RHS Plant Finder 2016

DEVISED BY CHRIS PHILIP
AND REALISED BY TONY LORD

EDITOR-IN-CHIEF
JANET CUBEY

RHS EDITORS
JAMES ARMITAGE DAWN EDWARDS
KÁLMÁN KÖNYVES NEIL LANCASTER
ROSALYN MARSHALL

COMPILER
JUDITH MERRICK

Royal
Horticultural
Society

Royal Horticultural Society

Published and compiled by
The Royal Horticultural Society
80 Vincent Square
London SW1P 2PE

Reg charity no: 222879/SC038262

First edition 1987
Thirtieth edition 2016

British Library Cataloguing Publication Data
A catalogue record for this book is available from the British Library

ISBN 978-1-907057-663

Publisher – Rae Spencer-Jones

RHS Editor – Simon Maughan

Designer – Peter Cooling

Cover Design – Mark Timothy

Maps – Alan Cooper

Printed and bound by Polestar Wheatons, Hennock Road, Marsh Barton, Exeter, Devon EX2 8RP

The compiler and the editors of the *RHS Plant Finder* have taken every care, in the time available, to check all the information supplied to them by the nurseries concerned. Nevertheless, in a work of this kind, containing as it does hundreds of thousands of separate computer encodings, errors and omissions will inevitably occur. The RHS, the Publisher and the Editors cannot accept responsibility for any consequences that may arise from such errors.

If you find any mistakes we hope that you will let us know so that the matter can be corrected in the next edition.

Front cover photograph: Mixed border of *Rudbeckia hirta* 'Prairie Sun' growing with purple kale 'Redbor'
(GAP Photos/Elke Borkowski)
Back cover: Nursery image (RHS/Tim Sandall)
Plant portraits from top to bottom: Harvesting raspberries (RHS/Tim Sandall)
Allium hollandicum 'Purple Sensation' (Neil Hepworth)
Harvesting chard (Tim Sandall)
Matteuccia struthiopteris and *Primula* Harlow Car hybrids (Jason Ingram)

The Royal Horticultural Society is the UK's leading gardening charity dedicated to advancing horticulture and promoting good gardening. Its charitable work includes providing expert advice and information, training the next generation of gardeners, creating hands-on opportunities for children to grow plants and conducting research into plants, pests and environmental issues affecting gardeners.

For more information visit www.rhs.org.uk or call 020 3176 5800.

Contents

INTRODUCTION

The *RHS Plant Finder* exists to put enthusiastic gardeners in touch with suppliers of plants. It is comprehensively updated every year.

The book is divided into two related sections: **PLANTS** and **NURSERIES.**

PLANTS includes an A-Z Directory of around 70,000 plant names, against which are listed a series of nursery codes. These codes point the reader to the full nursery details contained in the **NURSERIES** section towards the back of the book.

It is important to remember when ordering plants that many of the nurseries listed in the book are small, family-run businesses that propagate their own material. They cannot, therefore, guarantee to hold large stocks of the plants they list. Some will, however, propagate to order.

Nurseries appearing in the *RHS Plant Finder* for the first time or re-entering after an absence are printed in bold type in the **Nursery Index by Name** (pp.922-926).

NEW IN THIS EDITION

The 2016 edition reflects the decisions made by the RHS Nomenclature and Taxonomy Advisory Group (NATAG) during 2015. The **Nomenclatural Notes** section, p.22 gives a brief overview of these changes made since the compilation of the previous edition of the book.

For the first time we are including vegetables that have been awarded an RHS Award of Garden Merit (AGM). Descriptions, as well as nursery suppliers, can be found in the separate **AGM Vegetables** section (pp.812-828).

The **RHS Perfect for Pollinators** list is also included for the first time (pp.829-834).

LISTS OF NURSERIES FOR PLANTS WITH MORE THAN 30 SUPPLIERS

To prevent the book from becoming too big, we do not print nursery codes where more than 30 nurseries offer the same plant. The plant is then listed as being "widely available". See **How to Use the Plant Directory** (p.16).

A full list of all the nurseries held on file as current suppliers can be found by searching the RHS website Find a Plant facility or can be made available in printed form by post from the Compiler at the address below. For the latter, please ensure you include the full name of the plant (as given in the *RHS Plant Finder*) and enclose a stamped addressed envelope.

PLANTS LAST LISTED IN EARLIER EDITIONS

Plants cease to be listed for a variety of reasons. For more information, turn to **How to Use the Plant Directory** (p.16). A listing of more than 60,000 plants listed in earlier editions but for which we have no current suppliers will be made available on the RHS website.

RHS ONLINE

The plant data from the *RHS Plant Finder* is available on the Royal Horticultural Society's website at www.rhs.org.uk/plants under the Find a Plant section.

APPLICATION FOR ENTRY

If you would like your nursery to be considered for inclusion in the next edition of the *RHS Plant Finder*, please contact the Compiler. Entries to the book are free.

Contact details
The Compiler, *RHS Plant Finder*
RHS Garden Wisley
Woking
Surrey
GU23 6QB
Ⓣ (01483) 224234
Ⓔ plantfinder@rhs.org.uk

ACKNOWLEDGEMENTS

This edition was put together by Judith Merrick and Richard Sanford, with the assistance of Julie Humphries, Gill Skilton, June Skinner and Deborah Chubb. Rupert Wilson and Julia Barclay administered the RHS Horticultural Database using the BG-Base™ Collection Management Software.

RHS botanists James Armitage, Dawn Edwards, Kálmán Könyves, Neil Lancaster and Rosalyn Marshall undertook the task of editing the new plant names for this edition of the book.

We also acknowledge the contribution of John David and Yvette Harvey (RHS Science) and Louise Bowering, Diana Levy, Rae Spencer-Jones and Mark Timothy (RHS Media).

We are grateful for the professional support of Kerry Walter of BG-Base (UK) Ltd., Max Phillips of Strange Software Ltd. and Alan Cooper, who produces the maps. Finally, we are greatly indebted to Peter Cooling for his skill in turning our mass of raw data into a publishable form.

Our colleagues on the RHS Nomenclature and Taxonomy Advisory Group, along with the RHS International Cultivar Registrars, have all provided valuable guidance and information. Many nurseries have supplied useful details on new plants and have suggested corrections to existing entries. Some of these remain to be checked and will be entered in the next edition, although those that contravene the Codes of Nomenclature may have to be rejected. We appreciate your patience while these checks are made. We are also grateful to our regular correspondents and to all those readers who have made helpful comments.

Clematis	D.R. Donald, Int. Cultivar Registrar
Chrysanthemum	J. Barker
Conifers	S. McDonald, Int. Cultivar Registrar
Dahlia	S. McDonald, Int. Cultivar Registrar
Dianthus	Dr A.C. Leslie, Int. Cultivar Registrar
Delphinium	M.R. Underwood, Int. Cultivar Registrar
Heathers	Dr E.C. Nelson, Int. Cultivar Registrar
Ilex	S. Andrews
Lilium	D.R. Donald, Int. Cultivar Registrar
Narcissus	M.R. Underwood, Int. Cultivar Registrar
Nerine	Dr J.C. David
Orchids	J.M.H. Shaw, Int. Cultivar Registrar
Rhododendron	Dr A.C. Leslie, Int. Cultivar Registrar
Sorbus	Dr H. McAllister
Thymus	M. Easter, Int. Cultivar Registrar

Janet Cubey
RHS Editor in Chief
February 2016

CONSERVATION AND THE ENVIRONMENT

Invasive Plants

As the *RHS Plant Finder* demonstrates, gardens in Britain have been greatly enriched by the diversity of plants introduced to cultivation from abroad. While the vast majority of those introduced have enhanced our gardens, a few have proved to be highly invasive and to threaten native habitats. Once such plants are established it is very difficult, costly and potentially damaging to native ecosystems to eradicate or control the invasive "alien" species. Gardeners can help by choosing not to buy or distribute non-native invasive plants and by taking steps to prevent them escaping into the wild and by disposing of them in a responsible way.

Ten of the most serious invasive non-native species are no longer listed in the *RHS Plant Finder*. Any cultivars or varieties of them that are listed are believed to be less invasive than the species. These 10 plants are:

**Azolla filiculoides* – fairy fern
**Crassula helmsii* – New Zealand pygmy weed
Elodea nuttallii – Nuttall's waterweed
Fallopia japonica – Japanese knotweed
Heracleum mantegazzianum – giant hogweed
†**Hydrocotyle ranunculoides* – floating pennywort
Impatiens glandulifera – Himalayan balsam
†*Lagarosiphon major* – curly waterweed
†**Ludwigia grandiflora* – water primrose
†**Myriophyllum aquaticum* – parrot's feather

From April 2014 the five aquatic species indicated by a * above have been banned from sale in the UK. Anyone trading in these species is liable to a fine of up to £5000 or a six months' prison sentence.

The EU Regulation on Invasive Alien Species, which became law early in 2015, has a provision for a list of species of EU-wide concern. That list has now been published by the EU Commission and will become effective from March 2016. Species that are included in the list attract the strictest measures of control, including a ban on keeping, growing or cultivating, transporting or trading, use or exchange, as well as release into the wider environment. These controls will apply to individuals as well as organisations and businesses that own or hold any of these species. There are 14 plants on this list, most of which are of marginal importance to gardeners, or are already banned from sale in the UK (marked with † in the above list), but two widely grown species, *Eichhornia crassipes* (water hyacinth) and *Lysichiton americanus* (skunk cabbage), are included. Although there are transitionary measures allowing businesses to sell off their stock of these species within one year, to minimise potential for confusion, we have taken the step of not listing the species in the 2016 *RHS Plant Finder*. Those species affected are:

Baccharis halmifolia – tree groundsel
Cabomba caroliniana – Carolina fanwort
Eichhornia crassipes – water hyacinth
Ludwigia peploides – water primrose
Lysichiton americanus – American skunk cabbage
Parthenium hysterophorus – parthenium weed
Pueraria montana var. *lobata* – kudzu

Gardeners who already have these species in their gardens are not at risk of prosecution for possession as the Regulation is not retrospective, but will be required to meet the other requirements of the Regulation to ensure that they control the species effectively on their property and do not allow it to spread.

Species control provisions

The UK Government introduced new provisions in the Infrastructure Act (2015) to control invasive non-native species in England and Wales. There are two levels of control: a species control agreement and a species control order. In the former, the owner of land where an invasive non-native species is present, when approached by the relevant environmental authority, agrees to take action to limit or remove the species. If the landowner fails to do so, or does not agree, or where it is not known who the landowner is, then the environment authority can take action to enforce the control of the species. This may involve entry of the property by the authority to carry out the control if the owner fails to comply. In the case of an emergency then a species control order may be issued without going through the previous steps. Only those species listed on Schedule 9 of the Wildlife & Countryside Act can be subject to these control measures. For the purposes of the Act, Defra, Natural England, the Environment Agency and the Forestry Commission are defined as Environmental Authorities in England. For Wales it is Natural Resources Wales.

Bringing plants back from abroad

Travelling can be a great source of inspiration for gardeners and often provides an opportunity to encounter new and interesting plants. Anyone wishing to bring plants back into Britain from overseas must realise, however, that this is a complex matter. Various regulations are in force that apply to amateur gardeners as well as to commercial nurseries. The penalties for breaking these can be serious.

Most countries have regulations concerning the collection of plants from the wild, including seed.

These regulations are likely to ban collection from certain protected places, such as national parks, ban the collection of rare or endangered species, and require permits to collect where special protection measures are not in place. In addition there is likely to be an additional permit to export any collected plant material. Travellers are reminded of regulations in force at airports and other points of entry to a country. Anyone wishing to collect wild plants, for whatever purpose, will need to contact the country concerned well in advance of travel to seek the relevant permits. Breach of the regulations will result, as a minimum, in the confiscation of plant material if discovered. Any such material brought back to the UK is illegal.

The situation with plants in cultivation in another country is less clear and travellers are advised to check with the authorities in the country, particularly with regard to any Access and Benefit Sharing requirements (see **Nagoya Protocol** below), export permits or phytosanitary certificates that might be needed.

Plant Health regulations are in place to control the spread of pests and diseases. Plants are divided into the categories of prohibited, controlled and unrestricted, but there are also limits that vary according to the part of the world you are travelling from.

Ⓦ www.gov.uk/bringing-food-animals-plants-into-uk/plants

The Convention on International Trade in Endangered Species (CITES) affects the transport of animal and plant material across international boundaries. Its aim is to prevent exploitative trade and thereby to prevent harm and the ultimate extinction of wild populations. A tighter regime on trade in species of wild fauna and flora exists in the EU that requires export permits for any plants listed in Appendices A, B & C and import permits for Appendices A & B. There is a further Appendix D for non-CITES listed species that the EU consider to be endangered. A broad range of plants is covered in these Appendices, including *Cactaceae* and *Orchidaceae* and, although species are mentioned in the convention title, the restrictions cover all cultivars and hybrids of listed species too, except for specific exclusions, where there are annotations in the Appendices.

Ⓦ www.gov.uk/cites-imports-and-exports#cites-species

The Convention on Biological Diversity (CBD or the "Rio Convention") recognises the property rights of individual countries in relation to their own biodiversity. It exists to enable access to that biodiversity, but equally to ensure the sharing of any benefit derived from it. In principle it is possible to collect plant material from other countries that have asserted their rights under the CBD, by ensuring that you have obtained documentary evidence of prior informed consent on the basis of mutually agreed terms for any uses that the material will be put to in the future. In practice the legal requirements for collecting plant material vary from country to country and it is advisable to contact the National Focal Point for further information.

Ⓦ www.cbd.int

The **Nagoya Protocol** is a supplementary agreement of the CBD which entered into force late last year, and provides a framework for Access and Benefit Sharing. In the UK this is implemented by the European Union Regulation which is effective from 12 October 2014, and requires anyone utilising genetic resources from another country which is a signatory of the Nagoya Protocol, collected after 12 October 2014, to carry out due diligence to ensure that the material was collected in accordance with the Protocol and the CBD. While the most likely examples of utilisation are the development of new products or medicines from plants, breeding programmes to raise new plants for horticulture would also be covered. Although the burden to prove legitimate use of the genetic resource lies with the person or organisation utilising the genetic resource, anyone providing the source of the genetic resource (such as wild-collected plants) will need to be able to provide the relevant paperwork, such as a Material Transfer Agreement and Prior Informed Consent.

Ⓦ www.cbd.int/abs/about/

In March 2015 the UK Government put in place the scheme of penalties for failure to comply with the EU Regulation which includes a range of both civil and criminal penalties, with the ultimate sanction of a two-year prison sentence. This legislation also formally appointed the National Measurement and Regulation Office (NMRO) as the authority to enforce compliance in the UK, effective from June 2015.

Ⓦ www.gov.uk/guidance/abs

European Habitats Directive. The full implementation of this Directive into UK law in 2007 extended protection to all of the European Protected Species (EPS) listed in the Appendices of that Directive (these are Appendices II(b) and IV(b) for plants) whether they are native to the UK or not. This requires a licence for material of any of these species collected in the wild after 1994. These are issued by Natural England (for England), Natural Resources Wales (in Wales) and Scottish Natural Heritage (for Scotland).

Ⓦ www.jncc.gov.uk/page-1374.defra

Contact addresses

The UK authorities issue licences for UK plants. For other EU states a collector would need to contact the relevant national authorities.

Department for Environment, Food & Rural Affairs (Defra)
Nobel House
17 Smith Square
London
SW1P 3JR
For biodiversity queries:
Ⓔ biodiversity@defra.gsi.gov.uk

Plant Health is covered by the Plant Health and Seeds Inspectorate (PHSI) which is part of the Animal and Plant Health Agency.

Animal & Plant Health Agency (APHA)
Centre for International Trade – Bristol
1/17 Temple Quay House
2 The Square
Temple Quay
Bristol
BS1 6EB
Ⓣ 0117 372 8774
Ⓕ 0117 372 8206
Ⓔ wildlife.licensing@apha.gsi.gov.uk
Ⓦ www.gov.uk/plant-health-controls

Natural England
Wildlife Management & Licensing
First Floor, Temple Quay House
2 The Square
Bristol
BS1 6EB
Ⓣ 0845 601 4523
Ⓔ wildlife@naturalengland.org.uk

Non-Native Species Secretariat
Animal and Plant Health Agency
Sand Hutton
York
YO41 1LZ
Ⓦ www.nonnativespecies.org

National Measurement and Regulation Office
Stanton Avenue
Teddington
TW110JZ
Ⓣ 020 8943 7272
Ⓔ info@nmro.gov.uk

EXTENDED GLOSSARY

This glossary combines some of the helpful introductory sections from older editions in an alphabetical listing. A fuller, more discursive account of plant names, *Guide to Plant Names*, and a detailed guide to the typography of plant names, *Recommended Style for Printing Plant Names*, are both available as leaflets. To request a copy of either please send an A4 sae to The Compiler at the contact address given on page 4.

ADVISORY COMMITTEE ON NOMENCLATURE AND TAXONOMY

See **Nomenclature and Taxonomy Advisory Group**

AUTHORITIES

In order that plant names can be used with precision throughout the scientific world, the name of the person who coined the name of a plant species (its author, or authority) is added to the plant name. Usually this information is of little consequence to gardeners, except in cases where the same name has been given to two different plants or a name is commonly misapplied. Although only one usage is correct, both may be encountered in books, so indicating the author is the only way to be certain about which plant is being referred to. This can happen equally with cultivars. Authors' names, where it is appropriate to cite them, appear in a smaller typeface after the species or cultivar name to which they refer and are abbreviated following Brummitt and Powell's *Authors of Plant Names*.

🏆 AWARD OF GARDEN MERIT

The Award of Garden Merit (AGM) is intended as a practical guide for the gardener and is therefore awarded only after a period of assessment by the RHS Standing and Joint Committees. The AGM is awarded only to plants that are:

- excellent for ordinary use in appropriate conditions
- available
- of good constitution
- essentially stable in form and colour
- reasonably resistant to pests and diseases

The AGM symbol is cited in conjunction with the **hardiness** rating. A full list of AGM plants may be found on the RHS website at www.rhs.org.uk/agmplants.

The AGM list was originally reviewed every ten years, to ensure that every plant still merited the award. The last review took place in 2012; since 2013, the list has been subject to a "rolling review", and AGMs may now be rescinded at any time.

BOTANICAL NAMES

The aim of the botanical naming system is to provide each different plant with a single, unique, universal name. The basic unit of plant classification is the species. Species that share a number of significant characteristics are grouped together to form a genus (plural **genera**). The name of a species is made up of two elements; the name of the genus followed by the specific epithet, for example, *Narcissus romieuxii.*

Variation within a species can be recognised by division into subspecies (usually abbreviated to subsp.), varietas (or variety abbreviated to var.) and forma (or form abbreviated to f.). Whilst it is unusual for a plant to have all of these, it is possible, as in this example, *Narcissus romieuxii* subsp. *albidus* var. *zaianicus* f. *lutescens.*

The botanical elements are always given in italics, with only the genus taking an initial capital letter. The rank indications are never in italics. In instances where the rank is not known it is necessary to form an invalid construction by quoting a second epithet without a rank. This is an unsatisfactory situation, but requires considerable research to resolve.

In some genera, such as *Hosta*, we list the cultivar names alphabetically with the species or **hybrid** to which they are attributed afterwards in parentheses. For example, *Hosta* 'Reversed' (*sieboldiana*). In other situations where the aim is not to create a list alphabetically by cultivar name we would recommend styling this as *Hosta sieboldiana* 'Reversed'.

CLASSIFICATION OF GENERA

Genera that include a large number of species or with many cultivars are often subdivided into informal horticultural classifications or more formal Cultivar Groups, each based on a particular characteristic or combination of characteristics. Colour of flower or fruit and shape of flower are common examples and, with fruit, whether a cultivar is grown for culinary or dessert purposes. How such groups are named differs from genus to genus.

To help users of the *RHS Plant Finder* find the plants they want, the classifications used within cultivated genera are listed using codes and plants are marked with the appropriate code in brackets after its name in the Plant Directory. To find the explanation of each code, simply look it up under the genus concerned in the **Classification of Genera** starting on p.23. The codes relating to edible fruits are also listed here, but these apply across several genera.

Collectors' References

Abbreviations (usually with numbers) following a plant name refer to the collector(s) of the plant. These abbreviations are expanded, with a collector's name or expedition title, in the section **Collectors' References** starting on p.18.

A collector's reference may indicate a new, as yet unnamed range of variation within a species. The inclusion of collectors' references in the *RHS Plant Finder* supports the book's role in sourcing unusual plants.

The Convention on Biological Diversity calls for conservation of biodiversity, its sustainable use and the fair and equitable sharing of any derived benefits. Since its adoption in 1993, collectors are required to have prior informed consent from the country of origin for the acquisition and commercialisation of collected material.

Common Names

In a work such as this, it is necessary to refer to plants by their botanical names for the sake of universal comprehension and clarity. However, at the same time we recognise that with fruit and vegetables most people are more familiar with their common names than their botanical ones. Cross-references are therefore given from common to botanical names for fruit, vegetables and the commoner culinary herbs throughout the Plant Directory.

Cultivar

Literally meaning cultivated variety, cultivar names are given to denote variation within species and that generated by hybridisation, in cultivation. To make them easily distinguishable from botanical names, they are not printed in italics and are enclosed in single quotation marks. Cultivar names coined since 1959 should follow the rules of the International Code of Nomenclature for Cultivated Plants (**ICNCP**).

Descriptive Terms

Terms that appear after the main part of the plant name are shown in a smaller font to distinguish them. These descriptive elements give extra information about the plant and may include the **collector's reference**, **authority**, or what colour it is. For example, *Clematis henryi* B&SWJ 3402, *Penstemon* 'Sour Grapes' M. Fish, *Akebia quinata* cream-flowered.

Families

Genera are grouped into larger groups of related plants called families. Most family names, with the exception of eight familiar names, end with the same group of letters, *-aceae*. While it is still acceptable to use these eight exceptions, the modern trend adopted in the *RHS Plant Finder* is to use alternative names with *–aceae* endings. The families concerned are *Compositae* (*Asteraceae*), *Cruciferae* (*Brassicaceae*), *Gramineae* (*Poaceae*), *Guttiferae* (*Clusiaceae*), *Labiatae* (*Lamiaceae*), *Leguminosae* (split here into *Caesalpiniaceae*, *Mimosaceae* and *Papilionaceae*), *Palmae* (*Arecaceae*) and *Umbelliferae* (*Apiaceae*).

Apart from these exceptions we now follow (from 2010) *Mabberley's Plant-book* (3rd edition).

Genus (plural – genera)

Genera used in the *RHS Plant Finder* were originally based on Brummitt's *Vascular Plant Families and Genera* but are now based on a range of sources. For spellings and genders of generic names, Greuter's *Names in Current Use for Extant Plant Genera* has also been consulted. See **Botanical Names**.

Grex

Within orchids, hybrids of the same parentage, regardless of how alike they are, are given a grex name. Individuals can be selected, given cultivar names and propagated vegetatively. For example, *Pleione* Versailles gx 'Bucklebury', where Versailles is the grex name and 'Bucklebury' is a selected **cultivar**.

Group

This is a collective name for a group of cultivars within a genus with similar characteristics. The word Group is always included and, where cited with a cultivar name, it is enclosed in brackets, for example, *Actaea simplex* (Atropurpurea Group) 'Brunette', where 'Brunette' is a distinct cultivar in a group of purple-leaved cultivars.

Another example of a Group is *Rhododendron polycladum* Scintillans Group. In this case *Rhododendron scintillans* was a species that is now botanically 'sunk' within *R. polycladum*, but it is still recognised horticulturally as a Group.

Group names are also used for swarms of hybrids with the same parentage, for example, *Rhododendron* Polar Bear Group. These were formerly treated as

grex names, a term now used only for orchids. A single clone from the Group may be given the same cultivar name, for example, *Rhododendron* 'Polar Bear'.

Hardiness

Hardiness ratings are shown for **Award of Garden Merit** plants. To assist gardeners to determine more clearly which plants are hardy in their local area, the RHS introduced a new, enhanced, hardiness rating scheme in 2013, to coincide with the publication of the new **Award of Garden Merit** plant list. The categories now used are as follows:
Temperature ranges given are intended to be absolute minimum winter temperatures (°C).
H1a = Heated greenhouse – tropical >15
H1b = Heated greenhouse – subtropical 10 to 15
H1c = Heated greenhouse – warm temperate 5 to 10
H2 = Tender – cool or frost-free greenhouse 1 to 5
H3 = Half-hardy – unheated greenhouse/mild winter -5 to 1
H4 = Hardy – average winter -10 to -5
H5 = Hardy – cold winter -15 to -10
H6 = Hardy – very cold winter -20 to -15
H7 = Very hardy <-20

Further definition of these categories can be found on the RHS website, in the Feb 2013 edition of *The Garden* and in the *RHS Plant Finder 2013* essay.

Hybrids

Some species, when grown together, in the wild or in cultivation, are found to interbreed and form hybrids. In some instances a hybrid name is coined, for example hybrids between *Primula hirsuta* and *P. minima* are given the name *Primula* × *forsteri*, the multiplication sign indicating hybrid origin. Hybrid formulae that quote the parentage of the hybrid are used where a unique name has not been coined, for example *Rhododendron auriculatum* × *R. hemsleyanum*. In hybrid formulae you will find parents in alphabetical order, with the male (m) and female (f) parent indicated where known. Hybrids between different genera are also possible, for example × *Mahoberberis* is the name given to hybrids between *Mahonia* and *Berberis*.

There are also a few special-case hybrids called graft hybrids, where the tissues of two plants are physically rather than genetically mixed. These are indicated by an addition rather than a multiplication sign, so *Laburnum* + *Cytisus* becomes + *Laburnocytisus*.

ICNCP

The ICNCP is the International Code of Nomenclature for Cultivated Plants. First published in 1959, the 8th edition was published in 2009 and the 9th edition is due for publication during 2016.

Cultivar names that do not conform to this Code, and for which there is no valid alternative, are flagged I (for invalid). This code states that the minimum requirement is for a cultivar name to be given in conjunction with the name of the genus. However, in the *RHS Plant Finder* we choose to give as full a name as possible to give the gardener and botanist more information about the plant, following the Recommendation in the Code.

Nomenclature and Taxonomy Advisory Group

This Group advises the RHS on individual problems of nomenclature regarding plants in cultivation and, in particular, use of names in the *RHS Horticultural Database*, reflected in the annual publication of the *RHS Plant Finder*.

The aim is always to make the plant names in the *RHS Plant Finder* as consistent, reliable and stable as possible and acceptable to gardeners and botanists alike, not only in the British Isles but around the world. Recent proposals to change or correct names are examined with the aim of creating a balance between the stability of well-known names and botanical and taxonomic correctness. In some cases the conflicting views on the names of some groups of plants will not easily be resolved. The Group's policy is then to wait and review the situation once a more obvious consensus is reached, rather than rush to rename plants only to have to change them again when opinions have shifted.

In 2016 the Group is chaired by Dr John Grimshaw and includes: Susyn Andrews, Chris Brickell, Dr James Compton, Dr Janet Cubey (Vice-Chair), Mike Grant, Dr Stephen Jury, Dr Alan Leslie, Dr Tony Lord, Chris Sanders with Dr Crinan Alexander, Prof David Mabberley, Dr Charles Nelson and Julian Sutton (corresponding members), James Armitage, Dr John David and Julian Shaw (attending RHS staff) and Dr Dawn Edwards as Secretary.

Notes on Nomenclature and Identification

The **Notes on Nomenclature and Identification**, p.22, give further information for names that are complex or may be confusing. See also **Nomenclature and Taxonomy Advisory Group**.

Plant Breeders' Rights

Plants covered by an *active* grant of Plant Breeders' Rights (PBR) are indicated throughout the Plant Directory. Grants indicated are those awarded by both UK and EU Plant Variety Rights offices. Because grants can both come into force and lapse at any time, this book can only aim to represent the situation at one point in time, but it is hoped that this will act as a useful guide to growers and gardeners. UK and EU grants represent the published position as of the end of December 2016. We do not give any indication where PBR grants may be pending.

To obtain PBR protection, a new plant must be registered and pass tests for distinctness, uniformity and stability under an approved name. This approved name, under the rules of the **ICNCP**, established by a legal process, has to be regarded as the cultivar name. Increasingly however, these approved names are a code or "nonsense" name and are therefore often unpronounceable and meaningless, so the plants are given other names designed to attract sales when they are released. These secondary names are often referred to as selling names but are officially termed **trade designations**.

For further information on UK PBR contact:
Plant Variety Rights Office,
Animal and Plant Health Agency,
Eastbrook,
Shaftesbury Road,
Cambridge CB2 8DR
Ⓣ (0300) 060 0497
Ⓦ www.gov.uk/plant-breeders-rights

For details of plants covered by EU Community Rights contact:
Community Plant Variety Office (CPVO)
3 Boulevard Maréchal Foch, CS 10121
49101 Angers Cedex 2, France
Ⓣ 00 33 (02) 41 25 64 00
Ⓕ 00 33 (02) 41 25 64 10
Ⓦ www.cpvo.europa.eu

The *RHS Plant Finder* takes no responsibility for ensuring that nurseries selling plants with PBR are licensed to do so.

Reverse Synonyms

It is likely that users of this book will come across names in certain genera that they did not expect to find. This may be because species have been transferred from another genus (or **genera**).

Selling Names

See **Trade Designations**

Series

With seed-raised plants and some popular vegetatively propagated plants, especially bedding plants and pot plants such as *Petunia* or *Verbena*, Series have become increasingly popular. A Series contains a number of similar cultivars, but differs from a **Group** in that it is a marketing device, with cultivars added to create a range of flower colours in plants of similar habit. Individual colour elements within a Series may be represented by slightly different cultivars over the years.

The word Series is always included and, where cited with a cultivar name it is enclosed in brackets, for example *Aquilegia* 'Robin' (Songbird Series). The Series name usually follows the rest of the plant name, but sometimes in this book we list it before the cultivar name in order to group members of a Series together when they occur next to one another on the page.

Species

See under **Botanical Names**

Subspecies

See under **Botanical Names**

Synonyms

Although the ideal is for each species or cultivar to have only one name, anyone dealing with plants soon comes across a situation where one plant has received two or more names, or two plants have received the same name. In each case, only one name and application, for reasons of precision and stability, can be regarded as correct. Additional names are known as synonyms. Further information on synonyms and why plants change names is available in *Guide to Plant Names*. See the introduction to this glossary for details of how to request a copy.

See also **Reverse Synonyms**.

Trade Designations

A **trade designation** is the name used to market a plant when the cultivar name is considered unsuitable for selling purposes. It is styled in a different typeface and without single quotation marks.

In the case of **Plant Breeders' Rights** it is a legal requirement for the cultivar name to appear with the trade designation on a label at the point of sale. Most plants are sold under only one trade designation, but some, especially roses, are sold under a number of names, particularly when cultivars are introduced from other countries. Usually, the correct cultivar name is the only way to ensure that the same plant is not bought unwittingly under two or more different trade designations. The *RHS Plant Finder* follows the recommendations of the **ICNCP** when dealing with trade designations and PBR. These are always to quote the cultivar name and trade designation together and to style the trade designation in small capitals, for example *Choisya × dewitteana* GOLDFINGERS ('Limo'PBR). Here GOLDFINGERS is the trade designation and 'Limo' is the cultivar name that has been granted **Plant Breeders' Rights**.

TRANSLATIONS

When a cultivar name is translated from the language of first publication, the translation is regarded as a **trade designation** and styled accordingly. We endeavour to recognise the original cultivar name in every case and to give an English translation where it is in general use.

VARIEGATED PLANTS

Following a suggestion from the Variegated Plant Group of the Hardy Plant Society, a (v) is cited after those plants which are "variegated". The dividing line between variegation and less distinct colour marking is necessarily arbitrary and plants with light veins, pale, silver or dark zones, or leaves flushed in paler colours, are not shown as being variegated unless there is an absolutely sharp distinction between paler and darker zones.

For further details of the Variegated Plant Group, please write to:

Brian Dockerill
19 Westfield Road
Glyncoch
Pontypridd
Mid-Glamorgan
CF37 3AG

VARIETY

See under **Botanical Names** and **Cultivar**

Symbols and Abbreviations

Symbols Appearing to the Left of the Name

*	Name not validated. Not listed in the appropriate International Registration Authority checklist nor in works cited in the Bibliography. For fuller discussion see p.9
I	Invalid name. See *International Code of Botanical Nomenclature 2012* and *International Code of Nomenclature for Cultivated Plants 2016*. For fuller discussion see p.9
§	Plant listed elsewhere in the Plant Directory under a synonym
×	Hybrid genus
+	Graft hybrid genus

Symbols Appearing to the Right of the Name

✿	Plant Heritage National Plant Collection® exists for all of part of this genus. Further details can be found by searching the National Plant Collections online or in the Plant Heritage Directory available from www.plantheritage.com or by phone (01483) 447540.
♀H4	The Royal Horticultural Society's Award of Garden Merit, see p.9
(d)	double-flowered
(F)	Fruit
(f)	female
(m)	male
(v)	variegated plant, see p.13
PBR	Plant Breeders' Rights see p.11
new	New plant entry in this edition

For abbreviations relating to individual genera see **Classification of Genera** p.23

For **Collectors' References** see p.18

For symbols used in the **Nurseries** section see p.837

Symbols and Abbreviations Used as Part of the Name

×	hybrid species
aff.	affinis (akin to)
agg.	aggregate, a single name used to cover a group of very similar plants, regarded by some as separate species
ambig.	ambiguous, a name used by two authors for different plants and where it is unclear which is being offered
cf.	compare to
cl.	clone
f.	forma (botanical form)
gx	grex
sensu stricto	in the narrow sense
sp.	species
subsp.	subspecies
subvar.	subvarietas (botanical subvariety)
var.	varietas (botanical variety)

It is not within the remit of this book to check that nurseries are applying the right names to the right plants or to ensure nurseries selling plants with Plant Breeders' Rights are licensed to do so.

Please, never use an out of date edition

Plants

How to Use the Plant Directory

Nursery Codes

Look up the plant you require in the alphabetical Plant Directory. Against each plant you will find one or more four-letter codes, for example WCru, each code represents one nursery offering that plant. The first letter of each code indicates the main area of the country in which the nursery is situated. For this geographical key, refer to the **Nursery Codes and Symbols** on p.836.

Turn to the **Nursery Details by Code** starting on p.840 where, in alphabetical order of codes, you will find details of each nursery which offers the plant in question. If you wish to visit any nursery, you may find its location on one of the maps (following p.927). Please note that not all nurseries choose to be shown on the maps. For a fuller explanation of how to use the nursery listings please turn to p.837. **Always check that the nursery you select has the plant in stock before you set out.**

Plants with more than 30 Suppliers

In some cases, against the plant name you will see the term 'Widely available' instead of a nursery code. If we were to include every plant listed by all nurseries, the *RHS Plant Finder* would become unmanageably bulky. We therefore ask nurseries to restrict their entries to those plants that are not already well represented. As a result, if more than 30 nurseries offer any plant the Directory gives no nursery codes and the plant is listed instead as being 'Widely available'.

You should not have difficulty in locating these in local nurseries or garden centres. If, however, you are unable to find such plants, a list of all the current suppliers we have on file is available by post or online. See the Introduction (p.4).

Finding Fruit, Vegetables and Herbs

You will need to search for these by their botanical names. Common names are cross-referenced to their botanical names in the Plant Directory.

If you have Difficulty Finding your Plant

If you cannot immediately find the plant you seek, look through the various species of the genus. You may be using an incomplete name. The problem is most likely to arise in very large genera such as *Phlox* where there are a number of possible species, each with a large number of cultivars. A search through the whole genus may well bring success. For space reasons, we are not able to list in the Plant Directory annuals, orchids or cacti (except hardy terrestrial orchids and hardy cacti), or non-ornamental vegetables. For vegetables with an RHS Award of Garden Merit please see new section on p. 811.

Cross-references

It may be that the plant name you seek is a synonym. Our intention is to list nursery codes only against the correct botanical name. Where you find a synonym you will be cross-referred to the correct name.

Plants Last Listed in Earlier Editions

It may be that the plant you are seeking has no known suppliers and is thus not listed.

The loss of a plant name from the Directory may arise for a number of reasons – the supplier may have gone out of business, or may not have responded to our latest questionnaire and has therefore been removed from the book. Such plants may well be available but we have no knowledge of current suppliers. Alternatively, some plants may have been misnamed by nurseries in previous editions, but are now appearing under their correct name.

For further information on plants last listed in earlier editions please see the Introduction (p.4).

Please, never use an out of date edition

USING THE PLANT DIRECTORY

The purpose of the Plant Directory is to help the reader correctly identify the plant they seek and find stockists. Each nursery has a unique code which appears to the right of the plant name. **Nursery Details by Code** (p.840) gives details about each nursery. The first letter in each code denotes its geographical region. Turn to the **Map Index** (p.927) to find the correct code for an area.

The Plant Directory provides information about plants through symbols and notes. For example: if a plant has an alternative name; is new to the book; or has received the RHS Award of Garden Merit.

Abelia ✿ (*Caprifoliaceae*)

	chinensis misapplied	see *A.* × *grandiflora* 'Lake Maggiore'
§	***chinensis*** R. Br.	CBcs CExl CMCN CMac EBee EHyd ELan EPfP EWTr LRHS MAsh MGil MMuc SEND SPer SRms WGrn
§	***dielsii***	CBot
	'Edward Goucher' 🏆H5	Widely available
	engleriana	CExl CRos EHyd EPfP LRHS MAsh MBlu MGil NLar SLon
	floribunda	see *Vesalea floribunda*
§	× ***grandiflora***	CChe CTho ELan ETMg EWTr LCro LOPS LRHS MJak SRms SWeb WAvo
	- 'Aurea'	see *A.* × *grandiflora* 'Gold Spot'
	- 'Brockhill Allgold'	EMil EPfP LRHS SPoG
	- common clone	see *A.* × *grandiflora* 'Lake Maggiore'
	- 'Compacta'	WFar
	- CONFETTI ('Conti'PBR) (v)	CBcs CMac CRos CSBt ECrN EHyd ELan EMOT EMil EPfP GMcL LRHS LSRN MAsh MGos MRav NLar SCob SEle SGol SLim SPer SPoG SWvt WFar
§	- 'Francis Mason' (v)	Widely available
§	- 'Gold Spot' (v)	CBot EPfP NLar SPer
	- 'Gold Strike'	see *A.* × *grandiflora* 'Gold Spot'
	- GOLDEN PANACHE ('Minpan')	MRav
	- 'Goldsport'	see *A.* × *grandiflora* 'Gold Spot'
	- 'Hopleys'PBR (v) 🏆H5	CBcs CMac CRos CSBt CTri EHyd ELan EMil EPfP EWTr LRHS MAsh MGos NLar SCob SEle SGol SLon SRms SWvt WGrn WHar
	- 'Kaleidoscope'PBR (v)	CMac CRos CWGN ECrN EHoe ELan EPfP EShb ETMg LCro LRHS LSRN MAsh MGos MJak MPkF NLar NRHS SCob SGol SLim SPer SPoG SRms SWvt WCot WFar
	- LADY LIBERTY ('Keylib')	LRHS
§	- 'Lake Maggiore' 🏆H5	CBar CBot CMac CSBt CTri EHoe ELan EMOT EPfP MBlu MGil MGos MMuc MRav MSwo SCob SEND SPer SPoG SSta WHar
	- LUCKY LOTS ('Wevo2') (v)	LLHF NLar SCob SGol
	- 'Panache' (v)	LLHF WCot
	- 'Prostrate White'	ECrN LRHS NLar SPoG
	- 'Radiance' (v) **new**	NEoE
	- 'Semperflorens'	LRHS
	- 'Sherwoodii'	ECrN EHoe EPfP LRHS MAsh MGos SGol WRHF
	- 'Sparkling Silver' (v)	LRHS
	- SUNNY CHARMS ('Mindu01'PBR)	LCro
	- 'Sunrise' (v)	NLar

DESCRIPTIVE TERM
See p.10.

SYMBOLS TO THE LEFT OF THE NAME
Provides information about the name of the plant. See p.14 for the key.

SYMBOLS TO THE RIGHT OF THE NAME
Tells you more about the plant itself, e.g. (v) indicates that the plant is variegated, (F) = fruit. See p.14 for the key.

ABBREVIATIONS
To save space a dash indicates that the previous heading is repeated. If written out in full the name would be Abelia × grandiflora *'Kaleidoscope'.*

NEW
Plant new to this edition.

TRADE DESIGNATION
See p.12.

🏆H5
This plant has received the RHS Award of Garden Merit. See p.9.

CROSS-REFERENCES
Directs you to the correct name of the plant and the nursery codes. See p.16.

WIDELY AVAILABLE
Indicates that more than 30 Plant Finder nurseries supply the plant, and it may be available locally. See p.16.

PBR
Plant Breeders' Rights. See p.11.

NURSERY CODE
A unique code identifying each nursery. Turn to p.840 for details of the nurseries.

Supplementary Keys to the Directory

Collectors' References

Abbreviations following a plant name refer to the collector(s) of the plant. These abbreviations are expanded below, with a collector's name or expedition title. For a fuller explanation, see p.10.

A&JW	Watson, A. & J.
A&L	Ala, A. & Lancaster, Roy
AB&S	Archibald, James; Blanchard, John W. & Salmon, M.
AC	Clark, Alan J.
AC&H	Apold, J.; Cox, Peter & Hutchison, Peter
AC&W	Albury; Cheese, M. & Watson, J.M.
ACE	AGS Expedition to China (1994)
ACL	Leslie, Alan C.
AER	Robinson, Allan
AGS/ES	AGS Expedition to Sikkim (1983)
AGSJ	AGS Expedition to Japan (1988)
AH	Hoog, A.
AIM	Avent, Tony Mexico (1994)
Airth	Airth, Murray
Akagi	Akagi Botanical Garden
AL&JS	Sharman, Joseph L. & Leslie, Alan C.
APA	Cox, K.; Hootman, S.; Hudson, T.; et al, Expedition to Arunchal Pradesh (2005)
ARG	Argent, G.C.G.
ARGS	Alaska Rock Garden Society trip to China
ARJA	Ruksans, J. & Siesums, A.
B	Blanchard, John
B&F MA	Brown, Robert & Fisher, Rif & Middle Atlas (2007)
B L.	Beer, Len
B&L	Brickell, Christopher D. & Leslie, Alan C.
B&M & BM	Brickell, Christopher D. & Mathew, Brian
B&S	Bird P. & Salmon M.
B&SWJ	Wynn-Jones, Bleddyn & Susan
B&V	Burras, K. & Vosa, C.G.
BB	Bartholomew, B.
BBJMT	Boland, Brownless, Jamieson & McNamara
BC	Chudziak, W.
BC&W	Beckett; Cheese, M. & Watson, J.M.
Beavis	Beavis, Derek S.
Berry	Berry, P.
Berry & Brako	Berry, P. & Brako, Lois
BKBlount	Blount, B.K.
BKN	Bis, J., Kupčák, P. & Novak, H.
BL&M	University of Bangor Expedition to NE Nepal
BM	Mathew, Brian F.
BM&W	Binns, David L.; Mason, M. & Wright, A.
BOA	Boardman, P.
Breedlove	Breedlove, D.
BR	Rushbrooke, Ben
BS	Smith, Basil
BSBE	Bowles Scholarship Botanical Expedition (1963)
BSSS	Crûg Expedition, Jordan (1991)
Bu	Bubert, S.
Burtt	Burtt, Brian L.
BWJ	Wynn-Jones, Bleddyn
C	Cole, Desmond T.
C&C	Cox, P.A. & Cox, K.N.E.
C&Cu	Cox, K.N.E. & Cubey, J.
C&H	Cox, Peter & Hutchison, Peter
C&K	Chamberlain & Knott
C&R	Christian & Roderick
C&S	Clark, Alan & Sinclair, Ian W.J.
C&V	K.N.E. Cox & Vergera, S.
C&W	Cheese, M. & Watson, J.M.
CC	Chadwell, Christopher
CC&H	Chamberlain, David F.; Cox, Peter & Hutchison, P.
CC&McK	Chadwell, Christopher & McKelvie, A.
CC&MR	Chadwell, Christopher & Ramsay
CCH&H	Chamberlain, D.F.; Cox, P.; Hutchison, P. & Hootman, S.
CD&R	Compton, J.; D'Arcy, J. & Rix, E.M.
CDB	Brickell, Christopher D.
CDC	Coode, Mark J.E.; Dockrill, Alexander
CDC&C	Compton; D'Arcy; Christopher & Coke
CDPR	Compton; D'Arcy; Pope & Rix
CE&H	Christian, P.J.; Elliott & Hoog
CEE	Chengdu Edinburgh Expedition China (1991)

CGG	Glendoick Gardens Expedition to Guizou (2009)
CGV	Vosa, Canio
CGW	Grey-Wilson, Christopher
CH	Christian, P. & Hoog, A.
CH&M	Cox, P.; Hutchison, P. & Maxwell-MacDonald, D.
CHP&W	Kashmir Botanical Expedition
CL	Lovell, Chris
CLD	Chungtien, Lijiang & Dali Exped. China (1990)
CM&W	Cheese M.; Mitchel J. & Watson, J.
CN&W	Clark; Neilson & Wilson
CNDS	Nelson, C. & Sayers D.
COLA	Costin, J.J. & Lancaster, R., Japan (1990)
Cooper	Cooper, R.E.
Cox	Cox, Peter A.
CPC	Cobblewood Plant Collection
CPN	Compton, James
CS	Stapleton, Christopher
CSE	Cyclamen Society Expedition (1990)
CT	Teune, Carla
CW&T	Clark, A., Wilson, H. & Taggart, J., North Vietnam
CWJ	Colley, Finlay; Wynn-Jones, Bleddyn, Taiwan (2007)
Dahl	Dahl, Sally
DBG	Denver Botanic Garden, Colorado
DC	Cheshire, David
DF	Fox, D.
DG	Green, D.
DHTU	Hinkley, D., Turkey (2000)
DJF	Ferguson, Dave
DJH	Hinkley, Dan
DJHC	Hinkley D., China
DJHS	Hinkley, D., Sichuan
DJHV	Hinkley, D., Vietnam
DM	Millais, David
Doleshy	Doleshy, F.L.
DS&T	Drake, Sharman J. & Thompson
DWD	Rose, D.
DZ	Zummell, D.
ECN	Nelson, E. Charles
EDHCH	Hammond, Eric D.
EGM	Millais, T.
EKB	Balls, Edward K.
EM	East Malling Research Station
EMAK	Edinburgh Makalu Expedition (1991)
EMR	Rix, E.Martyn
EN	Needham, Edward F.
ENF	Fuller, E. Nigel
ETE	Edinburgh Taiwan Expedition (1993)
ETOT	Kirkham, T.S.; Flanagan, Mark
F	Forrest, G.
F&M	Fernandez & Mendoza, Mexico
F&W	Watson, J. & Flores, A.
Farrer	Farrer, Reginald
FK	Kinmonth, Fergus W.
FMB	Bailey, F.M.
G	Gardner, Martin F.
G&K	Gardner, Martin F. & Knees, Sabina G.
G&P	Gardner, Martin F. & Page, Christopher N.
GDJ	Dumont, Gerard
GG	Gusman, G.
GS	Sherriff, George
Green	Green, D.
Guitt	Guittoneau, G.G.
Guiz	Guizhou Expedition (1985)
GWJ	Goddard, Sally; Wynne-Jones, Bleddyn & Susan
G-W&P	Grey-Wilson, Christopher & Phillips
H	Huggins, Paul
H&B	Hilliard, Olive M. & Burtt, Brian L.
H&D	Howick, C. & Darby
H&M	Howick, Charles & McNamara, William A.
H&W	Hedge, Ian C. & Wendelbo, Per W.
Harry Smith	Smith, K.A.Harry
Hartside	Hartside Nursery
HCM	Heronswood Expedition to Chile (1998)
HECC	Hutchison; Evans; Cox, P.; Cox, K.
HEHEHE	Zetterlund, H. et al, Gothenburg Botanic Gardens Expedition to northern China
Hird	Hird
HH&K	Hannay, S & S & Kingsbury, N.
HK	Kuenzler, Horst
HLMS	Springate, L.S.
HM&S	Halliwell, B.; Mason, D. & Smallcombe
HOA	Hoog, Anton
HOLUB	Holubec, V.
HRS	Hers, J.
Hummel	Hummel, D.
HW&E	Wendelbo, Per; Hedge, I. & Ekberg, L.
HWEL	Hirst, J.Michael; Webster, D.
HWJ	Crûg Heronswood Joint Expedition
HWJCM	Crûg Heronswood Expedition
HWJK	Crûg Heronswood Expedition, East Nepal (2002)
HZ	Zetterlund, Henrik
ICE	Instituto de Investigaciónes Ecológicas Chiloé & RBGE
IDS	International Dendrological Society
ISI	Int. Succulent Introductions
J&JA	Archibald, James & Jennifer
J. Jurasek	Jurasek, J.
JCA	Archibald, James
JE	Jack Elliott
JJ	Jackson, J.
JJ&JH	Halda, J. & Halda, J.
JJH	Halda, Joseph J.
JL	Lode, Joel
JLS	Sharman, J.L.
JMH	Hoog, J. & M.
JM-MK	Mahr, J.; Kammerlander, M.

JMT	Mann Taylor, J.
JN	Nielson, Jens
JR	Russell, J.
JRM	Marr, John
JW	Watson, J.M.
K	Kirkpatrick, George
K&LG	Gillanders, Kenneth & Gillanders, L.
K&Mc	Kirkpatrick, George & McBeath, Ronald J.D.
K&P	Josef Kopec & Milan Prasil
K&T	Kurashige, Y. & Tsukie, S.
KC	Cox, Kenneth
KEKE	Kew/Edinburgh Kanchenjunga Expedition (1989)
KGB	Kunming/Gothenburg Botanical Expedition (1993)
KM	Marsh, K.
KMR	Kupčák, M.
KR	Rushforth, K.D.
KRW	Wooster, K.R. (distributed after his death by Kath Dryden)
KW	Kingdon-Ward, F.
KWJ	Crûg-World of Ferns Joint Expedition, Vietnam (2007)
L	Lancaster, C. Roy
L&S	Ludlow, Francis & Sherriff, George
LA	Long Ashton Research Station clonal selection scheme
LB	Bercht, L. (*Cactaceae*)
LB	Bird P.; Salmon, M.
LEG	Lesotho Edinburgh/Gothenburg Expedition (1997)
Lismore	Lismore Nursery, Breeder's Number
LM&S	Leslie, Mattern & Sharman
LP	Palmer, W.J.L.
LS&E	Ludlow, Frank; Sherriff, George & Elliott, E. E.
LS&H	Ludlow, Frank; Sherriff, George & Hicks, J. H.
LS&T	Ludlow, Frank; Sherriff, George & Taylor, George
LZ	Lutz, Eberhard
M&PS	Mike & Polly Stone
M&T	Mathew & Tomlinson
Mac&W	McPhail & Watson
McB	McBeath, R.J.D.
McLaren	McLaren, H.D.
MDM	Myers, Michael D.
MECC	Scottish Rock Garden Club, Nepal (1997)
MESE	Alpine Garden Society Expedition, Greece (1999)
MF	Foster, Maurice
MH	Heasman, Matthew T.
MK	Kammerlander, Michael
MP	Pavelka, Mojmir
MPF	Frankis, M.P.
MS	Salmon, M.
MS&CL	Salmon, M. & Lovell, C.

MSF	Fillan, M.S.
MUG	Uhlig, M.
NAPE	Hootman, S.; et al, Expedition to Naglaland and Arunachal Pradesh (2003)
NICE	North India Expedition (1997)
NJM	Macer, N.J.
NN	Nielsen & Nielsen (2009)
NNS	Ratko, Ron
NS	Turland, Nick
NVD	Expedition to Vietnam
NVFDE	Northern Vietnam First Darwin Expedition
Og	Ogisu, Mikinori
ORO	Oron, Peri
OS	Sonderhousen, O.
P. Bon	Bonavia, P.
P&C	Paterson, David S. & Clarke, Sidney
P&W	Polastri & Watson, J. M.
PAB	Barney, P.A.
PB	Bird, Peter
PBR	Bruggeman, P.
PC&H	Pattison, G.; Catt, P. & Hickson, M.
PD	Davis, Peter H.
PDM	Purdom, William
PF	Furse, Paul
PG	Pichler, G.
PJC	Christian, Paul J.
PJC&AH	P.J. Christian & A. Hogg
PNMK	Nicholls, P.; Kammerlander, M.
Polunin	Polunin, Oleg
Pras	Prasil, M.
PS&W	Polunin, Oleg; Sykes, William & Williams, John
PW	Wharton, Peter
R	Rock, J.F.C.
RB	Brown, R.
RBS	Brown, Ray, Sakharin Island
RCB AM	Brown, Robert, Expedition to Armenia
RCB/Arg	Brown, Robert, Argentina, (2002)
RCB E	Brown, Robert, Expedition to Spain (Andalucia)
RCB/Eq	Brown, Robert, Ecuador, (1988)
RCB RA	Brown, Robert
RCB RL	Brown, Robert, Expedition to Lebanon
RCB/TQ	Brown, Robert, Turkey (2001)
RE	Evans, Ron
RH	Hancock, R.
RJN	Neilsen, R.
RKMP	Ruksans, J.; Krumins, A.; Kitts, M.; Paivel, A.
RM	Ruksans, J. & Kitts, M.
RMRP	Rocky Mountain Rare Plants, Denver, Colorado
RS	Suckow, Reinhart
RSC	Richard Somer Cocks
RV	Richard Valder
RWJ	Crûg Farm-Rickards Ferns Expedition to Taiwan (2003)
S&B	Blanchard, J.W. & Salmon, M.

S&F	Salmon, M. & Fillan, M.
S&L	Sinclair, Ian W.J. & Long, David G.
S&SH	Sheilah & Spencer Hannay
Sandham	Sandham, John
SB	Brack, Steven
SB&L	Salmon, Bird & Lovell
SBEC	Sino-British Expedition to Cangshan
SBEL	Sino-British Lijiang Expedition
SBQE	Sino-British Expedition to Quinghai
Sch	Schilling, Anthony D.
SD	Sashal Dayal
SDR	Rankin, Stella & David
SEH	Hootman, Steve
SEP	Swedish Expedition to Pakistan
SF	Forde, P.
SG	Salmon, M. & Guy, P.
SH	Hannay, Spencer
Sich	Simmons, Erskine, Howick & Mcnamara
SJ	Johansson, Stellan
SLIZE	Swedish-Latvian-Iranian Zagros Expedition to Iran (May 1988)
SOJA	Kew/Quarryhill Expedition to Southern Japan
SS&W	Stainton, J.D. Adam; Sykes, William & Williams, John
SSNY	Sino-Scottish Expedition to NW Yunnan (1992)
T	Taylor, Nigel P.
T&K	Taylor, Nigel P. & Knees, Sabina
TCM	Mitchell, Thomas Carly
TG	Thomas, H-P. & Gilmer, K.
TH	Hudson, T.
TJR	Roberts, Tim
TS&BC	Smythe, T. & Cherry, B.
TSS	Spring Smyth, T.L.M.
TW	Weston, Tony
USDAPI	US Department of Agriculture Plant Index Number
USDAPQ	US Dept. of Agriculture Plant Quarantine Number
USNA	United States National Arboretum
VHH	Vernon H. Heywood
VV	Victor, David
W	Wilson, Ernest H.
W&B	Watkins, D. & Brown, R., Bulgaria (2012)
WJC	Wynn-Jones, B. & S. & Colley, F.
WM	McLewin, William
Woods	Woods, Patrick J.B.
Wr	Wraight, David & Anke
WWJ	Wharton, Peter; Wynn-Jones, Bleddyn & Susan
Yu	Yu, Tse-tsun
ZE&S	Zetterlund, H., Eriksson, A-I. & Strid, A.

Nomenclatural Notes

The following changes have been made during 2015 to the names used in the *RHS Plant Finder* based on decisions of the RHS Nomenclature and Taxonomy Advisory Group (NATAG). If you have any suggestions for other plant name changes within the *RHS Plant Finder*, then please write, stating your reasons in full to:

The Chairman & Vice-Chairman
Dr John Grimshaw & Dr Janet Cubey
Nomenclature and Taxonomy Advisory Group
Royal Horticultural Society
RHS Garden Wisley
Woking
Surrey
GU23 6QB

- Adopting the further splits of *Abelia: Diabelia* and *Vesalea*
- *Ammi visnaga* to *Visnaga daucoides*
- *Andrachne colchica* to *Leptopus chinensis*
- *Baloskion tetraphyllum* adopted for *Restio tetraphyllus*
- Adopting *Chaenostoma* for splits from *Sutera*, including *Sutera cordata*
- Separating *Charybdis* from *Urginea*
- *Chiastophyllum oppositifolium* to *Umbilicus oppositifolium*
- *Clerodendrum myricoides* to *Rotheca myricoides*
- Recognition of *Cyclamen hederifolium* subsp. *crassifolium* and *C. confusum*
- Separating *Clinanthus* from *Stenomesson*
- *Corymbia* distinct from *Eucalyptus*
- *Cosmos* × *Dahlia* 'Mexican Black' to *Dahlia* 'Mexican Black'
- Recognition of *Cornus* hybrids *C.* × *elwinortonii* (*C. kousa* × *C. nuttallii*) and *C.* × *rutgersensis* (*C. florida* × *C. kousa*)
- *Glandularia* separated as distinct from *Verbena*
- *Hutchinsia* and *Prizelago* sunk into *Hornungia*
- Recognising *Ismene* as distinct from *Hymenocallis*
- *Littonia modesta* to *Gloriosa modesta*
- Changes to *Meconopsis*, including transferring *M. cambrica* to *Papaver cambricum* and *M. villosa* to *Cathcartia villosa*
- *Murraya koenigii* replaced by *Bergera koenigii*
- *Nardostachys grandiflora* to *N. jatamansii* 'Grandiflora'
- *Onixotis stricta* to *Wurmbea stricta*
- *Othonna cheirifolia* to *Hertia cheirifolia*
- *Phlox* 'Bill Baker' and 'Morris Berd' both assigned to *P. glaberrima*
- *Phymatosorus diversifolius* to *Microsorium diversifolium*
- *Rhamnus pallasii replaced by R. erythroxyloides*
- *Rhodiola trollii* to *R. saxifragoides*
- *Sanvitalia procumbens* misattributed cultivars, to cultivars of *Melampodium montanum*
- Correcting the attribution of *Sedum* 'Chocolate Ball' from *S. hackonense* to *S. polytrichoides*
- Splits of *Senecio;* recognising *Curio, Caputia, Delairea, Jacobaea* and *Roldana*
- Incorporating *Spiloxene* within *Pauridia*
- Including *Stemmacantha* within *Rhaponticum*
- *Viburnum tinus* subsp. *subcordatum* to *V. treleasei*
- *Vigna caracalla* to *Cochliasanthus caracalla*
- *Wasabia wasabi* to *Eutrema japonicum*

This is not intended to be an exhaustive list of the changes made to the RHS Horticultural Database, reflected in the *RHS Plant Finder*; many more changes are made during the year by the RHS botanical team. This list is to highlight some of the some of the NATAG changes.

Changes already proposed for the 2017 edition of this book include:

- Adopting *Goeppartia,* as distinct from *Calathea*
- Separating *Hylotelephium* from *Sedum*
- Changes within *Wisteria* [*Bot. Mag.* Oct 2015, Vol 32]
- A revision of generic boundaries within *Rosaceae.*

Classification of Genera

Genera including a large number of species, or with many cultivars, are often subdivided into informal horticultural classifications, or formal cultivar groups in the case of *Clematis* and *Tulipa*. The breeding of new cultivars is sometimes limited to hybrids between closely related species, thus for *Saxifraga* and *Primula*, the cultivars are allocated to the sections given in the infrageneric treatments cited. Please turn to p.9 for a fuller explanation.

Acer

(A) Amoenum Group
(D) Dissectum Group
(Dw) Dwarf Group
(L) Linearilobum Group
(M) Matsumurae Group
(P) Palmatum Group

Actinidia

(s-p) Self-pollinating

Begonia

(C) Cane-like
(R) Rex Cultorum
(S) Semperflorens Cultorum
(T) × *tuberhybrida* (Tuberous)

Chrysanthemum

(By the National Chrysanthemum Society)
(1) Indoor Large (Exhibition)
(2) Indoor Medium (Exhibition)
(3a) Indoor Incurved: Large-flowered
(3b) Indoor Incurved: Medium-flowered
(3c) Indoor Incurved: Small-flowered
(4a) Indoor Reflexed: Large-flowered
(4b) Indoor Reflexed: Medium-flowered
(4c) Indoor Reflexed: Small-flowered
(5a) Indoor Intermediate: Large-flowered
(5b) Indoor Intermediate: Medium-flowered
(5c) Indoor Intermediate: Small-flowered
(6a) Indoor Anemone: Large-flowered
(6b) Indoor Anemone: Medium-flowered
(6c) Indoor Anemone: Small-flowered
(7a) Indoor Single: Large-flowered
(7b) Indoor Single: Medium-flowered
(7c) Indoor Single: Small-flowered
(8a) Indoor True Pompon
(8b) Indoor Semi-pompon
(9a) Indoor Spray: Anemone
(9b) Indoor Spray: Pompon
(9c) Indoor Spray: Reflexed
(9d) Indoor Spray: Single
(9e) Indoor Spray: Intermediate
(9f) Indoor Spray: Spider, Quill, Spoon or Any Other Type
(10a) Indoor, Spider
(10b) Indoor, Quill
(10c) Indoor, Spoon
(11) Any Other Indoor Type
(12a) Indoor, Charm
(12b) Indoor, Cascade
(13a) October-flowering Incurved: Large-flowered
(13b) October-flowering Incurved: Medium-flowered
(13c) October-flowering Incurved: Small-flowered
(14a) October-flowering Reflexed: Large-flowered
(14b) October-flowering Reflexed: Medium-flowered
(14c) October-flowering Reflexed: Small-flowered
(15a) October-flowering Intermediate: Large-flowered
(15b) October-flowering Intermediate: Medium-flowered
(15c) October-flowered Intermediate: Small-flowered
(16) October-flowering Large
(17a) October-flowering Single: Large-flowered
(17b) October-flowering Single: Medium-flowered
(17c) October-flowering Single: Small-flowered
(18a) October-flowering Pompon: True Pompon
(18b) October-flowering Pompon: Semi-pompon
(19a) October-flowering Spray: Anemone
(19b) October-flowering Spray: Pompon
(19c) October-flowering Spray: Reflexed
(19d) October-flowering Spray: Single
(19e) October-flowering Spray: Intermediate
(19f) October-flowering Spray: Spider, Quill, Spoon or Any Other Type
(20) Any Other October-flowering Type
(21a) Korean: Anemone
(21b) Korean: Pompon
(21c) Korean: Reflexed
(21d) Korean: Single
(21e) Korean: Intermediate
(21f) Korean: Spider, Quill, Spoon, or any other type
(22a) Charm: Anemone

(22b) Charm: Pompon
(22c) Charm: Reflexed
(22d) Charm: Single
(22e) Charm: Intermediate
(22f) Charm: Spider, Quill, Spoon or Any Other Type
(23a) Early-flowering Outdoor Incurved: Large-flowered
(23b) Early-flowering Outdoor Incurved: Medium-flowered
(23c) Early-flowering Outdoor Incurved: Small-flowered
(24a) Early-flowering Outdoor Reflexed: Large-flowered
(24b) Early-flowering Outdoor Reflexed: Medium-flowered
(24c) Early-flowering Outdoor Reflexed: Small-flowered
(25a) Early-flowering Outdoor Intermediate: Large-flowered
(25b) Early-flowering Outdoor Intermediate: Medium-flowered
(25c) Early-flowering Outdoor Intermediate: Small-flowered
(26a) Early-flowering Outdoor Anemone: Large-flowered
(26b) Early-flowering Outdoor Anemone: Medium-flowered
(27a) Early-flowering Outdoor Single: Large-flowered
(27b) Early-flowering Outdoor Single:Medium-flowered
(28a) Early-flowering Outdoor Pompon: True Pompon
(28b) Early-flowering Outdoor Pompon: Semi-pompon
(29a) Early-flowering Outdoor Spray: Anemone
(29b) Early-flowering Outdoor Spray: Pompon
(29c) Early-flowering Outdoor Spray: Reflexed
(29d) Early-flowering Outdoor Spray: Single
(29e) Early-flowering Outdoor Spray: Intermediate
(29f) Early-flowering Outdoor Spray: Spider, Quill, Spoon or Any Other Type
(29Rub) Early-flowering Outdoor Spray: Rubellum
(30) Any Other Early-flowering Outdoor Type

Clematis

(Cultivar Groups as per Matthews, V. (2002) *The International Clematis Register & Checklist 2002*, RHS, London.)

(A) Atragene Group
(Ar) Armandii Group
(C) Cirrhosa Group
(EL) Early Large-flowered Group
(F) Flammula Group
(Fo) Forsteri Group
(H) Heracleifolia Group
(I) Integrifolia Group
(LL) Late Large-flowered Group
(M) Montana Group
(T) Texensis Group
(Ta) Tangutica Group
(V) Viorna Group
(Vb) Vitalba Group
(Vt) Viticella Group

Dahlia

(Classification according to The International Dahlia Register (1969), 22nd Supp. (2012) formed through consultation with national dahlia societies.)

(Sin) 1 Single
(Anem) 2 Anemone-flowered
(Col) 3 Collerette
(WL) 4 Waterlily
(D) 5 Decorative
(Ba) 6 Ball
(Pom) 7 Pompon
(C) 8 Cactus
(S-c) 9 Semi-cactus
(Misc) 10 Miscellaneous
(Fim) 11 Fimbriated
(SinO) 12 Single Orchid (Star)
(DblO) 13 Double Orchid
(P) 14 Peony-flowered
(B) Botanical
(DwB) Dwarf Bedding
(Lil) Lilliput

Dianthus

(By the RHS)

(b) Carnation, border
(M) Carnation, Malmaison
(p) Pink
(p,a) Pink, annual
(pf) Carnation, perpetual-flowering
(pt) Carnation, pot

Fruit

(B) Black (*Vitis*), Blackberry (*Rubus*), Blackcurrant (*Ribes*)
(Ball) Ballerina (*Malus*)
(C) Culinary (*Malus, Prunus, Pyrus, Ribes*)
(Cider) Cider (*Malus*)
(D) Dessert (*Malus, Prunus, Pyrus, Ribes*)
(F) Fruit
(G) Glasshouse (*Vitis*)
(O) Outdoor (*Vitis*)
(P) Pinkcurrant (*Ribes*)
(Perry) Perry (*Pyrus*)

(R) Red (*Vitis*), Redcurrant (*Ribes*)
(S) Seedless (*Citrus*, *Vitis*)
(W) White (*Vitis*), Whitecurrant (*Ribes*)

Fuchsia

(E) Encliandra
(T) Variants and hybrids of *F. triphylla*

Gladiolus

(B) Butterfly
(E) Exotic
(G) Giant
(L) Large
(M) Medium
(Min) Miniature
(N) Nanus
(P) Primulinus
(S) Small
(Tub) Tubergenii

Hepatica nobilis

(Adapted from the International Hepatica Society classification for *Hepatica nobilis*)
(1) Hyoujun (normal)
(2) (degenerated anther)
(3) Otome (degenerated stamen)
(4) Henka (petal deformity)
(5/d) Herashibe (semi-double, primitive)
(5A/d) Choji (semi-double, primitive)
(6/d) Nidan (semi-double, advanced)
(7/d) Sandan (double, primitive)
(8/d) Karako (double, advanced)
(9/d) Sene-e (double, completed)

Hydrangea macrophylla

(H) Hortensia
(L) Lacecap

Impatiens

(NG) New Guinea Group

Iris

(Adapted from the American Iris Society Classification)
(AB) Arilbred
(BB) Border Bearded
(Cal-Sib) Series *Californicae* × Series *Sibiricae*
(CH) Californian Hybrid
(DB) Dwarf Bearded (not assigned)
(Dut) Dutch
(IB) Intermediate Bearded
(J) Juno (subgenus *Scorpiris*)
(La) Louisiana Hybrid
(MDB) Miniature Dwarf Bearded
(MTB) Miniature Tall Bearded
(Rc) Regeliocyclus (Section *Regelia* × Section *Oncocyclus*)
(Reticulata)
(SDB) Standard Dwarf Bearded
(Sib) Siberian
(Sino-Sib) Series *Sibiricae*, chromosome number 2n=40
(SpH) Species Hybrid
(Spuria) Spuria
(TB) Tall Bearded

Lilium

(Classification according to *The International Lily Register* (ed. 4, 2007))
(I) Asiatic hybrids derived from *L. amabile, L. bulbiferum, L. callosum, L. cernuum, L. concolor, L. dauricum, L. davidii, L.* × *hollandicum, L. lancifolium, L. lankongense, L. leichtlinii, L.* × *maculatum* and *L. pumilum, L.* × *scottiae, L. wardii* and *L. wilsonii.*
(II) Martagon hybrids derived from *L. dalhansonii, L. hansonii, L. martagon, L. medeoloides and L. tsingtauense*
(III) Euro-Caucasian hybrids derived from *L. candidum, L. chalcedonicum, L. kesselringianum, L. monadelphum, L. pomponium, L. pyrenaicum* and *L.* × *testaceum.*
(IV) American hybrids derived from *L. bolanderi, L.* × *burbankii, L. canadense, L. columbianum, L. grayi, L. humboldtii, L. kelleyanum, L. kelloggii, L. maritimum, L. michauxii, L. michiganense, L. occidentale, L.* × *pardaboldtii, L. pardalinum, L. parryi, L. parvum, L. philadelphicum, L. pitkinense, L. superbum, L. vollmeri, L. washingtonianum* and *L. wigginsii.*
(V) Longiflorum lilies derived from *L. formosanum, L. longiflorum, L. philippinense and L. wallichianum.*
(VI) Trumpet and Aurelian hybrids derived from *L.* × *aurelianense, L. brownii, L.* × *centigale, L. henryi, L.* × *imperiale, L.* × *kewense, L. leucantheum, L. regale, L. rosthornii, L. sargentiae, L. sulphureum* and *L. sulphurgale* (but excluding hybrids of *L. henryi* with all species listed in Division VII).
(VII) Oriental hybrids derived from *L. auratum, L. japonicum, L. nobilissimum, L.* × *parkmanii, L rubellum* and *L. speciosum* (but excl. all hybrids of these with *L. henryi*).
(VIII) Other hybrids not covered by any of the previous divisions (I-VII)
(IX) Species and cultivars of species
a/ upward-facing flowers
b/ outward-facing flowers
c/ downward-facing flowers
/a trumpet-shaped flowers

/b	bowl-shaped flowers
/c	flat flowers (or with only tepal tips recurved)
/d	recurved flowers

MALUS *SEE* FRUIT

NARCISSUS

(By the RHS, revised 1998)

(1)	Trumpet
(2)	Large-cupped
(3)	Small-cupped
(4)	Double
(5)	Triandrus
(6)	Cyclamineus
(7)	Jonquilla and Apodanthus
(8)	Tazetta
(9)	Poeticus
(10)	Bulbocodium
(11a)	Split-corona: Collar
(11b)	Split-corona: Papillon
(12)	Miscellaneous
(13)	Species

NYMPHAEA

(H)	Hardy
(D)	Day-blooming
(N)	Night-blooming
(T)	Tropical

PAEONIA

(S)	Shrubby

PELARGONIUM

(A)	Angel
(C)	Coloured Foliage (in combination)
(Ca)	Cactus (in combination)
(d)	Double (in combination)
(Dec)	Decorative
(Dw)	Dwarf
(DwI)	Dwarf Ivy-leaved
(Fr)	Frutetorum
(I)	Ivy-leaved
(Min)	Miniature
(MinI)	Miniature Ivy-leaved
(R)	Regal
(Sc)	Scented-leaved
(St)	Stellar (in combination)
(T)	Tulip (in combination)
(U)	Unique
(Z)	Zonal

PRIMULA

(Classification by Section as per Richards. J. (2002) *Primula* (2nd edition). Batsford, London)

(Ag)	*Auganthus*
(Al)	*Aleuritia*
(Am)	*Amethystinae*
(Ar)	*Armerina*
(Au)	*Auricula*
(A)	Alpine Auricula
(B)	Border Auricula
(S)	Show Auricula
(St)	Striped Auricula
(Bu)	*Bullatae*
(Ca)	*Capitatae*
(Cf)	*Cordifoliae*
(Ch)	*Chartaceae*
(Co)	*Cortusoides*
(Cr)	*Carolinella*
(Cu)	*Cuneifoliae*
(Cy)	*Crystallophlomis*
(Da)	*Davidii*
(De)	*Denticulatae*
(Dr)	*Dryadifoliae*
(F)	*Fedtschenkoanae*
(G)	*Glabrae*
(Ma)	*Malvaceae*
(Mi)	*Minutissimae*
(Mo)	*Monocarpicae*
(Mu)	*Muscarioides*
(Ob)	*Obconicolisteri*
(Or)	*Oreophlomis*
(Pa)	*Parryi*
(Pe)	*Petiolares*
(Pf)	*Proliferae*
(Pi)	*Pinnatae*
(Pr)	*Primula*
(Poly)	Polyanthus
(Prim)	Primrose
(Pu)	*Pulchellae*
(Py)	*Pycnoloba*
(R)	*Reinii*
(Si)	*Sikkimenses*
(So)	*Soldanelloides*
(Sp)	*Sphondylia*
(Sr)	*Sredinskya*
(Su)	*Suffrutescentes*
(Y)	*Yunnanenses*

PRUNUS *SEE* FRUIT

PYRUS *SEE* FRUIT

RHODODENDRON

(A)	Azalea (deciduous, species or unclassified hybrid)
(Ad)	Azaleodendron
(EA)	Evergreen azalea
(G)	Ghent azalea (deciduous)
(K)	Knap Hill or Exbury azalea (deciduous)
(M)	Mollis azalea (deciduous)
(O)	Occidentalis azalea (deciduous)
(R)	Rustica azalea (deciduous)
(V)	Vireya rhododendron
(Vs)	Viscosa azalea (deciduous)

Ribes *see* Fruit

Rosa

(A)	Alba
(Bb)	Bourbon
(Bs)	Boursault
(Ce)	Centifolia
(Ch)	China
(Cl)	Climbing (in combination)
(D)	Damask
(DPo)	Damask Portland
(F)	Floribunda or Cluster-flowered
(G)	Gallica
(Ga)	Garnette
(GC)	Ground Cover
(HM)	Hybrid Musk
(HP)	Hybrid Perpetual
(HT)	Hybrid Tea or Large-flowered
(Min)	Miniature
(Mo)	Moss (in combination)
(N)	Noisette
(Patio)	Patio, Miniature Floribunda or Dwarf Cluster-flowered
(Poly)	Polyantha
(Ra)	Rambler
(RH)	Rubiginosa hybrid (Hybrid Sweet Briar)
(Ru)	Rugosa
(S)	Shrub
(SpH)	Spinosissima Hybrid
(T)	Tea

Rubus *see* Fruit

Saxifraga

(Classification by Section from Gornall, R.J. (1987). *Botanical Journal of the Linnean Society,* 95(4): 273-292)

(1)	*Ciliatae*
(2)	*Cymbalaria*
(3)	*Merkianae*
(4)	*Micranthes*
(5)	*Irregulares*
(6)	*Heterisia*
(7)	*Porphyrion*
(8)	*Ligulatae*
(9)	*Xanthizoon*
(10)	*Trachyphyllum*
(11)	*Gymnopera*
(12)	*Cotylea*
(13)	*Odontophyllae*
(14)	*Mesogyne*
(15)	*Saxifraga*

Tulipa

(Classification by Cultivar Group from *Classified List and International Register of Tulip Names* by Koninklijke Algemeene Vereniging voor Bloembollencultuur 1996)

(1)	Single Early Group
(2)	Double Early Group
(3)	Triumph Group
(4)	Darwin Hybrid Group
(5)	Single Late Group (including Darwin Group and Cottage Group)
(6)	Lily-flowered Group
(7)	Fringed Group
(8)	Viridiflora Group
(9)	Rembrandt Group
(10)	Parrot Group
(11)	Double Late Group
(12)	Kaufmanniana Group
(13)	Fosteriana Group
(14)	Greigii Group
(15)	Miscellaneous

Verbena

(G)	Species and hybrids considered by some botanists to belong to the separate genus *Glandularia* are included in *Glandularia* in this edition for the first time.

Viola

(C)	Cornuta Hybrid
(dVt)	Double Violet
(ExVa)	Exhibition Viola
(FP)	Fancy Pansy
(P)	Pansy
(PVt)	Parma Violet
(SP)	Show Pansy
(T)	Tricolor
(Va)	Viola
(Vt)	Violet
(Vtta)	Violetta

Vitis *see* Fruit

THE PLANT DIRECTORY

A

Abelia ✿ (*Caprifoliaceae*)

	chinensis misapplied	see *A.* × *grandiflora* 'Lake Maggiore'
§	***chinensis*** R. Br.	CBcs CExl CMCN CMac EBee EHyd ELan EPfP EWTr LRHS MAsh MGil MMuc SEND SPer SRms WGrn
§	***dielsii***	CBot
	'Edward Goucher' 🏆H5	Widely available
	engleriana	CExl CRos EHyd EPfP LRHS MAsh MBlu MGil NLar SLon
	floribunda	see *Vesalea floribunda*
§	× ***grandiflora***	CChe CTho ELan ETMg EWTr LCro LOPS LRHS MJak SRms SWeb WAvo
	- 'Aurea'	see *A.* × *grandiflora* 'Gold Spot'
	- 'Brockhill Allgold'	EMil EPfP LRHS SPoG
	- common clone	see *A.* × *grandiflora* 'Lake Maggiore'
	- 'Compacta'	WFar
	- CONFETTI ('Conti'PBR) (v)	CBcs CMac CRos CSBt ECrN EHyd ELan EMOT EMil EPfP GMcL LRHS LSRN MAsh MGos MRav NLar SCob SEle SGol SLim SPer SPoG SWvt WFar
§	- 'Francis Mason' (v)	Widely available
§	- 'Gold Spot' (v)	CBot EPfP NLar SPer
	- 'Gold Strike'	see *A.* × *grandiflora* 'Gold Spot'
	- GOLDEN PANACHE ('Minpan')	MRav
	- 'Goldsport'	see *A.* × *grandiflora* 'Gold Spot'
	- 'Hopleys'PBR (v) 🏆H5	CBcs CMac CRos CSBt CTri EHyd ELan EMil EPfP EWTr LRHS MAsh MGos NLar SCob SEle SGol SLon SRms SWvt WGrn WHar
	- 'Kaleidoscope'PBR (v)	CMac CRos CWGN ECrN EHoe ELan EPfP EShb ETMg LCro LRHS LSRN MAsh MGos MJak MPkF NLar NRHS SCob SGol SLim SPer SPoG SRms SWvt WCot WFar
	- LADY LIBERTY ('Keylib')	LRHS
§	- 'Lake Maggiore' 🏆H5	CBar CBot CMac CSBt CTri EHoe ELan EMOT EPfP MBlu MGil MGos MMuc MRav MSwo SCob SEND SPer SPoG SSta WHar
	- LUCKY LOTS ('Wevo2') (v)	LLHF NLar SCob SGol
	- 'Panache' (v)	LLHF WCot
	- 'Prostrate White'	ECrN LRHS NLar SPoG
	- 'Radiance' (v) **new**	NEoE
	- 'Semperflorens'	LRHS
	- 'Sherwoodii'	ECrN EHoe EPfP LRHS MAsh MGos SGol WRHF
	- 'Sparkling Silver' (v)	LRHS
	- SUNNY CHARMS ('Mindu01'PBR)	LCro
	- 'Sunrise' (v)	NLar
	- SUNSHINE DAYDREAM ('Abelops'PBR) (v)	CEnd ECrN LCro LLHF LOPS LRHS MMrt MPkF NLar SCob SGbt SGol SRms
	- 'Tanya'	WAvo
	- 'Variegata'	see *A.* × *grandiflora* 'Francis Mason'
§	'Lynn'PBR	EMOT LLHF LRHS MGos MPkF SCob SPoG
	mosanensis	CBot CMCN CRos EHyd ELan EPfP LLHF LRHS MBlu MGil NLar SLon SPoG WGob
	- BRIDAL BOUQUET ('Monia')	LRHS SChF
	parvifolia	CBcs CBot CExl CMac CSBt CTri EHyd EPfP LRHS MGil NLar NRHS SGbt SLim SLon SPer SWvt WGrn
	- 'Bumblebee'	LCro LOPS MAsh MPkF NLar
	PASTEL CHARM ('Minduo2')	LRHS
	PETITE GARDEN ('Minedward'PBR)	LRHS SGol
	PINKY BELLS	see *A.* 'Lynn'
	rupestris misapplied	see *A.* × *grandiflora*
	rupestris Lindl.	see *A. chinensis* R. Br.
	serrata	see *Diabelia serrata*
	triflora	see *Zabelia triflora*
	zanderi	see *A. dielsii*

Abeliophyllum (*Oleaceae*)

distichum	CBcs CDul CEnd CRos ECrN EHyd ELan ELon EPfP IDee LRHS MAsh MBlu NRHS SGol SWvt WCFE WFar WSHC
- Roseum Group	CBcs CExl CRos CWld EHyd ELan ELon EPfP LCro LOPS LRHS MAsh MGil MMuc MRav SGol SLon SMad SPer SPoG

Abelmoschus (*Malvaceae*)

esculentus	SVic

Abies ✿ (*Pinaceae*)

sp.	LPra
alba	CAco CDul CPer MMuc
- 'Bystricka'	NLar
- 'Compacta'	CKen
- 'Fastigata' **new**	GMil
- 'Green Spiral'	NLar
- 'King's Dwarf'	CKen
- 'Microphylla'	CKen
- 'Münsterland'	CKen
- 'Nana' misapplied	see *Picea glauca* 'Nana'
- 'Nana' ambig.	CKen
- 'Pendula'	CKen
- 'Pyramidata' **new**	GMil
amabilis 'Spreading Star'	SLim
arizonica	see *A. lasiocarpa* var. *arizonica*
balsamea	MAsh MMuc
- 'Cook's Blue'	CKen

	- 'Eugene Gold'	NLar
	- Hudsonia Group	CKen LRHS SLim
	- - 'Hudsonia' ♀H7	NRHS
	- - 'Nana'	CKen ELan LRHS MGil MJak NEgg NRHS NWad
	- 'Jamie'	CKen
	- 'Kiwi'	NLar
	- 'Le Feber'	CKen
	- 'Little Carleigh'	NLar
	- var. ***phanerolepis*** 'Bear Swamp'	CKen
	- 'Piccolo'	CKen LRHS NLar SLim
	- 'Renswoude'	CKen
	- 'Sky Meadow' **new**	NLar
	- 'Tyler Blue'	CKen NLar
	- 'Verkade's Prostrate'	CKen
	borisii-regis	CDul
*	- 'Pendula'	CKen
	- 'Spring Delight'	LRHS
	brachyphylla dwarf	see *A. homolepis* 'Prostrata'
	cephalonica	CDul CKen
	- 'Greg's Broom'	CKen NLar
§	- 'Meyer's Dwarf'	GMil NEgg NLar SLim
	- 'Nana'	see *A. cephalonica* 'Meyer's Dwarf'
	chensiensis	LRHS
	cilicica 'Spring Grove'	CKen
	concolor	CAco CBcs CDul CTho LMaj LPra LRHS MMuc NRHS SEND
	- 'Archer's Dwarf'	CKen NEgg NLar SLim
	- 'Aurea'	NLar
	- 'Birthday Broom'	CKen
	- 'Blue Cloak'	CKen
	- 'Blue Sapphire'	CKen
	- 'Bryce Canyon'	NLar
§	- 'Compacta' ♀H7	CKen LRHS MGos NEgg NLar SLim
	- 'Fagerhult'	CKen
	- 'Gable's Weeping'	CKen
	- 'Glauca'	see *A. concolor* (Violacea Group) 'Violacea'
	- 'Glauca Compacta'	see *A. concolor* 'Compacta'
	- 'Hillier Broom'	see *A. concolor* 'Hillier's Dwarf'
§	- 'Hillier's Dwarf'	CKen
	- 'Husky Pup'	CKen
	- 'La Veta'	CKen
	- (Lowiana Group) 'Creamy'	CKen GMil NEgg NLar
	- 'Masonic Broom'	CKen NLar
	- 'Mike Stearn'	CKen
	- 'Mora'	CKen
	- 'Ostrov nad Ohri'	CKen
	- 'Piggelmee'	CKen MAsh NLar
	- 'Pygmy'	CKen
	- 'Scooter'	CKen NLar
	- 'Sherwood's Blue'	NEgg
	- Violacea Group	CKen SLim
§	- - 'Violacea' ♀H7	GMil
	- - 'Violacea Prostrate' ♀H7	NLar
	- 'Viona'	NLar
	- 'Wattezii'	CKen
	- 'Wintergold'	CAco CKen LRHS MBlu NEgg NLar SLim
	delavayi	EPfP LEdu LRHS
	- 'Buchanan'	NLar
	- var. ***delavayi***	CExl
	- - Fabri Group	see *A. fabri*
	- 'Major Neishe'	CKen
§	***fabri***	CDul CKen
	fargesii	CKen
	firma	CDul
	forrestii	CKen
	fraseri	CAco CBcs CDul CPer CTho MMuc WMou WTSh
	- 'Blue Bonnet'	CKen
	- 'Franklin' **new**	NLar
	- 'Kline's Nest'	SLim
	- 'Palmeri' **new**	NLar
	- 'Piglet's' witches' broom	NLar
	- 'Raul's Dwarf'	CKen
	grandis	CBcs CDul CJun CMCN CPer ELan EPfP LPra MMuc WTSh
	- 'Compacta'	CKen
	- 'Van Dedem's Dwarf'	CKen SLim
	homolepis	CDul CKen
§	- 'Prostrata'	CKen
	koreana ♀H7	Widely available
	- 'Alpin Star'	CKen MAsh NEgg NLar
	- 'Blaue Zwo'	CKen LRHS
	- 'Blauer Eskimo' ♀H7	CKen MAsh NLar SLim
	- 'Blauer Pfiff'	CKen
	- 'Blinsham Gold'	CKen
	- 'Blue Emperor'	CAco MBlu NLar
	- 'Blue Magic'	CAco CKen NLar
	- 'Brilliant'	CKen
	- 'Cis' ♀H7	CKen LRHS NLar SLim
	- CRYSTAL GLOBE	see *A. koreana* 'Kristallkugel'
	- 'Discus' **new**	NLar
	- 'Doni-tajuso'	CKen
	- 'Eisregen'	CKen
	- 'Festival'	NEgg
	- 'Frosty'	SLim
	- 'Gait'	CKen NLar
	- 'Golden Glow'	SLim
	- 'Goldener Traum'	CKen NLar
	- 'Green Carpet'	CKen GMil LRHS NLar
	- 'Green 'n' Cream' **new**	CAco
	- 'Horstmann'	CKen
	- 'Inge'	NLar
	- 'Inverleith'	CKen
	- 'Kleiner Prinz'	NLar
	- 'Kohout'	CKen
	- 'Kohout's Ice Breaker' PBR ♀H7	CAco CKen LRHS MAsh MGos NLar SLim
	- 'Kosmos' **new**	NLar
§	- 'Kristallkugel'	CKen MAsh NEgg NLar
	- 'Lippetal'	CKen
	- 'Luminetta'	CAco CKen LRHS
	- 'Nadelkissen'	CKen
	- 'Nisbet'	CAco NEgg
	- 'Oberon'	CKen MAsh NLar
	- 'Piccolo'	CKen
	- 'Pinocchio'	CKen NWad
	- 'Prostrata'	see *A. koreana* 'Prostrate Beauty'
§	- 'Prostrate Beauty'	GMil
	- 'Ry'	NLar
	- 'Schillerlocke' **new**	NLar
	- 'Schneestern'	NLar
	- 'Sherwood Compact'	CKen
	- 'Shorty'	CKen NLar
	- 'Silberkugel'	CKen CMen MAsh NLar NWad SLim
	- 'Silberlocke' ♀H7	CCVT CDul CKen LRHS MAsh MBlu MGos NLar NOra NRHS SCoo SLim WHar
	- 'Silbermavers'	CKen
	- 'Silberperl'	CKen CMen LRHS NLar SLim
	- 'Silberschmelze'	NLar
	- 'Silver Show'	CAco CDul LRHS NLar
	- 'Threave'	CKen
	- 'Tundra'	NEgg NLar
	- 'Wellenseind'	CKen NLar

	lasiocarpa	MMuc
	- 'Alpine Beauty'	CKen NLar
§	- var. ***arizonica***	CAco
	- - 'Compacta' Hornibr. ♀H7	CAco CCVT CKen GMil LRHS MAsh MGos SLim SPoG
	- - 'Kenwith Blue'	CKen NEgg SLim
	- 'Beano Broom'	CKen
	- 'Chikov'	CKen
	- 'Day Creek'	CKen NLar
	- 'Duflon'	CKen MAsh NLar
	- 'Elaine'	CKen
	- 'Green Globe'	CKen GMil NLar SLim
	- 'Joe's Alpine'	CKen
	- 'Kyle's Alpine'	CKen NLar
	- 'Logan Pass'	CKen
	- 'Lopalpun'	CKen
	- 'Mulligan's Dwarf'	CKen
	- 'Prickly Pete'	CKen NLar
	- 'Stevens Blue'	CKen
	- 'Toenisvorst'	CKen
	- 'Utah'	CKen
	magnifica 'Mount Si'	CKen NLar
I	- 'Nana'	CKen
	- witches' broom	CKen
	marocana	see *A. pinsapo* var. *marocana*
	nebrodensis	CKen
	- 'Sicilian Gold'	NLar
	nephrolepis	CAco
	nobilis	see *A. procera*
	nordmanniana	CAco CCVT CDul CJun CMCN CMac CPer CTho ELan EPfP GMcL IBoy LBuc LMaj LPra MJak MMuc NLar SEND SLim SPoG WHar WMou WTSh
	- 'Arne's Dwarf'	CKen
	- 'Barabits' Compact'	GMil LRHS NLar
	- 'Barabits' Spreader'	CKen
	- 'Dobřichovice'	NLar
	- subsp. ***equi-trojani***	CDul
	- - 'Archer'	CKen
	- - 'Franke'	NLar
	- 'Filip's Gold Heart' **new**	NLar
	- 'Filip's Perfect Column' **new**	NLar
	- 'Golden Spreader' ♀H7	CAco CKen CMac GMil LRHS MAsh MBlu MGos NEgg NLar SCoo SLim
	- 'Hasselt'	see *A. nordmanniana* 'Peve Hasselt'
	- 'Jakobsen'	CKen
	- 'Kbng'	NLar
	- 'Midwinter Gold'	NLar
	- 'Münsterland'	NLar
	- 'Peli'	NLar
	- 'Pendula'	LRHS MBlu SMad
§	- 'Peve Hasselt'	CKen
	- 'Silberspitze'	CKen
	numidica	CKen
	- 'Glauca'	CKen
	- 'Lawrenceville'	NEgg
	pinsapo	CDul WThu
	- 'Atlas'	CKen MAsh NLar
	- 'Aurea' ♀H5	CAco CCVT CKen ELan LRHS MPkF SLim
I	- 'Aurea Nana'	CKen
	- 'Fastigiata'	CAco MPkF SGol
	- 'Glauca' ♀H5	CAco CCVT CDul CKen CTho ELan LRHS MBlu NLar SLim
	- 'Hamondii'	CKen
I	- 'Horstmann'	CKen NEgg NLar SLim
§	- var. ***marocana***	CDul
	- 'Marokko'	NLar
	- 'Pendula'	CAco CKen LRHS
	- 'Quicksilver'	CKen
	- 'Ronda Mountain'	NLar
	- 'San Pedro'	CKen
	- 'Ubrique' **new**	NLar
§	***procera***	CBcs CDul CMCN CPer EPfP LPra WTSh
	- 'Aurea' **new**	LRHS
	- 'Bizarro'	NEgg
	- 'Blaue Hexe'	CKen LRHS NEgg SLim
	- 'Delbar Cascade'	CKen
	- Glauca Group	CAco CDul EPfP GKin LPra LRHS MBlu NLar SLim
	- - 'Glauca' ♀H6 **new**	CTho LMaj
	- - 'Glauca Prostrata' ♀H6	SLim
	- 'Hupp's Dwarf'	CKen NLar
	- 'La Graciosa'	NLar
	- 'Pospíšil' **new**	CKen
	- 'Rat Tail'	NLar
	- 'Seattle Mount'	CKen
	- 'Sherwoodii'	CKen NLar SLim
	Rosemoor hybrid	CKen
	sachalinensis	CKen
	sibirica	EPfP
	spectabilis	EPfP
	veitchii	LPra NEgg WTSh
	- 'Heddergott'	CKen NEgg NLar SLim
	- 'Heine'	CKen
	- 'Kramer'	CKen
	- 'Otovenack'	NLar
I	- 'Pendula'	CKen
	- 'Rumburk'	CKen NLar SLim
	- 'Secrest' **new**	NLar
	- 'Syców'	CKen

Abromeitiella see *Deuterocohnia*

Abutilon ✿ (*Malvaceae*)

	'Ashford Red'	CBcs CCCN ELan LRHS WCot WFar WKif
	'Canary Bird' ♀H1b	CBcs CCCN CHll ELan WKif
	'Cannington Carol' (v) ♀H1b	CCCN ELan EMil LLHF LSRN SEND SLim
	'Cannington Peter' (v) ♀H1b	CCCN LSRN
	'Cloth of Gold'	CMac
	'Cynthia Pike' (v)	CRos EHyd EPfP LRHS NRHS
	'Flamenco'	CCCN CWGN
	'Hinton Seedling'	CCCN CRHN
	indicum	EBtc
	'John Thompson'	CCCN CWGN LSRN WCot
	'Kentish Belle' ♀H3	Widely available
	LUCKY LANTERN TANGERINE ('Nuabtang')	SPad
	'Marion' ♀H1b	CCCN CRHN CRos EHyd EPfP LRHS LSRN NRHS SPlb
	'Master Michael'	CMac
	megapotamicum ♀H3	CAby CBcs CBot CCCN CChe CHll CMac CRHN CRos CTri ELan ELon EMOT EPfP EUJe LRHS MGos MRav MSCN SCob SEND SEle SGol SLim SPer SPoG SRms WSHC XLum
	- 'Big Bell'	WGob
	- 'Ines'	ELon SChF WPGP
	- 'Variegatum' (v) ♀H3	CAby CBcs CBot CCCN CMac CRos ELon EPfP EUJe LRHS MGil SEle SLim SLon SMad SNig SPer SPoG SWvt WGob

- 'Wisley Red'	CRHN CTsd LRHS
× ***milleri*** hort. ♀H3	CCCN CMac CRHN WCot
- 'Variegatum' (v)	CCCN CMac LRHS WCot
'Nabob' ♀H1b	CBcs CCCN CExl CRHN EMOT EShb EUJe SAko SEND
'Orange Hot Lava'	CBcs CBct CExl EBee SChF SMad WPGP
'Patrick Synge'	CBcs CCCN CHGN CHll EBee SPhx WPGP
pictum 'Thompsonii' (v) ♀H1b	CCCN
'Pink Lady'	CCCN
'Russels Dwarf'	CCCN
'Savitzii' (v) ♀H1b	MSCN
'Silver Belle'	CCCN
'Simcox White'	CCCN
'Souvenir de Bonn' (v) ♀H1b	CCCN CHll
× ***suntense***	CBcs CCCN CRos CSBt EHyd EPfP EUJe EWld LRHS MSCN NPer NRHS
- 'Jermyns' ♀H4	CExl ELon EPfP LSRN MGos SAko SCoo SPoG SWvt
- 'Violetta'	CBot WSHC WSpi
'Tango'	CCCN CKel CWGN EUJe WGob
'Victory'	CCCN CWGN
vitifolium	CBcs CBot CCCN CDTJ EBee MHer NChi NEgg SPad SPer SPtp WFar WKif WSpi
- 'Album'	CBcs CCCN CExl WSHC WSpi
- 'Buckland'	CCCN
- 'Tennant's White' ♀H4	CBot CCCN CExl CRos EHyd EPfP LRHS NRHS SAko WCot
- 'Veronica Tennant' ♀H4	CExl EBee EPfP LRHS SChF
'Waltz'	CCCN CWGN EMOT EShb EUJe LLHF SBod WCot WGob
YELLOW TRUMPET ('Oosttrump'PBR)	CBot

Acacia (*Mimosaceae*)

acinacea	SPlb
adunca	SPlb
angustissima	SPlb
axillaris	SPlb
baileyana ♀H2	CBcs CCCN CEnd CMac CSBt EHoe ELan EPfP LRHS LSRN MGos SBig SCoo SPer SPlb SWvt WFar
- var. ***aurea***	SPlb
- 'Purpurea' ♀H3	CAby CBcs CBod CCCN CDul CEnd CExl CMac CSBt CSpe CTri CTsd EBee ELan EPfP LSRN MGos NOra SBig SCoo SGol SMad SPlb SPoG SWvt WCot WFar WPGP
- 'Songlines'	CRos LRHS MGos NRHS
boormanii	CAbb GBin SPlb WPGP
cultriformis	CTsd
dealbata ♀H2	Widely available
- 'Gaulois Astier'	CRos CSBt EMil LRHS LSRN MGos NRHS SGol SPoG SWvt
- subsp. ***subalpina***	WPGP
'Exeter Hybrid'	CSBt
glaucoptera	SPlb
gregorii	SPlb
jibberdingensis	SPlb
julibrissin	see *Albizia julibrissin*
karroo	see *Vachellia karroo*
longifolia	CDTJ LRHS
macradenia	SPlb
melanoxylon	CBcs CDTJ CMCN SPlb
pataczekii	CSBt EPfP WPGP
pendula	SPlb
podalyriifolia	SPlb
pravissima ♀H3	CAbb CBcs CChe CDul CExl CHll CMac CRos CTri CTsd ELan EPfP GBin IDee ILea LRHS LSRN SAko SArc SLim SMad SPlb SWvt
retinodes	CBcs CCCN CDTJ CTsd MMuc SEND SPad SWvt
- blue-leaved	CTsd
- 'Lisette'	LRHS MGos
riceana	CTsd SVen
rubida	CTsd SPlb
sentis	see *A. victoriae*
spectabilis	SPlb
suaveolens	SPlb
truncata	SPlb
verticillata	CBcs CDTJ CHGN CHll EPfP
- riverine form	CCCN CExl EPfP LRHS SAko SEND
§ ***victoriae***	SPlb

Acaena (*Rosaceae*)

adscendens misapplied	see *A. affinis*, *A. saccaticupula* 'Blue Haze'
§ ***affinis***	EBee ECha
anserinifolia misapplied	see *A. novae-zelandiae*
§ ***anserinifolia*** (Forst. & Forst. f.) Druce	MMuc
argentea	GJos
buchananii	EBee EHoe EPPr GAbr GBin GCrg MBrN MMuc NLar SCob SRms
caerulea hort.	see *A. caesiiglauca*
§ ***caesiiglauca***	GAbr GMaP
inermis	SPlb
- 'Purpurea'	CSam EBee ECha ECtt EHoe EUJe EWes GAbr GCrg GMaP MMuc NDov NHpl NLar NWad SPlb WMoo XLum
magellanica	GAbr GCal GKev
microphylla ♀H5	CSam MBel MBrN NLar SPlb SRms WMoo
- COPPER CARPET	see *A. microphylla* 'Kupferteppich'
- 'Glauca'	see *A. caesiiglauca*
- 'Grüner Zwerg'	NLar
§ - 'Kupferteppich'	CSam ECtt EHoe ELan EPPr GAbr GBin GCal GCrg GKev GLog GMaP LEdu MHol MRav NBro NLar SCob SMHy SRms WMoo XLum
minor var. ***antarctica***	GBin
§ ***novae-zelandiae***	CTri EBee GJos GKev WMoo XLum
ovalifolia	GJos GKev
'Pewter'	see *A. saccaticupula* 'Blue Haze'
profundeincisa	see *A. anserinifolia* (Forst. & Forst. f.) Druce
'Purple Carpet'	see *A. microphylla* 'Kupferteppich'
'Purple Haze'	CSpe SCob
saccaticupula	GKev MMuc
§ - 'Blue Haze'	CRos EBee ECha EDAr EHyd GJos LRHS MBrN MRav NRHS SPer SPlb SRms WMoo
sanguisorbae	see *A. anserinifolia* (Forst. & Forst. f.) Druce
sericea	GJos
viridior	see *A. anserinifolia* (Forst. & Forst. f.) Druce

Acalypha (*Euphorbiaceae*)

§ ***herzogiana***	CCCN EShb
pendula misapplied	see *A. herzogiana*

Acanthocalyx see *Morina*

Acantholimon (*Plumbaginaceae*)

androsaceum	see *A. ulicinum*
armenum	XSen
glumaceum	LLHF
§ ***ulicinum***	XEll
venustum	LLHF

Acanthopanax see *Eleutherococcus*

ricinifolius	see *Kalopanax septemlobus*

Acanthus ✿ (*Acanthaceae*)

arboreus	XLum
balcanicus misapplied	see *A. hungaricus*
'Candelabra'	WHil
caroli-alexandri	see *A. spinosus* L.
dioscoridis	GCal WHil
- var. ***perringii***	CDor ECha IRob MNrw NLar WCot WFar WHil XLum
- smooth-leaved	WHil
eminens	WCot
hirsutus	CDor CFis EPri IFoB WCot WHil
- subsp. ***syriacus***	ECha EHrv GCal WHil
'Hollande du Nort'	CRos LRHS NRHS XLum
§ ***hungaricus***	CBod CDor CHid CMac CRos EBee ELan ILea LCro LOPS LRHS MBel MMuc MRav NChi NLar NRHS SCob WCot WFar WHil XLum
- AL&JS 90097YU	WHil
- MESE 561	WHil
- 'White Lips'	EBee MAvo MNrw NLar WCot WHlf
longifolius Host	see *A. hungaricus*
mollis	Widely available
- from Turkey	WHil
- 'Fielding Gold'	see *A. mollis* 'Hollard's Gold'
- free-flowering	GCal MAvo WHil XLum
§ - 'Hollard's Gold'	CBct CDor CExl CMac EBee ECha ECtt EHoe ELan EPPr EPfP GKin GMaP LRHS LSou MNrw NGdn NLar NRHS SPoG SRms WAvo WCot WFar WHil WSHC
- 'Jefalba'	see *A. mollis* (Latifolius Group) 'Rue Ledan'
- Latifolius Group	CDor MRav SRms WHil WHoo
§ - - 'Rue Ledan'	CRav EBee ECtt EPPr EWTr GBin LRHS MAvo MNrw NGdn NLar NPnk NSti SCob SMHy SPhx WCot WHil XLum
- - 'Sjaak'	MAvo WHil
- 'Long Spike'	GCal WHil
- 'Tasmanian Angel' (v)	CAbb CBct CDor CRos CWGN EBee ECtt EHyd ELan IBoy LCro LOPS LRHS MBNS MHol MJak MSCN NRHS SBig SCob SMad SPoG WCot WFar XLum
'Morning's Candle'	EBee ECtt MNrw NGdn NLar WFar WHil XLum
sennii	CAby IMou SMad SPhx WCot WHil WSHC XLum
spinosus misapplied	see *A. spinosus* Spinosissimus Group
§ ***spinosus*** L.	Widely available
- Ferguson's form	EBee MAvo WCot WHil XLum
- 'Lady Moore' (v)	CDor NLar WHil XLum
- 'Royal Haughty'	WHil XLum
§ - Spinosissimus Group	CBct CBod CTsd ECha ELan GBin GCal IBoy LEdu MAvo MGos MRav NChi NPnk SMad WCot WFar WHar WHil
'Summer Beauty'	ECtt EWes LRHS MAvo MRav WCot WFar WHil XLum
'Whitewater' (v)	CBct CDor CWGN EBee ECtt ELan GEdr GKin MHol NLar NSti NWad SBig SCob SMad SPad SPer SPoG SRms WCot WHil

Acca (*Myrtaceae*)

sp.	LPra
sellowiana (F)	CAby CAgr CBcs CCCN CCht CDTJ CDul CExl CMac CTsd ELan EPfP EShb LMaj LPra LRHS LSou MGos NPla SCob SEle SLim SPer SPlb SPoG SVic SWeb SWvt WFar
- 'Apollo' (F)	EUJe
- 'Mammoth' (F)	CBcs CCCN
- 'Triumph' (F)	CBcs CCCN SGol
- 'Unique' (F)	ERea EUJe
- 'Variegata' (F/v)	CCCN

Acer ✿ (*Sapindaceae*)

sp.	ETod LPra
amoenum B&SWJ 10916	WCru
- B&SWJ 10977	WCru
- 'Firecracker'	see *A. palmatum* 'Firecracker'
'Ample Surprise'	MBlu
buergerianum	CDul CJun CMen CTho ECrN MMuc MPkF NLar SBrt SGol WMou
- from South Korea B&SWJ 12676	WCru
- var. ***formosanum*** CWJ 12477	WCru
- 'Naruto'	CMCN MPkF
campbellii	MBlu
- subsp. ***campbellii*** GWJ 9360	WCru
- - NJM 12.069	WPGP
- - PAB 13.071	LEdu
- 'Exuberance'	CJun
campestre 🏆^{H6}	Widely available
- 'Anny's Globe'	MBlu
- 'Carnival' (v) 🏆^{H6}	CCVT CEnd ECrN ELon EMOT MAsh MBlu NPoe SCob SGol SMad SPer SWvt WHar WMou
- 'Elsrijk'	CCVT CLnd EMOT LMaj SCoo SGol
- 'Evelyn'	see *A. campestre* 'Queen Elizabeth'
- 'Evenley Red'	CDul EBee MBlu WPGP
- 'Green Column'	EMOT
- 'Louisa Red Shine' **new**	CLnd
- 'Pendulum'	CEnd
- 'Postelense'	MBlu
- 'Pulverulentum' (v)	NEgg
§ - 'Queen Elizabeth'	CDul MGos SGol
- 'Red Shine'	EBar EMOT SGol
- 'Royal Ruby'	MGos
- 'Ruby Glow' 🏆^{H6}	CEnd
I - 'Silver Celebration' (v)	CJun
- 'William Caldwell'	CEnd CTho MBlu
capillipes	CBcs CDul CMCN CTho ELan EMOT GQue IRob LMaj MJak MMuc NRog SCob SPlb WHCr WHar WTSh
- 'Antoine'	CJun MBlu NLar
- 'Candy Stripe'	see *A. × conspicuum* 'Candy Stripe'
- 'Honey Dew'	CJun SSta
cappadocicum	CCVT CDul CEnd CMCN ECrN LMaj WMou WPGP
- 'Aureum' 🏆^{H6}	CBcs CDul CEnd CLnd CMCN CTho EBee ECrN ELan EMOT EPfP GKin IArd MAsh MBlu MRav NLar

	NOra SCob SGol SMad SPer SPoG SWvt WFar WHor WMou WTSh
§ - subsp. ***lobelii***	LMaj
- var. ***mono***	see *A. pictum*
- 'Rubrum' ♀H6	CArg CBcs CDul CLnd CMCN EBee ECrN ELan EMOT EPfP GKin IDee LMaj MBlu MMuc MRav NOra SCob SEND SGol SPer WFar WHer WHor
- var. ***tricaudatum***	CExl
carpinifolium	CDul CMCN EBee EPfP IArd LRHS MBlu MPkF NLar WPGP
- B&SWJ 10955	WCru
- B&SWJ 11124	WCru
§ ***caudatifolium*** CWJ 12403	WCru
- RWJ 9843	WCru
§ ***caudatum*** GWJ 9279	WCru
- GWJ 9317	WCru
- HWJK 2240	WCru
- HWJK 2338	WCru
- subsp. ***ukurunduense***	MPkF
- - B&SWJ 8658	WCru
circinatum	CBcs CCVT CDul CJun CMCN EBee ECrN MBlu MMuc NEgg NLar SEND SPlb WMou
- B&SWJ 9565	WCru
- 'Burgundy Jewel'	CJun
- 'Monroe'	CJun SGol
- 'Pacific Fire'	CJun
- 'Sunny Sister'	LRHS
circinatum* × *palmatum	SBig
cissifolium	CMCN EPfP NHim NLar
- B&SWJ 10801	WCru
§ × ***conspicuum*** 'Candy Stripe'	CJun
- 'Elephant's Ear'	CJun MBlu NLar
- 'Phoenix'	CEnd CJun CMCN CRos EPfP GKin LRHS MBlu NHim NLar SPoG SSta WPGP
- 'Silver Ghost'	SWvt
§ - 'Silver Vein'	CEnd CJun CMCN EPfP NLar SSta SWvt
crataegifolium	CMCN SSta
- B&SWJ 11036	WCru
- B&SWJ 11355	WCru
- 'Ittai-san-nishiki'	SSta
- 'Meuri-keade-no-fuiri' (v)	MPkF
- 'Meuri-no-ōfu' (v)	MPkF SSta
- 'Veitchii' (v)	CDul CJun CMCN EBee EPfP MBlu MPkF SSta
creticum misapplied	see *A. sempervirens*
dasycarpum	see *A. saccharinum*
davidii	CBcs CDul CExl ECrN LCro MBlu MGos MMuc MRav NRog SCob SGol SSta WCot WHar
§ - 'Canton'	CJun SSta
- 'Cantonspark'	see *A. davidii* 'Canton'
- 'Cascade'	CJun MBlu SSta WHor
- 'Ernest Wilson'	SSta
- 'George Forrest' ♀H5	CBcs CDul CExl CJun CMCN CMac CTho EBee ECrN ELan EPfP GBin MMuc NLar NOra SCob SPoG SSta SWvt WHar WMou
- 'Hagelunie'	SBir SSta
- 'Hansu-suru' (v)	SSta
- 'Karmen'	CBcs CDul CJun EPfP SSta
- 'Purple Bark'	CExl CJun NLar SBir SSta
- 'Rosalie'	CBcs CJun EPfP LRHS MBlu NLar SBir SSta WHor
- 'Sekka'	SSta
- 'Serpentine'	CBcs CDul CJun CMCN EPfP IDee IRob MBlu NEgg NLar SSta WHor
- 'Silver Vein'	see *A.* × *conspicuum* 'Silver Vein'
- VIPER ('Mindavi')	EPfP LRHS NLar NOra SPer SPoG WHCr
diabolicum	CMCN
elegantulum	CExl CJun GBin
erythranthum B&SWJ 11733	WCru
- FMWJ 13157	WCru
fabri	CExl
- WWJ 11614	WCru
flabellatum	CJun CMCN EBee
- NJM 11.017	WPGP
- PAB 9865	LEdu
- var. ***yunnanense***	CMCN MMuc
forrestii	CExl CMCN LRHS MMuc NEgg
- BWJ 7515	WCru
- 'Alice'	CEnd CJun NRHS SSta
- 'Inoense'	SSta
- 'Sirene'	CJun SSta
- 'Sparkling'	CJun
× ***freemanii***	CMCN
- 'Armstrong'	CCVT EMOT SGol
- AUTUMN BLAZE ('Jeffersred') ♀H6	CBcs CCVT CDul CLnd CMCN CTho EMOT EPfP IArd LMaj LRHS MBlu MGos MMuc NOra SBir SCoo SGol SPer WMou
- CELEBRATION ('Celzam')	CArg CCVT CDul CTho EBee MGos
- 'Elegant'	CLnd
- 'Indian Summer'	see *A.* × *freemanii* 'Morgan'
§ - 'Morgan'	CJun EBee NLar
ginnala	see *A. tataricum* subsp. *ginnala*
globosum	see *A. platanoides* 'Globosum'
grandidentatum	see *A. saccharum* subsp. *grandidentatum*
griseum ♀H5	Widely available
- 'Golden Lucky'	NLar
grosseri	CMCN CTri SGol
- var. ***hersii***	CBcs CDul CLnd CMac EBee ECrN EPfP ESps LSRN MMuc MRav NOra SCob SSta SWvt
- 'Leiden'	EPfP
heldreichii	CMCN
henryi	CBcs CDul EPfP NEgg NLar
heptaphlebium B&SWJ 11695	WCru
- B&SWJ 11713	WCru
- FMWJ 13369	WCru
japonicum	CMCN LPra SEWo
- B&SWJ 12847	WCru
- CWJ 12840 <u>**new**</u>	WCru
§ - 'Aconitifolium' ♀H6	Widely available
- 'Aki-hi'	NLar
- 'Ao-jutan'	CJun
- 'Attaryi'	CMen NEgg NLar
- 'Aureum'	see *A. shirasawanum* 'Aureum'
- 'Emmit's Pumpkins'	CJun
- 'Ezo-no-momiji'	see *A. shirasawanum* 'Ezo-no-momiji'
- 'Fairy Lights'	NLar
- 'Filicifolium'	see *A. japonicum* 'Aconitifolium'
- 'Green Cascade' ♀H6	CAco CEnd CJun CMCN CMac CMen CRos LRHS MGos MPkF NEgg NLar NRHS SBig SGol
- 'King's Copse'	CJun CRos LRHS NRHS
- 'Laciniatum'	see *A. japonicum* 'Aconitifolium'
- f. ***microphyllum***	see *A. shirasawanum* 'Microphyllum'
- 'Ogurayama'	see *A. shirasawanum* 'Ogurayama'

	Name	Suppliers
	- 'Ō-isami'	SBig
	- 'Ō-taki'	CJun
	- 'Vitifolium' ♀H6	CDul CEnd CJun CMCN CMac CTho ELan EPfP GBin LRHS MBlu MGos MPkF NEgg NLar NRHS SBig SGol SPer SSta WCFE WTSh
	kawakamii	see *A. caudatifolium*
	laevigatum B&SWJ 11684	WCru
	- FMWJ 13378	WCru
	- FMWJ 13439 **new**	WCru
	- NJM 10.049	WPGP
§	- var. ***reticulatum*** B&SWJ 11698	WCru
	laurinum FMWJ 13412 **new**	WCru
	- KWJ 12232 **new**	WCru
	- NJM 10.111	WPGP
	laxiflorum	SSta
	lobelii Ten.	see *A. cappadocicum* subsp. *lobelii*
	macrophyllum	CDul CMCN EPfP MBlu
	mandshuricum	CMCN
	- B&SWJ 12592	WCru
§	***maximowiczianum***	CBcs CMCN MMuc MPkF SGol SSta
	maximowiczii	MPkF
	metcalfii	CFil
	micranthum ♀H6	CDul CMCN EPfP MBlu NLar
	miyabei	MPkF
	mono	see *A. pictum*
	monspessulanum	CDul CMCN MMuc SEND XSen
	morifolium B&SWJ 11473	WCru
	morrisonense Hayata	see *A. caudatifolium*
	negundo	CAco CDul CMCN ECrN EMOT ESps LPra SCob SWvt
	- B&SWJ 14060 **new**	WCru
	- 'Auratum'	CMCN SGol
	- 'Aureomarginatum' (v)	CCVT ECrN SGol
	- 'Aureovariegatum' (v)	LPra
§	- 'Elegans' (v)	CDul CEnd CMCN EMOT ESps SCoo
	- 'Elegantissimum'	see *A. negundo* 'Elegans'
	- 'Flamingo' (v)	CAco CBcs CCVT CDul CEnd CMCN CMac ECrN ELan EMOT EPfP ESps LPra LRHS MAsh NLar NOra SCob SGol SPer SPoG SWvt WFar
	- 'Kelly's Gold'	CBcs CCVT CMCN EMOT ESps NLar SCob SGol SPoG WHar
	- subsp. ***mexicanum***	CFil
	- 'Sensation'	NLar
	- 'Variegatum' (v)	ECrN LMaj LPra SGol
	- var. ***violaceum*** ♀H6	CEnd SVen
	- 'Winter Lightning' ♀H6	NLar
	nikoense misapplied	see *A. maximowiczianum*
	nipponicum	CDul CMCN
	'Norwegian Sunset'	CCVT EBee EMOT
	oblongum	CMCN
	oliverianum	CDul CExl MBlu
	- subsp. ***formosanum*** CWJ 12437	WCru
	opalus	CMCN SEND
	orientale misapplied	see *A. sempervirens*
	ORIENTALIA ('Minorient') **new**	LRHS
	orizabense	EBee
	PACIFIC SUNSET ('Warrenred')	NLar
	palmatum	CBcs CCVT CDul CMCN CMen CSBt CTri EMOT EPfP ESps ETMg ETod GKin LCro LMaj LPra MBlu MGos NEgg SArc SCob SEWo SGol SPlb SWvt WFar WHar WTSh
	- (D)	Widely available
	- 'Akane' (P)	CMen
§	- 'Aka-shigitatsu-sawa' (M)	CBcs CJun CMCN CMen ESMi GMil LRHS MGos MJak MPkF NLar SAko SGol SPer
	- 'Akegarasu' (M)	CMCN CMen NLar
	- 'Alpenweiss' (P)	CJun
	- 'Alpine Surprise'	SAko
	- 'Amagi-shigure' (M)	CJun LRHS MPkF
	- 'Amber Ghost' (M)	CJun
	- 'Anne Irene'PBR (P)	LRHS MPkF
	- 'Aoba-jo' (Dw)	CJun CMen MPkF NEgg
	- 'Ao-kanzashi' (P/v)	MPkF NLar
	- 'Ao-shidare' (D)	CJun
	- 'Aoshime-no-uchi'	see *A. palmatum* 'Shinobuga-oka'
	- 'Aoyagi' (P)	CEnd CJun CMCN CMen CRos ELon ESMi LRHS MGos NEgg NLar NRHS
	- 'Aoyagi-gawa'	CJun
§	- 'Arakawa' (P)	CEnd CMCN CMac CMen ESMi MPkF NEgg
	- 'Arakawa-ukon'	CJun NLar
	- 'Aratama' (Dw)	CJun CMCN CMen ESMi GMil MJak
	- 'Ariadne' (M/v) ♀H6	CEnd CJun LRHS MGos MPkF NLar SBig SCoo SPoG
	- 'Ariake-nomura' (A)	CMen MPkF
	- 'Asahi-zuru' (P/v)	CBcs CJun CMCN CMen CRos GMil LRHS MGos NLar NRHS SPer
	- 'Ashurst Wood'	SBig
	- 'Atrolineare' (L)	CMen MPkF NEgg NLar
	- 'Atropurpureum' (A)	Widely available
	- 'Atropurpureum Novum'	MPkF NLar SGol
	- 'Attraction' (P)	CMen NEgg
	- 'Aureum' (P)	CAco CMCN CMen CRos CTri ELan EPfP GMil IBoy LMil LRHS MAsh MBlu MGos MPkF NEgg NLar NRHS SPoG WCFE WFar
	- 'Autumn Fire' (D)	CJun
	- 'Autumn Glory' (M)	CAco CEnd CJun CMac CMen GMil
	- 'Autumn Red' (M)	CMen ESMi NEgg
*	- 'Autumn Showers'	CEnd CJun
	- 'Azuma-murasaki' (M)	CJun CMen MPkF NEgg NLar
	- 'Baby Lace' (Dw)	CWGN SAko
	- 'Balcombe Green' (D)	SBig
	- 'Baldsmith' (D)	CJun EUJe GMil LRHS MPkF SBod
	- 'Barrie Bergman' (D)	CJun
	- 'Beni-chidori' (P)	CMen
	- 'Beni-fushigi' (P)	MPkF
	- 'Beni-gasa' (M)	CJun MPkF NLar
	- 'Beni-hime' (Dw)	MPkF SAko
	- 'Beni-hoshi' (Dw)	MPkF
	- 'Beni-kagami' (M)	CEnd CJun CMCN MPkF NLar SGol
	- 'Beni-kawa' (P)	CJun CMCN CMen MPkF SBig SGol
	- 'Beni-komachi' (P)	CAco CEnd CMCN CMen CRos EPfP ESMi GMil LRHS MGos MPkF NLar NRHS SCob SSta
	- 'Beni-komachi' sport	CBcs
	- 'Beni-kosode' (v)	MPkF
	- 'Beni-maiko' (P) ♀H6	CEnd CJun CMCN CMen CRos EPfP ESMi EUJe LMil LRHS MGos MJak MPkF NLar NRHS SBig SBod SCob SCoo SWvt WCFE
	- 'Beni-musume'	MPkF
	- 'Beni-otake' (L)	CBcs CJun CMen ELan EPfP ESMi EUJe GMil LRHS MGos MPkF NEgg NLar SAko SBig SBod SCob SWeb
	- 'Beni-otome'	MPkF
	- 'Beni-schichi-henge' (P/v)	CBcs CEnd CJun CMCN CMen CRos CWGN ESMi GMil LRHS MAsh MGos MJak MPkF NEgg NLar

		NOra NRHS SAko SBig SBod SCob SCoo SGol SSta
	- 'Beni-shidare' (D)	NLar SCob
	- 'Beni-shidare Tricolor'	see *A. palmatum* 'Toyama-nishiki'
	- 'Beni-shidare Variegated'	see *A. palmatum* 'Toyama-nishiki'
	- 'Beni-shi-en' (P)	CJun MPkF NLar
	- 'Beni-shigitatsu-sawa'	see *A. palmatum* 'Aka-shigitatsu-sawa'
	- 'Beni-tsukasa' (P/v) ♀H6	CEnd CJun CMCN CMen CRos ESMi LMaj LMil LRHS NLar NRHS SSta
	- 'Beni-tsuru'	MPkF
	- 'Beni-yubi-gohon' (P)	CJun GMil MJak MPkF NLar
	- 'Berrima Bridge' (D)	CJun
	- 'Berry Broom'	MPkF NLar
	- 'Berry Dwarf' (Dw)	CJun MPkF
	- 'Bewley's Red' (D)	CJun
	- 'Bi Hō' (P)	CJun LCro LOPS LRHS MGos NLar SAko SBod SGol
	- 'Black Lace' (M)	LRHS MGos MPkF NLar NRHS
	- 'Bloodgood' (A) ♀H6	Widely available
	- 'Bonfire' misapplied	see *A. palmatum* 'Seigai'
	- 'Bonfire' ambig.	CJun
	- 'Bonnie Bergman'	CJun
	- 'Boskoop Glory' (A)	GKin
	- 'Brandt's Dwarf' (Dw)	NLar
	- 'Brocade' (D)	CJun MPkF
	- 'Bronzewing' (D)	CJun
	- 'Burgundy Lace' (M) ♀H6	CAco CBcs CEnd CJun CMCN CMen CRos ELan EPfP ESMi EUJe GKin GMil IBoy LMil LRHS LSRN MAsh MGos MJak MPkF NEgg NRHS SBig SBod SCoo SGol SPer SPoG SSta
	- 'Butterfly' (P/v)	Widely available
	- 'Calico' (P)	CJun
	- 'Caperci Dwarf' (Dw)	MPkF
	- 'Carlis Corner' (Dw)	CJun
	- 'Carminium'	see *A. palmatum* 'Corallinum'
	- 'Chantilly Lace' (D)	CJun IBoy
	- 'Chikuma-no' (A)	CMen MPkF
	- 'Chirimen-nishiki' (P/v)	MPkF
	- 'Chishio' (P)	CMCN CMen ESMi GMil LMil LRHS MPkF NLar SBig SBod
	- 'Chishio Improved' (P)	CEnd CJun CMCN CMac CMen CTho EPfP LRHS MAsh MGos MPkF NLar NRHS SBig SWvt
	- 'Chitose-yama' (M) ♀H6	CDul CEnd CJun CMCN CMen EPfP GKin LMaj LRHS MAsh MGos MPkF NLar NRHS SGol SLim SSta
§	- 'Chiyo-hime'	EBee EPfP GMil LCro LOPS NLar NPri WFar
	- 'Collingwood Ingram'	SGol
	- 'Coonara Pygmy' (Dw)	CJun CMCN CMac CMen ESMi GKin GMil LRHS MPkF SCoo
	- 'Coral Pink' (Dw)	CJun CMen MPkF SGol SSta
§	- 'Corallinum' (P) ♀H6	CAco CEnd CJun CMCN CMen GMil NLar SAko WCFE
	- var. ***coreanum*** B&SWJ 8606	WCru
	- 'Crimson Carol' (M)	CJun
	- 'Crimson Prince'	CJun MPkF SCoo
	- 'Crimson Princess' (D)	CBcs CRos EBee EPfP EUJe GMil LMaj LRHS MJak MPkF NRHS SBod SWeb
	- 'Crimson Queen' (D) ♀H6	Widely available
	- 'Crippsii' (D)	CBcs CMac CMen LRHS MPkF SBod SCoo SGol
	- 'Deshōjō' (P)	CMCN CMen ESMi LMaj MBlu MGos NLar NPoe SCoo SGol
	- 'Diana' (Dw)	CJun CMen NLar SGol
	- 'Dissectum' (D)	CAco CTho CTri EMOT LBuc LOPS LPra NOra WCFE WFar WHar WTSh
	- 'Dissectum Atropurpureum' (D)	LMil LPra
	- 'Dissectum Flavescens' (D)	CAco CBcs CEnd CJun CMac CMen EUJe GMil MBlu MGos MPkF NEgg SBod SPer SWeb
§	- 'Dissectum Nigrum' (D)	CAco CJun CMac CMen CRos ESMi LRHS MAsh MPkF NEgg NLar NRHS SWeb
	- 'Dissectum Palmatifidum' (D)	CAco CMen CRos EUJe LRHS MPkF NEgg NRHS SBod SCoo SGol SPer
	- 'Dissectum Rubrifolium' (D)	MPkF
§	- 'Dissectum Variegatum' (Dw/v)	CJun ESps LRHS MPkF
	- Dissectum Viride Group	Widely available
	- 'Donzuru-bo'	CJun
	- 'Dormansland'	SBig
	- 'Dragon's Fire'	CJun
	- 'Earthfire'	GMil MJak MPkF
I	- 'Ebbingei'	CMac
	- 'Eddisbury' (P) ♀H6	CEnd CJun CMen CSBt MBlu NLar SSta
	- 'Edna Bergman' (M)	CJun
	- 'Effegi'	see *A. palmatum* 'Fireglow'
§	- 'Elegans' (M) ♀H6	CMen CRos EPfP LRHS MPkF NEgg NRHS
	- 'Elizabeth' (Dw)	CJun
	- 'Ellen' (D)	CJun MPkF NLar
	- 'Emerald Lace' (D) ♀H6	CBot CJun CRos EBee EUJe GKin GMil LBuc LCro LOPS LRHS MGos MPkF NEgg NLar NRHS SBod SPoG SSta WCFE WFar
§	- 'Emperor 1' (A)	CJun ELan EUJe GMil IBoy LMaj LRHS MPkF SBod SCob SPer SWeb
	- 'Enkan' (L)	CEnd CJun CMen CRos CWGN ESMi GMil LRHS MGos MPkF NLar NOra NPri NRHS SBod SGol SPoG
	- 'Eono-momiji'	CMen
	- 'Ever Red'	see *A. palmatum* 'Dissectum Nigrum'
	- 'Fairy Hair' (L)	CJun NLar
	- 'Fall's Fire' (P)	CJun NLar
	- 'Fascination' (M)	CJun
	- 'Felice' (D)	CJun MPkF
	- 'Filigree' (Dw/v)	CAco CJun CMCN CMen CRos EPfP LMil LRHS MAsh MGos MPkF NLar NRHS SBig SSta WCFE
	- 'Fior d'Arancio' (M)	CJun MPkF NLar
	- 'Fireball'	CJun
§	- 'Firecracker'PBR (D)	LRHS MPkF NEgg NLar SBod
§	- 'Fireglow' (A)	CAco CBcs CEnd CJun CMCN CMen CRos CSBt ESMi GMil LMaj LMil LPra LRHS LSRN MGos MJak MPkF NLar NRHS SAko SBod SCob SCoo SGol SPer SWeb
	- 'First Ghost' (M/v)	CJun
	- 'Frederici Guglielmi'	see *A. palmatum* 'Dissectum Variegatum'
	- 'Garnet' (D) ♀H6	Widely available
	- 'Garnet Tower' (D) **new**	MPkF NLar
	- 'Garyū' (Dw)	MPkF
	- 'Geisha' (Dw)	MPkF
	- 'Geisha Gone Wild' (P/v)	CJun NLar
	- 'Gentaku'	CJun

	- 'Germaine's Gyration' (D)	CJun
	- 'Gibbsii'	CMen
I	- 'Globosum' (Dw)	IBoy MPkF
	- 'Glowing Embers' (P)	CJun MPkF
	- 'Going Green' **new**	LRHS MPkF NLar
	- 'Going Red' **new**	NLar
	- 'Golden Pond' (A)	CJun
	- 'Goshiki-kotohime' (Dw/v)	CMCN NLar
	- 'Goshiki-shidare'	see *A. palmatum* 'Toyama-nishiki'
	- 'Goten-nomura'	NLar
	- 'Grace'	CJun
	- 'Grandma Ghost' (M)	CJun
	- 'Green Flag'	CJun
	- 'Green Globe' (D)	CJun
	- 'Green Hornet' (D)	CJun
	- 'Green Lace' (D)	CMen LMaj MPkF
	- 'Green Mist' (D)	CJun CRos GMil LRHS NRHS
	- 'Green Trompenburg' (M)	CJun CMen GBin GMcL MPkF NEgg NLar
	- 'Groundcover' (Dw)	MPkF
§	- 'Hagoromo'	CMac CMen ESMi NEgg SCoo
	- 'Hana-matoi'PBR (v)	CMCN SAko
	- 'Hanami-nishiki' (Dw)	CMen MPkF
	- 'Happy Corallinum' (A)	CJun
	- 'Haru-iro'	CJun
	- 'Harusame' (P/v)	MPkF NLar
	- 'Hazeroino' (v)	CMen MPkF
	- 'Heartbeat' (D)	CJun GMil LRHS MPkF NRHS SBod
	- 'Heffner's Red'	CJun
	- var. ***heptalobum***	CMCN LRHS
	- 'Heptalobum Elegans Purpureum'	see *A. palmatum* 'Hessei'
	- 'Herbstfeuer' (P)	CJun GMil
§	- 'Hessei' (M)	CEnd CMen MPkF NLar
	- 'Higasa-yama' (P/v)	CAco CEnd CJun CMCN CMen CWGN ESMi GMil MPkF NLar SBod SGol
	- 'Hino-tori-nishiki'	CMen NLar SGol
	- 'Hogyōku' (A)	CJun CMCN CMen MPkF SBod
	- 'Hondoshi' (A)	NLar
	- 'Hōno-o'	MPkF
	- 'Hoshi-kuzu' (Dw)	MPkF
	- 'Hupp's Dwarf' (Dw)	CJun MPkF
	- 'Hupp's Red Willow'	NLar
	- 'Ibo-nishiki' (P)	CMen ESMi MPkF NEgg
	- 'Ichigyōji' (A)	CEnd CJun CMen MAsh NEgg NLar SBig SBod
	- 'Ightham Gold'	SSta
	- 'Iijima-sunago' (M)	CMen MPkF
	- 'Inaba-shidare' (D) ♀H6	Widely available
	- 'Inazuma' (M)	CAco CBcs CJun CMCN CMen CRos GMil LRHS MPkF NLar NRHS SBod SCoo SGol SLau
	- 'Irish Lace'	CJun
	- 'Irish Lace' × ***palmatum*** 'Yasemin'	CJun
	- 'Iso-chidori' (Dw)	MPkF
	- 'Issai-nishiki'	CMen MPkF
*	- 'Issai-nishiki-kawazu'	MPkF
	- 'Jane'	CJun MPkF
	- 'Japanese Sunrise' (P)	CJun GMil SBod
	- 'Jerre Schwartz' (Dw)	CRos EPfP LCro LOPS LRHS MGos MPkF NLar NRHS
	- 'Jirō-shidare' (P)	CJun LRHS MPkF NLar SBig
	- 'JJ'	CJun
	- 'Julia D.'	CJun
	- 'Kaba' (Dw)	CMen MPkF SPoG
	- 'Kagero' (A/v)	MPkF
§	- 'Kagiri-nishiki' (P/v)	CBcs CJun CMCN CMac CMen CWGN GMil IRob MPkF NEgg NLar SPer SWeb
	- 'Kamagata' (Dw)	CAco CEnd CJun CMCN CMen CRos ESMi GMil LRHS MAsh MGos MPkF NLar NRHS SCoo
	- 'Kandy Kitchen' (Dw)	CMen LRHS
	- 'Karaori-nishiki' (P/v)	CMen MPkF NLar
	- 'Karasu-gawa' (P/v)	CJun CMen CWGN MPkF
	- 'Kasagiyama' (M)	CEnd CJun CMen CRos LRHS MPkF NLar NRHS
	- 'Kasen-nishiki' (P)	CMen MPkF
	- 'Kashima' (Dw)	CEnd CJun CMCN CMen CRos GMil LRHS MPkF NEgg NLar NRHS SBod
	- 'Kashima-yatsubusa'	MPkF
	- 'Katja'	CJun CMen MPkF
	- 'Katsura' (P) ♀H6	Widely available
	- 'Katsura-nishiki'	MPkF
	- 'Kawahara Rose'	MPkF
I	- 'Kawaii' (D)	CJun
	- 'Ki-hachijō' (M)	CJun CMCN CMen GMcL MPkF NLar SBod
	- 'Killarney' (M)	CJun
	- 'Kinky Krinkle' (P)	CJun LRHS NLar
	- 'Kinran' (M)	CAco CMen CRos ESMi GMil LRHS MPkF NEgg NRHS SBod
	- 'Kinshii' (L) ♀H6	CEnd CJun CMCN CMen CRos EPfP GBin LRHS MPkF NEgg NLar NOra NRHS SAko
	- 'Kiri-nishiki' (D)	CJun CMen CRos LRHS MPkF NLar NRHS
	- 'Ki-shuzan' (M)	CJun
	- 'Kiyohime' (Dw) ♀H6	CMCN CMen GMil MPkF NEgg
	- 'Koba-shōjō' (M)	MPkF
	- 'Kogane-nishiki' (P)	CMen NLar SGol
	- 'Kogane-sakae' (A)	CJun MPkF
	- 'Kokobunji-nishiki' (v)	MPkF
	- 'Komachi-hime' (Dw)	CJun CMen MPkF
	- 'Komon-nishiki' (P/v)	CJun CMen MPkF NEgg
	- 'Korean Gem' (M)	CAco CJun CMen MPkF NEgg
	- 'Koriba' (P)	CJun MPkF NLar
	- 'Koshibori-nishiki' (P)	MPkF
	- 'Kotohime' (Dw)	CJun CMCN CMen MGos MPkF NLar SBig SCoo SPoG
	- 'Koto-ito-komachi' (Dw)	CJun CMen CRos ESMi LRHS MPkF NEgg NRHS
	- 'Koto-maru' (Dw)	NLar SGol
	- 'Koto-no-ito' (L)	CMCN LMaj LRHS MAsh MBlu MGos MPkF NLar NRHS SAko SBod SGol SPoG
	- 'Koya-san' (Dw)	CMen MPkF NLar
	- 'Kurabu-yama' (M)	CMen MPkF
	- 'Kurui-jishi' (Dw)	MPkF
	- 'Kyōryū'	MPkF
	- 'Kyra'	CMen MPkF
	- 'Lace Lady' (D)	GMil LRHS
	- 'Leather Leaf'	GMil
	- 'Limelight' (P)	LRHS NLar
§	- 'Linearilobum' (L)	CBcs CMen EPfP LRHS MGos MPkF NEgg NLar NOra SBod SCoo SLau SPer
*	- 'Lionheart' (D)	CBcs CJun CMen CRos CWGN ESMi EUJe LRHS MGos MPkF NLar NRHS SCoo
	- 'Little Princess'	see *A. palmatum* 'Chiyo-hime'
	- 'Lozita' (P)	NLar
	- 'Lutescens' (A)	CMen MPkF NEgg
	- 'Lydia'	MPkF
	- 'Maiko' (P)	CMen MPkF

- 'Mama' (P)	CMen
- 'Manyō-no-sato' (P/v)	LRHS MPkF
- 'Mapi-no-machi-hime' (Dw)	CEnd CJun CMCN CMen CRos LRHS MAsh MPkF NRHS
- 'Marakumo' (P)	MPkF
- 'Marasaki-yama'	MPkF
- 'Mardi Gras'	CJun
- 'Margaret'	MPkF
- 'Margaret Bee' (A)	CJun NLar
- 'Marjan' (M)	CJun MPkF SBod
- 'Marlo'PBR (D)	CRos LCro LOPS LRHS MAsh MGos NLar NRHS
- 'Masamurasaki'	CMen MPkF
- 'Masukagami' (P/v)	CEnd CJun MPkF NLar
- 'Matsu-ga-e' (P/v)	CMen MPkF
- 'Matsukaze'	CJun CMCN CMen
- var. ***matsumurae*** B&SWJ 11100	WCru
- - B&SWJ 11195	WCru
- 'Matsuyoi' (A)	CJun MPkF
- 'Meihō-nishiki'	CJun
- 'Melanie'	CJun SBig
- 'Meoto'	CJun
- 'Midori-no-teiboku' (Dw)	CJun
- 'Mikasa-nishiki' (v)	MPkF
- 'Mikawa-yatsubusa' (Dw)	CJun CMCN CMac CMen ESMi GMil LRHS MGos MPkF NEgg NLar SAko SBod SGol
- 'Mikazuki' (M/v)	CJun MPkF
- 'Mimaye'	CJun
- 'Mini Mondo'	MPkF
- 'Mirte' (M)	CJun CMen MPkF NLar SBig SGol
- 'Mizuho-beni' (P)	CJun CMen
- 'Mizu-kuguri' (A)	MPkF NLar
- 'Momoiro-koya-san' (Dw)	CJun LRHS MPkF NLar SGol
- 'Mon Papa' (M)	CJun CMen NLar
- 'Monzukushi' (A)	CJun MPkF
- 'Moonfire' (M)	CJun CMCN EPfP GMil MAsh MPkF SGol
* - 'Muncaster'	SBig
- 'Murasaki-hime' (Dw)	MPkF
- 'Murasaki-kiyohime' (Dw)	CAco CEnd CJun CMCN CMen CRos ESMi LRHS MPkF NRHS SBod
- 'Mure-hibari' (M)	CJun CMen MPkF
- 'Murogawa' (A)	CJun CMen
- 'Musashino' (M)	CJun SGol
- 'Nakata'	NLar
- 'Nanase-gawa' (A)	MPkF
- 'Nicholsonii' (M)	CMen MPkF NEgg NLar
- 'Nigrum' (A)	CMCN CTri SWeb
- 'Nishiki-gasane' (P/v)	CMen MPkF
§ - 'Nishiki-gawa' (P)	CEnd CJun CMen CRos ESMi LRHS MPkF NEgg NRHS
- 'Nishiki-momiji' (P)	CMen
- 'Nishiki-yamato'	NLar
- 'Nomura'	CJun CMen
- 'Nomura-nishiki' (Dw/v)	CMen
- 'Nomurishidare' misapplied	see *A. palmatum* 'Shōjō-shidare'
- 'Nomurishidare' Wada	CRos NRHS
- 'Nuresagi' (M)	CEnd CJun GMil MPkF SBod
- 'Octopus' (D)	CJun NLar
- 'Ōgi-nagashi' (P/v)	MPkF NLar
- 'Ōgi-no-sen'	MPkF
- 'Ōgon-sarasa' (A)	CJun MPkF
- 'Ojishi' (Dw)	CMen MPkF
- 'Ō-kagami' (P)	CAco CBcs CEnd CJun CMac CMen CRos EPfP ESMi EUJe GMil LRHS MAsh MGos MPkF NLar NRHS SCoo

- 'Okina'	NLar
- 'Okukuji-nishiki' (P)	CJun
- 'Okushimo' (P)	CEnd CJun CMCN CMen CRos ETod GQue LRHS MPkF NEgg NLar NRHS SSta
- 'Omato' (A)	CJun MAsh MPkF SBig
- 'Omure-yama' (M)	CAco CEnd CJun CMCN CMen CRos EPfP ESMi LRHS MGos MPkF NEgg NLar NRHS SBod SCob SCoo SGol SPer SSta
- 'Orange Dream' (P) ♀H6	Widely available
- 'Orangeola' (D) ♀H6	CJun CMen CRos CSBt CTri ESMi EUJe GMil IBoy LRHS MAsh MGos MJak MPkF NEgg NLar NRHS SBig SBod SCob SCoo SGol SPer SPoG SSta
- 'Oranges and Lemons'	CJun SGol
- 'Oregon Sunset' (M)	CJun GMil MJak MPkF
- 'Oridono-nishiki' (P/v)	CEnd CJun CMCN CMac CMen CRos CWGN ELan ELon EPfP ESMi LRHS MAsh MBlu MGos MPkF NEgg NLar NRHS SBod SLim SPoG SSta
- 'Oriental Mystery'	CJun
- 'Ornatum' (D) ♀H6	CMCN CMen EPfP ESMi ESps GMcL LMaj LSRN MGos MPkF MRav NEgg NLar NPri SCob SCoo WCFE
- 'Ōsakazuki' (A) ♀H6	Widely available
- 'Ōshio-beni' (A)	CJun CMen NEgg
- 'Ōshū-shidare' (M)	CJun CMen IBoy MPkF
- 'Oto-hime' (Dw)	CJun CMen CRos LRHS MPkF NRHS
- 'Otome-zakura' (P)	CJun CMen CRos LRHS NRHS
- 'Otto's Dissectum' (D)	CJun
- 'Peaches and Cream' (M/v)	CAco CJun CMen ESMi MPkF NLar SGol SPer
- 'Pendulum Julian' (D)	CMCN GMil LRHS MPkF SPer
- 'Peve Chameleon'	MPkF
- 'Peve Dave'	LRHS MPkF NLar SBod
- 'Peve Multicolor'	CJun
- 'Peve Ollie'PBR	MPkF
- 'Peve Stanley'	MPkF NLar
- 'Peve Starfish'	NLar
- 'Phoenix' (P)	CJun EBee EUJe LRHS MAsh MGos MPkF NLar NRHS SBod
- 'Pine Bark Maple'	see *A. palmatum* 'Nishiki-gawa'
- 'Pink Ballerina' (Dw/v)	CJun NLar
- 'Pink Filigree' (D)	CJun CMen NLar
- 'Pink Passion' (v)	LSRN NLar
- 'Pixie' (Dw)	CJun CMen GMil LRHS MGos MPkF NLar NOra SAko SBod SCob
- 'Princetown Gold'	CCVT EUJe IArd NLar
- 'Pung-kil'	LRHS MPkF SAko
- 'Purple Ghost' (M)	CJun NLar
- 'Raraflora' (D)	CJun
- 'Red Autumn Lace' (D)	CJun
- 'Red Baron' (A)	CJun IBoy
- 'Red Cloud' (L)	CJun MPkF
- 'Red Dragon' (D)	CJun CMen CRos CWGN ESMi LRHS MAsh MJak MPkF NRHS SAko SBig SBod
- RED EMPEROR	see *A. palmatum* 'Emperor 1'
- 'Red Falcon' (M)	GMil
- 'Red Feather' (D)	CJun MPkF
- 'Red Filigree Lace' (D)	CEnd CJun CMCN CMen CRos CWGN LRHS MPkF NRHS SBig
- 'Red Flame'	NLar
- 'Red Flash' (A)	CJun CMen MPkF
- 'Red Jonas'	MPkF NLar
- 'Red Pygmy' (L) ♀H6	Widely available

	- 'Red Select' (D)	MPkF
	- 'Red Spider' (L)	CJun
	- 'Red Wood' (P)	CJun SGol SLau
	- 'Redwine'^{PBR} (P)	CRos EPfP LRHS MPkF NLar NRHS
	- 'Renjaku-maru'	MPkF
	- 'Reticulatum'	see *A. palmatum* 'Shigi-tatsu-sawa'
	- 'Ribesifolium'	see *A. palmatum* 'Shishi-gashira'
	- 'Rising Sun'	CJun
	- 'Roseomarginatum'	see *A. palmatum* 'Kagiri-nishiki'
	- 'Rough Bark Maple'	see *A. palmatum* 'Arakawa'
	- 'Rubrum' (A)	CMen
I	- 'Rubrum Kaiser'	CJun
	- 'Ruby Ridge' (M)	CJun
	- 'Ruby Star'	CJun MPkF
	- 'Rufescens' (P)	MPkF
	- 'Ryokū-ryū' (P)	CMen MPkF
	- 'Ryusen'	CJun LRHS NLar
	- 'Ryuzu' (Dw)	CJun MPkF
	- 'Sagara-nishiki' (v)	CAco CEnd CMen CRos LRHS MPkF NEgg NRHS
	- 'Sai-ho'	MPkF
	- 'Saint Jean'	MPkF
	- 'Samidare' (A)	CJun MPkF NLar
	- 'Sandra' (Dw)	CMen MPkF
	- 'Sango-kaku' (P) ♀^{H6}	Widely available
	- 'Saoshika' (A)	CJun CMen MPkF NLar
	- 'Sa-otome' (P)	CMen MPkF
	- 'Satsuki-beni' (M)	CJun CMen ESMi MPkF NEgg
	- 'Sazanami' (M)	CEnd CJun CMen MPkF NEgg NLar
	- 'Scolopendriifolium'	see *A. palmatum* 'Linearilobum'
§	- 'Seigai' (M)	CJun
	- 'Seigen' (Dw)	CEnd CJun CMCN CMen CRos LRHS MBlu MPkF NRHS
	- 'Seiryū' (D) ♀^{H6}	Widely available
	- 'Seiun-kaku' (P)	CJun CMen MPkF NLar
	- 'Sekimori' (D)	CJun NLar SBig
	- 'Sekka-yatsubusa' (P)	CMCN CMen MPkF NLar
	- 'Semi-no-hane' (M)	CJun
	- 'Senkaki'	see *A. palmatum* 'Sango-kaku'
	- 'Septemlobum Elegans'	see *A. palmatum* 'Elegans'
	- 'Septemlobum Purpureum'	see *A. palmatum* 'Hessei'
	- 'Sessilifolium' dwarf	see *A. palmatum* 'Hagoromo'
	- 'Shaina' (P)	CBcs CEnd CJun CMen CRos CSBt CWGN EBee EPfP LBuc LCro LMaj LOPS LRHS MBlu MGos MJak MPkF NLar NRHS SAko SBod SCob SCoo SGol SLim SPoG
	- 'Sharp's Pygmy' (P)	CJun CMen GMil MPkF SBod SGol
	- 'Sherwood Flame' (M)	CJun CMen CRos LRHS MAsh MBlu MGos MPkF NEgg NLar NRHS SCoo SGol
	- 'Shichigosan'	CMen
	- 'Shichihenge' (P)	NLar
	- 'Shidava Gold' (Dw)	CJun GMil MPkF
	- 'Shigarami' (P)	CJun CMen MPkF
§	- 'Shigi-tatsu-sawa' (A/v)	CEnd CJun CMCN CMac CMen CRos LRHS MGos MPkF NEgg NLar NRHS SBig SWeb
	- 'Shigure-bato' (M)	CJun MPkF
	- 'Shigurezome' (M)	MPkF NLar
	- 'Shikageori-nishiki' (P)	CJun CMen MPkF
	- 'Shime-no-uchi' (L)	CJun SBig
	- 'Shin Nyo'^{PBR}	MBlu
	- 'Shin-chishio' (P)	CJun
	- 'Shin-deshōjō' (P) ♀^{H6}	CBcs CEnd CJun CMCN CMac CMen CRos CSBt CWGN EPfP GMil LMil LRHS LSRN MAsh MGos NEgg NLar NPla NPri NRHS SBod SCoo SGol SPer SPoG SReu SSta

§	- 'Shinobuga-oka' (L)	CBcs CJun CMCN CMen GMil LRHS MPkF SBod SGol SLau SWeb
	- 'Shinonome' (M)	CJun CMen MPkF NLar
	- 'Shirazz' (P/v)	CRos CWGN ESMi EUJe GMil IBoy LMil LRHS LSRN MGos MJak MPkF NLar NOra NRHS SBod SCob SPer SWeb SWvt
§	- 'Shishi-gashira' (P) ♀^{H6}	CJun CMCN CMac CMen CRos ESMi EUJe GMcL GMil LMaj LRHS MBlu MGos MPkF NEgg NLar NRHS SBod SCoo SGol SPoG
	- 'Shishio-hime' (Dw)	MPkF
	- 'Shishi-yatsubusa'	CJun MPkF
	- 'Shōjō' (A)	CJun CMCN NLar
	- 'Shōjō-no-mai' (P)	CJun
	- 'Shōjō-nomura' (A)	CEnd CMen MPkF SWeb
§	- 'Shōjō-shidare' (D)	CEnd CJun CMen GMil LRHS MPkF NOra
	- 'Shu-shidare' (D)	CJun GMil
	- 'Silhouette'^{PBR}	CJun LCro LOPS MPkF
	- 'Sister Ghost' (M)	CJun NLar
	- 'Skeeter's Broom' (Dw)	CAco CBcs CJun CMen CRos CSBt ELan EPfP ESMi EUJe GMil IArd IBoy LMaj LRHS MGos MPkF NEgg NLar NRHS SBig SBod SCoo SPoG
*	- 'Sode-nishiki' (P)	CJun MPkF NLar
	- 'Spring Delight' (D)	CJun MPkF SAko
	- 'Starfish'^{PBR}	ETMg LRHS MPkF
	- 'Stella Rossa' (D)	CEnd CJun GMil LRHS MJak MPkF NLar NPri SBod
	- 'Suisei' (Dw/v)	MPkF
	- 'Sumi-nagashi' (M)	CBcs CCVT CMen CRos ESMi GMil LRHS MAsh MGos MJak MPkF NEgg NLar NOra NRHS SBod SCoo SGol SLau
I	- 'Summer Gold' (P)	CAco CJun EBee LRHS MPkF NLar SAko SBod SWvt
	- 'Sunset' (D)	CJun MPkF
	- 'Sunshine' (D)	MPkF
	- 'Susan'	MPkF
	- 'Taiyō-nishiki' (P)	MPkF
	- 'Takao' (P)	CMen
	- 'Tama-hime' (Dw)	CJun CMen CRos ESMi LRHS MPkF NEgg NRHS
	- 'Tamukeyama' (D)	CAco CBcs CJun CMCN CMen CRos ELan ESMi EUJe GMil LRHS MAsh MGos MJak MPkF NEgg NLar NOra NRHS SAko SCob SCoo SGol SLau SWeb WHor
	- 'Tana' (A)	CJun CMCN CMen MPkF NLar
	- 'Tarō-yama' (Dw)	CJun MPkF
	- 'Tatsuta'	CMen MPkF
	- 'Taylor'^{PBR} (P/v)	CDul CEnd CRos CWGN EPfP LOPS LRHS LSRN MAsh MGos MPkF NEgg NLar NPri NRHS SCoo
	- 'Tennyo-no-hoshi' (P)	CMen MPkF NLar
	- 'Tiger Rose' (M)	CJun
	- 'Tiny Tim'	CJun
	- 'Tobiosho' (P)	CJun
§	- 'Toyama-nishiki' (Dw/v)	CJun CMCN CMen CWGN ESMi LRHS MPkF
	- 'Trompenburg' (M) ♀^{H6}	Widely available
	- 'Tsuchigumo' (P)	CJun CMen MPkF NLar
	- 'Tsukuma-no'	MPkF
	- 'Tsukushigata' (A)	MPkF SBod SGol
	- 'Tsuma-gaki' (A)	CAco CJun CMCN CMen EPfP ESMi GMil LRHS MGos MPkF NEgg NLar NRHS
	- 'Tsuri-nishiki' (M)	CJun CMen MPkF
	- 'Twombly's Red Sentinel'	CJun

- 'Ueno-homare' (P)	CMen EUJe MPkF
- 'Ueno-yama'	CBcs CJun GMil LRHS MPkF NEgg NLar SBod SGol SPer
- 'Uki-gumo' (P/v)	CAco CBcs CEnd CJun CMCN CMac CMen CRos ESMi GMil LRHS MGos MJak NRHS SBig SCoo SPer SPoG SSta
- 'Ukon'	CJun CMen CRos CTho ESMi GKin GMil LMil LRHS MJak MPkF NEgg NRHS SBod SCoo
- 'Umegae' (A)	CJun
- 'Uncle Ghost' (M)	CJun
- 'Usu-midori'	CJun
- 'Utsu-semi' (A)	CJun MPkF
- 'Van der Akker'	CJun
- 'Van der Maat' (D)	SBod
- 'Versicolor' (P/v)	CMCN MPkF
- 'Vic Pink' (D)	CJun
- 'Victoria'	SGol
- 'Villa Taranto' (L) 🏆H6	CEnd CJun CMCN CMen CRos EPfP ESMi GMil LRHS MBlu MGos MPkF NEgg NLar NOra NRHS SCoo SGol
- 'Volubile' (P)	CMCN CMen MPkF NEgg SBod
- 'Wabito' (P)	CJun CMen MPkF
- 'Waka-midori'	CMen
- 'Waka-momiji' (P/v)	CJun
- 'Wakehurst Pink' (M/v)	CMCN MPkF
- 'Waterfall' (D)	CJun CMCN
- 'Watnong' (D)	CJun MPkF
- 'Wendy' (P)	CJun CMen MPkF NLar SGol
- 'Wetumpka Red'	CJun
- 'Whitney Red' (A)	CMen
- 'Wild Goose' (P)	MPkF
- 'Will's Devine'	CJun
- 'Wilson's Pink Dwarf' (Dw)	CAco CEnd CJun CMen CRos LRHS MGos MJak MPkF NLar NRHS SAko SCoo SPoG WFar
- 'Winter Flame' (P)	CJun GMil LRHS MPkF SBod
- 'Wou-nishiki'	CMCN CMen MPkF
- 'Yana-gawa'	CMen
- 'Yasemin' (M)	CJun CMen CWGN GMil LRHS MJak MPkF NEgg NLar SBig SBod
- 'Yatsubusa' (Dw)	MPkF
- 'Yezo-nishiki' (A/v)	CMen MBlu MPkF NLar
- 'Yūba-e' (M)	MPkF
- 'Yūgure' (M)	MPkF
- 'Yuri-hime' (Dw)	MPkF
- 'Zaaling' (D)	CAco CMen NEgg
papilio	see *A. caudatum*
pauciflorum 'Blaze Away'	CJun CRos LRHS NRHS
pectinatum	MMuc WPGP
- DS&T 817 **new**	GKev
- GWJ 9354	WCru
- 'Mozart'	CBcs CJun MBlu SSta
- subsp. ***pectinatum***	EBee
- - HWJ 569	WCru
- - HWJ 944	WCru
pensylvanicum	CBcs CDul CMCN CTho EBee ECrN EPfP LPra MGos MJak MMuc MRav NEgg SCob SSta WHor
- 'Erythrocladum'	CBcs CEnd CJun CMCN EPfP IArd MAsh MGos NLar
pentaphyllum	SBig WPGP
§ ***pictum***	CMCN
- 'Mallet Court' **new**	CMCN
- subsp. ***okamotoanum***	CMCN
- - B&SWJ 12623	WCru
- subsp. ***pictum*** f. ***ambiguum*** B&SWJ 8806	WCru

- 'Shufu-nishiki'	CMCN
platanoides	CAco CBcs CCVT CDul CLnd CMCN CPer CSBt CTri ECrN EMOT EPfP GQue LMaj LPra MGos MMuc MSwo SEWo SGol SPer WHar WMou WTSh
- 'Columnare'	CLnd CMCN LMaj LPra SCoo
- 'Crimson King' 🏆H6	Widely available
- 'Crimson Sentry'	CArg CCVT CDul CEnd CLnd CMac CTri ECrN ELan EMOT ESps EUJe LCro LMaj LSRN MAsh MGos MRav SGol SPer SPoG SWvt WHar
- 'Deborah'	CBcs CDul CLnd CTho EPfP EWTr LMaj LPra SGol SPer
- 'Dissectum'	CAco CTho IArd
- 'Drummondii' (v)	Widely available
- 'Emerald Queen'	CDul ECrN ESps LMaj LPra
- 'Faassen's Black'	CDul LPra
§ - 'Globosum'	CDul CMCN ECrN LMaj NLar SWvt
- 'Jules' (v)	EMOT
- 'Laciniatum'	CMCN EBtc GBin
- PRINCETON GOLD ('Prigo'[PBR]) 🏆H6	CBcs CDul CTho EBee ECrN ELan EMOT ESps EUJe GQue LBuc LRHS MAsh MGos NEgg NOra SCoo SEWo SLim SPer SPoG SWvt WHar
- 'Reitenbachii'	CDul
- 'Royal Red'	CDul ECrN EPfP LMaj LPra MRav NLar SCoo SEWo
- 'Schwedleri' 🏆H6	CMCN LPra WTSh
- subsp. ***turkestanicum***	CMCN SSta
pseudoplatanus	CAco CBcs CCVT CDul CLnd CMCN CPer CTri ECrN ELan EMOT LPra MGos SGol SPer WHar WMou WTSh
§ - 'Atropurpureum'	CDul ECrN ESps LPra SEWo WHar
- 'Brilliantissimum' 🏆H6	Widely available
- 'Corstorphinense'	CDul
- f. ***erythrocarpum*** 'Erythrocarpum'	CMac
- 'Gadsby'	CDul EBee
- 'Leopoldii' misapplied	see *A. pseudoplatanus* f. *variegatum*
- 'Negenia'	CDul
- 'Prinz Handjéry'	CDul CEnd CMCN CTri ESps MGos NLar NOra SGol WHar
- 'Spaethii' misapplied	see *A. pseudoplatanus* 'Atropurpureum'
§ - f. ***variegatum*** (v)	LPra
- - 'Esk Sunset' (v)	CLnd EBee ELan LSRN MGos SPoG
- - 'Leopoldii' ambig. (v)	CBcs CCVT CDul CLnd CMCN ECrN EMOT ESps SWvt
- - 'Leopoldii' Vervaene (v)	SPer
- - 'Simon-Louis Frères' (v)	CBcs CCVT CDul CLnd CMCN ECrN EMOT ESps MAsh MGos NLar SGol SPer SWvt WHar
- 'Worley'	CDul CLnd CMCN CMac ECrN EMOT ESps MRav SGol SLim SPer
pseudosieboldianum	CMCN LRHS MBlu MPkF
- B&SWJ 8468	WCru
- B&SWJ 8746	WCru
- B&SWJ 8769	WCru
- var. ***microsieboldianum*** B&SWJ 8766	WCru
- subsp. ***takesimense***	MBlu
- - B&SWJ 8500	WCru
- - B&SWJ 8540	WCru
pubipalmatum	CRos LRHS NRHS
pycnanthum	EPfP

'Red Flamingo' (v)	CBcs CJun CMac CRos EPfP LRHS MBlu MGos NLar NOra SGol SMad SPoG
'Red Wings' (*A. palmatum* hybrid)	CJun
reticulatum	see *A. laevigatum* var. *reticulatum*
rubescens CWJ 12438	WCru
rubrum	CAco CAgr CBcs CDul CLnd CMCN CPer CSBt CTri EBee ECrN ELan EMOT EPfP LCro LMaj LOPS LPra LRHS MGos MMuc NEgg SCoo SEWo SGol WCFE WHar WTSh
- 'Autumn Flame'	CCVT WMou
- 'Autumn Spire'	CJun
- 'Brandywine'	CDul CJun CLnd CTho EBee EMOT EPfP LRHS LSRN MAsh MBlu NLar NOra SAko SBir SCoo WHCr
- 'Embers'	CJun
- FAIRVIEW FLAME	see *A. rubrum* 'Pete's Fairview'
- 'Firedance'	CJun
- 'Joseph'	NLar
- 'New World'	SCoo
- 'October Glory' ♀H6	Widely available
§ - 'Pete's Fairview'	CJun MMuc SPer
- 'Red King'	CJun
- RED SUNSET ('Franksred') ♀H6	CAco CDul CEnd CMCN CTho EBee ELan EMOT EPfP LPra NLar SBir SCoo SGol SLim SPer SPoG
- 'Scanlon'	CBcs CDul CEnd CJun CMCN CTho EPfP LMaj LPra LRHS NOra SLim SPer
- 'Schlesingeri'	CEnd CJun CLnd CMac EPfP SPer
I - 'Sekka'	MBlu
- 'Somerset'	CDul CJun CTho CTri EBee SCoo
- SUMMER RED ('Hosr')	CDul EBee EMOT EPfP SCoo
- 'Sun Valley'	CJun EBee MAsh NOra WMou
- 'Tilford'	CJun SSta
§ ***rufinerve***	CBcs CDul CLnd CMCN CTho CTri EBee ECrN EPfP ESps EWTr LPra MMuc NEgg NLar NOra SCoo SGol SSta SWvt WHar WTSh
- 'Albolimbatum' (v)	CEnd CJun CMCN SBig SSta
- 'Erythrocladum'	CJun MBlu
- 'Ko-fuji-nishiki'	SSta
I - 'Sunshine'	SSta
- 'Winter Gold'	CJun NLar SSta
- 'Yellow Ribbon'	WHor
§ ***saccharinum***	CBcs CCVT CDul CLnd CMCN CTri EBee ECrN ELan EPfP ESps LPra MGos MMuc NOra SCoo SGol SPer WTSh
- 'Born's Gracious'	CJun
- 'Fastigiatum'	see *A. saccharinum* 'Pyramidale'
- f. ***laciniatum***	EBee LPra MBlu MMuc SGol SPer
- - 'Laciniatum Wieri'	CDul CMCN NLar SGol
- 'Lutescens'	CDul CTho
§ - 'Pyramidale'	CLnd ECrN LMaj SPer
saccharum	CAgr CBcs CDul CLnd CMCN CTho EBee ECrN EPfP IArd LMaj LPra LRHS MBlu NEgg WTSh
- 'Brocade'	CJun
- 'Fiddlers Creek'	CJun
§ - subsp. ***grandidentatum***	CMCN EPfP
§ ***sempervirens***	EBee EPfP IArd IDee LEdu MPkF
'Sensu'	CJun
'Serendipity'	SSta
serrulatum	CMCN
- CWJ 12437	WCru
shirasawanum	CMCN
§ - 'Aureum' ♀H6	Widely available

- 'Autumn Moon'	CBcs CJun CMCN CMen CRos CWGN EPfP EUJe GMil LRHS MPkF NEgg NLar NOra NRHS SBod SCob SCoo SGol SPer SPoG
§ - 'Ezo-no-momiji'	CJun CMen MPkF NEgg
- 'Gloria'	MPkF SGol
- 'Jordan'PBR	CDul CEnd CMCN CRos CWGN EBee LRHS LSRN MAsh MGos MPkF NRHS SBod SPoG SWvt
- 'Kakure-gasa'	CJun
- 'Lovett'	CJun
§ - 'Microphyllum'	NEgg
- 'Mr Sun'	CJun
§ - 'Ogurayama'	CAco CJun CMen
- 'Palmatifolium'	CJun
- 'Red Dawn'	CJun
- 'Susanne'	CJun CMen SGol
- var. ***tenuifolium*** B&SWJ 11073	WCru
sieboldianum ♀H6	CDul CMCN CMen CTho CTri ECrN LRHS MAsh MBlu MMuc SEND SGol WMou
- B&SWJ 10849	WCru
- B&SWJ 11049	WCru
- B&SWJ 11090	WCru
- 'Sode-no-uchi'	CJun CMen
- var. ***tsushimense*** B&SWJ 10962	WCru
sikkimense B&SWJ 11689	WCru
- B&SWJ 11703	WCru
- FMWJ 13166 from northern Vietnam **new**	WCru
- NJM 10.134	WPGP
- WJC 13674 from Sikkim **new**	WCru
- WWJ 11601	WCru
- WWJ 11613	WCru
- WWJ 11853	WCru
'Silver Cardinal' (v)	CEnd CJun CMCN EPfP MBlu MGos NLar SSta
'Silver Vein'	see *A.* × *conspicuum* 'Silver Vein'
sinense	CMCN
spicatum	CMCN NLar
§ ***sterculiaceum***	EBee
- PAB 13.135	LEdu
- subsp. ***franchetii***	CMCN NLar
- subsp. ***sterculiaceum*** NJM 13.087	WPGP
tataricum	CMCN
§ - subsp. ***ginnala***	CAco CArg CBcs CDul CLnd CMCN CTri ECrN EWTr LPra MBlu MGos NLar SGol SPer
- - 'Flame'	CCVT CJun EBee ECrN EPfP LRHS MGos MMuc NLar
tegmentosum ♀H5	CDul CJun CMCN EPfP IArd MBlu SMad SSta WHor
- subsp. ***glaucorufinerve***	see *A. rufinerve*
- 'Joe Witt'	NLar
tonkinense subsp. ***liquidambarifolium*** DJHV 06173	WCru
trautvetteri	CMCN
triflorum ♀H6	CBcs CCVT CDul CJun CMCN EBee EPfP LMaj LRHS MBlu NLar NOra
truncatum	CDul MPkF
- 'Akikaze-nishiki' (v)	CJun MPkF
tschonoskii	GKin
- subsp. ***koreanum***	MPkF
- - B&SWJ 12596	WCru
- - B&SWJ 12603	WCru

	Name	Suppliers
	'Valley Phantom'	SSta
	velutinum	CMCN
	villosum	see *A. sterculiaceum*
	wardii **new**	LEdu WPGP
	'White Tigress'	CBcs CJun CTho EPfP LRHS NLar SSta
	× ***zoeschense***	CMCN MPkF
	- 'Annae'	MMuc SGol

Aceriphyllum see *Mukdenia*

Achillea (*Asteraceae*)

	Name	Suppliers
	ageratifolia ♀H5	CMea ECha ECtt EDAr GWyn NGdn SRms WSpi XLum XSen
§	***ageratum***	CBod ENfk GPSL GPoy LEdu MHer MNHC SRms WFar WGwG WHer WTre XLum XSen
	'Alabaster'	CRos LRHS NRHS WSpi
	ANTHEA ('Anblo'PBR)	EBee ECtt IBoy LRHS LSRN MCot MRav NRHS SHar SRms SWvt WFar
§	'Apfelblüte' (Galaxy Series)	CAby CBod EBee ECha ECtt ELan EPed GKin LRHS LSRN MMuc MRav NGdn NQui NRHS NSti SCob SEND SPer SRms XSen
	APPLEBLOSSOM	see *A.* 'Apfelblüte'
	'Apricot Beauty'	ECtt EWTr WSpi
	'Apricot Delight' (Tutti Frutti Series)	LRHS NLar WTor
	argentea misapplied	see *A. clavennae, A. umbellata*
	argentea Lamarck	see *Tanacetum argenteum*
	aurea	see *A. chrysocoma*
	'Bahama'	GBin GQue
	'Belle Epoque'	WSpi XSen
	biebersteinii	XLum
	brachyphylla	EPot
	'Breckland Bouquet'	EWes
	'Breckland Cream'	EPed
	'Breckland Ruby'	EWes
	'Carmina Burana'	CMea
	cartilaginea	see *A. salicifolia*
§	***chrysocoma***	WMoo
	- 'Grandiflora'	ECha MMuc NGdn WBrk
§	***clavennae***	GKev SRms WAbe
	clypeolata Sibth. & Sm.	CRos EHyd LRHS NRHS SPlb SRms XLum
	coarctata	XSen
	Colorado Group	CRos EHyd LRHS NPol NRHS WHar
	'Coronation Gold' ♀H7	CRos CWCL EBee ECtt ELan EPed EPfP ETMg IBoy LRHS MAsh MHol MRav MWat NChi NDov NRHS SCob SPer SRms SWvt WCAu WCot WSpi XLum XSen
	'Credo' ♀H7	CAby CDor CRos CWld ECha ECtt EPed EPfP EWTr GBin IBoy IPot LCro LOPS LRHS MArl MBel MRav MSpe NDov NGdn NLar NRHS NSti SMad SPer WCAu WSpi XSen
	crithmifolia	XLum XSen
	decolorans	see *A. ageratum*
	(Desert Eve Series) DESERT EVE CREAM ('Deseve')	CRos EBee EHyd LRHS NRHS
	- DESERT EVE DEEP ROSE ('Desderos')	EBee ECtt EHyd LRHS NRHS
	- DESERT EVE LIGHT YELLOW	CRos ECtt LRHS NRHS SRms
	- DESERT EVE RED ('Desred'PBR)	CRos EBee LRHS NRHS
	- DESERT EVE YELLOW ('Desyel'PBR)	EBee
	erba-rotta subsp. ***moschata***	NBro
	falcata	GKev
§	'Fanal'	CAby CRos CWCL EBee ECha ECtt ELan EPed EPfP GKin GWyn IBoy LRHS MCot MRav MSpe MTis NEgg NLar NRHS SPer SWvt WCAu
	'Faust'	CDor ELon
	'Feuerland'	CMac CSam EBee ECha ECtt ELon EPfP GKin LRHS MRav NDov NGdn NRHS SAko SMad SPer SPoG WFar WSpi XSen
	filipendulina 'Cloth of Gold' ♀H7	Widely available
	- 'Gold Plate' ♀H7	Widely available
	- 'Hymne'	EBee
	- 'Parker's Variety' ♀H7	EBee NBre WFar WMoo XLum XSen
	'Fleur van Zonneveld'	NDov
	FLOWERS OF SULPHUR	see *A.* 'Schwefelblüte'
	(Forncett Series) 'Forncett Beauty'	SWvt
	- 'Forncett Bride'	EBee
	- 'Forncett Citrus'	ECtt WFar
	- 'Forncett Fletton'	CWCL ECtt EHrv ELon EPed EPfP GBin GKin MBel MRav NGdn
	'Gloria Jean'	SHar
	'Golden Fleece'	GWyn
	grandifolia misapplied	see *Tanacetum macrophyllum* (Waldst. & Kit.) Sch.Bip.
§	***grandifolia*** Friv.	CSam MArl MHol NBro WFar WMoo WOld
	'Great Expectations'	see *A.* 'Hoffnung'
	'Hannelore Pahl'	IPot
	'Heidi' ♀H7	MRav NPnk XSen
	'Heinrich Vogeler'	EBee LPla MHol
	'Hella Glashoff' ♀H7	CMea CRos CWCL EBee ELon LRHS MAsh NRHS
§	'Hoffnung'	CWCL NRHS
	× ***huteri***	ECtt EDAr GCrg IRob MMuc NGdn NHpl NRya SEND SRms SWvt WFar
	'Inca Gold'	CBcs CSam CWCL ECha ECtt EHoe EHrv EPed LRHS MRav MSpe NDov NRHS NSti SPer SRms SWvt WFar WGwG WHoo WSpi WWtn
	× ***kellereri***	XLum XSen
	'King Alfred'	CMea NHpl SRms
	× ***kolbiana***	EWes SRms XSen
§	'Lachsschönheit' (Galaxy Series) ♀H7	CAby CBWd CKno CWCL EBee ECha ECtt ELan EPed EPfP GBin GMaP LRHS MBNS MCot MRav NDov NLar NRHS NSti SCob SPer SRms
	× ***lewisii*** 'King Edward' ♀H5	EDAr GCrg GMaP SRms WAbe WFar
	'Lucky Break' ♀H7	EBee ECha ECtt LEdu MHol WBrk WCot WRHF
	macrophylla	MBNS
	'Marie Ann'	CWCL LSRN NLar NPnk
	'Marmalade'	CDor MRav NDov
	'Martina' ♀H7	CAby CSam ECtt GBin GKin LRHS MAsh MBNS MBel MCot MRav NDov NGdn NRHS SRGP WCot WGwG WHoo
	'McVities'	CWCL ECtt
	millefolium	CHab EBWF ENfk GPoy MNHC NMir NPol SRms WHer WOut WSFF WSpi XLum
	- 'Apricot Seduction' **new**	WFar
	- 'Bloodstone'	ECtt EWes MRav
	- 'Carla Hussey'	WFar

	- 'Cassis'	CBod CRos CSam CSpe EHyd EPfP LRHS MCot NChi NGBl NLar NRHS SPtp WBor WFar WMoo WOut
§	- 'Cerise Queen'	Widely available
	- 'Chamois'	MNrw
	- 'Cherry King'	WMoo
	- 'Christel'	EWes
	- 'Circus'	XLum
	- 'Dark Lilac Beauty'	CWCL
	- KIRSCHKÖNIGIN	see *A. millefolium* 'Cerise Queen'
	- 'Lansdorferglut' ♕H7	CRos EBee IRob LRHS NDov NRHS SPhx
	- 'Laura'	CSam CWGN ECtt EPfP MBel MNrw
	- 'Lavender Beauty'	see *A. millefolium* 'Lilac Beauty'
§	- 'Lilac Beauty'	CRos ECha EHrv ELon EPfP GMaP GWyn IBoy IPot LCro LOPS LRHS LSRN MMuc MRav NEgg NLar NRHS SCob SEND SRms WCAu WFar WHar WSpi XLum
*	- 'Lilac Queen'	MArl
	- 'Little Suzie'	CWGN ECtt
	- (New Vintage Series) NEW VINTAGE LILAC	see *A. millefolium* (New Vintage Series) NEW VINTAGE VIOLET
	- - NEW VINTAGE RED ('Balvinred')	LRHS MHol WHil
	- - NEW VINTAGE ROSE ('Balvinrose')	LRHS WHil
	- - NEW VINTAGE VIOLET ('Balvinviolet') **new**	CBod
	- - NEW VINTAGE WHITE ('Balvinwite') **new**	CBod
	- 'Old Brocade'	EShb NDov
	- Pastel Shades	IFoB IFro WFar
	- 'Peggy Sue'	CWGN EBee ECtt WFar
	- 'Pomegranate' (Tutti Frutti Series)	CWGN IPot LCro LOPS MBel MNrw SCob SHar WTor XLum
	- 'Pretty Woman'	CBWd CSam CWGN EBee
	- 'Raspberry Ripple'	GBin GWyn
	- 'Red Beauty'	CWCL EPfP EWTr MBNS SRms XLum
	- 'Red Salmon'	EWes
	- 'Red Velvet'	Widely available
	- 'Rose Madder'	CWCL ECtt EHoe EPfP GKin GMaP LRHS MBel MCot MHol MMuc MNrw MPie MTis NChi NEgg NGdn NLar NRHS NSti SEND SPer SPoG SWvt WCot WFar WHoo WSpi XLum
	- 'Salmon Pink'	IBoy
	- 'Salmon Queen'	WFar WHar
	- 'Sammetriese'	ELon MNrw SMad SPhx
	- 'Schneetaler'	IRob
	- 'Serenade'	ECtt
	- 'Sonoma Coast'	CSpe
	- 'Sue's Pink'	CSam
	- (Summer Fruits Series) 'Summer Fruits Carmine'	EBee LRHS MTis WHar
	- - 'Summer Fruits Lemon'	EBee LRHS WFar WHar WSpi
	- - 'Summer Fruits Salmon'	EBee LRHS WHar
	- 'Summertime'	WFar
	- 'White Beauty'	EWTr
	- 'White Queen'	EBee
	- 'Wonderful Wampee'	CRos EBee EHyd EWTr LRHS MNrw NRHS SCob WCot
	'Mondpagode' ♕H7	ECtt EPfP EWTr LRHS MBNS MCot MRav NGdn NRHS SPhx SWvt WHoo
*	'Moonbeam'	GKin SEND
	'Moonshine' ♕H7	Widely available
	'Moonwalker'	EPfP SPav WCot XLum
	nana	WFar
	nobilis	XSen
	- subsp. ***neilreichii***	CBod EHoe EWTr MBNS MMuc NSti SEND SPer SWvt WFar WGwG
*	***odilis***	EWTr
	'Paprika' (Galaxy Series)	Widely available
	'Petra'	EBee ILea MNrw XLum
	pindicola subsp. ***integrifolia***	EWes
	'Pineapple Mango' PBR	SCob
	pink-flowered from Santa Cruz Island	CWCL
	'Pink Grapefruit' (Tutti Frutti Series)	GWyn IPot MAsh MTis NLar SCob
	'Pretty Belinda'	CDor CRos EBee ECtt EHyd EPfP GWyn IRob LPmr LRHS LSRN MAvo MSpe NDov NRHS NSti SAko SPoG SRms WCAu WFar
	'Prospero'	WCot
	ptarmica	CBod CBre EBWF MHer NMir SCob SRms WArt WWtn XLum
*	- 'Ballerina'	MBNS NDov NLar
	- 'Double Diamond' (d)	CRos EHyd LRHS NRHS
	- 'Nana Compacta'	CRos EHyd IBoy LRHS NRHS SPlb WCFE WCot WFar
	- 'Noblessa'	MHol
	- 'Perry's White' (d)	CBre ECha MNrw SRGP WCot
	- 'Stephanie Cohen'	see *A. sibirica* 'Stephanie Cohen'
	- The Pearl Group seed-raised (d)	CTri ELan GWyn MMuc SGbt SPlb WFar WMoo
	- - 'Boule de Neige' (clonal) (d)	ELan GKin IBoy MRav MSpe NPer NSti SHar SPer WFar WSpi XLum
	- - 'The Pearl' (clonal) (d)	Widely available
	pyrenaica	XLum
	'Rougham Salmon'	CDor
	'Ruby Wine'	WFar
	'Safran'	CRos EBee LRHS NRHS XLum
§	***salicifolia***	WFar
	- 'Silver Spray'	NLar SPav WOut
	SALMON BEAUTY	see *A.* 'Lachsschönheit'
	'Sandra Wagg'	ECtt
	'Sandstone'	see *A.* 'Wesersandstein'
	'Saucy Seduction' (Seduction Series)	CWCL EBee MHol MTis NBid
§	'Schwefelblüte'	MRav
	'Schwellenburg'	NBre WCot WFar
	sibirica subsp. ***camschatica*** 'Love Parade'	CBod CHid EBee MBNS MHol MMuc MNrw SGbt SPer SPtp WArt XLum
§	- 'Stephanie Cohen'	GBin WFar
	'Stephanie'	EWes LSRN
	SUMMER BERRIES MIXED	CBod EHyd LRHS NRHS WFar WHil
	Summer Pastels Group	CBod CRos EHyd EPfP IBoy LRHS NLar NRHS SRms WFar WHar XLum
	- 'Peachy Seduction' PBR (Seduction Series)	NLar
	- 'Strawberry Seduction' (Seduction Series)	ECtt
	'Summerwine' ♕H7	Widely available
	'Sunbeam'	SHar
	'Sunny Seduction' (Seduction Series)	ECtt ELon MAsh MTis
I	'Taygetea'	ELan EPfP GWyn LCro LOPS MBNS SCob SPer SPoG SRkn WCAu WCot WSpi XLum
	'Terracotta'	Widely available
	'The Beacon'	see *A.* 'Fanal'
	'Tissington Old Rose'	MNrw

	tomentosa ♀H5	CTri ECha ECtt GPSL
§	– 'Aurea'	CMea NBro XLum
	– 'Goldie'	CRos EHyd LRHS NRHS SWvt WFar
	– 'Maynard's Gold'	see *A. tomentosa* 'Aurea'
	'Tri-colour'	MBNS NGdn
§	***umbellata***	EPot NSla XSen
	'Velour'	GBin
	'W.B. Childs'	ELan MNrw MRav NDov SHar
	'Walther Funcke'	Widely available
§	'Wesersandstein'	CRos CWCL GMaP MNrw NRHS SCob SGbt
	'Wilczekii'	SRms
	'Yellowstone'	EWes

× *Achimenantha* (*Gesneriaceae*)

'Aries'	WDib
'Cool Inferno'	WDib
'Golden Jubilee'	WDib
'Himalayan Sunrise'	LAma WDib
'Inferno' ♀H1c	WDib
'Pisces'	WDib
'Texas Blue Bayou'	WDib

Achimenes (*Gesneriaceae*)

'Addano'	WDib
admirabilis	WDib
'Ambroise Verschaffelt' ♀H1c	EShb LAma SDir WDib
'Ami Van Houtte'	WDib
'Apricot Glow'	WDib
'Aquamarine'	WDib
'Aurora Charm'	WDib
'Ballerina'	WDib
'Beautiful Fire'	WDib
'Big Weiss'	WDib
'Blue Sparks' **new**	SDeJ
'Caligula'	WDib
'Cameo Rose'	WDib
'Candy Shop'	WDib
'Cascade Fairy Pink'	WDib
'Cascade Fashionable Pink'	WDib
'Cascade Rose Red'	WDib
'Cascade Violet Night'	WDib
'Cattleya'	LAma SDir
cettoana	WDib
'Charity'	WDib
'Charm'	LAma SDeJ WDib
'Claret'	WDib
'Crackerjack'	WDib
'Crummock Water'	WDib
'Double Picotee Rose' (d)	WDib
'Double Pink Rose' (d)	WDib
erecta	WDib
'Erlkönig'	WDib
'Escheriana'	LAma
'Extravaganza'	WDib
'Firefly'	WDib
'Flamenco'	WDib
'Glory'	WDib
'Golden Butterfly'	WDib
'Harry Williams'	EShb LAma SDir WDib
'Hilda Michelssen' ♀H1c	WDib
'Himalayan Angel'	LAma
'Himalayan Double'	LAma
'Himalayan Mandarin'	LAma
'Hugues Aufray'	WDib
'Ice Tea'	WDib
'India'	EShb
'Jay Dee Coral'	WDib
'Jay Dee Large White'	WDib
'Jay Dee Pink'	WDib
'Jay Dee Purple'	WDib
'Jennifer Goode'	WDib
'Johanna Michelssen'	WDib
'Just Divine'	WDib
'Kim Blue'	WDib
'Lady in Black'	WDib
'Light Lilac'	WDib
'Little Beauty'	WDib
longiflora 'Major'	WDib
'Maxima'	LAma
'Melon Ice Cream'	WDib
'Menuett'	WDib
mexicana	LAma SDeJ
misera	WDib
'Opal'	WDib
'Orange Delight'	WDib
'Pally'	WDib
'Patens Major'	WDib
'Peach Blossom'	EShb LAma SDeJ WDib
'Peach Glow'	WDib
pedunculata	WDib
'Petite Fadette'	WDib
'Primadonna'	SDeJ WDib
'Pulcherrima'	SDeJ
'Purple King'	WDib
'Purple Queen'	WDib
'Purple Triumph'	WDib
'Queen of Queens'	WDib
'Rai'	WDib
'Rainbow'	WDib
'Rainbow Warrior'	WDib
'Red Hilda Michelssen'	WDib
'Rozi Roza'	WDib
'Santa Claus'	WDib
'Schneewittchen'	WDib
'Serge Saliba'	WDib
'Serge's Fantasy'	WDib
'Show-off'	WDib
'Shy Sun'	WDib
skinneri	WDib
'Snow Princess'	EShb SDeJ
'Stan's Delight' (d) ♀H1c	WDib
'Sterntaler'	WDib
'Sugarland'	WDib
'Sun Wind'	WDib
'Sweet and Sour'	WDib
'Tango'	WDib
'Tarantella'	WDib
(Tetra Series) 'Tetra Himalayan Purple'	LAma SDir WDib
– 'Tetra Purple'	SDir
'Tiger Eye'	WDib
'Valse Bleu'	WDib
'Violacea Semiplena' (d)	WDib
'Vivid'	LAma WDib
'Weinrot Elfe'	WDib
'Wetterlow's Triumph'	WDib
'Yellow Beauty'	WDib

Achlys (*Berberidaceae*)

japonica	WCru
triphylla	IMou WCru

Achnatherum see *Stipa*

Achyranthes (*Amaranthaceae*)

bidentata var. ***longifolia*** PAB 8037	LEdu

Acidanthera see *Gladiolus*

Acinos (*Lamiaceae*)

§ ***alpinus***	CMea EBee EDAr GJos LLHF NHpl SBch SRms WAbe WArt XLum
§ ***corsicus***	WHoo WKif

Aciphylla (*Apiaceae*)

aurea	GBin GCal SPlb
colensoi	GKev
congesta	CMen
dieffenbachii	SPoG
glaucescens	EBee GCal SPlb
hectorii	CMen
montana	CMen
pinnatifida	CMen
simplex	CMen
spedenii	CMen

Acis (*Amaryllidaceae*)

§ ***autumnalis*** ♀H5	CAby CAvo CBro CElw CTal CTri ECha EHyd ELan EPot EWes GKev LRHS MPie NHpl NRHS NRog SBch SBrt SDir SMHy SRms SRot WAbe WFar WHoo WOld WPGP WSHC
- 'Cobb's Variety'	GCal
- var. ***oporantha***	CWCL EPri GKev LAma NRog
- - f. ***dispathacea***	GEdr GKev NRog
- var. ***pulchella***	NRog
- 'September Snow'	ELan EPri GKev LAma NRog
ionica	NRog
nicaeensis	CTal EHyd EPot GCal LRHS NRHS NWad WAbe WCot WThu
§ ***rosea***	CTal NRog WAbe
§ ***tingitana***	CBro
§ ***trichophylla***	EPot GKev
- pink-flowered	EPri
- f. ***purpurascens***	WCot
§ ***valentina***	NRog SRot WCot

Acnistus (*Solanaceae*)

australis	see *Iochroma australe*

Aconitum (*Ranunculaceae*)

sp.	ESps
'Album'	CBod EPfP MSCN WSpi
altissimum	see *A. lycoctonum* subsp. *vulparia*
anglicum	see *A. napellus* subsp. *napellus* Anglicum Group
§ ***anthora***	EPfP MHol
arcuatum	see *A. fischeri* var. *arcuatum*
austroyunnanense	WHal WSHC
- BWJ 7902	WCru
autumnale misapplied	see *A. carmichaelii* Wilsonii Group
autumnale Rchb.	see *A. fischeri* Rchb.
× ***bicolor***	see *A.* × *cammarum* 'Bicolor'
'Blue Lagoon'PBR	CWGN EBee EWTr GMcL WHil
'Blue Opal'	EBee ECtt EWes MAvo
'Blue Sceptre'	SRms
'Bressingham Spire' ♀H7	Widely available
bulbilliferum HWJK 2120	WSHC
× ***cammarum*** new	NChi
§ - 'Bicolor' ♀H7	Widely available
- 'Eleanora'	ECtt EPPr EPfP EWes EWld GMaP LSou SRms
- 'Grandiflorum Album'	CAby MNrw
- 'Pink Sensation'PBR	CAby GKev NLar NPnk
§ ***carmichaelii***	CBod CRos CSam EHyd ELan EPfP GAbr GKin IFoB IFro IRob LRHS MMuc MNrw NBro NChi NEgg NGdn NRHS SEND SRms WCot WFar WHar WHil WHoo WSpi WWtn
- Arendsii Group	ECtt LEdu SRot WCAu WHil
- - 'Arendsii' ♀H7	Widely available
- - 'Cloudy'PBR	CWGN EBee ECtt ELon EWTr LEdu MAvo MBel NGdn NLar NRHS SPer WCot WHil WSpi
- 'Moody Blues'	EBee
- 'Redleaf'	see *A. carmichaelii* 'Royal Flush'
- 'River Finn'	WCot
- 'River Lugg'	WCot
- 'River Medway'	CDor WCot
- 'River Nene'	WCot
- 'River Ouse'	ECtt WCot
- 'River Spey'	WCot
- 'River Tees'	WCot
- 'River Teifi'	WCot
- 'River Trent'	WCot
- 'River Welland'	WCot
§ - 'Royal Flush'PBR	CDor CWGN EBee ECtt IBoy LSun MBNS MCot MHol MNrw NEgg NLar SPad SPer SPoG WCot
- var. ***truppelianum***	WCot
- - HWJ 732	EBee WCot
§ - Wilsonii Group	EBee GMaP LEdu MCot MRav MWat NDov NEgg WHoo XLum
- - 'Barker's Variety'	CKno CRos ELon GCal LRHS NGdn NLar NRHS NSti SRms WCot WSpi
- - 'Kelmscott' ♀H7	ELon EWes MCot MRav SMHy WCot WFar WRHF WSpi
- - 'Spätlese'	CDor CSam CWGN EBee ECtt ELon GBin GCal GQue IRob LEdu LRHS MCot MHol NGdn NLar SGbt SPer SPoG WCAu WCot WRHF
§ ***chasmanthum***	CRos LRHS NRHS
- GWJ 9393	WCru
chiisanense B&SWJ 4446	WCru
cilicicum	see *Eranthis hyemalis* Cilicica Group
compactum	see *A. napellus* subsp. *vulgare*
confertiflorum	see *A. anthora*
delphiniifolium	CExl
elliotii	EBee
elwesii	EBee LEdu
episcopale	WCot WCru
excelsum	see *A. lycoctonum* subsp. *lycoctonum*
ferox	EBee EWes LLHF
- GWJ 9333 from Sikkim	WCru
- GWJ 9403	WCru
fischeri misapplied	see *A. carmichaelii*
§ ***fischeri*** Rchb.	CBod EBee LRHS NBid NLar WCot
- B&SWJ 8809	WCru
§ - var. ***arcuatum*** B&SWJ 774	WCru
formosanum B&SWJ 3057	WCru
fukutomei B&SWJ 337	LEdu MRav WCru
gammiei GWJ 9418	WCru
gmelinii	see *A. lycoctonum* subsp. *lycoctonum*
grossedentatum	LPla NLar
- subsp. ***paniculatum***	see *A. variegatum* subsp. *paniculatum*
§ ***hemsleyanum***	CAby CExl CRHN CTal CWGN ECtt EWTr EWld GKev GLog MBel NBid WCot WCru
- dark blue-flowered	WSpi
- 'Red Wine'	EWld WCot
hyemale	see *Eranthis hyemalis*

	'Ivorine'	CRos CSam EBee ECha EHyd ELan EPfP GMaP IBoy ILea IRob LEdu LRHS MCot MHol NEgg NGdn NLar NPnk NRHS SCob SPer WFar WPnP WWtn
	jaluense B&SWJ 8741	WCru
	japonicum	EBee GCal GQue NLar WCot
	- var. ***hakonense***	CExl
	- var. ***montanum*** B&SWJ 5507	WCru
§	- subsp. ***napiforme***	EWes
	- - B&SWJ 943	EBee ELon WCru
§	- subsp. ***subcuneatum*** B&SWJ 6228	WCru
	kitadakense B&SWJ 11173	WCru
	kusnezoffii	WCot
	laciniatum GWJ 9254	WCru
	- GWJ 9324	WCru
	lamarckii	see *A. lycoctonum* subsp. *neapolitanum*
	lasianthum	see *A. lycoctonum* subsp. *vulparia*
	leucostomum	EBee GCal
	loczyanum	GKev WCot
	- B&SWJ 11529	WCru WSHC
	lycoctonum	CTal NLar NSti WSpi
	- 'Darkeyes'	WCot WSpi
§	- subsp. ***lycoctonum***	LEdu SRms
§	- subsp. ***moldavicum***	WCot
§	- subsp. ***neapolitanum***	CDor EBee GCal GMaP IMou MMuc NLar SEND WHil WSpi
	- 'Russian Yellow'	EWld GCal
§	- subsp. ***vulparia***	CMac GPoy ILea MRav NEgg NGdn SRms WWtn
	mairei	see *A. vilmorinianum*
	moldavicum	see *A. lycoctonum* subsp. *moldavicum*
	nagarum	WCot
	- KR 7589	EBee
	napellus	CAby CBod CRav ECtt EPfP EWTr GAbr GBin GPoy ILea IRob LRHS MBel MCot MHol MMuc MNHC MWat SEND SPoG SRms WFar WHar WHoo WPnP WShi XLum
	- 'Bergfürst'	CAby EBee NDov
	- 'Blue Valley'	EBee EPfP EWes
	- 'Gletschereis'	CRos EBee LRHS NRHS WCAu
§	- subsp. ***napellus*** Anglicum Group	MCot MHol MMuc SEND WCot WWtn
	- - - 'Spring Yellow'	WCot
	- 'Rubellum'	IBoy IMou LRHS NBro NLar NSti SPoG WSpi
	- 'Schneewittchen'	CSpe EWes IRob SAko
§	- subsp. ***vulgare***	CTal
	- - 'Albidum'	CAby CBod ELon EPfP EWTr GAbr GMaP LEdu LRHS MBel NBid NLar NRHS SPer SPoG WBor WWtn
	- - 'Carneum'	WHer
	napiforme	see *A. japonicum* subsp. *napiforme*
	nasutum	WCot
	- white-flowered **new**	WCot
	neapolitanum	see *A. lycoctonum* subsp. *neapolitanum*
	'Newry Blue'	CRos EBee ECtt GMcL IMou LRHS MArl MBNS MRav NRHS NWad SRms WGwG WSpi
	orientale misapplied	see *A. lycoctonum* subsp. *vulparia*
	paniculatum misapplied	see *A. variegatum* subsp. *paniculatum*
	piepunense	EBee GKev
	proliferum	WCot
	- B&SWJ 4107	WCru
	pseudohuiliense	CExl
	pseudolaeve var. ***erectum*** B&SWJ 8466	WCru
	pubiceps white-flowered	GCal
	pyramidale	see *A. napellus* subsp. *vulgare*
	pyrenaicum misapplied	see *A. lycoctonum* subsp. *neapolitanum*
	ranunculifolium	see *A. lycoctonum* subsp. *neapolitanum*
	sachalinense	WCot
	- subsp. ***yezoense***	EBee LPla NLar WCot
	senanense var. ***incisum*** B&SWJ 11032	WCru
	- subsp. ***paludicola*** B&SWJ 10866	WCru
	seoulense	EBee
	- B&SWJ 694	WCru
	- B&SWJ 864	WCru
	- BWJ 4107	IMou
	septentrionale	see *A. lycoctonum* subsp. *lycoctonum*
	'Shirui Blue'	LEdu
	'Spark's Variety' 🏆^{H7}	Widely available
	spicatum GWJ 9394	WCru
	'Stainless Steel' 🏆^{H7}	Widely available
	subcuneatum	see *A. japonicum* subsp. *subcuneatum*
	'Surprise'	WCot
	× ***tubergenii***	see *Eranthis hyemalis* Tubergenii Group
	uchiyamae B&SWJ 1005	WCru
	- B&SWJ 1216	ELon WCru
	- B&SWJ 4446	NLar
	variegatum	EBee GCal
§	- subsp. ***paniculatum***	EBee GCal LPla WCot
§	***vilmorinianum*** BWJ 8055	WCru
	violaceum var. ***robustum***	see *A. chasmanthum*
	volubile misapplied	see *A. hemsleyanum*
	volubile Pall.	EBee
	vulparia	see *A. lycoctonum* subsp. *vulparia*
	yamazakii	WCru
	zigzag var. ***ryohakuense*** B&SWJ 8906	WCru

Aconogonon see *Persicaria*

Acorus ✿ (*Acoraceae*)

	calamus	CBen CKno CWat EBWF GPoy MNHC MSKA NPer WHer WMAq
	- subsp. ***angustatus***	GPoy
	- 'Argenteostriatus' (v)	CWat ECha MCot MMuc SCob SEND SRms WMAq
*	***christophii***	ELon EPPr
	gramineus	GPoy MSKA NPer WHer
	- 'Golden Delight'	SCob SRms
	- 'Golden Edge' (v)	ELon NRHS NWad
	- 'Hakuro-nishiki' (v)	CRos ESps GCrg GMcL GWyn MMoz NBid NRHS NWad SCob SRms SWvt WMoo XLum
	- 'Kinchinjunga' (v)	IFro
	- 'Licorice'	GBin GCal MMoz MSCN WGrn
	- 'Masamune' (v)	EWes GBin GCal
	- 'Minimus Aureus'	CBre GCal
	- 'Oborozuki' misapplied	see *A. gramineus* 'Ōgon'
	- 'Oborozuki' (v)	EHoe
§	- 'Ōgon' (v)	Widely available
	- var. ***pusillus***	NBro
	- 'Variegatus' (v)	Widely available
	'Intermedius'	NPer

Acradenia (Rutaceae)

frankliniae	CBcs CCCN CMac EBee EPfP LRHS MBlu SAko SEND SPlb WHor WPGP

Actaea (Ranunculaceae)

alba misapplied	see *A. pachypoda*, *A. rubra* f. *neglecta*
arizonica	CRos CTal EBee LRHS NLar NRHS SPhx WCru
asiatica B&SWJ 616	WCru
- B&SWJ 6351 from Japan	WCru
- B&SWJ 8694 from Korea	WCru
- BWJ 8174 from China	WCru
biternata B&SWJ 8917	NLar WCru
- B&SWJ 11190	WCru
'Chocoholic'	CBWd CBod CWGN EBee ECtt ELan GBin GEdr ILea IPot LRHS MAsh MAvo MBel MNrw NRHS WHil
§ ***cimicifuga***	ECha GCal GPoy
aff. ***cimicifuga*** WJC 13720 **new**	WCru
§ ***cordifolia***	CBot EBee ETMg GBin GMaP LRHS NGdn NLar SWvt
- variegated (v)	EBee
dahurica	GBin GQue IRob
- B&SWJ 8426	WCru
- B&SWJ 8573	WCru
- tall	GBin NBid
elata	CPla IMou
erythrocarpa	see *A. rubra*
frigida B&SWJ 2966	WCru
§ ***japonica***	CBot GCal MBel NLar
- B&SWJ 5828	WCru
- B&SWJ 11136	WCru
- B&SWJ 11526	WCru
- from Jejudo, South Korea	EBee ELon GBin IMou IPot LEdu MNrw NDov WWtn
- var. ***acutiloba*** B&SWJ 6257	WCru
- 'Cheju-Do' **new**	LPla
- compact B&SWJ 8758A	WCot WCru
mairei	CRos IMou LRHS NRHS
- BWJ 7635	WCru
- BWJ 7939	WCru
§ ***matsumurae***	CExl
- B&SWJ 11187	WCru
- B&SWJ 11528	WCru
- 'Elstead Variety' ♀H7	CExl GCal MRav
- 'Frau Herms'	IRob
- 'White Pearl'	Widely available
§ ***pachypoda***	CBro CExl CTal EBee EPfP EWTr GCal GLog GPoy MBel NBid NSti SMad WCru
- MISTY BLUE ('Lk05'PBR) **new**	CBct CBro CSpe CWGN EBee ECtt GEdr IRob MAvo MHol SCob SMad SPhm SPoG WCot WTor
- f. ***rubrocarpa***	GCal
§ ***podocarpa***	EBee SPlb SRms WCru
'Queen of Sheba'PBR	EBee LRHS NDov NRHS
racemosa ♀H7	CBod CMac CRos EBee ELan EPfP GCal GPoy NBid NGdn NLar NSti SCob SPer SWvt WFar WWtn XLum
§ ***rubra***	CBod CBro CTal EBee ECha ELan GCal IRob LEdu MBel MMrt NBid NLar SMad SPoG WCAu WCru
- B&SWJ 9555	WCru
- ***alba***	see *A. pachypoda*, *A. rubra* f. *neglecta*
§ - f. ***neglecta***	CBot GLog MBel WCot WCru
simplex	EBee GLog NEgg WCot
- B&SWJ 8653	WCru
- B&SWJ 8664	WCru
- B&SWJ 10957	WCru
- B&SWJ 11133	WCru
§ - Atropurpurea Group	Widely available
- - 'Black Negligee'	Widely available
- - 'Brunette' ♀H7	Widely available
- - 'Carbonella'	EBee ECtt ELan EWTr GBin MBel MHol MNrw WFar
- - 'Hillside Black Beauty'	CDor ECtt GKin GMaP LRHS MAsh MNrw MTis NLar NPnk SCob
- - 'James Compton' ♀H7	Widely available
- - 'Mountain Wave'	ECtt MAsh NDov
- 'Pink Spike'	Widely available
§ - 'Prichard's Giant'	CRos GCal LRHS MNrw MRav NLar NRHS WFar
- ***ramosa***	see *A. simplex* 'Prichard's Giant'
- 'Silver Axe'	GCal NGdn
- variegated (v)	WCot
spicata	CBot GBin GPoy LEdu WCru
- PAB 8131	LEdu
- from England	WCru
taiwanensis B&SWJ 3413	WCru
- RWJ 9996	WCru
yesoensis B&SWJ 6355	WCru
- B&SWJ 10860	WCru
yunnanensis	GCal

Actinella see *Tetraneuris*

Actinidia (Actinidiaceae)

BWJ 8161 from China	WCru
arguta	CRHN EBee MGil
- (f/F)	CAgr
- B&SWJ 4455 from Jejudo, South Korea	WCru
- B&SWJ 4823 from Japan	WCru
- B&SWJ 8529 from Ulleungdo, South Korea	WCru
- 'Ambrosia Grande'	NLar
- 'Ananasnaya' (f/F)	CAgr WPGP
- 'Bayern' (F)	CAgr CCCN
- 'Geneva 2' (f/F)	CAgr
- 'Honigbeere'	NLar
- 'Issai' (s-p/F)	CAgr CBcs CCCN EHyd EPom LBuc LRHS SVic WPGP
- 'Jumbo' (f/F)	CAgr LEdu SVic
- 'Ken's Red' (F)	CAgr CCCN CFGn SVic
- 'Meader' (m)	CAgr
- 'Purpurna Sadowa' (f/F)	NLar
- 'Shoko' (f)	WCru
- 'Unchae' (m)	WCru
- 'Weiki' (m)	CAgr CCCN SVic
chinensis misapplied	see *A. deliciosa*
chinensis Planch. var. ***setosa*** H.L. Li B&SWJ 3563	WCru
§ ***deliciosa***	ESps MRav WFar WSHC
- 'Atlas' (m)	NLar SDea
- 'Golden Delight' (F)	CBcs CFGn
- 'Hayward' (f/F)	CBcs CCCN EPfP LRHS LSRN SCob SDea SWvt WFar
- 'Jenny' (s-p/F)	CAgr CEnd CMac CRos CTri EHyd ELan EMOT EPfP EPom LCro LOPS LRHS MGos SCob SDea SPoG SPre SVic WFar
- 'Oriental Delight' (s-p/F)	CRHN

- SOLISSIMO ('Renact') (s-p/F) — CRos EHyd EUJe LRHS MCoo NRHS SPoG
- 'Solo' (s-p/F) — CBar CBcs CCCN CMac CRHN CRos ECrN EPfP LRHS LSRN NLar NPri SLim SPer SWvt
- 'Tomuri' (m) — CBcs CCCN EBee EPfP LRHS LSRN SWvt

hypoleuca B&SWJ 5942 — WCru
'Kiwai Bee' — CCCN
kolomikta ♀H5 — Widely available
- (m) — MBlu NPla
- B&SWJ 4243 — LSRN WCru
- 'Adam' (m) — ETho
- 'Doctor Szymanowski' — WPGP
- 'Sentyabraskaya' (f/F) — NLar
- 'Tomoko' (f/F) — WCru
- 'Yazuaki' (m) — WCru

melanandra — SPlb
petelotii FMWJ 13137 — WCru
- HWJ 628 — WCru

pilosula misapplied — see *A. tetramera* var. *maloides*
pilosula (Finet & Gagnep.) Stapf ex Hand.-Mazz. — CKel CRos EHyd ELan IArd LRHS NRHS SPoG SRms WKif
polygama — CMen GCal
- B&SWJ 5444 — WCru
- B&SWJ 8525 from Korea — WCru
- B&SWJ 8923 from Japan — WCru
- B&SWJ 12564 — WCru

rufa B&SWJ 3525 — WCru
strigosa WJC 13662 — WCru
- WJC 13807 — WCru

aff. ***strigosa*** HWJK 2367 — WCru
tetramera B&SWJ 3564 — WCru
§ - var. ***maloides*** ♀H5 — CBcs CBot CExl CWGN EBee EUJe GCal MGil NLar SBrt SCoo WBor WCru WPGP WSHC

Acystopteris (*Woodsiaceae*)

taiwaniana new — CBdn

Adansonia (*Malvaceae*)

grandidieri — SPlb
madagascariensis — SPlb
rubrostipa — SPlb
za — SPlb

Adelocaryum see *Lindelofia*

Adenanthos (*Proteaceae*)

sericeus — SPlb

Adenia (*Passifloraceae*)

glauca — LToo
keramanthus — LToo
spinosa — LToo

Adenium (*Apocynaceae*)

obesum ♀H1a — CCCN LToo
- subsp. ***boehmianum*** — LToo

Adenocarpus (*Papilionaceae*)

decorticans — SPlb

Adenophora (*Campanulaceae*)

sp. — MHol
'Afterglow' — see *Campanula rapunculoides* 'Afterglow'
asiatica — see *Hanabusaya asiatica*
bulleyana — ELan LRHS NBid NGdn NLar SPav SPlb WCot WFar
capillaris subsp. ***leptosepala*** — EWld
- - BWJ 7986 — WCru

coelestis — CExl EBee NBid
- B&SWJ 7998 — WCru

confusa — WSHC
divaricata B&SWJ 11018 — WCru
'Gaudi Violet' — EBee SEle SPoG
grandiflora B&SWJ 8555 — WCru
khasiana — CExl LLHF NLar XLum
lamarkii B&SWJ 8738 — WCru
latifolia misapplied — see *A. pereskiifolia*
latifolia ambig. white-flowered — MMuc
liliifolia — CMea EPfP GAbr GCal GKev NLar NPer WFar
maximowicziana B&SWJ 11008 — WCru
morrisonensis RWJ 10008 — WCru
§ ***nikoensis*** — GEdr NBid WCot
- B&SWJ 11201 new — WCru

§ ***pereskiifolia*** — EWes SHar SPlb WCot
- 'White Blaze' new — CKno

polyantha — EWTr NLar SRms
polymorpha — see *A. nikoensis*
potaninii — EBee MMuc SEND WHal
- pale-flowered — MAvo WHal

remotiflora — EWld
- B&SWJ 8714 — WCru
- B&SWJ 11016 — WCru

stricta subsp. ***sessilifolia*** — EBee
takedae — EBee SBrt
- B&SWJ 11424 — WCru

taquetii — CPla GEdr WAbe
tashiroi — GKev XLum
triphylla B&SWJ 10916 — WCru
- var. ***hakusanensis*** — LLHF
- var. ***japonica*** — GJos
- - B&SWJ 10933 — WCru

uehatae — GEdr
- B&SWJ 126 — WCru

Adenostyles (*Asteraceae*)

alpina — SBrt

Adesmia (*Papilionaceae*)

longipes — SPlb

Adiantum ✿ (*Pteridaceae*)

sp. — CMac
aethiopicum — NLos XBlo
§ ***aleuticum*** ♀H6 — CKel MMoz NBro NLar SPlb WFib
- 'Imbricatum' — CBdn CElw CRos EBee ECha ELon EShb EUJe GEdr LPla LRHS MAvo MGos MMoz NBid NBro NLar NLos NRHS SRms WCot WFar WFib XLum

§ - 'Japonicum' — WFar
- 'Miss Sharples' — CAby CBod CDTJ CRos ECha GEdr LPla LRHS MGos NLar NRHS SPoG SRms WCot WFar

§ - 'Subpumilum' ♀H5 — NBid NBro WCot WFib
- 'Tasselatum' — WCot

andicola B&SWJ 10448 — WCru
bonatianum — CExl
capillus-veneris — CBdn EBee NBro WFib
- 'Mairisii' — see *A.* × *mairisii*

chilense — NLos
hispidulum — CBdn CCCN CRos EBee LRHS NLos NRHS

- 'Bronze Venus'	CCCN CHid CRos LRHS NRHS SRms
§ × ***mairisii*** ♀H5	CBdn EBee EShb LRHS NLos NRHS
pedatum misapplied	see *A. aleuticum*
pedatum ambig.	EUJe NLos SPer
pedatum L.	CBcs CDor ECha EFer ELon EShb GMaP NBro WFar
- Asiatic form	see *A. aleuticum* 'Japonicum'
- 'Japonicum'	see *A. aleuticum* 'Japonicum'
- 'Roseum'	see *A. aleuticum* 'Japonicum'
- var. ***subpumilum***	see *A. aleuticum* 'Subpumilum'
poiretii	CBdn WCot
raddianum 'Fragrans'	see *A. raddianum* 'Fragrantissimum'
§ - 'Fragrantissimum'	EShb NLos
- 'Fritz Lüthi' ♀H1c	EShb NLos
- 'Lady Geneva'	WCot
- 'Legrand Morgan'	NLos
reniforme	NLos WAbe
venustum ♀H7	CBdn CExl CFil CRos CSpe CTsd EBee EFer EUJe GCal ITim LLWG LRHS MCot MHol MSCN NBid NBro NRHS SBrt SPer SPlb SRms WCot WFar WFib WHal WPGP

Adina (*Rubiaceae*)

rubella	NLar

Adlumia (*Papaveraceae*)

fungosa	CRos CSpe LRHS NRHS

Adonis (*Ranunculaceae*)

amurensis misapplied	see *A.* 'Fukujukai', *A. multiflora*
amurensis ambig.	CMea EBee EHrv GEdr GKev IDee LEdu NHpl
amurensis Regel & Radde 'Pleniflora'	see *A. multiflora* 'Sandanzaki'
- 'Sakhalin'	EBee
annua	SPhx
brevistyla	GEdr
'Chichibu-beni'	GEdr
§ 'Fukujukai'	ECha GEdr GKev XEll
§ ***multiflora***	SRot
- 'Beni-nadeshiko'	GEdr
- 'Hakuju'	GEdr
- 'Hanazono' (d)	GEdr
§ - 'Sandanzaki' (d)	EBee EPot GEdr GKev LEdu MMrt NLar
ramosa	GEdr
'Sado-no-maboroshi' (d)	GEdr
vernalis	GPoy NLar WCot

Adoxa (*Adoxaceae*)

moschatellina	CBre EBWF EBee EWld LEdu MNrw NRya WHer WSFF WSHC WShi WWtn

Adromischus (*Crassulaceae*)

maculatus ♀H2	LToo

Aechmea ✿ (*Bromeliaceae*)

sp.	XBlo
'Blue Rain'PBR	LCro
caudata	NLos
- var. ***variegata***	NLos
fasciata ♀H1a	WSFF XBlo
gamosepala	CFil NLos
nudicaulis ♀H1a	NLos
- var. ***capitata***	NLos
I - - f. ***albomarginata***	NLos
ramosa	XBlo
recurvata	CBlu CFil NLos
- 'Paraguay'	NLos
- var. ***recurvata***	NLos
'Suenos'	CFil
victoriana	XBlo
- var. ***discolor***	NLos

Aegle (*Rutaceae*)

sepiaria	see *Citrus trifoliata*

Aegopodium (*Apiaceae*)

aff. ***handellii*** PAB 9003 new	SPhx
podagraria 'Dangerous' (v)	CHid
- gold-margined (v)	EPPr
- 'Variegatum' (v)	CBod EBee ECha EHoe EPPr EShb GKev GMaP GQue LRHS LSou MBel MRav NBid NEgg NRHS NSti SEND SPer SPoG WCot WHil WMoo WSHC XLum

Aeollanthus (*Lamiaceae*)

subacaulis var. ***subacaulis*** new	LToo

Aeonium (*Crassulaceae*)

arboreum	CDTJ CKno CPbh CPla ELan EShb GCal NCft SEND
- 'Atropurpureum'	CAbb CCCN CDTJ ELan EShb NCft NPer SEND SPer
I - 'Magnificum'	EShb ETod GBin SArc
- 'Variegatum' (v)	CPbh NPer
balsamiferum	CCCN CDTJ CPbh EUJe SChr WCot
'Black Cap'	CCCN
'Blush'	CKno
canariense	CCCN CDTJ SVen
- var. ***palmense***	SVen
castello-paivae	SChr
ciliatum	SPlb
'Copper Kettle'	WAvo
'Cornish Tribute'	CCCN CPbh
'Cristata Sunburst'	CDTJ CPbh WCot
cuneatum	CDTJ CPbh SEND
'Cyclops'	CPbh
* ***decorum*** 'Variegatum' (v)	WCot
'Dinner Plate'	CDTJ CPbh
× ***domesticum***	see *Aichryson* × *aizoides* var. *domesticum*
'Du Rozzen'	CPbh
* ***escobarii***	SPlb
glandulosum	SVen
goochiae	SBch
haworthii ♀H1c	CDTJ EUJe NCft NHpl SAll SEND SVen
- 'Kiwi'	CCCN
- 'Variegatum' (v) ♀H1c	CDTJ CPbh EShb SAll SVen
hierrense	CPbh SPlb
holochrysum Webb & Berth.	CAbb
korneliuslemsii new	CFil
lindleyi	SChr
'Logan Rock'	CPbh
'Merry Maiden'	CPbh
* ***multiflorum*** 'Variegatum' (v)	CDTJ EUJe
nobile	CBrP
'Poldark'	CCCN CPbh
sedifolium	CPbh SAll
simsii	CDTJ CPbh NCft

	simsii × 'Zwartkop'	CCCN CPbh CPla ELan ETod GCal MHer SChr
	spathulatum	CDTJ CPbh WCot
	'Sunburst' (v) ♀H1c	CPbh WCot
	tabuliforme ♀H1c	CCCN CDTJ CPbh CSpe SMad SPlb WCot
	'Trewidden' **new**	WCot
	undulatum	EUJe SPlb
	urbicum	EShb
	'Velour'	CCCN CDTJ CPbh NPer
	'Voodoo'	ETod GCal WCot
	'Zwartkop' ♀H1c	CAbb CBcs CBod CCCN CCht CHll CKno CPbh CRos CSpe ECtt EShb EUJe GBin MCot MSCN NLos NPer NPla SArc SChr SEND SEle SMad SPlb SRot SWvt WAvo WCot WWFP

Aeschynanthus ✿ (*Gesneriaceae*)

	Black Pagoda Group	WDib
	buxifolius KR 7798	WAbe
	'Fire Wheel'	WDib
	'Hot Flash'	WDib
	'Little Tiger'	WDib
	longicalyx	WDib
§	***longicaulis*** ♀H1c	WDib
	marmoratus	see *A. longicaulis*
	radicans ♀H1c	WDib
	'Scooby Doo'	WDib
	speciosus ♀H1c	WDib

Aesculus ✿ (*Sapindaceae*)

	sp.	LPra
	arguta	see *A. glabra* var. *arguta*
	× ***arnoldiana***	CDul
	assamica WWJ 11886	WCru
	'Autumn Splendor'	EPfP
§	× ***bushii***	CDul
	californica	CBcs CDul CMCN CMac EPfP ERod SBrt WPGP
	- 'Canyon Pink'	CMCN
	× ***carnea***	CDul LPra SGol
	- 'Aureomarginata' (v)	ERod LLHF
	- 'Briotii'	CAco CBcs CCVT CDul CEnd CLnd CMac CSBt EBee ECrN ELan EMOT EPfP ESps EWTr LMaj LPra LRHS MGos MMuc NLar SCob SEND SEWo SPer WFar WTSh
	- 'Plantierensis'	CDul
*	- 'Variegata' (v)	CDul CMCN
	chinensis	CBcs CMCN
	flava ♀H5	CDul CMCN EBee ELan EPfP IArd LMaj MMuc SEND
	- f. ***vestita***	CDul MBlu
	georgiana	see *A. sylvatica*
	glabra	CDul CMCN
§	- var. ***arguta***	CMCN NLar
	- 'Autumn Blaze'	EPfP
	- 'October Red'	EPfP
	glaucescens	see *A.* × *neglecta*
	hippocastanum	CAco CBcs CCVT CDul CMac CPer CSBt CTri EBee ECrN ELan EMOT ESps LPra MGos MMuc MSwo NLar NOra SCob SEND SEWo SGol SPer WFar WTSh
	- 'Aureomarginata' (v)	CMac
§	- 'Baumannii' (d)	CDul CLnd CMCN ECrN ELan ESps LPra MGos MSwo SCob SPer
	- 'Digitata'	CDul CMCN WCot
	- 'Flore Pleno'	see *A. hippocastanum* 'Baumannii'
	- 'Hampton Court Gold'	CDul CMCN CMac
	- f. ***laciniata***	CDul CMCN NLar SMad WCot
	- 'Pyramidalis'	LPra
	- 'Wisselink'	CDul CMCN WCot
	indica	CDul CMCN ECrN ELan EPfP EWTr LEdu LMaj SEND SGol WTSh
	- 'Sydney Pearce' ♀H5	CBcs CDul CEnd CJun CMCN EPfP ERod IArd MBlu MGos NLar NOra
	× ***marylandica***	CDul
	× ***mississippiensis***	see *A.* × *bushii*
	× ***mutabilis*** 'Induta'	CDul CMCN EPfP NOra
§	- 'Penduliflora'	CDul
§	× ***neglecta***	CMCN
	- 'Autumn Fire'	EBee EPfP SPoG
	- 'Erythroblastos' ♀H5	CBcs CDul CEnd CJun CMCN EPfP ERod EUJe MBlu SCoo SMad SPer SPoG WCot
	parviflora ♀H5	CBcs CDul CMCN CMac CTri EBee ELan EPfP ESps EWTr GKin IDee LMaj LPra MBlu MGos MMuc MRav NLar NOra SEND SGol SMad SPer SWvt
	pavia	CBcs CMCN EPfP
	- 'Atrosanguinea'	CEnd CMCN EPfP ERod
	- var. ***discolor*** 'Koehnei'	CMCN EPfP NLar NOra
	- 'Penduliflora'	see *A.* × *mutabilis* 'Penduliflora'
	- 'Purple Spring'	WPGP
	- 'Rosea Nana'	CMCN
§	- Splendens Group	CMCN EPfP
	splendens	see *A. pavia* Splendens Group
§	***sylvatica***	CMCN
	turbinata	CBcs CDul CMCN
	wilsonii	CBcs CExl MBlu

Aethionema (*Brassicaceae*)

I	***antitaurii***	GJos
	armenum	GKev
	capitatum	CPBP
	coridifolium	GJos
§	***grandiflorum*** ♀H5	ELan GJos LPmr NBro SRms XSen
	- Pulchellum Group ♀H5	CSpe MMuc
*	***kotschyi*** hort.	EDAr GJos WAbe
	membranaceum	GJos
	oppositifolium	LLHF
	pulchellum	see *A. grandiflorum*
	saxatile	GJos
	schistosum	GJos LLHF
	subulatum	LLHF
	'Warley Rose' ♀H5	CRos EHyd ELan EPot GCrg LRHS NRHS NSla SBch SRms WThu WTor XSen
	'Warley Ruber'	CMea EPot

Afrocarpus (*Podocarpaceae*)

	falcatus	CBcs

Agapanthus ✿ (*Agapanthaceae*)

	'Aberdeen'	IBal
	'Adonis'	CPrp IBlr
	'African Moon'	CPrp IBal MAvo
	'African Skies'	CAbb CPrp CTal IBal SFai
	africanus misapplied	CBlu CElw CExl CTsd CWCL EBee EHrv ELan EPfP EPot ESps ETMg ETod EUJe GKev ILea ITim LCro LRHS MJak SArc SChr SCob SDeJ SPer SRot SVic WBor XLum XSen
	- 'Albus' misapplied	CBcs CBod CExl CWCL EBee ELan EPfP EPot ESps ETod ETMg EUJe GKev ILea LCro LOPS LRHS LSRN MGos MJak MNHC SCob SDeJ SEND SPer SRms WSpi XLum XSen

	- hybrid	IBoy
	- TWISTER ('Ambic001')	CPar IBal LCro SFai
	'Aimee'	CBro IBal
	'Alan Street'	CAvo IBal
	'Albus' ambig.	GMaP MHer
I	'Albus Nanus'	IBal
I	'Albus Roseus'	IBal
	'Alice Gloucester'	CPrp
	'Allisio'	IBal
	'Amsterdam'	EBee EWTr IBal IMou
	'Angela'	CPrp IBal
	'Ankara'	IBal
	'Anneke'	IBal
	'Antibe'	IBal
	'Aphrodite'	IBlr
	'Apple Court'	LRHS
	'Aquamarine'	CAvo EPri IBal
	'Arctic Star'	CAvo CBWd CCCN CExl CKno CMac CPne CPou CPrp CSpe CWCL EBee ELon ETMg IBal LRHS LSRN LSou NLar SDys SFai SPoG
	'Ardernei Hybrid'	CAvo CExl ECha ECtt EWes GAbr GCal IBal IBlr IRob WCot WGwG
	'Ascona' **new**	IBal
	'Atlas'	IBlr
	'Aureovittatus' (v)	IBal
	'Autumn Mist'	IBal
	'Avalanche'	EBee IBal SFai WSpi
	'Baby Blue'	see *A.* 'Blue Baby' Rom.
	'Baby Pete'PBR	EBee ELan IBal SFai
	BACK IN BLACK ('B in B'PBR)	CBro CCCN CExl CWCL ELan EPfP EShb IBal MBNS MRav NBid SCob SHyH SMad SPer WFar
	'Ballerina'	CPne IBal LRHS
	'Ballyrogan'	IBal IBlr
	'Bangor Blue'	IBlr
	'Barley Blue'	IBal
	'Barnfield Blue'	CPne CPrp EBee IBal SFai
	'Basutoland'	LRHS
	'Beatrice'	CPrp
	'Becky'	IBal
	'Beeches Dwarf'	IBal
	'Ben Hope'	CBro ESps IBal IBlr
	'Berlin'	IBal
	'Beth Chatto'	see *A. campanulatus* 'Albovittatus'
	'Bethlehem Star'	EPri
	'Bicton Bell'	EPri IBal IBlr
	'Bicton Bride'	IBal
	'Big Ben'	IBal
	'Big Blue'	CBod CCCN CChe CMac CPrp CWCL EBee SEND SLdr SRkn WSpi
	'Black Beauty'	CBod CPrp IBal LRHS WSpi
	'Black Buddhist'	CCCN CWCL EBee ECtt EPfP EPri EUJe GMcL IBal LRHS NGdn NSti SAko SFai SPer XSen
	'Black Magic'	CAbb CBWd CPar CPne CPrp EBee EUJe IBal LCro LOPS LSou NSti SFai
	'Black Pantha'PBR	Widely available
§	'Blauwe Valk'	EPfP
	'Bloemfontein'	IBal
§	'Blue Baby' Rom.	CCCN EHyd ELan ELon IBal LRHS MJak NRHS XTur
	'Blue Bayou'	IBal
	'Blue Beauty'	LRHS
	BLUE BIRD	see *A.* 'Blauwe Valk'
	'Blue Bird'	LRHS
	'Blue Brush'	CPrp EHyd EPfP LRHS NRHS SCoo
	'Blue Cascade'	IBlr
	'Blue Companion'	CPrp IBlr
	'Blue Diamond' ambig.	CMac
	'Blue Dot'	CPrp ECtt EPfP LLHF LRHS LSou SDys
	'Blue Flare'	IBal
	'Blue Flash'	IBal
	'Blue Formality'	IBal IBlr
	'Blue Giant'	CBro CCCN CChe CDor CKno CPrp EBee ELan IBal LRHS MGos SCob WAvo WSpi
	'Blue Globe'	CBod CHid EBee EPri GMaP LRHS
	'Blue Gown'	CSam
	'Blue Heaven'PBR	CPne CWGN IBal SCob
	'Blue Horizons'PBR (v)	CCCN IBal LRHS
	'Blue Ice'	CAbb CAco CPne CPou CPrp EBee IBal LRHS SAko
	'Blue Imp'	CBro IBal IBlr
	'Blue Jay'	IBal
	'Blue Magic'	EBee IBal SFai
	'Blue Moon'	CBro CPrp EBee ECha ECtt EPri GMcL IBal IBlr ILea IPot LRHS MHol NLar SEND SHyH SLdr WCot
	'Blue Nile'	CPne CPrp IBal
	'Blue Pixie'	IBal
	'Blue Prince'	EBee
	'Blue Rinse'	IBal
	'Blue Skies' ambig.	LRHS
I	'Blue Skies' Dunlop	IBlr
	'Blue Steel'	IBal
	'Blue Triumphator'	CBWd CDor EPfP GKev GMaP IBal ILea IRob LRHS MAvo MHer SCob WSpi
	'Blue Umbrella'	CDor ELan GMcL SRkn WHar WSpi
	'Blue Yonder'	EBee
	blue-flowered	WAvo WCFE
	BLUESTORM ('Atiblu'PBR)	CPrp EHyd EPfP IBal LBuc LRHS NRHS SArc SCob SEND
	'Bluety'PBR	IBal
	'Bray Valley'	CPne CPrp
	'Bressingham Blue'	CAbb CBro CSam CTri ESps EWes GCal IBal IBlr IRob LRHS MAvo MRav SFai WSpi
	'Bressingham Bounty'	IBal LRHS
	'Bressingham White'	ESps LRHS MRav
	'Bridal Bouquet'	EBee IBal LCro LSRN SFai
	'Bright Blue'	IBal
	BRILLIANT BLUE ('Aga0451')	EBee IBal LCro LRHS SFai
	'Bristol'	IBal
	'Buckingham Palace'	CBro EBee EWes GAbr IBal IBlr NChi WCot
	'Calimero'	IBal
	'Cally Blue'	GAbr GCal IBal IRob
	'Cally Large White' **new**	GAbr
	'Cally Longstem'	EBee EPri GCal
	'Cally Pale Blue'	IBal
	campanulatus	CBlu CMac CPbh CPrp ELan EPfP GKin IBal IBlr LRHS MRav NChi NEgg WAvo WFar WKif WSpi
	- var. ***albidus***	CBWd CPrp ECha ELan EPfP GKev GKin IBlr LEdu LRHS MMuc MWat NBid NGdn SEND SPer WGwG WHoo WSHC WSpi
§	- 'Albovittatus' (v)	IBal
	- bright blue-flowered	GCal IBal
	- 'Cobalt Blue'	CPrp ELan EPri GKin IBal LRHS LSou MAsh MAvo MMuc NEgg NGdn WHoo
	- 'Oxford Blue'	IBlr
	- subsp. ***patens*** ♀H4	CPrp EPfP IBal LRHS MRav
	- - deep blue-flowered	IBlr LRHS
	- 'Profusion'	CBro ECha EPri IBal IBlr LRHS
	- 'Ultramarine'	IBal

	- variegated (v)	EBee ECha NPer
	- 'Wedgwood Blue'	EBee IBal IBlr LRHS
	- 'Wendy'	CPne EBee IBal IBlr IRob LRHS
	- 'White Hope'	IBal IBlr IRob
	'Carefree'	CPrp
	'Castle of Mey'	CAvo CBod CBro CExl CFil CPrp EBee GAbr GCal IBal IBlr LCro LOPS LRHS LSou SFai WSpi
	'Catharina'	IBal
§	***caulescens*** ♀H2	CPrp IBal IBlr LRHS
	- subsp. ***angustifolius***	CHid ELon IBal IBlr MHol SEND
	- subsp. ***caulescens***	IBlr
	'Cedric Morris'	EPri IBal IBlr SMHy
	'Celebration'	IBal
	'Chandra'	IBal IBlr
	'Charlotte'PBR	CMac EBee ELan EPfP IBal LRHS SFai SPoG
	'Cheney's Lane'	SMHy
	'Cherbours'	IBal
	'Cherry Holley'	ELon IBal WSpi
	'Chika's Blue'	IBal MAvo
	'Clarence House'	CBro CPrp IBal
	'Cloudy Days'	IBal
	coddii	CExl CTal EPri EWes IBal IBlr MHer WCot
	'Columba'	CPrp EBee ELon IBal LAma NBid XSen
	comptonii	see *A. praecox* subsp. *minimus*
	'Cool Blue'	IBal MAvo
	'Corina'	EBee
	'Crystal'	GCal
	'Crystal Drop'	CAbb CExl CPne CPou CPrp EBee EPri IBal SFai
	DANUBE	see *A.* 'Donau'
	'Dart Valley'	CPrp IBal
	'Dartmoor'	CPne
	'Debbie'	IBal
	'Delft'	CPrp EBee IBal IBlr
	'Delft Blue'	ELan EWTr IBal LRHS
	'Density'	IBlr
	'Dnjepr'	CBro EBee IBal
	'Dokkum'	IBal
	'Dokter Brouwer'	CKno ECrN GKev IBoy ILea LRHS LSRN MCot SHyH
§	'Donau'	CBro CPrp EBee EPri EShb IBal WCot
	DOUBLE DIAMOND ('Rfdd'PBR)	CPne EBee EHyd EPfP EPri EWes IBal LRHS LSRN LSou NRHS SAko SCob SFai SPoG WSpi XEll
	'Dublin'	IBal
	'Duivenbrugge Blue'	IBal
	'Duivenbrugge White'	IBal
	'Durban'	IBal
	dyeri	see *A. inapertus* subsp. *intermedius*
	'Early Blue'	EBee IPot
	'Ed Carman' (v)	LSou
	'Eggesford Sky'	CPne CPrp EBee IBal
	'Elaine'	IBal
	'Elisa'	IBal
	'Elisabeth'	LRHS
	'Elizabeth Salisbury'	IBal
	'Ellamae'	IBal
	'Enigma'	Widely available
	'Enigma Variations'	EBee
	'Ethel's Joy'	ELan EPri IBal
	'Eve'	IBlr
	'Evening Eclipse'	IBal
	'Evening Star'	EPri
	'Exmoor'	CPne IBal LRHS MAvo
	'Findlay's Blue'	LRHS MAvo SMHy WHil
	'Finnline' (v)	SRms
	'Flore Pleno' (d)	CBcs CExl CMac CPrp EBee ECha ECtt EHrv ELan GAbr GKin IBal IBlr LSou MHer MHol NEgg NGdn WCot WFar WPGP WSHC
	'Fulsome' **new**	IBlr
	'Gayle's Lilac'	CBcs CCCN CElw CExl CPrp ECtt ELan ELon EPfP EWTr GKin LRHS MRav NGdn WGwG XTur
	'Gem'	CPrp ELon LRHS
	'Genua'	IBal
	'Getty White'	LRHS
	'Glacier'	IBal
	'Glacier Stream'	CBro CDor EPri IBal XSen XTur
	'Glen Avon'	CAbb CCCN CExl CPrp EBee EHyd EPfP GBin IBal LRHS NLar SCoo SFai SLon
	'Gold Strike'PBR (v)	IBal LCro LOPS SFai
	'Golden Drop'PBR (v)	EHyd LRHS NRHS SFai SRms
	'Golden Rule' (v)	EHoe IBlr
	'Gothenburg'	IBal
	'Greenfield'	EBee IBal
	'Hamar'	IBal
	'Hanneke'	IBal
	'Hannover'	IBal
	'Happy Blue'	IBal
	'Harvest Blue'	IBal
§	Headbourne hybrids	Widely available
	- dark blue-flowered	LRHS
	'Headbourne White'	CAvo EPri
	'Heavenly Blue'	CCCN
	'Helen'	IBlr
	'Helsinki'	IBal
	'His Majesty' **new**	IBal
	'Holbrook'	CSam
	'Hoyland Blue'	EBee IBal
	'Ice Blue Star'	CBro
	'Ice Lolly'	CBro EShb IBal
	inapertus	CAvo CBod CBro CFil CPbh CPrp EWes SMHy WPGP WSHC
	- dwarf	IBlr
	- subsp. ***hollandii***	IBal IBlr
	- - 'Zealot'	IBlr
	- 'Ice Cascade'	CCCN EBee IBal LRHS
	- 'Icicle'	GCal
	- subsp. ***inapertus***	IBlr
I	- - 'Albus'	IBlr
	- - 'Cyan'	IBlr
	- - 'White'	CPrp IBal
§	- subsp. ***intermedius***	CPrp EPfP IBlr
	- - 'Long Tom'	CExl CPne CPrp CSpe EBee EPri IBal
	- - white-flowered	CPou
	- large	IBal
	- 'Margaret'	CCCN
	- 'Midnight Cascade'	CCCN CExl CPar EBee ECtt ELan IBal IPot LEdu NBid SCob SFai SRms
I	- 'Nigrescens'	IPot
	- subsp. ***parviflorus***	IBlr
	- subsp. ***pendulus***	IBal IBlr LRHS
	- - 'Black Magic'	IBal
	- - 'Graskop'	CAvo CBcs CCCN CExl CPrp CSam CSpe EBee EHyd ELan EPfP EPri GBin IBal IBlr LRHS MNrw NRHS NSti SFai SMHy SRms
	- - 'Violet Dusk'	IBlr
	- 'Tempest' **new**	WPGP
	'Indigo Dreams'	CPne CPrp CTal EBee IBal LLHF LPla MAvo SFai

	'Inkspots'	CCCN CMac EHyd EPfP IBal LRHS LSou NRHS SFai SPoG WHlf
	'Intermedius' Leichtlin	CWCL IBal LEdu
I	'Intermedius' van Tubergen	EBee IBal NBid
	'Isis'	CAvo CBro CSam ECha EPri IBal IBlr LRHS MAvo
	'Jacaranda'	CMac EBee IBal LRHS SFai
	'Jack Elliott'	MAvo
	'Jack's Blue'	CBro CDor CElw CPne CSam EBee ECtt ELan ELon EPri GMaP IBal LRHS LSRN MAvo MHol MNrw NGdn NLar SEND SLdr SMad WCot WFar WSpi
	'Jersey Giant'	CPrp IBal
	'Jodie'	CPne ELon MAvo
	'Johanna'	EBee IBal
	'Johannesburg'	IBal
	Johannesburg hybrids	ECha EPfP
	'Jolanda'	CPrp IBal LAma
	'Jonie'	IBal
	'Jonny's White'	IBal
	'Kalmthout Blue'	IBal
	'Kilmurry Blue'	IBal
	'Kilmurry White'	IBal
	'Kingston Blue'	IBlr LRHS NBid
	'Kobold'	CBro IBal WFar
	'Lady Edith'	IBlr
§	'Lady Grey'	IBlr
	'Lady Moore'	IBlr SMHy
	'Lapis'	CAbb CAvo CBod CHid CMac CPne CPrp EBee EPri IBal LRHS SFai SHyH SLdr
	'Latent Blue'	IBlr
	'Lavender Haze'	CCCN CMac EHyd EPfP ETMg IBal LRHS NRHS SFai WSpi
	'Leanne'	IBal LRHS
	'Leicester'	IBal
	'Liam's Lilac'	CCCN CExl CKno CPne CPou CPrp EHyd ELon IBal LCro LOPS LRHS MAvo NLar NRHS SFai
	'Lilac Flash'	IBal LRHS
	'Lilac Lullaby' **new**	IBal
	'Lilac Time'	CExl CPrp IBlr WCot
	'Lilliput'	CBcs CBro CCCN CMac CMea CSpe ECha ECtt ELan EPfP EShb EWTr GKev GMaP IBal LRHS MRav NGdn SPer SRms WCFE WFar XEll XSen
	'Lissabon'	IBal
	'Lisse'	IBal
	'Little Dutch Blue'	IBal WCot
	'Little Dutch White'^{PBR}	IBal WCot
	'Little White'	IBal
	'Littlecourt'	CBro IBal MAvo
	'Loch Hope' 🏆^{H6}	CAby CAvo CBod CBro CPrp CSam ECtt ELon EPfP GCal IBal LPla LRHS MHol MRav SLdr WCot WHoo WSpi
	'Los Angeles'	IBal
	'Luly'	CPrp CTal EPfP IBal LRHS MGos WFar
	'Luna'	EBee IBal
	'Lydenburg'	CPne EBee EPri IBal IBlr
	'Lyn Valley'	CPrp EBee IBal
	'Mabel Grey'	see *A.* 'Lady Grey'
	'Madurodam'	IBal
	'Magnifico'	CPrp IBal IBlr
	'Malaga'	IBal
	'Malmo'	IBal
	'Marchants Cobalt Cracker'	SMHy
	'Marchant's Midnight Blue'	SMHy
	'Marcus'	EBee IBal SDir
	'Margaret'	GCal GKev IBal LRHS LSRN
	'Marianne'	IBal
	'Mariètte'	EBee
	'Marijke'	IBal
	'Marjorie'	LRHS
	'Marnie'	CPne
	'Martine'	EBee IBal MAvo
	'Maureen'	CPne CPrp EBee IBal LSRN
	'Maurice'	IBal
	'May Snow' (v)	LRHS WCot
	'Medan'	IBal
	'Medusa'	IBal
	'Megan's Mauve'	CBro CKno CPne CPou CPrp EBee ELon EPri IBal LCro LOPS LRHS LSRN LSou NSti SFai SHyH
	'Meibont' (v)	IBal
	'Melbourne' **new**	SPad
	'Mercury'	IBlr
	'Messina'	IBal
	'Mi Casa' **new**	SFai
	'Michelle'	IBal
	'Middleburg'	IBal
	MIDKNIGHT BLUE ('Monmid')	WSHC XTur
	'Midnight'	EWes IBal
	'Midnight Blue' ambig.	CAby ELan EPfP EShb EUJe IBal SMHy WFar
	'Midnight Blue' P. Wood	GCal IBlr LRHS
	'Midnight Dream'	EBee ECtt IBal LEdu STPC
§	'Midnight Star'	Widely available
	'Mini Blue' **new**	IBal
	'Miniature Blue'	EUJe
	'Misty Dawn' (v)	CWGN EBee ECtt IBal MHol SEND SHyH SLdr WCot
	mixed white-flowered	WCFE
	'Mole Valley'	IBal
	'Molly Howick'	EBee LRHS
	'Monique'	IBal
	'Montreal'	IBal
	'Mood Indigo'	CPne CPrp EBee EPri IBal
	'Moonlight Star'	EBee IBal IPot
	'Moonshine'	IBal
I	'Mooreanus' misapplied	EBee EPfP IBal NBid
	'Mooreanus' H.R. Wehrh.	GCal MAvo
	'Morning Star'	IBal
	'Mount Stewart'	IBal IBlr
	'Nana Blue'	SHyH
	'Nancy'	IBal
	'Napoli'	IBal
	'Navy Blue'	see *A.* 'Midnight Star'
	'Newa'	EBee
	'Newcastle'	IBal
	'Nikki'	CMea CPne IBal
	'Norman Hadden'	IBlr
	'Northern Light'	CBWd IBal LLHF
	'Northern Star'^{PBR}	CAbb CAvo CExl CKno CPne CPrp CTal CWGN EBee EHyd EPri ETMg EWes IBal LCro LOPS LRHS LSRN LSou NLos NRHS NSti SCob SFai SLon SPoG SRms
	nutans	see *A. caulescens*
	'Nyx'	IBlr
	'Odessa'	IBal
	'Oslo'	IBal
	'Oxbridge'	IBlr
	'Oxford'	IBal
	'Pacific Blue'^{PBR}	CWCL EBee EHyd EWTr IBal LRHS NRHS SFai SHyH SLdr

Palmer's hybrids	see *A.* Headbourne hybrids
'Patent Blue'	CPrp IBal IBlr
'Patriot'	EPfP LRHS
'Pavlova'	EUJe IBal
'Penelope Palmer'	CPrp IBal IBlr
'Peter Franklin'	CPne CPrp EBee IBal
'Peter Pan' ambig.	Widely available
'Peter Pan American'	GKev
'Phantom'	CAbb CPne CPrp EBee IBal IBlr IMou LRHS SFai SWeb WCot
'Picton Blue'	WFar
Pine Cottage hybrids	CPne
'Pino'	LRHS
'Pinocchio'	GKev IBal IMou SDeJ
'Pirame'	IBal
'Plas Merdyn White'	IBal IBlr
'Podge Mill'	IBal IBlr
'Polar Ice'	CPrp EBee ELon EPri GBin GKev IBal IBoy ILea IPot IRob LAma LRHS LSRN MAvo MNrw WSpi XTur
'Polar Star'	IBal
'Porcelain'	IBal IBlr
praecox ♀H2	CPrp ESps GKev IBlr LRHS
- 'Albiflorus' ♀H2	CAco CBcs CBro CPou CPrp CTri EPri ESps GWyn LRHS MTin NEgg SEND
- 'Maximus Albus'	CPou IBal IBlr
§ - subsp. ***minimus***	CElw CPou IBal IBlr SEND
- - 'Adelaide'	CPrp IBal
- 'Neptune'	IBlr
§ - subsp. ***orientalis***	CBro CCCN IBlr
- - 'Full Moon'	IBal
- subsp. ***praecox***	IBlr
- 'Saturn'	IBlr
- Slieve Donard form	IBlr
- 'Storms River'	IBal
- 'Uranus'	IBlr
- 'Venus'	IBlr
'Premier'	IBlr LRHS
'Pretty Wendy'	IBal
'Princess Margaret'	IBal
§ 'Purple Cloud'	Widely available
'Purple Delight'	CAvo CPne CPrp EBee IBal LCro LOPS LRHS SAko SFai
'Purple Emperor'	CPne SFai
'Purple Fountain'	CPne CPrp IBal SFai SRms
'Purple Haze'	IBal
'Purple Magic'	IBal
'Purple Ripple'	IBal
'Purple Star'	CCCN CKno
'Queen Anne'	IBal
'Queen Mother'	CHid IBal LRHS WSpi
QUEEN MUM ('Pmn06'PBR)	Widely available
'Queen of the Ocean'	IBal
'Quink Drops'	SMHy
'Radiant Star'	IBal LRHS
'Regal Beauty'	CBro CPrp CSBt EBee ETMg IBal LRHS LSRN NBid SFai
'Rhone'	CBro IBal IBlr
'Robin'	IBal
'Rosewarne'	CBcs CBod CCCN CExl CPrp IBal IBlr NLar
'Rotterdam'	IBal XSen
'Roxanne'	EBee IBal
'Royal Blue'	CBro CPrp GMaP IBal WCot WSpi
'Royal Knight'	IBal
'Ruan Vean'	CPrp
'Sabang'	IBal
'Sally Anne'	CPne CPrp

'San Gabriel' (v)	CPne
'San Remo'	IBal
'Sandringham'	CAbb CBod CPrp CSpe EBee ELon EPfP EPri EWes IBal LRHS LSRN LSou MMuc SFai WFar
'Sandy'PBR	IBal
'Sapphire'	CPrp IBlr
'Sarah'PBR	CCCN CWCL EBee IBal LSRN MTin SEND SFai SHyH SLdr
'Saville Blue' **new**	CPrp
'Sea Coral'	CCCN CMac CPrp EBee EPri IBal LRHS MAvo NSti
'Sea Foam'	CMac NLar XLum
'Sea Mist'	CCCN CPrp EBee
'Sea Spray'	CCCN EBee EPri IBal WFar
'Selma Bock'	IBal
'Semarang'	IBal
'Senna'PBR	CCCN CExl EBee IBal
'Septemberhemel'	IBal
'Shooting Stars' **new**	IBal
'Silberpfeil'	IBal
'Silver Anniversary'	IBal
'Silver Baby'	CAbb CBod CKno CPne CPrp CWGN EBee EHyd ELon EPfP EPri ETod IBal LEdu LRHS MAvo MHol NRHS SFai SRms
'Silver Jubilee'	IBal
'Silver Lining'	ECtt IBal LRHS
'Silver Mist'	IBal IBlr
SILVER MOON ('Notfred'PBR) (v)	CAbb CCCN EBee EHyd ELan EPfP EWes GKev IBal LRHS LSou MGos MJak NLar NRHS NSti SCob SFai SPoG WCot XTur
'Silver Sceptre'	IBlr
'Silver Suzy'	IBal
'Sky'	CAbb CPne CPrp EHyd EPfP EPri EWTr IBal IBlr LRHS NBid NRHS SFai SRms
'Sky Rocket'	CPrp IBal IBlr
'Sky Star'	IBal
'Skyscraper'	IBal
'Slieve Donard'	IBlr
'Snow Cloud'	CAbb CBro CExl CPrp CTsd EBee EHyd EPfP LCro LOPS LRHS NLar NRHS SEND SFai SLdr SLon WSpi
'Snow Pixie'	CSpe EBee IBal LRHS LSRN LSou SFai SHyH SLdr WSpi
'Snow Princess'	ELon EPfP IBal
'Snow Shadows'	CBro IBal
'Snowball'	CBcs CExl LSou NLos WSpi
'Snowdrops'	CCCN EBee ELan WFar
'Snowstorm'PBR	EBee EPfP IBal LBuc LRHS SArc
'Sofie'PBR	CBod EBee EUJe SCob STPC XTur
'Sorento'	IBal
'Southern Cross'	EBee EHyd IBal LRHS NRHS SFai
'Southern Star'	IBal
'Star Quality'	IBal LBuc LRHS MNrw SFai
'Starburst'	IBlr
'Starburst Blue' **new**	IBal
'Starburst White' **new**	EWTr IBal
'Stardust'	IBal LBuc LRHS
'Stargazer'	EBee IBal LBuc LRHS
'Stars and Stripes'	IBal
'Stéphanie Charm'	IBal
'Stockholm'	GAbr IBal IRob
'Storm Cloud' Reads	see *A.* 'Purple Cloud'
'Storm Cloud' (d)	CBro IBal
'Strawberry Ice'	EBee IBal SFai
'Streamline'	CAvo CBcs CBod CElw CKno CMea EBee ECtt EHyd ELon EPfP EShb

	ETod GAbr GKin GMaP GMcL IBal LRHS LSou MRav SDys SEND SFai
'Su Casa' **new**	SFai
'Summer Blue'	IBal
'Summer Clouds'	ELan
'Summer Days'	CPne CPrp EBee IBal SFai
'Summer Delight'	IBal
'Summer Skies'	IBal
'Sunfield'	CDor CKno CPrp EPfP IBal ILea LAma LRHS MNrw NLar NPer NRHS SPoG
'Super Star'	CBro CPrp IBal
'Sweet Surprise'	EBee IBal SFai
'Sylvia'PBR	IBal
'Sylvine'	IBal
'Tall Boy'	CPrp IBal IBlr
'Tarka'	CExl CPne CPrp ELon EPfP EPri IBal LRHS LSou NLar SDys SFai
'Taw Valley'	CAbb CAvo CKno CPne CPrp CTal EBee ELon IBal LCro LOPS LRHS MGos SHyH SPoG
'Thorn'	IBal
'Thumbelina'	CBro CMac EBee IBal LRHS LSou NLar XLum
'Timaru'	CAco CBro CElw CPrp ECtt ELan ELon EPfP GAbr GMaP GMcL IBal MHol NGdn NLar SFai SHyH SLdr WCot
'Tinkerbell' (v)	CBcs CBro CCCN CPne CPrp EBee EHoe ELan EPfP EPri EShb IBal LRHS MGos MRav NPer SPoG SRms SWvt
'Tiny White'	EPri
'Titan'	IBlr
'Titch'	IBal
'Tom Thumb'PBR	CAvo CExl CPrp ECtt EHyd EPau EPfP GBin IBal LRHS LSou MAsh NCou NRHS SFai SRkn SRot
'Torbay'	CBod CElw CPrp ECtt ELon EPau EPfP EShb GAbr GCal GKin IBal LRHS MAvo MMuc MNrw NEgg SBod WAvo WHoo
'Tornado'	CBod CPrp EBee ECtt ELon GBin IBal ILea LRHS SEND SFai STPC WCot
'Triangle'	CPbh
'Tsolo'	IBal
'Twilight'	IBlr
'Twilight Zone'	IBal
umbellatus Redouté	see *A. praecox* subsp. *orientalis*
'Underway'	EWes GCal GKev IBal IBlr
'Vallée Blanche'	XTur
'Vallée Bleue'	XTur
'Vallée de la Belle'	XTur
'Vallée de la Loire'	XTur
'Vallée de la Sarthe'	XTur
'Vallée de l'Authion'	XTur
'Vallée du Cap'	XTur
'Vallée du Lathan'	XTur
Ventnor hybrid **new**	SVen
'Volendam'	IBal
'Washington'	IBal
'Wavy Navy'	IBal
'Wedding Day'	EBee IBal
'Wembworthy'	CPne CPrp EBee IBal SFai
'White Baby'	XTur
'White Cloud'	IBal
'White Dwarf'	see *A.* white-flowered, dwarf
'White Flash'	IBal
'White Giant'	WSpi
'White Heaven'PBR	Widely available
'White Ice'	CBcs IBal
'White Pixie'	IBal
'White Smile'	EPri
'White Superior'	CBod EBee EPfP GMaP
'White Swan'	SCob
'White Triumphator'	CBWd
'White Umbrella'	EHyd ELan GMcL LRHS NRHS WHar
'White Wings'	IBal
white-flowered	WAvo
§ white-flowered, dwarf	CBro CKno EBee ECha ECtt EPfP EShb IBal LRHS MPie NGdn
'Whitestorm'	SCob
'Whitney'PBR	IBal IBlr LRHS
'Windlebrooke'	CCCN EAJP EPri IBal MAvo SDeJ WCot
'Windsor Castle'	CPrp IBal IBlr
'Windsor Grey'	Widely available
'Winsome'	IBlr
'Winter Sky'	IBal
'Wolga'	CBro EBee IBal
'Wolkberg' Kirstenbosch	IBal IBlr
'Yves Klein'	CPrp IBlr
'Zachary'	CPou CPrp ELon EPri
'Zeal Thomas'	IBal
'Zigzag White'	WCot

Agapetes (*Ericaceae*)

'Ludgvan Cross' ♀H2	CBcs CCCN CTsd EShb MGil SPad
serpens ♀H2	CBcs CCCN CHll CTsd SLon
– 'Scarlet Elf'	CCCN CTsd LRHS
smithiana var. ***major***	GGGa

Agastache (*Lamiaceae*)

'After Eight'	EBee ECtt IBoy LRHS
anethiodora	see *A. foeniculum* (Pursh) Kuntze
anisata	see *A. foeniculum* (Pursh) Kuntze
'Astello Indigo' **new**	MNHC
aurantiaca	NGBl SPhx WMoo
– 'Apricot Sprite'	CBod EPfP ESps NGdn SPhm SRkn WHar
'Ayala'	SAko
'Blackadder'	Widely available
'Blaue Sangria'	LPla MAvo NDov
'Blue Boa'PBR	CBod CPla CWGN EBee ECtt IPot LCro LRHS MAvo MHol NCou NDov NLar SPoG
'Blue Delight'	SBch
'Blue Fortune' ♀H6	CBWd CBcs CBod CRos ECha EHyd EPfP GWyn IBoy LCro LOPS LRHS MCot MRav NDov NLar NRHS SAko SCob SMad SPer SPhx SRms SWvt WCAu WSpi XSen
'Bolero'	CSpe IBoy LRHS MHol MSpe NGBl SPhx
breviflora	SPhx
§ ***cana***	SPhx
– 'Heatwave'PBR	EPfP NDov
– 'Purple Pygmy'	EPfP
'Cotton Candy'PBR	ECtt IBoy LCro LOPS
'Firebird'	CWGN EBee ECtt ELan EPfP LSou SAko SPer SRms SWvt
'Fleur'	ECtt
foeniculum misapplied	see *A. rugosa*
§ ***foeniculum*** (Pursh) Kuntze	EBee ELan ENfk GPoy MCot MHer MNHC SPav SPhx SRms WTre
– 'Alabaster'	CBcs EBee LCro
– 'Alba'	NBre SPav
– 'Blaustrahl'	SAko

- 'Blue Spike' **new**	XAbr
'Globetrotter'	CBod ELan SPhx WArt
'Grapefruit Nectar' (Nectar Series)	SCob
'Kolibri'	ECtt ILea
(Kudos Series) 'Kudos Ambrosia'[PBR]	ECtt LRHS SPoG
- 'Kudos Coral'[PBR]	CMea LRHS SPoG
- 'Kudos Gold'	CMea LRHS SPoG
- 'Kudos Mandarin'[PBR]	CMea LRHS MMrt SPoG
- 'Kudos Silver Blue'	ECtt NEoE SPhm
'Linda'	CWGN NDov WCot
§ ***mexicana***	SPav
- 'Champagne'	NWad
- 'Red Fortune'[PBR]	CBod CRos CWGN EAJP ECtt EHyd ILea LCro LOPS LRHS MCot MHol NEgg NRHS SAko SCob SPad WCot
- 'Rosea'	see *A. cana*
- 'Sangria'	CWGN ELon ILea NGdn SPad SPhx SRms XLum
micrantha	SPhx
nepetoides	CBod EPPr NDov SPav
- 'Green Candles' **new**	WFar
occidentalis	SPhx
ORANGE NECTAR (Nectar Series)	EBee MHol MPie SPoG WCot
'Painted Lady'	CSpe ECtt
pallidiflora var. ***neomexicana***	SPhx
- - 'Lavender Haze'	SPhm
- - 'Rose Mint'	CSpe
'Pink Perfume'[PBR]	WOut
'Pink Pop'	EPfP MHol WHil
'Purple Haze'	LRHS NDov NRHS SAko
'Raspberry Summer'[PBR]	CBod CWGN ECtt EPfP ILea LRHS MNHC NRHS SCob WAul
§ ***rugosa***	CAby CBod ECha GPoy LEdu MNHC SPav SPhx SPlb SRms WMoo
- f. ***albiflora***	WCAu
- - 'Alabaster'	NDov
- - 'Liquorice White'	CBWd CBod EBee ELan EPed EPfP GWyn MArl MBel NGBl NLar SPer SPlb SRms
- 'Golden Jubilee'	CAby CBod CSpe EBee ECha ECtt ELan ELon EPfP IBoy LRHS MAvo MHer NLar NRHS NSti SCob SRms SWvt WMoo WTre XLum
- 'Heronswood Mist'	EBee
- 'Korean Zest'	WCru
- 'Liquorice Blue'	CBod CDor CTsd ELan EPed EPfP LRHS MBel MSpe MWat NEgg NGBl NGdn SPoG SRms SSut SWvt WMoo
- 'Little Adder' **new**	CBod ECtt LSou MHol
rupestris	CSpe SPhx XSen
- 'Apache Sunset'	SPlb XSen
'Serpentine'	ECtt MAvo NDov SPhx
'Spicy'	NDov
'Summer Fiesta'[PBR]	EBee ECtt IBoy LSou MNrw
'Summer Glow'[PBR]	CDor CKno CWGN EBee ECtt EPfP ETMg EUJe LRHS LSou MNrw NDov NGBl NRHS SCob SDys SPad SPoG WRHF
'Summer Love'[PBR]	ECtt LRHS MNrw NDov
'Summer Sky'[PBR]	CBod EBee ECtt LRHS NDov
'Summer Sunset'[PBR]	CDor CSpe CWGN EBee ELan LCro LOPS LPla LRHS LSou MHol NRHS SCob
'Tangerine Dreams' ♀H3	ECtt ELan EPfP LRHS NEgg NRHS SCoo
'Tango'	SGbt WKif
'Tutti-frutti'	ECtt
urticifolia	WArt
'Violet Vision'[PBR] **new**	ECtt LCro LOPS

Agathaea see *Felicia*

Agathosma (*Rutaceae*)

ovata	CCCN

Agave ✿ (*Asparagaceae*)

albomarginata	CDTJ
americana ♀H2	CAbb CAco CBcs CBen CBot CPla ELan EPfP EShb ESps EUJe IDee LRHS LSun NLos SArc SChr SCob SEND SPlb SPre SVen SWvt WCot WGrn
§ - subsp. ***americana*** JL 2007-01	CCac
- blue-flowered **new**	SPlb
- 'Marginata' (v) ♀H2	CBot CBrP CDTJ CFil CHll GMcL NQui SEND SVen WCot WSFF
- 'Mediopicta' misapplied	see *A. americana* 'Mediopicta Alba'
- 'Mediopicta' (v) ♀H2	CDTJ CFil EUJe SArc SBig WGrn
§ - 'Mediopicta Alba' (v) ♀H2	CAbb CBrP CCCN CDTJ CFil CJun CPbh ELan SPlb WCot WGrn
- 'Mediopicta Aurea' (v)	CFil WCot
- var. ***oaxacensis***	WPGP
- subsp. ***protamericana***	CDTJ
- subsp. ***protamericana*** × ***scabra*** F&M 310	WPGP
- 'Striata' (v)	CDTJ EShb WCot
- 'Variegata' (v) ♀H2	CAbb CAco CBcs CBen CFil CPbh ELan EPfP EShb ESps EUJe LRHS LSun MGos NPer NPla SArc SChr SCob SMad SPlb SWvt WCot
angustifolia	see *A. vivipara* var. *vivipara*
- var. ***marginata*** hort.	SBig WCot
applanata	CFil CJun SPlb WPGP
asperrima	CDTJ
§ - subsp. ***maderensis***	SPlb
asperrima × ***lechuguilla***	CCac
atrovirens	SPlb WCot
- from Carneros, Coah, Mexico	CCac
- from Concepción del Oro, Mexico	CCac
- var. ***mirabilis***	CDTJ CFil
- - F&M 245	WPGP
attenuata	CAbb CDTJ NLos SBig SPlb
'Bloodspot'	WCot
boldinghiana	WCot
bracteosa	CBlu CCCN CDTJ EUJe WCot
celsii	see *A. mitis* var. *mitis*
cerulata subsp. ***nelsonii***	CDTJ
chrysantha	CAco CBlu CCCN CDTJ CPbh EBee WCot WGrn
- 'Black Canyon'	WCot
chrysoglossa	CDTJ
colimana	see *A. ortgiesiana*
colorata	CCCN CDTJ CJun WCot
cordillerensis	see *A. americana* subsp. *americana*
'Cornelius'	WCot WGrn
cupreata	CDTJ
decipiens	SPlb
deserti	CAco CDTJ CJun CPbh LRHS WCot
- var. ***simplex***	WCot
difformis	CDTJ
- NJM 05.034	WPGP

	durangensis	SPlb
	elongata	see *A. vivipara* var. *vivipara*
	ensifera	CJun
	felgeri	CDTJ
	ferdinandi-regis	see *A. victoriae-reginae*
	ferox	see *A. salmiana* var. *ferox*
	filifera ♀H2	CCCN CDTJ CJun CPbh SChr SPlb WCot
	flexispina	SPlb
	- from Parral, Chihuahua, Mexico	CCac
	garciae-mendozae	CDTJ
	geminiflora	CCCN CDTJ CFil CJun CPbh EShb
	gentryi	CCht CDTJ CFil EUJe SPlb WCot
	ghiesbreghtii	CPbh
	gigantea	see *Furcraea foetida*
§	***gracillima***	SPlb
	guadalajarana	CDTJ CPbh
	guttata	WCot
	havardiana	CBlu CDTJ CFil CPbh XSen
	- DJF 1326 from Davis Mountains, Texas	CCac
	horrida	CDTJ CFil CJun SBig
	- subsp. ***horrida***	SPlb
	- 'Perotensis'	CDTJ EShb
	hurteri	CDTJ
	impressa	CDTJ WCot
	isthmensis	SPlb
	kerchovei	WCot
	lechuguilla	CDTJ WCot XSen
	lophantha	see *A. univittata*
	- var. ***caerulescens***	see *A. univittata*
	'Macha Mocha'	WCot
	macroacantha ♀H1c	CBlu CDTJ EUJe NLos
§	***maculosa***	WCot
	marmorata	CBlu CJun WCot
	maximilliana	SPlb
	mckelveyana	WCot
	- DJF 1575 from Bagdad, Arizona	CCac WCot
	- from Hillside, Arizona	CCac
	mitis **new**	CCht
	- var. ***albidior***	CFil
§	- var. ***mitis***	CDTJ CFil CPla SPlb
	- var. ***mitis* × *variegata***	WCot
	montana	CBlu CCac CCht CDTJ CFil ETod EUJe NLos SArc SChr SPlb XSen
	multifilifera	XSen
§	***obscura***	CDTJ WCot
	oroensis	WCot
	- from Estanción Margarita, Zacatecas, Mexico	CCac
§	***ortgiesiana***	WCot
	ovatifolia	CBlu CDTJ CFil CJun EUJe SPlb WCot XSen
	- NJM 09.002	WPGP
	palmeri	CCCN CCac CDTJ CFil EBee SPlb WCot XSen
	panamana	see *A. vivipara* var. *vivipara*
	parrasana ♀H2	CDTJ EUJe WCot
	- from Sierra Parras, Mexico	CCac
	parryi ♀H2	CDTJ CPbh ETod EUJe GKev SPlb WCot XSen
	- DJF 138	CCac
	- HK 1684	CCac
	- var. ***couesii***	CCac CDTJ XSen
	- 'Cream Spike' (v)	CBcs CFil EMFm EUJe SPad WArt WCot WGrn
	- var. ***huachucensis***	CBlu CCac CDTJ WCot
	- subsp. ***neomexicana***	CCCN CDTJ CFil SPlb XSen

	- - SB 948 from W of Artesia, New Mexico	CCac WCot
	- 'Ohi-kissho-ten-nishiki' (v)	WCot
	- subsp. ***parryi***	CBlu CDTJ WCot WPGP
	- small	ETod
	- var. ***truncata***	CBlu CCac CDTJ ETod SPlb
	- - variegated (v)	WCot
	parviflora ♀H2	WCot
	polyacantha	see *A. obscura*
	var. ***xalapensis***	
	potatorum 'Gary Fisher'	WCot
	salmiana	CCac CDTJ CFil SBig SPlb
	- subsp. ***crassispina***	SPlb
§	- var. ***ferox***	CCac CDTJ CPbh EUJe SArc SBig SChr SPlb
	- - from Tlacotepec, Pue, Mexico	CCac
	scabra	CCCN CPbh WCot
	- subsp. ***maderensis***	see *A. asperrima* subsp. *maderensis*
	schidigera	EUJe
	- 'Shira-ito-no-ohi' (v)	WCot
	- 'White Stripe' (v) **new**	CBlu
	schottii	CDTJ WCot
	'Sharkskin Shoes'	NLos WCot
	shrevei subsp. ***magna***	SPlb
§	***sileri***	WCot
	sisalana	CDTJ
	stictata	WCot
	striata subsp. ***falcata***	WCot
*	- 'Rubra'	CDTJ SPlb WCot
	stricta ♀H2	CCCN CDTJ EUJe WCot
	- 'Nana'	CDTJ SMad
	- 'Rubra' **new**	WCot
	aff. ***stricta***	WCot
	tenuifolia	CPla
	titanota ♀H1c	CBlu SPlb
	toumeyana ♀H2	CPbh SPlb WCot
	- from Globe, Arizona	CCac
	- var. ***bella***	CDTJ XSen
	triangularis	CDTJ
§	***undulata***	WCot
	- 'Chocolate Chips'	WCot
§	***univittata***	CBlu CDTJ CJun NLos WCot
	- 'Quadricolor' (v)	CDTJ EUJe LLWG NLos SMad SPlb WCot
	utahensis ♀H3	CCac CDTJ SEND SPlb WCot XSen
	- DJF 1521 from Peach Springs, Arizona	CCac WCot
	- LZ 2042 from Beaver Dam Mountains, Utah	CCac
	- from Kingman, Arizona	CCac
	- var. ***eborispina***	CCac WCot
	- subsp. ***kaibabensis***	CCac WCot
§	***variegata***	WCot
	- B&SWJ 10234	WCru
§	***victoriae-reginae*** ♀H2	CCCN CDTJ CJun CPbh NLos SChr SPlb WCot XSen
	- dwarf	CBlu WCot
§	***virginica***	WCot
§	***vivipara*** var. ***vivipara***	WCot
	wocomahi	WCot
	xylonacantha	CDTJ SChr SPlb WCot
	zebra	CBlu CDTJ

Ageratina (Asteraceae)

§	***altissima***	CDor CHid CMac EBee GJos
	- 'Braunlaub'	CBod NLar SAko SHar WCAu WPtf WWtn
	- 'Chocolate'	Widely available

§ ***aromatica***	MRav SHar
§ ***ligustrina***	CBod CExl CRHN CRos CTri EBee ECha EHoe ELan EWTr LRHS MBlu SBrt SEND SPer SPoG SRkn SRms WSFF WSHC

Ageratum (*Asteraceae*)

sp.	ESps
'Blue Champion'	NPri
corymbosum	CHII CSpe
houstonianum 'Blue Danube' ♀H2	ETMg
- 'Blue Horizon' ♀H2 **new**	CRav
- 'High Tide Blue'	NPri
- PINCUSHION MIXED **new**	ETMg
petiolatum	LRHS

Agrimonia (*Rosaceae*)

eupatoria	CBod CHab CWld EBWF ENfk GPoy MHer MNHC NMir SRms WHer
* - var. ***alba***	NLar
- 'Cambridge Lace' (v) **new**	WCot
odorata misapplied	see *A. procera*
odorata (L.) Mill.	see *A. repens*
§ ***procera***	EBWF
§ ***repens***	WMoo

Agropyron (*Poaceae*)

glaucum	see *Elymus hispidus*
magellanicum	see *Elymus magellanicus*
pubiflorum	see *Elymus magellanicus*

Agrostemma (*Caryophyllaceae*)

coronaria	see *Lychnis coronaria*
githago	CHab EBWF MNHC SRms WTre
- 'Ocean Pearl'	CSpe MCot SPhx

Agrostis (*Poaceae*)

calamagrostis	see *Stipa calamagrostis*
capillaris	CHab EBWF
nebulosa	SPhx
- 'Fibre Optics'	see *Panicum* 'Fibre Optics'
stolonifera 'Julia Ann' (v)	WCot

Aichryson (*Crassulaceae*)

§ × ***aizoides*** var. ***domesticum***	SAll
- - 'Variegatum' (v) ♀H1c	CDTJ CPbh EBak WCot

Ailanthus (*Simaroubaceae*)

sp	LPra
§ ***altissima***	CBcs CCVT CDul CExl CMac EBee EPfP EUJe LPra SPer SPlb SWvt
- 'Purple Dragon'	MBlu
- var. ***tanakae*** CWJ 12452	WCru
- - RWJ 9906	WCru
glandulosa	see *A. altissima*

Ainsliaea (*Asteraceae*)

apiculata var. ***acerifolia*** B&SWJ 6059	WCru
chapaensis B&SWJ 11720	WCru
- B&SWJ 11732	WCru
latifolia FMWJ 13426	WCru
nervosa B&SWJ 11344	WCru
petelotii FMWJ 13427	WCru
tonkinensis B&SWJ 11819	WCru
uniflora	GEdr

Ajania (*Asteraceae*)

pacifica 'Silver Edge'	XLum

Ajuga (*Lamiaceae*)

genevensis	GCal GWyn SPhx WOut
incisa	EPPr EWld GCal
- 'Bikun' (v)	EBee SPoG SRGP WCot
- 'Blue Enigma'	CExl ELon IMou NLar
- 'Blue Ensign'	WSHC
'Little Court Pink'	see *A. reptans* 'Purple Torch'
lupulina	GEdr
metallica hort.	see *A. pyramidalis*
'Pink Lightning' (v)	EBee LSou NHpl WHil
'Pink Spires'	WFar
§ ***pyramidalis***	XAbr
- 'Metallica Crispa'	CBre EBee ELan EWes NEoE NHpl NLar NPnk SRms SWvt WTor XSen
reptans	CHab CTri EBWF ECtt ENfk EPed GKev GPoy LCro MBel MHer MNHC SRms WOut XLum
- f. ***albiflora***	CDor
- - 'Alba'	CBod CBre EBee ELon ETMg MBel MRav NBro SRms WFar WMoo
- 'Arctic Fox' (v)	GEdr LSou MRav NBro NRHS SWvt
- 'Argentea'	see *A. reptans* 'Variegata'
§ - 'Atropurpurea'	CRos CTri ECha EHyd ELan EPfP ESps GAbr GBin GWyn LCro LRHS MGos MMuc NRHS NWad SEND SGol SPer SPlb SRms SWvt WBrk XLum
- BLACK SCALLOP ('Binblasca'PBR)	Widely available
- 'Blueberry Muffin'	ECtt EWTr LCro LOPS NHpl
- 'Braunherz'	CRos CTri ECtt EHoe EHyd ELan EPfP GMaP IBoy LRHS MWat NHpl NLar NPri NRHS SCob SGol SPer SRms SWvt WFar WHar WMoo
- 'Burgundy Glow' (v)	Widely available
§ - 'Catlin's Giant' ♀H7	Widely available
- 'Choc Ice'	EWTr
- 'Chocolate Chip'	see *A. reptans* 'Valfredda'
- 'Ebony'	LSRN
- 'Evening Glow'	CBod WBrk WMoo
- 'Flisteridge'	CNat
- 'Golden Beauty'	SRms WOut
- 'Harlequin' (v)	SWvt
- 'John Pierpoint'	SHar
- 'Jumbo'	see *A. reptans* 'Jungle Beauty'
§ - 'Jungle Beauty'	EPfP MRav XLum
- 'Macrophylla'	see *A. reptans* 'Catlin's Giant'
- 'Mahogany'	SRms
§ - 'Multicolor' (v)	CBcs ELan LRHS NPri NRHS SPer SPlb SPoG SRms SWvt WMoo
- PARTY COLORS ('Binparcol'PBR)	SCob
- 'Pink Elf'	CDor MRav NBro
- 'Pink Surprise'	EHoe EPri MHer NRya
- 'Purple Brocade'	EHoe
§ - 'Purple Torch'	MPie NLar SRms SWvt WCAu
- 'Purpurea'	see *A. reptans* 'Atropurpurea'
- 'Rainbow'	see *A. reptans* 'Multicolor'
- 'Rosea'	CBod GWyn MBel WMoo XLum
- 'Rowden Amethyst'	MHCG WHil
- 'Tricolor'	see *A. reptans* 'Multicolor'
§ - 'Valfredda'	CBod CRos ECrN EHyd EPfP GAbr GBin GKev GWyn LRHS MHCG NHpl NLar NRHS SRms SWvt WBrk WHar WMoo

§ - 'Variegata' (v)	ECtt EPfP NHpl SPer SPoG SRms WFar WTor
'Rose Glow'	NHpl
'Sparkler' (v)	EBee NHpl

Akebia ✿ (*Lardizabalaceae*)

longeracemosa	CRHN EBee SBrt SChF
- B&SWJ 3606	CExl LEdu WCot WCru WPGP
× ***pentaphylla***	CBcs CRHN CRos EBee EHyd ELan EPfP LRHS MAsh MGil MRav SPer
- B&SWJ 2829	WCru
quinata	Widely available
- B&SWJ 4425	WCru
- 'Amethyst Glow'	CRos CWCL EHyd EMil EPfP LRHS NLar SEle SPer SPoG
- cream-flowered	CBot CCCN CKel CRHN CRos EBee EHyd EPfP EWld LCro LOPS LRHS MGos MRav NLar SPer SRms SSta SWvt WCru WPGP
- 'Shirobana'	CBcs CHll CMen CWGN EUJe MBlu MGil NLar WAvo
- 'Silver Bells'	LRHS
- variegated (v)	CBcs LLHF
- 'White Chocolate' 🏆[H5]	NLar WCru WSHC
trifoliata	CBcs CMen CRHN CRos EBee EHyd EPfP LRHS MGil MGos SLon WOld
- B&SWJ 5063	WCru
- 'Amethyst'	CBot

Alangium (*Cornaceae*)

platanifolium	CBcs CBot CExl EBee WPGP
- var. ***macrophyllum***	CCCN EPfP MGil MMrt WBor

Albizia (*Mimosaceae*)

chinensis	EPfP LRHS
distachya	see *Paraserianthes lophantha*
§ ***julibrissin***	CBlu CDTJ EBee EPfP EUJe IDee MGil NEgg NLos
- 'Evy's Purple'	ERea
- OMBRELLA ('Boubri'[PBR])	CBcs EBee EPfP ERea NOra WPGP
- f. ***rosea*** 🏆[H2]	CAco CBcs CDul CExl CLnd CMCN CRos CWGN EBee ELan EPfP LEdu LRHS SArc SEND SLim SPad SPlb SPoG SPtp WPGP WSHC
I - 'Rouge Selection'	EPfP LRHS
- 'Shidare'	EBee NOra
- 'Summer Chocolate'[PBR] 🏆[H2]	CBcs CDul CRos CWGN EBee EHyd ELan EPfP ERea IDee LRHS MAsh NOra NRHS SCoo SPer SPoG
- TROPICAL DREAM ('Pos 1') **new**	EBee
kalkora	SPlb
lophantha	see *Paraserianthes lophantha*

Albuca ✿ (*Asparagaceae*)

JCA 15856	CTca
from Namibia	LToo
angolensis	CPou
aurea	CTca
'Ausgrabies Hills' **new**	WHil
canadensis (L.) F.M. Leight.	CPou WHil
'Dirk Wallace'	CExl
flaccida	WHil
glauca	EBee
humilis	CExl LLHF WAbe WHil
namaquensis	WHil
nelsonii	CAvo CPne CPrp CTca EBee LAma SChr WHil
setosa	CTca
shawii	CAvo CBod CBro CPne CPou CPrp CTca CWld EAJP EBee EHoe EPot EPri ERCP EWld MHer NPnk SPhm SPoG WAbe WGwG WHil
spiralis	WHil
- 'Frizzle Sizzle' **new**	WHil
wakefieldii	WHil

× *Alcalthaea* (*Malvaceae*)

suffrutescens 'Freedom'	CBod ELan LPla SPad WFar
- 'Parkallee' (d)	CBod CRos EBee ECha ECtt ELan ELon GMaP GWyn LRHS MAvo MCot MHol MNrw NGBl NGdn NLar NRHS SEND SPhx WBrk WCot XLum
- 'Parkfrieden' (d)	CSpe ECtt ELon LRHS MAvo MCot MNrw SPhx XLum
- 'Parkrondell' (d)	CBod CRos ECha ECtt ELan ELon LCro LOPS LRHS MAvo MNrw NRHS SHar SPhx WCot XLum
- 'Poetry'	CBod EBee ECtt ELan ELon LPla LRHS MAvo
- white-flowered	IFro

Alcea (*Malvaceae*)

'Apple Blossom' (d)	EPfP
'Arabian Nights'	SPav
'Blackcurrant Whirl'	SPav
'Burgundy Towers'	SEND
ficifolia	NChi SPav WFar WMoo WSpi
'Happy Lights'	CBot
kurdica	CBot
'Las Vegas'	ELon
nudiflora	GCal
'O'Hara' **new**	CBot
pallida	XSen
'Peaches 'n' Dreams'	CBot EPfP
§ ***rosea***	ESps SVic WFar
- 'Blacknight' (Spotlight Series)	CBod CBot EPfP GKev MHer
- Chater's Double Group (d)	EPfP GMcL IBoy SPoG SRms WBor WFar WHar
- - chamois (d)	EPfP
- - chestnut-brown-flowered (d)	EPfP
- - maroon-flowered (d)	EPfP ESps LCro LOPS SPoG
- - pink-flowered (d)	ELan EPfP ESps
- - red-flowered (d)	ELan EPfP GMcL SPoG
- - rose-pink-flowered (d)	LCro LOPS
- - salmon-pink-flowered (d)	EPfP
- - scarlet-flowered (d)	EPfP IBoy SPoG
- - violet-flowered (d)	EPfP
- - white-flowered (d)	ELan EPfP GMcL LCro LOPS SPoG
- - yellow-flowered (d)	EPfP GMcL LCro LOPS SPoG SRms
- 'Crème de Cassis'	CBot ELan EPfP LRHS SPav
- 'Double Banana' (d) **new**	CBot
- 'Fiesta Time' (d)	CBot
- (Halo Series) 'Halo Apricot'	CBot CRos EHyd EPfP LRHS NRHS SPoG WHoo
- - 'Halo Blossom' **new**	CBot
- - 'Halo Blush'	CBot CRos EHyd EPfP LRHS NRHS SPoG WHil
- - 'Halo Candy' **new**	CBot
- - 'Halo Cerise'	CBot CRos EHyd LRHS NRHS SPoG
- - 'Halo Cream'	CBot CRos EHyd LRHS NRHS SPoG
- - 'Halo Pink' **new**	CBot
- - 'Halo Red'	CBot EPfP LRHS NRHS SPoG
- - 'Halo White'	CBot CRav CRos EHyd LRHS NRHS SPoG
- 'Jet Black'	CBot

- 'Mars Magic' (Spotlight Series)	CBod CBot EPfP LCro LOPS LRHS MHer
- 'Nigra'	CBod CBot CRav CSpe ECtt ELan EPfP ESps GMcL IBoy LCro LOPS LRHS LSRN MNHC NGdn SPer SPhx SRms WHar XEll XSen
- 'Polarstar' (Spotlight Series)	CBod ELan LCro LOPS LRHS
- 'Radiant Rose' (Spotlight Series)	CBod ELan LRHS MHer
- single-flowered	MMuc SEND SRms
- Spring Celebrities Series (d)	CBot
- - 'Spring Celebrities Crimson' (d)	CRos LRHS NRHS
- - 'Spring Celebrities Lemon' (d)	CRos LRHS NRHS
- - 'Spring Celebrities Pink' (d)	CRos LRHS NRHS
- - 'Spring Celebrities Scarlet' (d) **new**	NRHS
- - 'Spring Celebrities White' (d)	CRos LRHS NRHS
- Summer Carnival Group	SRms
- 'Sunshine' (Spotlight Series)	CBod EPfP LRHS
§ ***rugosa***	CBot EPPr LEdu MSpe SHar SPav XSen

Alcea × *Althaea* see × *Alcalthaea*

Alchemilla ✿ (*Rosaceae*)

abyssinica	EBee
alpina misapplied	see *A. conjuncta*, *A. plicatula*
alpina ambig.	MCot SCob
alpina L.	CRos EBee EHoe ELan EPfP GPoy IRob LEdu LRHS MBel MMuc MRav NChi SBch SEND SRms WMoo WPGP WSHC
§ ***conjuncta***	CDor CMac CSam CSpe EBee ECha EHrv ELan EPfP GAbr GMaP GMcL GWyn MHer MRav NBid NRya NSti SPer SPlb SRms WCAu WHoo
ellenbeckii	GAbr IMou NChi WTor
epipsila	EBee ELan EPfP EShb GCal LRHS LSun NLar SPhx WSHC
erythropoda ♀H5	Widely available
- (Cepa Group) 'Alma'	EUJe
- Turkish form	ECha
faeroensis	WMoo WPtf XLum
- var. ***pumila***	EBee GEdr GKev
fissa	EBee EPPr
glabra **new**	EBee
glaucescens	CNat
hoppeana misapplied	see *A. plicatula*
hoppeana (Reichenb.) Dalla Torre	EBee
iniquiformis	EBee
'Irish Silk' **new**	CBod
mollis ♀H7	Widely available
I - 'Auslese'	SWvt
- 'Robustica'	GQue LSun MMuc SEND SPlb WFar WMoo WPnP
- 'Thriller'	CBod CRos EHyd EPfP LRHS NRHS WFar
- 'Variegata' (v)	CNat
'Mr Poland's Variety'	see *A. venosa*
pedata	CHid EBee NChi
peristerica	EBee
§ ***plicatula***	NLar
saxatilis	NLar
sericata 'Gold Strike'	EBee ECtt ELan EPfP GLog IMou SHar SWvt
straminea	MRav
valdehirsuta	EBee
§ ***venosa***	EBee SHar SMHy
vetteri	CRos EBee LRHS NRHS WHrl
vulgaris agg. **new**	EBWF
vulgaris misapplied	see *A. xanthochlora*
§ ***xanthochlora***	GPoy NLar SRms WFar WHer

alecost see *Tanacetum balsamita*

Alectorurus (*Liliaceae*)

yedoensis var. ***platypetalus***	EBee GEdr

Alectryon (*Sapindaceae*)

excelsus	CBcs

Alisma (*Alismataceae*)

lanceolatum	MSKA XBlo
plantago-aquatica	CBen CHab EBWF MSKA MWts NPer WMAq WWtn XBlo
- var. ***parviflorum***	MSKA SPlb WWtn

Allamanda (*Apocynaceae*)

cathartica	CCCN

Alliaria (*Brassicaceae*)

petiolata	EBWF GPoy WHer WOut WSFF

Allium ✿ (*Alliaceae*)

See also AGM Vegetables Section.

RCB AM 21	WCot
SSSE 250	GEdr
§ ***acuminatum***	GKev NRog
I - 'Album'	CRos LRHS NRHS
acutiflorum	GKev LAma NRog
aflatunense misapplied	see *A. hollandicum*
aflatunense ambig.	CRos GMcL LCro LRHS LSRN SCob SDeJ SEND
akaka	NRog
'Akbulak'	EBee GKev LAma
albidum	see *A. denudatum*
albopilosum	see *A. cristophii*
alexeianum	NRog
altissimum	GKev LAma NRog
- 'Goliath'	CRos LRHS NRHS NRog WCot
amabile	see *A. mairei* var. *amabile*
'Ambassador'	CAvo CMea CRos CTca CWCL ERCP GKev ILea LAma LRHS NRHS NRog SDir WCot
amethystinum	GKev
- 'Red Mohican'	CMea CTca EBee ERCP GKev IPot LAma MMrt SDeJ WCot
ampeloprasum	EBWF EBee ECha GKev LAma NRog SPlb WHer WShi
- var. ***babingtonii***	CAgr CTca GKev GPoy LEdu NRog SRms WHer WPGP WShi
§ - 'Elephant'	CRav LCro LEdu LOPS
- 'Pink Lady' **new**	GKev
- 'Purple Mystery' **new**	GKev
amphibolum	EBee GKev LAma NRog
amplectens	LAma NRog
- 'Graceful Beauty'	CRav EBee EPfP EPot ERCP GKev LAma LCro LOPS NRog SCob SDeJ SPer SPhx XEll
anceps	NRog
§ ***angulosum***	CAvo CTca GKev LAma LEdu NHpl NRog WCot

	– 'Sara' new	GKev
	aschersonianum	EBee GKev SDeJ WCot
	atropurpureum	CRos EAJP EBee ECha ELan EPfP EPot ERCP GBin GKev GWyn LAma LCro LOPS LRHS MJak NRHS NRog SDeJ SDir SPhx WRHF
	atropurpureum* × *schubertii	LSRN
	atroviolaceum W&B BG A-5 new	WCot
	auctum	EBee
	azureum	see *A. caeruleum*
	backhousianum	GKev LAma NRog
	barszczewskii	NRog
	'Beau Regard' ♀H7	CRos CTca CWCL EBee ELan ERCP GKev ILea LAma LRHS NLar NRHS NRog SDir
	beesianum misapplied	see *A. cyaneum*
	beesianum W.W.Sm. ♀H5	EBee EPot LLHF NHpl
	bisceptrum	NRog
	'Bizar'	LAma
	blandum	see *A. carolinianum*
	bodeanum	see *A. cristophii*
	'Bolero'	CRos EBee LAma LRHS NRHS NRog
	brevicaule	GKev
	bulgaricum	see *Nectaroscordum siculum* subsp. *bulgaricum*
§	***caeruleum*** ♀H5	CAvo CDor CRav CRos CTca EBee EPot ERCP GKev LAma LCro LRHS MGos MNrw NLar NPer NRHS NRog NRya SCob SDeJ SPhx
	– *azureum*	see *A. caeruleum*
	caesium ♀H5	EBee ERCP GKev NRog WCot
	– 'Pskem's Beauty'	GKev WCot
	callimischon subsp. ***callimischon***	EPot GKev NRog
	– subsp. ***haemostictum***	NRog WCot
	'Caméléon'	CDor CRos EBee ERCP GKev LAma LCro LOPS LRHS NPnk NRHS NRog SCob SDir WCot
	campanulatum	NRog
	canadense	SHar
	candolleanum new	GKev
§	***carinatum***	GKev WHer
§	– subsp. ***pulchellum*** ♀H5	CBro CRos CSpe EBee ECha EPot GKev LAma LRHS MHer MMuc MNrw NRHS NRog SDeJ SPhx WArt WThu
	– – f. ***album*** ♀H5	CBro EBee ECha GKev LEdu LSun MNrw NRog SPhx WPtf
	– – 'Bill Baker'	LEdu
	– – 'Olympic Mist' new	GKev
§	***carolinianum***	LAma NRog
	cepa	CBod SVic
	– Aggregatum Group	GPoy SRms
	– 'Kew White'	WCot
	– 'Perutile'	CHby GPoy LEdu MHer
	– Proliferum Group	CAgr GPoy LEdu MHer MNHC SRms WGwG WHer XAbr XLum
	– 'Red Brunswick'	SVic
	– var. ***viviparum***	GKev LAma NRog
	cernuum	Widely available
§	– 'Hidcote' ♀H5	CSam EBee WArt WKif XSen
	– 'Major'	see *A. cernuum* 'Hidcote'
	– 'White Dwarf'	CMea EBee GKev LAma NRog
	– 'White Max'	GKev
	chinense	CAgr GPoy LEdu
	– 'October Mist'	LEdu
	cirrhosum	see *A. carinatum* subsp. *pulchellum*
*	***cneorum***	LAma
	colchicifolium	NRog
	commutatum	GKev
	convallarioides	GKev LAma
	– pink-flowered	GKev
	cowanii	see *A. neapolitanum* Cowanii Group
	crenulatum	LAma NRog
	crispum	NRog
§	***cristophii*** ♀H7	Widely available
	cupanii	GKev
	cupuliferum	GKev NRog
	curtum RCB RL 13	WCot
§	***cyaneum*** ♀H5	CPBP CRos GEdr GKev LAma LBee LRHS MHer NHpl NRHS NRog NRya WCot
§	***cyathophorum*** var. ***farreri***	CBro CElw CRos EPot GKev LAma LEdu LRHS MHer MNrw MRav NHpl NRHS NRya WCot WPtf WThu XEll
	cyrilli	GKev
	darwasicum	WCot
	decipiens	GKev LAma NRog
§	***denudatum***	GKev
	diabaloense	NRog
	dichlamydeum	NRog
	dolichostylum new	GKev
	douglasii	NRog
§	***drummondii***	CRos LRHS NRHS
	'Early Emperor'	CRav CRos CWCL EBee EPfP ERCP GKev LAma LRHS NRHS NRog SCob
	elatum	see *A. macleanii*
	elburzense	NRog
	'Emir'	GKev NRog
	ericetorum	NRog WCot
	– PAB 1009	LEdu
	'Eros'	EBee GKev LAma LCro LOPS
	falcifolium	CTal GKev LAma LLHF NRog WCot WRHF
	farreri	see *A. cyathophorum* var. *farreri*
	fasciculatum	LAma
	fimbriatum	NRog
	– var. ***purdyi***	NRog
	'Firmament'	CWCL ECha ERCP GKev LAma LRHS NRog SDeJ SPhx WCot XEll
	fistulosum	CAgr CHby ENfk GKev GPoy LAma MHer MNHC NPri SEND SRms SVic WCot WGwG XLum
	fistulosum* × *pskemense new	GKev
	flavum ♀H4	CBro CRos CTca ECha EPot ERCP LAma LRHS NHpl NRHS NSla SDeJ SDir WGwG WPtf WThu
	– subsp. ***flavum***	GKev NRog SPhx
	– – var. ***minus***	MMuc NRog SEND
	– var. ***nanum***	EPot NRog
	– subsp. ***tauricum***	CSpe GKev NRog SPhx WCot
	'Forelock'	CTca EPfP ERCP GKev LAma MNrw NRog SCob SDir WCot XEll
	forrestii	NSla WCot
	geyeri	EBee GBin
	giganteum	Widely available
	– 'Twinkling Stars'	GKev LAma
	'Gladiator' ♀H7	CAvo CRos CWCL EBee EPfP ERCP ETMg GKev GMaP LAma LCro LOPS LRHS NRHS NRog SCob SDeJ SDir SPhx
	glaucum	see *A. senescens* subsp. *glaucum*
	'Globemaster' ♀H7	Widely available

	'Globus'	EBee GKev LAma NRog
	'Guardsman' ♀H4 **new**	EMsh MShS
	guttatum subsp. ***dalmaticum***	GKev NRog
	- subsp. ***sardoum***	GKev NRog
	gypsaceum	NRog
	haemanthoides	WCot
	haematochiton	NRog
	'Hair'	see *A. vineale* 'Hair'
	heldreichii	NRog
*	***hirtifolium*** var. ***album***	EBee GKev LAma NRog
	'His Excellency'	CRos CWCL EBee ERCP GBin GKev LAma LRHS NRHS NRog SCob
§	***hollandicum*** ♀H7	CArg CAvo CRav ECha GKev LAma LCro LOPS NRog SPlb WFar
	- 'Purple Sensation' ♀H7	Widely available
	- 'Purple Surprise' ♀H7	WCot
	hookeri	GKev LEdu SPhx
	- ACE 2430	LEdu WCot
	- var. ***muliense***	GEdr LEdu
	- 'Zorami'	CAgr ELan LEdu WPGP
	howellii var. ***clokeyi***	NRog
	huber-morathii	EBee GKev
	humile	GEdr
	hyalinum	GKev NRog
	- pink-flowered	WCot
	inconspicuum	LAma NRog
§	***insubricum*** ♀H5	CSpe GEdr MNrw NHpl NRog NRya NSla SChF WAbe
	'Jackpot'	CWCL EBee ERCP GKev ILea LAma NRog SPhx
	jajlae	see *A. rotundum* subsp. *jajlae*
	jesdianum 'Michael Hoog'	see *A. rosenorum* 'Michael H. Hoog'
	- 'Purple King'	CRos GKev LAma LRHS NRHS NRog
	- 'White Empress' PBR	CRos EBee LRHS NRHS NRog
	kansuense	see *A. sikkimense*
	karataviense ♀H5	CAby CAvo CRos EBee ECha ELan EPot GAbr GKev LAma LCro LOPS LRHS LSun NHpl NLar NRHS NRog SCob SDeJ SWvt
	- subsp. ***henrikii***	LAma NRog WCot
	- 'Ivory Queen'	CAby CAvo CTca EBee ECha EPfP ERCP GKev LAma LCro LOPS LRHS LSRN NHpl NLar NRHS NRog SCob SDeJ SDir SPlb WWFP
	- red- and pink-flowered **new**	GKev
	kharputense	NRog
	komarovianum	see *A. thunbergii*
	komarovii	GKev LAma NRog
	lacunosum	NRog
	- var. ***lacunosum***	NRog
	ledebourianum	GKev LAma NRog SPhx
	lemmonii	NRog
	lenkoranicum	LAma NRog WCot
	litvinovii	EBee LAma NRog WCot
	loratum	EBee LAma NRog
	- 'Marshmellow' **new**	GKev
	'Lucy Ball'	CRos EPfP ERCP GKev LAma LRHS NLar NRHS NRog SDeJ
§	***lusitanicum***	CBro CSpe ECha ERCP GKev NBre NDov NRog SRms XSen
§	***macleanii***	CRos EBee EPfP GKev LAma LRHS NRHS NRog
	macranthum	CSpe EBee GKev LAma NHpl NRog WCot
	mairei	CRos EHyd LAma LRHS MMuc NRHS NRya
§	- var. ***amabile***	GEdr LEdu NRya NSla WThu
	maximowiczii	GKev NHpl
	- white-flowered	LAma
	'Mercurius' PBR	EBee GKev LAma NRog SDeJ SPhx WCot
	'Metallic Shine' **new**	ERCP GKev LAma
	meteoricum	GKev NRog WCot
	'Miami'	CRos EBee ERCP GKev LAma LRHS NRHS NRog SDeJ SDir SPhx
	'Millennium'	WCot
	moly	CAgr CWCL GKev LAma LCro LOPS MRav NRog NRya SCob SDeJ SRms WCot XLum
	- 'Jeannine' ♀H5	CMea CRos EBee EPot GKev IRob LAma LRHS NRHS NRog
	'Mont Blanc'	CMea CRos EBee ELan ERCP GBin GKev ILea LAma LRHS NLar NRHS NRog SCob SPhx
	moschatum **new**	GKev
	multibulbosum	see *A. nigrum*
	murrayanum misapplied	see *A. unifolium*
	murrayanum Regel	see *A. acuminatum*
	myrianthum	NRog
	narcissiflorum misapplied	see *A. insubricum*
§	***narcissiflorum*** Vill.	CSpe GCal LEdu MNrw NWad
	neapolitanum	CAgr CRos EPot GKev LAma LRHS NRHS NRog SEND SRms WGwG
§	- Cowanii Group	CRav CRos GKev LCro LOPS LRHS NRHS NRog SDeJ WCot
§	***neriniflorum***	WAbe
	nevii	NRog
	nevskianum	GKev LAma NRog
§	***nigrum***	CArg CAvo CBWd CBro CDor CRos ECha EHrv EPfP EPot ERCP GKev GWyn IBoy LAma LCro LOPS LRHS MCot NPer NRHS NRog SCob SDeJ SDir SPhx WCot WRHF
	- f. ***roseum***	CBro
	nutans	GKev IRob LAma LEdu MHer NRog SMHy SRms WHal
	nuttallii	see *A. drummondii*
§	***obliquum***	CAvo CBro CSpe ECha EPri ERCP GEdr GKev MNHC NRog SDeJ SPhx WCot
	ochotense	WCot
	odorum L.	see *A. ramosum* L.
	oleraceum	WHer
	olympicum	NRog
§	***oreophilum***	CRos CSam ECha GJos GKev LAma LCro LOPS LRHS NRHS NRog SRms WCot
	- 'Agalik Giant'	NRog
	- 'Samur'	WCot
	- 'Zwanenburg' ♀H5	EPot
	orientale	GKev NRog
	oschaninii	LAma NRog
	'Ostara'	ERCP GKev
	ostrowskianum	see *A. oreophilum*
	ovalifolium var. ***leuconeurum***	GEdr WCot
	pallasii	NRog
	pallens	CBre
§	***paniculatum***	LAma NRog
*	- var. ***minor***	GKev LAma NRog
	paradoxum	LEdu
	- var. ***normale***	CBro EPot EWld GKev NRog WCot
	parciflorum	GKev NRog
	parvum	NRog
	pedemontanum	see *A. narcissiflorum* Vill.
	pendulinum	GKev NRog

	'Pinball Wizard'	CAvo CRos CTca CWCL EHyd ERCP GKev LAma LRHS NRHS NRog
	'Ping Pong'	EBee
	'Pink Jewel'	CAvo CTca EBee ERCP GKev LAma NRog SPhx WCot
	platycaule	LAma NRog WCot
	plummerae	EBee GKev NRog
	plurifoliatum	LAma
	polyphyllum	see *A. carolinianum*
	'Powder Puff'	CAvo CTca EBee GKev LAma
	prattii	EBee
	protensum	NRog
	przewalskianum	LAma NRog SBch
	pskemense	LAma NRog WCot
	pulchellum	see *A. carinatum* subsp. *pulchellum*
	'Purple Rain'	CRav CRos CWCL ELan ERCP GKev LAma LRHS NRHS NRog SDeJ WCot WRHF
	'Purple Suze'	LAma
	pyrenaicum misapplied	see *A. angulosum*
	pyrenaicum ambig.	SEND
	pyrenaicum Costa & Vayr.	XSen
	ramosum Jacq.	see *A. obliquum*
§	***ramosum*** L.	GKev LAma LEdu NRog
	'Red Eye'	EBee SDir SPhx
	'Rien Poortvliet'	GKev LAma
	roborowskianum	GKev
	robustum	NRog
	rosenbachianum misapplied	see *A. stipitatum*
	rosenbachianum Regel	CBro CRos LRHS NRHS
	- 'Akbulak'	CRos GKev LRHS NRHS
	- 'Album'	CRos EPfP GKev LAma LRHS NRHS NRog WCot
	- 'Michael Hoog'	see *A. rosenorum* 'Michael H. Hoog'
	- 'Shing'	GKev LAma
§	***rosenorum*** 'Michael H. Hoog'	CRos EPot GKev LAma LRHS NRHS NRog
	roseum	CMea CRos EAJP GKev LAma LCro LOPS LRHS NRHS NRog SCob SDeJ XLum
	- ***albiflorum***	GMcL
	rotundum	GKev
§	- subsp. ***jajlae***	LAma NRog WCot
	'Round and Purple'	CAvo CRos ERCP GKev LAma LRHS NRHS NRog
	rupestre	GKev
	sarawschanicum	NRog
	sativum	ENfk NPri SPoG SRms
	- 'Elephant'	see *A. ampeloprasum* 'Elephant'
	- var. ***ophioscorodon***	GKev GPoy LAma SPlb
	saxatile	GKev NRog WCot
	- pink-flowered	GKev
	schmitzii	LEdu
	schoenoprasum	Widely available
	- f. ***albiflorum***	ECha GKev LEdu MHer SRms
	- 'Black Isle Blush'	EBee GPoy LEdu MHer WPGP
	- 'Colesbourne Giant'	EBee LEdu
	- 'Corsican White'	LEdu XSen
	- 'Elbe'	LEdu
	- fine-leaved	GQue
	- 'Forescate'	CRos ECha GKev LAma LEdu LRHS MHer MRav NRHS SRms WAul XLum
	- medium-leaved	NPri
	- 'Pink Perfection'	GPoy IRob LEdu MHer NDov
	- 'Polar Bere' **new**	LEdu
	- PROFUSION ('Sterile') **new**	LEdu
	- 'Rising Star' **new**	XSen
	- 'Shining Silver'	LEdu
	- var. ***sibiricum***	WShi
	- 'Silver Chimes'	CAvo EBee MRav
	- thick-leaved	SRms
	schubertii ♀^{H4}	CAvo CBod CRav CRos CSpe CTca CWCL EHyd ELan EPfP EPot ERCP GKev GMcL LAma LCro LOPS LRHS MJak MNHC NRHS NRog SCob SDeJ SPer SPhx WCot WFar WWFP
	- 'Magic' **new**	LAma
	scorodoprasum	EBWF LAma
	- 'Art'	ERCP GKev LAma NRog
	- subsp. ***jajlae***	see *A. rotundum* subsp. *jajlae*
	- 'Passion'	ERCP GKev LAma NRog
	- 'Purple Caila'	GKev
	- subsp. ***scorodoprasum***	NRog
	senescens	CBro CRos CTca CTri EDAr EPot GJos GKev GNew IMou LAma LEdu LRHS MRav NRHS SBch SRms WBrk XLum XSen
§	- subsp. ***glaucum***	CAvo CMea CPBP CRos CSpe CTal EBee ECha EDAr EWTr GKev LEdu LRHS NDov NGdn NLar NRHS NRog NRya SEND WCot WHoo XSen
	- subsp. ***senescens***	GKev LEdu NRog WPGP
	serra	WCot
	sewerzowii	NRog
	shelkovnikovii	CTal GKev
	sibthorpianum	see *A. paniculatum*
	siculum	see *Nectaroscordum siculum*
§	***sikkimense***	CRos EBee EWTr GEdr GKev LRHS MHer MMuc NHpl NRHS NSla WCot
	'Silver Spring'	CRav EPot ERCP GKev IPot MNrw NRog SDeJ SDir
	sphaerocephalon	Widely available
	- subsp. ***arvense***	NRog WCot
	'Spider'	CRav CWCL EBee EPot ERCP GKev IBoy ILea LAma LRHS NRog SPhx WCot
I	***splendens*** var. ***kurilense***	GEdr
	stamineum W&B BGF-2	WCot
	'Statos'	CRos EBee GKev LAma LRHS NRHS WCot
	stellatum	CRos LRHS NRHS NRog SPhx WGwG
	stellerianum	GKev
	- var. ***kurilense***	NRya WAbe WThu
§	***stipitatum***	GKev LAma NRog WCot
	- 'Album'	NRog
	- 'Mars'	CRos EBee GKev GMcL LAma LRHS NRHS NRog
	- 'Mount Everest'	CAvo CBro CRav CRos CTca EPfP EPot ERCP ETMg GKev GMaP GWyn ILea LAma LCro LOPS LRHS LSRN MJak NRHS NRog SDeJ SDir SPer SPhx
	- 'Violet Beauty'	CCse CRav CRos CWCL GKev LAma LCro LOPS LRHS MWat NRHS WCot WRHF
	- 'White Giant'	CRos CWCL EBee ERCP GKev LAma LRHS NRHS NRog
	stracheyi	WCot
	subhirsutum	GKev NRog XLum
	subvillosum	EPot GKev NRog
	'Summer Beauty'	see *A. lusitanicum*
	'Summer Drummer'	CBWd CTca EPfP ERCP GKev LRHS NRog SDeJ SDir SPhx WCot

suworowii	GKev NRog
'Sweet Discovery'	LAma NRog
taquetii	see *A. thunbergii*
tauricola	GKev NRog
texanum	GKev LAma NRog
§ ***thunbergii*** ♀H5	EBee EPot LAma MHer NRog NRya SPhx WAbe
- PAB 3821	LEdu
- 'Album'	NRya WAbe
- 'Ozawa'	EBee GEdr SRms WAbe WCot
tibeticum	see *A. sikkimense*
tolmiei var. ***platyphyllum***	NRog
- var. ***tolmiei***	NRog
triquetrum	ELan EPot GKev LAma LEdu SEND WCot WHer WMoo WPnP XLum
tschimganicum	EBee LAma NRog SPhx
tuberosum	CAgr CAvo CBro CFGn CHby CRos CTca ECha ENfk GKev GPoy LAma LEdu LRHS MHer MMuc MNHC NGdn NPol NRHS NRog SDeJ SEND SPoG SRms SVic WCot XAbr XLum XSen
- B&SWJ 8881	WCru
- purple/mauve-flowered	CHby
- 'White Dwarf'	GKev SPhx WCot
tuncelianum	GKev WCot
umbilicatum	GKev NRog
§ ***unifolium*** ♀H4	CAvo CMea CRav EBee EPfP EPot ERCP GKev GWyn IBoy LAma LCro LOPS MRav NPer NQui NRog SDeJ SEND SRms WCot
ursinum	CHab CHby CWld EBWF ENfk GJos GKev GPoy LAma LEdu MHer MMuc NPoe NPri NRog SRms WSFF WShi XAbr XLum
validum NNS 06-41	WCot
victorialis 'Cantabria'	EBee GKev NRog WCot
vineale	EBWF WHer
- PAB 2763	LEdu
- 'Dready'	ERCP GKev LAma NRog
§ - 'Hair'	CRos ERCP GKev LAma LRHS NPer NRHS NRog SCob SDeJ SDir
violaceum	see *A. carinatum*
virgunculae	CMea CPBP EDAr GEdr WAbe
- f. ***albiflorum*** new	GEdr
wallichii	EBee EPot EWes LEdu LLHF MBNS NChi WCot XLum
- CLD 1500	NBid
- PAB 2976	LEdu WPGP
- PAB 9191	LEdu
- dark-flowered	LPla WCot WFar
'White Cloud'	EBee GKev XEll
'World Cup'	LAma
woronowii	GKev NRog SDir
zaprjagajevii	WCot
zebdanense	EBee GKev LAma NRog

almond see *Prunus dulcis*

Alniphyllum (*Styracaceae*)

eberhardtii FMWJ 13121	WCru
fortunei FMWJ 13013	WCru

Alnus ✿ (*Betulaceae*)

sp.	LPra
cordata ♀H5	Widely available
cremastogyne	EBtc
fauriei from Niigata, Japan	CSto
firma	CSto
formosana	IArd
glutinosa	Widely available
- 'Aurea'	CDul CEnd MGos
- var. ***barbata***	CSto
- 'Imperialis' ♀H6	CCVT CDul CEnd CLnd CTho EBee ECrN ELan EMOT EPfP ESps EWTr IDee MBlu MMuc MPkF NLar NOra SCob SGol SPer SPoG WHar WTSh
- 'Laciniata'	CCVT CDul CMac CTho ECrN MGos NLar WMou
- 'Pyramidalis'	CDul
hirsuta	CSto
incana	CBcs CCVT CDul CLnd CMCN CPer CSto CTho ECrN EMOT ESps LBuc LMaj LPra MGos NLar SCob SGol SPer WHar WMou WTSh
- 'Aurea' ♀H6	Widely available
- 'Laciniata'	ELan ESps NLar SCoo WFar WMou
- 'Pendula'	CDul CTho
japonica	MBlu
maximowiczii	CSto
- from Ulleungdo	WCru
nitida	EBtc
oregana	see *A. rubra*
pendula B&SWJ 10895	WCru
rhombifolia	EBtc
§ ***rubra***	CDul CMCN CPer CTho ELan MCoo WTSh
- f. ***pinnatisecta***	CMCN MBlu
serrulata new	CMCN
sieboldiana	CSto EBee GKev WCru
× ***spaethii***	EWTr LMaj LPra MBlu
subcordata	CSto
- NJM 13.009	EBee WPGP
viridis	CAgr CSto MCoo WTSh
- subsp. ***sinuata***	CAgr CSto

Alocasia (*Araceae*)

× ***amazonica*** ♀H1a	XBlo
- 'Polly'	LCro NLos
'Bambino' (Bambino Series)	NLos
'Black Velvet'	NLos
'Calidora'	CDTJ EUJe NLos
cucullata	NLos XBlo
macrorrhiza	CDTJ EUJe NLos SBig
odora	EUJe XBlo
plumbea	XBlo
'Portodora'	NLos
wentii	NLos
zebrina	NLos

Aloe ✿ (*Asphodelaceae*)

africana	CAbb
arborescens	CDTJ CPbh EShb EUJe NLos SEND
- 'Variegata' (v) ♀H1c	SRms
aristata ♀H3	CCac EUJe NLos SArc SChr SEND SPad SPlb XLum
- 'Cathedral Peak'	SChr
- 'Green Pearl' PBR	SMad
aristata × ***striatula***	CCac
barbadensis	see *A. vera*
barberae	CCCN CPbh
boylei	CPbh
brevifolia ♀H2	CAbb CPbh EShb SArc
broomii	CAbb CCCN CPbh SPlb
camperi 'Maculata'	SEND
ciliaris	CCac CHll EShb SChr
'Cleopatra'	WCot
comptonii	CAbb
cooperi	CCCN CDTJ
descoingsii ♀H1b	LToo

dichotoma	CAbb CPbh SPlb
'Doran Black'	LToo
ecklonis	CBlu CCCN SPlb
erinacea	LToo
ferox	CAbb CBod CCCN CDTJ CPbh SBig
fosteri	CDTJ
greatheadii var. ***davyana***	SChr SPlb
humilis	SChr SEND
juvenna	SRms
kedongensis	SEND
krapohliana	CAbb
lineata	CAbb
littoralis	CAbb
maculata	CDTJ
marlothii	CAbb CCCN SPlb
melanacantha	CAbb
microstigma	CCCN CPbh
millotii	LToo
mitriformis	NGBl SChr SEND
mutabilis	SChr SEND
peglerae	SRms
petricola	CAbb
plicatilis ♀H2	CBlu CCCN CDTJ EShb LToo
pluridens	CAbb
polyphylla ♀H3	CBlu CCCN CCac CDTJ CPbh LToo MHer WPGP
pratensis	CCCN CDTJ
rauhii ♀H1b	CPbh LToo
'Red Dragon' new	LToo
reitzii	CAbb CBlu CPbh SPlb
saundersiae new	LToo
'Snowflake'	NLos
somaliensis ♀H1b	LToo NLos
speciosa	CAbb
spicata	CAbb
× ***spinosissima***	SChr
striata	CAbb CBlu CCCN CPbh EShb EUJe SPlb
striatula ♀H3	CAbb CBrP CCac CDTJ CSam CTca ETod EUJe IBlr LEdu SArc SBig SChr SEND SMad SPlb SVen WCot WPGP
- var. ***caesia***	WPGP
succotrina	CAbb
suprafoliata	CAbb CBlu
thraskii	CAbb
variegata (v) ♀H1b	EShb LSun NLos
§ ***vera*** ♀H1b	CCCN CSpe ELan ESps GPoy LCro MHer MNHC NPer NPla NPri SChr SEND SMad SPlb SPre SRms SVic XAbr
wickensii	SPlb
yavellana	SPlb

Aloe × *Gasteria* see × *Gasteraloe*

Aloinopsis × *Nananthus* (*Aizoaceae*)

A. spathulata × ***N. transvaalensis*** new	CPBP

Alonsoa (*Scrophulariaceae*)

'Bright Spark'	CSpe
incisifolia	CCCN CSpe
meridionalis	CCCN
- 'Rebel'	CBod CPla ECtt SRkn
'Pink Beauty'	CSpe
warscewiczii	CCCN MSCN
- 'Peachy-keen'	CSpe

Alopecurus (*Poaceae*)

alpinus	see *A. magellanicus*
§ ***magellanicus***	ELan GBin
pratensis	CHab EBWF
- 'Aureovariegatus' (v)	CTri EHoe EPPr EShb GMaP GMcL NBid SPer SRms
- 'Aureus'	NBro SPlb
- 'No Overtaking' (v)	EPPr

Alophia (*Iridaceae*)

lahue	see *Herbertia lahue*

Aloysia (*Verbenaceae*)

chamaedryfolia	EBee EPfP LRHS
citriodora	see *A. citrodora*
§ ***citrodora*** ♀H3	Widely available
- 'Spilsbury Mint'	ELan
triphylla	see *A. citrodora*

Alpinia (*Zingiberaceae*)

japonica	CExl LEdu
- B&SWJ 8889	WCru
- PAB 6441	LEdu
nutans misapplied	see *A. zerumbet*
speciosa	see *A. zerumbet*
§ ***zerumbet***	XBlo
- 'Variegata' (v)	NLos XBlo

Alsobia see *Episcia*

Alstroemeria ✿ (*Alstroemeriaceae*)

sp.	ESps NRHS
'Adonis'PBR	WViv
'Aimi'	ELan MNrw SWvt WViv
'Alexis'PBR	WViv
'Aliénor' (Midi Series)	LPmr XTur
'Amarillo'	WViv
'Andigné' (Garden Series)	XTur
'Angelina'	CTsd SWvt
'Anne' (Midi Series)	XTur
'Antoine' (Maxi Series)	XTur
'Apollo' ♀H4	CRav CTsd EHyd ELan LRHS MNrw NBre NRHS SWvt WViv
'Arthur' (Maxi Series)	XTur
'Athena'	WViv
'Aubance' (Garden Series)	XTur
aurantiaca	see *A. aurea*
§ ***aurea***	CPla GWyn MRav SRms XLum
- 'Apricot'	GCal
- 'Lutea'	GKev LPmr NLar SDeJ SPlb
- 'Orange King'	ELan EPfP EWTr GKev LPmr NLar SDeJ
'Authion' (Garden Series)	XTur
'Avanti'	EHyd ELan LRHS NRHS WViv
'Avrillé' (Garden Series)	XTur
'Baracé' (Garden Series)	LPmr WHlf XTur
'Baugé' (Garden Series)	XTur
'Béatrice' (Midi Series)	XTur
'Blushing Bride'	CTsd SWvt WViv
'Bodega'PBR	WViv
'Bolero'	WViv
'Bonanza'	WViv
brasiliensis	CTsd GCal SBrt SHar WCot WRHF WSHC WViv XLum
- 'Cally Star' (v)	EBee GCal NLar
'Brezé' (Garden Series)	XTur
'Briançon' (Garden Series)	WHlf XTur
Butterfly hybrids	ETMg
'Cahors' (Planet Series) ♀H4	LCro LOPS
'Camille' (Mini Series)	LPmr XTur
'Candé' (Garden Series)	XTur
'Candy'	WViv

	'Candy Floss'	ELan EPfP
	'Caroline' (Midi Series)	LPmr XTur
	'Charles' (Maxi Series)	XTur
	'Charlotte' (Mini Series) **new**	XTur
	'Charm'	CRav CTsd WSpi WViv
	'Chartrené' (Garden Series)	XTur
	'Chi Chi'	WCot
	'Chinon' (Garden Series)	XTur
	'Chloé' (Mini Series)	XTur
§	'Christina'[PBR]	ELan SWvt WViv
	'Christine' (Midi Series)	XTur
	'Christine Marsh'	WViv
	'Cindy'	WViv
	'Coronet' ♀[H4]	WViv
	'Dandy Candy'	CBod EBee ECtt EHyd LLWG LRHS MHol NGdn NLar WBrk WCot
	'Davina'[PBR]	NLar
	'Dayspring Delight' (v)	GCal MNrw
§	DIANA, PRINCESS OF WALES ('Stablaco')	CRos EHyd LRHS NRHS
	'Diane' (Midi Series)	XTur
	diluta subsp. ***chrysantha*** F&W 8700	WCot
	Doctor Salter's hybrids	SRms
	'Dorothée' (Midi Series)	LPmr XTur
	'Douceur d'Automne'	WHlf
	'Eleanor'	WViv
	'Elvira'	CRav ELan MNrw WViv
	'Etna'[PBR]	WViv
	'Evening Song'	EHyd LRHS MNrw NRHS SWvt
	exserens	WCot
	'Flaming Star'	CRav LSvl WViv
	'Fougeré' (Garden Series)	LPmr XTur
	'Frances' (v)	CAvo CBro
	'François' (Maxi Series)	XTur
	'Freedom'	CBod CNor CWGN ECtt ELon LSou MHol NEgg NLar NSti SCob SMad SPoG WCot
	'Friendship' ♀[H5]	CRav CTsd EHyd ELan LRHS NBre NRHS SWvt WViv
	'Gaspard' (Mini Series)	LPmr XTur
	'Georges' (Maxi Series)	XTur
	'Gloria'	LRHS NRHS SWvt WViv
	'Glory of the Andes' (v)	CWGN NLar
	'Golden Delight'	EHyd ELan LRHS MNrw NRHS WViv
I	'Hatch Hybrid'	GCal
	'Hawera'	GBin GCal IRob
	'Héloïse' (Mini Series)	XTur
	'Henri' (Maxi Series)	LPmr XTur
	INCA ADORE ('Koadore')	CExl
	INCA AVANTI ('Koncavanti'[PBR])	CWGN LBuc SCob WViv
	INCA AZURE ('Konazur'[PBR])	GBin WViv
	INCA CLASSIC ('Konclassic')	WViv
	INCA CORAL ('Konocoral')	IBoy WViv
	INCA DEVOTION ('Konevotio'[PBR])	NLar
	INCA DREAM ('Kodream')	WViv
	INCA EXOTICA ('Koexotica')	WViv
	INCA GLOW ('Koglow')	CBod CExl CWGN EHyd ELon GBin LRHS LSou MHol NLar NRHS SDeJ SRms WViv
	INCA GOAL ('Koncagoal')	CBcs CBod CPla WViv
	INCA HUSKY ('Konhusky')	CBcs CBod CPla CRos CWGN EHyd LRHS MHol NRHS SCob SPoG WViv
	INCA ICE ('Koice') (Inca Series)	CWGN NLar WViv
	INCA JOLI ('Koncajoli'[PBR])	LBuc WViv
	INCA LAKE ('Koncalake')	CWGN LBuc NRHS SCob WViv
	INCA LOLLY ('Koncalolly'[PBR]) (Inca Series)	WViv
	INCA MAMBO ('Koncamambo'[PBR])	NRHS WViv
	INCA MILK ('Koncamilk')	WViv
	INCA NOBLE ('Koncanoble')	WViv
	INCA OBSESSION ('Koobsion')	WViv
	INCA PULSE ('Konpulse'[PBR])	CWGN ELon GBin LSou NLar SDeJ SMad WViv
	INCA SERIN ('Koserin'[PBR])	CWGN WViv
	INCA SMILE ('Koncasmile'[PBR])	ETMg SCob WViv
	INCA SWEETY ('Koncasweet'[PBR])	WViv
	INCA TOTO ('Koncatoto'[PBR])	WViv
	INCA TROPIC ('Kotrop')	CExl CWGN WViv
	INCA VITO ('Koncavito'[PBR])	CBcs CBod CRos CWGN EHyd LRHS LSou MHol NLar NRHS SCob SPoG WViv
	INCA YUKO ('Koncayuko'[PBR])	CBod CRos CWGN EHyd LBuc LRHS LSou MHol NRHS SPoG WSpi WViv
	INDIAN SUMMER ('Tesronto'[PBR])	CBod CRos CWGN ECtt EHyd EPfP ETMg LPmr LRHS NRHS NSti SPoG WCot WFar WViv
	INTICANCHA ANTARCTICA ('Tesantarc'[PBR])	WViv
	INTICANCHA BRYCE ('Tesbryce'[PBR])	LPmr LSou WFar WViv
	INTICANCHA CABANA ('Tescaban') **new**	CBod CRos EHyd LSou NRHS
	INTICANCHA CREAMY DARK PINK ('Tescreda')	SDeJ WViv
	INTICANCHA DARK PURPLE ('Tesdarklin'[PBR])	EWTr IBoy LPmr MHol WFar WViv
	INTICANCHA IMALA ('Tesima'[PBR]) **new**	CRos EHyd NRHS
	INTICANCHA INDIGO ('Tesindie') **new**	CBod MHol
	INTICANCHA KANIKA ('Tesikani') **new**	CRos EHyd NRHS
	INTICANCHA MACHU ('Tesmach'[PBR])	WFar WViv
	INTICANCHA MAYA ('Tesmaya'[PBR])	CRos CWGN ECtt EHyd LRHS NRHS WFar WViv
	INTICANCHA NAVAYO ('Tesnava'[PBR])	ECtt LPmr LSou MHol WFar
	INTICANCHA PASSION ('Tespassion'[PBR])	CRos ECtt EHyd LRHS LSou NRHS WViv
	INTICANCHA PURPLE ('Tespurplin'[PBR])	CWGN WFar WViv
	INTICANCHA RED ('Tesrobin'[PBR])	CWGN EBee LPmr WFar WViv
	INTICANCHA SUNDAY ('Tessunday'[PBR])	WViv
	INTICANCHA SUNLIGHT ('Tessunlight'[PBR])	ECtt LSou WFar WViv
	INTICANCHA SUNSHINE ('Tesshine') **new**	LSou MHol
	INTICANCHA WHITE PINK BLUSH ('Tesblushin'[PBR])	CRos EHyd NRHS WFar WViv
	INTICANCHA WHITE PINK HEART ('Tesheartin')	LPmr
	ISABELLA ('Stalis')	LSRN
§	***isabellana***	WCru
	'Isabelle' (Midi Series)	XTur
	'Jacques' (Maxi Series)	XTur

'Jalesne' (Garden Series)	XTur
'Jazze Purple Rose' (Jazze Series)	GMcL
'Joséphine' (Midi Series)	XTur
'Junon' (Planet Series)	LCro
'Laguna'	WViv
LAURA ('Stalauli'PBR)	ECtt SCob
'Layon' (Garden Series)	LPmr XTur
'Léo' (Mini Series)	LPmr XTur
ligtu hybrids	CAvo CBcs ECha EPfP GKev LCro LOPS MNrw NPer SDeJ SRms SWvt WBrk WHoo XLum
– var. ***ligtu***	SMHy
'Liré' (Garden Series)	XTur
'Little Eleanor'	EHyd LRHS NRHS WViv
'Little Miss Catherine'	WViv
'Little Miss Christina'	see *A.* 'Christina'
'Little Miss Davina'	EHyd LRHS NRHS WViv
'Little Miss Emily'	WViv
'Little Miss Gina'	WViv
'Little Miss Isabel'	WViv
'Little Miss Jessica'	WViv
'Little Miss Lucy'	WViv
'Little Miss Matilda'	WViv
'Little Miss Miranda'	WViv
'Little Miss Natalie'	see *A.* 'Natalie'
'Little Miss Rosanna'	WViv
'Little Miss Roselind'	see *A.* 'Roselind'
'Little Miss Sophie'	see *A.* 'Sophie'
'Little Miss Tara'	see *A.* 'Tara'
'Little Miss Veronica'	WViv
'Longué' (Garden Series)	WHlf XTur
'Louis' (Maxi Series)	XTur
'Louise' (Midi Series)	LSRN XTur
'Lucas' (Mini Series) **new**	XTur
'Lucca'	WViv
'Lucinda'	SWvt WViv
'Maestro'PBR	WViv
'Marcé' (Garden Series)	XTur
'Marguerite' (Midi Series)	LPmr XTur
'Marie' (Midi Series)	XTur
'Marissa'	GMaP IBoy
'Mars' (Planet Series)	CRos EHyd LRHS NRHS
'Mathilde' (Midi Series)	LPmr NLar XTur
'Mauve Majesty'	ECtt ELon IBoy ILea LLWG LRHS MHol NLar SPoG WCot WViv
'Mazé' (Garden Series)	LPmr XTur
'Montsoreau' (Garden Series)	LPmr XTur
'Moulin Rouge'	ELan WViv
§ 'Natalie'PBR	CSBt EHyd LRHS NRHS WViv
'Neptune'	LCro
'Nicolas' (Maxi Series)	LPmr XTur
'Noah' (Mini Series) **new**	XTur
'Océane' (Mini Series)	XTur
'Orange Glory' ♀H4	EHyd ELon GMaP IBoy LRHS NRHS SWvt WViv
'Orange Supreme'	EHyd LRHS NRHS WViv
'Oriana' ♀H4	SWvt WViv
pallida	SPlb
'Pandora'PBR	WViv
patagonica	WAbe
'Perfect Orange'	WViv
'Philippe' (Maxi Series)	XTur
philippii	WCot
'Phoenix' (v) ♀H4	SWvt WViv
'Pink Lady'	WViv
'Pink Perfection'	NLar
'Pink Sensation'	LRHS NRHS WViv
'Polka'	WViv
presliana RB 94103	WCot
PRINCESS AMINA ('Zapriamin'PBR)	CBcs CRos EHyd LRHS NRHS SPoG WViv
PRINCESS ANGELA ('Staprilan')	ELan
PRINCESS ANOUSKA ('Zaprinous'PBR)	NLar WViv
PRINCESS ARIANE ('Zapriari'PBR)	CBcs WViv
PRINCESS BEATRIX ('Stadoran')	SChr
PRINCESS CAMILLA ('Stapricamil')	CRos EHyd LRHS NRHS SPoG
PRINCESS CLAIRE ('Zapriclair'PBR)	CBcs CRos EHyd LRHS NRHS
PRINCESS DANIELA ('Stapridani')	SCoo
PRINCESS DIANA	see *A.* DIANA, PRINCESS OF WALES ('Stablaco'), *A.* PRINCESS DIANA ('Zapridapal')
§ PRINCESS DIANA ('Zapridapal'PBR)	EHyd WViv
PRINCESS ELIANE ('Zaprielia'PBR)	CRos EHyd LRHS NRHS WViv
PRINCESS FABIANA ('Zaprifabi'PBR)	CBcs CRos EHyd LRHS NLar NRHS SPoG WViv
PRINCESS FREDERIKA ('Stabronza')	ECha MCot
PRINCESS ISABELLA ('Zapribel'PBR)	EHyd LRHS LSRN NRHS WViv
PRINCESS IVANA ('Staprivane'PBR)	SPoG
PRINCESS JULIETA ('Zaprijul'PBR)	IBoy NLar
PRINCESS KATE ('Zaprikate'PBR)	CBcs CRos EHyd LRHS NRHS
PRINCESS LETIZIA ('Zaprilet'PBR)	CBcs CRos EHyd LRHS NRHS SPoG
PRINCESS LILIAN ('Zaprilian'PBR)	CBcs CRos EBee EHyd LRHS NRHS WViv
PRINCESS LOUISE ('Zaprilou'PBR)	CRos EHyd LRHS LSRN NRHS WViv
PRINCESS MARGARET ('Staprimar')	NLar
PRINCESS MARILENE ('Staprilene'PBR)	WViv
PRINCESS MARY ('Zaprimary'PBR)	NLar
PRINCESS MATHILDE ('Zaprimat'PBR)	CRos EHyd LRHS NRHS WViv
PRINCESS OXANA ('Staprioxa'PBR)	EBee
PRINCESS PAOLA ('Stapripal'PBR)	CBcs CRos EHyd LRHS NRHS SCoo SPoG WViv
PRINCESS SARA ('Staprisara'PBR)	CBcs CRos EHyd EPfP LRHS NRHS SPoG WViv
PRINCESS SUSANA ('Staprisusa')	SCoo
PRINCESS THERESA ('Zapriteres'PBR)	EPfP NLar
PRINCESS ZAVINA ('Staprivina'PBR)	NLar SPoG
pseudospathulata	WCot
§ ***psittacina***	CAvo CBro CHll CMea CPne CSam CTsd ECha EHrv ELan EPfP GBin GCal MCot MHer SHar SRms WAvo WBrk WFar WViv XLum
– 'Mona Lisa'	CBod XLum
– 'Royal Star' (v)	CAby CBod CBro CExl CWCL EHyd ELan ELon EPfP EPri EWTr LRHS

	MPie NRHS SHar SPhm SPoG SRms WCot WHoo WSHC WSpi XLum
pulchella Sims	see *A. psittacina*
'Purple Rain'	ELan SWvt WViv
'Querré' (Garden Series)	XTur
'Red Beauty' (v)	see *A.* 'Spitfire'
'Red Beauty'	EHyd ELan GMaP LRHS NRHS SWvt
'Red Elf' 🏆H4	IBoy SMHy SWvt WViv
'René' (Maxi Series)	XTur
'Rhubarb and Custard'	ELan EPfP
'Rivale'	LCro
ROCK 'N' ROLL ('Alsdun01' PBR) (v)	CBod CDor EBee EPfP ETMg LCro LOPS MHol MNrw SPoG WCot WViv
§ 'Roselind'	CSBt ELan SWvt WViv
'Rosie' (Mini Series)	XTur
'Roxane' (Mini Series) **new**	XTur
'Saturne' (Planet Series)	EPfP LCro LOPS
'Sedna' (Planet Series) **new**	LCro LOPS
'Segré' (Garden Series)	LPmr XTur
'Selina'	CRos EHyd IRob LRHS MNrw NBre NRHS WViv
'Serenade'	ELan WViv
'Serrant' (Garden Series)	XTur
'Sirius' (Planet Series) 🏆H4	LCro LOPS
'Sonata' 🏆H4	WViv
§ 'Sophie' PBR	ELan SWvt WViv
§ 'Spitfire' (v) 🏆H4	CRos EHyd EPfP IBoy LRHS NRHS SWvt WCot WViv
'Strawberry Lace'	EBee ELan EPfP
'Summer Breeze'	CRos ECtt EHyd ETMg LPmr LRHS LSou NRHS WViv
'Summer Party' **new**	CRos ECtt EHyd NRHS
'Summertime'	WViv
'Sunstar'	GMaP
'Sweet Laura' PBR	CBod ECtt ELan ELon LEdu LRHS LSRN MHol MNrw MPie NEgg NGdn NLar NSti SMad SPoG WCot WHar WSpi WViv
'Tangerine Tango'	WViv
'Tanya'	MNrw WViv
§ 'Tara' PBR	CSBt ELan NLar SWvt WViv
'Tessa' 🏆H4	CRav CRos EHyd LRHS NBre NRHS WViv
'Thorigné' (Garden Series)	XTur
'Tiercé' (Garden Series)	LPmr XTur
'Timoté' (Mini Series) **new**	XTur
'Turkish Delight'	EPfP
'Ventura'	WViv
'Venus' (Planet Series)	LCro LOPS
'William' (Maxi Series)	LPmr XTur
'Yellow Friendship' 🏆H4	IRob MNrw NLar SWvt WViv
'Yellow Queen'	IBoy
'Zoé' (Mini Series)	XTur

Alternanthera (*Amaranthaceae*)

reineckii	XBlo
- 'Lilacina'	XBlo
I - 'Rosaefolia'	XBlo

Althaea (*Malvaceae*)

armeniaca	EBee GCal WCot
cannabina	CAby CFis CSpe ELan EPPr GCal IBoy IPot MAvo MHer MMuc MNrw NGBl SHar SPhx WBor WCot WHal WHil WOld WSHC
officinalis	CBod CHab EBWF ELan ENfk EPPr GPoy MAvo MHer MMuc MNHC NLar SRms WHer WSpi XAbr XLum XSen
- ***alba***	LSou
§ - 'Romney Marsh'	MAvo MRav WFar WKif
rosea	see *Alcea rosea*
rugosostellulata	see *Alcea rugosa*

Altingia (*Hamamelidaceae*)

poilanei B&SWJ 11756	WCru

× *Alworthia* (*Asphodelaceae*)

'Black Gem'	EBee EPfP EShb EUJe

Alyogyne (*Malvaceae*)

§ ***huegelii***	CCCN EShb EUJe SEle SPlb
- 'Santa Cruz'	CCCN CHll CSam
MAGIC MOMENTS ('Hutwow' PBR)	CSpe CWGN SRkn

Alyssum (*Brassicaceae*)

aizoides Boiss.	CPla
montanum	ECha GJos SPlb SRms
§ - 'Berggold'	EPfP XLum
- MOUNTAIN GOLD	see *A. montanum* 'Berggold'
- 'Tekara'	CMea
oxycarpum	EPot
saxatile	see *Aurinia saxatilis*
- 'Summit'	SRms
spinosum	ESps GKev
- 'Roseum' 🏆H5	CMea CSpe CTri ECha ELan EPot ESps GCrg WAbe
* - 'Roseum Variegatum' (v)	GCrg
- 'Rubrum'	EPot
'Takara Yellow'	GWyn
tortuosum	SEND
'Variegatum' (v)	CBod
wulfenianum	EDAr GAbr GJos IFoB XLum

Amaranthus (*Amaranthaceae*)

'Autumn Palette'	CSpe
caudatus	LCro
- 'Viridis'	SPhx
hypochondriacus 'Pygmy Torch' 🏆H2	CSpe
'Red Army'	LCro
tricolor	SRms

× *Amarcrinum* (*Amaryllidaceae*)

'Dorothy Hannibal'	WCot
memoria-corsii	CPrp
- 'Howardii'	EPri EShb GKev LEdu NRog SDeJ WCot

× *Amarine* (*Amaryllidaceae*)

tubergenii Belladiva Series	CBro EBee ERCP LAma LCro LOPS LRHS
- - 'Anastasia' **new**	EBee ERCP GKev LAma
- - 'Aphrodite' **new**	EBee GKev LAma
- - 'Elvi' **new**	LAma
- - 'Emanuelle' PBR **new**	ERCP
- - 'Smilla' **new**	LAma
- 'Fletcheri'	WCot
- 'Zwanenburg'	GKev LAma WCot

× *Amarygia* (*Amaryllidaceae*)

§ ***bidwillii*** 'Alba'	CAvo CBro CPrp NRog WCot
- 'Rosea'	NRog WCot

Amaryllis (*Amaryllidaceae*)

§ ***belladonna*** 🏆H3	CAby CBcs CBod CBro CPne CPrp CTca CTsd EBee EPfP ERCP EShb

	GKev LAma LCro MPie NRog SDeJ SEND WCot WWFP
- 'Hathor'	CBro
- 'Johannesburg'	CBro WCot
- 'Kimberley'	CPne
- 'Parkeri Alba'	see × *Amarygia bidwillii* 'Alba'
- 'Purpurea'	WCot
- white-flowered	SDeJ

Ambrosina (*Araceae*)

bassii	WCot

Amelanchier ✿ (*Rosaceae*)

sp.	LPra
alnifolia	CTho EBtc ERea
- 'Forestburg'	MBlu NLar
- 'Jb30' (F) **new**	CAgr MCoo
- 'Martin' (F)	CAgr NOra
- 'Northline' (F)	CAgr MCoo NOra
- 'Obelisk' PBR	CAgr CDul CRos EBee EHyd ELan EMOT EPfP GKin GQue LBuc LLHF LRHS LSRN MAsh MCoo MGos MJak NLar NOra NPri SAko SCoo SPer SPoG WCot
- pink-fruited	NLar
§ - var. ***pumila***	MMrt WCot
- 'Regent' (F)	CAgr NLar
- 'Smokey'	CAgr CDul MBlu MCoo NLar NOra SPoG
- 'Thiessen' **new**	MCoo
§ ***arborea***	CTho LPra
- TRADITION ('Trazam')	NLar SAko
'Autumn Glory'	EPfP
bartramiana	SSta
- 'Eskimo'	EMOT NLar
canadensis K. Koch	see *A. lamarckii*
canadensis Sieb. & Zucc.	see *A. arborea*
canadensis ambig.	CAco CDul CFGn CTsd EMOT ESps GMcL IBoy IRob MMuc NEgg NOra NPri SCob SEND SEWo SPoG WFar WHar
canadensis (L.) Medik.	CAgr CJun CLnd CMac CRos CSBt CTho CTri EBee ECrN ELan EPfP LEdu LRHS MGos MRav MSwo SPer
§ - 'Glenn Form'	CEnd EMOT LRHS NLar NOra NRHS SGol SLim SPoG
- 'Prince William'	CAgr MCoo SGol
- RAINBOW PILLAR	see *A. canadensis* 'Glenn Form'
× ***grandiflora***	SCob
- 'Autumn Brilliance'	CEnd CJun EPfP MBlu NLar NRHS SGol
- 'Ballerina'	Widely available
- 'Cole's Select'	CAby LRHS SWvt
- 'Forest Prince'	NLar
- 'Princess Diana' 🏆H6	NLar SCoo
- 'Robin Hill' 🏆H6	Widely available
- 'Rubescens'	CEnd CJun EBee EUJe NLar SLon SWvt
'La Paloma' 🏆H6	EPfP LRHS LSRN MGos NOra SCoo SLim
laevis	CBcs CDul CTri EPfP LMaj NLar
- 'Prince Charles'	NLar
- 'R.J. Hilton' 🏆H6	EPfP LRHS NLar NOra SCoo
- 'Snow Cloud'	EPfP NRHS
- 'Snowflakes'	CEnd CJun EBee EMOT ESps LRHS LSRN MAsh NOra SEWo SLim SPer SPoG SWvt WMou
§ ***lamarckii*** 🏆H6	Widely available
ovalis misapplied	see *A. spicata* (Lam.) K. Koch
ovalis Medik.	SPlb
- 'Edelweiss'	CJun EWTr IArd MRav NEgg NLar SCoo
pumila	see *A. alnifolia* var. *pumila*
rotundifolia ambig.	CAgr MCoo NEgg
sanguinea 'Chimney Rock'	NLar
§ ***spicata*** (Lam.) K. Koch	CAgr MCoo
stolonifera	CTri

× *Amelasorbus* (*Rosaceae*)

raciborskiana	MBlu

Amicia (*Papilionaceae*)

zygomeris	CAbb CBcs CCse CDTJ CHGN CHll CSpe EUJe EWes GCal IPot MCot MGil SEle SMad SPhm SPhx SPoG WCot WPGP
- 'John's Big Splash' (v)	WCot

Ammi (*Apiaceae*)

majus 🏆H6	CBod CRav CSpe LCro LEdu LRHS MAvo MNHC SPav SPhx WCot WSFF
- 'Graceland' 🏆H6 **new**	SPhm
visnaga	see *Visnaga daucoides*

Ammocharis (*Amaryllidaceae*)

coranica	WCot
longifolia	WCot

Ammophila (*Poaceae*)

arenaria	CKno EBWF IMou XLum XSen
breviligulata	IMou XLum

Amomum (*Zingiberaceae*)

subulatum	SPre

Amomyrtus (*Myrtaceae*)

§ ***luma***	CBcs CTri CTsd EBee ELan LEdu MMuc SEND WPGP

Amorpha (*Papilionaceae*)

canescens	EBee LRHS MGil MNrw NRHS SPhx SPlb
fruticosa	CAco EBtc MBlu MGil MMuc SEND SPlb
herbacea	NLar
nana	XLum
ouachitensis	SMad
paniculata	NLar

Amorphophallus ✿ (*Araceae*)

sp.	SDir
albus	CDTJ LEdu SPlb WCot
bulbifer	CDTJ EUJe LAma LRHS NRHS SBig SDeJ SDir SPlb XLum
dunnii	CDTJ LEdu
henryi	WCot
kerrii	CExl WCot
kiusianus B&SWJ 4845	WCru
konjac	CDTJ CExl CFil CSpe CTal EUJe GCal LEdu LRHS NRHS SChF SDeJ SDir SPlb WCot XLum
nepalensis	WCot XLum
stipitatus	LEdu WCot
yuloensis	WCot

Ampelaster (*Asteraceae*)

§ ***carolinianus***	XEll

Ampelocalamus (*Poaceae*)

§ ***mocrophyllum*** ERod
scandens WPGP

Ampelocissus (*Vitaceae*)

sikkimensis HWJK 2066 WCru

Ampelodesmos (*Poaceae*)

mauritanicus CHid CKno CSam CSpe ECha EHoe EShb EWes MAvo SEND SMad SPlb WCot XSen

Ampelopsis (*Vitaceae*)

aconitifolia NLar WAvo WCru
- 'Chinese Lace' EBee EHyd EShb EUJe EWTr MRav NLar WBor

arborea WCru
brevipedunculata ELan MGil MMrt SCoo SLim SPer WHar
- 'Citrulloides' WCru
- 'Elegans' (v) CBcs CMac EBee EHyd ELan ELon EPfP EShb LRHS MGil MGos MMuc MRav NBro SNig SPer SPoG SWvt WAvo WCot WSHC

delavayana EShb MGil MMuc
glandulosa var. ***hancei*** B&SWJ 1793 WCru
henryana see *Parthenocissus henryana*
megalophylla CBot EShb GCal NLar
sempervirens hort. ex Veitch see *Cissus striata*
tricuspidata 'Veitchii' see *Parthenocissus tricuspidata* 'Veitchii'

Amphicome see *Incarvillea*

Amsonia (*Apocynaceae*)

'Blue Ice' CAby CBWd CBod CRos EBee ECha ECtt EMFm EPPr GMaP IBoy IPot IRob LEdu LPla LRHS LSun MHol MNrw NDov NPnk NRHS SCob SPad SPoG WCAu WCot WHil WRHF
ciliata IDee LEdu NLar SHar XLum
§ ***elliptica*** EBee EPPr SPhx
'Ernst Pagels' MAvo WCot
hubrichtii CAby CBWd CCse CHid CRos CSpe EBee ECha EPPr IPot LEdu LRHS LSun NDov NRHS SBrt SMHy SMad SPhx SWvt WCAu WPGP WPtf WSHC
illustris CRos CSpe EPPr GCal LEdu LRHS NLar NRHS SHar SMHy SPhx WHil WHoo
jonesii EBee SBrt SMHy SPhx
§ ***orientalis*** CHll CMea CRos CSpe CTri ECha GWyn IPot LEdu LRHS MCot MRav NDov NLar NRHS SPhx SVen SWvt WCot WFar WKif XEll XLum
- from Turkey **new** SMHy
- 'Cally Dark Stem' GCal

peeblesii SPhx
rigida GEdr
sinensis see *A. elliptica*
tabernaemontana Widely available
- 'Montana' SPer SWvt
- var. ***salicifolia*** CBWd CRos EBee IMou IPot LCro LEdu LPla LRHS NDov NRHS SBee WCAu
- 'Stella Azul' IPot

tharpii SPhx
tomentosa EBee SPhx
var. ***stenophylla***

Amygdalus see *Prunus*

Amyris (*Rutaceae*)

madrensis CFil

Anacamptis (*Orchidaceae*)

pyramidalis WHer

Anacyclus (*Asteraceae*)

pyrethrum GPoy
- var. ***depressus*** ♀H4 ELan EPfP GKev MMuc NEgg SPlb SRot
- - 'Garden Gnome' CTri SRms
- - 'Silberkissen' CMea EDAr NSla

Anagallis (*Primulaceae*)

monellii subsp. ***linifolia*** 'Blue Light' CSpe
- 'Skylover' CCCN CRav

tenella LLWG
- 'Studland' MHer WAbe

Ananas (*Bromeliaceae*)

comosus (F) CCCN SPre
- 'Champaca' (F) CCCN LCro SPre

Anaphalioides (*Asteraceae*)

§ ***bellidioides*** CTri

Anaphalis (*Asteraceae*)

alpicola EBee
margaritacea CBcs ECha ECtt GMaP GNew NBid NLar SRms WFar WHar WMoo
§ - 'Neuschnee' GJos ILea LPla NBre NLar XLum
- NEW SNOW see *A. margaritacea* 'Neuschnee'
- var. ***yedoensis*** CTri

§ ***nepalensis*** var. ***monocephala*** EBee MCot NSti SRms
nubigena see *A. nepalensis* var. *monocephala*
transnokoensis EBee EWes
§ ***trinervis*** CExl LSun XLum
triplinervis ♀H7 CBod EHoe ELan ELon EPfP EWTr EWld GAbr GKev GMaP IBoy IFoB ILea LRHS MMuc MRav NBid NLar NRHS SBod SPer WCAu WHoo WMoo
- CC 1620 EPPr
§ - 'Sommerschnee' ♀H7 CMac EAJP ECha ECtt EHoe EPfP GMcL GWyn IBoy LRHS MCot MHol MRav NEgg NLar NRHS NWad SPer WGwG WWtn
- SUMMER SNOW see *A. triplinervis* 'Sommerschnee'

Anchusa (*Boraginaceae*)

sp. CHab
§ ***azurea*** NLar SPhx
- 'Dropmore' EBee EPfP GPSL LCro LRHS MRav NEgg NLar SCob SRms WHar
- 'Feltham Pride' CDor EBee ELan EPfP SRms SWvt WHoo
- 'Little John' SRms
- 'Loddon Royalist' Widely available
- 'Opal' CBod ECtt LRHS MPie NRHS

capensis 'Blue Angel' MNHC SWvt
cespitosa ELan EWes LLHF WAbe

italica	see *A. azurea*
laxiflora	see *Borago pygmaea*
myosotidiflora	see *Brunnera macrophylla*
officinalis	MNHC SRms
sempervirens	see *Pentaglottis sempervirens*
undulata	EBee

Ancylostemon (*Gesneriaceae*)

convexus B&SWJ 6624	WCru
- B&SWJ 7182	WCru

Andrachne (*Phyllanthaceae*)

colchica	see *Leptopus chinensis*

Androcymbium (*Colchicaceae*)

longipes new	CPla

Andromeda (*Ericaceae*)

polifolia 'Alba'	EHyd ELan LRHS MAsh SPer SPlb SWvt WFar
- 'Alisa' new	GKev
- 'Blue Ice'	CRos EBee EHyd ELan GBin IDee LRHS LSRN MAsh NLar SPer SPoG WFar
- 'Blue Lagoon'	NLar
- 'Compacta' ♀H5	CMac CRos EHyd GEdr LRHS LSRN MAsh MGil NLar NWad SWvt WFar WGwG
- 'Grandiflora'	ELan GKev
- 'Kirigamine'	CRos LRHS MAsh
- 'Macrophylla' ♀H5	GEdr ITim WThu
- 'Nana'	EPfP
- 'Nikko'	CMac NLar

Andropogon (*Poaceae*)

gerardii	CKno CRos EBee EHoe EPPr LRHS NRHS NWsh XLum
- 'Prairie Sommer'	NDov
glomeratus	CAco
var. ***glaucopsis*** new	
scoparius	see *Schizachyrium scoparium*
ternarius	GCal

Androsace (*Primulaceae*)

alpina	WAbe
* ***bayanharshanensis***	WAbe
bisulca var. ***aurata***	GKev
brachystegia	EPot GKev
bulleyana	EPot GKev WAbe
cantabrica	EPot
carnea	GKev IFoB
- subsp. ***brigantiaca***	GCrg GKev NHpl NRHS NSla WAbe WHoo
- var. ***halleri***	see *A. carnea* subsp. *rosea*
- subsp. ***laggeri*** ♀H5	GCrg GKev LLHF NRHS NSla WAbe
§ - subsp. ***rosea*** ♀H5	GCrg GKev IFoB ITim NHpl
carnea × pyrenaica	EPot LLHF
chaixii	IFoB
chamaejasme subsp. ***carinata***	LLHF
ciliata	CPBP WAbe
cylindrica	CRos EPot ITim LRHS NRHS
cylindrica × hirtella	CRos EHyd EPot LRHS NRHS
delavayi	GKev SPlb WAbe
- ACE 1786	WAbe
elatior	WAbe
flavescens	EPot
geraniifolia	ECha SBch SRms
globifera	GKev WAbe
halleri	see *A. carnea* subsp. *rosea*
hausmannii × hirtella	LLHF
hedraeantha	GCrg NSla WAbe
himalaica	CPBP EPot GEdr WAbe
hirtella	IFoB ITim LLHF WAbe
idahoensis	WAbe
idahoensis × laevigata	WAbe
jacquemontii	see *A. villosa* var. *jacquemontii*
lactea	WAbe
laevigata	GCrg ITim WAbe
- 'Gothenburg'	GKev
- var. ***laevigata***	GKev
- 'Saddle Mount'	GKev
lanuginosa ♀H5	CBod CMea CSpe CTal ECtt EDAr EHoe EPfP EPot GBin GEdr MMuc NHpl SBch SRms SRot WAbe WOld WTor
lehmanniana	WAbe
- 'Götëborg Yellow'	WAbe
limprichtii	see *A. sarmentosa* var. *watkinsii*
mariae	GKev LLHF
× ***marpensis***	EPot WAbe
mathildae	LLHF
microphylla	see *A. mucronifolia* G. Watt
'Millstream'	IFoB
minor	WAbe
§ ***mollis***	CPBP
montana	WAbe
mucronifolia misapplied	see *A. sempervivoides*
§ ***mucronifolia*** G. Watt	EPot WAbe
mucronifolia G. Watt × ***sempervivoides***	CPBP CTal WAbe
muscoidea	GKev WAbe
- 'Breviscapa'	EPot
- 'Dolpo Lilac'	WAbe
- Schacht's form	EPot WAbe
nivalis	SPlb
- Chumstick form	GKev LLHF
ochotensis	WAbe
× ***pedemontana***	LLHF
primuloides	see *A. studiosorum*
pubescens	CRos EHyd EPot ITim LLHF LRHS NRHS
pyrenaica	CRos EHyd EPot ITim LLHF LRHS NRHS WAbe
rigida	EPot LLHF WAbe
rioxana new	GKev
robusta subsp. ***purpurea***	WAbe
- subsp. ***purpurea*** 'Dolpo Dwarf'	EPot WAbe
rotundifolia	GKev
sarmentosa misapplied	see *A. studiosorum*
sarmentosa ambig.	NHpl SPlb XLum
sarmentosa Wall.	GKev SRms WHoo
- CC 5557	GKev
- from Namche, Nepal	EPot WAbe
- Galmont's form	see *A. studiosorum* 'Salmon's Variety'
- 'Sherriffii'	EPot SRms WHoo
§ - var. ***watkinsii***	CTal EPot GKev SBch
- var. ***yunnanensis*** misapplied	see *A. studiosorum*
- var. ***yunnanensis*** Knuth	see *A. mollis*
selago	WAbe
- 'Red Eye'	WAbe
§ ***sempervivoides*** ♀H5	CRos EDAr EHyd EPot GBin GCrg GKev GMaP LRHS MBel NRHS NSla SBch SPlb SRms WOld
- 'Susan Joan'	EPot GKev WAbe WOld
septentrionalis 'Stardust'	MHol
spinulifera	GKev LLHF

stenophylla	MAsh
strigillosa	GKev NHpl WAbe
- CC 7533	GKev
§ ***studiosorum*** ♀H5	EPot GAbr GCrg GKev IFoB WAbe
- 'Chumbyi'	EPot LLHF NHpl SBch SRms WThu
- 'Conwy Gem' **new**	WAbe
- 'Conwy Jewel' **new**	WAbe
- 'Doksa'	CPBP CTal EPot IFoB WAbe
§ - 'Salmon's Variety'	CMea CTri SBch WAbe
tapete	WAbe
vandellii	ITim WAbe
villosa	EPot IFoB WAbe
- var. ***arachnoidea***	GKev
- var. ***incana*** **new**	GKev
§ - var. ***jacquemontii***	CPBP CTal
- - lilac-flowered	EPot WAbe
- - pink-flowered	EPot WAbe
vitaliana	see *Vitaliana primuliflora*
wardii	WAbe
watkinsii	see *A. sarmentosa* var. *watkinsii*
yargongensis	LLHF WAbe
zambalensis	WAbe

Andryala (*Asteraceae*)

agardhii	GKev
glandulosa	WCot
lanata	see *Hieracium lanatum*

Anemanthele (*Poaceae*)

§ ***lessoniana*** ♀H4	Widely available
- 'Autumn Tints'	EHoe
- 'Gold Hue'	EHoe ELon
- 'Sirocco'	CBod EUJe WCot WFar

Anemarrhena (*Asparagaceae*)

asphodeloides	WCot

Anemia (*Schizaeaceae*)

mexicana	WPGP
tomentosa	CRos LRHS NRHS

Anemone ✿ (*Ranunculaceae*)

Chen Yi T49	WCot
aconitifolia Michx.	see *A. narcissiflora*
altaica	GKev NLar SRms
amurensis	CExl
apennina ♀H4	CAvo GEdr WShi
- var. ***albiflora***	EPPr EPot GKev
- double-flowered (d)	EPPr LLHF MAvo
- 'Petrovac'	EPot GKev LEdu LLHF
baicalensis	WSHC
baldensis	GEdr GKev ITim SRms
barbulata	CExl EAJP EBee EWes GEdr GKev GPSL
biflora var. ***petiolulosa***	GKev
blanda ♀H4	CAby CRos ESps LAma LCro LRHS NLar NRHS SCob SEND WBor WFar WHar WShi
I - 'Alba'	CRos EHyd LRHS NRHS
- blue-flowered	CAvo CMea CRav CRos CTri EHyd ELan EPfP EPot ERCP GAbr GKev GMaP LCro LOPS LRHS MJak NPnk NRHS SCob SDeJ SDir SPer SPhx SPoG SRms WCot WHoo
- 'Charmer'	CGrW EPot GKev NHpl SDeJ SDir WCot
- 'Ingramii'	EPot GKev WCot
- var. ***rosea***	CRos EHyd GKev LAma LRHS NRHS SDeJ SPoG
- - 'Pink Star'	CAvo ERCP GKev LAma
- - 'Radar' ♀H4	EPot ERCP GKev LAma MNrw NHpl SDeJ
- 'Violet Star'	CMea GKev SDeJ
- 'White Splendour' ♀H4	CAby CAvo CMea CRav CRos CTri ELan EPfP EPot ERCP GAbr GKev IRob LAma LCro LOPS LRHS NRHS SDeJ SDir SPhx SPoG SRms WCot WWFP
- white-flowered	LRHS NRHS
'Bowles's Mauve'	GEdr MAsh
caerulea	LEdu
canadensis	ELon EPPr GEdr LEdu NWad WCot
caroliniana	GKev
caucasica	LEdu
chapaensis HWJ 631	WCru
'Cinderella'PBR (Fantasy Series)	EBee EHyd LRHS NRHS SPoG
coronaria	SCob SVic
- var. ***coronaria***	IBoy
- De Caen Group	CHid CRos EHyd EPfP GKev LAma LOPS LRHS NPnk NRHS SCob SDir SPoG WBor
- - 'Bicolor'	CHid GKev LAma SDeJ
- - blue-flowered	LRHS NRHS
- - 'Bordeaux'	EPfP LCro LOPS SCob
§ - - 'Die Braut'	CRav ERCP GKev LAma LCro LOPS SDeJ
- - 'His Excellency'	see *A. coronaria* (De Caen Group) 'Hollandia'
§ - - 'Hollandia'	GKev IBoy LAma SDeJ
- - 'Mister Fokker'	CRav CTca ERCP GKev IBoy LAma LCro LOPS SDeJ
- - pink-flowered	LRHS NRHS
- - red-flowered	LRHS NRHS
- - THE BRIDE	see *A. coronaria* (De Caen Group) 'Die Braut'
- - 'The Governor'	CMea ERCP GKev SDeJ
- (Harmony Series) 'Harmony Orchid'	CRos EHyd LRHS NRHS
- - 'Harmony Pearl'	CRos EHyd LRHS NRHS
- - 'Harmony Scarlet'	CRos EHyd LRHS NRHS
- 'Mistral Blue'	NPnk
- Saint Bridgid Group (d)	CRos EHyd GKev LAma LRHS NRHS SDir
- - 'Lord Lieutenant' (d)	CMea ERCP GKev SDeJ
- - 'Mount Everest' (d)	ERCP GKev SDeJ
- - 'Saint Bridgid' (d)	CHid
- - 'The Admiral' (d)	GKev SDeJ
- 'Sylphide' (Mona Lisa Series)	CRav ERCP GKev LAma LCro LOPS SDeJ WRHF
crinita	NLar
cylindrica	GEdr MHer NDov NLar XEll
'Dainty Swan' **new**	IPot LRHS MNrw NRHS
'Danish White'	MNrw
decapetala	LLHF MHer
demissa	LLHF WCot
- var. ***major***	EBee
'Dreaming Swan'	CWGN GBin IPot LLHF LRHS MBel MNrw NPnk SHar SPoG
drummondii	GKev
'Elfin Swan' **new**	EBee MNrw
fasciculata	see *A. narcissiflora*
filisecta	CAby EBee MBel MHol MPie MTis WCot WRHF
flaccida	CAby CBro CRos EHrv EHyd EPPr GEdr IRob LEdu LPla LRHS MAvo MNrw NRHS WCot WHal WSHC
- 'Futabazuru' (d) **new**	GEdr
- 'Ginpai' (d)	GEdr
globosa	see *A. multifida* Poir.

	'Guernica'	EWes
	'Hatakeyama Double' (d)	GCal LPla WSHC
	'Hatakeyama Single'	LPla
	hepatica L.	see *Hepatica nobilis*
§	***hortensis***	EBee
§	***hupehensis***	CBod CExl EBee GMaP LSun
	- BWJ 8190	WCru
	- NJM 11.068	WPGP
	- f. ***alba***	CExl CSpe IFro
§	- 'Bowles's Pink' ♀H7	CDor CElw CExl
	- 'Crispa'	see *A.* × ***hybrida*** 'Lady Gilmour' Wolley-Dod
	- 'Eugenie'	ECtt EPfP LRHS NRHS
	- 'Hadspen Abundance' ♀H7	Widely available
	- var. ***hupehensis***	WFar
§	- var. ***japonica***	CPou EPed SRms WAvo XLum
	- - B&SWJ 4886	WCru
	- - PAB 8884	LEdu
	- - 'Bodnant Burgundy'	LRHS SWvt WBrk
§	- - 'Bressingham Glow'	CExl CMac ECtt ELan EPfP EPot EShb EWTr GKin ILea LRHS NEgg NRHS SPer WBrk WCAu WFar WHil
§	- - 'Pamina' ♀H7	Widely available
	- - 'Pink Saucer'	EBee GMcL WFar
	- - PRINCE HENRY	see *A. hupehensis* var. *japonica* 'Prinz Heinrich'
§	- - 'Prinz Heinrich'	Widely available
§	- - 'Rotkäppchen'	CDor CRos ECtt GBin GKin GQue IBoy LRHS MHol MMuc NLar NRHS NSti SPad SWvt WCot WSHC
	- - 'Splendens'	CMea CRos EHyd EPfP LCro LOPS LRHS MCot NLar NRHS SCob SPer SPoG SRms SWvt WHal WSpi XLum
	- 'Little Princess'PBR	EBee ECtt MNrw
	- 'Ouvertüre'	ECtt
	- 'Pocahontas'PBR (Fantasy Series)	CRos EBee ECtt EHyd EPfP GBin LRHS MNrw NRHS SPoG
	- 'Praecox'	CMea CRos EPfP IRob LRHS LSou MBNS NRHS NSti SRms SWvt WCAu
	- 'Red Riding Hood' (Fantasy Series) **new**	CRos NRHS
	- 'September Charm'	see *A.* × ***hybrida*** 'September Charm'
	- 'Superba'	WSpi
§	× ***hybrida***	ESps NChi NEgg WHar WMoo
	- 'Alba' misapplied (UK)	see *A.* × ***hybrida*** 'Honorine Jobert'
	- 'Alba Dura'	see *A. tomentosa* 'Albadura'
	- 'Albert Schweitzer'	see *A.* × ***hybrida*** 'Elegans'
	- 'Andrea Atkinson'	Widely available
	- 'Bowles's Pink'	see *A. hupehensis* 'Bowles's Pink'
	- 'Bressingham Glow'	see *A. hupehensis* var. *japonica* 'Bressingham Glow'
	- 'Coupe d'Argent'	EBee ECtt MBel WCot
§	- 'Elegans' ♀H7	CSam ECtt GMaP LCro LOPS LRHS MMuc SEND SWvt WFar
	- 'Frau Marie Maushardt'	WBrk
§	- 'Géante des Blanches'	IRob LPla
§	- 'Honorine Jobert' ♀H7	Widely available
	- 'Josephine'	WFar
§	- 'Königin Charlotte' ♀H7	Widely available
	- 'Lady Gilmour' misapplied	see *A.* × ***hybrida*** 'Montrose'
	- 'Lady Gilmour' ambig.	CAvo GMaP GMcL GWyn XLum
§	- 'Lady Gilmour' Wolley-Dod	CRos CSpe ECtt EPfP LEdu LRHS MRav NChi NRHS SRms WCot WSpi XLum
	- 'Loreley'	CRav EPfP NLar SCob SWvt WAvo WCot
	- 'Luise Uhink'	CPou
	- 'Märchenfee'	MNrw
	- 'Margarete' Kayser & Seibert	CExl CRos ECtt ELan EPfP LRHS MHol NDov NRHS WCot
	- 'Max Vogel'	see *A.* × ***hybrida*** 'Elegans'
	- 'Monterosa'	see *A.* × ***hybrida*** 'Montrose'
§	- 'Montrose'	CPou CRos EBee ECha EWes GMaP LCro LOPS LRHS NLar NRHS SRms WCAu
	- 'Nightingale' (Fantasy Series)	EBee
	- 'Pamina'	see *A. hupehensis* var. *japonica* 'Pamina'
	- PINK KISS ('Pkan'PBR) **new**	CBod EBee ELon
	- Pretty Lady Series **new**	NRHS
	- - 'Pretty Lady Diana'PBR	ECtt LBuc LCro LRHS MNHC NRHS SCob SWvt WHil
	- - 'Pretty Lady Emily'PBR	EPfP LBuc LRHS NRHS SCob SWvt WHil
	- - 'Pretty Lady Julia'PBR	EBee LBuc SCob SHar WHil
	- - 'Pretty Lady Maria'	EBee LRHS NRHS
	- - 'Pretty Lady Susan'	CWGN EBee LBuc LCro LOPS LRHS SCob SHar SWvt WHil
	- PRINCE HENRY	see *A. hupehensis* var. *japonica* 'Prinz Heinrich'
	- 'Profusion'	CRos CTri EBee LBuc LRHS NRHS WHal
	- QUEEN CHARLOTTE	see *A.* × ***hybrida*** 'Königin Charlotte'
	- 'Richard Ahrens'	CAvo CBod CRos ECtt EPed EPfP EShb GCal GMaP LRHS LSRN MGos NEgg NGdn NLar NRHS SWvt WGwG WHar
§	- 'Robustissima'	CBWd CBod CRos EBee EPfP GMaP ILea LRHS LSRN MCot MHol MMuc MNrw NEgg NGdn NLar NRHS NSti SEND SPer SRms SWvt WAvo WCAu WMoo
	- 'Rosenschale'	CRos LRHS MNrw NRHS
	- 'Rotkäppchen'	see *A. hupehensis* var. *japonica* 'Rotkäppchen'
§	- 'September Charm' ♀H7	Widely available
	- 'Serenade'	CRos CSam ECtt EPfP ESps ETMg GMcL LRHS LSRN MRav NLar NRHS SPoG WCAu WMoo XLum
	- TOURBILLON	see *A.* × ***hybrida*** 'Whirlwind'
§	- 'Whirlwind'	Widely available
	- 'White Queen'	see *A.* × ***hybrida*** 'Géante des Blanches'
	- WIRBELWIND	see *A.* × ***hybrida*** 'Whirlwind'
	japonica	see *A. hupehensis, A. hupehensis* var. *japonica, A.* × ***hybrida***
	- 'Crustata'	CMac
	keiskeana	GEdr WCru
§	× ***lesseri***	CBro CSpe ECha ELan GEdr GKev SRms
	leveillei	Widely available
	- BWJ 7919	WCru
§	× ***lipsiensis***	CAby CBro CRav EBee ECtt EHrv EPPr EPfP EPot EWTr GAbr GEdr GKev GMaP IFro LEdu MAvo MBel MMoz MNrw NHpl NLar NPnk SBch WCru WFar WHal WPGP WSHC WSpi
	- 'Pallida' ♀H5	CElw CSam CSpe ELon EShb GEdr GKev LEdu NLar WCot WShi XEll
	- 'Schwefelfeuer'	LEdu MAvo
	- 'Vindobonensis'	EBee GEdr GKev MAvo WCot
	lithophila	GEdr
	magellanica hort. ex Wehrh.	see *A. multifida* Poir.
	matsudae B&SWJ 1452	WCru

	multifida misapplied, red-flowered	see *A.* × *lesseri*
§	***multifida*** Poir.	ECha EHyd EPfP GJos ILea LRHS NRHS NSti SPer WFar WHoo
	- SDR 8101	GKev
	- Annabella Series	GKev
	- - 'Annabella White'	GJos
	- var. ***globosa***	GKev
	- 'Major'	CMea CSpe EPfP GPSL SPhx
	- 'Rubra'	EHrv EPfP GBin GEdr GKev GPSL GWyn ILea LRHS LSou NEgg NLar NPnk NRHS WBor WHar WHil WHoo
	- white-flowered	NPnk
	- yellow-flowered	CBro GEdr
§	***narcissiflora***	CFis CSpe EBee GKev NChi WPtf
	nemorosa	Widely available
	- 'Alba'	CRos LRHS NRHS WFar
	- 'Alba Plena' (d)	CSam EAJP ECha ECtt EPPr EPfP GKev NGdn NLar NPnk WFar WSHC
	- 'Allenii' ♀H5	CBro CElw CRos EHrv ELon EPPr EPot GEdr GKev GMaP ITim LRHS MAvo MMoz MRav NRHS NRya WFar WShi
	- 'Apuseni'	LEdu
	- 'Atley'	EBee GEdr GKev MAvo WCot WFar
	- 'Atrocaerulea'	IBlr NLar NPnk
	- 'Ballyrogan Blue'	MAvo MNrw
	- 'Behemoth Blue'	LEdu
	- 'Bill Baker's Pink'	LEdu
	- 'Blue Beauty'	EBee ELon GMaP IBlr MAvo SBch
	- 'Blue Bonnet'	CAby ITim LEdu MAvo
	- 'Blue Eyes' (d)	CAby CAvo CElw EBee GAbr GEdr GKev GMaP IBlr ITim LEdu MAvo MMoz NHpl NPnk WSHC
	- 'Blue Queen'	ELon
	- 'Blush'	LEdu
	- 'Bohemia'	MAvo
	- 'Bowles's Purple'	CAby CSam EBee ELon EPot GEdr GMaP LRHS MAvo MHol NBid NHpl NPnk NRya WBor WCot WFar
	- 'Bracteata'	CAby CBro CTca GEdr GKev MMoz MMrt
	- 'Bracteata Pleniflora' (d)	EHrv EPot GKev GMaP IBlr LEdu MAvo MNrw NPnk SBch WCot WHal WShi XEll
	- 'Buckland'	EBee EPfP EPot IBlr MAvo
	- 'Caerulea'	EPot GKev ITim
	- 'Cedric's Pink'	EPPr IBlr LLHF MAvo WFar
	- 'Celestial'	ELan EPPr MAvo
	- 'Dee Day'	CElw EBee LEdu MAvo
	- 'Dell Garden'	EPPr
	- 'Flore Pleno' (d)	CAby GAbr IFro MMoz WBor WFar
	- 'Flushing'	GEdr GKev MAvo
	- 'Frenzy' **new**	WCot
	- 'Frühlingsfee'	GKev MAvo
	- 'Frühlingsfest'	EBee
	- 'Gerda Ramusen'	ELan ELon EWes LEdu LLHF
	- 'Gerry'	MAvo
I	- 'Gigantea Rubra'	MAvo WCot
	- 'Glyncock Gold' **new**	MAvo
	- 'Good Blue'	MAvo
	- 'Green Dream'	MAvo WSHC
	- 'Green Fingers'	EHrv EPPr GEdr GKev GMaP ITim MMrt WSHC XEll
	- 'Hakumane Senjuizaki'	WCot
	- 'Hannah Gubbay'	IBlr
	- 'Helsinki'	MAvo
	- 'Hilda'	EBee ECtt GEdr GKev LEdu MNrw NPnk NRya
	- 'Ice and Fire'	GKev LEdu
	- 'Jack Brownless'	LEdu
	- 'Kentish Pink'	GBin GMaP NPnk
	- 'Knightshayes Vestal' (d)	CExl MAvo MRav WSHC
	- 'La Rochanne' **new**	MAvo MNrw
	- 'Lady Doneraile'	EPot LEdu WFar WSHC
	- 'Latvian Pink'	EPot GEdr GKev LEdu MAvo
	- 'Leeds' Variety'	EPot GKev GMaP LEdu MNrw NPnk
	- 'Lionel Bacon'	LEdu MAvo
	- 'Lismore Blue'	EPPr EPot GKev
	- 'Lismore Pink'	GEdr LEdu
	- 'Lucia'	EPot GEdr GKev LEdu MAvo WCot WFar
	- 'Lychette'	EHrv EPPr GAbr GEdr GKev IBlr MAvo MNrw NPnk WSHC
	- 'March Blue'	EPfP
	- 'Marie Rose'	EPot WFar
	- 'Mart's Blue'	EBee EPfP GKev MAvo WCot
	- 'Monstrosa'	EPot GKev MAvo NPnk
	- 'New Pink'	IBlr
	- 'Noémie'	XEll
	- 'Parlez Vous'	CExl EHrv EPPr GEdr LEdu MAvo MNrw NHpl WFar WPnP XEll
	- 'Pat's Pink'	WShi
	- 'Pentre Pink'	EPot IBlr
	- 'Picos Pink'	EHrv
	- 'Pink Carpet'	GEdr LEdu
	- 'Pink Delight'	LEdu
	- pink-flowered	MMuc
	- 'Robinsoniana' ♀H6	Widely available
	- 'Rosea'	LEdu MAvo NLar NPnk
	- 'Royal Blue'	CAby CBro CSpe CTca EBee ECtt EHrv EPPr EPot ERCP EUJe GAbr GEdr GKev GMaP LAma LEdu MAvo NDov NHpl NLar NPnk WCot WFar WPnP
	- 'Salt and Pepper'	LEdu MAvo
	- 'Slack Top Pink'	MAvo
§	- 'Stammerberg' (d)	EPPr MAvo WSHC
	- 'Stammheim'	see *A. nemorosa* 'Stammerberg'
	- 'Tilo'	MAvo
	- 'Tomas'	EAJP ELon EPot GEdr LEdu MAvo NHpl NPnk NRya WFar
	- 'Tups'	LEdu
	- 'Vestal' (d) ♀H5	Widely available
	- 'Virescens' ♀H5	CAvo CWCL EHrv ELon EPPr EPot GEdr GKev GMaP LEdu MAvo MMoz NPnk SDir WShi
	- 'Viridiflora'	CExl EPfP GBin MAvo MNrw WSHC
	- 'Westwell Pink'	EPPr LLHF MNrw WBor WCot WShi
	- white-flowered	LRHS NRHS
	- 'Wilks' White'	ELon EPPr GEdr IRob MAvo NPnk
	- 'Wisley Pink'	EPot LEdu MAvo WFar
I	- 'Wisley White Form'	MAvo
	- 'Wyatt's Pink'	ELon EPot GKev LEdu MAvo
	- 'Yerda Ramusem'	EPPr LEdu MAvo WSHC
	nemorosa* × *ranunculoides	see *A.* × *lipsiensis*
	obtusiloba	GEdr LLHF WAbe WHal
	- CLD 1549	GEdr
	- 'Alba'	GEdr WAbe
	- 'Large Blue'	EPot GEdr LEdu NSla WAbe
	- 'Pradesh'	GEdr
I	- 'Sulphurea'	GEdr WAbe
	palmata	EWes GEdr GPSL IBoy LEdu NPnk NSum SMad WKif
	parviflora	GKev LLHF XEll

patens	see *Pulsatilla patens*
pavonina	CAby CSpe ECha IBoy LPla LRHS MHol NRHS SLon SMHy SPoG WCot
polyanthes	CRos EBee GEdr GKev LLHF LRHS NRHS
prattii	CExl EPPr GEdr LEdu
pseudoaltaica	GEdr LEdu WCru
- blue-flowered	GEdr
- pink-flowered	GEdr
- 'Yuki-no-sei' (d)	GEdr WCot
pulsatilla	see *Pulsatilla vulgaris*
raddeana	GKev
* - f. ***rosea***	GEdr
ranunculoides ♀H5	Widely available
- 'Bill Baker'	LEdu MAvo
- 'Crazy Vienna'	WCot
- 'Ferguson's Fancy'	GCal
- 'Frank Waley'	WCot
- 'Fuchsis Traum'	WCot
- 'Grandiflora'	MAvo
* - ***laciniata***	MAvo WCot
- 'Pleniflora' (d) ♀H5	CAvo CRos ECha EPPr GKev LRHS MAvo NLar NPnk NRHS WFar
- subsp. ***ranunculoides***	GKev
- 'Semi-Plena'	GEdr GKev LEdu
- subsp. ***wockeana***	CSam EBee LEdu
reflexa	EBee GKev LLHF
riparia	see *A. virginiana* var. *alba*
rivularis	CAvo CPar CRos CSpe CTsd EWTr GBin GEdr GKev GPoy ILea IPot IRob LRHS MNrw NLar NPnk NRHS NWad SBrt SChF SMad SRms WCru WFar WHoo WKif WMoo XEll
- B&SWJ 13944	WCru
- BWJ 7611	WCru
- CC 4588	CExl
- PAB 2477	LEdu
- SDR 4229	GKev
- 'Glacier'	CWCL EBee MHol NSti WHil
aff. ***rivularis***	WSpi
'Ruffled Swan'	CWGN EWTr GBin IPot LLHF LRHS MNrw NPnk NSti SHar SLon SPoG STPC
rupicola	GEdr LLHF WCot
× ***seemannii***	see *A.* × *lipsiensis*
stellata Lam.	see *A. hortensis*
stolonifera double-flowered (d)	GEdr LEdu LPla WCot WSHC
sulphurea misapplied	see *Pulsatilla alpina* subsp. *apiifolia*
sumatrana B&SWJ 11265	WCru
sylvestris	Widely available
- 'Elise Fellmann' (d)	CSpe WHal
- 'Macrantha'	EPfP
- 'Snow White' new	CBod
tetrasepala	WCot XEll
§ ***tomentosa***	LRHS NRHS SRms
§ - 'Albadura'	EBee
- 'Robustissima'	see *A.* × *hybrida* 'Robustissima'
trifolia L.	EBee EPPr LEdu NBid NLar WCot
trullifolia	GBin GCal LLHF
- var. ***linearis***	WAbe
udensis	EBee GEdr GKev WCot
vernalis	see *Pulsatilla vernalis*
vesicatoria	SBrt
virginiana	EBee LEdu MNrw NBid NWad WCot WHrl
§ - var. ***alba***	GEdr
vitifolia misapplied	see *A. tomentosa*
vitifolia Buch.-Ham. ex DC. WJC 12743	WCru
WILD SWAN ('Macane001'PBR)	Widely available

Anemonella (*Ranunculaceae*)

thalictroides	CElw EHrv ELon GAbr GEdr GKev IRob ITim LAma MAvo MBel MMoz NHpl NLar NPnk NRya WAbe WFar WPnP WSHC WSpi XLum
- 'Alba Plena' (d)	NPnk
- 'Amelia'	EPPr GEdr NHpl NPnk
- 'Babe'	WCot
- 'Betty Blake' (d)	EBee ELon GBin GEdr LAma LLHF MAvo MMrt NHpl NPnk NRya WCot
- 'Cameo'	EPPr GEdr LAma MAvo MNrw NHpl NPnk NRya SDir WCot WFar
- 'Charlotte'	GEdr NPnk
- 'Dark Pink'	EBee MAvo
- 'Diamante'	CElw WCot
- 'Double Diamante' (d)	WCot
- 'Flore Pleno' (d)	NPnk
- 'Full Double White' (d)	NHpl
- 'Green Hurricane' (d)	GEdr LAma NPnk NRya SDir WCot
- 'Hakikomi-fu' (v)	GEdr
- 'Kikuzaki Pink' (d)	GEdr LAma
- 'Kikuzaki White' (d)	GEdr LAma
- f. ***rosea***	CAby CElw ELan GKev LLHF NLar WAbe
- - 'Oscar Schoaf' (d)	EBee GEdr MAvo NHpl NPnk WAbe WCot
- - semi-double pink-flowered (d)	CElw EHrv MAvo
- 'Rosea Plena' (d)	LAma
- semi-double white-flowered (d)	CElw EPPr WAbe
- 'Snowflakes' (d)	MAvo
- 'Spring Nymph'	SMHy
- 'Tairin'	GEdr LAma WCot

Anemonopsis (*Ranunculaceae*)

macrophylla	CAby CBot CExl CPBP CSpe CTal EPfP EWes GCal GEdr LEdu MNrw MRav NHpl NLar SBch SPhx WCru WFar WOld WPGP WSHC
- double-flowered	GKev WSHC
- 'White Swan'	CTal GEdr WCru WSHC

Anemopsis (*Saururaceae*)

californica	EBee EWat GEdr IFoB LLWG LOPS MSKA MWts SBrt WCot

Anethum (*Apiaceae*)

graveolens	CRav ENfk GPoy MHer MNHC NPri SRms SVic XAbr

angelica see *Angelica archangelica*

Angelica (*Apiaceae*)

acutiloba	WFar
- var. ***iwatensis*** B&SWJ 11197	WCru
anomala B&SWJ 10886	WCru
archangelica	Widely available
atropurpurea	CRos ECtt EHyd EPfP LRHS MHer MNrw MRav NRHS SWvt
brevicaulis new	LEdu WPGP

breweri B&SWJ 14083 **new**	WCru
cartilaginomarginata B&SWJ 12663	WCru
cyclocarpa WJC 13658	WCru
dahurica	CBot NDov SPhx WFar WOut
decursiva B&SWJ 5746	WCru
edulis	WHer WPGP
- B&SWJ 10968	LEdu WCru
gigas	Widely available
- B&SWJ 4170	WCru
- 'Atropurpurea'	CSpe
hendersoni	LEdu
hispanica	see *A. pachycarpa*
japonica B&SWJ 11480	WCru
montana	see *A. sylvestris*
morii RWJ 9802	WCru
nubigena WJC 13763 **new**	WCru
§ ***pachycarpa***	CBre CRos CSam CSpe EBee GBin GMaP LRHS MHer MRav NGBl NLar NRHS WFar
pubescens	NDov
- B&SWJ 5593	WCru
sachalinensis	EBee
sinensis	GPoy LEdu
'Summer Delight'	see *Ligusticum scoticum*
§ ***sylvestris***	CBre CHab EBWF LLWG WHil WOut
- PAB 8136	LEdu
- 'Burgundy'	CSpe NGBl
- 'Ebony'	CBct CBre CRos CSpe ECtt LCro LEdu LLWG LRHS MBel MHer MHol MSCN MTis NRHS NSti SAko SCob SPad SPhx SPoG WCot WFar WPGP
* - 'Purpurea'	CDor CSam EWes GMaP
- 'Vicar's Mead'	CBod EBee LEdu LRHS NChi NLar SPer SPhx SWvt
taiwaniana	CBre CDTJ CDor CRos EBee ELan IMou LRHS MMuc NLar NRHS
ursina	NGBl WCru

Angelonia (*Plantaginaceae*)

ARCHANGEL DEEP ROSE ('Balarcrose')	CRos EHyd LRHS NRHS

Anigozanthos (*Haemodoraceae*)

(Bush Gems Series) BUSH BONANZA ('Rambubona'PBR) **new**	SEle
- BUSH DIAMOND ('Rambodiam'PBR) **new**	SEle
- 'Bush Inferno'PBR **new**	SEle
- 'Bush Ranger'	CCCN
flavidus	SPlb
- 'Ember'	CCCN
- 'Illusion'	CCCN
- 'Opal'	CCCN
- 'Pearl'	CCCN
- red-flowered	SPlb
- 'Splendour'	CCCN
- 'Yellow Gem'	CCCN
manglesii ♀H1c	SPlb SVen
rufus	SEle

Anisacanthus (*Acanthaceae*)

quadrifidus var. ***wrightii***	WCot

anise see *Pimpinella anisum*

Anisodontea (*Malvaceae*)

bryoniifolia	SVen
§ ***capensis***	CCCN CHGN CRos ELan EPri SChF SEle SLim SPhm SPlb SRkn SRms SVen SWvt
- 'Elegans Princess'	CCCN
'Crystal Rose'	CRos EPfP LRHS MGos NRHS XLum
'El Rayo'	CSpe CWGN EBee ECtt MAvo MHol MPie NCou SDys SPad SPoG SRkn WAvo WBor WCot WFar XLum
huegelii	see *Alyogyne huegelii*
× ***hypomadara*** misapplied	see *A. capensis*
§ × ***hypomadara*** (Sprague) D.M. Bates	SEle
julii	SVen
LADY IN PINK ('Nuanilaninp')	NCou
'Large Magenta'	ELon LRHS LSou SWvt
scabrosa 'Miss Pinky'PBR	CRos LRHS NRHS

Anisodus (*Solanaceae*)

carniolicodes BWJ 7501	WCru

Anisotome (*Apiaceae*)

imbricata var. ***imbricata***	WAbe
lyallii	GKev

Annona (*Annonaceae*)

cherimola (F)	CCCN XBlo
squamosa (F)	SPlb

Anoiganthus see *Cyrtanthus*

Anomalesia see *Gladiolus*

Anomatheca (*Iridaceae*)

cruenta	see *Freesia laxa*

Anopterus (*Escalloniaceae*)

glandulosus	CFil WSHC

Anredera (*Basellaceae*)

§ ***cordifolia***	CRHN EShb GKev LEdu

Antennaria (*Asteraceae*)

aprica	see *A. parvifolia*
dioica	CTri ECtt EDAr EWld GAbr GBin GJos GPoy NSla SPlb SRms WAbe XLum
- 'Alba'	EHoe
- 'Alex Duguid'	GPSL NWad
- 'Aprica'	see *A. parvifolia*
- 'Minima'	EPot GCrg ITim NBro NRHS NSla WAbe
- 'Nyewoods Variety'	SRms
- var. ***rosea***	see *A. rosea*
- 'Rotes Wunder'	CMea ECha EPot GCrg SBch WAbe
* - 'Rubra'	ECha ECtt EDAr MHer MMuc SRms XLum
'Joy'	WAbe
§ ***parvifolia***	CTri SRms SRot
- 'Alba' **new**	EDAr
plantaginifolia	EBee
§ ***rosea*** ♀H5	CRos EHyd GMaP LRHS NRHS NSla SPlb SRms WHal WHoo

Antenoron see *Persicaria*

Anthemis ✿ (*Asteraceae*)

from Turkey	ECtt EWes
arvensis	CHab EBWF

§ 'Beauty of Grallagh'	WSpi
'Cally Cream'	ELon GCal GWyn LRHS SMHy SPhx
'Cally White'	GBin GCal WBrk WHil
carpatica	MMuc NBro
- 'Karpatenschnee'	CRos EHyd EPfP LRHS NRHS SAko SRms
cretica subsp. ***leucanthemoides***	EPot
- subsp. ***tenuiloba***	EWes
frutescens Voss	see *Argyranthemum frutescens*
'Grallagh Gold' misapplied, orange-yellow	see *A.* 'Beauty of Grallagh'
'Grallagh Gold'	ECtt EWes NPer SPhx
§ ***marschalliana***	CRos ECha ECtt EDAr EPot LRHS NHpl NRHS SPlb WAbe WCot
- subsp. ***pectinata***	GCrg
nobilis	see *Chamaemelum nobile*
punctata subsp. ***cupaniana*** 🏆^{H4}	Widely available
- - 'Nana'	NPer SHar
rudolphiana	see *A. marschalliana*
sancti-johannis	CRos EPfP ESps LPmr LRHS NPer NRHS SAko SRms WMoo
SUSANNA MITCHELL ('Blomit')	CBod CRos EBee ECtt ELon GMaP LRHS LSRN MAvo MBel MHol MNrw MWat NDov NLar NRHS NWad SWvt WSHC XLum
'Tetworth'	ECha EHrv ELan EPfP GBin LRHS SAko SMad WCot
tinctoria	CBod CHby CMac EBee ENfk GPoy MHer MNHC NPer SRms SWvt WSFF XLum
- 'Alba'	CRos EBee LRHS NRHS NWad WArt WFar
- 'Charme'^{PBR}	CRos EPfP LRHS NLar NRHS SPoG SRms SWvt
- 'Compacta'	EWes GCal XLum
- dwarf	SAko
- 'E.C. Buxton' 🏆^{H4}	Widely available
- 'Eva'	NDov
- 'Hall Farm Frilly'	ECtt ELon
- 'Kelwayi'	CRos CSBt EPfP ESps GLog GMcL GWyn LRHS NBro NLar NPer NRHS SPer SRms WFar WMoo XLum
- 'Lemon Ice'	CBod EBee GBin GWyn
- 'Lemon Maid'	ECtt ELon
- 'Sauce Hollandaise'	Widely available
- 'Wargrave Variety'	CBod CElw CMac CRos CSam ECha ECtt EHrv ELan EPfP GBin GWyn LRHS MAvo MHol NChi NGdn NRHS NWad SPhx SWvt WCAu WFar WGwG
'Tinpenny Sparkle'	CBod CSam EBee ECtt GMcL GWyn MHol MPie NLar NSti WBrk WFar WHoo WRHF
triumfettii	NDov NPer WCot
tuberculata	NChi SBch

Anthericum (*Asparagaceae*)

algeriense	see *A. liliago*
* ***bovei***	CBro
§ ***liliago***	CRos CSpe ELan EWld GCal GKev GMaP IDee IFoB LRHS MCot MPie MRav NLar NRHS SPer WAul WPtf XEll
- 'Major' 🏆^{H5}	CAvo CBro EBee ECha EHrv IBlr LEdu SPhx
plumosum	see *Trichopetalum plumosum*
ramosum	CAby CFis CRos CSpe ECha EPPr EPot EPri EWes GCal GKev IBoy LEdu LRHS MBrN NBid NLar NRHS NSla SPhx WCot

Antholyza (*Iridaceae*)

coccinea	see *Crocosmia paniculata*
× ***crocosmioides***	see *Crocosmia* × *crocosmioides*
paniculata	see *Crocosmia paniculata*

Anthoxanthum (*Poaceae*)

odoratum	CHab EBWF GPoy GQue XAbr XLum

Anthriscus (*Apiaceae*)

cerefolium	CHby ENfk GPoy MHer MNHC SRms WSFF XAbr
sylvestris	CBre CHab EBWF LRHS NMir SPhx WFar WOut WSFF
- 'Broadleas Blush'	CNat
- 'Going for Gold'	CNat EPPr EWes NChi WCot WOut
- 'Ravenswing'	Widely available
- 'Snape Cottage Brown' **new**	CNat

Anthurium (*Araceae*)

andraeanum 'Glowing Pink'	XBlo
- 'Red Heart'	XBlo
- 'Tivolo'	XBlo
'Aztec'	XBlo
BALENO ('Anthauf4'^{PBR})	XBlo
'Caribo'	XBlo
crenatum	XBlo
'Crimson'	XBlo
'Magenta'	XBlo
'Mikra'	XBlo
'Octavia'	XBlo
PICO BELLO ('Anthcupcup'^{PBR})	XBlo
PINK CHAMPION ('Antinkeles'^{PBR})	LCro XBlo
'Porcelaine White'	XBlo
RED CHAMPION ('Anthbnena'^{PBR})	LOPS XBlo
'Vitara'	XBlo
WHITE CHAMPION ('Anthefaqyr'^{PBR})	LCro XBlo

Anthyllis (*Papilionaceae*)

hermanniae 'Compacta'	see *A. hermanniae* 'Minor'
§ - 'Minor'	EPot WAbe
montana	XSen
- subsp. ***atropurpurea***	CRos LRHS NRHS
- 'Rubra' 🏆^{H5}	CPla EDAr EPot LLHF NSla
vulneraria	CHab EBWF GJos NMir NRya SPhx WSFF
- var. ***coccinea***	ELan GAbr GKev IBoy MBel NRHS NSla SPhx WCFE WHal WOut XSen
- dark red-flowered	CSpe
- 'Fireberry'	ECtt

Antirrhinum (*Plantaginaceae*)

asarina	see *Asarina procumbens*
australe	GCal
barrelieri	SEND
braun-blanquetii	GLog WCot
CANDY SHOWERS MIXED **new**	ETMg
glutinosum	see *A. hispanicum* subsp. *hispanicum*

hispanicum 'Avalanche' ECtt
§ - subsp. ***hispanicum*** CSpe
- - 'Roseum' CMea
majus 'Admiral White' **new** LCro LOPS
- 'Black Prince' CSpe ECtt LPla SPhx
- (Liberty Classic Series) 'Liberty Classic Crimson' **new** CRav
- - 'Liberty Classic Scarlet' CRav
- 'Madame Butterfly' (mixed) (d) **new** ETMg
- 'Night and Day' CRav CSpe WMoo WWFP
- 'Royal Bride' **new** ETMg
- Sonnet Series, formula mixed **new** NPri
- 'White Giant' **new** CRav
MINI BUTTERFLIES MIXED **new** ETMg
molle CSpe GKev MCot NPer SChF WAbe
- pink-flowered MCot WAbe
- white-flowered EBee GKev WAbe
PRETTY IN PINK ('Pmoore07') LCro LOPS LRHS SHar SLon SPoG WHlf
sempervirens EWTr MHer WAbe
valentinum **new** WHil

añu see *Tropaeolum tuberosum*

Aphelandra (*Acanthaceae*)

squarrosa EShb
- 'Citrina' XBlo

Aphyllanthes (*Asparagaceae*)

monspeliensis SBrt XLum XSen

Apios (*Papilionaceae*)

§ ***americana*** EWes LEdu WCot WCru WSHC
- 'Nutty' CAgr
tuberosa see *A. americana*

Apium (*Apiaceae*)

graveolens CHab EBWF ENfk GPoy MHer MNHC SRms SVic
- (Secalinum Group) 'Par-cel' MHer SRms
nodiflorum EBWF

Apium × *Petroselinum* (*Apiaceae*)

hybrid, misapplied see *A. graveolens* Secalinum Group

Apocynum (*Apocynaceae*)

cannabinum GPoy

Aponogeton (*Aponogetonaceae*)

desertorum EWat
distachyos CBen CWat EWat LCro LLWG LOPS MSKA MWts NPer SVic WMAq XLum

apple see *Malus domestica*

apricot see *Prunus armeniaca*

Aptenia (*Aizoaceae*)

cordifolia CCCN NPer SChr SPlb SVen
- 'Variegata' (v) CCCN

Aquilegia ✿ (*Ranunculaceae*)

akitensis misapplied see *A. flabellata* var. *pumila*
'Alaska' (State Series) 🏆H5 EBee LRHS NRHS
alpina CBot CMea EBee EPfP ESps GMcL LCro LPmr MNHC NGdn SCob SPer SRms WHoo WMoo WSpi XEll XLum
amaliae see *A. ottonis* subsp. *amaliae*
aragonensis see *A. pyrenaica*
§ ***atrata*** CBot CPou
aurea Janka LLHF
barnebyi CWCL
bernardii GKev
bertolonii 🏆H5 CMea EWld GKev LRHS NRHS NSla SRms WHoo
Biedermeier Group EAJP EPfP ESps GJos LRHS NGdn NNor NRHS SRot WFar WHil
'Blackcurrant' CWCL
'Blue Pleats' CWCL
'Blue Star' (Star Series) CWCL ELan EPfP GBin GMaP GWyn LRHS MAvo NEgg NPnk NRHS SPtp
'Bluebird' (Songbird Series) 🏆H4 LBuc LRHS NPer WFar
'Bob Hares' **new** WAvo
brevistyla NNor
buergeriana CFis GKev SPhx
- 'Calimero' CFis CTsd CWCL EAJP LRHS MBNS NLar SBee SPtp
- var. ***oxysepala*** see *A. oxysepala*
aff. ***buergeriana*** NPnk
'Bunting' (Songbird Series) 🏆H4 MHer SGbt
canadensis 🏆H3 CBot CSpe ELan GCrg GKev GLog NBro SPhx SRms WFar WSpi XEll XLum
- 'Little Lanterns' EAJP EPPr GKev NHpl NLar
- 'Nana' GKev WThu
'Cardinal' (Songbird Series) LBuc LRHS
chaplinei GKev SBch
chrysantha CBot EHrv GJos GWyn MCot SRms SWvt WKif XSen
- 'Denver Gold' CSam EShb SPhx WHil
I - 'Flore Pleno' (d) CBot
- 'Yellow Queen' 🏆H5 CExl CWCL ELon EPPr EPfP GBin GMaP IRob LRHS MAvo NGdn NRHS SCob SGbt SPhx SWvt WCFE WHil WTor XEll XLum
clematiflora see *A. vulgaris* var. *stellata*
Clementine Series EPfP
coerulea 🏆H5 GJos GKev IRob NNor SRms
- var. ***ochroleuca*** CWCL
'Colorado' (State Series) LRHS NRHS
'Crimson Star' CWCL ELan EPfP GMcL LRHS NRHS SPoG WHar WMoo
discolor GKev LLHF WThu XEll
double black-flowered (d) WHar
'Double Rubies' (d) CPla ELan WMoo
'Dove' (Songbird Series) 🏆H5 LBuc LRHS MHer SGbt SHar SPer
I 'Dragonfly' CBcs ELan EPfP LRHS MJak NEgg NRHS SPoG
ecalcarata see *Semiaquilegia ecalcarata*
einseleana LLHF
elegantula GKev
eximia B&SWJ 14053 **new** WCru
flabellata f. ***alba*** CTri ELan
- - 'White Jewel' (Jewel Series) GKev
- 'Blackcurrant Ice' CWCL EPfP LRHS NRHS
- Cameo Series GMaP WFar
- - 'Cameo Blue and White' GMcL SRms SRot WFar WTor
- - 'Cameo Pink and White' GMcL MHer
- - 'Cameo Red and White' GMcL

	- - 'Cameo Rose'	WFar
	- - 'Cameo White'	GMcL SRot WFar
	- 'Georgia' (State Series) ♀H5	LRHS NRHS
	- 'Ministar'	EDAr GCrg GWyn MHol WFar WHil XLum
	- 'Nana Alba'	see *A. flabellata* var. *pumila* f. *alba*
§	- var. ***pumila*** ♀H5	CWCL ECha EDAr ELon EPPr GEdr GKev LRHS LSun NGdn NRHS
§	- - f. ***alba*** ♀H5	ECha GKev LRHS LSun NRHS
	- - 'Atlantis'	CWCL GMcL LRHS MHol
I	- - f. ***kurilensis*** 'Rosea'	WAbe
	- 'Vermont' (State Series)	EBee
	flavescens	GKev
	'Florida' (State Series) ♀H5	LRHS NRHS
	formosa	CBot EPPr NChi
	- var. ***formosa*** B&SWJ 13543 **new**	WCru
	- var. ***truncata*** B&SWJ 14072 **new**	WCru
§	***fragrans***	GAbr GBin GEdr GJos IBoy SGbt WArt
	'Fruit and Nut Chocolate'	EBee MHol WCot
	glandulosa	GKev GWyn LLHF
	glauca	see *A. fragrans*
	'Golden Guiness'	ELon GPSL MMrt
	'Goldfinch' (Songbird Series)	LBuc LRHS MHer SGbt SPer
	grahamii	WAbe
	'Heavenly Blue'	CDor EBee GWyn LRHS NRHS
	'Hensol Harebell'	SHar SRms WSpi
	'Honeydew'	GWyn
	hybrida 'Double Pleat Blackberry' (d)	EPed
	japonica	see *A. flabellata* var. *pumila*
	jonesii	EPot GKev SPlb
	jonesii × ***saximontana***	GKev
	'Koralle'	CBod CDor GWyn MMrt WHil
	'Kristall'	CBar EShb SGbt
*	***kuhistanica***	EBee GKev GWyn
	laramiensis	GKev
	'Leprechaun Gold' (v)	EPfP MHol NGdn
	'Lime Sorbet'	LEdu LRHS SRms
	longissima	CWld MHer SHar WHoo
	'Louisiana' (State Series) ♀H5	EBee LRHS NRHS SCob
	'Magpie'	see *A. vulgaris* 'William Guiness'
	'Maxi'	CBod WHil
	McKana Group	CBod CTri EAJP ELan ELon EPfP GAbr GJos GMaP GMcL LRHS MGos MJak NEgg NGdn NLar NRHS SCob SPer SPlb SPoG SRms SWvt WFar WHar WMoo XLum
	Mrs Scott-Elliot hybrids	CSBt ECtt EPfP MHol
	Music Series	SRms
	- 'Music Blue and White' **new**	CBod
	- 'Music Red and White'	CBod
	'Nightingale' (Songbird Series)	SGbt
	nigricans	see *A. atrata*
	nivalis	LLHF
	'Oregon' (State Series)	EBee
	(Origami Series) 'Origami Blue and White'	IBoy
	- 'Origami Red and White' ♀H5	IBoy
	- 'Origami Rose and White'	NRHS
	- 'Origami White'	IBoy
§	***ottonis*** subsp. ***amaliae***	CPBP LLHF WAbe
§	***oxysepala***	CExl GLog MMrt
	- B&SWJ 4775	WCru
	- var. ***kansuensis***	GKev

	Perfumed Garden Group	WFar
	pleated burgundy-flowered	CBot
	'Purple Emperor' PBR	EPfP
§	***pyrenaica***	EPot GKev
	- dwarf	GKev WAbe
	'Red Hobbit'	CSpe CWCL EBee ELan EPfP GMcL IBoy LRHS MBel MHol NEgg NGdn NHpl NLar NRHS SPtp WBor WFar
	'Red Star' (Star Series)	CWCL EAJP EPfP MAvo NEgg SHar WHil
	'Rhubarb and Custard'	LRHS
	'Robin' (Songbird Series)	SGbt SPer
	rockii	EWld GKev SBrt
	- B&SWJ 7965	WCru
	'Roman Bronze'	see *Aquilegia* × *Semiaquilegia* 'Roman Bronze'
	'Rose Queen'	CBod CDor CWCL EPfP GWyn NNor SPtp WFar WHoo
	'Roundway Chocolate'	CBot
	saximontana	EPot GEdr GKev NSla
§	'Schneekönigin'	CWCL EBee LRHS NRHS WCFE
	scopulorum	GKev LLHF
	sibirica	GKev LLHF
	'Silver Queen'	EBee ELan GBin
	'Simone's White'	EBee
	skinneri	CBot CExl CSpe ELan GEdr GLog NWad
	- 'Tequila Sunrise'	CSpe CWCL ELan MHer NNor SPtp
	SNOW QUEEN	see *A.* 'Schneekönigin'
	Spring Magic Series	LRHS NPri
	- SPRING MAGIC BLUE AND WHITE	LRHS SCob
	- SPRING MAGIC ROSE AND IVORY	NRHS
	- SPRING MAGIC ROSE AND WHITE	GMcL
	- SPRING MAGIC WHITE	GMcL SCob
	- SPRING MAGIC YELLOW	GMcL
	stellata	see *A. vulgaris* var. *stellata*
	'Stoulton Blue'	WAvo
	'Sunburst Ruby'	CWCL WMoo
	(Swan Series) 'Swan Lavender'	LRHS NRHS
	- 'Swan Red and White'	LRHS NRHS WFar
	- 'Swan Violet and White' **new**	CRos NRHS
	triternata	GWyn NNor
	'Virginia' (State Series)	LRHS NRHS
	viridiflora	CBot EBee ELan EPfP GCal MMrt SBee SPhx WAbe WCot
	- var. ***atropurpurea***	LEdu
	- 'Chocolate Soldier'	CSpe CWCL CWld
	'Volcano!' (mixed)	WHil
	vulgaris	CHab CWCL CWld EBWF EPfP ESps GKev GPoy GWyn LCro LOPS LRHS MHer MNHC NBro NDov NGdn NMir SPlb WCAu WMoo WShi XAbr XSen
	- 'Adelaide Addison'	ECha WAvo
	- var. ***alba***	CMea EPfP LRHS MMuc NDov NRHS SCob
	- 'Altrosa'	GWyn
	- 'Aureovariegata'	see *A. vulgaris* Vervaeneana Group
	- 'Blackbird' (Songbird Series) (d)	CWCL
	- ***clematiflora***	see *A. vulgaris* var. *stellata*
	- (Clementine Series) 'Clementine Blue' (d)	EPfP LRHS NRHS SPoG WCot

	- - 'Clementine Dark Purple' (d)	EPfP LRHS NRHS SPoG
	- - 'Clementine Red' (d)	EPfP
	- - 'Clementine Rose' (d)	LRHS NRHS SPoG
	- - 'Clementine Salmon Rose' (d)	EPfP LRHS NRHS SPoG
	- - 'Clementine White' (d)	CWCL EPfP LRHS NRHS SPoG WSpi
	- 'Crystal Star'	EPfP LRHS NRHS
	- 'Eyecatcher'	WCot
	- var. ***flore-pleno*** (d)	WFar
	- - black-flowered (d)	MMuc SEND WCot
	- - 'Dorothy Rose' (Dorothy Series) (d)	SPtp
	- - 'Double Pleat' (d)	EPfP
	- - 'Double Pleat' blue/white-flowered (d)	CBot
	- - 'Double Pleat' pink/white-flowered (d)	CWCL
	- - 'Jane Hollow' (d)	CPou
	- - pink-flowered (d)	CWCL
	- - 'Strawberry Ice Cream' (d)	NBro NNor
*	- - 'White Bonnet' (d)	CWCL
	- 'Heidi'	GWyn MMuc SEND
	- 'Mellow Yellow'	CTsd EHoe ELon LRHS NRHS WMoo
	- MUNSTEAD WHITE	see *A. vulgaris* 'Nivea'
§	- 'Nivea' ♀^{H7}	CBWd CBod CBot CDor CPou CRav CSpe EBee ECha ELan EPfP LCro LOPS NChi SEND SPoG WArt WCot WSpi
	- Pom Pom Series	WSpi
	- - 'Pom Pom Crimson'	NBro WCot
§	- var. ***stellata***	CDor CTsd ELan ESps GAbr GKev GWyn MCot NBro NNor WMoo
	- - Barlow Series (d)	WFar
	- - - 'Black Barlow' (d)	Widely available
	- - - 'Blue Barlow' (d)	CBod CBot CDor CSpe EBee ECtt EPfP GMaP GQue ILea IPot LRHS LSRN MJak NRHS SCob SPer SPhx SWvt WCot WSpi XLum
	- - - 'Bordeaux Barlow' (d)	LRHS NRHS STPC
	- - - 'Christa Barlow' (d)	EBee EPfP LRHS MBel NLar NRHS SHar WRHF
	- - - 'Nora Barlow' (d)	Widely available
	- - - 'Rose Barlow' (d)	EPfP LRHS LSRN NRHS WSpi
	- - - 'White Barlow' (d)	CAby CDor EPfP GMaP IBoy LCro LOPS LRHS MBel NRHS SPer SWvt
	- - blue-flowered	MMuc SEND
	- - 'Firewheel'	WMoo
	- - 'Greenapples' (d)	CDor CNor CWCL EBee ELan EPfP GAbr GKev GQue LRHS MCot NRHS SCob WHil WHoo
*	- - 'Iceberg'	WSpi
	- - 'Royal Purple' (d)	NBro NNor WMoo
	- - 'Ruby Port' (d)	Widely available
	- - white-flowered	CSpe NBro
	- variegated foliage	see *A. vulgaris* Vervaeneana Group
§	- Vervaeneana Group (v)	CDor CWCL ELan EPfP LRHS NPer SPlb SRms WHoo WMoo
	- - 'Woodside Blue' (v)	NWad
	- - 'Woodside White' (v)	WBrk
§	- 'William Guiness'	Widely available
	- 'William Guiness Doubles' (d)	GWyn WMoo
	'White Star' (Star Series)	CDor CWCL EBee ELan EPfP GMaP LRHS NPnk
	white-flowered	NRHS
	Winky Series	ELan GJos NNor SWvt WFar
	- 'Winky Blue-White'	GBin LRHS NLar NRHS WCFE
	- 'Winky Double Red-White' (d)	LRHS NRHS
	- 'Winky Purple-White'	GPSL LRHS NRHS
	- 'Winky Red-White'	LRHS NRHS SWvt
	- 'Winky Rose-Rose'	LRHS NRHS
	- 'Winky Wooh' (Winky Series)	NEgg
	yabeana	GKev GPSL SPad WMoo
	'Yellow Star' (Star Series) ♀^{H4}	CDor CWCL ECtt EPfP NPnk

Aquilegia × Semiaquilegia (*Ranunculaceae*)

	hybrid, blue-flowered	NGdn
§	'Roman Bronze'	WMoo

Arabis (*Brassicaceae*)

	alpina	MAsh SPlb
	- subsp. ***caucasica*** 'Arctic Joy' (v)	MAvo WCot
	- - 'Corfe Castle'	ECtt
	- - 'Douler Angevine' (v)	CBod ECtt ELon NEoE NHpl SPoG SRms
	- - 'Flore Pleno' (d) ♀^{H5}	CElw CFis CHid CSpe CTri ECtt ELan ESps EWld GAbr GJos SBch SRms WBrk WHoo XLum
	- - 'Hedi'	MJak
	- - 'Little Treasure White'	GWyn
	- - 'Lotti Deep Rose'	MHol
	- - 'Pixie Cream'	ECtt MHol MMuc NGdn
	- - 'Rosea'	GJos LRHS SRms
§	- - 'Schneehaube' ♀^{H6}	CTri EAJP ECtt EPfP GMaP GWyn LRHS MJak NGdn SPoG SRms
	- - SNOWCAP	see *A. alpina* subsp. *caucasica* 'Schneehaube'
	- - 'Variegata' (v)	ELan GMaP MJak SPoG SRms
	androsacea	CPla SRms
	× ***arendsii*** 'Compinkie'	SPlb SRms
	blepharophylla	CPla EPfP MHol NPri
§	- 'Frühlingszauber' ♀^{H5}	CTri EAJP ELan EPfP GJos MMuc NGdn SPoG SRms WCot
	- 'Rose Delight'	LRHS NRHS
	- 'Rote Sensation'	ELan NGdn
	- SPRING CHARM	see *A. blepharophylla* 'Frühlingszauber'
	carduchorum	XLum
	cypria	CPla
	ferdinandi-coburgi 'Aureovariegata' (v)	CMea CTri ECtt ELan SWvt
	- 'Old Gold'	CTal EHoe EPfP EPot ESps GWyn MAsh MHer MJak NRya SPoG SRms SRot SWvt WCFE WRHF
	- 'Variegata'	see *A. procurrens* 'Variegata'
	procurrens	WCot XLum XSen
	- 'Glacier'	GJos
§	- 'Variegata' (v) ♀^{H5}	CTal ECtt EHoe ELan EPfP ESps EWes GAbr GKev GPSL MBrN MHer MJak SPlb SRms SRot WCot
	pumila	GKev
	SNOW CAP	see *A. alpina* subsp. *caucasica* 'Schneehaube'

Arachniodes (*Dryopteridaceae*)

aristata	NLos
davalliaeformis	CBdn CRos EBee LRHS NLos NRHS WPGP
miqueliana	CBdn NLos
rhomboidea new	CBdn
simplicior	CCCN CRos EBee EShb EUJe LLWG LRHS NLos NRHS SCob SPlb WCot
standishii	CBdn CRos EBee EShb LEdu LRHS NLos NRHS WCot WPGP

Araiostegia (*Davalliaceae*)

faberiana	CExl
hymenophylloides	WCot
parvipinnata	see *A. perdurans*
§ ***perdurans***	CFil NLos WCot WPGP
- B&SWJ 1608	EBee WCru
pulchra HWJ 1007	WCru

Aralia ✿ (*Araliaceae*)

CW&T 6257	CMCN
apioides	IMou LEdu
- EDHCH 9720	SBrt WCru
armata B&SWJ 6916	WCru
bipinnata Blanco CWJ 12407	WCru
- RWJ 10101	WCru
cachemirica	CDTJ GCal MBrN NBid SMad SPlb WCru WHal WMoo
californica	EBee GCal GPoy LEdu NLar SBrt WCru
castanopsidicola CWJ 12411	WCru
chapaensis B&SWJ 11812	WCru
- HWJ 1013	WCru
chinensis misapplied	see *A. elata*
chinensis L. BWJ 8102	WCru
continentalis	LEdu MPie NLar WHoo
- B&SWJ 8437	WCru
- B&SWJ 8524	WCru
cordata Thunb.	CAgr GCal LEdu WFar
- B&SWJ 5596	WCru
- var. ***sachalinensis***	NLar
- - B&SWJ 4773	WCru
- 'Sun King'	CAby CBct CBod CCht EBee ECtt EPfP EUJe IBoy LCro LOPS LRHS LSou MHol MNrw MPie NBid NLar NSti SCob SPad SPoG SWvt WFar WHil WMoo
dasyphylla new	LEdu
decaisneana B&SWJ 6794	WCru
- RWJ 9910	WCru
§ ***elata***	CAby CBcs CDul CExl CHll CMac CRos CTsd EBee ELan EPfP EUJe LRHS LSRN MBlu MGos MMuc SArc SCob SGol SPer SPoG SWvt WFar WSpi
- B&SWJ 5480	WCru
- 'Albomarginata'	see *A. elata* 'Variegata'
- 'Aureo-marginata' (v)	WSpi
- 'Aureovariegata' (v) ♀H5	CBcs EWes NLar SCob
- 'Golden Umbrella' (v)	EUJe LSRN NLar
- 'Silver Umbrella' (v)	EUJe NLar WSpi
§ - 'Variegata' (v) ♀H5	CBcs CDul NLar SCob SWvt
foliolosa B&SWJ 8360	WCru
- NJM 13.033 new	WPGP
- NJM 13.061 new	WPGP
kansuensis BWJ 7650	WCru
- CD&R 2289	WCru
leschenaultii B&SWJ 9515	WCru
- B&SWJ 11789	WCru
nudicaulis L.	GPoy
papyrifera	see *Tetrapanax papyrifer*
racemosa	CBod GPoy LEdu SRms WMoo
- B&SWJ 9570	WCru
searelliana B&SWJ 11736	WCru
sieboldii de Vriese	see *Fatsia japonica*
spinosa L.	EBtc GQue MBlu NChi SPlb
subcordata HWJK 2385	WCru
verticillata B&SWJ 11797	WCru
vietnamensis B&SWJ 12349E	WCru

Araucaria (*Araucariaceae*)

sp.	LPra MAsh
angustifolia	CDTJ WPGP
angustifolia* × *araucana	CBrP GMcL
§ ***araucana***	Widely available
bidwillii	MMuc SEND
excelsa misapplied	see *A. heterophylla*
§ ***heterophylla*** ♀H2	CCCN
imbricata	see *A. araucana*

Araujia (*Apocynaceae*)

sericifera	CBcs CHll CMac ECre LRHS SVen WCot WSHC

Arbutus ✿ (*Ericaceae*)

sp.	LPra
× ***andrachnoides*** ♀H4	CHGN CJun CRos CTho ELan EPfP LEdu LRHS LSRN MAsh MRav NRHS SArc SPoG WPGP WSpi
menziesii	CBcs EPfP MBlu
× ***reyorum*** 'Marina'	CJun CRos EBee ELan EPfP LEdu LRHS MAsh MBlu SMad SPoG WPGP
unedo	Widely available
- 'Atlantic' ♀H5	CCCN CJun CRos EPfP LRHS LSRN MAsh MGos SAko SBig SGbt SGol SWvt
- 'Compacta'	CBcs CCCN CRos EUJe LRHS MAsh NLar SGol SLon SPoG SWvt WFar
- 'Elfin King'	CRos EPfP LRHS MAsh SLon SWvt
- 'Quercifolia'	CCCN CDul CHll CJun ELan LEdu LLHF LRHS MAsh NLar WHor
- ROSELILY ('Minlily'PBR)	SBig
- f. ***rubra*** ♀H5	CAgr CBcs CDul CJun CMac CRos CSBt CTri ELan EPfP LRHS LSRN MAsh MBlu MMuc MRav NLar SEND SGol SMad SPer SPoG SSta SWvt WPGP XSen
xalapensis	CFil SPlb

Archontophoenix (*Arecaceae*)

cunninghamiana	XBlo

Arctanthemum (*Asteraceae*)

§ ***arcticum***	ECha MMuc NLar XLum
- 'Polarstern'	WFar
- 'Roseum'	EBee ELon WFar
- 'Schwefelglanz'	EBee WFar

Arcterica see *Pieris*

Arctium (*Asteraceae*)

lappa	GPoy SRms SVic WHer WSFF
minus	EBWF

Arctostaphylos (*Ericaceae*)

uva-ursi	GMcL GPoy NLar SPlb
- 'Snowcap'	MAsh
- 'Vancouver Jade'	CMac CRos EBee ELan GKin LRHS LSRN MAsh SCoo SLon SPer SPoG SWvt

Arctotheca (*Asteraceae*)

calendula	EBee WPGP WSHC

Arctotis (*Asteraceae*)

HANNAH ('Archnah'PBR)	CAby CCht CRav ECtt MBNS

HAYLEY ('Archley'PBR)	CCCN ECtt MBNS
'Heidi'	CCht CRav MBNS
'Holly'	CCht CRav
× ***hybrida*** hort. 'Apricot'	CCCN ECtt SVen
- 'Flame' ♀H2	CAby CCCN CRav ECtt MBNS SCoo SVen
- 'Red Devil'	CCCN CPla CRav LSou MBNS SCoo SVen
- 'Wine'	CCCN CCht CPla CRav LSou MBNS SCoo SRkn

Ardisia (*Primulaceae*)

PAB 7988 from Mizoram, India	LEdu
japonica	WCot
- B&SWJ 1032	SMad WCru
- var. ***angusta***	WCot
- 'Ito Fukurin' (v)	EBee WPGP
- var. ***minor***	GEdr
- - B&SWJ 1841	WCru
- - B&SWJ 3809	WCru

Areca (*Arecaceae*)

triandra	XBlo

Arecastrum see *Syagrus*

Arenaria (*Caryophyllaceae*)

§ ***alfacarensis***	EPot NLar SPlb WAbe WOld
balearica	CWCL EWes GCrg LLWG MAsh NHpl NRHS NSla SPlb SRms
capillaris	CTri
festucoides	CPBP GKev WAbe
grandiflora	XLum
kansuensis	NLar
ledebouriana	EDAr NLar SBrt
montana ♀H5	CAby CMea CRos ECha ECtt EDAr EPfP GMaP LRHS MGos NRHS NSla SPlb SRms SRot WAbe WFar WKif WWFP
- 'Avalanche'	ECtt LSun MHol
- 'Blizzard'	EPfP
pulvinata	see *A. alfacarensis*
purpurascens	EPot EWes GCrg LLHF NLar SRms WAbe WThu
tetraquetra subsp. ***amabilis***	EPot
'The Pearl'	CBod

Arenga (*Arecaceae*)

micrantha	EUJe WCot

Argania (*Sapotaceae*)

spinosa	WPGP

Argemone (*Papaveraceae*)

grandiflora	CSpe EPPr SBch
mexicana	ELan IMou SPhx

Argyranthemum ✿ (*Asteraceae*)

'Bridesmaid'	MHom
broussonetii	MHom
canariense hort.	see *A. frutescens* subsp. *canariae*
CHERRY HARMONY ('Supa532') (Daisy Crazy Series) (d)	MCot
CHERRY LOVE ('Supacher') (Daisy Crazy Series) (d) ♀H2	CCCN
'Cornish Gold' ♀H2	CBcs CCCN CPla ECtt EShb
double pink-flowered (d)	SVen
'Everest'	CRos LRHS NRHS SPoG
'Flamingo'	see *Rhodanthemum gayanum*
§ ***foeniculaceum*** misapplied	ELan
- pink-flowered	see *A.* 'Petite Pink'
§ ***foeniculaceum*** (Willd.) Webb & Sch.Bip.	MCot
- 'Royal Haze' ♀H2	CCCN CHll NPer
§ ***frutescens***	LCro LOPS SEND WKif
§ - subsp. ***canariae*** ♀H2	CCCN MHom
'Gill's Pink'	MHom
gracile	CHll
- 'Chelsea Girl' ♀H2	CCCN CSpe MBNS MCot MHom WKif
'Guernsey Pink'	MHom
GYPSY ROSE ('M9/18d')	CCCN
'Jamaica Primrose' ♀H2	CSpe CTri ECtt
'Jamaica Snowstorm'	see *A.* 'Snow Storm'
LARITA BANANA SPLIT ('Kleaf10067') (LaRita Series) ♀H2	CRos LRHS NRHS
'Levada Cream' ♀H2	MHom
(Madeira Series) MADEIRA CHERRY RED ('Bonmadcher'PBR) ♀H2	CRav
- MADEIRA CRESTED DOUBLE WHITE **new**	LSou
- MADEIRA CRESTED HOT PINK ('Bonmad 11277') **new**	LSou
- MADEIRA CRESTED IVORY ('Bonmadcivy') (d)	SPoG
- MADEIRA CRESTED PINK ('Bonmadcink'PBR)	SPoG
- MADEIRA CRESTED YELLOW ('Bonmadcrel'PBR)	LSou SPoG
- MADEIRA RED ('Bonmadre'PBR)	LSou SPoG
- MADEIRA WHITE IMPROVED ('Bonmadwitim'PBR)	SPoG
- MADEIRA WHITE ('Ohmadleva') **new**	CRav
§ ***maderense*** ♀H2	CHll MHom
'Mary Wootton' (d)	ECtt MHom
mawii	see *Rhodanthemum gayanum*
METEOR RED ('Supa742') (Daisy Crazy Series)	CBcs CPla CWGN MBNS
ochroleucum	see *A. maderense*
PACIFIC GOLD ('Pacargone'PBR) (d)	CBcs CWGN
§ 'Petite Pink' ♀H2	CCCN
PING-PONG ('Innping'PBR) (d)	CCCN
'Pink Australian' (d)	MHom
'Pink Delight'	see *A.* 'Petite Pink'
POMPONETTE PINK ('Supa392'PBR) (d)	CBcs
'Powder Puff' (d)	ECtt
'Reflection Pink'	CRav
'Shirley's Yellow'	MHom
'Silver Queen'	see *A. foeniculaceum* misapplied
§ 'Snow Storm' ♀H2	MHom
'Starlight' ♀H2	MCot MHom
'Sugar and Ice' (d)	CCCN
'Sugar Baby' (d)	CCCN
'Summer Cloud'	MCot
'Summer Melody' (d)	CBcs CCCN
'Summer Pink'	CCCN
'Vancouver' (d) ♀H2	CCCN ECtt EShb

'Vera'	CCCN
'Weymouth Pink'	MHom
'White Spider'	CCCN ELan

Argyrocytisus (*Papilionaceae*)

battandieri	Widely available
- 'Yellow Tail' ♀H4	CBot CDul CEnd CRos ELan EPfP EUJe LRHS MGos NLar NOra NRHS SPoG SSta WHar

Arisaema (*Araceae*)

CC 4904	CExl
CC 5511	CExl
album	XLum
amurense	CElw CFil LAma LLHF MMoz WThu
§ - subsp. ***robustum***	WBor
angustatum	WCru
var. ***peninsulae*** B&SWJ 8639 new	
auriculatum	GKev LAma
- var. ***hungyaense***	LRHS
brachyspathum	see *A. heterophyllum*
brevipes	CExl
candidissimum ♀H4	CElw CFil CPne CSpe CTal ECha EHrv ELon EPPr EPfP EPot GEdr GKev IRob LAma MMoz MRav NLar NSla SDeJ SDir WBor WCot WHal WPnP
- from Yunnan	IRob
- white-flowered	CFil GEdr LAma SDir
ciliatum	CPla GEdr LAma MMoz NLar SRot
- var. ***liubaense***	CAby CWCL EPfP EPot GKev MMoz WCot
- - CT 369	CExl EPfP SDys WPGP
- - GG 97091	WCot
concinnum	EUJe GEdr GKev LAma SDir WPnP XLum
consanguineum	CAby CBcs CExl CTal EBee EPfP GBin GCal GEdr GKev LAma MMoz WCot WPGP WPnP XLum
- from Burma new	GCal
- subsp. ***kelung-insulare*** B&SWJ 256	WCru
- 'The Perfect Wave'	WCot
- variegated (v)	WCot
costatum	CCCN CFil EBee EPfP EPot GKev LAma MMoz SChF SDir WCot WPGP XLum
dracontium	EUJe XLum
ehimense	LAma
elephas	LAma
engleri	GKev LAma LRHS
erubescens	XEll
exappendiculatum	CAby CExl CFil LAma LRHS MMoz
fargesii	CExl CFil EPot EUJe GKev LAma MMoz SChF XLum
flavum	CFil CWCL EPfP EPot GCal GKev LAma MMoz NPnk SDir SPlb WHil
- CC 6303	ITim
- subsp. ***abbreviatum*** CC 6300	ITim
formosanum B&SWJ 280	WCru
§ ***franchetianum***	CExl GKev LAma
galeatum	EPot GKev LAma LRHS WCot XLum
grapsospadix B&SWJ 7000	WCru
§ ***griffithii***	EUJe GEdr GKev LAma LRHS MMoz NBid NLar SDeJ SDir XLum
- var. ***pradhanii***	GEdr GKev LAma XLum
- - WJC 13660 new	WCru
aff. ***griffithii***	SDir
helleborifolium	see *A. tortuosum*
§ ***heterophyllum***	GKev ITim LAma
inkiangense	LAma
intermedium	LAma MMoz MNrw XLum
iyoanum	LAma
subsp. ***nakaianum***	
jacquemontii	CAby CFil GEdr GKev GLog LAma MMoz NLar SDir XLum
- CC 5184	ITim
aff. ***jacquemontii***	SDir
japonicum Blume	see *A. serratum* var. *mayebarae*
japonicum Komarov	see *A. serratum*
jinshajiangense	CExl
kishidae	GEdr LAma
kiushianum	GKev LAma LRHS SDir WCot
- 'Kikkou-fu'	GEdr
lichiangense	GKev LAma LRHS
lingyunense	LAma
§ ***lobatum***	CExl LAma
maximowiczii	GEdr LAma
§ ***nepenthoides***	CFil EPot EUJe GEdr GKev LAma LRHS MMoz SDir WPnP XLum
ochraceum	see *A. nepenthoides*
onoticum	see *A. lobatum*
petelotii B&SWJ 9706	WCru
propinquum	GKev LAma MMoz NLar XLum
purpureogaleatum	see *A. franchetianum*
rhombiforme	LAma
ringens misapplied	see *A. amurense* subsp. *robustum*
ringens ambig.	CDTJ EPfP GEdr GKev LRHS MMoz SChF
ringens (Thunberg) Schott	LAma LEdu
- f. ***sieboldii*** B&SWJ 551	WCru
aff. ***ringens***	SDir
robustum	see *A. amurense* subsp. *robustum*
sazensoo	GEdr LAma
§ ***serratum***	GKev LAma MMoz
§ - var. ***mayebarae***	GEdr GKev LAma
- var. ***serratum***	LAma
sikokianum	EPot GEdr GKev LAma LLHF LRHS NHpl NLar SDir WPnP
- variegated (v)	GEdr
speciosum	CExl CFil GEdr GKev LAma LRHS MMoz SDeJ SDir SPlb WCot WPnP XLum
* - var. ***magnificum***	CBcs GEdr GKev LAma NLar XLum
- var. ***mirabile***	GKev LAma LRHS XLum
taiwanense	CAby GEdr
- B&SWJ 269	WCru
- f. ***cinereum*** B&SWJ 19121	WCru
tashiroi	GKev LAma
ternatipartitum	GKev LAma LRHS
thunbergii	GEdr LAma WBor
- subsp. ***autumnale*** B&SWJ 1425	WCru
- subsp. ***urashima***	GKev LAma
§ ***tortuosum***	CExl CFil CPne ECha EPfP EUJe GKev LAma LEdu NLar SDir WPnP XLum
- 'Black Rod'	CFil
- var. ***helleborifolium***	NBid XLum
tosaense	GKev LAma LRHS
triphyllum	CElw CExl EPot EUJe GKev GPoy LAma NLar SPlb
§ ***utile***	EPot EUJe GEdr GKev LAma XLum
verrucosum	see *A. griffithii*
- var. ***utile***	see *A. utile*
yamatense	LAma
subsp. ***sugimotoi***	

yunnanense	LAma

Arisarum (*Araceae*)

proboscideum	Widely available
vulgare	GKev

Aristea (*Iridaceae*)

§ ***capitata***	CHll
ecklonii	CBcs CExl CPou CPrp CTsd EBee EPri EShb MHer SBrt
- GWJ 9469	WCru
ensifolia	ELan
thyrsiflora	see *A. capitata*

Aristolochia (*Aristolochiaceae*)

baetica	CExl SBrt
bianorii	SBrt
californica	LEdu SBrt
chilensis	CCCN SPlb
clematitis	GPoy LEdu
contorta B&SWJ 12613	WCru
cucurbitifolia B&SWJ 7043	WCru
durior	see *A. macrophylla*
fimbriata B&SWJ 13612	WCru
gigantea 🏆H1b	CCCN CHll
grandiflora	CCCN
griffithii B&SWJ 2118	WCru
- Mabiluo Strain **new**	GCal
kaempferi	CCCN
- B&SWJ 293	WCru
× ***kewensis***	CCCN
§ ***macrophylla***	CBcs CCCN CMac EPfP MRav SBrt WSpi
manshuriensis	EWld
- B&SWJ 12557	WCru
moupinensis BWJ 8181	WCru
paucinervis	SBrt
sempervirens	CMac LEdu WCru WSHC
- B&SWJ 13600 **new**	WCru
serpentaria	SBrt
sipho	see *A. macrophylla*
trilobata	SBrt

Aristotelia (*Elaeocarpaceae*)

§ ***chilensis***	LEdu
- 'Variegata' (v)	CCCN CMCN CMac EBee SPlb
macqui	see *A. chilensis*
peduncularis	CExl
serrata	SVen

Armeria (*Plumbaginaceae*)

§ ***alliacea*** (Cav.) Hoffmanns. & Link	ECha SPhx XSen
- f. ***leucantha***	SPhx SRms WMoo
alpina	GJos GKev
arenaria	EBWF
'Avalanche'	MHol
'Brutus'	MAvo MHCG
caespitosa	see *A. juniperifolia*
- 'Bevan's Variety'	see *A. juniperifolia* 'Bevan's Variety'
curvifolia	GAbr
Joystick Series	MMuc
- 'Joystick Lilac Shades'	CRos EBee ELan EPfP GEdr LPmr LRHS NRHS SPoG
- 'Joystick Red'	CRos ELan EPfP EShb GEdr LPmr LRHS NRHS SPoG WWFP
- 'Joystick White'	CRos ELan EPfP LPmr LRHS NRHS SPoG
§ ***juniperifolia*** 🏆H5	CMea CRos ELan EPfP GCrg LRHS MHer NRHS NSla SPlb SPoG SRms XLum
- 'Alba'	CMea ELan EPfP GBin GCrg GMaP ITim MHer MMuc NHpl SPoG SRms SRot WAbe WHoo WThu
- 'Beechwood'	GCrg
§ - 'Bevan's Variety' 🏆H5	ECha ELan ELon EPfP EPot GEdr GMaP MMuc NCou NLar NRya SPoG SRms SRot WAbe WHoo
- dark-flowered	WAbe
- rose-flowered	ITim
§ ***maritima***	CHab CRos CWld EBWF ECtt ELan EPfP GJos LRHS MBel MSCN NEgg NRHS SWvt WCFE WMoo
- 'A Little in the Red'	GCrg
- 'Alba'	CAby CBcs CElw CTri ECha ELan EPfP ESps ETMg GJos GMaP LSun MBel MCot MHol MMuc NHpl NRHS NRya SEND SPlb SPoG SRms WCFE WMoo
- 'Armada Rose'	CRos GKev LRHS NRHS
- 'Bloodstone'	CTri ELan
- 'Corsica'	CMea CTri ECha MMuc
- DÜSSELDORF PRIDE	see *A. maritima* 'Düsseldorfer Stolz'
§ - 'Düsseldorfer Stolz'	CBod CElw CRos ECha ECtt EDAr ELan EPfP GCrg GKev GMaP LRHS MCot NRHS SPoG SWvt XLum
- 'Glory of Holland'	EPot
- 'In the Red'	CAby CMea ECha EHoe EPPr EShb GCal GCrg GMaP MAvo MHer MMuc NHpl NRya NSla SEND SPad SRms SRot SWvt WFar WHoo WRHF
- 'Laucheana'	WHoo WMoo
- 'Ministicks Rose'	CRos LRHS
- 'Ministicks White'	CRos LRHS
- 'Morning Star White'	CBod
- 'Nifty Thrifty' (v)	CTri ECtt EHoe MHer MHol NLar SPoG SRms
- 'Pink Lusitanica'	NLar
- 'Ruby Glow'	CTri
- 'Schöne von Fellbach'	XLum
- 'Splendens'	CBcs CRos CTri EDAr EPfP ESps GMaP LRHS MHer MHol MJak MMuc NHpl NMir NRHS NRya SPhx SPoG WMoo XLum
- 'Splendens Alba'	XLum
- 'Vindictive' 🏆H5	CMea EPfP
- white foliage	LRHS NRHS
plantaginea misapplied	see *A. alliacea* (Cav.) Hoffmanns. & Link
pseudarmeria	ELan EPfP XLum
- (Ballerina Series) 'Ballerina'	CRos NRHS
- - 'Ballerina Lilac' **new**	LRHS WFar
- - 'Ballerina Red'	CRos GEdr LRHS NRHS SRms WFar WTor
- - 'Ballerina White'	CRos LRHS NRHS
- hybrids	CTri ELan
splendens 'Perfecta'	CRos LRHS NRHS
'Vesuvius'	XLum
vulgaris	see *A. maritima*
welwitschii	IFoB SBrt

Armoracia (*Brassicaceae*)

§ ***rusticana***	CBod CFGn CHby CTri ENfk GPoy LOPS MHer MMuc MNHC NPer SPoG SRms SVic WHer WHrl WSpi XAbr

- 'Variegata' (v)	CRos EBee ELan GCal IFoB LEdu NRHS NSti SMad SRms WHer WMoo

Arnebia (*Boraginaceae*)

densiflora	LLHF
echioides	see *A. pulchra*
longiflora	see *A. pulchra*
§ ***pulchra***	LLHF

Arnica (*Asteraceae*)

chamissonis Less.	CBod CHby EBee ENfk MNHC NLar SRms
cordifolia	CPla
montana	GPoy MHer MNHC SRms XAbr

Arnoglossum (*Asteraceae*)

§ ***plantagineum***	SBrt SPhx
reniforme	SBrt

Aronia ✿ (*Rosaceae*)

arbutifolia	CAco CDul CTri EPfP LSRN MBlu MMuc SGol SLon SPlb
- 'Erecta'	CDul CRos CTho EBee ELan EWTr LRHS MBlu MGil MMuc NLar SPoG SRms SWvt WCFE
melanocarpa	CCVT CDul CMCN CRos CSpe CTsd ELan EPfP EWTr GKin LRHS MAsh MMuc NRHS WGrn
- var. ***grandifolia***	CJun
- 'Hugin'	CAgr CJun LEdu MCoo NLar
× ***prunifolia***	WGrn
- 'Aron' (F)	CAgr CJun MCoo
- 'Autumn Magic'	CBcs CJun CTho EBee ELan LRHS MAsh NEgg
- 'Brilliant'	CBcs CDul CRos CTri EBee EPfP ETMg LRHS MGil MMuc NEgg SGol SPer WAvo WHar
- 'Karhumäki' (F)	NLar
- 'Nero' (F)	CAgr CBcs GBin LEdu MCoo NLar WPGP
- 'Serina' (F)	CJun
- 'Viking' (F)	CAgr CDul CJun CTho EBee ECrN EPfP EPom EWTr GBin IDee LBuc LCro LEdu LOPS LRHS MBlu NLar SGol WFar WPGP

Arrhenatherum (*Poaceae*)

elatius	CHab EBWF
- var. ***bulbosum***	GMcL
- - 'Variegatum' (v)	EBee EHoe ELan EPPr GBin GKev GMaP GQue MMoz MMuc NBid NWad SEND WMoo

Artedia (*Apiaceae*)

squamata new	SPhx

Artemisia ✿ (*Asteraceae*)

RBS 0207	CExl
from Taiwan	WHer
§ ***abrotanum***	CBod CEls CExl CHby EBee ECha ECtt ELan ENfk GBin GMaP GPoy IDee LEdu MCot MHer MMuc MNHC MRav NLar NSti SMad SPad SPer SRms WHer WHoo XAbr XLum XSen
- 'Courson'	XSen
absinthium	CBod CEls CHab ELan ENfk ESps GPoy MHer MNHC NLar NSti SRms SVic WHer WTre XAbr XSen
- 'Lambrook Giant'	CEls
- 'Lambrook Mist'	CEls CFis CMac CRos ECtt ELan EPfP GQue LRHS MBel MRav NRHS XLum
- 'Lambrook Silver'	CEls CExl CRos CSam EBee ECha EHrv ELan EPfP ESps GMaP LRHS LSRN MHer MMuc MRav NBro NRHS SCob SLim SPer SRms SWvt
- 'Silver Ghost'	CEls
afra	CEls XSen
§ ***alba***	CBod CEls GPoy SRms XSen
§ - 'Canescens' ♀H4	CBot CEls CSam EBee ECha ELan EPfP GMaP LRHS MAsh MHer MRav NLar SBrt WCFE XSen
annua	CEls
anomala	CEls
§ ***arborescens*** ♀H3	CBot CEls GAbr GMcL SPer
- 'Brass Band'	see *A.* 'Powis Castle'
- 'Faith Raven' ♀H3	CEls GBin MBNS NLar
- 'Porquerolles'	CEls
arbuscula	CEls
argentea misapplied	see *A. arborescens*
argentea L'Hér.	CEls
argyi	CEls
§ ***armeniaca***	CEls CRos LRHS WHer
assoana	see *A. caucasica*
atrata	CEls
barrelieri	CEls
caerulescens	CEls WCot
subsp. ***cretacea***	
- subsp. ***gallica***	CEls
californica	CEls WHer
- 'Canyon Gray'	CEls
- 'Montara' new	CEls
campestris	XLum XSen
- subsp. ***borealis***	CEls
- subsp. ***campestris***	CEls
- subsp. ***maritima***	CEls
- - from Wales	CEls
camphorata	see *A. alba*
cana	CEls
canariensis	see *A. thuscula*
canescens misapplied	see *A. alba* 'Canescens'
canescens Willd.	see *A. armeniaca*
capillaris	CEls XLum
carruthii	CEls
§ ***caucasica*** ♀H4	CEls EWes MHer SPhx SRms SRot
chamaemelifolia	CBod CEls MHer SRms XSen
cretacea	see *A. nutans*
discolor Dougl. ex Besser	see *A. michauxiana*
douglasiana	CEls
- 'Valerie Finnis'	see *A. ludoviciana* 'Valerie Finnis'
dracunculus	ECha EWTr MNHC MRav SPlb SRms WBrk XSen
- French	CBod CEls CHby CRav CTsd ENfk GPoy LEdu MHer NPri SEND SPhm WGwG XAbr XLum
- Russian	CEls ENfk LOPS SVic
- 'Thüringen'	IMou
ferganensis	CEls
filifolia	CEls
fragrans	CEls
frigida ♀H5	CEls
genipi	CEls
glacialis	CEls
gmelinii	CEls
gnaphalodes	see *A. ludoviciana*
gorgonum	CEls SEND
gracilis hort.	see *A. scoparia*
'Hausserman'	XLum

herba-alba CEls XSen
indica var. ***momiyamae*** CEls
japonica CEls
kitadakensis 'Guizhou' see *A. lactiflora* Guizhou Group
laciniata CEls
lactiflora ♀H7 CEls CRos EBee ECha ELan GMaP MRav NDov NGdn SPer SRms WMoo WWtn XLum
- NJM 11.010 WPGP
- 'Elfenbein' EBee EPPr GCal IMou MNrw MRav SMHy
§ - Guizhou Group Widely available
- - 'Dark Delight' CEls ECtt EWes LEdu
- 'Jim Russell' CDor CEls CElw EBee ECtt EWes MPie SPhx WWFP
- 'Laigong' LEdu
- ***purpurea*** see *A. lactiflora* Guizhou Group
- 'Weisses Wunder' EBee
lanata Willd. see *A. caucasica*
lanata Lam. XSen
laxa see *A. umbelliformis*
'Little Mice' CEls NLar
longifolia XSen
§ ***ludoviciana*** CEls ELan IFoB NLar NPer SRms WCFE WFar XLum
- subsp. ***ludoviciana*** var. ***incompta*** CEls
- - var. ***latiloba*** CEls EHoe NBro SWvt
- subsp. ***mexicana*** var. ***albula*** CEls
- 'Silver Queen' Widely available
- 'Valerie Finnis' ♀H7 Widely available
maritima 'Coca-Cola' EBee XSen
- var. ***maritima*** CEls
mauiensis CEls
§ ***michauxiana*** CEls
molinieri CEls XSen
mutellina see *A. umbelliformis*
niitakayamensis CEls
nova CEls
§ ***nutans*** CEls MRav
palmeri hort. see *A. ludoviciana*
aff. ***parviflora*** CLD 1531 CEls
pedemontana see *A. caucasica*
pontica CBod CEls EBee ECha EHoe ELan GMaP GPoy LEdu MAvo MNHC MRav NBro NSti SEND SPer SRms WFar WHil WHoo WPGP XSen
§ 'Powis Castle' ♀H3 Widely available
princeps CEls GPoy LEdu
procera Willd. see *A. abrotanum*
purshiana see *A. ludoviciana*
pycnocephala CEls
- 'David's Choice' CEls
ramosa CEls
'Rosenschleier' CEls EPPr EWes GCal GQue SHar WWtn
schmidtiana ♀H5 CEls ECha SRms
- 'Nana' ♀H5 CBcs CEls CMea CRav CRos EBee ECtt EDAr EHoe ELan EPfP EPot EUJe GMaP LRHS MAsh MCot MHer MRav MSwo NLar NRHS SPer SPlb SPoG SRms SRot WCFE XLum XSen
- 'Nana Attraction' CBod CRos LRHS NLar NRHS SRot
§ ***scoparia*** SMad
selengensis CEls
splendens misapplied see *A. alba* 'Canescens'
splendens Willd. var. ***brachyphylla*** MAsh
stelleriana CEls CTri ECha GKev IFoB MAvo NBro NLar SRms
- RBS 0207 CEls
- from Alaska WCot
- 'Boughton Silver' CBod CDor CEls CRos EBee ECtt EHoe ELan EPfP EShb ESps GMaP LRHS MAsh MBel MRav NEgg NLar NRHS NSti SPer SPoG SRms SWvt
- 'Mori' see *A. stelleriana* 'Boughton Silver'
- 'Nana' CEls SWvt
- 'Prostrata' see *A. stelleriana* 'Boughton Silver'
- 'Shemya' **new** CEls
- 'Silver Brocade' see *A. stelleriana* 'Boughton Silver'
taurica CEls
§ ***thuscula*** CEls
tridentata WHer
- subsp. ***tridentata*** CEls
- subsp. ***wyomingensis*** CEls
§ ***umbelliformis*** CEls
vallesiaca CEls
verlotiorum CEls
vulgaris CBod CEls GPoy MNHC WHer
- 'Cragg-Barber Eye' (v) EBee
- ORIENTAL LIMELIGHT ('Janlim') (v) CBod CEls EBee EHoe EPfP GAbr GMcL NEgg NLar SWvt WHrl WOut WPnP
- 'Variegata' (v) CEls ELan EPfP SRms WMoo XLum
× ***wurzellii*** CEls

Arthropodium (*Asparagaceae*)

candidum CBot MPie
- 'Little Lilia' (v) **new** WCot
- 'Maculatum' LEdu NHpl SPlb
- 'Purpureum' GEdr NWsh
cirratum CPbh CSpe CTsd MHer MPie
- 'Matapouri Bay' CBcs SEND
milleflorum SBrt
minus CExl

artichoke, globe see *Cynara cardunculus* Scolymus Group

artichoke, Jerusalem see *Helianthus tuberosus*

Arum (*Araceae*)

byzantinum GKev
'Chameleon' CDor EPri SEND SMad SPer WBrk WCot WRHF
§ ***concinnatum*** CTal GKev
- 'Mount Ida' LEdu
cornutum see *Sauromatum venosum*
creticum CBro CFil CPne CTal EBee GCal MNrw SDir WBor
- 'Karpathos' CExl MMoz WCot
- 'Marmaris White' EBee WCot
- white-flowered **new** CMea
- white-spotted EWes
creticum × ***italicum*** EBee
cyrenaicum CFil
dioscoridis GKev SDir
- JCA 195.197 WCot
- var. ***cyprium*** EBee
§ - var. ***dioscoridis*** GKev
- var. ***liepoldtii*** see *A. dioscoridis* var. *dioscoridis*
- var. ***smithii*** see *A. dioscoridis* var. *dioscoridis*
- var. ***syriacum*** GKev
dracunculus see *Dracunculus vulgaris*
euxinum GKev
hygrophilum WCot

italicum	CBod CTri GBin GWyn IBoy IRob LAma LCro LOPS MHol SDeJ WCot WShi
- subsp. ***albispathum***	CFil MMoz
- 'Angelique'	WCot
- 'Edward Dougal'	WCot WFar
- 'Green Marble'	WFar
- subsp. ***italicum***	GKev WBrk
§ - - 'Marmoratum' ♀H6	Widely available
- - 'Spotted Jack'	WCot
- - 'Tiny'	CExl GCal NChi SMHy SWvt WRHF
- - 'Uniquity' **new**	WCot
§ - - 'White Winter'	WBrk WCot
- 'Nancy Lindsay'	MMoz
- subsp. ***neglectum***	SChr
- - 'Miss Janay Hall' (v)	EHoe MMoz WCot
- 'Pictum'	see *A. italicum* subsp. *italicum* 'Marmoratum'
aff. ***italicum***	SDir
italicum* × *maculatum	EHrv WHer
korolkowii	WCot
maculatum	EBWF EPot GKev GPoy LAma MHer MRav NLar WHer WShi
- 'Painted Lady' (v)	WCot
- 'Pleddel'	MRav
- Tar Spot Group	SEND
nickelii	see *A. concinnatum*
§ ***nigrum***	GKev LLHF SBrt
palaestinum	GKev
petteri misapplied	see *A. nigrum*
pictum	CExl CMac CTal EWes GKev LEdu
- 'Taff's Form'	see *A. italicum* subsp. *italicum* 'White Winter'
purpureospathum	CFil GKev
rupicola var. ***rupicola***	GKev

Aruncus ✿ (*Rosaceae*)

aethusifolius ♀H7	Widely available
- 'Little Gem'	WCru
asiaticus B&SWJ 8624	WCru
'Bastei'	IMou
dioicus	Widely available
§ - (m) ♀H7	CBar CBen CMac EHoe ELan IBoy MBNS MRav MWts NBro NSti SMad SPer SRms WMoo
- CHILD OF TWO WORLDS	see *A. dioicus* 'Zweiweltenkind'
- 'Glasnevin'	ECtt ESps MRav WFar
- var. ***kamtschaticus***	EWes NLar NWad WHrl
- - RBS 0208	NGdn
- 'Kneiffii'	Widely available
- 'Whirlwind'	LPla SPoG
§ - 'Zweiweltenkind'	GAbr LPla LRHS NLar SMad XLum
'Guinea Fowl'	CBod ECtt ELon LEdu LLWG MBel MHol NBid NGdn NLar SCob WCAu WWtn
'Horatio'	Widely available
'Johannifest'	EBee ECtt IMou IPot WCot
'Misty Lace'	ECtt GBin NGdn NLar SAko
'Netzwerk'	IMou
'Noble Spirit'	GMcL LSun MBel NGdn NLar
'Perlehuhn'	EBee IMou
plumosus	see *A. dioicus*
* ***sinensis***	NBre
sylvestris	see *A. dioicus*
- 'Sommeranfang'	IMou
'Woldemar Meier'	IMou MAvo MCot NLar SAko WCot

Arundinaria (*Poaceae*)

anceps	see *Yushania anceps*
auricoma	see *Pleioblastus viridistriatus*
disticha	see *Pleioblastus pygmaeus* 'Distichus'
fargesii	see *Bashania fargesii*
fastuosa	see *Semiarundinaria fastuosa*
fortunei	see *Pleioblastus variegatus*
§ ***gigantea***	CDTJ
- subsp. ***tecta***	CBcs
hindsii	see *Pleioblastus hindsii*
hookeriana misapplied	see *Himalayacalamus falconeri* 'Damarapa'
hookeriana Munro	see *Himalayacalamus hookerianus*
humilis	see *Pleioblastus humilis*
japonica	see *Pseudosasa japonica*
jaunsarensis	see *Yushania anceps*
maling	see *Yushania maling*
marmorea	see *Chimonobambusa marmorea*
murielae	see *Fargesia murielae*
nitida	see *Fargesia nitida*
oedogonata	see *Clavinodum oedogonatum*
palmata	see *Sasa palmata*
pumila	see *Pleioblastus argenteostriatus* f. *pumilus*
pygmaea	see *Pleioblastus pygmaeus*
quadrangularis	see *Chimonobambusa quadrangularis*
simonii	see *Pleioblastus simonii*
spathiflora	see *Thamnocalamus spathiflorus*
tessellata	see *Bergbambos tessellata*
vagans	see *Sasaella ramosa*
variegata	see *Pleioblastus variegatus*
veitchii	see *Sasa veitchii*
viridistriata	see *Pleioblastus viridistriatus*
'Wang Tsai'	see *Bambusa multiplex* 'Floribunda'

Arundo (*Poaceae*)

donax	CAbb CKno CPla ELan ELon ETod EUJe EWes GMaP IDee MAvo MBlu MBrN MNrw MRav SArc SCob SEND SMad SPlb SPoG SSut WHal
- 'Golden Chain' (v)	CKno EPPr EWes LRHS SMad
- 'Macrophylla'	CExl CFil CHGN CKno ETod LEdu WPGP
- 'Variegata'	see *A. donax* var. *versicolor*
§ - var. ***versicolor*** (v)	CAbb CBcs CBlu CBod CKno CRos CTsd ELan ELon ETod EUJe EWes LEdu LLWG LRHS MRav NLos NRHS SArc SCob SEND SMad SPer SPlb SPoG WAvo XLum XSen
I - - 'Aureovariegata' (v)	CBod CDTJ SEND
formosana	CKno EPPr
- 'Golden Showers'	NLos

Asarina (*Plantaginaceae*)

antirrhiniflora	see *Maurandella antirrhiniflora*
barclayana	see *Maurandya barclayana*
erubescens	see *Lophospermum erubescens*
lophantha	see *Lophospermum scandens*
lophospermum	see *Lophospermum scandens*
§ ***procumbens***	CTri CWld EBee IBoy NRya SChF SPhx SRms WBrk WKif

Asarum (*Aristolochiaceae*)

arifolium	EBee EHrv EPPr
- 'The Giant'	EBee NLar
- white-flowered	EBee
canadense	CDor CTal EBee GEdr GPoy LEdu MMoz NLar

caudatum	EBee ECha EPfP GEdr LEdu LPla NBro NLar SMad SRms WCot WCru WSpi
- 'Little Murphy' **new**	WCot
caulescens	LAma
delavayi	LAma NLar WCot
- giant	EBee XEll
epigynum	CBot EBee GEdr LEdu MNrw NLar NPnk WFar
- 'Silver Web'	WCot
europaeum ♀H6	Widely available
- PAB 4377	LEdu WPGP
infrapurpureum B&SWJ 1994	LEdu
lemmonii	LEdu
longirhizomatosum	GEdr WCru
maculatum B&SWJ 1114	WCru
maximum	CTal LAma
- 'Green Panda'	NLos
- 'Silver Panda'	CAby CBct CBod CExl EUJe GEdr NGBl NPnk SMad WCot WMoo
sieboldii	WCru
splendens	CAby CBct CBod CBro EHrv ELan EPfP EPot EUJe GKev ILea LAma LEdu MHol MRav NLar NLos NPnk NSti SMHy SPlb SPoG WCot WFar XLum
wulingense	CExl CTal

Asclepias ✿ (*Apocynaceae*)

asperula **new**	SPhx
'Cinderella'	SGol
cordifolia	SPhx
curassavica	CCCN EShb LLWG SRkn XLum
exaltata	SBrt
§ ***fascicularis***	SBrt
fasciculata	see *A. fascicularis*
fruticosa	see *Gomphocarpus fruticosus*
hallii	EBee
incarnata	CRos IFoB LRHS MRav NRHS SBrt SPhx SPlb WOld XLum
- 'Ice Ballet'	CBod GKev IFoB MSCN NLar SPer
* - 'Iceberg'	SGol
- 'Soulmate'	CBod EBee EPfP SPer WHar
latifolia	SPhx
purpurascens	EBee XAbr
rubra	SBrt
speciosa	EBee MMuc NBre SBrt
sullivantii	SPhx
syriaca	EBee LPla MMuc XLum
tuberosa	CBWd CBcs CBod CSpe EBee EShb EUJe GKev GPoy LRHS MHer MNHC MPie MSCN NDov NRHS SCob SPad SPer SPhx SPoG WGwG WHar WWtn XLum XSen
- subsp. ***interior*** **new**	MHol

Asimina (*Annonaceae*)

triloba (F)	CAby CBcs CCCN CDTJ EBee IBal MBlu NLar SGol SPlb
- 'Sunflowers'	CCCN SAko

asparagus see also AGM Vegetables Section

Asparagus (*Asparagaceae*)

PAB 13.0321 from Nagaland	LEdu
acutifolius	XSen
asparagoides ♀H1c	EShb
densiflorus 'Mazeppa'	EShb
- 'Myersii' ♀H1c	EShb SEND
- Sprengeri Group ♀H1c	NGBl SEND
falcatus	SEND
filicinus	XBlo
- NJM 12.024 **new**	WPGP
- var. ***giraldii***	WCot
aff. ***meioclados*** B&SWJ 8309	WCot WCru
officinalis 'Ariane'	LCro LOPS WHar
- 'Backlim' ♀H4	ECrN EMsh EPom
- 'Connover's Colossal' ♀H4	CSBt EKin ELan EUnw LCro LOPS LSRN MCtn MNHC NRob SEND SVic
- 'Crimson Pacific'	SVic
- 'Dariana' ♀H4	SDea
- 'Franklim'	CTri NRHS
- 'Gijnlim' ♀H4	CRav ECrN EKin EMsh EPom LCro LOPS NRob SDea
- 'Guelph Millennium' ♀H5	CRav EPom LCro LOPS NRob
- 'Jersey Knight'	SVic
- 'Mondeo'	EPom LCro LOPS
- 'Pacific 2000'	EPfP EPom LCro LOPS LSRN
- 'Pacific Purple'	EPfP EPom LCro LEdu LOPS NRHS
- 'Stewart's Purple'	EPom WHar
- 'Vitalim'^{PBR} **new**	LCro
pseudoscaber 'Spitzenschleier'	EBee EShb WCot
retrofractus	WCot
scandens	EShb WCot
schoberioides	LEdu
- B&SWJ 8814	WCru
setaceus 'Pyramidalis' ♀H1c	XBlo
verticillatus	SEND
virgatus	EShb SPlb WPGP

Asperula (*Rubiaceae*)

§ ***arcadiensis*** ♀H3	EPot WAbe
aristata subsp. ***scabra***	CSpe ECha MMuc WCot WSHC
- subsp. ***thessala***	see *A. sintenisii*
boissieri	EPot SPlb WAbe
daphneola	ELan EPot EWes LLHF WAbe
gussonei	EPot LLHF WAbe WHoo WOld
nitida	EPot
- subsp. ***puberula***	see *A. sintenisii*
odorata	see *Galium odoratum*
§ ***sintenisii***	CMea CPBP EPot LLHF WAbe WHoo WThu
suberosa misapplied	see *A. arcadiensis*
taurina	WPtf
- subsp. ***caucasica***	NLar WBor
tinctoria	GPoy MHer SRms XAbr

Asphodeline (*Asphodelaceae*)

§ ***brevicaulis***	XSen
liburnica	CBro CPla CSam ECha ELan EPri IMou MMuc SEND SPhx XSen
§ ***lutea***	Widely available
§ - 'Gelbkerze'	CRos EBee EPfP LRHS NRHS
- YELLOW CANDLE	see *A. lutea* 'Gelbkerze'
taurica	EPot MBNS SMHy

Asphodelus (*Asphodelaceae*)

acaulis	CTal LLHF WCot WWFP
§ ***aestivus***	EBee EWes MBel WCot XSen
albus	CAvo CBot CBro CPla CSam CSpe ECha EPPr EPfP GAbr GJos IFoB NBid SPlb SRms XLum XSen
brevicaulis	see *Asphodeline brevicaulis*
cerasiferus	see *A. ramosus*
fistulosus	CBro LEdu SVen XSen
lusitanicus	see *A. ramosus*

luteus	see *Asphodeline lutea*
microcarpus	see *A. aestivus*
§ ***ramosus***	CPar CTal GCal LPla MCot WCot XSen

Aspidistra (*Asparagaceae*)

Chen Yi 135	WCot
B&SWJ 6645 from Thailand	WCru
attenuata	IMou
- 'Dungpu Dazzler' **new**	WCru
- 'Xitou Starlet' **new**	WCru
caespitosa 'Jade Ribbons'	see *A. hainanensis* 'Jade Ribbons'
'China Star'	CFil WCot
daibuensis 'Taiwan Stars' **new**	WCru
- 'Totally Dotty' (v)	WCru
- 'Yuli Yummy' **new**	WCru
- 'Tidy Trim'	WCru
elatior ♀H2	CBct CTsd EBak EBee EShb LEdu LOPS MRav NLos NPla SAko SEND SMad WCot
- 'Akebono' (v)	WCot
- 'Asahi' (v)	WCot
- 'Hoshi-zora' (v)	WCot
- 'Lennon's Song' (v)	WCot
- 'Milky Way' (v)	EBee EShb MMoz MMuc SAko SEND XLum
- 'Okame' (v)	WCot
- 'Variegata' (v) ♀H2	IFoB
- 'Variegata Exotica' (v)	XBlo
§ ***hainanensis*** 'Jade Ribbons'	WCot
linearifolia 'Leopard'	WCot
lurida	EShb
- 'Ginga'	see *A. sichuanensis* 'Ginga'
- 'Ginga Giant' (v)	WCot
minutiflora	WCot
mushaensis B&SWJ 3727	WCru
aff. ***mushaensis*** 'Spotty Dotty' (v)	WCru
omeiensis	WCot
saxicola 'Uan Fat Lady'	see *A. zongbayi* 'Uan Fat Lady'
§ ***sichuanensis*** 'Ginga' (v)	WCot
sutepensis B&SWJ 5216	WCru
tonkinensis	WCot WCru
typica 'China Sun'	WCot
zongbayi	WCot
§ - 'Uan Fat Lady'	WCot WCru

Asplenium ✿ (*Aspleniaceae*)

§ ***aethiopicum***	CBdn
antiquum 'Osaka'	CRos LRHS NRHS
bulbiferum misapplied	see *A.* × *lucrosum*
bulbiferum Forst.f.	GBin
§ ***ceterach***	WHer XLum
× ***ebenoides*** ♀H4	CBdn
furcatum Thunb.	see *A. aethiopicum*
incisum	CBdn
integrifolium marbled fronds Chen Yi T-5981	WCot
§ × ***lucrosum*** ♀H1c	EShb
lyallii	CBdn
'Maori Princess'	EBee GBin WFib
monanthes	CBdn
nidus ♀H1b	XBlo
- 'Crispy Wave'PBR **new**	EShb
protensum	CBdn
scleroprium **new**	GKev
§ ***scolopendrium*** ♀H6	Widely available
- 'Angustatum' ♀H6	Widely available
- Crispum Group ♀H6	EFer ELan NBid SRms SRot WAbe WFar WFib
- - 'Crispum Bolton's Nobile'	WFib
- Crispum Cristatum Group	CTal MMuc SCob
- - 'Crispum Cristatum Bolton'	WCot
- Cristatum Group	CAby CBdn CDor CRos CWCL EBee ECtt EHrv ELan ELon EPfP LRHS MGos MMoz MRav NBro NLar NRHS SPer SPoG SRms SRot WBor WFib WHoo WMoo
- Fimbriatum Group	CRos LRHS NRHS
- 'Furcatum'	CBdn CDTJ EBee ELan ELon EUJe GCal MMuc NLar SPad
- 'Kaye's Lacerated' ♀H5	EFer WFib
- Marginatum Group	CBdn EFer EPed
- 'Muricatum'	ELan MRav NBid WFib WHoo
- 'Sagittatoprojectum Sclater'	WFib
- Undulatum Group	CDTJ CRos EBee ECha EPed EPfP GEdr GQue LRHS MMoz MMuc MWat NEgg NLar NRHS SRms WCot WFar WGwG WMoo XLum
trichomanes ♀H6	Widely available
- Cristatum Group	LRHS NRHS
- Incisum Group ♀H6	EFer WAbe
- 'Ramocristatum'	WAbe

Astelia (*Asteliaceae*)

banksii	CBcs CBod CPla CRos CSpe EUJe IBal LRHS LSRN MGos NRHS SCoo WCot
'Bronze Spear'	GKev
§ ***chathamica*** ♀H3	Widely available
- 'Silver Spear'	see *A. chathamica*
cunninghamii	see *A. solandri*
fragrans	CBcs IBlr LEdu
graminea	GCal
grandis	IBlr LEdu WPGP
nervosa	IBlr LSRN SArc
- 'Alpine Ruby'	IBlr
- 'Bronze Giant'	IBlr
- 'Silver Sabre'	IBlr
- 'Westland'	CBcs CBod CRos CSpe CTsd EUJe GBin GCal GWyn ILea LEdu LRHS LSRN MGos NLos NRHS SCob SEND SWvt
nivicola 'Golden Gem'	IBlr
- 'Red Gem'	LEdu
petriei	IBlr
'Red Devil'	CBcs CBod CPla CRos CSpe EPfP GBin GWyn IBoy LRHS MGos MHol MJak SPoG WHer
'Red Shadow' **new**	SPad
'Silver Mound'	EPfP SCob
'Silver Shadow'PBR	CRos EBee EPfP LCro LRHS MJak MMrt NLos NRHS SPad SWvt WCot WFar WSpi
§ ***solandri***	IBlr

Aster ✿ (*Asteraceae*)

acris	see *Galatella sedifolia*
ageratoides	see *A. trifoliatus* subsp. *ageratoides*
§ ***albescens*** WJC 13657	WCru
alpinus ♀H5	EBee EPfP MHol NRya SRms WFar
- var. ***albus***	CRos EDAr EPfP ESps GKev LRHS NRHS WArt WCot
- 'Antje'	MAvo MNrw
- DARK BEAUTY	see *A. alpinus* 'Dunkle Schöne'

	- var. ***dolomiticus***	NSla
§	- 'Dunkle Schöne'	EAJP EDAr SRms WArt WFar XSen
	- 'Goliath'	CPla ELan EPfP SPlb
	- 'Happy End'	CRos EPfP GMcL LRHS NRHS SRms XLum XSen
	- 'Pinkie'	EAJP EBee EDAr EPfP WArt
	- 'Trimix'	SRms
	- violet-flowered	GMcL
	amelloides	see *Felicia amelloides*
	amellus	ELon
	- 'Blue King'	ECtt EWTr EWes NWsh SWvt WSpi
	- 'Breslau'	EBee ELon MAvo
	- 'Brilliant'	CBod ECha ECtt ELon EPPr IRob LRHS LSou MAvo MBNS MRav MWat NEgg NLar NRHS NWsh SAko SEND SPer WHoo WOld WSpi
	- 'Butzemann'	ELon WCot
	- 'Danzig'	XLum
	- 'Doktor Otto Petschek'	EBee ELon WCot
	- EMPRESS	see *A. amellus* 'Glücksfund'
	- 'Forncett Flourish'	ECtt MHCG SMHy WCot WOld
	- 'Framfieldii' ♀H7	ECtt SMHy WCot WOld
§	- 'Glücksfund'	SAko
	- 'Gründer'	IMou IPot MAvo MHCG MWat WCot WOld
	- 'Jacqueline Genebrier' ♀H7	MHCG NDov WOld
	- 'King George' ♀H7	Widely available
	- 'Kobold'	ESps WOld
	- 'Lac de Genève'	WCot XLum
	- 'Lady Hindlip'	CSam ECtt IMou WCot
	- 'Louise'	MBrN MHCG SBch
	- 'Mira'	EBee ELon MNrw SAko SPtp
	- 'Moerheim Gem'	ECtt IMou WCot WOld
	- 'Mrs Ralph Woods'	WOld
	- 'Nocturne'	ELon MAvo WCot WOld
	- 'Peach Blossom'	WOld
	- PINK ZENITH	see *A. amellus* 'Rosa Erfüllung'
§	- 'Rosa Erfüllung'	CBod CDor CMac CRos EBee ECtt ELan ELon EPPr EPfP GMaP LRHS LSou MAvo MNrw MRav NLar NRHS SCob SPhx SPoG SRGP SWvt WCAu WOld WSpi
	- 'Rotfeuer'	ELon WSpi
	- 'Rudolph Goethe'	CRos EBee ECtt ELan ELon EMil EPPr EPfP ESps LRHS MWat NLar NRHS SCob WHar WOld WSpi
	- 'September Glow'	WOld
	- 'Silbersee'	CSam IMou SAko
	- 'Sonia'	CRos EBee ECtt ELon LRHS NRHS SWvt WOld
	- 'Sonora'	IRob MAvo MNrw SPhx WKif WOld
	- 'Sternkugel'	EBee ELon WOld
	- 'Ultramarine'	WOld
	- 'Vanity'	WOld
§	- 'Veilchenkönigin' ♀H7	Widely available
	- VIOLET QUEEN	see *A. amellus* 'Veilchenkönigin'
	- 'Weltfriede'	ECtt WOld
	× ***amethystinus***	see *Symphyotrichum* × *amethystinum*
	'Anita Pfeiffer'	CRos LRHS NRHS
	asperulus misapplied	see *A. peduncularis*
	'Beauté du Nord'	WCot
	capensis 'Variegatus'	see *Felicia amelloides* variegated
	carolinianus	see *Ampelaster carolinianus*
	'Cheavers'	CRos LRHS NRHS
	'Chilly Fingers'	MAvo MNrw MTis MWat
	ciliolatus	see *Symphyotrichum ciliolatum*
	'Climax' misapplied	see *Symphyotrichum laeve* 'Arcturus', *S. laeve* 'Calliope'
	coelestis	see *Felicia amelloides*
	coloradoensis	see *Xanthisma coloradoense*
	'Connecticut Snow Flurry'	see *Symphyotrichum ericoides* f. *prostratum* 'Snow Flurry'
	conspicuus	see *Eurybia conspicua*
	cordifolius	see *Symphyotrichum cordifolium*
	corymbosus	see *Eurybia divaricata*
	'Cotswold Gem'	ECtt MHCG MNrw WCot WOld
	diffusus	see *Symphyotrichum lateriflorum*
	diplostephioides	EPPr EPfP GEdr GKev GLog MBNS MMrt SPlb WCot WOld
	divaricatus	see *Eurybia divaricata*
	dumosus	see *Symphyotrichum dumosum*
	'Dwarf Barbados'	CRos EPfP LRHS NRHS
	'Eleven Purple' PBR	MAvo MNrw
	ericoides	see *Symphyotrichum ericoides*
	falcatus	see *Symphyotrichum falcatum*
	'Fanny's Fall'	see *Symphyotrichum oblongifolium* 'Fanny's'
	farreri	NWad
	× ***frikartii***	CMac EPfP MRav SWvt WSHC
	- 'Eiger'	IRob WOld
	- 'Flora's Delight'	CMea CRos EBee ECtt GCal LPla LRHS MArl MMrt MRav NLar NRHS SPoG SRms WCAu WHoo WOld WSpi
	- 'Jungfrau'	CRos CWGN EBee EPPr GMaP ILea IRob LRHS MRav NLar NRHS SPhx SRms WMoo WOld
	- 'Mönch' ♀H7	Widely available
	- WONDER OF STAFA	see *A.* × *frikartii* 'Wunder von Stäfa'
§	- 'Wunder von Stäfa' ♀H7	CBod CEnd CExl CKno CRav CRos EBee ECtt ELan ELon EPPr EPed EPfP EWTr GMaP LRHS MBNS MCot MHol MWat NLar NRHS SRGP SWvt WCot WOld WSpi XLum
	furcatus	see *Eurybia furcata*
	glehnii 'Aglenii'	IMou MNrw NDov SMad
	greatae	see *Symphyotrichum greatae*
	× ***herveyi***	see *Eurybia* × *herveyi*
	himalaicus	NSla
	hybridus luteus	see *Solidago* × *luteus*
	'Ice Cool Pink'	SMHy
	'Ivy House'	ECtt
*	***kotarimus***	XLum
	laevis	see *Symphyotrichum laeve*
	lateriflorus	see *Symphyotrichum lateriflorum*
	laterifolius 'Snow Flurry'	see *Symphyotrichum ericoides* f. *prostratum* 'Snow Flurry'
	limonifolius new	GKev
	linosyris	see *Galatella linosyris*
	maackii	WCot
	macrophyllus	see *Eurybia macrophylla*
	mongolicus	see *Kalimeris mongolica*
	'Mrs Dean'	ECtt
	natalensis	see *Felicia rosulata*
	'Natasha'	LSRN
	novae-angliae	see *Symphyotrichum novae-angliae*
	'Novemberlaan'	MSpe
	novi-belgii	see *Symphyotrichum novi-belgii*
	oblongifolius	see *Symphyotrichum oblongifolium*
	OCTOBERLIGHT	see *Symphyotrichum* 'Oktoberlicht'
	oolentangiensis	see *Symphyotrichum oolentangiense*
	pappei	see *Felicia amoena*

§ ***peduncularis***	CKno CPou EBee EPPr IMou LEdu MAvo MHol MMuc MPie MTis MWat NCou NRHS NSti WCot WFar WOld
petiolatus	see *Felicia petiolata*
pilosus	see *Symphyotrichum pilosum*
ptarmicoides	see *Solidago ptarmicoides*
puniceus	see *Symphyotrichum puniceum*
pyrenaeus 'Lutetia'	CBod CKno CMea CSam ECha EPPr EWTr GCal GMaP LRHS MAvo MNrw MPie MWat NLar NRHS SPoG SPtp SRGP WCAu WKif WOld XLum
radula	see *Eurybia radula*
'Rose Queen'	MNrw MPie NWsh
rotundifolius 'Variegatus'	see *Felicia amelloides* variegated
rugulosus 'Asrugo'	CKno
× ***salignus***	see *Symphyotrichum* × *salignum*
§ ***scaber***	GCal NPnk WCot
scandens	see *A. carolinianus*
schreberi	see *Eurybia schreberi*
sedifolius	see *Galatella sedifolia*
- 'Jean Polignier'	see *Galatella sedifolia* 'Jean Polignier'
sericeus	see *Symphyotrichum sericeum*
sibiricus	see *Eurybia sibirica*
'Small-Ness'	GKev NWad
'Snow Flurry'	see *Symphyotrichum ericoides* f. *prostratum* 'Snow Flurry'
souliei	CPBP
spathulifolius	WCot XLum
spectabilis	see *Eurybia spectabilis*
stracheyi	GKev LLHF
subcaeruleus	see *A. tongolensis*
'Sunspring'	SRGP
tataricus 'Jindai'	EBee MAvo MWat
thomsonii	GBin WCot WOld
- 'Nanus'	CAby GBin GMaP ILea LRHS MCot MRav SPer SPhx SPoG WCot WOld WSHC WSpi
§ ***tongolensis***	GKev NHpl
- 'Berggarten'	CRos IPot LRHS MHol MNrw MPie NPnk NRHS SPoG WOld
- 'Napsbury'	CRos LRHS NRHS
- 'Wartburgstern'	EPfP LRHS SGbt XLum
tradescantii misapplied	see *Symphyotrichum pilosum* var. *pringlei*
tradescantii L.	see *Symphyotrichum tradescantii*
§ ***trifoliatus*** subsp. ***ageratoides***	CPou WCot WOld
- - PAB 9347	LEdu
- - 'Ashvi'	CBod CKno CMil CSpe ECtt LSun MAvo MBel MHol MTis NCou NSti SPoG WCot WFar WOld WRHF
- - 'Asran'	EBee ECtt EHoe EPPr EWes GCal IMou LEdu MMuc MPie NLar SEND WBrk WCot WFar WOld WOut WTor XLum
- - 'Ezo Murasaki'	CSpe IPot MAvo NDov SAko SPoG WCot XLum
- - var. ***firmus***	WPGP
- - 'Harry Smith'	LSou MAvo MTis NDov SAko SPoG WCot WRHF
- - 'Little Theo'	CKno EBee
- - 'Stardust'	WOld
- - 'Starshine'PBR	CBod CKno CRos CWGN EBee ECtt EPfP IBoy LRHS MTis NRHS WCot WRHF
trinervius var. ***harae***	ELon WOld
tripolium	see *Tripolium pannonicum*
'Triumph'	WCot
turbinellus ambig.	see *Symphyotrichum turbinellum*
vahlii	GAbr
vimineus Lam.	see *Symphyotrichum lateriflorum*
- 'Ptarmicoides'	see *Solidago ptarmicoides*
'Yvonne'	CBre

Asteranthera (*Gesneriaceae*)

ovata	CExl CRos EPfP GGGa LRHS LSou SLon WPGP WSHC

Asteriscus (*Asteraceae*)

'Gold Coin'	see *Pallenis maritima*
maritimus	see *Pallenis maritima*

Asteromoea (*Asteraceae*)

mongolica	see *Kalimeris mongolica*
pinnatifida	see *Kalimeris pinnatifida*

Asteropyrum (*Ranunculaceae*)

cavaleriei	GEdr
peltatum	GEdr

Asterotrichion (*Malvaceae*)

discolor	SPlb SVen

Astilbe ✿ (*Saxifragaceae*)

CC 5201	CExl
'Alive and Kicking'	MAsh SCob
'Amerika' (× *arendsii*)	CSBt SRms
'Amethyst' (× *arendsii*)	CMac CRos ELon EPfP LRHS MRav NRHS SPer WArt WFar WMoo
'Angel Wings' (× *arendsii*)	NEoE
'Anita Pfeifer' (× *arendsii*)	ELon IBoy NLar XLum
'Aphrodite' (*simplicifolia* hybrid)	CBcs GCal GMcL MAsh XLum
× ***arendsii***	EPfP IFoB NBre WHar WMoo XLum
(Astary Series) 'Astary Pink' (× *arendsii*)	CBod CRos LRHS NRHS
- 'Astary Red' (× *arendsii*)	CRos LRHS NRHS
- 'Astary Rose' (× *arendsii*) **new**	NRHS
- 'Astary White' (× *arendsii*)	CBod CRos LRHS NRHS
astilboides	SWvt
'Avalanche'	CAby CTsd NEoE WSpi
§ 'Beauty of Ernst' (× *arendsii*)	CAbb CBod CMea EBee ELon EPfP LRHS SRms WMoo
§ 'Beauty of Lisse' (× *arendsii*)	CBod ELon WHil WOut
'Betsy Cuperus' (*thunbergii* hybrid)	NBre WCAu
'Bonn' (*japonica* hybrid)	CWCL CWat NLar NQui SCob SCoo SRms
'Boogie Woogie'PBR (× *arendsii*)	MAsh
§ 'Brautschleier' (× *arendsii*) ♀H7	CBod CExl CMac CRos ECtt EPfP GBin GKev GWyn LRHS LSRN MHol NEgg NGdn NLar NQui NRHS WPnP XLum
'Bressingham Beauty' (× *arendsii*)	CBod CExl CRos CSam CWCL EBee ECtt ELan EPfP GBin GKev GMaP ILea LCro LOPS LRHS MHol MJak MRav NEgg NEoE NRHS SPer SWvt WBor WMoo
BRIDAL VEIL (× *arendsii*)	see *A.* 'Brautschleier'
§ 'Bronce Elegans' (*simplicifolia* hybrid) ♀H7	ECha ELon EPfP GLog GMaP GMcL GWyn NLar SCob SRms WMoo WOut WSpi
'Bronze Sprite' (*simplicifolia* hybrid)	WFar
* ***bumalda*** 'Bronze Pygmy'	MMoz

	'Bumalda' (× *arendsii*)	CRos CSBt ELon GBin GLog GMaP IBoy LRHS MAsh NChi NEoE NGdn NRHS SPlb WMoo WWtn
	'Bunter Zauber' (× *arendsii*)	XLum
	'Burgunderrot' (× *arendsii*)	MNrw NLar
	'Cappuccino' (× *arendsii*)	CBod ILea LSou MAsh MSCN SPad WTor
*	'Carmine King'	MMuc
	'Catherine Deneuve'	see *A.* 'Federsee'
	'Cattleya' (× *arendsii*)	CRos CSam GBin GMcL GWyn IRob LRHS NLar NRHS SAko WMoo WSpi XLum
	'Ceres' (× *arendsii*)	EBee
	'Cherry Ripe'	see *A.* 'Feuer'
	chinensis	CBWd CRos GBin LRHS NRHS WSHC
	- B&SWJ 8178	WCru
	- from Russia	GCal
	- 'Brokat'	GBin IRob
	- var. ***davidii***	XLum
	- - B&SWJ 8583	WCru
	- - B&SWJ 8645	WCru
	- 'Diamonds and Pearls'PBR	CWGN ECtt IRob LLWG LSou SCob WFar WSpi
	- 'Finale'	ELon WOut
	- 'Intermezzo'	GBin GCal GMaP NEoE NLar
	- 'Little Vision in Pink'PBR	WFar WHil
	- 'Love and Pride'	LSou
	- 'Milk and Honey'PBR	CWGN ECtt ELon LSou MBNS WFar WSpi
§	- var. ***pumila*** ♀H5	Widely available
	- - 'Serenade'	CMac CRos LRHS NGdn NRHS
I	- - 'Tiny Form' **new**	GCrg
	- 'Purple Glory'	ECtt
	- var. ***taquetii***	CMac ELan EPfP LRHS NSti SRms XLum
	- - PURPLE LANCE	see *A. chinensis* var. *taquetii* 'Purpurlanze'
§	- - 'Purpurlanze'	Widely available
§	- - 'Superba' ♀H7	CMac CRos ECha GMcL IBoy LRHS NBro NRHS NWad SPer SRms WMoo
	- 'Troll'	GBin
	- 'Veronika Klose'	GBin IRob NLar
	- 'Vision in Pink'PBR	CWCL ELan EPfP MBNS MHol MNrw NDov WFar WHil WMoo
	- 'Vision in Red'PBR	CBod CWCL CWat ECtt ELan EPfP IBoy IRob MBNS MHol MNrw NDov NEgg NLar SAko SGbt SPoG WCAu WFar WMoo
	- 'Vision in White'	EPfP IRob NEoE SAko SPoG WFar WHil WMoo
	- 'Visions'	CMac CRos CWCL EPfP IBoy LRHS LSou MBNS NBro NEoE NGdn NRHS WMoo
	'Chocolate Shogun'	CBcs ECtt SCob
	COLOGNE	see *A.* 'Köln'
	COLOR FLASH	see *A.* 'Beauty of Ernst'
	COLOR FLASH LIME	see *A.* 'Beauty of Lisse'
	'Country and Western'PBR (× *arendsii*)	NEoE SCob
	'Crimson Feather'	see *A.* 'Gloria Purpurea'
	× ***crispa*** 'Lilliput'	ECtt NEoE NLar NRya NWad SCob SMad
§	- 'Perkeo' ♀H5	CBcs CRos EBee ECtt ELan EPfP GMaP LRHS NEoE NHpl NLar NRHS SPoG SRms WFar WHil WMoo
	- 'Peter Pan'	see *A.* × *crispa* 'Perkeo'
	- 'Red Rog'	NEoE
	- 'Snow Queen'	NEoE
	'Darwin's Dream'	IBoy MNrw NEoE NLar WFar
	'Darwin's Favourite' (× *arendsii*)	CWCL
	'Delft Lace'	CAbb CRos EBee LBuc LRHS MBel NRHS SRms WMoo
	'Deutschland' (*japonica* hybrid)	Widely available
§	'Diamant' (× *arendsii*)	LSRN MMuc MNrw NGdn SEND WFar
	DIAMOND	see *A.* 'Diamant'
	'Drayton Glory' (× *arendsii*)	see *A.* × *rosea* 'Peach Blossom'
	'Drum and Bass'PBR	IBoy LSou NLar
	'Dunkelachs' (*simplicifolia* hybrid)	EBee
	'Dusseldorf' (*japonica* hybrid)	CRos CWCL EBee LRHS NRHS
	'Eden's Odysseus'	IBoy
	'Eden's Phoenix' **new**	CBod
	'Eden's Twinkle'	CBod EBee WWtn
	'Elegans' (*simplicifolia* hybrid)	CMac
	'Elisabeth' van Veen (× *arendsii*)	ETMg WHar
	ELIZABETH BLOOM ('Eliblo'PBR) (× *arendsii*)	CRos ELon GAbr LLWG LRHS MHol MRav NEgg NGdn NRHS
	'Ellie' (× *arendsii*)	CMac CRos CWCL EPfP EShb LLWG LRHS LSRN LSou MAsh MBNS MBel NGdn NLar NRHS SPoG WFar WHar
	'Else Schluck' (× *arendsii*)	ECha
	'Erica' (× *arendsii*)	CAby CExl CRos CTri CTsd EWTr GBin GLog LRHS NEoE NLar NRHS WMoo
	'Etna' (*japonica* hybrid)	CBcs CSam ECtt IBoy LRHS NEgg NGdn NLar NRHS SRms WFar WHar WHoo
	'Europa' (*japonica* hybrid)	CMac CRos ECtt GMcL GWyn LRHS MGos NEgg NGdn NLar NRHS SPoG WCAu WHar WMoo
	'Fanal' (× *arendsii*) ♀H7	Widely available
§	'Federsee' (× *arendsii*)	CBcs CRos CWCL EBee ECha ECtt ELan ESps LRHS MBNS NBro NEoE NGdn NRHS SPer WFar WWtn XLum
§	'Feuer' (× *arendsii*)	CMac ECtt ELan EPed NEgg NEoE NGdn NLar WBor WMoo
	FIRE	see *A.* 'Feuer'
	'Fireberry'PBR (Short 'n' Sweet Series)	EBee LSou NLar
	'Flamingo'PBR (× *arendsii*)	CRos ECtt MBNS MBel NRHS
§	***formosa***	EBee
	- B&SWJ 10946	WCru
	'Gertrud Brix' (× *arendsii*)	CWat MMuc NGdn SEND XLum
§	***glaberrima***	NBid
§	- var. ***saxatilis*** ♀H5	EPfP GBin GCrg GEdr IFro WAbe WHal WThu
	- - 'Candy Floss'	NEoE
	- ***saxosa***	see *A. glaberrima* var. *saxatilis*
	'Gladstone' (× *arendsii*)	see *A.* 'W.E. Gladstone'
§	'Gloria Purpurea' (× *arendsii*)	ELon NQui WMoo
	'Gloria' (× *arendsii*)	CMac CRos CTri ECtt LRHS MRav NRHS
	GLOW	see *A.* 'Glut'
§	'Glut' (× *arendsii*)	CRos CWCL ECtt LRHS MMuc NGdn NRHS SAko SEND SRms WFar WWtn
	'Granat' (× *arendsii*)	CMac NEgg NGdn NLar WMoo
*	Grande Group (× *arendsii*)	NBre

	grandis	WHer
	- BWJ 8076A	NLar
	'Grete Püngel' (× *arendsii*)	ECha SRms WFar
	'Harmony' (× *arendsii*)	CRos LRHS NRHS
	'Heart and Soul'[PBR]	CWGN EPfP IRob LSou SAko
	'Hennie Graafland' (*simplicifolia* hybrid)	CBcs CWCL LSou NLar WFar
	'Henry Noblett'	LRHS NRHS
	HYACINTH	see *A.* 'Hyazinth'
§	'Hyazinth' (× *arendsii*)	CExl CRos EBee GMaP LLWG LRHS LSou NRHS
	'Icecream' (× *arendsii*)	CBod WHar
	'Inshriach Pink' (*simplicifolia* hybrid)	CBcs CRos ECtt EHoe ELan GBin LRHS NLar NRHS SBch WHal WOut
	'Irrlicht' (× *arendsii*)	CMac CMea CRos EBee ELan EPfP EShb IBoy LRHS NRHS NWad SPer SRms WPnP WWtn
	'Isa Hall'	NEoE NWad
	japonica	CExl
*	- 'Pumila'	NGdn
	- var. ***terrestris***	see *A. glaberrima*
	'Jo Ophorst' (*davidii* hybrid)	CRos LRHS NGdn NLar NRHS
	'Jump and Jive'[PBR]	LSou MAsh WFar
	'Juno'	XLum
	'Key West' (*simplicifolia* hybrid)	CGar
§	'Köln' (*japonica* hybrid)	CRos CWat ELon LRHS NRHS
	'König Albert' (*davidii* hybrid)	GCal
	koreana	WCot
	- B&SWJ 8611	WCru
	- B&SWJ 8680	WCru
	'Kvěle' (× *arendsii*)	CRos LRHS NRHS WMoo
	'Lilli Goos' (× *arendsii*)	GBin GCal
	'Little Vision in Purple'[PBR] **new**	CBod
	'Lollipop'	ECtt GBin MBNS NEoE SRms
	longicarpa B&SWJ 6711	WCru
	'Look at Me'[PBR] (× *arendsii*)	CBod ETMg LCro LLWG LOPS LSou MBel MHol SPoG
	'Maggie Daley'	EWTr IBoy NBro NEoE SRms WMoo
	'Mainz' (*japonica* hybrid)	CRos EBee ECtt LRHS NRHS
	microphylla B&SWJ 11085	WCru
	'Mighty Chocolate Cherry' **new**	WWtn
	'Mighty Pip' (× *arendsii*)	CBod
	'Moerheim Glory' (× *arendsii*)	GBin IBoy NBre NGdn NLar
	'Montgomery' (*japonica* hybrid)	CRos EBee ELon EShb ETMg GAbr GMcL ILea LLWG LRHS LSRN LSou MAsh MBNS MNrw NBro NEgg NGdn NRHS SPoG
	'Nemo'	CBod
	'New Wave'	LLWG
	'Nikki'	NEoE NLar
§	***okuyamae*** B&SWJ 10975	WCru
	OSTRICH PLUME	see *A.* 'Straussenfeder'
	'Peaches and Cream'	NBro NLar
	'Peter Barrow' (*glaberrima* hybrid)	GBin SRms
	'Pink Lightning'[PBR] (*simplicifolia* hybrid)	CWCL ECtt EShb GAbr LLWG MBNS NLar SPad SPoG WFar
	PINK PEARL (× *arendsii*)	see *A.* 'Rosa Perle'
	'Poschka'	NEoE
	'Professor van der Wielen' (*thunbergii* hybrid)	CBWd CRos EBee ECha LRHS NLar NRHS SAko SRms WSpi
	pumila	see *A. chinensis* var. *pumila*
	'Purple Rain'[PBR] (× *arendsii*)	ILea NQui
	'Radius'	CBod ELon NGdn NLar WPnP
	'Raspberry' (Short 'n' Sweet Series) **new**	LSou
	'Red Baron'	CAby CTsd NEoE SPad
	RED LIGHT	see *A.* 'Rotlicht'
	'Red Sentinel' (*japonica* hybrid)	CBcs CBod CRos CWCL CWat EBee ELon EPfP GBin GMaP GWyn IBoy LRHS LSou LSun MHol NBro NEgg NEoE NGdn NLar NRHS WHil WOut WWtn
	'Rheinland' (*japonica* hybrid) 🏆[H7]	CBcs CRos CWCL ELon GBin GMcL GWyn LRHS MBel MMuc NGdn NLar NRHS SCob SEND SRot WHoo WPnP
	'Rhythm and Blues'[PBR]	ECtt NEgg NLar
	rivularis	EBee WCot
	- CC 5201	GKev
	- GWJ 9366	WCru
	- PAB 7353	LEdu
	- PAB 9763	LEdu
I	- 'Grandiflora'	GBin
§	- var. ***myriantha***	EBee WMoo WPGP
	- - BWJ 8076a	WCru
	- - SICH 757	CExl
	'Robinson's Pink'	NGdn
	'Rock and Roll'[PBR]	CAby IRob LSRN MAsh NEoE
§	'Rosa Perle' (× *arendsii*)	CSam
§	× ***rosea*** 'Peach Blossom'	CBcs CRos ELon IBoy ILea LRHS NEoE NGdn NRHS SGbt SPoG SWvt WHoo WMoo
	- 'Queen Alexandra'	XLum
	'Rot Straussenfeder' (× *arendsii*)	CBod
§	'Rotlicht' (× *arendsii*)	CMac CRos GBin LLWG LRHS NEgg NEoE NGdn NLar NRHS
	'Salland'	CRos LRHS NRHS
	'Saxosa'	see *A. glaberrima* var. *saxatilis*
	'Sheila Haxton' (*chinensis*)	CRos LRHS NRHS
	Showstar Group (× *arendsii*)	SRms WHil WRHF WWtn
	simplicifolia 🏆[H5]	CAby CFis WFar
	- BRONZE ELEGANCE	see *A.* 'Bronce Elegans'
	- 'Darwin's Snow Sprite'	CMac GBin NLar WFar
	- 'Jacqueline'	LSou
*	- 'Nana Alba'	NEoE
	- 'Rose of Cimarron'	NEoE NWad
	- 'White Sensation'[PBR]	CRos EBee GQue LRHS NLar NRHS SAko
	'Snowdrift' (× *arendsii*)	CHid CRos CWat ESps GMaP LLWG LRHS MBNS MBel MMuc NEgg NEoE NRHS SEND
	'Spartan' (× *arendsii*)	see *A.* 'Rotlicht'
	'Spinell' (× *arendsii*)	GMcL NBre WMoo WPnP
	'Spotlight'[PBR]	GBin
	'Sprite' (*simplicifolia* hybrid) 🏆[H7]	Widely available
	'Stand and Deliver'[PBR]	ECtt
§	'Straussenfeder' (*thunbergii* hybrid) 🏆[H7]	CMac CRos EBee ECtt EPfP GBin GMaP GQue LRHS NBro NEgg NGdn NLar NRHS SPer SRms WCAu WMoo
	'Sugar Plum' (*simplicifolia* hybrid)	NGdn
	'Sugarberry'[PBR] (Short 'n' Sweet Series)	NLar
	'Superba'	see *A. chinensis* var. *taquetii* 'Superba'
	thunbergii	CExl CRos LRHS NRHS
	- var. ***congesta*** B&SWJ 10961	WCru
	- var. ***formosa***	see *A. formosa*

- var. ***hachijoensis*** EBee
- - B&SWJ 5622 WCru
- var. ***okuyamae*** see *A. okuyamae*
- var. ***sikokumontanum*** B&SWJ 11164 WCru
- - B&SWJ 11534 WCru
- var. ***terrestris*** B&SWJ 6125 WCru
'Thunder and Lightning' (*chinensis* hybrid) **new** NEoE
'To Have and To Hold' LSou MNrw
'Venus' (× *arendsii*) ECtt GMaP MBNS MCot MMuc NGdn SEND WFar WMoo
'Vesuvius' (*japonica* hybrid) CBcs ECtt NBro NLar
virescens see *A. rivularis* var. *myriantha*
§ 'W.E. Gladstone' (*japonica* hybrid) LRHS NRHS
'Walter Bitner' GBin LLWG LRHS MBNS NBre NRHS
'Washington' (*japonica* hybrid) ETMg LRHS NBre NGdn WPnP
§ 'Weisse Gloria' (× *arendsii*) CBod CMac CRos ECha GMcL IRob LLWG LRHS NBro NEgg NEoE NRHS SCoo WBor WCAu WMoo WWtn
'White Diamond' (× *arendsii*) WFar
WHITE GLORIA see *A.* 'Weisse Gloria'
'William Reeves' (× *arendsii*) NWad
'Willie Buchanan' (*simplicifolia* hybrid) CBcs CHid EHoe GAbr GBin GCrg GMaP LRHS NEgg NHpl NRHS NWad SPer SPhm SRms WAbe WCFE WFar WGwG WMoo WOut
YOUNIQUE CERISE ('Verscerise'PBR) ILea
YOUNIQUE PINK ('Verspink'PBR) MAsh
YOUNIQUE RED ('Versred') MAsh
YOUNIQUE SILVERY PINK ('Versilverypink'PBR) WFar WHil
YOUNIQUE WHITE ('Verswhite'PBR) MAsh
'Zuster Theresa' (× *arendsii*) CRos EBee ELon IBoy LRHS MBNS MNrw NRHS

Astilboides (*Saxifragaceae*)

§ ***tabularis*** Widely available

Astragalus (*Papilionaceae*)

canadensis EBee GJos LRHS NRHS
centralpinus GJos
crassicarpus **new** SPhx
desperatus **new** CPBP
glycyphyllos GJos SPhx
looseri SPlb
naturitensis **new** CPBP
neglectus SPhx
odoratus EBee
sericoleucus **new** CPBP

Astrantia ✿ (*Apiaceae*)

bavarica GCal GKev MFie
'Berendien Stam' CElw MAvo MFie
'Bloody Mary' CWCL EBee MAvo MFie MNrw NGdn
'Bradfield Rose' EHrv
'Buckland' Widely available
'Bury Court' NDov
carniolica NEgg
- ***major*** see *A. major*
- 'Rubra' CBcs GKev GMaP MFie WMoo WSpi
- 'Variegata' see *A. major* 'Sunningdale Variegated'
'Censation Milano' **new** WHlf
'Clear Pink' NDov
'Dark Shiny Eyes' CExl CWCL ECtt IBoy ILea LLHF MTis NGdn NLar NSti SWvt
'Good Pink' LRHS MAvo NRHS
'Hadspen Blood' Widely available
'Harvington Adrian's Choice Pink' CRos LRHS NRHS
'Harvington Selected Red' CRos LRHS NRHS
helleborifolia see *A. maxima*
'Larch Cottage Clear Pink' NLar
'Larch Cottage Magic' MAvo
'Madeleine' see *A. major* 'Madeleine van Bennekom'
§ ***major*** Widely available
- 'Abbey Road'PBR CExl CKno CWCL ECtt EWTr IBoy IPot LRHS LSou MBel MFie MPnt NLar NPnk SCob SRkn SRms WCAu
I - 'Alba' CBcs EBee EHrv GKev LRHS MCot MFie MRav NGdn NPer WMoo WPnP WSpi
- 'Berdien' EBee
- 'Best Pink' MAvo
- subsp. ***biebersteinii*** CRos EBee LRHS MFie NRHS
- 'Bo-Ann' IBoy MFie WFar
- 'Can Candy' MAvo
- 'Celtic Star' CSpe MFie SWvt
- 'Claret' Widely available
- Cliff's form MFie
- 'Côte d'Azur' WSpi
- 'Cottage Herbery' MAvo
- 'Dark Desire' LEdu NDov
- 'Elaine's Pink' WHoo
- 'Elmblut' IMou MAvo MFie
- 'Florence'PBR CBct CKno CNor CRos CWCL CWGN ECtt EPfP EWTr GPSL IRob LRHS MAvo MBel NDov NLar NRHS SPoG SWvt WHar
- Gill Richardson Group Widely available
- 'Gracilis' EBee
- 'Green Tapestry' (v) WCot
- 'Greenfingers' EWes
- 'Gwaun Valley' WFar
- subsp. ***involucrata*** CRos LRHS MFie NRHS
- - 'Avondale' MAvo
- - 'Barrister' CSam MAvo MFie NLar
- - 'Canneman' EBee EWes MFie NLar SMHy WCot
- - 'Huntsman' MAvo
- - 'Jumble Hole' EBee NDov
- - 'Margery Fish' see *A. major* subsp. *involucrata* 'Shaggy'
- - 'Moira Reid' CExl CSam CWCL ECtt EWld GCal GMaP IRob LSRN MFie MRav
- - 'Orlando' MAvo MFie
§ - - 'Shaggy' ♀H7 Widely available
- - 'Snape Cottage' EBee
- 'Jade Lady' WFar
- 'Jitse' MAvo
- 'Large White' LCro LOPS
- 'Lars' CExl CWCL ECtt ELon GBin GMcL IFoB LRHS MFie MHol MNrw NBid NGdn NLar SPer SPoG SRms SWvt WCAu
- 'Lola' CBcs CBod CDor EBee IBoy MTis NLar SPad WHar WWtn

§	– 'Madeleine van Bennekom'	CNor CWCL EBee ECha ECtt
	– 'Midnight Owl'	CRos ECtt LRHS MHol NRHS NSti
	– 'Penny's Pink'	CWCL EBee ELan LCro MAvo MFie NPnk WSpi
	– 'Pink Crush'	CRos EBee EPfP LRHS NRHS
	– 'Pink Pride'	CWCL GMcL GWyn IPot LSou MHol MTis WCAu WFar
	– 'Pink Sensation'	EBee GBin GMcL
	– 'Pink Surprise'	GMcL MAvo NLar
	– 'Primadonna'	CBod CRos EPri GMaP LRHS MFie MHol MTis NLar NRHS SPlb WMoo
	– 'Princesse Sturdza'	CWCL EBee EWTr
	– 'Red Joyce' **new**	SPad WHar
	– 'Reverse Sunningdale Variegated' (v)	MFie
	– 'Rosa Lee'	CWCL MFie
	– var. ***rosea***	CRos CWCL EHrv EPfP EWTr GWyn LRHS MFie MRav MSpe NGdn NRHS SPer WCAu WFar WMoo
	– – George's form	CWCL LSRN MFie
	– 'Rosensinfonie'	CWCL EBee GMaP GWyn MFie NBro WPnP
§	– 'Rubra'	CBod CRos CSpe CWCL ELan EPfP GKin GMcL IBoy LCro LOPS LRHS MFie MGos MHol MSpe NChi NPer NRHS SCob SRms WBor WCAu WHal WHar
	– 'Ruby Cloud'	CBod CHid ECtt ELan ELon EPri EWTr MFie NBro NGdn NRHS SRot WFar WHar WMoo WSpi WWtn
	– 'Ruby Giant'	GKin SHar
	– 'Ruby Glow'	MFie
	– 'Ruby Wedding'	Widely available
	– 'Silver Glow'	EBee ECtt
	– 'Star of Beauty'^{PBR}	CKno CRos CWCL ECtt ELan EPed GWyn IBoy LRHS LSou MFie NLar NPri NRHS NSti SCob SPoG SRms SRot SWvt WSpi
	– 'Star of Billion'^{PBR}	CBod CRos EBee ECtt ELan IBoy IRob LLWG LRHS MHol NLar NPri NRHS SCob SPoG SWvt WCAu WCot WRHF
	– 'Star of Fire'^{PBR}	CWGN EBee ECtt LRHS LSou MBel SCob SRot WFar WHil
	– 'Star of Magic'^{PBR} (v)	LRHS SPoG WCAu
	– 'Star of Royals'^{PBR}	CWCL ECtt IPot LSou SPoG WFar
	– 'Star of Summer'	CBod EBee LSou
	– 'Starburst'	EBee MFie
	– 'Sue Barnes' (v)	MFie
§	– 'Sunningdale Variegated' (v) ♀H7	Widely available
	– 'Titoki Point'	MFie WCot
	– 'Venice'^{PBR}	CBct CDor CKno CRos CWCL CWGN ECtt ELan IBoy LRHS LSou MAvo MHol MNrw NEgg NEoE NLar NRHS SPoG SRms SWvt WCAu WFar WHil WSpi
§	***maxima*** ♀H6	Widely available
	– 'Mark Fenwick'	MFie
I	– 'Rosea'	CDor ECtt EWTr MNrw NGdn
	minor	EBee LRHS WCru
	'Moulin Rouge'^{PBR}	Widely available
§	'Mrs MacGregor'	MAvo
	'Old Warwickshire Pink'	see *A.* 'Mrs MacGregor'
	'Queen's Children'	CDor
	'Rainbow'	MFie NLar
	'Roma'^{PBR} ♀H7	Widely available
	rubra	see *A. major* 'Rubra'
	'Ruby Bere'	LEdu

	'Ruby Star'^{PBR}	Widely available
	'Sheila's Red'	LSRN NDov
	'Snow Star'^{PBR}	CRos CWCL EBee EHrv ELan EPfP LRHS MBNS MFie NLar NRHS
	'Star of Heaven'	NLar
	'Star of Passion'^{PBR}	EBee ECtt ELan NLar SCob
	'Star of Treasure'^{PBR}	ELan IBoy IPot NLar
	'Superstar'^{PBR}	CAvo CBod CDor CMil CSpe EBee ECtt ELon EPfP IBoy IPot IRob LCro LOPS LRHS MBNS MHol MNrw MRav NDov NEgg NLar NSti SPer SWvt WCot WHoo WSpi XEll
	'Warren Hills'	EBee GMaP MFie NLar NPnk
	'Washfield'	CWCL MTis NDov NEoE

Asyneuma (*Campanulaceae*)

	campanuloides	SBch
	canescens	CRos LRHS LSou NRHS
	limonifolium	WAbe
	pulvinatum	CPBP EPot NSla WAbe

Asystasia (*Acanthaceae*)

	bella	see *Mackaya bella*

Athamanta (*Apiaceae*)

	turbith	CSpe LEdu MNrw SBrt
	vestina	LRHS SBrt SPhx

Athanasia (*Asteraceae*)

§	***parviflora***	SPlb

Atherosperma (*Atherospermataceae*)

	moschatum	CFil CHll WSHC

Athrotaxis (*Cupressaceae*)

	cupressoides	CBcs CKen WThu
	laxifolia	CKen LRHS

Athyrium ✿ (*Woodsiaceae*)

	auriculatum **new**	CBdn
	'Branford Beauty'	CCCN CRos LRHS NRHS
	'Branford Rambler'	CBdn EBee
	filix-femina ♀H7	Widely available
§	– subsp. ***angustum*** ♀H7	CRos ELan LRHS MMoz MRav NGdn NRHS WMoo
	– – f. ***rubellum*** 'Lady in Red' ♀H7	CAby CBdn CBod CCCN CKel CRos CWCL EBee EPfP EUJe GBin IBal LCro LEdu LLWG LRHS LSRN MGos MSCN NEgg NLar NRHS SCob SPoG WMoo
	– 'Crispum Grandiceps Kaye'	NGdn
	– Cristatum Group	EFer ELan ESps LSRN MMoz NGdn WCot WFib
	– 'Dre's Dagger'	CBdn EBee SCob SMad SPoG WPGP
	– 'Fieldii'	EFer
	– 'Frizelliae' ♀H7	Widely available
	– 'Frizelliae Capitatum'	WFib
	– 'Lady-in-Lace' ♀H7	EBee LLHF LLWG
	– 'Minutissimum'	CRos ELan LRHS MMoz NRHS WCot
	– Plumosum Group	EShb MRav WFib XLum
	– 'Plumosum Axminster'	EFer WFar
	– 'Plumosum Druery'	EFer
	– RED STEM	see *A. filix-femina* 'Rotstiel'
§	– 'Rotstiel'	CDTJ EBee MMoz NBro NLos WMoo WPnP
	– 'Setigerum Cristatum'	WFar
	– 'Vernoniae' ♀H7	ELan MMoz MRav NLar
	– 'Vernoniae Cristatum'	WFib

- 'Victoriae'	CBdn CCCN CDTJ CRos CWCL EBee ECtt EFer ELan EPfP GBin GMaP IBal LLWG LRHS NBid NHim NLar NRHS WMoo WSpi XLum
- Victoriae Group	see *A. filix-femina* subsp. *angustum*
- aff. 'Victoriae'	CKel CTal EWTr WFar
'Ghost' 🏆^{H6}	CBdn CCCN CRos EBee LLWG LRHS LSou MGos NRHS NSti SPlb SPoG WCot
goeringianum 'Pictum'	see *A. niponicum* var. *pictum*
minimum	CAby CBdn LLHF NHim
niponicum	CBdn CRos LRHS NRHS WHal
- 'Godzilla'	CBdn EBee
- f. ***metallicum***	see *A. niponicum* var. *pictum*
§ - var. ***pictum*** 🏆^{H5}	Widely available
- - 'Apple Court'	CBdn CCCN CRos EBee ESps LRHS NLar NRHS
- - 'Burgundy Lace'	CBdn EBee ECtt MPnt NBro NLar SPoG WCot
* - - 'Cristatoflabellatum'	CRos EBee LRHS NRHS
- - 'Pearly White' **new**	CBdn
- - 'Pewter Lace'	CBdn EBee ECtt NBro NLar
- - 'Red Beauty'	CAby CBcs CBod CDTJ CRos ECha ECtt ELan EMOT EPfP EUJe GBin GEdr GMcL IBal IBoy LEdu LRHS LSRN MMoz MMuc MSCN NLar NRHS SRkn WCot WFar WMoo
- - 'Regal Red'	CBdn CRos EBee LRHS NLos NRHS
- - 'Silver Falls' 🏆^{H5}	CBcs CRos EBee EShb LRHS NRHS SPoG WCot
- - 'Ursula's Red'	EBee EShb IRob LCro LEdu LLWG LOPS LRHS LSRN NBid NHpl NLar SPoG WCot WFar WPGP
- - 'Wildwood Twist'	WCot
'Ocean's Fury'	CAby CBdn EBee ECtt EShb GBin LPla SPoG WCot
otophorum 🏆^{H4}	MRav NBid NLos WPGP
- var. ***okanum*** 🏆^{H5}	Widely available
vidalii	CBdn CRos EBee IBal LLWG LRHS LSou MMoz MSCN NBro NLar NLos NRHS WCot WFar WFib XLum
wardii	CBdn

Atractylodes (*Asteraceae*)

japonica	GEdr LEdu

Atragene see *Clematis*

Atriplex (*Amaranthaceae*)

canescens	CAgr XSen
halimus	CAgr CBcs CFGn ECha EHoe EPPr MRav NLar SLon SPer SPlb WCot XAbr
- 'Cascais'	WCot
- 'Limelight' (v)	EPPr
hortensis	ENfk
- var. ***rubra***	CSpe ELan LSou MNHC SRms

Atropa (*Solanaceae*)

belladonna	EBWF GPoy MMuc SEND
mandragora	see *Mandragora officinarum*

aubergine see AGM Vegetables Section

Aubrieta (*Brassicaceae*)

'Agnetta' **new**	ECtt GCrg
'Alba'	see *A.* 'Fiona'
albomarginata	see *A.* 'Argenteovariegata'
'Alix Brett'	CMea
'Ann Kendall'	ECtt
'April Joy' (d)	ELon
§ 'Argenteovariegata' (v) 🏆^{H5}	CRos ELan LRHS MJak NRHS
'Astolat' (v)	ECtt GCrg
'Audrey Blue' (Audrey Series)	GWyn
§ 'Aureovariegata' (v) 🏆^{H5}	CMea NPer XLum
(Axcent Series) AXCENT BLUE WITH EYE ('Audelbley'^{PBR})	LBuc LRHS
- AXCENT BURGUNDY	CRos LRHS NRHS
- AXCENT DEEP PURPLE ('Audelpur'^{PBR})	ETMg LBuc LRHS
- AXCENT LIGHT BLUE	CRos EPfP LRHS NRHS
- AXCENT MAGENTA ('Audelmag'^{PBR})	LRHS
bicoloured	CMea
BLAUE SCHÖNHEIT	see *A.* 'Blue Beauty'
'Blaumeise'	IRob LRHS MHol
§ 'Blue Beauty'	CBod CMea ECtt EPfP EUJe GBin GKev GMaP NHpl NLar WHoo
'Blue Emperor'	ECtt
'Blue Whale'	CBod ECtt GAbr MHol NLar SRms SRot SWvt
§ 'Bob Saunders' (d)	CMea ECtt ELon
'Bressingham Pink' (d) 🏆^{H5}	ECtt EPfP SRms
'Bressingham Red'	ECtt ELan EPfP ESps GCrg GMaP SRms
'Bubble Purple'	EPfP
canescens	CPBP
Cascade Series	SPoG
- 'Blue Cascade'	CTri GMaP MBNS MBel MJak SPlb SPoG SRms
- 'Lilac Cascade'	SPoG SRms
- 'Purple Cascade'	CTri LCro LSRN MAsh MBNS MBel MJak NSla SPlb SPoG SRms WRHF
- 'Red Cascade' 🏆^{H5}	CTri ECtt LSRN MBNS MJak NSla SPlb SPoG
× ***cultorum***	SVic XSen
deltoidea	WCFE
- Variegata Group (v)	ECtt MHol
- - 'Nana Variegata' (v)	CMea EPot
'Doctor Mules' 🏆^{H5}	ECtt ESps SRms
'Doctor Mules Variegata' (v)	ECtt EHoe ELan ELon EPfP ESps ETMg GCrg GMaP GWyn MAsh MHer NLar NWad SPoG SRot SWvt WHoo
double pink-flowered (d)	CBod ELan EPfP GMaP MHol
'Downers Variegata' (v)	ECtt EPot NWad
'Elsa Lancaster'	EPot NHpl NSla
§ 'Fiona'	ECtt EWes MMuc
glabrescens	CMea NHpl WAbe
'Gloria'	CBod CMea ECtt EUJe GAbr NHpl NLar SRot WHoo
'Golden Emperor'	MHer
'Golden King'	see *A.* 'Aureovariegata'
gracilis 'Kitte Rose'	CRos ECtt LBuc LRHS MHol NRHS
'Greencourt Purple' 🏆^{H5}	ECtt MHer
'Hamburger Stadtpark'	CWCL ECtt ELan ELon EPfP GCrg GMaP SRms SRot
'Hemswell Purity'	see *A.* 'Snow Maiden'
'Hürth' **new**	SAko
'Ida'	CSma ECtt
'Kati'	GMaP LRHS
'Kitte'	CSma ECtt ELan EPfP GCrg LRHS MHer NEoE NLar SPoG SRms
'Kitte Blue'	CRos EPfP LBuc LRHS MHol NPri NRHS SPoG SRms
'Kitte Purple'	CSma ELan EPfP SPoG

	'Kitte White'	CRos CSma LRHS MHer NRHS
	'Leichtlinii'	XLum
	'Lime Variegated' (v)	NHpl
	macedonica	EPot
	'Oakington Lavender'	ECtt
	'Pink Beauty'	ECtt
	'Purple Charm'	SRms
	'Red Carpet'	ELan EPot MAsh MHer SRms
	'Rose Queen'	CMea ECtt
	(Royal Series) 'Royal Blue'	ELan EPfP MJak NEgg NLar SRms SRot WMoo
	- 'Royal Red'	ELan EPfP GBin GWyn SRms WMoo
	- 'Royal Violet'	ELan EPfP WMoo
	'Schofield's Double'	see *A.* 'Bob Saunders'
	'Shobden' (v)	ECtt
	'Silberrand' (v)	ECha
§	'Snow Maiden'PBR	NHpl
	'Somerfield Silver'	ELan EPfP
	'Somerford Lime' (v)	ECtt ELan EPfP SRms
	'Swan Red' (v)	CBod CPla ECtt EHoe ELon EPot MHer NEgg NEoE NHpl NLar NSla SRot WTor
	'Valerie' (v)	ECtt EPot EWes
	'Westacre Gold' (v)	ECtt EWes LSou MAsh MHol
	'Whitewell Gem'	WMoo XLum
	'Winterberg'	ECtt

Aucuba ✿ (*Garryaceae*)

	chlorascens	CFil
	- B&SWJ 11815	WCru
	himalaica	CFil SBrt
	var. ***dolichophylla***	
	- - Og 95038	WCru
	japonica	CAco CCVT CDul ESps GMcL SCob SEWo WCru WFar
	- 'Angelon'	CRos LRHS NRHS
	- var. ***borealis*** (f) CWJ 12898	WCru
	- 'Clent Wortley Hall' (m) **new**	WCFE
	- 'Crassifolia' (m)	EBtc ELon SArc
	- 'Crotonifolia' (f/v) ♀^{H5}	Widely available
	- 'Crotonifolia' (m/v)	CMac MAsh SGol SRms
	- 'Dentata'	WAvo WCru
	- 'Golden Girl' (v)	CRos LRHS MAsh NRHS
	- 'Golden King' (m/v) ♀^{H5}	CMac CRos ELan ELon EMOT EPfP LRHS MAsh MGos NLar SCob SGol SLim SPoG WFar
	- 'Golden Spangles' (f/v)	CBcs EBee EMil LRHS SMad SWvt
	- 'Hillieri' (f)	EBtc
	- 'Leucocarpa' (f) **new**	SPer
	- f. ***longifolia***	CBot CMac EPfP NLar SArc WCru
	- - 'Salicifolia' (f) ♀^{H5}	EBee MRav NLar SCob WCru WFar WPGP
	- 'Maculata' misapplied	see *A. japonica* 'Variegata'
	- 'Marmorata' (v)	CRos LRHS MAsh NRHS
	- 'Mr Goldstrike' (m/v)	CRos EPfP ESps LRHS MAsh
	- PEPPER POT ('Shilpot') (m/v) ♀^{H5}	CRos CTsd EPfP LRHS MAsh MJak SLon
	- 'Pepperspot'PBR (m/v)	MJak WMoo
	- 'Picturata' (m/v)	CDul CMac CRos CSBt ELan ELon ESps LRHS MAsh MJak MMuc NLar NRHS SEND WFar
	- 'Rozannie' (f/m) ♀^{H5}	Widely available
	- 'Sulphurea Marginata' (f/v)	CMac CRos CTri EBee EShb LRHS NLar NRHS SPer WFar
§	- 'Variegata' (f/v)	Widely available
	- 'Variegata' white-flowered (m/v)	SGbt
	omeiensis	CBcs CDTJ CExl CFil
	- B&SWJ 2864	WCru
	- BWJ 8048	WCru
	- L 614	CFil WPGP

Aulax (*Proteaceae*)

	cancellata	CCCN SPlb

Aurinia (*Brassicaceae*)

§	***saxatilis*** ♀^{H5}	CPla ELan EPfP MMuc SPlb WRHF XSen
	- 'Citrina' ♀^{H5}	ECha ECtt SRms
	- 'Compacta'	ECtt GJos
	- 'Dudley Nevill'	ELon
	- 'Dudley Nevill Variegated' (v)	ECha ECtt ELon EWes MHer
	- GOLD BALL	see *A. saxatilis* 'Goldkugel'
	- 'Gold Dust'	SRms WRHF
§	- 'Goldkugel'	CMea EPfP GWyn MHol SPoG SRms
	- 'Variegata' (v)	SPoG SRms

Austrocedrus (*Cupressaceae*)

§	***chilensis***	CKen SBig SLim

Avena (*Poaceae*)

	candida	see *Helictotrichon sempervirens*

Avenula see *Helictotrichon*

Averrhoa (*Oxalidaceae*)

	carambola (F)	CCCN

avocado see *Persea americana*

Azalea see *Rhododendron*

Azara ✿ (*Salicaceae*)

	sp.	NEgg
	dentata	CBcs CHll CMac WFar
	- 'Variegata'	see *A. integrifolia* 'Variegata'
	integrifolia	CCCN MGil
	- 'Uarie'	CCCN
§	- 'Variegata' (v)	CCCN LRHS
	lanceolata	CBcs CExl CTri CTsd LEdu NSti
	microphylla ♀^{H4}	CBcs CCCN CDul CExl CMac CRos CTri EBee ELan ELon EPfP EUJe LRHS LSRN MAsh MGil MGos MMuc MNHC SArc SEND SLim SPer SPlb SWeb WFar WPGP WSpi
*	- 'Albovariegata' (v)	CTri
	- 'Gold Edge' (v)	CBcs EPfP WFar
	- 'Variegata' (v)	CBcs CBct CExl CMac CRos CTsd EHoe ELan EPfP GMcL LRHS MAsh MGil MMuc NLar SEND SPoG WAvo WFar WSHC
*	***patagonica***	MBlu
	petiolaris	CTri MGil
	serrata ♀^{H4}	CBcs CBot CCCN CDul CEnd CRos CTsd EPfP EShb EUJe GBin LRHS MGil NLar SEND SGol SPer SPoG SRms SVen WBor WFar WHar WKif WSHC WSpi
	uruguayensis	CBcs CCCN CExl CTsd

Azorella (*Apiaceae*)

	glebaria misapplied	see *A. trifurcata*
	glebaria A. Gray	see *Bolax gummifer*
	gummifer	see *Bolax gummifer*
	lycopodioides	EPot WAbe
	patagonica	EPot SPlb WAbe

§ ***trifurcata***	CPar CSpe CTri GAbr GCrg GKev MMuc SPlb WAbe
- 'Nana'	GEdr GMaP WThu XLum

Azorina (*Campanulaceae*)

§ ***vidalii***	NWad SPlb

B

Babiana (*Iridaceae*)

sp.	SDir
ambigua	CTal
nana	CTal CTca GKev
- 'Claudia' **new**	GKev
patersoniae	SPlb
purpurea	CTal
pygmaea	CTal
sambucina	CTal NRog
stricta 𝕐H2	CCCN CTal GKev SDeJ
- Kew hybrids	GKev
- 'Purple Star'	CExl NRog
thunbergii	CPbh
tubulosa	CTal NRog
vanzyliae	CTal
* ***volubilis***	NRog
'Zwanenburg's Glory'	CPrp

Baccharis (*Asteraceae*)

patagonica	LRHS MMuc SArc SVen

Backhousia (*Myrtaceae*)

citriodora	GPoy MHer

Bacopa (*Plantaginaceae*)

sp.	SWvt
'Snowflake'	see *Chaenostoma cordatum* 'Snowflake'

Baeckea (*Myrtaceae*)

gunniana	CExl
linifolia	SPlb
virgata	SPlb

Balbisia (*Ledocarpaceae*)

peduncularis	CCCN

Baldellia (*Alismataceae*)

ranunculoides	WMAq
- f. ***repens***	LLWG

Ballota (*Lamiaceae*)

acetabulosa	ECha EWes MNHC WCot
'All Hallow's Green'	see *Marrubium bourgaei* var. *bourgaei* 'All Hallows Green'
hirsuta	XSen
nigra	GPoy NMir SRms
§ - 'Archer's Variegated' (v)	MAvo
- 'Variegata'	see *B. nigra* 'Archer's Variegated'
pseudodictamnus 𝕐H4	CBcs CBod CMac CRos EBee ECha EHoe ELan EPfP GMaP LRHS LSRN MNHC MRav NPer NRHS NSti SCob SEND SLon SPer WAvo XLum XSen
- B&M 8119	WCot WPGP
- from Crete	ECha
- compact **new**	CBct
rupestris 'Frogswell Carolyn' (v)	IFro

Baloskion (*Restionaceae*)

§ ***tetraphyllum***	CCht CPbh GBin GCal LRHS SPlb SPoG
- 'Cornish Gold' (v)	CPbh MPkF

Balsamita see *Tanacetum*

Balsamorhiza (*Asteraceae*)

incana	SBrt

Bambusa (*Poaceae*)

glaucescens	see *B. multiplex*
§ ***multiplex***	XBlo
- 'Alphonso-Karrii'	SBig
- 'Elegans'	see *B. multiplex* 'Floribunda'
- 'Fernleaf'	see *B. multiplex* 'Floribunda'
§ - 'Floribunda'	EShb XBlo
- 'Golden Goddess'	XBlo
- 'Silverstripe'	see *B. multiplex* 'Variegata'
§ - 'Variegata' (v)	XBlo
- 'Wang Tsai'	see *B. multiplex* 'Floribunda'
pubescens	see *Dendrocalamus strictus*
ventricosa	SBig XBlo
vulgaris	XBlo
- 'Vittata'	ERod XBlo

banana see *Ensete*, *Musa*

Banksia ✿ (*Proteaceae*)

canei	SPlb
ericifolia	CDTJ CPbh
- var. ***ericifolia***	CCCN
- var. ***macrantha***	SPlb
grandis	CCCN CPbh LRHS
integrifolia	CBcs CCCN CDTJ CKel CPbh LRHS SPlb
marginata	CTsd LRHS SPlb
media	SPlb
oblongifolia	SPlb
paludosa	SPlb
praemorsa	CCCN
- yellow-flowered **new**	CCCN
prionotes **new**	CCCN LRHS
robur	CBcs CCCN CPbh SPlb
serrata	CCCN SPlb
speciosa	SPlb
spinulosa	CPbh
- 'Birthday Candles'	CPbh
- var. ***collina***	SPlb
- var. ***spinulosa***	CCCN
violacea	SPlb

Baptisia (*Papilionaceae*)

§ ***alba***	EBee ILea LPla MBel MNrw WHil
- var. ***alba***	IPot WCAu
- - 'Wayne's World'	EBee
§ - var. ***macrophylla***	CRos EWes LRHS MNrw NRHS SPhx
australis 𝕐H7	Widely available
- 'Blueberry Sundae' **new**	EBee EWTr ILea SPer
- 'Caspian Blue'	CExl LEdu WHil
- 'Exaltata' 𝕐H7	CGar EBee ECtt LPla MBNS MHer MHol NCou SBod WCot
- var. ***minor***	MMrt SPhx
× ***bicolor*** 'Starlite' (Prairieblues Series)	MAvo MNrw NDov
bracteata var. ***leucophaea***	LSou SPhx

'Carolina Moonlight'	EBee ECtt EWTr EWes IPot MMrt MNrw NDov NPnk NSti SPer
'Cherries Jubilee' **new**	EBee ILea WHil
'Chocolate Chip'	SHar
'Dutch Chocolate' (Decadence Series)	CWGN EBee ECtt EWTr ILea IPot LRHS MAvo NSti SPer SPoG WHil XEll
'Indigo Spires' **new**	EBee ILea
lactea	see *B. alba* var. *macrophylla*
'Lemon Meringue' **new**	EBee WHil
leucantha	see *B. alba* var. *macrophylla*
pendula	see *B. alba*
'Purple Smoke'	CAby CExl CSpe EBee ECtt ILea IPot IRob LCro LEdu LOPS LRHS MAvo MBel MCot MHol MNrw NPnk SMHy SPhx WAul
'Solar Flare' (Prairieblues Series)	ILea
sphaerocarpa	SPhx SPlb
tinctoria	SPhx
'Vanilla Cream' **new**	IPot
× ***variicolor*** 'Twilite' (Prairieblues Series)	EBee EPfP EWes NDov

Barbarea (*Brassicaceae*)

praecox	see *B. verna*
rupicola 'Sunnyola'	WCot
§ ***verna***	GPoy MHer SRms SVic
vulgaris **new**	EBWF
- 'Variegata' (v)	NBro WMoo

Barleria (*Acanthaceae*)

oenotheroides	CCCN
suberecta	see *Dicliptera sericea*

Barnardia (*Asparagaceae*)

japonica **new**	WCot

Barosma see *Agathosma*

Bartlettina (*Asteraceae*)

§ ***sordida***	CCCN EUJe

Basella (*Basellaceae*)

rubra	SPre

Bashania (*Poaceae*)

§ ***fargesii***	CBdn ENBC ERod MMuc MRav MWht SEND
I ***qingchengshanensis***	ERod MWht

basil see *Ocimum basilicum*

Bauhinia (*Caesalpiniaceae*)

alba hort.	see *B. variegata*
* ***lutea***	CCCN
natalensis	SPlb
purpurea L.	CCCN SPlb
tomentosa	CAco CCCN
§ ***variegata***	CAco
'White Lady'	CCCN
yunnanensis	SPlb

Baumea see *Machaerina*

bay see *Laurus nobilis*

beans see AGM Vegetables Section

Beaucarnea (*Asparagaceae*)

recurvata ♀H1c	LOPS SPlb

Beaufortia (*Myrtaceae*)

sparsa	CTsd
squarrosa	SPlb

Beckmannia (*Poaceae*)

eruciformis	XLum

Bedfordia (*Asteraceae*)

linearis	SPlb SVen

Beesia (*Ranunculaceae*)

§ ***calthifolia***	CBct CDTJ CDor CSpe CTal EBee EHrv EPfP EWld GEdr IMou LEdu LLHF SChF SMad WCot WCru WPGP WSHC
- DJHC 98447	CExl
deltophylla misapplied	see *B. calthifolia*

beetroot see AGM Vegetables Section

Begonia ✿ (*Begoniaceae*)

from Taiwan	GCal
'Abel Carrière' (R)	WDib
aconitifolia (C)	EShb
'Adam'	WFib
albopicta (C)	EBak
- 'Rosea' (C)	EShb WDib
'Angela Jane' (T)	WFib
§ ***annulata*** ♀H1b HWJK 2424	WCru
'Apricot Delight' (Fragrant Falls Improved Series) (T) **new**	ETMg WFib
'Apricot Nectar' (Fragrant Falls Improved Series) (T) **new**	NRHS
I 'Apricot Shades Improved' **new**	ETMg SDeJ
'Argentea' (R)	EBak
'Argenteo-guttata'	EShb
'Aya' (C)	WDib
balansana **new**	CBct
'Benitochiba' (R) ♀H1b	CAvo CBct CExl CHll CSpe EBee ECtt GBin LLWG MHol NLar SPoG WCot WDib WGrn
'Beryl Rhodes' (T)	WFib
'Bethlehem Star'	WDib
§ 'Bettina Rothschild' (R)	WDib
'Billy Langdon' (T)	WFib
'Black Fang' ♀H1b	WDib
'Black Knight' (R)	WDib
'Blackberry Swirl' (R)	WDib
'Blazing Star' (T)	LCro LOPS
'Blushing Star' (T)	LCro LOPS
'Bokit'	WDib
'Bokit' × ***imperialis***	WDib
boliviensis 'Firecracker'	WDib
BONFIRE ('Nzcone'PBR) ♀H1b	EPfP SPoG
'Bouton de Rose' (T)	SDeJ
'Buffey'PBR (T)	NPri
'Buttermilk' (T)	WFib
'Can-can' (T)	WFib
'Candy Floss'	WCru
carolineifolia ♀H1b	WDib
'Cascade Florence' **new**	SDeJ
'Cascade Sunray' **new**	SDeJ
'Casey Corwin' (R)	WDib
cathayana	EBee GCal
'Champagne'	LCro LOPS
I ***chapaensis*** HWJ 642	WCru

	CHERRY BON BON	NPri
	'China Curl' (R) ♀H1b	WDib
	chitoensis B&SWJ 1954	GCal WCru
	'Cleopatra' ♀H1b	WDib
	coccinea (C)	WDib
	'Cocoa Enchantment' (T) **new**	ETMg
	'Comte de Lesseps' (C)	WDib
	'Connee Boswell' ♀H1b	CHll WDib
§	***corallina*** (C)	EBak
	'Crispa Marginata' (T) **new**	ETMg
	cucullata var. ***arenosicola*** (S)	CFil ECtt WCot
	'Curly Fireflush' (R) ♀H1b	WDib
	'Daffadowndilly' (T) **new**	ETMg
	'David Blais' (R) ♀H1b	WDib
	'Dawnal Meyer' (C)	WDib
I	'De Elegans'	WDib
	DEVOTION ('Yadev'PBR) (Million Kisses Series) ♀H1b	NPri
	'Dewdrop' (R) ♀H1b	WDib
	'Dibleys Pink Showers'PBR ♀H1b	WDib
	discolor	see *B. grandis* subsp. *evansiana*
	'Don Miller' (C)	WDib
	'Doublet Pink' (Doublet Series) (S/d)	NPri
	DRAGON WING RED ('Bepared'PBR) ♀H1b	EShb
§	***dregei*** (T) ♀H1b	CSpe
	ELEGANCE ('Yagance'PBR) (Million Kisses Series) ♀H1b	NPri
	'Embrace' (Million Kisses Series)	NPri
	emeiensis	CFil CSpe EBee
	'Emerald Giant' (R)	WDib
	'Escargot' (R) ♀H1b	SMad WDib
	'Fairy Lights' (T)	WFib
	Fimbriata Group (T)	SDeJ
	'Fire Flush'	see *B.* 'Bettina Rothschild'
	'Fireworks' (R) ♀H1b	WDib
	'Flo'Belle Moseley' (C)	WDib
§	***foliosa*** var. ***miniata*** ♀H1b	CHll CSpe CTsd EBak MArl WCot
	- - pink-flowered	CCCN WCot
	'Fortune Peach Shades' (T) **new**	ETMg
	Fragrant Falls Improved Series	SPoG
	fuchsioides	see *B. foliosa* var. *miniata*
	fusca	WPGP
	'Garden Angel Blush' (Garden Angel Series) **new**	CAbb CBct LLWG LSou
	'Gay Gordon' (T)	WFib
	'Glowing Embers' ♀H1b	CRav ECtt ETMg LBuc NWad SPoG
	gracilis (T) F&M 266	CFil
	- F&M 337	CFil
	grandis (T)	IDee XLum
§	- subsp. ***evansiana*** ♀H3	CAby CBct CBot CHll CPne CSpe CTal CTsd ELon EShb EUJe GCal LEdu SBch SEND SPlb WCot WCru WFar WMoo
	- - B&SWJ 11188	WCru
	- - var. ***alba*** hort. ♀H5	CAby CFil CSpe CTal EBee EPPr EShb EUJe EWld GCal LEdu NLos SBch WCot WMoo WPGP XLum
	- - 'Claret Jug'	CExl CFil EBee ECtt WGrn
	- - 'Pink Parasol'	WCru
	- - pink-flowered	NLos WFar
	- - 'Sublime'	LEdu
	- 'Sapporo'	CFil EBee EPPr GCal SChr WCru
	- silver-spotted **new**	GCal
§	- subsp. ***sinensis*** (T)	EBee NWad
I	- - 'Red Undies'	WCru
	- - 'Snowpop'	WPGP
	- aff. subsp. ***sinensis*** (T) BWJ 8133	WCru
	'Green Gold' (R) ♀H1b	WDib
	griffithii	see *B. annulata*
	haageana hort. ex W. Watson	see *B. scharffii*
	hatacoa silver-leaved	WDib
	'Helen Teupel' (R)	WDib
	'Helena Hall' (T)	WFib
	'Hilo Holiday' (R) ♀H1b	WDib
	homonyma	see *B. dregei*
	HONEYMOON ('Yamoon'PBR) (Million Kisses Series)	NPri
	Illumination Series (T/d) **new**	ETMg
	- 'Illumination Apricot' (T/d)	ESps SCoo
	- 'Illumination Orange' (T/d) ♀H2	ESps
	- 'Illumination Peaches 'n' Cream' (T/d)	ESps
	- 'Illumination Peachy Pink' (T/d)	ESps
	- 'Illumination Rose' (T/d)	ESps SCoo
	- 'Illumination Salmon Pink' (T/d) ♀H2	ESps SCoo
	- 'Illumination White' (T/d)	ESps SCoo
	Inferno Series (S) **new**	ETMg
	× ***intermedia*** 'Bertinii' (T)	LCro LOPS SDeJ
	'Jennifer Wilson' (T)	WFib
	'Jessie Cruickshank' (T)	WFib
	'Joburg' (T)	WFib
	'John Smith' (T)	WFib
	'La Paloma' (C)	WDib
	Large-flowered Double Group (T/d)	SDeJ
	'Lianne' (T)	WFib
	'Lime Green' **new**	GCal
	'Lime Swirl'	WDib
	'Limeade' ♀H1b	WDib
	'Linda Jackson' (T)	WFib
	listada ♀H1b	WDib
	'Little Brother Montgomery' ♀H1b	EShb NWad WDib
	'Lois Burks' (C)	WDib
	'Looking Glass' (C)	WDib
	LOTTO MIXED (S) **new**	ETMg
	'Lucerna' (C)	EBak ELan EShb NLos WDib
	luxurians ♀H1b	CAbb CBct CBod CBot CHll CSpe EBee ECtt ELan EUJe GBin GCal MNrw MPie SMad SPlb WCot WGrn WPGP
	macduffieana	see *B. corallina*
	maculata 'Wightii' (C)	CSpe WDib
	(Majestic Series) 'Majestic Golden Picotee' (T) **new**	ETMg
	- 'Majestic Pink' (T) **new**	ETMg
	- 'Majestic Pink Picotee' (T) **new**	CRos ETMg NRHS
	- 'Majestic Red' (T) **new**	ETMg
	- 'Majestic White' (T) **new**	ETMg
	- 'Majestic Yellow' (T) **new**	ETMg
	'Majesty' (T)	WFib
	Marginata Group (T)	SDeJ
*	'Marginata Crispa White'	SDeJ

	'Marmaduke' ♀H1b	WDib
	'Marmorata' (T)	SDeJ
	'Martin Johnson' (R) ♀H1b	WDib
	masoniana ♀H1b	GCal WDib WSFF
I	'Matador' (T)	WFib
	'Matisse' (Impressionist Series) **new**	CRos NRHS
	'Melissa' (T)	WFib
	'Merry Christmas' (R)	WDib
	'Metallic Mist'PBR	CSpe
	'Midnight Magic' (R) ♀H1b	WDib
	Million Kisses Series	CRav LBuc NPri
	'Mishmi Silver'	CBct GCal WPGP
	'Monet' (Impressionist Series) **new**	CRos NRHS
	'Moonwalker' **new**	ETMg
	'Mother's Day' (T)	LCro LOPS
	'Mrs E. McLaughlan' (T)	WFib
	'Mrs Peters' (T)	WFib
	'Munchkin' ♀H1b	WDib
	'My Best Friend'	WDib
	'Namur' (R) ♀H1b	WDib
	natalensis	see *B. dregei*
	'Nick Woodfield'	WFib
	Nonstop Series (T/d)	ESps ETMg SDeJ
	- 'Nonstop Deep Red' (T/d)	ESps
	- 'Nonstop Pink' (T/d)	ESps SDeJ
	- 'Nonstop Red' (T/d)	ESps SDeJ
	- 'Nonstop Rose Petticoat' (T/d)	ESps
	- 'Nonstop Rosepink' (T/d)	ESps
	- 'Nonstop Salmon' (T/d) **new**	SDeJ
	- 'Nonstop White' (T/d) **new**	SDeJ
	- 'Nonstop Yellow' (T/d) **new**	SDeJ
	(Nonstop Mocca Series) 'Nonstop Mocca Mix' (T/d)	ESps ETMg
	- 'Nonstop Mocca White' (T/d)	ESps
	- 'Nonstop Mocca Yellow' (T/d)	ESps
	'Northern Lights Pink Burst' (T) **new**	ETMg
	'Odorosa' **new**	SDeJ
	'Ollykey' (T)	WFib
	'On Top Pink Blush' (On Top Series) (T) **new**	ETMg
	'Orange Rubra' (C)	WDib
	'Orangeade' (c) **new**	NWad
	'Organdy' (mixed)	ETMg
	palmata	CBct CDTJ CExl GCal
	panchtharensis	CFil
	- B&SWJ 2692	WCru
	- PAB 9007	LEdu
	partita	see *B. dregei*
	'Peardrop'PBR	NPri
	pedatifida DJHC 98473	EWld WCru
	Pendula Group (T)	SDeJ
	- 'Pink Giant' (T)	LCro LOPS
	- 'Red Giant' (T)	LCro LOPS
	- 'White Giant' (T)	LCro LOPS
	'Picasso' (Impressionist Series) **new**	CRos NRHS
	'Picotee' (T)	SDeJ
	'Pink Cascade' **new**	SDeJ
	'Pink Champagne' (R) ♀H1b	WDib
	'Pink Flamingo' (T)	LCro LOPS
	'Pink Twist' **new**	WDib
	'Pollux' ♀H1b	WDib
	'Powder Puff' (T)	WFib
	'Président Carnot' (C) ♀H1b	NWad
	'Princess Alice' (T)	WFib
	'Princess of Hanover' (R) ♀H1b	WDib
	putii B&SWJ 7245	WCru
	'Queen Olympus'	WDib
	'Raspberry Swirl' (R)	WDib
	ravenii (T)	EBee
	'Ray Peters'	WFib
	'Razzmatazz' (R)	WDib
	'Red Admiral' (T)	WFib
	'Red Glory' (T)	LCro LOPS
	'Red Robin' (R) ♀H1b	WDib
	'Red Tempest' **new**	WDib
	'Red Undies' (*grandis*)	see *B. grandis* subsp. *sinensis* 'Red Undies'
	'Regal Minuet' (R) ♀H1b	WDib
	'Renoir' (Impressionist Series) **new**	CRos NRHS
	'Rocheart' (R) ♀H1b	WDib
	'Roy Hartley' (T/d)	WFib
	'Sal's Comet' (R) ♀H1b	WDib
	'Sal's Moondust'	WDib
	'Sammy' (T)	WFib
	'Sandra Haynes' (T)	WFib
	'Sceptre' (T)	WFib
	'Sceptre Cross' (T)	WFib
§	***scharffii***	EBak
	'Scherzo'	WDib
	'Sea Urchin'	WDib
	Semperflorens Cultorum Group bronze-leaved, red-flowered (S)	ESps
	- bronze-leaved, white-flowered (S)	ESps
	- green-leaved, rose-flowered (S)	ESps
	- green-leaved, scarlet-flowered (S)	ESps
	- green-leaved, white-flowered (S)	ESps
	serratipetala ♀H1b	EBak WDib
	'Shamus'	WDib
*	***shepherdii***	WDib
	SHERBET BON BON ('Yabon') ♀H1b	NPri
	sikkimensis	GCal
	silletensis	WCot
	- subsp. ***mengyangensis***	GCal
	'Silver Cloud' (R) ♀H1b	WDib
	'Silver Jewell' ♀H1b	WDib
	'Silver Lace'	WDib
	'Silver Splendor'	CSpe ECtt IBoy XEll
	sinensis	see *B. grandis* subsp. *sinensis*
	sizemoreae	GCal WDib
	'Snow Storm'	WDib
I	'Snowcap' (C) ♀H1b	WDib
	solananthera A. DC. ♀H1b	WDib
	'Solid Silver' (R)	WDib
	soli-mutata	WDib
	sonderiana (T)	GCal
	'Stained Glass'	WDib
	'Star Bright' **new**	WDib
	'Star Light' **new**	WDib
	STARSHINE MIXED **new**	ETMg
	'Sugar Candy' (T/d)	WFib

	'Sugar Plum'	MAsh
	SUMMER JEWELS MIXED (S) new	ETMg
	SUMMERWINGS DARK ELEGANCE ('Insumdaele'PBR) (Summerwings Series)	CSpe SPoG
	'Sunset Yellow Champagne' new	LCro LOPS
	'Susan' (T)	WFib
	sutherlandii (T) ♀H2	CAvo CCCN CExl CFil EBak EBee EShb EWld NPer SAdn SBch WCot WDib WGrn WPGP
	- 'Papaya' (T)	CSpe
	'Sweet Dreams' (T/d)	WFib
	SWEET SPICE CITRUS new	NPri
	SWEET SPICE ENGLISH ROSE new	LSou NPri
	'Switzerland' (T)	SDeJ
	'Tahiti' (T)	WFib
	taliensis EDHCH 042	WCot WCru
	'Tessa Robinson' (T)	WFib
	'Thurstonii' ♀H1b	EShb
	'Tiny Gem'	WDib
*	***tripartita*** (T)	WDib
	'Truffle Cream'	NPri
	'Truffle Peach'	NPri
	'Two Face'	WDib
	'Tye Dye'	GCal
	'Van Gogh' (Impressionist Series) new	CRos NRHS
	venosa	EShb
	'Vera Coates' (T)	WFib
	'Vesuvius' (R)	WDib
	'Vibrant Star' (T)	LCro LOPS
	'Wavy Green'	CBct EBee GCal WPGP
	'Whispers' (T)	WFib
	Whopper Series	ETMg
	'Wild Swan'	WCru
*	***wynn-jonesiae*** 'Pink Lady'	WCru
	'Ziggy' (T)	WFib

Belamcanda see *Iris*

chinensis	see *Iris domestica*

Bellendena (*Proteaceae*)

montana new	CPla

Bellevalia (*Asparagaceae*)

	atroviolacea	GKev
	'Cream Pearl'	WCot
	desertorum JCA 0.227.690	WCot
	dubia	GKev WCot
	forniculata	GKev WCot
	hyacinthoides	WCot
§	***paradoxa***	CAby CHid CMea ERCP GBin GKev MNrw SDeJ
	pycnantha misapplied	see *B. paradoxa*
	pycnantha ambig.	SDeJ
	pycnantha (K. Koch) Losinsk. 'Green Pearl'	CAby ERCP GKev SDeJ
	romana	CAvo ERCP GKev SDeJ WCot
	tabriziana	WCot

Bellis (*Asteraceae*)

§	***caerulescens***	ECtt GAbr
	perennis	EBWF GQue
	- 'Alice'	ECtt GAbr WHer
	- Bellissima Series new	ETMg
	- - 'Bellissima Red'	ESps
	- - 'Bellissima White'	ESps
	- 'Big Bob' (d)	ECtt WCot
	- 'Dresden China'	WCot WHer
	- 'Galaxy White' (Galaxy Series)	EPfP
	- HEN AND CHICKENS	see *B. perennis* 'Prolifera' single-flowered
	- 'Hula'	CNat
	- 'Miss Mason'	WCot WHer
	- old strain	WCot
	- 'Prolifera' double-flowered (d)	WHer
§	- 'Prolifera' single-flowered	CFis ECtt WHer
	- 'Rusher Rose'	EPfP
	- 'Single Blue'	see *B. caerulescens*
	- 'Stafford Pink'	WHer
	- 'The Pearl'	GAbr WCot
	- 'Upper Seagry'	CNat
	rotundifolia 'Caerulescens'	see *B. caerulescens*
	sylvestris	WCot

Belloa (*Asteraceae*)

chilensis	SPlb

Beloperone see *Justicia*

Bensoniella (*Saxifragaceae*)

oregona	CExl

Benthamiella (*Solanaceae*)

nordenskjoldii	WAbe
patagonica	SPlb WAbe
- F&W 9345	ITim WAbe
- white-flowered	WAbe
- yellow-flowered	WAbe

Berberidopsis (*Berberidopsidaceae*)

corallina	CBcs CKel CMac CRHN CRos CTri ELan EPfP EUJe IArd IDee LRHS MGil MGos MRav NLar SAko SLim SPer SPoG SWvt WHar WSHC

Berberis (*Berberidaceae*)

	CC 4730	CExl
	aggregata	SPer SRms
	amurensis var. ***latifolia*** B&SWJ 8539	WCru
	aquifolium	see *Mahonia aquifolium*
	- 'Fascicularis'	see *Mahonia* × *wagneri* 'Pinnacle'
	asiatica	CExl GPoy WPGP
	- PAB 5438	LEdu
	bealei	see *Mahonia bealei*
	'Boughton Red'	WHor
	buxifolia 'Nana' misapplied	see *B. microphylla* 'Pygmaea'
	calliantha	WFar
	candidula C.K. Schneid.	CDul ESps LRHS MMuc MSwo NLar SCob SEND SPer
	- 'Jytte'	see *B.* 'Jytte'
	× ***carminea*** 'Buccaneer'	WSpi
	- 'Pirate King'	CRos CSBt EBee EPfP LRHS MAsh SPer SPoG SWvt
	darwinii ♀H5	Widely available
I	- 'Compacta'	CMac CRos CSBt EBee ELan EMOT EPfP ESps GMcL LBuc LRHS MAsh MGos NEgg NLar NRHS SCob SLim SPoG SWvt WCot WFar
	dictyophylla	CBot EBee ELan EPfP LRHS MMuc NLar SCob SPer SPoG WSHC WSpi

dulcis 'Nana'	see *B. microphylla* 'Pygmaea'
empetrifolia	LEdu WSpi
× ***frikartii*** 'Amstelveen' ♀H5	CCVT ELan EPfP MBNS MMuc MRav SCob SEND WMoo
- 'Telstar'	EMOT ESps NEoE SCob WMoo
gagnepainii misapplied	see *B. gagnepainii* var. *lanceifolia*
gagnepainii C.K.Schneid.	CDul CMac SCob
§ - var. ***lanceifolia***	CTri MMuc SEND SGol WAvo WHar
- - 'Fernspray'	EBee EPfP MRav SRms
- 'Purpurea'	see *B.* × *interposita* 'Wallich's Purple'
'Georgei' ♀H5	CRos EPfP LRHS NRHS
'Goldilocks'	CDul EBee EPfP MBlu SCob SPoG
goudotii B&SWJ 10769	WCru
hamiltoniana H&M 1919	GKev
heterophylla	GKev
× ***hybridogagnepainii*** 'Chenault'	ELan
- 'Robin Hood'	NEgg
hypokerina	CMac
insignis	IDee
- subsp. ***insignis*** var. ***insignis***	ELon LLHF
- - - B&SWJ 2432	WCru
§ × ***interposita*** 'Wallich's Purple'	CCVT CRos EPfP LRHS MRav MSwo SGol SPer WMoo
jamesiana	LLHF WCFE
julianae	CAco CArg CBcs CDul CMac ELan EPfP GMcL MGos MJak MMuc MSwo NEgg SCob SEND SGol SPer SRms SWvt WFar WHar WSHC WSpi
§ 'Jytte'	EBee
koreana	EPfP NLar WFar
'Little Favourite'	see *B. thunbergii* f. *atropurpurea* 'Atropurpurea Nana'
× ***lologensis*** 'Apricot Queen' ♀H5	CBcs CMac CRos EBee EPfP LRHS MAsh MGos NLar SCob SPer SPoG SWvt
- 'Mystery Fire'	IArd MAsh MGos NEgg NLar SGol SWvt WHar WRHF
- 'Stapehill'	CMac CRos ELan EPfP LRHS MAsh SPoG
× ***media*** 'Dual Jewel'PBR	NLar
- PARK JEWEL	see *B.* × *media* 'Parkjuweel'
§ - 'Parkjuweel'	CMac IArd MRav SCob SRms WFar
- 'Red Jewel' ♀H5	CMac CRos EPfP ESps GMcL LRHS MAsh MGos MMuc MRav NEgg SCob SEND SPer SPoG WCFE WFar WMoo
microphylla	EPfP GKev WCFE WFar
- SDR 7027	GKev
§ - 'Pygmaea'	CRos EPfP GMcL LRHS MAsh MGos MMuc MRav SCob SLim SPer
mitifolia	NLar
montana	WPGP
× ***ottawensis*** 'Auricoma'	SGol SWvt
- f. ***purpurea***	CCVT CMac WHar
§ - - 'Silver Miles' (v)	EHoe MRav WFar
§ - - 'Superba'	CBar CBcs CDul CSBt CTri EBee ECrN EHoe ELan ELon EMOT EPfP GMcL MGos MJak MMuc MRav MSwo NEgg SCob SEND SEWo SLim SPer SRms SWvt WFar WHar WMoo
panlanensis 'Cally Rose'	EBee GCal WPGP
poiretii	CExl
polyantha var. ***polyantha***	CTri
pruinosa	GKev
'Red Tears'	MRav SPer WFar WMoo

× ***rubrostilla*** 'Cherry Ripe'	CMac
- 'Wisley'	CRos EBee LRHS
sieboldii	ELon LEdu LLHF MAsh MRav WCFE WSpi
§ ***soulieana***	EPfP
stenophylla Hance	see *B. soulieana*
× ***stenophylla*** Lindl. ♀H5	CCVT CDul CMac CSBt CTri EPfP ESps GMcL LBuc MMuc MRav SGol SPer SRms WFar
- 'Autumnalis'	NEgg
- 'Claret Cascade'	EBee EMil MRav NLar SPer SPoG
- 'Compacta'	NEgg WFar
- 'Corallina Compacta' ♀H5	CMac CMea CRos ELan EPfP EPot GCrg LRHS MAsh MHer SCob SPer SPoG SRms
- 'Cornish Cream'	see *B.* × *stenophylla* 'Lemon Queen'
- 'Crawley Gem'	NLar
- 'Cream Showers'	see *B.* × *stenophylla* 'Lemon Queen'
- 'Etna'	CRos ELan LRHS MAsh SCoo SPoG
- 'Irwinii'	CMac LRHS
- 'Lemon Queen'	WSpi
- 'Nana'	CRos LRHS
subacuminata FMWJ 13290	WCru
- NJM 09.165	WPGP
sublevis PAB 8943	LEdu
taliensis	CExl
temolaica ♀H5	EHoe EPfP EWes MGos NLar SCob SPer WPGP WSpi
thunbergii	CArg CBcs CDul CMac CPer EMOT EPfP ESps GMcL LBuc LPra MJak SCob SPer SWvt WFar WMou
- f. ***atropurpurea***	CAco CBcs CCVT CMac CSBt CTri EBee ECrN ELan EPfP ESps GMcL LBuc MGos MMuc MRav MSwo NEgg NLar SCob SGol SPer SPlb SRms WAvo WHar WMoo WMou WTSh
- - 'Admiration'PBR ♀H7	Widely available
§ - - 'Atropurpurea Nana' ♀H7	Widely available
- - 'Bagatelle'	CRos ELan EPfP ESps GMcL IArd LRHS LSRN MAsh MGos MRav NLar SCob SLim SPer SPoG SWvt WCFE WHar WMoo
- - 'Concorde' ♀H7	CRos ELan EPfP LRHS MAsh NRHS SCob
- - 'Dart's Red Lady' ♀H7	CExl CRos CSBt EHoe ELan EPfP ESps GMcL LRHS MAsh NLar NRHS SCob SPer SWvt WAvo WFar
- - 'Golden Ring' (v) ♀H7	CAco CBcs CDul CMac CRos EHoe ELan EMOT EPfP ESps GMcL LRHS MAsh MGos MRav NEgg NRHS SCob SGbt SPer SPoG SWvt WAvo WFar WMoo
- - 'Harlequin' (v) ♀H7	CChe CRos ELan EPfP ESps GMcL LCro LOPS LRHS LSRN MAsh MGos NEgg NRHS SCob SEle SGol SPer SPoG SRms SWvt WFar WHar
- - 'Helmond Pillar'	Widely available
- - 'Pink Queen' (v)	CDul CPer ELan EPfP ESps LRHS MAsh SCob WFar
- - 'Red Chief'	CBcs CMac CRos EHoe ELan EMOT EPfP ESps GMcL LRHS MAsh MGos MJak MSwo NEgg NRHS SCob SGol SLim SLon SPer SPoG SRms SWvt WFar WHar WMoo
- - 'Red Pillar'	CChe CMac CRos EHoe ELan EMOT ESps LRHS MAsh MGos NEgg SWvt WRHF

- - 'Red Rocket'	CRos EBee ELan EPfP EUJe GMcL LRHS MPkF NEgg NLar NRHS SCob SCoo SPer WMoo
- - 'Rose Glow' (v) ♀H7	Widely available
- - 'Rosy Rocket'PBR (v)	CWGN EBee ELan EMOT EMil EPfP LRHS MAsh MRav NLar SPer SPoG WFar
- 'Atropurpurea Superba'	see *B.* × *ottawensis* f. *purpurea* 'Superba'
- 'Aurea'	CBcs CDul CMac CRos EHoe ELan EMOT EPfP ESps GMcL IRob LRHS LSRN MBlu MGos MRav NLar NRHS SCob SLim SPlb SRms SWvt WMoo
- BONANZA GOLD ('Bogozam'PBR)	CBcs CRos EBee ELan EPfP LRHS MAsh MRav NLar SCob SLim SPer
- 'Crimson Pygmy'	see *B. thunbergii* f. *atropurpurea* 'Atropurpurea Nana'
- 'Diabolic'	CRos ESps LRHS MAsh NPri NRHS SPer SPoG
- 'Erecta'	CMac EPfP MRav SPer WCFE
- 'Fireball'PBR ♀H7	CRos EPfP LRHS
- FLAMINGO ('Hoho 1') **new**	SGol
- 'Golden Dream'PBR **new**	EMOT
- 'Golden Rocket'PBR	CRos EBee ELan EPfP LLHF LRHS MAsh MGos MJak MPkF MRav NEgg NLar NRHS SCoo SPer SPoG WFar
- GOLDEN RUBY ('Goruzam') (v)	LCro
- 'Golden Torch'	CRos CSBt ELan EMOT EPfP ESps LRHS MAsh MRav NEgg NRHS SLim SWvt
- 'Green Carpet'	CMac ESps EUJe LRHS MBlu NLar SGol SPoG SWvt WFar
- 'Green Mantle'	see *B. thunbergii* 'Kelleriis'
- 'Green Marble'	see *B. thunbergii* 'Kelleriis'
§ - 'Kelleriis' (v)	CRos GMcL LRHS MRav
- 'Kobold'	CMac CRos EPfP LRHS MGos NEgg SCob SPer SPoG WMoo
- 'Lutin Rouge'PBR	LCro
- 'Maria'PBR ♀H7	CRos CWGN EHoe ELon EMOT EPfP ESps GMcL IRob LLHF LRHS LSou MGos MJak MPkF NLar NRHS SCob SGol SPoG WGrn WHar WMoo
- 'Orange Dream'PBR	EBee EMOT
- 'Orange Rocket'PBR	CRos EBee ELan EMOT EMil EPfP ESps GMcL LRHS MAsh MGos MPkF MRav NEgg NRHS SCoo SEle SPer SPoG WFar
- 'Pow-wow'	CRos ELan EMOT ESps LRHS MGos NLar NRHS SCob SCoo SGol SLim SPoG SWvt
- 'Redtorch'PBR	CRos LRHS NRHS
- 'Silver Beauty' (v)	EHoe
- 'Silver Mile'	see *B.* × *ottawensis* f. *purpurea* 'Silver Miles'
- 'Somerset'	CMac GMcL
- 'Starburst'PBR (v)	CBcs CDul CRos CSBt EBee EMOT EPfP ESps LCro LOPS LRHS LSRN MGos MJak MPkF NEgg NRHS SCoo SLim SLon SRms SWvt
- 'Tiny Gold'PBR	CRos ELan LCro LRHS LSou MAsh MGos NEgg SCob SLim SLon SWvt WFar
* - 'Tricolor' (v)	CMac MRav WFar
trigona 'Jewel'	ESps
- 'Orange King'	CBcs CMac CTri ELan EPfP LRHS MAsh MGos NEgg NLar SCob SPer SPoG
valdiviana ♀H4	CBcs CBot CExl CJun EBee EPfP GBin IArd IDee SChF SMad WPGP
verruculosa ♀H5	CBcs CDul CRos EPfP ESps GMcL LRHS MBlu MGos NLar SCob SPer SRms SWvt WFar
aff. ***verticillata*** B&SWJ 10672	WCru
virescens B&SWJ 2646D	WCru
vulgaris	CAgr CNat EBWF GPoy MCoo
- 'Wiltshire Wonder' (v)	CNat
wilsoniae	CBcs CDul CFil CMac CTri ECre ELan ELon EPfP GLog GMcL MMuc SCob SPer SRms WAvo WFar WSpi
- blue-leaved	MAsh WFar
- var. ***guhtzunica***	EWes
xanthoclada NJM 11.007	WPGP

Berchemia (*Rhamnaceae*)

racemosa	NLar

bergamot see *Citrus* × *limon* Bergamot Group

Bergbambos (*Poaceae*)

§ ***tessellata***	ERod MMuc MWht SEND

Bergenia ✿ (*Saxifragaceae*)

'Abendglocken'	CMac CRos ECha ECtt EPfP MWat NRHS NSti WCot WFar
§ 'Abendglut'	Widely available
'Admiral'	CBct CMac ECha WCot
afghanica	XLum
* ***agavifolia***	CBct XLum
'Andrea'	WCot
'Angel Kiss' (Dragonfly Series)	EBee ECtt GBin MNrw WCot
'Apple Blossom'	CRos EPfP LRHS NRHS
'Apple Court White'	CBct
'Autumn Magic'	CBct CBod CRos ELon EPfP LRHS LSou NCou WFar
'Baby Doll'	Widely available
'Bach'	CBct CBod CDor CRos EBee ECtt EPfP GEdr LPla LRHS LSou MBel MCot MMuc NLar NRHS NSti NWad SCob SWvt WCAu WCot WFar WHar WMoo WWtn
§ 'Ballawley' clonal	CRos ECha GBin GCal IMou LRHS MRav NEgg NRHS WCot XLum
'Ballawley Guardsman'	CBct
§ Ballawley hybrids	CMac WSpi
'Ballawley' seed-raised	see *B.* Ballawley hybrids
'Bartók'	CBct CMil CRos EBee ECtt EUJe LLWG LRHS NRHS WCot WMoo
beesiana	see *B. purpurascens*
'Beethoven'	CBct ECha GBin MRav WCot
BELL TOWER	see *B.* 'Glockenturm'
'Biedermeier' ♀H7	ECha
'Bizet'	CBct XLum
'Borodin'	CBct
'Brahms'	CBct WCot
'Bressingham Bountiful'	CBct
'Bressingham Ruby'PBR	CBct CBod CRos CWCL EBee ECha ECtt ELon EPed GBin IRob LRHS LSRN MBel MGos MHol MRav NEgg NRHS SCob SPer SWvt WCot WHoo WSpi
'Bressingham Salmon'	CBct EBee ECha ECtt ELon GMaP IRob MRav NLar SRms WCAu WCot
'Bressingham White' ♀H6	Widely available
'Britten' ♀H7	CBct CMac GBin IMou WCot

	ciliata	CBct CDor CMac CTal ECha EHrv EPri EShb EUJe GEdr GMaP LEdu LRHS MRav NLar NPnk SPer WPGP WSHC WSpi XLum
	- 'Dumbo'	CAbb CBct EBee GBin LLHF LRHS
	- f. ***ligulata***	see *B. pacumbis*
	- 'Wilton'	CBct CTal EWld LEdu SHar WCot WSHC
	ciliata × crassifolia	see *B. × schmidtii*
	'Claire Maxine' ♀H7	CBct ECtt GBin GCal GQue MPie NLar NWad SPad WCAu WCot WSHC
	cordifolia	Widely available
	- 'Flore Pleno' (d)	CBct
	- 'Jelle'	CBct EBee GBin WCAu
	- 'Lunar Glow'	EBee ECha ECtt ELan EPfP EUJe LSou NEgg NLar SRms WFar
	- 'Purpurea'	CBcs CBod CMac CRos CWCL EBee ECha ELan EPed EPfP GBin GMcL LBuc LCro LOPS LRHS MRav NRHS SCob SPer SRms SWvt WFar XLum
	- 'Rosa Schwester'	CBct ECha
	- 'Rosa Zeiten' ♀H7	CBct GBin IMou
	- 'Tubby Andrews' (v)	CBct CMac CTal EShb GEdr LEdu LRHS MAvo MBel MBrN NEgg NEoE NLar NPnk SRms WHil WHrl
	- 'Vinterglöd'	CBod CBot CRos EBee ELan ELon EPfP ESps EUJe GMaP IFoB LRHS LSun MBel MGos NLar SPad SWvt WHar WPnP XLum
	crassifolia	EPfP GKev SRms XLum
	- DF 90028	CBct GBin
	- 'Autumn Red'	CBct ECha
	- 'Orbicularis'	see *B. × schmidtii*
I	- var. ***pacifica***	XLum
	- - 'Cally Gem'	GCal
	'Croesus'	GBin
*	***cyanea***	WCot
	'Dark Damsel' **new**	CBct IBal
	'David'	CBct EBee ECha EWes GBin
	'Delbees'	see *B.* 'Ballawley' clonal
	'Diamond Drops' **new**	IBal
	'Doppelgänger'	EBee
	'Eden's Dark Margin'	CBct CBod ECtt ELan ELon GBin LSou MHol MNrw NEoE NLar WCot WHoo
	'Eden's Magic Giant' ♀H7	CBct CRav CRos ECtt ELan ELon EUJe GBin GQue LRHS MPie NEgg NLar NRHS SRms WCot
	emeiensis	CBct CDor CTal GCal IMou LEdu WCot WPGP WSHC
	- hybrid	MWat
	'Eric Smith' ♀H7	ECha GCal IRob SWvt WCAu
	'Eroica' ♀H7	Widely available
	'Evening Glow'	see *B.* 'Abendglut'
	'Flower Joy'	GBin
§	'Glockenturm'	CBct GBin NEgg
	'Godfrey Owen'	EBee
	'Harzkristall'	CBct CBod CDor CMac CMea CPla CRos EPfP GBin GWyn LRHS NCou NRHS STPC SWvt WSpi
	'Hellen Dillon'	see *B. purpurascens* 'Irish Crimson'
	'Herbstblute'	CRos EPfP GBin LRHS NRHS WCAu
	'Ice Queen'	CBct CMil EBee ELan EWTr GBin LLHF LPla MBel SWvt WCAu WCot
	'Jo Watanabe'	CBct MRav
	'Kashmir'	XLum
	'Kerstin' **new**	CRos NRHS
	'Lambrook'	see *B.* 'Margery Fish'
	'Little Pine'	WCot
§	'Margery Fish'	CBct CFis ECha SPer
	milesii	see *B. stracheyi*
§	'Morgenröte' ♀H6	CBcs CBct CBod CMac CRos ECha ELon EPfP GMaP IRob LRHS LSRN MRav NLar NSti SAko SCob SPer SRms SWvt WCAu WCFE WCot
	'Morning Light'	ECtt
	MORNING RED	see *B.* 'Morgenröte'
	'Mrs Crawford'	ECha
	'Oeschberg'	CBct GBin GCal
	'Opal'	CBct EBee GBin
	'Overture'	Widely available
§	***pacumbis***	CTal EBee GBin GCal NBid NSti
	- B&SWJ 2693	WCru
	- CC 1793	SBch WCot
	- CC 3616	CBct
	'Pink Dragonfly'	CBct CMac CRos CTal ECtt ELon EPfP ETMg LPla LRHS NLar NRHS SCob SWvt WCAu WCot WFar
	'Pink Frostwork'	ECtt GBin WCot WWFP
	'Pink Ice'	CBct CDor EBee
	'Pinneberg'	CBct EBee GBin
	'Pugsley's Pink' ♀H7	CBct
§	***purpurascens*** ♀H5	CMac EBee EPfP GMaP SPer WSpi
	- SDR 4548	GKev
	- var. ***delavayi*** ♀H5	CRos CWCL LRHS NLar NRHS SRms
§	- 'Irish Crimson' ♀H7	CBct ECha WCot
	aff. ***purpurascens***	NGdn
	- ACE 2175	WCot
	'Purpurglocken'	ECtt GCal WCAu
	'Red Beauty'	EHoe EPfP IBoy
	'Red Rush'	EBee
	'Rietheim'	CBct EBee GBin
	'Rosenkristall'	CRos LRHS NRHS
	'Rosi Klose'	CBct CDor CRos EBee ECha ECtt EHoe ELon EWes GBin GMcL LRHS MHol MRav NGdn NRHS WCot WFar
	'Rosi Ruffles'	EBee
	'Rotblum'	CBct ECtt EHoe ELon EPfP GMaP LBuc NGdn NRHS SCob SRkn WHar
	'Sakura' (Dragonfly Series)	EBee ETMg GBin LRHS MNrw NRHS WHar
§	× ***schmidtii***	CBct CMac GBin MRav NLar
	'Schneekissen'	CBct CMac ECtt EPri LRHS MCot NRHS WCAu WGwG
§	'Schneekoenigin'	CBct ECha GBin GCal SWvt WCot
§	'Silberlicht' ♀H6	Widely available
	SILVERLIGHT	see *B.* 'Silberlicht'
	'Simply Sweet'	WCot
	SNOW QUEEN	see *B.* 'Schneekoenigin'
	'Spring Fling'	GBin
§	***stracheyi***	CBct CExl ECha GBin GCal GKev NBid NLar WCot WFar
	- CC 4609	EBee
	- Alba Group	CTal ECha GCal
	'Sunningdale' ♀H7	CBcs CBct CBod CMac CRav ECha ELan EPfP GMaP LRHS MRav NGdn NRHS SWvt WAvo WCAu
	'Tim'	EBee
	'Walter Kienli'	GBin
	WINTER FAIRY TALES	see *B.* 'Wintermärchen'
§	'Wintermärchen' ♀H7	CBct CBod CBot CChe CRos ECha ECtt ELan ELon EPfP EShb GWyn LRHS MMuc MRav NEoE NRHS SCob SEND SPoG SRms SWvt WCot WMoo
	'XXL'	WCot

Bergenia × *Mukdenia* see × *Mukgenia*

Bergera (*Rutaceae*)

§ ***koenigii***	EOHP GPoy SCit SPre SVen WSFF

Bergeranthus (*Aizoaceae*)

vespertinus	XLum

Berkheya (*Asteraceae*)

cirsiifolia	EBee ELon WSHC
'Helios' new	GCal
macrocephala	SPlb
multijuga	CRos LRHS NRHS
- 'Golden Spike'	ECtt WHil
purpurea	CAby CBcs CDor CRos ELon EPfP ESps EWTr GBin IBoy IRob LRHS MHol MNrw NRHS SPad SPlb WCot WHer WKif WSHC WTor
- 'Silver Spike'	EPfP NGdn
- 'Zulu Warrior'	CMac
radula	EBee GCal

Berlandiera (*Asteraceae*)

lyrata	LPmr XAbr

Berula (*Apiaceae*)

erecta	NPer

Berzelia (*Bruniaceae*)

galpinii	SPlb
intermedia new	LRHS

Beschorneria (*Asparagaceae*)

albiflora	CFil CSpe EBee WCot
calcicola	WCot
'Red Bells'	WCot
rigida	WCot
septentrionalis	CAby CDTJ CFil CSpe EUJe IBoy LRHS LSou LSun MBNS MHol MSCN NLos SPad WCot WGrn
- variegated (v)	WCot
septentrionalis × ***yuccoides***	CFil
tubiflora	CDTJ CFil
wrightii	CFil WCot
yuccoides ♀H3	CAbb CBcs CExl CFil CPne EUJe SArc SEND SPlb
- subsp. ***dekosteriana***	CFil
- 'Quicksilver'	CBcs CCCN CEnd CExl CSBt ELan EPfP EUJe LRHS NLos SLim SPoG WGrn

Bessera (*Asparagaceae*)

elegans	CAby CAvo CGrW EBee EPot LAma SDeJ SDir WCot

Besseya (*Plantaginaceae*)

alpina new	LLHF
wyomingensis	GKev

Beta (*Amaranthaceae*)

vulgaris	SVic WHer
- 'Bull's Blood'	CSpe LCro
- 'Burpee's Golden' new	CRav
- subsp. ***maritima***	CAgr CFGn

Betonica see *Stachys*

Betula ✿ (*Betulaceae*)

alba	see *B. pendula*, *B. pubescens*
albosinensis misapplied	see *B. utilis*
albosinensis Burkill	CBrP CLnd CMCN EMOT EPfP MMuc SEND
- W 4106	CSto
- from Gansu, China	CSto
- 'Bowling Green'	CExl CJun MBlu WPGP
§ - 'China Rose' ♀H6	CJun CSto EBee WPGP
- 'China Ruby' K.Ashburner	see *B. albosinensis* 'China Rose'
- 'China Ruby' ambig.	CJun CLnd EPfP
- 'China Ruby' B. Humphrey ♀H6	CBcs ERea
- 'Chinese Garden'	CJun EBee MBlu WPGP
- 'Chris Lane'	WPGP
- clone F	see *B. albosinensis* 'Ness'
- hybrid	CDul
- 'Joseph Rock'	CJun
- 'K.Ashburner'	CJun CTho
§ - 'Ness'	CJun CTho
- 'Pink Champagne'	CJun CSto EBee EPfP LRHS MBlu WPGP
- 'Red Panda' ♀H6	CJun EBee ERea WPGP
- 'Rhinegold'	MBlu
- 'Sable'	SLim
- var. ***septentrionalis***	CBcs CCVT CDul CEnd CMac CTho EBee ECrN ELan ELon EPfP ESps EWTr GBin MBlu MGos MMuc MRav MSwo SCob SGol SLim SPer WMou WPGP WSpi
- - PDM 752	WPGP
- - 'Kansu'	CEnd CJun CLnd CTsd EBee NLar NOra SBig
- - 'Purdom'	CJun CLnd EBee SBig
§ ***alleghaniensis***	CCVT CDul CMCN CSto EPfP MMuc NLar SEND WCru
ashburneri	GKev
- S&L 5297	GKev
chichibuensis	CJun CMCN GKev MMrt
chinensis	CMCN
'Conyngham'	CJun CTho MBlu SLau
cordifolia	CSto
costata misapplied	see *B. ermanii* 'Grayswood Hill'
costata ambig.	CMCN ESps LMaj SGol
costata Trautv.	EBee MSwo
- 'Daleside'	EBee ERea LRHS NDal NOra
* - 'Fincham Cream'	CJun SBig
'Crimson Frost'	EBee GBin
cylindrostachya	WPGP
dahurica Pall.	CBrP CSto
- 'Maurice Foster'	CJun CSto CTho EBee MBlu WPGP
- 'Stone Farm'	CJun
ermanii	CBcs CCVT CDul CLnd CMCN CMac CTri ECrN ELan EMOT ESps GBin LMaj LPra LRHS MBlu MGos MMuc MRav SCob SGol
- B&SWJ 8801 from South Korea	WCru
- B&SWJ 10852 from Aomori, Japan	WCru
- B&SWJ 12600 from South Korea	WCru
- from Hokkaido, Japan	CSto
- 'Blush'	CJun EPfP MBlu SBig SCoo
§ - 'Grayswood Hill' ♀H6	CDul CEnd CJun CLnd CMCN CSBt CTho CTri EBee EPfP GBin LCro LRHS MBlu SCoo SWvt WPGP
- 'Hakkoda Orange'	CJun CTho EMOT SCoo WPGP
- 'Holland'	IArd LMaj

	- 'Kwanak Weeping'	CJun EBee LLHF MBlu SBig SBir
	- 'Mount Zao'	CJun CSto CTho EBee WPGP
	- 'Polar Bear'	CJun CLnd EPfP MAsh MBlu NLar SAko SCoo
	- 'Zao Purple'	CDul
	'Fascination' ♀H6	CCVT CDul CJun CLnd CMCN EBar EBee EPfP ERea IArd LMaj LPra MBlu MGos NOra NRHS SCob SCoo SLim SSta WHCr WSpi
	'Fetisowii'	CDul CJun LRHS MBlu NOra SBig
	fruticosa	see *B. humilis*
	globispica	CJun GKev
	gmelinii	see *B. ovalifolia*
	grossa	IDee
	'Hergest' ♀H6	CJun EBee ECrN EPfP ERea MAsh MGos NOra SLau SPer WHCr
§	***humilis***	EBee
	insignis	CSto EBee GKev WPGP
	- subsp. ***fansipanensis***	IArd IDee SAko
	- - B&SWJ 11751	WCru
	- - FMWJ 13149 new	WCru
	'Inverleith'	see *B. utilis* var. *jacquemontii* 'Inverleith'
	jacquemontii	see *B. utilis* var. *jacquemontii*
	kamtschatica H. Buek	see *B. humilis*
	lenta	CDul CMCN CSto EPfP IArd IDee MBlu MMuc
	luminifera	CJun EBee EBtc IArd WPGP
	lutea	see *B. alleghaniensis*
	maximowicziana	CDul CMCN CSto EMOT ESps MBlu NLar SGol WSpi
	medwediewii	CDul CJun CMCN CSto EBee EPfP GKev NLar WPGP
	- 'Gold Bark' ♀H7	CJun CMCN EPfP MBlu
	megrelica	GKev IArd
	michauxii	EBee GKev NLar WCru
	'Mount Apoi'	CJun CLnd SBig
	nana	CDul MRav
	- 'Glengarry'	EPot GCrg GEdr
	nigra	CBcs CCVT CDul CEnd CLnd CMCN CTri EBee ESps LMaj LPra MMuc NLar SCob SEWo SGol WMou WTSh
	- 'Black Star'	CDul LRHS NOra
§	- 'Cully'	CCVT CDul CLnd EBee ECrN LMaj NOra SBig SGol WHCr
	- HERITAGE	see *B. nigra* 'Cully'
	- 'Little King'	CJun CMCN
	- 'Peter Collinson'	CJun
	- 'Shiloh Splash'	SReu SSta
	- 'Summer Cascade'[PBR]	EBee LRHS LSRN MAsh NOra SLon
	- TECUMSEH COMPACT ('Studetec')	SGol
	- Wakehurst form	EPfP SPer SPoG WPGP WSpi
§	***ovalifolia*** MF 357 new	GKev
	papyrifera	CAco CCVT CDul CLnd CMCN CMac CPer CSto CTri EBee ECrN ELan EMOT EPfP ESps LBuc LRHS MGos MMuc MSwo NOra SCob SEND SGol SPer WHar WTSh
	- 'Belle Vue'	CSto EBee
	- var. ***cordifolia*** 'Clarenville'	CJun CSto
	- var. ***papyrifera***	CSto
	- 'Saint George'	CJun CSto CTho EBee WHCr
	- 'Vancouver'	CTho
§	***pendula***	Widely available
	- 'Black Prince'	WHCr
	- f. ***crispa***	see *B. pendula* 'Laciniata'
	- 'Dalecarlica' misapplied	see *B. pendula* 'Laciniata'
	- 'Dalecarlica' ambig.	CBcs CSBt ECrN EMOT LPra LRHS MRav NOra SWvt WFar WHCr WTSh
	- 'Dark Prince'	CJun
	- 'Fastigiata'	CCVT CDul CJun CLnd CSBt CTho EBee ECrN ELan EMOT LPra MGos SCoo SGol SPer
	- 'Golden Beauty'	CDul CJun CMac EMOT ERea IRob MAsh MGos MJak NOra SGol SLim SPer
	- 'Golden Cloud'	MJak
§	- 'Laciniata' ♀H7	CDul CMCN CMac EBee ELan ESps LMaj MAsh MBlu MGos MSwo SCob SCoo SGol SPer WCFE WHar WMou WTSh
	- 'Long Trunk'	CDul LLHF MBlu SGol SLim
	- 'Purpurea'	CCVT CDul CMCN CMac CSBt ECrN ELan EMOT ESps GKin LPra LSRN MGos MSwo SCoo SGol SMad SPer WFar WTSh
	- 'Silver Grace'	CJun ECrN LSRN
§	- 'Spider Alley'[PBR]	EBee ERea EUJe GBin LRHS NEgg NLar
	- 'Swiss Glory'	LMaj
	- 'Tristis' ♀H7	CBcs CCVT CDul CEnd CLnd CMCN CMac CSto CTho CTri EBee ECrN EMOT EPfP ESps LMaj LPra LRHS LSRN MGos MRav MSwo NOra SCob SGol SLim SPer WFar WHar WMou
	- 'Youngii'	Widely available
	- 'Zwitsers Glorie'	CDul CJun NLar
	platyphylla misapplied	see *B. platyphylla* subsp. *mandshurica*
	platyphylla Sukaczev DAKOTA PINNACLE ('Fargo')	CDul EBee NLar NOra SCoo
§	- subsp. ***mandshurica***	CSto MMuc
	populifolia	CSto EBtc
	- 'Whitespire'	CDul
	pseudomiddendorffii	GKev
§	***pubescens***	CAco CCVT CDul CHab CPer CSto CTho CTri EBee LMaj MMuc SCob SEND WTSh
	- 'Armenian Gold'	CLnd
	- var. ***pubescens***	CSto
	raddeana	EBtc
	'Royal Frost'	CBcs CDul CJun EBee EUJe GQue LSRN MAsh MBlu NEgg NLar SGol
	'Silver Trestles'	see *B. pendula* 'Spider Alley'
	szechuanica 'Liuba White'	CJun MBlu
§	***utilis***	CDul CMCN CSto ECrN ESps LMaj LPra SSta
	- BL&M 100 from central Nepal	CSto
	- GWJ 9259	WCru
	- H&M 1480 from Sichuan, China	CSto
	- HWJK 2250	WCru
	- HWJK 2345	WCru
	- Sch 2168	EBee
	- SICH 667 from Sichuan, China	CSto
	- S&L from Nepal	CDul
	- Yu 10163 from Yunnan, China	CSto
	- from eastern Nepal	CSto
	- 'Bhutan Sienna'	CJun CSto WPGP
	- 'Buckland'	EBee
	- 'Buddha'	CJun EBee SAko WPGP

	- 'China Bronze'	CSto WPGP
	- 'Cobhay Sentinel'	CJun
	- 'Dark-Ness'	EBee NOra SLon WHCr WPGP
*	- 'Fastigiata'	CJun SBig SSta
	- 'Forest Blush' 🏆^{H6}	CDul CJun CSto EBee SBig WPGP
	- 'Himalayan Pink'	CJun WSpi
§	- var. ***jacquemontii***	Widely available
	- - Polunin collection	WPGP
§	- - 'Doorenbos' 🏆^{H6}	Widely available
	- - 'Grayswood Ghost' 🏆^{H6}	CDul CEnd CJun CLnd CMCN CSto CTho CTri ECrN ELan EPfP ERea ETod LCro LOPS LRHS MBlu NLar NOra SBig SBir SLau SLim SPer SSta WHar WHor WPGP WSpi
§	- - 'Inverleith'	CDul CJun SBig SCoo WPGP
	- - 'Jermyns' 🏆^{H6}	CBcs CDul CEnd CJun CTri EPfP LSRN MBlu NOra SCoo SLau SLim SPer SSta SWvt WHCr WPGP
	- - 'McBeath'	SLau
	- - 'Moonbeam'	CDul CJun CSBt EBee ERea LRHS MAsh SBig SCoo SEWo SLim SPoG WHCr
	- - 'Silver Shadow' 🏆^{H6}	CDul CEnd CJun CLnd CMCN CTho EBee EPfP EWTr LRHS LSRN MAsh MBlu NLar NOra NRHS SBig SCoo SLau SLim SPer SPoG SSta WHCr WSpi
	- - 'Snow Leopard'	CSto
	- - 'Snow Queen'	see *B. utilis* var. *jacquemontii* 'Doorenbos'
	- - 'Trinity College'	CDul CJun CLnd CTri LRHS MAsh SBig SCoo WPGP
	- 'Knightshayes'	CTho EBee WPGP
	- 'Mount Luoji'	CJun CSto WPGP
	- 'Nepalese Orange'	CJun CSto EBee WPGP
	- var. ***occidentalis*** 'Kyelang'	CJun
	- 'Park Wood' 🏆^{H6}	CJun CSto WPGP
	- var. ***prattii***	CJun CTho MBlu
	- 'Ramdana River'	CJun WPGP
	- 'Schilling'	CJun
	- 'Sichuan Red'	CSto
	- 'Silver Queen'	WSpi
	- subsp. ***utilis*** 'Edinburgh'	CJun CLnd EWTr
	- 'Wakehurst Place Chocolate' 🏆^{H6}	CJun CSBt ERea GBin MBlu SBig SCoo SLim WSpi
	cf. ***utilis***	CTri SGol
	verrucosa	see *B. pendula*

Biarum ✿ (*Araceae*)

S&L 604	WCot
SB&L 597	WCot
carratracense from Spain	WCot
davisii	LAma WCot
dispar SB&L 294	WCot
- SB&L 564	WCot
ditschianum from Turkey	WCot
marmarisense	EPot GKev NRog WCot
tenuifolium	WCot
- LB 295	WCot
- PB 357	WCot
- S&L 174	WCot
- subsp. ***abbreviatum***	GKev
- - MS 974	WCot
- subsp. ***arundanum***	WCot
- subsp. ***galianii*** PB 435	WCot
- subsp. ***idomenaeum*** MS 738	WCot
- subsp. ***tenuifolium*** new	GKev
- subsp. ***zelebori***	WCot
- - CRL 502	WCot
- - LB 300	WCot
- - PB 224	WCot
- - PB 334	WCot

Bidens (*Asteraceae*)

	atrosanguinea	see *Cosmos atrosanguineus*
§	***aurea***	CFis EAJP ECtt EPPr ESps EWes LEdu MSpe NPer SBee WBor XLum
	- cream-flowered	MNrw
	- 'Hannay's Lemon Drop'	CAby CFis CKno EAJP EBee ECtt ELan ELon EPPr EPfP ILea LEdu MNrw MSpe SGbt SPoG SPtp SRms WBor WFar WMoo WPGP
*	- 'Lemon Queen'	SMad
	- 'Mellow Yellow'	WCot
	- 'Rising Sun'	ECtt EWes
	- 'Super Nova'	EPPr GCal
	- white-flowered	EBee ELon EPPr GCal NSti
	BEEDANCE PAINTED RED ('Sunbidevb2') new	ETMg
	ferulifolia	NPer
	- 'Golden Eye'	ECtt LSou SPoG
	- YELLOW CHARM ('Danyel9')	LSou
	heterophylla Ortega	see *B. aurea*
	heterophylla misapplied	CAby ECtt MCot MMuc MRav MWat WFar WHal WMoo XLum
	integrifolia	SMad
	'Pirate's Treasure'	ECtt
	'Rockstar'	CPla NPri
	triplinervia	ETMg
	var. ***macrantha*** 'Gold Nuggets' (d) new	

Bignonia (*Bignoniaceae*)

capreolata	CCCN CRHN EBee ECre EWld WSHC
lindleyana	see *Clytostoma calystegioides*
tweedieana	see *Dolichandra unguis-cati*
unguis-cati	see *Dolichandra unguis-cati*

Bilderdykia see *Fallopia*

Billardiera (*Pittosporaceae*)

cymosa	CTsd
longiflora 🏆^{H3}	CBcs CMac CRos CSBt CTri EBee ELan EPfP EUJe GKev IArd IDee ITim LRHS MAsh MGil MGos MMuc MRav SLim SPer SPoG SWvt WKif
- 'Cherry Berry'	CBcs CFlo CRos ELan EPfP EUJe LRHS SLim SPer SPoG SRms SWvt
- 'Fructu-albo'	CBcs CFlo CRos EBee ELan EPfP EWes LRHS NLar SLon SPer SPoG SWvt

Billbergia ✿ (*Bromeliaceae*)

	'Borracho'	NLos
	distachya var. ***maculata***	NLos
	'Fosters Striate'	NLos
	nutans	CCCN CHll EBak EUJe LEdu NLos SChr SEND SPlb WSFF
	- var. ***schimperiana***	EShb
*	- 'Variegata' (v)	CCCN CHll EShb EUJe NLos SChr WCot
	pyramidalis 🏆^{H1a}	NLos XBlo
	'Santa Barbara' (v)	SChr
	× ***windii*** 🏆^{H1a}	EBak NLos

Bismarckia (*Arecaceae*)

nobilis	CCCN

Bistorta see *Persicaria*

blackberry see *Rubus fruticosus* agg.

blackcurrant see *Ribes nigrum*

Blechnum ✿ (*Blechnaceae*)

alpinum	see *B. penna-marina* subsp. *alpinum*
attenuatum	NLos
auriculatum	CBdn
australe	NLos
brasiliense ♀H1a	CBdn EShb NLos SPlb WCot
- 'Volcano'	CBdn ETMg IBal LLWG LRHS NLos SCob SPoG WBor WCot WPGP
§ ***chilense*** ♀H4	CBcs CBdn CDTJ CKel CRos EBee EPfP EWes GAbr GBin GCal IBal IBlr LEdu LRHS MMoz NBro NLos NRHS SArc SBig SPlb SRms WCru WMoo
cycadifolium	NLos
discolor	GCal NLos
divergens	NLos
fluviatile	CDTJ MMoz NLos
gibbum	CKel NLos SPlb
- 'Silver Lady'	NLos
gracile	NLos
magellanicum misapplied	see *B. chilense*
magellanicum (Desv.) Mett.	SBig SPlb
minus	CBdn
novae-zelandiae	NLos
nudum	CDTJ CKel NLos
penna-marina	Widely available
§ - subsp. ***alpinum***	CBdn ECha EPfP GEdr GKev NWad SBrt WMoo
- - BR 68	GEdr
- 'Cristatum'	GAbr GEdr GWyn NWad
procerum	NLos
spicant ♀H6	Widely available
tabulare misapplied	see *B. chilense*
tabulare (Thunb.) Kuhn	CBcs CBdn CDTJ CKel EPfP NLos
wattsii	EBee NLos

Blepharocalyx (*Myrtaceae*)

§ ***cruckshanksii***	CCCN CExl CRos EBee ELon LRHS MGil SEND SVen WPGP
- 'Heaven Scent'	see *B. cruckshanksii*

Blephilia (*Lamiaceae*)

ciliata	SPhx

Bletilla (*Orchidaceae*)

sp.	NDav SDir
hyacinthina	see *B. striata*
ochracea	CExl CTal LAma
Penway Paris gx	CTal
Penway Sunset gx	GKev
sinensis	CExl
§ ***striata*** ♀H4	CAby CBct CExl CTal CTri EPot GAbr GKev LAma LCro LEdu LOPS LRHS MHer MNrw NRHS SDeJ SPer WCot WFar WHlf WPGP XLum
- ***alba***	see *B. striata* f. *gebina*
- 'Albostriata'	CBct CExl ELan LAma WCot XLum
- blue-flowered	GKev
§ - f. ***gebina***	CExl CTal CTri LCro LEdu LOPS LRHS SDeJ SDir SPer WCot WPGP
- - variegated (v)	LEdu WHlf
- 'Kuchi-beni'	LAma WHlf
- 'Lips'	SDir
- purple-flowered	GKev
- 'Shi-ran' **new**	WHlf
- 'Soryu'	CTal LAma SDir
- variegated (v)	GKev
- yellow-flowered	GKev
Yokohama gx	CTal

blueberry see *Vaccinium corymbosum*

Blumea (*Asteraceae*)

balsamifera	CHab

Bocconia (*Papaveraceae*)

cordata	see *Macleaya cordata* (Willd.) R. Br.
frutescens B&SWJ 10654	WCru
microcarpa	see *Macleaya microcarpa*

Boehmeria (*Urticaceae*)

nivea	WCot
platanifolia	IMou
sieboldiana	EBee EPPr SBrt WFar
tricuspis	IMou SBrt

Boenninghausenia (*Rutaceae*)

albiflora B&SWJ 1479	WCru
- CC 7147	ITim
- pink-flowered B&SWJ 3112	WCru

Bolax (*Apiaceae*)

glebaria	see *B. gummifer*
§ ***gummifer***	EPot GEdr GKev WAbe WFar

Bolboschoenus (*Cyperaceae*)

§ ***maritimus***	EBWF

Boltonia (*Asteraceae*)

asteroides	GQue MMuc NWsh SEND SPer WRHF XLum
- var. ***latisquama***	GMaP GQue LSou MRav MWat NLar SHar WBor WFar WHal
- - JIM CROCKETT ('Masbolimket'PBR)	LRHS SPoG
- - 'Nana'	LPla NChi
- - 'Snowbank'	ELan
decurrens	CBod EBee EPPr IMou MMuc SEND WBor
- 'Warrior's Blush'	MNrw
incisa	see *Kalimeris incisa*

Bomarea (*Alstroemeriaceae*)

acuminata	see *B. andreana*
acutifolia	CFil
- F&M 104	WPGP
§ ***andreana*** B&SWJ 14310 **new**	WCru
- B&SWJ 14376 **new**	WCru
aff. ***andreana*** B&SWJ 10617	WCru
boliviensis misapplied	see *Alstroemeria isabellana*
boliviensis Baker	WCot
caldasii	see *B. multiflora*
costaricensis	EBee GCal
- B&SWJ 10467	WCru
distichifolia	CExl WCot WCru

§ ***edulis*** ♀H1c	CBlu CHll CPla CPne CRHN EWld MGil SBrt WCot
- B&SWJ 9017	WCru
- F&M 104	CExl
frondea	see *B. multiflora*
aff. ***frondea*** B&SWJ 10681	WCru
hirsuta B&SWJ 14442 new	WCru
hirtella	see *B. edulis*
§ ***multiflora*** ♀H2	CBcs CCCN CExl CPbh EBee GCal NLos WCru WSHC
- B&SWJ 14419 new	WCru
'Orange Sunset'	WCot
patacocensis JCA 13987	WCot
salsilla ♀H1c	CAvo CCCN CFil CPne EBee NLos SBrt WSHC

Bombax (*Malvaceae*)

ceiba	SPlb

Bongardia (*Berberidaceae*)

chrysogonum	CAvo CRos EPot GKev LLHF LRHS NRHS

Bonia (*Poaceae*)

§ ***solida***	CBdn ERod MMoz MMuc MWht SEND

Boophone (*Amaryllidaceae*)

disticha	LRHS

Boquila (*Lardizabalaceae*)

trifoliolata	WCru

borage see *Borago officinalis*

Borago (*Boraginaceae*)

laxiflora	see *B. pygmaea*
officinalis	CHby CRav ENfk EPfP GPoy LCro MHer MNHC NPri SRms SVic XAbr
- 'Alba'	CBre ENfk SRms
- 'Bill Archer' (v)	CNat
§ ***pygmaea***	CExl CHid CSpe ELan GCal LEdu MHer MNrw NChi NSti SRms WHer WMoo

borecole see AGM Vegetables Section

Borinda (*Poaceae*)

KR 4558	ERod
KR 5287	MWht
KR 5600	MWht
KR 5950	ERod
KR 6438	MWht
KR 6439	MWht
KR 7346	MWht
KR 7613	MWht
KR 7662	MWht
albocerea ♀H4	EPfP ERod MWht
- Yunnan 1	ERod
- Yunnan 2	CDTJ ERod MAvo MMoz
- Yunnan 3a	CDTJ ERod
- Yunnan 3b	ERod
- Yunnan 4	see *B. lushuiensis* Yunnan 4
angustissima	CBdn CDTJ CExl CFil EPfP ERod MMuc MWht SBig
boliana	SBig SSut
frigida	CDTJ
- KR 4059	ERod MWht
fungosa	CBdn CBlu IBoy
grossa KR 5931	MWht
§ ***lushuiensis*** Yunnan 4	CDTJ MWht
macclureana KR 5051	MWht
- KR 5177 from Gyala, Nepal	ERod MWht
- KR 5602	ERod
- KR 5950	ERod
- KR 6243	ERod
aff. ***macclureana*** KR 6900	MWht
nujiangensis	CDTJ
papyrifera	ERod WPGP
- CS 1046	CBdn MAvo MWht
scabrida ♀H4	CBdn CDTJ ENBC ERod MAvo MMoz MWht SSut WPGP
- 'Asian Wonder'	CBod ENBC LRHS NLar SBig
Yunnan 4	see *B. lushuiensis* Yunnan 4

Boronia (*Rutaceae*)

crenulata	CBcs CCCN
heterophylla	CBcs CCCN CTsd EBee EPfP IDee LRHS MPkF SEle WCot
- 'Ice Charlotte'	CCCN SEle

Bossiaea (*Papilionaceae*)

riparia	SPlb
scolopendria	SPlb

Bothriochloa (*Poaceae*)

§ ***bladhii***	CKno EPPr
caucasica	see *B. bladhii*

Bougainvillea (*Nyctaginaceae*)

'Alexandra'	CCCN SPre SWeb
'Brilliant' misapplied	see *B.* × *buttiana* 'Raspberry Ice'
§ × ***buttiana*** 'Raspberry Ice' (v)	EShb
glabra ♀H1c	EShb IDee SPre
§ - 'Sanderiana'	EUJe
'Sanderiana'	see *B. glabra* 'Sanderiana'
'Sentimento'	CCCN
'Tropical Rainbow'	see *B.* × *buttiana* 'Raspberry Ice'
Vera Series	CCCN

Boussingaultia (*Basellaceae*)

baselloides Hook.	see *Anredera cordifolia*

Bouteloua (*Poaceae*)

curtipendula	CBod
§ ***gracilis***	CAby CRos EAJP EBee EHoe LRHS NRHS SMad SPoG XSen

Bouvardia (*Rubiaceae*)

ternifolia	CBcs CBod CWGN EBee MNrw SMad WCot

Bowiea (*Asparagaceae*)

volubilis	GKev

Bowkeria (*Stilbaceae*)

sp.	CCCN
cymosa	SPlb SVen
verticillata	CHll

Boykinia (*Saxifragaceae*)

aconitifolia	CElw CMac GEdr GKev GLog IMou MRav NRya SMad WCru WMoo WSHC
elata	see *B. occidentalis*
heucheriformis	see *B. jamesii*
§ ***jamesii***	CPla GKev
lycoctonifolia	LEdu NLar
major	EBee

§ ***occidentalis*** WCru WMoo WPtf XLum
rotundifolia GJos WCru WMoo
tellimoides see *Peltoboykinia tellimoides*

boysenberry see *Rubus* 'Boysenberry'

Brachychilum see *Hedychium*

Brachychiton (*Malvaceae*)

acerifolius SPlb
populneus CBcs SPlb
§ ***rupestris*** EShb

Brachyelytrum (*Poaceae*)

japonicum NLar

Brachyglottis (*Asteraceae*)

bidwillii 'Basil Fox' WAbe
§ ***compacta*** CRos ELan EPfP ESps LRHS MAsh SPer
(Dunedin Group) 'Drysdale' CRos EBee ELan EPfP ESps LRHS NRHS SLon SWvt
§ - 'Moira Reid' (v) CExl CTsd
§ - 'Sunshine' 🏆H4 CAgr CBar CDul CRos CSBt CTri EBee ELan EPfP ESps GMcL LCro LRHS MGos MJak MMuc MRav MSwo NPer NRHS SCob SEND SLim SPer SPlb SRms SWvt WHar
greyi misapplied see *B.* (Dunedin Group) 'Sunshine'
§ ***greyi*** (Hook. f.) B. Nord. CMac ESps SGol
huntii SVen
huntii* × *stewartii SEND
laxifolia misapplied see *B.* (Dunedin Group) 'Sunshine'
§ ***monroi*** CBcs CMac CRos CSBt CTsd EHoe ELan EPfP LRHS MAsh MRav SGol SLon SVen WFar
repanda EWld
- 'Purpurea' CBcs
- var. ***rangiora*** CTsd
§ ***rotundifolia*** CCCN
'Silver Waves' CCht CRos LRHS NRHS
I 'Sunshine Improved' CBcs EHoe MAsh
'Sunshine Variegated' see *B.* (Dunedin Group) 'Moira Reid'
WALBERTON'S SILVER DORMOUSE ('Walbrach'^{PBR}) 🏆H4 CBct CBot CRos CSBt EBee EPfP ESps GBin LRHS MGos MRav NRHS SPoG SWvt WFar WHil

Brachypodium (*Poaceae*)

phoenicoides XSen
pinnatum EPPr
sylvaticum CHab EBWF MMuc SEND

Brachyscome (*Asteraceae*)

MAUVE MYSTIQUE ('Pacimamy'^{PBR}) CPla
multifida 'Blue Haze' **new** CRav
rigidula CPBP

Brachystachyum (*Poaceae*)

densiflorum ERod

Bracteantha see *Xerochrysum*

Brahea (*Arecaceae*)

sp. ETod
armata CBrP CDTJ CPHo EPfP EShb ETod SPlb WCot
dulcis NLos
edulis CCCN CPHo ETod NLos
'Super Silver' NLos WCot

Brassaia see *Schefflera*

Brassica (*Brassicaceae*)

japonica see *B. juncea* var. *crispifolia*
juncea SVic
§ - var. ***crispifolia*** MNHC
oleracea CAgr EBWF SVic WHer
- var. ***ramosa*** LEdu
- - 'Cotswold Cream' (v) **new** WCot
- - 'D'Aubenton Panaché' (v) WCot
* ***rapa*** var. ***japonica*** MNHC
- subsp. ***nipposinica*** var. ***laciniata*** **new** CRav

× *Brigandra* (*Gesneriaceae*)

calliantha WAbe

Brighamia (*Campanulaceae*)

insignis CCCN

Brillantaisia (*Acanthaceae*)

kirungae CCCN
owariensis CSpe

Brimeura (*Asparagaceae*)

§ ***amethystina*** 🏆H5 CExl GBin GKev LEdu SBrt SDeJ SPhx WCot WPGP WThu
- 'Alba' GKev SDeJ SPhx

Briza (*Poaceae*)

maxima CRav CTri EHoe LCro NGdn NSti NWad SPhx
media Widely available
- 'Golden Bee' CBWd CKno CWCL EHoe ELon EPPr EPfP EWes LEdu LRHS MMrt NDov NLar NRHS SMad SPhx WPGP
- 'Limouzi' CElw CKno CRos EHoe ELon EPPr EUJe GCal IRob LEdu LRHS MAvo NRHS NSti NWsh SMad SPer SPoG WPGP XLum
- 'Romany Silver' **new** LEdu
- 'Russells'^{PBR} CBod CHid CKno EBee EHoe ELan EPfP LRHS MGos NRHS NWad NWsh SCob SPer SPoG SRms SWvt
subaristata EPPr
triloba CRos LRHS NRHS NWsh

Brocchinia (*Bromeliaceae*)

hechtioides NLos

broccoli see AGM Vegetables Section

Brodiaea (*Asparagaceae*)

§ ***californica*** EBee ERCP GKev WCot
- NNS 00-109 WCot
- NNS 06-102 WCot
- 'Babylon' CAvo ERCP GKev
capitata see *Dichelostemma capitatum*
'Corrina' see *Triteleia* 'Corrina'
ida-maia see *Dichelostemma ida-maia*
laxa see *Triteleia laxa*
§ ***minor*** GKev
peduncularis see *Triteleia peduncularis*
purdyi see *B. minor*

Bromus (*Poaceae*)

	erectus	CHab
	- W&B BG B-5 new	WCot
	inermis 'Skinner's Gold' (v)	EBee EHoe EPPr NLar WCot
	ramosus	EBWF

Broussonetia (*Moraceae*)

	kazinoki	EBee
	papyrifera	CBcs CDul CMCN CTsd EBtc ELan MGil SPer WBor WCot
	- 'Billardii'	NLar
	- 'Laciniata'	EBee SChF SMad

Browallia (*Solanaceae*)

	from Sikkim	CSpe
	americana	SPhx

Bruckenthalia see *Erica*

Brugmansia (*Solanaceae*)

	'Angel's Baby' (d)	WOth
	'Angel's Sunbeam' new	ELan
§	***arborea***	CBcs CDTJ
§	- 'Knightii' (d) ♀H1c	CDTJ
	- 'Rosea' variegated (v)	ELan
	- variegated (v)	ELan
	aurea	CCCN SAdn
	'Bergische Symphonie' (d)	WOth
	× ***candida***	CCCN
	- 'Bergkönigin' (d)	WOth
§	- 'Grand Marnier' ♀H1c	CDTJ CHII CSam WOth
	- 'Plena'	see *B. arborea* 'Knightii'
	- 'Rosalla'	WOth
§	- 'Variegata' (v)	CCCN CDTJ CHII CSam
	'Dalen's Pink Amour' (d)	WOth
	'Fleming Island Spider' (d)	WOth
	'Flowerdream' (d)	EUJe
§	× ***insignis***	CHII
§	- pink-flowered	SEND
	'L'Amour'	WOth
	'Madame Bovary'	WOth
	'Miss Emily Mackenzie'	WOth
	'Morgensonne'	WOth
	'Nicoline'	WOth
	'Painted Lady'	WOth
§	***sanguinea***	CCCN EUJe GCal SEND SPlb WOth
	- 'Rosea'	see *B.* × *insignis* pink-flowered
§	***suaveolens*** ♀H1c	CBcs CHII EUJe
	- 'Flore Pleno' (d)	EUJe
	- ***rosea***	see *B.* × *insignis* pink-flowered
	- 'Variegata' (v)	EShb
	- yellow-flowered	EShb
	suaveolens* × *versicolor	see *B.* × *insignis*
	'Variegata Sunset'	see *B.* × *candida* 'Variegata'
	versicolor misapplied	see *B. arborea*
§	***versicolor*** Lagerh.	CCCN
*	'Yellow Trumpet'	ELan

Brunfelsia (*Solanaceae*)

	americana	CCCN WFib
	australis	WFib
	calycina	see *B. pauciflora*
	lactea	CCCN
§	***pauciflora*** ♀H1c	CCCN ELan EShb

Brunia (*Bruniaceae*)

	albiflora	SPlb

Brunnera ✿ (*Boraginaceae*)

§	***macrophylla***	Widely available
	- 'Agnes Amez'	IMou
	- 'Aimee Angus'	EPPr
	- 'Alba'	see *B. macrophylla* 'Betty Bowring'
	- 'Alexander's Great'	CBod CPla ECtt ETMg EUJe MAvo MPnt MSCN NBid NCou NLar SCob SPoG WCot WFar WSpi
§	- 'Betty Bowring'	Widely available
	- 'Blanc d'Adoué'	CBot
	- 'Blaukuppel'	CTal EWes GCal WCAu
	- 'Dawson's White' (v)	CBcs CDor CRos CWCL ECha ECtt ELan ELon EPfP GKev GMaP GMcL LRHS NBid NHpl NLar NRHS SCob SPer SRGP SRms SWvt WCAu WCot WFar
	- 'Diane's Gold'PBR	CBct CRos CTal EBee ECha ECtt LRHS MGos MHol MPnt NLar NPnk NRHS SCob
	- 'Emerald Mist'PBR (v)	CBod EBee ECtt GBin GEdr MGos NLar SWvt WSpi
	- 'Golden Jack Frost' new	MPnt
	- 'Gordano Gold' (v)	EHoe WCot
	- 'Green Gold' (v)	EBee WFar
	- 'Hadspen Cream' (v) ♀H6	Widely available
	- 'Henry's Eyes'	EBee ECtt EPfP
	- 'Jack Frost'PBR ♀H6	Widely available
	- 'Jennifer'	EBee MBel WCAu
	- 'King's Ransom'PBR (v)	CBct CNor CWGN ECtt GPSL NLar NSti WFar
	- 'Langford Hewitt' (v)	MNrw
	- 'Langtrees'	CBct CMac EBee ECha GAbr GBin GCal LRHS MCot MHol MMuc NGdn NRHS SEND WCFE WSpi
	- 'Little Jack' (v)	CRos LRHS LSou NRHS SPoG
	- 'Looking Glass'PBR ♀H6	Widely available
	- 'Marley's White'	SCob SGbt WPnP
§	- 'Mister Morse'PBR (v)	Widely available
	- 'Sea Heart'	EBee ECtt ETMg GBin IPot NLar SCob WCAu
	- 'Silver Heart'	CWGN ECtt ETMg IRob MTis SCob SPad WBor WPnP
	- 'Silver Spear' new	WCot
	- 'Silver Wings'	CBod CElw CRos CWCL EBee ECtt EPfP GEdr GKev LRHS LSou MBel MGos NGdn NLar NRHS NSti NWad WCAu WFar
	- 'Spring Yellow'	ECtt
	- 'Starry Eyes'	MTis SCob
	'Mrs Morse'	see *B. macrophylla* 'Mister Morse'
	sibirica	CElw EBee EPPr EWes NBid

Brunsvigia (*Amaryllidaceae*)

	bosmaniae	WCot
	- white-flowered	WCot
	elandsmontana	WCot
	grandiflora	WCot
	gregaria	WCot
	josephinae	WCot
	- LAV 30394	WCot
	litoralis	WCot
	marginata	WCot
	multiflora	see *B. orientalis*
§	***orientalis***	WCot
	pulchra	WCot
	radulosa	WCot
	rosea 'Minor'	see *Amaryllis belladonna*

Brussels sprouts see AGM Vegetables Section

Bryonia (*Cucurbitaceae*)

dioica	GPoy NMir

Bryophyllum see *Kalanchoe*

Buddleja ✿ (*Scrophulariaceae*)

	sp.	CPer
	HCM 98.017 from Chile	WPGP
	agathosma	CBot CExl CFil SLon WKif WSHC
	albiflora	SLon
	alternifolia ♀H5	Widely available
	- KR 4881	GKev
	- 'Argentea'	CBcs CBot CRos EBee ELan EPfP LRHS MBNS MNHC MRav NLar SPer SPoG SWvt WCot WSHC XSen
	- UNIQUE ('Pmoore12') **new**	LCro LOPS NLar SLon
	asiatica ♀H2	CHid IDee SLon
	- B&SWJ 11278	WCru
	asiatica × ***lindleyana*** **new**	WSpi
	auriculata	CBcs CBot CExl CHll CMCN CRos EBee ELan EPfP LRHS NSti SBod SLon SPlb SVen WGwG
	'Bel Argent'	EBee WPGP
	'Berries and Cream' **new**	SPoG
	'Blue Chip'[PBR] (Lo and Behold Series)	CBot CRos EMil EPfP LBuc LRHS MAsh MGos MJak NLar NRHS SCob SLim SLon SRms SWvt WCot WFar
*	'Blue Trerice'	CExl
	caryopteridifolia	EBtc SEND SLon
	colvilei	CAby CBcs CBod CCCN CDul ELan EPfP GBin GCal GKin IArd IDee LRHS SBrt SLon SWvt WBor WHer WSpi
	- B&SWJ 2121	WCru
	- GWJ 9399	WCru
	- WJC 13760	WCru
	- 'Kewensis'	CBot CExl CHGN CHid CRHN CWld EWes GCal NLar SLon SVen WCFE WCru WSHC
	- pink-flowered	NLar
	cordata	CFil LRHS SLon
	- B&SWJ 10433	WCru
	coriacea	SLon
§	***crispa***	CBcs CBct CBot CExl CHid CRos CSpe EBee ECha ELan EPfP LRHS SLon SPer SRkn SVen SWvt WFar WKif WPGP WSHC WSpi
	- var. ***farreri***	CBot CHGN CHid EUJe SLon SPoG
	- 'Stone House Cottage' **new**	WSHC
	crotonoides subsp. ***amplexicaulis***	SLon
	'David Griffin'	CRos LRHS
	davidii	CCVT CPer ESps NPol SCob WTSh
	- B&SWJ 8083	WCru
	- ADONIS BLUE ('Adokeep'[PBR])	CBcs CRos CSBt CWCL EMOT ESps LBuc LRHS SLon SPoG
	- 'African Queen'	CRos LRHS SLon SRGP
	- var. ***alba***	ESps
§	- 'Autumn Beauty'	CAni SLon
	- 'Autumn Delight'	SLon
	- 'Bath Beauty'	CAni
	- 'Beijing'	see *B. davidii* 'Autumn Beauty'
	- 'Bishop's Velvet'	CAni
	- 'Black Knight' ♀H5	Widely available
	- 'Blue Horizon' ♀H5	CAni CRos LRHS NLar NRHS SLon SRGP WCot WMoo WRHF
	- 'Border Beauty'	CAni CRos LRHS NRHS SCob SLon
	- 'Brown's Beauty'	CAni
	- Buzz Series	LBuc SLon
	- - BUZZ CANDY PINK ('Tobudsopin') **new**	SPoG
	- - BUZZ INDIGO **new**	CBod ELan ETMg
	- - BUZZ IVORY ('Tobudivory'[PBR])	CEnd CMac CRos EBee ELan ELon EMOT EPfP ESps ETMg GMcL LRHS LSRN LSou MGos MJak NLar NRHS SLim SLon SPer SPoG WHil WSpi
	- - BUZZ LILAC	ELan MGos SCob SLon
	- - BUZZ MAGENTA ('Tobudpipur'[PBR])	CBod CEnd CMac CMea CNor CRos ELan ELon EMOT ETMg GAbr GMcL LRHS LSRN LSou MGos MJak NEgg NLar NPri NRHS SCob SLon SPad SPoG SRms SWvt WFar WSpi
	- - BUZZ SKY BLUE ('Tobudskybl'[PBR])	CMac CRos EPfP ETMg GMcL LRHS LSou MGos NEgg NLar NPri NRHS SPad SPoG SRms WFar
	- - BUZZ VELVET ('Tobudvelve'[PBR])	LRHS NRHS SPad SPer
	- - BUZZ VIOLET ('Tobudviole')	CMac ELan ELon GMcL LRHS LSou MGos MJak NLar NPri NRHS SEle SLim SLon SPer SPoG SWvt WHil
	- CAMBERWELL BEAUTY ('Camkeep') (English Butterfly Series) ♀H5	CHll CRos ESps LRHS LSRN SLon
	- 'Car Wash'	CAni
	- 'Castle Blue'	CRos LRHS NRHS SLon
	- 'Castle School'	CAni CSam
§	- 'Charming'	CDul WMoo WSHC
	- 'Clive Farrell'	see *B. davidii* 'Autumn Beauty'
	- 'Corinne Tremaine'	WHer
	- 'Darent Valley' ♀H5	SLon
	- 'Dartmoor' ♀H5	Widely available
	- 'Dart's Ornamental White'	MRav SLon
	- 'Dart's Papillon Blue'	CAni LRHS SLon
	- 'Dart's Purple Rain'	CAni CRos LRHS NRHS SLon
	- 'Dubonnet'	CAni SLon
	- 'Dudley's Compact Lavender'	CAni
	- 'Ecolonia'	CAni SLon
	- 'Empire Blue'	CAni CBcs CDul CRos CSBt ECtt EPfP ESps GKin LRHS LSRN MGos NPer NRHS SCob SEND SPer SPlb SPoG SRGP SRms SWvt XSen
	- 'Fascinating'	CAni GCal MRav SLon
	- 'Flaming Violet'	CAni SLon
	- 'Florence'	LSRN NEgg NLar SLon WFar WMoo
	- 'Fortune'	CAni
	- 'Glasnevin Hybrid'	CAni CRos LRHS NLar SLon
	- 'Gonglepod'	CAni CRos LRHS NRHS SLon
	- 'Greenway's River Dart'	CAni LRHS SLon
	- 'Griffin Blue'	MAsh
	- 'Gulliver'[PBR]	CRos EMOT LRHS NLar NRHS SGol SLon WFar
	- 'Harlequin' (v)	Widely available
	- 'Île de France'	CAni CBcs NLar SLon SRms
	- 'Leela Kapila'	LRHS SLon
	- 'Les Kneale'	CAni SLon
	- 'Lyme Bay'	CAni
	- MARBLED WHITE ('Markeep'[PBR]) (English Butterfly Series)	CRos CSBt LRHS NEoE NRHS SLon WMoo
	- MASQUERADE ('Notbud') (v)	MRav SLon
	- MOONSHINE ('Buddma'[PBR])	LSou MTin NEoE WFar
§	- NANHO BLUE ('Mongo')	CAni CBcs CMac CRos CSBt EBee ECrN EPfP ESps ETMg GBin GKev GKin GMcL LRHS MAsh MGos MJak MRav MSwo NLar NRHS SCob SGol SLim WHar WMoo WSpi XSen

- 'Nanho Petite Indigo'	see *B. davidii* NANHO BLUE
- 'Nanho Petite Plum'	see *B. davidii* NANHO PURPLE
- 'Nanho Petite Purple'	see *B. davidii* NANHO PURPLE
§ - NANHO PURPLE ('Monum') ♀H5	CBcs CMac CRos CTri EBee EPfP ESps LRHS LSRN MGos MRav NLar NRHS SCob SGol SLim SLon SPer SPlb SRms XSen
- NANHO WHITE ('Monite') ♀H5	CMac CRos EPfP ESps LRHS SCob SGol SLon SPer SRms
- var. ***nanhoensis***	CAni CDul SEND SGol WFar
- - blue-flowered	EPfP NWad SLon SPer
- 'Orchid Beauty'	CAni LRHS SLon
- 'Orpheus'	CAni SLon
- 'Panache'	CRos EPfP LRHS MAsh NRHS SLon
- 'Peace'	CMac CTri CWCL LSRN MRav NLar SLon SPoG
- PEACOCK ('Peakeep'PBR) (English Butterfly Series)	CSBt GMcL LCro LOPS MAsh MJak NEgg SEle
- 'Persephone'	SLon
- 'Petite Indigo'	see *B. davidii* NANHO BLUE
- 'Pink Beauty'	LSRN MBlu SRGP WFar
- 'Pink Charming'	see *B. davidii* 'Charming'
- 'Pink Pearl'	CAni CRos LRHS NRHS SEND SLon
- 'Pink Spreader'	CAni CRos LRHS SLon
- 'Pixie Blue'	CAni CRos GMcL LRHS MAsh NLar SLon
- 'Pixie Red'	CAni CRos GMcL LBuc LRHS MAsh NLar SEND
- 'Pixie White'	LBuc MAsh NLar SEND SGol
- PURPLE EMPEROR ('Pyrkeep') (English Butterfly Series)	NEgg SLon
- 'Purple Friend'	CAni LRHS SLon
- 'Purple Prince'	CAni
- 'Red Admiral'	CAni CRos LLHF LRHS SLon SRGP
- RÊVE DE PAPILLON ('Minpap')	CRos LRHS MAsh NRHS
- 'Royal Purple'	CAni SLim SWvt
- 'Royal Red' ♀H5	Widely available
- 'Saith Ffynnon Early'	WSFF
- 'Santana' (v)	CAni CBcs CBod CDul CMac CRos EBee EHoe ELon EMil EPfP EWes GMcL LRHS LSou MGos MRav NEgg NLar NRHS NWad SGol SPoG SRms SWvt WAvo WCFE WMoo WSpi
- 'Shapcott Blue'	CAni
- 'Southcombe Splendour'	CAni CRos LRHS NRHS
- 'Summer Beauty'	CAni CDul MBlu SLon XSen
- 'Summer House Blue'	CRos LRHS SLon
- 'Variegata' (v)	CAni MAsh SLon SWvt
- 'White Ball'	ELan NLar SLon
- 'White Bouquet'	CAni CCVT CSBt EPfP GKin MSwo NLar SCob SEND SPer SRGP SWvt XSen
- 'White Cloud'	CAni ECrN LRHS NRHS SRms WGwG
- 'White Harlequin' (v)	SLon WCFE
- 'White Profusion' ♀H5	Widely available
- 'White Wings'	CRos LRHS NRHS SLon
- 'Widecombe'	CAni
- 'Windtor'	CRos LRHS NRHS
davidii × fallowiana new	WSpi
§ ***delavayi***	CBot CExl ECre GBin SEND WCru
'Ellen's Blue'	CExl CFil CRos LRHS NLar
fallowiana misapplied	see *B.* 'West Hill'
fallowiana Balf. f. & W.W. Sm.	CRos ELan LRHS
- ACE 2481	LRHS
- BWJ 7803	WCru

- var. ***alba*** ♀H5	CBot CHGN CMac CRos ECrN ELan EPfP LRHS MRav NLar NRHS SLon SPer WSHC
- 'Bishop's Violet'	CTsd
'Flower Power'	see *B. × weyeriana* 'Bicolor'
(Flutterby Series) FLUTTERBY LAVENDER ('Podaras 11'PBR) new	CSBt
- FLUTTERBY PEACE ('Podaras 6'PBR) new	CSBt
- FLUTTERBY PINK ('Podaras No 9'PBR) new	CCht CSBt
FLUTTERBY FLOW LAVENDER ('Podaras No 12') (Flutterby Flow Series)	LCro
(Flutterby Petite Series) FLUTTERBY PETITE BLUE HEAVEN ('Podaras 8'PBR)	CMea ETMg LCro LOPS NLar
- FLUTTERBY PETITE DARK PINK ('Podaras 10'PBR)	LCro NLar
- FLUTTERBY PETITE SNOW WHITE ('Podaras 15'PBR)	LCro LOPS
- FLUTTERBY PETITE TUTTI FRUITTI PINK ('Podaras 13'PBR)	CMea ETMg LBuc LCro SRms
forrestii	WCru
- BWJ 8020	WCru
globosa ♀H5	Widely available
- RCB/Arg C-11	WCot
- 'Cally Orange'	GCal WGwG
- 'Lemon Ball'	MBlu NPer SLon
glomerata	EShb SLon SPlb
- 'Silver Service'	CBod CBot LRHS
heliophila	see *B. delavayi*
'Ice Chip'PBR (Lo and Behold Series)	EPfP
indica	SLon
INSPIRED PINK	see *B. × weyeriana* 'Pink Pagoda'
japonica	SLon
- B&SWJ 8912	WCru
* ***knappii***	CBot
× ***lewisiana*** 'Margaret Pike'	SLon
'Lilac Chip' (Lo and Behold Series)	LRHS NLar NRHS
limitanea	SLon
- from Cangshan, Yunnan, China	SBrt
lindleyana	Widely available
- 'Miss Vicie'	CRos LRHS NRHS
aff. ***lindleyana***	CBot GWyn WSpi
- B&SWJ 11478	WCru
'Lochinch' ♀H5	Widely available
longifolia	SLon
'Longstock Gem'	SLon
'Longstock Silver'	LRHS SLon
loricata	CBot CExl CHGN CMCN CRos CTsd EBee EPfP GBin GCal GWyn IDee LRHS SLon SPlb WSpi
macrostachya HWJ 602	WCru
- PAB 4198	LEdu WPGP
- WWJ 12016	WCru
§ ***madagascariensis*** ♀H2	CRHN NLar SLon SPlb SVen
'Malvern Blue'	CAni
megalocephala B&SWJ 9106	WCru WPGP
'Miss Ruby'PBR ♀H5	CRos EBee EMOT EPfP LBuc LRHS MAsh NRHS SGol
§ 'Morning Mist'PBR	CExl CMac CPer CRos CSBt CWGN EBee EHoe EPfP LCro LOPS LRHS

	LSRN NEgg NLar NRHS SCob SGol SLon SPoG SRms SWvt WCot
myriantha	CExl EBee SLon WPGP
nappii	CBot SLon
nicodemia	see *B. madagascariensis*
nivea	CBot CExl CHid EBee SLon XSen
- B&SWJ 2679	WCru
- pink-flowered	SLon
aff. ***nivea***	CBot WSpi
officinalis ♀^{H2}	CBot CExl SLon XSen
paniculata	SLon
- GWJ 9286 from Sikkim	WCru
- from Sikkim	SBrt
parvifolia	SLon
× ***pikei*** 'Hever'	SRms XSen
'Pink Delight' ♀^{H5}	Widely available
'Pink Perfection'	CAni WFar
'Pride of Hever'	SDys
'Pride of Longstock'	SLon SPoG
'Purple Chip' (Lo and Behold Series)	LRHS NRHS
saligna	SLon
'Salmon Spheres'	SLon
salviifolia	CBcs CBct CBot CExl CHid CMac CRos CTsd CWCL EBee ELan LRHS MBlu NLar SBrt SEND SPlb SVen WGwG WHer WPGP
- white-flowered	EBee SLon WPGP
SILVER ANNIVERSARY	see *B.* 'Morning Mist'
stenostachya	CExl SLon
sterniana	see *B. crispa*
SUGAR PLUM ('Lonplum'^{PBR})	CRos CSBt EPfP LBuc LCro LOPS LRHS NEoE NRHS SLon SPoG
tibetica	see *B. crispa*
tubiflora	SLon
venenifera	SLon
- B&SWJ 895	WCru
- B&SWJ 6036	WCru
wardii KR 4881	EBee WPGP
§ 'West Hill' ♀^{H5}	CRos LRHS NRHS SLon
× ***weyeriana***	CBot CDul ECtt MBNS MGil MMuc MNHC MNrw MSwo SPad SPlb SWvt WAvo WOut
§ - 'Bicolor'	EBee EPPr EPfP IDee LCro LLHF LOPS LSRN MNrw NLar NQui SCob SLon SRms
- 'Boy Blue'	SLon
- 'Golden Glow'	CTri ECrN GBin GWyn LSRN NLar SLon SWvt WSFF
- 'Honeycomb'	MGos NLar
- 'Lady de Ramsey'	SEND
- 'Moonlight'	CBcs CExl CRos ELan EPPr GBin GWyn LRHS SLon SPer WCot WSpi
§ - 'Pink Pagoda'^{PBR}	CRos EPfP LCro LOPS LRHS NRHS SLon SPoG
- 'Sungold' ♀^{H4}	Widely available
'White Chip' (Lo and Behold Series)	LRHS NRHS
'Winter Sun'	SLon
yunnanensis	CBcs GCal NLar SLon
- B&SWJ 8146	WCru

Buglossoides (*Boraginaceae*)

§ ***purpurocaerulea***	CHll CSpe ECha ELan EPfP EWld LPla MNrw NBid NChi SPhx WCot WFar WSHC XLum

Bukiniczia (*Plumbaginaceae*)

cabulica	GKev

Bulbine (*Asphodelaceae*)

SH 74	CCse
annua misapplied	see *B. semibarbata*
bulbosa misapplied	see *B. semibarbata*
caulescens	see *B. frutescens*
§ ***frutescens***	CBod CHll IDee MHer NChi SVen
- 'Hallmark'	CCCN
latifolia	CCCN EBee
§ ***semibarbata***	CCCN

Bulbinella (*Asphodelaceae*)

angustifolia	EBee GKev MHer
cauda-felis	GKev
hookeri	CExl CRos EBee GBin GEdr GKev IRob LRHS NRHS SRms WCot WHal WThu
latifolia subsp. ***latifolia***	IBlr
nutans	EBee
- white-flowered	CPne

Bulbinopsis see *Bulbine*

Bulbocodium (*Colchicaceae*)

vernum	EPot GKev LAma LLHF SDeJ

bullace see *Prunus insititia*

Bunias (*Brassicaceae*)

orientalis	CAgr LEdu

Bunium (*Apiaceae*)

bulbocastanum	CAgr CSpe EBee IMou LEdu WHil WPGP
ferulaceum	WCot
W&B BG B-10 **new**	

Buphthalmum (*Asteraceae*)

salicifolium	EBee ELan EPfP ESps MMuc NBro NGdn SPer SRms WCot WFar WWtn XLum
- 'Alpengold'	CSam ECha GMaP NLar
- 'Dora'	ECtt WCot WFar
- 'Sunwheel'	CBod CRos LRHS MHol NRHS SRms
speciosum	see *Telekia speciosa*

Bupleurum (*Apiaceae*)

angulosum copper-leaved	see *B. longifolium*
candollei	WSHC
falcatum	CSpe ECha LPla LRHS NDov SPhx WCot
fruticescens **new**	XSen
fruticosum	CBcs CFil CSpe ELan EPfP LRHS SCob SEND SLon SPoG WCot WCru WPGP XSen
- bronze-leaved	LRHS
gibraltaricum	XSen
§ ***longifolium***	CElw CFis CSpe EBee EWes LEdu LRHS MNrw NChi NSti SBrt SMad WBor WPGP
- subsp. ***aureum***	LPla NDov SPhx
- 'Bronze Beauty'	GEdr
ranunculoides	LPla SPhx XLum
rotundifolium	CRav CSpe IMou LEdu SPhx WCot
- 'Copper'	NDov

Bursaria (*Pittosporaceae*)

spinosa	CCCN CHll

Butia (*Arecaceae*)

	sp.	ETod
	capitata	CCCN CDTJ CPHo ETod EUJe LRHS SArc
§	- var. ***odorata***	SPlb
	eriospatha	CPHo LRHS
	odorata	see *B. capitata* var. *odorata*
	yatay	LRHS NLos SBig

Butomus (*Butomaceae*)

	umbellatus	CBen CWat ECha EPfP EWat MNrw MRav MSKA MWts NPer WMAq WWtn XLum
	- f. ***albiflorus***	MSKA
	- 'Rosenrot'	EWat LLWG
	- 'Schneeweisschen'	EWat LLWG MWts

butternut see *Juglans cinerea*

Buxus (*Buxaceae*)

	sp.	LPra
	aurea 'Marginata'	see *B. sempervirens* 'Marginata'
	balearica	WSpi
	'Green Gem'	NWad
	harlandii misapplied	CMen SRiv
	japonica 'Nana'	see *B. microphylla*
	macrophylla new	WSpi
§	***microphylla***	NWad SGol
	- 'Asiatic Winter'	see *B. microphylla* var. *japonica* 'Winter Gem'
§	- 'Compacta'	CMen LLHF MHer SRiv WCot
	- 'Curly Locks'	NWad
	- 'Faulkner' ♀H5	CCVT ELan EPfP ESps LBuc LMaj LTop MGos SCob SGol SPer SRiv SRms WMoo WSpi
	- 'Golden Triumph'PBR	CBot NLar
	- 'Green Pillow'	MHer SRiv WSpi
	- 'Herrenhausen'	WSpi
	- var. ***japonica***	SGol
	- - 'Morris Midget'	NWad
	- - 'National'	WSpi
§	- - 'Winter Gem'	MRav
	- 'John Baldwin'	SRiv
	- var. ***sinica***	LTop
	sempervirens	Widely available
§	- 'Angustifolia'	MRav NWad SMad
	- 'Argenteo-variegata' (v)	ESps IFoB MJak SGol WFar
	- 'Aurea'	see *B. sempervirens* 'Aureovariegata'
	- 'Aurea Maculata'	see *B. sempervirens* 'Aureovariegata'
	- 'Aurea Marginata'	see *B. sempervirens* 'Marginata'
§	- 'Aureovariegata' (v)	EPfP EShb ESps LTop MGos MRav NLar SPer SRiv SRms WMoo
	- 'Bentley Blue'	LTop
	- 'Blauer Heinz'	ELan GQue MHer MRav SRiv WMoo WSpi
	- 'Bowles's Blue'	EWes WCFE
I	- 'Brilliantissima'	WMoo
	- clipped ball	EPfP LSRN MGos NLar SGol SRiv SRms
	- clipped bird	SRiv
	- clipped cone	LSRN SGol SRiv SRms
	- clipped pyramid	EPfP LSRN MGos NLar SGol SRiv SRms
	- clipped spiral	LSRN NLar SGol SRiv SRms
	- 'Elegans'	IFoB
§	- 'Elegantissima' (v) ♀H5	Widely available
	- 'Fiesta'	SRms
	- 'Gold Tip'	see *B. sempervirens* 'Notata'
§	- 'Graham Blandy' ♀H5	MHer SAko SGol SRiv WSpi
	- 'Green Balloon'	EPfP LBuc
	- 'Greenpeace'	see *B. sempervirens* 'Graham Blandy'
	- 'Handsworthensis'	CLnd CTri SEND SRms WCFE WSpi
	- 'Ickworth Giant'	WSpi
	- 'Japonica Aurea'	see *B. sempervirens* 'Latifolia Maculata'
	- 'Kensington Gardens'	WSpi
	- 'King Midas'	SAko
	- 'Kingsville'	see *B. microphylla* 'Compacta'
	- 'Kingsville Dwarf'	see *B. microphylla* 'Compacta'
§	- 'Latifolia Maculata' (v) ♀H5	EPfP LRHS MMuc NPer SEND SPoG SRiv WRHF WSpi
	- 'Longifolia'	see *B. sempervirens* 'Angustifolia'
§	- 'Marginata' (v)	CPne IFoB LTop SGol WSpi
	- 'Memorial'	LTop NWad SMHy SRiv WSpi
	- 'Myosotidifolia'	NEoE SRiv WCot WSpi
	- 'Myrtifolia'	WSpi
§	- 'Notata' (v)	IFoB MAsh WMoo WSpi
	- 'Prostrata'	WSpi
	- 'Pylewell'	WSpi
	- 'Rosmarinifolia'	MRav
	- 'Rotundifolia'	ELan MMuc SEND WMoo WSpi
	- 'Silver Variegated'	see *B. sempervirens* 'Elegantissima'
	- 'Suffruticosa'	Widely available
	- 'Suffruticosa Variegata' (v)	SRms SWvt
	- 'Twisty'	WFar
	- 'Vardar Valley'	NEoE SRiv WSpi
*	- 'Variegata' (v)	MSwo SArc
	- 'Wisley Blue'	WSpi
	sinica var. ***insularis*** 'Filigree'	NWad WSpi
	- - 'Justin Brouwers'	LPla MHer SRiv WSpi
	- - 'Tide Hill'	LTop SRiv WFar WSpi

C

cabbages see AGM Vegetables Section

Cacalia (*Asteraceae*)

plantaginea	see *Arnoglossum plantagineum*
suaveolens	see *Hasteola suaveolens*

Cachrys (*Apiaceae*)

alpina	SPhx

Caesalpinia (*Caesalpiniaceae*)

gilliesii ♀H1c	CBcs CSpe EBee LRHS NLos SPlb WCot
pulcherrima ♀H1b	CCCN
spinosa	SPlb

Caiophora (*Loasaceae*)

coronata	GEdr

calabrese see AGM Vegetables Section

Caladium (*Araceae*)

'Candidum' (v)	SDeJ
'Carolyn Whorton'	SDeJ
'Florida Cardinal' (v)	SDeJ
'Frieda Hempel'	SDeJ
praetermissum 'Hilo Beauty'	XBlo
'White Christmas' (v)	SDeJ

Calamagrostis (*Poaceae*)

× ***acutiflora***	XLum
- 'Avalanche'	CKno CRos ECha ECtt EHoe EPPr EPed EPfP EShb EWes GCal GMcL GQue GWyn LRHS MAsh MAvo NDov NRHS NWsh SPoG WPtf
- 'Eldorado' (v)	CKno MAvo MMuc WCot
- 'England' (v)	EPPr GBin
- 'Karl Foerster'	Widely available
- 'Overdam' (v)	Widely available
- 'Stricta'	EBee EPPr
- 'Waldenbuch'	CKno EBee
argentea	see *Stipa calamagrostis*
arundinacea	CElw CExl CMac SPlb WMoo XSen
§ ***brachytricha*** ♀H7	Widely available
- 'Mona'	NDov
emodensis	CAby CMea CSam CSpe EBee ECha EHoe GCal IRob MAvo MMoz NBid SEND WGrn WMoo
epigejos	CKno EBWF LEdu WHrl WPGP
foliosa	EPPr
'Glenorchy Fireworks' new	EPPr
splendens misapplied	see *Stipa calamagrostis*
splendens Trin.	LPla NDov
varia	CKno EHoe ELon GBin LPla WHrl

Calamintha (*Lamiaceae*)

alpina	see *Acinos alpinus*
§ ***ascendens***	EBee WMoo
clinopodium	see *Clinopodium vulgare*
cretica	SPhx
§ ***grandiflora***	CBod ECha ELan GJos GPoy MNHC MNrw MRav NLar NPer SPer SPlb SRms WCAu WMoo WSHC XSen
- 'Elfin Purple'	EBee EPfP
- 'Variegata' (v)	ELan ENfk EPfP LSou MPie SRms
§ ***nepeta***	CBWd CBod CHab CMea CRos ECha ENfk GBin GMaP LRHS MHer MNHC NBro NRHS SCob SEND SPhx SPlb SPoG SRms WCAu WHer WMoo WOut WPtf XAbr XSen
- subsp. ***glandulosa***	WMoo
- - ACL 1050/90	EBee WHoo
- - 'White Cloud'	CBWd EBee ECtt EHrv ELan IBoy MRav SPoG SRms WCAu WMoo
- 'Gottfried Kuehn'	LPla MRav
§ - subsp. ***nepeta***	ELan ELon EPfP IMou MCot MHer MMuc MRav NDov NSti SPer WFar WHal XLum
- - 'Blue Cloud'	CFis CSam CSpe EBee ECha ECtt EHrv EPfP EPri GWyn MRav MSpe NDov SPhx SPoG SPtp SRms WArt WCAu WFar WMoo WTor
- 'Weisse Riese'	CMea EBee NDov
nepetoides	see *C. nepeta* subsp. *nepeta*
officinalis misapplied	see *C. ascendens*
sylvatica	see *Clinopodium menthifolium*
vulgaris	see *Clinopodium vulgare*

calamondin see *Citrus* × *microcarpa*

Calandrinia (*Portulacaceae*)

grandiflora	CPla
sibirica	see *Claytonia sibirica*
umbellata	EDAr MAsh
- 'Ruby Tuesday'	WTor XLum

Calanthe (*Orchidaceae*)

alismifolia	LAma
aristulifera	GKev LAma LRHS
bicolor	see *C. striata*
discolor	EBee GKev LAma LRHS SDir
- var. ***flava***	see *C. striata*
Kozu gx	GKev LEdu WPGP
- 'Orange'	GKev
nipponica	GKev LAma LRHS
reflexa	GKev LAma LRHS SDir
sieboldii	see *C. striata*
§ ***striata***	EBee GKev LAma LRHS SDir
sylvatica	GKev LAma
tricarinata	LAma SDir
triplicata	GKev LAma

Calathea (*Marantaceae*)

argyrophylla 'Exotica'	XBlo
louisae 'Maui Queen'	XBlo
majestica ♀H1b	XBlo
makoyana ♀H1b	XBlo
picturata 'Argentea' ♀H1b	XBlo
roseopicta ♀H1b	XBlo
- 'Rosastar'	XBlo
rufibarba ♀H1b	XBlo
* ***stromata***	XBlo
veitchiana 'Medaillon'	XBlo
zebrina ♀H1b	XBlo
'Zoizia'	XBlo

Calceolaria (*Calceolariaceae*)

arachnoidea	EWes GEdr SPlb
§ ***biflora***	EWes EWld GAbr GCrg GKev
- 'Goldcrest Amber'	SPlb
cana new	SBrt
cavanillesii	SPlb
chelidonioides	GKev
corymbosa	GKev GLog
falklandica	GKev
filicaulis	GKev
- subsp. ***luxurians*** new	GKev
fothergillii	GKev GLog WAbe
'Goldcrest'	LRHS
integrifolia ♀H1c	CAbb CBcs CDTJ CExl CFis CPla CTri ECtt ELan EShb MGil MSCN SAdn SEND SPer SRms WAbe WBor WHer
- bronze	MSCN SPer
- 'Gaines' Yellow'	EBee GCal
'Kentish Hero'	CRos CSpe EBee GCal MGil NRHS SDys WAbe
meyeniana	GCal
subsp. ***nahuelbutae*** new	
mollissima	GKev
pavonii	MGil
aff. ***pavonii***	CRHN
plantaginea	see *C. biflora*
rugosa	see *C. integrifolia*
'Sultan'	EBee
tenella	NSla WAbe
uniflora var. ***darwinii***	GKev NHpl
'Walter Shrimpton'	WAbe

Calendula ✿ (*Asteraceae*)

'Apricot Twist' new	LSou
arvensis	CCCN
'Bronze Beauty'	CSpe
officinalis	ENfk GPoy LCro MHer MNHC SPav SRms SVic SWvt WSFF XAbr
- 'Indian Prince' (Prince Series)	CRav LCro SPhx
- 'Touch of Red Buff' (Touch of Red Series)	CSpe
'Tarifa'	SEND

(Winter Wonders Series) WINTER WONDERS AMBER ARCTIC ('212372D') **new** ETMg
- WINTER WONDERS BANANA BLIZZARD ('2012357D') **new** ETMg
- WINTER WONDERS GOLDEN GLAZE ('2012329D') **new** ETMg
- WINTER WONDERS PEACH POLAR ('2012391D') **new** ETMg

Calibanus (*Asparagaceae*)

hookeri EShb

Calibrachoa (*Solanaceae*)

(Cabaret Series) CABARET BRIGHT RED ('Balcabrite'PBR) NPri
- CABARET DEEP BLUE ('Balcabdebu'PBR) CRav
- CABARET DEEP YELLOW ('Balcabdepy'PBR) LSou NPri
- CABARET PURPLE ('Balcabpurp') LSou

CALLIE SUNRISE ('Cal Sunre'PBR) (Callie Series) LSou

(Can-can Series) CAN CAN PRIMROSE LSou
- CAN-CAN APPLEBLOSSOM **new** LSou
- CAN-CAN BLACK CHERRY CRav LSou
- CAN-CAN CORAL REEF ('Balcanoree') **new** LSou
- CAN-CAN DOUBLE DARK YELLOW NPri
- CAN-CAN DOUBLE MAGENTA LSou NPri
- CAN-CAN DOUBLE PROVENCE BLUE **new** LSou
- CAN-CAN NEON PINK ('Balcaneoni') **new** LSou
- CAN-CAN ORANGE ('Balcanoran') LSou

(Carillon Series) CARILLON BURGUNDY ('Sk9-354') ESps
- CARILLON LEMON ESps
- CARILLON RED ('Sk7-1155') ESps
- CARILLON WHITE ESps

'Crackerjack' **new** ETMg

Kabloom Series ETMg
- KABLOOM DEEP BLUE ('Pas10203441') NPri
- KABLOOM DEEP PINK ('Pas1020305') NPri
- KABLOOM TERRACOTTA **new** ETMg
- KABLOOM WHITE ('Pas1020307') NPri

(Million Bells Series) MILLION BELLS CHERRY ('Sunbelchipi'PBR) ESps
- MILLION BELLS PINK MORN ('Sunbelkupapi'PBR) ESps
- MILLION BELLS RED ('Sunbelre'PBR) ESps
- MILLION BELLS TRAILING BLUE ('Sunbelkubu'PBR) ESps
- MILLION BELLS TRAILING FUCHSIA ('Sunbelrkup') ♀H2 ESps
- MILLION BELLS TRAILING LAVENDER VEIN ('Sunbelbura'PBR) ESps
- MILLION BELLS TRAILING SOFT PINK ('Sunbelkuopi'PBR) ESps
- MILLION BELLS TRAILING WHITE ('Sunbelkuho') ESps

'Starlight Blue' **new** NPri

'Starlight Pink' **new** NPri

(Superbells Series) SUPERBELLS BANANA CHOCOLATE CPla
- SUPERBELLS DOUBLE RUBY ('Uscal83901'PBR) CPla
- SUPERBELLS GRAPE PUNCH ('Uscal84704') NPri
- SUPERBELLS IMPERIAL PURPLE ('Uscali100'PBR) LSou
- SUPERBELLS ORANGE ('Uscali41109') LSou
- SUPERBELLS PINK ('Uscali11'PBR) ♀H2 LSou
- SUPERBELLS POMEGRANATE PUNCH ('Uscal08501') NPri

Calla (*Araceae*)

sp. NRHS

aethiopica see *Zantedeschia aethiopica*

palustris CBod CRos CWat ESps EWat LLWG MSKA NPer SRms WMAq

Calliandra (*Mimosaceae*)

'Dixie Pink' CCCN

portoricensis CCCN

surinamensis CCCN

tweediei ♀H1c CCCN

Callianthemum (*Ranunculaceae*)

anemonoides EPot GEdr WAbe WCot

coriandrifolium GEdr

kernerianum GEdr WAbe

Callicarpa (*Lamiaceae*)

CW&T 6228 CMCN

acuminata CFil

americana CExl
- var. ***lactea*** CMCN

bodinieri CHll WHar
- var. ***giraldii*** ESps LMaj MRav NLar SGol
- - 'Profusion' ♀H5 Widely available
- 'Imperial Pearl' LRHS

'Cardinal' CJun

cathayana NLar

dichotoma CBcs CExl LRHS NLar SCob
- 'Issai' EPfP EUJe LRHS MBlu

japonica CExl CMen NLar SBrt
- B&SWJ 12621 WCru
- f. ***albibacca*** LRHS
- 'Heavy Berry' NLar
- 'Koshima-no-homate' NLar
- 'Leucocarpa' CBcs CExl CMac EBee ELan EPfP EWTr MRav NLar SPer SPoG WGob

- var. ***luxurians*** B&SWJ 8521	WCru
kwangtungensis	CBcs NLar
mollis	CBcs CExl
psilocalyx NJM 13.057	WPGP
shikokiana	NLar
× ***shirasawana***	NLar
aff. ***tikusikensis*** B&SWJ 7127	WCru
Van den Broek selection	NLar
yunnanensis	NLar

Callirhoe (*Malvaceae*)

bushii	EBee
involucrata	LPla SBrt WHrl WSHC XLum
- var. ***tenuissima***	EBee GCal SPhx

Callisia (*Commelinaceae*)

elegans	EShb
fragrans	EOHP EShb
repens	EShb

Callistemon (*Myrtaceae*)

acuminatus	CCCN
brachyandrus	SVen
citrinus	CBcs CHll CTri EPfP EPri ESps SEle SPlb WGrn
- 'Albus'	see *C. citrinus* 'White Anzac'
- 'Firebrand'	CRos LRHS MAsh
- 'Splendens' $\mathbb{Y}^{H3}$	Widely available
§ - 'White Anzac'	CHll CMac CSBt CTsd ELan EMil EPfP LRHS SAko SEND SPoG
comboynensis	CCCN
'Dawson River Weeper'	CMCN
glaucus	see *C. speciosus*
'Inferno'	LRHS NEgg
'Kings Park Special'	CMCN
laevis hort.	see *C. rugulosus*
linearifolius	LSRN
linearis $\mathbb{Y}^{H2}$	CMac CRos CTri ELan EPfP ESps IDee LRHS LSRN MAsh MGos MHer SEND SLim SLon SPlb SWvt WSHC
macropunctatus	SPlb SVen
'Masotti'PBR	CRos MPkF SPoG
'Mauve Mist'	CCCN CRos ELan EMil EPfP LRHS MAsh SAko SEle SPad SPoG SVen WGrn
pallidus	CBcs CCCN CMCN CMac CRos CTsd ELan EPfP EWTr IDee LRHS MAsh MMuc MRav NRHS SAko SEND SEle SPer SPlb SVen
paludosus	see *C. sieberi* DC.
'Perth Pink'	CBcs CCCN CSBt ELan EPfP LRHS SPad SVen WGrn
pinifolius	SPlb SVen
§ ***pityoides***	CExl NLar SEle SVen
'Red Clusters'	CBcs CMac CRos ELan EMOT EMil EPfP IArd LRHS MAsh MJak SAko SWvt WFar
rigidus	CBcs CChe CHll CRos CTri CTsd ELan EMOT EPfP ESps EUJe GAbr GMcL IArd LRHS LSRN MGos MMuc MRav NLar NRHS SAko SEle SPer SVen SWvt
§ ***rugulosus***	CCCN GMcL LRHS SVen SWvt
salignus $\mathbb{Y}^{H2}$	CBcs CCCN CCht CMac CTri EMOT EPfP MHer MRav NEgg NLar SEle SLim SPer SVen
sieberi misapplied	see *C. pityoides*
§ ***sieberi*** DC.	CBcs CMCN EBee ELan EPfP LRHS MGil MMuc NLar SLim SPlb
§ ***speciosus***	CDul LRHS NLar SEND SPlb
subulatus	SArc SPlb
- 'Crimson Tail'	MGil MMuc NLar SPtp
viminalis	CCCN CMCN SPlb
- 'Captain Cook'	CMac EMOT LRHS LSRN NEgg SVen SWvt WFar WGrn
- 'Endeavour'	CCCN
- 'Hannah Ray'	EMOT WFar
- HOT PINK ('Kkho1'PBR)	CRos LRHS MGos MPkF SLim
- 'Little John'	LSRN MAsh SEND SPad SWvt
'Violaceus'	NLar SPlb SVen
viridiflorus	CMCN CTsd MMuc SEND SPlb WGwG
'White Anzac'	see *C. citrinus* 'White Anzac'

Callistephus (*Asteraceae*)

chinensis	CPla SVic

Callitriche (*Plantaginaceae*)

sp.	WSFF
brutia subsp. ***hamulata***	LLWG
§ ***palustris***	CBen MSKA MWts
stagnalis	WMAq
verna	see *C. palustris*

Callitris (*Cupressaceae*)

endlicheri	CBrP

Callitropsis see *Chamaecyparis*

× ***leylandii***	see × *Cuprocyparis leylandii*
nootkatensis	see *Xanthocyparis nootkatensis*

Calluna ✿ (*Ericaceae*)

vulgaris	ESps SWhi WOut
- 'Adrie'	SWhi
- 'Alba Elongata'	see *C. vulgaris* 'Mair's Variety'
§ - 'Alba Plena' (d)	CRos
§ - 'Alba Rigida'	CFst
- 'Alexandra'PBR (Garden Girls Series)	SCoo SPoG
- 'Alicia'PBR (Garden Girls Series) $\mathbb{Y}^{H7}$	SCoo SPoG
- 'Allegro'	EPfP MMuc SCoo
- 'Amethyst'PBR (Garden Girls Series)	MJak MMuc SPoG SWhi
- 'Amilto'	CFst
- 'Anette'PBR (Garden Girls Series)	MJak SCoo
- 'Angie'	SWhi
- 'Annabel' (d)	SWhi
- 'Annemarie' (d) $\mathbb{Y}^{H7}$	CFst CSBt EPfP SCoo SPlb SWhi
- 'Anne's Goldzwerg'	CFst
- 'Anne's Zwerg'	CFst
- 'Aphrodite'PBR (Garden Girls Series)	CFst
- 'Arabella'PBR	SWhi
- 'Arina'	MAsh SCoo
- 'Athene'PBR (Garden Girls Series)	CFst SWhi
- 'Aurea'	MJak
- 'Beoley Crimson'	SCoo
- 'Beoley Gold' $\mathbb{Y}^{H7}$	CSBt CTri EPfP MAsh SCoo
- 'Beoley Silver'	SCoo SWhi
- 'Blazeaway'	CTri EPfP MAsh MJak SCoo
- 'Bonfire Brilliance'	CSBt
- 'Bonita'PBR (Garden Girls Series)	CFst
- 'Boskoop'	MAsh SWhi

	- 'C.W. Nix'	CSBt
	- 'Con Brio'	CFst CSBt SCoo SWhi
	- 'Cottswood Gold'	SCoo
	- 'County Wicklow' (d) ♀H7	CTri ELan EPfP MMuc SCoo SWhi
	- 'Cuprea'	EPfP MJak SCoo SWhi
	- 'Dark Beauty'PBR (d) ♀H7	CBcs CFst CSBt ELan EPfP LCro LOPS MAsh SCoo SWhi
	- 'Dark Star' (d) ♀H7	CFst CSBt EPfP GJos MAsh SCoo SWhi
	- 'Darkness' ♀H7	CBcs CFst CTri EPfP MAsh MJak SCoo SWhi
	- 'David Hagenaars'	SWhi
	- 'Disco Queen'	SWhi
	- 'Dunnet Lime'	SPlb
	- 'Easter-bonfire'	MJak SCoo
	- 'Eckart Miessner'	SWhi
	- 'Elsie Purnell' (d) ♀H7	CFst ELan EPfP MAsh SCoo SPlb
	- 'Feuerwerk'	SCoo
	- 'Firefly' ♀H7	CFst CSBt EPfP MJak SCoo SPer SWhi
	- 'Flamingo'	SCoo
	- 'Forest Fire'	CFst
	- 'Foxii Nana'	CFst SWhi
	- 'Fred J. Chapple'	MJak SWhi
	- 'Galaxy'PBR	CFst
	- 'Gina'PBR	SWhi
	- 'Glenfiddich'	CSBt MAsh
	- 'Gold Haze'	CTri MAsh SCoo
	- 'Gold Knight'	ELan EPfP MAsh SCoo
	- 'Gold Spronk'	SWhi
	- 'Golden Angie'	SWhi
	- 'Golden Carpet'	CFst MAsh
	- 'Golden Fleece'	CFst
	- 'Golden Turret'	MAsh
	- 'Grey Carpet'	CFst
	- 'Guinea Gold'	MAsh SWhi
§	- 'H.E. Beale' (d)	CTri EPfP GJos MJak SCoo
	- 'Hammondii Aureifolia'	MJak SPlb
	- 'Hammondii Rubrifolia'	SWhi
	- 'Hera'PBR	SWhi
	- 'Highland Rose'	SPlb
	- 'J.H. Hamilton' (d)	CTri ELan MAsh SCoo SWhi
	- 'Jana' (d)	CFst
	- 'Johnson's Variety'	SCoo
	- 'Josefine'	SWhi
	- 'Joy Vanstone'	EPfP
	- 'Julia'	SWhi
	- 'Kerstin' ♀H7	CFst SCoo SPlb SWhi
	- 'Kinlochruel' (d) ♀H7	CBcs CFst CTri EPfP MAsh SPlb SWhi
	- 'Kirby White'	MAsh SPlb SWhi
	- 'Klaudine'PBR (Garden Girls Series)	CFst
	- 'Lemon Queen'	CFst
	- 'Leslie Slinger'	SCoo
	- 'Lilli'PBR	SWhi
	- 'Little John'	LSRN
	- 'Loki'PBR	SWhi
	- 'Long White'	SWhi
§	- 'Mair's Variety'	SCoo SWhi
	- 'Marleen'	CSBt MJak
	- 'Melanie' (Garden Girls Series)	CSBt SCoo SWhi
	- 'Mickkle-Dickkle' **new**	SWhi
	- 'Mrs Pat'	MAsh
	- 'Multicolor'	MAsh
§	- 'My Dream' (d)	CSBt EPfP SCoo
	- 'Nana Compacta'	CFst
	- 'Nora'	SWhi
	- 'October White'	CFst
	- 'Orange Queen'	CSBt
	- 'Peter Sparkes' (d) ♀H7	CBcs CSBt EPfP MAsh MMuc SCoo
	- 'Pink Beale'	see *C. vulgaris* 'H.E. Beale'
	- 'Purple Passion'	ELan EPfP SCoo
	- 'Radnor' (d)	CSBt
	- 'Ralph Purnell'	ELan SCoo
	- 'Red Beauty'	CBcs CFst SWhi
	- 'Red Favorit' (d)	CFst SWhi
	- 'Red Fred'	SCoo
	- 'Red Haze'	EPfP SCoo
	- 'Red Pimpernel'	ELan EPfP SCoo SWhi
	- 'Redbud'	SWhi
	- 'Rigida Prostrata'	see *C. vulgaris* 'Alba Rigida'
	- 'Robert Chapman' ♀H7	CFst CSBt CTri MAsh SPer SWhi
	- 'Rosalind' ambig.	EPfP
	- 'Rosalind, Underwood's'	EPfP
	- 'Rosita'PBR	CFst
	- 'Sandy'PBR (Garden Girls Series)	SPoG SWhi
	- 'Serlei Aurea'	CSBt EPfP
	- 'Silvana'PBR	CFst SWhi
	- 'Silver Fox'	CBcs CFst
	- 'Silver Knight'	CSBt ELan EPfP MAsh MJak SCoo SPlb SWhi
	- 'Silver Queen' ♀H7	CFst MAsh MJak SWhi
	- 'Sir John Charrington'	CFst EPfP MAsh SWhi
	- 'Sister Anne' ♀H7	CFst CSBt EPfP MJak MMuc SCoo
	- 'Snow White'	SWhi
	- 'Snowball'	see *C. vulgaris* 'My Dream'
	- 'Spitfire'	MAsh
	- 'Spring Cream' ♀H7	CBcs CFst MAsh MMuc SCoo SPer SWhi
	- 'Spring Torch'	CBcs CFst CSBt MAsh MJak SCoo SPer SWhi
	- 'Stefanie'	SWhi
	- 'Strawberry Delight' (d)	ELan EPfP SCoo
	- 'Sun Sprinkles'	CFst
	- 'Sunrise'	EPfP
	- 'Sunset'	CFst
	- 'Theresa' (Garden Girls Series)	CFst SWhi
	- 'Tib' (d) ♀H7	CSBt MAsh SWhi
	- 'Tricolorifolia'	EPfP MAsh SCoo
	- 'Trinklet' **new**	SWhi
	- 'Velvet Fascination' ♀H7	EPfP SCoo SWhi
	- 'White Angie'	SWhi
	- 'White Bouquet'	see *C. vulgaris* 'Alba Plena'
	- 'White Coral' (d) ♀H7	ELan EPfP SCoo
	- 'White Lawn'	CFst MMuc
	- 'Wickwar Flame' ♀H7	CBcs CFst CSBt ELan EPfP GJos MAsh MJak SCoo SPlb SWhi
	- 'Winter Chocolate'	CSBt EPfP MAsh SCoo
	- 'Yellow Beauty'PBR	CFst
	- 'Yvette's Gold'	CFst SPer
	- 'Yvette's Silver'	CFst

Calocedrus (*Cupressaceae*)

§	***decurrens*** ♀H6	CAco CBcs CDul CLnd CMac CTho EPfP EUJe LMaj LPra MBlu SLim WTSh
	- 'Aureovariegata' (v) ♀H6	CBcs
	- 'Berrima Gold' ♀H6	NLar SLim SPoG
§	- 'Depressa'	CKen
	- 'Nana'	see *C. decurrens* 'Depressa'
	- 'Pillar'	CKen NLar

Calocephalus (*Asteraceae*)

	brownii	see *Leucophyta brownii*

Calochortus (*Liliaceae*)

	'Cupido'PBR	CExl GKev LAma SDeJ WTor

luteus 'Golden Orb'PBR	CExl GKev SDeJ SDir
splendens 'Violet Queen'	GKev SDeJ
superbus	GKev SDeJ SDir
'Symphony'PBR	CExl GKev SDeJ
venustus	GKev SDeJ SDir
- 'Burgundy'	GKev SDeJ

Calonyction see *Ipomoea*

Caloscordum see *Allium*

Calostemma (*Amaryllidaceae*)

luteum	GKev
purpureum	GKev
- dark-flowered	GKev

Calothamnus (*Myrtaceae*)

quadrifidus	CKel
validus	SPlb
villosus	SPlb

Calpurnia (*Papilionaceae*)

aurea	SPlb

Caltha ✿ (*Ranunculaceae*)

howellii	see *C. leptosepala* subsp. *howellii*
laeta	see *C. palustris* var. *palustris*
leptosepala	EBee EWat GEdr GKev LLWG NLar
- SDR 8134	GKev
§ - subsp. ***howellii*** NNS 07-87	GKev
natans	LLWG
palustris	Widely available
- var. ***alba***	CBen CMac CRos CSpe CWat EBee ECha ELan ELon EWat GEdr GKev GKin LRHS MMuc MNrw MRav MWts NBid NChi NEgg NGdn NLar NRHS SPer SRms WFar WMAq WMoo WPnP
- 'Auengold'	LLWG
- 'Auenwald'	LLWG
- var. ***barthei***	GEdr
- 'Flore Pleno' (d) ♀H7	CAby CBen CMac CWCL EBee ECha ELan EWat GAbr GKin GMaP MMuc MRav NChi NEgg NGdn NLar NPer NRya SCob SEND SPer SPlb SRms WFar WMAq WMoo WPnP XLum
- 'Girls Eyes' **new**	MNrw
- 'Himalayan Snow'	EBee ECtt LLWG WFar
- 'Honeydew'	CAby ELon EWat LLWG MNrw WCot WFar WSHC
§ - var. ***major***	CAby
- 'Marilyn'	LLWG
- 'Multiplex' (d)	CDor ECtt SRot
- Newlake hybrid	LLWG
- 'Pallida Plena' (d)	SCob
§ - var. ***palustris***	CBen CBre ECha ELan EUJe EWat GCal LLWG WWtn
- - 'Plena' (d)	CWat EWat LRHS MCot MSKA NRHS SGol WGwG
- var. ***radicans***	EWat GEdr
- - 'Flore Pleno' (d)	WWtn
- 'Stagnalis'	MSKA MWts
- 'Yellow Giant'	MSKA
polypetala misapplied	see *C. palustris* var. *major*
polypetala Hochst. ex Lorent	CWat GCal MSCN MSKA NPer SMad WMAq
sagittata	WSHC

Calycanthus (*Calycanthaceae*)

'Aphrodite' **new**	CMCN
chinensis	CBcs CCCN CHll CJun CMCN ELan EPfP EUJe GKin LRHS MBlu MGil MPkF NLar
fertilis	see *C. floridus* var. *glaucus*
floridus	Widely available
- 'Athens'	CBcs CJun NLar WCot
§ - var. ***glaucus***	CRos EPfP LRHS MAsh SPer
- - 'Purpureus'	CBcs CJun MBlu NLar
- var. ***laevigatus***	see *C. floridus* var. *glaucus*
- 'Michael Lindsay'	CJun NLar WPGP
mohrii	NLar
occidentalis	CBcs CMCN CSpe MAsh MBlu MGil SBrt WCFE
× ***raulstonii*** 'Hartlage Wine' ♀H5	CBcs CJun CMCN CRos EPfP EUJe GKin IArd IDee LCro LLHF LOPS LRHS MAsh MBlu MGos NLar SPoG WKif
'Venus'	CBcs CMCN EPfP IArd LCro LOPS LRHS MAsh MBlu NLar

Calylophus (*Onagraceae*)

§ ***berlandieri*** **new**	XSen

Calystegia (*Convolvulaceae*)

§ ***hederacea*** 'Flore Pleno' (d)	SMad
japonica 'Flore Pleno'	see *C. hederacea* 'Flore Pleno'
soldanella	CPla
- NNS 99-85	WCot

Calytrix (*Myrtaceae*)

tetragona	SPlb

Camassia (*Asparagaceae*)

'Blue Candle'	CTca EBee EPot GKev LAma NHsp SDir SPhx
'Blue Heaven'	CMea CRos EBee ERCP GKev IRob LAma LRHS NHsp NRHS SDeJ SDir SPhx
cusickii	CBWd CBod CBro CExl CPla CRav CRos CTca CTri CWCL EBee ECtt ELan EPfP EPot ERCP EWTr GBin GKev IFro LAma LRHS MCot NLar NRHS SDeJ SDir WPnP
- white-flowered	CBod IFoB
- 'Zwanenburg'	CRos CTca EBee ERCP GKev IPot LRHS NHpl NHsp NRHS WCot
esculenta Lindl.	see *C. quamash*
'John Treasure' (d)	GCal MAvo
'Lavender Mist'	MAvo
leichtlinii misapplied	see *C. leichtlinii* subsp. *suksdorfii*
leichtlinii (Baker) S.Watson	MArl
- 'Alba' misapplied	see *C. leichtlinii* subsp. *leichtlinii*
* - 'Alba Plena'	CRav LSun MNrw NHpl
- BLUE DANUBE	see *C. leichtlinii* subsp. *suksdorfii* 'Blauwe Donau'
- 'Blue Wave'	NWad SDir
- 'Harlequin' (v)	GKev NHsp
§ - subsp. ***leichtlinii***	Widely available
- 'Magdalen'	MAvo
- pale pink-flowered **new**	GKev
- 'Plena' (d)	ECha
- 'Sacajawea'	CAvo CMea CTca ERCP GKev LAma LRHS NHsp NRHS SDeJ SDir WCot WTor
- 'Semiplena' (d)	CAvo CBro CMea CRos CTca EBee ECtt EPfP EPot ERCP GKev LAma

		LRHS MBel MNrw NRHS NSti SDir SPhx WBor WCot WPnP WShi
§	- subsp. ***suksdorfii***	LCro LOPS WCot
	- - 'Alba'	CRos EPot GBin GMaP IBoy IRob LCro LOPS LRHS NRHS NSti SCob
	- - 'Albocaerulea'	NPnk
§	- - 'Blauwe Donau'	ILea
	- - Caerulea Group	Widely available
	- - - 'Maybelle' <u>new</u>	CAvo CMea
	- - 'Electra'	CAvo ECha MAvo WCot
	- - 'Lady Eve Price'	WCot
§	***quamash***	CAvo CBWd CBro CRav CRos CTca CWCL EBee ECha ELan EPot ERCP GKev LAma LEdu LLWG LRHS MBel MCot NRHS SCob SDeJ SDir SRms WFar WHar WPnP WShi XLum
	- 'Blue Melody' (v)	CBro CSam CTca EBee EPot GKev GMaP LEdu LRHS NHsp NRHS SDeJ SDir WTor
	- 'Orion'	CBro EBee GKev IRob LRHS NHsp NRHS WCot
	- var. ***quamash*** <u>new</u>	IBoy

Camellia ✿ (*Theaceae*)

	'Adorable' (*pitardii* hybrid)	LRHS LSRN
	'Alpen Glo'	LRHS
	'April Blush'	WFar WHar
	'Auburn White'	see *C. japonica* 'Mrs Bertha A. Harms'
	'Baby Bear'	LRHS MPkF
	'Barbara Clark' (*reticulata* × *saluenensis*)	LRHS LSRN NRHS
	'Bertha Harms Blush'	see *C. japonica* 'Mrs Bertha A. Harms'
	'Black Lace' ♀H5	CBcs CSgt CTrh CTri EPfP LRHS LSRN MMuc NPri NRHS SArc SEND SWeb SWvt
	'Blissful Dawn'	CBcs CTrh
	'Bonnie Marie'	CBcs SCam
	'Califonia Sunset'	LRHS
	'Canterbury'	LRHS MPkF SCam
	'China Lady' (*granthamiana* × *reticulata*)	SCam
	'Christmas Daffodil' (*japonica* hybrid)	CBcs LRHS MPkF
	'Cinnamon Cindy'	LRHS MPkF
	'Congratulations'	CSBt LSRN
	'Contessa Lavinia Maggi'	see *C. japonica* 'Lavinia Maggi'
	'Cornish Snow' (*cuspidata* × *saluenensis*) ♀H4	CBcs CMac CSBt CTri EPfP SAko SCam SWvt
	'Cornish Spring' (*cuspidata* × *japonica*) ♀H4	CCCN CSBt CTrh CTsd LRHS NRHS SCam SPer
	crassipes	CPne
	'Crimson Candles' ♀H5	LRHS
	cuspidata	SCam
	'Czar'	see *C. japonica* 'The Czar'
	'Dainty Dale'	SCam
	'Delia Williams'	see *C.* × *williamsii* 'Citation'
	'Diamond Head' (*japonica* × *reticulata*)	LSRN
	'Doctor Clifford Parks' (*japonica* × *reticulata*) ♀H4	CBcs
	'Donckelaeri'	see *C. japonica* 'Masayoshi'
	edithae	LRHS
	'Extravaganza' (*japonica* hybrid) ♀H5	CTrh IArd MAsh SCoo
	'Fairy Blush'	LRHS MPkF
	'Fairy Wand'	LRHS MPkF
	'Fascination'	SWvt
	'Faustina Lechi'	see *C. japonica* 'Faustina'
	'Felice Harris' (*reticulata* × *sasanqua*)	SCoo
	'Festival of Lights'	LRHS
	'Fiesta Grande'	MPkF
	'Forty-niner' (*japonica* × *reticulata*)	CBcs CSgt LRHS MAsh NRHS
	'Fragrant Pink'	CTrh
	'Francie L' ♀H4	CBcs CMac EPfP
	'Frau Minna Seidel'	see *C. japonica* subsp. *rusticana* 'Otome'
	'Free Spirit'	CTrh
	'Freedom Bell' ♀H5	CTrh EPfP GKin LRHS NPri NRHS SCam
	'Frosted Star'	LRHS
	'Gay Baby'	MPkF
	'Golden Anniversary'	see *C. japonica* 'Dahlohnega'
	grijsii	CBcs CExl CTrh LRHS
	handelii	CExl
	'Happy Anniversary'	CSBt LSRN SWvt
§	***hiemalis*** 'Bonanza'	CSgt CTrh LRHS MPkF SCam
	- 'Chansonette'	CSgt ELon
§	- 'Dazzler'	LRHS NRHS SCam
	- 'Elfin Rose'	LRHS
	- 'Interlude'	MPkF
	- 'Kanjirō'	SCam
	- 'Shishigashira'	CTrh
	- 'Shōwa-no-sakae'	LRHS MPkF
	'High Fragrance'	LRHS
	'Hooker'	CSgt LRHS NRHS
	'Imbricata Rubra'	see *C. japonica* 'Imbricata'
	'Innovation'	CSgt
	'Inspiration' (*reticulata* × *saluenensis*) ♀H4	CBcs CMac CSgt CTrh EPfP LRHS LSRN MGos NLar SCam
	japonica	CAco ESps LMaj LPra SEWo SPre
	- 'Aaron's Ruby'	ELon LRHS NRHS SCam
	- 'Ace of Hearts'	SCoo
	- 'ACS Jubilee'	LRHS
	- 'Ada Pieper'	CTrh
	- 'Adelina Patti' ♀H5	CBcs CSgt CTrh
	- 'Adeyaka'	CSgt LRHS NRHS
	- 'Adolphe Audusson' ♀H5	Widely available
§	- 'Akashigata' ♀H5	CBcs ELon EPfP LRHS LSRN NRHS SCam SSta
	- 'Alba Plena' (d) ♀H5	CSBt CTrh ELan LRHS SPer SWvt
	- 'Alba Simplex'	CMac CSgt CTrh EPfP GMcL LMaj MAsh NPri SCam SCob SSta SWeb
	- 'Alexander Hunter' ♀H5	CSgt LRHS NRHS SCam
§	- 'Althaeiflora'	CBcs ELon LRHS NRHS SCam
	- 'Amazing Graces'	SCam
	- 'Anemoniflora'	CBcs CTsd EPfP LRHS NRHS
	- 'Angel'	CBcs LSRN SCam WBor
	- 'Angela Cocchi'	SWeb
	- 'Angello'	CSgt LRHS NRHS
	- 'Ann Sothern'	CBcs
	- 'Annie Wylam' ♀H5	CTrh LRHS NRHS SCoo
	- 'Apollo 14'	MAsh
	- 'Apollo' ambig.	CBcs GMcL LRHS NRHS
	- 'Apollo' Paul, 1911	MSwo SCam
§	- 'Apple Blossom'	CBcs CTrh CTsd ESps LRHS NRHS
	- 'April Blush' <u>new</u>	CSgt
	- 'April Kiss' <u>new</u>	CSgt
	- 'April Remembered'	NRHS WFar
	- 'April Rose'	CSgt WFar
	- 'Arajishi' misapplied	see *C. japonica* subsp. *rusticana* 'Beni-arajishi'
	- 'Augustine Supreme'	CMac
	- 'Augusto Leal de Gouveia Pinto'	CBcs
	- 'Ave Maria' ♀H5	CSgt CTrh LRHS MGos NRHS
	- 'Baby Pearl'	LSRN

	– 'Baby Sis'	LRHS NRHS
	– 'Ballet Dancer' ♀H5	ELon LSRN SCam
	– 'Baron Gomer'	see *C. japonica* 'Comte de Gomer'
	– 'Baronne Leguay'	SCam
	– 'Beau Harp'	LRHS NRHS SCam
	– 'Bella Romana'	SCam
	– 'Berenice Boddy' ♀H5	LRHS NRHS
	– 'Berenice Perfection'	SCam
	– 'Betty Foy Sanders'	CTrh LRHS NRHS
	– 'Betty Robinson'	LRHS NRHS
	– 'Betty Sheffield'	LRHS NRHS
	– 'Betty Sheffield Pink'	LRHS NRHS SCam
	– 'Betty Sheffield Supreme'	CBcs SCam
	– 'Betty's Beauty'	LRHS
	– 'Black Magic'	CSgt CTrh LRHS NRHS SCam
	– 'Black Tie'	CBcs CTrh ELon LRHS MAsh MGos NEgg NRHS SCam WFar
	– 'Blackburnia'	see *C. japonica* 'Althaeiflora'
§	– 'Blood of China'	CBcs CSBt CSgt EUJe LRHS LSRN MAsh MGos NLar NRHS SCam SCoo SWvt
	– 'Blush Tinsie'	LRHS NRHS
	– 'Bob Hope' ♀H5	CBcs CTrh CTri LRHS NRHS SCam SWeb
	– 'Bob's Tinsie' ♀H5	CBcs CSBt CTsd ECre EPfP LRHS LSRN MGos NRHS SPoG
§	– 'Bokuhan' ♀H5	MPkF SCam
	– 'Bonomiana'	SWeb
	– 'Bright Buoy'	LRHS NRHS
	– 'Brushfield's Yellow'	CBcs CSBt CSgt CTrh CTsd EBee ELan ELon EPfP IArd LRHS LSRN MAsh MGos NLar NRHS SCam SCoo SPer SSta WSpi
	– 'Bush Hill Beauty'	see *C. japonica* 'Lady de Saumarez'
§	– 'C.M. Hovey' ♀H5	CMac CSgt LRHS NRHS
	– 'C.M. Wilson'	CMac
	– 'Campsii Alba'	CSgt CTsd SCam SCoo
	– 'Can Can'	ELon
	– 'Candy Apple'	CTrh
	– 'Cara Mia'	CTsd LRHS NRHS SCam SCoo
	– 'Carolyn Tuttle'	CSgt LRHS NRHS
	– 'Carter's Sunburst' ♀H5	EPfP
	– 'Cassandra'	EPfP LRHS NRHS
	– 'Centifolia Alba'	SWeb
	– 'Chandleri Elegans'	see *C. japonica* 'Elegans'
	– 'Charlotte de Rothschild'	CTrh CTri
	– 'Cinderella'	LRHS NRHS SCam
	– CLASSIQUE ('Kerguelen'PBR) (v)	LRHS MPkF MSCN
	– 'Colonel Firey'	see *C. japonica* 'C.M. Hovey'
	– 'Commander Mulroy' ♀H5	CBcs SCoo
§	– 'Comte de Gomer'	ELon EPfP LRHS NPri NRHS SCam
	– 'Conspicua'	CBcs
§	– 'Coquettii' ♀H5	CSgt LRHS MAsh NRHS
	– 'Curly Lady'PBR	MJak NPri
§	– 'Dahlohnega'	CSBt CSgt CTrh ELon EPfP LMil LRHS LSRN MGos MPkF NRHS SPer
	– 'Daikagura'	LRHS NRHS
	– 'Dainty'	CBcs
	– 'Daitairin'	see *C. japonica* 'Dewatairin'
	– 'Daphne du Maurier'	LRHS NRHS
	– 'Dark of the Moon'	LRHS NRHS
	– 'Dear Jenny'	CSgt
	– 'Debutante'	CBcs CMac ELon SCam
	– 'Desire' ♀H5	CBcs CSBt CSgt CTrh CTsd EPfP GMcL LCro LMil LOPS LRHS LSRN MAsh MGos MJak MPkF NEgg NRHS SCam SPoG WFar
	– 'Devonia'	CBcs
§	– 'Dewatairin' (Higo)	CBcs SCam

	– 'Diddy's Pink Organdie'	LRHS NRHS
	– 'Dixie Knight'	CBcs LRHS NRHS SCam
	– 'Dobreei'	CMac
	– 'Doctor Burnside'	CBcs CTrh LMaj LRHS SCam SWeb
	– 'Doctor King'	CSgt EBee EPfP LRHS NPri NRHS SCoo SPoG
	– 'Doctor Tinsley' ♀H5	CSgt EPfP LRHS MAsh NPri NRHS SCam
	– 'Dona Herzilia de Freitas Magalhães'	CBcs ELon
	– 'Dona Jane Andresson'	SCam
	– 'Donckelaeri'	see *C. japonica* 'Masayoshi'
	– 'Donnan's Dream'	CBcs CTrh
	– 'Drama Girl' ♀H5	CBcs CTsd LMaj LRHS NRHS SCam
	– 'Duchesse Decazes'	CBcs
	– 'Edelweiss'	ELon SCam
§	– 'Elegans'	ELon EPfP ESps GMcL LCro LMil LOPS LRHS MGos NRHS SCam SLim SPer SPoG SWvt
	– 'Elegans Champagne'	CSgt EPfP
	– 'Elisabeth'	LRHS NRHS
	– 'Elizabeth Arden'	CTsd
	– 'Elizabeth Cooper'	CTrh LSRN
	– 'Elizabeth Hawkins'	CSgt CTrh EUJe LRHS MAsh NRHS
	– 'Emmett Pfingstl'	SCam
	– 'Emperor of Russia'	CBcs LRHS NRHS
	– 'Eric Baker'	SCam
	– 'Eugène Lizé'	SCam
	– 'Eximia'	EPfP LRHS NRHS
	– 'Fanny'	CSgt
§	– 'Faustina'	LRHS NRHS
	– 'Finlandia Variegated' (v)	ELon SCam
	– 'Firebird'	CBcs CTsd
	– 'Flashlight'	EPfP LRHS NRHS
§	– 'Fleur Dipater'	CBcs CSgt LRHS MAsh NRHS SCam
	– 'Flowerwood'	SCam
	– 'Fred Sander'	ELon LRHS NRHS SCam
§	– 'Gigantea'	LRHS NRHS SCam
	– 'Giuditta Rosani'	LRHS NRHS
	– 'Glen 40'	see *C. japonica* 'Coquettii'
	– 'Gloire de Nantes' ♀H5	CTrh SCam
	– 'Gold Tone'	ELon SCam
	– 'Grace Albritton' (d)	LRHS
	– 'Grace Bunton'	ELon
	– 'Grand Prix' ♀H5	ELon LSRN NLar SCam SWeb
	– 'Grand Slam' ♀H5	CBcs SCam
	– 'Guest of Honor'	CSgt EUJe LRHS NRHS
	– 'Guilio Nuccio' ♀H5	CBcs CTri ELon EPfP IArd LRHS LSRN NEgg NPri NRHS SCam SLim SWeb
	– 'Gus Menard'	SCam
	– 'Gwenneth Morey'	CBcs
	– 'H.A. Downing'	SCam
§	– 'Hagoromo' ♀H5	CBcs CSBt CTrh CTsd LRHS NRHS SWeb
	– 'Hakugan'	EPfP
§	– 'Hakurakuten' ♀H5	CTrh CTri SCam SCoo
	– 'Hanafūki'	LRHS NRHS SCam
	– 'Happy Birthday'	LSRN
	– 'Haru-no-utena'	CTrh
	– 'Hatsuzakura'	see *C. japonica* 'Dewatairin'
	– 'Hawaii'	CMac CTrh ELon LRHS NRHS SCam
	– HERME	see *C. japonica* 'Hikarugenji'
	– 'High Hat'	CBcs
§	– 'Hikarugenji'	LRHS NRHS
	– 'Hinomaru'	CMac
	– 'Holly Bright'	CTrh MPkF
§	– 'Imbricata'	CSgt CTrh LRHS NRHS
	– 'Imperator'	SCam
	– 'Italiana Vera'	CSgt LRHS MAsh NRHS

	- 'J.J.Whitfield'	CMac
§	- 'Japonica Variegata' (v)	LRHS NRHS
	- 'Joseph Pfingstl' 🏆^{H5}	CSgt CTri EPfP LRHS MMuc NLar NRHS SCam
	- 'Jovey Carlyon'	CSgt LRHS NRHS
	- 'Joy Sander'	see *C. japonica* 'Apple Blossom'
	- 'Jubilee Gem'	CTsd
	- 'Juno'	CBcs LRHS NRHS
	- 'Jupiter' Paul, 1904 🏆^{H5}	CMac CSgt CTri EPfP LSRN MAsh SCam WHar
	- 'Kellingtoniana'	see *C. japonica* 'Gigantea'
	- 'Kentucky'	LRHS NRHS
	- 'Kick-off'	CTrh SCam
	- 'Kimberley'	CTsd EUJe LSRN SCam
	- 'King's Ransom'	CSgt LRHS NRHS
	- 'Kingyoba-shiro-wabisuke'	SCam
	- 'Kingyo-tsubaki'	SCam SSta
	- 'Kitty Berry'	CTrh
	- 'Kokinran'	SCam
§	- 'Konronkoku' 🏆^{H5}	CSgt LRHS NRHS
	- 'Kouron-jura'	see *C. japonica* 'Konronkoku'
	- 'Kramer's Supreme' 🏆^{H5}	CBcs CCCN CSgt ELon GMcL LRHS LSRN MGos NRHS SCam SCoo SGol
§	- 'Kumasaka'	CTri LRHS NRHS
	- 'Lady Campbell'	CTri EPfP GMcL LRHS NPri NRHS SCam SCoo WFar
	- 'Lady Clare'	see *C. japonica* 'Akashigata'
§	- 'Lady de Saumarez'	CBcs CMac CTsd
	- 'Lady Loch'	CTrh SCam
	- 'Lady Marion'	see *C. japonica* 'Kumasaka'
	- 'Lady McCulloch'	LRHS NRHS
	- 'Lady Vansittart'	CSgt CTrh EPfP LMil LRHS LSRN MGos NEgg NRHS SCam SLim SPer SPoG SSta
§	- 'Lady Vansittart Pink'	CMac
	- 'Lady Vansittart Red'	see *C. japonica* 'Lady Vansittart Pink'
	- 'Lady Vansittart Shell'	see *C. japonica* 'Yours Truly'
	- 'Latifolia'	SCam
	- 'Laura's Red'	CTsd
	- 'Laurie Bray'	SCoo SWeb
§	- 'Lavinia Maggi' 🏆^{H5}	CBcs CSgt CTri ELon EPfP GMcL LRHS LSRN MGos NPri NRHS SCam SCoo SPoG SReu SRms SSta
	- 'Lavinia Maggi Rosea'	LMaj
	- 'Lemon Drop'	CBcs CTrh LRHS
	- 'Lily Pons'	CTrh
	- 'Little Bit'	ELon SCam SSta
	- 'Little Man'	LRHS NRHS
	- 'Look-away'	LRHS
	- 'Lovelight' 🏆^{H5}	CSgt CTrh LRHS NRHS
	- 'Ludgvan Red'	LRHS NRHS
	- 'Mabel Blackwell'	ELon SCam
	- 'Madame de Strekaloff'	CMac CSBt SCam
	- 'Madame Lebois'	SCam
	- 'Madge Miller'	CSgt LRHS NRHS
	- 'Magnoliiflora'	see *C. japonica* 'Hagoromo'
	- 'Magnoliiflora Alba'	see *C. japonica* 'Miyakodori'
	- 'Maiden's Blush'	CMac
	- 'Manuroa Road'	LRHS
	- 'Margaret Davis' 🏆^{H5}	CCCN CSBt CSgt EBee ELan ELon EPfP LCro LOPS LRHS LSRN MAsh MGos NEgg NRHS SCam SCoo SGol SLim SWeb WFar
	- 'Margaret Davis Picotee'	CBcs CTrh SPer
	- 'Margaret Rose'	SCam
	- 'Margaret Short'	CTsd
	- 'Marguérite Gouillon' Drouard-Gouillon	SSta
	- 'Marian Mitchell'	SCam
	- 'Mariana'	ELon
	- 'Mariottii Rubra'	CMac
	- 'Marjorie Magnificent'	CSgt LRHS MAsh
	- 'Mark Alan'	LRHS LSRN SCam
	- 'Maroon and Gold'	CSgt LRHS NRHS
	- 'Mars' 🏆^{H5}	CBcs SCam
	- 'Marshmallow'	LRHS
	- 'Mary Costa'	CBcs CTrh SCam
	- 'Mary J. Wheeler'	LSRN
§	- 'Masayoshi' 🏆^{H5}	CBcs CSBt LRHS NRHS
	- 'Mathotiana Alba'	CMac CTri CTsd EPfP GMcL LSRN MGos SCam SPer WSpi
§	- 'Mathotiana Rosea'	CBcs CMac IRob NLar
	- 'Mathotiana Supreme'	SCam
	- 'Matilija Poppy'	CTrh SCam
	- 'Matterhorn'	CTrh
	- 'Mattie Cole'	SCam
	- 'Mercury' 🏆^{H5}	CMac EPfP GGGa NEgg
	- 'Mermaid'	LRHS NRHS SCam
	- 'Midnight'	CBcs CTsd LRHS NRHS
	- 'Midnight Magic'	CBcs CSgt CTrh CTri LRHS NRHS
	- 'Midnight Serenade'	LRHS NRHS
	- 'Midnight Variegated' (v)	LRHS MPkF
	- 'Midsummer's Day'	CBcs
§	- 'Mikenjaku'	CBcs CSgt EPfP LRHS NRHS
	- 'Miriam Stevenson'	SCam
§	- 'Miyakodori'	SWeb
	- 'Monstruosa Rubra'	see *C. japonica* 'Gigantea'
	- 'Monte Carlo'	SCam
	- 'Moshe Dayan'	CCht CSgt CTsd LRHS MAsh NRHS SCam
§	- 'Mrs Bertha A. Harms'	LRHS NRHS SCam
	- 'Mrs Charles Cobb'	LRHS
	- 'Mrs D.W. Davis'	CBcs EPfP
	- 'Mrs William Thompson'	LRHS NRHS SCam
	- 'Myorenji'	SCam
	- 'Nagasaki'	see *C. japonica* 'Mikenjaku'
	- 'Nancy Bird'	SCam
	- 'Nigra'	see *C. japonica* 'Konronkoku'
	- 'Nina Avery'	SCam
	- 'Nobilissima' 🏆^{H5}	CBcs CMac CSgt CTrh CTri EPfP LCro LMil LOPS MBlu MJak MMuc NEgg SCam SPer SPoG WFar WHar
	- 'Nokogiriba-tsubaki'	MPkF
	- 'Nuccio's Cameo' 🏆^{H5}	CSgt CTrh GMcL LRHS NPri NRHS
	- 'Nuccio's Gem' 🏆^{H5}	CBcs CSgt EPfP LRHS MAsh NRHS SGol SWeb
	- 'Nuccio's Jewel' 🏆^{H5}	CSBt CSgt CTrh EPfP LRHS LSRN MAsh NRHS SCam
	- 'Nuccio's Pearl' 🏆^{H5}	CSgt EPfP LMaj LRHS LSRN NPri NRHS
	- 'Nuccio's Pink Lace'	CBcs CSgt CTri LRHS MAsh NRHS
	- 'Onetia Holland'	CBcs EPfP LSRN SCam SLim
	- 'Oo-La-La'	CTrh LRHS NRHS
	- 'Optima'	CBcs ELon LRHS NRHS SCam
	- 'Orandakō'	LRHS NRHS SCob
	- 'Patricia Ann'	LSRN
	- 'Paulette Goddard'	SCam
	- 'Paul's Apollo'	see *C. japonica* 'Apollo' Paul, 1911
	- 'Peachblossom'	see *C. japonica* 'Fleur Dipater'
	- 'Pearl Harbor'	SCam
	- 'Pearl Maxwell'	SWeb
	- 'Pink Chiffon'	CSgt LRHS NRHS
	- 'Pink Clouds'	CBcs
	- 'Pink Perfection'	see *C. japonica* subsp. *rusticana* 'Otome'
	- 'Pope John Paul XXIII'	SCam
	- 'Preston Rose'	CBcs
	- 'Pride of Descanso'	see *C. japonica* 'Yukibotan'
	- 'Primavera'	CTrh LRHS NRHS

– 'Prince Murat'	LRHS NRHS
– 'Princess Baciocchi'	SCam
– 'Princess du Mahe'	CMac
– 'R.L. Wheeler' ♀H5	CBcs CSBt CSgt CTri EPfP GMcL LMaj LRHS LSRN MGos NPri NRHS SCam SCoo
– 'Raspberry Ripple'	MPkF
– 'Red Dandy'	CSgt SCam
– 'Red Red Rose'	LRHS NRHS SCam
– 'Robert Lasson'	LRHS
– 'Roger Hall'	CBcs CSgt CTrh LRHS LSRN NRHS SPoG
– 'Rosa Baroveira Nella'	NLar
– 'Rosa Mundi'	LPra
– 'Rosularis'	ELon
– 'Royal Velvet'	CTrh
– 'Rubescens Major'	CBcs
– 'Ruddigore'	CTrh
§ – subsp. ***rusticana***	CBcs
– – 'Arajishi' misapplied	see *C. japonica* subsp. *rusticana* 'Beni-arajishi'
– – 'Arajishi' Ko'emon	SCam
§ – – 'Beni-arajishi'	CBcs LRHS NRHS
§ – – 'Otome'	SCam
– – 'Otome' sport	SWeb
– – 'Reigyoku' (v)	CBcs
– 'Sabiniana'	LRHS NRHS
– 'Sacco Nova'	LMaj
– 'Sacco Vera'	SWeb
– 'Saint André'	CMac CSgt LRHS MAsh NRHS
– 'San Dimas' ♀H5	CTrh ELon LRHS MPkF NRHS SCam SWeb
– 'Sanpei-tsubaki'	LRHS
– 'Saturnia'	CSgt ELon LRHS MJak NRHS
– 'Sawada's Dream'	SCam
– 'Scentsation' ♀H5	CTri LRHS NRHS
– 'Sea Foam'	LRHS NRHS
– 'Shikibu'	CTrh SCam
– 'Shiragiku'	CBcs EPfP LMaj SWeb
– 'Shiro Chan'	ELon SCam
– 'Shirobotan'	CSgt ELon LRHS NRHS SCam
– 'Silver Anniversary' ♀H5	CBcs CSBt CSgt CTri ELon EPfP ESps GMcL LCro LMil LOPS LRHS LSRN MAsh MGos MJak NEgg NLar NPri NRHS SCam SCoo SLim SPer SPoG SReu SWvt WFar
– 'Silver Ruffles'	CTrh ELon LRHS NRHS SCam
– 'Something Beautiful'	SCam
– 'Souvenir de Bahuaud-Litou' ♀H5	CBcs SCam
– 'Spencer's Pink'	CBcs
– 'Splendens Carlyon'	CSgt LRHS MAsh NRHS
– 'Spring Fling'	CTrh LRHS NRHS SPoG
– 'Spring Formal'	CTrh LRHS NRHS
– 'Spring Frill'	SCam
– 'Stacy Susan'	MPkF
– 'Strawberry Swirl'	CBcs
– 'Sugar Babe'	CTrh LRHS NRHS SCam
– 'Sylva' ♀H5	EUJe GGGa
– 'Sylvia'	CMac
– 'Takanini'	CBcs CTrh MPkF SCam
– 'Tama-no-ura'	SCam
– 'Tammia'	CSgt LRHS NRHS
– 'Teresa Ragland'	SCam
§ – 'The Czar'	CBcs
– 'The Mikado'	LRHS NRHS
– 'Tiffany'	ELon LRHS NRHS SCam
– 'Tiki'	SCoo
– 'Tinker Bell'	ELon SCam
– 'Tinker Toy'	CTrh

– 'Tom Pouce'	LRHS
– 'Tom Thumb' ♀H5	CTrh LRHS NRHS SRms
– 'Tomorrow'	MAsh NEgg SCam
– 'Tomorrow's Dawn'	SCam
– 'Touchdown'	SCam
– 'Trewithen White'	CSgt LRHS NRHS
§ – 'Tricolor' ♀H5	CBcs CMac CSBt CTrh ELon LRHS MGos MMuc NRHS SCam
– 'Tricolor Red'	see *C. japonica* 'Lady de Saumarez'
– 'Trinket'	SCam
– 'Vergine di Collebeato'	SWeb
– 'Victor Emmanuel'	see *C. japonica* 'Blood of China'
– 'Ville de Nantes'	LRHS NRHS
– 'Virginia Carlyon'	CBcs
– 'Visconti Nova'	LRHS NRHS
– 'Vittorio Emanuele II'	CSgt CTrh LRHS MAsh NRHS
– 'Volunteer'	EPfP LCro LOPS LRHS
– 'Warrior'	SCam
– 'Wheel of Fortune'	LRHS NRHS
– 'White Swan'	CMac CSBt CSgt LRHS NRHS
– 'Wildfire'	LRHS NRHS
– 'William Bartlett'	CTrh SCoo
– 'William Honey'	CTrh
– 'Wisley White'	see *C. japonica* 'Hakurakuten'
– 'Witman Yellow'	CTrh
§ – 'Yours Truly'	CMac CSgt CTrh CTsd LRHS LSRN MAsh NRHS
§ – 'Yukibotan'	CBcs
– 'Yukimi-guruma'	SWeb
'Jury's Yellow'	see *C.* × *williamsii* 'Jury's Yellow'
'Koto-no-kaori' (*lutchuensis* hybrid)	LRHS
'Leonard Messel' (*reticulata* × (× *williamsii*)) ♀H5	CMac CTrh CTri CTsd EPfP LRHS MGos MPkF NHim NLar NRHS SCam SPer SReu SWeb WHor
'Liz Henslowe'	CTsd
lutchuensis	LRHS MPkF
'Magic Mum'	LSRN
'Maud Messel' (*reticulata* × (× *williamsii*))	SCam
'Mimosa Jury'	LRHS
'Nicky Crisp' (*japonica* × *pitardii*)	CSgt CTrh LRHS NRHS SPoG
oleifera	CExl CTrh
'Paolina Guichardini'	LRHS
'Pink Goddess' (*hiemalis* hybrid)	LRHS MPkF
'Pink Icicle' (*oleifera* hybrid)	CBcs ELon SCam
'Pink Spangles'	see *C. japonica* 'Mathotiana Rosea'
pitardii WWJ 11925 from Vietnam **new**	WCru
'Portuense'	see *C. japonica* 'Japonica Variegata'
'Quintessence' (*japonica* × *lutchuensis*)	CTrh LRHS
'Red Crystal'	CTrh
reticulata 'Arch of Triumph'	LRHS
– 'Captain Rawes'	LRHS
– 'Jean Morel'	LRHS
– 'Mary Williams'	SPoG
– 'Satsuma-kurenai'	LRHS
– 'Simpatica'	LRHS
– 'William Hertrich'	CBcs
rosthorniana CUPIDO	see *C. rosthorniana* 'Elina'
§ – 'Elina'	ELan EPfP LCro LOPS LRHS NRHS SAko
rusticana	see *C. japonica* subsp. *rusticana*
I ***sasanqua*** 'Alba'	CMac CTri
– 'Baronesa de Soutelinho'	ELon SCam
– 'Bonanza'	see *C. hiemalis* 'Bonanza'

	- 'Cleopatra'	EPfP SCob SWeb
	- 'Cotton Candy'	SCam
	- 'Crimson King' ♀H4	CSgt CTrh LRHS NRHS
	- 'Dazzler'	see *C. hiemalis* 'Dazzler'
	- 'Dwarf Shishi'	CTrh
	- 'Early Pearly'	LRHS
	- 'Flamingo'	see *C. sasanqua* 'Fukuzutsumi'
	- 'Fragrans'	ELon SCam
	- 'Fuji-no-mine'	ELon SCam
	- 'Fuji-no-yuki' **new**	LRHS
§	- 'Fukuzutsumi'	CSBt
	- 'Gay Border'	LRHS
	- 'Gay Sue'	CTrh SCam
	- 'Hinode-gumo'	SEWo SWeb
	- 'Hiryū'	CSgt LRHS NRHS SCam
	- 'Hugh Evans' ♀H4	CBcs CTrh ELan EPfP LRHS NRHS SCam SSta
	- 'Jean May' ♀H4	CSgt EPfP LRHS NRHS SCam WCot
	- 'Kenkyō'	ELon SCam SPer SSta
	- 'Maiden's Blush'	LRHS NRHS WCot
	- 'Mignonne'	CTrh
	- 'Narumigata' ♀H4	CBcs CDul CMac CSgt CTrh CTsd EPfP LCro LOPS LRHS MBlu MGos NRHS SCam SPoG SSta WSHC
	- 'New Dawn'	SCam
	- 'Nyewoods'	CMac
	- 'Papaver'	SCam
	- 'Paradise Audrey'	LMil LRHS SPoG
	- 'Paradise Belinda'	EPfP LMil LRHS SPoG
	- 'Paradise Blush'	CBcs LRHS NRHS
	- 'Paradise Glow'	CBcs LMil LRHS NRHS
	- 'Paradise Helen'	LRHS
	- 'Paradise Hilda'	LRHS
	- 'Paradise Pearl'	EPfP LMil LRHS NRHS
	- 'Paradise Venessa'	CTsd EPfP LRHS
	- 'Plantation Pink'	CSgt CTrh EPfP LCro LOPS LRHS NRHS SRkn WCot
	- 'Rainbow'	CBcs CSgt CTrh ELan ELon EPfP LRHS MPkF NRHS SCoo SSta
	- 'Rosea'	CMac ELon LRHS NRHS SCam
	- 'Sasanqua Rubra'	CMac SCam
	- 'Sasanqua Variegata' (v)	CTrh ELon MPkF SCam
	- 'Sekiyō'	LRHS
	- 'Setsugekka'	LRHS
	- 'Snowflake'	SSta
	- 'Sparkling Burgundy'	see *C.* 'Sparkling Burgundy'
	- 'Tanya'	CTrh SCam
	- 'Versicolor'	CSgt EPfP LRHS NRHS
	- 'Winter's Joy'	CBcs SCam
	- 'Winter's Snowman'	LCro LOPS LRHS NRHS SCam
	'Scented Gem'	LRHS
	'Scented Sun'	CTrh
	'Scentuous' (*japonica* × *lutchuensis*)	CBcs
	'Show Girl' (*reticulata* × *sasanqua*) ♀H4	LRHS SCam
§	***sinensis***	CBcs CCCN CSgt CTrh CTsd GPoy LRHS NLar NRHS SCam SPlb SPre SWvt
	- var. ***assamica***	CCCN SPre
	- var. ***sinensis***	CCCN
	- 'Tea Breeze'	WCot
	'Snow Flurry'	CBcs CSgt CTrh LRHS NEgg NRHS
§	'Sparkling Burgundy' ♀H5	EPfP LCro LRHS MGos NRHS SCam
	'Spring Festival' (*cuspidata* hybrid) ♀H4	CBcs CSBt CTrh EPfP LCro LMil LOPS LRHS MGos NPri NRHS SCam SWeb
	'Spring Mist' (*japonica* × *lutchuensis*)	CTrh
	'Sugar Dream'	CTrh LRHS SCam

	'Superscent'	CTrh
	'Survivor'	LRHS
	'Swan Lake'	EPfP LRHS NPri NRHS
	'Sweet Emily Kate' (*japonica* × *lutchuensis*)	LRHS MPkF
	'Sweet Jane'	LRHS MPkF SCam
	'Sweet Olive' (d)	LRHS
	'Tarōkaja' (wabisuke)	SCam
	thea	see *C. sinensis*
	'Tinsie'	see *C. japonica* 'Bokuhan'
	'Tom Knudsen' (*japonica* × *reticulata*) ♀H4	CTrh LRHS NRHS
	transnokoensis ♀H4	CExl CTrh LRHS MPkF
	'Tricolor Sieboldii'	see *C. japonica* 'Tricolor'
	'Tristrem Carlyon' (*reticulata* hybrid)	CCht CSgt CTri CTsd EPfP LRHS NPri NRHS
	'Usu-otome'	see *C. japonica* subsp. *rusticana* 'Otome'
	× ***vernalis*** 'Yuletide'	CTrh LCro LOPS LRHS LSRN MPkF NRHS SCam SCob SWeb
	'White Retic' (*japonica* × *reticulata*)	LRHS
	× ***williamsii*** 'Angel Wings'	LRHS NRHS
	- 'Anticipation' ♀H5	CBcs CCht CDul CMac CSBt CSgt CTrh ELan EPfP GGGa GKin GMcL LCro LMil LOPS LRHS MAsh MGos MSwo NEgg NRHS SCob SLim SPer SPoG SWvt WFar WHar WHor
	- 'Anticipation Variegated' (v)	LRHS NRHS
	- 'Ballet Queen'	CBcs CSBt SCam
	- 'Ballet Queen Variegated' (v)	ELon
	- 'Bartley Number Five'	CMac
	- 'Beatrice Michael'	CBcs CMac
	- 'Blue Danube'	SCoo
	- 'Bow Bells'	CDul CTri
	- 'Bowen Bryant' ♀H5	CSgt CTrh EPfP GMcL LRHS MAsh NRHS
	- 'Brigadoon' ♀H5	CBcs CSgt CTri EPfP GGGa LRHS NRHS SCam
	- 'Burncoose'	CBcs
	- 'Buttons 'n' Bows'	LRHS MPkF
	- 'C.F. Coates'	SCam
	- 'Caerhays'	CBcs
	- 'Celebration'	CSBt LSRN
	- 'Charles Colbert'	LRHS SCam
	- 'Charles Michael'	CBcs
	- 'China Clay' ♀H5	CBcs EPfP LRHS NRHS
§	- 'Citation'	CBcs CMac
	- 'Contribution'	CTrh LRHS NRHS SPoG
	- 'Coral Delight'	LRHS MPkF
	- 'Debbie' ♀H5	Widely available
	- 'Debbie's Carnation'	LRHS NRHS SCam
	- 'Deloraine'	CTsd
	- 'Donation' ♀H5	Widely available
	- 'Dream Boat'	LRHS
	- 'E.G. Waterhouse'	CBcs CSBt CSgt CTrh CTri ELan ELon EPfP GKin GMcL LRHS MGos NEgg NRHS SCam SSta
	- 'E.T.R. Carlyon' ♀H5	CBcs CSgt CTrh CTri EPfP LMil LRHS MAsh MGos NLar NRHS SLim
	- 'Elegant Beauty' ♀H5	CTrh ELon LRHS NLar NRHS SCam SPer
	- 'Elizabeth Anderson'	CTrh CTsd
	- 'Ellamine'	CBcs
	- 'Elsie Jury' ♀H5	CBcs CMac CSgt CTri ELan GKin LRHS MGos NLar NRHS SCam SGol SPer
	- 'Fiona Colville'	SCam

- 'Francis Hanger' CTrh LRHS NRHS SCam SPer
- 'Galaxie' CBcs SCam
- 'Gay Time' LRHS NRHS
- 'George Blandford' ♀H5 CMac
- 'Glenn's Orbit' ♀H5 NLar SCam
- 'Golden Spangles' (v) CMac ELan EPfP GKin LRHS MGos MMuc NEgg NRHS SCam SEND SPer SPoG WHor
- 'Grand Jury' LRHS NRHS
- 'Gwavas' CBcs CCCN CSgt CTrh LRHS MAsh NRHS SCam
- 'Hilo' SCam
- 'J.C. Williams' ♀H5 CBcs CMac CTri LRHS
- 'Jenefer Carlyon' CBcs
- 'Jill Totty' CTrh
- 'John Pickthorn' CBcs
- 'Julia Hamiter' ♀H5 CBcs CSgt LRHS NRHS
§ - 'Jury's Yellow' ♀H5 CBcs CCCN CSBt CSgt CTrh CTri ELan EPfP GGGa LCro LMil LOPS LRHS LSRN MAsh MGos NEgg NPri SCam SLim SPer SPoG SSta SWvt
- 'Lady's Maid' SCam
- 'Laura Boscawen' CBcs CTrh SCam
- 'Les Jury' ♀H5 CBcs CSBt CTrh LMil LRHS LSRN MGos NHim NRHS SLim
- 'Margaret Waterhouse' CBcs SCam
- 'Marjorie Waldegrave' CSgt LRHS MAsh NRHS
- 'Mary Phoebe Taylor' ♀H5 CBcs CSgt LMaj NLar SLim
- 'Mirage' CTrh
- 'Monica Dance' CBcs
- 'Muskoka' ♀H5 CBcs
- 'Night Rider' MPkF SCam WPGP
- 'November Pink' SCam
- 'Philippa Forward' CMac
- 'Pink Wave' CSgt LRHS NRHS
- 'Rendezvous' CTrh SCam
- 'Rose Parade' CSgt
- 'Rose Quartz' CSgt
- 'Rosemary Williams' CBcs CMac
- 'Ruby Wedding' (d) ♀H5 CBcs CSBt CSgt CTrh CTsd EPfP LMil LRHS LSRN MAsh MGos MJak NEgg NPri NRHS SCam SCoo SLim SPer SPoG SWvt WFar
- 'Saint Ewe' ♀H5 CBcs CSBt CSgt CTrh CTri EPfP LRHS MGos NRHS SCam
- 'Saint Michael' CBcs
- 'Sayonara' LMaj
- 'Senorita' ♀H5 CSgt CTrh ELon GMcL LRHS NLar NRHS SCam
- 'Shocking Pink' CSgt LRHS NRHS
- 'The Duchess of Cornwall' LRHS NRHS SCam
- 'Tiptoe' CTrh SCoo
- 'Toni Finlay's Fragrant' CTrh
- 'Tulip Time' LRHS
- 'Twinkle Star' CSgt LRHS NRHS
- 'Water Lily' ♀H5 CBcs CTri ELon EPfP LRHS NLar NRHS SCam
- 'Wilber Foss' ELon LRHS NRHS SCam
- 'William Carlyon' CSgt LRHS NRHS

'Winter's Charm' CBcs CSgt LRHS NRHS
'Winter's Interlude' CBcs LRHS NRHS
'Winter's Toughie' CSgt LRHS NRHS SCam
'Winton' (*cuspidata* × *saluenensis*) CBcs
'Yoimachi' (*fraterna* × *sasanqua*) CTrh LRHS
'Yume' LRHS

Camissonia (*Onagraceae*)

bistorta 'Sunflakes' CSpe

Campanula ✿ (*Campanulaceae*)

sp. GNew
RCB AM 13 WCot
from Sicily WCot
alata EWTr WHil WMoo XLum
'Albert Kirkham' EBee
§ ***alliariifolia*** Widely available
- DHTU 0126 WCru
- 'Ivory Bells' see *C. alliariifolia*
alpina GJos
alsinoides GEdr
americana WFar XLum
ardonensis GEdr NSla
argaea GKev
armena GJos
arvatica CPBP CRos EACa EPot LRHS NRHS NSla SRms WAbe
aucheri see *C. bellidifolia* subsp. *aucheri*
'Audrey Widdison' LRHS
'Barbara Valentine' EBee EWTr SCob
barbata EACa EBee EPfP EWTr GKev WAbe WMoo
'Belinda' CPBP EPot SBch
bellidifolia LLHF NSla
§ - subsp. ***aucheri*** EPot GEdr GKev
§ - subsp. ***besenginica*** SBrt
- subsp. ***saxifraga*** CPla GEdr
bellidifolia × ***tridentata*** GKev
besenginica see *C. bellidifolia* subsp. *besenginica*
§ ***betulifolia*** ♀H5 EACa GCrg GEdr GKev NSla
biebersteiniana GEdr LLHF NSla
'Birch Hybrid' CRos EACa ECtt ELan ELon GCrg LRHS MMuc NRHS SAko SEND SRms XLum
'Blithe Spirit' WAbe
'Blue Octopus' CRos CWGN LRHS MPnt NPnk NRHS SCob SRms WNPC
'Blue Pearl' **new** WAbe
bononiensis SRms
bornmuelleri CPBP
'Burghaltii' NLar SHar
'Cantata' WAbe
carpatha white-flowered CPBP WHar
carpatica ♀H5 EPfP NBro NGdn SPlb SRms WFar WHar XLum
- f. ***alba*** CRos LRHS NGdn NRHS SPlb WHar XLum
§ - - 'Weisse Clips' CBar CRos ECtt ELan EPfP GKin GMaP LCro LOPS LRHS MAsh MJak NEgg NGdn NRHS SCob SPer SPoG SRms SWvt WFar WHar
§ - 'Blaue Clips' CBar CBcs CRos ECtt ELan EPfP ESps ETMg GKin GMaP IFoB IPot LRHS MAsh MGos MJak NEgg NGdn NRHS SCob SPer SPoG SRms SWvt WFar WHar
- BLUE CLIPS see *C. carpatica* 'Blaue Clips'
- 'Blue Moonlight' CRos EACa LRHS NRHS
- blue-flowered ECrN
- 'Chewton Joy' CRos EACa LLHF LRHS NRHS
- 'Kathy' EPot GCrg
- 'Pearl White' MHol
- 'Rapido Blue' **new** MHol
- var. ***turbinata*** SRms
- - f. ***alba*** 'Snowsprite' ESps
- - 'Foerster' CRos EACa GCrg LRHS NRHS XLum

- - 'Isabel'	CRos EACa LLHF LRHS NRHS XLum
- - 'Jewel'	CRos EACa LRHS NRHS
- WHITE CLIPS	see *C. carpatica* f. *alba* 'Weisse Clips'
§ ***cashmeriana***	GKev WAbe
- white-flowered **new**	GKev
cenisia	WAbe
cephallenica	see *C. garganica* subsp. *cephallenica*
cervicaria	GJos
§ ***chamissonis***	EPot GEdr LLHF NWad
- 'Major'	EWes
- 'Oyobeni'	EACa
§ - 'Superba' ♀H5	EACa NHpl WAbe
'Chloe' **new**	EBee EWTr
choruhensis	CPla EWes GEdr LLHF SPlb
ciliata **new**	GEdr
§ ***cochlearifolia*** ♀H5	CRos CSpe EBee EDAr EPfP GJos GMaP LRHS MAsh MMuc NHpl NRHS NWad SBch SEND SPoG WHoo XLum
- var. ***alba***	CSpe CTri EDAr ITim MHer MMuc NHpl NRya SBch SEND SRms WHoo XLum
- - 'White Baby' (Baby Series)	CRos EACa EPfP EPot ESps ITim LRHS NRHS NWad SPoG SRms XLum
- 'Bavaria Blue'	GJos XLum
- 'Bells Blue'	MHol
- 'Blue Baby' (Baby Series)	ECtt EPfP ESps GJos LRHS MHer NHpl SPoG SRms SRot
- 'Blue Wonder'	ECtt GCrg ITim
- 'Elizabeth Oliver' (d) ♀H5	CRos CTri EACa ECtt EDAr EPot GCrg GEdr GMaP LRHS MHer MHol NHpl NRHS SPlb SRms WAbe WFar WHoo
- 'Flore Pleno' (d)	WFar
- var. ***pallida*** 'Silver Chimes'	ITim
- 'R.B. Loder' (d)	CRos LRHS MHer NRHS WAbe
- 'Tubby'	CRos EACa EPot ITim LLHF LRHS MHer NRHS SRms
- 'Warleyensis'	see *C.* × *haylodgensis* W. Brockbank 'Warley White'
collina	EACa LLHF WCFE XLum
'Constellation'	EACa
'Covadonga'	CMea CPBP CRos EACa LRHS NRHS SBch WAbe WThu
cretica	MHol
'Crystal'	CFis ECtt MAvo MCot MNrw WCot WFar
cymbalaria	GKev
dasyantha	see *C. chamissonis*
divaricata	LPla
dolomitica	EACa LLHF
'E.K. Toogood'	CElw CPBP EACa ECtt MWat SRms XLum
'Faichem Lilac'	WCot
fenestrellata	EACa XLum
§ - subsp. ***istriaca***	GKev
finitima	see *C. betulifolia*
foliosa	EACa
fragilis	IFoB
garganica ♀H5	CRos EACa EPfP ESps GMaP GWyn LRHS MAsh MMuc MRav NRHS SRms SVic SWvt WFar WMoo XLum
- 'Aurea'	see *C. garganica* 'Dickson's Gold'
- 'Blue Diamond'	EACa ELon NLar
§ - subsp. ***cephallenica***	EACa NBro
§ - 'Dickson's Gold'	CElw CMac CMea CPBP CRos CTri EACa ECtt EHoe ELan ELon EPfP EPot ESps GMaP IBoy LRHS LSou MHer MRav NLar NRHS NSla SPlb SPoG SRms SWvt WAbe WHoo XLum
- 'Erinus Major'	EACa XLum
- 'Filigree' **new**	WBrk WCot
- subsp. ***istriaca***	see *C. fenestrellata* subsp. *istriaca*
- 'Major'	SPoG
- 'Mrs Resholt'	CTri ECtt EPau IRob LRHS NLar NRHS SRms SWvt
- 'Senior'	EWTr
- 'W.H. Paine' ♀H5	EACa ECtt IFoB NLar NSla WAbe WFar WHoo
'Glandore'	EACa SAko XLum
glomerata	CExl CWld EBWF ESps GAbr GJos GNew IBoy LSRN MHer NBro NEgg NGBl NMir WFar
- var. ***acaulis*** hort.	EACa EPfP GMcL ITim NEgg NLar SRms WFar XLum
- var. ***alba***	CBcs CRos CSpe EACa ECtt ELan EPfP GBin GJos GMaP IBoy LRHS MBel NEgg NRHS SCob SPer SPlb SPoG WCAu WGwG
§ - - 'Schneekrone'	ECha LCro LOPS WFar
- BELLEFLEUR BLUE (Bellefleur Series)	GMcL
- 'Caroline' ♀H7	Widely available
- CROWN OF SNOW	see *C. glomerata* var. *alba* 'Schneekrone'
- var. ***dahurica***	CRos EAJP EBee ELon LRHS NEgg NLar NRHS SHar XLum
- 'Emerald'	CBod CRos EACa EBee ECtt EPfP LRHS MHer MSCN NLar NRHS SPad SRms WFar XSen
- 'Freya'^{PBR} ♀H7	EACa EBee ECtt EPfP LPla LSun MHol MNrw SCob SPad WCot WFar WHil
- 'Genti Blue'	WFar
- 'Genti Twisterbell'	LSun NEoE WHil
- 'Genti White'	CWGN NLar WFar
- 'Joan Elliott'	CSam EBee ECha ECtt LEdu LSRN MWat XSen
- 'Purple Pixie'	LRHS SRms
- 'Superba' ♀H7	Widely available
grossekii	CRos EBee LLHF LRHS NRHS
'Hannah'	CRos EACa LRHS NRHS
× ***haylodgensis*** misapplied	see *C.* × *haylodgensis* 'Plena'
§ × ***haylodgensis*** W. Brockbank 'Marion Fisher' (d)	EPot WAbe WHoo
§ - 'Plena' (d)	CRos EACa ECtt EPfP EPot LRHS NRHS SRms WAbe WKif
§ - 'Warley White' (d)	EPot XLum
- 'Yvonne'	CBod ECtt EPot GCrg NHpl WHil
'Hemswell Starlight'	WAbe
hercegovina 'Nana'	CPBP ITim WAbe
'Hilltop Snow'	WAbe
hofmannii	CTsd GJos GKev NWad
hypopolia	CPBP WAbe
§ ***incurva***	EACa EWld GKev WAbe
IRIDESCENT BELLS ('Iribella'^{PBR})	CWGN EACa EBee EWes LCro LOPS LRHS LSou MBel NCou NPnk NSti SPad SPer WCAu WHil WPnP
isophylla ♀H2	EPot
- 'Alba' ♀H2	EPot
jaubertiana	WAbe
JENNY ('Harjen'^{PBR})	CWGN SHar
'Joe Elliott'	WAbe

	kemulariae	EDAr LLHF WCot XLum
	- 'Alba'	ITim
	'Kent Belle' ♀H7	Widely available
	khasiana	EBee
	kirpicznikovii	GEdr
	komarovii	WCot
	lactiflora	CAby CElw CFGn CMac EACa EBee ECha EPfP ESps GAbr IFoB LRHS MCot MNrw NEgg NRHS SPer WCAu WFar WHar WMoo WSpi WWtn XLum
	- ***alba***	see *C. lactiflora* white-flowered
	- 'Alba' ♀H7	CAby EBee ECha EPfP EWTr GBin GMaP IBoy ILea IRob MAvo MBel MHol MMuc SCob WBrk WCot WSpi
	- 'Assendon Pearl' ♀H7	EACa LPla SPhx WCot
	- AVALANCHE ('Camblo')	EACa EBee ECtt LCro LOPS MBNS MBel MTis WCAu
	- 'Blue Cross'	EBee IRob
	- 'Border Blues'	EBee ECtt ELon EPfP EWTr MHol MNrw WFar
	- 'Dixter Presence'	IPot LPla SMHy
	- dwarf pink-flowered	EACa EAJP EBee EPfP
	- 'Favourite' ♀H7	CSpe ECtt NGdn
	- 'Lidie's Choice'	CSam
	- 'Loddon Anna' ♀H7	Widely available
	- 'Moorland Rose'	WMoo
	- 'Platinum'	EACa LPla SMHy
	- 'Pouffe'	CRos EACa EAJP EBee ECtt EPfP GMaP GWyn LRHS MHol MNrw MRav NBro NGdn NLar NRHS SGbt SPer SPoG SWvt
	- 'Prichard's Variety' ♀H7	Widely available
	- 'Superba' ♀H7	ECtt
	- 'Violet'	WSpi
	- 'White Pouffe'	CBod CRos EACa ECtt EPfP EWTr GMaP GMcL LRHS LSRN NChi NLar NRHS SGbt SPer SPoG WFar
§	- white-flowered	ECha ESps NEgg SPer
	latifolia	EACa EBWF ESps GJos MCot NBid NChi NMir SPer SRms WCAu WMoo WShi WSpi
	- var. ***alba***	CRos EBee EPfP ESps GJos GWyn LRHS MMuc MSCN NGdn NRHS SEND SPav SPer SRms WHal WSpi
*	- 'Amethyst'	WSpi
	- blue-flowered	SEND
	- 'Brantwood'	CDor CRos EPfP GAbr IRob LRHS MRav NLar NRHS WSpi
	- 'Gloaming'	CRos ECtt LRHS NRHS WSpi
	- var. ***macrantha***	CDor CMea CRos EBee ELan EPfP GMaP LRHS MBel NEgg NRHS NSti SWvt WMoo
	- - 'Alba'	CMea CRos ECtt GLog GMaP MHol MRav NLar WCAu WMoo
	latiloba	WCot WKif
§	- 'Alba'	GAbr GCal MCot NEgg NLar NWad WBrk
	- 'Hidcote Amethyst'	CAby CDor CWGN ECtt ELan ELon GCal LRHS MCot MHol MMuc NBid NGdn NLar NRHS SEND SPer WCAu WCot WSpi
	- 'Highcliffe Variety' ♀H7	CGar EACa ECtt ELan EPfP LRHS MPie MRav NLar NRHS SPer SPoG WCAu WCot WRHF WSpi WWtn
	- 'Percy Piper' ♀H7	CRos EACa EBee LRHS MRav NBro NLar NRHS WSpi
	- 'Splash'	MAvo
	'Linda'	LSRN

	'Lynchmere'	CMea EPot NWad WAbe
	makaschvilii	CHid CPla CSpe EACa EPfP GWyn ILea MHer MMuc WCot WOut WSHC
	- pink-flowered	EBee
	makaschvilii* × *trachelium	WCot
	'Margaret Brine'	CMea CPBP WAbe
	'Marion Fisher'	see *C.* × *haylodgensis* W. Brockbank 'Marion Fisher'
	medium	EPfP
§	- var. ***calycanthema*** hort.	WSpi
	- 'Cup and Saucer'	see *C. medium* var. *calycanthema* hort.
	'Mevr. V. Vollenhove'	CSpe EBee ECtt MAvo MHol NSti
	'Misty Dawn' ♀H7	MAvo WCot
	modesta	GJos
	moesiaca	GKev
	'Monic'	EPfP
*	***morettiana*** 'Alba' × ***raineri*** 'Alba'	CPBP
	muralis	see *C. portenschlagiana*
	myrtifolia	CPBP
	nitida	see *C. persicifolia* var. *planiflora*
	'Norman Grove'	EPot
	ochroleuca	CMea EBee GBin IMou WCFE WCot
I	- 'Nana'	GEdr
	odontosepala from Iran	EPPr NLar
	'Oliver's Choice'	WHrl
	olympica misapplied	see *C. rotundifolia* 'Olympica'
	orphanidea	IMou
	ossetica	ECtt WBor
	pallida subsp. ***tibetica***	see *C. cashmeriana*
	parviflora Lam.	see *C. sibirica*
	patula	EACa WCot WKif XLum
	'Paul Furse'	CMea ECtt NSti SHar WCot WHrl
	'Pearlescent Pink' **new**	LSou
	'Pearlescent White' **new**	LSou
	pendula	CPla GJos SRot
	persicifolia	Widely available
	- var. ***alba***	Widely available
§	- 'Alba Coronata' (d)	GAbr SRms WHar
	- 'Alba Plena'	see *C. persicifolia* 'Alba Coronata'
	- 'Azure Beauty'	EBee ECtt NLar WCot WSpi XSen
	- 'Beau Belle'	LSou NLar
§	- 'Bennett's Blue' (d)	EPfP MRav
	- blue and white-flowered	SRms
	- 'Blue Bell'	GWyn
	- 'Blue Bloomers' (d)	CDor CRos EACa ECtt EPri EWes LRHS MBel MRav MSCN NQui NRHS NWad SRms WCFE WCot WHal WRHF XLum
	- blue cup-in-cup (d)	WPtf
	- 'Blue-eyed Blonde'PBR (v)	NLar WHil
	- blue-flowered	GMcL IFoB SPlb
	- 'Boule de Neige' (d)	CDor WSpi
§	- 'Chettle Charm'PBR	CDor CGar CRos CTri CWCL ECtt EHrv ELan EPfP EShb GAbr LRHS LSou MAvo MBel MRav NLar NRHS SCob SPer SRms SWvt WCot WFar WWtn
	- 'Cornish Mist'	CExl CRos EACa EBee ECtt ELan EPfP GBin MBel MHol MPie WCAu WCot WRHF WSpi
	- 'Fleur de Neige' (d)	MRav
	- 'Frances' (d)	WCot
	- 'Gawen'	CMac EACa ECtt GMaP LRHS NBre NRHS SGbt WCAu WCot
	- 'George Chiswell'	see *C. persicifolia* 'Chettle Charm'
	- 'Grandiflora'	CDor EAJP GBin IBoy

	– 'Grandiflora Alba'	EAJP GBin NLar NWad WArt
	– 'Hampstead White' (d)	GCal NLar WHil WSpi
	– 'Kelly's Gold'	MHol MJak SRms
	– 'La Belle' (d)	EBee MNrw NLar
	– 'La Bello'PBR	EBee MNrw
	– 'La Bonne Amie' (d)	EBee EPfP IBoy MCot MNrw NLar SPoG XEll
	– 'Moerheimii' (d)	EPfP WSpi
	– 'Perry's Boy Blue'	NPer
§	– var. ***planiflora***	CPBP
	– – f. ***alba***	CPBP NHpl WAbe WCot
	– 'Powder Puff' (d)	EPfP GMcL GWyn MHol NEgg WArt XEll
	– 'Pride of Exmouth' (d) ♀H7	CDor IBoy MHer MRav WSpi
	– subsp. ***sessiliflora*** 'Alba'	see *C. latiloba* 'Alba'
	– 'Snowdrift'	SRms
	– (Takion Series) 'Takion Blue'	CRos ELan GWyn LRHS NRHS SPoG
	– – 'Takion White'	ELan EPfP GWyn SPoG
	– 'Telham Beauty' ambig.	CBod MCot NEgg NGBl SCob SPhm SWvt WSpi XLum
	– 'Telham Beauty' misapplied	CRos CSBt EBee ELan EPfP LRHS MRav NRHS SPer SRms SWvt WArt
	– 'Telham Beauty' D.Thurston	NLar
	– 'Tinpenny Blue'	WCot
	– 'Wortham Belle' misapplied	see *C. persicifolia* 'Bennett's Blue'
	– 'Wortham Belle' ambig.	MRav WCAu
	– 'Wortham Belle' Blooms	CRos ECtt GBin LRHS MBNS NEgg WGwG
	'Peter Nix'	EACa
	petrophila	WAbe
	pilosa	see *C. chamissonis*
	– 'Superba'	see *C. chamissonis* 'Superba'
	'Pink Octopus'PBR	CAby CRos CWGN ECtt EHrv ELon EPfP EUJe IBoy IRob LRHS MBNS MHol MSCN MTis NGdn NLar NPnk NRHS SCob SEle SPad SPoG SRkn SRms WSpi XLum
	planiflora	see *C. persicifolia* var. *planiflora*
§	***portenschlagiana*** ♀H5	Widely available
	– 'Biokovo'	XLum
	– 'Blue Ocean'	GCrg
	– 'Catharina'	CRos EACa ECtt EPPr EShb LRHS MHol NRHS SPoG SRms
	– 'Lieselotte'	CElw CPBP EACa ECtt SAko
	– 'Major'	CBod EACa NCou WGwG WMoo
	– 'Resholdt's Variety'	CBar CMea CRos CSam EACa ECtt EDAr ELan EPfP GMaP LRHS MCot MHol MRav NRHS SAko SRms WCot WMoo XLum XSen
	poscharskyana	Widely available
	– 'Blauranke'	EACa EWes SAko XLum
	– 'Blue Gown'	EACa ECtt GCrg SAko XLum
	– 'Blue Rivulet'PBR	ECtt
	– 'Blue Waterfall'	CWCL CWGN EACa ECtt LSun MBNS NDov SPoG WBrk WCot XLum
	– 'E.H. Frost'	CElw EACa ECtt EDAr ELan EPPr EPfP EWTr GKev GMaP IBoy MCot MMuc NLar NRya SAko SEND SPer SRGP SRms SWvt WAbe WBrk WMoo WSpi XLum
	– 'Erich G.Arends'	SAko
I	– 'Freya'	EACa SAko XLum
	– 'Frühlingszauber'	WCot
	– 'Hirsch Blue'	EPfP SRms
	– 'Lilacina'	EACa EPPr
	– 'Lisduggan Variety'	CBre CElw EACa EBee ECtt EDAr EPPr EWes GMaP IBoy MHer NBro NLar SAko SRms WBrk WFar WMoo XLum
	– 'Nana Alba'	EACa EPPr SAko WBrk
	– 'Pinkins'PBR	CSma EACa ECtt
	– 'Schneeranke'	XSen
	– 'Silberregen'	SAko
	– 'Stella' ♀H5	CRos ECha ECtt ELan EPPr EPfP EWTr IBoy IPot IRob LRHS LSRN MAvo MRav NBro NDov NRHS SAko SPer SWvt WBrk WCot WHoo WMoo XLum
	– 'Trollkind'	EACa EPPr SAko XLum
	– variegated (v)	EBee EHoe EPPr
	– white-flowered	CTri ELan WFar
	× ***pseudoraineri*** hort.	CRos EACa EWes LRHS NRHS
	pulla	CRos EACa ECtt EDAr ELan EPot GCrg GEdr LRHS NHpl NRHS NSla SCob SPoG SRms SRot WAbe
	– 'Alba'	CRos EACa EPot LRHS NRHS NSla WAbe
	× ***pulloides*** hort. 'G.F.Wilson' ♀H5	EACa ECtt EPot GMaP NLar SBee SRkn
	– 'Jelly Bells'PBR	IPot NLar
	punctata	ESps MCot NBro NSti WCAu WFar WGwG WMoo
	– f. ***albiflora***	WFar
	– – 'Nana Alba'	GEdr
	– 'Alina's Double' (d)	MSCN MSpe NLar
	– 'Cherry Pie'	EPfP
	– dwarf	CPBP
	– var. ***hondoensis***	GKev
	– hose-in-hose (d)	MMrt WGwG
	– 'Hot Lips'	CMac EPfP MHol
*	– var. ***howozana***	GKev
	– 'Kurokawa'	WFar
	– var. ***microdonta*** B&SWJ 5553	WCru
*	– 'Nana'	GEdr WFar
	– 'Pantaloons' (d)	CMac CWGN EACa EWes NLar NPnk SRms WCot
	– 'Pink Chimes'	CDor MBNS MHol NLar SEle
	– 'Plum Wine'	NWad
	– purple-flowered	ELan LRHS
	– f. ***rubriflora***	CBod CDor CRos CSpe ECtt EHrv ELan EPfP IRob LRHS MCot MHol MNHC MNrw NEgg NRHS SCob SPer SPhm SRms WCAu WGwG WHar
	– – 'Beetroot'	GKev GWyn MHer NLar
	– – 'Bowl of Cherries'	CRos ECtt EPfP LRHS MMrt NPnk SRms SRot
	– – 'Cherry Bells'	CDor ECtt LSRN
	– – 'Vienna Festival'	CSBt
	– – 'Wine 'n' Rubies'	EACa EBee ECtt MHol
I	– 'Silver Bells'	EACa EBee ECtt EPfP IPot MSpe NSti SPad SRms WCAu WFar WHil
	– 'Wedding Bells'	CWCL EACa EAJP EBee EHrv EPri LRHS LSRN MBel MHol MSpe MTis NEgg NLar NPnk NRHS SCob SRkn SRms WHil
	– white hose-in-hose (d)	MNrw XLum
	'Purple Sensation'PBR	CSpe CWGN EBee EPfP LSou MBel MHol MNrw MSCN NLar NPnk WCot
	pusilla	see *C. cochlearifolia*
	pyramidalis	CSpe EACa EBee ELan EPfP ESps GJos GMcL MMuc NGBl SEND SPav SPlb WHar XLum

	– 'Alba'	CSpe EACa ELan EPfP GJos NGBl SPav SPlb XLum
	– lavender blue-flowered	GMcL
	raddeana	EACa GKev SBrt WBrk
	raineri	CPBP EPot NRHS NSla WAbe
	– 'Nettleton Gold'	CRos EACa LRHS NRHS
§	***rapunculoides***	GKev WCFE XLum
§	– 'Afterglow'	MAvo WFar
	– 'Alba'	MAvo WFar XLum
	rapunculus	MNHC WOut XLum
	recurva	see *C. incurva*
	rhomboidalis Gorter	see *C. rapunculoides*
	rhomboidalis L.	WCot XLum
	rigidipila	WHer
	(Ringsabell Series)	LRHS WTor
	'Ringsabell Indigo Blue'	
	– 'Ringsabell Mulberry Rose' **new**	WTor
	rotundifolia	CMac CWld EACa EBWF ELan EPfP GAbr GEdr GJos GLog LCro LOPS MCot MHer MNHC SPhx SPlb SRms WBrk
	– var. ***albiflora***	CElw EWes WAbe
	– 'Jotunheimen'	EACa WAbe
§	– 'Olympica'	EACa EBee ECtt WHoo
	– 'Thumbell Blue'	WHar
	– 'White Gem'	CMea EACa EBee EPfP GJos LRHS NBre NRHS WHoo
	'Royal Wave'	EBee ECtt EPot GEdr IPot MBel MHol NLar SCob
	rupestris	LLHF
	rupicola	WAbe
	'Samantha'	EACa ECtt ELon GBin IBoy LRHS LSRN MCot NHpl SHar WTor XEll
	'Sarastro'	Widely available
	sarmatica	EACa EBee EPfP NBid SBch SRms WFar
	– 'Hemelstraling'	IPot MAvo MCot NLar
	'Senior'	ECtt EPPr MHol SAko WBrk WCot WRHF
§	***sibirica***	GJos
	– 'Royal Wedding'	IPot
	speciosa	EBee
	'Spring Bell White' **new**	MHol
	'Stansfieldii'	CRos EACa EPot LLHF LRHS NRHS
	stevenii	see *C. stevenii* subsp. *beauverdiana*
§	– subsp. ***beauverdiana***	SBrt
	suanetica	GMaP
	subramulosa	see *C. cochlearifolia*
	'Summer Pearl'	CBod ECtt
	'Summertime Blues'^{PBR}	ECtt ELan IBoy LSou
§	'Swannables'	CPou CRos EACa LRHS MAvo MRav NRHS WFar WOut
	takesimana	CBod CBro CRos CSpe ECtt ELan EPfP ESps GKev GKin LEdu LRHS NEgg NRHS NSti SPer SRms SWvt WMoo XLum
I	– 'Alba'	GNew IBoy WFar WMoo
	– 'Beautiful Trust'	EBee NPnk WCot
	– 'Elizabeth'	Widely available
	– 'Elizabeth II' (d)	EPPr WCot
	– 'Feenrock JP'	XLum
	– purple-flowered	WWtn
	thyrsoides	CSpe EACa EBee GJos SPav
	'Timsbury Chimes'	CPBP WAbe
	'Timsbury Perfection'	GCrg WAbe
	tommasiniana ♀^{H5}	LLHF SBrt WAbe
	topaliana subsp. ***delphica*** SDR 8254	GKev
	trachelium	CRos EACa EBWF EBee ELon GJos GKev LRHS MHer MNHC MRav NMir NRHS WCot WFar WHer WMoo WOut WShi WSpi XLum
	– f. ***alba***	CRos EBee GJos IFro IMou LRHS NLar NRHS SGbt WCot WFar WMoo
	– – 'Alba Flore Pleno' (d)	LEdu SMHy
	– 'Bernice' (d)	CDor CSpe EACa ECtt ELan EPfP GMaP LRHS MBel MHol MNrw MSCN NLar NSti SCob SPer WBor WCAu WCot WFar WHil WSpi XSen
	– 'Purple Break'	EBee MHol MPie WCot
	– 'Snowball'	CMac LSRN
	tridentata	GEdr
	troegerae	EACa
	'Van-Houttei'	CDor EBee EWes NLar SMHy WCot
	versicolor	CPBP SRms
	vidalii	see *Azorina vidalii*
	'Viking'^{PBR}	ECtt LRHS
	waldsteiniana	LLHF WAbe
	wanneri	GJos
	'Warley White'	see *C.* × *haylodgensis* W. Brockbank 'Warley White'
	'Warleyensis'	see *C.* × *haylodgensis* W. Brockbank 'Warley White'
	'White Octopus'	ECtt GPSL SCob SEle WNPC
	× ***wockei*** 'Puck'	CHid CPBP CRos EACa ECtt EPot GCrg LLHF LRHS NRHS WAbe WOld
	zangezura	EACa EDAr GJos GKev SGbt XLum
	zoysii	WAbe

Campanula × *Symphyandra* see *Campanula*

Campanumoea see *Codonopsis*

Campsis (*Bignoniaceae*)

	grandiflora	CBcs CFlo CKel CRos CWGN ELan EPfP ESps LRHS LSRN SPer SWvt WCFE
	radicans	CBcs CMac CRHN CRos CWCL ECrN ELan EPfP ESps LRHS MGil MJak MSwo NEgg NRHS SLon SNig SPer SPlb
	– 'Atrosanguinea'	SVen
	– 'Flamenco'	CBcs CMac CWCL EBee ELan EPfP LRHS LSRN MGil SAdn SCoo SLim SPoG SVen SWvt
§	– f. ***flava*** ♀^{H4}	CBcs CFlo CMac CRos CTri CWCL EBee ELan EPfP ESps LRHS MBlu MGil MGos MJak NPla NRHS SLim SPer SPoG SVen SWvt
	– 'Stromboli'	CAco EPfP
	– 'Yellow Trumpet'	see *C. radicans* f. *flava*
	× ***tagliabuana***	ESps
	– DANCING FLAME ('Huidan'^{PBR})	CRos CWCL CWGN LRHS
	– INDIAN SUMMER ('Kudian'^{PBR})	CBcs CFlo CKel CRos CWCL CWGN ELon EMOT EPfP ETMg LRHS LSRN LSou MGil MGos SCoo
	– 'Madame Galen' ♀^{H4}	Widely available
	– 'Takarazuka Yellow' (Summer Jazz Series)	CRos LRHS NRHS
	– 'Takarazuka Zujin' (Summer Jazz Series)	LRHS NRHS

Camptosorus see *Asplenium*

Camptotheca (*Nyssaceae*)

	acuminata	WPGP

Campylandra see *Tupistra*

Campylotropis (*Papilionaceae*)

	macrocarpa	SBrt WSHC

Canarina (*Campanulaceae*)

	canariensis ♀H2	CCCN CFil CMCN CPne CTsd SBrt SVen
	- from Anaga Mountains, Tenerife	WCot
	- from Los Silos, Tenerife	WCot
	eminii	CFil

Candollea see *Hibbertia*

Canna ✿ (*Cannaceae*)

	'Adam's Orange'	CDTJ XBlo
	'Alaska' ♀H3	SAdu
	'Alberich'	SHaC
	'Alfred Cole' **new**	SAdu
	altensteinii	CDTJ SAdu SHaC SPlb XBlo
	'Ambassador'	LAma SDeJ
	'Ambassadour'	LLWG SAdu SHaC
	'Angel Pink'	SAdu
	'Annaeei' ♀H3	SAdu SHaC
	'Annei-Rubra'	SAdu
	'Anthony and Cleopatra' (v)	WCot
	'Argentina'	SAdu SHaC
	'Asia' **new**	SAdu
	'Assaut'	SAdu SHaC
	'Atlantis'	XBlo
	'Australia'	CDTJ EUJe SAdu SHaC XBlo
	'Austria'	SAdu
	'Baron Seguier'	XLum
	'Bethany' ♀H3	SAdu
	'Bird of Paradise' **new**	SHaC
	'Black Knight'	LAma LSvl SAdu SDeJ SHaC XBlo XTur
	'Black Prince' **new**	SAdu
	'Bonfire'	CDTJ SDir
	'Bonnezeaux'	XTur
	brasiliensis	CTsd SAdu SHaC XBlo
	'Brillant'	LAma SAdu SDeJ XTur
	'Britannia'	SAdu
	'Burbank'	CDTJ SAdu
	'Caballero'	SHaC XLum
	'Calimèro'	SHaC
	'Camille Bernardin' **new**	SAdu
	'Canary'	XBlo
	Cannova Series **new**	SHaC
	- 'Cannova Lemon' **new**	SHaC
	- 'Cannova Mango' **new**	SHaC
	- 'Cannova Orange Shades' **new**	SHaC
	- 'Cannova Red Shades' **new**	SHaC
	- 'Cannova Rose' **new**	SHaC
	- 'Cannova Scarlet' **new**	SHaC
	- 'Cannova Yellow' **new**	SHaC
	'Carnaval'	EUJe SHaC XTur
	'Centenaire de Rozain-Boucharlat'	SAdu SDeJ SHaC XLum XTur
	'Champion'	SAdu XTur
	'Chocolate Sunrise'	LCro LOPS SAdu
	'Chouchou'	LLWG SAdu SHaC
I	'Citrina'	XBlo
§	'City of Portland'	LAma SAdu SDeJ XTur
§	'Cleopatra'	CCCN EUJe LAma SAdu SDeJ SHaC XBlo
*	'Cléopâtre'	SAdu
	coccinea	SArc
	compacta	SHaC
	'Corail'	XTur
	'Corrida'	XLum
	'Corsica' (Island Series)	SAdu
	'Creamy White'	XBlo
	'Délibáb'	SDir
	'Di Bartolo'	XBlo
	'Doyen Jean Liabaud' **new**	SAdu
	'Durban' Hiley, orange-flowered	see *C.* 'Phasion'
	'Durban' ambig.	CChe CWGN EPfP ETod LAma SHaC
	'E. Neubert'	ELan EUJe SAdu SHaC
	edulis	CDTJ SAdu
	- purple-leaved	SAdu
§	× ***ehemanii*** ♀H3	CDTJ SAdu SBrt SHaC
	'Emblème'	SHaC
	'En Avant'	SHaC SPlb XTur
	'Endeavour'	EUJe MSKA SAdu SHaC
	'Erebus' ♀H3	EUJe MSKA SAdu SHaC
	'Ermine'	EUJe SHaC
	'Étoile du Feu'	XBlo
	'Extase'	SHaC
	'Fatamorgana'	SHaC
	'Feuerzauber'	SHaC XTur
	'Fiesta'	SHaC
	FIREBIRD	see *C.* 'Oiseau de Feu'
	flaccida	SAdu SHaC
	'Flame'	XBlo
§	'Florence Vaughan'	SAdu
	'General Eisenhower' ♀H3	EUJe SAdu SHaC
	generalis × ***indica***	SHaC
	glauca	SAdu SHaC
	'Gnom'	SAdu SDeJ SHaC
	'Golden Girl'	SAdu
	'Golden Lucifer'	LAma SDeJ
	'Golden Orb'	SAdu SHaC
	'Gran Canaria'	SAdu
	'Grande'	SAdu SHaC SPlb XLum
	'Grandiose'	SHaC
	'Heinrich Seidel'	SAdu
	Henlade hybrids	CDTJ
	'Henlade Pink'	SAdu
	'Henlade Red'	SAdu
	'Henri Cohn'	SAdu
	'Herman' **new**	SHaC
	'Horn'	XTur
	'Hossegor'	XLum
	'Hungaria'	SAdu
	'Ibis'	XTur
	'Ibiza' (Island Series)	SAdu
	'Indiana'	SAdu SHaC
	indica	CAbb CBlu CDTJ CPla SAdu SArc SHaC SMHy SPlb
	- 'Kreta' (Island Series)	SAdu
	- 'Purpurea'	CDTJ SAdu SHaC SPlb
	- 'Red King Rupert'	CCCN
	- 'Russian Red' ♀H3	SAdu SHaC
	- TROPICANNA GOLD ('Mactro'PBR)	CCCN EPfP LCro LOPS SAdu SPhm
	'Intrigue'	EUJe SAdu SHaC
	iridiflora misapplied	see *C.* × *ehemanii*
	iridiflora Ruiz & Pav.	CDTJ CSpe SArc
	'Italia'	CDTJ SAdu
	'J.D. Cabos' **new**	SAdu
	jacobiniflora	SAdu SHaC

	jaegeriana	SHaC
	'Jivago'	SHaC
	'John Lochner' **new**	SAdu
	'Kalimpong'	CDTJ
I	'King Humbert' (blood-red)	CBcs CBod CDTJ SDeJ XBlo
	KING HUMBERT (orange-red)	see *C.* 'Roi Humbert'
	'King Midas'	see *C.* 'Richard Wallace'
	'Klondyke' **new**	SAdu
	'Königin Charlotte'	SAdu SDeJ SHaC
	'La Belle Dame sans Merci' **new**	SAdu
	'La France'	SAdu
	'La Gloire'	XTur
	latifolia	SHaC
	'Leilani' **new**	SAdu
	'Lesotho Lil'	SAdu SHaC
	'Libération'	XLum
	'Liberté'	see *C.* 'Wyoming'
	'Lion Rouge'	XLum
	'Llanthony'	SAdu
	'Lohengrin' **new**	SAdu
	'Lolita'	SHaC
	'Louis Cayeux' ♀H3	LAma SHaC
	'Louis Cottin'	CBcs CCCN CDTJ LAma SAdu SDir XTur
	'Louisiana' **new**	SAdu
	'Love Child'	SAdu
	'Lucifer'	CCCN LAma NPer SDeJ XLum
	lutea	SHaC XBlo
	'Madame Angèle Martin'	SAdu XBlo XTur
	'Madame Crozy'	SAdu
	'Madame Paul Casaneuve'	SHaC
	'Madeira' (Island Series)	EUJe SAdu SHaC
	'Malawiensis Variegata'	see *C.* 'Striata'
	'Marabout'	SAdu XTur
	'Marjorie Cole' **new**	SAdu
	'Marlena' **new**	SHaC
	'Marshmallow' **new**	SHaC
	'Mirizia' **new**	SHaC
	'Montaigne'	SHaC
	'Moonshine'	CCCN LCro LOPS
	'Morwent' **new**	SAdu
	'Mrs Kate Gray'	SAdu
	'Mrs Oklahoma'	SDeJ
	'Musifolia' ♀H3	CDTJ ETod EUJe EWes SAdu SHaC XBlo
I	'Musifolia Rubra'	SAdu
	'Mystique' ♀H3	SAdu SHaC
	'Ointment Pink'	XBlo
§	'Oiseau de Feu'	SAdu XLum
	'Oiseau d'Or'	XLum XTur
	'Orange Chocolate'	SHaC
	'Orange Punch'	SAdu SHaC XTur
	'Orchid'	see *C.* 'City of Portland'
	'Panache'	CDTJ SAdu SHaC
	'Panama'	SHaC
	paniculata	SHaC
	'Parkridge Peach' **new**	SAdu
	'Parthenope' **new**	SAdu
	'Peach Pink'	XBlo
	'Pearlescent Pink'	XBlo
	'Pennsylvania' **new**	SAdu
	'Perkeo'	LLWG SAdu SHaC
§	'Phasion' (v) ♀H3	CCCN CHll CSpe ELan EPfP EUJe EWes LAma LCro LOPS NPer NPla SAdu SHaC SPhm WCot XBlo
	'Phoebe' **new**	SAdu
	'Picadore'	XTur
	'Picasso' ♀H3	CBcs CCCN CDTJ CExl LAma SAdu SDir SHaC XBlo
	'Pink Champagne'	XBlo
	'Pink Futurity' (Futurity Series)	CCCN
	'Pink Perfection'	SHaC
	'Pink Sunburst' (v)	SAdu
	'Plaster Pink'	XBlo
	'President'	LAma SAdu SDeJ SHaC XBlo XLum
	'Pretoria'	see *C.* 'Striata'
	'Pretoria Variegata'	see *C.* 'Striata'
	'Prince Charmant'	SHaC XTur
	'Pringle Bay' (v)	SAdu
	'Professor Lorentz'	see *C.* 'Wyoming'
	'Professor Wendt' **new**	SAdu
	'Puck'	SHaC
	'Ra' ♀H3	EUJe MSKA SHaC
	'Red Cherry'	SDeJ XTur
	'Red Stripe'	SAdu
§	'Richard Wallace'	CExl SAdu SDeJ SHaC SPlb XBlo
	'Robert Kemp'	SHaC
§	'Roi Humbert'	SAdu SHaC
	'Roi Soleil'	SHaC XLum XTur
	'Roma'	SAdu SHaC
	'Rosemond Coles'	SAdu SDeJ SHaC XBlo
	'Saladin'	SHaC XLum
	'Salmon Punch' **new**	SAdu
	'Salsa'	SHaC
	'Sassy Sandy' **new**	SAdu
	SAVENNIÈRES ('Turcasav')	XTur
	'Sémaphore'	EUJe SAdu SHaC WCot XBlo
	'Shenandoah' ♀H3	LLWG SAdu SHaC
	'Singapore Girl'	SAdu SHaC
	'Snow-white'	XBlo
	'Society Belle' ♀H3	SHaC
	'Soudan'	CDTJ SAdu
	'South Pacific' **new**	SHaC
	'South Pacific Scarlet' **new**	SAdu
	speciosa	CDTJ SPlb XBlo
	'Stars and Stripes' **new**	SAdu
	'Statue of Liberty'	SAdu
	'Strasbourg'	NPer SAdu XLum
	'Strawberry Delight' **new**	SAdu
	'Strawberry Pink'	XBlo
	'Striata' misapplied	see *C.* 'Stuttgart'
§	'Striata' (v) ♀H3	CCCN CDTJ CSpe CWGN ETod EUJe NLos SAdu SEND SHaC WCot XBlo XTur
	'Striped Beauty' (v)	CCCN CDTJ EUJe LAma SAdu
§	'Stuttgart' (v)	CDTJ CSpe EWes SAdu SHaC XTur
	'Summer Gold'	XBlo
	'Sunset'	WCot
	'Südfunk'	SAdu
	'Tafraout'	XTur
	'Tali'	SAdu SHaC
	'Talisman'	XBlo
	'Taney'	EUJe MSKA SHaC
	'Taroudant'	SHaC XLum
	'Tenerife' (Island Series)	SAdu
	'Triomphe'	SHaC
	(Tropical Series) 'Tropical Bronze Scarlet'	SAdu SHaC
	- 'Tropical Orange'	XTur
	- 'Tropical Red'	SAdu SHaC XTur
	- 'Tropical Rose'	SAdu SHaC XTur
	- 'Tropical Salmon'	SAdu SHaC
	- 'Tropical White'	SAdu SHaC XTur
	- 'Tropical Yellow'	SAdu SHaC XTur
	TROPICANNA	see *C.* 'Phasion'
	TROPICANNA BLACK ('Lon01'PBR)	EPfP LCro LOPS SAdu
	tuerckheimii	SAdu SHaC

'Valentine'	SAdu WCot
'Vanilla Cream' new	SDeJ
'Vanilla Pink'	XBlo
'Verdi' ♀H3	LAma SAdu SHaC
warscewiczii	CDTJ CExl SAdu SHaC
'Weymouth'	CDTJ SAdu
'Whithelm Pride' ♀H3	SAdu SDeJ SHaC
'Wintzer's Colossal'	SAdu SHaC
'Woodbridge Pink'	XBlo
§ 'Wyoming' ♀H3	CBcs CCCN CDTJ EUJe LAma LCro LOPS SAdu SDeJ SDir SEND SHaC XBlo XTur
'Yara'	SAdu SDeJ SHaC
'Yellow Humbert' misapplied	see *C.*'Cleopatra', *C.*'Florence Vaughan', *C.*'Richard Wallace'
'Yellow Humbert'	SAdu SDeJ
'Zoodikers!'	SAdu

Cannomois (*Restionaceae*)

grandis	CPbh SPlb

Cantua (*Polemoniaceae*)

buxifolia ♀H2	CAbb CBcs CBod CCCN CExl CHid CHll CPne ECre EShb LRHS MGil
- 'Alba'	CBcs CCCN CHid WWFP
- 'Dancing Oaks'	SVen

Cape gooseberry see *Physalis peruviana*

Capeochloa (*Poaceae*)

§ ***cincta***	WCot

Capnoides see *Corydalis*

Capparis (*Capparaceae*)

spinosa	CCCN
- subsp. ***rupestris***	SPlb

Capsicum (*Solanaceae*)

See also AGM Vegetables Section.

annuum	CCCN SVic
- 'Ancho'	SVic
- var. ***annuum*** (Cerasiforme Group) 'Piccante Calabresé'	SVic
- - (Conioides Group) 'Bell Boy'	LCro NRHS
- - (Longum Group) cayenne	CCCN
- - - 'Fish'	SVic
- - - 'Golden Cayenne'	SVic
- - - jalapeño	NRHS SVic
- - - 'Joe's Long Cayenne'	SVic
- - - 'Ring of Fire'	SVic
- - - 'Serrano'	SVic
- - - 'Tokyo Hot'	SVic
- - 'Marconi Rosso'	SVic
- 'Bulgarian Carrot'	SVic
- 'Cayenne Red'	SPre SVic
- 'Cheyenne' new	CRos NRHS
- var. ***glabriusculum***	SVic
- 'Las Cruces Cayenne'	SVic
- 'Masquerade' new	CRos NRHS
- 'Medusa' new	CRos NRHS
- 'Nosferatu'	SVic
- 'Numex Big Jim'	SVic
- 'Numex Garnet'	SVic
- 'Numex Piñata'	SVic
- 'Numex Primavera'	SVic
- 'Numex Twilight'	CRos NRHS SPre SVic
- 'Padron' new	LCro
- 'Peter Pepper'	SVic
- 'Pinocchio's Nose'	SVic
- 'Vampire'	SVic
baccatum 'Aji Limon'	SVic
- 'Aji Omnicolor'	SVic
- 'Christmas Bell'	SVic
- 'Lemon Drop'	SPre
chinense Habanero Group ♀H1c	EHyd EKin LSds MCtn MShS NRHS NRob
- - 'Habanero Caribbean Red'	SVic
- - 'Naga Morrich'	SVic
- 'Numex Suave Orange'	SVic
- 'Numex Suave Red'	SVic
- 'Scotch Bonnet'	CRos NRHS SPre
frutescens Tabasco Group	SVic
'Rodeo'	SVic

Caputia (*Asteraceae*)

§ ***tomentosa*** ♀H1c	EShb

Caragana (*Papilionaceae*)

CC 3945	CExl
arborescens	CAgr CDul CMCN EBee ELan EPfP NLar SCob SPer SPlb
- PAB 13.376 new	LEdu
- 'Lorbergii'	CEnd MBlu NLar SPer
- 'Pendula'	CAco CMac ELan ESps GBin MAsh MBlu NEgg NLar SCoo SPer
- 'Walker'	CDul CEnd CMac ELan MAsh MBlu MGos NLar SCoo SPer
aurantiaca	NLar
pygmaea	NLar

carambola see *Averrhoa carambola*

caraway see *Carum carvi*

Cardamine (*Brassicaceae*)

asarifolia misapplied	see *Pachyphragma macrophyllum*
bipinnata	WCot
bulbifera	EBee ELon EPPr GBin GEdr LEdu MAvo NRya WCru
californica	EPPr LEdu MAvo NRya WCru WMoo
concatenata	WCru
digitata	EBee
diphylla	CAby EBee LEdu WCot WCru
- 'American Sweetheart'	CExl
- 'Eco Cut Leaf'	CAby CExl EBee MAvo WCru
- 'Eco Moonlight'	WCru
aff. ***diphylla***	CTal
enneaphylla	EWld GWyn NBid NLar
glanduligera	CElw EBee ECha ELon EPPr EPri GEdr LEdu MAvo MMoz MNrw SBrt WCot WCru WFar
§ ***heptaphylla***	CAby ECha ELon EWTr GBin GQue ILea LLHF WCru
- from the Pyrenees	GCal NLar
- 'Big White'	EBee GCal IRob NLar WPnP
- Guincho form	EPPr MAvo WCot
§ ***kitaibelii***	CAby CTal EPPr GCal LEdu MNrw NLar SBrt WCot WCru
latifolia Vahl	see *C. raphanifolia*
macrophylla	EBee GBin GEdr LEdu WCot WSHC
- 'Bright and Bronzy'	CExl IMou MAvo WCru
maxima	LEdu MAvo SHar WCru
microphylla	GKev

pentaphylla ♀H5	CBro CSpe ELan ELon EPPr GAbr GBin GKev GMaP IFro LEdu MCot NHpl SPhx WCot WCru WSHC
- bright pink-flowered	WCot
pratensis	CWat EBWF GJos LCro MCot MHer MNHC MSKA NMir NRHS SPhx WHer WMoo WSFF WShi
- 'Diane's Petticoat'	MAvo
- 'Edith' (d)	EBee MMoz
- 'Flore Pleno' (d)	CAby CBre CSpe ECha EPfP GCal GQue IFro LEdu MHer MNrw NBid NBro NLar NRHS WBor WSFF
- 'Flore Pleno' white-flowered (d)	LEdu
- 'William' (d)	LEdu
quinquefolia	CAby CElw CMea CRos ECha EHrv ELon ILea LEdu LRHS MAvo MBel MCot MMoz MNrw MPie NLar NRHS SDys WBrk WCot WCru WFar WPnP
- PAB 9992	LEdu
§ ***raphanifolia***	CBre CExl EBee GAbr GBin GCal IFro IMou LLWG MAvo NBid NBro NRya NSti WBor WMoo
- PAB 204	LEdu
trifolia	CAby CElw CMac CTal EBee ECha EHrv ELon EPPr EWld GBin GCal GEdr GMaP IFro ILea IMou LEdu MAvo MRav NBro NLar NRya WCot WCru WFar WMoo
waldsteinii	CElw CExl CTal EBee EHrv EPPr GCal GEdr ILea LEdu MAvo MMoz NLar SMHy WCru WFar WPGP WSHC
yezoensis	GBin
- B&SWJ 4659	EBee WCru

cardamon see *Elettaria cardamomum*

cardoon see *Cynara cardunculus*

Cardiandra (*Hydrangeaceae*)

alternifolia B&SWJ 5719	WCru
- B&SWJ 5845	WCru
- B&SWJ 6177	WCru
- B&SWJ 6354	WCru
- subsp. ***moellendorffii***	CExl CFil WPGP
- 'Pink Geisha'	WCru
amamiohshimensis	WCru
formosana	CExl IArd IDee WPGP
- B&SWJ 2005	WCru
- 'Crûg's Abundant'	WCru
- 'Hsitou'	WCru
- 'Hsitou Splendour'	WCru

Cardiocrinum ✿ (*Liliaceae*)

cordatum	GAbr WCot
- B&SWJ 2812	WCru
- B&SWJ 4841	WCru
- B&SWJ 5427	WCru
- B&SWJ 6336	WCru
- B&SWJ 11069	WCru
- var. ***glehnii***	CCCN GEdr LRHS
- - B&SWJ 10827	WCru
- - B&SWJ 10843	WCru
- red-veined	MNrw
giganteum	CAby CBcs CCCN CHid CRos EBee GAbr GBin GEdr GKev LAma LRHS MNrw NBid NHpl NLar NRHS SMad WAbe WCot WCru WPnP
- B&SWJ 2419	WCru
- GWJ 9219 from Sikkim	WCru
- HWJK 2158 from Nepal	WCru
- WJC 13661 from Sikkim **new**	WCru
- WJC 13698 from Sikkim **new**	WCru
- pure white-flowered	GKev
- var. ***yunnanense***	CSpe EPfP GEdr ITim NBid WCru WPGP
- - NJM 11.023 from Guizhou **new**	WPGP
- - PAB 8347	LEdu
aff. ***giganteum*** NJM 12.060 from Nagaland **new**	WPGP

Carduus (*Asteraceae*)

defloratus subsp. ***argemone***	SBrt
- subsp. ***defloratus***	SBrt

Carex (*Cyperaceae*)

from Kyoto, Japan **new**	EPPr
acuta	CHab MSKA
- 'Aureovariegata' (v) **new**	EUJe WMoo
- 'Variegata' (v)	CBen CMac CWat EHoe EShb GMaP IFro LLWG MMoz NBro WMoo WWtn
acutiformis	EBWF NMir
alba	CKno WCot
'Amazon Mist'	EUJe WFar
arenaria	CKno EBWF
atrata	EHoe WHrl
§ - subsp. ***pullata*** KEKE 494	EBee
aurea	GWyn IFoB
baccans	CExl GCal SBrt
berggrenii	CRos ELan NRHS SPlb
binervis	EBWF
brizoides	IMou
brunnea	CMac ESps
- 'Jenneke' (v)	CRos ESps LRHS NRHS SLim SWvt
- 'Jubilo'[PBR] **new**	EBee
- 'Variegata' (v)	EHoe WHoo
buchananii	Widely available
- 'Green Twist'	EBee EShb NWsh
- 'Red Rooster'	NWsh WHar
- 'Viridis'	ELan XLum
chathamica	LRHS SVen WCot
'China Blue'	MMoz
ciliatomarginata 'Treasure Island' (v)	EBee
colchica	XLum
comans	EPfP NBro
- 'Bronze Perfection'	ETMg
- bronze-leaved	CPla CRos CSBt EHoe EHrv ELan EMOT EPfP ESps EUJe GBin GCal GKev GMcL IFro LRHS MAsh MBNS NEgg NRHS NSti NWad NWsh SCob SLim SPer SRms SWvt WHar WMoo
- 'Bronzita'	WFar
- 'Dancing Flame'	CWCL ELon
- 'Frosted Curls'	Widely available
- 'Hot Chocolate' **new**	CBod
- 'Kupferflamme'	CBod
- red-leaved	NLar SRms WHar
- 'Small Red'	see *C. comans* 'Taranaki'
§ - 'Taranaki'	MBNS SCoo
conica 'Hime-kan-suge'	see *C. conica* 'Snowline'

§ - 'Snowline' (v)	CMac EHoe ELan EShb GKev GMaP LEdu MMoz NBro NLar NWsh SGol SWvt XLum
dallii	WHrl
davalliana	EBee
depauperata	EHoe
dioica	EBWF LLWG
dipsacea	CKno CMac CRos CWCL EHoe EShb GMaP LRHS MMoz NLar NRHS NWad NWsh WHal
- 'Dark Horse'	EHoe MMuc WPtf
divulsa	CKno
- subsp. ***divulsa***	EBWF
- subsp. ***leersii***	EPPr
§ ***dolichostachya*** 'Kaga-nishiki' (v)	CSBt ESps LEdu LRHS SLim
duthiei	see *C. atrata* subsp. *pullata*
echinata	EBWF
elata	EBWF
§ - 'Aurea' ♀H6	Widely available
- 'Bowles's Golden'	see *C. elata* 'Aurea'
- 'Knightshayes'	CKno WCot
elongata	CHab
'Evergold'	see *C. oshimensis* 'Evergold'
firma 'Variegata' (v)	EPot GEdr
flacca	CHab CKno EBWF EPPr GBin WBor XLum XSen
- 'Bias' (v)	MMoz
- 'Blue Zinger'	CBod CKno
§ - subsp. ***flacca***	EBee MMoz NSti
flagellifera	CBcs CBod CMac CRos CSpe CTri CWCL EBee EHoe ELan ELon EPfP EShb GCal GMaP LRHS MMuc NRHS NWsh SCob SEND SPlb SPoG WWtn
- 'Auburn Cascade'	CBod ELan SPtp
- 'Kiwi'	EShb NWsh
- red-leaved	SCob
flava	CKno EHoe
fortunei	see *C. morrowii* Boott
fraseri	see *Cymophyllus fraserianus*
fraserianus	see *Cymophyllus fraserianus*
glauca Scop.	see *C. flacca* subsp. *flacca*
'Gold Fountains'	see *C. dolichostachya* 'Kaga-nishiki'
grayi	CAby CRos CWCL EHoe GBin LEdu LLWG LRHS MBlu MSKA NLar NRHS SPlb SPtp WBor WPGP
hirta	EBWF
hostiana	EBWF
'Ice Dance' (v)	CBod CKno CRos CWCL EBee ECrN ESps GBin GKev GMaP GMcL GQue GWyn LRHS LSun MMoz MMuc MSCN NRHS NWad NWsh SCob SEND SGol SPad SPtp SWvt WCot WMoo
kaloides	EHoe XLum
'Kan-suge'	see *C. morrowii* Boott
laxiculmis 'Bunny Blue'PBR	LRHS NLar
* ***leformeri***	XLum
§ ***leporina***	EBWF
limosa	EBWF LLWG
lupulina	GBin
lurida	EPfP XLum
melanocephala	EBee
mertensii NNS 07-98	ELon
MILK CHOCOLATE ('Milchoc'PBR) (v)	CBod ECtt EPfP ESps SCob
morrowii misapplied	see *C. oshimensis*
§ ***morrowii*** Boott	CRos ESps LRHS NRHS
I - 'Fisher's Form' (v)	CBot CTri ELan EPPr ESps MMoz MRav SCob SWvt WAvo WGrn
- 'Gilt' (v)	EHoe EPPr MBNS NWad
- 'Gold Band'	GMcL
- 'Nana Variegata' (v)	CTri
- 'Pinkie'	CPla WPtf
- var. ***temnolepis***	IMou
- 'Variegata' (v)	CBod EHoe ELan EPPr GCal GMaP MJak MMoz MMuc NSti SRms WAvo XLum
muricata	XSen
muskingumensis	CExl CKno CWCL EHoe ELan EPPr EPfP EShb ESps GBin GCal LEdu LLWG NBro NLar SLim SMad WMoo WPnP
- 'Little Midge'	CKno CMac EPPr EShb GBin GCal LEdu NLar
- 'Oehme' (v)	CKno CRos CWCL EBee EPPr EShb LEdu LLWG LRHS NBid NRHS NWad WPtf
- 'Silberstreif' (v)	CKno EBee EPPr EShb GBin LEdu MMuc XLum
nigra (L.) Reichard	EBWF EPPr WAvo XLum
§ - 'On-line' (v)	EPPr
- 'Variegata'	see *C. nigra* 'On-line'
No 1, Nanking (Greg's broad leaf)	MMoz
No 4, Nanking (Greg's thin leaf)	EPPr MMoz
obnupta	CKno
ornithopoda 'Aurea'	see *C. ornithopoda* 'Variegata'
§ - 'Variegata' (v)	EBee GBin NRHS NWsh WMoo
§ ***oshimensis***	EPPr MMoz WCot
- 'Everdi'PBR	LRHS
- EVEREST ('Fiwhite'PBR) (v)	CBod CKno CSBt EBee EShb ESps GBin GMcL GWyn LLWG LRHS LSun MAsh MBel MMuc NEoE NWad NWsh SArc SCob SEND SPoG WCot WFar WSHC
§ - 'Evergold' (v) ♀H7	Widely available
- 'Evergreen'	LRHS
- 'Everillo'PBR	CBcs CBod CKno EHoe EUJe GBin IRob LRHS MAsh NLar NWad NWsh SPoG WCot
- 'Everlime'PBR	CBct LLWG LRHS
- 'Everoro' (v)	CKno LRHS WCot
- 'Eversheen'	LRHS
- 'J.S. Greenwell'	EBee
otrubae	CHab EBWF XLum
ovalis	see *C. leporina*
pallescens	EBWF
panicea	CKno CWCL EBee EHoe EPPr EShb LLWG MMoz MSKA WMoo
paniculata	EBWF XLum
pendula	CBcs CBen CHab CKno CTri CWat EBWF ECha EHoe ELan EPfP GAbr GMaP GMcL IBoy MJak MMuc MRav NBid NBro NEgg NLar NMir SCob SEND SLim SMad WMoo XLum XSen
- 'Cool Jazz' (v)	EPPr MSKA
- 'Moonraker' (v)	EHoe EPPr MSKA NWad WCot
petriei	EBee ECha ELon XLum
phyllocephala	EShb
- 'Sparkler' (v)	EHoe EPfP GMcL LRHS SPad SPoG SWvt XLum
plantaginea	EBee EHoe EPPr EShb GBin LEdu WPGP
praegracilis	CKno EPPr
Pritchard's selection (v)	IFro

pseudocyperus	CBen EBWF EHoe GBin MMoz MSKA MWts NPer NWsh WMoo WPnP
pulicaris	EBWF
punctata	XLum
remota	CKno EBWF EHoe EPPr EShb LPla
riparia	CHab EBWF MMoz MMuc MSKA MWts NPer WShi
- 'Bowles's Golden'	see *C. elata* 'Aurea'
sabynensis	see *C. umbrosa* subsp. *sabynensis*
scaposa KWJ 12304	LEdu WCru
secta	CKno CRos EPPr EPfP GMaP IMou LRHS NRHS SAko WMoo
- from Dunedin, New Zealand	EPPr
siderosticta	WSHC
- 'Banana Boat'	see *C. siderosticta* 'Golden Falls'
§ - 'Golden Falls' (v)	LEdu SMad SPtp
- 'Kisokaido' (v)	EShb
- 'Old Barn'	EBee
- 'Shima-nishiki' (v)	EBee EPfP LRHS
- 'Variegata' (v)	CTri CTsd EBee EHoe ELan ELon EShb GCal GKev GMcL LEdu NLar NSti NWsh SLim WBor WWtn
'Silver Sceptre' (v)	CBod EShb ESps GMaP LRHS MBNS MGos NRHS NSti NWad NWsh SLim SPlb SWvt WBrk WHar WMoo
solandri	CKno NRHS XLum
spicata	CHab EBWF
spissa	MNrw
stricta Gooden. 'Bowles's Golden'	see *C. elata* 'Aurea'
stricta Lam.	MMuc SEND
sylvatica	CHab EBWF EHoe
tenuiculmis	CBod CWCL EAJP EBee LRHS NRHS NSti NWad SPtp WCot XLum
testacea	Widely available
- dark-leaved	EPfP
- 'Limeshine'	EWes GBin SPoG WFar
- 'Old Gold'	EWes SMad SPlb WMoo
- 'Prairie Fire'	CRos CSpe GMaP LRHS NLar NRHS SCob SRms WGrn
texensis	EPPr
'The Beatles'	EHoe ESps
trifida	CKno EHoe GAbr
- 'Chatham Blue'	CBod GBin MMuc SEND
* - 'Glauca'	CWCL
- 'Rekohu Sunrise'^{PBR} (v)	CKno EBee ELon EPfP GMcL LRHS MMuc NEoE NSti SAko SEND SLon WCot
umbrosa	EBee EShb
subsp. ***sabynensis*** 'Thinny Thin' (v)	
viridula	EBWF

Carica (*Caricaceae*)

papaya (F)	XBlo
- 'Babaco'	CCCN
pubescens	see *Vasconcellea pubescens*

Carissa (*Apocynaceae*)

grandiflora	see *C. macrocarpa*
§ ***macrocarpa*** (F)	CCCN

Carlina (*Asteraceae*)

acanthifolia	SPhx
acaulis	ELan SPlb
- subsp. ***acaulis***	GPoy
I - 'Bronze Form'	SMad
- var. ***caulescens***	see *C. acaulis* subsp. *simplex*
§ - subsp. ***simplex***	CRos ECha ELon NRHS
- - bronze-leaved	SBrt SPhx
vulgaris	EBWF
- 'Silver Star'	SPhx

Carmichaelia (*Papilionaceae*)

australis	WSHC
odorata	CExl
petriei	SMad
stevensonii	MBlu SBrt WPGP WThu

× *Carmispartium* see *Carmichaelia*

Carpenteria (*Hydrangeaceae*)

californica	CCCN CRos CSBt CTri CWCL EBee ELan EPfP EWTr GBin LCro LOPS LRHS MGil MGos NRHS SCob SMad SPer SWvt WCot WFar WSpi
- 'Bodnant' ♀^{H4}	CBcs CDul CRos EBee ELan LRHS LSRN MAsh MGos NLar NRHS SEle SPer SWvt WFar WPGP WSpi
- 'Elizabeth' ♀^{H4}	CBcs CRos CSBt CWGN EPfP LRHS LSRN MAsh NLar SPoG SSta
- 'Eskimo'	LRHS SWvt
- 'Ladhams' Variety'	CBcs CDul CMac CRos EPfP LRHS MRav NLar SAko SEle SPer SRkn SWvt WKif WSpi

Carpinus ✿ (*Betulaceae*)

sp.	LPra
betulus ♀^{H6}	Widely available
* - 'A. Beeckman'	CLnd SGol
- 'Columnaris'	CDul CLnd CTho ESps
* - 'Columnaris Nana'	LLHF MPkF WCot
§ - 'Fastigiata' ♀^{H6}	Widely available
- 'Frans Fontaine'	CCVT CDul CEnd CLnd CMCN CMac CTho EBee EMOT EPfP ESps EWTr IArd LMaj MBlu MGos NLar NOra SCoo SEWo SGol SLim SPer SPoG WHar WMou
- 'Globus'	MBlu
- 'Incisa'	WMou
- 'Lucas'	CCVT EBee EMOT MBlu NOra SBir SGol
- 'Monument'	MPkF
- 'Pendula'	CDul CEnd CTho EBee LLHF LMaj MBlu SWvt WMou
- 'Purpurea'	CDul CEnd MBlu
- 'Pyramidalis'	see *C. betulus* 'Fastigiata'
- 'Quercifolia'	CDul LPra
- 'Rockhampton Red'	MBlu WMou
- 'Stegemanns Primus'^{PBR}	EBee
caroliniana	CDul CLnd CMCN EPfP SBir
- 'Red Fall'	EPfP MBlu
- 'Sentinel Dries'	LRHS MBlu
cordata	CDul MBlu SSta
coreana	CMCN SBir
fangiana	CBcs CEnd CExl CJun CMCN CTho EBee EPfP IArd LLHF LRHS MBlu WPGP
fargesiana	WPGP
- KR 8780 **new**	WPGP
fargesii	see *C. viminea*
henryana	CExl CMen EBtc SBir
- var. ***simplicidentata***	CMCN MBlu
japonica ♀^{H6}	CDul CEnd CLnd CMCN CMen CTho EPfP MBlu NLar NOra SAko SBir SCoo SEWo SSta
- B&SWJ 10803	WCru

- B&SWJ 11072 WCru
- 'Chinese Lantern' LRHS SGol
kawakamii CMCN
- CWJ 12412 WCru
- CWJ 12449 WCru
laxiflora CExl CMen
- B&SWJ 10809 WCru
- B&SWJ 11035 WCru
- var. ***longispica*** B&SWJ 8772 WCru
- var. ***macrostachya*** see *C. viminea*
omeiensis EBee
- KR 280 WPGP
orientalis CMCN SBir
polyneura EBee SBir SSta WPGP
pubescens EBee WPGP
- 'Abbotsbury' SSta
rankanensis SSta
- RWJ 9839 WCru
× ***schuschaensis*** EBee EBtc LRHS
shensiensis CDul EBee WPGP
tschonoskii EBee
- B&SWJ 10800 WCru
- BBJMT 297 WPGP
turczaninowii CDul CMCN CMen MBlu NLar SBir SSta
§ ***viminea*** CEnd CExl CMCN SSta WCot

Carpobrotus (*Aizoaceae*)

acinaciformis SVen
§ ***edulis*** CCCN CCac CDTJ SArc SEND SVen WHer XLum
- 'Gugh Dawn' (v) CCac SVen
- var. ***rubescens*** CCCN CCac
muirii CCCN SVen
sauerae CCCN

Carrierea (*Salicaceae*)

calycina CBcs EBee IArd IDee SAko WPGP

carrot see *Daucus carota* for species; also AGM Vegetables Section for cultivars

Carthamus (*Asteraceae*)

dianius SBrt
mitissimus GEdr
tinctorius MNHC SPav SRms SVen

Carum (*Apiaceae*)

carvi CBod ENfk GPoy MHer MJak MNHC SRms SVic XAbr
petroselinum see *Petroselinum crispum*

Carya ✿ (*Juglandaceae*)

cathayensis new EGFP
cordiformis MBlu
glabra CBcs CMCN
illinoinensis (F) CAgr CBcs CDul CMCN MBlu MRai
- 'Carlson No 3' seedling (F) CAgr
- 'Colby' seedling (F) CAgr
- 'Cornfield' (F) CAgr
- 'Lucas' (F) CAgr
laciniosa (F) EPfP
- 'Henry' (F) CAgr
- 'Keystone' seedling (F) CAgr
ovata (F) CAgr CBcs CDul CLnd EPfP MBlu WPGP
- 'Grainger' seedling (F) CAgr
- 'Neilson' seedling (F) CAgr
- 'Weschcke' seedling (F) CAgr
- 'Yoder No 1' seedling (F) CAgr
tomentosa CMCN EPfP NLar WPGP

Caryophyllus see *Syzygium*

Caryopteris (*Lamiaceae*)

× ***clandonensis*** CAco CMac ECtt ESps MGil
- 'Arthur Simmonds' ♀H4 CTri ECha SCob
- BEST PINK ('Lisspin') new CRos LCro LOPS NRHS
- 'Dark Knight' CBod CBot CRos CSpe CTsd EBee ECtt ELan EMOT EPfP ESps EWTr IRob LBuc LCro LRHS MAsh MCot NRHS SCob SEle SPer SPoG SWvt WFar WHil WHoo
- 'Ferndown' EWTr NLar SEND SRms
- 'First Choice' ♀H5 CMac CRos ECrN ELan EPfP LRHS LSRN MAsh MGos NRHS SLim SPer SPoG SRkn SWvt
- 'Gold Giant' CRos EPfP LRHS MAsh NRHS
- GRAND BLEU ('Inoveris'PBR) CDul CMac CRos CSBt EBee ELan EPfP LRHS LSRN MGos NLar NRHS SAko SCob SGbt SGol SWvt
- 'Heavenly Baby' ♀H4 CRos EPfP LRHS MAsh SLon
- 'Heavenly Blue' Widely available
- 'Hint of Blue' new SGol
- HINT OF GOLD ('Lisaura'PBR) ♀H4 CRos CSBt ELan EMOT EPfP ESps LCro LOPS LRHS MAsh MCot NLar NRHS
- 'Kew Blue' Widely available
- 'Longwood Blue' CRos EPfP LRHS
- 'Pershore' WAvo
- PETIT BLEU ('Minbleu'PBR) EBee LRHS MPkF
- STEPHI ('Lissteph') new CRos LRHS
- STERLING SILVER ('Lissilv'PBR) ♀H4 CMac CRos EBee EPfP GMcL LRHS LSRN MAsh NEoE NRHS SCob SPer SPoG SRms SSta
- 'Summer Gold' CMac MAsh
- 'Summer Sorbet'PBR (v) ♀H4 CBod CMac CRos CWGN EBee ECrN EHoe ELan EPfP EWes GMcL LRHS MAsh MGos MJak NLar SCob SCoo SEND SGbt SGol SLim SPer SRms SWvt WFar WHar WHil
- weeping EPPr
- 'White Surprise'PBR CMac CRos CWGN ELan EMOT EMil EPfP LRHS MGos NEgg NLar NRHS SCob SGol SPer SPoG WFar WHil
- 'Worcester Gold' ♀H4 Widely available
divaricata CMCN SBrt WHil
- 'Electrum' LSou WCot WFar WSHC
- 'Jade Shades' WSHC
§ ***incana*** XSen
- 'Blue Cascade' EBtc ELan LRHS MRav NLar SRms WGrn
- 'Delft Blue' CChe LRHS
§ - 'Jason'PBR EBee ECrN EMOT NEgg NLar SCob SPoG
- SUNSHINE BLUE see *C. incana* 'Jason'
mastacanthus see *C. incana*

Caryota (*Arecaceae*)

mitis CCCN
- 'Himalaya' NLos

Cassandra see *Chamaedaphne*

Cassia (*Caesalpiniaceae*)

corymbosa Lam. see *Senna corymbosa*
marilandica see *Senna marilandica*
nemophila SPlb

Cassinia (Asteraceae)

fulvida	CBcs SVen
leptophylla	CBcs
vauvilliersii	EBee ELan SEle SVen
'Ward Silver'	EHoe LRHS

Cassinia × *Helichrysum* (Asteraceae)

hybrid	WKif

Cassiope ✿ (Ericaceae)

	'Askival Snowbird'	ITim NWad
	'Askival Snow-wreath'	see *C.* Snow-wreath Group
	'Askival Stormbird'	ITim NWad
	'Badenoch'	GKev WThu
	'Edinburgh' ♀H5	EPot GBin NWad WThu
	lycopodioides ♀H5	ITim
	- 'Beatrice Lilley'	EBee EPot GKev WThu
	- 'Jim Lever'	ITim WAbe
	- 'Rokujō'	ITim
	mertensiana 'California Pink'	NWad
	- var. ***californica***	ITim NWad WThu
	- var. ***gracilis***	NWad WThu
	'Muirhead' ♀H5	WThu
	'Randle Cooke' ♀H5	EPot GBin WThu
	selaginoides LS&E 13284	EPot WAbe WThu
§	Snow-wreath Group	ITim
	tetragona	ITim
	wardii	EPot

Castanea ✿ (Fagaceae)

	'Bouche de Bétizac' (F)	CAgr
	crenata	CAgr
	dentata	CBcs
	henryi	CMCN
	'Maraval' (F)	CAgr CTho ERea MCoo
	'Maridonne' (F)	CAgr
	'Marigoule' (F)	CAgr EPom ERea MCoo SPer
	'Marsol' (F)	CAgr CFGn ECrN ERea MCoo
	mollissima	CBcs
	'Précoce Migoule' (F)	CAgr
	sativa	Widely available
§	- 'Albomarginata' (v) ♀H6	CDul CEnd EBee EPfP NOra SPoG
	- 'Anny's Summer Red'	CDul EUJe SPer
	- 'Argenteovariegata'	see *C. sativa* 'Albomarginata'
	- 'Aspleniifolia'	CDul
	- 'Aureomarginata'	see *C. sativa* 'Variegata'
	- 'Belle Epine' (F)	CAgr
	- 'Bournette' (F)	CAgr
*	- 'Doré de Lyon'	CAgr
	- 'Marlhac' (F)	CAgr CFGn NOra
	- 'Marron Comballe' (F)	CAgr
	- 'Marron de Goujounac' (F)	CAgr
	- 'Marron de Lyon' (F)	CAgr CDul CEnd CFGn CHab CTho EPfP EPom SVic
	- 'Regal' (F)	EPom
§	- 'Variegata' (v)	CMCN ELan SPer
	seguinii	EGFP WPGP

Castanopsis (Fagaceae)

sieboldii	CBcs

Castilleja (Orobanchaceae)

integra	GKev SPlb
miniata	SPlb WAbe
scabrida new	GKev
sessiliflora	SPlb

Casuarina (Casuarinaceae)

cunninghamiana	SPlb

Catalpa ✿ (Bignoniaceae)

	sp.	LPra
	bignonioides ♀H6	Widely available
	- 'Aurea' ♀H6	Widely available
*	- 'Aurea Nana'	LPra
	- 'Nana'	LPra
	- 'Purpurea'	see *C.* × *erubescens* 'Purpurea'
	- 'Variegata' (v)	EBee ELon EPfP LRHS MAsh
	bungei	CCVT CMCN MBlu SArc SGol
	- 'Purpurea'	EMOT
§	× ***erubescens*** 'Purpurea' ♀H6	CBcs CBot CCVT CDul CEnd CMCN CMac CTho EBee ELan ELon EPfP ESps EUJe LMaj MAsh MBlu MGil MRav NLar NOra SCob SMad SPer SPoG SWvt WMou WPGP
	fargesii f. ***duclouxii*** ♀H5	CBcs CDul CEnd EBee EPfP MBlu NLar SAko SChF WPGP
	ovata	CMCN CTho SPad
	- 'Slender Silhouette'	NLar
	speciosa ♀H6	CDul CMCN CTho GBin SVen
	- 'Frederik'	NLar
	- 'Pulverulenta' (v)	CDul EBee LLHF MBlu SBig SMad

Catananche (Asteraceae)

caerulea	CBod CMea CRos CSBt CSpe CTri EAJP ECha ELan EPfP EShb ESps LRHS MBel MNHC MSpe NEgg NRHS SCob SPad SPer SPhx SPoG SWvt WArt WCAu WHar WHoo WMoo XSen
- 'Alba'	CBod CMea CRos EAJP ECha ELan EPfP EWTr GNew IFoB LRHS MBel MNrw NRHS SCob SPad SPer SPoG SWvt WArt WCAu WHar WMoo
- 'Amor Blue'	CRos EPfP LRHS NRHS
- 'Bicolor'	MSpe WMoo
- 'Major' ♀H5	CRos EWTr LRHS NRHS SRms

Catha (Celastraceae)

edulis	GPoy

Cathcartia (Papaveraceae)

§	***villosa***	GGGa

Catopsis (Bromeliaceae)

morreniana	NCft

cauliflower see AGM Vegetables Section

Caulokaempferia (Zingiberaceae)

petelotii B&SWJ 11818	LEdu WCru
- HWJ 541	WCru

Caulophyllum (Berberidaceae)

thalictroides	CAby EPPr GKev IMou LEdu SRot WCru WPGP WPnP WSHC
- subsp. ***robustum***	EBee WCru

Cautleya ✿ (Zingiberaceae)

	cathcartii	CExl LEdu
	- 'Tenzing's Gold'	EBee GCal WCru WPGP WSHC
§	***gracilis***	CAby CDTJ CExl EBee EPfP EUJe GCal IBlr IBoy MMoz MPie SBig
	- BWJ 7843	WCru
	- from Manipur, India new	WPGP
	- 'Crûg Gold'	LEdu WCru WPGP
	- 'Dzoukou' new	LEdu

- var. ***gracilis***	NLos
- var. ***robusta***	NLos
lutea	see *C. gracilis*
spicata	CAby CBct CCCN CDTJ CSpe CTsd EUJe GKev IBlr IRob MMoz MPie NLos SBig
- CC 3676	CExl
- 'Arun Flame'	CBct GCal LEdu WCru WPGP
- 'Bleddyn's Beacon'	WCru
- 'Crûg Canary'	LEdu WCru WPGP
- 'Crûg Compact'	WCru
* - var. ***lutea***	CBct LEdu WBor WPGP
- 'Robusta'	CAvo CExl EBee GCal IBlr LEdu MNrw SMad WBor WCot WCru WPGP

Cayratia (*Vitaceae*)

japonica B&SWJ 6636	WCru
§ ***thomsonii***	SDea
- BWJ 8123	EPPr WCru

Ceanothus ✿ (*Rhamnaceae*)

'A.T. Johnson'	SGol SRms
arboreus	SArc
- 'Trewithen Blue' ♀H4	Widely available
'Autumnal Blue' ♀H4	Widely available
'Blue Cushion'	CBcs CRos CTri EPfP LRHS MAsh MGos MJak NLar SLon SWvt
'Blue Diamond'PBR	LSRN
'Blue Jeans'	CBcs MMuc NLar SWeb
'Blue Mound' ♀H4	Widely available
'Blue Sapphire'PBR	CWGN ELan EPfP GMcL LRHS LSRN MAsh MGos NEgg NEoE NLar SPoG SRms SWvt
'Blue Sensation' **new**	NLar
'Burkwoodii' ♀H4	CBcs CRos CSBt EMOT EPfP ESps LRHS MAsh MGos MRav NEgg SCob SEle SLim SPer SPoG SRms SWvt
'Cascade' ♀H4	CBcs ESps LSRN SPer SPlb WAvo WHar
'Concha' ♀H4	Widely available
§ ***cuneatus*** var. ***rigidus***	WSHC
'Cynthia Postan'	CRos EPfP ESps LRHS LSou MHer NEgg NLar SCob
'Dark Star' ♀H4	CBcs CRos CSBt CTri CWGN ELan ELon EPfP ESps EUJe GMcL LRHS LSRN MAsh MGos SBod SCob SPoG SSta SWvt
'Delight'	CBcs EPfP ESps
× ***delileanus*** 'Gloire de Versailles' ♀H4	CBcs CDul CRos CTri ELan EMOT EPfP ESps ETMg EWTr GMcL LRHS MGos MRav MSwo NLar NRHS SCob SCoo SGol SPer SPoG SWvt WKif WSHC
- 'Henri Desfossé'	CRos ELan EPfP LRHS LSRN MRav MSwo NLar NRHS SCob SPer SPoG WKif
- 'Topaze' ♀H4	CRos EPfP GMcL LRHS MRav NLar NRHS SGol SLon WKif
dentatus misapplied	see *C.* × *lobbianus*
dentatus Torr. & A. Gray	SPer SPlb
'Diamond Heights'	see *C. griseus* var. *horizontalis* 'Diamond Heights'
'Edinburgh'	NEgg
EL DORADO ('Perado') (v)	ELan MJak SGol WAvo
gloriosus 'Anchor Bay'	EPfP
- 'Emily Brown'	CBcs ELan MRav NLar
§ ***griseus*** var. ***horizontalis*** 'Diamond Heights' (v)	CBcs CMac EPfP LSRN MAsh NLar SPer
- - 'Silver Surprise'PBR (v)	EPfP LBuc LSRN NEgg NLar NPri SRms
- - 'Yankee Point'	CBar CBcs CMac CRos CSBt ECrN EPfP ESps LRHS LSRN MGos MRav MSwo NLar NRHS SCoo SEND SGol SLim SPlb SPoG SWvt WHar
impressus	CTri EPfP ESps MAsh SWvt
'Italian Skies'	CBcs CRos CSBt ECrN ELan EMOT EPfP ESps GMcL LRHS LSRN MAsh MGos MSwo NEgg NLar NRHS SCob SCoo SGol SLim SLon SPer SPlb SPoG SWvt
'Julia Phelps'	SGol WAvo
'Lemon and Lime'PBR	LBuc LRHS NRHS
§ × ***lobbianus***	CBcs CTri
'Madagascar'	EMOT SCoo SPoG
MARIE-ROSE ('Minmarose')	WHlf
× ***pallidus***	WHar
- 'Marie Simon'	CBcs CRos ELan EPfP EWTr GMcL LRHS LSRN MAsh MGos NRHS SCob SGol SPer SPoG SRms SWvt WCFE WKif
- 'Perle Rose' ♀H4	CBcs CRos EMOT EPfP LRHS MGos NRHS SPer WKif WSHC
papillosus	IArd SBrt
§ 'Pershore Zanzibar'PBR (v)	CBcs CBod CChe CMac CRos CSBt CTri EHoe EPfP EShb ESps GMcL LRHS MGos MJak MRav MSwo NEgg NRHS SGol SLim SPer SPoG SRms WAvo
'Pin Cushion'	CRos EPfP LRHS MAsh WAvo
'Point Millerton'	see *C. thyrsiflorus* 'Millerton Point'
'Popcorn'	LRHS
'Puget Blue' ♀H4	Widely available
'Puget Blue' × ***thyrsiflorus*** var. ***repens***	ESps LOPS
'Ray Hartman'	NLar
repens	see *C. thyrsiflorus* var. *repens*
rigidus	see *C. cuneatus* var. *rigidus*
'Skylark' ♀H4	CBar CBcs CBod CChe CDul CMac CRos ELan EMOT EPfP ESps GBin GMcL GWyn LCro LOPS LRHS LSRN MAsh MGos NRHS SEND SEle SGol SLim SPer WAvo WFar WHar
'Snow Flurries'	see *C. thyrsiflorus* 'Snow Flurry'
'Snow Showers'	CBcs
'Southmead' ♀H4	CRos CTri ECrN ELan EPfP GMcL LRHS MGos MSwo NEgg NRHS
thyrsiflorus	CTri SRms SWvt WAvo
§ - 'Millerton Point'	CRos ELan EPfP LRHS NLar WAvo
- 'Mystery Blue' ♀H4	CRos EPfP LRHS NRHS SWvt
§ - var. ***repens*** ♀H4	Widely available
§ - 'Snow Flurry'	ELan MSwo NEgg SGol
'Tilden Park'	CRos LRHS
'Tuxedo'PBR	LRHS MAsh MRav NLar SGol
× ***veitchianus***	CRos CSBt EPfP LRHS NRHS SEND SPer
'Victoria'	CEnd CRos EBee ESps LRHS LSRN MSwo NLar NRHS SGol SRGP SRms WHar
'Zanzibar'	see *C.* 'Pershore Zanzibar'

Cedrela (*Meliaceae*)

sinensis	see *Toona sinensis*

Cedronella (*Lamiaceae*)

§ ***canariensis***	CBod EBee ENfk GPoy MNHC SRms

mexicana	see *Agastache mexicana*
triphylla	see *C. canariensis*

Cedrus (*Pinaceae*)

sp.	LPra
atlantica	CAco CDul CMac ESps LMaj LPra SEND SGol WHar WMou WTSh
- 'Aurea' ♀H6	LRHS MJak NLar SSta
- 'Fastigiata'	CDul NEgg NLar
- Glauca Group	Widely available
- - 'Glauca' ♀H6	CAco EMOT GMil LMaj SAko WTSh
- - 'Glauca Pendula' ♀H6	CAco CCVT CDul GMil LRHS MBlu MGos NEgg NLar SGol SLim SSta WHar
- - 'Silberspitz'	CKen NLar
- 'Pendula'	CAco MAsh SMad
- 'Pyramidalis' **new**	LMaj
- 'Sahara Frost'	NLar
- 'Sapphire Nymph'	CKen MAsh NLar SLim
brevifolia	GMil LRHS NLar
- 'Epstein'	NLar
- 'Hillier Compact'	CKen
- 'Jade Medusa'	LRHS
- 'Kenwith'	CKen NLar
deodara ♀H6	Widely available
- 'Albospica' (v)	SWvt
- 'Anny's Dwarf' **new**	NLar
- 'Aurea' ♀H6	CCVT CKen EPfP ESps GMil LMaj MAsh MGos NEgg NOra SGol WFar
I - 'Aurea Pendula'	CAco GMil
- 'Blue Dwarf'	CKen
* - 'Blue Mountain Broom'	CKen
- 'Blue Snake'	CKen
- 'Blue Surprise'	CAco
- 'Bush's Electra'	LRHS MBlu NLar
- 'Devinely Blue'	CKen
- 'Eisregen'	LRHS
- 'Feelin' Blue' ♀H6	CKen ELan ESps GMil LMaj LRHS MAsh MJak NEgg NLar NRHS SMad SWvt WFar
- FEELIN' SUNNY ('Monkinn') **new**	NLar
- 'Golden Horizon'	CKen CMen ELan GMil MAsh NEgg SPoG WFar
- 'Golden Jubilee'	SGol
- 'Karl Fuchs'	LRHS NLar NRHS
- 'Klondyke'	CAco
- 'Lime Glow'	CKen NEgg
- 'Mr Blue' **new**	SPoG
- 'Nana'	CKen
- 'Pendula' ♀H6	CKen
- 'Pygmy'	CKen
- 'Robusta'	LMaj LPra WPGP
- 'Roman Candle'	GMil NEgg
- 'Scott'	CKen
- 'Silver Mist'	CKen
- 'Silver Spring'	CAco NLar
libani ♀H6	Widely available
- 'Alibaba' **new**	NLar
- 'Blue Angel'	NLar SLim
- 'Blue Fountain' **new**	NLar
- 'Comte de Dijon'	LRHS NLar
- 'Fontaine'	NLar
- 'Glauca'	CAco EWTr
- 'Green Prince'	NLar
- 'Hedgehog'	CKen NLar
- 'Home Park'	CKen NLar
- 'Italie' **new**	NLar
- 'May'	LRHS NLar
- Nana Group	CAco CKen ELan NEgg
- 'Pendula'	CAco NLar
- 'Sargentii'	GMil LRHS MBlu NEgg NLar
- 'Taurus'	NLar
- 'Whitehouse Wb' **new**	NLar

Ceiba (*Malvaceae*)

pentandra	SPlb

Celastrus (*Celastraceae*)

dependens CWJ 12478	WCru
flagellaris B&SWJ 8572	WCru
hookeri B&SWJ 11667	WCru
kusanoi CWJ 12445	WCru
orbiculatus	CBcs ELan LRHS MRav SLon SPer WHar WHer
- 'Diana' (f)	CMac
- 'Hercules' (m)	CMac
- Hermaphrodite Group ♀H6	EWTr MGil MMuc
- var. ***papillosus*** B&SWJ 591	WCru
- var. ***punctatus*** CWJ 12439	WCru
scandens	CMac SPhx SPlb
stephanotiifolius B&SWJ 4727	WCru
stylosus WJC 13746	WCru

celeriac see AGM Vegetables Section

celery see AGM Vegetables Section

Celmisia (*Asteraceae*)

allanii	GKev WAbe
angustifolia ♀H5	GKev WAbe
argentea	WAbe
bellidioides	EPot GAbr ITim NSla WAbe
coriacea misapplied	see *C. semicordata*
densiflora	GKev
discolor	WAbe
gracilenta	GKev ITim NSla WAbe
haastii × viscosa	NSla
hectorii	ITim WAbe
hookeri	NHpl
longifolia	IBlr
monroi	IBlr
ramulosa	EPot ITim WAbe
- var. ***tuberculata***	NSla
§ ***semicordata***	IBlr ITim NHpl
- subsp. ***stricta***	IBlr
sessiliflora	EPot WAbe

Celsia see *Verbascum*

× *Celsioverbascum* see *Verbascum*

Celtica see *Stipa*

Celtis (*Cannabaceae*)

australis	CBcs CDul CLnd CMCN EBee EBtc LEdu MBlu
biondii	NLar
caucasica	CFil
choseniana B&SWJ 12774	WCru
glabrata	see *C. planchoniana*
occidentalis	CDul EBtc EWTr
§ ***planchoniana***	EGFP
sinensis	CMen

Cenolophium (*Apiaceae*)

denudatum	CSam CSpe EPPr EWes GAbr GBin LCro LEdu LOPS LPla LRHS MAvo MBel MMuc MPie MSpe NChi NDov SPtp WCot WPGP WSHC WSpi

Centaurea ✿ (*Asteraceae*)

HH&K 271	NBid
RCB AM 6	WCot
W&B BGB-1	WCot
affinis new	GKev
alba	IBoy
alpestris	MSpe NLar SPhx
'Amethyst'	CRos LRHS NRHS
'Amethyst on Ice'	LBuc LRHS NRHS
§ ***atropurpurea***	CAby CBWd CFis CRos CSpe EBee EPfP EWes GQue IBoy LRHS MSpe NBid NLar NRHS NSti SBrt SHar SPhx SPlb WHil
bagadensis	GKev
bella	CBod CRos EBee ECtt ELon GCal LRHS LSou MBel MRav MSpe NBro NDov NRHS NSti SBod SMHy SPhx WGwG WKif XLum XSen
- 'Katherine' (v)	MSpe
benoistii misapplied	see *C. atropurpurea*
benoistii ambig.	CSpe MRav
benoistii ambig. × ***orientalis***	SPhx
cana	see *C. triumfettii* subsp. *cana*
candidissima misapplied	see *C. cineraria*
'Caramia'	CRos EBee ECtt EPfP LEdu LRHS MHol MNrw MSpe NBid NHpl NRHS WHil
carniolica SDR 5443	EBee
cheiranthifolia	CFis EPPr MNrw MSpe NBid NLar SHar WBrk
§ ***cineraria***	ECre
- subsp. ***cineraria*** ♀H3	SEND WCot
I 'Copper Hybrid'	CPla
cyanoides	SPhx
cyanus	CHab CSpe EBWF LCro MHer MNHC SVic
- 'Black Ball'	CSpe LCro LOPS LRHS MNHC SPhx
- 'Blue Ball'	CSpe
- 'Blue Boy'	CRav LRHS
- 'Pinkie' (d)	MNHC SPhx
- Polka Dot Series new	CRav
- 'Snowman'	SPhx
cynaroides	see *Rhaponticum centaureoides*
dealbata	CBod CMac CRos EAJP EBee ELon EPfP ESps GJos GMcL IFoB LPmr LRHS MBel MHol MMuc MSpe NBro NLar NMir NRHS SCob SEND SRms WHar WMoo XLum
- 'Steenbergii'	CMac EPPr GCal IRob MBel MSpe NBid NEgg NGdn NPer NSti SPer SPoG WCAu WCot
declinata RCB UA 18	WCot
glastifolia	EBee LEdu
grinensis	WOut
gymnocarpa	see *C. cineraria*
hypoleuca	NBid
jacea	CSam GAbr GWyn LEdu MMuc MSpe NBid NLar SEND SPhx WCot WOut WPGP
- PAB 8821	LEdu
'John Coutts'	Widely available
'Jordy'	Widely available
karabaghensis	GCal GKev MAvo MSpe
kotschyana	WPGP
macrocephala	CBWd CRos ECha ECtt ELan ELon EPfP GAbr IBoy ITim LEdu LRHS MBel MHol MSpe NBid NBro NChi NEgg NGBl NLar NRHS SMad SPer SPoG SRms WCAu WMoo XLum
microptilon	EBee LEdu
mollis	NBid
montana	Widely available
- 'Alba'	Widely available
- 'Amethyst Dream'PBR	CRos EBee LRHS MNrw NLar NRHS SPoG
- 'Amethyst in Snow'	CElw CRos EAJP EBee ECtt EPfP IRob LRHS MHol MSpe NLar NRHS NWad SCob SPoG WBor WTor
- 'Black Sprite'	CNor CRos CSpe CWGN EAJP EBee ECtt EPfP ILea LRHS MNrw NLar NPnk NRHS NSti SPoG WBor WBrk WFar WNPC
- 'Blewit'	CAby CElw EBee ECtt ELon EPPr MSpe NLar WBor WCAu WOut
§ - 'Carnea'	CElw CSam ELon EPPr GMaP IRob MSpe NChi NLar SPhx WBrk WCAu WFar WMoo WOut
- 'Elworthy Glacier'	CElw
- 'Gold Bullion'	CRos CSpe EBee ECtt EPfP EWes GMaP LRHS MAvo MHol MRav NBid NLar NRHS SMad WSHC
- 'Grandiflora'	EBee ELon MJak MPie MSpe
- 'Joyce'	CElw MAvo MMuc MTis NBid NLar SHar WBor WCAu WSHC
- 'Lady Flora Hastings'	CCse CElw CRos CSam CSpe EBee ELon EPPr LRHS MMuc NBid NRHS WBor WBrk
- 'Lavender Mist' new	CBod MHol
- lilac-flowered	NBid NLar
- 'Ochroleuca'	CElw MSpe NBid
- 'Parham'	CRos ECtt ELon GAbr GCal GQue LRHS LSou MNrw MRav NEgg NLar NRHS NSti SPer SPlb WMoo WSHC
- 'Purple Heart'	CAby CRos CWGN EBee ECtt ELon EPfP EWTr MBNS MBel MHer MMuc MNrw MSpe NGBl NLar SMad SPad SPer WCAu WCot WHil WMoo
- 'Purple Prose'	CElw EPPr LPla
- 'Purpurea'	CElw MSpe WBor
- 'Rosea'	see *C. montana* 'Carnea'
I - 'Violacea'	NBid
- 'Violetta'	ELon MAvo MSpe NBid WBrk WCAu WMoo
nervosa	NBid NBro XLum
nigra	CBod CDor CHab EBWF EPfP GJos MSpe NLar NMir SPhx SRms WMoo WOut WSFF
- var. ***alba***	CBre NBid WOut
- 'Elstead'	MSpe
- 'Mardi Gras' (v)	ECtt
- subsp. ***rivularis***	NBid XLum
nogmovii	MAvo MSpe
orientalis	CSpe EWes IBoy LRHS LSou MHol NGBl NRHS SPhx WHoo WWtn
pannonica	EPPr
- subsp. ***pannonica*** HH&K 259	NBid
pestalozzae	GKev
phrygia	MMuc MSpe NLar SEND
pterocaula RCB/TQ 18	WCot

	pulcherrima	MNrw MSpe SCob SMad WHil XSen
	'Pulchra Major'	see *Rhaponticum centaureoides*
	pullata	CRos LRHS NRHS
	rupestris	EBee EPfP SPhx
	ruthenica	CDor CFis SCob SPer SPhx SPlb
	salonitana RCB AM 1	WCot
	scabiosa	CBre CDor CHab CWld EBWF IBoy LCro MHer MNHC MSpe NBid NMir SPhx SRms
	'Silver Feather'	CKno CRos LRHS NRHS
	simplicicaulis	CSam ELon MAsh NChi NHpl SBch SHar SRms WHoo WSHC XSen
	thracica	CSpe EBee WCot
	triumfettii	CPBP
I	- subsp. ***cana*** 'Rosea'	WBrk
	- 'Hoar Frost'	EBee ELon NDov
	uniflora	EBee
	woronowii	MAvo MSpe

Centaurium (*Gentianaceae*)

	erythraea	EBWF GPoy
	scilloides	GCrg NRHS NSla WAbe

Centella (*Apiaceae*)

§	***asiatica***	GPoy LEdu XAbr

Centradenia (*Melastomataceae*)

	inaequilateralis	CCCN

Centranthus (*Caprifoliaceae*)

§	***lecoqii***	ECha ECtt EPPr EWes LRHS SPhx WCot
	macrosiphon	CMac
§	***ruber***	Widely available
*	- 'Alba Pura'	GAbr
§	- 'Albus'	Widely available
	- 'Atrococcineus'	ECha MMuc
	- var. ***coccineus***	CBWd CBcs CBod CRos EBee ELan EPed EPfP GAbr GBin GKin GMaP GMcL LRHS LSun MJak MRav MWat NRHS SCob SEND SPer SPhm SPhx SRot WCot WFar WGwG XSen
	- mauve-flowered misapplied	see *C. lecoqii*
	- 'Roseus'	CRos EBee EPfP LRHS NRHS WMoo
	- 'Snowcloud'	CWld EBee ECtt ENfk EPfP MNHC SRms WHil
	'White Cloud'	SPad

Centropogon (*Campanulaceae*)

	costaricae B&SWJ 10455	WCru
	ferrugineus B&SWJ 10665	WCru
	hirsutus B&SWJ 10657	WCru

Cephalanthus (*Rubiaceae*)

	'Magical Moonlight' **new**	ETMg
	occidentalis	CDul CRos EBee LRHS LSou MAsh MBNS MBlu NLar NQui SLim SPer SPoG WCFE

Cephalaria (*Caprifoliaceae*)

§	***alpina***	CRos EPPr EPfP LRHS MAsh MMuc MNrw NRHS SHar SPhx SRms WBrk WCot WFar XLum
	caucasica	see *C. gigantea*
	dipsacoides	MSpe SPhx SRms WMoo
§	***flava***	LRHS NRHS
	galpiniana	SPlb
§	***gigantea***	Widely available
	graeca	see *C. flava*
	leucantha	CFis MMuc NLar SEND SPhx WBrk WMoo
	litvinovii	SPhx
	radiata	NDov SPhx
	tatarica hort.	see *C. gigantea*
	tchihatchewii	ILea NLar WCot
	transsylvanica	CSpe SPhx
	- W&B BGJ-1	WCot

Cephalotaxus (*Taxaceae*)

	fortunei	CAco CDul LEdu WCru
	harringtonia	CMCN LEdu
	- var. ***drupacea***	CAco
	- 'Fastigiata'	CAco CDul IArd LRHS MAsh MGos NRHS SLim SPoG
	- 'Gimborn's Pillow'	MAsh NLar
	- 'Korean Gold'	SLim SPoG

Cephalotus (*Cephalotaceae*)

	follicularis ♀^{H2}	NLos SHmp

Cerastium (*Caryophyllaceae*)

	alpinum	IFoB SRms
	- var. ***lanatum***	EWes XLum
	biebersteinii	MBel XLum
	candidissimum	CPla EWes
	fontanum	CHab
	tomentosum	CBar CSBt ELan EPfP ESps EWTr GAbr GWyn MHol MMuc SEND SPer SPlb SPoG WFar
	- var. ***columnae***	ECha EWes GMaP XLum XSen

Ceratonia (*Caesalpiniaceae*)

	siliqua	SEND SPlb

Ceratophyllum (*Ceratophyllaceae*)

	demersum	CBen CWat EWat LOPS MSKA MWts WMAq WSFF XBlo
	submersum	LLWG

Ceratostigma (*Plumbaginaceae*)

	abyssinicum	CBcs ELan LEdu
	asperrimum B&SWJ 7260	WCru
	'Autumn Blue'	EPfP LRHS
	capensis	CMac
	griffithii	CBcs CDul CMac CRos EBee EHoe ELan EPfP ESps LRHS MAsh MRav MSwo NLar SCoo SEND SGol SLim SPer SPoG SRms SVen SWvt WGwG WKif WSHC XLum XSen
§	***plumbaginoides*** ♀^{H4}	Widely available
	'Summer Skies' **new**	WHlf
	willmottianum ♀^{H4}	Widely available
	- BWJ 8140	WCru
	- DESERT SKIES ('Palmgold'^{PBR})	CBcs CMac ELan EPfP ESps NLar SCob SLim SPer SWvt
	- FOREST BLUE ('Lice'^{PBR}) ♀^{H4}	CMac CRos CSBt ELan EPfP ESps LCro LOPS LRHS LSRN MAsh MGos MRav NEgg NLar NPri NRHS SAko SCob SCoo SEle SLim SPer SPoG SSta SWvt
	- SAPPHIRE RING ('Lissbrill'^{PBR})	CBcs CRos ELan EMil EPfP LRHS MAsh NRHS SCoo SPoG

Cercidiphyllum ✿ (*Cercidiphyllaceae*)

	japonicum ♀^{H5}	Widely available
	- 'Boyd's Dwarf'	CJun CRos ELan EPfP LLHF LRHS MAsh MBlu NLar SPoG SSta
	- 'Chameleon' (v)	MBlu NLar

- GLOWBALL ('Jww4') LRHS
- 'Herkenrode Dwarf' MBlu
- 'Heronswood Globe' ♀H5 CJun CMCN EPfP MBlu NLar SSta
- 'Kreukenberg Dwarf' CJun NLar SSta
- 'Morioka Weeping' CJun CTho EBee MPkF NLar SChF SMad SSta
- 'Peach' CJun NLar

§ - f. ***pendulum*** ♀H5 Widely available
- - 'Amazing Grace' CTho MBlu NLar SSta
- 'Raspberry' CJun MBlu NLar
- RED FOX see *C. japonicum* 'Rotfuchs'

§ - 'Rotfuchs' CBcs CEnd CJun CMCN CMac CRos CTho EBee ELan EMOT EPfP EWTr GMcL LRHS MAsh MBlu MGos MPkF NHim NLar SAko SChF SCob SPoG SSta WFar
- 'Ruby' CJun EBee MBlu NLar WPGP
- 'Strawberry' CBcs CJun MBlu NLar SSta
- 'Tidal Wave' CJun MBlu NLar SSta
- 'Titania' NLar SSta

magnificum CBcs CDul CEnd CExl CMCN MBlu NLar
- f. ***pendulum*** see *C. japonicum* f. *pendulum*

Cercis ✿ (*Caesalpiniaceae*)

canadensis CAco CAgr CBcs CDul CMCN CWGN ESps LMaj MGil MGos MMuc NEgg NLar SCob SPer
- 'Ace of Hearts'PBR MPkF
- f. ***alba*** CBcs LSRN
- - 'Royal White' CDul CJun EPfP MBlu SPer
- 'Appalachian Red' CJun CTho MBlu MGos NTre
- 'Cascading Hearts' CRos LRHS NRHS NTre
- 'Flame' CJun NLar SSta
- 'Forest Pansy' ♀H5 Widely available
- 'Hearts of Gold'PBR CRos CTho CWGN EBee EMOT IBoy LRHS MGos MPkF MRav NOra NRHS NTre SLon SMad SPoG
- LAVENDER TWIST ('Covey') CDul EBee ELan EPfP ERea LCro LOPS LSRN MBlu MGos NLar NOra NRHS NTre SCob SGol SLon SPer SPoG WMou
- LITTLE WOODY ('Litwo'PBR) MGos MPkF SGol
- 'Melon Beauty' NLar SMad
- 'Merlot' EMOT MGos NTre
- 'Pauline Lily' NLar
- 'Pink Heartbreaker' SGol
- 'Pink Pom Poms' NTre
- RED FORCE ('Minrouge3'PBR) EBee WCot
- 'Ruby Falls'PBR ♀H5 CBcs CMac CRos CTho EBee ELan EMOT ERea EWTr LCro LOPS LRHS MGos MPkF NOra NRHS NTre SCob SPoG
- 'Rubye Atkinson' CJun NLar
- 'Silver Lining' (v) EBee
- 'Tennessee Pink' SCob
- var. ***texensis*** 'Oklahoma' CJun EBee MGos MPkF NTre WPGP
- - 'Texas White' CEnd CJun CMac CTho EBee EPfP ERea MPkF NLar SCob
- - 'Traveller' NTre SGol
- 'The Rising Sun' MGos NTre
- 'Vanilla Twist' LRHS NTre SPoG
- 'Whitewater' (v) NTre

chinensis EGFP EWTr LEdu NLar SPer WMou
- B&SWJ 12665 WCru
- NJM 11.047 WPGP
- f. ***alba*** CTho MGos
- 'Avondale' ♀H5 Widely available
- 'Don Egolf' ♀H5 CJun MBlu MGos MPkF NLar NTre SGol
- 'Shirobana' NTre

chingii CExl
gigantea NLar WPGP
griffithii CMCN LEdu NLar SSta
occidentalis LEdu SSta
racemosa CExl WPGP
siliquastrum Widely available
- f. ***albida*** CRos CTho ECrN ELan EPfP EWes LRHS
- 'Bodnant' ♀H4 CMac CRos CTho EPfP ESps EWes IArd LLHF LRHS LSRN MBlu MGos NLar NOra NTre SCob
- 'Rubra' ESps
- 'White Swan' CJun CTho

Cerinthe (*Boraginaceae*)

major SWvt
- 'Kiwi Blue' CHll
- 'Purpurascens' CRav CSpe ELan EPfP ESps ETMg IBoy LCro LOPS LPmr MNHC SPer SPhx SPoG WKif

Ceropegia (*Apocynaceae*)

§ ***linearis*** subsp. ***woodii*** ♀H1c EShb LToo
sandersonii ♀H1c CCCN EShb
woodii see *C. linearis* subsp. *woodii*

Cestrum (*Solanaceae*)

aurantiacum EShb SEND
buxifolium WCru
B&SWJ 14395 new
× ***cultum*** CHll
- 'Cretan Pink' CCCN
- 'Cretan Purple' CBcs CCCN CHGN CHll ELan ELon EPfP EShb IDee LRHS SEND SWvt WKif WSHC

diurnum × ***nocturnum*** EShb

§ ***elegans*** CAby CExl CHll EBee ELon EPfP EWTr LRHS MGil NQui SEND SLon SWvt WCFE

fasciculatum EShb
'Newellii' ♀H1c CBcs CCCN CExl EBak EBee ELan ELon EPfP EShb EUJe LRHS SEND SPlb SVen SWvt WKif
nocturnum CBcs CCCN CHll EBak EShb GCal WCFE
parqui ♀H3 CAbb CBcs CCCN CHll CMCN CTsd EBee ELan EPfP EUJe IDee LRHS MGil SEND SLon SMad SWvt WKif WSHC
psittacinum CExl
purpureum (Lindl.) Standl. see *C. elegans*
roseum CExl
- B&SWJ 10255 from Oaxaca State, Mexico WCru

Ceterach see *Asplenium*

officinarum see *Asplenium ceterach*

Chaenomeles (*Rosaceae*)

cathayensis CAgr CDul CTho EBee LEdu NLar SBrt WCru WHer WPGP

§ ***japonica*** CAco CCCN ESps MMuc SEND
- 'Chojubai' CMen
- 'Cido' CAgr LEdu MCoo
- 'Orange Beauty' LRHS SPer
- 'Rising Sun' NLar

- 'Sargentii'	ELan ETMg MBlu NLar SGol
MADAME BUTTERFLY ('Whitice')	CRos EBee ELan EPfP ESps LRHS LSRN MAsh MMuc MRav NRHS SCob SEND SGol SLim SPer SPoG SRms
maulei	see *C. japonica*
'Orange Star'	CEnd
'Red Kimono'	LCro LOPS LRHS SGol
sinensis	see *Pseudocydonia sinensis*
speciosa 'Apple Blossom'	see *C. speciosa* 'Moerloosei'
- 'Brilliant'	EPfP
- 'Contorta'	LRHS MAsh WFar
- 'Eximia'	LRHS
- 'Falconnet Charlet' (d)	CRos LRHS MRav NRHS SRms
- 'Flocon Rose'	EPfP LRHS SGol
- 'Friesdorfer'	LRHS
- 'Geisha Girl' (d) ♀H6	CBcs CEnd CMac CRos CSBt EBee ELan EPfP IRob LCro LOPS LRHS LSRN MAsh MGos MRav MSwo NRHS SCob SGbt SGol SLim SPer SPoG SRms SWvt WFar
- HOT FIRE ('Minvesu')	EPfP LRHS
- 'Kinshiden'	EPfP LRHS LSRN NLar SGol
§ - 'Moerloosei' ♀H6	Widely available
- 'Nivalis'	Widely available
- 'Orange Storm' **new**	SGol
- 'Pink Storm' **new**	SGol
- 'Rubra Grandiflora'	LRHS
- 'Scarlet Storm' **new**	SGol
- 'Simonii' (d)	CBcs MRav SPer
- 'Snow'	MAsh MSwo SRms
- 'Umbilicata'	MBlu SPer SRms
- 'Yukigotan' (d)	CRos LCro LEdu LLHF LOPS LRHS NLar SCob SGol SWvt
× ***superba***	ESps IBoy
- 'Boule de Feu'	CTri MCoo
- 'Cameo' (d)	CChe CEnd ELon EPfP LEdu LRHS MBNS MRav NLar SGol SRms WFar
- 'Coquelicot'	NLar
- 'Crimson and Gold' ♀H6	Widely available
- 'Elly Mossel'	CMac NLar SRms WFar
- 'Ernst Finken'	NLar
- 'Etna'	GMcL WFar
- 'Fire Dance'	CDul CHll CTsd EUJe MSwo NLar SGol SPer SPoG WCot WRHF
- 'Fusion'	CAgr
- 'Hollandia'	SRms
- 'Issai White'	MRav NLar
- 'Jet Trail'	CBcs CMac CRos CSBt ECrN ELan EPfP ESps GMcL LRHS LSRN MAsh MGos MJak MRav MSwo NLar NRHS SCob SGol SLim SPoG SRms SWvt WFar
- 'Knap Hill Scarlet'	CDul CRos CWCL EBee ELan EPfP IRob LRHS MAsh MGos NRHS SCob SEND SLim SNig SPer SPoG SRms SWvt
- 'Lemon and Lime'	ELan EWTr LRHS MAsh MGos MRav NLar SBod SLon SRms
- 'Nicoline' ♀H6	CBcs CDul EPfP ESps IBoy LRHS MGos NEgg SCob WMoo
- 'Pink Lady' ♀H6	Widely available
- 'Pink Trail'	NLar SRms
- 'Red Joy'	EBee EPfP LRHS MRav NLar
- 'Red Trail'	MRav
- 'Rowallane' ♀H6	CHll ELan EPfP MRav
- 'Salmon Horizon'	IArd NLar
- 'Tortuosa'	LRHS MBNS NLar WGrn
'Toyo-nishiki'	MBlu

Chaenorhinum (*Plantaginaceae*)

glareosum	ITim NHpl
§ ***origanifolium***	CBod SBee SPlb
- 'Blue Dream'	CSpe EPfP GKev LRHS MAsh NRHS SCob SPoG SWvt WFar WMoo
- 'Dreamcatcher'	EPfP WFar

Chaenostoma (*Scrophulariaceae*)

ABUNDA COLOSSAL WHITE ('Balabowite'PBR) (Abunda Series)	NPri
§ ***cordatum*** 'Blutopia' **new**	ETMg
- 'Olympic Gold' (v)	SCoo
- (Scopia Series) SCOPIA GOLDEN LEAVES WHITE ('Dancop15')	NPri
- - SCOPIA GREAT CLASSIC PINK ('Dancop46')	NPri
§ - 'Snowflake'	NPer SCoo SPoG SWvt
- SNOWTOPIA ('Pas430726') **new**	CRav ETMg
§ ***neglectum***	WPGP
SCOPIA GREAT REGAL BLUE ('Dancop30') (Scopia Series)	NPri
'Secrets Central Pink' (Secrets Series)	LSou

Chaerophyllum (*Apiaceae*)

azoricum	LPla MAvo WOut
hirsutum	IMou
- 'Roseum'	Widely available
temulum	LEdu

Chamaebatiaria (*Rosaceae*)

millefolium	SBrt

Chamaecyparis ✿ (*Cupressaceae*)

funebris	see *Cupressus funebris*
lawsoniana	CAco CDul CPer ESps LMaj LPra WMou WTSh
- 'Allumii Aurea'	see *C. lawsoniana* 'Alumigold'
I - 'Allumii Green'	CAco
- 'Allumii Magnificent'	MAsh
§ - 'Alumigold'	MAsh MJak
- 'Alumii'	CAco LPra MJak
- 'Aurea'	CDul
- 'Aurea Densa' ♀H6	CKen CSBt CTri MGos NRHS
- 'Aurea Nana' **new**	GMil
- 'Bleu Nantais' ♀H6	CAco CKen EMOT EPfP ESps GMil LBee LRHS MGos SCoo SLim SPoG WCFE
- 'Blom'	CKen
- 'Blue Surprise'	CKen
- 'Brégéon'	CKen NLar
- 'Broomhill Gold' ♀H6	CSBt EMOT GMcL GMil LBee MGos NRHS SCoo SLim SPoG
- 'Burford Gold' **new**	NRHS
- 'Caudata'	CKen
§ - 'Chilworth Silver' ♀H6	CSBt ESps LBee LRHS MAsh NRHS
- 'Columnaris'	CAco EMOT EPfP ESps LBee LPra MJak NEgg SCoo SPoG
- 'Columnaris Glauca'	CMac ESps GMcL GMil MGos NEgg NLar SAko SCoo
- 'Compact Blue' **new**	LSvl
- 'Cream Crackers'	EMOT
- 'Cream Glow'	CKen CSBt GMil NRHS
- 'Dik's Weeping' ♀H6	NLar SLim
- 'Duncanii'	EMOT

	- 'Dutch Gold'	MAsh
	- 'Dwarf Blue'	see *C. lawsoniana* 'Pick's Dwarf Blue'
	- 'Eclipse'	CKen
	- 'Elegantissima' ambig.	CMac SLim
	- 'Ellwoodii' ♀^{H6}	CAco CDul CMac CSBt CTri ELan EMOT EPfP ESps GMcL GMil LRHS MGil MGos NEgg NPri NRHS SCoo SLim SPer
I	- 'Ellwoodii Glauca'	SPlb
	- 'Ellwood's Empire'	NRHS
	- 'Ellwood's Gold' ♀^{H6}	CAco CBcs CDul CMac CSBt ELan EMOT EPfP ESps GMcL GMil LBee LRHS MAsh MGos MJak NPri NRHS SPer SPlb SPoG
	- 'Ellwood's Gold Pillar' ♀^{H6}	GMcL GMil LBee SBod SLim
§	- 'Ellwood's Nymph'	CKen MAsh
	- ELLWOOD'S PILLAR ('Flolar') ♀^{H6}	CAco CMac EMOT ESps GMcL LBee LRHS MGos NLar SCoo SLim
	- 'Ellwood's Pygmy'	CMac
	- 'Ellwood's Silver Threads'	CMac LBee
	- 'Ellwood's Variegata'	see *C. lawsoniana* 'Ellwood's White'
§	- 'Ellwood's White' (v)	CAco CMac CSBt EMOT GMcL SPoG
	- 'Emerald Spire'	MAsh
	- 'Erecta'	ESps
	- 'Erecta Viridis'	GMcL MJak NEgg
	- 'Filip's Golden Tears'	ELan MAsh NLar SLim
	- 'Fleckellwood'	MAsh NRHS
	- 'Fletcheri' ♀^{H6}	CMac
	- 'Fletcheri Aurea'	see *C. lawsoniana* 'Yellow Transparent'
	- 'Forsteckensis'	NLar
I	- 'Forsteckensis Aurea'	NLar
	- 'Gimbornii' ♀^{H6}	CDul NLar NRHS
	- 'Glauca'	CDul ESps
	- 'Globosa'	GMcL
	- 'Gnome'	CKen CMac EMOT SCoo SPoG
§	- 'Golden Pot'	CSBt GMcL LBee
	- 'Golden Wonder' ♀^{H6}	CAco EMOT MAsh NEgg NLar SCoo
	- 'Goldfinger'	NLar
	- 'Grayswood Feather' ♀^{H6}	ESps GMcL GMil LBee NRHS SPlb
	- 'Grayswood Gold'	GMcL
	- 'Grayswood Pillar'	ESps
	- 'Green Globe' ♀^{H6}	CKen CMen CSBt ESps LBee LRHS
§	- 'Green Hedger'	CSBt
§	- 'Green Pillar'	CAco CDul EMOT ESps GMcL LBee NEgg
	- 'Green Spire'	see *C. lawsoniana* 'Green Pillar'
	- 'Hillieri'	CAco
	- 'Imbricata Pendula' ♀^{H6}	CKen IDee MBlu NLar WPGP
	- 'Ivonne' ♀^{H6}	CAco CDul EMOT EPfP GMcL GMil LRHS MAsh MGos NLar NRHS SLim SPoG
	- 'Jackman's Green Hedger'	see *C. lawsoniana* 'Green Hedger'
	- 'Jackman's Variety'	see *C. lawsoniana* 'Green Pillar'
	- 'Jeanette'	CKen
	- 'Kilmacurragh' ♀^{H6}	CAco CDul CMac WCFE
	- 'Kilworth Column'	LRHS NLar
	- 'Knowefieldensis'	CMac EMOT
	- 'Lane' misapplied	see *C. lawsoniana* 'Lanei Aurea'
	- 'Lane' den Ouden	EMOT MJak NEgg
§	- 'Lanei Aurea' ♀^{H6}	ESps LMaj
	- 'Lemon Pillar'	WHar
	- 'Lemon Queen'	LBee
	- 'Little Spire' ♀^{H6}	ESps EUJe GMil LRHS NLar NRHS
§	- 'Lutea Nana'	CMac ESps NLar
§	- 'Lutea Smithii'	CAco
	- 'Luteocompacta'	LBee
	- 'Minima Argentea'	see *C. lawsoniana* 'Nana Argentea'
	- 'Minima Aurea' ♀^{H6}	CKen CMac CSBt EMOT EPfP ESps GMcL GMil LBee LRHS MAsh MGil MGos MJak NEgg NRHS SLim SPoG WCFE
	- 'Minima Glauca' ♀^{H6}	CAco CMac EMOT ESps GMcL GMil MJak NEgg NRHS SCoo SLim WFar
	- 'Moonsprite' ♀^{H6}	CAco CKen EMOT GMil NLar SCoo SLim SPoG
	- 'Nana'	ESps
	- 'Nana Albospica' (v)	EMOT LBee NRHS
§	- 'Nana Argentea'	CKen CMac EMOT EPfP GMil SPoG
	- 'Nana Lutea'	see *C. lawsoniana* 'Lutea Nana'
	- 'Nicole'	EMOT GMil MAsh SCoo
	- 'Nyewoods'	see *C. lawsoniana* 'Chilworth Silver'
	- 'Nymph'	see *C. lawsoniana* 'Ellwood's Nymph'
	- 'Pearly Swirls' (v)	LRHS NLar SPoG
§	- 'Pelt's Blue'	CAco CBcs CDul CSBt ESps MJak NLar
	- 'Pembury Blue' ♀^{H6}	CCVT CDul EMOT EPfP ESps GMcL GMil LBee LPra LRHS MAsh MGos MJak NEgg NLar NRHS SCoo SLim SPoG
§	- 'Pick's Dwarf Blue'	GMil
	- 'Pina Colada'^{PBR}	LRHS
	- POT OF GOLD	see *C. lawsoniana* 'Golden Pot'
	- 'Pottenii'	ESps GMcL LBee NLar
	- 'Pygmaea Argentea' (v) ♀^{H6}	CKen CMac CSBt ELan EMOT ESps GMil MGos NEgg NRHS SLim SPoG
	- 'Pygmy'	ESps NLar
	- 'Rijnhof'	LBee
	- 'Rimpelaar'	CKen NWad
	- 'Royal Gold'	GMil
	- 'Silver Queen' (v)	CKen
	- 'Silver Threads' (v)	CAco ELan EMOT EPfP ESps LBee LRHS NRHS SLim SPoG
	- 'Silver Tip' (v)	EMOT
	- 'Smithii'	see *C. lawsoniana* 'Lutea Smithii'
	- 'Snow Flurry' (v)	CKen
	- 'Snow White'^{PBR} (v) ♀^{H6}	EMOT ESps GMcL GMil LBee LRHS MAsh MGos NRHS SCoo SPoG
	- 'Springtime'^{PBR}	CSBt GMil LBee LRHS NRHS
	- 'Stardust' ♀^{H6}	CBcs CDul CSBt ELan ESps GMcL LPra LRHS MGos MJak NEgg NRHS
	- 'Stewartii'	CDul ESps LPra NEgg
	- 'Summer Snow' (v) ♀^{H6}	CAco EMOT EPfP GMcL GMil NRHS SCoo
	- 'Sunkist'	NRHS
	- 'Tamariscifolia'	WCFE
	- 'Treasure' (v)	CDul MAsh NRHS
	- 'Van Pelt'	see *C. lawsoniana* 'Pelt's Blue'
	- 'Waterfall'	CAco
	- 'White Spot' (v)	EMOT GMcL NRHS
	- 'White Wonder'	GMil
	- 'Winston Churchill'	IRob
	- 'Wisselii' ♀^{H6}	CKen CMac EMOT ESps MGos NLar SLim WCFE
	- 'Wisselii Nana'	CKen
	- 'Wissel's Saguaro' ♀^{H6}	CKen NLar
	- 'Witzeliana'	NLar
	- 'Yellow Spire' **new**	NLar
§	- 'Yellow Transparent'	CMac NRHS
	× ***leylandii***	see × *Cuprocyparis leylandii*
	nootkatensis	see *Xanthocyparis nootkatensis*
	obtusa	ESps LPra
	- 'Albovariegata' (v)	CKen
	- 'Arneson's Compact'	CKen

	- 'Aurora' 🏆H7	CKen ELan EMOT SLim SPoG
	- 'Bambi'	CKen WAbe WThu
	- 'Barkenny'	CKen
	- 'Bartley'	CKen
	- 'Bassett'	CKen
	- 'Bess'	CKen
	- 'Brigitt'	CKen
	- 'Bronze Pygmy'	LRHS NLar
	- 'Butterball'	CKen LRHS
	- 'Caespitosa'	WAbe
	- 'Chabo-yadori'	NLar
	- 'Chilworth'	CKen NWad
	- 'Chima-anihiba'	CKen
	- 'Chirimen'	CKen NLar
	- 'Clarke's Seedling'	CKen LRHS
	- 'Confucius'	EUJe
	- 'Corley Gold'	EUJe NLar
§	- 'Crippsii' 🏆H7	CBcs CMac LPra
	- 'Crippsii Aurea'	see *C. obtusa* 'Crippsii'
	- 'Dainty Doll'	CKen NLar NWad
	- 'Densa'	see *C. obtusa* 'Nana Densa'
	- 'Draht'	NLar
	- 'Draht Hexe'	CKen
	- 'Elf'	CKen NLar
	- 'Ellie B'	CKen
	- 'Ericoides'	CKen
	- 'Erika'	NLar
	- 'Fernspray Gold' 🏆H7	CCVT CDul CKen CTri EMOT EPfP ESps GMcL GMil LRHS MGos NEgg NLar NRHS SCoo SLim SPoG
	- 'Flabelliformis'	CKen NWad
	- 'Gemstone' **new**	NLar
	- 'Gitte'	SLim
	- 'Gnome'	CKen CMen
	- 'Gold Fern'	CKen
	- 'Golden Fairy'	CKen NLar
	- 'Golden Filament' (v)	CKen
	- 'Golden Nymph'	CKen
	- 'Golden Sprite'	CKen WAbe
	- 'Gracilis'	GMil NEgg
	- 'Gracilis Aurea'	CKen CMac GMil
	- 'Graciosa'	see *C. obtusa* 'Loenik'
	- 'Green Cushion'	CKen
	- 'Green Diamond'	CKen
	- 'Hage'	CKen
	- 'Hannah'	NLar
	- 'Hypnoides Nana'	CKen
	- 'Intermedia'	CKen WAbe
	- 'Ivan's Column'	CKen
	- 'Junior'	CKen
	- 'Juniperoides'	CKen
	- 'Juniperoides Compacta'	WAbe
	- 'Kamarachiba' 🏆H7	CKen CSBt EMOT GMcL LBee MAsh NEgg NLar SCoo SLim SPoG
	- 'Kerdalo'	LRHS NLar
	- 'Konijn'	GMcL GMil
	- 'Kosteri' 🏆H7	CKen CMac ELan EMOT ESps GMil LBee SCoo
	- 'Kyoto Creeper'	CKen
	- 'Leprechaun'	WAbe
	- 'Limerick'	CKen
	- 'Little Markey'	CKen
§	- 'Loenik'	EMOT
	- 'Lucas' PBR	LRHS NLar
	- 'Lutea Nova' **new**	CAco
	- 'Marian'	CKen NLar
§	- 'Mariesii' (v)	CKen LRHS
	- 'Melody'	CKen NLar
	- 'Meroke'	NLar
	- 'Minima'	CKen
	- 'Nana' 🏆H7	CAco CKen CMac CMen ESps LBee NWad
	- 'Nana Aurea' 🏆H7	CMac CSBt EMOT EPfP ESps LRHS MJak NEgg NRHS
§	- 'Nana Densa'	CKen CMac
	- 'Nana Gracilis' 🏆H7	CDul CKen CMen CSBt ELan EMOT EPfP GMcL GMil LRHS MGos MJak NEgg NRHS NWad SBod SCoo SLim SPoG
I	- 'Nana Gracilis Aurea'	CAco CMen GMil NEgg
I	- 'Nana Lutea' 🏆H7	CKen ELan EMOT GMcL GMil LBee LRHS MAsh MGos NWad SLim
	- 'Nana Rigida'	see *C. obtusa* 'Rigid Dwarf'
	- 'Nana Variegata'	see *C. obtusa* 'Mariesii'
	- 'Pygmaea'	CSBt EMOT ESps NEgg SCoo SLim
	- 'Rashahiba'	LRHS NRHS
	- 'Reis Dwarf'	EUJe
	- 'Rezek Dwarf' **new**	CKen CMen
§	- 'Rigid Dwarf'	CKen LBee SLim
	- 'Saffron Spray'	NLar
	- 'Slim Jim' **new**	NLar
	- 'Snowflake' (v)	CKen ELan NEgg NWad
	- 'Snowkist' (v)	CKen
	- 'Southern Lights' **new**	NLar
	- 'Sparkles'	NLar
	- 'Spiralis'	CKen
	- 'Split Rock'	NLar
	- 'Stoneham'	CKen CMen NEgg SBod
	- 'Strangman' **new**	CKen
	- 'Tempelhof'	CKen NEgg NLar SCoo
	- 'Tetragona Aurea'	CMac NWad
	- 'Timothy'	CMac
	- 'Tonia' (v)	CKen
	- 'Tsatsumi'	NLar
	- 'Tsatsumi Gold' 🏆H7	CAco CKen ELan EPfP LRHS MPkF NLar SCoo SLim SPoG
	- 'Verdon'	CKen
	- 'Villa Marie'	NLar
	- 'Wiels Baby' **new**	NLar
	- 'Wissel'	CKen
	- 'Wyckoff'	CKen
	- 'Yellowtip' (v)	CKen EPfP MAsh NEgg
	pisifera 'Argenteovariegata' (v) **new**	GMil
	- 'Aurea Nana' misapplied	see *C. pisifera* 'Strathmore'
	- 'Aureovariegata' **new**	GMil
	- 'Baby Blue'	ELan EPfP LRHS SCoo SLim SPoG
	- 'Blue Globe'	CKen
	- 'Boulevard' 🏆H7	CBcs CBod CDul CMac CSBt ELan EMOT EPfP ESps GMcL GMil LBee LRHS MAsh MGos MJak NEgg NRHS SLim SPer WBor
	- 'Compacta Variegata' (v)	GMil NEgg
	- 'Curly Top' 🏆H7	CAco CSBt EMOT EPfP ESps GMil SCoo SLim SPoG
	- 'Devon Cream'	NEgg
	- 'Filifera'	CMac CSBt
	- 'Filifera Aurea' 🏆H7	CKen CMac ELan EMOT EPfP ESps LBee LMaj MAsh MGos MJak NEgg SCoo
	- 'Filifera Aureovariegata' (v)	ESps
	- 'Filifera Nana'	CAco ELan LRHS NRHS SLim
	- 'Filifera Nana Aurea'	see *C. pisifera* 'Golden Mop'
	- 'Filifera Sungold'	see *C. pisifera* 'Sungold'
	- 'Fuiri-tsukomo'	CKen
	- 'Gold Cushion'	CKen
	- 'Gold Dust'	see *C. pisifera* 'Plumosa Aurea'
	- 'Gold Spangle'	CKen
§	- 'Golden Mop'	CAco CKen NLar
	- 'Green Pincushion'	CKen CMen

	- 'Hime-himuro'	CKen
	- 'Hime-sawara'	CKen CMen
	- 'Iceberg'	NLar
	- 'Lime Tart'	CKen
	- 'Nana'	CKen CMen EMOT ESps GMcL
	- 'Nana Aureovariegata' (v)	CSBt GMil LBee NRHS
I	- 'Nana Compacta'	CMac
	- 'Nana Variegata' (v)	CMac LBee
I	- 'Parslorii'	CKen
	- 'Pici'	CKen
§	- 'Plumosa Aurea'	CKen MAsh
	- 'Plumosa Aurea Compacta'	CKen NWad
	- 'Plumosa Aurea Nana'	MAsh
I	- 'Plumosa Aurea Nana Compacta'	CMac
	- 'Plumosa Aurescens'	CMac
§	- 'Plumosa Compressa' ♀H7	CKen NWad
	- 'Plumosa Densa'	see *C. pisifera* 'Plumosa Compressa'
I	- 'Plumosa Juniperoides'	CKen ESps NRHS
I	- 'Plumosa Pygmaea'	ESps
§	- 'Plumosa Rogersii'	GMcL
I	- 'Pygmaea Tsukumo'	NLar
	- 'Rogersii'	see *C. pisifera* 'Plumosa Rogersii'
	- 'Silver Lode' (v)	CKen
	- 'Snow' (v)	CKen
	- 'Snowflake'	CKen
	- 'Spaan's Cannon Ball'	CKen
	- 'Squarrosa Dumosa'	CKen
I	- 'Squarrosa Lombarts'	CMac CSBt GMil
	- 'Squarrosa Lutea'	CKen
	- 'Squarrosa Sulphurea'	CSBt ELan ESps NRHS
§	- 'Strathmore'	CAco
§	- 'Sungold' ♀H7	CKen CSBt ELan ESps GMil LRHS MAsh MGos NRHS SCoo SLim SPoG
	- 'Tama-himuro'	CKen GMil
	- 'Teddy Bear'	NEgg NLar
	- 'True Blue'	CAco ELan GMil
	- 'White Beauty' (v)	EMOT GMil
	thyoides 'Andelyensis'	CMac CSBt EMOT
	- 'Ericoides'	CKen CTri EMOT ESps LBee SPlb
	- 'Little Jamie'	CKen
	- 'Red Star'	see *C. thyoides* 'Rubicon'
§	- 'Rubicon'	CMac CSBt EMOT EPfP ESps LBee LRHS MAsh NEgg NRHS SLim SPoG
	- 'Top Point'	LBee LRHS MAsh SCoo SPoG

Chamaedaphne (*Ericaceae*)

	calyculata	CBcs

Chamaedorea (*Arecaceae*)

	elegans ♀H1a	NLos
	metallica misapplied	see *C. microspadix*
§	***microspadix***	CPHo
	radicalis	CBrP CPHo NLos

Chamaemelum (*Asteraceae*)

§	***nobile***	CBod CHby CPrp CTri EBWF ENfk EPfP GPoy LCro MHer MMuc MNHC NGdn NPri SEND SPlb SRms SVic WSpi WTre XAbr
	- dwarf	SMor SVic
	- dwarf, double-flowered (d)	LEdu
	- 'Flore Pleno' (d)	CBod CBre CElw CMea CPrp CTri ECha ENfk EPfP GPoy MHer MHol MNHC MRav NBro NGdn SBch SPer SRms WHal WTre
	- 'Treneague'	CBod CBre CPrp CTri ECha ELan ENfk EPfP GAbr GKin GPoy MCot MHer MNHC MRav SMor SPer SPlb SRms WFar WHal WHer WTre

Chamaenerion (*Onagraceae*)

§	***angustifolium***	WSFF
§	- 'Album'	Widely available
	- 'Isobel'	MRav WCot
	- 'Stahl Rose'	CAby CHid CMea CRav EPfP EWes LEdu NSti SGbt SMad SPhx WCot WSHC
§	***dodonaei***	CFis EWes IMou SMHy SPhx WCot WSHC
§	***fleischeri***	MMuc

Chamaepericlymenum see *Cornus*

Chamaerhodos (*Rosaceae*)

	altaica new	GKev

Chamaerops (*Arecaceae*)

	sp.	ETod
	excelsa misapplied	see *Trachycarpus fortunei*
	excelsa Thunb.	see *Rhapis excelsa*
	humilis ♀H4	CAbb CAco CBcs CBrP CTsd ELan EPfP ESps ETod EUJe LRHS MGos NPla SArc SChr SEND SPlb SPoG STrG SWeb WCot XSen
§	- var. ***argentea***	CBlu CBrP CDTJ CPHo ETod LRHS MGos SChr SPlb WCot
	- var. ***cerifera***	see *C. humilis* var. *argentea*
	- 'Stella'	ETod
	- 'Vulcano'	CDTJ EUJe SChr

Chamaespartium see *Genista*

Chamaesphacos (*Lamiaceae*)

	ilicifolius misapplied	see *Siphocranion macranthum*

Chamelaucium (*Myrtaceae*)

	uncinatum	CCCN EShb
	- 'Snowflake'	CCCN EBee

Chamerion see *Chamaenerion*

chard see AGM Vegetables Section

Charybdis (*Asparagaceae*)

§	***maritima***	LAma WCot

Chasmanthe (*Iridaceae*)

	aethiopica	CPbh EPri
	bicolor	CExl CPrp CTca EPri EWld
	floribunda	CPrp EPri GKev SDeJ
	- var. ***duckittii***	CPrp GKev SDeJ
	- - 'Golden Wave'	CPrp GKev

Chasmanthium (*Poaceae*)

§	***latifolium***	CBWd CBod CKno CSpe EAJP ECha EHoe ELan ELon EPPr EShb EUJe GMcL LEdu LRHS MAvo MMuc NRHS SCob SGol SMad SPad SPoG SRms WCot XLum
	- 'Golden Spangles'	CKno
	- 'River Mist' (v)	CBod EBee ECha ELan SCob SPoG
	laxum	CBod

Cheilanthes ✿ (*Pteridaceae*)

	acrostica	CBdn
	argentea	EBee
	distans	WAbe
	eatonii	WAbe
	***ecklonia*na**	WAbe

farinosa new	CBdn
grisea	WAbe
lanosa	CBod CCCN CRos EBee EFer EPot EWes LRHS NLos NRHS SPlb SPoG WAbe WCot
lindheimeri	WAbe
myriophylla	WAbe
tomentosa	CBdn CCCN CRos EBee LRHS NRHS WAbe
wootonii	WAbe

Cheiranthus see *Erysimum*

Cheirolophus (*Asteraceae*)

benoistii misapplied	see *Centaurea atropurpurea*
benoistii (Humb.) Holub	CSpe MRav WSHC

Chelidonium (*Papaveraceae*)

japonicum	see *Hylomecon japonica*
majus	EBWF GPSL GPoy NMir WHer WHil WSFF XAbr
- 'Flore Pleno' (d)	CBre GJos NBid NBro
- var. ***laciniatum***	WCot

Chelone (*Plantaginaceae*)

barbata	see *Penstemon barbatus*
§ ***glabra***	CBod CMac CRos EBee ECha ELan EPfP GMaP GWyn ILea LRHS MMuc NBid NBro NEgg NGdn NLar SPer SPlb SRms WFar WHar WMoo WPnP WSHC WWtn
lyonii	EBee ILea NLar WShi
- 'Hot Lips'	WHil WPnP
- 'Pink Temptation'	EBee GEdr MMoz
obliqua	Widely available
- var. ***alba***	see *C. glabra*
- 'Ieniemienie'	EBee LEdu
- 'Pink Sensation'	WFar
I 'Pink Turtle'	EBee GBin

Chelonopsis (*Lamiaceae*)

moschata	EBee GEdr LEdu MBel MHer SBrt SMad SPlb WHil WMoo
yagiharana	CAby CMea NBid WMoo

Chengiopanax (*Araliaceae*)

sciadophylloides	WCru

Chenopodium (*Amaranthaceae*)

bonus-henricus	CAgr CFGn CHab CHby ENfk GPoy MCoo MHer MNHC SRms WHer WTre
giganteum	MNHC SRms

cherimoya see *Annona cherimola*

cherry, Duke see *Prunus* × *gondouinii*

cherry, sour or morello see *Prunus cerasus*

cherry, sweet see *Prunus avium*

chervil see *Anthriscus cerefolium*

chestnut, sweet see *Castanea sativa*

Chiastophyllum (*Crassulaceae*)

oppositifolium	see *Umbilicus oppositifolius*
- 'Frosted Jade'	see *Umbilicus oppositifolius* 'Jim's Pride'
simplicifolium	see *Umbilicus oppositifolius*

chicory see *Cichorium intybus*; also AGM Vegetables Section

Chiliotrichum (*Asteraceae*)

diffusum	CCCN MMuc
- 'Siska'	CBcs

chilli pepper see *Capsicum*; also AGM Vegetables Section

Chimonanthus ✿ (*Calycanthaceae*)

fragrans	see *C. praecox*
nitens	CBcs CMCN NLar
§ ***praecox***	Widely available
- 'Brockhill Goldleaf'	NLar
- 'Grandiflorus' 🏆H5	CEnd CJun CRos ELan EPfP LRHS MAsh SPer SPoG WCot
- 'Luteus' 🏆H4	CEnd CJun ELan EPfP LEdu LRHS MAsh MGos NLar SChF SPoG WCot
- 'Sunburst'	CJun
- 'Trenython' 🏆H4	CEnd CJun

Chimonobambusa (*Poaceae*)

KR 7592	MWht
hookeriana misapplied	see *Himalayacalamus falconeri* 'Damarapa'
§ ***marmorea***	CDTJ ERod MMuc SBig
- 'Variegata' (v)	CDTJ ERod
§ ***quadrangularis***	CBcs CDTJ EPfP ERod IMou MMoz MWht
- 'Nagaminei' (v)	ERod
- 'Suow' (v)	CDTJ
- 'Tatejima'	ERod
tumidissinoda	CBdn CDTJ ERod IMou MMoz MWht SBig

Chinese chives see *Allium tuberosum*

Chinese cabbage see AGM Vegetables Section

Chiogenes see *Gaultheria*

Chionanthus (*Oleaceae*)

retusus	CBcs CCCN CDul CMCN CRos EBee EPfP EWTr LRHS MPkF NLar SAko SPer
- 'Arnold's Pride'	WPGP
virginicus	CBcs CCCN CDul CMCN CRos ECrN ELan EPfP EWTr GBin IArd LRHS MBlu MGil MMuc MRav NEgg NLar SAko SPer SPlb WSpi

Chionochloa (*Poaceae*)

conspicua	CAby CBod EBee GAbr GCal GKev MAvo NBid WPGP
- subsp. ***conspicua***	WCot
- 'Rubra'	see *C. rubra*
flavescens	EBee EHoe MAvo WPGP
flavicans	GBin IMou SMad
rigida	MAvo
§ ***rubra*** 🏆H7	CCht CElw CKno CSpe EBee EHoe ELan EWes GBin GCal IMou IRob MAsh MRav SMad WCot WMoo WPGP
- PAB 67	LEdu
- subsp. ***cupreus***	CAby

Chionodoxa ✿ (*Asparagaceae*)

§ ***forbesii***	CRav CRos EPfP EPot GKev LAma LRHS NHpl NRHS SCob SDeJ SDir SPer SRms WShi
- 'Alba'	SDir
- 'Blue Giant'	ELan EPot ERCP GKev SCob SDir
- 'Rosea'	GKev LAma NHpl
- 'Violet Beauty'	GKev IRob SDeJ SDir
- 'Zwanenburg'	GKev
gigantea	see *C. luciliae* Gigantea Group
luciliae misapplied	see *C. forbesii*
luciliae ambig.	CAvo LCro LOPS LRHS MWat NRHS SEND
luciliae Boiss. ♀H5	CAby EPfP LAma SPer
- 'Alba'	CRos IRob LAma LRHS NHpl NRHS SDeJ SDir SPer
§ - Gigantea Group	GKev
- - 'Alba'	EPot GKev SCob
- 'Rosy Queen'	GKev LAma
'Pink Giant'	CAvo CRos ELan EPfP EPot ERCP GKev LAma LRHS NRHS SCob SDeJ SDir WBor XLum
sardensis ♀H5	CRos EPot ERCP GKev LAma LRHS NRHS SDeJ SPhx WShi
'Valentine Day'	EPot

Chionographis (*Melanthiaceae*)

japonica	GEdr

Chionohebe (*Plantaginaceae*)

pulvinaris	NSla WAbe
'Vera Cox'	WAbe

× *Chionoscilla* (*Asparagaceae*)

§ ***allenii***	SPhx WCot

Chiranthodendron (*Malvaceae*)

pentadactylon	SPlb

Chirita (*Gesneriaceae*)

'Aiko'	WDib
'Candy'	WDib
'Chastity'	WDib
'Diane Marie'	WDib
'Erika'	WDib
flavimaculata	WDib
heterotricha	WDib
'Keiko'	WDib
linearifolia	WDib
linearifolia × sinensis	WDib
longgangensis	WDib
'New York'	WDib
sinensis ♀H1c	WDib
- 'Hisako'	WDib
speciosa 'Crûg Cornetto'	WCru
'Stardust'	WDib
'Sweet Dreams'	WDib
tamiana	WDib

Chironia (*Gentianaceae*)

baccifera	SPlb

× *Chitalpa* (*Bignoniaceae*)

tashkentensis	CBcs CEnd EPfP EUJe MMrt SBrt
- 'Morning Cloud'	MBlu
- 'Pink Dawn'	CBcs MBlu
- SUMMER BELLS ('Minsum')	CCCN ELon WCot

chives see *Allium schoenoprasum*

Chlidanthus (*Amaryllidaceae*)

fragrans	CCCN GKev SDeJ SEND

Chloranthus (*Chloranthaceae*)

fortunei	SCob WCot
glaber B&SWJ 11102	WCru
henryi	WCot
japonicus	GEdr WCru
oldhamii	CTal WPGP
- B&SWJ 2019	GEdr LEdu WCru
serratus	GEdr WCru
sessilifolius 'Domino'	WCot

Chloris (*Poaceae*)

distichophylla	see *Eustachys distichophylla*

Chlorogalum (*Asparagaceae*)

pomeridianum 'Berkeley Hills'	SBrt
- tall, from Siskiyou Mountains, Oregon	SBrt

Chlorophytum (*Asparagaceae*)

capense 'Variegatum' (v) **new**	CPla
comosum	EShb SEND SVic
- 'Aureomarginata' (v)	SEND
- 'Variegatum' (v) ♀H2	CTsd EShb LOPS NGBl SEND SPre
- 'Vittatum' (v) ♀H2	EShb NGBl
graminifolium	EBee
krookianum	WCot
macrophyllum	EShb
nepalense	IMou WPGP
- B&SWJ 2528	WCru
- PAB 13.034 **new**	LEdu
saundersiae	CExl

Choisya (*Rutaceae*)

× ***dewitteana*** APPLE BLOSSOM ('Pmoore09') **new**	LCro LOPS SLon
- 'Aztec Gold'PBR	CBcs CRos EPfP LRHS MAsh MGos NLar NRHS SCob WFar
- 'Aztec Pearl' ♀H4	Widely available
- GOLDEN GIFT ('Lismarty'PBR)	CRos LRHS NRHS
- GOLDFINGERS ('Limo'PBR)	CBcs CDul CMac CRos CWGN EBee ELan EMOT EPfP EShb ESps EUJe GMcL LRHS LSRN MGos MJak MRav NEgg NLar NPri NRHS SCob SGbt SLon SPer SPoG SRms SWvt
- SNOW FLURRIES ('Lisflurry'PBR)	ELan EPfP LLHF LRHS MAsh MRav NRHS SPoG
- WHITE DAZZLER ('Londaz'PBR) ♀H4	Widely available
'Royal Lace'	LRHS SLon
ternata ♀H4	Widely available
- MOONSHINE ('Walcho'PBR)	EBee NLar
- MOONSLEEPER	see *C. ternata* SUNDANCE
§ - SUNDANCE ('Lich'PBR) ♀H4	Widely available

Chondrosum (*Poaceae*)

gracile	see *Bouteloua gracilis*

Chordospartium see *Carmichaelia*

Chorisia (*Malvaceae*)

speciosa	CCCN SPlb

Chorispora (*Brassicaceae*)

sp. **new**	CPla

Chorizema (*Papilionaceae*)

cordatum ♀H2	SVen
dicksonii	SPlb

Chronanthus see *Cytisus*

Chrysalidocarpus see *Dypsis*

Chrysanthemopsis see *Rhodanthemum*

Chrysanthemum ✿ (*Asteraceae*)

E.H.Wilson s.n.	EWes MNrw WCot
'Action Bronze' (22)	EPfP NWsh
'Action Yellow' (22) ♀H3	WFar
'Agnes Ann' (21d)	MNrw
'Ahlemer Rote' (21)	MNrw NWad
'Alan Brown' (25a)	MCms
'Alan Foxall Yellow' (3b)	MCms
'Alec Bedser' (25a)	NHal
'Alex Young' (25b)	MCms
'Aline' (21)	MHCG
'Alison' (29c)	ELon MNrw
'Alison's Dad'	MNrw
'Allouise' (25b) ♀H3	NHal
'Allouise Orange' (25b)	CRav MCms NHal
'Allouise Pink' (25b)	MCms
'Allyson Peace' (14a)	MCms NHal
alpinum	see *Leucanthemopsis alpina*
'Alyece Shaw' (29d) **new**	NHal
'Amber Matlock' (24b)	MCms
'American Beauty Lemon' (5b)	MCms
'American Beauty Snowball' (5b)	MCms
'American Beauty White' (5b)	MCms
'Anastasia' ambig.	SAko
'Anastasia' (21c)	CHid EBee ELon ETMg GCal LRHS MNrw MRav NRHS NSti SRms WBor
'Anastasia Green'PBR **new**	CRav
'Anderton' (6b)	MCms
'Angela Blundell' (19b)	WCot
'Angela Cosimini' (25b)	MCms
'Angelic' (21b) ♀H4	EBee ELon
'Anne Ratsey' (21)	CSam MNrw WBrk
'Anne, Lady Brocket' (21d)	ECtt NWsh
'Anthony Peace' (25b)	MCms
'Antigua'PBR	MCms
'Apollo' H. Shoesmith	MNrw WCot
'Apollo' (21)	SPhx WFar WHoo
'Apricot'	see *C.* 'Cottage Apricot'
'Apricot Chessington' (25a)	MCms NHal
'Apricot Courtier' (24a)	MCms NHal
'Apricot Enbee Wedding'	see *C.* 'Bronze Enbee Wedding'
'Apricot Mundial' (6b)	MCms
'Arctic Beauty' (4b)	MCms
'Arctic Queen'PBR (23a)	MCms
'Arctic Queen Yellow'	MCms
arcticum L.	see *Arctanthemum arcticum*
argenteum	see *Tanacetum argenteum*
'Arthur Ellis' (25b) **new**	MCms
'Artist Orange'	MCms
'Astro' (25b)	MCms NHal
'Aunt Millicent' (21d) ♀H4	MHCG NHal WCot
'Balcombe Perfection' (5a)	MCms NHal
balsamita	see *Tanacetum balsamita*
BARBARA ('Yobarbara') (22)	NHal
'Barca'	MCms
'Beacon' (5a) ♀H2	MCms NHal
'Beechcroft' (29Rub)	MNrw SPhx
'Bella Orange' **new**	CRav
'Belle' (21d)	MHCG MNrw NWad
'Beppie Bronze' (29e)	MCms
'Beppie Purple' (29e)	MCms
'Beppie Red' (29e)	MCms
'Beppie Rose' (29e)	MCms
'Beppie Yellow' (29e)	MCms
'Bessie Rowe' (25a)	MCms
'Best Man' (29d)	MCms
'Bienchen' **new**	SAko
'Bill Holden' (14a)	MCms NHal
'Bill Wade' (25a)	MCms NHal
'Billy Bell' (15a)	MCms NHal
'Blanche Poitevene' (5b)	EMal MCms NHal
'Blenda Purple'	CRav
'Bob Green' (13b)	MCms
'Bobby Swinburn' (13b)	MCms NHal
boreale **new**	WCot
BRAVO ('Yobra') (22c) ♀H3	NHal
* 'Breitner's Supreme'	ECtt MHCG MNrw
'Brennpunkt'	MNrw
'Bretforton Road'	ECtt MNrw WCot WFar WOld
'Brierton Violet' (17b)	NHal
'Brightness' (21)	MNrw
'Bronze Cassandra' (5b) ♀H2	MCms NHal
'Bronze Darren Pugh' (3b)	NHal
'Bronze Dee Gem' (29c)	MCms NHal
§ 'Bronze Elegance' (21b) ♀H4	CDor CTri ECtt EPPr LRHS MNrw NGdn NRHS NSti NWsh SHar SRms WBor
§ 'Bronze Enbee Wedding' (29d) ♀H3	MCms NHal
'Bronze Gigantic' (1)	NHal
'Bronze Matlock' (24b)	MCms NHal
'Bronze Max Riley' (23b) ♀H3	MCms NHal
'Bronze Mayford Perfection' (5a) ♀H2	MCms
'Bronze Mei-kyo'	see *C.* 'Bronze Elegance'
'Bronze Talbot Parade' (29c) ♀H3	MCms
'Bronze William Florentine' (15a)	MCms
'Brooke Farm Red'	NWsh
'Brown Eyes' (21b) ♀H4	MNrw
'Bruno Bronze' (24)	CRav
'Bryony Wade' (13b)	MCms NHal
'Buff Peter Rowe' (23b)	MCms
'Buff William Florentine' (15a)	MCms
'Bunty' (28)	SMad
burnt orange-flowered	CAby CDor CFis MNrw
'Burntwood Belle' (3b)	MCms
'Buxton Ruby'	EWTr
'Candy John Wingfield' (14b)	MCms
'Capel Manor'	EBee MHCG MNrw WCot
'Capella' (10a)	MCms
'Cardinal Red'	LRHS
'Carlene Welby' (25b)	MCms

'Carmine Blush' (21d) ♀H4	GAbr MHCG MNrw WBrk WCot WFar
'Caroline Barclay' (14b)	MCms
'Casablanca' (25a)	NHal
'Cassandra' (5b) ♀H2	MCms NHal
'Cawthorne' (29d)	MCms WFar
'Charles Tandy' (5a)	MCms
'Charles Tandy Primrose' (15a)	MCms
'Charles Tandy Yellow' (15b)	MCms
'Charlie' (24b)	MCms
'Chatsworth' (29c)	NHal
'Chelsea Physic Garden'	CAby EBee ELon GAbr MHCG MNrw WCot WFar
'Chempak Rose' (14b)	MCms
'Cherilyn Arlett' (5a)	MCms
'Cherry Chessington' (25a)	MCms NHal
'Cherry Riley's Dynasty' (14a)	MCms
'Chesapeake Primrose' (10a)	MCms
CHESAPEAKE ('Yochesapeake'PBR) (10a)	GBin MCms NHal
'Chessington' (25a)	MCms
'Chessington Oyster' (25a)	MCms
'Chesswood Beauty' (7b)	MCms
'Chestnut Talbot Maid' (29c)	MCms
'Chestnut Talbot Parade' (29c) ♀H3	MCms WFar
'Chloe Ball' (13b)	MCms
'Christmas'	MNrw NWad
'Christopher Lawson' (24b)	MCms NHal
cinerariifolium	see *Tanacetum cinerariifolium*
'Citronella' **new**	MNrw
'Clapham Delight' (23a)	MCms NHal
'Clara Curtis' (21d)	Widely available
'Clare Louise' (24b)	MCms
'Clarksdale' (15b)	MCms NHal
coccineum	see *Tanacetum coccineum*
'Colsterworth'	MNrw
'Coral Reef' (10b)	MCms NHal
'Corinna' (21d)	GBin MNrw
'Cornetto' (25b)	MCms NHal
corymbosum	see *Tanacetum corymbosum*
§ 'Cottage Apricot' (21)	CDor EPfP LRHS MBNS MRav NRHS SMHy SRms WFar
'Cottage Bronze'	MNrw NWad
'Cottage Lemon'	MNrw NWad
'Cottage Pink'	see *C.* 'Emperor of China'
'Courtier' (24a)	NHal
'Cousin Joan' (21d) ♀H4	EBee ELon MHCG MNrw WCot WOld
'Cream Dorridge Crystal' (24a)	MCms
'Cream Elegance' (9c)	NHal
'Cream John Hughes' (3b)	MCms
'Cream Patricia Millar' (14b)	NHal
'Cream Talbot Maid' (29c)	MCms
'Cream Talbot Parade' (29c) ♀H3	MCms
'Cream West Bromwich' (14a)	MCms
'Crimson Purple Glow' (5a)	MCms
DANA ('Yodana') (25b) ♀H3	MCms NHal
DANCE ('Fidance'PBR) (9f)	MCms
'Dance Red' (9f)	MCms
DANCE SALMON ('Fidancesal') (9f)	GBin MCms
'Dance Sunny' (9f)	MCms
'Dance White' (9f)	MCms
'Daniel Cooper' (21d) ♀H4	EBee MNrw SBch WFar
'Danny Peace' (25b)	MCms
'Daphne Davis' (29d)	NHal
'Darren Pugh' (3b)	MCms NHal
'Darren Pugh Primrose' (3b)	MCms
'David Shoesmith' (25a)	MCms
'Dawn Charlton' (14a)	MCms
'Dee Gem' (29c) ♀H3	MCms NHal WFar
'Delianne'PBR	MCms
'Delianne New Green'PBR **new**	MCms
'Delianne Yellow'PBR	MCms
'Delistar'PBR (9f)	MCms
'Delistar Bronze' (9f)	MCms
'Delistar Cream'PBR (9f)	MCms
'Delistar Lemon' (9f)	MCms
'Delistar Lilac' (9f)	MCms
'Delistar Mint' (9f)	MCms
'Delistar Pink' (9f)	MCms
'Delistar Pink Star' (9f)	MCms
'Delistar Saffira' (9f)	MCms
'Delistar Sunny' (9f)	MCms
'Delta' (5b)	NHal
'Delta Copper Bronze' (9d)	NHal
'Delta Crimson' (29d)	NHal
'Delta Yellow' (29)	NHal
'Denise Oatridge' (5a)	MCms
'Dennis Gill' (25b)	MCms
'Dennis Turner' (25b)	MCms
'Dennis Turner Primrose' (15b)	MCms
'Dernier Soleil'	EBee MNrw XLum
'Deva Glow' (25a)	MCms NHal
'Disco Club'	MCms
'Dixter Orange'	EBee EWes GCal IRob MHCG SBee SMad SPhx WBor
§ 'Doctor Tom Parr' (21c)	CExl ELan MNrw
'Domingo' (14b)	MCms
'Don't Start' (7a)	MCms
'Doreen Hall' (15a)	MCms NHal
'Doreen Statham' (4b)	MCms NHal
'Doris Ozols' (25a)	MCms NHal
'Dorothy Stone' (25b)	MCms NHal
'Dorridge Crystal' (24a)	MCms NHal
'Dorridge King' (4b)	MCms
'Downpour' (10a)	MCms
'Dublin'	MCms
'Duchess of Edinburgh' (21d)	EBee ECtt ELan ELon EPfP LRHS LSun NRHS SPhx XLum
'Dulwich Pink' (21d) ♀H4	MHCG MNrw NWad WCot WOld
'Dutchy'PBR (9d)	MCms
'Early Yellow'	EBee ELon MNrw WCot WFar
'Edelweiss' (21)	CAby MNrw NWad
'Edina' (29d)	NHal
'Edmund Brown'	WCot WFar
'Edward Shaw' (5a)	MCms
'Egret' (23b)	MCms NHal
'Elaine's Hardy White' **new**	WCot
'Elegance' (9c)	NHal
'Elizabeth Lawson' (5b)	MCms NHal
§ 'Emperor of China' (21)	CAby CDor CElw ECha ECtt MHCG MNrw MRav NHal SBee SPhx SRms WBor WFar XLum
'Enbee Wedding' (29d) ♀H3	MCms NHal
'Energy'PBR (9)	MCms

	'Erebus White' **new**	CRav
	'Esther' (21d)	EBee ELon MHCG MHer MNrw SMad
	'Eva Allen' (25b)	MCms
	'Evelyn Bush' (25b)	MCms
	'Exopolis'	MCms
	'Fairweather' (3b)	MCms NHal
	'Fairweather Cream' (3b)	MCms
	'Fairweather Peach' (3b)	MCms
	'Fanfare Cherry'	LRHS
	'Fanfare Claret'	LRHS
	'Fanfare Flame'	LRHS
	'Fanfare Glowing Embers'	LRHS
	'Fanfare Orange'	LRHS
	'Fanfare Pink Blush'	LRHS
	'Fanfare Pink Pastel'	LRHS
	'Fanfare Rosetta'	LRHS
	'Fanfare Ruby'	LRHS
	'Fanfare Salmon'	LRHS
	'Fanfare Sunset'	LRHS
	'Feeling Green Dark' PBR	MCms
	'Feeling Sunny' PBR	MCms
	'Fleur de Lis' (10a)	MCms
	'Flo Cooper' (25a)	MCms
	foeniculaceum	see *Argyranthemum foeniculaceum*
	'Folk Song' (4b)	MNrw
	'Fondant'	NHal
	'Formcast' (24a)	MCms
	'French Rose'	MNrw
	'Froggy' PBR (9)	CRav MCms
	frutescens	see *Argyranthemum frutescens*
	'Gala Burgundy'	EPfP
	'Gambit' (24a)	MCms NHal
	'Geoff Aird' (15b)	MCms
	'Geoff Amos' (3b)	MCms
	'Geoff Brady' (5a)	MCms NHal
	'George Griffiths' (24b) ♀H3	MCms NHal
	'Gillette' (23b)	MCms
	'Ginger Nut' (25b)	MCms
	'Ginger Nut Yellow' (25b)	MCms
I	'Gladys' (12a)	NHal
	'Gladys Emerson' (3b)	MCms NHal
	'Gold Enbee Wedding' (29d) ♀H3	MCms
	'Gold Mundial' (6b) ♀H2	MCms
	'Golddukaten' (21)	NWad
	'Golden Cassandra' (5b) ♀H2	MCms NHal
	'Golden Chalice' (12a)	NHal
	'Golden Courtier' (24a)	MCms NHal
	'Golden Masons' (7b)	MCms
	'Golden Mayford Perfection' (5a) ♀H2	MCms
	'Golden Plover' (22)	NHal
	'Golden Rain' (10a) ♀H2	MCms NHal
	'Golden Roy Coopland' (5b)	MCms
	'Golden Seal' (7b)	MCms
	'Golden Shoesmith Salmon' (4a)	MCms
	'Golden Splendour' (10a)	MCms
	'Golden Wedding' (21)	MNrw
	'Golden William Florentine' (15a)	MCms
	'Golden Woolman's Glory' (7a)	NHal
	'Goldengreenheart' (21d) ♀H4	EBee ECtt ELon EPPr EShb MHCG MNrw SPhx WBrk WHoo
	'Goldmarianne' (21)	GBin WFar XLum
	'Gompie Red'	CRav
	'Goodlife Sombrero' (29a) ♀H3	MCms
	'Goshu Penta' (10a)	MCms
	'Grace Riley' (24a)	MCms
	'Grace Wade' (25b)	MCms
	'Grand Cherry'	MCms
	'Grand Pink'	MCms
	'Grand Salmon' **new**	MCms
	'Grandchild' (21c) ♀H4	MNrw NHal SBch
§	× ***grandiflorum***	CTri
	'Green Goddess' (2) **new**	MCms
	'Hanenburg' (25b)	MCms NHal
	haradjanii	see *Tanacetum haradjanii*
	'Harold Lawson' (5a)	MCms NHal
*	'Harry Lawson'	MCms
	'Harry Tolley' (14b)	MCms
	'Harry Woolman' (13b)	MCms
	'Heather James' (3b)	MCms NHal
	'Hebe' (21d)	EBee MNrw
	'Heide' (29c) ♀H3	NHal
	'Helen Louise' (25b)	MCms NHal
	'Herbie McCauley' (24b)	MCms NHal
	'Herbstbrokat'	GBin WFar XLum
	'Herbstfeuer' (21)	NWad
	'Hesketh Knight' (5b) ♀H2	MCms
	'Hillfield Apricot'	EShb
	'Hillside Apricot' **new**	ECtt
	'Hoagy' (29d)	MCms NHal
	'Holly Elizabeth' (14a)	MCms
	HOLLY ('Yoholly') (22b) ♀H3	NHal
	'Honey Enbee Wedding' (29d)	MCms NHal
	'Horningsea Pink' (19d)	WBor
	hosmariense	see *Rhodanthemum hosmariense*
	indicum	SVic
	- 'Louis Germ White' **new**	CRav
	'Innocence' (21d) ♀H4	CDor CFis ECtt ELan ELon MNrw MRav NGdn SHar WBrk WFar WHoo
	'Jack Wood' (25a)	MCms
	'Jan Wardle' (5a)	MCms
	'Janet South'	MNrw
	'Jante Wells' (21b) ♀H4	MNrw WBor
	'Jennifer Shephard' (25b)	MCms
	'Jenny Wren' (12a)	NHal
	'Jessie Cooper' misapplied	see *C.* 'Mrs Jessie Cooper' (21)
	'Jessie Cooper' Perry	CElw
	'Jimmy Simpson' (25b)	MCms
	'Jimmy Tranter' (14b)	NHal
	'Joan Waugh' (14b)	MCms
	'John Harrison' (25b)	MCms NHal
	'John Hughes' (3b)	MCms NHal
	'John Lowry' (24a)	MCms NHal
	'John Riley' (14a)	CRav MCms NHal
	'John Wingfield' (14b)	MCms NHal
	'John Wingfield Honey' (14b)	MCms
	'John Wingfield Pearl' (14b)	MCms
	'Jolie Rose'	WCot
	'Joyce Fountain' (24a)	MCms NHal
	'Joyce Frieda' (13b)	MCms NHal
	'Julia' (28)	EPfP MNrw
	'Julia Arnold'	WHoo
	'Julia Peterson'	MHCG MHer MNrw WCot WFar WHoo
	'Julie Lagravère' (28)	MHCG MNrw WFar XLum
	'Karen Taylor' (29c) ♀H3	NHal

'Kath Stephenson' (7b)	MCms NHal
'Kath Stephenson Honey' (7b)	MCms
'Kath Stephenson Peach' (7b)	MCms
'Kath Stephenson Primrose' (7b)	MCms NHal
'Kath Stephenson Rose' (7b)	MCms NHal
'Kath Stephenson Salmon' (7b)	MCms
'Kay Woolman' (13b)	MCms NHal
'Kay Woolman Cream' (13b) **new**	MCms
'Kay Woolman Primrose' (13b)	MCms
'Kay Woolman Yellow' (13b)	MCms
'Killerton Tangerine'	MNrw
'Kimberley Marie' (15b)	MCms NHal
'Kiyomi-no-meisui'	MCms NHal
'Kleiner Bernstein'	MNrw
'Königssohn' **new**	WCot
× ***koreanum***	see *C.* × *grandiflorum*
'La Damoiselle'	WCot
§ 'Lady in Pink' (21)	MNrw MPie
'Lakelanders' (3b)	MCms NHal
'Laura Jayne' (25a)	MCms
'Laura Norris' (15a)	MCms
'Lava' (10a)	MCms
'Leo' (21b) ♀H4	EBee
leucanthemum	see *Leucanthemum vulgare*
'Lexy'PBR (9)	GBin MCms
'Lexy Red'PBR (9)	GBin MCms
'Lighthouse'	NHal
'Lilac Chessington' (25a)	MCms NHal
'Lilian Shoesmith' (5b)	MCms
LINDA ('Lindayo') (22c) ♀H3	NHal
'L'Innocence' (21)	CAby
'Little Ricky' (25b)	MCms
'Littleton Red' **new**	CRav
'Liverpool Festival' (23b)	MCms
'Lollipop'PBR (9)	GBin MCms
LOLLIPOP PURPLE ('Filollipop Purple'PBR)	MCms
'Lorna Wood' (13b)	MCms NHal
'Louise Park' (24a)	MCms
'Luba' (9c)	MCms
'Luba Bronze' (9c)	MCms
'Luba Orange' (9c)	MCms
'Lucy' (29a)	MCms NHal
'Lydia Mannion' (7b)	MCms
'Lynn Johnson' (15a)	MCms
LYNN ('Yolynn') (22c) ♀H3	NHal
macrophyllum	see *Tanacetum macrophyllum* (Waldst. & Kit.) Sch.Bip.
'Malcolm Perkins' (25a)	MCms NHal
'Mancetta Comet' (29a)	MCms NHal
'Mancetta Symbol' (5a)	MCms
'Mandarin' (5b)	SAko
maresii	see *Rhodanthemum hosmariense*
'Margaret Dear' (25a)	MCms
'Margaret Lawson' (14b)	MCms NHal
'Margery Fish'	MNrw
'Marion' (25a)	MNrw WCot
'Martin Bell' (29d)	MCms WFar
'Mary' (21f)	MHCG NHal
'Mary Stoker' (21d)	CAby CDor CSam CTri EBee ECtt ELan EPfP LRHS MNrw MPie MRav NHal NLar NRHS NWsh WAul WCAu XLum

'Mary's Miracle' (24a)	MCms
'Mason's Bronze' (7b)	MCms
'Matlock' (24b)	NHal
'Mauve Gem' (21f) ♀H3	MNrw NHal
'Mavis' (21) ♀H3	MHCG MNrw
mawii	see *Rhodanthemum gayanum*
'Max Riley' (23b) ♀H3	MCms NHal
maximum misapplied	see *Leucanthemum* × *superbum*
maximum Ramond	see *Leucanthemum maximum* (Ramond) DC.
'Maxine Charlton' (24b)	MCms NHal
'Maxine Johnson' (25b)	MCms NHal
'May Shoesmith' (5a) ♀H2	MCms NHal
'Maybach' (9)	MCms
'Mayford Perfection' (5a) ♀H2	MCms
'Mei-Kyō' (28b) ♀H4	CDor CFis CMea CTri ECtt EPPr LRHS MNrw MPie NRHS SRms WBor WBrk WCAu WFar
'Membury' (24b)	MCms NHal
'Michelle Preston' (13b)	NHal
'Millennium' (25b) ♀H3	MCms NHal
'Millie Mathews' (14b)	MCms
'Misty Cream' (25b)	MCms
'Misty Golden' (25b)	MCms
'Misty Lemon' (25b)	MCms
'Moonlight' (29d/K)	MRav
'Moonlight' (24a)	LRHS NRHS
'Morning Star' (12a)	NHal
'Mount Fuji' (10b)	MCms
§ 'Mrs Jessie Cooper' (21d) ♀H4	CAby CHGN EBee ELon EPPr GQue MNrw NLar SDys SRms WCot WFar WHoo WPtf
'Mrs Jessie Cooper No 1'	NWsh SBch
'Mrs Jessie Cooper No 2'	MNrw
'Mundial' (6)	MCms
'Mundial Peach' (6b/9a)	MCms
'Mundial Rose' (6b)	MCms
'Mundial Ruby' (6b)	MCms
'Muriel Odell' (7b)	MCms
'Music' (23b)	MCms NHal
'Muxton Sable' (10a)	GBin MCms
'Myss Debbie' (29e)	NHal
'Myss Dorothy' (29c)	MCms NHal
'Myss Eliza' (29c)	MCms
'Myss Goldie' (29c)	MCms
'Myss Rihanna' (29c)	MCms NHal
'Myss Saffron' (29c) ♀H3	MCms NHal
'Nancy Perry' (21d)	CSam MRav XLum
'Nantyderry Sunshine' (28b) ♀H4	CDor ELon IRob LRHS MHCG MNrw MPie NRHS NWsh SPhx SRms WBor WCot WFar WOld
'Naru' (9c)	NHal
'Naru Crimson' (9c)	NHal
'Natalie Rachelle' (25b)	MCms
'Natalie Sarah' (29d) ♀H3	MCms NHal
'Nell Gwynn' (21d)	MNrw NHal
'New Stylist' (24b)	MCms
NICOLE ('Yonicole') (22c) ♀H3	NHal
nipponicum	see *Nipponanthemum nipponicum*
'Nora Brook' (25b)	MCms
'Nutcracker' (23b) **new**	MCms
'Old Norwell' **new**	MNrw
'Olwyn' (4b)	MCms
'Olwyn Yellow' (4b)	MCms
'Optimist'	MCms

'Orange Enbee Wedding' (29d)	NHal
'Paloma Mist' (29d)	NHal
'Paloma Redeye' (29d)	NHal
'Paloma Regent' (29d)	NHal
'Paloma Sands' (29d)	NHal
parthenium	see *Tanacetum parthenium*
'Pat Bahn' (29c)	NHal
'Patricia Millar' (14b)	MCms NHal
'Patricia Millar Cerise' (14b)	MCms
'Patricia Millar Coral' (14b)	MCms
'Patricia Millar Orange' (14b)	MCms
'Patricia Millar Yellow' (14b)	MCms NHal
'Paul Boissier' (30Rub)	CAby CDor CFis ECtt MNrw NSti SPhx WBor
'Paul Cornelius' (24b)	MCms NHal
'Pauline White' (15a)	MCms
'Payton Blaze' (29c)	CRav
'Peach Courtier' (24a)	NHal
'Peach Enbee Wedding' (29d) ♀H3	MCms NHal
'Peach John Wingfield' (14b)	MCms NHal
'Peach Patricia Millar' (14b)	MCms
'Peach Southway Sheeba' (29d)	NHal
'Pearl Celebration' (24a)	MCms
'Pearl Enbee Wedding' (29d)	MCms
'Pearl Smith' (25b)	MCms
'Pennine Bullion'	NHal
'Pennine Club' (29d)	MCms
'Pennine Gambol' (29a)	MCms
'Pennine Jude' (29a)	MCms
'Pennine Marie' (29a) ♀H3	MCms
'Pennine Oriel' (29a) ♀H3	MCms NHal
'Pennine Point' (19c)	NHal
'Pennine Polo' (29d) ♀H3	MCms NHal
'Pennine Poppet' (29a)	MCms
'Pennine Swan' (29c)	MCms NHal
'Penny's Yellow'	WBrk
'Percy Salter' (24b)	NHal
'Perry's Peach' (21d) ♀H4	ELon MHCG MNrw NHal NPer SPhx
'Peter Jolley' (25b)	MCms
'Peter Rowe' (23b)	MCms NHal
'Peterkin'	CMac EBee ECtt ELon LRHS NRHS XLum
'Picasso'	MHCG MNrw WCot
'Ping Pong' (8a)	MCms
'Pink John Wingfield' (14b)	NHal
'Pink Progression'	see *C.* 'Lady in Pink'
'Pocahontas' (10a)	MCms
'Poesie'	IPot MNrw SAko WCot
'Polar Gem' (3a)	MCms NHal
'Pomander' (25b)	MCms
'Porto Purple' **new**	CRav
'Pot Black' (14b)	MCms
'President Osaka'	MNrw NWad
'Primrose Allouise' (24b) ♀H3	MCms NHal
'Primrose Chessington' (25a)	MCms
'Primrose Courtier'	see *C.* 'Yellow Courtier'
'Primrose Dorothy Stone' (25b)	MCms NHal
'Primrose Dorridge Crystal' (24a)	MCms
'Primrose Egret' (23b)	MCms
'Primrose Enbee Wedding' (29d) ♀H3	MCms NHal
'Primrose Fairweather' (3b)	MCms
'Primrose John Hughes' (3b)	MCms
'Primrose Mayford Perfection' (5a) ♀H2	MCms
'Primrose Olwyn' (4b)	MCms
'Primrose Pauline White' (15a)	MCms
'Primrose Pennine Oriel' (29a)	MCms
'Primrose West Bromwich' (14a)	MCms
'Princess' (21d)	MNrw
'Promise' (25a)	MCms NHal
'Purleigh White' (28b)	ECtt ELon EPPr MNrw NSti
'Purple Chempak Rose' (14b)	MCms
'Purple Dee Gem' (29c)	NHal
'Purple Doreen Hall' (15a)	MCms
'Purple Glow' (5a)	MCms
'Quinty' (19)	GBin
'Raquel' (21)	MNrw
'Ray's Red' **new**	MNrw
'Red Balcombe Perfection' (5a)	MCms NHal
'Red Chempak Rose' (14b)	MCms
'Red Goodlife Sombrero' (29a)	MCms
'Red Louise Park' (14a)	MCms
'Red Mayford Perfection' (5a)	MCms
'Red Pennine Gift' (29c)	NHal
'Red Regal Mist' (25b)	MCms NHal
'Red Shirley Model' (3a)	MCms NHal
'Redbreast' (12a)	NHal
'Regal Mist' (25b)	NHal
'Regal Mist Purple' (25b)	MCms
'Regent' (5b) **new**	MCms
'Rejoyce'	GBin
I 'Rhumba'	WCot
'Rihanna'	MCms
'Riley's Dynasty' (14a)	MCms
'Ringdove' (12a)	NHal
'Rita Fox' (25b)	MCms
'Rita McMahon' (29d) ♀H3	NHal
ROBIN ('Yorobi') (22c)	NHal
'Roen Sarah' (29c)	NHal
'Romantica'	MNrw WOld
'Rose Enbee Wedding' (29d)	MCms NHal
'Rose Madder'	GAbr MNrw WCot
'Rose Mayford Perfection' (5a) ♀H2	MCms
'Rose Patricia Millar' (14b)	MCms NHal
'Rose Talbot Parade' (29c)	MCms
'Rosetta'	MNrw
roseum	see *Tanacetum coccineum*
'Roter Spray'	NWad
'Roy Bevan' (29d)	MCms
'Roy Coopland' (5b) ♀H2	MCms
'Royal Command' (21a)	MHCG MNrw WCot WHoo
rubellum	see *C. zawadskii*
'Ruby Enbee Wedding' (29d) ♀H3	MCms NHal WFar
'Ruby Glow' (7b)	MCms
'Ruby Mound' (21c) ♀H4	CSpe MHCG MNrw NHal SDys SHar SPhx WBrk WCot WFar

'Ruby Raynor' (21c) ♀H4	MNrw NHal WFar
'Rumpelstilzchen' (21d)	CFis CMea ECtt MHer MNrw NWsh
'Salhouse Dream' (10a)	MCms NHal
'Salhouse Joy' (10a)	MCms NHal
'Salmon Allouise' (25b)	MCms NHal
'Salmon Enbee Wedding' (29d) ♀H3	NHal
'Salmon Fairweather' (3b)	MCms
'Salmon John Wingfield' (24b)	MCms
'Salmon Patricia Millar' (14b)	MCms
'Salmon Pauline White' (15a)	MCms
'Salmon Talbot Maid' (29c)	MCms
'Salmon Talbot Parade' (29c) ♀H3	MCms WFar
'Salmon Venice' (24b)	MCms
'Sam Vinter' (5a)	MCms NHal
'Samba'	WCot WFar
'Sarah Louise' (25b)	NHal
'Saratov Lilac' **new**	CRav
'Savanna Charlton' (25a)	MCms NHal
'Schaffhausen' **new**	WFar
'Sea Urchin' (21f) ♀H3	NHal SDys
'Seaton's Ashleigh' (10b)	MCms
'Seaton's Galaxy' (10a)	MCms NHal
'Senkyo Karyu' (10a)	MCms
'Senkyo Kenshin' (10a)	GBin MCms NHal
'Shamrock' (10b)	CRav MCms
'Sheer Purple' **new**	CRav
'Sheffield'	XLum
'Sheila Coles' (7b)	MCms NHal
'Sheila Harris' (3b)	MCms
'Shining Light' (21f)	WCot
'Shoesmith Salmon' (4a)	MCms
'Shoesmith Salmon Bright Bronze' (4a)	MCms
'Shoesmith Salmon Crimson' (4b)	MCms
'Shoesmith Salmon Purple' (4a)	MCms
'Showmaker Action Bronze'	ESps
sinense	see *C.* × *grandiflorum*
'Smokey Purple' **new**	CRav
'Soir d'Orient' **new**	WFar
'Sound' (9d)	MCms
'Southway Semtex' (29d)	MCms
'Southway Sheba' (29d) ♀H3	MCms NHal
'Southway Sheba Bronze' (29d)	MCms NHal
'Southway Shimmer' (29d)	MCms NHal
'Southway Shiraz' (29d)	MCms WFar
'Southway Sloe' (29d)	MCms NHal
'Southway Spectacular' (29d)	MCms
'Southway Spritzer' (29d)	MCms NHal
'Southway Strontium' (29d)	MCms NHal
'Southway Sunbeam' (29d)	MCms
'Spartan Canary' (21d) ♀H4	IRob
'Spartan Display'	EWes
'Spartan Linnet'	IRob
'Spartan Seagull' (21d)	MNrw
'Spencer's Cottage' (13b)	MCms
'Stallion' PBR (9)	GBin MCms
'Stallion Yellow'	MCms
'Stan Addison' (5b)	MCms
'Starlet' (21f) ♀H4	NHal
'Stella' (29c)	IRob

'Steve Packham' (23b)	MCms NHal
'Stockton' (3b) ♀H2	MCms NHal
'Suffolk Pink'	ECtt EShb MNrw NWsh
'Sunny John Wingfield' (14b)	MCms
'Super-Bronze Shoesmith Salmon' (4a)	MCms
'Susan Kate' (25b)	MCms
'Swan Cream'	MCms
SWAN ('Fiswan' PBR) (9)	MCms
'Swan Sunny' **new**	MCms
'Sweetheart Pink'	MNrw
'Syllabub' (21f) ♀H3	ECtt MNrw
'Symphony' (10a)	MCms NHal
'Talbot Maid' (29c)	MCms
'Talbot Parade' (29c) ♀H3	MCms
'Talbot Parade Pink' (29c)	MCms
'Tapestry Rose' (21d)	CMea MNrw NWsh SPhx WBor WFar WHoo
'Tara Olivio' (24b)	MCms
'Terry Brook' (29e)	MCms NHal
'Terry Morris' (7b)	MCms
'Thoroughbred' (24a)	MCms NHal
'Tickle Pink' (29f/K)	MNrw NWad
'Tim Sandall' (25a)	MCms
'Tom Parr'	see *C.* 'Doctor Tom Parr'
'Tom Snowball' (3b)	MCms
'Tracey Waller' (24b)	MCms
TRIUMPH ('Yotri') (22)	NHal
uliginosum	see *Leucanthemella serotina*
'Uri'	CAby CFis EBee ELon MHCG MNrw SPhx
'Vagabond Prince'	ELon MHCG MNrw WBor WBrk WFar WHoo WOld
'Venice' (24b)	MCms NHal
'Venice Peach' (24b)	MCms
'Venice Rose' (24b)	MCms
'Venus' (21)	NWad WCot
'Venus One'	ECtt MNrw NHal
'Vibrant' (9c) ♀H2	NHal
'Viking' (9)	MCms
'Viscount' (4b)	MCms
'Vision On' (24b)	MCms
'Vulcano Dark' (9)	MCms
'Wedding Day' (29k)	MNrw
'Wedding Sunshine' (21)	MNrw NWad
welwitschii	see *Glebionis segetum*
'Wembley' (24b)	MCms
'Wendy Tench' (21d)	EBee ECtt MNrw NWsh
'West Bromwich' (14a)	MCms
weyrichii	CTri EBee GCrg GPSL LEdu MNrw NHpl SBch SRms
'White Allouise' (25b) ♀H3	MCms NHal
'White Beppie' (29e)	MCms WFar
'White Cassandra' (5b)	MCms NHal
'White Denise Oatridge' (5a)	MCms
'White Enbee Wedding' (29d)	MCms NHal
'White Fairweather' (3b)	MCms NHal
'White Gem' (21f)	NHal
'White Gloss' (21e)	MNrw SPhx
'White Pearl Celebration' (24a)	MCms
'White Spider' (10a)	CRav
'White Tower' (27)	MNrw MPie NWad
'Wilder Charms'	NWad
'William Florentine' (15a)	MCms NHal
'Wills Wonderful' (21d) ♀H4	MHCG

'Win' (9c)	NHal
'Wind Dancer' (10a)	MCms
'Winning's Red' (21)	MHCG SMad WCot WFar
'Winter Queen' (5b)	MCms
'Winter Queen Yellow' (5b)	MCms
'Woolley Globe' (15b)	MCms
'Woolman's Glory' (7a)	MCms NHal
'Woolman's Glory Red' (7a)	MCms
'Woolman's Star' (3a)	MCms NHal
'Woolman's Venture' (14b)	MCms NHal
'Woolman's Venture Red' (14b)	MCms
'Xiang'	NWad
'Yellow Allouise' (25b)	MCms
'Yellow American Beauty' (5b) ♀^{H2}	MCms
'Yellow Billy Bell' (15a)	NHal
'Yellow Clapham Delight' (23a)	MCms NHal
§ 'Yellow Courtier' (24a)	MCms NHal
'Yellow Duke of Kent' (1)	NHal
'Yellow Egret' (23b)	MCms
'Yellow Enbee Wedding' (29d)	MCms NHal
'Yellow Goodlife Sombrero' (29a)	MCms
'Yellow Heide' (29c) ♀^{H3}	NHal
'Yellow John Harrison' (25b)	MCms
'Yellow John Hughes' (3b) ♀^{H2}	MCms NHal
'Yellow John Wingfield' (14b)	MCms NHal
'Yellow May Shoesmith' (5a)	NHal
'Yellow Mayford Perfection' (5a) ♀^{H2}	MCms
'Yellow Pennine Oriel' (29a) ♀^{H3}	MCms NHal
'Yellow Spider' (10a)	MCms
'Yellow Talbot Parade' (29c)	MCms
'Yellow Woolman's Glory' (7a)	MCms
yezoense	CDor MNrw SRms
- B&SWJ 10872	WCru
- 'Roseum'	ECtt
'Yvonne Gray' (25b)	MCms
'Yvonne's Rot-Goldene'	SAko
§ ***zawadzkii***	CMac SRms
'Zembla'^{PBR}	MCms
'Zembla Lime'^{PBR} **new**	MCms
'Zembla Yellow'^{PBR}	MCms

Chrysocephalum (*Asteraceae*)

'Desert Flame'	LRHS NRHS

Chrysogonum (*Asteraceae*)

australe	LRHS NRHS
virginianum	CMea EBee EWes SPer WFar
- 'Golden Acres'	ECtt

Chrysopogon (*Poaceae*)

gryllus	EBee WPGP

Chrysosplenium (*Saxifragaceae*)

alternifolium	EBee GEdr MMoz
davidianum	CBre CSam CSpe EBee EWld GCal GEdr GJos GKev ILea IMou NHpl NLar NRHS WBor WCru WMoo WSHC
- SBEC 233	CExl
lanuginosum var. ***formosanum***	GEdr
- - B&SWJ 6979	WCru
macrophyllum	CExl CSpe CTal EPPr EWld GBin GCal GKev GMaP IMou LEdu MPie NLar SHar WBor WCot WCru WSHC
oppositifolium	EBWF ECha NMir WSFF WShi

Chusquea (*Poaceae*)

breviglumis misapplied	see *C. culeou* 'Tenuis'
culeou ♀^{H4}	CAbb CBcs CRos EPfP LEdu MAvo MGos MWht NRHS SBig SPlb SSta
- 'Breviglumis'	see *C. culeou* 'Tenuis'
- 'Purple Splendour'	CDTJ
§ - 'Tenuis'	ERod
- weeping	CDTJ
delicatula from Machu Picchu, Peru	CExl CFil
gigantea ♀^{H3}	CBdn CDTJ CExl CFil EPfP ERod MMoz MWht SBig WPGP
montana	CDTJ
mulleri F&M 104A from Mexico	CExl
nigricans	CFil MAvo
quila	MMoz

Cibotium (*Cibotiaceae*)

barometz	NLos

Cicerbita (*Asteraceae*)

§ ***alpina***	GAbr NBid SBrt SPlb
bourgaei	CFis MMuc
macrorhiza CC 6912	EBee
plumieri	GAbr SBrt WCot WFar WMoo WSHC
- 'Blott' (v)	WCot

Cichorium (*Asteraceae*)

See also AGM Vegetables Section.

endivia 'Pancalieri' ♀^{H3} **new**	CHby EKin LSds MCtn MShS
intybus	CHby CSpe CWld EBWF ELan ENfk GAbr GPoy LSun MBel MCot MHer MNHC NGBl NMir NPnk SPer SPlb SPoG SRms SVic WFar WHrl WMoo WSHC WTre
- f. ***album***	CBod ECha ECtt LRHS MBel MCot MPie NPnk NRHS SHar SPer
- 'Indigo' ♀^{H4} **new**	NRHS
- 'Palla Rossa' ♀^{H4}	CHby EUnw LSds MCtn MShS SRms
- 'Pan di Zucchero' ♀^{H4} **new**	CHby EUnw LSds MCtn
- 'Red Rib'	SRms
- 'Roseum'	CBod ECha ECtt ELan GKin LRHS MBel NPnk NRHS SBod SHar SPer SPoG

Cicuta (*Apiaceae*)

virosa	LLWG

Cimicifuga see *Actaea*

acerina	see *Actaea japonica*
americana	see *Actaea podocarpa*
cordifolia (DC.) Torrey & A. Gray	see *Actaea cordifolia*
cordifolia Pursh	see *Actaea podocarpa*
foetida	see *Actaea cimicifuga*
racemosa var. ***cordifolia***	see *Actaea cordifolia*
- 'Purpurea'	see *Actaea simplex* Atropurpurea Group

ramosa	see *Actaea simplex* 'Prichard's Giant'
rubifolia	see *Actaea cordifolia*
simplex var. ***matsumurae***	see *Actaea matsumurae*

Cineraria (*Asteraceae*)

maritima	see *Jacobaea maritima*

Cinnamomum (*Lauraceae*)

camphora	CExl LRHS SPlb

Circaea (*Onagraceae*)

alpina	EBee
lutetiana	EBWF WHer
- 'Caveat Emptor' (v)	NBid WCot

Cirsium (*Asteraceae*)

arvense	WSFF
canum	CSpe GQue
ciliatum	EBee
diacantha	see *Ptilostemon diacantha*
eriophoroides	GEdr
helenioides	see *C. heterophyllum*
§ ***heterophyllum***	CBod CDor CHid EBWF EBee EWld LEdu LRHS MAvo NChi NLar SHar WHil
- PAB 067	LEdu WPGP
- 'Pink Blush'	GBin LCro LOPS NSti SPoG
japonicum 'Rose Beauty'	SCob WSpi
'Mount Etna'	CBWd CBod CFis EBee ELan EPed EPfP GCal GKin IRob LRHS MBNS MBel MMuc MPie MSpe NDov NGdn NPnk NRHS SEND WCAu
oleraceum	LEdu NBid NLar SBrt WCAu
purpuratum	MNrw
rivulare 'Atropurpureum'	Widely available
- FROSTED MAGIC ('Loweir') **new**	IPot LBuc LCro LOPS MBel SHar WHil
- 'Trevor's Blue Wonder'	Widely available
tuberosum	CAby LEdu LPla LRHS SPhx
vulgare	WSFF

Cissus (*Vitaceae*)

antarctica ♀H1c	CCCN EShb SEND
pedata B&SWJ 2371	WCru
rhombifolia ♀H1c	EOHP EShb
- 'Ellen Danica' ♀H1c	EShb
§ ***striata***	CBcs CMac CRos CWCL EBee ELon EShb IBoy LRHS MGil MRav NChi SBrt SEND SLim SWvt WSHC

Cistus ✿ (*Cistaceae*)

acutifolius misapplied	see *C. inflatus*, *C.* × *pulverulentus*
× ***aguilarii***	CBcs CSBt CTri MRav WSHC
- 'Maculatus' ♀H4	CAby CBcs CBod CDul CExl CRos CSBt CSam ELan EPfP LRHS LSRN MMuc NLar SEle SPer SPoG SWvt WKif WPGP WSpi
albidus	WSpi XSen
algarvensis	see *Halimium ocymoides*
'Anne Palmer'	see *C.* × *fernandesiae* 'Anne Palmer'
× ***argenteus*** 'Blushing Peggy Sammons'	CAby ELan EPfP LRHS NLar NRHS SWvt WAvo XSen
- 'Paper Moon'	CBod LRHS LSRN NLar
§ - 'Peggy Sammons'	CBot CDul CRos ECha ELan EPfP LRHS LSRN MAsh MGos NLar SAko SCob SEND SLim SPer SWvt XSen
- 'Silver Ghost'	CAby EPfP LRHS SWvt
- 'Silver Pink' ambig.	CBar CBcs CBot CChe CDul CRos EBee ELan EPfP ESps LCro LRHS MAsh MGos MJak MRav MSwo SCob SEND SLim SPer SPoG SSta SWvt WAvo WFar WHar WKif WSpi
atriplicifolius	see *Halimium atriplicifolium*
'Blanche'	see *C. ladanifer* 'Blanche'
× ***bornetianus*** 'Jester' ♀H4	CRos CSBt ELan EPfP LRHS MAsh NLar NRHS SWvt
× ***canescens*** f. ***albus***	XSen
clusii subsp. ***multiflorus***	XSen
× ***corbariensis***	see *C.* × *hybridus*
creticus	CAby CBcs CExl CRos CSam ESps GPoy LRHS MAsh MGos NEgg SLon SPoG SRms SWvt WKif
- subsp. ***corsicus***	XSen
§ - subsp. ***creticus***	EBee ELan EPfP MRav SCoo SPer
- subsp. ***eriocephalus***	CBod
§ - subsp. ***incanus***	WCot
× ***crispatus***	XSen
§ - 'Warley Rose'	GMaP WKif XLum
crispus misapplied	see *C.* × *pulverulentus*, *C.* × *purpureus*
§ ***crispus*** L.	ELan SEND SGol
- 'Prostratus'	see *C. crispus* L.
- 'Sunset'	see *C.* × *pulverulentus* 'Sunset'
§ × ***cyprius*** ♀H4	CDul CRos EBee ELan EPfP ESps LRHS NRHS SEND SPer SRms SWvt WKif WSpi
§ - var. ***ellipticus*** 'Elma' ♀H4	CRos ELan EPfP EWTr LRHS MAsh NLar NRHS SPer WAvo WCot
§ × ***dansereaui***	CBot CMac CSBt LRHS NLar SWvt WSpi
- 'Decumbens' ♀H4	CBod CDul CRos CTri CTsd EBee ELan EPau EPfP ESps EUJe LRHS MAsh MBNS MJak MRav MSwo NEgg NLar NRHS SArc SCoo SGbt SPer SPhx SPoG SWvt WFar WPGP
- 'Jenkyn Place' ♀H4	CBod EBee GMaP LSRN MBNS MMuc NLar SPer SPoG WKif
'Elma'	see *C.* × *cyprius* var. *ellipticus* 'Elma'
§ × ***fernandesiae*** 'Anne Palmer'	CRos EPfP LLHF LRHS MAsh NLar
× ***florentinus*** misapplied	see × *Halimiocistus* 'Ingwersenii'
× ***florentinus*** ambig.	XLum
§ × ***florentinus*** Lam.	GMaP XSen
* - 'Tramontane'	XSen
'Gordon Cooper' ♀H4	LSRN MMrt MMuc NLar SCob SPoG WSpi
× ***heterocalyx*** 'Chelsea Bonnet'	CBod EUJe GMaP LRHS MBNS NLar SCoo SPoG
'Highlights'	EPfP MAsh
hirsutus Lam. 1786	see *C. inflatus*
- var. ***psilosepalus*** misapplied	see *C. inflatus*
§ × ***hybridus***	Widely available
- 'Gold Prize' (v)	CWGN NLar SWvt WGrn
- LITTLE MISS SUNSHINE ('Dunnecis'PBR) (v)	CRos LRHS MAsh MGos NLar NRHS SRms SWvt
- ROSPICO ('Rencis'PBR) (v)	EPfP LRHS NLar
incanus	see *C. creticus* subsp. *incanus*
§ ***inflatus***	XSen
ingwerseniana	see × *Halimiocistus* 'Ingwersenii'
'Jessamy Beauty'	WAvo WHar
'Jessamy Charm'	SPhx
ladanifer misapplied	see *C.* × *cyprius*
ladanifer ambig.	CMac ECha SArc WKif
ladanifer L.	CBcs CBot CSBt CTri ELan EPfP GPoy LRHS MRav MSwo SWvt WSpi XSen
§ - 'Blanche'	CBot EPfP LLHF LSRN NLar SEND SPer SWvt WKif WSpi

	- var. ***maculatus*** new	CBod
§	- 'Paladin'	EPfP EUJe
	- Palhinhae Group	see *C. ladanifer* var. *sulcatus*
	- 'Pat'	CRos ELan EPfP LRHS LSRN MAsh NLar NRHS SPer SPoG SWvt
	- var. ***petiolatus*** 'Bennett's White' new	WAvo
§	- var. ***sulcatus***	CRos CTsd ELan LRHS
	lasianthus	see *Halimium lasianthum*
	laurifolius	EPfP LRHS MGos SCob SPer SWvt WSpi XSen
	- subsp. ***atlanticus***	XSen
	× ***laxus*** 'Snow White' ♀^{H4}	CWGN EBee EPfP GMcL LRHS MGos NLar NPer SAko SLon
	× ***ledon***	EBee
§	× ***lenis*** 'Grayswood Pink' ♀^{H4}	Widely available
	× ***loretii*** misapplied	see *C.* × *dansereaui*
	× ***lusitanicus*** Maund	see *C.* × *dansereaui*
	'Merrist Wood Cream'	see × *Halimiocistus wintonensis* 'Merrist Wood Cream'
	monspeliensis	CMac EPfP GMcL LRHS MAsh MBNS MMuc SLon SPer SPoG XSen
	- 'Vicar's Mead'	CCCN CRos MBNS
	monspeliensis × ***salviifolius***	see *C.* × *florentinus* Lam.
	× ***oblongifolius***	SWvt XSen
	× ***obtusifolius*** ambig.	ELan LRHS
	× ***obtusifolius*** Sweet	EPfP WPGP XSen
§	- 'Thrive' ♀^{H4}	CRos EPfP LRHS MGos NRHS SCoo
	ocymoides	see *Halimium ocymoides*
	'Paladin'	see *C. ladanifer* 'Paladin'
	palhinhae	see *C. ladanifer* var. *sulcatus*
	parviflorus misapplied	see *C.* × *lenis* 'Grayswood Pink'
	parviflorus Lam.	WSHC
	'Peggy Sammons'	see *C.* × *argenteus* 'Peggy Sammons'
	× ***platysepalus***	SPhx
	populifolius	CBot CMac CRos ECha EPfP LLHF LRHS NLar SGol SPer SWvt
	- var. ***lasiocalyx***	see *C. populifolius* subsp. *major*
§	- subsp. ***major***	CRos EPfP LRHS LSRN WPGP WSpi
	psilosepalus misapplied	see *C. inflatus*
§	× ***pulverulentus***	CExl CTri ECha WSHC XSen
§	- 'Sunset' ♀^{H4}	Widely available
	- 'Warley Rose'	see *C.* × *crispatus* 'Warley Rose'
§	× ***purpureus*** ♀^{H4}	Widely available
	- 'Alan Fradd'	Widely available
	- 'Betty Taudevin'	see *C.* × *purpureus*
	- f. ***strictus***	EPfP LRHS WAvo
	× ***rodiaei*** 'Jessabel'	CBot CRos EPfP LRHS MAsh MRav NLar SPer SWvt WPGP
	- 'Jessica'	NLar
	'Ruby Cluster'	CBod CCCN LRHS MMuc NLar
	sahucii	see × *Halimiocistus sahucii*
	salviifolius	CCCN XSen
	- 'Avalanche'	WAbe
	- 'Gold Star'	ELan LRHS NLar
	- 'May Snow'	EHoe LRHS MAsh
	- 'Prostratus'	CAby CRos ELan EPfP LRHS SWvt
	'Silver Pink' misapplied	see *C.* × *lenis* 'Grayswood Pink'
	× ***skanbergii***	CBod CMac CTri ELan EPfP MGos MHol MMuc MRav NLar SCob SEND SPer WCFE WSpi XLum XSen
	'Snow Fire' ♀^{H4}	CAby CCCN CRos EBee ELan EPfP LRHS LSRN MAsh MGos MMuc NEgg NLar SAko SBod SCoo SEle SWeb SWvt WAvo WGrn WHar
	'Thrive'	see *C.* × *obtusifolius* 'Thrive'
	× ***verguinii***	XSen
	villosus	see *C. creticus* subsp. *creticus*
	wintonensis	see × *Halimiocistus wintonensis*

Citharexylum (*Verbenaceae*)

	quadrangulare Jacq.	see *C. spinosum*
	spicatum	CExl CFil WBor
§	***spinosum***	CHll

citrandarin see *Citrus reticulata* × *C. trifoliata*

citrange see *Citrus* × *insitorum*

citrangequat see *Citrus* × *georgiana*

× *Citrofortunella* see *Citrus*

	mitis	see *Citrus* × *microcarpa*

citron see *Citrus medica*

Citronella (*Icacinaceae*)

§	***gongonha***	SVen
	mucronata	see *C. gongonha*

Citrullus (*Cucurbitaceae*)

	lanatus 'Charleston Gray'	SVic

Citrus (*Rutaceae*)

§	× ***aurantiifolia*** (F)	CCCN EPfP ETod NRHS SCit SPre
	- key lime	see *C.* × *aurantiifolia*
§	× ***aurantium*** (F)	SCit
	- 'Aber's Narrowleaf' (F)	SCit
	- subsp. ***bergamia***	see *C.* × *limon*
	- 'Bergamot de Versailles' (F) new	NRHS
	- 'Bouquet de Fleurs'	see *C.* × *aurantium* (Sour Orange Group) 'Bouquet'
	- 'Gou-tou Cheng' (F)	SCit
§	- Grapefruit Group (F)	CCCN EUJe SPre SVic
	- - 'Foster' (F)	SCit
	- - 'Golden Special' (F)	SCit SVic
	- - 'Marsh' (F)	SCit
	- - 'Oroblanco' (F)	SCit
	- - 'Red Blush' (F/S)	SCit
	- - 'Star Ruby' (F/S)	CCCN SCit SPre
	- - 'Wheeny'	see *C. maxima* 'Wheeny'
	- var. ***myrtifolia***	see *C.* × *aurantium*
	- 'Pursha' (F)	LRHS NRHS
	- 'Robinson' (F)	SCit
§	- (Sour Orange Group) 'Bouquet' (F)	SCit
	- - 'Bouquetier de Nice' (F)	SCit
	- - 'Chinotto' (F)	SCit SPre
	- - 'Seville' (F)	LSRN SCit SPre
	- - 'Smooth Flat Seville' (F)	SCit
§	- Sweet Orange Group (F)	CCCN ETod EUJe NRHS SCit SPre SVic
§	- - 'Baia' (F/S)	SCit
	- - 'Embiguo' (F)	SCit
	- - 'Fukumoto' (F)	CCCN
	- - 'Jaffa'	see *C.* × *aurantium* (Sweet Orange Group) 'Shamouti'
	- - 'Lane Late' (F)	CCCN NLar SCit
§	- - 'Malta Blood' (F)	SCit
	- - 'Maltaise Sanguine'	see *C.* × *aurantium* (Sweet Orange Group) 'Malta Blood'
	- - 'Navelate' (F)	SCit
	- - 'Navelina' (F/S)	CCCN SCit SPre SVic
	- - 'Newhall' (F/S)	NLar SCit
	- - 'Salustiana' (F/S)	SCit
§	- - 'Sanguinelli' (F)	CCCN SCit SPre SVic

§	- - 'Shamouti' (F)	SCit
	- - 'Spanish Sanguinelli'	see *C.* × *aurantium* (Sweet Orange Group) 'Sanguinelli'
	- - 'Succari' (F)	SCit
	- - 'Tarocco' (F)	SCit
	- - 'Valencia' (F)	CCCN SCit
	- - 'Valencia Late' (F)	LRHS NRHS
	- - 'Washington'	see *C.* × *aurantium* (Sweet Orange Group) 'Baia'
	- - 'Washington Navel'	see *C.* × *aurantium* (Sweet Orange Group) 'Baia'
§	- (Tangelo Group) 'Minneola' (F)	SCit
§	- - 'Nova' (F/S)	CCCN SCit SVic
	- - 'Orlando' (F)	SCit
	- - 'Seminole' (F)	SCit
	- - 'Ugli' misapplied	see *C.* × *aurantium* (Tangelo Group) 'Minneola'
	- - 'Ugli' (F)	SCit
	- (Tangor Group) 'Dweet' (F) **new**	SCit
	- - 'Ellendale' (F)	SCit
	- - 'Murcott' (F)	SCit
	australasica (F)	SCit SPre
	bergamia	see *C.* × *limon*
	- bergamot	see *C.* × *limon* Bergamot Group
	- 'Castagnaro' (F) **new**	SCit
	'Buddha's Hand'	see *C. medica* 'Fingered'
	calamondin	see *C.* × *microcarpa*
§	***cavaleriei*** (F)	WPGP
	citrandarin	see *C. reticulata* × *trifoliata*
	deliciosa	see *C. reticulata* 'Willowleaf'
	× ***floridana*** 'Eustis' (F)	SCit SPre
	- 'Lakeland' (F)	SCit
	× ***georgiana*** 'Thomasville' (F)	SCit
§	***hystrix***	CCCN ELan IDee LSRN NLar NPla SCit SPre
	Ichang lemon	see *C. cavaleriei*
	ichangensis	see *C. cavaleriei*
	× ***insitorum*** 'C-35' (F)	SCit
	- 'Carrizo' (F)	SCit
	- 'Citromon' (F) **new**	SCit
	- 'Curafora' (F)	SCit
	- 'Swingle' (F)	SCit
	- 'Us119' (F)	SCit
	- 'Venasca' (F)	SCit
	jambhiri	see *C.* × *taitensis*
§	***japonica*** (F) ♀H1c	CBcs ELan EPfP NRHS SCit SPre SVic
	- Hong Kong kumquat (F)	SCit
	- 'Nagami' (F)	SPre
	- 'Reale' PBR (F)	SPre
§	× ***junos***	SCit SPre
	kinokuni	see *C. japonica*
	kotokan	see *C.* × *aurantium*
	'Kucle' (F)	SCit SPre
	'Kulci' (F)	CCCN
	kumquat	see *C. japonica*
	'La Valette' (F)	CCCN LSRN SPre
	× ***latifolia*** (F/S)	CCCN EPfP EUJe LRHS NLar NRHS SCit SPre
	- 'Bearss' (F)	SCit SVic
	- variegated (F/v)	SPre
	latipes Hook. f. & Thomson ex Hook. f.	see *C. hystrix*
	limetta (F)	CCCN SPre SVic
	limettioides (F)	SCit SPre
§	× ***limon*** (F)	ETod EUJe LSRN NRHS SCit SVic
§	- Bergamot Group (F)	SPre
	- - 'Fantastico' (F)	SCit
	- 'Eureka'	see *C.* × *limon* 'Garey's Eureka'
	- 'Eureka Variegated' (F/v)	SCit
	- 'Fino' (F)	CCCN SCit
	- 'Four Seasons'	see *C.* × *limon* 'Garey's Eureka'
§	- 'Garey's Eureka' (F)	CCCN ELan EPfP LCro LSRN NLar SCit SPre SVic
	- 'Imperial' (F)	SCit
	- 'Improved Meyer'	see *C.* × *limon* 'Meyer'
	- 'Lemonade' (F)	SCit
	- 'Lisbon' (F)	SCit
	- 'Lunario' (F)	SCit
§	- 'Meyer' (F) ♀H2	CBcs CCCN CHll CTri ELan EPfP LRHS LSRN NLar NRHS SCit SPre
	- 'Ponderosa' (F)	SCit
	- 'Quatre Saisons'	see *C.* × *limon* 'Garey's Eureka'
	- 'Rangpur' (F)	SCit
	- 'Romana' (F) **new**	SCit
	- 'Sfusato d'Amalfi' (F)	SCit
	- 'Siracusano' (F)	SCit
	- 'Variegata' (F/v) ♀H2	CCCN SCit SPre
	- 'Verna' (F)	CCCN SCit
	- 'Villa Franca' (F)	SCit
	- 'Yen Ben' (F)	SCit
	- 'Zagara Bianco' (F)	SCit
	× ***limonia***	see *C.* × *limon*
	'Lipo' (F)	CCCN NLar SCit SPre
	macrophylla (F)	SCit
	madurensis	see *C. japonica*
§	***maxima*** 'Wheeny' (F)	SCit
	medica 'Cedra' (F)	SPre
	- 'Cidro Digitado'	see *C. medica* 'Fingered'
	- var. ***digitata***	see *C. medica* 'Fingered'
	- 'Ethrog' (F)	SCit SPre
§	- 'Fingered' (F)	EUJe SCit SPre
*	- 'Rubra'	SPre
	- var. ***sarcodactylis***	see *C. medica* 'Fingered'
	× ***meyeri***	see *C.* × *limon*
§	× ***microcarpa*** (F) ♀H1c	CCCN LRHS NLar NRHS SCit SPre
	- Philippine lime	see *C.* × *microcarpa*
§	- 'Tiger' (F/v)	SCit SPre
	- 'Variegata'	see *C.* × *microcarpa* 'Tiger'
	× ***mitis***	see *C.* × *microcarpa*
	natsudaidai	see *C.* × *aurantium*
	'Nippon'	SCit
	× ***nobilis*** Lour.	see *C. reticulata* 'Willowleaf'
	- var. ***inermis***	see *C. japonica*
	- Ortanique Group	see *C.* × *aurantium* Sweet Orange Group
	× ***obovata*** (F)	SPre
§	- 'Fukushu' (F)	CCCN SCit
	× ***paradisi***	see *C.* × *aurantium* Grapefruit Group
	- 'Wheeny'	see *C. maxima* 'Wheeny'
	'Pursta' (F)	CCCN
	reshni	see *C.* × *aurantium*
§	***reticulata*** (F)	CCCN SCit SPre
	- 'Clausellina' (F/S)	SCit
	- var. ***deliciosa***	see *C. reticulata* 'Willowleaf'
	- 'Fina' (F/S)	SCit
	- 'Hashimoto' (F/S)	SCit
	- 'Hernandina' (F)	CCCN
	- Mandarin Group (F)	EPfP EUJe SPre
	- - 'Clementine' (F)	EPfP SPre
	- - 'Encore' (F)	SCit
	- - 'Esbal' (F)	CCCN
	- - 'Fortune' (F)	SCit
	- - 'Fremont' (F)	SCit
	- - 'Nules' (F/S)	CCCN SCit
	- 'Marisol' (F/S)	SCit

- 'Miyagawa' (F)	CCCN SCit
- 'Nour' (F)	SCit
- 'Nova'	see *C.* × *aurantium* (Tangelo Group) 'Nova'
- 'Okitsu' (F/S)	CCCN SCit
- 'Owari' (F/S)	SCit
- Satsuma Group	see *C. reticulata*
- (Tangerine Group) 'Dancy' (F)	SCit
§ - 'Willowleaf' (F)	SCit
§ ***reticulata*** × ***trifoliata***	SCit
sinensis	see *C.* × *aurantium* Sweet Orange Group
- 'Jaffa'	see *C.* × *aurantium* (Sweet Orange Group) 'Shamouti'
- 'Washington'	see *C.* × *aurantium* (Sweet Orange Group) 'Baia'
§ × ***taitensis*** (F)	SCit SPre
- 'Otaheite' (F)	CCCN SCit
§ - rough lemon (F)	SCit
- Schaub rough lemon	see *C.* × *taitensis* rough lemon
§ ***trifoliata***	CAgr CBcs CCCN CDul EBee ELan EPfP IDee LRHS MBlu MGil MMuc MRav SCit SMad SPer SPlb SVic WSHC
- 'Flying Dragon'	LEdu SCit
unshiu	see *C. reticulata*
volkameriana	see *C.* × *limon*
wilsonii	see *C.* × *junos*

Cladium (*Cyperaceae*)

mariscus	EBWF XLum

Cladrastis (*Papilionaceae*)

§ ***kentukea***	CBcs CDul CLnd CMCN CTho EBee ELan EPfP EUJe EWTr LMaj MBlu MRav NLar NOra WHar WPGP
§ - 'Perkins Pink'	MBlu
- 'Rosea'	see *C. kentukea* 'Perkins Pink'
lutea	see *C. kentukea*
sinensis	CExl CFil EBee EPfP IArd MBlu WPGP
wilsonii	WPGP

Clavinodum (*Poaceae*)

§ ***oedogonatum***	MWht

Claytonia (*Portulacaceae*)

alsinoides	see *C. sibirica*
caroliniana	GKev WCot
§ ***perfoliata***	GPoy MNHC WHer
§ ***sibirica***	CAgr IMou LSou MMoz XLum
- f. ***albiflora***	EWld MMoz MPie WCot WMoo
virginica	EBee GKev LAma MPie WFar WMoo WPnP

Clematis ✿ (*Ranunculaceae*)

sp.	NRHS
BWJ 7630 from China	WCru
CC 4710	CExl
CC 711	CExl
SDR 6151	GKev
SDR 7835	GKev
'Abigail' (Vt)	NHaw
ABILENE ('Evipo027'PBR) (EL)	CFlo CKel CRos CWGN ELan EPfP ETho LRHS MAsh NRHS SNig SPoG SWCr
'Abundance' (Vt) ♀H6	CArg CBcs CFlo CKel CRHN CWCL EPfP ESps ETho GMcL LCro LRHS LSRN MAsh SNig WFar
ACROPOLIS ('Evipo078') (Boulevard Series)	CWGN
addisonii	ESps NHaw
'Advent Bells' (C)	CWGN
afoliata	WThu
'Ai-Nor' (EL)	ETho
'Akaishi' (EL)	ETho
akebioides	NHaw
akoensis	NHaw
ALABAST ('Poulala'PBR) (EL) ♀H6	ETho LRHS SCoo
ALAINA ('Evipo056'PBR) (EL)	CKel CRos LRHS NRHS SLon SPoG SWCr
'Alba Luxurians' (Vt)	CBcs CFlo CKel CRHN CRos CTri CWCL ELan ELon EPfP ETho LCro LRHS LSRN MAsh MGos NRHS SCob SLim SNig SPer SPoG SWCr
'Albatross' (EL)	LSRN
'Albina Plena' (A/d)	ETho
'Aleksandrit' (EL)	NHaw
'Alice Fisk' (EL)	CKel ETho LSRN MSwo SNig
'Aliide' (LL)	NHaw
'Alionushka' (I) ♀H6	CKel CRHN CRos CWCL ELan EPfP ETho LRHS LSRN NLar SLim SPoG SWCr
ALITA ('Evipo070'PBR) (Vt)	CRos CWCL EBee LRHS NRHS SNig
'Allanah' (LL)	CWCL ELon ETho LRHS LSRN NHaw SCoo SLim SNig SPet WHar
alpina	ESps GKev GKin GLog IBoy LCro LRHS LSRN MAsh MRav NPer SCob SEWo SPlb SPre SWvt WFar
- 'Albiflora'	see *C. sibirica*
- 'Columbine White'	see *C.* 'White Columbine'
§ - 'Pamela Jackman' (A) ♀H6	CKel CMac CRos CWCL ELan LRHS LSRN MAsh MMuc NEgg NRHS SCoo SLim SNig SPer SPoG SRkn SWvt WFar
- pink-flowered	GKev
- 'Stolwijk Gold' (A)	CWGN EBee ETho IBoy MBlu SRms
alternata	CWGN EBee NHaw
'Amethyst Beauty' (A)	EPfP LRHS
AMETHYST BEAUTY ('Evipo043'PBR) (LL)	ETho MAsh SLon SPoG
'Andante' (I)	CWGN
'Andromeda' (EL)	CRos EBee ETho LRHS NHaw NLar NRHS SNig SWCr
ANETA ('Evipo055'PBR)	CFlo CRos CWGN EBee LCro LRHS NRHS
ANGELA ('Zoang'PBR) (EL)	ELan
ANGELIQUE ('Evipo017') (EL)	CFlo CKel CRos CWGN ELan EPfP ETho LRHS MAsh MGos NRHS SCoo SLon SNig SPer SWCr
'Anissa' (V) **new**	NHaw
'Anita' (Ta)	CFlo EBee EPfP ETho LSRN NHaw
ANNA LOUISE ('Evithree'PBR) (EL) ♀H6	CRos CWCL EPfP ETho LRHS LSRN MGos SCoo SLim SLon SNig
'Annabel' (EL)	LSRN MAsh
ANNIVERSARY ('Pynot') (EL)	LSRN SCoo
'Aotearoa' (LL) ♀H6	ETho IPot NHaw
'Aphrodite' (I)	MAsh
'Aphrodite Elegafumina' (I)	CRHN CRos CWGN LRHS NHaw
'Apollonia'	CWGN EBee IPot
'Apple Blossom' (Ar) ♀H4	Widely available
'Arabella' (I) ♀H6	CFlo CKel CRHN CRos CWCL CWGN ELan ELon EPfP EShb ESps ETho LCro LRHS LSRN MAsh MGos NEgg NLar NRHS SLim SNig SPer SRkn SWCr SWvt WBor WFar WHar

§	ARCTIC QUEEN ('Evitwo'PBR) (EL) ♀H6	CFlo CKel CRos EPfP ETho LBuc LCro LRHS LSRN MAsh NPri NRHS SCoo SLon SPoG SWCr WHar
	armandii	Widely available
	- 'Enham Star'	CRos EPfP LRHS MGos NRHS
§	- 'Little White Charm'	CRos EBee ELan LBuc LRHS NRHS SWCr
	- 'Meyeniana'	see *C. armandii* 'Little White Charm'
§	- 'Snowdrift'	CBcs CFlo CKel CRos EBee ELan EPfP ESps ETho GMcL LCro LOPS LRHS LSRN MAsh MGos MSwo NLar NRHS SCob SEle SPer SPoG SRms SWCr
	× ***aromatica***	CFlo CKel CRos CWGN ELan EPfP ETho IPot LRHS MMrt
	'Asao' (EL)	CArg CRos ELan EPfP ETho IBoy LRHS SCoo SNig SPoG WFar
	'Ascotiensis' (LL)	CRHN CRos EBee EPfP LRHS NHaw SCoo SLim SLon SNig
	'Ashva' (LL)	CWGN
	ASTRA NOVA ('Zo09085') (Vt)	CFlo CWGN ETho IPot
	AVANT-GARDE ('Evipo033'PBR) (Vt)	CFlo CKel CRos CWCL CWGN ELan EPfP ETho EUJe LRHS SLon
§	AZTEK ('Daihelios') (Ta)	CKel CRos LRHS SCoo
	BABY DOLL ('Zobadol'PBR) (EL)	CKel CWGN EBee ETho
	'Baby Pink' (I) **new**	NHaw
	BABY STAR ('Zobast'PBR) (EL)	CKel CWGN ETho
§	'Bagatelle' (LL)	CRos GMcL LRHS NHaw SNig
	'Bal Maiden' (Vt)	CRHN NHaw
	'Barbara' (LL)	LSRN
	'Barbara Dibley' (EL)	CFlo CKel CRos CTri CWCL LRHS MAsh NHaw SCoo SLim SNig SPet
	'Barbara Harrington'PBR (LL)	CRos LRHS LSRN
	'Barbara Jackman' (EL)	CArg CKel CRos CWCL ESps ETho LRHS LSRN MAsh MGos MSwo NEgg SCoo SLon SNig
	'Beata' (LL)	CWCL NHaw SNig
	'Beautiful Bride'PBR (EL)	LCro LOPS
	'Beauty of Worcester' (EL)	CKel CRos CWCL ELan ELon EPfP ESps ETho LRHS LSRN MAsh MSwo NEgg NHaw SCoo SLim SNig SPer SPet
	'Bees' Jubilee' (EL)	CArg CBcs CKel CMac CRos CWCL EBee ELan ELon EPfP ESps ETho LCro LOPS LRHS LSRN MAsh MGos MSwo NEgg NLar SLim SNig SPer SPoG SWvt
	'Bella' (EL)	LSRN
	'Belle Nantaise' (EL)	CRos LRHS NRHS SCoo SRms
	'Belle of Woking' (EL)	CRos ELan ELon ESps LRHS LSRN NEgg SCoo SPoG SWvt
	'Ben's Beauty' (A)	CFlo CKel
	BERNADINE ('Evipo 061'PBR) (EL)	CFlo CRos LRHS NRHS SWCr
	'Berry Red' (A)	CWGN
	'Best Wishes'	CKel CRos EBee ETho LRHS NRHS SNig SPoG SWCr
§	'Beth Currie' (EL)	CRos EPfP LRHS SNig SWCr
	'Betty Corning' (Vt)	CFlo CKel CRHN CRos CWGN EBee ELan EPfP ETho IPot LRHS LSRN MGos NRHS SCoo SLon SNig SPoG SRms SWCr SWvt
	'Betty Risdon' (EL)	ETho
	BIJOU	see *C.* THUMBELINA
	'Bill MacKenzie' (Ta) ♀H6	CArg CFlo CKel CMac CRav CRos CSam CSpe CTri ELan EPfP ESps ETho GKev IRob LRHS LSRN MAsh MGos MRav NPri NRHS SCob SLim SPer SPoG SRms SWCr SWvt WSHC
	'Black Prince' (Vt)	CFlo CKel CRHN CRos CWGN ELan EPfP ETho IPot LCro LRHS LSRN NHaw NLar NRHS SLim SLon SNig SPer SPoG SRms
	'Black Tea' (LL)	CKel CRos EPfP IPot LRHS LSRN NEgg NHaw NRHS SLim SLon SNig
§	'Błękitny Anioł' (LL) ♀H6	CFlo CKel CRHN CRos CWCL CWGN EBee ELon ETho LRHS MAsh NLar NRHS SCob SCoo SNig SPer SPoG SWCr WBor
	BLUE ANGEL	see *C.* 'Błękitny Anioł'
	'Blue Belle' (Vt)	CRHN ELan IPot LRHS NEgg NLar SLon WFar
	'Blue Bird' (A/d)	CArg CBcs CWCL EBee ELan GMcL LRHS MAsh SRms
	BLUE BLOOD	see *C.* 'Königskind'
	'Blue Boy' (EL)	see *C.* 'Elsa Späth'
	'Blue Boy' (I)	see *C.* × *diversifolia* 'Blue Boy' (I)
	'Blue Dancer' (A)	CBcs CKel CRos EPfP ETho LRHS MGos NLar SNig
	'Blue Eclipse' (A)	CFlo CKel CRos CWGN ETho LRHS NHaw NRHS SPoG
	'Blue Eyes' (EL)	ELon ETho LSRN NLar SNig
§	'Blue Light'PBR (EL/d)	CFlo CRos CWGN ELan LRHS NLar
	BLUE MOON ('Evirin'PBR) (EL)	CRos ETho LRHS LSRN NLar SCoo SLon SNig SWCr
	BLUE OCEAN ('Zo09045') (I)	EBee IPot
	BLUE PIROUETTE ('Zobluepi'PBR) (I)	CWCL IPot MJak NEgg
	BLUE RAIN	see *C.* 'Sinii Dozhd'
	'Blue Ravine' (EL)	CRos EPfP LRHS NLar SCoo
	BLUE RIVER ('Zoblueriver'PBR)	CWCL CWGN ELan ETho
	'Bolam Belle' (Vt)	NHaw
	BONANZA ('Evipo031'PBR) (Vt)	CRos EPfP LRHS NLar SCoo SLon SNig SPoG SWCr
	× ***bonstedtii*** 'Crépuscule' (H)	ECtt GCal
	BOURBON ('Evipo018'PBR) (EL)	CRos ELan EPfP ETho LRHS SCoo SLon SNig
	'Brianna' (Vt)	NHaw
	'Brocade' (Vt)	CRHN NHaw
	'Broughton Bride' (A)	CFlo CKel CWCL CWGN ETho LOPS LRHS NLar SPoG SRms WHar
	'Broughton Star' (M/d) ♀H4	Widely available
	'Brunette' (A)	CFlo CKel CRos ELan EPfP ETho LRHS MAsh NLar SLon SNig
	buchananiana Finet & Gagnep.	see *C. rehderiana*
	'Buckland Beauty' (V)	CFlo CWGN ETho LCro LOPS MJak NHaw
	'Buckland Pixie' (Vt)	NHaw
	'Burford Bell' (V)	NHaw
	'Burford Princess' (Vt)	CRHN NHaw
	'Burford White' (A)	NLar
	'Burma Star' (EL)	CFlo CKel CWCL CWGN EPfP ETho SNig
	CADDICK'S CASCADE	see *C.* 'Semu'
	calycina	see *C. cirrhosa* var. *balearica*
§	***campaniflora***	EShb ETho GCal NHaw
	campestris **new**	GKev

'Candy Stripe'	CRos LRHS SCoo SNig SPoG
'Capitaine Thuilleaux'	see *C.* 'Souvenir du Capitaine Thuilleaux'
'Cardinal Wyszynski'	see *C.* 'Kardynał Wyszyński'
'Carlotta' (Vt)	NHaw
'Carmencita' (Vt)	CRHN EBee LRHS LSRN NHaw SCoo SLon
'Carnaby' (EL)	CArg CBcs CKel CRos CWCL ELan ELon EPfP ETho LRHS LSRN MAsh NEgg SCoo SLim SNig SWCr SWvt WHar
'Carol Klein' (I)	NHaw
'Carol Leeds' (Vt)	NHaw
'Caroline' (LL)	CWGN ETho LSRN
× ***cartmanii*** 'Avalanche'^{PBR} (Fo/m)	CFlo CKel CRos ELan EPfP ETho LRHS MGos NLar NPri NRHS SCoo SLon SPoG SWCr SWvt
- 'Joe' (Fo/m) ♀^{H4}	CBcs CFlo CKel CRos CTsd CWCL ELan EPfP ETho EWes ITim LRHS LSRN NRHS SCob SCoo SPoG SWCr SWvt
- 'Joe' × ***marmoraria*** (Fo)	MAsh SWCr
- 'Joe' × 'Sharon'	LSRN
- MICHIKO ('Evipo044'^{PBR}) (Fo)	CRos EBee LRHS NRHS SNig SPoG
- 'White Abundance'^{PBR} (Fo/f)	CRos LRHS NLar
CASSIS ('Evipo020'^{PBR})	CKel CRos EBee ELan ETho LRHS LSRN MAsh SCoo SLon SNig SPer
'Catherine Clanwilliam' (T)	CWGN
'Catherine Penny' (VT) **new**	NHaw
'Celebration' Caddick	see *C.* 'Pink Celebration'
'Celebration'^{PBR} Godfrey (EL)	CFlo ETho
CEZANNE ('Evipo023'^{PBR}) (EL)	CFlo CKel CRos ELan EPfP ETho LRHS MAsh MGos NLar NRHS SCoo SLon SNig SWCr
'Chacewater' (Vt)	CRHN
'Chalcedony' (EL)	CWGN ETho
CHANTILLY ('Evipo021'^{PBR}) (EL)	CFlo CKel CRos ELan EPfP ETho LRHS LSRN NRHS SCoo SLon SNig SWCr
'Charissima' (EL)	CRos CWGN LRHS NLar SCoo
'Charlie Brown' (LL)	CRHN NHaw
'Charlotte' (EL) **new**	CFlo
CHARMAINE ('Evipo022'^{PBR}) (EL)	CFlo CKel CRos CWGN LRHS NRHS SPoG
'Chatsworth' (Vt)	CRHN CRos CWGN LRHS NHaw SLon
CHELSEA ('Evipo100')	CRos EPfP ETho LRHS NRHS SLon SWCr
CHEROKEE	see *C.* OOH LA LA
CHEVALIER ('Evipo040'^{PBR}) (EL)	CRos ELan EPfP LRHS MAsh NRHS SLon SNig SPoG SWCr
chiisanensis	WSHC
- B&SWJ 4560	WCru
- B&SWJ 12725	WCru
- 'Lemon Bells' (A)	CRos ELan EPfP LRHS MAsh SCoo SLon SPoG SWCr
- 'Love Child' (A)	ELan IPot
chinensis misapplied	see *C. terniflora*
CHINOOK ('Evipo013'^{PBR})	CRos LRHS SRms
chrysantha	see *C. tangutica*
chrysocoma misapplied	see *C. spooneri*
chrysocoma Franch.	WSpi
'Cicciolina' (Vt)	CRHN ETho NHaw
cirrhosa	CRos CTri LRHS MAsh SArc SCob MSwo SBrt SCob SEND SLim SPer SPoG SWvt
§ - var. ***balearica***	CBcs CFlo CKel CMac CRos CTri CWCL ELan EPfP ETho LCro LOPS LRHS LSRN MAsh MGos MRav
- 'Jingle Bells' (C)	CFlo CKel CMac CRos CWCL EPfP ETMg ETho LCro LOPS LRHS LSRN MAsh MGos NLar NRHS SCob SCoo SLim SLon SNig SRms SWCr
- 'Ourika Valley' (C)	CWGN ELon MAsh NLar SPoG
- var. ***purpurascens*** 'Freckles' (C) ♀^{H4}	Widely available
- - 'Lansdowne Gem' (C)	CFlo CKel CMac CRos CWCL CWGN LBuc LRHS NLar SPoG SWCr SWvt WSpi
- 'Winter Parasol' (C) **new**	LBuc
- 'Wisley Cream' (C) ♀^{H4}	CBcs CFlo CKel CMac CRos CWCL EBee ELan EPfP ESps ETho LCro LOPS LRHS LSRN MAsh MSwo NLar NRHS SCob SCoo SEND SLim SNig SPer SPoG SRms SWCr SWvt WFar
clarkeana misapplied	see *C. urophylla* 'Winter Beauty'
'Cloudburst' (LL)	ETho
coactilis	NHaw SBrt
columbiana	GKev
§ - var. ***tenuiloba***	LLHF
- - 'Ylva' (A)	WAbe
'Columbine' (A)	CDul CRos EBee LRHS MSwo SNig SPer
'Columella' (A)	EBee ETho NLar
'Comtesse de Bouchaud' (LL) ♀^{H6}	CArg CFlo CKel CRos CTri CWCL EBee ELan ELon EPfP EShb ESps ETho IRob LCro LOPS LRHS LSRN MAsh MGos MRav NPri NRHS SLim SNig SPer SPoG SWCr WBor
CONFETTI ('Evipo036'^{PBR}) (Vt)	CFlo CRos EPfP ETho LRHS LSRN SLon
'Congratulations' (EL)	CRos ELon LRHS LSRN NRHS SNig SPoG
aff. ***connata*** HWJK 2176 from Nepal	WCru
'Constance' (A) ♀^{H6}	CArg CFlo CKel CRos CWCL EBee EPfP ESps ETho GMcL LRHS LSRN NEgg NLar NRHS SCoo SNig SPre SRms SWCr WFar
'Continuity' (M)	CWGN
'Cora' (I)	CWGN
CORINNE ('Evipo063') (EL)	CFlo CRos LRHS NRHS SNig SPoG SWCr
'Cornish Spirit' (Vt)	CRHN
'Corona' (EL)	ELon EPfP LRHS SCoo
'Côte d'Azur' (H)	CExl CKel GCal LRHS MNrw NLar
'Countess of Lovelace' (EL)	CBcs ELan EPfP ETho LRHS LSRN SCoo SNig
COUNTRY ROSE ('Zocoro'^{PBR}) (A)	CFlo EPfP
'Cragside' (A)	CFlo CKel CRos LRHS NRHS
§ 'Crimson King' (LL)	NLar
'Crinkle'^{PBR} (M)	CCCN
§ ***crispa***	CWGN NHaw
§ CRYSTAL FOUNTAIN ('Evipo038'^{PBR}) (EL)	CFlo CKel CRos CWCL CWGN ELan EPfP ETMg ETho LBuc LCro LOPS LRHS LSRN MGos SCoo SLon SNig SPoG SRms SWCr
'Danae' (Vt)	NHaw
DANCING DORIEN ('Zodado'^{PBR}) (EL)	IPot
DANCING KING ('Zodaki'^{PBR}) (EL)	CKel
DANCING QUEEN ('Zodaque'^{PBR}) (EL)	ETho
DANCING SMILE ('Zodasmi'^{PBR}) (EL)	CKel EBee

	Name	Suppliers
	'Daniel Deronda' (EL) 🏆H6	CArg CFlo CKel CRos CWCL CWGN EBee ELan ETho IBoy IPot LRHS LSRN MAsh NRHS SCoo SLim SNig SPet SPoG SWCr
	'Darius' (EL)	EBee
	'Dark Eyes' (Vt)	CKel CWGN ETho IPot LOPS
	dasyandra NJM 11.075	WPGP
	'Dawn' (EL)	CCCN CFlo CRos ETho LRHS LSRN SCoo
	'De Vijfhoeven' (Vt)	NHaw
	'Débutante' (EL)	NHaw
	delavayi	ESps
	'Denny's Double' (EL/d)	CKel CWCL CWGN ETho LRHS SNig
	'Destiny' (EL)	CWGN
	DIAMANTINA ('Evipo039'PBR) (EL)	CFlo CKel CRos EBee EPfP ETho LBuc LRHS NRHS SLon SNig SWCr
	'Diamond Anniversary' (A)	CWCL
	'Diamond Ball'PBR (EL)	ETho
	'Diana' (LL)	EBee ETho LSRN NHaw
	DIANA'S DELIGHT ('Evipo026'PBR)	CKel CRos EPfP ETho LRHS LSRN MAsh NRHS SLon SPoG SWCr
	dioscoreifolia	see *C. terniflora*
§	× ***diversifolia***	CRHN LRHS NHaw SWvt WCot
	- 'Benedikt' (I)	CWGN
§	- 'Blue Boy' (I)	CRHN NHaw
	- 'Heather Herschell' (I)	CFlo CRHN CTsd NHaw
§	- 'Hendersonii' (I)	CFlo CRos CWCL ELan ETho GKev LRHS LSRN MCot MRav MWat SMHy SPer SWvt WCot
§	- 'Olgae' (I)	CExl NHaw
	'Doctor Mary' (V)	NHaw
	'Doctor Ruppel' (EL)	CArg CFlo CKel CMac CRos CWCL ELon ESps ETho GMcL IBoy LRHS LSRN MAsh MSwo NRHS SCob SLim SNig SPer SPet SWCr WFar
	'Dominika' (LL)	NHaw
	'Dorath'	CKel CRos CWGN EPfP LRHS NHaw
	'Dorothy Tolver' (EL)	ETho
	'Dorothy Walton'	see *C.* 'Bagatelle'
	'Double Delight' (M)	CFlo CWGN
	'Duchess of Albany' (1897) (T)	CArg CFlo CKel CRos CTri CWCL ELan EPfP ETho LRHS LSRN MAsh MGos NEgg SNig SPer SRkn
	'Duchess of Edinburgh' (EL)	CBcs CKel CMac CWCL ELan ELon EPfP ESps ETho IBoy LRHS LSRN MAsh MGos MSwo NEgg NRHS SLim SNig SPoG SWCr SWvt WHar
	× ***durandii*** 🏆H6	CBcs CFlo CKel CRHN CRos CSpe CWCL ELan EPfP ETho LRHS LSRN MAsh MGos MRav NRHS SCoo SPer SPoG SWCr SWvt WCot WSpi
	'Dutch Sky' (LL)	CWGN ETho
	'Early Sensation' (Fo/f)	Widely available
	EAST RIVER ('Zoeastri'PBR) (I)	ELan
	'Eclipse' (H)	EBee LRHS
	EDDA ('Evipo074') (Boulevard Series) (EL)	CFlo CRos EPfP LRHS NRHS SWCr
	'Edith' (EL) 🏆H6	CWCL ETho LSRN NHaw NLar SNig
	'Édouard Desfossé' (EL)	LRHS
	'Edward Prichard'	CFlo CKel EPfP ETho SNig
	'Eetika' (LL)	CRHN ETho NHaw
	'Effie Dewey' (LL) **new**	NHaw
	'Ekstra' (LL)	NHaw
	'Eleanor' (Fo/f)	GEdr
	'Elf' (Vt)	CWGN
	'Elgar' (A)	see *C.* 'Sir Edward Elgar'
	'Elizabeth' (M) 🏆H4	Widely available
§	'Elsa Späth' (EL)	CArg CExl CKel CMac CRos CTri ELan EMOT EPfP ESps ETho LRHS LSRN MAsh NEgg NRHS SLim SNig SPer SPoG SWCr SWvt
	'Elten' (M)	CKel
	'Elvan' (Vt)	CRHN NHaw NLar SNig
	'Ember' (I)	CWGN
	'Emerald Dream'PBR	LRHS NPnk
	'Emilia Plater' (Vt)	CRHN EPfP ETho NHaw SLon
	'Emma' (EL) **new**	CFlo
	'Empress Amy Lai'	CWCL NHaw
	EMPRESS ('Evipo011'PBR) (EL)	CFlo CRos ELan EPfP LRHS NRHS SLon SNig
	ENDELLION ('Evipo076') (EL)	CRos LRHS NRHS SWCr
	'Entel' (Vt)	CRHN EBee NHaw SNig
	× ***eriostemon***	see *C.* × *diversifolia*
	'Ernest Markham' (LL) 🏆H6	CBcs CKel CMac CRos CWCL ELan EPfP ESps ETho IBoy LRHS LSRN MAsh MGos MJak MSwo NEgg NPri NRHS SLim SNig SPer SPoG SWCr SWvt
	ESME ('Evipo048'PBR)	EBee SNig
	'Esperanto' (LL)	EBee NHaw
	ESTHER ('Zo09143') **new**	IPot
	'Étoile Rose' (Vt)	CMac CRHN CRos CTri CWCL EBee ELan EPfP ESps ETho IPot LRHS LSRN MAsh NEgg NHaw SCoo SLim SLon SNig SPer WBor
	'Étoile Violette' (Vt) 🏆H6	Widely available
	EVENING STAR ('Evista') (EL)	EPfP
	'Fair Rosamond' (EL)	NLar
	FAIRY BLUE	see *C.* CRYSTAL FOUNTAIN
	'Fairydust' (Vt)	NHaw
	fargesii var. ***souliei***	see *C. potaninii* var. *potaninii*
	× ***fargesioides***	see *C.* 'Paul Farges'
	fasciculiflora KWJ 12160	WCru
	- L 657	CBot EBee EPfP WCru WPGP
	'Fascination'PBR (I)	CFlo CWCL CWGN WCot
	'Fay' (Vt) **new**	NHaw
	FILIGREE ('Evipo029'PBR) (EL)	CFlo CRos ETho LBuc LRHS MAsh MGos NRHS
	'Filomae' (Vt)	NHaw
	finetiana misapplied	see *C. paniculata* J.G. Gmel.
	'Fireworks' (EL)	CArg CFlo CKel CRos CWCL CWGN ELon EPfP ESps ETho IBoy LRHS LSRN MAsh MRav NEgg NLar SLim SNig SPer SPoG SWCr
	flammula	CArg CFlo CKel CRos EBee ELan EPfP ETho LCro LOPS LRHS LSRN MAsh MBlu MRav NLar NRHS SPoG SRms SWCr SWvt WSpi XSen
	- 'Rubra Marginata'	see *C.* × *triternata* 'Rubromarginata'
	FLEURI ('Evipo042'PBR) (Boulevard Series) (EL)	CFlo CKel CRos CWCL EPfP ETho LRHS LSRN LSou NRHS SCoo SLon SNig SPoG SWCr
	florida	CWGN SWvt
	- 'Bicolor'	see *C. florida* var. *florida* 'Sieboldiana'
	- var. ***flore-pleno*** 'Plena' (d)	CCCN CFlo CRos CWCL EBee ELan EPfP ETho IPot LRHS LSRN MAsh NEgg NRHS SNig SPoG SWCr
§	- var. ***florida*** 'Sieboldiana' (d)	CBcs CFlo CKel CRos CWCL CWGN ELan EPfP ETMg ETho LCro LOPS LRHS LSRN MAsh NEgg NRHS SNig SPoG SRkn SWCr SWvt WFar

	- var. ***normalis*** PISTACHIO ('Evirida'^{PBR}) (LL)	CCCN CFlo CKel CRos CWGN ELan EPfP ETho LRHS MAsh MGos NLar NRHS SLon SNig SPoG SWCr
	'Floris V' (I)	GKev MCot NHaw NLar
	'Fluffy Duck' (Vt/d)	NHaw
	'Fond Memories' (EL)	CFlo CKel CRos CWCL CWGN EBee EPfP ETho IPot LCro LOPS LRHS LSRN NHaw NLar NRHS SLon SNig SWCr
	FOREVER FRIENDS ('Zofofri'^{PBR}) (LL)	CRos CWGN ETho IPot LRHS NRHS SLon SWCr
	'Forget-me-not NLP1'	LSRN NLar WHar
	forrestii	see *C. napaulensis*
§	***forsteri***	IDee WSHC
	'Foxtrot' (Vt)	CRHN
	'Foxy' (A) ♀^{H6}	CFlo LRHS NLar SLon
	FRAGRANT OBERON ('Hutbron'^{PBR}) (Fo)	CFlo LCro LOPS SWvt
	'Fragrant Spring' (M)	CKel CRos CSBt CWGN ELon ETho GMcL IBoy LRHS NLar NRHS SLim SNig SPet SWCr
	'Frances Rivis' (A) ♀^{H6}	CArg CBot CFlo CKel CMac CRos CWCL ELan EPfP ETMg ETho LCro LOPS LRHS LSRN MAsh MBlu MRav MSwo NLar SPer SPoG SRms SWCr
	'Francesca' (A)	LSRN
	'Frankie' (A) ♀^{H6}	CFlo CKel CRos ELan EPfP ETho LCro LOPS LRHS LSRN MAsh MGos MHer SCoo SWCr
	FRANZISKA MARIA ('Evipo008') (EL)	CFlo CRos EPfP LCro LRHS MAsh MGos SCoo SLon
	'Frau Susanne' (EL)	ETho
	'Freda' (M) ♀^{H4}	CKel CRHN CRos CTri CWGN ELan EPfP ESps ETho LCro LOPS LRHS LSRN MAsh MBlu MRav NEgg NRHS SLim SNig SPer SRms SWCr
	FREEDOM ('Zo06128') **new**	CFlo IPot
	fremontii	NHaw SBrt
	'Fryderyk Chopin' (EL)	EBee NLar SNig SPet
	'Fudō' (V)	NHaw
	'Fujimusume' (EL) ♀^{H6}	CFlo CKel CRos CWGN ETho IPot LRHS MAsh NHaw NRHS SPoG SWCr
	'Fukuzono'	CRos LRHS LSRN NHaw NRHS
	fusca misapplied	see *C. japonica*
	fusca Turcz. dwarf	CWGN
§	- var. ***fusca***	ETho WSHC
	- var. ***kamtschatica***	see *C. fusca* Turcz. var. *fusca*
	- large-flowered B&SWJ 8431	WCru
	'Fusca Peveril' (V)	NHaw
	'Fuyu-no-tabi' (EL)	ETho
	'Gabrielle' ambig.	LSRN
	GALORE	see *C.* VESUVIUS
	'Garnet' (V)	NHaw
	GAZELLE ('Evipo014'^{PBR}) (I)	CRos LRHS MAsh SRms
	'Generał Sikorski' (EL)	CBcs CFlo CKel CMac CRos CWCL ELan EPfP ESps ETMg ETho LRHS LSRN MAsh MGos NRHS SCoo SLim SNig SPer SWCr SWvt
	gentianoides	SBrt WAbe
	'Geoffrey Tolver' (LL)	CWGN ETho NHaw SNig
	'Georg Ots' (LL)	NHaw
	GIANT STAR ('Gistar'^{PBR}) (M)	CKel CRos ELon GMcL IBoy LRHS NEgg NLar NPer SLim SRkn
	'Gillian Blades' (EL) ♀^{H6}	CFlo CKel CRos EBee ELan EPfP ETho LBuc LRHS LSRN MAsh MGos NHaw NRHS SCoo SNig SPoG SWCr SWvt
	'Ginny' (V) **new**	NHaw
§	'Gipsy Queen' (LL) ♀^{H6}	CArg CBcs CMac CRos CWCL ELan ELon EPfP ESps ETho IBoy LRHS LSRN MAsh MGos NEgg SLim SNig SPer SPoG SWCr SWvt
	GISELLE ('Evipo051'^{PBR})	CFlo CRos EPfP ETho LRHS NRHS SLon SPoG SWCr
	'Gladys Picard' (EL)	NHaw
	glauca Turcz.	see *C. intricata*
	glaucophylla	NHaw WSHC
	'Golden Harvest' (Ta)	NLar
	GOLDEN TIARA ('Kugotia'^{PBR}) (Ta) ♀^{H6}	CKel CWGN ESps ETho LSRN NLar SRms WCot
	'Grace' (Ta)	EPfP IPot NHaw NLar
	gracilifolia BWJ 8002	WCru
	grandiflora	ETho LBuc SRms
I	'Grandiflora' (F)	WFar
	'Grandiflora Sanguinea' (Vt)	NHaw
	grata misapplied	see *C. × jouiniana*
	'Gravetye Beauty' (T)	CFlo CKel CRHN CRos CWCL EBee ELan EPfP ETho LRHS LSRN MAsh MGos MJak SLon SNig SPoG SRms SWCr SWvt
§	'Grażyna' (LL)	ETho
	'Guernsey Cream' (EL)	CFlo CRos CWCL EPfP ETMg ETho LCro LOPS LRHS LSRN MAsh MGos NLar SCoo SLim SNig SRkn SWCr
	GUIDING PROMISE ('Evipo053'^{PBR})	CRos LRHS NRHS SLon SNig
	'Guiding Star' (EL)	EBee
	'H.F. Young' (EL)	CFlo CKel CRos ELan EPfP ETho LRHS LSRN MAsh MGos NLar SCoo SNig SPer SPet SWCr SWvt
	'Hågelby Pink' (Vt) ♀^{H6}	CRHN CWGN NHaw
	'Hagley Hybrid' (LL)	CArg CMac CRos CWCL EBee ELan EPfP ESps ETho GMcL IRob LRHS LSRN MAsh MGos MJak MRav NEgg NLar NRHS SCob SLim SNig SPer SPet SPoG SRms SWCr SWvt
	'Hakuōkan' (EL)	CRos EPfP ETho LRHS LSRN NLar SCoo
	'Hakuree' ambig.	CKel
	'Hakuree' K. Ozawa (I)	ETho
	'Hanaguruma' (EL)	CKel ETho LSRN SNig SPet
	'Hanajima' (I)	ETho SChF
	'Hania' (EL)	EBee ETho
	'Happy Anniversary' (EL)	LBuc LCro LOPS LSRN NLar
§	HAPPY BIRTHDAY ('Zohapbi'^{PBR}) (LL)	LCro LOPS LSRN
	HARLOW CARR ('Evipo004'^{PBR})	CMac CRos EPfP LRHS NRHS SCoo SLim SRms
	'Haru Ichiban' (EL)	ETho
	'Hayate'	CWGN
	'Helen Cropper' (EL)	ETho
	'Helios'	see *C.* AZTEK
	'Helsingborg' (A) ♀^{H6}	CFlo CKel CRos ELan EPfP ETho LRHS MAsh NPri SCoo SNig SPoG SRms SWCr
I	'Hendersonii' (I)	CFlo CKel LSRN
	hendersonii Koch	see *C. × diversifolia* 'Hendersonii'
	hendersonii Stand.	see *C. × diversifolia*
I	'Hendersonii Rubra' (Ar)	LRHS
	'Hendryetta'^{PBR} (I)	CRos EMOT LRHS NEgg SWvt
	henryi	EShb ESps LSRN MAsh SNig SPet
	- B&SWJ 3402	WCru
	- var. ***morii*** B&SWJ 1668	WCru
	'Henryi' (EL)	CFlo CKel CMac CRos CTri CWCL EBee ELan EPfP ETho LCro LOPS LRHS LSRN MRav MSwo NEgg NRHS SPer SPoG SWCr

heracleifolia CBod CMac CPou CRos ECtt GJos GLog LRHS NLar WArt WBor WOld
- ALAN BLOOM see *C. tubulosa* ALAN BLOOM
- 'Blue Dwarf' (H) CWGN ETho WAbe
- 'Cassandra' (H) CBot CFlo CRos CSpe CWGN ECtt ELon EPfP ETho GLog LRHS LSRN MCot NRHS
- 'China Purple' (H) CBod CExl CPou ECtt GBin ILea LRHS MHol NLar SNig WHar
- 'Pink Dwarf' (H) CWGN NLar WAbe
- 'Roundway Blue Bird' (H) CBot

'Herbert Johnson' (EL) NHaw
hexapetala Forster see *C. forsteri*
hexasepala see *C. forsteri*
hirsutissima GKev SBrt SPhx
'Honora' (LL) CFlo CRos CWGN LRHS MAsh NRHS SCoo SNig
'Horn of Plenty' (EL) CRos LRHS NHaw
'Hoshi-no-flamenco' (T) CWGN ETho
huchouensis NHaw
HUDSON RIVER ('Zo06137') (I) **new** IPot
'Huldine' (LL) ♀H6 CBcs CKel CRHN CRos CWCL ELan EPfP ETho LRHS LSRN MAsh MRav SLon SNig SPer SWCr SWvt
'Huvi' (LL) CWGN ETho NHaw
'Hybrida Sieboldii' (EL) SCoo
HYDE HALL ('Evipo009'[PBR]) (EL) CFlo CKel CMac CRos CWGN EBee ELan EPfP LRHS MAsh MGos NRHS SCoo SLim SLon SNig SRms SWCr
'Hythe Egret' (Fo) LLHF
I AM A LITTLE BEAUTY ('Zolibe') (Vt) CRHN EBee NHaw
I AM HAPPY ('Zoiamha') (Vt) CWGN SCob
I AM LADY J ('Zoiamlj') (Vt) IPot NHaw SCob
I AM LADY Q ('Zoiamladyq'[PBR]) (Vt) CWGN EBee LRHS NHaw SCob
I AM RED ROBIN ('Zorero'[PBR]) (A) CWGN
ianthina 'Josie's Midnight Blue' (V) NHaw
- var. ***kuripoensis*** NHaw
- - B&SWJ 700 WCru

'Ibi' (EL) CWGN
ICE BLUE ('Evipo003'[PBR]) (Prairie Series) (EL) CRos ELan EPfP ETho LRHS MAsh SCoo SLim SLon SNig SWCr
'Ice Queen' (EL) MAsh
'Ilka' (EL) NHaw
indivisa Willd. see *C. paniculata* J.G. Gmel.
INES ('Evipo059') (Boulevard Series) **new** CRos NRHS SPoG
'Ingrid Biedenkopf' (Vt) NHaw
'Innocent Blush'[PBR] (EL) ETho
'Innocent Glance'[PBR] (EL) ETho
INSPIRATION ('Zoin'[PBR]) (I) ELan NLar SCoo
integrifolia CExl CFis ELan EPfP EWTr GKev IFoB IPot LRHS NChi NLar NPer SRms WArt WHil WHoo
I - 'Alba' (I) CFlo CRos ECtt GKev LRHS LSRN NHaw NLar SCoo SRms
- 'Blue Ribbons' (I) CSpe MMrt NLar SBee SPhx
- 'Budapest' (I) EBee
- dark blue-flowered GKev
- 'Hendersonii' Koch see *C.* × *diversifolia* 'Hendersonii'
- 'Olgae' see *C.* × *diversifolia* 'Olgae'
- 'Ozawa's Blue' (I) CWGN ETho MBNS
- violet-flowered GKev
- white-flowered see *C. integrifolia* 'Alba'

§ ***intricata*** CExl
ispahanica NHaw
'Iubileinyi-70' (LL) NHaw
'Ivan Olsson' (EL) CWCL ETho IPot
'Izumi' M.Takeuchi (LL) ETho
'Jackmanii' (LL) ♀H6 CArg CBcs CKel CMac CRos CTri EBee EPfP ESps ETMg ETho GMcL IBoy LCro LOPS LRHS LSRN MAsh MGos MJak SCoo SLim SNig SPoG SWCr SWvt WHar
'Jackmanii Alba' (EL) CRos CWCL ELan ELon EPfP ETho LRHS LSRN MAsh SCoo SLim SNig SPoG
JACKMANII PURPUREA ('Zojapur'[PBR]) (LL) ETho
'Jackmanii Superba' misapplied see *C.* 'Gipsy Queen'
'Jackmanii Superba' ambig. (LL) CDul CFlo CKel CMac CRos CWCL ELan EPfP ESps ETho LCro LRHS MAsh MGos MRav MSwo NEgg NPer NPri SCob SLim SNig SPer SPoG SWCr
'Jacqueline du Pré' (A) ♀H6 CBcs CFlo CKel EBee ELan EPfP ETho LRHS SNig
'Jacqui' (M/d) CKel CWCL
'James Mason' (EL) ETho LSRN SNig
'Jan Fopma'[PBR] (I) CWGN
'Jan Lindmark' (A/d) CRos EPfP ETho LRHS MAsh NLar SCoo SPoG SPre SWCr
§ 'Jan Paweł II' (EL) CRos ELan ETho LRHS SCoo SPer SPet
'Jane Ashdown' (M) **new** NHaw
§ ***japonica*** NHaw
- B&SWJ 11204 WCru

'Jasper' (V) ETho
'Jean Caldwell' (Vt) NHaw
'Jean Cumpston' (C) NHaw
'Jeanne's Pink' CWCL ETho LCro LOPS
'Jenny' (M/d) CFlo CKel CRos CWCL ETho LCro LOPS LRHS LSRN SPoG SWCr
I 'Jenny' (Cedergren) (LL) **new** NHaw
'Jenny Caddick' (Vt) NHaw
'Jerzy Popiełuszko' (EL) ETho
JESSICA ('Evipo012'[PBR]) (I) CRos LRHS
JEWEL OF MERK see *C.* HAPPY BIRTHDAY
JOHN HOWELLS ('Zojohnhowells'[PBR]) (Vt) CFlo CWCL CWGN ETho LSRN SLon
'John Huxtable' (LL) ♀H6 CFlo CKel CRos ETho LRHS SNig
JOHN PAUL II see *C.* 'Jan Paweł II'
'John Treasure' (Vt) CRHN NHaw NLar
'John Warren' (EL) CRos LRHS MAsh NHaw NRHS SCoo SWCr
'Jolly Jake' (Vt) CFlo
JOSEPHINE ('Evijohill'[PBR]) (EL) CFlo CKel CRos CWCL CWGN EPfP ETho EUJe LCro LOPS LRHS LSRN MAsh MGos NLar NRHS SCoo SLim SNig SPer SPoG SRkn SWCr SWvt WHar
§ × ***jouiniana*** MRav SEND SWvt WSHC
'Julka' (EL) CFlo CWCL ETho NHaw
'Justa' (Vt) NHaw
'Juuli' (I) LSRN
'Kaaru' (LL) CRHN
'Kacper' (EL) NHaw
'Kaen' (EL) ETho
'Kaiser'[PBR] ETho
'Kaiu' (V) CFlo CKel CRos CWCL CWGN ETho LRHS NHaw

§	'Kakio' (EL)	CRos CWCL ETho LRHS LSRN MAsh MGos NEgg SNig SPer SPet SWCr
I	'Kamilla' (EL)	CWGN
§	'Kardynał Wyszyński' (EL)	ETho
§	'Kasmu' (Vt)	NHaw
	KASSIA ('Evipo067') (Flora Series)	CRos LRHS NRHS
	'Kathleen Dunford' (EL)	LSRN SCoo
	'Kathryn Chapman' (Vt)	CRHN NHaw
	'Kaunitar' (LL)	NHaw
	'Ken Donson' (EL) ♀H6	LRHS SCoo
	'Ken Pyne' (LL)	CFlo
	'Kermesina' (Vt) ♀H6	CKel CRHN CRos EBee ELan EPfP ETho IBoy LCro LOPS LRHS MAsh MJak SCoo SLim SNig SPer SPoG SRms SWCr WBor
	'Ketu Õde' (LL)	NHaw
	'Kiev' (Vt)	NHaw
	'Killifreth' (Vt)	CRHN NHaw
	'King Edward VII' (EL)	LRHS NHaw
	KINGFISHER ('Evipo037'^{PBR}) (EL)	CFlo CKel CRos CWCL ELan EPfP LRHS SCoo SLon SPoG SWCr
	'Kinju Atarashi' (LL)	CWCL ETho
	'Kiri Te Kanawa' (EL)	CKel CWCL ELon ETho LRHS LSRN NLar SNig
	'Kirsi' (LL)	NHaw
	'Kommerei' (LL)	NHaw
§	'Königskind' (EL)	ETho NLar
	koreana	MAsh WCru
	'Krakowiak'^{PBR} (Vt)	NHaw
	'Külli' (LL)	NHaw
	ladakhiana	NHaw
	'Lady Betty Balfour' (LL)	CMac CRos ETho LRHS SCoo SNig SWvt
	'Lady Bird Johnson' (T)	CFlo CRos CWCL LRHS LSRN SCoo
	'Lady Caroline Nevill' (EL)	CRos LRHS NRHS
	'Lady Londesborough' (EL)	NHaw SCoo
	'Lady Northcliffe' (EL)	CKel CRos CTri CWCL EPfP ETho LRHS MAsh SNig
	'Lambton Park' (Ta) ♀H6	CKel CRHN CWCL EBee ETho NHaw NLar
	lasiandra	NHaw
	'Last Dance' (Ta)	CRHN EBee
	LASTING LOVE	see *C.* 'Grażyna'
	'Lasurstern' (EL) ♀H6	CArg CBcs CExl CFlo CKel CMac CRos CTri EBee ELan EPfP ETho LCro LOPS LRHS LSRN MAsh NEgg SNig SPer SPet SPoG SWCr SWvt WFar
	'Laura Denny' (EL)	ETho
	'Lavender Twirl' (Vt)	CRHN
	'Lawsoniana' (EL)	CMac LRHS SNig
	'Lech Wałęsa' (EL)	ETho
	'Lemon Beauty' (A)	ETho
	'Lemon Chiffon' (EL)	CRos LRHS
	'Lemon Dream'^{PBR} (A)	ETho
	LIANNE ('Evipo064') (EL)	SNig
	LIBERATION ('Evifive'^{PBR}) (EL)	CRos LRHS NLar SCoo SLim SLon SNig
	LIBERTY ('Zo08095') (EL)	ETho IPot
	ligusticifolia	NHaw
	'Lily the Pink' (Vt)	NHaw
	'Lincoln Star' (EL)	CArg CMac CRos ELon ESps LRHS MAsh NEgg SLim SNig SPer SWvt
	'Lisboa' (Vt)	NHaw
	'Little Bas' (Vt)	CRHN CWGN IPot NHaw NLar SLon SNig
	'Little Butterfly' (Vt)	CRHN NHaw
	'Little Mermaid' (EL)	CFlo CWCL ETho
	'Little Nell' (Vt)	CCCN CRHN EBee ELan EPfP ETho LRHS LSRN MAsh SCoo SLon SNig WFar
I	'Longiflora'	CFlo
	'Lord Herschell'	CFlo CKel CWCL CWGN ETho NHaw SNig
	'Lord Nevill' (EL)	CRos EPfP LRHS
	'Louise Rowe' (EL)	CFlo CRos CWCL ELan ETho LRHS LSRN NHaw SNig
	'Love Jewelry' (EL)	ETho SNig
	LUCKY CHARM ('Zo09067') (LL) **new**	CFlo CWGN IPot LCro LOPS
	LULA ('Evipo057') (Boulevard Series)	CWGN
	'Lunar Lass' (Fo/f)	CFlo EBee ETho LRHS WAbe
	'Lunar Lass Variegata' (Fo/v)	LLHF
	'Luther Burbank' (LL)	SNig
	'Luxuriant Blue' (Vt)	CRHN NHaw
	'M. Koster' (Vt)	CRHN ETho LRHS NHaw SLon SRms
	macropetala (d)	CBcs CRos ELan EPfP ESps ETho GKev GMcL LRHS MAsh MGos MMuc MRav NRHS SNig SPer
	- 'Blue Lagoon'	see *C. macropetala* 'Lagoon' Jackman 1959
	- 'Lagoon' Jackman 1956	see *C. macropetala* 'Maidwell Hall' Jackman
	- 'Lagoon' ambig.	LSRN
§	- 'Lagoon' Jackman 1959 (A/d) ♀H6	CRos ETho LCro LOPS LRHS LSRN MAsh MSwo NRHS SCoo
	- 'Maidwell Hall' ambig. (A)	SCob
§	- 'Maidwell Hall' Jackman (A/d)	CTri EPfP LSRN MAsh WSHC
	- 'Wesselton' (A/d) ♀H6	CFlo CKel CRos CTri CWCL EPfP ETho LCro LOPS LRHS MAsh NLar SPoG SPre SRms SWCr
	- 'White Moth'	see *C.* 'White Moth'
	'Madame Baron-Veillard' (LL)	CRos LRHS SCoo SNig
	'Madame Edouard André' (LL)	CRos CWCL EPfP LRHS MAsh NRHS SCoo SNig SPet
	'Madame Grangé' (LL) ♀H6	CRos LRHS NHaw SCoo
	'Madame Julia Correvon' (Vt) ♀H6	Widely available
	'Madame le Coultre'	see *C.* 'Mevrouw Le Coultre'
	'Majojo' (Fo)	GEdr LLHF
	mandschurica	EBee ETho GBin GCal NHaw NLar XEll
	marata	GKev WThu
	'Margaret Hunt' (LL)	ETho IBoy LSRN NHaw SNig
	'Mari' (LL)	NHaw
	'Maria' Kivistik (LL)	NHaw
	'Maria Cornelia'^{PBR} (Vt)	CWGN ETho LCro LOPS
	'Maria Skłodowska-Curie'^{PBR} (EL)	ETho
	'Marie Boisselot' (EL) ♀H6	CArg CBcs CFlo CKel CMac CRos CTri CWCL ELan EPfP ETho IBoy LRHS LSRN MAsh MGos MSwo NLar NPri SNig SPer SPet SPoG SWCr SWvt
	'Marinka'	CWGN
	'Marjorie' (M/d)	CArg CBcs CKel CRos CTri CWCL ELan EPfP ESps GKin GMcL IBoy LRHS LSRN MAsh MGos MRav NEgg NRHS SLim SNig SPer SPoG SRms SWCr WFar
	'Markham's Pink' (A/d) ♀H6	Widely available
	marmoraria	CRos EPot LRHS NRHS SPlb SRms WAbe
	- 'Timpany Treasure'	ITim

	'Marmori' (LL)	CWGN ETho NHaw
	MARTA ('Evipo071'[PBR])	SNig
	'Mary Habberley' (Vt)	NHaw
	'Mary Rose'	see *C. viticella* 'Flore Pleno'
	'Mary-Claire' (EL/d)	SNig
	maximowicziana	see *C. terniflora*
	'Mayleen' (M) ♀H4	CRos CSam CTri EPfP ETMg ETho IBoy LRHS MAsh MRav NEgg NRHS SCoo SLim SNig SPer SPoG SRms SWCr SWvt WFar
	'Mazury' (LL)	ETho
	'Meeli' (LL)	NHaw
I	'Melodie' (Vt)	NHaw
§	'Mevrouw Le Coultre' (EL)	ETMg GMcL MJak
	MIENIE BELLE ('Zomibel'[PBR]) (T)	CWGN ETho IPot NHaw
	'Mikelite' (Vt)	EBee NHaw
	'Miniseelik' (LL)	NHaw
	'Minister' (EL)	SNig
	'Minuet' (Vt) ♀H6	CRHN CRos EBee EPfP ETho LCro LOPS LRHS MAsh MGos SCob SCoo SLon SPer SPoG SWCr SWvt
	MIRABELLE ('Evipo072') **new**	CRos NRHS
	MIRANDA ('Floclemi'[PBR]) (I)	CWGN
	'Miss Bateman' (EL)	CFlo CKel CMac CRos CTri CWCL EBee ELan EPfP ESps ETho GMcL LCro LOPS LRHS LSRN MAsh MGos NEgg NRHS SLim SNig SPer SPet SPoG SWCr WBor
	'Miss Christine' (M)	CFlo CSam ELan LCro LOPS LSRN SPoG SWvt
	MISSISSIPPI RIVER ('Zomisri') (I)	IPot
	'Mister Hans Horn' (Vt)	NHaw
	MON AMOUR ('Zomoa'[PBR]) (EL)	CWGN
	MON CHERRY ('Zomonch') (EL)	CWGN IPot
	'Moniuszko' (EL)	CWGN
	montana	CExl CPla CSBt ESps MAsh SCob SEWo
	- B&SWJ 6724 from Taiwan	WCru
	- B&SWJ 6930	WCru
	- WJC 13713 from the Himalaya **new**	WCru
	- var. ***alba***	see *C. montana* var. *montana*
	- 'Alexander' (M)	CRos EPfP LRHS NRHS SWCr
	- 'Da Yun' (M)	CWGN EBee
	- var. ***grandiflora*** (M) ♀H4	CArg CChe CDul CKel CMac CRos CWCL ELan EPfP ESps ETho GKin GMcL LBuc LCro LOPS LRHS MJak MMuc NPri NRHS SCob SEND SLim SNig SPer SPoG SRms SWCr SWvt
§	- var. ***montana***	CBar CBcs GMcL LCro LOPS LRHS MAsh SCob SPer SPoG WFar
	- var. ***rubens*** misapplied	see *C. montana* var. *montana*
	- var. ***rubens*** E.H.Wilson	CRos CSBt CTri ELan EPfP ESps GMcL LRHS NRHS SNig SPlb
I	- - 'Odorata' (M)	EPfP ETho GKin LRHS MRav SCoo SLim WHar WHlf
	- - 'Pink Perfection' (M)	CKel CMac CRHN CRos ELan EPfP ESps GKin LCro LOPS LRHS LSRN MAsh NRHS SCob SCoo SLim SNig SPer SPoG SWCr SWvt WFar WHar
	- - 'Tetrarose' (M) ♀H4	Widely available
I	- 'Rubens Superba' (M)	CTri ECtt GKin NEgg SRms SWCr WFar
	- var. ***sericea***	see *C. spooneri*
	- var. ***wilsonii***	CFlo CKel CRav CRos CWCL ECtt ELan EPfP ETho GKin GLog GQue LRHS LSRN MRav MSwo SNig SPer SPet SPoG SRms SWCr SWvt
	'Monte Cassino' (EL)	CWGN SNig SPet
	'Moonbeam' (Fo)	EPot GEdr ITim
	MOONFLEET ('Evipo046'[PBR]) (LL)	CRos LRHS
§	'Moonlight' (EL)	LRHS MAsh
	'Moonman' (Fo)	LLHF
	MORNING CLOUD	see *C.* 'Yukikomachi'
	'Morning Heaven' (Vt)	NHaw
	MORNING STAR ('Zoklako'[PBR]) (EL)	CWGN ETho LRHS
	MORNING YELLOW ('Cadmy'[PBR]) (M)	CCCN CFlo EBee EUJe GMcL IBoy LRHS
	'Mrs Cholmondeley' (EL) ♀H6	CKel CRos CWCL ELan EPfP ESps ETho LRHS LSRN MAsh MGos MSwo NPri SCob SLim SNig SPer SPet SPoG SWCr
	'Mrs George Jackman' (EL) ♀H6	CFlo CRos CWCL EBee ESps ETho LRHS NLar SCoo
	'Mrs James Mason' (EL)	EBee
	'Mrs N. Thompson' (EL)	CArg CKel CMac CRos CTri CWCL EBee ELan ELon ETho IBoy LRHS LSRN MAsh MGos NEgg NPer SLim SNig SPer
	'Mrs P.B. Truax' (EL)	CRos LRHS
	'Mrs Robert Brydon' (H)	ECtt NLar SRms
	'Mrs T. Lundell' (Vt)	CRHN NHaw
	'Multi Blue' (EL)	CArg CBcs CFlo CKel CRos CWCL ELan ELon EPfP ESps EUJe GMcL IBoy LRHS LSRN MAsh MGos SLim SNig SPer SPoG SRkn SRms SWCr WHar
	'My Angel'[PBR] (Ta)	ELan IPot NHaw NLar SCob
	'Myojō' (EL)	LRHS
	'Nadezhda' (LL)	NHaw
§	***napaulensis***	CFlo CTri CWCL EPfP ETMg ETho LCro LOPS NHaw WCru WSHC
I	'Natacha' (EL)	EBee NHaw SCoo
	'Natascha' (EL)	CWCL LRHS LSRN SNig SPet SWvt
	'Negritianka' (LL)	CRos LRHS LSRN NHaw
	'Negus' (LL)	NHaw
	'Nelly Moser' (EL) ♀H6	Widely available
	'Nelly Moser Neu' (EL)	GMcL
	NEVA ('Evipo050') (Boulevard Series) (EL)	CRos LRHS NRHS SNig
	'New Love'[PBR] (H)	ETMg ETho LSRN NLar
	'Night Veil' (Vt)	NHaw
	NINON ('Evipo052') (Boulevard Series)	CWGN SNig
	'Niobe' (EL) ♀H6	Widely available
	'North Star' (EL)	CKel EPfP SNig
	NORTH STAR (LL)	see *C.* 'Põhjanael'
	NUBIA ('Evipo079') (Boulevard Series) **new**	CRos NRHS
	'Nunn's Gift' (Fo)	ETho
	nutans var. ***thyrsoidea***	see *C. rehderiana*, *C. veitchiana*
	'Oberek' (Vt)	CRHN NHaw
	'Ocean Pearl' (A)	CFlo ETho LSRN NLar
	ochotensis	GKev LLHF
	OCTOPUS ('Zooct'[PBR]) (A)	CFlo CWGN
	'Odoriba' (V)	CRHN CWGN ETho NHaw
	'Olimpiada-80' (EL)	NHaw
	'Omoshiro' (EL)	CWCL CWGN ETho IPot LRHS NHaw
§	OOH LA LA ('Evipo041'[PBR]) (Boulevard Series) (EL)	CFlo CKel CRos CWCL ELon EPfP ETho LRHS LSou MAsh NRHS SCoo SNig SPer SPoG SWCr
	orientalis misapplied	see *C. tibetana* subsp. *vernayi*
	orientalis ambig.	SRms
	orientalis L.	EBee EPfP SCoo SWvt
	- PAB 13.731 **new**	LEdu

	- from Kyrgyzstan **new**	WPGP
	- 'Orange Peel'	see *C. tibetana* subsp. *vernayi* var. *vernayi* 'Orange Peel'
	- 'Sherriffii'	see *C.* 'Sherriffii'
	- var. ***tenuiloba***	see *C. columbiana* var. *tenuiloba*
	orientalis* × *tangutica	SWvt
	'Oshikiri' (V) **new**	NHaw
	otophora	NHaw SBrt
	'Ovation'PBR (Fo)	IBal NPnk
	'Paala' (EL)	NHaw
	'Pagoda' (Vt)	CRHN EBee EPfP LRHS SCoo SLon SRms
	PALETTE ('Evipo034'PBR) (Vt)	SLon
	'Pamela' (F)	ETho NHaw
	'Pamela Jackman' (Vt)	NEgg
	'Pamela Jackman' (A)	see *C. alpina* 'Pamela Jackman'
	'Pamiat Serdtsa' (I)	ELon ETho NHaw
	'Pamina' (EL)	ETho
	'Pangbourne Pink' (I) ♀H6	CFlo CKel CRos CWCL EPfP ETho LRHS NHaw NRHS SCoo
	paniculata Thunb.	see *C. terniflora*
§	***paniculata*** J.G. Gmel.	MNrw
	'Paola' (EL/d)	EBee
	'Paradise Queen' (EL)	LBuc NLar
	PARISIENNE ('Evipo019'PBR) (Boulevard Series) (EL)	CFlo CRos CWCL ELon EPfP ETho EUJe LRHS LSou MAsh NRHS SCoo SLon SNig SPoG SWCr
	parviflora DC.	see *C. campaniflora*
	parviloba var. ***bartlettii*** B&SWJ 6788	WCru
	'Pat Coleman' (EL)	CWCL ETho
	patens 'Korean Moon' (EL)	WCru
§	- 'Manshuu Ki' (EL)	CFlo CRos CWCL EBee ELon ETho LRHS NEgg SNig
	- 'Yukiokoshi' (EL)	EBee ETho
	PATRICIA ANN FRETWELL ('Pafar') (EL)	ETho
§	'Paul Farges' (Vb) ♀H6	CArg CKel CWGN EShb ETho GLog MNrw NEgg NHaw NLar
	'Pauline' (A/d) ♀H6	CBcs CRos LRHS LSRN NRHS SCoo
	'Peggy West' (LL) **new**	NHaw
	'Pendragon' (Vt)	CRHN NHaw
	'Pennell's Purity' (LL)	CFlo
	PEPPERMINT ('Evipo005'PBR) (d)	CFlo ELan EPfP LRHS SCoo SLon SNig
	'Perida' (LL)	CWGN
	'Perle d'Azur' (LL)	CBcs CKel CMac CRHN CRos CTri CWCL EBee ELan ELon EPfP ETho IRob LCro LOPS LRHS LSRN MAsh MGos MSwo NEgg SCob SLim SNig SPer SPoG SRms SWCr WFar WSpi
	'Perrin's Pride' (Vt)	CRos EBee LRHS MGos NHaw NLar SCoo SNig
	PETIT FAUCON ('Evisix'PBR) (I) ♀H6	CFlo CRos EPfP ETho LRHS LSRN MGos MMrt NLar SCob SCoo SLim SNig SPer SRms SWCr SWvt
	petriei	WThu
	'Peveril Pristine' (Vt)	CWGN NHaw
	PICARDY ('Evipo024'PBR) (EL)	CFlo CRos EPfP ETho LRHS NRHS SCoo SLim SNig SPoG SWCr
	PICOTEE ('Zo09124') **new**	CFlo IPot
I	'Picton's Variety' (M)	CTri SPoG
	'Piilu' (EL)	CArg CKel CRos CWCL CWGN EBee ELan ETho GMcL LCro LOPS LRHS LSRN MAsh MBNS NHaw NLar SCob SCoo SLim SNig SPet SRkn SWCr
	'Pille' (LL)	NHaw
§	'Pink Celebration' (EL)	ETho
	PINK CHAMPAGNE	see *C.* 'Kakio'
	'Pink Dream' (A)	ETho
	'Pink Fantasy' (LL)	CFlo CRHN CRos CTri ETho LRHS MAsh NLar SCob SCoo SLim SNig SRkn
	'Pink Flamingo' (A) ♀H6	CRos CWCL ELan EPfP LRHS MGos NRHS SCoo SNig SPoG SWCr
	'Pink Ice' (I)	CKel CWCL NHaw
	'Pink Swing' (A)	ETho
	'Pirko' (Vt)	NHaw
§	***pitcheri***	CWGN NHaw WSHC
	'Pixie' (Fo/m)	CFlo CKel EBee ELan ELon EPfP ETho GMcL LRHS MGos NLar NPnk SCoo SPoG
	pogonandra	NHaw
§	'Põhjanael' (LL)	NLar
	POLAR BEAR	see *C.* ARCTIC QUEEN
	'Poldice' (Vt) ♀H6	CRHN
	'Polish Spirit' (LL) ♀H6	Widely available
	'Polonez' (Vt)	NHaw
	potaninii	ETho
§	- var. ***potaninii***	WSHC
	- var. ***souliei***	see *C. potaninii* var. *potaninii*
	- 'Summer Snow'	see *C.* 'Paul Farges'
	'Praecox' (H) ♀H6	CBod CRHN CRos CWCL EBee ELan EPfP ETho IRob LRHS MCot NQui NSti WAul WCot
	PRETTY IN BLUE ('Zopre'PBR) (F)	EBee SCob SWvt
	'Primrose Star'	see *C.* 'Star'
	'Prince Charles' (LL) ♀H6	CFlo CKel CRHN CRav CTri CWCL EBee ELan EPfP EShb ETMg ETho LRHS LSRN MAsh MJak NHaw NLar SCoo SLim SNig SPer SWCr SWvt
	'Prince George' (LL)	CWCL ETho LCro LOPS LSRN NLar NPri
	'Princess Charlotte' (EL) **new**	LCro LOPS
§	'Princess Diana' (T) ♀H5	CBcs CFlo CKel CRHN CTri CWGN EBee ELan ESps ETMg ETho IPot LBuc LCro LRHS LSRN MAsh MBlu MSwo SCob SCoo SLim SNig SPer SPoG SRms SWCr SWvt
	PRINCESS KATE ('Zoprika'PBR) (T)	CFlo CRos CWGN EBee EPfP ETho EWTr IPot LCro LOPS LRHS MAsh MBlu NRHS SPoG SWCr WBor WCot
§	'Princess of Wales' (1875) (EL)	CWCL LSRN NLar SLon SWvt
	'Prinsesse Alexandra'PBR (EL)	ETho
	'Propertius' (A)	CArg CFlo CKel CRos CWCL CWGN EBee ETho GEdr LRHS MGos SPoG
	'Prosperity' (M)	CRHN ETho
	'Proteus' (EL)	CRos ELan ELon EPfP LRHS MAsh MGos SCoo SNig WHar
	psilandra CWJ 12377	WCru
	'Purple Dream'PBR (A)	ETho
	'Purple Haze' (Vt)	CRHN NHaw
	'Purple Princess' (H)	SPoG
	'Purple Spider' (A/d)	CFlo EPfP ETho LRHS MAsh MBlu NLar SCoo
	'Purpurea Plena Elegans' (Vt/d) ♀H6	CBcs CKel CMac CRHN CRos CTri CWCL EBee ELan ELon EPfP ETho IBoy LCro LOPS LRHS LSRN MAsh MSwo NEgg NRHS SLim SPer SPoG SWCr SWvt WBor
	quadribracteolata	NHaw

QUEEN MOTHER ('Zoqum') (Vt)	CWGN EPfP ETho LRHS
'Radiance'	CWGN
'Rahvarinne' (LL)	ETho
'Ramona' (LL)	CRos LRHS LSRN NHaw SNig
ranunculoides	NHaw
'Rasputin' (LL)	CWCL ETMg ETho
REBECCA ('Evipo016'PBR) (EL)	CFlo CKel CRos CWCL CWGN ELan EPfP ETho EUJe LCro LOPS LRHS LSRN MAsh NRHS SCob SCoo SLon SNig SPer SPoG SWCr
recta	CWCL ECtt IPot MNrw NLar
- PAB 9005	LEdu
- 'Lime Close' seedlings	CAby
- 'Purpurea' (F)	CDor CFlo CRos EHoe ELan EPfP ETho GKev GWyn ILea IPot LRHS MAvo MNrw NChi SEND SPer WArt XLum
- 'Velvet Night' (F)	CSpe ECtt EUJe LRHS NEgg NLar WCot
'Red Ballon' (Ta)	EBee IPot
'Red Cooler'	see *C.* 'Crimson King'
'Red Pearl' (EL)	CFlo CRos LRHS LSRN SNig SWCr
REFLECTIONS ('Evipo035') (LL)	CRos EBee EPfP LRHS SLon SNig
§ ***rehderiana*** ♀H5	CDul CKel CRHN CWCL EBee ELan EPfP ETho MBlu NSti SWvt WCot WPGP WSHC
'Reiman' (LL)	NHaw
'Remembrance' (LL)	CFlo CWCL EPfP ETMg ETho LSRN NHaw
repens 'Bells of Emei Shan'	ETho
'Reverie' (T) **new**	NHaw
'Rhapsody' ambig.	EPfP ETho LBuc MAsh MGos SCoo SNig SWCr
'Rhapsody' B. Fretwell (EL)	CRos EBee LRHS LSRN NHaw
'Ribble Red' (V)	NHaw
'Richard Pennell' (EL) ♀H6	CRos LRHS SNig SPet SWCr
'Richard's Picotee' (Vt)	NHaw
'Rising Star'	NHaw SNig
'Ristimägi' (LL)	NHaw
'Rituaal' (LL)	NHaw
'Robud'PBR (M/d)	NPer
'Roelie' (Vt)	NHaw
'Roko-Kolla' (LL)	ETho NHaw
'Romantika' (LL)	CFlo CRos ELan ELon ETho IBoy LCro LRHS LSRN MAsh NHaw NRHS SCoo SNig XEll
'Rooguchi' (I)	CFlo CWCL CWGN ETho LRHS NHaw
'Rooran' (EL)	CWCL ETho
'Rosa Königskind' (EL)	ETho NLar
ROSALYN ('Zo09087') (Vt)	CWGN
'Rosamunde' (LL)	ETho
I 'Rosea' (A/d)	CRos
I 'Rosea' (I)	CWCL EPfP ETho GKev LRHS LSRN WHoo
I 'Rosea' Westphal. (Vt)	NHaw
ROSEMOOR ('Evipo002'PBR) (EL)	CFlo CKel CRos CWCL CWGN EPfP ETho LRHS MAsh NRHS SCoo SLim SLon SNig SWvt
'Rosy O'Grady' (A) ♀H6	MAsh NLar SRms
'Rosy Pagoda' (A)	CRos ELan LRHS NLar
'Rouge Cardinal' (LL)	CArg CBcs CFlo CMac CRos EBee ELan ELon EPfP ESps ETho GMcL IBoy LRHS LSRN MAsh MGos MJak NEgg NRHS SCob SLim SNig SPer SPet SPoG SRms SWCr
'Royal Velours' (Vt)	CFlo CKel CRHN CRav CRos CTri CWCL ELan EPfP ETMg ETho IPot LCro LOPS LRHS LSRN MAsh MGos NLar NRHS SCob SCoo SLim SNig SPer SPoG SWCr
ROYAL VELVET ('Evifour'PBR) (EL)	CRos LRHS LSRN SCoo
'Royalty' (EL)	CRos CWCL ELan EPfP LRHS LSRN MAsh SCoo SWCr
'Rubens Superba'	see *C. montana* 'Rubens Superba'
'Ruby' (A)	CRos CWCL ELan EPfP ETMg ETho LRHS LSRN MAsh NEgg SCoo SNig SPer SRms SWCr WFar
'Ruby Glow' (EL)	CRos EPfP LRHS LSRN SCoo SNig
'Ruby Tuesday' (V) **new**	NHaw
'Ruby Wedding' Fretwell (T)	CFlo CWCL CWGN EPfP LBuc LCro LOPS LSRN SWvt
'Rüütel' (EL)	CFlo CKel CRos CWCL ELon ETho LRHS MAsh NHaw SCoo SNig
'Saalomon' (LL)	NHaw
SACHA ('Evipo060') **new**	CRos LRHS NRHS
SALLY ('Evipo077') (EL)	CFlo CRos LRHS MAsh NRHS SPoG SWCr
'Sally Cadge' (EL)	NHaw
SAMARITAN JO ('Evipo075')	CFlo CRos EPfP ETho LRHS MAsh NRHS SPoG SWCr
'Sanssouci' (M) **new**	EBee
SAVANNAH ('Evipo015'PBR) (Vt)	MAsh
'Scartho Gem' (EL)	CRos LRHS SCoo SNig
'Sealand Gem' (EL)	NHaw
§ 'Semu' (LL)	CWGN ETho NHaw
serratifolia	CRHN ECtt ETho GAbr GKev GLog SBrt SPlb
- B&SWJ 8458 from Korea	WCru
'Sheila Thacker' (EL)	ETho
I 'Sherriffii' (Ta)	SWvt
'Shikoo' (EL)	CWCL ETho LSRN
SHIMMER ('Evipo028'PBR) (LL)	CKel CRos EPfP LRHS NRHS SLon SWCr
'Shirayukihime' (EL)	NLar
'Sialia' (A/d)	CFlo CKel
§ ***sibirica***	CRos EPfP ESps LRHS NRHS
- var. ***tianschanica***	NHaw
'Signe' (Vt)	see *C.* 'Kasmu'
'Siirus' (EL)	NHaw
'Silmakivi' (EL)	NHaw
'Silver Moon' (EL)	CFlo CWCL EPfP ETho LRHS MAsh NLar SCoo
simensis	LEdu
simsii Small	see *C. pitcheri*
simsii Sweet	see *C. crispa*
'Sinee Plamia' (LL)	NHaw
§ 'Sinii Dozhd' (I)	CWCL NHaw
§ 'Sir Edward Elgar' (A) **new**	LCro LOPS LRHS NRHS
'Sir Eric Savill' (M)	ETho LSvl
'Sir Trevor Lawrence' (T)	CRos LRHS NHaw
'Sireen' (LL)	NHaw
'Skyfall' (LL)	ETho
smilacifolia NJM 10.094	WPGP
aff. ***smilacifolia*** HWJ 1049	WCru
'Snow Queen' (EL)	CFlo CKel CRos ELon EPfP ETMg ETho LRHS SLim SNig SRms
'Snowbird' (A/d)	CFlo CKel CRos LRHS SNig SPer SPoG SWCr
'Snowdrift'	see *C. armandii* 'Snowdrift'
socialis **new**	NHaw
'Södertälje' (Vt)	CRHN EPfP ETho NHaw SCoo
'Sokojiro' (EL) **new**	CRos NRHS
'Solidarność' (EL)	ETho
'Solina' (Vt)	NHaw
songarica	NHaw

	Name	Suppliers
	'Sonnette' (V)	CFlo CRHN CWGN ETho IPot NHaw
	'Sophie' (V) **new**	NHaw
	SORBET ('Zosor'PBR) (A) **new**	CFlo
§	'Souvenir du Capitaine Thuilleaux' (EL)	CKel ELon SNig
	'Special Occasion' (EL)	CRos CWGN EPfP LRHS LSRN NLar SCoo SNig SWCr
	SPIKY ('Zospi'PBR) (A/d)	CFlo
§	***spooneri***	CTri EPfP LRHS SCoo SWvt
	SPRING JOY ('Zo12053') (M) **new**	CFlo
	'Sputnik' (I)	NHaw
	stans	CBot CExl CPou CRos EWTr IFro LLHF LRHS NLar SWCr
	- B&SWJ 5073	WCru
	- B&SWJ 6345	WCru
§	'Star'PBR (M/d)	CRos EPfP LRHS MSwo NLar SPer
	'Star of India' (LL)	CKel CRos CWCL EPfP ETho LRHS MGos SCoo SLim SNig SPer
	STAR OF PAKISTAN ('Zostapa')	CWGN
	STAR RIVER ('Zostarri'PBR) (I)	ELan IPot
I	'Starfish' (EL)	NHaw
	'Starlight' (M)	CKel CWCL ELon SNig
	'Stasik' (LL)	NHaw
	'Stefan Franczak' (EL)	ETho
	'Stephanie' (A)	CFlo CKel
	STILL WATERS ('Zostiwa'PBR) (EL)	ETho
	'Strawberry Kiss' (V)	NHaw
	SUCCESS CANDY ('Tra415'PBR) **new**	ETMg
	SUCCESS LAVENDER ('Tra27'PBR) (EL) **new**	ETMg
	SUCCESS MAGENTA ('Tra73'PBR) (LL) **new**	ETMg
	SUGAR CANDY ('Evione'PBR) (EL)	LRHS MAsh SCoo SLim SNig
	SUMMER SNOW	see *C.* 'Paul Farges'
	SUMMERDREAM ('Zosumdre') (EL)	ETho
	SUNNY SKY ('Zosusk'PBR) (Vt)	CFlo CKel NHaw
	'Sunrise' (M/d)	EBee IPot MSwo NLar
	'Sunset' (EL) 🏆H6	CArg CRos CWCL ELon LRHS LSRN MGos NEgg NLar SCoo SNig
	SUPER NOVA ('Zo09088') (Vt) **new**	CFlo IPot
	'Swedish Bells' (I)	CWGN EBee
	'Sweet Scentsation' (F)	CFlo EPfP LOPS NHaw NLar
	'Sweet Summer Love'PBR (F)	CWGN EBee ETho NHaw
	SWEETHEART ('Witswe'PBR) (I)	ELan EPfP ETho
	'Sylvia Denny' (EL)	CArg EPfP ETho MAsh
	'Syrena' (LL)	NHaw
	szuyuanensis B&SWJ 6791	WCru
	- CWJ 12455	WCru
	'Tae'	see *C.* 'Toltae'
	'Tage Lundell' (A)	CFlo EPfP LRHS NLar
	'Tamakazura' (V) **new**	NHaw
	'Tango' (Vt)	CRHN EBee NHaw
§	***tangutica***	Widely available
	'Tapestry' (I)	NHaw
	'Tartu' (EL)	NHaw
	tashiroi purple-flowered B&SWJ 7005	WCru
	- 'Yellow Peril'	WCru
	TEKLA ('Evipo069'PBR) (LL)	CRos LRHS NRHS SNig SPoG SWCr
	'Teksa' (LL)	NHaw
	TEMPTATION ('Zotemp'PBR) (EL)	EBee
	tenuiloba	see *C. columbiana* var. *tenuiloba*
§	***terniflora***	EPfP ETho NHaw WHar
	- B&SWJ 5751	WCru
	'Teshio' (EL)	EBee IPot
	texensis	ETho NHaw WSHC
	- 'The Princess of Wales'	see *C.* 'Princess Diana'
	- 'Wellmax'PBR **new**	NHaw
	'The Bride' (EL)	CWCL CWGN ETho LRHS LSRN
	THE COUNTESS OF WESSEX ('Evipo073') (EL)	CRos EPfP ETho LRHS MAsh NRHS SPoG SWCr
	'The First Lady' (EL)	CWCL ETho SNig
	'The President' (EL) 🏆H6	Widely available
	'The Princess of Wales' (EL)	see *C.* 'Princess of Wales' (1875) (EL)
	'The Princess of Wales' (T)	see *C.* 'Princess Diana' (T)
	'The Vagabond' (EL)	CRos CWCL CWGN ELan EPfP ETho LRHS LSRN MAsh NHaw NLar SCoo SLim SNig SPet
	'The Velvet' (EL)	SNig
§	THUMBELINA ('Evipo030'PBR) (EL)	CKel CWCL ETho GMcL LRHS NRHS SNig
	thunbergii misapplied	see *C. terniflora*
	'Thyrislund' (EL)	CKel SNig
	'Tibetan Mix' (Ta)	NHaw
	tibetana	NHaw
	- CC 7447	GKev
	- 'Black Tibet' (Ta)	NHaw
§	- subsp. ***vernayi***	LLHF
	- - 'Glasnevin Dusk' (Ta)	WSHC
§	- - var. ***vernayi*** 'Orange Peel' LS&E 13342 (Ta)	CBcs ETho LRHS SEND
	'Tie Dye' (LL)	CWGN EBee ELan EPfP ETho NHaw SPoG
	'Tiiu' (LL)	NHaw
	'Tim's Passion' (Vt) **new**	CRHN
	'Titipu' (V)	NHaw
	'Together' (I)	NHaw
	'Toki' (EL)	CWGN
§	'Toltae'PBR (EL)	CFlo CRos CWGN ETho LRHS NRHS
	tongluensis	WPGP
	- GWJ 9358	WCru
	- HWJK 2368	WCru
	tosaensis f. ***cremea***	NHaw
	'Tranquility'	CWGN
	'Triinu' (Vt)	NHaw
§	× ***triternata*** 'Rubromarginata'	CFlo CKel CMac CRHN CRos CWGN ELan ELon EPfP ETho LCro LOPS LRHS LSRN MAsh MGos MMrt MRav NLar NRHS SCob SLim SLon SNig SPer SPoG SRms SWCr
	'Tsunami Child' (M)	IMou
§	***tubulosa*** ALAN BLOOM ('Alblo'PBR) (H)	CRos LRHS NRHS
	- 'Wyevale' (H)	CFlo CMac CRos ELan ELon EPfP LRHS MCot MRav NLar NRHS NSti SCoo SPad SPer WAul WGwG
	'Tuchka' (EL)	NHaw
	'Twilight' (EL)	CFlo CKel CRos EPfP LRHS MAsh SNig SWCr
	TWINKLE ('Zotwi') (I)	CWGN
	'Uno Kivistik'PBR (LL)	NHaw
	urophylla	SPhx

§ - 'Winter Beauty' CFlo CWCL EBee ETMg ETho LCro LOPS LRHS LSRN SBrt SCoo SPoG WPGP WSHC
urticifolia B&SWJ 8651 WCru
- B&SWJ 8852 WCru
'Utopia' (EL) CWGN
'Valge Daam' (LL) CWGN ETho NHaw
'Valle' (LL) NHaw
'Van Gogh' (M) CWGN ETho
'Vanessa' (LL) CRHN NHaw
'Vanso' see *C.* 'Blue Light'
§ ***veitchiana*** EWld NHaw
'Venosa Violacea' (Vt) ♀H6 CFlo CKel CRHN CRos ELan EPfP ETho LRHS LSRN MAsh NHaw SCoo SNig SPer SPoG SRms SWCr
'Vera' (M) LRHS LSRN SCoo SLim
vernayi see *C. tibetana* subsp. *vernayi*
'Veronica's Choice' (EL) CFlo CWCL ELan NHaw SNig
VERSAILLES ('Evipo025'PBR) (EL) CRos EPfP LRHS SNig
§ VESUVIUS ('Evipo032'PBR) (Vt) CRos LRHS MAsh SCoo SLon
'Vetka'PBR (LL) NHaw
VICTOR HUGO ('Evipo007'PBR) (LL) CFlo CRos LRHS NLar SCoo SNig
'Victoria' (LL) ♀H6 CRos ETho LRHS LSRN NHaw SCoo
VIENNETTA ('Evipo006'PBR) (d) CFlo CKel CRos CWCL CWGN EPfP ETho LRHS MGos NRHS SCoo SLon SNig SRms SWCr
'Vihma' (LL) NHaw
'Ville de Lyon' (LL) CBcs CFlo CKel CRHN CWCL ELan EPfP ESps GMcL IBoy LRHS LSRN MAsh MGos NEgg NRHS SLim SNig SPer SPet SPoG SWCr WHar
vinacea NHaw
'Vince Denny' (Ta) EBee ETho NHaw SNig
VINO ('Poulvo'PBR) (EL) CRos LRHS NHaw SCoo
'Viola' (LL) CFlo CWGN ELon ETho LSRN NHaw
'Violet Charm' (EL) NEgg
viorna CWGN NHaw WSHC
virginiana misapplied see *C. vitalba*
§ ***vitalba*** CPer CWld EBWF ECrN ETho NHaw WHer WSFF WSpi
- SDR 6610 GKev
viticella CDul CRHN ESps ETho NHaw WSHC
- subsp. ***campaniflora*** see *C. campaniflora*
§ - 'Flore Pleno' (Vt/d) CFlo CKel CRHN CRos ELan ELon EPfP ETho IPot LCro LOPS LRHS LSRN NHaw NRHS SLon SNig SPoG SWCr
- 'Hågelby Blue' (Vt) NHaw
- 'Hågelby White' (Vt) CRHN CWGN NHaw
- 'Hanna' (Vt) CRHN LSRN NHaw
- 'Mary Rose' see *C. viticella* 'Flore Pleno'
'Viva Polonia'PBR (EL) ETho
'Vivienne' see *C.* 'Beth Currie'
'Voluceau' (Vt) CRHN CRos CWCL ELan EPfP LRHS LSRN SNig SRms SWCr
VOLUNTEER ('Evipo080') **new** CRos NRHS
'Vostok' (LL) NHaw
'Vyvyan Pennell' (EL) CArg CBcs CFlo CKel CMac CRos CTri CWCL ELan EPfP ESps ETMg ETho EUJe IBoy LRHS LSRN MAsh MSwo NEgg NLar SLim SNig SPer SPet SPoG SWCr SWvt WFar
'W.E. Gladstone' (EL) CRos ETho LRHS
WADA'S PRIMROSE see *C. patens* 'Manshuu Ki'
'Walenburg' (Vt) ♀H6 CKel CRHN CWGN ETho NHaw SLon
'Walter Pennell' (EL) CBcs CRos LRHS SCoo
'Warsaw' (Ta) NLar
'Warszawska Nike' (EL) ♀H6 CMac CRHN CRos CWCL ELan EPfP ETho GMcL LCro LOPS LRHS MAsh MGos SCob SCoo SNig SPoG SWCr
'Warszawska Olga' (EL) ETho
'Warwickshire Rose' (M) CFlo CKel CMac CRHN CRos CTri CWGN EBee ELan ESps ETho LRHS LSRN MAsh NEgg SLim SNig SPoG SWCr WHar
'Wedding Day' (EL) CFlo ETho LCro LOPS LSRN NLar
'Wee Willie Winkie' (M) GMcL SCoo SRms
'Westerplatte' (EL) CFlo CKel CRos CWCL CWGN EBee EPfP ETMg ETho LRHS MGos NHaw SLim SNig SPoG SWCr WHar
§ 'White Columbine' (A) ♀H6 ELan ETho LRHS SNig SPer
'White Heart' (Vt) **new** NHaw
'White Magic'PBR (Vt) ETho
§ 'White Moth' (A/d) LSRN MAsh
'White Prince Charles' (LL) NHaw
'White Satin' (A) CRos EPfP LRHS SRms
'White Swan' (A/d) ETho MAsh NLar SCoo
'White Wings' (A/d) CFlo LSRN
'Will Goodwin' (EL) ♀H6 CBcs CRos CWCL ELan EPfP ETho LRHS SNig SRms
'William Kennett' (EL) CWCL ELan ETho IBoy LRHS MJak
'Willy' (A) CArg CRos EBee ELan EPfP ETho LRHS MAsh MGos NLar NRHS SPer SRms WFar
WISLEY ('Evipo001'PBR) (Vt) ♀H6 CKel CRos EPfP LRHS MGos NLar SLim SLon
'Xerxes' misapplied see *C.* 'Elsa Späth'
'Yatsuhashi' ambig. SNig
'Yellow Queen' Holland see *C. patens* 'Manshuu Ki'
'Yellow Queen' Lundell/Treasures see *C.* 'Moonlight'
§ 'Yukikomachi' (EL) ETho NHaw
yunnanensis EBee SBrt WPGP
ZARA ('Evipo062'PBR) (EL) ELan SLon
'Zephyr' (Vt) NHaw

Clematopsis see *Clematis*

Clementsia see *Rhodiola*

Cleome (*Cleomaceae*)

hassleriana COLOUR FOUNTAIN MIXED **new** CRav
- 'Helen Campbell' ♀H2 CSpe
- 'Violet Queen' **new** LCro LOPS
SENORITA ROSALITA ('Inncleosr'PBR) CSpe NPri

Cleretum (*Aizoaceae*)

§ ***bellidiforme*** ESps

Clerodendrum (*Lamiaceae*)

CW&T 6506 CMCN
bungei Widely available
- PAB 8953 LEdu
- 'Diamond' **new** SGol
- 'Pink Diamond' (v) CCCN CWGN ELan EPfP EWes LRHS LSRN LSou MGos NLar SPer SPoG SWvt
§ ***chinense*** var. ***chinense*** (d) ♀H1b CCCN CHll
- 'Pleniflorum' see *C. chinense* var. *chinense*

colebrookianum B&SWJ 6651	WCru
- PAB 7794	LEdu
fragrans var. ***pleniflorum***	see *C. chinense* var. *chinense*
myricoides 'Ugandense'	see *Rotheca myricoides* 'Ugandense'
philippinum	see *C. chinense* var. *chinense*
× ***speciosum***	CHll
aff. ***subscaposum*** WWJ 11735	WCru
thomsoniae 🏆H1b	EShb WSFF
tomentosum new	CBot
trichotomum	CAby CBcs CBot CEnd CExl CLnd CMCN CRos CSam CSpe CTho CTri EPfP EUJe IArd LRHS NLar SLim SLon SPer WBor WHor
- var. ***fargesii*** 🏆H4	Widely available
- - 'Carnival' (v) 🏆H4	CBcs CCCN CExl CMac CRos CWCL EBee ELan EPfP EWes LRHS MAsh NLar SEle SLim SMad SPer SPoG SWvt WAvo WCot
- 'Purple Blaze'	EBee
- 'Purple Haze'	MMrt NLar
- 'Shiro'	WCru
- white calyx new	CBot
wallichii	EShb

Clethra ✿ (*Clethraceae*)

CW&T 6497	CMCN
acuminata	NLar
alnifolia	CBcs CDul CExl CTsd MPkF SPer SRms WCot WFar
- 'Anne Bidwell'	MBlu NLar
- 'Creel's Calico' (v)	NLar
- 'Fern Valley Pink'	CCCN CMac EBee ELon LLHF LRHS NLar SRms WFar
- 'Hokie Pink'	NLar
- 'Hummingbird' 🏆H5	CCCN CEnd CExl CMac CRos ECrN ELan EPfP LRHS MAsh MBlu NEgg NLar SChF SEle SPad SPoG SWvt WFar
- 'Paniculata'	CRos ELon EPfP LRHS MGil MMuc WBor
- 'Pink Spice' new	CRos
- 'Pink Spires'	CAco CBcs CExl CWld ECrN GKin LEdu LSou MMuc MRav NEgg NLar SCob SCoo SEle SPer WBor
- 'Rosea'	CTri GKin MPkF
- 'Ruby Spice' 🏆H5	CBcs CCCN CEnd CExl CJun CMac CRos ELan ELon EWTr GBin GGGa GKin IDee LCro LOPS LRHS LSRN MAsh MBlu NLar SEle SPad SPer SPoG SWvt
- 'September Beauty'	CJun NLar
- 'Sixteen Candles'	GGGa MPkF NLar
- VANILLA SPICE ('Caleb')	CBcs NLar
arborea	CBcs
barbinervis 🏆H5	CBcs CExl CRos CTho EPfP GGGa IDee LRHS MBlu MGil NLar WFar WPGP WSHC
- B&SWJ 11562	WCru
- GREAT STAR ('Minbarb')	EPfP LRHS WPGP
- 'White Star'	EBee EPfP LRHS SPer
conzattiana new	CFil
delavayi Franch.	CBcs CCCN CFil CPne EBee EPfP GCal GGGa IDee LLHF MGil NLar WPGP
- SBEC 1513	CExl
fabri B&SWJ 11702	WCru
- FMWJ 13037 new	WCru
fargesii	CExl CFil EPfP IDee NLar
kaipoensis NJM 11.020	WPGP
- NJM 11.058	WPGP
- PAB 8571	LEdu
luzmariae	CFil
mexicana	CFil
monostachya	CExl EBee GGGa NLar WPGP
pringlei	CBcs CFil EBee NLar WPGP WSHC
tomentosa 'Cottondale'	CJun NLar

Cleyera (*Pentaphylacaceae*)

fortunei	see *C. japonica* 'Fortunei'
- 'Variegata'	see *C. japonica* 'Fortunei'
§ ***japonica*** 'Fortunei' (v)	CCCN CMac CRos LRHS SSta
- var. ***japonica***	EBee WPGP
- 'Tricolor' (v)	CBcs IDee SAko
- var. ***wallichii***	WPGP

Clianthus ✿ (*Papilionaceae*)

maximus	CTsd GDun
- 'Kaka King'	EWes GDun SPoG
§ ***puniceus*** 🏆H3	CAbb CBcs CCht CExl CHll CKel CRos CSpe CTsd EBee EPfP EUJe GDun IBoy LRHS MGil NRHS SEle SGbt SPer SPlb SPoG SWvt WSHC
§ - 'Albus' 🏆H3	CAby CBcs CExl CHGN CKel CRos CSpe EPfP GDun IBoy LRHS MGil NRHS SPer SPoG SWvt
- 'Flamingo'	see *C. puniceus* 'Roseus'
- 'Red Admiral'	see *C. puniceus*
- 'Red Cardinal'	see *C. puniceus*
§ - 'Roseus' 🏆H3	CBcs CExl CKel CRos EPfP GDun LRHS NRHS SMad SPer SPoG
- 'White Heron'	see *C. puniceus* 'Albus'

Clinanthus (*Amaryllidaceae*)

§ ***coccineus***	NRog
§ ***incarnatus*** apricot-flowered	NRog
§ ***variegatus***	WCot
- orange-flowered	NRog
- red-flowered	NRog
- yellow-flowered	NRog

Clinopodium (*Lamiaceae*)

ascendens	see *Calamintha ascendens*
calamintha	see *Calamintha nepeta*
grandiflorum	see *Calamintha grandiflora*
§ ***menthifolium***	EBWF NBre NLar
§ ***vulgare***	CHab CSpe EBWF EBee GPSL MHer MNHC NMir SRms WMoo WOut
- PAB 7562	LEdu

Clintonia (*Liliaceae*)

udensis	WCru
umbellulata	GCal WCru

Clivia ✿ (*Amaryllidaceae*)

caulescens	WCot
- pink-flowered	WCot
gardenii	WCot
miniata 🏆H1c	CAbb CBcs CCCN CTca CTsd LCro SAdn SEND SPlb WCot
- 'Anshan Variegated' (v)	WCot
- 'Arturo's Yellow'	WCot
- 'Ato-Shan'	WCot
- 'Aurea'	CSpe
- Belgian hybrids	WCot
- 'Beverley's Delight'	WCot
- broad-leaved, variegated (v)	WCot

- var. ***citrina*** ♀H1c	CTca LAma
- - variegated (v)	WCot
- 'Dancing Sisters'	WCot
× 'Terracotta Green Throat'	
- Daruma Group	WCot
- green-centred	WCot
- 'Light of Buddha' (v)	WCot
- 'Mitsuhashi Multipetal'	WCot
- pastel shades	WCot
- 'Pink Perfection'	WCot
- 'Red Dawn'	WCot
- 'Striata' (v)	CBlu WCot
- 'Terracotta Treasure' (v)	WCot
- 'Vico Shima'	WCot
- 'Wide Leaf Monk'	WCot
nobilis ♀H1c	SPlb WCot
robusta	WCot
'San Marcus Yellow'	WCot
× 'Solomone Yellow'	
'Sweet Undress'	WCot

Clusia (*Clusiaceae*)

rosea	CCCN

Clytostoma (*Bignoniaceae*)

§ ***calystegioides***	CCCN CHll CRHN

Cnidium (*Apiaceae*)

officinale	GPoy LEdu

Cobaea (*Polemoniaceae*)

paneroi	CFil
pringlei	CRHN WPGP WSHC
- CD&R 1323	SBrt
scandens ♀H2	CCCN CDTJ CRav CSpe EShb SPer
- f. ***alba***	CRav CSpe EShb LCro LOPS SPer

cobnut see *Corylus avellana*

Cocculus (*Menispermaceae*)

laurifolius	EUJe
§ ***orbiculatus***	CExl
- B&SWJ 535	WCru
trilobus	see *C. orbiculatus*

Cochlearia (*Brassicaceae*)

armoracia	see *Armoracia rusticana*
officinalis	EBWF WHer

Cochliasanthus (*Papilionaceae*)

§ ***caracalla***	CCCN WHil

Cocos (*Arecaceae*)

plumosa	see *Syagrus romanzoffiana*

Codonanthe (*Gesneriaceae*)

gracilis	WDib
'Paula'	WDib

× *Codonatanthus* (*Gesneriaceae*)

'Golden Tambourine'	WDib
'Sunset'	WDib
'Tambourine'	WDib

Codonopsis ✿ (*Campanulaceae*)

ACE 1625	EWld
HWJK 2105 from Nepal	WCru
SDR 3019	GKev
affinis	EBee
- HWJCM 70	WCru
- HWJK 2151	WCru
benthamii GWJ 9352	WCru
bhutanica	GKev
cardiophylla	EBee EWld GCal WSHC
clematidea	CDor CSpe EBee ECha EPfP EWld GAbr GCal GKev MNHC MNrw NEgg NLar SPhx SPlb SWvt WRHF WSHC
- 'Lilac Eyes'	NEgg
convolvulacea misapplied	see *C. grey-wilsonii*
convolvulacea ambig.	GBin
- 'Alba'	see *C. grey-wilsonii* 'Himal Snow'
- Forrest's form	see *C. forrestii* Diels
- var. ***hirsuta*** B&SWJ 7812	WCru
'Dangshen'	see *C. pilosula*
aff. ***deltoidea*** SSSE 86	EBee EWld
forrestii misapplied	see *C. grey-wilsonii*
§ ***forrestii*** Diels	CPne EBee EWld GKev WCot
- BWJ 7776	WCru
- BWJ 7847	WCru
§ ***grey-wilsonii*** ♀H5	CAby CBro CPne EWld GEdr
- B&SWJ 7532	WCru
§ - 'Himal Snow'	CAby CPne EWld GEdr WCru
inflata GWJ 9442	WCru
kawakamii	EBee EWld
- B&SWJ 1592	WCru
- RWJ 10007	WCru
§ ***lanceolata***	CAby EWld SBrt
- B&SWJ 562	EBee WCru
nepalensis Grey-Wilson	see *C. grey-wilsonii*
obtusa	EBee EWld
ovata	EBee EWld NBro NLar
§ ***pilosula***	CDor EBee EWld GKev GPoy SBrt
- var. ***modesta***	EBee EWld
pinifolia new	GKev
§ ***rotundifolia*** var. ***angustifolia***	EBee EWld SBrt WCru
- var. ***grandiflora***	EBee EWld WSHC
silvestris	see *C. pilosula*
tangshen misapplied	see *C. rotundifolia* var. *angustifolia*
ussuriensis	see *C. lanceolata*
vinciflora	CPne EWld GEdr
viridiflora	WCru
viridis HWJK 2435	WCru

Coffea (*Rubiaceae*)

arabica	CCCN LCro SPlb SPre

coffee see *Coffea*

Coincya (*Brassicaceae*)

wrightii PJL 20098	CHid

Colchicum (*Colchicaceae*)

agrippinum ♀H4	CAvo CBro CTal ECha EPot GBin GKev LAma MRav NRog WAbe WCot WHoo WThu
alpinum	GKev
'Antares'	ECha NRog
atropurpureum	GKev LAma
'Autumn Herald'	LAma NRog
'Autumn Queen' ♀H5	CTca NRog
§ ***autumnale***	CAvo CBro CHab EPot GBin GKev GPoy GQue IFro LAma NRog NRya SDeJ SEND WShi
- 'Alboplenum'	ERCP GKev LAma NRog SDeJ
- 'Album'	CAvo CBro CTca ELan EPot GKev LAma LCro LOPS WShi
- 'Atropurpureum'	NRog

	- var. ***major*** hort.	see *C. byzantinum* Ker Gawl.
	- var. ***minor*** hort.	see *C. autumnale*
§	- 'Nancy Lindsay' ♀H5	CBro CTal EPot GKev NRog WShi XEll
	- 'Pannonicum'	see *C. autumnale* 'Nancy Lindsay'
§	- 'Pleniflorum' (d)	GKev IRob LAma NRog
	- 'Roseum Plenum'	see *C. autumnale* 'Pleniflorum'
	baytopiorum	GKev NRog
	'Beaconsfield'	NRog
§	***bivonae***	EPot
	- 'Apollo'	GKev NRog
	- 'Mount Giona'	GKev
§	***boissieri***	GKev
	bornmuelleri misapplied	see *C. speciosum* var. *bornmuelleri* hort.
	bornmuelleri Freyn	CBro GKev IRob LAma NRog
	bowlesianum	see *C. bivonae*
	byzantinum ambig.	GKev NRog
§	***byzantinum*** Ker Gawl. ♀H5	CBro ELan LAma SDeJ WShi
	- ***album***	see *C. byzantinum* 'Innocence'
§	- 'Innocence'	GKev NRog WCot
	cilicicum	LAma NRog
	- 'Purpureum'	CTca EPot GKev LAma NRog
	'Conquest'	see *C.* 'Glory of Heemstede'
	corsicum	GKev WThu
	cupanii AH 9707	GKev
	- var. ***pulverulentum***	GKev NRog
	davisii	CTal GKev NRog
	'Dick Trotter'	EPot GKev NRog SDeJ SDir WFar WOld
	'Disraeli'	EPot GKev NRog
	falcifolium	NRog
§	***giganteum***	GKev LAma NRog
§	'Glory of Heemstede'	NRog
	'Gracia'	NRog
	graecum	GKev
	'Hannibal'	GKev
	'Harlekijn'	GKev LAma NRog
	hungaricum	EPot GKev NRog
	- f. ***albiflorum***	EPot GKev NRog
	- 'Roseum'	GKev
	- 'Valentine'	GKev
	- 'Velebit Star'	GKev NRog
	illyricum	see *C. giganteum*
	'Jaroslavna'	NRog
	'Jochem Hof'	NRog
	kesselringii	NRog
	laetum misapplied	see *C. parnassicum*
	laetum Stev.	NRog
	'Lilac Bedder'	GKev NRog
	'Lilac Wonder'	ELan GKev IRob LAma MRav NRog SDeJ WCot
	longifolium	see *C. neapolitanum*
	lusitanum	LAma
	luteum	NRog
	'Lysimachus'	GKev
	macrophyllum	GKev LAma NRog
	minutum	NRog
	munzurense	NRog
§	***neapolitanum***	GKev NRog
	'Neptun'	NRog
	'Oktoberfest'	EPot
	parlatoris	GKev NRog
§	***parnassicum***	ECha GKev NRog WThu
	'Pink Goblet' ♀H5	CBro LAma
	'Poseidon'	GKev NRog
	procurrens	see *C. boissieri*
	psaridis	GKev
	pusillum	GKev NRog
	'Rosy Dawn' ♀H5	CBro ECha GKev NRog WOld
	'Rosy Wonder'	LAma
	sibthorpii	see *C. bivonae*
	'Spartacus'	GKev
	speciosum ♀H5	CAvo CBro ELan EPot GBin GKev LAma NRog WCot WShi
	- 'Album' ♀H5	CAvo CBro ECha EPfP EPot ERCP GAbr GKev LAma NRog SDeJ
	- 'Atrorubens' ♀H5	ECha EPot LAma
I	- var. ***bornmuelleri*** hort.	WHoo WOld
	- 'Dombai'	NRog
	- var. ***illyricum*** hort.	see *C. giganteum*
	szovitsii	GKev
	subsp. ***brachyphyllum***	
	- 'Snow White'	GKev
	- 'Tivi'	NRog
	- white-flowered	GKev
	tenorei ♀H4	CTal EPot GKev LAma NRog
	'The Giant'	CAvo CBro EPfP EPot GKev IRob LAma NRog SCob SDeJ WFar
	triphyllum	GKev NRog
	'Violet Queen'	EPot ERCP GAbr GKev LAma NRog
	'Waterlily' (d) ♀H5	CAvo CBro CTca ELan EPfP EPot ERCP GBin GKev GMcL IRob LAma LCro LOPS NRog SCob SDeJ WCot WFar WHoo
	'William Dykes'	NRog
	'Zephyr'	LAma

Coleonema (*Rutaceae*)

	album	EBee
§	***pulchellum***	CCCN CSpe SVen
§	- 'Pink Fountain'	CAbb CCht EBee ELan EPfP LRHS MPkF NRHS SEle SPoG
	pulchrum misapplied	see *C. pulchellum*
§	'Sunset Gold'	CAbb CBod CCCN CCht CPbh CSBt CSpe ELan EPfP LRHS MPkF NRHS SCoo SEle SPlb SPoG

Coleus see *Plectranthus, Solenostemon*

Colignonia (*Nyctaginaceae*)

ovalifolia B&SWJ 10644	WCru

Colletia (*Rhamnaceae*)

	armata	see *C. hystrix*
	cruciata	see *C. paradoxa*
§	***hystrix***	CBcs CMac CTri CTsd ELon MGil NLar SMad
	- 'Rosea'	CMac GCal MBlu SArc WSHC
§	***paradoxa***	CBcs CCCN EBee ELan EPfP SArc SMad SPoG
	paradoxa × ***spinosissima***	SMad
	ulicina	SVen

Collinsonia (*Lamiaceae*)

canadensis	LEdu

Collomia (*Polemoniaceae*)

grandiflora	WCot

Colocasia (*Araceae*)

	affinis var. ***jeningsii***	CDTJ
	antiquorum	see *C. esculenta*
§	***esculenta*** ♀H1a	CDTJ EUJe LCro LLWG LOPS MSKA NLos SDir SPlb XBlo
	- 'Black Coral'	CAbb SPad SPhm
	- 'Black Magic'	CBct CDTJ EUJe LAma LRHS NLos NRHS SBig SDir XBlo
	- burgundy-stemmed	CDTJ EUJe LAma SBig

- 'Fontanesii'	CDTJ EUJe MPkF
- 'Illustris'	CAbb CDTJ EUJe LLWG
- 'Mammoth'	EUJe
- 'Pink China'	MPkF
- 'Purple Stem'	EUJe
- 'Ruffles'	EUJe
- 'Sangria'	EUJe
fallax	EUJe SPlb
formosana B&SWJ 6909	WCru
gaoligongensis	CPHo
gigantea	CDTJ
'Kachhu'	LAma
'Madeira'	EUJe

Colquhounia (*Lamiaceae*)

coccinea	CCCN CHll EUJe LRHS MBlu MGil MRav NLar SBrt SChF SLon SPoG WCot
- Sch 2458	EPfP WPGP
§ - var. ***mollis*** B&SWJ 7222	WCru
- var. ***vestita*** misapplied	see *C. coccinea* var. *mollis*
- var. ***vestita*** (Wall.) Prain	CBcs CTsd EBee EPfP LRHS MBNS SEND

Columnea (*Gesneriaceae*)

'Aladdin's Lamp'	WDib
× ***banksii*** ♀H1c	WDib
§ 'Broget Stavanger' (v) ♀H1c	WDib
'Chanticleer' ♀H1c	WDib
I 'Firedragon'	WDib
'Gavin Brown'	WDib
gloriosa	EBak
'Inferno'	WDib
'Katsura'	WDib
'Merkur'	WDib
I 'Midnight Lantern'	WDib
'Rising Sun'	WDib
schiedeana	WDib
'Sherbert'	WDib
'Stavanger' ♀H1c	WDib
'Stavanger Variegated'	see *C.* 'Broget Stavanger'

Coluria (*Rosaceae*)

geoides	WCot

Colutea (*Papilionaceae*)

arborescens	CAgr CBcs CExl ELan EWTr LRHS MBlu MGil MGos MMuc SCob SEND SPer SPlb
× ***media***	CTsd EWld
- 'Copper Beauty'	CBcs ELan EWTr NLar SCob SPer
orientalis	CCCN

Colvillea (*Caesalpiniaceae*)

racemosa	SPlb

Comarum see *Potentilla*

Combretum (*Combretaceae*)

fruticosum	CCCN

Commelina (*Commelinaceae*)

benghalensis	XBlo
coelestis	see *C. tuberosa* Coelestis Group
dianthifolia	GCal GEdr LEdu NHpl SBrt WHil
- 'Electric Blue'	ELan LRHS NRHS SVic WCot
robusta	SBrt WCot
tuberosa	GKev MAvo NWad
- B&SWJ 10353	SBrt WCru
- blue-flowered	SDeJ
§ - Coelestis Group	CAby CPla CSpe ECha SDys WKif WSHC
- - 'Sleeping Beauty'	MSpe

Comptonia (*Myricaceae*)

peregrina	EBee WPGP

Conandron (*Gesneriaceae*)

ramondoides B&SWJ 8929	WCru

Conicosia (*Aizoaceae*)

pugioniformis	SVen

Coniogramme (*Pteridaceae*)

japonica	CBdn WFib
- 'Flavomaculata' ♀H4	CBod CSpe EBee EUJe LLWG MSCN WCot WFar

Conium (*Apiaceae*)

maculatum	EBWF

Conoclinium (*Asteraceae*)

§ ***coelestinum***	CBod CRos EBee LRHS NRHS SBrt WArt XLum

Conopodium (*Apiaceae*)

majus	CEls EBWF WOut WShi

Consolida (*Ranunculaceae*)

§ ***ajacis***	CSpe LRHS
- Giant Imperial Series	SVic
- 'Mauve' **new**	CRav
ambigua	see *C. ajacis*

Convallaria ✿ (*Asparagaceae*)

japonica	see *Ophiopogon jaburan*
keiskei	EPPr MAvo
I - 'Marginata' (v)	WCot
- 'Shiro-shima-fu' (v)	GEdr
majalis ♀H7	Widely available
- 'Albostriata' (v)	CBct CBot CRos CTal CWCL EHoe EHrv ELan EPPr EUJe GKev GMaP IRob LEdu LRHS MAvo MHer MHol MMoz MNrw MRav NEgg NPnk NRHS NSti WCot WFar WHer WHoo WPnP
- 'Berlin Giant'	NRya SDeJ
- 'Blush'	CAvo
- 'Bordeaux'	CBro CExl CWld EBee EPPr GKev GPSL MAvo NEgg NLar WCot
- 'Bridal Choice'	EBee ELan GKev NLar XEll
- 'Dorien'	CBct CBre EPPr IMou MAvo
- 'Fernwood's Golden Slippers'	CAvo GEdr LLHF WCot
- 'Flore Pleno' (d)	GEdr WFar
- 'Géant de Fortin'	CAvo CBct CBro CExl EPot GCal GEdr MMoz MRav NLar SBch WCot WFar
- 'Gerard Debureaux'	see *C. majalis* 'Green Tapestry'
- 'Golden Jubilee'	CBct CBot LEdu MNrw WCot
§ - 'Green Tapestry' (v)	CBct MAvo WCot
- 'Haldon Grange' (v)	CAby EPPr MAvo
- 'Hardwick Hall' (v)	CBct CCse CDor CExl CTal EBee EHoe EHrv GEdr GKev LEdu MAvo SMHy WAul WCot WFar WHil XEll
- 'Hitschberger Riesenperle'	XLum
- 'Hofheim' (v)	CAby CAvo CBct GEdr GKev LEdu MAvo WCot WHal
- 'Landgraaf' (v)	MAvo

	- 'Marcel' (v)	MAvo
	- 'Prolificans'	CBct CBod CCse CTal EBee ECtt EHrv EPPr EPfP GEdr GKev ILea LAma LCro LOPS LSou MAvo MRav MSCN NLar NPnk NSti WCot WFar WPnP
	- var. ***rosea***	Widely available
	- 'Rosea Plena' (d)	WHar
	- 'Silbercconfolis' (v)	WCot
	- 'Variegata' (v)	EAJP EPot GCal SBch SMad WThu
	- 'Vic Pawlowski's Gold' (v)	CAby CBct CBro CExl CMac EPPr GEdr LEdu MAvo MMoz WPGP WSHC
	transcaucasica	EBee GKev

Convolvulus (*Convolvulaceae*)

	althaeoides	CFis CMea ELan
§	- subsp. ***tenuissimus***	EWes WCot
§	***boissieri***	WAbe XEll
	cantabrica	CRos LRHS NRHS SPhx XLum
	chilensis	CCCN
	cneorum ♀H4	Widely available
	- 'Snow Angel'	CRos LRHS SWvt
	elegantissimus	see *C. althaeoides* subsp. *tenuissimus*
	lineatus	EWes
	mauritanicus	see *C. sabatius*
	nitidus	see *C. boissieri*
§	***sabatius*** ♀H3	CCCN CRav CSam CTri ECtt ELan EPfP EShb MCot SEND SLim SPer SPlb SPoG SVen SWvt WCFE WSHC XLum XSen
	- dark-flowered	CCCN CSpe
	- 'Moroccan Beauty'PBR	CSpe ECtt
	- white-flowered	CCCN

× *Cooperanthes* see *Zephyranthes*

Cooperia see *Zephyranthes*

Coprosma (*Rubiaceae*)

	baueri misapplied	see *C. repens*
	'Beatson's Gold' (f/v)	CBcs CDTJ CExl CHGN CHll ELan EShb LRHS SEND SWvt WGrn WSHC
	'Black Cloud'	ELon SEND
	'Brunette' (f)	MAsh
	brunnea (f)	WThu
	- (m)	WThu
	'Cappuccino'	EShb SEle
	'Coppershine'	CExl
	depressa	WThu
	'Evening Glow'PBR (f/v)	CCCN CDTJ CRos CSBt ELan ESps EUJe LRHS MGos NRHS SEle SLim SRms WHar
	'Fire Burst'PBR (f/v)	CAbb CBcs CCCN CRos EBee ELan ESps LRHS MGos SEle SLim SLon SRms WHar
	'Green Globe'	CHll
	'Inferno'PBR	CAbb CRos LRHS SEle
	'Karo Red'PBR (v)	SLim SRms
I	× ***kirkii*** 'Kirkii' (f)	CHll
	- 'Variegata' (f/v)	CTsd ELan EPfP EShb GBin LRHS SLim
	'Lemon and Lime'PBR (v)	CRos EBee ELan ESps EUJe LRHS MGos NRHS SEle SPoG SRms WHar
	petriei	GAbr WThu
	- 'White Pearls'	WThu
	'Rainbow Surprise'PBR (v)	CCCN CExl CRos CSBt ELan ESps LRHS MGos SLim SRms WFar WHar
§	***repens***	CExl EShb SPlb SVen
	- 'County Park Plum' (v)	CBcs
	- 'Marble Queen' (m/v) ♀H2	EShb
	- 'Midnight Martini' (v)	CRos LRHS NRHS
	- PACIFIC NIGHT ('Hutpac'PBR) (m)	CCht CRos CSBt ELan ESps EUJe LRHS MGos SLon
	- PACIFIC SUNSET ('Jwncopps') (v)	EBee ELan ESps LCro SEle
	- 'Painter's Palette' (m)	SEle SVen
	- 'Picturata' (m/v) ♀H2	EShb
	- 'Pina Colada'PBR (v)	CAbb CRos CSBt LRHS NRHS SEle SPoG
	- 'Tequila Sunrise'	CAbb CCht CRos CSBt EBee ESps LRHS MTin NRHS SEle
	'Roy's Red' (m)	CCht CMac EShb LSRN
	rugosa (f)	CExl
	'Scarlet O'Hara'	CCht SEle SPoG
	'Walter Brockie'	CHGN CHll EShb

Coptis (*Ranunculaceae*)

chinensis B&SWJ 12865	WCru
japonica	GPoy WCru
- var. ***dissecta***	WCru
- var. ***major***	EBee WCru WSHC
laciniata B&SWJ 12863 **new**	WCru
omeiensis	CTal WCru
quinquefolia	CTal
- B&SWJ 1677	WCru
ramosa B&SWJ 6000	WCru
- B&SWJ 6030	WCru
trifolia	WCru

Corallospartium see *Carmichaelia*

Cordyline ✿ (*Asparagaceae*)

australis ♀H3	Widely available
- 'Albertii' (v) ♀H3	CCCN SArc
- 'Atlantic Green'	CRos LRHS NRHS
- 'Atropurpurea'	CCCN
- 'Black Night'	CCCN
- BURGUNDY SPIRE ('Jel01'PBR)	EPfP
- 'Claret'	CBcs
- 'Karo Kiri'	CCCN
- 'Olive Fountain'	CCCN
- 'Peko'PBR	CCCN
- 'Purple Heart'	CCCN MSwo
- Purpurea Group	CBcs CDTJ ELan ESps MGos MMuc SEND SPlb WFar
- 'Red Comet' **new**	SPad
- 'Red Sensation'	CCCN CRos LRHS NRHS SWvt
- 'Salsa' **new**	CRos NRHS
- 'Sparkler'	CCCN CRos EPfP LRHS NRHS SCob SEND
- 'Torbay Dazzler' (v) ♀H3	CAbb CBcs CBod CPla CRos CSBt ELan EMOT EPfP ESps EUJe LRHS LSRN MAsh MGos MJak NEgg NPla NPri NRHS SCob SLim SPoG SWvt WFar
- 'Torbay Sunset'	CCCN CRos LRHS NRHS SCob
'Autumn'	CCCN
'Can Can'PBR **new**	SEND
'Cardinal'PBR	CBcs
'Cha Cha'PBR	CCCN CRos EUJe LRHS MJak NRHS SEND WAvo
'Cherry Sensation' (v)	CRos EPfP LBuc LRHS NRHS WFar
'Coffee Cream'	CCCN
'Dark Star'	CCCN CDTJ
'Eurostar'	CCCN

'Eurostripe'PBR	CRos LRHS NRHS
FESTIVAL GRASS ('Jurred')	MPkF
'Firecracker'	CCCN CRos LRHS
fruticosa 'Kiwi'	CRos LRHS NRHS
- 'Red Edge' ♀H1b	XBlo
§ ***indivisa***	CBcs CCCN CDTJ CPbh CTsd EUJe NLos SArc SChr SPlb SWeb WPGP
kaspar	CCCN
mauritiana	WCot
obtecta	CCCN
'Pink Champagne'	CCCN CRos EMOT LRHS MSwo SCob
PINK PASSION ('Seipin'PBR)	CCCN CPla CRos EPfP EUJe LBuc LRHS NRHS
'Pink Stripe' (v)	CCCN EPfP LSRN SLim SWvt
'Polka'PBR **new**	SEND
'Purple Sensation'	CBcs CCCN CRos LRHS NRHS
'Purple Tower' ♀H3	ESps
'Red Bush'	XBlo
'Red Heart'	CCCN MJak
'Red Star'	CAbb CBcs CBod CCCN CChe CEnd CRos CSBt EMOT EPfP EUJe GMcL LCro LOPS LRHS MJak MSwo NPer NRHS SCob SPoG SWvt WFar
'Southern Splendour'	CCCN CPla CRos ELan ESps LRHS NPri NRHS SPoG
'Sundance' ♀H3	CBcs CRos EMOT EPfP LRHS MGos MSwo NPer SCob SLim SPoG SRms SWvt WFar
'Sunrise' (v)	CEnd CPla CRos EUJe LRHS NRHS
terminalis	see *C. fruticosa*
'Torbay Red' ♀H3	CCCN CMac CPla CRos CTsd EPfP ESps LRHS LSRN MAsh NPri SPer SWvt

Coreopsis (*Asteraceae*)

'Astolat'	CBod EPed LSou MRav NEgg
auriculata CUTTING GOLD	see *C.* 'Schnittgold'
- 'Elfin Gold'	EDAr ELan EPfP
- 'Nana'	ELon MNrw NBre
- 'Superba'	MRav
- 'Zamphir'	CDor EBee EPfP MNrw WCot
'Baby Gold'	see *C. lanceolata* 'Sonnenkind' (unblotched)
BABY SUN	see *C.* 'Sonnenkind' (red-blotched)
'Calypso' (v)	SPoG XLum
'Cha Cha Cha'	SEle
'Cherry Pie'PBR (Pie Series)	SCob
'Citrine'PBR (Hardy Jewel Series)	CWGN
'Cosmic Evolution' (Big Bang Series)	EBee ELan ETMg LRHS
'Cosmic Eye' (Big Bang Series)	EBee ELan ETMg WFar
'Cranberry Ice'	LRHS NRHS
'Daybreak' (Li'l Bang Series) **new**	CRos NRHS
'Dream'	SRkn
'Enchanted Eve' (Li'l Bang Series) **new**	MHol WFar
'Fool's Gold'	EBee
'Full Moon'PBR (Big Bang Series)	CBod EBee ELan ETMg STPC WFar XLum
'Galaxy' (Big Bang Series)	ELan WFar
gigantea	SPlb
'Golden Pompom' (d)	EBee
grandiflora	ESps ETMg NEgg NPnk
- 'Bernwode' (v)	CMac EBee LSou SWvt
- 'Domino'	EBee LSun
- 'Early Sunrise' ♀H5	CRos CSBt EAJP EBee EPed EPfP IBoy LPmr LRHS MAsh MNHC NGBl NPer NRHS SCob SGbt SPoG SWvt WFar WHar XLum
- FLYING SAUCERS ('Walcoreop'PBR)	CRos EPfP LRHS NRHS SCoo SPoG
- 'Illico'	EBee
- 'Mayfield Giant'	CBod CSBt EBee ELan EPfP MNrw SPer SRms SWvt WHrl
- 'Presto' (d)	NGBl SPad
- 'Rising Sun'	ELan LPmr
- 'Sun Up' **new**	CBod
- 'Sunburst'	EPfP NBre XLum
- 'Sunfire'	CBod CRos IBoy LRHS NRHS WFar
- 'Sunray'	CBcs CChe CRos CSBt ECtt ELon EPed EPfP GMcL LRHS MAsh NGdn NRHS SPlb SPoG SRms SWvt WHar WMoo XLum
- 'Tetra Riesen'	NBre
'Jethro Tull'PBR	CBod CPla EBee
'Jive'PBR (Coloropsis Series)	CWGN NPnk SCob SEle
lanceolata	NBre
- 'Goldfink'	MRav SRms
- 'Goldteppich'	CRos EBee EPfP LRHS NRHS
- 'Little Sundial'	LSou
§ - 'Sonnenkind' (unblotched)	GMaP MAsh XLum
- 'Walter'	LSou MNrw NDov NEgg SPoG WCot WFar WGwG XLum XSen
'Limbo' (Coloropsis Series)	SCob
'Limerock Passion'PBR	CRos EPfP LRHS NRHS SRkn
'Limerock Ruby'PBR	CRos GMaP LRHS NRHS SCob SPer SRkn SWvt WFar WHar XLum
major	WFar
'Mambo' (Coloropsis Series)	SEle
'Mango Punch' (Punch Series)	EBee WFar
maximiliani	see *Helianthus maximiliani*
'Mercury Rising'PBR (Big Bang Series)	SHar
palmata	SPhx
'Pineapple Pie'PBR (Pie Series)	SCob
'Pink Lady'PBR	CBod
'Polaris' (Big Bang Series) **new**	WFar
pubescens	LSou
- 'Sunshine Superman'	EBee ELan
'Pumpkin Pie'PBR (Pie Series)	SCob
'Red Elf' (Li'l Bang Series) **new**	CRos NRHS
'Red Satin' (Permathread Series)	WTor
'Redshift'	ILea
rosea	NGBl
- 'American Dream'	CBod CRos CSBt CSam ELan EPed EPfP ETMg GMaP LRHS NEgg NGdn NRHS SPer SPlb SRms SWvt WArt WFar WGwG XLum
- 'Heaven's Gate'PBR	CSBt LRHS MHol NGBl SCob WFar
- 'Nana'	XLum
'Route 66'PBR	EBee WCAu WFar
'Ruby Frost' (Hardy Jewel Series)	CBod EBee SPoG
'Salsa' (Coloropsis Series)	SEle
§ 'Schnittgold'	NBre SHar
'Snowberry'	LRHS NEoE NRHS
SOLANNA GOLDEN SPHERE	EPfP MHol SPoG
I 'Sonnenkind' (red-blotched)	CRos EBee LRHS NBre NRHS

'Star Cluster' (Big Bang Series)	CWGN EBee ELan MHol WFar
'Starlight' (Li'l Bang Series) **new**	CRos NRHS WFar
'Sterntaler'	CRos EBee ELon EPfP GWyn LRHS NCou NRHS SEle SPad SWvt WHrl XLum
SUN CHILD	see *C.* 'Sonnenkind' (red-blotched)
SUNNY DAY ('Balcorsunay') **new**	WFar
'Tequila Sunrise' (v)	MNrw
tinctoria	MNHC SRms XAbr
tripteris	CAby CBWd ELan EPfP SMad WMoo XLum
- 'Mostenveld'	EBee
- 'Pierre Bennerup'	SAko
- 'Red November'	MNrw
verticillata	CMac CTri EBee ECha GCal MBel MBrN MHer MWat NLar NPer SRms WCAu WHal WOld
- 'Bengal Tiger'^{PBR}	CMea
- CRÈME BRÛLÉE ('Crembru'^{PBR})	CRos ECtt LRHS MJak NRHS SCoo SRkn
I - 'Golden Gain'	CBod ECtt EWTr MArl NGdn WFar
- 'Golden Shower'	see *C. verticillata* 'Grandiflora'
§ - 'Grandiflora' 🏆^{H5}	CBcs CBod CRos ELan ELon EPfP GMaP LRHS MArl MAvo MRav NGdn NPnk NRHS NWad SHar SPer SPhm WFar XLum
- 'Limerock Dream'^{PBR}	EBee SCob
- 'Moonbeam'	Widely available
- 'Ruby Red'	CRos EAJP LRHS NRHS
- 'Solar Dance' **new**	CRos EWTr NRHS WFar
- 'Sunbeam'	ELon SCob
- 'Tweety'^{PBR}	WFar
- 'Zagreb' 🏆^{H6}	Widely available

coriander see *Coriandrum sativum*

Coriandrum (*Apiaceae*)

sativum	ENfk GPoy MHer MNHC NPri SPoG SRms XAbr
- 'Calypso'^{PBR} 🏆^{H2} **new**	EKin EMsh EUnw
- 'Confetti' 🏆^{H2}	EKin
- 'Leisure'	CRav SVic

Coriaria ✿ (*Coriariaceae*)

arborea	WCru
intermedia B&SWJ 019	WCru
japonica	NLar SVen WCru
- B&SWJ 2833	WCru
- subsp. ***intermedia*** B&SWJ 3877	WCru
kingiana	WCru
§ ***microphylla***	GCal WCru
- B&SWJ 8999	WCru
myrtifolia	WCru
- B&SWJ 14003	WCru
nepalensis	NLar WCru
- BWJ 7755	WCru
pteridoides	WCru
ruscifolia	WCru
- HCM 98178	WCru
sarmentosa	WCru
terminalis f. ***fructu-rubro***	WCru
- var. ***xanthocarpa***	GCal SBrt WCru
- - GWJ 9204	WCru
- - HWJK 2112c	WCru
thymifolia	see *C. microphylla*

Cornus ✿ (*Cornaceae*)

NJM 12.048 **new**	WPGP
alba L.	CArg CCVT CDul CLnd ECrN EMOT ESps MRav SCob SEWo SRms WMou WTSh
- 'Alleman's Compact'	LRHS
- 'Argenteovariegata'	see *C. alba* 'Variegata'
- 'Atrosanguinea'	WWtn
- 'Aurea' 🏆^{H7}	Widely available
- BATON ROUGE ('Minbat'^{PBR})	CAby CRos EBee ELon EPfP IRob LRHS MAsh NRHS SPoG SWvt WFar
- 'Cream Cracker'^{PBR} (v)	MRav
- 'Elegantissima' (v) 🏆^{H7}	Widely available
- 'Gouchaultii' (v)	CMac CRos EPfP ESps GKin LRHS MGos MJak MRav NEgg NLar NRHS SGol SPer SRms WFar WMoo
- 'Hessei' misapplied	see *C. sanguinea* 'Compressa'
- IVORY HALO ('Bailhalo'^{PBR})	EMil EPfP ESps LRHS LSRN MAsh MRav SPer
- 'Kesselringii'	Widely available
- RED GNOME ('Regnzam')	ELon EPfP LLHF MAsh
- 'Siberian Pearls'	CBcs ELan GKin MBlu NLar
§ - 'Sibirica' 🏆^{H7}	Widely available
- 'Sibirica Variegata' (v) 🏆^{H7}	CDul CRos EBee ECrN ELon EPfP ESps GKin GMcL LRHS LSRN MAsh MBlu MGos NEgg NRHS SCob SLim SPer SWvt WCFE WHar WMoo
- 'Spaethii' (v) 🏆^{H7}	Widely available
§ - 'Variegata' (v)	WFar
- 'Westonbirt'	see *C. alba* 'Sibirica'
alternifolia	CCVT CMCN CTho ELan ESps EWTr LPra WMou
§ - 'Argentea' (v) 🏆^{H6}	Widely available
- 'Brunette'	CJun MBlu
- GOLDEN SHADOWS ('Wstackman'^{PBR}) (v)	CRos CWGN EBee IArd LRHS SAko SMad WHor
- 'Golden Surprise'	CJun
- 'Goldfinch' (v)	CJun MBlu
- 'Moonlight' (v)	CJun
- PINKY SPOT ('Minpinky')	LSRN NLar
- 'Silver Giant' (v)	CJun NEgg NLar SAko WSpi
- 'Variegata'	see *C. alternifolia* 'Argentea'
- 'Yellow Spring'	CJun NLar
amomum	EBtc NLar
- 'Blue Cloud'	EPfP LRHS MBlu
- 'Lady Jane'	NLar
'Ascona'	CBcs CEnd CJun CLnd EWTr NLar SPer SSta WGob
canadensis	Widely available
capitata	CAby CBcs CDul CHid CJun CMac CRos CTsd EPfP EWTr GKev IArd IDee IMou LRHS MGos MMuc NRHS SAko SEND SGol SMad WCru WFar WPGP
- subsp. ***emeiensis***	CJun
- 'Foreness Fog' (v)	SEND
- 'Kilmacurragh Rose' **new**	IDee
'Celestial Shadow'	LRHS MPkF SGol
'Centennial'	CRos LRHS
chinensis	SSta SWvt
controversa	CAco CBcs CCVT CDul CMCN CTri ECrN ELan EPfP ESps EWTr LCro LMaj LOPS LPra MBlu MGil MJak NLar SEND SEWo SGol SSta SWvt WHar
I - 'Aurea'	LRHS MAsh
- 'Candlelight'	MBlu NLar
§ - 'Frans Type' (v)	CJun
- 'Green Carpet'	NLar

- 'Laska'	CJun LMaj NLar
- 'Lucia'	CJun NLar
I - 'Marginata Nord'	NLar
- 'Pagoda'	CJun MBlu NLar SArc
- 'Troya Dwarf'	CJun NLar
- 'Variegata' (v) ♀H5	Widely available
- 'Variegata' Frans type	see *C. controversa* 'Frans Type'
'Dorothy'	CJun
'Eddie's White Wonder' ♀H5	Widely available
elliptica 'Full Moon'	CJun
× ***elwinortonii*** VENUS ('Kn30 8'PBR) (Jersey Star Series)	CJun CWGN ELan EPfP LCro LOPS LRHS MAsh MBlu MPkF NLar SLon SSta WPGP
excelsa F&M 57 **new**	WPGP
florida	CAco CDul CMCN CRos CTho ESps EWTr LCro LPra MMuc NOra SPer WHar WMou WTSh
- 'Appalachian Spring'	CJun
- 'Apple Blossom'	CJun CMac CMen GQue WGob
- 'Autumn Gold'	SSta
- CHEROKEE BRAVE ('Comco No 1')	CBcs CJun CMen CRos LMil LRHS MAsh NEgg NRHS SGol SPoG SSta WGob
- 'Cherokee Chief'	CBcs CDul CEnd CJun CMen CTho CTri EWTr LSRN NEgg SAko SGol WSpi
- 'Cherokee Daybreak'	see *C. florida* 'Daybreak'
- 'Cherokee Princess'	CJun CRos EWTr LRHS MAsh NOra SGol SSta
- 'Cherokee Sunset'	see *C. florida* 'Sunset'
- 'Cloud Nine'	CBcs CJun CMen CTho EWTr GKin NEgg SAko WGob
§ - 'Daybreak' (v) ♀H5	CBcs CJun CRos LRHS LSRN MAsh NOra NRHS SPoG
- 'Eternal Dogwood' (d)	SGol
- 'First Lady' (v)	CMen WGob
- 'Fragrant Cloud'	SWvt
- 'Granary Gold'	SSta
- 'Junior Miss'	CEnd
- 'Pink Flame' (v)	SSta
- 'Purple Glory'	CJun SPer
- 'Rainbow' (v) ♀H5	CBcs CDul CJun CRos GKin LRHS MAsh MMrt NOra NRHS SGol SPer SPoG
- f. ***rubra***	CDul CLnd CTri ELan ESps GKin LCro LOPS LRHS MGil MMrt MRav NEgg SPer SPoG WGob
- - 'Red Giant'	CBcs EWTr MPkF
- - 'Spring Song'	CJun CMac CMen NEgg WGob
- 'Spring Day'	CMac CMen NEgg WGob
- 'Springtime'	CJun
- 'Stoke's Pink'	CEnd CJun CMen WGob
§ - 'Sunset' (v)	CEnd CMen CRos ELan ESps LCro LRHS MAsh NRHS SSta SWvt WGob
- 'Sweetwater'	CJun SAko WGob
- subsp. ***urbiniana***	WPGP
- 'Variegata'	GKin
- 'White Cloud'	CJun EWTr NOra
- yellow-leaved **new**	SPer
'Gloria Birkett'	CJun CRos ELan LMil LRHS MAsh NEgg WGob
'Gold Splash' (v)	NEgg
hessei misapplied	see *C. sanguinea* 'Compressa'
hongkongensis	CRos LRHS NLar NRHS WPGP
- B&SWJ 11700	WCru
- HWJ 1033	EPfP WPGP
- PAB 8237	LEdu
- subsp. ***gigantea*** KWJ 12225	WCru
- subsp. ***melanotricha***	EBee
- subsp. ***tonkinensis*** B&SWJ 11791	WCru
'Jerry Mundy'	CMac NEgg
'Kelsey Dwarf'	see *C. sericea* 'Kelseyi'
'Kenwyn Clapp'	CJun
kousa	CBcs CCVT CMCN CMac CTho ELan EPfP ESps GKin GMcL LCro LMaj LPra MJak NEgg NLar SCob SGol SPer SPlb WFar WHar WMou
- B&SWJ 12610 from Korea	WCru
- 'Akabana'	CJun
- 'Akatsuki' (v)	CJun MPkF SSta
- 'All Summer'	CJun
- 'Autumn Rose'	CJun IArd NLar
- 'Beni-fuji'	EWTr LRHS MPkF NLar SMad WPGP
- 'Big Apple'	CJun CRos LLHF LMil LRHS MAsh NLar SBir WGob
- 'Blue Shadow'	CBcs CJun LRHS MBlu NHim NLar SSta
- 'Bultinck's Beauty'	LRHS NLar
- 'Bultinck's Giant'	LRHS NLar WGob
- 'Cappuccino' **new**	EWTr MPkF
- 'Cherokee'	CJun LRHS NLar
- 'China Dawn' (v)	CJun SSta
- var. ***chinensis***	Widely available
- - 'Barmstedt' **new**	SAko
- - 'Bodnant Form'	CAby CEnd CJun CMac CTho EPfP EUJe NLar SSta WBor WGob
- - 'China Girl' ♀H5	Widely available
- - 'Claudia'	EPfP IArd LRHS NLar SSta
- - 'Great Star'	LRHS MAsh
- - 'Greta's Gold' (v)	CJun SSta
- - 'Ikone'	SAko
- - 'PVG'	CJun
- - 'Snowflake'	CJun
- - 'Spinners'	CJun NEgg
- - 'Summer Stars'	CJun
- - 'Tri-Splendor'	NLar
- - 'White Dusted' (v)	CJun EPfP MBlu NLar SMad
- - 'White Fountain'	EPfP LSRN MPkF MPnt NLar NOra
- - 'Wieting's Select'	CJun EWTr MBlu MPkF NEgg NLar SAko
- - 'Wisley Queen' ♀H5	CJun CRos EPfP LMil LRHS MAsh SPoG SSta WPGP
- - 'Xanthocarpa' **new**	CBcs
- 'Claudine'	CJun
- 'Copacabana'	MBlu
- 'Daybreak'	SGol
- 'Doctor Bump'	CJun
- 'Doubloon'	CJun
- 'Dwarf Pink'	CJun LRHS
- 'Ed Mezitt'	CJun LRHS NLar
- 'Elizabeth Lustgarten'	CJun MBlu MPkF SSta
- 'Eurostar'	ELan LRHS MBlu
- 'Fanfare'	CJun
- 'Fernie's Favourite'	CJun
- GALILEAN ('Galzam')	CJun MPkF WGob
- 'Gay Head'	CJun
- giant-flowered **new**	MPkF
I - 'Girard's Nana'	CJun
- 'Gold Cup' (v)	CJun SSta
- 'Gold Star' (v)	CBcs CEnd CJun CMCN CMac CRos ELan ESps LMil LRHS MAsh MBlu NEgg NLar SGol SPoG SSta WGob
- 'Greensleeves'	CJun CRos EPfP GKev LLHF LMil LRHS MAsh SSta WGob
- 'Heart Throb'	CJun NLar SGol WGob
- 'Highland'	CJun

- 'John Slocock' ♀H5	CJun IArd NLar WGob
- 'Kim'	NEgg
- 'Koree'	NLar
- 'Kreutzdame'	CJun LRHS MBlu
- 'Laura'	CWGN MBlu SGol SSta
- 'Little Beauty'	CJun
- 'Lizzie P'	NLar
- 'Lustgarten Weeping'	CJun
- 'Madame Butterfly'	CJun CRos LRHS MBlu NEgg NLar SPoG
- 'Marwood Dawn'	SSta
- 'Milky Way'	CBod CJun CLnd CMCN CTho EPfP EWTr GMcL LMaj LRHS LSRN MAsh MBlu MGos MPkF MRav NEgg NLar SGol WGob WSpi
- 'Milky Way Select'	CBcs CJun CRos LRHS NRHS
- 'Miss Petty'	CJun NLar
- 'Miss Satomi' ♀H5	Widely available
- 'Moonbeam'	CJun EWTr NLar
- 'Mount Fuji'	CJun MBlu NLar SSta
- 'National'	CJun LMaj LMil LRHS MAsh NLar SSta WGob
- 'Nicole'	LRHS NLar WGob
- 'Ohkan'	CJun
- 'Pevé Foggy'	LRHS NLar
- 'Pevé Limbo' (v)	CJun NLar
- 'Pevé Satomi Compact'	CJun NLar
- 'Polywood'	CJun NLar
- RADIANT ROSE ('Hanros')	CJun MPkF NLar SBir SSta WGob
- 'Rasen'	CJun NLar
- 'Rel Whirlwind'	CJun NLar
* - 'Robert'	NLar
- 'Rosea'	CJun
- 'Rosemoor Pink' **new**	CJun
- SAMARATIN ('Samzam') (v)	CBcs CEnd CJun LRHS LSRN SGol SSta
- 'Schmetterling'	CJun EWTr LRHS MBlu NLar
- 'Snowbird'	CJun LRHS
- 'Snowboy' (v)	CDul CEnd CLnd MBlu SMad
- 'Snowflurries'	CJun
- 'Southern Cross'	CJun WGob
- 'Square Dance'	CJun
- 'Steeple'	CJun NEgg
- 'Summer Fun' ♀H5	CJun CRos LMil LRHS SPoG SSta
- 'Summer Majesty'	CJun
- 'Sunsplash' (v)	CJun LRHS SPoG SSta
- 'Temple Jewel' (v)	CJun
- 'Teresa'	LRHS
- 'Teutonia' ♀H5	CJun ELan IArd LRHS MGos NLar SAko SSta WGob
- 'Trinity Star'	CJun
- 'Triple Crown'	CJun
- 'Tsukubanomine'	CJun CLnd NLar
- 'Weaver's Weeping'	CJun MPkF NLar
- 'Weisse Fontäne'	CJun LRHS NLar
- 'White Dream'	CJun LRHS NLar
- 'White Giant'	CJun SPer
- 'Willy Boy'	WHor
- 'Wolf Eyes' (v) ♀H5	CBcs CJun ELan LMil LRHS MAsh MBlu NHim NLar SGol SPoG SSta
macrophylla Wall.	CMCN WCru
mas	Widely available
- 'Aurea' (v) ♀H6	CBcs CJun CRos ELan ELon EPfP LRHS MAsh MBlu MRav NEgg NLar SGol SSta
§ - 'Aureoelegantissima' (v)	CJun CMac CRos EBee LRHS SPer WCot
- 'Elegant' (F)	CAgr
- 'Elegantissima'	see *C. mas* 'Aureoelegantissima'
- 'Golden Glory' ♀H6	CJun CLnd EPfP LRHS NLar WHor
- 'Gourmet' (F)	CAgr
- 'Hillier's Upright'	CJun
- 'Jolico' (F) ♀H6	CAgr CJun LEdu LRHS MBlu NLar
- 'Kasanlaker' (F)	CAgr LEdu NLar
- 'Pancharevo' (F)	CAgr
- 'Pioneer' (F)	CJun NLar
- 'Redstone' (F)	CJun
- 'Shan' (F)	CAgr
- 'Shumen' (F)	CAgr
- 'Spring Glow'	CJun NLar
- 'Variegata' (v) ♀H6	CBcs CDul CJun CMCN CMac CRos CTho EPfP ESps LRHS MAsh MBlu MGos NLar SGol SPer
- 'Vraća Kaštel' (F) **new**	CAgr
- 'Xanthocarpa'	CJun
- 'Yellow'	CAgr
mas* × *officinalis	CJun
'Norman Hadden' ♀H5	Widely available
nuttallii	CDul CLnd CTri ELan EPfP EWTr LPra SPer SWvt
- 'Colrigo Giant'	CJun
- 'Gold Spot' (v)	CJun CMac
- 'Monarch'	CJun EWTr NEgg
- 'North Star'	CDul CJun NLar
- 'Portlemouth'	CEnd CJun CRos LRHS NLar
- 'Zurico'	CJun
oblonga	CExl EBee LEdu WPGP
officinalis	CAgr CBcs CDul CJun CMCN CRos EPfP IMou LRHS MBlu NLar SWvt WSpi
- 'Kintoki' ♀H6	NLar
'Ormonde' ♀H5	CJun EPfP NEgg NLar SMad SSta WGob WPGP
'Pink Blush'	CJun
'Porlock' ♀H5	CJun CMCN CRos EPfP ITim LRHS NLar SWvt WGob WHor
pumila	NLar
racemosa	EBtc NLar
rugosa	EBtc NLar
× ***rutgersensis***	LRHS
- (Stellar Series) AURORA ('Rutban')	CJun MBlu NLar SGol
§ - - CELESTIAL ('Rutdan')	CBcs CDul CJun CRos LRHS NEgg NLar NRHS SGol WGob
- - CONSTELLATION ('Rutcan')	CJun SGol
- - RUTH ELLEN ('Rutlan')	CJun LRHS NLar
- - STARDUST ('Rutfan')	CJun
- - STELLAR PINK ('Rutgan')	CBcs CJun CRos EWTr LRHS MGos MPkF NLar NRHS SGol WGob WPGP
× ***rutgersiensis*** GALAXY	see *C.* × *rutgersensis* CELESTIAL
sanguinea	CBcs CCVT CDul CHab CLnd CMac CPer CTho CTri ECrN EPfP ESps LBuc LPra MMuc MRav MSwo SCob SEWo SGol SPer SVic WHar WMou WTSh
§ - 'Anny'	CJun ETMg MBlu
- 'Anny's Winter Orange' ♀H6	CJun CRos ELon LRHS LSvl MAsh NRHS SGol WAvo WCot
- 'Beteramsii'	LRHS
§ - 'Compressa'	MBlu MGil MRav NLar WAvo
- 'Magic Flame' ♀H6	CJun CRos ELon EMil EPfP LRHS MAsh NLar NRHS SPoG SWvt WCot
- 'Midwinter Fire'	Widely available
- 'Winter Beauty'	CJun CSBt EBee EPfP ESps EUJe MBlu NLar NRHS SArc SLon SWvt WAvo WCFE WHar WWtn
- 'Winter Flame'	see *C. sanguinea* 'Anny'
§ ***sericea***	LPra

- 'Bud's Yellow'	CRos ELon EPfP LRHS MBlu NLar NRHS
- 'Cardinal'	CDul CHGN CRos EBee ELon EPfP LRHS MAsh MGos NLar NRHS
- 'Flaviramea' ♀H7	Widely available
- 'Hedgerows Gold' (v) ♀H7	CRos EBee ELan ELon EMil EPfP LRHS MAsh MGos NEoE NRHS SCob SPoG WFar
§ - 'Kelseyi'	CMac CRos ELan EPfP ESps GMcL MRav NLar SCob SPoG WMoo
- KELSEY'S GOLD ('Rosco')	CRos IRob LRHS MAsh NRHS SPoG
- subsp. ***occidentalis*** 'Sunshine'	ELon EPfP NEoE NLar
§ - 'White Gold' (v)	EHoe ELon EPfP MRav NLar SBod SPer SPoG SRms WFar WMoo
- 'White Spot'	see *C. sericea* 'White Gold'
stolonifera	see *C. sericea*
'Summer Sky Tree' new	LCro LOPS
× ***unalaschkensis***	LLHF WAbe
walteri	CBcs EBtc
- B&SWJ 8776	WCru
wilsoniana	CRos
'Winter Orange'	CJun NLar WHor

Corokia ✿ (*Argyrophyllaceae*)

buddlejoides	CBcs CHGN CTsd EBee GBin NLar SEND WFar
cotoneaster	CBcs CDul CMac CRos CSBt CTri EBee ECre ELan EPfP EUJe LRHS MGil MGos NLar SBod SCob SEle SPer SPoG SWvt WAvo WCot WFar WGrn WSHC
× ***virgata***	CChe CRos CTri CTsd ELan EPfP LRHS NLar SArc SWvt WKif WSHC
- 'Bronze King'	CRos LRHS SPer SVen
- 'Frosted Chocolate'	CCht CRos CTsd EBee ELan EPfP LLHF LRHS SEND SLim SPoG SSta SVen SWvt WAvo WFar WGrn
- 'Geenty's Green'	CRos LRHS WGrn
- 'Pink Delight'	EPfP MRav
- 'Red Wonder'	CMac CRos ELan EPfP LRHS SEND SPoG SVen WAvo WGrn
- 'Sunsplash' (v)	CCht CMac CRos CTsd EBee ELan EPfP LLHF LRHS NLar SEND SEle SPoG SSta SWvt WFar WGrn
- 'Yellow Wonder'	CBcs CRos EBee ELan LRHS NLar SBod SEND SWvt

Coronilla (*Papilionaceae*)

cappadocica	see *C. orientalis*
comosa	see *Hippocrepis comosa*
coronata	CRos LRHS NRHS
emerus	see *Hippocrepis emerus*
glauca	see *C. valentina* subsp. *glauca*
minima	WAbe
'Nan Hicks'	EWld
§ ***orientalis***	CAby
valentina	CRHN GMcL MGil
- 'Clotted Cream'	CHid
- 'Cotswold Cream' (v)	WCot
§ - subsp. ***glauca*** ♀H4	CDul CMac CRos CSBt CTri EBee ELan EPfP LRHS LSRN MGil MMuc SEND SLim SNig SPer SRms SVen SWvt WAbe WOut XSen
- - 'Brockhill Blue'	EPfP LRHS MCot SAko WCot
- - 'Citrina' ♀H4	Widely available
* - - 'Pygmaea'	LRHS SEle SRms WAbe WCot
- - 'Variegata' (v)	CBcs CKel CMac CRos CTri CWCL EBee EHoe ELan EPfP LRHS MAsh MCot MGil MNHC MRav NQui SEle SLim SLon SNig SPer SPoG SRms SVen WCot
- 'Variegata' (v)	SEle SMad
varia	see *Securigera varia*

Correa ✿ (*Rutaceae*)

alba	CCCN CExl EPfP
- 'Pinkie' ♀H2	CCCN CExl CTsd
alba × ***backhouseana***	SEle
backhouseana ♀H2	CAbb CBcs CCCN CExl CHll CMac CRos CTri CTsd ELan EPfP GCal IDee LRHS MGil NLar SBrt SEle SPoG SVen WAvo WSHC
- 'Peaches and Cream'	CCCN SEle SRkn
'Dusky Bells' ♀H2	CAbb CBcs CCCN CHll CRos CTri CTsd ELan EPfP LRHS MAsh MGil SEle SPlb SPoG SRkn SVen WAvo
'Dusky Maid'	CCCN CExl
'Federation Belle'	CCCN SVen
glabra	SEle WAvo
'Harrisii'	see *C.* 'Mannii'
'Ivory Bells'	LRHS
lawrenceana	CExl CFil CTsd EBee LRHS SEND WPGP
- var. ***grampiana***	SVen
§ 'Mannii' ♀H2	CBcs CCCN CExl CTsd ECre ELan ELon EPfP LRHS MGil WSHC
'Marian's Marvel' ♀H2	CBcs CCCN CExl ELan EPfP MAsh SEND SEle SRkn SVen
'Peachy Cream'	CAbb CCCN LRHS
'Poorinda Mary'	CCCN SEle
pulchella ♀H2	CExl CMac CTri MGil SEle WAvo
- orange-flowered	WAbe
reflexa ♀H2	CExl
- green-flowered new	SBrt
- var. ***nummulariifolia***	MAsh MGil WAbe WCot
- var. ***reflexa***	CExl
* - ***virens***	CExl
schlechtendalii	CCCN CTsd MGil SEle SVen

Cortaderia ✿ (*Poaceae*)

argentea	see *C. selloana*
fulvida misapplied	see *C. richardii* (Endl.) Zotov
§ ***fulvida*** (Buchanan) Zotov ♀H6	EUJe EWes IArd IDee WCot
richardii misapplied	see *C. fulvida* (Buchanan) Zotov
richardii ambig.	CBod CChe CExl EHoe IMou MMuc SMad SWvt WHrl
§ ***richardii*** (Endl.) Zotov ♀H5	CAby CBcs CBot CCht CKno CRos EBee ECha EWes IMou LRHS NRHS SArc SRms WPGP
- Brown's strain	LSun WCot
rudiuscula new	EBee
§ ***selloana***	CAco CBcs CBod CTri CTsd EMOT ESps IBoy MGos MJak SCob SGol SPlb
§ - 'Albolineata' (v)	CBcs CBot ELon MWht SEND SPoG SWvt
§ - 'Aureolineata' (v) ♀H5	CBcs CBot CMac CRos ELan EPfP GMaP LRHS MWht NBid NRHS SCob SEND SLim SPer SPoG SWvt
- 'Evita'PBR ♀H5	ECtt MAvo NLar SPer SPoG SWvt WFar
- 'Gold Band'	see *C. selloana* 'Aureolineata'
- 'Golden Goblin'PBR	EHoe NLar SCob
- 'Icalma'	EPPr
- 'Monstrosa' ♀H5	SEND SMad
- 'Patagonia' ♀H5	EPPr
- 'Pink Feather'	CRos EPfP GMcL LPmr LRHS NRHS SEND SPer WFar

	- 'Pointe du Raz'	CBot EBee SWvt
	- 'Pumila' Υ^{H5}	Widely available
	- 'Rendatleri'	CBcs ELan SCoo SLim SWvt
	- 'Rosea'	CBod CDul CRos EMOT EPfP ESps MJak NLar SCob SGol WHar
	- 'Senior'	NLar
	- SILVER FEATHER ('Notcort') (v) Υ^{H5}	CRos SCob
	- 'Silver Fountain' (v)	ELan EPfP LRHS MAsh NRHS
	- 'Silver Stripe'	see *C. selloana* 'Albolineata'
	- 'Splendid Star'^{PBR} (v)	CBcs CRos EHoe LRHS MAsh MGos MJak NLar NRHS SLim SPoG SWvt
	- 'Sunningdale Silver' Υ^{H5}	CDul CMac CRos ECha ELan ELon EPfP ESps EUJe GMcL LRHS LSRN MGos NRHS SCob SEND SLim SMad SPer SPoG SWvt
*	- 'White Feather'	CBod CRos GMcL LPmr LRHS NLar NRHS SCob SPer WFar WHar
	- 'White Plume'	EPed
	Toe Toe	see *C. richardii* (Endl.) Zotov

Cortusa (*Primulaceae*)

	brotheri	EBee
*	***caucasica***	EBee GKev
*	- 'Alba'	CPla EBee GKev
	matthioli	EWld GKev GPSL NHpl WFar
	- 'Alba'	GKev MAvo NLar
	- var. ***congesta***	GKev
	- subsp. ***pekinensis***	EDAr MPnt NBid NLar WSHC
	- - var. ***sachalinensis***	EBee GKev
	turkestanica	LLHF NWad

Corydalis ✿ (*Papaveraceae*)

	angustifolia	WCot
	anthriscifolia	CSpe EWes IFro LEdu MMrt
	'Blackberry Wine'	CExl CSpe CWCL EBee ECtt EPfP EWTr MPnt SPoG WTor
	BLUE LINE ('Couriblue')	CWGN LLHF LSou SPoG
	'Blue Panda'	see *C. flexuosa* 'Blue Panda'
	bracteata	EPot
	'Bronze Beauty'	WMoo
	brunneovaginata	WCot
	bulbosa misapplied	see *C. cava*
	bulbosa (L.) DC.	see *C. solida*
	buschii	CAby EBee ELon GEdr GKev NRya
	calycosa	MAvo
	'Canary Feathers'^{PBR}	ECtt ETMg LRHS MBNS NHpl NRHS
	cashmeriana	CRos GKev LRHS NBid NRHS WAbe WHal
	- 'Kailash'	CRos EBee LRHS NRHS
	cashmeriana* × *flexuosa	CBro WAbe
	caucasica var. ***alba*** misapplied	see *C. malkensis*
§	***cava***	EBee GKev LAma NHpl WShi
	chaerophylla	EWld
	cheilanthifolia	CExl CSpe EPfP EWld IMou LEdu SRms
	'Craigton Blue'	EBee EPPr EWTr EWld GEdr GKev IMou IPot MMoz MNrw WAbe WFar
	curviflora	WAbe
	- subsp. ***rosthornii***	CExl
	- - 'Blue Heron'	CBod CWCL CWGN ECtt EPot EWld GEdr MBNS MHol MPnt NLar NPnk SPad WFar WSHC
	davidii	CExl
	decipiens Schott, Nyman & Kotschy	see *C. solida* subsp. *incisa*
	decipiens misapplied	EPot GKev
	densiflora	GKev
	elata	CRos CSpe EPot EWes GAbr GEdr GWyn IFro LRHS MArl MBel MCot MMuc MNrw NBid NChi NRHS NSla SPhx SPoG SPtp WCru WHal WHoo WOut WSHC
	- 'Blue Summit'	CRos ECtt EPPr IMou LRHS MPnt NRHS
	elata* × *flexuosa	IMou
	elata* × *flexuosa clone 1	CCse CExl GEdr
	flexuosa Υ^{H5}	CSpe EPfP GMcL GWyn MArl MNrw WAbe WSHC XLum
	- CD&R 528	IFro NRya
	- 'Balang Mist'	CExl
	- 'Blue Dragon'	see *C. flexuosa* 'Purple Leaf'
§	- 'Blue Panda'	CExl CWCL EPPr EWTr EWes GMaP MPnt MWat NLar WCru
	- 'Blue Skies'	MHol
	- 'China Blue'	Widely available
	- 'Golden Panda' (v)	NHpl
	- 'Hale Cat'	ECtt EPPr
	- 'Hidden Purple'	CHid
	- 'Nightshade'	CExl EWld LLHF NBid WCot
I	- 'Norman's Seedling'	EPPr
	- 'Père David'	CBod CDor CMac CRos CSBt CSam CSpe CWCL EBee ECha ELan EPPr EPfP GBin GWyn LRHS MHer MMoz NEgg SPlb SPoG SRms SWvt WCru WPnP XLum
§	- 'Purple Leaf'	Widely available
	glauca	see *C. sempervirens*
	'Heavenly Blue'	GKev
	heterocarpa	EBee IMou
	incisa	LAma SDir
	integra	GKev
	'Kingfisher'	CAby CSma GEdr LEdu NLar NSla WAbe WSHC
	leucanthema DJHC 752	CExl
	- 'Silver Spectre' (v)	CExl CRos
	linstowiana	ELan
	- CD&R 605	CExl
§	***lutea***	CBcs EPfP IFoB IFro MMuc NPer NWad SEND SRms WCot WMoo
§	***malkensis*** Υ^{H5}	CMea CWCL EBee EHrv EPot GKev LLHF NRya WThu
	'Maya' (v)	XLum
	moorcroftiana	CExl
	mucronipetala <u>new</u>	GKev
	nobilis	CHid GKev IFoB LLHF SPhx
	ochotensis	CRos IMou LRHS NRHS
§	***ochroleuca***	CElw CSpe EPot EWTr GCal NLar WMoo
	omeiana	WCot
	ophiocarpa	EHoe ELan GCal WMoo
	ornata	EPot
	pachycentra	CExl WAbe
	paczoskii	CRos LRHS NRHS
	pseudofumaria alba	see *C. ochroleuca*
	'Rainier Blue'	WFar
	'Rukšāns Red'	CWCL
	'Sapphire'	CBro
	scandens	see *Dactylicapnos scandens*
§	***sempervirens***	GWyn
	- 'Alba'	WArt
	shimienensis 'Berry Exciting'^{PBR}	CAby CBcs CDor EBee ECtt EPfP MBNS MHol MPnt NPer SPoG
	siamensis	IFoB IMou
	- B&SWJ 7200	WCru
§	***solida***	CAvo CElw CRos EBee ECtt EPfP EPot GKev LAma LEdu LRHS MPie

	MRav NLar NRHS NRya SDeJ SPhx WBrk WCot WShi
- 'Advocet'	GEdr
- 'Coscoroba' **new**	GKev
- 'Evening Shade'	GEdr SDir
- 'Fire Bird'	GEdr GKev
- 'Firecracker'	CRos GKev LLHF LRHS NRHS SPhx
- 'Frodo'	LAma
- 'Galah'	GKev
- 'Gaviota'	GEdr GKev
§ - subsp. ***incisa*** ♀H5	EPot GKev SDeJ SPhx
- lilac-flowered	IFoB
- 'Linnet'	GKev
- 'Lucky Bird'	GKev
- 'Purple Beauty'	EBee GEdr GKev SPhx WTor
- 'Purple Bird'	CAvo EBee GKev LLHF SDeJ WFar
- 'Quiet Elegance'	SDir
- RAINBOW MIXED	GKev
- 'Red Giant' **new**	GKev
- 'Rosefinch'	GKev
§ - subsp. ***solida***	EPot NRya SPhx WArt WCot
- - from Penza, Russia	SDir
- - 'Beth Evans'	CBro CMea CWCL ECha ELon EPPr EPot ERCP EWTr GEdr GKev IFro LAma LEdu LLHF MCot MHer MNrw MSCN NHpl NLar NPnk NWad SDeJ SPhx WBor WCot WFar
- - 'Blushing Girl'	GEdr LAma WFar
- - 'Dieter Schacht' ♀H5	EPPr EPot GEdr LAma NLar
- - 'Evening Shade'	GEdr LAma
- - 'George Baker' ♀H5	Widely available
- - 'Nettleton Pink'	GKev
- - Prasil Group	GEdr GKev NHpl SPhx WBor
- - 'White Knight'	GKev LAma NHpl SDir WCot
- f. ***transsylvanica***	see *C. solida* subsp. *solida*
- 'White King'	WCot
- 'White Swallow'	EPot GEdr GKev SDeJ WFar
- 'Zwanenberg'	GKev
'Spinners'	CAby CDor CElw CFis CSpe EBee ECha ECtt ELon EPPr GKev GLog GPSL IMou NEgg NQui WPnP WSHC XLum
stipulata B&SWJ 2951	WCru
'Sylvia's Castle Haven'	MPie
taliensis	CExl GCal GKev GLog
tauricola	GEdr
temulifolia 'Chocolate Stars'	CBod CHid CSpe CWGN EBee ECtt EWTr EWld ILea LEdu LLHF MBNS MCot MHol MPie SCob SPoG WCot WSHC WWFP
'Tory MP'	CDor CExl CHid CRos CSam CSpe EBee EPPr GEdr IFro LRHS MNrw MPie NBid NChi NRHS WFar WPGP
transsylvanica hort.	see *C. solida* subsp. *solida*
turtschaninovii	EPot
vittae	GKev IFoB
- 'Goliath'	GKev
vivipara	EPPr
wendelboi	IFoB
'Wildside Blue'	EWld WSHC
wilsonii	CExl GKev IFoB

Corylopsis (*Hamamelidaceae*)

SDR 7921	GKev
glabrescens	CHGN CJun CRos EPfP LRHS NLar WCFE
- var. ***gotoana***	CJun CRos EPfP LRHS MAsh NLar
- - 'Chollipo'	CBcs CJun CRos LRHS NLar SSta
- 'Lemon Drop'	CJun IArd NLar
glandulifera	CJun
pauciflora ♀H5	Widely available
platypetala	see *C. sinensis* var. *calvescens*
- var. ***laevis***	see *C. sinensis* var. *calvescens*
sinensis	CBcs EBee EPfP GKev
§ - var. ***calvescens***	CBcs CJun CTho EPfP NLar
§ - - f. ***veitchiana*** ♀H5	CJun CRos EPfP IMou LRHS MAsh NLar WCFE
§ - var. ***sinensis*** ♀H5	CDul CJun CMCN CRos CTho ELon EPfP LRHS MAsh NLar SGol SLon WSpi
- - 'Spring Purple'	CBcs CEnd CJun CMac CRos EPfP GMcL IDee LRHS MGos NLar NRHS SChF SPoG WPGP
- 'Veitch's Purple'	CJun NLar
spicata	CBcs CDul CJun CMCN IArd IDee LRHS MBlu MGil MRav NEgg NLar SCob SGol SLim WHor
- 'Golden Spring'	NLar
- 'Red Eye'	CJun NLar
veitchiana	see *C. sinensis* var. *calvescens* f. *veitchiana*
willmottiae	see *C. sinensis* var. *sinensis*

Corylus ✿ (*Betulaceae*)

avellana (F)	Widely available
- 'Anny's Purple Dream'PBR	IDee MBlu NLar SMad
- 'Anny's Red Dwarf'	NLar
- 'Aurea'	CBcs CDul CEnd CRos CTri ELan EPfP ESps EUJe LRHS MAsh MBlu MGos NLar SCob SLim SPer SPoG SSta SWvt WFar
- 'Bollwylle'	see *C. maxima* 'Halle'sche Riesennuss'
§ - 'Butler' (F)	CAgr CDul CMac CTho CTri EMOT ERea IArd MJak SDea SRms WHar
- 'Casina' (F)	CAgr CTho
- 'Contorta' ♀H6	Widely available
- 'Corabel' (F)	CAgr NOra SKee SRms
- 'Cosford' (F)	CAgr CCVT CDul CFGn CMac CSBt CTho CTri EBee ECrN EPom ERea IArd LBuc LEdu MBlu MGos NLar NOra SDea SEWo SGol SKee SPer SRms SWvt WHar
§ - 'Ennis' (F)	CAgr EMOT NOra SDea
- 'Feriale' (F) **new**	CAgr
§ - 'Fuscorubra' (F)	EPom EShb MRav NLar SPoG SWvt WFar
- 'Gustav's Zeller' (F)	NOra
§ - 'Heterophylla'	CDul EBee NLar SSta
- 'Laciniata'	see *C. avellana* 'Heterophylla'
§ - 'Lang Tidlig Zeller' (F)	CAgr ERea NOra
- 'Lewis' (F) **new**	CAgr
- 'Merveille de Bollwyller'	see *C. maxima* 'Halle'sche Riesennuss'
- 'Nottingham Prolific'	see *C. avellana* 'Pearson's Prolific'
- 'Pauetet' (F)	CAgr
§ - 'Pearson's Prolific' (F)	CAgr CFGn CSBt CTho EMOT LBuc SDea SGol
- 'Pendula'	MAsh MBlu SCoo SRms WCot
- 'Princess' (F)	SVic
- 'Purpurea'	see *C. avellana* 'Fuscorubra'
- 'Red Majestic'PBR ♀H6	Widely available
- 'Rouge de Zeller' (F) **new**	SGol
- 'Tonda di Giffoni' (F)	NOra SKee
- 'Webb's Prize Cob' (F)	CAgr CDul CTho CTri ELan ERea IArd LEdu MBlu MJak NLar SDea SEND SGol SKee SVic
chinensis	EBee
colurna ♀H5	CAgr CCVT CDul CMCN EBee ECrN ELan EPfP ESps IArd LEdu

LMaj LPra MBlu MGos NLar NOra NPri SCoo SGol SPer SRms WHar WMou
× ***colurnoides*** 'Chinoka' (F) — CAgr MCoo
– 'Freeoka' (F) — CAgr MCoo
EARLY LONG ZELLER — see *C. avellana* 'Lang Tidlig Zeller'
fargesii — WPGP
ferox — CJun
maxima (F) — CDul CLnd CTri EPom ESps LPra MSwo SDea
– 'Butler' — see *C. avellana* 'Butler'
– 'Ennis' — see *C. avellana* 'Ennis'
– 'Fertile de Coutard' — see *C. maxima* 'White Filbert'
– 'Frühe van Frauendorf' — see *C. maxima* 'Red Filbert'
– 'Grote Lambertsnoot' — see *C. maxima* 'Kentish Cob'
– 'Gunslebert' (F) — CCVT CDul CMac CTho CTri ECrN EMOT ERea NOra SDea SPoG SRms WHar
– HALLE GIANT — see *C. maxima* 'Halle'sche Riesennuss'
§ – 'Halle'sche Riesennuss' (F) — CAgr CTho EMOT ERea MMuc NLar NOra SDea SEND SKee WHar
§ – 'Kentish Cob' (F) — CAgr CBcs CDul CMac CSBt CTho CTri ECrN ELan EMOT EPfP EPom ERea IArd LBuc LRHS MGos NLar SDea SEWo SKee SLim SPer SPoG SRms SVic SWvt WHar WMou
– 'Lambert's Filbert' — see *C. maxima* 'Kentish Cob'
– 'Longue d'Espagne' — see *C. maxima* 'Kentish Cob'
– 'Monsieur de Bouweller' — see *C. maxima* 'Halle'sche Riesennuss'
– 'Nottingham Cobnut' (F) — ERea SVic
– 'Purple Filbert' — see *C. maxima* 'Purpurea'
§ – 'Purpurea' (F) — Widely available
§ – 'Red Filbert' (F) ♀H6 — CDul CEnd CHab CTho EMOT EPom ERea IArd LEdu MAsh MBlu NLar NOra SCoo SGol SKee SLim SRms SSta WCot WHar
– 'Red Zellernut' — see *C. maxima* 'Red Filbert'
– 'Spanish White' — see *C. maxima* 'White Filbert'
§ – 'White Filbert' (F) — CHab ERea
– 'White Spanish Filbert' — see *C. maxima* 'White Filbert'
– 'Witpit Lambertsnoot' — see *C. maxima* 'White Filbert'
'Nottingham Early' (F) — NLar
sieboldiana B&SWJ 11056 — WCru
– var. ***mandshurica*** — MBlu
'Te Terra Red' — CDul CMCN EPfP MAsh MBlu SLon SRms WMou
tibetica — CMCN LEdu

Corymbia (*Myrtaceae*)

§ ***citriodora*** — CWCL MHer SKin SPlb SVic
§ ***eximia*** — SPlb
* – 'Nana' — SPlb
§ ***ficifolia*** — CDTJ IDee

Corynabutilon see *Abutilon*

Corynephorus (*Poaceae*)

canescens 'Spiky Blue' **new** — CBod

Corynopuntia (*Cactaceae*)

grahamii SB 1885 from Candelaria, Texas — CCac

Cosmos (*Asteraceae*)

§ ***atrosanguineus*** — CBcs CMea CPla CRav CSBt CSpe CWGN EAJP ECtt ELan EPfP EWTr LCro LOPS LSRN MRav NLar SCob SDeJ SPer SPoG SWvt WHoo
– CHOCAMOCHA ('Thomocha'PBR) — CBcs CBod CCCN CChe CDor CHid CPla CRav CRos CSpe CWGN ECtt EPfP ESps GMaP IBoy LCro LOPS LPmr LRHS MGos NLar NRHS SCob SEle SPer SPoG SRot WBor
– DARK SECRET ('3013/01') — ETMg
– 'Eclipse' **new** — ETMg
– 'New Choco'PBR — LSou
– 'Spellbound' — ECtt
bipinnatus 'Antiquity' — CRav NPri SPhx
– Bright Lights mixed (d) — CRav
– 'Candy Stripe' **new** — CRav
– 'Dazzler' — CRav LCro LOPS SPhx
– (Double Click Series) 'Double Click Cranberries' (d) **new** — CRav SPhx
– – 'Double Click Snow Puff' (d) **new** — SPhx
– 'Psyche Rose Picotee' **new** — CRav
– 'Psyche White' **new** — CRav
– 'Purity' — CRav CSpe LCro LOPS LRHS SPhx
– 'Rubenza' — CRav LCro LOPS SPhx
– (Sensation Series) 'Sensation Picotee' **new** — LOPS
– – 'Sensation Pinkie' ♀H3 **new** — CRav
– Sonata Series — SEle
– – 'Sonata Carmine' — EPfP LSou NPri SPoG
– – 'Sonata Pink Blush' **new** — NPri
– – 'Sonata Pink' — CRav EPfP LSou NPri SPoG
– – 'Sonata White' — CRav CSpe EPfP LSou NPri SPoG
– 'Sweet Sixteen' — SPhx
– 'Xanthos Lemon Sherbet' **new** — ETMg LCro LOPS NPri
peucedanifolius — CSpe GPSL WSHC
– 'Flamingo' — CGrW EBee EPfP ERCP SDeJ
'Razzmatazz Pink' — NPri
sulphureus 'Bunte Lichter' — CSpe
'Yellow Garden' **new** — SPhx

Cosmos × *Dahlia* (*Asteraceae*)

'Mexican Black' — see *Dahlia* 'Mexican Black'

costmary see *Tanacetum balsamita*

Costus (*Costaceae*)

pulverulentus — LRHS

Cotinus ✿ (*Anacardiaceae*)

americanus — see *C. obovatus*
'Candy Floss' — CRos LCro LOPS LRHS NRHS
§ ***coggygria*** — CAco CBcs CDul CMCN CMac ECrN ELan EPfP ESps MRav MSwo NLar SCob SEND SGol SPer SRms SWvt WFar XAbr XSen
– GOLDEN SPIRIT ('Ancot'PBR) ♀H5 — Widely available
– GREEN FOUNTAIN ('Kolcot'PBR) — EBee LRHS
– 'Kanari' — NLar
– 'Lilla'PBR **new** — LRHS
– 'Notcutt's Variety' — MRav
– 'Old Fashioned'PBR — MPkF NEoE NLar
– 'Pink Champagne' — EPfP MAsh NLar SSta
– Purpureus Group — EPfP IBoy SGol SRms
– 'Red Beauty' — NLar
– RED SPIRIT ('Firstpur') — NLar

- 'Royal Purple' ♀H5	Widely available
- Rubrifolius Group	CBcs CDul EPfP SEND SGol SPer SWvt
- SELECTION	EPfP
- SMOKEY JOE ('Lisjo'[PBR])	CBcs CBod CRos EPfP LRHS MAsh SLon SPoG SSta SWvt
- 'Smokey Joe Purple'	LSou
- 'Velvet Cloak'	CRos EBee ELan EPfP ESps LRHS MGos MPkF NLar SLon SWvt
- 'Westonbirt Orange' **new**	NLar
- 'Young Lady'[PBR] ♀H5	CBcs CMac CRos CSBt ECrN ELon EPfP EUJe EWes GBin GMcL LRHS LSou MAsh MBlu MJak MPkF MRav NLar SCob SCoo SGol SPer SRms SWvt WFar WHar
DUSKY MAIDEN ('Londus'[PBR])	CRos CSBt CTsd EBee ELon EPfP LLHF LRHS MGos NLar NRHS SCob SLon WFar
'Flame' ♀H5	CBcs CDul CRos ECrN ELan ELon EPfP ESps LRHS MAsh MGos MRav NLar NRHS SCob SGbt SLim SPer SPoG SWvt WAvo WFar
'Grace'	Widely available
§ ***obovatus***	CMCN ELon EPfP IArd LLHF LRHS MBlu MPkF MRav NLar SSta WPGP
'Ruby Glow'	CRos LCro LOPS LRHS MGos NRHS

Cotoneaster ✿ (*Rosaceae*)

sp.	ESps
acuminatus	SRms
acutifolius var. ***laetevirens***	see *C. laetevirens*
adpressus	CAco SCob
§ - 'Little Gem'	NLar
- var. ***praecox***	see *C. nanshan*
- 'Tangstedt'	SGol
- 'Tom Thumb'	see *C. adpressus* 'Little Gem'
affinis	SRms
albokermesinus	SRms
ambiguus Rehder & E.H.Wilson	NLar
amoenus	NLar SRms
§ ***apiculatus***	NLar SRms
§ ***ascendens***	SRms
assamensis	SRms
§ ***astrophoros***	CMac MBlu NLar
atropurpureus	NLar SRms
§ - 'Variegatus' (v) ♀H6	Widely available
aurantiacus	NLar
boisianus	NLar SRms
bradyi	GBin GKev SRms
brickellii	NLar
§ ***bullatus***	CDul CTri EPfP ESps MMuc NLar SPer SRms
- 'Firebird'	see *C. ignescens*
- f. ***floribundus***	see *C. bullatus*
- var. ***macrophyllus***	see *C. rehderi*
bumthangensis	NLar SRms
buxifolius blue-leaved	see *C. lidjiangensis*
- 'Brno'	see *C. marginatus* 'Brno'
- f. ***vellaeus***	see *C. astrophoros*
camilli-schneideri	NLar SRms
canescens	NLar SRms
chadwellii	NLar
chuanus	NLar
chungtiensis	NLar
cinnabarinus	SRms
§ ***cochleatus***	SRms
§ ***congestus***	CDul CSBt ESps MSwo NLar SPer SPlb SRms XLum
- 'Nanus'	GCrg GEdr
conspicuus	CBcs EWTr SRms
- 'Decorus' ♀H6	CRos CSBt EPfP ESps GMcL LRHS MGos MJak MMuc MSwo NEgg SCob SEND SGol SLim SPer SPlb SPoG SWvt WMoo
- 'Leicester Gem'	SRms
- 'Red Glory'	CMac
cooperi	SRms
cordifolius	MBlu NLar SRms
cornifolius	SRms
§ 'Cornubia' ♀H6	Widely available
crispii	NLar
cuspidatus	MBlu NLar
dammeri	Widely available
§ - 'Major'	CBar ESps LBuc WFar
§ - 'Mooncreeper'	MMuc SCob
- var. ***radicans*** misapplied	see *C. dammeri* 'Major'
dammeri* × *microphyllus	MJak
dielsianus	NLar SPer SRms
divaricatus	EPfP NLar SPer SRms
duthieanus	NLar
- 'Boer'	see *C. apiculatus*
elatus	SRms
elegans	SRms
emeiensis	NLar SRms
encavei	NLar
'Erlinda'	see *C.* × *suecicus* 'Erlinda'
'Exburiensis'	CBcs CBod CCVT CDul EBee ECrN EMOT EPfP ESps MGos MMuc MRav NLar NOra SCob SEND SGol SPer WFar WHar
falconeri	SRms
fastigiatus	SRms
flinckii	NLar SRms
floccosus	GMcL IArd SEND
floridus	SRms
forrestii	NLar SRms
franchetii	Widely available
frigidus	CTho EWTr SRms
§ - 'Pershore Coral'	WAvo
fulvidus	NLar
gamblei	SRms
ganghobaensis	CMCN NLar SRms
- B&L 12234	WCru
glabratus	SRms
glacialis	SRms
glaucophyllus	IArd SRms
§ ***glomerulatus***	NLar SRms
gonggashanensis	NLar
gracilis	SRms
granatensis	NLar SRms
harrovianus	SRms
harrysmithii	NLar
hebephyllus	NLar
I ***hedegaardii*** 'Fructu Luteo'	SRms
henryanus	SRms
- 'Corina'	SRms
'Herbstfeuer'	see *C. salicifolius* 'Herbstfeuer'
'Highlight'	see *C. pluriflorus*
hillieri	NLar
§ ***hjelmqvistii***	LBuc NLar SRms
- 'Robustus'	see *C. hjelmqvistii*
- 'Rotundifolius'	see *C. hjelmqvistii*
hodjingensis	NLar SRms
horizontalis	Widely available
- 'Variegatus'	see *C. atropurpureus* 'Variegatus'
- var. ***wilsonii***	see *C. ascendens*
hualiensis	NLar SRms

	- B&SWJ 3143	WCru
	humifusus	see *C. dammeri*
	hummelii	SRms
	hupehensis	NLar
§	'Hybridus Pendulus'	CBcs CCVT CDul CMac CTri EBee ECrN EMOT ESps GMcL LCro LSRN MGos MJak MRav NEgg NLar NOra NPri SLim SPer SPoG SRms SWvt WHar WJas
§	***hylmoei***	NLar SRms
	hypocarpus	SRms
	ignavus	SRms
§	***ignescens***	NLar SRms
	ignotus	SRms
	incanus	NLar
	induratus	SRms
	insculptus	SRms
	insolitus	NLar
	integerrimus	SRms
§	***integrifolius***	MAsh NLar SRms WMoo
	kangdingensis	SRms
	kingdonii	NLar
	kitaibelii	NLar
	konishii	NLar
	kweitschoviensis	NLar
	lacteus 🏆^{H6}	Widely available
	- 'Milkmaid' (v)	NLar
§	***laetevirens***	NLar
	lancasteri	NLar SRms
	langei	SRms
	laxiflorus	SRms
§	***lidjiangensis***	NLar SRms
	lucidus	NLar SRms
	ludlowii	SRms
	magnificus	SRms
§	***mairei***	NLar SRms
	marginatus Lindl. ex Loudon	SRms
§	- 'Blazovice'	NLar SRms
§	- 'Brno'	SRms
	marquandii	NLar SRms
§	***meiophyllus***	MBlu NLar
	melanocarpus	NLar
	meuselii	NLar SRms
	meyeri	NLar
	microphyllus misapplied	see *C. purpurascens*
	microphyllus ambig.	CBcs ESps GMcL SCob
	microphyllus Wall. ex Lindl.	CDul CRos CTri LRHS MGos SPer WMoo
	- NICE 004	WCFE
	- var. ***cochleatus*** (Franch.) Rehder & E.H.Wilson	see *C. cochleatus*
	- var. ***cochleatus*** ambig.	NSla
	- 'Donard Gem'	see *C. astrophoros*
	- 'Tanja'	CRos LRHS NRHS
	- 'Teulon Porter'	see *C. astrophoros*
	- var. ***thymifolius*** (Lindl.) Koehne	see *C. integrifolius*
	- var. ***thymifolius*** ambig.	CRos LRHS MMuc
	milkedandaensis	SRms
	miniatus	SRms
	mirabilis	NLar SRms
	monopyrenus	SRms
	- F 11422	GKev
	'Mooncreeper'	see *C. dammeri* 'Mooncreeper'
	morrisonensis	SRms
	moupinensis	GLog SRms
	- BWJ 8167	WCru
	mucronatus	NLar SRms
	'My Pet'	GAbr
§	***nanshan***	SRms WAvo
	- 'Boer'	see *C. apiculatus*
	naoujanensis	EPfP NLar
	- 'Berried Treasure'	CRos EPfP LRHS NRHS
	nepalensis	NLar
	newryensis	SRms
	nitens	NLar SRms
	nitidifolius	see *C. glomerulatus*
	nohelii	NLar SRms
	notabilis	SRms
	nummularioides	SRms
	nummularius Fisch. & C.A.Mey.	SRms
	obscurus	SRms
	obtusus Wall. ex Lindl.	NLar SRms
	ogisui	GBin
	- Og 95105	EBee GKev
	omissus	NLar
	pangiensis	SRms
	pannosus	SRms
	paradoxus	SRms
	parkeri	NLar SRms
	pekinensis	SRms
	permutatus	see *C. pluriflorus*
	perpusillus	SRms
	'Pershore Coral'	see *C. frigidus* 'Pershore Coral'
§	***pluriflorus***	SRms
	poluninii	NLar SRms
	polycarpus	SRms
	praecox 'Boer'	see *C. apiculatus*
	procumbens	SRms
	- 'Queen of Carpets' 🏆^{H6}	CBod CRos ELan EPfP ESps IBoy LRHS LSRN MAsh MGos MMuc MRav NEgg NLar NRHS SCoo SLim SPoG SRms SWvt WMoo
	- 'Streib's Findling'	see *C.* 'Streib's Findling'
	prostratus	SRms
	przewalskii	SRms
	pseudo-obscurus	SRms
§	***purpurascens***	CRos CSBt LRHS NLar NRHS
	pyrenaicus misapplied	see *C. congestus*
	qungbixiensis	NLar SRms
	raboutensis	NLar
	racemiflorus	SRms
§	***rehderi***	NLar SRms
	reticulatus	NLar
	rhytidophyllus <u>**new**</u>	GKev
	rokujodaisanensis	NLar
	roseus	NLar SRms
	'Rothschildianus' 🏆^{H6}	Widely available
	rubens W.W.Sm.	NLar
	rugosus E. Pritz. ex Diels	NLar SRms
	'Saint Monica'	MBlu
	salicifolius	CTri MMuc MSwo NLar SRms WFar
	- AUTUMN FIRE	see *C. salicifolius* 'Herbstfeuer'
§	- 'Avonbank'	CEnd NLar WAvo
	- 'Brno Orangeade'	SRms
	- 'Emerald Carpet'	SEND
	- 'Gnom' 🏆^{H6}	CChe CMac CRos ELan EPfP ESps GMcL LRHS MAsh MGos MRav NEgg SCob SLim SPer SPoG SRms WAvo WHar WMoo
§	- 'Herbstfeuer'	MRav MSwo SRms WMoo
	- 'Pendulus'	see *C.* 'Hybridus Pendulus'
	- 'Pink Champagne' 🏆^{H6}	CMac MRav
	- 'Repens'	EPfP ESps NOra NPla SCob SGol SLim SPer SPoG SRms
	- var. ***rugosus***	see *C. hylmoei*
	salwinensis	NLar SRms

sandakphuensis	SRms
scandinavicus	SRms
schantungensis	NLar SRms
schlechtendalii 'Blazovice'	see *C. marginatus* 'Blazovice'
- 'Brno'	see *C. marginatus* 'Brno'
schubertii	SRms
* ***sengorensis*** new	NLar
serotinus misapplied	see *C. meiophyllus*
serotinus Hutch.	SRms
shannanensis	SRms
shansiensis	NLar SRms
sherriffii	NLar SRms
sikangensis	GBin GLog NLar SRms
simonsii	CCVT CDul CLnd CMac CPer CRos EBee ECrN ELan EPfP ESps GMcL LBuc LRHS MGos MMuc NLar NWad SCob SGol SRms
soczavianus	NLar
§ ***splendens***	GKev SRms
- 'Sabrina'	see *C. splendens*
spongbergii	NLar SRms
staintonii	SRms
sternianus ♀H6	EPfP NLar SRms
- ACE 2200	MSwo
§ 'Streib's Findling'	CRos IBoy LRHS MAsh NRHS SCob SGol
suavis	SRms
subacutus	SRms
subadpressus	SRms
submultiflorus	NLar
× ***suecicus*** 'Coral Beauty' ♀H6	Widely available
§ - 'Erlinda' (v)	SRms
- 'Ifor'	SRms
- 'Juliette' (v) ♀H6	CRos EHoe EMOT EShb GMcL LRHS LSRN MAsh MJak MMuc MRav NLar NRHS SCob SCoo SLim SPer SPoG
- 'Skogholm'	CBcs CRos ELan EPfP ESps LRHS MAsh MGos MMuc SCob SPer SRms WHar
svenhedinii	NLar
taoensis	SRms
tardiflorus	NLar SRms
tauricus	SRms
teijiashanensis	NLar SRms
tengyuehensis	SRms
thimphuensis	NLar SRms
tomentellus	WCFE
tomentosus	SRms
transcaucasicus	NLar
trinervis	GKev
turbinatus	NLar SRms
'Valkenburg'	SRms
vandelaarii	NLar SRms
veitchii	MAsh NLar SRms
verruculosus	SRms
vestitus	NLar
villosulus	SRms
vilmorinianus	SRms
wardii misapplied	see *C. mairei*
wardii W.W. Sm.	SRms
× ***watereri***	CBod CCVT ECrN ELon EMOT EPfP ESps MJak MSwo WJas
- 'Avonbank'	see *C. salicifolius* 'Avonbank'
- 'Cornubia'	see *C.* 'Cornubia'
- 'John Waterer'	EPfP SPer SPoG
- 'Pendulus'	see *C.* 'Hybridus Pendulus'
wilsonii	NLar SRms
yalungensis	SRms
yinchangensis	SRms
zabelii	SRms

Cotula (*Asteraceae*)

coronopifolia	CBen CWat NPer
hispida ambig.	CPla ECtt EWld GKev
§ ***hispida*** (DC.) Harv.	CTri CWCL EDAr EHoe ELon GMaP MAsh MHer NPer NRya SPoG SRms XLum
leariloba (DC.) Hilliard	ECha EWes
minor	see *Leptinella minor*
pectinata	see *Leptinella pectinata*
'Platt's Black'	see *Leptinella squalida* 'Platt's Black'
potentilloides	see *Leptinella potentillina*
pyrethrifolia	see *Leptinella pyrethrifolia*
reptans	see *Leptinella scariosa*
scariosa	see *Leptinella scariosa*
squalida	see *Leptinella squalida*

Cotyledon (*Crassulaceae*)

chrysantha	see *Rosularia chrysantha*
oppositifolia	see *Umbilicus oppositifolius*
orbiculata	CPbh CPla CTal ETod SPlb
- var. ***oblonga***	EShb LToo WCot
- 'Silver Waves'	MCot
simplicifolia	see *Umbilicus oppositifolius*
tomentosa subsp. ***ladismithensis*** ♀H1c	SAll

courgette see AGM Vegetables Section

Crambe (*Brassicaceae*)

abyssinica	SPhx
cordifolia ♀H5	Widely available
maritima	Widely available
- 'Lilywhite'	CAgr LEdu SVic
tatarica	GJos

cranberry see *Vaccinium macrocarpon*, *V. oxycoccos*

Crassula ✿ (*Crassulaceae*)

anomala	see *C. atropurpurea* var. *anomala*
arborescens	EShb EUJe SChr XAbr
argentea	see *C. ovata*
§ ***atropurpurea*** var. ***anomala***	SChr
- subsp. ***arborescens*** 'Blue Mist'	SAll SEND
coccinea	CPbh CPla EShb SPlb
lycopodioides variegata	see *C. muscosa* 'Variegata'
multicava	SEND
muscosa	EShb SChr SPlb SRot
§ - 'Variegata' (v)	EShb
obtusa	SRot
§ ***ovata*** ♀H2	EBak NCft NPer NPla SAll SChr SEND SPlb SPre SVen WThu
- 'Blue Bird'	LToo
- 'Gollum' ♀H2	NCft SAll SEND
- 'Hummel's Sunset' (v) ♀H2	CBlu EShb SAll
- 'Minima'	SAll
* - ***nana***	SEND
- 'Undulata'	WCot
- 'Variegata' (v)	EBak EShb SAll WCot
pellucida subsp. ***marginalis*** f. ***rubra***	EShb
perfoliata var. ***falcata*** ♀H2	SEND SRot WCot

	perforata ♀H2	CPla
	- 'Variegata' (v)	NWad SRot
	portulacea	see *C. ovata*
	rupestris ♀H2	SAll
§	***sarcocaulis*** ♀H3	CBcs CPla CTri ELon GCrg GMaP MAsh NHpl SBrt SPlb SPoG SRms SRot SVen WAbe WHoo WSHC XSen
I	- 'Alba'	NHpl
	sedifolia	see *C. setulosa* 'Milfordiae'
	sediformis	see *C. setulosa* 'Milfordiae'
	setulosa	SPlb
§	- 'Milfordiae'	CTri NRya WAbe
	socialis	LLHF WAbe
	tetragona	SAll SEND
*	***tomentosa*** 'Variegata' (v)	EShb
	trachysantha new	SEND

+ *Crataegomespilus* (*Rosaceae*)

'Jules d'Asnières'	NLar

× *Crataegosorbus* (*Rosaceae*)

miczurinii 'Ivan's Belle'	CAgr

Crataegus (*Rosaceae*)

	sp.	LPra SWvt
	arnoldiana	CAgr CDul CLnd CTri EBee ECrN EPfP MAsh MCoo MMuc NLar SEND SPer SPoG
	'Autumn Glory'	CEnd CLnd EBee ECrN
	azarolus	CDul CTho
	chrysocarpa	EPfP
§	***coccinea*** L.	CAgr CDul CLnd CTho EBee LMaj
	coccinioides	EPfP
	cordata	see *C. phaenopyrum*
	crus-galli misapplied	see *C. persimilis* 'Prunifolia'
	crus-galli L.	CCVT CDul CLnd CRos ECrN EPfP MAsh SPer WJas
	dahurica	EPfP
	douglasii	EBtc
	dsungarica	EPfP
	× ***durobrivensis***	CAgr CDul CLnd EPfP MBlu
	ellwangeriana	CAgr ECrN EPfP WCot
	- 'Fire Ball'	MBlu
	eriocarpa	CLnd
	gemmosa	CAgr
	greggiana	EPfP
	× ***grignonensis*** ♀H6	CDul CLnd CTho ECrN ELan MAsh MMuc SPer WJas
	harbisonii	IArd
	jonesiae	EPfP
	laciniata misapplied	see *C. orientalis*
§	***laevigata***	CCVT ESps LPra SCob
	- 'Coccinea Plena'	see *C. laevigata* 'Paul's Scarlet'
	- 'Crimson Cloud'	see *C. laevigata* 'Punicea'
	- 'Gireoudii'	CBod EMOT NLar NSti WJas
	- 'Mutabilis'	CTri SGol
§	- 'Paul's Scarlet' (d) ♀H6	Widely available
	- 'Pink Corkscrew'	EPfP LLHF MAsh MBlu WCot
	- 'Plena' (d)	CDul CLnd CMac CSBt CTri EBee ECrN ELan EMOT EPfP ESps MGos MRav MSwo NOra SEWo SGol SLim SPer SWvt
§	- 'Punicea' ♀H6	CArg CCVT CDul CEnd CLnd CTsd ECrN ELan EMOT EPfP EWTr GKin LSRN MGos MJak MMuc MSwo NLar NOra NPri SCob SCoo SEND SLim SLon SPer SPoG WJas WMou
	- 'Rosea'	GKin
	- 'Rosea Flore Pleno' (d) ♀H6	Widely available
	× ***lavalleei***	CCVT CDul CLnd CMCN CTri ECrN ELan EMOT ESps MMuc MRav MSwo SCoo SEND SLon SPer WTSh
	- 'Aurora'	NLar
	- 'Carrierei' ♀H6	CDul CMac CTho EPfP EWTr LMaj LSRN SCoo SEWo SPoG WMou
	mexicana	see *C. pubescens* f. *stipulacea*
	mollis	CAgr CTho ECrN EPfP WSpi
	monogyna	Widely available
§	- 'Biflora'	CDul CEnd CTho CTri MAsh MCoo MGos NLar SLim WSpi
	- 'Compacta'	LLHF LPra MAsh MBlu WCot
	- 'Praecox'	see *C. monogyna* 'Biflora'
	- 'Stricta'	CCVT CDul CLnd CSBt ECrN EPfP IDee LMaj LPra MMuc SGol SPer
	- 'Variegata' (v)	ECrN SWeb
	× ***mordenensis*** 'Toba' (d)	CDul CLnd SGol
	nigra	CDul
§	***orientalis*** ♀H6	CCVT CDul CEnd CLnd CMCN CTho CTri ECrN EMOT EPfP ESps EWTr IArd MAsh MCoo MGos NLar SCoo SLim SPoG WHar WJas WMou WSpi
	oxyacantha misapplied	see *C. laevigata*
	pedicellata	see *C. coccinea* L.
	persimilis	LMaj
§	- 'Prunifolia' ♀H6	Widely available
	- 'Prunifolia Splendens'	CAgr CCVT CRos EBar EBee ESps EWTr LBuc LMaj NOra
§	***phaenopyrum***	CDul CLnd CTho EBee EPfP
	pinnatifida	EPfP
	- var. ***major***	CDul CEnd EPfP LEdu LRHS MCoo
	- - 'Big Golden Star'	CAgr CFGn CLnd CRos CTho EBee ECrN EMOT EPfP MBlu MCoo NOra
	'Praecox'	see *C. monogyna* 'Biflora'
	prunifolia	see *C. persimilis* 'Prunifolia'
§	***pubescens*** f. ***stipulacea***	CDul CTho ECrN EPfP
	punctata	EPfP
	- f. ***aurea***	EPfP MBlu
	pycnoloba new	GKev
	sanguinea	EPfP
	schraderiana	CAgr CDul CLnd CTho EBtc EPfP EWTr NLar WHar
	submollis	CLnd
	succulenta 'Jubilee'PBR	CAgr EBee MCoo NOra
	- var. ***macracantha***	CMCN
	tanacetifolia	CAgr CDul CTho EPfP MBlu
	viridis 'Winter King'	CAgr EPfP
	wattiana	CDul CLnd EBee ELan EPfP

× *Crataemespilus* (*Rosaceae*)

grandiflora	CDul CLnd CRos IArd

Craterocapsa (*Campanulaceae*)

congesta	CPBP

Cremanthodium (*Asteraceae*)

SDR 7968	GKev
arnicoides	EBee GKev
decaisnei	GKev

Crenularia see *Aethionema*

Crepis (*Asteraceae*)

incana ♀H4	CMea ECtt EWld GBin NChi NRHS NSla SRms WAbe
rubra	CSpe

Crinitaria see *Aster*

Crinodendron (*Elaeocarpaceae*)

hookerianum ♀H4	Widely available
- 'Ada Hoffmann'	CBcs CBod CBot CEnd CExl CMac CRos CTsd ELon EPfP GCal GKin GMcL IBoy LRHS MBlu MGil MGos MJak MPkF NHim NLar SCob SEle SLim SWvt WFar WHlf WSHC
patagua	CBcs CBot CCCN CDul CExl CHid CMac CRos CTsd EBee ELan ELon EPfP GBin LRHS MGil NLar SAko SEND SEle SPlb SVen WSHC

Crinum (*Amaryllidaceae*)

amoenum	CCCN EBee EShb GKev
§ ***bulbispermum***	CPrp
campanulatum	EBee
capense	see *C. bulbispermum*
'Carolina Beauty'	WCot
'Cintho Alpha'	EPfP GKev SDeJ SPer
'Elizabeth Traub'	WCot
'Ellen Bosanquet'	CCCN CRos ELan EPri GKev LAma LRHS NRHS SDir WCot
'Emma Jones'	WCot
'Hanibal's Dwarf'	CFil WPGP
moorei	CBro CTca LEdu SChr WPGP
- f. ***album***	CCCN CFil CTca EBee EPri GKev LAma
'Ollene'	WCot
§ × ***powellii***	CAby CBcs CBod CBro CExl CPrp CRos CTca EBak ECha ELan ELon EPfP GCal GKev LAma LEdu LRHS MAvo MNrw MRav MWat NRHS NWad SDeJ SEND SMad SPer SRms WCot
- 'Album'	Widely available
- 'Bak-madder' **new**	EBee
- 'Harlemense'	EBee
- 'Krelagei'	EBee
- 'Longifolium'	see *C. bulbispermum*
- 'Roseum'	see *C. × powellii*
'Sangria'	EUJe WCot
'Summer Nocturne'	WCot
'White Queen'	WCot
yemense misapplied	GKev

Criogenes see *Cypripedium*

Crithmum (*Apiaceae*)

maritimum	CEls EBWF GPoy LRHS MNHC SPhx SPlb SRms WHoo WTre

Crocosmia (*Iridaceae*)

sp.	SDir
'African Beauty'	ECtt IBal
'Anna Marie'	CRos CTca EBee ECtt ELan GKev LAma LRHS MAvo NRHS WFar
'Anniversary'	IBlr
'Apricot'	CTca ECrc IBal
'Apricot Surprise'	ECtt IBal
aurea misapplied	see *C.* × *crocosmiiflora* 'George Davison' Davison
aurea ambig.	CPrp CRos EShb GCal LRHS NRHS
aurea (Pappe ex Hook.f.) Planch.	CPou ECrc IBal IBlr LEdu
- from Swaziland	GCal IBal
- subsp. ***aurea***	CTca ECrc GKev IBlr
- - 'Maculata'	IBlr
- subsp. ***pauciflora***	IBlr
- 'Zomba'	GCal
'Auricorn'	IBal IBlr LEdu
'Auriol'	IBlr
'Aurora'	NGdn
'Ballyrogan Sundown'	CTca IBlr
'Baywalker'	MAvo
'Beth Chatto'	CTca ECrc IBal
'Big Top' **new**	IBal
'Blaze'	IBal
'Bowland Blaze'	IBal MAvo
BRESSINGHAM BEACON ('Blos')	CRos IBlr LRHS MSpe NRHS
'Bressingham Blaze'	CBre CPrp CRos CTca IBal IBlr LRHS NGdn NRHS
Bridgemere hybrid	ECrc
BRIGHT EYES ('Walbreyes'^{PBR})	CRos EPfP LRHS NRHS
'Buttercups'	MTis WSpi
'Cadenza'	IBal IBlr NWad
'Caistor Sunset'	IBal
'Carnival'	IBlr
'Cascade'	IBal IBlr
'Chinatown'	IBal IBlr
'Chrome'	CSam
'Chrome Spray'	CTca IBlr
'Citronella' misapplied	see *C.* × *crocosmiiflora* 'Honey Angels'
'Comet' Knutty	CRos CTca IBal IBlr LRHS MAvo NRHS WMoo
'Cornish Copper'	CTca SMad
× ***crocosmiiflora***	CTca CTri IBlr SPlb SRms WBrk WMoo WShi
- 'A.J. Hogan'	CPrp IBal IBlr
- 'African Glow'	CTca EBee ECrc IBal
- 'Amberglow'	CElw CExl GWyn IBal IBlr NPer
- 'Apricot Queen'	IBlr
- 'Autumn Gold'	ECrc IBlr
- 'Baby Barnaby'	CBre CSam EBee WFar
- 'Babylon'	Widely available
- 'Best of British'	ECtt
- 'Bicolor'	CElw CTca IBlr
- 'Burford Bronze'	CTca IBal IBlr
- 'Burnt Umber'	IBal
- 'Butterball'	CRos LRHS NRHS
- 'Buttercup'	CDor CRos CSam CTca ECrc ECtt EPfP GKev IBal LAma LRHS MAvo MCot NRHS SMad SRkn WFar WMoo WSpi
- 'Canary Bird'	CBro CSam ECrc ECtt IBal NGdn WBrk WSpi
- 'Cardinale'	IBlr
§ - 'Carmin Brillant' ♀H4	Widely available
- 'Challa'	ECrc ECtt IBal
- 'Citrina'	MNrw
- (Lemoine) N.E. Br. 'Citronella' J.E. Fitt	CBro CExl CRos CSam EBee ECrc EPfP GMaP LRHS MBel NGdn NRHS
§ - 'Coleton Fishacre'	Widely available
§ - 'Columbus'	CAvo CBod CPrp CRos CSam CTca ECrc EPfP EPri GKev IBal IBlr ILea LRHS MAvo MSCN MTis NRHS SMad SPer SRms WFar WMoo WWtn
- 'Colwall'	IBal IBlr NWad
- 'Comet'	EBee IBal
- 'Constance'	CBro CDor CRos CSam CTca ECtt EPri IBal IBlr LAma LRHS MAvo NBid NGdn NRHS WBrk
- 'Corona'	CPrp IBal IBlr MAvo

	- 'Corten'	IBlr
§	- 'Croesus'	IBal IBlr
	- 'Custard Cream'	CPrp CRos ECrc IBlr LRHS NRHS
	- 'D.H. Houghton'	IBlr
	- 'Daisy Hill'	IBlr
	- 'David Fitt'	MAvo WFar
	- 'Debutante'	CPrp CTca EBee ECrc EPri IBal IBlr WSHC
§	- 'Diadème'	CSam CWCL IBal
	- 'Dusky Maiden'	CMac ECtt EHoe ELon EPri ESps GKin GMaP IBal MMuc MSwo SRms SWvt
	- 'Dwarf Gold'	IBal
§	- 'E.A. Bowles'	CPou ECrc MSpe
	- 'Eastern Promise'	CBre IBal IBlr MAvo
	- 'Elegans'	ECrc ECtt IBal
§	- 'Emily McKenzie'	Widely available
	- 'Fantasie'	ECrc IBal
	- 'Fire Jumper'	CTca EBee GWyn IBal MAvo MSpe
	- 'Fireglow'^{PBR}	CRos CTca EBee ECtt GKev IBal LRHS NRHS
	- 'George Davison' misapplied	see *C.* × *crocosmiiflora* 'Golden Glory' ambig., *C.* 'Sulphurea'
§	- 'George Davison' Davison	Widely available
	- 'Gillian'	IBal
	- 'Gloria'	CTca ECrc IBal MAvo MSpe SMad
	- 'Golden Glory' misapplied	see *C.* × *crocosmiiflora* 'Diadème'
§	- 'Golden Glory' ambig.	CBod CDor CExl CWCL EAJP ELan ELon EShb GKev GWyn IBal IBoy LPmr MSwo MWat SCob SRms WHar
	- 'Goldfinch'	ECrc
	- 'Goldie'	MAvo WFar
	- 'Hades'	IBal IBlr
	- 'Harvest Sun'	IBlr
	- 'His Majesty'	CBro CPrp CTca ECrc IBal IBlr WFar WMoo
	- 'Hoey Joey'	ECrc
§	- 'Honey Angels'	Widely available
	- 'Honey Bells'	ECrc WBrk WOld
	- 'Irish Dawn'	ECrc IBal IBlr MAvo NWad
§	- 'Jackanapes'	CRos ECtt ELon GCal IBal IBlr LRHS MNrw MSpe SRms
	- 'Jackanapes VI'	IBal
	- 'James Coey' misapplied	see *C.* × *crocosmiiflora* 'Carmin Brillant'
	- 'James Coey' J.E. Fitt	ECha EHoe EPfP GKin IBal IFoB LSou NGdn NLar SPoG WMoo
§	- 'Jessie'	CElw
	- 'Judith'	IBlr
	- 'Kapoor'	IBlr
	- 'Kiautschou'	CWCL IBal IBlr
	- 'Lady Hamilton'	CExl CRos CTca ECtt GCal IBal IBlr IRob LRHS MAvo NRHS WMoo
	- 'Lady McKenzie'	see *C.* × *crocosmiiflora* 'Emily McKenzie'
	- 'Lady Oxford'	IBal IBlr
	- 'Lady Wilson' **new**	CRos LRHS NRHS
	- 'Lambrook Gold'	CAvo ECrc IBal IBlr MAvo
	- 'Lord Nelson'	CExl IBal
	- 'Loweswater'	ECrc IBal
	- 'Lutea'	ECrc ECtt IBal
	- 'Marjorie'	IBal
	- 'Mars'	ECrc EWes IBal IFoB MAvo NGdn
	- 'Mephistopheles'	CPrp CTca IBlr MAvo WFar
	- 'Merryman'	ECrc IBal MAvo
	- 'Météore'	CRos ECtt EPfP LRHS MBNS NEgg NRHS WFar
	- 'Morgenlicht'	ECrc MSpe WFar
	- 'Mount Usher'	CCse CPrp CTca ECrc ECtt GCal IBal MNrw
§	- 'Mrs Geoffrey Howard'	CRos IBal IBlr LRHS NRHS SRms WCru
	- 'Mrs Morrison'	see *C.* × *crocosmiiflora* 'Mrs Geoffrey Howard'
	- 'Newry Seedling'	see *C.* × *crocosmiiflora* 'Prometheus'
	- 'Nimbus'	CPrp CTca IBal IBlr
§	- 'Norwich Canary'	CRos CTca ECha ECtt EPri IBal IBlr LAma LRHS MRav NGdn NRHS SPer WMoo WSpi
	- 'Olympic Fire'	IBlr
	- 'Pepper'	IBlr
	- 'Ping Pong'	CTca
	- 'Plaisir'	IBal IBlr NBid
	- 'Polo'	CRos CSam CTca CWCL ECrc ECtt IBal LRHS NRHS
	- 'Princess'	see *C. pottsii* 'Princess'
§	- 'Princess Alexandra'	IBlr
	- 'Prolificans'	ECrc IBal
§	- 'Prometheus'	CRos CTca IBal IBlr LRHS NRHS
	- 'Queen Alexandra' misapplied	see *C.* × *crocosmiiflora* 'Princess Alexandra'
§	- 'Queen Alexandra' J.E. Fitt	EBee ECha EWes IBlr WHal WMoo
	- 'Queen Charlotte'	IBal IBlr
	- 'Queen Mary II'	see *C.* × *crocosmiiflora* 'Columbus'
	- 'Queen of Spain'	IBal
	- 'Rayon d'Or'	ECrc IBal
	- 'Red King'	CBro CDor CRos CWld EBee EPfP GKev IBal IBoy LRHS NLar NRHS WBrk WFar WMoo WRHF
	- 'Red Knight'	IBal
	- 'Rheingold' misapplied	see *C.* × *crocosmiiflora* 'Diadème'
	- 'Saint Clements'	CTca IBal IBlr
	- 'Saracen'	CAby CBcs CBro CMac CTca CWCL EBee ECtt ELon GBin GCal GKin IBal IBoy LEdu LRHS MAvo MBNS MHer MHol MNrw NRHS NSti SPoG WAul WAvo WCot WMoo
	- 'Severn Seas'	ECtt
	- 'Sir Mathew Wilson'	IBal
	- 'Solfatare' ♀^{H4}	Widely available
	- 'Solfatare Coleton Fishacre'	see *C.* × *crocosmiiflora* 'Coleton Fishacre'
	- 'Star of the East' ♀^{H4}	Widely available
	- 'Sultan'	CExl WFar WMoo
	- 'Twilight Fairy Gold'	CBod CPou CTca EBee ECha ECtt IBal LLWG LSou MBNS MHol NCou NHpl SMad SPer WCot WSpi
	- 'Venus'	CBre CDor ECtt GPSL IBal MAvo MHer WMoo
	- 'Vesuvius'	ECrc GCal WSHC
	- 'Vic's Yellow'	IBal
	- 'Voyager'	CRos ECtt ERCP GKev IBal LRHS NLar NRHS SDeJ WHar
	- Wasdale strain	ECrc IBal
	- 'Zeal Tan'	CBod CElw CExl CSam CTca CWCL EBee ECtt ELan ELon EPri GBin IBal IRob LEdu LLWG LRHS MBNS MNrw NEgg NLar NRHS NSti SPoG WAul WAvo WCot WFar WHoo WMoo
§	× ***crocosmioides***	IBlr
	- 'Castle Ward Late'	CBod CPrp ECtt EPfP GCal IBal IBlr LEdu LRHS MAvo NEgg NLar NRHS SRms WCot WFar WMoo
	- 'Mount Stewart Late'	IBlr

§	– 'Vulcan' Leichtlin	CTca IBlr
	'Darkleaf Apricot'	see *C.* × *crocosmiiflora* 'Coleton Fishacre'
	'Doctor Marion Wood'	IBal
	'Eldorado'	see *C.* × *crocosmiiflora* 'E.A. Bowles'
	'Elegance'	IBlr
	'Ellenbank Canary'	MAvo
	'Ellenbank Firecrest'	CTca EBee ECrc MAvo MHCG
	'Ellenbank Goldcrest'	WSHC
	'Ellenbank Skylark'	MAvo
	'Emberglow'	Widely available
	'Fandango'	IBal IBlr
	'Fernhill'	ECrc IBal IBlr
	'Fire King' misapplied	see *C.* × *crocosmiiflora* 'Jackanapes'
	'Fire King' ambig.	CRos GKev IBal LAma LRHS NLar NRHS NSti SWvt
	'Fire Sprite'	IBlr
	'Firebird'	CRos ECtt ELon IBal IBlr LRHS MHol NRHS SRms WCot
	'Firecracker'	IBlr
	'Firefly'	CRos CTca EBee ECtt GKev IBlr IBoy LRHS MAsh NRHS
	'Flaire'	IBlr
	'Fleuve Jaune'	IBal
	'Forest Fire'	IBal LLHF
	fucata 'Jupiter'	see *C.* 'Jupiter'
	fucata* × *paniculata	IBal
	'Fugue'	CTca IBlr SMad
	'Fusilade'	IBlr
	'Gold Sprite'	IBlr
	'Golden Ballerina'PBR	CAbb EBee ECtt EWes IBal LSou MWat SCob SPoG
	'Golden Dew'	ECtt IBal MBNS WCot WFar WMoo
	GOLDEN FLEECE *sensu* Lemoine	see *C.* × *crocosmiiflora* 'Coleton Fishacre'
	'Harlequin'	CBod CElw CPrp CTca EBee ECrc GKev IBal ILea LLHF LRHS MAsh MAvo MBNS MHer MSCN MTis SPoG SWvt WFar WTor
	'Harmonia'	EPri
	'Hellfire'	Widely available
	'Highlight'	ECrc IBal IBlr MAvo NWad
	'Jennine'	IBal
	JENNY BLOOM ('Blacro'PBR)	CRos EBee IBal LRHS NRHS
	'John Boots'	ECtt ELon IBal IBoy LAma LRHS MCot NBid NLar SMad SRms
§	'Jupiter'	CBot CDor CSam CTca CWCL EBee GCal IBal LRHS MAvo MNrw NChi NLar
	'Karin'	CRos CTca EBee ECrc GKev LRHS NRHS WFar
	'Kathleen'	ECrc
	'Krakatoa'	CAbb CHll CPrp ECrc IBal LLHF MBel MHer SWvt WFar WMoo
	'Lady Ann'	EBee ECrc GKev
	'Lady Jane'	CRos CTca EBee ECrc GKev LRHS NRHS
	'Lady Wilson' misapplied	see *C.* × *crocosmiiflora* 'Norwich Canary'
	'Lana de Savary'	CPrp CTca EBee ECtt EWes GCal IBal IBlr MNrw NBid NWad SMad WCot
	'Late Cornish'	see *C.* × *crocosmiiflora* 'Queen Alexandra' J.E. Fitt
	'Late Lucifer'	CTri GCal IBal IBlr MNrw
	'Late Yellow'	IBal
	× ***latifolia***	see *C.* × *crocosmioides*
	'Lemon Spray'	CTca IBal IBlr
	'Limpopo'	Widely available
	'Lincolnshire Gold' **new**	ECrc
	'Lucifer' ♀H5	Widely available
	LUCIFER'S CHILDREN	ELan EPfP
	'Malahide Castle Red'	GBin SMad WMoo
	'Mandarin'	IBlr
	'Marcotijn'	GNew IBal
	masoniorum ♀H4	Widely available
	– from Satan's Nek, South Africa	IBal
	– 'African Dawn'	CTca EBee ECrc ECtt
	– 'Amber'	IBlr
	– 'Dixter Flame'	IBlr IFoB IRob WOut
	– 'Flamenco'	IBlr IRob
	– 'Golden Swan'	SRms
	– Holehird strain	ECtt
	– hybrid **new**	ECrc
	– 'Kiaora'	IBlr
	– 'Moira Reid'	ECtt IBal
	– red-flowered	IBlr
	– 'Rowallane Apricot'	IBlr
	– 'Rowallane Orange'	GBin IBal IBlr
	– 'Rowallane Yellow' ♀H4	CRos CTca EBee GAbr GCal IBal IBlr IMou LRHS MNrw NRHS SMHy WSHC
	– 'Sherbert Orange'	IBal MAvo
	– Slieve Donard selection	IBal
	– 'Sunflare'	IBlr
	– 'Tropicana'	IBlr
	mathewsiana	IBlr
	'Mex'	LEdu SMad
	'Ministar'	CRos CTca EBee ECrc GKev LRHS NRHS WFar
	'Minotaur'	IBlr
	'Miss Scarlet'	CRos EPfP LRHS NRHS SAko
	'Mistral'	CBcs CCCN CRos CTca ECtt EPfP GAbr GKev IBal IBlr LAma LEdu LRHS NLar NRHS SCob WFar WMoo
	'Moorland Blaze'	WMoo
	'Moorland Sunset'	IBal WMoo
	'Mount Stewart'	see *C.* × *crocosmiiflora* 'Jessie'
	'Mr Bedford'	see *C.* × *crocosmiiflora* 'Croesus'
	'Okavango'PBR	CBre CBro CMac CTca ECtt ELon EPfP EPot EPri GAbr GBin IBal IRob LPla LSun MAvo MBNS MHol MNrw NEgg NLar NSti WCAu WCot WFar
	OLD HAT	see *C.* 'Walberton Red'
	'Orange Devil'	CBre ECtt EUJe GKin IBal IBlr LLHF LRHS MBNS NRHS
	ORANGE PEKOE ('Pek Or') **new**	IBal LCro LOPS NSti WHlf
	'Orange River'	MAvo WCot WFar
	'Orangeade'	CTca ECtt GKev IBal IBlr SRms
	'Pageant'	IBal
§	***paniculata***	CMac CPou CTca ECtt GAbr GBin NBid SCob WBrk WMoo WOut WShi
	– from Kologha	CTca
	– brown/orange-flowered	IBlr
	– 'Cally Greyleaf'	EBee GCal IBal MAvo MNrw SMHy WCot
	– 'Cally Sword'	GCal IBal MAvo
	– 'Major'	CTri IBlr
	– 'Natal'	CPrp CTca ECtt IBal
	– red-flowered	IBal IBlr SWvt
	– triploid	IBlr
	aff. ***paniculata***	IBlr
	'Paul's Best Yellow'	Widely available
	'Peach Spray' **new**	CTca

	'Peach Sunrise' **new**	IBal
	pearsei	IBlr
	'Phillipa Browne'	ECtt EHoe IBal MNrw SCob WCot WMoo
	'Plancheon' **new**	IBal
	pottsii	CRos CTca EBee GMcL GWyn IBlr LEdu LRHS NRHS WPtf
	- CD&R 109	CPou
	- 'Culzean Pink'	CElw CExl CPrp CTca EBee GBin GCal GNew IBal IBlr LPla MNrw NBid WFar WOut
	- deep pink-flowered	IBlr WMoo
	- 'Grandiflora'	IBal IBlr
§	- 'Princess'	CRos EBee ECtt GKev IBal LAma LRHS NRHS
	- tall	IBal MSpe
	'Pride of Plantion'	CTca ECrc ILea
	'Prince of Orange'	CBod CRos EBee ERCP GKev LAma LLHF LRHS MSCN NRHS SDeJ WFar WWtn
	'Quantreau'	IBlr
	'Queen Alexandria'	CRos LRHS NRHS
	'R.W. Wallace'	IBal
	'Raspberry Spray'	IBlr
	'Red Star'	IBal
	rosea	see *Tritonia disticha* subsp. *rubrolucens*
	'Rowden Bronze'	see *C.* × *crocosmiiflora* 'Coleton Fishacre'
	'Rowden Chrome'	see *C.* × *crocosmiiflora* 'George Davison' Davison
	'Ruby Velvet'	IBlr
	'Rubygold'	IBlr
	'Saffron Queen'	IBlr
	'Sampford Yellow'	IBal
	'Saturn'	see *C.* 'Jupiter'
	'Scarlatti'	CRos CTca EBee ECtt GAbr GKev IBal IBlr LRHS NRHS
	'Scarlet Wonder'	CTca
	'Severn Sunrise' 🏆H5	Widely available
	'Shocking'	IBal IBlr MAvo
	'Sonate'	ECrc
	'Sorento'	IBlr
	'Spitfire'	CExl CPrp CSam CTca ECha ECtt ELan GAbr GQue IBal IBlr IRob MArl MAvo MRav SWvt WFar WOld
§	'Sulphurea'	CExl CPou CRos CSam ECtt EPfP IBal IBlr LRHS MSpe
	'Sun Flare' **new**	CTca
	'Sunglow'	EBee ECtt EPfP ERCP GKev IBal LAma MNrw SHar SPad WHil WOut
	'Sunzest'	ECrc ECtt WHoo
	'Suzanna'	EBee ECrc ECtt MAvo
	'Tamar Double Red'	CTca SMad
	'Tamar Glow'	CTca WOld
	'Tamar Golden Ring'	CTca
	'Tamar New Dawn'	CTca
	'Tamar Peace'	CTca SMad
	'Tangerine Dream'	IBlr
	'Tangerine Queen'	GAbr IBal IBlr NWad WMoo
	'Tangerine Spray'	IBlr
	'Tiger'	CElw CTca MSpe
	'Toccata'	IBlr
	'Twilight Fairy Crimson'	CTca CWGN EBee ECrc ECtt EPri GBin LEdu MAvo NHpl
I	'Vulcan' A. Bloom	CTca IBal IBlr MAvo
	'Vulcan' Leichtlin	see *C.* × *crocosmioides* 'Vulcan' Leichtlin
§	'Walberton Red'	CSam CTca EBee EWes IBal MAvo NWad SMad
	WALBERTON YELLOW ('Walcroy'^{PBR})	CRos EPfP LRHS NRHS SMad
	'Zambesi'^{PBR}	CBro CMac ECtt ELon GBin IBal IRob LSou MBNS MCot MNrw MTis NEgg WCot
	'Zeal Giant'	CTca ECtt IBal IBlr MAvo
	'Zeal Unnamed'	CPrp CTca ECrc ECtt IBal

Crocus ✿ (*Iridaceae*)

	adanensis	EPot
	'Advance'	CRav EPot ERCP GKev LAma SDeJ SDir
§	***albiflorus***	GKev
	- blue-flowered **new**	GKev
	- purple apex **new**	GKev
	ancyrensis	EPot GKev SDeJ
	- 'Golden Bunch'	SDeJ WShi
§	***angustifolius*** 🏆H5	EPot GKev SDeJ WShi
	- 'Berlin Gold'	GKev
	- bronze-flowered	GKev
	- 'Minor'	EPot
	'Ard Schenk'	GKev LAma LRHS NRHS SDir
	asturicus	see *C. serotinus* subsp. *salzmannii*
	asumaniae	EPot GKev NRog
	- white-flowered	NRog
	'Aubade'	EPot GKev LAma
	aureus	see *C. flavus* subsp. *flavus*
	autranii	NRog
	banaticus 🏆H5	EPot GKev LLHF NHpl NRog WThu
	- 'Early Bird'	NRog
	- 'Snowdrift'	GKev
	biflorus 'Blue Pearl' 🏆H5	CAvo EPfP EPot ERCP GKev LCro MJak SCob SDeJ SDir SPer SPhx WCot WShi
	- subsp. ***melantherus***	GKev NRog
	- 'Miss Vain'	EPot ERCP GKev LAma
	- subsp. ***pulchricolor***	GKev
	- 'Serevan'	EPot
	- subsp. ***stridii***	GKev
	- subsp. ***tauri***	EPot
	- subsp. ***weldenii*** 'Albus'	EPot GKev LAma
	- - 'Fairy'	GKev LAma
	'Blue Bird'	EPot GKev
	blue-flowered	NRHS
	boryi	CRos GKev LRHS NRHS NRog
	cambessedesii	NRog
	cancellatus	SDeJ
§	- subsp. ***cancellatus***	EPot LAma NRog
	- var. ***cilicicus***	see *C. cancellatus* subsp. *cancellatus*
	- subsp. ***damascenus***	NRog
	- subsp. ***lycius***	EPot NRog
	- subsp. ***mazziaricus***	EPot NRog
	- subsp. ***pamphylicus***	NRog
	candidus var. ***subflavus***	see *C. olivieri* subsp. *olivieri*
	cartwrightianus 🏆H4	CRos GKev LRHS NRHS NRog WShi
	- 'Albus' misapplied	see *C. hadriaticus*
	- 'Albus' Tubergen 🏆H4	EPot GKev NRog SDeJ
	- 'Marcel'	NRog
	- 'Michel'	NRog
	chrysanthus 🏆H5	CHab
	- 'Blue Peter'	EPot
	- 'Constellation'	EPot
	- 'Cream Beauty' 🏆H5	CAvo EPfP EPot ERCP GKev LAma LCro LOPS LRHS NRHS SCob SDeJ WShi
	- 'E.A. Bowles' misapplied	see *C. chrysanthus* 'E.P. Bowles'
§	- 'E.P. Bowles' 🏆H5	LAma
	- var. ***fuscotinctus***	EPot GKev LAma LCro LOPS MJak SDeJ

- 'Goldene Sonne'	EPot
- 'Zwanenburg Bronze' ♀H5	SDeJ WShi
'Cloth of Gold'	see *C. angustifolius*
clusii	see *C. serotinus* subsp. *clusii*
corsicus ♀H4	EPot GKev
dalmaticus	EPot
- 'Petrovac'	GKev
'Dorothy'	EPot GKev
'Dutch Yellow'	see *C.* × *luteus* 'Golden Yellow'
'Early Gold'	GKev
'Ego'	GKev
etruscus ♀H5	GKev
- 'Rosalind'	GKev
- 'Zwanenburg'	EPot GKev LAma SDeJ SDir
'Fantasy'	GKev WShi
§ ***flavus*** subsp. ***flavus*** ♀H5	EPot GKev LAma WShi
fleischeri	EPot GKev LAma
'Flower Record'	CArg GKev LAma LRHS MJak SDeJ SDir
'Gipsy Girl'	CAvo EPfP EPot ERCP GKev LAma LCro LOPS SCob SDir
'Golden Mammoth'	see *C.* × *luteus* 'Golden Yellow'
'Goldilocks' ♀H5	GKev LAma SDeJ
goulimyi ♀H4	CAvo CRos CTal EPot GKev LAma LRHS NRHS NRog SDeJ WCot
- 'Albus'	see *C. goulimyi* subsp. *goulimyi* 'Mani White'
§ - subsp. ***goulimyi*** 'Mani White' ♀H4	CTal EPot
- subsp. ***leucanthus***	NRog
'Grand Maître'	CAvo GKev LAma SDeJ
'Haarlem Gem'	GKev
§ ***hadriaticus*** ♀H4	CRos GKev LAma LRHS NRHS NRog
- 'Alepohori'	GKev
- 'Annabelle'	GKev
- var. ***chrysobelonicus***	see *C. hadriaticus*
- 'Jumbo'	NRog
'Herald'	CAvo GKev LAma SDeJ
heuffelianus	GKev WShi
subsp. ***heuffelianus***	
- - 'Snow Princess' **new**	GKev
§ - subsp. ***scepusiensis***	GKev
imperati	EPot
subsp. ***suaveolens***	
- - 'De Jager'	CAvo ERCP GKev LAma SDeJ
'Jeanne d'Arc'	CAby CArg CAvo EPot GKev LAma LCro LOPS LRHS MJak SDeJ WShi
'Jeannine'	GKev SDeJ
karduchorum	EPot GKev LAma NRog
'Karin'	EPot
'King of the Striped'	GKev LAma SDeJ SPer
korolkowii	GKev LAma
- 'Golden Nugget'	EPot GKev
- 'January Gold'	GKev
- 'Kiss of Spring'	EPot GKev
kosaninii	GKev
kotschyanus ♀H5	SDeJ
- 'Albus'	GKev NRog SDeJ
- subsp. ***cappadocicus***	NRog
§ - subsp. ***kotschyanus***	EPot GKev NRog SDeJ
- 'Reliance'	GKev NRog
'Ladykiller'	CAvo EPot GKev LAma LCro LOPS SPhx WShi
laevigatus ♀H3	NRog
- CE&H 612	EPot
- 'Fontenayi'	EPot ERCP GKev NRog
'Large Yellow'	see *C.* × *luteus* 'Golden Yellow'
§ ***ligusticus*** ♀H5	EPot GKev LAma
- 'Millesimo'	NRog
longiflorus ♀H4	CRos EPot LRHS NRHS NRog
§ × ***luteus*** 'Golden Yellow' ♀H5	CArg CAvo EPot GKev LAma LCro LOPS LRHS MJak WShi
§ - 'Stellaris' ♀H5	EPot
malyi ♀H4	GKev
- 'Sveti Roc'	GKev
mathewii	EPot NHpl
- 'Dream Dancer'	EPot
medius	see *C. ligusticus*
minimus	EPot ERCP GKev LAma LLHF
- 'Spring Beauty'	CRav EPfP ERCP SDeJ
'Negro Boy'	EPot
niveus	CRos EPot GKev LAma LLHF LRHS NRHS NRog
nudiflorus	EPot GKev LAma LLHF NRog
ochroleucus	EPot GKev NRog SDeJ
olivieri AH 0156	GKev
- subsp. ***balansae*** 'Zwanenburg'	EPot GKev
§ - subsp. ***olivieri***	GKev
'Orange Monarch'	EPfP ERCP LAma LLHF SCob SDir
oreocreticus	NRog
pallasii VV KR.75	GKev
- subsp. ***dispathaceus***	NRog
- subsp. ***turcicus***	GKev
paschei	EPot
'Pickwick'	CAby CArg CAvo EPot GKev LAma LCro LOPS LRHS MJak SDeJ WShi
'Prins Claus'	EPfP EPot ERCP GKev LAma SDeJ SDir
pulchellus ♀H4	CAvo GKev LAma NRog SDeJ WCot
- 'Albus'	EPot GKev NRog
- 'Inspiration'	NRog
- 'Michael Hoog'	NRog
'Purple Heart'	GKev NRog
'Purpureus'	see *C.* 'Purpureus Grandiflorus'
§ 'Purpureus Grandiflorus'	EPot SDeJ
'Queen of the Blues'	EPot SDeJ
'Rainbow Gold' **new**	GKev
'Remembrance'	CAby CArg CAvo EPot GKev LAma LCro LOPS LRHS SDeJ WShi
reticulatus	EPot
robertianus	NRog
'Romance'	CAvo EPot GKev LAma MJak SDeJ
'Ruby Giant'	CAvo CRos EPfP EPot ERCP GKev LAma LCro LOPS LRHS MJak NRHS SCob SDeJ SPer SPhx WShi
rujanensis	EPot
salzmannii	see *C. serotinus* subsp. *salzmannii*
sativus	CAvo CBod CTca ELan EPot ERCP GKev GPoy ILea LAma LCro LOPS NRog SCob SDeJ SVic WFar XAbr
'Saturnus'	EPot LAma
scepusiensis	see *C. heuffelianus* subsp. *scepusiensis*
§ ***serotinus*** subsp. ***clusii***	GKev LAma NRog
§ - subsp. ***salzmannii***	GKev LAma NRog
- - f. ***albus***	NRog
- - 'Atropurpureus'	WCot
- - 'Erectophyllus'	GKev NRog
sibiricus	see *C. sieberi*
§ ***sieberi***	EPot
- 'Albus'	see *C. sieberi* 'Bowles's White'
- subsp. ***atticus*** 'Amfiklia'	GKev
- - 'Firefly'	CRos EPfP EPot ERCP GKev LAma LRHS NRHS SDeJ
§ - 'Bowles's White' ♀H5	EPot GKev SDeJ
- 'Hubert Edelsten' ♀H5	EPot GKev LAma
- 'Ronald Ginns'	EPot

- subsp. ***sublimis***	GKev
- - 'Tricolor' ♀H4	CArg CAvo CRos CTca EPfP EPot GKev LAma LCro LOPS LRHS NRHS SDeJ WOld
- 'Vardousia'	GKev
- 'Violet Queen'	LAma
'Snow Bunting' ♀H5	CAvo CRav CTca ELan EPfP EPot GKev LAma LCro LOPS SCob SDeJ SDir SPer WShi
speciosus ♀H4	CAvo EPfP LAma LCro LOPS SDeJ WCot WShi
- 'Aino'	GKev NRog
- 'Aitchisonii'	CRos GKev LRHS NRHS NRog
- 'Albus' ♀H4	CAvo EPot ERCP GKev LCro LOPS NRog SDeJ WShi
- 'Artabir'	CRos GKev LRHS NRHS NRog SDeJ
- 'Cassiope'	CRos GKev LAma LRHS NRHS NRog SDeJ
- 'Conqueror'	CRos ELan EPfP ERCP GKev LAma LCro LOPS LRHS NRHS NRog SDeJ
- 'Oxonian'	CRos ELan EPot GKev LAma LRHS NRHS NRog WOld
- subsp. ***speciosus***	EPot GKev NRog SDeJ
- subsp. ***xantholaimos***	GKev NRog
× ***stellaris***	see *C.* × *luteus* 'Stellaris'
'Striped Beauty'	GKev
susianus	see *C. angustifolius*
suterianus	see *C. olivieri* subsp. *olivieri*
thomasii	EPot GKev NRog
tommasinianus ♀H5	CArg CAvo CGrW CHab CRav CTca EPot GKev IRob LAma LCro LOPS MRav SDeJ SDir SPhx SRms WShi
- 'Albus'	EPot GKev LAma WShi
- 'Barr's Purple'	EPot GKev LAma LCro LOPS LRHS NRHS SDeJ SDir
- 'Eric Smith'	EPot
- 'Lilac Beauty'	EPot GKev LAma
- 'Pictus'	EPot GKev LAma LLHF WShi
- 'Roseus'	EPot ERCP GKev LAma SDeJ SDir SPhx WCot WShi
- 'Rubinetta'	GKev
- 'Whitewell Purple'	CAvo CRos EPot ERCP GKev LAma LCro LOPS LRHS NRHS SDeJ WCot WShi
tournefortii ♀H3	CAvo CRos EPot GKev LRHS NRHS NRog
'Twinborn'	EPot
vallicola	GKev
'Vanguard' ♀H5	EPot GKev LAma LCro LOPS SDeJ WCot
veneris	NRog
vernus	CRav GKev
- subsp. ***albiflorus***	see *C. albiflorus*
- 'Drina Marvel'	GKev
- 'Graecus'	EPot GKev
- 'Krasno Polje'	GKev
- 'Michael's Purple'	GKev
- Uklin strain	GKev
- subsp. ***vernus*** 'Grandiflorus'	see *C.* 'Purpureus Grandiflorus'
versicolor JMH 8215	GKev
- 'Picturatus'	EPot GKev LAma LLHF SDeJ WShi
vitellinus	EPot GKev
'Yalta'	CAvo ERCP GKev SDir SPhx WCot
'Yellow Giant'	SDeJ
'Yellow Mammoth'	see *C.* × *luteus* 'Golden Yellow'
'Zenith'	EPot
'Zephyr' ♀H4	NRog SDeJ WOld
zonatus	see *C. kotschyanus* subsp. *kotschyanus*

Croomia (*Stemonaceae*)

heterosepala	WCru

Crossandra (*Acanthaceae*)

infundibuliformis ♀H1a	EShb

Crossyne (*Amaryllidaceae*)

flava	NRog WCot

Crotalaria (*Papilionaceae*)

laburnifolia ♀H2	CCCN

Crowea (*Rutaceae*)

exalata × ***saligna***	CExl

Crucianella (*Rubiaceae*)

stylosa	see *Phuopsis stylosa*

Cruciata (*Rubiaceae*)

§ ***laevipes***	EBWF NMir

Crusea (*Rubiaceae*)

coccinea	CSpe SBrt WCot
- 'Crûg Crimson'	CAby WCru

× *Cryptbergia* (*Bromeliaceae*)

'Rubra' new	SChr

Cryptocarya (*Lauraceae*)

alba	GBin SVen

Cryptocoryne (*Araceae*)

× ***willisii***	XBlo

Cryptogramma (*Pteridaceae*)

crispa	WHer

Cryptomeria ✿ (*Cupressaceae*)

fortunei	see *C. japonica*
§ ***japonica***	CAco CDul CMen CPer CTho EPfP ESps MBlu LPra MMuc SEND SPer SWvt WMou WTSh
- 'Antique Gold'	LRHS
- Araucarioides Group	GMil NEgg SLim
- 'Atawai'	NLar
- 'Aurea'	EUJe
- 'Bandai-sugi' ♀H6	CKen CMac CMen EPfP GMil IArd MGos NLar SRms
- 'Barabits Gold'	LRHS
- 'Birodo'	CKen
- 'Black Dragon'	SLim
- 'Blue Diamond'	CAco
- 'Compressa'	CKen EMOT EPfP LBee LRHS MAsh NLar NWad SRms
§ - 'Cristata'	CAco CBcs CMac ELan GMil LRHS MGos MPkF NEgg SRms
- 'Dacrydioides'	LRHS NLar
- 'Dinger'	CKen LRHS
- Elegans Group	CBcs CDul CMac CSBt ELan EMOT EPfP ESps EUJe GMil LRHS MGos NEgg NLar NOra NRHS SCoo SEND SLim SPoG SRms WFar
- - 'Elegans' ♀H6 new	CAco GMil
- 'Elegans Aurea'	CCVT CRos ELan GMil MAsh NEgg NRHS SPoG SWvt WFar
- 'Elegans Compacta' ♀H6	CMac CRos CSBt ELan GBin GMcL GMil LBee LRHS MAsh MMuc NLar NRHS SRms SWvt
- 'Elegans Nana'	SRms

	- 'Elegans Viridis' 🏆H6	LRHS NOra SLim
I	- 'Elegantissima'	CCVT
	- 'Filip's Winter Magic' **new**	NLar
	- 'Globosa Nana' 🏆H6	CAco EMOT EPfP ESps GMcL GMil LBee MGos NEgg NPoe SArc SCoo SPoG
	- 'Golden Promise' 🏆H6	CAco CBcs MAsh NWad SLim SPer SWvt
	- 'Jindai-sugi'	NLar
	- 'Kilmacurragh'	CKen
	- 'Kohui-yatsubusa'	CKen
	- 'Koshiji-yatsubusa'	NLar
	- 'Koshyi'	CKen
	- 'Little Champion'	CKen LRHS NRHS SLim
	- 'Little Diamond'	CKen GMil NEgg
	- 'Little Sonja'	CKen SLim
	- 'Little Yoko'	CKen NLar
	- 'Littleworth Dwarf'	see *C. japonica* 'Littleworth Gnom'
§	- 'Littleworth Gnom'	LRHS
	- 'Lobbii'	CAco
	- 'Lobbii Nana' hort.	see *C. japonica* 'Nana'
	- 'Midare' **new**	CAco
	- 'Monstrosa'	NLar
	- 'Mushroom'	GMil SLim
§	- 'Nana'	SRms
	- 'Osaka-tama'	CKen
	- 'Pipo'	CKen
	- 'Pygmaea'	NLar NWad SRms
	- 'Rasen-sugi'	GMil IDee NLar SMad
	- 'Sekkan-sugi' 🏆H6	CAco CBcs CCVT CDul CMac EPfP GBin GKin GMil IArd LBee LRHS MAsh MGos NEgg NLar NPoe SCoo SLim SPoG SWvt
	- 'Sekka-sugi'	see *C. japonica* 'Cristata'
§	- 'Spiralis' 🏆H6	CAco CKen CMac ELan EPfP ESps GMil LBee LRHS MAsh MGos NEgg NLar SAko SCoo SLim SPoG SRms SWvt
§	- 'Spiraliter Falcata'	NLar
§	- 'Tansu'	CKen GMil LRHS
	- 'Tenzan-sugi' 🏆H6	CKen WThu
	- 'Tilford Gold'	EMOT GMcL GMil
	- 'Toda'	CKen
	- 'Vilmoriniana' 🏆H6	CKen CMen CRos CTri ELan EPfP ESps GKin GMcL GMil LRHS MAsh MGil MGos NEgg NLar NRHS SCoo SEND SLim SPer SPoG SWvt WMoo
	- 'Winter Bronze'	CKen
	- 'Yatsubusa'	see *C. japonica* 'Tansu'
	- 'Yellow Twig' **new**	NLar
	- 'Yore-sugi'	see *C. japonica* 'Spiralis', 'Spiraliter Falcata'
	- 'Yoshino'	CKen NEgg SLim
	sinensis	see *C. japonica*

Cryptostegia (*Apocynaceae*)

	grandiflora	CCCN

Cryptotaenia (*Apiaceae*)

	japonica	CAgr CHby CPou GPoy LEdu MNHC SRms WHer
	- f. ***atropurpurea***	CDor CSpe EBee EHoe LEdu LPla MNrw WBor WPGP XAbr

Ctenanthe (*Marantaceae*)

	lubbersiana 🏆H1b	XBlo
	oppenheimiana	XBlo

Cucubalus (*Caryophyllaceae*)

	baccifer	NLar

cucumber see AGM Vegetables Section

Cudrania see *Maclura*

cumin see *Cuminum cyminum*

Cuminum (*Apiaceae*)

	cyminum	SRms SVic XAbr

Cumulopuntia (*Cactaceae*)

§	***boliviana*** subsp. ***dactylifera***	CCac

Cunninghamia (*Cupressaceae*)

	konishii	CExl
§	***lanceolata***	CAco CBcs CDTJ CDul CKen CMCN CMac CTho EPfP MGil SSta WPGP
	- 'Glauca'	CAco CExl CJun
	sinensis	see *C. lanceolata*
	unicaniculata	see *C. lanceolata*

Cunonia (*Cunoniaceae*)

	capensis	CExl

Cuphea (*Lythraceae*)

	caeciliae	CSam
	cyanea	LSvl
	hyssopifolia 🏆H1c	CTsd EShb LSou SWvt
	- 'Alba'	CCCN CPbh CRav EShb SWvt
	- pink-flowered	CCCN CPbh
	- red-flowered	CCCN
	- 'Rosea'	SWvt
§	***ignea*** 🏆H1c	CTsd
	- 'Matchless'	SVic
	'Lilac Belle'	CSpe
§	***llavea*** 'Georgia Scarlet'	CCCN
	- 'Tiny Mice'	see *C. llavea* 'Georgia Scarlet'
I	***macrophylla*** hort.	CHll
	maculata	CCCN
	platycentra	see *C. ignea*
	'Regal Purple'	CPla
	viscosissima	CFis CSpe ELan MCot

× *Cupressocyparis* see × *Cuprocyparis*

Cupressus (*Cupressaceae*)

	arizonica	ESps
	- 'Conica Glauca'	CAco
I	- 'Fastigiata Aurea'	ESps SWeb
	- var. ***glabra*** 'Aurea'	MAsh SGol
	- - 'Blue Ice'	CAco CDul CMac CTho ESps MAsh MGos NEgg SLim SWvt
	- - 'Compacta'	CKen
I	- - 'Fastigiata'	CCVT ECrN EPfP ETod
	- - 'Glauca'	NRHS
*	- - 'Lutea'	NEgg
	- 'Pyramidalis' 🏆H5	SEND SGol
	cashmeriana 🏆H3	CAco CDTJ
	dupreziana	CAco
	var. ***atlantica***	
§	***funebris***	CAco CDul
	× ***leylandii***	see × *Cuprocyparis leylandii*
	lusitanica 'Brice's Weeping'	CKen NEgg SLim
	- 'Pygmy'	CKen
	macnabiana	GLog
	macrocarpa	CBcs CBod CCVT CDul CPer CTho SEND

	- 'Compacta'	CKen
	- 'Gold Spread'	SLim
	- 'Goldcrest' ♀H4	CBcs CCVT CDul CMac ECrN ELan EMOT ESps GMcL GMil LRHS MGos NPri NRHS SEWo SGol SLim SWeb SWvt
	- 'Golden Cone'	ESps
	- 'Golden Pillar'	SWvt
	- 'Lohbrunner'	CKen
	- 'Pygmaea'	CKen
	- 'Sulphur Cushion'	CKen
	- 'Wilma' ♀H4	CSBt ELan EMOT GMil LBee LRHS MAsh MGos NRHS SCoo SEND SGol SLim SPoG SWvt
	- 'Woking'	CKen
	nootkatensis	see *Xanthocyparis nootkatensis*
	sempervirens	ETMg EUJe LPra LRHS SPlb SWeb
	- 'Agrimed'	CCVT
	- 'Bolgheri'	LSRN SBig
	- 'Green Pencil'	CKen
	- 'Pyramidalis'	see *C. sempervirens* Stricta Group
	- var. ***sempervirens***	see *C. sempervirens* Stricta Group
§	- Stricta Group	CAco CBcs CCVT CDul CTho ESps LMaj LPra LRHS NLar SArc SEND SEWo SGol WCFE
	- 'Swane's Gold'	CBcs CKen MAsh NEgg
	- 'Totem Pole'	CAco CCVT CKen CSBt CTho CTri ELan EMOT EPfP EUJe LBee LRHS MAsh MGos SCoo SEND SPoG SWvt
	torulosa	CAco

× *Cuprocyparis* ✿ (*Cupressaceae*)

§	***leylandii***	Widely available
I	- '2001'	CCVT SGol
	- 'Blue Jeans'PBR	SEND
§	- 'Castlewellan'	CBcs CCVT CDul CMac CSBt CTri EMOT EPfP ESps ETMg GMil LBuc LPra LSRN MAsh MGos MJak MMuc NPri SCob SEND SGol SLim SPer SPoG SWvt WAvo WFar WHar WTSh
	- EXCALIBUR GOLD ('Drabb'PBR)	CPer
	- 'Ferngold'	MAsh
	- 'Galway Gold'	see × *C. leylandii* 'Castlewellan'
	- 'Gold Rider' ♀H6	CBod CMac ELan ESps MAsh MGos MMuc NEgg SCob SCoo SEND SGol SPer SPoG SWvt
§	- 'Harlequin' (v)	CMac SEND SWvt
	- 'Leighton Green'	WTSh
	- 'Naylor's Blue'	CMac SEND
	- 'Olive's Green'	SWvt
	- 'Robinson's Gold'	CMac SGol
	- 'Silver Dust' (v)	WAvo
	- 'Variegata'	see × *C. leylandii* 'Harlequin'
	- 'Winter Sun'	WCFE

Curculigo (*Hypoxidaceae*)

capitulata	XBlo
crassifolia B&SWJ 2318	WCru
- HWJ 683 from Vietnam	WCru

Curcuma ✿ (*Zingiberaceae*)

alismatifolia	SDeJ
longa	SPlb SPre
roscoeana	SDeJ
zedoaria 'Bicolor Wonder'	CCCN
- 'Pink Wonder'	CCCN
- 'White Wonder'	CCCN SDeJ

Curio (*Asteraceae*)

§	***articulata***	EShb SEND
§	***ficoides***	EShb
§	***repens***	EShb EUJe SEND
§	***rowleyanus***	EBak EShb
	talinoides	WCot
	subsp. ***mandraliscae*** 'Blue Finger'	

Curtonus see *Crocosmia*

Cussonia ✿ (*Araliaceae*)

gamtoosensis	WCot
natalensis	WCot
paniculata	CDTJ CWGN
sphaerocephala	WCot
spicata	CDTJ SPlb
zuluensis	WCot

custard apple see *Annona cherimola*

Cyananthus (*Campanulaceae*)

	incanus	GEdr
	integer misapplied	see *C. microphyllus*
	lobatus ♀H5	GKev LLHF
	- SDR 7476	GKev
	- 'Albus'	EPot WAbe
	- giant	GEdr WAbe
	lobatus × ***microphyllus***	EWld GCrg GEdr WAbe
§	***microphyllus*** ♀H5	EPot GCrg GEdr GKev NSla WAbe
	sherriffii	GJos IFoB WAbe
	spathulifolius	WAbe

Cyanastrum (*Tecophilaeaceae*)

cordifolium	GKev

Cyanella (*Tecophilaeaceae*)

orchidiformis	NRog

Cyanotis (*Commelinaceae*)

beddomei ♀H1c **new**	EShb
somaliensis ♀H1c	EShb

Cyathea ✿ (*Cyatheaceae*)

	australis	CBct CBdn CDTJ CKel IDee LRHS NLos SPlb
	baileyana	NLos
	brownii	CKel NLos
	cooperi	CAbb CBdn CDTJ CKel EUJe NLos WFib
*	- 'Brentwood'	CBdn EBee NLos
	- 'Cinnamon'	NLos
	- single-crested	NLos
	cunninghamii	CKel
	dealbata	CBdn CDTJ CKel GBin
	dregei	SPlb
	exilis	NLos
	glauca	NLos
	leichardtiana	NLos
	medullaris	CBdn CKel NLos
	rebeccae	NLos
	robusta	CKel
	smithii	CDTJ CKel
	tomentosissima	CDTJ CKel
	woollsiana	NLos

Cyathodes (*Ericaceae*)

colensoi	see *Leucopogon colensoi*
fraseri	see *Leucopogon fraseri*

Cycas (*Cycadaceae*)

	panzhihuaensis	CBrP SPlb
	revoluta ♀H2	CAbb CBcs CBrP CCCN EPfP EShb ESps ETod EUJe NLos SArc SChr SEND SMad SPlb XBlo
	revoluta* × *taitungensis	CBrP
§	***rumphii***	CBrP
	taitungensis	CBrP
	thouarsii	see *C. rumphii*

Cyclamen ✿ (*Primulaceae*)

	abchasicum	see *C. coum* subsp. *caucasicum*
	africanum	CBro CRos GKev LRHS MAsh NRHS XEll
§	***alpinum***	CBro CRos EPot GKev LAma LRHS MAsh NRHS SDeJ XEll
	- 'Nettleton White'	MAsh
	balearicum	CBro CRos EPot GKev LAma LRHS MAsh NRHS
	cilicium ♀H3	CAby CBro CRos EPfP EPot ERCP GJos GKev GMcL LAma LCro LOPS LRHS MAsh NHpl NRHS NSla WHoo WShi XEll
	- f. ***album***	CBro CRos EPot GKev LAma LLHF LRHS MAsh NRHS XEll
	colchicum	MAsh
	confusum	GKev
§	***coum*** ♀H5	Widely available
	- var. ***abchasicum***	see *C. coum* subsp. *caucasicum*
	- 'Ashwood Snowflake' new	MAsh
§	- subsp. ***caucasicum***	GKev MAsh
	- subsp. ***coum***	CBro
	- - f. ***albissimum***	GKev
	- - - 'George Bisson'	MAsh
	- - - 'Golan Heights'	MAsh
	- - - 'Lake Effect' new	MAsh
	- - f. ***coum*** Nymans Group	MAsh
	- - - Pewter Group ♀H5	GEdr GKev WCot
	- - - - 'Maurice Dryden' ♀H5	CBro CRos EPot GKev LAma LRHS MAsh NPnk NRHS WHoo
	- - - - 'Tilebarn Elizabeth'	MAsh WHoo
	- - - 'Roseum'	CAvo IRob
	- - - Silver Group	CBro CRos GKev LRHS NRHS NRya WHoo
	- - - - red-flowered	WHoo
	- - magenta-flowered	WHoo
	- - f. ***pallidum*** 'Album'	CAvo CWCL EPot GEdr GKev GMaP GWyn IRob LAma LCro LOPS SDeJ SDir SPer WHoo WShi
	- dark pink-flowered	CAvo WHoo
	- hybrid	ERCP
	- marble-leaved	WHoo
	- 'Meaden's Crimson'	GKev LAma
	- red-flowered	IRob
I	- 'Rubrum'	GKev GWyn IRob LCro LOPS
	- silver speckled leaf	CAvo EHrv
	creticum	MAsh
	cyprium	CBro CRos GKev LRHS MAsh NRHS XEll
	- 'E.S.'	MAsh WThu
	- 'Galaxy'	MAsh
	× ***drydeniae***	MAsh
	elegans	MAsh
	europaeum	see *C. purpurascens*
	graecum	CBro CPne CRos EPot GKev LAma LLHF LRHS MAsh NRHS WHil WThu XEll
	- subsp. ***candicum***	MAsh
	- subsp. ***graecum*** f. ***album***	CBro CRos GKev LAma LRHS MAsh NRHS XEll
	- - f. ***graecum*** 'Glyfada'	EPot GKev LAma MAsh XEll
§	***hederifolium*** ♀H5	Widely available
	- S&L 175/1	WCot XLum
	- 'Amaze Me'	ECtt IRob LSou MAvo MHol NCou WCot
	- subsp. ***crassifolium***	GKev
	- var. ***hederifolium***	CAby CAvo CBro GKev LCro LEdu
	f. ***albiflorum*** ♀H5	LOPS NWad SCob SDeJ WHoo WPnP XLum
	- - - 'Album'	CWCL EHrv EWTr IRob SDeJ WShi
	- - - Bowles's Apollo Group	NWad
	- - - 'Discovery'	WCot
	- - - 'Nettleton Silver'	see *C. hederifolium* var. *hederifolium* f. *albiflorum* 'White Cloud'
	- - - 'Perlenteppich'	GMaP
	- - - silver-leaved	SDys
§	- - - 'White Cloud' ♀H5	MAsh NHpl WHoo
	- - f. ***hederifolium*** Bowles's Apollo Group	CHid
	- - - 'Fairy Rings'	MAsh
	- - - 'Rosenteppich'	CAby
	- - - 'Ruby Glow'	CRos CWCL LRHS MAsh NRHS WThu
	- - - Silver Cloud Group ♀H5	CAby CBro CHid EHrv MAsh WHoo
	- - - 'Silver Shield'	MAsh
	- - - 'Stargazer'	MAsh
	- island scented strain	WCot
	- 'Lysander'	GKev MAsh
	- 'Pewter Mist'	LAma SDir
	- 'Red Sky'	CBro LAma NWad
	- 'Rose Pearls'	SRot
	- 'Silver Mist'	SDir
	- Silver-leaved Group	CRav CRos EPot GKev LRHS NPnk NRHS NSla SRot
	- - 'Silver Leaf Pink'	GMaP NWad
	- - 'Silver Leaf Red'	NWad
	- - 'Silver Leaf White'	GMaP NWad
	× ***hildebrandii***	LLHF
	ibericum	see *C. coum* subsp. *caucasicum*
	intaminatum	CBro CPne CRos EPot GKev LAma LLHF LRHS MAsh NRHS WHoo XEll
	- plain-leaved	WThu
	latifolium	see *C. persicum*
	libanoticum	CBro CRos GKev LAma LRHS MAsh NRHS XEll
	maritimum	XEll
	mirabile ♀H4	CBro CPne CRos EPot GKev LAma LLHF LRHS MAsh NHpl NRHS SDeJ WThu
	- 'Alba'	GKev SDeJ XEll
	- f. ***mirabile*** 'Tilebarn Anne'	MAsh
	- - 'Tilebarn Nicholas'	MAsh
	- f. ***niveum***	SDeJ
	- - 'Tilebarn Jan'	MAsh
	neapolitanum	see *C. hederifolium*
	orbiculatum	see *C. coum*
	parviflorum	MAsh
§	***persicum***	CBro CRos CWCL GKev LRHS MAsh NRHS WCot
	- f. ***albidum***	MAsh
	- Ashwood silver-leaved new	MAsh
	pseudibericum ♀H4	CBro CPne CRos EPot GKev LAma LLHF LRHS MAsh NRHS SDeJ WCot
	- AC&W 664	NWad

	– f. ***roseum***	MAsh
§	***purpurascens***	CAby CBro GKev LLHF MAsh NHpl NSla WHoo WThu
	– 'Lake Garda'	MAsh
	repandum	CAby CAvo CBro CRos EPot GKev LAma LRHS MAsh NRHS WHer
	– 'Pelops' misapplied	see *C. rhodium* subsp. *peloponnesiacum*
	rhodium	GKev MAsh
§	– subsp. ***peloponnesiacum***	GKev MAsh
	– subsp. ***vividum***	MAsh
	rohlfsianum	CRos GKev LRHS MAsh NRHS WThu XEll
	× ***schwarzii***	MAsh
	'Trena'	SDeJ
	trochopteranthum	see *C. alpinum*
	× ***wellensiekii***	MAsh
	× ***whiteae***	LLHF

Cyclea (*Menispermaceae*)

	polypetala KWJ 12157	WCru

Cyclosorus ✿ (*Thelypteridaceae*)

	tottoides	CBdn

Cydonia ✿ (*Rosaceae*)

	japonica	see *Chaenomeles japonica*
	oblonga (F)	ECrN ESps EUJe
	– 'Agvambari' (F)	SKee
	– 'Aromatnaya' (F)	ERea MCoo NOra SKee WHar
	– 'Champion' (F)	CAgr CHab ECrN EMOT EPom ERea LBuc MCoo NEgg NOra SKee SVic WHar
	– 'Early Prolific' (F)	SEND
	– 'Ekmek' (F)	SKee
	– 'Gamboa' (F)	MRai SKee
	– 'Iranian' (F)	CAgr
	– 'Isfahan' (F)	ERea SKee
	– 'Krymsk' (F)	CAgr WWct
	– 'Leskovac' (F)	CAgr EPom ERea LMaj NLar NOra WWct
§	– 'Lusitanica' (F)	CAgr CHab CLnd ELan EMOT EPom ERea LRHS NLar WHar
	– 'Meech's Prolific' (F) 🏆H5	CAgr CDul CHab CLnd CTri ECrN EMil EPom ERea LRHS MAsh MGos MRav NLar NOra SDea SKee SLim SPer SPoG SSFT WHar WWct
	– pear-shaped (F)	CHab ECrN NEgg SPer
	– PORTUGAL	see *C. oblonga* 'Lusitanica'
	– 'Rea's Mammoth' (F)	CHab ECrN ERea NLar
	– 'Serbian Gold' (F)	CDul CMac CTho ECrN EMOT EPom ERea GQue LRHS MAsh NLar NOra SKee SSFT WHar
	– 'Smyrna' (F)	NLar NOra SKee WHar
	– 'Sobu' (F)	SKee
	– 'Vranja' ambig. (F)	CBcs EMOT MAsh SPoG
	– 'Vranja' Nenadovic (F) 🏆H5	Widely available

Cylindropuntia (*Cactaceae*)

	acanthocarpa from Meadview, Arizona	CCac
§	***echinocarpa*** MUG 167	CCac
	imbricata	CCac SPlb XLum XSen
	– DJF 928.19 from Union County, New Mexico	CCac
	– DJF 1575 from Delhi, Colorado	CCac
	– KMR 429	CCac
	– SB 99 from Manzano Mountains, New Mexico	CCac
	– from Caon City, Colorado	CCac
	– from Fremont County, Colorado	CCac
	– 'Pinky'	CCac
	kleiniae	CCac
	leptocaulis	XSen
	– from Valencia County, New Mexico	CCac
	rosea PG	CCac
§	***spinosior***	XLum
	versicolor	CCac XSen
	× ***viridiflora***	CCac
	– SB 957 from Santa Fe, New Mexico	CCac
	whipplei DJF 131.24 from Show Low, Arizona	CCac
	– DJF 167 from Snowflake, Arizona	CCac
	– MUG 125 from San Juan, New Mexico	CCac
	– from Coconino County, Arizona	CCac
	– 'Monstrosus'	CCac
*	– var. ***multidigitata*** from Meadview, Arizona	CCac
	– 'Waiblingen'	CCac
	– 'Würzburg'	CCac

Cymbalaria (*Plantaginaceae*)

	aequitriloba 'Alba'	GAbr GEdr NRya
§	***hepaticifolia***	CSma SBrt SPlb
§	***muralis***	EBWF ECtt GAbr GJos LPmr MHer MSCN WArt WHer WTor
	– 'Albiflora'	see *C. muralis* 'Pallidior'
	– 'Kenilworth White'	GJos WCot WMoo
	– 'Nana Alba'	ECtt GCrg MSCN
§	– 'Pallidior'	SPhx
	– 'Snow Wave'	ECtt WCot WFar
§	***pallida***	CPBP CSma MAsh MMuc SBch SEND SPlb WMoo
	– 'Alba'	WMoo
§	***pilosa***	ECtt NLar
	'Snow Wave'	ECtt WFar

Cymbopogon (*Poaceae*)

	citratus	CBod CCCN CRav CTsd ENfk ERea GPoy MNHC SPre SRms SVic WTre XAbr
	flexuosus	CCCN MHer MNHC SRms
	nardus	GPoy

Cymophyllus (*Cyperaceae*)

§	***fraserianus***	CFil EBee GCal

Cynanchum (*Apocynaceae*)

	ascyrifolium	EBee GEdr IPot LEdu WHil

Cynara (*Asteraceae*)

	cardunculus 🏆H6	Widely available
	– from Chelsea Physic Garden	MAvo
	– 'Bianco Avorio'	SVic
I	– 'Cardy'	LCro
	– dwarf	SMHy
	– subsp. ***flavescens***	SBrt
I	– 'Florist Cardy'	NLar
	– 'Gobbo di Nizza'	SRms
	– 'Porto Spineless'	CAgr
§	– Scolymus Group	CBcs CMea CRos EPfP EWes GPoy IBoy LCro LOPS LRHS

	LSRN MNHC MRav NRHS SEND SPav SPhx SPoG SVic WHer
- - 'Bere'	LEdu
- - 'Gros Camus de Bretagne'	MAvo WCot
- - 'Gros Vert de Lâon' ♀H5	CBcs CRos ELan LRHS WCot
- - 'Monica Lynden-Bell'	WCot
- - 'Purple Globe'	LCro LEdu SRms
- - 'Romanesco'	LCro SRms SVic
- - 'Rouge d'Alger'	CAgr
- - 'Tavor'	SVic
- - 'Vert Globe'	CSBt ENfk LEdu NLar NPer SPad SRms SVic SWvt WHil
- - 'Violet de Provence'	CSBt MHer SPad SRms
- - 'Violetto di Chioggia' ♀H4	WHil
* ***gomerensis***	WCot
humilis	SBrt
- white-flowered	SBrt
scolymus	see *C. cardunculus* Scolymus Group
syriaca	SPhx

Cynodon (*Poaceae*)

aethiopicus	EHoe EPPr

Cynoglossum (*Boraginaceae*)

amabile ♀H3	SPhx
- f. ***roseum*** 'Mystery Rose'	LLWG
grande	SBrt
nervosum	CBod EBee ELan EPPr GPSL MMuc SEND SPer WCAu WCot WGwG
officinale	EBWF

Cynosurus (*Poaceae*)

cristatus	CHab EBWF NMir

Cypella (*Iridaceae*)

aquatilis	EWat LLWG
§ ***coelestis***	CSpe
plumbea	see *C. coelestis*

Cyperus (*Cyperaceae*)

§ ***albostriatus***	CCCN EShb
alternifolius misapplied	see *C. involucratus*
alternifolius L.	CBen CCCN EPfP MSKA SArc WMAq WMoo XBlo
- 'Compactus'	see *C. involucratus* 'Nanus'
'Chira'	NWsh
§ ***cyperoides***	NLos
diffusus misapplied	see *C. albostriatus*
diffusus ambig.	NLos
§ ***eragrostis***	EHoe EPPr GCal MWts NSti SPlb WGrn WMAq WMoo
esculentus	CAgr EShb
fuscus	WMoo
glaber	IBoy
haspan misapplied	see *C. papyrus* 'Nanus'
haspan L.	MSKA NLos
§ ***involucratus*** ♀H1c	EShb EWat MSKA MWts SEND WMoo
- 'Gracilis'	LLWG
§ - 'Nanus'	EShb NLos
longus	CBen CWat EHoe ETMg EWat MMuc MWts NPer SEND SPlb WMAq WWtn XLum
papyrus ♀H1a	CCCN CDTJ EUJe LCro LOPS LRHS MHer MSKA NLos SBig SPlb XBlo
§ - 'Nanus' ♀H1a	XBlo
- 'Perkamentus' PBR	CCCN
prolifer	LLWG
sumula hort.	see *C. cyperoides*
vegetus	see *C. eragrostis*
'Zumila'	EShb

Cyphomandra see *Solanum*

Cyphostemma (*Vitaceae*)

juttae	LToo
mappia new	SPlb

Cypripedium (*Orchidaceae*)

sp.	SDir
acaule	GEdr
Achim gx	GEdr XFro
Aki gx	GEdr XFro
- 'Pastel'	GEdr XFro
× ***andrewsii***	GEdr
Anna gx	GEdr XFro
Annegret gx	SDir
Annette gx	GEdr
Bärbel Schmidt gx	GEdr
× ***barbeyi***	see *C.* × *ventricosum*
Barry Phillips gx	GEdr
Bernd gx	GEdr
Bill gx	GEdr
Birgit gx pastel-flowered	GEdr XFro
Boots gx	GEdr
calceolus	GKev LAma SDir
calceolus × ***henryii***	LAma
californicum	LAma
Carol Ilene gx	GEdr
Chauncey gx	GEdr XFro
Cleo Pinkepank gx	GEdr XFro
corrugatum	see *C. tibeticum*
Dawn Edwards gx	GEdr
debile	LAma
Dietrich gx ♀H5	GEdr XFro
Emil gx	GEdr XFro
Eurasia gx	XFro
fasciolatum	GEdr LAma LRHS NRHS
flavum	GEdr GKev LAma SDir
- white-flowered	GKev
- white-flowered × ***reginae***	LAma
formosanum ♀H3	GEdr GKev LAma
Gabriela gx 'Kentucky Maxi'	GKev LAma NHpl
Gisela gx	CAvo GEdr XFro
- 'Pastel'	GEdr
Hank Small gx ♀H5	GEdr XFro
Hans Erni gx	GEdr XFro
henryi	GKev LAma SDir
Inge gx	GEdr XFro
Ingrid gx	GEdr XFro
Irene gx	GEdr XEll
Ivory gx	GEdr LAma
James Armitage gx	GEdr
japonicum	GKev
Jens gx	GEdr
Judith Merrick gx	GEdr
Julia Barclay gx	GEdr
Kathleen Anne Green gx	GEdr
kentuckiense ♀H5	CCCN GEdr GKev LAma LRHS NHpl NRHS SDir XEll
- **Lady Dorine gx**	LAma
'Kentucky Pink'	see *C.* Philipp gx 'Kentucky Pink'
Kristi Lyn gx	GEdr XFro
Lothar Pinkepank gx	GEdr
Lucy Pinkepank gx	GEdr XFro
- 'Kentucky Pink Blush'	GKev LAma LRHS NHpl NRHS
macranthos	GEdr GKev
- 'Hotei'	GEdr

- var. ***hotei-atsumorianum*** Sadovsky	GEdr
- John Hagger Group	XFro
- var. ***speciosum***	GEdr
Maria gx	GEdr XFro
Memoria Gerd Kohls gx	GEdr
Memoriam Shawna Austin gx	GEdr
Michael gx ♀H5	GEdr XFro
- 'Pastel'	GEdr
Monto gx	XFro
Neil Lancaster gx	GEdr
Otto gx	GEdr
parviflorum	GEdr GKev SDir
- var. ***parviflorum***	LAma
§ - var. ***pubescens***	GEdr GKev LAma SDir
'Parville'	LRHS NHpl
Paul gx	GEdr XFro
Peter gx	GEdr XFro
Philipp gx ♀H5	GEdr XFro
§ - 'Kentucky Pink'	GKev LAma NHpl SDir
Piccolo gx	GKev
Pixi gx	GEdr
Pluto gx	GEdr XFro
pubescens	see *C. parviflorum* var. *pubescens*
'Pueblo'	GKev LRHS NHpl
Rascal gx	GEdr
reginae ♀H5	CCCN GEdr GKev IRob LAma LRHS NHpl SDir WHlf XEll
- f. ***albolabium***	NHpl
- f. ***album***	GEdr GKev LAma LRHS SDir XEll
Renate gx	GEdr
- pastel-flowered	XFro
Rhodopoxis gx	GEdr
Sabine gx ♀H5	GEdr XFro
- pastel-flowered	CTal GEdr XFro
Schoko gx	CTal
Sebastian gx	GEdr XFro
- 'Frosch's Mountain King'	XFro
- 'Multiflower White'	LAma NHpl
segawae	LAma
Selston High School gx	GEdr
Siggi gx	GEdr
Sunny gx	CTal GEdr XFro
§ ***tibeticum***	EBee GEdr LAma
Tilman gx	GEdr LAma XFro
Tower Hill gx	GEdr
Ulla Silkens gx ♀H5	GEdr GKev LAma XEll XFro
Ursel gx	GEdr XFro
§ × ***ventricosum***	GEdr LAma XFro
- 'Pastel'	XFro
Victoria gx	GEdr XFro
Werner Frosch gx	GEdr

Cyrilla (*Cyrillaceae*)

racemiflora	CMac

Cyrtanthus (*Amaryllidaceae*)

§ ***brachyscyphus***	EShb GKev
breviflorus	CPbh WCot WPGP
'Edwina'	CCCN
§ ***elatus*** ♀H1c	CPne CSam CTal EShb GKev LEdu NSti SPtp WCot
- salmon-flowered	GKev
- white and orange-flowered	GKev
- white-flowered	GKev
- yellow-flowered	GKev
elatus × ***fergusoniae***	CPne
'Elizabeth'	CCCN
epiphyticus	WCot
falcatus ♀H2	CPne
mackenii	EShb WPGP
- var. ***cooperi***	CAby CPne
- cream-white-flowered	CCCN GKev
- 'Himalayan Pink'	CCCN GKev
- pink-flowered	GKev
- red-flowered	CCCN GKev
- yellow-flowered	CTal
parviflorus	see *C. brachyscyphus*
purpureus	see *C. elatus*
sanguineus	CFil WCot
speciosus	see *C. elatus*
suaveolens new	WCot

Cyrtomium ✿ (*Dryopteridaceae*)

devexiscapulae	CAby CBdn LLWG NHim WPGP
§ ***falcatum*** ♀H2	CAby CBod CHid CKel CRos EFer ELan ELon EPfP EUJe GBin GMaP LEdu LRHS NLar NLos NRHS SEND SPlb SPoG SPtp SRms SRot WMoo XBlo XLum
- 'Rochfordianum'	CCCN CRos GBin LRHS MRav NRHS WFib
§ ***fortunei*** ♀H3	CBod CHid CKel CRos EFer ELan ELon EMOT EPed EPfP EUJe GBin LCro LRHS MGos MRav NBid NBro NLar NLos NRHS SPer SPoG SRms WCFE WFib WMoo WPnP XLum
- var. ***clivicola***	CBdn CKel CRos EBee EPfP EShb MGos MMoz MRav NBro NLar NRHS SPad SPtp WCot XLum
macrophyllum	CHid CRos EBee LRHS NRHS
tukusicola	EBee NLos

Cystopteris ✿ (*Woodsiaceae*)

bulbifera	WCot
dickieana	WFib
fragilis	EFer GKev WFib
moupinensis B&SWJ 6767	WCot WCru

Cytisus (*Papilionaceae*)

'Andreanus'	see *C. scoparius* f. *andreanus*
× ***beanii*** ♀H5	CRos ELan EPfP LRHS MAsh NLar SLon
'Boskoop Glory'	NLar
× ***boskoopii*** 'Apricot Gem'	NLar
- 'Boskoop Ruby' ♀H5	CMac CRos CSBt EPfP ESps EWTr GKin GMcL LCro LOPS LRHS LSRN MAsh MJak NEgg NRHS SCob SWvt WHar
- 'Dukaat'	NLar
- 'Hollandia' ♀H5	CBcs CSBt EPfP ESps GKin MMuc MRav SGol
- 'La Coquette'	EPfP LRHS NEgg NRHS SPlb
- 'Windlesham Ruby'	CExl ELan EPfP LRHS LSRN NEgg NLar NRHS SLim SPer WFar
- 'Zeelandia' ♀H5	CMac CRos EBee EPfP ESps EWTr LRHS SCob SPer WFar
'Burkwoodii' ♀H5	CBcs CDul CRos ELan ELon EPfP ESps EUJe GMcL LRHS LSRN MSwo NEgg NRHS SPoG WFar
canariensis	see *Genista canariensis*
'Cottage'	EPot
§ ***decumbens***	MAsh
'Dorothy Walpole'	WFar
'Golden Cascade'	CBcs CRos ELan LRHS MAsh NEgg NRHS SLim
'Goldfinch'	CRos CSBt ELan GMcL LRHS MJak MSwo NEgg NLar NRHS SCob WFar

§	***hirsutus***	CExl SBrt
	× ***kewensis*** ♀H5	CRos ELan EPfP LRHS MAsh MGos MRav NLar NRHS SPer SRms
	- 'Niki'	CBod CRos EPfP GMcL LRHS MAsh MMuc NLar SPer WRHF
	'Killiney Red'	ELan
	'Killiney Salmon'	GKin LSRN MRav
	'Lena' ♀H5	CMac CRos CSBt EPfP GKin GMcL LRHS LSRN MGos NEgg NLar NRHS SCob SGol SLim SPoG WFar WHar
	'Luna'	CRos EPfP GMcL NEgg
	maderensis	see *Genista maderensis*
	'Maria Burkwood'	NLar
	'Minstead'	ELan SPer
	'Moyclare Pink'	LCro LOPS
	'Mrs Norman Henry'	NLar
	'Newry Seedling'	CMac
	nigricans 'Cyni' ♀H5	CRos ELan IArd LRHS MAsh MMuc SPer SPoG
	'Porlock'	see *Genista* 'Porlock'
	× ***praecox***	CMac CRos ELon EPfP ESps EWTr LRHS MAsh NEgg NRHS SGol SPlb SPoG WFar WHar
	- 'Albus'	CBcs CMac CRos ELan EPfP ESps GMcL LRHS LSRN MAsh MGos MJak MMuc MRav NRHS SCob SEND SGol SPer WFar WHar
	- 'Allgold' ♀H5	Widely available
	- 'Frisia'	WFar
	- 'Lilac Lady'	CRos LRHS SBrt
	- 'Warminster' ♀H5	EPfP GKin MRav SEND SPer SRms
	proliferus	CExl
	purpureus	EBee ELan EPfP GMcL LRHS MRav SBrt WCot WSHC
	- 'Atropurpureus'	EPfP
	racemosus	see *Genista* × *spachiana*
	'Red Wings'	MMuc SGol
	scoparius	CDul CPer EBWF WTSh
§	- f. ***andreanus***	CTri EPfP
	- - 'Splendens'	SPer
	- 'Cornish Cream'	CDul CSBt ELan EPfP NEgg SPer
	- 'Firefly'	CBcs CMac
	- 'Fulgens'	EPfP
	- 'Golden Sunlight'	CSBt GMcL MSwo
§	- subsp. ***maritimus***	CMac
	- var. ***prostratus***	see *C. scoparius* subsp. *maritimus*
	× ***spachianus***	see *Genista* × *spachiana*
	supinus	see *C. hirsutus*
	supranubius	SBrt
	'White Lion'	CMac EBee

D

Daboecia ✿ (*Ericaceae*)

	cantabrica	LRHS MMuc
§	- f. ***alba***	CSBt NWad SWhi
	- - 'Creeping White'	CFst
	- - 'David Moss'	MMuc
	- 'Alberta White'	CFst SWhi
	- 'Amelie' PBR	CFst SPer SWhi
	- 'Andrea'	CFst SWhi
	- 'Arielle'	CFst SWhi
	- 'Atropurpurea'	CFst CSBt NWad SWhi
	- 'Bicolor'	CFst
	- f. ***blumii*** 'Purple Blum'	CFst SPer
	- - 'White Blum'	CFst SPer SWhi
	- 'Bubbles'	CFst
	- 'Celtic Star'	CFst
	- 'Chaldon'	CFst
	- 'Covadonga'	CFst
	- 'Cupido'	SWhi
	- 'Glamour'	CFst
I	- 'Globosa Pink'	NWad SWhi
	- 'Heather Yates'	CFst
	- 'Hookstone Purple'	NWad
	- 'Praegerae'	CTri
	- 'Rainbow' (v)	CFst
	- 'Romantic Muxoll'	CFst
	- subsp. ***scotica*** 'Ben'	CFst
	- - 'Cora'	CFst
	- - 'Ellen Norris'	CFst
	- - 'Golden Imp'	CFst SWhi
	- - 'Goscote'	MGos SWhi
	- - 'Jack Drake'	CFst
	- - 'Katherine's Choice'	CBcs CFst CTri
	- - 'Red Imp'	CFst
	- - 'Robin'	CFst
	- - 'Silverwells' ♀H5	CBcs MAsh SWhi
	- - 'William Buchanan' ♀H5	CFst GAbr GJos MAsh NWad SCoo SWhi
	- 'Stardust Muxoll'	CFst
	- 'Tinkerbell'	CFst GJos SWhi
	- 'Vanessa' PBR	CFst SWhi
	- 'Waley's Red' ♀H5	NWad SWhi

Dacrycarpus ✿ (*Podocarpaceae*)

§	***dacrydioides***	CBrP LEdu

Dacrydium ✿ (*Podocarpaceae*)

	cupressinum	SPlb WThu
	franklinii	see *Lagarostrobos franklinii*
	laxifolium	see *Lepidothamnus laxifolius*

Dactylicapnos (*Papaveraceae*)

	macrocapnos	CBcs CSpe GKev IDee IFro WBor WCru
	platycarpa	WPGP
§	***scandens***	CRHN EBee GEdr IRos MSCN SBrt WHlf
	- GWJ 9438	WCru
	- WJC 13793	WCru
	- 'Shirley Clemo'	CExl
§	***ventii*** GWJ 9376	WCru
	- WJC 13786 new	WCru

Dactylis (*Poaceae*)

	glomerata	CHab EBWF SVic WSFF
	- 'Variegata' (v)	MMuc NBid SEND

Dactylorhiza (*Orchidaceae*)

	sp.	SDir
	baltica	LAma
	× ***braunii***	ECha EHrv
§	***elata*** ♀H5	GKev LAma WCot
	- 'Glasnevin' new	GCal
§	***foliosa*** ♀H4	CCCN ECha MAvo NChi
§	***fuchsii***	CCCN CMil GKev LEdu MNrw NRya WHer WHlf WSFF
	× ***grandis***	IBlr
	- Blackthorn hybrid	CJun IBlr
	hybrid	LEdu NRya
	incarnata	LAma NBid
§	***maculata***	CHid CRos EHrv EPfP GKev LAma LRHS NRHS WBor WHlf
	maderensis	see *D. foliosa*
§	***majalis***	GKev LAma LRHS MNrw WHlf WSFF XEll

- subsp. ***sphagnicola***	GKev
mascula	see *Orchis mascula*
praetermissa	CCCN GKev LRHS NRHS
purpurella	EPot GAbr GJos GKev NRya

Dahlia ✿ (*Asteraceae*)

'A la Mode' (D)	CWGr
'Abba' (D)	CWGr ECtt
'Abbie' (D)	NHal
'Abingdon Ace' (D)	SGbt
'Abridge Ben' (D)	CWGr
'Abridge Florist' (WL)	CWGr
'Abridge Taffy' (D)	CWGr GRid
I 'Acapulco' (S-c)	ERCP
'Ace Summer Emotions'^{PBR} (D) **new**	SDeJ
'Ace Summer Sunset'^{PBR} (D) **new**	CBod
'Addison June' (Ba)	ERCP
'Adelaide Fontane' (D)	CWGr
'Admiral Rawlings' (D)	CFil CWGr
'Afiong' (D) **new**	CWGr
'Aitara Caress' (C)	NHal SGbt
'Aitara Majesty' (S-c)	GRid
'Akita' (Misc)	CWGr ELan LCro LOPS SGbt
'Aladdin's Lamp' (WL)	NJRG
'Alauna Clair-Obscur' (Fim)	CRav CWGr ERCP LCro LOPS
'Albert Schweitzer' (S-c)	CWGr SGbt
'Alden Regal' (C)	CWGr
'Alfred C' (S-c)	CWGr
'Alfred Grille' (S-c)	LCro LOPS SDeJ SDir SGbt
'Alf's Mascot' (D)	NJRG
'Alison Shingler' (S-c) **new**	CWGr
'Aljo' (S-c)	CWGr
'Allan Snowfire' (S-c)	NHal
'Allan Sparkes' (WL) ♀H3	CWGr
'Alloway Candy' (Misc)	ERCP
'Alloway Cottage' (D)	CWGr NHal SGbt
'Alltami Apollo' (S-c)	CWGr
'Alltami Cherry' (Ba)	CWGr
'Alltami Classic' (D)	CWGr
'Alltami Corsair' (S-c)	CWGr
'Alltami Ruby' (S-c)	CWGr
'Almand's Climax' (D) ♀H3	CWGr GRid SGbt
'Alpen Beauty' (Col)	CWGr
'Alpen Flame' (C)	CWGr
'Alpen Fury' (Anem) **new**	NJRG
'Alpen Mary Lloyd' (Col) **new**	NJRG
'Alpen Mildred' (S-c)	CWGr
'Alpen Sun' (S-c)	CWGr
'Alstergruss' (Col)	SDeJ
'Alva's Doris' (S-c) ♀H3	CWGr LAyl
'Alva's Lilac' (D)	CWGr
'Alva's Supreme' (D) ♀H3	CWGr GRid LAyl NHal
'Amaran Guard' (D)	CWGr
'Amaran Relish' (D)	CWGr GRid SGbt
'Amaran Return' (D)	CWGr
'Amaran Royale' (D)	CWGr
'Amaran Troy' (WL)	CWGr
I 'Amazone' (Sin/DwB)	SPoG
'Amazonia' (C) **new**	CWGr
'Amber Banker' (C)	CWGr SGbt
'Amber Festival' (D)	GRid NHal
'Amberglow' (Ba)	CWGr
'Amberley Joan' (D)	CWGr
'Amberley Victoria' (D)	CWGr
'Ambition' (S-c)	CAvo CRav CWGr ERCP LCro LOPS
'Amelia's Surprise' (D)	CWGr
'American Copper' (D)	CWGr

'American Dawn' (D)	CRav ERCP LCro LOPS
'American Moon' (D)	LCro LOPS
AMERICAN PIE ('Vdtg26'^{PBR}) (Dark Angel Series) (Sin)	SDeJ
'American Sun' (D) **new**	ERCP
'Amethyst' (D)	CWGr
'Amgard Coronet' (D)	CWGr GRid
'Amgard Delicate' (D)	CWGr SGbt
'Amgard Rosie' (D)	CWGr
'Amira' (Ba)	CWGr GRid
'Amorangi Joy' (C)	CWGr
'Amy Cave' (Ba)	GRid NHal
'Amy Madison' (S-c) **new**	CWGr
'Anchorite' (D)	CWGr
'Andrea Clark' (D)	GRid NHal
'Andrea Lawson' (Ba)	GRid NHal
'Andrew Lockwood' (Pom)	CWGr
'Andrew Mitchell' (S-c)	CWGr GRid NHal
'Andries' Amber' (S-c)	CWGr
'Andries' Orange' (C)	ECtt
'Andries' Orange As' (S-c)	CWGr
'Andy Murray' (Sin)	CWGr
'Angora' (Fim)	SGbt
'Anita Summerhayes' (Misc)	CWGr
'Ann Breckenfelder' (Col) ♀H3	CWGr ECtt ERCP EUJe GRid NHal NJRG
'Anna Lindh' (WL)	GRid
'Annika' (Sin)	LCro LOPS SDeJ
'Anniversary Ball' (Ba)	CWGr
'Another Pet'	see *D.* 'Mystic Enchantment'
'Antique'^{PBR} (Sin)	LRHS
'Apache' (Fim)	CWGr ERCP SDeJ SGbt SPer
'Apache Blauw' (Fim)	ERCP
'Apopa Sky' (Sin) **new**	NJRG
'Apple Blossom' (C)	SGbt
I 'Appleblossom' (Col)	CWGr
'Apricot Honeymoon Dress' (D)	CWGr
I 'Apricot Parfait' (Fim)	CWGr
'April Dawn' (D)	CWGr
'April Heather' (Col) ♀H3	NHal
'Arabian Night' (D)	CAby CAvo CBcs CWCL CWGr ECtt EHrv ELan EPfP ERCP IRob LAyl LCro LOPS LRHS LSRN LSun MHol NLar SDeJ SEND SGbt WCot WSpi
'Arc de Triomphe' (D)	CWGr
'Arlequin' (D)	SGbt
'Arnhem' (D)	CWGr
'Arthur Godfrey' (D)	CWGr
'Arthur Hankin' (D)	CWGr
'Arthur's Delight' (D)	CWGr
'Asahi Chohje' (Anem) ♀H3	CWGr
'Askwith Joan' (D)	NHal
'Askwith Minnie' (D)	NHal
'Atilla' (D)	CWGr
I 'Atlanta' (D)	CWGr SGbt
atropurpurea	CWGr
'Audacity' (D)	CWGr LAyl SGbt
'Aurora's Kiss' (Ba)	CWGr ERCP NHal SGbt
I 'Aurore' (C) **new**	CWGr
'Aurwen's Violet' (Pom)	CWGr NHal
australis	CFil CSpe CWGr EBee
- B&SWJ 10389	WCru
australis* × *tenuicaulis **new**	CFil
I 'Autumn Fairy' (S-c)	ERCP SDeJ
'Autumn Lustre' (WL)	CWGr
'Avignon' (D)	SDeJ
'Avoca Amanda' (D)	NHal

	'Avoca Comanche' (S-c)	GRid NHal
	'Avoca Salmon' (D)	GRid NHal
	'Avon Snowflake' (C)	NJRG
	'Awaikoe' (Col)	CWGr
	'B.J. Beauty' (D)	GRid NHal NJRG
	'Babette' (S-c)	GRid
	'Baby Fonteneau' (S-c)	CWGr
	'Babylon' (D)	LRHS SGbt
§	'Babylon Brons' (D)	ERCP LRHS SDir SGbt
	'Babylon Bronze'	see *D.* 'Babylon Brons'
	'Babylon Lila' (D)	SGbt
§	'Babylon Paars' (D)	ECtt LRHS SDeJ SGbt
	'Babylon Purple'	see *D.* 'Babylon Paars'
	'Babylon Rose' (D)	LRHS SGbt
	'Bacardi' (D)	CRav ERCP
	'Badger Twinkle' (S-c)	GRid
	'Bahama Lemon'	see *D.* 'Lemon Cane'
	'Balham' (Sin)	WCot
	'Ballego's Glory' (D)	CWGr SGbt
	'Bambino' (Lil)	CWGr
	'Banker' (C)	CWGr
	'Bantling' (Ba)	CWGr ERCP SDir SGbt
	'Barbara Schell' (D)	CWGr
	'Barbara's Pastelle' (S-c)	CWGr NJRG SGbt
	'Barbara's Yellow' (S-c) **new**	NJRG
	'Barbarossa' (D)	CWGr
	'Barbarry Ball' (Ba)	CWGr
	'Barbarry Banker' (D)	CWGr LAyl
	'Barbarry Bluebird' (D)	SGbt
	'Barbarry Cadet' (D)	CWGr
	'Barbarry Carousel' (Ba)	CWGr
	'Barbarry Civic' (D) **new**	GRid
	'Barbarry Cosmos' (D)	CWGr
	'Barbarry Dominion' (D)	CWGr
	'Barbarry Drifter' (D)	CWGr
	'Barbarry Flag' (D)	CWGr
	'Barbarry Gem' (Ba)	CWGr
	'Barbarry Maverick' (D)	GRid
	'Barbarry Melody' (D)	NHal
	'Barbarry Monitor' (Ba)	CWGr SGbt
	'Barbarry Olympic' (Ba)	CWGr
	'Barbarry Oracle' (D)	CWGr
	'Barbarry Pinky' (D)	CWGr
	'Barbarry Pip' (D)	NHal
	'Barbarry Red Devil' (Dec) **new**	GRid
	'Barbarry Sultan' (D)	NHal
	'Barbarry Sunbeam' (D)	NHal
	'Barbarry Token' (D)	GRid
	'Barbarry Triumph' (D)	CWGr
	'Barbarry Vintage' (D) **new**	GRid
	'Barbette' (D)	CWGr
	'Bareham's Beauty' (D)	CWGr
	'Baret Joy' (S-c)	CWGr GRid NHal
	'Bargaly Blush' (D)	GRid NHal
	'Baron Ray' (D)	CWGr
	'Barry Williams' (D)	CWGr SGbt
	'Bart' (D)	CWGr
	'Barton Memory' (S-c)	GRid
	'Bassingbourne Beauty' (D)	CWGr
	'Bayou'PBR (Anem)	CRav CWGr ERCP LAyl LCro LOPS NHal NJRG SGbt SPer
	'Bedford Sally' (D)	CWGr
	'Bednall Beauty' (Misc/DwB) ♀H3	CHll CRos CSpe CWGr ECtt EHrv ELan EUJe EWes LRHS NJRG WHoo WSpi
	'Bell Boy' (Ba)	SGbt
	'Belle Epoque' (C)	CWGr
	'Ben Huston' (D)	GRid
	'Bengale' (D) **new**	CWGr
	'Berger's Rekord' (S-c)	CWGr
	'Berliner Orange' (D)	ERCP
	'Berner Oberland' (D) **new**	CRav
	'Bernice Sunset' (S-c)	CWGr
	'Berolina' (D)	CWGr
	'Berwick Banker' (Ba)	CWGr
	'Berwick Wood' (D)	CWGr GRid NHal SGbt
	'Bess Painter' (D)	CWGr
	'Best Bett'	see *D.* MYSTIC SPIRIT
	'Beth's Chaplet' (Sin)	WCot
	'Betty Ann' (Pom)	CWGr
	'Biddenham Fairy' (D)	CWGr
	'Biddenham Strawberry' (D)	CWGr SGbt
	'Biddenham Sunset' (S-c)	CWGr
	'Big Orange' (D)	CWGr
	'Bilbao'PBR (Jumbo Collection) (D)	SDeJ
	'Bill Holmberg' (D)	CWGr GRid SGbt
	'Bingo' (D)	SGbt
	'Bishop of Auckland'PBR (Misc)	CAby CAvo CRav CRos CWGN CWGr ECtt EPfP ERCP LAma LCro LOPS LRHS MGos NJRG NRHS SDeJ SDir SGbt WCot
	'Bishop of Cambridge' (Sin)	SDir
	'Bishop of Canterbury'PBR (P)	CRav CRos CWGr ECtt ELan EPfP LAma LCro LOPS LRHS MGos NHal NRHS SDeJ SDir SGbt SPer SPoG
	'Bishop of Dover' (Sin)	CRav CWGr EPfP LAma LCro LOPS LRHS SDeJ SDir SGbt WBrk
	'Bishop of Lancaster' (Misc)	CWGr IRob LAma LCro LOPS NLar SDir
	'Bishop of Leicester' (Misc)	CRav CWGr ECtt ELan EPfP LAma LCro LOPS LRHS NLar NRHS SDeJ SDir SGbt SHar SPer
	'Bishop of Llandaff' (P) ♀H3	Widely available
	'Bishop of Oxford' (Misc)	CAby CBod CRos CWGr ELan EPfP ERCP IRob LAma LCro LOPS LRHS MGos NJRG NRHS SDeJ SDir SGbt SPoG
	'Bishop of York' (Misc)	CAby CAvo CBod CRos CWGr ECtt ELan EPfP IRob LAma LAyl LCro LOPS LRHS MGos NGdn NRHS SDeJ SDir SGbt SPer SPoG
	'Bishop Peter Price' (Sin)	CWGr
	'Bista' (Ba) **new**	GRid
	'Black Fire' (D)	CWGr ECtt
	'Black Jack' (D)	EBee ERCP NHal NJRG
	'Black Monarch' (D)	CWGr NHal SGbt
	'Black Narcissus' (C)	CWGr SGbt
I	'Black R Jack'	NJRG
	'Black Spider' (S-c)	CWGr
	'Black Star' (Sin)	EPfP
	'Black Touch' (Fim)	CWGr ERCP
	'Blackberry Ripple' (S-c)	CWGr
	'Blaisdon Red' (D)	CWGr
	'Blanc y Verde' (D) **new**	CRav
	'Blaze' (D)	CWGr
	'Blithe Spirit' (D)	CWGr
	'Bloemfontein' (D)	CWGr
	'Bloodstone' (D)	CWGr SGbt
	'Bloody Mary' (D) **new**	ERCP
	'Bloom's Graham' (S-c)	CWGr
	'Bloom's Kenn' (D)	CWGr SGbt
	'Blue Beard' (S-c)	CWGr
	'Blue Bell' (D)	ERCP SPer
	'Blue Boy' (D)	CWGr ERCP LCro LOPS
	'Blue Record' (S-c/DwB)	ERCP
	'Blue Wish' (WL)	ERCP GRid LCro LOPS NJRG SDir

	Name	Suppliers
	‘Blyton Everest’ (D) **new**	NHal
	‘Blyton Golden Girl’ (D)	GRid NHal
	‘Blyton Lady in Red’ (D)	GRid LAyl NHal NJRG
	‘Blyton Romance’ (D)	NHal
	‘Blyton Royal Velvet’ (D) **new**	GRid
	‘Blyton Softer Gleam’ (D) 🏆H3	CWGr GRid NHal NJRG SGbt
	‘Blyton Valentine’ (D) **new**	NHal
	‘Bob’s Bonaventure’ (D)	CWGr GRid NHal
	‘Bokay’ (WL)	CWGr
	‘Bonesta’ (D)	CWGr
	‘Bonny Blue’ (Ba)	CWGr
	‘Boogie Woogie’ (Anem)	CWGr SDeJ
	‘Boom Boom Red’ (Ba)	SPer
	‘Boom Boom White’ (Ba)	CRav ERCP
	‘Boom Boom Yellow’ (Ba)	ERCP SDeJ
	‘Bora Bora’ (S-c)	CWGr
	‘Border Princess’ (C/DwB)	CWGr SGbt
	‘Boy Scout’ (Ba)	CWGr
	‘Bracken Lorelei’ (WL)	NJRG
	‘Brackenridge Ballerina’ (WL)	CWGr GRid NHal NJRG SGbt
	‘Brandaris’ (S-c)	CWGr SGbt
	‘Brandon James’ (D)	SDeJ
	‘Brandysnap’ (D)	CWGr SGbt
	‘Brantwood’ (Sin)	CWGr
	‘Brasilia’ (D) **new**	CWGr
	BRAVEHEART (‘Vdtg67’PBR) (Dark Angel Series) (Sin)	LCro LOPS SDeJ
	‘Brian’s Dream’ (D)	LAyl NHal
	‘Bride’s Bouquet’ (Col)	ERCP LRHS
	‘Bridge View Aloha’ (S-c) 🏆H3	CWGr SGbt
	‘Bright Diamond’ (D) **new**	SDeJ
	‘Bright Eyes’ (Sin)	CRav ERCP
	‘Brindisii’ (Anem) **new**	SDeJ
	‘Bristol Petite’ (D)	CWGr
	‘Brookfield Delight’ (Sin/Lil) 🏆H3	CWGr
	‘Brookfield Rachel’ (Ba)	CWGr
	‘Brookfield Rene’ (D)	CWGr
	‘Brookfield Snowball’ (Ba)	CWGr
	‘Brookfield Sweetie’ (Misc/DwB)	CWGr
	‘Brookside Cheri’ (C)	CWGr
	‘Brookside Snowball’ (Ba)	CWGr
	‘Bryce B. Morrison’ (D)	CWGr
	‘Bryn Terfel’ (D)	CWGr GRid GWyn NHal SGbt
	‘Bull’s Pride’ (D)	CWGr
	‘Bunty Wright’ (Col) **new**	NJRG
	‘Burlesca’ (Ba) **new**	ERCP
	‘Butch’ (D)	CWGr
	‘Butterball’ (D/DwB)	SDeJ
*	‘Buttercup’ (Pom)	CWGr
	‘By George’ (D)	CWGr
	‘Caballero’ (WL)	CWGr GRid
	‘Café au Lait’ (D)	CAby CWGr ELan EPfP ERCP LCro LOPS LRHS NHal SDeJ SGbt SPer WHar WSpi
	‘Calgary’ (D)	CWGr
	‘California Sunset’ (Misc) **new**	CAby
	‘Calin’ (WL) **new**	CWGr
	‘Camano Ariel’ (C)	CWGr
	‘Camano Choice’ (D)	CWGr
	‘Camano Passion’ (S-c)	CWGr
	‘Camano Poppet’ (Ba)	CWGr
	‘Camano Regal’ (S-c)	CWGr
I	‘Cameo’ (WL)	LAyl NHal NJRG SGbt
	campanulata	CFil CWGr
	‘Campos Hush’ (S-c)	CWGr
	‘Campos Philip M’ (D)	CWGr
	‘Canary Fubuki’ (Fim)	CWGr ERCP SDeJ SGbt SPer
	‘Cancun’ (D) **new**	CRos NRHS
I	‘Candlelight’ (D)	GRid
	‘Candy Cane’ (Ba)	CWGr
	‘Candy Cupid’ (Ba)	CWGr
	CANDY EYES	see *D.* ‘Zone Ten’
	‘Candy Hamilton Lilian’ (D)	CWGr
	‘Candy Keene’ (S-c)	CWGr GRid NHal
	‘Caprice’ (D) **new**	CWGr
	‘Capulet’ (Ba)	CWGr
	‘Careless’ (D)	CWGr
	‘Caribbean Fantasy’ (D)	CWGr
	‘Carole Chamberlain’ (Col) **new**	NJRG
	‘Carolina Moon’ (D)	CWGr GRid GWyn NHal SGbt
	‘Carol’s Spanish Dancer’ (C)	LAyl NHal NJRG
	‘Carstone Firebox’ (Col)	LAyl
	‘Carstone Ruby’ (D)	NHal
	‘Carstone Sunbeam’ (D)	CWGr
	‘Carstone Suntan’ (C)	CWGr GRid
	‘Carstone Valiant’ (Ba)	NHal
	‘Cartouche’ (D) **new**	CWGr ERCP
	‘Catherine Deneuve’ (Misc)	CWGN CWGr NJRG SGbt
	‘Catherine Ireland’ (D)	CWGr
	‘Cerise Prefect’ (S-c)	CWGr
	‘Cha Cha’ (S-c)	CWGr SGbt
	‘Challenger’ (D)	GWyn
	‘Chanson d’Amour’ (D)	CWGr
	‘Charles de Coster’ (D)	CWGr
	‘Charles Dickens’ (Ba)	CWGr
	‘Charlie Briggs’ (Ba)	NHal
	‘Charlie Dimmock’ (WL) 🏆H3	CWGr GRid MSmi NHal NJRG SGbt
	‘Charlie Two’ (D)	CWGr GRid NHal
I	‘Charlotte’ (Sin) **new**	CWGr
	‘Charlotte Bateson’ (Ba)	CWGr
	‘Chat Noir’ (S-c) 🏆H3	CRav CWGr ERCP IRob LAyl LCro LOPS LRHS SGbt
	‘Chee’ (WL)	CWGr
	‘Cheerio’ (S-c)	ECtt LRHS NRHS
	‘Cherokee Beauty’ (D)	CWGr
	‘Cherry Wine’ (D)	CWGr
	‘Cherrywood Millfield’ (S-c)	CWGr
	‘Cherrywood Turnpike’ (D)	CWGr
	‘Cherrywood Wilderness’ (D)	CWGr
	‘Cherubino’ (Col)	CWGr
	‘Cherwell Goldcrest’ (S-c)	CWGr GRid NHal SGbt
	‘Cherwell Lapwing’ (S-c)	GRid
	‘Cherwell Linnet’ (Ba) **new**	GRid
	‘Cherwell Skylark’ (S-c)	GRid NHal
	‘Cherwell Waxwing’ (D) **new**	GRid
	‘Chessy’ (Sin/Lil) 🏆H3	CWGr
	‘Chic Red’ (Misc) **new**	NRHS
	‘Chilson’s Pride’ (D)	CWGr SGbt
	‘Chiltern Amber’ (D)	CWGr
	‘Chiltern Sylvia’ (S-c)	CWGr
	‘Chimacum Topaz’ (S-c)	CWGr GRid
	‘Chimborazo’ (Col)	CWGr EUJe LAyl SGbt
	‘Chinese Lantern’ (D)	CWGr
	‘Chloe’s Keene’ (S-c)	CWGr
	‘Chorus Girl’ (D)	CWGr
	‘Christine’ (D)	CWGr
I	‘Christine’ (WL)	SGbt
	‘Christmas Carol’ (Col)	CWGr ECtt GRid GWyn NHal NJRG
	‘Christopher Nickerson’ (S-c)	CWGr SGbt
	‘Christopher Taylor’ (WL)	NHal SGbt SHar

	'City of Leiden' (S-c)	CRav LCro LOPS NHal
	'Clair de Lune' (Col) ♀H3	CWCL CWGr ECtt ERCP GRid LRHS MCot NHal NJRG SGbt WCot WSpi
	'Claire Diane' (D)	CWGr
	'Clara May' (Fim)	CWGr
	'Clarion' (S-c)	CRos LRHS NRHS
I	'Clarion' (Sin)	CWGr
	'Classic A.1' (C)	CWGr
	'Classic Poème'PBR (Misc)	ERCP
	'Classic Rosamunde'PBR (Misc)	CRav ERCP NHal
	'Classic Summertime' (Misc)	CWGr
§	'Classic Swanlake'PBR (Misc)	CRav CWGr EPfP ERCP LCro LOPS LRHS NJRG
	'Claudette' (D)	MHol
	'Clayt's Candy' (S-c)	GRid NHal
	'Clearview Arlene' (S-c) **new**	GRid
	'Clearview Edie' (DblO) **new**	GRid NHal
	'Clearview Irene' (S-c)	GRid NHal
	'Clearview Louise' (S-c)	NHal
	'Clearview Sundance' (C)	GRid NHal
	'Cleo Laine' (S-c) **new**	CWGr NHal
	'Cloverdale' (D)	CWGr
	coccinea	CExl CFil CRos CSpe CWGr EBee MCot SGbt SMHy WPGP
	- NJM 05.072	WPGP
	- hybrids	NSti
	- orange-flowered	CFil CWGr
	- var. ***palmeri***	CAvo CFil WPGP XEll
	- yellow-flowered	CFil CWGr
	'Cocktail' (S-c)	CWGr
	'Colac' (D)	CWGr
	'Color Spectacle' (S-c)	CWGr LRHS
	'Colour Magic' (S-c)	CWGr
	'Coltness Gem' (Sin/DwB)	CWGr
	'Comet' (Anem)	CWGr
	'Como Polly' (D)	CWGr
	'Con Amore' (D) **new**	CRav
	'Contessa' (D)	CWGr SDeJ
	'Coral Jupiter' (S-c)	CWGr GRid
	'Coral Strand' (D)	CWGr
	'Cornel' (Ba)	CWGr ERCP NHal NJRG SGbt
	'Cornel Brons' (Ba)	ERCP
	'Cornell' (D) **new**	GRid
	'Cornish Minx' (Pom)	CWGr
	'Cornish Ruby' (Sin)	EPfP
I	'Corona' (S-c/DwB)	SDeJ
	'Coronella' (D)	CWGr SGbt
	'Cortez Silver' (D)	CWGr
	'Cortez Sovereign' (S-c)	CWGr
	'Corton Bess' (D)	CWGr
	'Corton Olympic' (D)	CWGr GRid
	'Corydon' (D)	CWGr
	'Cottontail' (Col)	CWGr
	'Country Boy' (S-c)	CWGr GRid
	'Coupe de Soleil' (D)	CWGr LCro LOPS
	'Craigowan' (S-c)	GRid NHal
	'Crazy Legs' (DblO)	CWGr SGbt
	'Crazy Love' (D)	LCro LOPS
	'Cream Alva's' (D) ♀H3	CWGr GRid
I	'Cream Beauty' (WL)	CWGr
	'Cream Capella' (D) **new**	GRid
	'Cream Klankstad' (C)	CWGr
	'Cream Linda' (D)	CWGr
	'Cream Moonlight' (S-c)	CWGr GRid NJRG SGbt
	'Cream Reliance' (D)	CWGr
	'Crème de Cassis' (D)	CWGr ERCP LCro LOPS
	'Crève Coeur' (D)	CWGr GRid
	'Crichton Cherry' (D)	CWGr
	'Crichton Honey' (Ba)	CWGr
	'Croesus' (S-c)	CWGr
	'Crossfield Allegro' (S-c)	CWGr
	'Crossfield Anne' (D)	CWGr
	'Crossfield Festival' (D)	CWGr GRid
	'Croydon Ace' (D)	CWGr
	'Croydon Jumbo' (D)	CWGr
	'Croydon Snotop' (D)	CWGr
	'Croydon Superior' (D)	SGbt
	'Cryfield Harmony' (Ba)	CWGr
	'Cryfield Jane' (Ba)	CWGr
	'Cryfield Keene' (S-c)	CWGr
	'Cryfield Max' (C)	CWGr
	'Cryfield Rosie' (Ba)	CWGr
	'Culdrose' (D)	SGbt
	'Cupidor' (Sin) **new**	NJRG
	'Curate' (Misc)	CWGr
	'Curiosity' (Col)	GRid NJRG
	'Currant Cream' (Ba)	CWGr SGbt
	cuspidata	CFil EBee
	'Cyclone' (D)	CWGr
	'Cycloop' (S-c)	CWGr
	'Cynthia Chalwin' (Ba)	CWGr
	'Cynthia Louise' (D)	CWGr
	'Czar Willo' (Pom)	CWGr
	'Czardas' (C)	GCal
	DAHLIETTA JENNY	see *D.* 'Jenny'
	'Daily Mail' (D)	CWGr
	'Daisy Duke' (D)	ERCP
	DALAYA SHIVA ('Kledh13033')	NPri
	DALAYA YOGI ('Kledh11031'PBR)	NPri
	'Daleko Gold' (D)	CWGr
	'Daleko Jupiter' (S-c)	CWGr GRid NHal
	'Daleko National' (D)	CWGr
	'Daleko Tangerine' (D)	CWGr
	'Dame Deidre' (S-c)	CWGr
	'Dana Audrey' (C)	CWGr
	'Dana Dream' (S-c)	CWGr
	'Dana Iris' (S-c)	CWGr
	'Dana Sunset' (C)	CWGr
	'Dancing Queen' (S-c)	CWGr
I	'Dandy' (Col)	SVic
	'Danjo Doc' (D)	CWGr SGbt
	'Dannevirke' (Sin)	CWGr
	'Danum Belle' (D)	CWGr
	'Danum Fancy' (D)	CWGr
	'Danum Gail' (D)	CWGr GRid
	'Danum Hero' (D)	CWGr
	'Danum Meteor' (S-c)	CWGr
	'Danum Rebel' (S-c)	CWGr
	'Danum Rhoda' (D)	CWGr
	'Danum Salmon' (S-c)	CWGr
	'Danum Torch' (Col)	CWGr ECtt SGbt
	'Dark Butterfly' (D) **new**	CRav LCro LOPS
	'Dark Desire' (Sin/DwB)	CBod CRav CWGr
	'Dark Fubuki' (Fim)	ERCP
§	'Dark Side Of The Sun'PBR (Sin)	CRos LRHS NRHS SPoG
	'Dark Spirit' (D)	CSpe ECtt SDeJ SGbt
	'Dark Stranger' (C)	CWGr
	'Darkarin' (Misc)	CBod CRav
	'Darlington Diamond' (S-c)	CWGr
	'Darlington Jubilation' (S-c)	CWGr
	'Davenport Anita' (D)	CWGr
	'Davenport Honey' (D)	CWGr GRid
	'Davenport Lesley' (D)	CWGr

'Davenport Sunlight' (S-c)	CWGr
'Dave's Choice' (Ba)	GRid NJRG
'Dave's Snip' (D)	CWGr
'David Digweed' (D)	CWGr NHal SGbt
'David Howard' (D) ♀H3	CAby CRos CWGr ECtt EHrv ELan EPfP ERCP EUJe LAyl LCro LOPS LRHS NHal NJRG NRHS SGbt SPer SWvt WBrk WCot WFar WGwG WSpi
'David Wright' (S-c) **new**	CWGr
'David's Choice' (D)	CWGr
'Dawn Chorus' (D)	CWGr
'Dawn Sky' (D)	LAyl
'Dazzler' (D/DwB)	CWGr
'Deborah's Kiwi' (C)	CWGr GRid NHal SGbt
'Debra Anne Craven' (S-c)	CWGr GRid NHal
'Decorette' (D/DwB)	CWGr SGbt
'Deepest Yellow' (Ba)	CWGr SDeJ SGbt
'De-la-Haye' (S-c)	NHal
'Demi Schneider' (Col)	CWGr
'Dentelle de Venise' (C)	CWGr
'Deuil du Roi Albert' (D)	CWGr
'Deutschland' (D)	CWGr
'Devon Elegance' (S-c)	CWGr
'Devon Joy' (D)	CWGr
'Devon Temptation' (C)	CRos CWGr NRHS
'Diamond Rose' (Anem/DwB)	CWGr
'Diamond Wedding' (D)	SGbt
'Diamond Years' (D)	SGbt
'Diana Gregory' (Pom)	CWGr SGbt
'Diana's Memory' (D)	LCro LOPS
'Dick Westfall' (S-c)	CWGr
'Dikara Jodie' (D)	NHal
'Dikara Kent' (Ba) ♀H3	GRid
'Dikara Moon' (D)	NHal
'Dikara Superb' (D)	CWGr GRid NHal
'Dilys Ayling' (Col)	NHal
'Dinah Shore' (S-c)	CWGr
I 'Disneyland' (Col)	SGbt
dissecta	CExl CFil CWGr EBee
'Diva US' (D)	ERCP SDeJ
'Doc van Horn' (S-c)	CWGr
'Doktor Hans Ricken' (D)	CWGr
'Don Hill' (Col) ♀H3	GRid NJRG
'Doris Bacon' (Ba)	CWGr
'Doris Day' (C)	CWGr NHal SGbt
'Doris Knight' (C)	LSvl
'Doris Rollins' (C)	CWGr
'Dorothy Rose' (D)	NHal
'Dottie D.' (Ba)	CWGr
'Double Dream Fantasy' (Dreamy Series) (Misc)	CRos EPfP LRHS NRHS
'Dovegrove' (Sin) ♀H3	CWGr
'Downham Royal' (Ba)	CRav CWGr ERCP LCro LOPS
'Dr Caroline Rabbit' (D)	CWGr SGbt
DRACULA ('Vdtg17'PBR) (Dark Angel Series) (Sin)	ERCP
DRAGON BALL ('Vdtg31'PBR) (Dark Angel Series) (Sin)	SDeJ
(Dreamy Series) DREAMY BLUSH WHITE (Misc) **new**	CRos NRHS
- DREAMY EYES (Misc)	NLar
- DREAMY FANTASY (Misc)	CRos CWGr ELan LRHS NRHS
- DREAMY FUSION (Sin)	CRos CWGr LRHS NRHS
- DREAMY INSPIRE (Misc)	CRos LRHS NLar NRHS
- DREAMY KISS (P)	CRos CWGr LRHS NLar NRHS
- DREAMY LIPS (P)	CRos LRHS NLar NRHS
- DREAMY MOONLIGHT (Sin)	CRos LRHS NRHS
- DREAMY NIGHTS (Misc)	CRos LRHS NRHS
- DREAMY PASSION (Sin)	CRos LRHS NRHS
'Drummer Boy' (D)	CWGr GRid
'Duddon Grace' (WL)	NHal
'Duet' (D)	CWGr ELan SGbt
'Dusky Harmony' (WL)	SGbt
'Dutch Boy' (D)	CWGr
'Dutch Explosion' (S-c)	ELan
'Earl Haig' (D)	CWGr
'Earl Marc' (C)	CWGr
'Early Bird' (D)	CWGr
'Early Harvest' (D)	SGbt
'Easter Sunday' (Col)	CWGr
'Eastwood Moonlight' (S-c)	CWGr GRid NHal SGbt
'Eastwood Star' (S-c)	CWGr
'Ebbw Vale Festival' (D)	CWGr
'Edge of Gold' (D)	CWGr
'Edge of Joy' (D)	CRav EPfP LCro LOPS
'Edgeway Joyce' (Ba)	CWGr GRid
'Edinburgh' (D)	CWGr ERCP GRid GWyn NHal SDeJ SDir SGbt
'Edith Jones' (Col)	CWGr NJRG
'Edith Mueller' (Pom)	CWGr
'Edmund' (Sin)	WCot
'Edna C' (D)	CWGr
'Edwin's Sunset' (WL) ♀H3	GRid NHal
'Eileen Denny' (S-c)	CWGr GRid
'El Cid' (D)	CWGr
'El Paso' (D)	CWGr SDeJ
'Elaine Beedle' (D) **new**	CWGr
'Eldon Wilson' (Misc)	CWGr
'Elga-Bergerhoff' (C)	ERCP LRHS
'Elgico Leanne' (C)	CWGr SGbt
'Elizabeth Snowden' (Col)	GRid
'Ella Britton' (D)	LRHS NRHS
'Ellen Huston' (Misc/DwB) ♀H3	CWGr ECtt ERCP GRid NHal SGbt
'Elma E' (D)	CWGr ERCP GRid NHal
'Elmbrook Chieftain' (D)	CWGr
'Elmbrook Rebel' (S-c)	CWGr GRid
'Elmdon Superb' (Ba) **new**	GRid
'Elsie Merina' (D) **new**	CWGr
I 'Embrace' (C)	NHal NJRG
'Emma's Coronet' (D)	CWGr GRid
'Emmaus' (Fim) **new**	CWGr
'Emmie Lou' (D)	CWGr
'Emory Paul' (D)	CWGr ERCP
'Emperor' (D)	CWGr
I 'Encore' (Fim)	CWGr ERCP
'Engadin' (D)	CWGr
'Engelhardt's Matador' (D)	ECtt ERCP EUJe LRHS MCot MHol MJak NJRG SGbt WCot
'Enid Adams' (D)	CWGr
'Epping Forest' (D)	CWGr
'Eric's Choice' (D)	CWGr
'Esau' (D)	CWGr
'Essex Chronicle' (D)	CWGr
'Esther' (Col) **new**	SDeJ
'Esther Chamberlain' (Col) **new**	NJRG
'Etheral' (Sin)	CWGr
'Eunice Arrigo' (S-c)	CWGr
I 'Eurydice' (Fim) **new**	CWGr
'Eveline' (D)	CAby CWGr ERCP LCro LOPS SDeJ SGbt
'Evelyn Foster' (D)	CWGr GRid
'Evelyn Rumbold' (D)	CWGr SGbt
'Evelyn Taylor' (S-c)	NJRG
'Evening Lady' (D)	CWGr
'Evening Mail' (S-c) **new**	GRid

I	'Evita' (Anem)	NJRG
	excelsa (B)	CHll NJRG
	- B&SWJ 10238	WCru
	- 'Penelope Sky' (Sin)	WCru
	'Excentrique' (Misc)	CWGr ERCP NJRG
	'Exotic Dwarf' (Sin/Lil) ♀H3	NJRG
	'Explosion' (S-c)	CWGr SDir
	'Extase' (S-c)	CRos CWGr NRHS
	'Eye Candy' (Sin)	LRHS NJRG NRHS
	'Eyed Beauty' (Anem)	EPfP
	'Fabula' (Col)	CWGr
	'Fairfield Frost' (Col)	NHal
	'Fairway Pilot' (D)	CWGr NHal
	'Fairway Spur' (D)	CWGr GRid NHal
	'Fairy Queen' (C)	CWGr SGbt
§	'Famoso' (Col)	ERCP
	'Fantastico' (Col)	CWGr ERCP
	'Fascination' (P) ♀H3	CAby CBcs CBod CRos CWGr ECtt ERCP LAyl LPmr LRHS LSRN MCot MSCN NJRG NLar NRHS SDeJ SDir SGbt WHoo WSpi
	'Fascination Aus' (Col)	CWGr
	'Fashion Monger' (Col)	CWGr ECtt EHrv ERCP GRid NHal NJRG SGbt
	'Fata Morgana' (Anem)	CWGr NJRG SGbt
	'Fay Dyer' (Col)	NJRG
	'Fern Irene' (WL)	CWGr
	'Fern Ridge Painted Lady' (D) **new**	GRid
	'Ferncliff Illusion' (D)	CWGr ERCP SGbt
	'Ferncliff Inspiration' (S-c)	ERCP
	'Fernhill Champion' (D)	CWGr
	'Festivo' (Col)	CWGr
	'Feu Céleste' (Col)	CWGr
	'Fidalgo Blacky' (D)	CWGr
	'Fidalgo Bounce' (D)	CWGr
	'Fidalgo Climax' (Fim)	CWGr
	'Fidalgo Magic' (D)	CWGr
	'Fidalgo Snowman' (S-c)	CWGr
	'Fidalgo Splash' (D)	CWGr
	'Fidalgo Supreme' (D)	CWGr GRid LAyl
I	'Fiesta' (Pom)	SDeJ
	Figaro Series (Misc/DwB)	NPri
	'Figurine' (WL) ♀H3	GRid NJRG SHar
	'Fille du Diable' (S-c)	CWGr SGbt
	'Finchcocks' (WL) ♀H3	CWGr LAyl
	'Fiona Stewart' (Ba)	CWGr GRid
	'Fire and Ice' (Misc)	CWGr SDeJ
	'Fire Magic' (S-c)	CWGr
	'Fire Mountain' (D)	GRid LAyl NHal NJRG
	'Firebird' (Sin)	CWGr
	'Firebird' (S-c)	see *D.* 'Vuurvogel'
	'Firebrand' ambig. (S-c)	CWGr SGbt
	'Firepot' ambig. (WL)	ERCP SGbt
	'First Lady' (D)	CWGr
	'Flavien' (D)	ERCP
	'Fleur'	see *D.* 'Fleurel'
	'Fleur Mountjoy' (Col)	CWGr
§	'Fleurel' PBR (Fim)	ERCP SDeJ
	'Floorinoor' (Anem)	ERCP GWyn LCro LOPS SGbt
	'Florence Vernon' (Ba)	CWGr
	'Flutterby' (WL)	CWGr
	foeniculifolia	CFil
	'Fontmell Kaz' (Col)	NJRG SGbt
	'Formby Art' (D)	LAyl NHal
	'Formby Perfection' (D)	GRid
	'Formby Supreme' (D)	CWGr SGbt
	'Forrestal' (S-c)	CWGr
	'Fortuna' (Col/DwB)	CWGr ERCP
	'Frank Holmes' (Pom)	CWGr GRid NHal
	'Frank Hornsey' (D)	CWGr
	'Frank Lovell' (S-c)	CWGr
	'Franz Kafka' (Pom)	CAvo CWGr ERCP GRid NHal NJRG SDeJ
	'Fred Wallace' (C)	CWGr
	'Freelancer' (C)	CWGr SGbt
	'Freestyle' (C)	CWGr GRid NJRG
§	'Freya's Paso Doble' (Anem) ♀H3	CWGr GRid LAyl NJRG SGbt
	'Freya's Thalia' (Sin/Lil)	CWGr
	'Friendship' (C)	CWGr
	'Frigoulet' (C)	CWGr ERCP SGbt
	'Fripon' (C) **new**	CWGr
	'Funfair' (D)	CWGr
	'Funny Face' (Misc)	CWGr
	'Furka' (C) **new**	CRav
	'Furswood Park' (Pom)	NJRG
	'Fusion' (D) ♀H3	CWGr SGbt SHar WCot
	'G.F. Hemerik' (Sin)	CWGr
	'G.I. Joe' (D)	SGbt
	'Gala Parade' (D)	CWGr
	'Gale Lane' (Pom)	CWGr GRid
	(Gallery Series) 'Gallery Art Deco' PBR (D) ♀H3	CRos CWGr ERCP LRHS NHal NRHS SGbt
	- 'Gallery Art Fair' PBR (D) ♀H3	CRos CWGr ERCP LCro LOPS LRHS NHal NRHS SDeJ
	- 'Gallery Art Nouveau' PBR (D) ♀H3	CRos CWGr ERCP LRHS NHal NRHS SDeJ
	- 'Gallery Bellini' PBR (D)	CRos LRHS NRHS SDeJ
	- 'Gallery Cézanne' PBR (D)	CRos CWGr LRHS NRHS SDeJ SGbt
	- 'Gallery Cobra' PBR (D)	ERCP
	- 'Gallery La Tour' PBR (D) ♀H3	SDeJ
	- 'Gallery Leonardo' PBR (D) ♀H3	CWGr LCro LOPS SDeJ
	- 'Gallery Matisse' PBR (D)	CRos LRHS NRHS
	- 'Gallery Pablo' PBR (D) ♀H3	CRos CWGr LRHS NRHS SGbt
	- 'Gallery Pinto' PBR (D)	CRos CWGr LRHS NRHS
	- 'Gallery Rembrandt' PBR (D) ♀H3	CWGr LCro LOPS
	- 'Gallery Renoir' PBR (D) ♀H3	CRos CWGr LRHS NRHS
	- 'Gallery Rivera' PBR (D)	CRos LRHS NRHS SDeJ
	- 'Gallery Salvador' PBR (D)	ERCP SGbt
	- 'Gallery Serenade' PBR (D)	ERCP
	- 'Gallery Singer' PBR (D)	CWGr SDeJ
	- 'Gallery Valentin' PBR (D)	CRos LRHS NRHS
	- 'Gallery Vermeer' PBR (D)	CWGr SGbt
	- 'Gallery Vincent' PBR (D) ♀H3	CWGr
	'Gardaia' (Anem) **new**	CWGr
	'Garden Festival' (WL)	CWGr ERCP GRid
	'Garden Miracle' (D) **new**	NJRG
	'Garden Party' (C) ♀H3	LAyl
	'Garden Princess' (C/DwB)	CWGr SDir SGbt
	'Garden Wonder' (D)	CWGr SDeJ
	'Gargantuan' (S-c)	CWGr
	'Gateshead Festival' (D) **new**	GRid
	GATESHEAD FESTIVAL	see *D.* 'Peach Melba'
	'Gay Mini' (D)	CWGr
	'Gay Princess' (WL)	CWGr
	'Gay Triumph' (S-c)	CWGr
	'Geerlings Babette' (Ba)	ERCP
	'Geerlings Beatrice' (Ba)	CWGr
	'Geerlings Cupido' (WL)	CWGr SGbt
	'Geerlings Indian Summer' (S-c)	CRav CWGr NHal
	'Geerlings Moonlight' (D)	CWGr

§ 'Geerlings Sorbet' (S-c) CAby NHal SGbt
'Geerlings Yellow' (S-c) CWGr
'Gelber Vulkan' (S-c) SGbt
'Gemma Darling' (D) CWGr GRid
'Gemma's Place' (Pom) CWGr
'Genova' (Ba) CAvo EPfP ERCP SDeJ SGbt
'Geoffrey Kent' (D) ♀H3 GRid
'Gerald Grace' (S-c) CWGr
'Gerlos' (D) CWGr
I 'Geronimo' (S-c) **new** CWGr
'Gerrie Hoek' (WL) CRav CWGr ERCP NJRG SDeJ SGbt WSpi
'Gill's Pastelle' (S-c) GRid
'Gilt Edge' (D) CWGr
'Gilwood Terry G' (C) GRid NHal
'Gina Lombaert' (S-c) CWGr SEND
'Ginger Willo' (Pom) CWGr
'Gipsy Boy' (D) CWGr LAyl
'Gipsy Night' (Ba) ERCP SDeJ
'Giraffe' (DblO) CAby CWGr ERCP SGbt
'Gitty' (Ba) CWGr
'Glad Huston' (S-c/DwB) CWGr
'Glen Afton' (Pom) CWGr GRid
'Glen Gharry' (Col) CWGr
'Glenbank Honeycomb' (Pom) GRid
'Glenbank Paleface' (Pom) CWGr
'Glenbank Twinkle' (C) CWGr
'Globular' (Ba) CWGr
'Glorie van Heemstede' (WL) ♀H3 CWGr ERCP LAyl LCro LOPS NHal NJRG SDeJ SGbt
'Glorie van Naardwijk' (D) CWGr
'Glorie van Noordwijk' (S-c) ERCP SDeJ SGbt
'Glow Orange' (Ba) CWGr
'Go American' (D) CWGr NHal
'Gold Crown' (S-c) SDeJ
'Goldean' (D) CWGr
I 'Golden Emblem' (D) CWGr ECtt SDeJ
'Golden Fizz' (Ba) CWGr
'Golden Glitter' (S-c) CWGr
'Golden Heart' (S-c) CWGr
'Golden Horn' (S-c) CWGr
'Golden Impact' (S-c) CWGr GRid
'Golden Scepter' (D) CWGr ERCP SDeJ SGbt
'Golden Symbol' (S-c) CWGr
'Golden Turban' (D) CWGr
'Goldfield' (D) CWGr
'Goldie Gull' (Anem) NJRG
'Goldorange' (S-c) CWGr
'Good Earth' (C) CWGr SDeJ
I 'Good Hope' (D) CWGr
'Good Intent' (Ba) CWGr
'Goshen Beauty' (WL) CWGr
'Goya's Venus' (S-c) CWGr
'Grace Kendall' (D) **new** GRid
'Grace Rushton' (WL) CWGr
'Gracie S' (C) CWGr NHal NJRG
'Gramma's Lemon Pie' (D) CWGr
'Grand Finale' (S-c) **new** SDeJ
'Grand Prix' (D) CWGr ERCP SDeJ SGbt
'Grand Willo' (Pom) CWGr
'Grenadier' (D) ♀H3 CWGr ECtt ERCP LRHS NJRG NLar SGbt WCot
'Grenidor Pastelle' (S-c) CWGr GRid NJRG
'Gretchen Heine' (D) CWGr
'Grock' (Pom) CWGr
'Gryson's Yellow Spider' (C) ERCP
'Gunyuu' (D) CWGr
'Gurtla Twilight' (Pom) CWGr GRid NHal NJRG
'Gute Laune' (C) CWGr
'Gwyneth' (WL) GRid NHal NJRG
'Gypsy Girl' (D) CWGr SGbt
'Hadrian's Sunlight' (Sin) NHal
'Hadrian's Sunset' (Sin) **new** NHal
'Hallmark' (Pom) CWGr GRid GWyn NJRG
'Hallwood Coppernob' (D) CWGr
'Hallwood Satin' (D) CWGr
'Hallwood Tiptop' (D) CWGr
'Hamari Accord' (S-c) ♀H3 CWGr GRid LAyl
'Hamari Bride' (S-c) ♀H3 CWGr
'Hamari Girl' (D) CWGr GRid NHal SGbt
'Hamari Gold' (D) ♀H3 CWGr GRid NHal SGbt
'Hamari Katrina' (S-c) CWGr
'Hamari Rosé' (Ba) ♀H3 CWGr GRid NHal SGbt SHar
'Hamari Sunshine' (D) NHal SGbt
'Hamilton Amanda' (D) CWGr
'Hamilton Lillian' (D) ♀H3 CWGr
'Hans Ricken' (D) CWGr
* 'Happy Birthday' (S-c) CWGr
'Happy Boy' (S-c) **new** GRid
'Happy Caroline' (D) CWGr
HAPPY DAYS CHERRY RED ('Hdchr23'PBR) (Sin) **new** CRos NRHS
HAPPY DAYS CREAM ('Hdw79'PBR) (Sin) CRos LRHS NRHS
HAPPY DAYS LEMON ('Hdle105'PBR) (Sin) **new** CRos ERCP NRHS
HAPPY DAYS PURPLE ('Hdpu165'PBR) (Sin) ♀H3 CRos ERCP LRHS NRHS
HAPPY DAYS RED (Sin) EPfP
'Happy Go Lucky' (D) **new** SDeJ
'Happy Halloween' (D) CRav CWGr
(Happy Single Series) CWGr ERCP LRHS SDeJ
HAPPY SINGLE DATE ('HS Date'PBR) (Sin)
- HAPPY SINGLE FIRST LOVE ('HS First Love'PBR) (Sin) CWGr ERCP LRHS SDeJ
- HAPPY SINGLE FLAME ('HS Flame'PBR) (Sin) ♀H3 CAvo CWGr ERCP LRHS NJRG
- HAPPY SINGLE JULIET ('HS Juliet'PBR) (Sin) CRav CWGr ERCP LRHS SDeJ
- HAPPY SINGLE KISS ('HS Kiss'PBR) (Sin) CAvo CWGr LRHS
- HAPPY SINGLE PARTY ('HS Party'PBR) (Sin) CAvo CWGr SDeJ
- HAPPY SINGLE PRINCESS ('HS Princess'PBR) (Sin) ♀H3 CRos CWGr ERCP LRHS SDeJ
- HAPPY SINGLE ROMEO ('HS Romeo'PBR) (Sin) CWGr LRHS SDeJ
- HAPPY SINGLE WINK ('HS Wink'PBR) (Sin) ♀H3 CWGr ERCP IBoy LCro LOPS LRHS LSou NPri SDeJ SDir
'Haresbrook' (Sin) NGdn SHar WSpi
'Harriet G' (WL) NHal NJRG
'Hartenaas' (Col/DwB) SDeJ
'Harvest' (Fim) CWGr
§ 'Harvest Samantha' (Sin/Lil) ♀H3 CWGr NHal
'Haseley Goldicote' (D) CWGr
'Haseley Triumph' (D) CWGr
'Hawai'PBR CWGr
'Hawaiian Dreams'PBR (Sin) CBod CWGr ELan IBoy LRHS WAvo
'Hayley Jayne' (C) CWGr ERCP NJRG SGbt
'Heather Huston' (D) CWGr
'Heather Jean' (Col) NJRG
'Heather Linford' (Fim) CWGr NHal
'Helma Rost' (S-c) CWGr
'Hemera' (Sin) **new** CWGr
'Henri Lewi' (S-c) CWGr

'Henriette' (C)	CWGr
'Herbert Smith' (S-c)	CWGr
'Hexton Copper' (Ba)	CWGr SGbt
'Highgate Bobby' (Ba)	CWGr
'Highgate Torch' (S-c)	CWGr
'Highness' (S-c)	CWGr
'Hilda Clare' (Col)	CWGr
'Hildepuppe' (Pom)	CWGr
'Hillcrest Albino' (S-c)	CWGr
'Hillcrest Amour' (D)	CWGr GRid SGbt
'Hillcrest Aura' (D) **new**	GRid
'Hillcrest Bobbin' (Ba)	CWGr
'Hillcrest Camelot' (S-c)	CWGr
'Hillcrest Candy' (S-c) 🏆H3	CWGr GRid NHal NJRG SGbt
'Hillcrest Carmen' (D)	CWGr GRid
'Hillcrest Chelsey' (D) **new**	GRid
'Hillcrest Cheryl' (SinO)	NHal
'Hillcrest Contessa' (Ba)	CWGr
'Hillcrest Delight' (D)	GRid NHal SGbt
'Hillcrest Desire' (C) 🏆H3	GRid
'Hillcrest Divine' (D)	GRid
'Hillcrest Duncan Edwards' (S-c)	NHal
'Hillcrest Embers' (D)	GRid
'Hillcrest Fiesta' (S-c)	CWGr
'Hillcrest Firecrest' (D) **new**	NHal
'Hillcrest Hannah' (D)	GRid
'Hillcrest Harvest' (D) **new**	GRid
'Hillcrest Heights' (S-c)	CWGr
'Hillcrest Hillton' (S-c)	GRid
'Hillcrest Jake' (S-c)	GRid NHal
'Hillcrest Jersie' (S-c) **new**	NHal NJRG
'Hillcrest Jessica J' (C)	GRid
'Hillcrest Kismet' (D)	GRid LAyl NHal NJRG
'Hillcrest Liam' (S-c) **new**	GRid
'Hillcrest Margaret' (D)	GRid
'Hillcrest Matt' (D)	GRid
'Hillcrest Millennium' (S-c) **new**	GRid
'Hillcrest Pearl' (D)	CWGr
'Hillcrest Regal' (Col) 🏆H3	CWGr GRid SGbt
'Hillcrest Royal' (C) 🏆H3	CRav CWGr LAyl NHal SGbt
'Hillcrest Suffusion' (D)	CWGr GRid NJRG
'Hillcrest Thomas J' (D) **new**	GRid
'Hillcrest Ultra' (D)	GRid
'Hill's Delight' (S-c)	CWGr
'Hindu Star' (Ba)	CWGr
hjertingii	CWGr
'Hockley Maroon' (D)	CWGr
'Hockley Nymph' (WL)	CWGr
'Holbrook Honey' (Sin)	CSam
'Holbrook Lilac' (Sin)	CSam
'Holbrook Magenta' (Sin)	CSam
'Holland Festival' (D)	CWGr GRid SGbt
'Hollyhill Big Pink' (S-c)	SGbt
'Home Run' (Sin)	CWGr
'Homer T' (S-c)	CWGr
'Honest John' (C)	CWGr
'Honey' (Anem/DwB)	CWGr SDeJ
'Honeypot' (Ba)	SGbt
'Honka' (SinO) 🏆H3	CWGr ECtt ERCP LAyl LCro LOPS LRHS NHal NJRG SDeJ WCot
'Honka Fragile' (SinO)	CAby ERCP LCro LOPS SDeJ WHlf
'Honka Orange' (SinO)	ERCP NJRG
'Honka Pink Edge' (SinO)	NJRG
'Honka Red' (SinO)	CAby CWGr ERCP LCro LOPS SDeJ
'Honka Rose' (SinO)	ERCP NJRG SDeJ
'Honka Surprise' (SinO)	CAby CWGr EBee ECtt ERCP EUJe LCro LOPS NJRG SDeJ WBrk WCot
'Honka White' (SinO)	CAby CWGr ERCP

'Honor Francis' (Misc)	WCot
I 'Hootenanny' (Col)	NHal NJRG
'Hot Chocolate' (D)	CWGr NJRG SGbt
'Hotcakes' (Anem) **new**	CRav
'Hugh Mather' (WL)	CWGr GRid
'Hulin's Carnival' (D)	CWGr
'Hy Clown' (D)	CWGr
'Hy Fire' (Ba)	CWGr
'Hy Totem' (D) **new**	GRid
'Ian Hislop' (Sin)	CWGr
'Ice Crystal' (Fim)	ERCP
'Ice Cube' (D)	ERCP SDeJ
'Ice Queen' (WL)	CWGr
I 'Idylle' (S-c) **new**	CWGr
'Ieda' (Sin) **new**	NJRG
'Ike' (Fim)	CWGr
imperialis (B)	CDTJ CFil CHll CWGr EBee EWes ILea LEdu LRHS NJRG SBig SChr SDir SGbt
– B&SWJ 8997	WCru
– B&SWJ 14341 **new**	WCru
– 'Alba' (B)	CFil CWGr
– pink double-flowered (B)	CExl CFil
aff. ***imperialis***	CWGr SDir XLum
'Impression Famosa'	see *D.* 'Famoso'
'Inca' (Anem)	IBoy SDeJ
'Inca Dambuster' (S-c)	CWGr NHal SGbt
'Inca Glamour' (D)	CWGr
'Inca Matchless' (D)	CWGr
'Inca Metropolitan' (D)	CWGr
'Inca Panorama' (D)	CWGr
'Inca Spectrum' (S-c)	CWGr
'Inca Vanguard' (D)	CWGr
'Inca Vulcan' (S-c)	CWGr
'Independence' (D)	SGbt
'Inglebrook Jill' (Col)	CWGr NJRG
'Inland Dynasty' (S-c)	CWGr GRid
'Inn's Gerrie Hoek' (D)	CWGr
'Irene Ellen' (D)	GRid
'Irene van der Zwet' (Sin)	CWGr
'Irene's Pride' (S-c) **new**	GRid
'Iris' (Pom)	CWGr GRid GWyn
'Islander' (D)	CWGr ERCP
'Ivanetti' (Ba)	CWGr ERCP GRid NHal SGbt
'Ivy Della' (D)	CWGr
'J Boy' (Ba) **new**	GRid
'J.R.G.' (Misc) 🏆H3	NJRG
'Jack Hood' (D)	CWGr SGbt
'Jackie Magson' (S-c)	CWGr
'Jacqueline Tivey' (D)	CWGr
'Jake's Pastelle' (S-c) **new**	GRid
'Jaldec Jerry' (S-c)	CWGr
'Jaldec Joker' (C)	CWGr
'Jamaica' (WL)	CWGr SGbt
'Jamie' (S-c)	CWGr
'Jan Lennon' (S-c)	CWGr
'Jan van Schaffelaar' (Pom)	ERCP SDeJ
'Janal Amy' (S-c)	CWGr GRid NHal SGbt
'Jane Cowl' (D)	CWGr
'Jane Horton' (Col)	CWGr GRid SGbt
'Janet Beckett' (C)	CWGr
'Japanese Waterlily' (WL)	CWGr
'Jayne Wărton' (S-c)	NHal
'Jazzy' (Col)	CWGr
'Je Maintiendrai' (D)	CWGr
'Jean Fairs' (WL) 🏆H3	CWGr SGbt
'Jean Marie' PBR (D)	CWGr ERCP
'Jean Melville' (D)	CWGr
'Jean Shaw' (D)	GRid NHal
'Jeanne d'Arc' (C)	CWGr

	'Jeannie Leroux' (Fim)	CWGr
	'Jean's Carol' (Pom)	CWGr
I	'Jennie' (Fim)	CWGr GRid
§	'Jenny' (Dahlietta Select Series) (Misc)	SGbt
	'Jersey Beauty' (D)	CWGr
	'Jescot Buttercup' (D)	CWGr
	'Jescot India' (D)	CWGr
	'Jescot Jess' (D)	CWGr
	'Jescot Jim' (D)	CWGr
	'Jescot Julie' (DblO)	CRav CWGr ERCP LAyl LCro LOPS NJRG
	'Jescot Lingold' (D)	CWGr SGbt
	'Jescot Redun' (D)	CWGr
	'Jessica' (S-c)	CWGr
	'Jessie G' (Ba)	CWGr NJRG
	'Jessie Ross' (D/DwB)	CWGr
	'Jet' (S-c)	CWGr
I	'Jet Fire' (D) **new**	GRid
	'Jill Day' (C)	CWGr
	'Jill Doc' (D)	CWGr
	'Jill's Delight' (D)	CWGr
	'Jim Branigan' (S-c)	CWGr NHal
	'Jive' (Anem)	ELan ERCP SDeJ
	'Jo Anne' (S-c)	CWGr
	'Joan Beecham' (D)	GRid
	'Joan Walker' (D)	GRid
	'Jocondo' (D)	CWGr GRid NHal SGbt
	'Jodie Wilkinson' (Ba) ♀H3	NHal
	'Joe Swift' (Sin)	CWGr
	'Johann' (Pom)	CWGr GRid NHal
	'John Hill' (D)	GRid NHal
	'John Prior' (D)	CWGr
	'John Street' (WL)	CWGr WSpi
	'John's Champion' (D)	CWGr
	'Jolly Good' (Sin) **new**	NJRG
	'Jomanda' (Ba) ♀H3	CWGr GRid NHal NJRG SGbt
	'Jorja' (S-c)	GRid
	'Jo's Choice' (D)	CWGr
	'Josie Gott' (Ba) ♀H3	NJRG SGbt
	'Jowey Ingrid' (D) **new**	GRid
	'Jowey Linda' (Ba)	ERCP
	'Jowey Winnie' (Ba)	ERCP
	'Joy Donaldson' (C)	CWGr
	'Joyce Green' (S-c)	CWGr GRid SGbt
	'Joyce Margaret Cunliffe' (D)	CWGr
	'Juanita' (S-c)	CWGr
	'Jules Dyson' (Misc)	SDys
	'Julie One' (DblO)	CWGr ECtt SGbt
	'Julie's Delight' (S-c)	CWGr
	'Julio' (Ba)	CWGr
	'Jura' (S-c)	CWGr
	'Juul's Allstar' (SinO) ♀H3	CWGr
	'Kaftan' (D)	CWGr
	'Kaga-komachi' (D)	LRHS NRHS
	'Kaiser Wilhelm' (Ba)	CWGr
	'Kaiserwalzer' (Col)	CWGr
	'Kaisha Lea' (D)	ERCP
	'Karen G' (Col) **new**	NJRG
	'Karenglen' (D) ♀H3	GRid NHal NJRG SGbt
	'Kari Quill' (C)	CWGr
	'Karma Amanda'PBR (D)	CWGr LRHS
	'Karma Bon Bini'PBR (C)	CAby SGbt
	'Karma Choc'PBR (D) ♀H3	CAby CRav CRos CSpe CWGr EBee EPfP ERCP EWes IBoy LCro LOPS LRHS MHol NRHS SDir SEND SGbt SPer WBor WCot WFar WHoo
	'Karma Corona'PBR (C)	CWGr SGbt
	'Karma Fiesta'PBR (D)	ERCP

	'Karma Fuchsiana' (D)	CRav CWGr ERCP IBoy LCro LOPS SGbt
	'Karma Irene'PBR (D)	CWGr ERCP
	'Karma Lagoon'PBR (D)	CRos CWGr ERCP LRHS NRHS SGbt
	'Karma Maarten Zwaan'PBR (WL)	CWGr ERCP
	'Karma Naomi'PBR (D)	ERCP SDir SGbt
	'Karma Pink Corona'PBR (C)	LCro LOPS
	'Karma Prospero'PBR (D)	ERCP LCro LOPS
	'Karma Red Corona'PBR (C)	SDeJ SGbt
	'Karma Sangria'PBR (C)	CWGr LCro LOPS SDeJ SGbt
	'Karma Serena'PBR (D)	SDeJ
	'Karma Yin Yang' (D)	LRHS SGbt
	'Karras 150' (S-c)	CWGr
	'Kasasagi' (Pom)	CWGr
	'Kate Mountjoy' (Col)	CWGr SGbt
	'Katie Dahl' (D)	NHal
	'Katisha' (D)	CWGr
	'Kayleigh Spiller' (Col)	SGbt
	'Kea Magic' (D)	GRid
	'Keith's Choice' (D)	GRid NHal SGbt
	'Kelsea Carla' (S-c) ♀H3	CWGr
	'Kelsey Annie Joy' (Col) **new**	NJRG
	'Kelvin Floodlight' (D)	CWGr IRob SDeJ SDir SGbt
	'Kennemerland' (S-c)	LCro SDeJ SDir SGbt
	'Kenora Canada' (S-c)	CWGr
	'Kenora Challenger' (S-c)	CWGr GRid NHal NJRG SGbt
	'Kenora Christmas' (Ba)	CWGr
	'Kenora Clyde' (S-c)	CWGr
	'Kenora Fireball' (Ba)	GRid
	'Kenora Frills' (Fim)	NHal
	'Kenora Jubilee' (S-c)	GRid GWyn SGbt
	'Kenora Lisa' (D)	CWGr
	'Kenora Macop-B' (Fim)	CWGr ECtt ERCP NHal
	'Kenora Moonbeam' (D)	CWGr GRid
	'Kenora Ontario' (S-c)	CWGr
	'Kenora Sunset' (S-c) ♀H3	CWGr GRid NHal SGbt
	'Kenora Superb' (S-c)	CWGr GRid SGbt
	'Kenora Valentine' (D) ♀H3	CWGr NHal SGbt
	'Kenora Wildfire' (D)	CWGr GRid
	'Kenora Wow' (S-c)	LAyl NHal
	'Ken's Choice' (Ba)	GRid
	'Ken's Coral' (WL)	CWGr
	'Ken's Flame' (WL)	CWGr SGbt
	'Ken's Rarity' (WL)	NHal NJRG SGbt
	'Key West' (D)	CWGr
	'Kidd's Climax' (D) ♀H3	CWGr GRid
	'Kiev' (Jumbo Collection) (D)	LCro
	'Kikoski' (C)	SGbt
	'Kilburn Fiesta' (S-c)	GRid NHal
	'Kilburn Glow' (WL)	NHal NJRG
	'Kilburn Rose' (WL) ♀H3	NJRG
	'Kilmorie' (S-c)	GRid NHal
	'Kingston' (D)	CWGr SGbt
	'Kirsty G' (Col) **new**	NJRG
	'Kismet' (Ba)	CWGr
	'Kiss' (D)	CBod
	'Kit Kat' (C)	CWGr
	'Kiwi Brother' (S-c)	CWGr
	'Kiwi Gloria' (C)	CWGr GRid NHal NJRG
	'Kiwi Sister' (S-c)	CWGr
	'Klondike' (S-c)	CWGr ERCP NJRG
I	'Knockout'PBR (Sin) ♀H3	CBcs CChe CWGr EPfP ERCP LRHS LSRN LSou NRHS SPoG
	'Kochelsee' (Ba)	CWGr
	'Kogane Fubuki' (Fim)	CWGr
	'Kotare Jackpot' (S-c)	CWGr
	'Kung Fu' (D)	CWGr

	'Kym Willo' (Pom)	CWGr
I	'Kyoto' (WL)	CWGr SGbt
	'L.A.T.E.' (Ba)	CWGr GRid NHal SGbt
	'La Cierva' (Col)	CWGr
	'La Gioconda' (Col)	CWGr GRid
	'La Recoleta' (D)	CRav CWGr ERCP
	'Labyrinth' (D)	CRav ERCP
	'Lady Darlene' (D)	CWGr ERCP
	'Lady Kate' (D) **new**	LCro LOPS
	'Lady Kerkrade' (C)	CWGr
	'Lady Liberty' (D)	ERCP
	'Lady Linda' (D)	CWGr GRid NHal SGbt
	'Lady Orpah' (D)	CWGr
	'Lady Sunshine' (S-c)	CWGr
	'Laguna Beach' (Ba) **new**	CWGr
	'Lake Carey' (D) **new**	LCro LOPS
	'Lakeland Polly' (Pom)	GRid NHal NJRG
	'Lambada' (Anem)	ELan ERCP
	'L'Ancresse' (Ba)	GRid LAyl NHal NJRG
	'Larkford' (D)	CWGr
	'Last Dance' (D)	CWGr
	'Laura's Choice' (D)	CWGr
	'Lauren's Moonlight'	see *D.* 'Pim's Moonlight'
	'Lavendale' (D)	CWGr
	'Lavender Chiffon' (S-c)	CWGr
	'Lavender Freestyle' (C)	CWGr
	'Lavender Leycett' (D)	CWGr
	'Lavender Line' (S-c)	GRid NHal SHar
	'Lavender Nunton Harvest' (D)	CWGr
	'Lavender Perfection' (D)	CWGr SDeJ
	'Lavengro' (D)	CWGr GRid
	'Le Baron' (D)	ERCP
	'Le Castel' (WL) ♀H3	CWGr SDeJ
	'Le Feu du Soleil' (Fim)	NHal
	'Le Patineur' (D)	CWGr
	'Le Vonné Splinter' (S-c)	CWGr GRid
	'Leander' (S-c)	CWGr
	'Lee Marshall' (C) **new**	CWGr
	'Leila Savanna Rose' (S-c) **new**	ERCP
§	'Lemon Cane' (D)	CWGr ECtt
	'Lemon Elegans' (S-c) ♀H3	CWGr GRid NHal NJRG
	'Lemon Meringue' (D)	CWGr ECtt SGbt
	'Lemon Puff' (Anem)	CWGr
	'Lemon Symbol' (S-c)	CWGr
	'Lemon Zing' (Ba)	GRid LAyl NHal SGbt
	'Leopold Chloe' (D)	GRid NHal
	'Leopold Sophie' (D)	CWGr GRid
	'Leslie's Willo' (Pom)	GRid
	'Lexington' (Pom)	CWGr
	'Leycett' (D)	CWGr
	'Libretto' (Col)	CWGr
	'Life Force' (D)	CWGr SGbt
	'Life Style' (Anem)	GWyn
	'Lifesize' (D)	GRid
	'Light Music' (S-c)	CWGr
	'Lilac Athalie' (C)	CWGr
	'Lilac Bull' (D)	LRHS
	'Lilac Marston' (D) ♀H3	GRid NHal
	'Lilac Pathfinder' (Sin) **new**	NJRG
	'Lilac Shadow' (S-c)	CWGr
	'Lilac Taratahi' (C) ♀H3	CSam CWGr
I	'Lilac Time' (D)	CWGr ERCP SDeJ SGbt
	'Lilac Willo' (Pom)	CWGr
	'Lilian Alice' (Col)	GRid
	'Lilian Marston' (D) **new**	GRid
	'Lilianna W' (Sin/Dw.B.)	NJRG
	'Linda's Baby' (Ba)	ERCP
	'Linda's Chester' (C)	CWGr
	'Linda's Diane' (D)	CWGr
	'Linda's Polly' (Pom)	NJRG
	'Lindsay' (WL) **new**	GRid
	linearis **new**	CFil
	'Lismore Carol' (Pom)	CWGr GWyn NHal
	'Lismore Chaffinch' (D)	GRid
	'Lismore Moonlight' (Pom)	CWGr GRid NHal
	'Lismore Robin' (D)	GRid NHal
	'Lismore Sunset' (Pom)	CWGr GRid SGbt
	'Lismore Willie' (WL) ♀H3	CWGr GRid NJRG
	'Little Beeswing' (C)	ERCP
	'Little Dorrit' (Sin/Lil)	CWGr NJRG
	'Little Lamb' (S-c)	CWGr
	'Little Laura' (Ba)	CWGr
	'Little Matthew' (Pom)	CWGr SGbt
	'Little Reggie' (S-c)	CWGr
	'Little Robert' (D)	CWGr ERCP SGbt
	'Little Sally' (Pom)	CWGr SGbt
	'Little Scottie' (Pom)	CWGr
	'Little Shona' (D)	CWGr
	'Little Snowdrop' (Pom)	CWGr SGbt
	'Little Tiger' (D)	CWGr
	'Little Willem' (Pom)	SDeJ SGbt
	'Lloyd Huston' (S-c)	CWGr
	'Lois Walcher' (D)	CWGr
	'Lololove' (Sin)	SPer
	'Loraine Mitchell' (WL) **new**	NJRG
	'Loretta' (Ba)	GRid NJRG
	'Lorona Dawn' (SinO)	ERCP LAyl NJRG
	'Loud Applause' (C)	CWGr
	'Louie Meggos' (D)	NHal
	'Louis V' (Fim)	SGbt
*	'Louis Walchen' (D)	CWGr
	'Louise Bailey' (D)	CWGr
	'Louise'^{PBR} (Dahlietta Surprise Series) (D/DwB)	CWGr
	lovatii	CWGr
	'Lovelife'^{PBR} (D)	ERCP
	'Lucky Devil' (WL)	CWGr
	'Lucky Number' (D)	CWGr ERCP
	'Ludwig Helfert' (S-c)	CWGr
	'Luka Johanna' (WL)	ERCP
	'Lula Pattie' (D) **new**	GRid
	'Lupin Dixie' (C)	CWGr
	'Lyn Mayo' (D)	CWGr
	'Mabel Ann' (D)	CWGr GRid LAyl
	'Madaline Ann' (D)	CWGr
	'Madame Simone Stappers' (WL)	CWGr ECtt EUJe LAyl LRHS NRHS WSpi
	'Madame Vera' (D)	CWGr
	'Maddie Grace' (D)	CWGr
	'Mafolie' (S-c)	CWGr
	'Magenta Magenta' (D)	LAyl SGbt
	'Magenta Magic' (Sin/DwB)	NHal
	'Magenta Star' (Sin) ♀H3	CRav CWGr ERCP SGbt
I	'Magic Moment' (S-c)	CWGr
	'Magnificat' (D)	CWGr
	'Maiko Girl' (DblO) ♀H3	LAyl
	'Maisie' (D)	CWGr
	'Maisie Mooney' (D)	CWGr
	'Majestic Kerkrade' (C)	CWGr
	'Majjas Symbol' (S-c)	CWGr
	'Maldiva' (D)	ERCP
	'Malham Portia' (WL)	CWGr
	'Maltby Fanfare' (Col)	CWGr
	'Malvern Martha' (D) **new**	GRid
I	'Mambo' (Anem)	CRav SDeJ
	'Manhattan Island' (D)	CWGr ERCP SDeJ
	'Manuel' (D) **new**	CWGr
	'Marble Ball' (D)	CWGr EPfP ERCP SDeJ SGbt

	'Margaret Anne' (D)	CWGr
	'Margaret Brookes' (D)	CWGr
	'Marie' (D)	CWGr
	'Marie Schnugg' (SinO) ♀H3	CWGr NJRG SGbt
	'Mariposa' (Col)	CWGr
	'Marissa' (WL)	GRid
	'Mark Damp' (S-c)	CWGr
	'Mark Hardwick' (D)	CWGr GRid
	'Mark Lockwood' (Pom)	CWGr
	'Market Joy' (S-c)	CWGr
	'Marla Lu' (C)	CWGr
	'Marlene Joy' (Fim)	CWGr SGbt
	'Marrakech' (WL) **new**	CWGr
I	'Mars' (Col)	CWGr NJRG SGbt
	'Marston George' (Ba)	GRid NHal NJRG
	'Marston Suzanne' (D)	GRid NHal
	'Marston Velvet' (D) **new**	GRid
	'Martina' (D)	GRid
	'Martin's Yellow' (Pom)	GRid NHal
	'Mary Crichton' (D) **new**	GRid
I	'Mary Eveline' (Col)	ECtt NHal
	'Mary Evelyn' (C)	ERCP NJRG SGbt
	'Mary Hammett' (D)	WSpi
	'Mary Layton' (Col)	CWGr
	'Mary McLelland' (Col) **new**	GRid
	'Mary Partridge' (WL)	CWGr
	'Mary Pitt' (D)	CWGr SGbt
	'Mary Richards' (D)	CWGr
	'Mary's Jomanda' (Ba) ♀H3	CWGr GRid GWyn NHal NJRG SGbt
	'Mascot Maya' (D)	NJRG
	'Master Michael' (Pom)	CWGr
	'Match' (S-c)	CWGr GRid
	'Matchless' (C)	CWGr
	'Matilda Huston' (S-c)	CWGr LAyl NHal
	'Matt Armour' (Sin)	CWGr
	'Maureen Hardwick' (D)	CWGr SGbt
	'Maureen Jones' (Col)	NJRG
	'Maxime' (D)	ERCP
	'Maxine Bailey' (D)	CWGr
	'Mayan Blood' (DblO) **new**	CWGr
	'Mayan Pearl' (DblO) ♀H3	CWGr LAyl NHal SGbt
	'Mayan Swan' (S-c)	SGbt
	'Mayan Warrior' (S-c) **new**	NJRG
	'Mediterrannee' (D)	ERCP
	'Megan Dean' (Ba)	GRid NHal
	'Meiro' (D)	CWGr
	'Melanie Jane' (S-c)	CWGr
	'Melody Allegro'[PBR] (D)	ERCP MHol
	'Melody Bolero'[PBR] (D)	CWGr SDeJ
	'Melody Dixie'[PBR] (D)	CWGr ERCP
	'Melody Dora'[PBR] (D)	CWGr GRid LCro LOPS LRHS
	'Melody Fanfare'[PBR] (D)	ERCP SDeJ
	'Melody Gipsy'[PBR] (S-c)	CWGr ERCP LRHS
	'Melody Harmony'[PBR] (D) ♀H3	CRav ERCP SDir
	'Melody Pink Allegro' (D)	ERCP
	'Melody Swing'[PBR] (D)	CWGr ERCP
	'Mel's Orange Marmalade' (Fim)	ERCP LCro LOPS
	'Melton' (D)	CWGr
	merckii	CBot CExl CFil CHll CRos CSpe CWGr EUJe EWes LRHS MCot MMrt MNrw MRav NRHS NSti SHar SPtp
	- 'Alba' (B)	CExl CFil CSpe
	- compact	CFil
	- dark-flowered **new**	WPGP
	'Mero Star' (D)	SPer
	'Mevrouw Clement Andries' (Fim)	ERCP
§	'Mexican Black' (Misc)	CWGr ECtt ERCP NJRG SMHy WPGP
	'Mexico Mogul' (D)	SGbt
	'Mi Wong' (Pom)	GRid
	'Miami' (D)	CWGr
	'Michael J' (D)	CWGr
	'Michigan' (D)	CWGr
	'Mick' (C)	CWGr
	'Mick's Peppermint' (S-c)	CAby CWGr SGbt
	'Midas' (S-c)	CWGr
	'Midnight' (Pom)	CWGr SGbt
	'Midnight Star' (SinO)	NJRG
	'Mies' (Sin)	CWGr
	'Milk Shake' (D)	CWGr
	'Mingus Alex' (S-c)	CWGr
	'Mingus Arthur K' (Fim) **new**	GRid
	'Mingus Erik' (Fim) **new**	GRid
	'Mingus Gregory' (S-c)	CWGr ERCP SDeJ
	'Mingus Heather' (WL) **new**	GRid
	'Mingus Julie' (C) **new**	GRid
	'Mingus Kyle D' (D)	CWGr
*	'Mingus Max'	ERCP
	'Mingus Nichole' (D)	CWGr
	'Mingus Toni' (D)	ERCP
	'Mingus Tracy Lynn' (S-c)	CWGr GRid
	'Mingus Whitney' (S-c)	GRid
	'Mini Red' (S-c)	CWGr
	'Minley Carol' (Pom)	CWGr GRid NHal NJRG
	'Minley Iris' (Pom)	CWGr
	'Minnesota Migrant' (S-c) **new**	CWGr
	'Miramar' (D)	CWGr
	'Mish-Mash' (Fim)	GRid
	'Miss Blanc' (WL)	CWGr
	'Miss Ellen' (Misc) ♀H3	CWGr
	'Miss Rose Fletcher' (S-c)	CWGr
	'Miss Swiss' (D)	CWGr
	'Misterton' (D)	CWGr SGbt
	'Mistill Beauty' (C)	CWGr
	'Mistill Delight' (D)	CWGr
	mollis	CFil
	mollis* × *rudis **new**	CFil
	'Mom's Special' (D)	CWGr ERCP
	'Monet Mystique' (WL)	SGbt
	'Monet Sunlight' (WL)	SGbt
	'Monk Marc' (C)	CWGr
	'Monkstown Diane' (C)	CWGr
	'Monrovia' (Ba)	CWGr
	'Moonfire' (Misc/DwB) ♀H3	CAby CBcs CRos CWGN CWGr ECtt EHrv ELan EPfP ERCP EUJe IRob LAyl LRHS NHal NJRG NLar NRHS SGbt SPer WCot WHoo WSpi
	'Moonglow' (S-c)	CWGr ERCP LRHS
	'Moor Place' (Pom)	CWGr GRid NHal NJRG SGbt
	moorei	WPGP
	'Moray Susan' (WL)	CWGr
	'Moret' (S-c)	CWGr
	'Morley Lady' (D)	CWGr
	'Morna Whitlock' (S-c) **new**	CWGr
	'Morning Dew' (WL)	CWGr
	'Motto' (D)	CWGr
	'Moulin Rouge' (C) **new**	SPer
	'Mount Noddy' (Sin)	CWGr
	'Mr Sandman' (Fim) **new**	MSCN
	'Mrs A. Woods' (D)	CWGr
	'Mrs Black' (Pom)	CWGr
	'Mrs Eileen' (D)	ERCP SDeJ SGbt
	'Mrs H. Brown' (Col)	SGbt
	'Mrs McDonald Quill' (D)	CWGr GRid SGbt
	'Mrs Silverston' (D)	CWGr

	'Ms Kennedy' (Ba)	NHal
	'München' (D)	CRos NRHS SDeJ SGbt
	'Murdoch' ambig. (D)	ECtt LRHS MHol WCot WSpi
	'Murillo' ambig. (Sin)	LAyl
	'Murray May' (WL)	CWGr
	'Murray Petite' (S-c)	CWGr
	'Musette' (D)	CWGr SGbt
	'My Irene' (WL)	NJRG
	'My Joy' (Pom)	CWGr
	'My Love' (S-c)	CWGr ECtt ERCP LCro LOPS SEND SGbt
	'My Neddy' (D)	SGbt
I	'My Pride' (D) **new**	GRid
	'Myama Fubuki' (Fim)	ELan ERCP
	'My-nute Blend' (Misc)	CWGr
	'Myrtle's Folly' (Fim)	CBod ERCP SDeJ
	'Mystère' (Anem) **new**	CWGr
	'Mystery Day' (D)	CWGr
	MYSTIC DESIRE	see *D.* 'Zone Ten'
	MYSTIC DREAMER	see *D.* 'Knockout' (Sin)
§	'Mystic Enchantment' PBR (Sin)	CRos ELan IBoy LRHS LSou NRHS SPoG
	'Mystic Haze'	see *D.* 'Dark Side Of The Sun'
	MYSTIC ILLUSION	see *D.* 'Knockout' (Sin)
	MYSTIC MARS	see *D.* 'Scarlet Fern'
§	MYSTIC SPIRIT ('Hamspirit' PBR) (Sin)	ELan LRHS
	'Mystic Wonder' (Sin) **new**	ELan WAvo
	'Nadia Ruth' (Fim)	ERCP
	'Nagano' (D)	CWGr SDeJ
	'Nancy H' (Ba)	CWGr
	'Nancy Margaret' (S-c) **new**	GRid
	'Nargold' (Fim)	CWGr LAyl
	'Narrow's Tricia' (S-c)	GRid NJRG
	'Natal' (Ba)	CAvo ECtt SDeJ
	'Natalie G' (D)	EPfP NJRG
	'Nathalie's Wedding' (WL)	ERCP
	'Nationwide' (D)	CWGr
	'Neal Gillson' (D)	CWGr
	neglecta	CWGr
	'Nelly Geerlings' (Sin)	CWGr
	'Nenekazi' (Fim)	CWGr GRid LAyl NJRG
	'Néo' (D) **new**	CWGr
	'Nepos' (WL)	CWGr GRid GWyn NJRG SGbt
	'Nescio' (Pom)	CWGr ERCP SDeJ
	'Nettie' (Ba)	CWGr
I	'New Baby' (Ba)	CWGr ERCP LCro LOPS SGbt
	'New Look' (S-c)	CWGr
	'Newby' (D)	CWGr
	'Newquay' (Sin)	CWGr
	'Newsham Wonder' (D)	CWGr
	'Nicholas' (D)	ERCP SPer
	'Nicola' (S-c)	CWGr
	'Nicolette' (D)	CWGr
	'Nienke' (D) **new**	NJRG
	'Night Butterfly' (Col)	CAby CRav
	'Night Editor' (D)	CWGr
I	'Night Queen' (Ba)	EPfP ERCP
	'Nijinsky' (Ba)	CWGr
	'Nina Chester' (D)	CWGr GRid
	'Nippon' (Sin)	EPfP LRHS
	'Nogent' (D) **new**	CWGr
	'Nonette' (WL)	CWGr EBee ECtt SGbt WBrk WCot
	'Norbeck Dusky' (S-c)	CWGr
	'Noreen' (Pom)	CWGr GRid NHal NJRG
	'Norman Lockwood' (Pom)	CWGr
	'Normandie Wedding Day' (Fim) **new**	NHal
	'Northland Primrose' (C)	CWGr
	'Northwest Cosmos' (Sin) ♀H3	CWGr
	'Ntac Eileen' (Col)	NJRG
§	'Nuit d'Eté' (S-c)	CAby CAvo CWGr ELan ERCP LCro LRHS SDeJ SGbt
	'Nuland's Josephine' (Ba)	LAyl NHal NJRG
	'Nunton Form' (D)	CWGr
	'Nunton Harvest' (D)	CWGr GRid
	'Nymphenburg' (WL)	CWGr
	'Oakwood Belle' (C) **new**	CWGr
	'Oakwood Bridesmaid' (C) **new**	CWGr
	'Oakwood Dazzle' (D) **new**	CWGr
	'Oakwood Diamond' (Ba)	CWGr
	'Oakwood Fire' (S-c) **new**	CWGr
	'Oakwood Firelight' (S-c) **new**	CWGr
	'Oakwood Goldcrest' (S-c)	GRid NHal
	'Oakwood Heather' (Ba) **new**	CWGr
	'Oakwood Katie' (S-c) **new**	CWGr
	'Oakwood Marian S' (D) **new**	CWGr
	'Oakwood Naranga' (D) ♀H3 **new**	CWGr
	'Oakwood Natasha' (Pom) **new**	CWGr
	'Oakwood Royale' (D) **new**	CWGr
	'Ocean Bird' PBR (D) **new**	ERCP
	'Offshore Dream' (D)	ERCP
I	'Old Gold' (D)	CWGr SGbt
I	'Olivia' (Col)	CWGr GRid NJRG
	'Olivia Mari' (WL)	GRid NHal
	'Omo' (Sin/Lil) ♀H3	NJRG
	'Onesta' (D)	CWGr ERCP SDeJ SPer
	'Only Love' (S-c)	CWGr
	'Onslow Michele' (D)	CWGr
	'Onslow Renown' (S-c)	CWGr
	'Opal' (Ba)	CWGr
	'Optic Illusion' (D)	CWGr
	'Opus' (D)	CWGr SGbt
	'Orange Chum' (D) **new**	CWGr
	'Orange Cushion' (D)	CWGr
	'Orange Explosion' (Misc)	CWGr SGbt
	'Orange Fire' (S-c)	CWGr
	'Orange Fubuki' (D)	ERCP
	'Orange Keith's Choice' (D)	CWGr GRid
	'Orange Kiss' (Col) **new**	NJRG
	'Orange Mullett' (D/DwB)	CWGr
	'Orange Nugget' (Ba)	CWGr SDeJ
	'Orange Pathfinder' (Misc)	CWGr NJRG
I	'Orange Queen' (C)	CWGr SGbt
	'Orange Sun' (D)	CWGr
	'Orchid Lace' (C)	CWGr
	'Orchid Princess' (S-c)	ERCP
	'Orel' (Col)	CWGr GRid SGbt
	'Oreti Bliss' (C)	GRid LAyl NHal
	'Oreti Classic' (D)	NHal
	'Oreti Duke' (Pom)	CWGr
	'Oreti Stacey' (Fim) **new**	GRid
	'Orfeo' (C)	CWGr ERCP LCro MNrw SDeJ SGbt
I	'Orion' (D)	CWGr
	'Ornamental Rays' (C)	CWGr
	'Osaka' (D)	CWGr
	'Osirium' (D)	ERCP
	'Ossie Latham' (Sin)	CWGr SGbt
	'Othello' (S-c)	CWGr GRid
	'Otto's Thrill' (D) ♀H3	ERCP
	'Our Dad' (S-c)	NHal
	'Pacific Argyle' (D)	NHal

	'Pacific Ocean' (WL)	ERCP
	'Paint Box' (S-c)	CWGr
	'Painted Girl' (D)	ERCP
	'Paisley Gem' (Sin)	CWGr
	'Pale Excentrique' (Sin/DwB)	NJRG
	'Pale Roxy' (Misc)	NJRG
	'Palomino' (D)	CWGr
	'Pam Howden' (WL)	NHal NJRG SGbt
	'Pamela' (D)	CWGr
	'Paradise City' (D)	ERCP
	'Pari Taha Sunrise' (S-c)	CWGr
	'Park Princess' (C/DwB)	CWGr LAyl NHal NRHS SDeJ SGbt
	'Park Record' (S-c)	LCro LOPS
	'Parkland Rave' (S-c)	CWGr
	'Paroa Gillian' (C)	CWGr
	'Paso Doble' misapplied	see *D.* 'Freya's Paso Doble'
	'Pat Knight' (Col)	CWGr NHal NJRG
	'Pat Mark' (S-c)	CWGr
	'Pat 'n' Dee' (D)	CWGr
	'Pat 'n' Perc' (Col)	NJRG SGbt
	'Pat Seed' (D)	CWGr
	'Paul Chester' (C)	CWGr
	'Paul Critchley' (C)	CWGr
	'Paul Magson' (S-c)	GRid
	'Paul Smith' (Ba)	CWGr
	'Peace Pact' (WL)	CWGr
	'Peach Athalie' (C)	CWGr
	'Peach Cupid' (Ba)	CWGr
	'Peach Delight' (S-c)	NHal SGbt
§	'Peach Melba' (D)	CWGr NHal
I	'Peaches' (Ba)	ERCP
	'Peaches and Cream'PBR (D)	CWGr ECtt
	'Peachette' (Misc/Lil)	CWGr
	'Pearl Hornsey' (D)	CWGr
	'Pearl of Heemstede' (D) ♀H3	CWGr LAyl NHal NJRG
	'Pearl Sharowean' (S-c)	CWGr
	'Pearson's Ben' (S-c)	CWGr GRid NJRG
	'Pearson's Melanie' (C)	CWGr
	'Pearson's Patrick' (S-c)	CWGr
	'Pembroke Levenna' (Ba)	LAyl NHal
	'Pembroke Pattie' (Pom)	GRid
	'Penhill Autumn Shade' (S-c)	GRid NJRG SGbt
	'Penhill Dark Monarch' (D) **new**	ERCP
	'Penhill Watermelon' (D) **new**	ERCP SDeJ
	'Pennsclout' (D)	CWGr
	'Penny Lane' (D)	ERCP
	'Pensford Marion' (Pom)	CWGr GRid
I	'Perfect' (D) **new**	CWGr
	'Perfect Partner' (Sin)	CWGr
	'Perfectos' (C)	CWGr
	'Peter' (D)	CWGr SGbt
	'Petit Byoux' (Col/DwB)	CWGr
	'Petite Harvest' (Misc/DwB)	NJRG
	'Petite Sunrise' (Sin)	NJRG
	'Petite Sunset' (Misc/Lil)	NJRG
	'Pfitzer's Joker' (C)	CAby
	'Pianella' (S-c)	CWGr SGbt
§	'Pim's Moonlight' (S-c)	GRid
	'Pineapple Lollipop' (Ba)	CWGr
	'Pineholt Princess' (D)	CWGr
	'Pinelands Pam' (Fim)	CWGr GRid
	'Pinelands Princess' (Fim)	ERCP EUJe SGbt
	'Pink Attraction' (D)	CWGr
	'Pink Breckland Joy' (D)	CWGr
	'Pink Carol' (Pom)	CWGr GRid NJRG
	'Pink Giraffe' (DblO) ♀H3	CAby CWGr ERCP SGbt
	'Pink Honeymoon Dress' (D)	CWGr
	'Pink Isa'PBR (D)	CWGr ERCP MSCN WHar
	'Pink Jean Fairs' (WL)	CWGr
	'Pink Jupiter' (S-c)	CWGr GRid NHal SGbt
	'Pink Katisha' (D)	CWGr
	'Pink Kerkrade' (C)	CWGr
	'Pink Leycett' (D)	CWGr
	'Pink Loveliness' (WL)	CWGr
	'Pink Pastelle' (S-c) ♀H3	GRid NHal SGbt
	'Pink Pat and Perc' (Col)	NHal NJRG
	'Pink Preference' (S-c)	CWGr
	'Pink Risca Miner' (Ba)	CWGr
	'Pink Robin Hood' (Ba)	CWGr
	'Pink Sensation' (C) ♀H3	CWGr
	'Pink Shirley Alliance' (C)	CWGr
	'Pink Skin' (D)	ECtt LRHS SDeJ
	'Pink Spur' (D) **new**	GRid
	'Pink Suffusion' (D)	GRid
	'Pink Sylvia' (D)	CWGr
	'Pink Symbol' (S-c)	CWGr
	'Pink Worton Ann' (D)	CWGr
	pinnata	CFil
	– B&SWJ 10240	WCru
	'Piperoo' (C)	CWGr SGbt
	'Piper's Pink' (S-c/DwB)	CWGr ECtt GRid LRHS NRHS SGbt
I	'Pippa' (WL)	CWGr
I	'Pippi' (D)	CWGr
	'Pitchoun' (Sin) **new**	CWGr
	'Platinium Blonde' (Anem) **new**	NJRG
	'Playa Blanca' (C/DwB)	SDir SGbt
	'Playboy' (D)	CWGr
	'Plum Surprise' (Pom)	CWGr
	'Polar Sight' (C)	CWGr
I	'Polka' (Anem)	NJRG SDeJ SGbt
	'Polly Peachum' (D)	CWGr
	'Polventon Supreme' (Ba)	CWGr
	'Polyand' (D)	CWGr
	'Pontiac' (C)	CWGr SGbt
	'Pooh' (Col)	see *D.* 'Pooh - Swan Island'
§	'Pooh - Swan Island' (Col) ♀H3	CWGr EBee ECtt ERCP EUJe GRid LAyl NCou NHal NJRG WCot
	'Pop Harris' (D)	CWGr
	'Pop Willo' (Pom)	GRid NJRG
I	'Poppet' (Pom)	CWGr
	'Poppyscotland' (Sin)	CWGr
	'Popular Guest' (Fim)	CWGr
	'Porcelain' (WL)	WSpi
	'Pot Black' (Ba)	CWGr
	'Potgeiter' (Ba)	CWGr
	'Prefect' (S-c)	CWGr
	'Prefere' (Sin)	CWGr
	'Preference' (C)	CWGr ERCP SDeJ SGbt
	'Preston Park' (Sin/DwB) ♀H3	CWGr LAyl NHal
	PRETTY WOMAN ('Vdtg43'PBR) (Dark Angel Series) (Sin) ♀H3	ERCP LCro LOPS
	PRIDE OF BERLIN	see *D.* 'Stolz von Berlin'
	'Prime Minister' (D)	CWGr
	'Primrose Diane' (D)	CWGr GRid
	'Primrose Pastelle' (S-c)	GRid NHal
	'Primrose Rustig' (D)	CWGr
	'Prince Valiant' (D)	CWGr
I	'Princess' (Col)	SDeJ
	'Princess Beatrix' (D)	CWGr
	'Princess Marie José' (Sin)	CWGr
	'Princesse Elisabeth' (D)	ERCP
	'Princesse Gracia' (D)	ERCP

'Princesse Laetitia' (D) ERCP
'Procyon' (D) CWGr SGbt
'Prom' (Pom) CWGr
'Promise' (Fim) CWGr ECtt ERCP SDeJ
pteropoda CWGr
aff. ***pteropoda*** CWGr
– F&M 312 WPGP
'Puerto Rico' (Fim) **new** ERCP
PULP FICTION ('Vdtg61'[PBR]) (Dark Angel Series) (Sin) ERCP
'Punky' (Pom) CWGr
'Purbeck Lydia' (S-c) CWGr
'Purity' (S-c) CWGr
'Purpinca' (Anem) CWGr
'Purple Cottesmore' (WL) CWGr
'Purple Flame'[PBR] (D) CRav ERCP
'Purple Fox'[PBR] (Ba) **new** ERCP
'Purple Gem' (S-c) CBod CWGr ERCP EUJe LCro LOPS SDeJ SGbt SPer
'Purple Haze' (Misc) ERCP LCro LOPS LSRN NQui
'Purple Pearl' (D) ERCP NHal
'Purple Petite' (Sin) NJRG
'Purple Puff' (Anem) LAyl NHal NJRG
'Purple Sensation' (S-c) CWGr
'Purple Splash' (WL) CWGr
'Purple Taiheyō' (D) CWGr
'Purpurröschen' (D) CWGr
purpusii CFil CWGr
aff. ***purpusii*** B&SWJ 10321 WCru
'Pussycat' (D) CWGr
'Que Sera' (Misc) CWGr NJRG
'Quel Diable' (S-c) CWGr
'Quick Step' (Anem) NJRG
'Rachel de Thame' (Sin) CWGr
'Rachel's Place' (Pom) CWGr
'Radiance' (C) CWGr
'Raffles' (D) CWGr
'Ragged Robin' (Misc) CSpe CWGr ECtt ERCP LCro LRHS
'Raspberry Ripple' (S-c) CWGr
'Raspberry Valiant' (B) NHal
* 'Raymond Guernsey' ECtt
'Razzle Dazzle' (D) ERCP
'Rebecca Lynn' (D) CWGr
'Rebecca's World' (D) ECtt EPfP SPer
'Red and White' (D) CRos CWGr NRHS SGbt
'Red Arrows' (D) CWGr
'Red Balloon' (Ba) CWGr
'Red Cap' (D) CWGr
'Red Carol' (Pom) CWGr GRid
'Red Diamond' (D) NHal
'Red Emperor' (D) **new** GRid
'Red Fox'[PBR] (Ba) LCro LOPS
'Red Fubuki' (D) SDeJ
'Red Highlight' (S-c) CWGr
'Red Kaiser Wilhelm' (Ba) CWGr
'Red Majorette' (S-c) CWGr SDeJ
'Red Pathfinder' (Sin) NJRG
'Red Pimpernel' (D) CWGr
'Red Pygmy' (S-c) CRos CWGr NRHS SDeJ
'Red Riding Hood' (Sin) CWGr GRid
'Red Rock' (D) ERCP
'Red Sun' (D) CWGr
'Red Velvet' (WL) CWGr GRid
'Red Warrior' (Pom) CWGr
'Reddy' (Sin/Lil) CWGr
'Reedly' (D) CWGr
'Rees' Dream' (D) CWGr GRid
'Regal Boy' (Ba) CWGr
'Reginald Keene' (S-c) CWGr GRid NHal
'Reliance' (Ba) CWGr
'Renato Tosio' (D) CWGr
'Reputation' (C) CWGr SGbt
'Requiem' (D) CWGr ECtt ERCP NJRG
'Reverend P. Holian' (S-c) CWGr SGbt
'Revive' (Misc) CWGr
'Rhanna Tammy' (D) GRid
'Rhonda' (Pom) GRid NHal
'Rhonda Suzanne' (Pom) ♀H3 GRid
'Richard Marc' (C) CWGr
'Richard S' (S-c) NHal
'Riisa' (Ba) CWGr
'Rip City' (S-c) CAvo CRav CWGr ERCP LCro LOPS LRHS MCot
'Ripples' (D) **new** CRav
'Risca Miner' (Ba) CWGr
'Rita Easterbrook' (D) CWGr
'Rita Shrimpton' (Misc) CWGr
'Roan' (D) CWGr
'Robann Regal' (D) CWGr
'Robann Royal' (Ba) CWGr
'Robert Too' (D) CWGr
I 'Robin Hood' (Ba) CWGr
'Rocco' (Ba) ERCP LCro LOPS SGbt
'Rockcliffe Billy' (S-c) NJRG
'Rockcliffe Gold' (S-c) CWGr
'Rokewood Opal' (C) CWGr
'Romance' (C) CWGr
'Ron's Dark Ember' (Fim) **new** GRid
'Rosalinde' (S-c) CWGr
'Rosamunde' (D) **new** NRHS
'Rose Jupiter' (S-c) CWGr GRid NHal
'Rose Tendre' (S-c) CWGr
'Rosella' (D) CWGr SDeJ SGbt
'Rosemary Webb' (D) CWGr SGbt
I 'Rosita' (Col) CWGr
'Rossendale Flamenco' (D) NHal
'Rossendale Heide' (D) NHal
'Rossendale Izzy' (D) **new** GRid
'Rossendale Joshua' (D) GRid
'Rossendale Lewis' (D) GRid
'Rossendale Lottie' (D) **new** GRid
'Rossendale Luke' (D) CWGr GRid
'Rossendale Mollie' (D) NHal
'Rossendale Natasha' (Ba) NHal SGbt
'Rossendale Parky' (D) **new** GRid NHal
'Rossendale Peach' (D) GRid
'Rossendale Stephanie' (D) GRid NHal
'Rossendale Tara' (D) **new** GRid
'Rossendale Vicki' (D) **new** GRid
'Rosy Cloud' (D) CWGr
'Rothesay Castle' (D/DwB) CWGr
'Rothesay Herald' (D/DwB) CWGr
'Rothesay Reveller' (D) CWGr
'Rothesay Robin' (D) GRid
'Rothesay Rose' (WL) CWGr GRid
'Rothesay Superb' (Ba) CWGr
'Rotonde' (C) CWGr
I 'Roxy' (Sin/DwB) CAby CBcs CRav CRos CWGr EBee ECtt EHrv ELan EPfP ERCP LAyl LRHS LSRN NCou NHal NJRG NRHS SGbt WCot WSpi
'Royal Amethyst' (D) CWGr
'Royal Mail' (D) SGbt
'Royal Visit' (D) CWGr SGbt
'Royal Wedding' (S-c) CWGr
'Ruby' (D) **new** GRid
'Ruby Puff' (Anem) CWGr
'Ruby Red' (Ba) CWGr

	'Ruby Wedding' (D)	CWGr SGbt
	rudis	CExl CFil CWGr WPGP
	'Ruskin Amanda' (S-c)	GRid
	'Ruskin Andrea' (S-c)	GRid LAyl NHal
	'Ruskin Avenger' (S-c)	NJRG
	'Ruskin Belle' (S-c)	CWGr
	'Ruskin Bride' (S-c)	GRid NHal
	'Ruskin Buttercup' (D)	CWGr SGbt
	'Ruskin Charlotte' (S-c)	CWGr GRid
	'Ruskin Diana' (D)	CWGr GRid NHal NJRG
	'Ruskin Dynasty' (D)	CWGr
	'Ruskin Emile' (S-c)	CWGr
	'Ruskin Gypsy' (Ba)	CWGr
I	'Ruskin Harmony' (S-c)	CWGr GRid NHal
	'Ruskin Impact' (D)	GRid
	'Ruskin Lilactime' (Ba) **new**	GRid
	'Ruskin Limelight' (C)	NHal
	'Ruskin Marigold' (S-c)	CWGr GRid NHal
	'Ruskin Mars' (D)	GRid GWyn
	'Ruskin Michelle' (S-c)	GRid NHal
	'Ruskin Myra' (S-c)	CWGr GRid NHal
	'Ruskin Petite' (Ba)	CWGr
	'Ruskin Respectable' (S-c)	NJRG
	'Ruskin Sensation' (S-c)	NHal
	'Ruskin Splendour' (S-c)	GRid
	'Ruskin Sunshine' (S-c)	GRid
	'Ruskin Tangerine' (Ba)	NHal SGbt
	'Russell Turner' (S-c)	CWGr
	'Rustig' (D)	CWGr
I	'Rusty' (Sin)	CWGr
I	'Ruth Ann' (Ba) **new**	NHal
	'Ryecroft Brenda T' (D)	GRid NHal NJRG
	'Ryecroft Claire' (D)	NHal
	'Ryecroft Delight' (Ba)	NHal
	'Ryecroft Gem' (Ba)	GRid
	'Ryecroft Helen' (S-c) **new**	NHal
	'Ryecroft Ice' (D)	SGbt
	'Ryecroft Isobel' (D) **new**	GRid
	'Ryecroft Jan' (Ba) ♀H3	GRid NHal NJRG
	'Ryecroft Jim' (Anem)	LAyl NHal
	'Ryecroft Laura' (Ba)	NHal
	'Ryecroft Pixie' (C)	GRid NHal
	'Ryecroft Rebel' (D)	GRid NHal
	'Ryecroft Sparkler' (C)	SGbt
	'Ryecroft Yellow Orb' (Ba)	NHal
	'Ryecroft Zoe' (S-c)	NHal
	'Ryedale Pinky' (D)	CWGr
	'Ryedale Prince' (D)	CWGr
	'Ryedale Rebecca' (S-c)	CWGr GRid
	'Ryedale Ria' (D) **new**	GRid
	'Safe Shot' (D)	CWGr
	'Sailor' (Fim)	CWGr
	'Saint Giles 150' (Misc) **new**	GRid
	'Saint-Saëns' (S-c)	ERCP SDeJ
	'Sakura Fubuki' (Fim)	ERCP
I	'Saladin' (Misc)	CWGr
	'Salmon Athalie' (C)	CWGr
	'Salmon Carpet' (D)	CWGr
	'Salmon Hornsey' (D)	CWGr
	'Salmon Keene' (S-c)	GRid
	'Sam Hopkins' (D)	CRav ERCP LAyl NHal
	'Sam Huston' (D)	CWGr SGbt
	'Samantha'	see *D.* 'Harvest Samantha'
	'Sandia Melody' (WL) ♀H3 **new**	GRid
	'Sandia Rose' (WL)	NHal
	'Sandra' (D)	ERCP LCro
	'Sans Souci' (C)	CWGr
	'Santa Claus US' (D)	CWGr SGbt
	'Sarabande' (S-c)	CWGr

	'Sarah' (S-c)	CWGr ECtt EUJe LRHS NRHS
	'Sarah G' (S-c)	CWGr
	'Sarah Louise' (WL)	CWGr
	'Sarah Thomas' (Col)	CWGr
	'Sarum Aurora' (D)	CWGr
	'Sascha' (WL) ♀H3	GRid
	'Sassy' (D)	SGbt
	'Satellite' (S-c)	CWGr
	scapigeroides	CFil
	'Scarborough Ace' (D)	CWGr
	'Scarlet Comet' (Anem)	CWGr
§	'Scarlet Fern' (Sin)	CRos CWGr LRHS NRHS
	'Scarlet Kokarde' (D)	CWGr
	'Scarlet O'Hara' (D)	NJRG
	'Scarlet Rotterdam' (S-c)	CWGr
	'Scarlet Star' (S-c)	CWGr
	'Scarlett Claire' (Col)	CWGr
	'Scaur Blaze' (D) **new**	GRid
	'Scaur Christine' (D) **new**	GRid
	'Scaur Glen' (Pom) **new**	GRid
	'Scaur Major' (Ba) **new**	GRid
	'Scaur Promise' (D) **new**	GRid
	'Scaur Queen' (D) **new**	GRid
	'Scaur Ruby' (D) **new**	GRid
	'Scaur Saffron' (D) **new**	GRid
	'Scaur Sunrise' (D)	NJRG
	'Scaur Sunset' (D) **new**	GRid
	'Scaur Swinton' (D)	CWGr GRid NHal SGbt
	'Scaur Tango' (D) **new**	GRid
	'Scaur Topper' (Ba) **new**	GRid
	'Scaur Vale' (D) **new**	GRid
	'Scaur Whisper' (D) **new**	GRid
	'Schweitzer's Kokarde' (D)	CWGr
	'Scottish Rhapsody' (S-c)	CWGr GRid
	'Scura' (Sin)	CRav CWGr
	'Seattle' (D)	CBod CWGr
	'Seduction' (D)	ERCP
	'Seirō' (S-c)	SGbt
	'Senior Ball' (Ba)	CWGr
	'Senzoe Ursula' (D)	CWGr GRid
	'Severin's Triumph' (D)	CWGr
	'Shandy' (S-c)	CWGr LAyl SHar
	'Shannon' (D)	CWGr
I	'Sheila' (Ba)	GRid
	'Sheila Mooney' (D)	CWGr GRid
	'Shep's Memory' (WL) ♀H3	NJRG
	sherffii	CWGr NJRG
	'Sherwood Titan' (D)	CWGr
	'Sherwood's Peach' (D)	CWGr
	'Sheval Megan' (D) **new**	NHal
	'Shining Star' (C)	CWGr
	'Shirley' (D)	CWGr
	'Shirley Pillman' (Misc)	CWGr
	'Shirwell George' (D) **new**	GRid
	'Shirwell Greta' (D)	GRid NHal
	'Shooting Star' (S-c)	CRav CWGr
	'Show 'n' Tell' (Fim)	CWGr SGbt
	'Shy Princess' (C)	CWGr
	'Siedlerstolz' (D)	CWGr
	'Siesta' (Sin) **new**	CWGr
	'Silver City' (D)	CWGr NHal SGbt
	'Silver Years' (D)	CWGr
	'Silvie's Queen' (D) **new**	SDeJ
	'Sir Alf Ramsey' (D)	CWGr GRid LAyl NHal SGbt
	'Sisa' (D)	CWGr
	'Skipper Rock' (D)	CWGr
	'Small World' (Pom) ♀H3	CWGr GRid LAyl NHal
	'Smokey' (D)	CWGr SDir
	'Smoots' (Fim)	CWGr
	'Schneeflocke' (Ba)	CWGr

'Sneezy' (Sin/DwB) CWGr
'Snip' (S-c) CWGr
'Snoho Peggy' (Ba) GRid
'Snoho Tammie' (Ba) CWGr
'Snow Cap' (S-c) CWGr SDeJ
'Snow Fairy' (C) CWGr
'Snowbound' (D) GRid SGbt
I 'Snowflake' (Pom) ERCP SDeJ
I 'Snowstorm' (D) CWGr LRHS SGbt
'Snowy' (Ba) CWGr
'So Dainty' (S-c) ♀H3 CWGr
I 'Sofia' (WL) **new** CWGr
'Soheim' **new** GRid
'Song of Olympia' (WL) CWGr
'Sonia Henie' (Ba) CWGr
'Sophie Taylor' (SinO) NJRG
'Sorbet' (DwB) LAyl
I 'Sorbet' (D) NHal
'Sorbet' (S-c) see *D.* 'Geerlings' Sorbet' (MS-c)
sorensenii CFil CWGr
'Sorrento Flush' (D) NJRG
'Soulman' (Anem) CWGr ERCP NJRG SGbt
'Souvenir d'Eté' (Pom) CWGr SDeJ
'Spanish Conquest' (D) CWGr NHal SGbt
I 'Sparkler' (S-c) ERCP
'Spartacus' (D) ERCP NHal
'Spassmacher' (S-c) CWGr
spectabilis CWGr
'Spectacular' (D) CWGr SGbt
'Spencer' (D) CWGr
'Spennythorn Aristocrat' (Ba) **new** GRid
'Spennythorn King' (D) CWGr
I 'Spike' (S-c) SGbt
'Spikey Symbol' (S-c) CWGr
'Sprinter' (C) CWGr
'Staleen Condesa' (S-c) ♀H3 GRid SGbt
'Stan's Nirvana' (WL) **new** CWGr
'Star Child' (SinO) CWGr
'Star Elite' (C) CWGr
'Star Spectacle' (S-c) CWGr
'Star Surprise' (C) CWGr SDeJ
STAR WARS ('Vdtg14'PBR) (Dark Angel Series) (Sin) ERCP LCro LOPS SDeJ WHil
'Starlight Keene' (S-c) CWGr
'Starry Night' (S-c) CWGr
'Star's Favourite' (C) ERCP SDeJ
'Star's Lady' (C) CWGr
'Stellyvonne' (Fim) CWGr
'Stephanie' (S-c) CWGr
'Stevie D' (D) ♀H3 CWGr SGbt
§ 'Stolz von Berlin' (Ba) CWGr ERCP SDeJ SGbt
'Stoneleigh Joyce' (Pom) CWGr
'Storm Warning' (D) CWGr
'Storrs Julie' (Pom) NJRG
'Streets Ahead' (D) GRid
'Strike a Light' (C) CWGr
'Striped Vulcan' (S-c) CAby
'Sue Mountjoy' (Col) CWGr
'Sue Willo' (Pom) CWGr
'Sue's Kilmorie' (S-c) NHal
'Suffolk Fantasy' (D) CWGr
'Suffolk Punch' (D) CWGr LAyl
'Sugar Diamond' (C) EPfP ERCP
'Sugartime Sunrise' (D) GRid
'Suitzus Julie' (Misc) CWGr
'Summer Festival' (D) CWGr SGbt
'Summer Gold' (D) **new** GRid
'Summer Night' (S-c) see *D.* 'Nuit d'Eté'
'Summer Night' ambig. NHal
'Summer Nights' (Misc) NJRG
'Summertime' CRav
'Sunlight' (Ba) CWGr
'Sunlight Pastelle' (S-c) CWGr GRid
'Sunny Boy' (D) SDeJ
'Sunray Silk' (S-c) CWGr
I 'Sunshine' (Sin) LCro LOPS LRHS
'Sunshine Girl' (Col) NHal NJRG
'Super Trouper' (D) CWGr
'Superfine' (C) CWGr
'Sure Thing' (C) CWGr
'Susan Gilbert' (Col) NHal NJRG
'Susan Gilliott' (S-c) GRid NHal
'Susan Willo' (Pom) CWGr
'Sutton Gem' (Ba) **new** GRid
I 'Suzanne' (Col) NJRG
'Suzette' (D/DwB) SGbt
'Swallow Falls' (D) CWGr
'Swan Lake' see *D.* 'Classic Swanlake'
'Swanvale' (D) CWGr GRid SGbt
'Sweet Content' (D) CWGr SGbt
'Sweet Lady' (D) **new** CRav
'Sweet Love' (D) **new** ERCP
'Sweet Surprise' (D) **new** ERCP
'Sweetheart' (D) CWGr NJRG SDeJ
'Swiss Miss' (Ba) CWGr
I 'Sylvia' (Ba) CWGr ERCP LCro NJRG
'Sylvia's Desire' (C) CWGr
'Symbol' (S-c) CWGr
'Sympathy' (WL) CWGr GRid
'Syston Harlequin' (D) CWGr
'Syston Sophia' (Ba) CWGr
'Tahiti Sunrise' (S-c) CWGr EPfP
'Tahoma Moonshot' (SinO) CRav CWGr
'Tahoma Star' (SinO) LCro LOPS
'Take Off' (Anem) SDeJ
'Tally Ho' (Misc) ♀H3 CRos CWGr ECtt EHrv EPfP LRHS NJRG NRHS SDys WCot
'Tam Tam' (Ba) CWGr SPer
'Tamburo' (S-c) EPfP ERCP SPer
'Tangerine Pathfinder' (Misc) **new** NJRG
I 'Tapestry' (Sin) CWGr SGbt
'Taratahi Ruby' (WL) ♀H3 CWGr ERCP GRid NHal NJRG
'Tartan' (D) CWGr
'Tartarus' (P) **new** CWGr
TAXI DRIVER ('Vdtg57'PBR) (Dark Angel Series) (Sin) ERCP
'Teesbrooke Audrey' (Col) CWGr ECtt GRid LCro LOPS NHal NJRG
'Teesbrooke Red Eye' (Col) CWGr ERCP GRid NJRG SGbt
'Temptation Golden' (Misc) **new** CRos NRHS
'Temptation Lavender' (Misc) **new** CRos NRHS
'Temptation Pink Bicolour' (Misc) **new** CRos LRHS NRHS
'Temptation Red' (Misc) **new** CRos NRHS
'Temptation Yellow' (Misc) **new** CRos NRHS
'Temptress' (S-c) CWGr
'Tender Moon' (D) CWGr
tenuicaulis CDTJ CExl CWGr SBig
– F&M 257 CFil
– F&M 355 CFil
aff. ***tenuicaulis*** CWGr
'Terracotta' (Misc/DwB) NHal
'Terrie Bandey' (Fim) LAyl NHal
'Thais' (Col) NJRG

	'Thames Valley' (D)	CWGr
	'That's It!' (D)	CWGr
	'The Baron' (D)	CWGr
	'The Phantom' (Anem)	ERCP NJRG SDeJ
I	'The Queen' (S-c)	CWGr
	'Thelma Clements' (D)	CWGr
	'Thelma Joyce' (D) **new**	GRid
	'Theo Sprengers' (D)	CWGr
	'Thomas A. Edison' (D)	CAvo CRav CWGr ERCP LOPS SDeJ SGbt
	'Thoresby Jewel' (D)	CWGr
I	'Tiara' (D)	CWGr
	'Tiffany Lynn' (SinO)	CWGr
I	'Tiger' (Sin/DwB)	CWGr
	'Tiger Eye' (D)	SGbt
	'Tiger Tiv' (D)	CWGr
	'Timeless' (D)	SPer
	'Timmo' (D) **new**	ERCP
	'Tinker's White' (D)	CWGr
	'Tioga Chantilly' (Fim) **new**	GRid
	'Tioga Dawn' (Fim) **new**	GRid
	'Tioga Seahawk' (Fim) **new**	GRid
	'Tioga Spice' (Fim)	CWGr GRid
	'Tip Toe' (D) **new**	GRid
	'Toga' (WL)	CWGr
	'Tohsuikyoh' (Misc)	CWGr SGbt
	'Tom McLelland' (S-c)	NHal
	'Tommy Doc' (S-c)	CWGr
	'Tommy Keith' (Ba)	CWGr
	'Tomo' (D)	LAyl NHal
	'Top Affair' (S-c)	CWGr
	'Top Choice' (S-c)	CWGr
	'Top Totty' (D)	GRid NHal
I	'Topaz Puff' (Anem)	CWGr
	'Topmix' (Sin/DwB)	SDeJ
	'Topmix Mama' (Sin)	NJRG
	'Topmix Orange' (Sin)	NJRG SDeJ
	'Topmix Pink' (Sin/DwB)	SDeJ
	'Topmix Purple' (Sin)	NJRG
	'Topmix Red' (Sin/DwB)	NJRG SDeJ
	'Topmix Reddy' (Sin)	NJRG
I	'Topmix Rose' (Sin)	NJRG
	'Topmix Salmon' (Sin) **new**	ERCP
	'Topmix White' (Sin/DwB)	ERCP SDeJ
	'Topmix Yellow' (Sin/DwB)	SDeJ
	'Totally Tangerine' (Anem) **new**	CRav
	'Toto' (Anem)	ERCP SDeJ
	'Tour de Monde' (WL) **new**	CWGr
	'Towneley Class' (D)	CWGr
	'Tramar' (C)	CWGr
	'Trelissick Purple'	CWGr LSvl
	'Trelyn Crimson' (Col) ℽH3	NHal
	'Trelyn Daisy' (Col) ℽH3	CWGr
	'Trelyn Kiwi' (S-c) ℽH3	CWGr GRid NHal NJRG SGbt
	'Trelyn Red Dragon' (SinO)	NHal
	'Trelyn Seren' (SinO)	GRid LAyl NHal
	'Trendy' (D)	CWGr
	'Trengrove Autumn' (D)	CWGr SGbt
	'Trengrove Jill' (D)	CWGr
	'Trengrove Millennium' (D)	CWGr GRid NHal NJRG SGbt
	'Trengrove Tauranga' (D)	CWGr
I	'Trevor' (Col)	CWGr ECtt SGbt
	'Tricolor' ambig.	MSCN
	'Trooper Dan' (S-c)	GRid NHal
	'Trotter's Jo-Anne' (S-c)	CWGr
	'Troy Dyson' (Misc)	SDys
	'Truly Scrumptious' (S-c)	SGbt
	'Tsuki-yori-no-shisha' (Fim)	CWGr LCro LOPS
	tubulata	CFil EBee
	'Tudor 1' (Misc/DwB)	NHal
	'Tui Avis' (C)	CWGr NJRG
	'Tui Connie' (D) **new**	GRid
	'Tui Orange' (S-c)	CWGr
	'Tula Rosa' (Pom)	CWGr
	'Tutankhamun' (Pom)	CWGr
	'Tu-tu' (S-c)	CWGr SGbt
	'Twiggy' (WL)	CWGr SGbt
	'Twilight Time' (D)	CWGr SDeJ
*	'Twinkle Stars'	SDeJ
	'Twyning's After Eight' (Sin) ℽH3	CAby CAvo CBot CExl CRos CSpe CWGN CWGr ECtt EHrv ELan EPfP ERCP LAyl LCro LOPS LRHS MJak NHal NJRG NRHS NSti SDys SGbt SPer WBor WCot WHoo
	'Twyning's Aniseed' (Sin)	CWGr
	'Twyning's Black Cherry' (D)	CWGr ECtt
	'Twyning's Candy' (Sin)	CWGr
	'Twyning's Chocolate' (Sin)	CWGr
	'Twyning's Peppermint' (Sin)	CWGr
	'Twyning's Purple Cherry' (D)	CWGr
	'Twyning's Revel' (Sin) ℽH3	CWGr
	'Twyning's Smartie' (Sin)	CAby CWGr EBee ECtt LCro LOPS SPer
	'Twyning's Velvet' (Sin) **new**	CWGr
	'Twyning's White Chocolate' (Sin)	CWGr ERCP
	'Tyrell' (D)	EPfP
	'Uchuu' (D)	CWGr
	'Uncle Hankey' (D)	ERCP
	'Union Jack' (Sin)	CWGr
	'United' (D)	CWGr
	'Urchin' (C) **new**	CRav
	'Usugesho' (D)	CWGr
	'Vader Abraham' (D)	CWGr
	'Vaguely Noble' (Ba)	CWGr
I	'Valentino' (Dw)	CWGr
	'Val's Candy' (S-c)	GRid NHal
	'Vancouver' (Misc)	CWGr ERCP LCro LOPS SDeJ
	'Variace' (Ba)	CWGr
	'Vassio Meggos' (D)	ERCP GRid NHal
	'Vera's Elma' (D)	CWGr
	'Veritable' (S-c)	LCro LOPS
	'Verrone's Obsidian' (SinO)	ERCP LCro LOPS
	'Vicky Jackson' (WL)	CWGr
	'Victory Day' (C)	CWGr
	'Vigor' (WL)	CWGr
	'Viking' (Pom)	CWGr
	'Vino' (Pom)	CWGr
	'Violet Davies' (S-c)	CWGr
	'Vivex' (Pom)	CWGr
	'Vivian Russell' (WL)	NHal NJRG
	'Volkskanzler' (Sin)	CWGr
	'Vulcan' (S-c)	CWGr ERCP SGbt
§	'Vuurvogel' (S-c)	CWGr ERCP SDeJ
	'Walter Hardisty' (D)	CWGr GRid
	'Walter James' (D)	CWGr
	'Waltzing Mathilda' (Misc) ℽH3	CRav ERCP LCro LOPS
	'Wanborough Gem' (Ba)	CWGr
	'Wanda's Aurora' (D)	GRid
	'Wanda's Capella' (D)	CWGr GRid
	'Wanda's Moonlight' (D)	CWGr
	'Wandy' (Pom)	CWGr
	'War of the Roses' (D)	CWGr EWes WHer
	'Warkton Willo' (Pom)	CWGr
I	'Waterlily' (Sin)	CRos LRHS NRHS

I	'Welcome Guest' (S-c)	CWGr
I	'Wendy' (Ba)	CWGr
	'Wendy's Place' (Pom)	GRid
	'Westerton Folly' (Ba) ♀H3	NHal
	'Westerton Harry' (D)	NHal
	'Westerton JWH' (D) **new**	NHal
	'Westerton Lilian' (D)	GRid NHal
	'Westerton Southside' (D)	NHal
	'Weston Aramac' (S-c)	CWGr
	'Weston Buccaneer' (C)	NHal
	'Weston Corsair' (C)	NJRG
	'Weston Cream' (C) **new**	GRid
	'Weston Forge' (C)	CWGr
	'Weston Kelpie' (C)	NJRG
	'Weston Melody' (S-c) **new**	GRid
	'Weston Miss' (S-c)	CWGr GRid GWyn NHal NJRG
	'Weston Nugget' (C)	CWGr
	'Weston Pirate' (C) ♀H3	GRid LAyl NHal NJRG
	'Weston Spanish Dancer' (C) ♀H3	CWGr ERCP NHal NJRG SGbt
	'Weston Stardust' (C) ♀H3	GRid NJRG
	'Weston Tea-time' (C)	CWGr
	'Wheels' (Col)	GRid NJRG
	'White Alva's' (D) ♀H3	CWGr GRid LAyl NHal SGbt
	'White Aster' (Pom)	CWGr ERCP SDir
	'White Ballerina' (WL)	NHal SGbt
	'White Ballet' (D) ♀H3	CWGr LAyl SGbt
	'White Charlie Two' (D)	GRid NHal
	'White Hunter' (D)	CWGr
	'White Klankstad' (C)	CWGr
	'White Knight' (D)	GRid NHal
	'White Lace' (Fim) **new**	GRid
	'White Linda' (D)	CWGr GRid NHal
	'White Magenta Star' (Sin)	CWGr
	'White Moonlight' (S-c)	CWGr GRid NHal
	'White Nettie' (Ba)	CWGr SGbt
	'White Onesta' (D)	ERCP SDeJ
	'White Pastelle' (S-c)	GRid
	'White Perfection' (D)	CWGr ECtt ERCP SDeJ SDir WSpi
	'White Rustig' (D)	CWGr
	'White Seedling' (Sin)	CWGr
	'White Star' (S-c)	CRav CWGr ERCP LCro LOPS LRHS SDeJ
	'White Swallow' (S-c)	NHal
	white-flowered B&SWJ 14340 from Colombia **new**	WCru
	'Who Dun It' (D)	ERCP
	'Wicky Woo' (D)	CWGr
	'Wildwood Marie' (WL)	CWGr NHal NJRG
	'William B' (D)	CWGr
	'William John' (Pom)	CWGr
	'Williamsburg' (S-c)	CWGr
	'Willo's Borealis' (Pom)	CWGr GRid NHal
	'Willo's Flecks' (Pom)	CWGr
	'Willo's Night' (Pom)	CWGr
	'Willo's Place' (Pom) **new**	GRid
	'Willo's Surprise' (Pom)	CWGr GRid NHal SGbt
	'Willo's Violet' (Pom)	CWGr GRid NHal NJRG SGbt
	'Willowfield Matthew' (D)	GRid
	'Willowfield Mick' (D)	CWGr
	'Will's Ringwood Rosie' (Pom) **new**	GRid
	'Wilma McCulloch'	GWyn
	'Wine & Roses' (WL)	CWGr SGbt
	'Winholme Diane' (D)	GRid NHal
	'Winkie Colonel' (D)	CWGr GRid
	'Winkie Lambrusco' (Pom) **new**	NHal NJRG
	'Winnie' (Pom)	CWGr
	'Winsome' (WL)	CWGr
	'Winston Churchill' (WL)	CWGr WSpi
	'Winter Springs' (S-c)	ERCP
	'Wise Guy' (D)	CWGr
	'Wishes n Dreams' (Sin)	NJRG
	'Wisk' (Pom)	CWGr
	'Wittem' (D)	CWGr
	'Witteman's Best' (S-c)	CRav CWGr ERCP MCot SGbt
	'Witteman's Superba' (S-c) ♀H3	CWGr NHal
	'Wizard of Oz' (Ba)	CRav ERCP LCro LOPS
	'Woodbridge' (Sin)	CWGr SGbt
	'Woodside Finale' (D)	NHal
	'Wootton Carnival' (C)	CWGr
	'Wootton Cupid' (Ba) ♀H3	CWGr
	'Wootton Impact' (S-c) ♀H3	GRid NHal
	'Wootton Phebe' (D)	CWGr
	'Wootton Tempest' (S-c)	CWGr
	'Wootton Windmill' (Col)	CWGr
	'Worton Blue Streak' (S-c)	CWGr ERCP SGbt
	'Worton Revival' (D)	CWGr
	'Worton Superb' (D)	CWGr
	'Wyndal Horizon' (S-c)	CWGr
	'XXL Grand Central' (D)	CWGr
	'Yamabiraki' (D)	CWGr
	'Yellow Baby' (Pom)	CWGr
I	'Yellow Bird' (Col)	CWGr
	'Yellow Bulldog' (Sin)	CWGr
	'Yellow Galator' (C)	SGbt
	'Yellow Hammer' (Sin/DwB) ♀H3	CWGr NHal NJRG SGbt
	'Yellow Lakeland Sunset' (C) **new**	GRid
	'Yellow Linda's Chester' (C)	CWGr
	'Yellow Lorona Dawn' (Col)	NJRG
	'Yellow Pages' (D)	CWGr
	'Yellow Passions' (D)	ERCP
	'Yellow Perception' (WL) **new**	SDeJ
	'Yellow Pet' (D)	CWGr
	'Yellow Present' (D) **new**	GRid
	'Yellow Sneezy' (Sin/Lil)	SDeJ
	'Yellow Spiky' (S-c)	CWGr
	'Yellow Star' (S-c)	CWGr ERCP EUJe SDeJ
	'Yellow Vulcan' (S-c)	CWGr
	'Yelno Enchantment' (WL)	CWGr
	'Yelno Petite Glory' (D)	CWGr
	'York and Lancaster' (D)	CWGr EBee SGbt WAvo WBrk
	'Yukino' (Col)	CWGr
	'Zagato' (D)	CWGr
	'Zakuro-hime' (D)	CWGr
I	'Zelda' (D)	CWGr GRid
	'Zest' (D)	CWGr
	'Zingaro' (D)	LCro LOPS
	'Zirconia' (D)	ERCP
§	'Zone Ten' PBR (Sin/DwB)	CAby CRav CRos CWGr EPfP IBoy LRHS LSou NRHS SHar SPoG WBor
	'Zorro' (D) ♀H3	CWGr ERCP GRid NHal SGbt
	'Zundert Mystery Fox' PBR (Ba)	ERCP
	'Zurich' (S-c)	CWGr

Daiswa see *Paris*

Dalea (*Papilionaceae*)

gattingeri	SBrt
purpurea	EBee SPhx WHil

damson see *Prunus insititia*

Danae (*Asparagaceae*)

§ ***racemosa*** 🏆H5 — CBcs CFil CMac CRos CTri EBee EPfP EWes LEdu MGil MGos MMuc MRav SEND SPer SRms SWvt WCot WCru WPGP WSpi

Daphne ✿ (*Thymelaeaceae*)

DJHC 98164 from China — WCru
acutiloba — GKev WSpi
- 'Fragrant Cloud' — CExl CJun EWes SChF WPGP

albowiana — CJun GKev LCro LOPS WSpi
alpina — GKev WThu XEll
altaica — CJun
arbuscula 🏆H5 — EPot
arisanensis B&SWJ 6983 — WCru
aurantiaca — EPot
- 'Gang-ho-ba' — CJun

bholua — CJun EPfP LRHS
- B&SWJ 8275 from Fansipan, Vietnam — WCru
- GWJ 9436 from India **new** — WCru
- NJM 13.115 — WPGP
- I – 'Alba' — EPfP GKev SSta WPGP
- 'Cobhay Snow' — CJun
- 'Darjeeling' — CCCN CExl CJun CTho EPfP GKev WPGP WSpi
- 'Garden House Enchantress' — WPGP
- 'Garden House Ghost' — WPGP
- 'Garden House Red Stem' — WPGP
- 'Garden House Sentinel' — WPGP
- var. ***glacialis*** 'Gurkha' 🏆H4 — CExl CJun EPfP WPGP
- – – × ***mezereum*** **new** — WSpi
- 'Glendoick' — CJun
- 'Hazel Edwards' — LRHS
- 'Heale House' — WPGP
- 'Jacqueline Postill' 🏆H4 — CExl CJun CRos CTri GKev LBuc LCro LRHS LSRN MAsh MBlu MGil MGos SChF SCob SReu SSta WPGP WSpi
- 'Limpsfield' — CJun LRHS SSta WPGP
- 'Penwood' — CJun
- 'Peter Smithers' — CExl CJun EPfP SSta WPGP
- 'Wisley Purple' — CJun

blagayana — SRms
- 'Brenda Anderson' — CJun EPot WAbe

'Bramdean' — see *D.* × *napolitana* 'Bramdean'
× ***burkwoodii*** — CMea LSRN SCob
- 'Albert Burkwood' — CJun
- 'Astrid' (v) — CBcs ELon LCro LOPS MGil SCob SGol
- § – 'Carol Mackie' (v) — CJun
- 'G.K. Argles' (v) — CJun MAsh
- I – 'Gold Sport' — CJun
- 'Golden Treasure' — CJun MAsh SChF
- 'Lavenirii' — CJun
- 'Somerset' 🏆H4 — CBcs CJun ELan LCro LOPS MGil MGos MSwo SCob WSpi
- § – 'Somerset Gold Edge' (v) — CJun
- § – 'Somerset Variegated' (v) — EPot WThu
- 'Variegata' broad cream edge — see *D.* × *burkwoodii* 'Somerset Variegated'
- 'Variegata' broad gold edge — see *D.* × *burkwoodii* 'Somerset Gold Edge'
- 'Variegata' narrow gold edge — see *D.* × *burkwoodii* 'Carol Mackie'

caucasica — CJun
circassica — SChF
cneorum — CBcs ELan ELon GKev MGil
- 'Benaco' — EPot
- 'Eximia' 🏆H5 — WAbe
- var. ***pygmaea*** — EPot
- 'Variegata' (v) — EPot GEdr
- var. ***verlotii*** — EPot

collina — see *D. sericea* Collina Group
domini — EPot GKev
§ ***gemmata*** — LCro LRHS NLar
- 'Royal Crown' **new** — CCCN

giraldii — GKev
gnidium — CMCN
- PAB 8371 — LEdu

'Guardsman' — CJun MAsh
× ***hendersonii*** 'Apple Blossom' **new** — EPot
- 'Aymon Correvon' — WThu
- 'Blackthorn Rose' — WAbe
- 'Bonnie Glen' **new** — EPot
- 'Ernst Hauser' — SChF WAbe WThu
- 'Fritz Kummert' — WAbe WThu
- 'Jeanette Brickell' — WThu
- 'Kath Dryden' — EPot GEdr
- 'Rosebud' — EPot WAbe WThu
- 'Solferino' — WAbe

'Hinton' — CJun
× ***houtteana*** — CJun
japonica 'Striata' — see *D. odora* 'Aureomarginata'
jasminea upright — EPot
kamtschatica — GKev
'Kilmeston Beauty' — CJun
kosaninii — GKev
kurdica — GKev
× ***latymeri*** 'Spring Sonnet' — SChF WAbe
laureola — CJun EPfP GKev GPoy MMrt NBid NLar NPer SChr WSpi
- 'Margaret Mathew' — EPot NLar SChF WSpi
- subsp. ***philippi*** — CBcs CCCN CJun CMac EBee ELan EPfP EWes LCro LOPS LRHS MAsh MBlu MGil MGos NLar WCot WPGP WSpi

× ***mantensiana*** 'Audrey Vockins' — CJun
- 'Manten' — CJun

× ***mauerbachii*** 'Perfume of Spring' — CJun
'Meon' — see *D.* × *napolitana* 'Meon'
mezereum — CTri GKev GMaP GPoy IFoB IRob LRHS MAsh MGil MGos NChi SChF SCob SGol SWvt WCot WFar WHar WPGP
- f. ***alba*** — CJun GKev GLog MAsh MGos NChi SRms SWvt WAbe WSpi
- – – 'Bowles's Variety' — CJun EPot
- 'Rosea' — MAsh SRms
- var. ***rubra*** — CBcs CCCN CJun ELan GKin LRHS MGil MGos MJak MRav MSwo SPer WAbe WCFE WSpi

modesta **new** — XEll
× ***napolitana*** 🏆H4 — CJun
- § – 'Bramdean' — CJun SChF
- § – 'Meon' — CJun ELan EPot GEdr LRHS MAsh SChF WThu

odora — CBcs CCCN CJun CRos EPfP LCro LOPS LRHS LSRN MSwo NRHS SCob SEle SGol SPer WSpi
- § – f. ***alba*** — CCCN LRHS
- – – 'Sakiwaka' — CCCN CExl
- § – 'Aureomarginata' (v) — Widely available
- I – 'Aureomarginata Alba' (v) — SEle WSpi

- 'Double Cream' (v) CJun
- 'Geisha Girl' (v) MAsh
- var. ***leucantha*** see *D. odora* f. *alba*
- 'Mae-jima' (v) CExl CRos EPfP GMcL LRHS MAsh MGos SLon
- 'Marginata' see *D. odora* 'Aureomarginata'
- MARIANNI ('Rogbret') (v) CCCN LCro MGil MJak NLar SGol SWvt
- REBECCA ('Hewreb') (v) CBct CMea CRos EPfP LBuc LRHS LSRN MAsh MBNS MGos NRHS SLon SPoG WSpi
- var. ***rubra*** CCCN CMac GKev SGol
- 'Sweet Amethyst' **new** LCro LOPS
- 'Walberton' (v) CRos EPfP LRHS MNHC NRHS

oleoides GKev
- var. ***buxifolia*** GKev

papyracea CExl CFil

PERFUME PRINCESS ('Dapjur01') **new** CCCN ETMg GBin LCro LOPS LRHS NRHS

petraea WAbe XEll
- 'Garnet' WAbe
- 'Grandiflora' WAbe

pontica CJun CMac CMea CRos EBee EPfP LRHS MAsh NLar NRHS SChF SPoG WPGP WSpi

retusa see *D. tangutica* Retusa Group

× ***rollsdorfii*** 'Arnold Cihlarz' CJun SChF WAbe
- 'Wilhelm Schacht' ♀H5 CJun CRos EPot LRHS MAsh SChF WThu

'Rosy Wave' SChF

× ***schlyteri*** 'July Glow' EPot GEdr SChF
- 'Lovisa Maria' EPot GEdr

sericea XEll

§ - Collina Group SChF

'Spring Beauty' CJun LRHS SChF WPGP

'Spring Herald' CJun WPGP

× ***suendermannii*** 'Franz Suendermann' WOld

× ***susannae*** 'Anton Fahndrich' GKev SChF WThu
- 'Cheriton' ♀H5 ELan EPot NLar SChF WThu
- 'Tichborne' EPot SChF WThu

tangutica ♀H5 CBcs CExl CJun CSpe CTri EBee ELan EPfP GKev LCro LOPS LSRN MAsh MGil MGos SRkn SRms WAbe WKif WOld WPGP WSpi
- 'Golden Thread' (v) EPfP

§ - Retusa Group ♀H5 CExl CJun ELan EPot GBin GEdr GKev GMaP LCro MGil NHim SRms WSpi

× ***transatlantica*** CBot
- 'Beulah Cross' (v) CJun MAsh SChF
- ETERNAL FRAGRANCE ('Blafra'PBR) ♀H5 CBcs CCCN CExl CRos CWGN ELan EPfP EUJe GBin GKev LCro LOPS LRHS LSRN MAsh MGil MGos MJak NRHS SCoo SGol SLim SLon SPer SPoG WSpi XEll

§ - PINK FRAGRANCE ('Blapink'PBR) CBcs CRos ELan EPfP GBin GKev LCro LOPS LRHS MAsh MMrt NRHS SGol SPoG WSpi XEll
- SPRING PINK ETERNAL FRAGRANCE see *D.* × *transatlantica* PINK FRAGRANCE

'Valerie Hillier' CJun GKev

velenovskyi 'Weber's Findling' SChF

'White Queen' **new** LCro LOPS

× ***whiteorum*** 'Beauworth' EPot WAbe WOld
- 'Kilmeston' WAbe

wolongensis 'Kevock Star' CExl GKev SChF

Daphniphyllum (*Daphniphyllaceae*)

aff. ***angustifolium*** B&SWJ 8225 WCru
- B&SWJ 11804 WCru
- WWJ 12020 WCru

chartaceum KWJ 12244 WCru
- KWJ 12313 WCru

glaucescens WCru

subsp. ***oldhamii*** var. ***kengii*** B&SWJ 6872
- - - B&SWJ 7119 WCru
- - var. ***oldhamii*** B&SWJ 7056 WCru
- - - CWJ 12351 WCru

himalaense IDee

humile see *D. macropodum* var. *humile*

aff. ***longeracemosum*** B&SWJ 11788 WCru
- NJM 10.147 WPGP

macropodum CBcs CBct CCCN CFil EBee EPfP IArd LRHS NLar SArc SVen WCru WHor WPGP
- B&SWJ 581 WCru
- B&SWJ 2898 WCru
- B&SWJ 6809 from Taiwan WCru
- B&SWJ 8507 from Ulleungdo, South Korea WCru
- B&SWJ 8763 from Jejudo, South Korea WCru
- B&SWJ 11489 from Yakushima, Japan WCru
- B&SWJ 12691 **new** WCru
- dwarf WCru

§ - var. ***humile*** B&SWJ 11232 WCru

majus B&SWJ 11744 WCru

paxianum B&SWJ 9755 WCru

pentandrum B&SWJ 6888 WCru
- B&SWJ 7056 WCru
- CWJ 12393 WCru
- RWJ 9836 WCru

teysmannii B&SWJ 11110 from Japan WCru
- B&SWJ 11112 WCru
- B&SWJ 11358 from Japan WCru

aff. ***teysmannii*** CWJ 12350 from Taiwan WCru

Darlingtonia (*Sarraceniaceae*)

californica ♀H3 SHmp WSSs

Darmera (*Saxifragaceae*)

peltata ♀H6 Widely available
- 'Nana' EBee ECha ELan EPfP GCal LLWG NBid NLar WFar WMoo

Dasylirion (*Asparagaceae*)

§ ***acrotrichum*** CDTJ CExl EShb SArc

berlandieri CExl

cedrosanum CDTJ CJun SPlb

glaucophyllum CCht CFil CJun

gracile Planchon see *D. acrotrichum*

leiophyllum CFil

longissimum CCCN EShb ETod XSen

miquihuanense CBlu CCht SMad XSen
- F&M 321 EBee

quadrangulatum CFil EBee SPlb XSen

serratifolium ETod EUJe

wheeleri ♀H2 CBlu CBrP SPlb XSen

Dasyphyllum (*Asteraceae*)

diacanthoides	WPGP

date see *Phoenix dactylifera*

Datisca (*Datiscaceae*)

cannabina	CDTJ CSpe ECha GCal IMou LRHS SBrt SMHy SMad WHer WMoo WSHC XAbr

Datura (*Solanaceae*)

arborea	see *Brugmansia arborea*
cornigera	see *Brugmansia arborea*
metel	CBod
rosea	see *Brugmansia* × *insignis* pink-flowered
rosei	see *Brugmansia sanguinea*
sanguinea	see *Brugmansia sanguinea*
stramonium	EBtc
suaveolens	see *Brugmansia suaveolens*
versicolor	see *Brugmansia versicolor* Lagerh.
- 'Grand Marnier'	see *Brugmansia* × *candida* 'Grand Marnier'

Daucus (*Apiaceae*)

See also AGM Vegetables Section.

carota	CHab EBWF LRHS NMir SVic WHer WHil WSFF

Davallia ✿ (*Davalliaceae*)

canariensis 🏆^{H1c}	CMen
divaricata	NLos
mariesii 🏆^{H2}	CMen CPne NLos
- var. ***stenolepis***	CMen
tasmanii	CMen
trichomanoides	CMen NLos
- f. ***barbata***	CMen

Davidia (*Nyssaceae*)

involucrata 🏆^{H5}	Widely available
- 'Sonoma'	LRHS MBlu NLar SMad SWeb
- var. ***vilmoriniana*** 🏆^{H5}	CBcs CDul CRos ELan EPfP LMaj LRHS MAsh MBlu MGos SLim SPtp

Daviesia (*Papilionaceae*)

cordata	SPlb
* ***ovalifolia***	SPlb
pectinata	SPlb

Debregeasia (*Urticaceae*)

longifolia	SVen
- WWJ 11686	WCru

Decaisnea (*Lardizabalaceae*)

fargesii	Widely available
- B&SWJ 8070	WCru
insignis WJC 13740	WCru

Decodon (*Lythraceae*)

verticillatus	LLWG

Decumaria (*Hydrangeaceae*)

barbara	CMac MMuc NLar WCru WSHC
- 'Vicki'	NBro NLar
sinensis	CBot CRos EBee EPfP EUJe LRHS MMuc NRHS SBrt SLon SPoG WCru WSHC

Degenia (*Brassicaceae*)

velebitica	WAbe WOld

Deinanthe ✿ (*Hydrangeaceae*)

sp.	SDir
bifida	CBct CExl CMil CRos EBee EPfP EWes GEdr LRHS MMrt NRHS WCru WPGP
- B&SWJ 5436	WCru
- B&SWJ 5551	WCru
- B&SWJ 5655	LEdu NLar
- 'Pink-Kii'	WCru
- 'Pink-Shi'	CMil WCru WSHC
bifida × ***caerulea***	WCru
'Blue Blush'	WCru
caerulea	CMil CPne GEdr GKev IMou LEdu MMrt NLar NPnk WCru WSHC
- 'Blue Wonder'	CExl IPot LLHF MNrw
- white-flowered	IMou

Delairea (*Asteraceae*)

§ ***odorata***	CCCN CExl EShb WPGP

Delonix (*Caesalpiniaceae*)

decaryi	SPlb
regia	SPlb

Delosperma (*Aizoaceae*)

sp.	ESps
from Graaf Reinet, South Africa	EPot NSla XLum
from Ouberg Pass, South Africa	CPBP
§ ***aberdeenense*** 🏆^{H3}	SAko XLum XSen
alpinum	see *Ectotropis alpina*
ashtonii	CCCN EWes NSla WThu XLum
basuticum	NHpl NRHS NSla
'Beaufort West'	CRos EDAr EPot EWes LRHS NRHS NSla XLum
congestum misapplied	see *Malotigena frantiskae-niederlovae*
cooperi	CCCN CRos CTri ECtt EDAr EPfP EPot EUJe GBin GKev ITim LRHS LSou MHer MSCN NHpl NRHS SChr SPlb SRot SVen XLum XSen
dyeri RED MOUNTAIN ('Psdold')	CRos EDAr LRHS NRHS SAko XLum
ecklonis	GKev
FIRE SPINNER ('P001s')	EDAr XLum
floribundum SEQUINS ('Balosquin')	CAbb
- 'Starburst'	MHol
- 'Stardust'	EWes
GOLDEN WONDER ('Wowd20111'^{PBR}) (Wheels of Wonder Series)	CCCN LCro LOPS SPoG
jansei	NSla
(Jewel of Desert Series) 'Jewel of Desert Garnet'^{PBR}	CAbb CCCN CRos ECtt LCro LOPS LRHS NHpl NRHS SPad
- 'Jewel of Desert Moon Stone'^{PBR}	CCCN CRos ECtt LRHS NHpl NRHS
- 'Jewel of Desert Peridott'^{PBR}	CCCN CRos CWGN ECtt LRHS NHpl NRHS SPad
- 'Jewel of Desert Rosequartz'	CCCN CRos LRHS NRHS
- 'Jewel of Desert Ruby'^{PBR}	CCCN CWGN LRHS NHpl
- 'Jewel of Desert Topaz'^{PBR}	CAbb CCCN CRos CWGN ECtt EWTr LRHS NHpl NRHS SPad
§ 'John Proffitt'	CCCN GKev SAko SPlb XLum
lavisiae	ELon NSla SPlb
'Lesotho Pink'	EWes

lineare	XLum XSen
'Magenta Falls' **new**	CSma
MESA VERDE ('Kelaidis')	ECtt SAko XLum
nubigenum	CSma CTal CTri ECtt EPot EUJe GAbr GCrg GKev NHpl SPlb
- HOT PINK WONDER ('Wowdry1'^{PBR}) (Wheels of Wonder Series) **new**	LCro LOPS
ORANGE WONDER ('Wowdoy3'^{PBR}) (Wheels of Wonder Series)	CCCN SPoG
'Ruby Coral'	CRos ECtt EPot LRHS NRHS
sphalmanthoides	CPBP EPot GEdr NHpl NSla SPlb
sutherlandii ♀H3	CCCN CSma CTal EDAr EUJe GBin NHpl SRot XLum
- 'Peach Star'	CCCN EDAr GEdr NHpl
TABLE MOUNTAIN	see *D.* 'John Proffitt'
VIOLET WONDER ('Wowdrw5'^{PBR}) (Wheels of Wonder Series)	CCCN SPoG
WHITE WONDER ('Wowdw7'^{PBR}) (Wheels of Wonder Series)	CCCN SPoG

Delphinium ✿ (*Ranunculaceae*)

'After Midnight'	LHom
'Alice Artindale' (d)	EWes EWld IFoB LHom MAvo WCot
ambiguum	see *Consolida ajacis*
'Ann Woodfield'	CNMi LHom
'Apollo'	WSpi
'Ariel' ambig.	LRHS
Astolat Group	CBcs CBod CRos CTri EAJP ELan EPfP ESps GMaP GMcL IBoy LCro LOPS LRHS MGos MHol NLar NRHS SPer SPoG SWvt WCAu WHar
'Atholl' ♀H5	CNMi
'Baby Doll'	ESps
'Bambi'	CNMi
Belladonna Group	ELan EPfP WHar
- 'Atlantis'	CRos ECha IBoy LRHS NLar NRHS WCot WSpi
- 'Bellamosum'	EPfP GMaP LRHS MNrw SPer WSpi
- 'Casa Blanca'	EPfP GMaP LRHS MBel NLar WSpi
- 'Cliveden Beauty'	EPfP GMaP LRHS NLar SPer WHar WSpi
- 'Gute Nacht'	EBee
§ - 'Janny Arrow'	LRHS
- 'Moerheimii'	WSpi
- 'Piccolo'	ECha NLar
- 'Pink Sensation'	see *D.* × *ruysii* 'Pink Sensation'
- 'Snow White'	IBoy
- 'Völkerfrieden'	GMaP IBoy LRHS MNrw NLar WCot WSpi
'Berghimmel'	EBee LRHS
'Beryl Burton'	CNMi
Black Knight Group	Widely available
'Black Pearl'	ECtt
'Black-eyed Angels' (New Millennium Series)	ELan IPot SCob SGbt
'Black-eyed Beauty'	MHol
'Blauwal'	LRHS WSpi
'Blue Arrow'	see *D.* (Belladonna Group) 'Janny Arrow', *D.* 'Blue Max Arrow', *D.* 'Kings Blue Arrow'
Blue Bird Group	CBcs CRos CTri ELan EPfP ESps EUJe GMaP GMcL IRob LRHS MGos MJak NMir NRHS SGbt SPer SPoG WCAu
'Blue Butterfly'	see *D. grandiflorum* 'Blue Butterfly'
'Blue Dawn' ♀H5	CNMi LHom
Blue Fountains Group	EPfP LSRN SPoG SRms
'Blue Jay'	EPfP LSRN MWat WSpi
I 'Blue Lace' (New Millennium Series) **new**	CRos ECtt IPot LCro LOPS LRHS NCou NLar NRHS WSpi
§ 'Blue Max Arrow'	LRHS
'Blue Nile' ♀H5	CNMi LHom LRHS NRHS SPoG
'Blue Oasis'	CNMi
Blue Springs Group	NGdn
'Blue Tit'	CNMi ECtt LHom
'Bob Geldof'	CNMi
'Bolero'	CBcs ECtt IBoy SPoG WCot
'Boudicca'	CNMi
'Bruce' ♀H5	CNMi LHom
'Butterball'	CNMi LHom WSpi
Cameliard Group	CBcs CRos ELan EPfP LRHS NLar NRHS SPer SPoG
carolinianum	SBrt
cashmerianum	CPne
'Cassius'	LHom
'Centurion White' (Centurion Series) **new**	LCro
'Cha Cha'	CBcs EBee LRHS WCot
'Chelsea Star'	EBee LHom LRHS
'Cher'	CNMi
'Cherry Blossom'	CBod EPfP EWTr NLar
'Cherub' ♀H5	CRos LRHS NRHS
chinense	see *D. grandiflorum*
'Christel'	LRHS LSRN NLar
'Claire'	CNMi
'Clifford Sky' ♀H5	CRos LRHS NRHS
'Conspicuous' ♀H5	CNMi
'Constance Rivett'	LHom
'Coral Sunset' (d)	CBcs
'Cranberry Delight'	CNMi
'Crown Jewel'	EBee EWes LRHS
'Cupid'	LHom
'Dark Blue Black' (Excalibur Series) **new**	EPfP
'Dark Blue White Bee' (Excalibur Series)	EWTr GMcL
'Darling Sue'	CNMi LHom
'Darwin's Pink Indulgence'^{PBR}	CBcs
'Diamant'^{PBR}	LRHS
'Dreaming Spires'	SRms
'Dunsden Green'	CNMi LHom
Dusky Maidens Group	ELan IFoB LCro LOPS LRHS MHol NLar SGbt SPoG
elatum	GCal
- 'Dasante Blue'	MHol
- (New Millennium Series) 'Blushing Brides'	EBee LRHS SPoG
- - 'Double Innocence' (d)	CPla ECtt ELan IPot LRHS MHol NLar NRHS
- - 'Morning Lights'	ECtt EPfP IPot LRHS MHol NLar NRHS SPoG
- - 'Sweethearts' ♀H5	EBee ECtt
'Elizabeth Cook' ♀H5	CNMi LHom
'Elmfreude'	IBoy LRHS WSpi
'Emily Hawkins' ♀H5	CNMi LHom
exaltatum	CSpe LPla
'Fanfare'	LHom
'Faust' ♀H5	CNMi CRos LHom LRHS NRHS SPoG WSpi
'Fenella' ♀H5	CNMi CRos LHom LRHS NRHS
'Finsteraarhorn'	LRHS MAvo WSpi
'Flamenco'	CBcs ECtt SPoG WCot
'Foxhill Nina' ♀H5	LHom

Galahad Group	CBcs CBod CWCL EAJP ECtt ELan EPfP ESps GMaP GMcL LRHS MJak MWat NGdn NRHS SPer SPlb SPoG WCAu WHar
'Galahad' (Pacific Hybrid Series)	CRav IRob LCro LSun MGos MHol NLar
'Galileo' ♀H5	CNMi
'Gemini'	CNMi LHom
'Gemma'	CNMi LHom
'Gillian Dallas'	LHom LRHS
glaciale HWJK 2299	WCru
'Gordon Forsyth'	LHom
'Gossamer'	CNMi ECtt
§ ***grandiflorum***	GKev
§ - 'Blauer Zwerg'	WHar
§ - 'Blue Butterfly'	CMea CRos CSpe EPfP ESps LRHS NRHS SPlb SPoG WSHC
- BLUE DWARF	see *D. grandiflorum* 'Blauer Zwerg'
- Delfix Series	LRHS
- - 'Delfix Rose'	EPfP
- (Summer Series) 'Summer Blues'	LRHS SRot
- - 'Summer Nights'	CRos EPfP LRHS NRHS SPoG WHar
- 'White Butterfly'	CRos LRHS NRHS
'Green Twist' (New Millennium Series)	CRos ECtt LRHS NRHS SCob SPoG
Guardian Series **new**	NRHS
- 'Guardian Blue'	CRos EBee LCro LOPS LRHS MHol NRHS SPoG
- 'Guardian Lavender'	CRos LCro LOPS LRHS MHol NRHS SPoG
- 'Guardian White'	CRos LCro LOPS LRHS NRHS SPoG
Guinevere Group	CBcs CBod CWCL ECtt EPfP MBel SPer SPoG
- 'Lady Guinevere'	IBoy
'Guy Langdon'	CNMi
'Highlander Blueberry Pie'	ECtt IBoy LPla LRHS SPoG WCot WSpi
'Highlander Crystal Delight'	ECtt LCro LOPS LPla LRHS MHol SPoG WCot
'Highlander Morning Sunrise'	NSti SPoG WCot
himalayae	GKev
'Honey Pink'	CNMi
I 'Independence'	LRHS
'Innocence'	LRHS SCob WSpi
ithaburense **new**	SPhx
'Jenny Agutter'	CNMi
'Jill Curley' ♀H5	CRos LRHS NRHS
'Kathleen Cooke'	CNMi
'Kennington Classic' ♀H5	LHom
'Kestrel' ♀H5	CNMi LHom
King Arthur Group	CBcs CBod EAJP ELan EPfP IRob LSRN LSun MBel MGos MHol MWat SHar SPer SPoG WHar
§ 'Kings Blue Arrow'PBR	LRHS
'La Bohème'	WSpi
'Langdon's Orpheus'	LHom
§ 'Langdon's Royal Flush'	CRos LRHS
'Lanzenträger'	LRHS
'Leonora'	CNMi
'Light Blue' (Excalibur Series) **new**	EPfP
'Lillian Basset'	LHom
'Loch Leven'	CNMi
'Loch Nevis'	LHom
'Lord Butler' ♀H5	CNMi EBee EWes LRHS
'Lucia Sahin' ♀H5	CNMi LHom
maackianum	GCal LLHF WCot
Magic Fountains Series	CRos IFoB IRob LRHS SPlb SPoG SVic
- 'Magic Fountains Blue/White Bee'	IBoy
- 'Magic Fountains Bright Eye'	ESps
- 'Magic Fountains Cherry Blossom'	EPfP SPoG
- 'Magic Fountains Dark Blue'	CBod EAJP EPfP GMaP IBoy LPmr LSRN NEgg NLar SPoG
- 'Magic Fountains Lavender'	EAJP EPfP LPmr NLar NRHS
- 'Magic Fountains Lilac Pink'	EPfP SPoG
- 'Magic Fountains Lilac Rose'	CRos EAJP LRHS NRHS
- 'Magic Fountains Pure White'	CBod CRos EAJP EPfP IBoy LPmr LRHS NEgg NRHS
- 'Magic Fountains Sky Blue'	EPfP MHol SPoG
- 'Magic Fountains The Blues'	ESps
'Margaret' ♀H5	LHom
'Marilyn Clarrissa'	CNMi
'Melanie Avery' **new**	LHom
'Merlin' ambig.	LRHS
'Michael Ayres' ♀H5	CNMi LHom
'Mighty Atom'	CNMi IPot LHom LRHS
'Min' ♀H5	CNMi LHom
'Misty Mauves' (New Millennium Series) (d)	IRob LRHS WSpi
'Molly Buchanan'	CNMi
'Moon Light'PBR (Highlander Series) (d)	ECtt EPfP EWTr LBuc LRHS MHol NLar NPri SPad SPoG WCot WSpi
'Moonbeam'	LRHS NRHS SPoG
'Moonlight Blues' (New Millennium Series)	LPla LRHS SGbt
'Morgentau'	LRHS
'Morning Sunrise'PBR	IBoy LPla
'Mrs Newton Lees'	LRHS NLar
'Mydark' **new**	LHom
nudicaule	GKev SPlb
- 'Laurin'	LRHS
'Olive Poppleton' ♀H5	LHom
'Oliver' ♀H5	LHom
'Our Deb' ♀H5	LHom
'Ouvertüre'	LRHS
oxysepalum	LLHF
Pacific hybrids	EPfP ESps IBoy IRob LSRN MHer NLar SRms SWvt WHar
'Pagan Purples' (New Millennium Series) (d)	CRos EAJP ECtt EWTr IFoB LCro LOPS LRHS NCou NLar NRHS WSpi
'Patricia Johnson'	CNMi
Percival Group	CBod EPfP
'Pericles'	CNMi CRos LHom LRHS NRHS
'Pink' (Excalibur Series) **new**	EPfP
'Pink Punch' (New Millennium Series)	ELan EPfP LRHS SCob
'Pink Ruffles'	CNMi LHom
'Plagu Blue'PBR	NLar WSpi
PRINCESS CAROLINE ('Odabar'PBR)	CBcs
'Purple Passion' (New Millennium Series)	EAJP ELan EPfP LRHS NLar SCob SPoG
'Red Caroline'	CBcs
requienii	CBgR CSpe EWld SPhx
'Rose Butterfly' (d)	CRos LRHS NRHS
'Rosemary Brock' ♀H5	LHom
'Royal Aspirations' (New Millennium Series)	ELan LRHS SCob SGbt SPoG

'Royal Flush'	see *D.* 'Langdon's Royal Flush'
'Ruby'	CNMi
'Ruby Tuesday'	CNMi
'Ruby Wedding'	CNMi LHom
§ × ***ruysii*** 'Pink Sensation'	EWTr IBoy NLar WSpi
'Sandpiper'	CNMi LHom
'Schönbuch'	LRHS
'Secret' PBR	LRHS WCot
'Shieldbearer'	LRHS
'Silver Jubilee'	CNMi
'Sky Sensation'	IBoy LRHS
'Snow Queen Arrow'	LRHS
'Sommerabend'	LRHS
'Sooty'	CNMi
'Spindrift' 🏆H5	CNMi CRos LHom LRHS NRHS
staphisagria	XAbr
'Starlight' PBR	LRHS WSpi
'Strawberry Fair'	LRHS NLar NRHS SPoG
Summer Skies Group	CBcs CRav ELan EPfP ESps LCro LOPS LRHS MGos MWat NRHS SPer SPhm SPoG WCAu
'Summerfield Diana'	CNMi
'Summerfield Oberon'	LHom WCot
'Sungleam' 🏆H5	ECtt EWes LHom WSpi
'Sunkissed' 🏆H5	CNMi LHom
'Sunny Skies' (New Millennium Series)	ELan LRHS SPoG
'Sweet Sensation' PBR (Highlander Series) (d)	ECtt EPfP IBoy LPla LRHS NLar SPoG WCot WSpi
'Sweetheart'	CRos LRHS NRHS
tatsienense	IFoB
'Tiger Eye'	CNMi LHom
'Titania'	LHom
tricorne	MAvo
'Trudy'	CNMi
'Turkish Delight'	LHom
'Vanessa Mae'	CNMi LHom
'Walton Benjamin'	LHom
'Walton Gemstone' 🏆H5	LHom
'West End Blue' PBR	CRos NRHS
'White Swan'	EPfP
'Wishful Thinking' PBR	CBcs
Woodfield strain	WHrl
'Yvonne'	LRHS NLar
'Zauberflöte'	LRHS

Dendranthema see *Chrysanthemum*

Dendriopoterium see *Sanguisorba*

Dendrobenthamia see *Cornus*

Dendrocalamus (*Poaceae*)

asper	XBlo
giganteus	XBlo
§ ***strictus***	XBlo

Dendromecon (*Papaveraceae*)

rigida	CRos LRHS WPGP WSHC

Dendropanax ✿ (*Araliaceae*)

cf. ***kwangsiensis*** FMWJ 13274	WCru
trifidus B&SWJ 11230	WCru

Dendroseris (*Asteraceae*)

litoralis new	CCCN

Dentaria see *Cardamine*

pinnata	see *Cardamine heptaphylla*
polyphylla	see *Cardamine kitaibelii*

Deparia (*Woodsiaceae*)

conilii	NLos

Dermatobotrys (*Scrophulariaceae*)

saundersii	ECre

Derwentia see *Parahebe*

Deschampsia ✿ (*Poaceae*)

cespitosa	CBod CKno EBWF EPPr EPfP LCro LOPS LRHS SCob SPhx SPlb WCot WMoo XLum XSen
- BRONZE VEIL	see *D. cespitosa* 'Bronzeschleier'
§ - 'Bronzeschleier'	CBWd CBod CDor CMea CRos CWCL EBee EHoe ELan ELon EPPr EPed EPfP GBin GMaP GWyn LRHS MAsh MAvo MBel NGdn NRHS SCob SPer SPhx SRms SWvt WMoo WPtf XLum
- 'Cabana Buta' new	LEdu
- 'Coral Cloud'	GQue
- 'Fairy's Joke'	see *D. cespitosa* var. *vivipara*
- 'Garnet Schist'	GQue LRHS SPhx
- GOLD DUST	see *D. cespitosa* 'Goldstaub'
- GOLDEN DEW	see *D. cespitosa* 'Goldtau'
- GOLDEN PENDANT	see *D. cespitosa* 'Goldgehänge'
- GOLDEN SHOWER	see *D. cespitosa* 'Goldgehänge'
- GOLDEN VEIL	see *D. cespitosa* 'Goldschleier'
§ - 'Goldgehänge'	CSam EHoe XLum
§ - 'Goldschleier'	CBar CBod CRos CSam CSpe EBee ECha ELon EPPr EPfP GBin GMaP GQue IRob LRHS NGdn NRHS NWsh SCob SPhx SWvt WMoo XLum
§ - 'Goldstaub'	EPPr
§ - 'Goldtau'	Widely available
- 'Mill End'	CKno LEdu
- 'Morning Dew'	WFar
- 'Northern Lights' (v)	CSBt ELan EPfP LRHS MBel SLim SPer SPoG SRms SWvt XLum
- 'Pixie Fountain'	CBWd EBee GQue LRHS LSun NWsh SPtp
- 'Schottland'	CKno EBee ELon EPPr EPed GBin LEdu MAvo
- 'Tardiflora'	CKno EPPr
- 'Tauträger'	CKno EBee ELon EPPr GQue SMHy XLum
§ - var. ***vivipara***	EHoe EPPr GBin NBro
- 'Waldschatt'	CKno EBee EPPr
- 'Willow Green'	GCal SCoo
flexuosa	CBWd CKno CRos EBWF EHoe LRHS NRHS NWsh SPhx
- 'Tatra Gold'	CBWd CBod CRos CWCL ECha ECtt EHoe ELan ELon EPed EPfP ESps GMaP LRHS MAsh MRav NBro NGdn NRHS NSti SCob SLim SPer SPoG SRot SWvt

Descurainia (*Brassicaceae*)

bourgaeana new	SBrt

Desfontainia (*Loganiaceae*)

§ ***spinosa*** 🏆H4	CAbb CAby CBcs CBot CDul CMac CRos CTri EBee ELan ELon EPfP EUJe GAbr GKin GMcL IArd LRHS MAsh MBlu MGil NHim NLar SLim SPer SPoG SRms WFar WSHC
- 'Harold Comber'	CMac NLar WHor

- f. ***hookeri***	see *D. spinosa*
- Treseder form **new**	CTsd

Desmodium (*Papilionaceae*)

callianthum	CMac CRos LRHS SBrt WSHC
canadense	EBee IArd IDee MNrw NLar SBrt SPhx
cuspidatum	SPhx
var. ***longifolium***	
§ ***elegans***	CBcs CExl CHid CRos EBee ELan EPfP LRHS NLar SBrt SChF SPhx SVen WHer WPGP WSHC
- dark-flowered **new**	WPGP
glutinosum	SPhx
paniculatum	SBrt
praestans	see *D. yunnanense*
sessilifolium	CBot
tiliifolium	see *D. elegans*
§ ***yunnanense***	CBot CExl WSHC

Deuterocohnia (*Bromeliaceae*)

brevifolia ♀H2	CFil WCot WPGP
lotteae	WCot

Deutzia ✿ (*Hydrangeaceae*)

CC 4548	CExl
CC 4550	CExl
SDR 7953 **new**	GKev
bhutanensis HWJK 2180	WCru
'Bright Eyes'	WPGP
calycosa BWJ 8007	WCru
- 'Dali'	CExl CFil IArd NLar SDys
chunii	see *D. ningpoensis*
compacta	CMCN SLon WPGP
- 'Lavender Time'	CBot CExl CMac EPfP LRHS NLar SWvt
cordatula B&SWJ 3720	WCru
- B&SWJ 6917	WCru
corymbosa	MRav
- GWJ 9202 **new**	WCru
- GWJ 9203 **new**	WCru
- GWJ 9339 **new**	WCru
- var. ***corymbosa*** **new**	WSpi
crenata	CBot
- B&SWJ 8886	WCru
- B&SWJ 8896	WCru
- B&SWJ 8924	WCru
- 'Flore Pleno'	see *D. scabra* 'Plena'
- var. ***heterotricha*** B&SWJ 5805	WCru
- - B&SWJ 8879	WCru
- var. ***nakaiana***	SBrt
- - B&SWJ 11184	WCru
- - 'Nikko'	see *D. gracilis* 'Nikko'
§ - 'Pride of Rochester' (d) ♀H5	CAco CBcs CMCN ECrN GKin LRHS LSou MBlu MMuc MRav NLar SCob SEND SEle SGol SLim SPoG SWvt WGrn
'Dark Eyes'	CExl CFil EBee SAko
discolor 'Major'	CExl CFil IDee WCru WPGP
× ***elegantissima***	SRms
- 'Fasciculata'	CBod CRos EBee ELan EPfP EWTr LRHS NLar SPer SWvt WBor
- 'Rosealind' ♀H5	CBcs CBot CCCN CDul CExl CMac CRos CTri EBee ELan EPfP GKin IArd LRHS LSRN LSou MGil MRav SLim SPer SRms SWvt WCFE WKif WSHC WSpi
glabrata B&SWJ 617	WCru
- B&SWJ 8427	WCru
glomeruliflora BWJ 7742	WCru
gracilis	CBod CRos CSBt ELan EPfP EWTr GKin LRHS MAsh MGil MGos MRav MSwo NLar NRHS SPad SPer WFar WHar WSpi
- B&SWJ 8927	WCru
- 'Aurea'	CMac EPfP LRHS
- 'Carminea'	see *D.* × *rosea* 'Carminea'
§ - 'Nikko' ♀H4	CBcs CBot CExl CMCN CMac CRos EBee ELan EPfP EShb EWes GKin LRHS MGos MHer MMuc MRav NGdn NLar SEND SGol SPlb SRms SWvt WFar WKif WSHC
- var. ***ogatae*** B&SWJ 8911	WCru
- 'Rosea'	see *D.* × *rosea*
grandiflora	WPGP
'Hillieri'	CFil
hookeriana	CRos EBee EPfP LBuc LLHF LRHS MSCN NRHS SWvt
× ***hybrida*** 'Contraste' ♀H5	CMac
- 'Iris Alford'	CExl CRos EPfP LRHS MGos NRHS SChF SLon WFar WPGP
- 'Joconde' ♀H5	CExl WFar
- 'Magicien' misapplied	see *D.* × *hybrida* 'Strawberry Fields'
- 'Magicien' Lemoine	CDul CExl CMac CRos CSBt EBee ECrN ELan ELon EPfP EShb LEdu LRHS LSou MAsh MRav MSwo NEgg SLon SPer SRms SWvt WFar WKif WSHC WSpi
- 'Mont Rose' ♀H5	Widely available
§ - 'Strawberry Fields' ♀H5	Widely available
× ***kalmiiflora***	CExl CMac CSBt CTri EBee GKin MAsh MGil MJak MMrt MRav NLar SRms WFar
× ***lemoinei***	MJak NGdn
longifolia	CMCN WPGP
- 'Veitchii'	CDul CSBt EPfP MGil MRav
- 'Vilmoriniae'	MRav
× ***magnifica***	CDul MMrt NLar SGbt SRms
- 'Rubra'	see *D.* × *hybrida* 'Strawberry Fields'
× ***maliflora***	CFil
maximowicziana B&SWJ 11567	WCru
monbeigii ♀H5	CBot CExl CFil EPfP LLHF LRHS MRav SWvt WKif
- BWJ 7728	WCru
multiradiata	CExl CFil EBee WPGP
§ ***ningpoensis***	CExl CFil CRos CTsd EBee EPfP MGil NLar SMad WCFE WPGP
paniculata B&SWJ 8592	WCru
parviflora var. ***barbinervis*** B&SWJ 8478	WCru
'Pink Pompon'	see *D.* 'Rosea Plena'
prunifolia B&SWJ 8588	WCru
pulchra	CAby CBot CDul CMCN EBee ELan EPfP EWTr IDee LRHS MGil MRav SBrt SLon SPer SPoG SWeb WPGP WSpi
- B&SWJ 1738	WCru
- B&SWJ 3870	WCru
- B&SWJ 3948 from the Philippines **new**	WCru
- B&SWJ 6908	WCru
- pink-tinged	WPGP
purpurascens	GKev
- BWJ 7859	WCru
rehderiana	CFil
§ × ***rosea***	CDul CRos EPfP ESps LRHS MAsh NRHS SRms WKif

- 'Campanulata'	CExl MAsh MSwo
§ - 'Carminea'	MGil SPlb SRms
- YUKI CHERRY BLOSSOM ('Ncdx2') **new**	LCro LOPS
§ 'Rosea Plena' (d)	CBot CExl CMac CRos CSBt ELan EPfP GKin GMcL LBuc LRHS MAsh MGos MMuc NLar NRHS SEle SLim SPoG SWvt WFar
rubens	LLHF
scabra	CTri
- B&SWJ 11127	WCru
- B&SWJ 11168	WCru
- B&SWJ 11178	WCru
§ - 'Candidissima' (d) 🏆H5	CDul MGil MMuc MRav SCob SEND SPer
- 'Codsall Pink' 🏆H5	CFil MRav
§ - 'Plena' (d)	CExl ECrN EPfP GKin NLar SPer SPoG WCFE
- 'Pride of Rochester'	see *D. crenata* 'Pride of Rochester'
- 'Punctata' (v)	EHoe MMuc SEND SRms
- 'Robert Fortune'	SPlb
- 'Variegata' (v)	CDul CMac
setchuenensis	CMac MRav WCFE WSHC
- PAB 7449	LEdu
- var. ***corymbiflora*** 🏆H5	CBcs CBot CDul CExl CRos CTri EBee ECre ELan EPfP IDee LRHS MMuc MSwo NLar SAko SChF SEle SPoG SWvt WFar WKif WPGP WSpi
- - NJM 11.096	WPGP
- - 'Kiftsgate' **new**	WPGP
taiwanensis	EPfP SGol WPGP
- B&SWJ 6858	WCru
- CWJ 12443	WCru
- CWJ 12459	WCru
× ***wellsii***	see *D. scabra* 'Candidissima'
× ***wilsonii***	SRms
YUKI SNOWFLAKE ('Ncdx1') **new**	LCro LOPS

Diabelia (*Caprifoliaceae*)

§ ***serrata*** **new**	SBrt

Dianella ✿ (*Hemerocallidaceae*)

caerulea	CBcs CJun CMac EBee EPri IBoy IMou NLar
- CASSA BLUE ('Dbb03'PBR)	CHll EPfP LRHS SPer SPoG
- LITTLE JESS ('Dcmp01'PBR)	CExl EBee
- 'Variegata'	see *D. tasmanica* 'Variegata'
ensifolia	LEdu
nigra	CBcs CExl IMou LEdu
- 'Margaret Pringle' (v)	CBcs CExl
§ ***revoluta*** 'Allyn Citation'PBR	LRHS
- 'Blue Stream'	EBee
- COOLVISTA	see *D. revoluta* 'Allyn Citation'
- LITTLE REV ('Dr5000'PBR)	EBee EPfP SEle
'Silver Streak' (v)	LRHS NRHS
'Streetscape'	EBee
tasmanica	CAbb CBar CBcs CElw CExl CKno CMac CPne CTal CTri CTsd ECre ELan EPfP EShb EUJe GBin IBoy LEdu SEle SMad SRms WSHC
- from Logan	GCal
- 'Emerald Arch'	LEdu SPer
- 'Splice'	CDTJ MJak
- TASRED ('Tr20'PBR)	CBod CExl ELan EPfP EUJe MBNS NPla SPer
§ - 'Variegata' (v)	CCCN CDTJ CExl ELan NLar

Dianthus ✿ (*Caryophyllaceae*)

'Alan Titchmarsh' (p)	CRos ECtt EPfP ESps LRHS LSRN MGos NEgg NRHS SPoG SWvt
'Albert Hill' (p)	SAll
'Albus Plenus' (p)	MJak
'Aldridge Yellow' (b)	SAll
'Alfred Galbally' (b)	SAll
'Alice' (p)	LSRN SAll
'Alice Forbes' (b)	SAll
'Alice Lever' (p)	WAbe
§ 'Allen's Maria' (p)	SAll
'Allspice' (p)	CFis MRav WHoo
Allwoodii Group (p)	NNor
- (Cocktails Series) CHERRY DAIQUIRI ('Wp15 Pie42') (p)	MTis WHlf
-- SHIRLEY TEMPLE ('Wp15 Pie44') (p)	MTis WHlf
-- TEQUILA SUNRISE ('Wp15 Pie45') (p)	MTis WHlf WTor
- 'Doris' (p) 🏆H6	Widely available
Allwoodii Alpinus Group (p)	NGdn SRms XLum
'Allwood's Celebration' (p)	SAll
'Allwood's Crimson' (pf)	SAll
'Allwood's Delight' (p)	SAll
alpinus 🏆H6	ESps GCrg GJos MMuc NRHS NSla
- 'Albus' (p)	GCrg NWad
- 'Joan's Blood' (p) 🏆H6	EPot GCrg LSRN NHpl WAbe WRHF
'Alyson' (p)	SAll
amurensis	EPPr GCal NNor SPhx XLum
- 'Andrey' (p)	NNor
- 'Siberian Blue' (p)	EPPr GPSL
anatolicus	CRos EDAr GJos LRHS MHer NGdn NRHS XLum
'Anders Fay Seagrave' (p)	SAll
'Anders Irene Ann' (pf)	CNMi
'Anders Melody' (p)	SAll
'Anders Patricia Griffiths' (p)	CNMi SAll
'Angela Carol' (pf)	CNMi
'Annabelle' (p)	SAll
'Annette' (p)	CMea CPBP CRos EDAr GCrg IPot LRHS LSRN MAsh NGdn NRHS SRGP SWvt
'Annie Claybourne' (pf)	CNMi
'Apricot Sue' (pf)	SAll
ARCTIC STAR	see *D.* 'Devon Arctic Star'
arenarius	GKev LEdu NGdn SAll SPlb WWFP XLum
- 'Little Maiden' (p)	CSpe GWyn MMuc NGdn
- 'Snow Flurries' (p)	ITim
'Argus' (p)	SAll
'Aristocrat' **new**	SAll
* 'Arlene' (b)	SAll
armeria	CBgR CFis EBWF WHer WOut
arpadianus var. ***pumilus***	EPot
§ × ***arvernensis*** (p) 🏆H6	ECha EPot SBch SMHy
'Ashley Reay' (p) **new**	CNMi
'Audrey Robinson' (pf)	CNMi
'Aurora' (b)	SAll
'Auvergne'	see *D.* × *arvernensis*
'Averiensis'	see *D.* 'Berlin Snow'
'Badenia' (p)	ECha
'Bailey's Celebration' (p)	MTis
barbatus	SVic
- AURICULA EYED MIXED (p,a) **new**	CRav
- 'Black Adder' (p,a)	CSpe

	- 'Dash Crimson' (p,a) **new**	MHol
	- 'Dash Magician' (p,a) **new**	MHol
	- GREEN TRICK ('Temarisou'[PBR]) (p,a) **new**	CRav EBee
	- 'Heart Attack' (p,a)	WCot
	- 'Indian Carpet' (p,a)	LCro
	- Midget Group (p,a)	CBod GJos
	- 'Monksilver Black' (p,a)	CSpe EBee ECtt EUJe LSou MAvo MBNS MBel MHol MPie NCou NSti SMad SPad WCot
	- Nigrescens Group (p,a) ♀H7	CBre CSpe SPhx WHil
	- - 'Sooty' (p,a)	CBod CRav GJos GWyn WFar WHer
	- 'Oeschberg' (p,a)	GWyn SAko
*	- 'Roseus' (p,a)	GWyn
	- 'Super Parfait Strawberry' (Super Parfait Series) (p,a) ♀H7	CRos LRHS NRHS
	- Sweet Series (p,a) **new**	ETMg
	- 'Tuxedo Black' (p,a)	WMoo
	'Barley Sugar' (pf)	CNMi
	basuticus	CPbh
§	'Bat's Double Red' (p)	SAll
	'Becky Robinson' (p) ♀H6	CNMi SAll
	'Belmont Duchess' (p)	SAll
§	'Berlin Snow' (p)	CPBP CRos EPot GCrg ITim LRHS NRHS
	'Betsy' (pf)	SAll
	'Betty Miller' (b)	SAll
	'Betty Morton' (p) ♀H6	CRos IFoB LRHS NRHS WKif
	'Betty's Choice' (pf)	CNMi
	'Bill Smith' (pf)	CNMi
	'Binsey Red' (p)	SBch
	'Blackjack' (b) **new**	ETMg
	'Blue Hills' (p)	GKev
	'Blue Ice' (b)	SAll
	'Blush'	see *D.* 'Souvenir de la Malmaison'
	'Bobby' (p)	SAll
	'Bob's Highlight' (pf)	CNMi
	'Bombardier' (p)	ECtt
	'Bookham Gleam' (b)	SAll
	'Bookham Grand' (b)	SAll
	'Bookham Heroine' (b)	SAll
	'Bookham Lad' (b)	SAll
	'Border Special' (b)	SAll
	'Bouquet Purple' (p)	CSpe
	'Bovey Belle' (p)	SAll
	'Bramdean' (pf)	CNMi
	brevicaulis subsp. ***brevicaulis***	LLHF
	'Brian Tumbler' (b) ♀H6	SAll
	'Bridal Veil' (p)	SAll SBch WHer
	'Brilliance' (p)	WMoo
	'Brilliant'	see *D. deltoides* 'Brilliant'
	'Brilliant Star' (p) ♀H6	CRos ECtt LRHS NRHS SEND SWvt
	'Brockenhurst' (pf)	CNMi
	'Brympton Red' (p)	CFis ECha SAll
	'Bryony Lisa' (b) ♀H6	SAll
	caesius	see *D. gratianopolitanus*
	callizonus	LLHF
	'Calypso' (pf)	CTri
	'Calypso Star' (p)	ECtt SPoG
	'Can-can' (pf)	ECtt MHol
	'Candy Clove' (b)	SAll
	CANDY FLOSS	see *D.* 'Devon Flavia'
	'Candy Spice' (p)	MRav
§	'Carmine Letitia Wyatt'[PBR] (p) ♀H6	CRos ECtt LRHS NRHS SPoG
	carthusianorum	Widely available
	- W&B BGL-1	WCot
I	- 'Rupert's Pink' (p)	EBee NGdn SWvt
	caryophyllus	ENfk SVic WSFF
	CASSANDRA ('Bardranasca'[PBR]) (pf)	SAll
	'Casser's Pink' (p)	NWad
	'Castleroyal Sceptre' (p) **new**	SAll
	'Charles' (p)	SAll
	'Charles Edward' (p)	SAll
	'Charles Musgrave'	see *D.* 'Musgrave's Pink'
	'Chastity' (p)	ECtt LLHF SAll WHoo
	Cheddar pink	see *D. gratianopolitanus*
	'Cherly'	LSRN
	'Cherry Clove' (b)	SAll
	'Cheryl'	see *D.* 'Houndspool Cheryl'
	'Chesswood Barbara Arif' (b) ♀H6 **new**	SAll
	'Chesswood Dorothy Cottam' (b)	SAll
	'Chetwyn Ruth Gillies' (pf)	CNMi
	CHILI	see *D.* CRACKER
	chinensis 'Black and White' (p,a)	CSpe
	'Chomley Farran' (b)	MCot
	'Chris Crew' (b) ♀H6	SAll
	'Christopher' (p)	SAll
	'Circus Clowns' (b) **new**	ETMg
	'Clare' (p)	ECtt SAll
	'Claret Joy' (p) ♀H6	ECtt EPfP ESps MMuc SAll SEND
	'Cleopatra' (pf)	EMal
	'Clifford Pipperoo' (pf)	SAll WCot
	'Clunie' (b)	SAll
§	'Cockenzie Pink' (p)	SAll SBch WHer
	COCONUT SUNDAE ('Wp 05 Yves'[PBR]) (Scent First Series) (p)	CRos ECtt ELan ELon LCro LOPS LRHS LSRN MCot NNor NRHS SEND SRot WTor
	'Constance' (p)	SAll
	'Constance Finnis'	see *D.* 'Fair Folly'
	'Consul' (b)	SAll
	'Conwy Silver' (p)	WAbe
	'Conwy Star' (p)	WAbe
	'Coral Reef'[PBR] (Scent First Series) (p)	CRos ECtt ELan LRHS NNor NRHS SPoG
	'Corona Iceberry Magic' (p,a) **new**	CRos NRHS
	'Coronation Ruby' (p) ♀H6	SAll
	corsicus	XSen
	COSMOPOLITAN ('Wp15 Pie43') (p)	MTis
	'Coste Budde' (p)	SBch WSHC
§	CRACKER ('Wp10 Sab06'[PBR]) (Early Bird Series) (p)	CRos LRHS
	'Cranberry Crush' (pf)	CNMi
	'Cranmere Pool' (p) ♀H6	CBcs CRos ECtt ELan EPfP LRHS NNor NRHS SEND SPoG SWvt WBrk WTor
	'Crimson Chance' (p)	NSla
	'Crimson Rim' (b) **new**	ETMg
	'Crimson Warrior' (pf)	CNMi
	'Crock of Gold' (b)	SAll
	'Crompton Classic' (pf)	CNMi
	'Crompton Princess' (pf)	CNMi
	cruentus	CAby CBWd CFis CSpe ELan EPPr EWes GCal LCro LRHS MBel NDov SHar SPhx SPtp SWvt WCAu
	'Cumbria' (pf) **new**	CNMi
	'D.D.R.'	see *D.* 'Berlin Snow'
	'Dad's Favourite' (p)	SAll

	'Dainty Dame' (p) ♀H4	CRos CSpe CTri ECtt EPfP LRHS MNHC NRHS SAll SBch
§	'Dancing Queen'PBR (p)	NNor
	'Daphne' (p)	SAll
	'David' (p)	LSRN SAll SCob
	'David Russell' (b) ♀H6	SAll
	'Dawn' (b)	SAll
	'Dawn's Delight' (pf) **new**	CNMi
	'Dedham Beauty' (p)	MPie SEND WCot
	deltoides ♀H6	CPbh CWld EBWF ECha ENfk EPfP EWld LEdu MAsh MBel MMuc MNHC SPlb SRms WPtf
	- 'Albus' (p)	ECha EPfP GBin GWyn NGdn WMoo
	- 'Arctic Fire' (p)	EPfP GAbr GJos GWyn MBel NGdn NSla SBee WFar WMoo
§	- 'Brilliant' (p)	CChe EAJP GJos GWyn NGdn SAll SRms WHar WHoo
	- 'Broughty Blaze' (p)	GCrg
	- 'Dark Eyes' (p)	EWes
	- 'Erectus' (p)	EPfP
	- FLASHING LIGHT	see *D. deltoides* 'Leuchtfunk'
§	- 'Leuchtfunk' (p)	GJos GPSL MJak NNor NRHS SPoG WMoo WTor
I	- 'Luneburg Heath Maiden Pink' (p)	NGdn
	- Microchips Group (p)	WMoo
	- 'Nelli' (p)	NGdn WMoo
	- red-flowered (p)	SVic
	- 'Shrimp' (p)	EAJP ECtt NGdn
	'Dennis' (p)	LSRN SAll
	'Desert Song' (b)	SAll
	'Desmond'	EPfP
§	'Devon Arctic Star' (Early Bird Series) (p)	CMea CRos CTri ELan GMaP LRHS NRHS SPoG SRot SWvt
	'Devon Cream'PBR (p)	ECtt ELan ESps LRHS NEgg
	'Devon Dove'PBR (p) ♀H6	CRos CSBt CTri ECtt ELan EPfP LRHS MRav MTis NEgg NRHS
	'Devon Esther'	see *D.* POP STAR
	'Devon Fatima'	see *D.* ICED GEM
§	'Devon Flavia'PBR (Scent First Series) (p) ♀H6	CRos ELan LCro LRHS LSou MTis NRHS SPoG
	'Devon Flores'	see *D.* SHOOTING STAR
	'Devon General'PBR (p)	CRav
	'Devon Glow' (p)	EPfP
	'Devon Magic'PBR (p)	ECtt
	'Devon Opal'	see *D.* LADY MADONNA
	'Devon Sapphire'	see *D.* MYSTIC STAR
	'Devon Verity'	see *D.* 'Dancing Queen'
§	'Devon Winnie'PBR (p)	MAsh MTis
	'Devon Wizard'PBR (p) ♀H6	CRav CRos CSBt ECtt EPfP LRHS MRav MSpe MTis NDov NEgg NNor NRHS WCAu
§	'Devon Xera' (p) ♀H6	MTis SEND
§	'Devon Yolande'PBR (Scent First Series) (p)	ECtt ELan EPfP LRHS LSRN NRHS SEND SPoG
	'Dewdrop' (p)	CMea EPot EWTr MAsh MHer MMuc NGdn SAll SEND WHal
	'Dian Cape' (b)	SAll
	'Diana'	see *D.* DONA
	'Diane' (p) ♀H6	ECtt ELan EPfP ESps ETMg NEgg SAll SPoG SWvt WHar
	DIANTICA DARK RED PINK EYE **new**	CRos NRHS
	DIANTICA WHITE WITH EYE ('Kledg11116') **new**	CRos NRHS
	'Dinetta Lilac' (p)	CRos LRHS NRHS
	'Dinetta Pink' (p)	CRos LRHS NRHS
	'Diplomat' (b)	SAll
§	DONA ('Brecas') (pf)	LSRN SRGP
	'Dora' (p)	CRos LRHS NRHS
	'Doreen Hodgson' (p)	ECtt SAll
	'Doris Allwood' (pf)	CNMi CSBt EMal SAll
	'Doris Elite' (p)	SAll
	'Doris Galbally' (b)	SAll
	'Doris Majestic' (p)	SAll
	'Doris Ruby'	see *D.* 'Houndspool Ruby'
	'Doris Supreme' (p)	SAll
	'Double Lace' (b)	ECtt
	'Double North' (p)	CTri
	DUBAI ('Bardibua'PBR) (pf)	SAll
	'Dubarry' (p)	ECtt
	'Duchess of Fife' (p)	EPfP
	'Duchess of Roxburghe' (pf)	EMal SAll
	'Duchess of Westminster' (M)	EMal SAll
	'Duke of Norfolk' (pf)	EMal SAll
	'Dunkirk Spirit' (pf)	CNMi
	'Dusky Janelle' (pf)	CNMi
	'Earl Kelso' (pf)	EMal
	'Earl of Essex' (p)	SAll
	'Edenside Scarlet' (b)	SAll
	'Edenside White' (b)	SAll
	'Edna' (p)	SAll
	'Edward Allwood' (pf)	SAll
	'Edwin Cross' (b)	SAll
	'Eileen' (p)	SAll
	'Eileen Lever' (p)	CPBP EPot GCrg IFoB WAbe
	'Eileen O'Connor' (b) ♀H6	SAll
	'Eira Wen' (p)	WAbe
	'Eleanor Parker' (p)	EPot WAbe
	'Eleanor's Old Irish' (p)	ECtt ELon LRHS MBel MHol MPie SEND WBrk WCot WHoo
	'Elizabeth Nelson' (b)	SAll
	'Elizabethan' (p)	CFis CSpe EWTr MCot MHCG SDys
*	'Elizabethan Pink' (p)	SAll
	'Elsie Ketchen' (pf)	CNMi
	'Emile Paré' (p)	CFis
	'Emjay' (b)	SAll
	'Emmeline Pankhurst' (pf)	CNMi
	'Emperor'	see *D.* 'Bat's Double Red'
	erinaceus	GCrg GJos
	- var. ***alpinus***	EPot ITim NSla
	- Duguid's	WAbe
	'Erycina' (b)	SAll
	'Ethel Hurford' (p)	WHoo
	'Eva Humphries' (b)	SAll
	'Evelyn Berry' (p)	CNMi
	'Evening Star' (p) ♀H6	CRos CTri LRHS NRHS SPoG SWvt
	EVERLAST RASPBERRY CREAM ('Kledg13158'PBR) **new**	CRos NRHS
	'Eve's Holly' (pf)	CNMi
	'Exquisite' (b)	SAll
§	'Fair Folly' (p)	SAll WHer
	'Farnham Rose' (p)	SAll
	'Fettes Mount' (p)	WAvo WBrk WCot
	'Feuerhexe' (p)	ECtt GCrg XLum
	'Fimbriatus' (p)	WHoo
	'Fiona' (p)	SAll
	FIRE STAR	see *D.* 'Devon Xera'
	'Firestar' (p)	CRos CTri ELan GMaP LRHS MAsh NRHS SRot SWvt
	'First Lady' (b)	SAll
	FIZZY ('Wp08 Ver03'PBR) (Early Bird Series) (p)	CRos ELan LRHS MHol NRHS
	'Flanders' (b) ♀H6	SAll
	'Flashdance' (pf)	CNMi
	'Fleur' (p)	SAll

	'Florence Franklin' (pf)	CNMi
	'Floristan Mix' (p,a)	NNor
	'Forest Glow' (b)	SAll
	'Forest Princess' (b)	SAll
	'Forest Sprite' (b)	SAll
	'Forest Treasure' (b)	SAll
	'Forge Pink'	LLHF
	'Fortuna' (p)	SAll
	'Fragrant Ann' (pf) Υ^{H6}	EMal SAll
	'Frances Isabel' (p)	SAll
	'Freda' (p)	SAll
	'Freda Woodliffe' (p)	ECtt GCrg SBch WAbe WHoo
	freynii	EPot EWes GKev WAbe
*	- var. ***nana***	GKev
	FRILLY ('Wp08 Ulr03'^{PBR}) (Early Bird Series) (p) **new**	CRos NRHS
	fringed pink	see *D. superbus*
	'Fusilier' (p)	CBod CPla CRos CTri ECtt EDAr EPfP GCrg GMaP LRHS MAsh NRHS SAll SHar SRot SWvt
	'Gail Graham' (b)	SAll
	'Gail Tilsley' (b)	SAll
	'Garland' (p)	CMea
	'Gaydena' (b)	SAll
	'Gingham Gown' (p)	ECtt EPot SAll
*	***glacialis elegans***	GKev
	'Gold Dust' (p)	ECtt EPot EWTr SAll SBch
	'Gold Embrace' (pf)	CNMi
	'Grace's Scarlet Clove' (b)	SAll
	'Grandma Calvert' (p)	SAll
	'Gran's Favourite' (p) Υ^{H6}	CBcs CRav CRos CSBt ECtt ELan EPfP ESps ETMg GJos LCro LOPS LRHS LSRN MCot MGos MMuc MTis NEgg NGdn NNor SAll SEND SPer SPlb SPoG SRGP SWvt WGwG WHer
§	***gratianopolitanus*** Υ^{H6}	CBod CPBP CTri CWld EBWF EDAr ENfk EPfP GJos LEdu MHer MNHC MRav NBid SAll
	- 'Albus' (p)	EPot MHer
	- 'Babi Lom' (p)	GCrg
	- dwarf	WAbe
§	- 'Tiny Rubies' (p)	EDAr LLHF SDys WAbe
	'Greensides' (p)	SAll
	'Gypsy Star' (p)	SPoG
	haematocalyx	EPot GJos NSla
	- 'Alpinus'	see *D. haematocalyx* subsp. *pindicola*
§	- subsp. ***pindicola***	LLHF NSla WAbe
	'Hamish Berry' (p)	CNMi
	'Hampshire' (pf)	CNMi
	'Hannah Gertsen' (p)	SAll
	'Harkell Special' (b)	SAll
	'Harmony' (b)	SAll
	'Hayden' (pf)	CNMi
	'Hayley's Choice' (b)	SAll
	HAYTOR	see *D.* 'Haytor White'
	'Haytor Rock' (p) Υ^{H6}	ELan EPfP MTis NNor WGwG
§	'Haytor White' (p) Υ^{H6}	CBcs CTri EPfP ESps ETMg GQue LCro LOPS SAll SCob
	'Heath' (p)	SAll
	'Heaven Scent' (p) **new**	SAll
	'Helen' (p)	ELon LSRN SAll
	'Helena Allwood' (pf)	EMal
	'Helena Hitchcock' (p)	SAll
	'Herbert's Pink' (p)	ECtt SPhx
	'Hercules' (pf)	CNMi
	'Hereford Butter Market' (p)	EBee
	'Hidcote' (p)	CRos CTri LLHF LRHS NRHS
	Highland Group (p)	SGbt
	'Highland Fraser' (p)	WKif
	'Hope' Allwood, 1946 (p)	SAll
	'Hot Spice' (p)	SPoG
§	'Houndspool Cheryl' (p) Υ^{H6}	CBcs CSBt ECtt EPfP ESps GJos SAll SRGP
§	'Houndspool Ruby' (p) Υ^{H6}	CBcs EPfP ESps LSRN SAll
	hungaricus **new**	CPla
	hyssopifolius	WOut
	'Ian' (p)	LSRN SAll
§	ICED GEM ('Wp06 Fatima'^{PBR}) (Scent First Series) (p)	CRos ELan ELon LRHS LSRN LSou MTis NNor NPnk NRHS SPoG SRot
	'Icomb' (p)	WHoo
	'Inchmery' (p)	LRHS SAll WHer
	'India Star'^{PBR} (p) Υ^{H6}	CRos CTri EPfP ESps LRHS MTis NEgg NRHS SRot
	'Inshriach Dazzler' (p) Υ^{H6}	CPBP CPla ECtt EPot GCrg GMaP LLHF MAsh MHer NEgg NSla SRot WAbe WHal WTor
	'Inshriach Startler' (p)	CMea
	'Irene Della-Torré' (b) Υ^{H6}	SAll
	'Janelle Welch' (pf)	CNMi
	'Janet Walker' (p)	GMaP
	'Jess Hewins' (pf)	CNMi SAll
	'Joan Schofield' (p)	CPBP
	'Joanne' (pf)	CNMi
	'Joanne's Highlight' (pf)	CNMi
	'Joy' (p) Υ^{H6}	EPfP ESps ETMg SAll SPoG
	'Julian' (p)	SAll
	'Julie Ann Davis' (b)	SAll
	'Julie Martin' (pf)	CNMi
	'Just Jodie' (pf)	CNMi
	'Kathleen Hitchcock' (b) Υ^{H6}	SAll
	'Kelly's Kiss' (p)	CNMi
	'Kent' (pf)	CNMi
	'Kesteven Kirkstead' (p) Υ^{H6}	MNrw SAll
	'Kim' (p)	NDov
	knappii	GWyn SHar SPhx WHer XLum
	- 'Yellow Harmony' (p,a)	SAll SBee
	'La Bourboule' (p) Υ^{H6}	CMea CRos ECtt EDAr GAbr GCrg GMaP LRHS NRHS
	'La Bourboule Alba' (p) Υ^{H5}	CTri ECtt GCrg MAsh
	'Laced Joy' (p)	SAll
	'Laced Monarch' (p)	CBcs CRav CRos CSBt ECtt ELan EPfP LRHS MCot MMuc NEgg NNor NRHS SAll SEND SPlb SPoG WGwG WHer
	'Laced Mrs Sinkins' (p)	SAll WHer
	'Laced Prudence'	see *D.* 'Prudence'
	'Laced Romeo' (p)	SAll
	'Laced Treasure' (p)	SAll
	'Lady Granville' (p)	MHCG SAll SBch
	LADY IN RED ('Wp04 Xanthe'^{PBR}) (p)	CRos ECtt ELan EPfP LRHS MTis NNor NRHS
§	LADY MADONNA ('Wp04 Opal'^{PBR}) (p) Υ^{H6}	ELan
	'Lady Wharncliffe' (p)	SBch
	'Lady Windermere' (M)	EMal SAll
	'Lancing Supreme' (p)	SAll WHer
	'Langford Manor' (pf)	CNMi
	'Langport Lady' (pt)	CNMi
	'Laura' (p)	SAll
	'Layla Jane' (p)	CNMi
	'Leatham Pastel' (pf)	CNMi
	'Lemsii' (p) Υ^{H6}	NGdn

'Len Hutton' (p)	SBch
'Letitia Wyatt' (p) ♀^{H6}	CMea CRos LRHS NRHS SBch SPoG SRGP
'Leuchtkugel' (p)	LLHF WAbe
'Lily Lesurf' (b)	SAll
LILY THE PINK ('Wp05 Idare'^{PBR}) (p) ♀^{H6}	CRos ELan LRHS NRHS SRGP
'Lime Crush' (pf)	CNMi
'Linfield Annie's Fancy' (pf)	CNMi
'Linfield Doreen Ashmore' (p)	SAll
'Linfield Dorothy Perry' (p) ♀^{H6}	SAll
'Linfield Isobel Croft' (p)	SAll
'Linfield Julie' (p)	SAll
'Linfield Kathy Booker' (p) ♀^{H6}	SAll
'Linfield Pink Margaret' (p)	CNMi SAll
'Little Ben' (p)	SAll
'Little Jock' (p)	CRos ECtt EDAr EPot GCrg LRHS MAsh NRHS SAll SPlb
'Liz Rigby' (b)	SAll
'London Brocade' (p)	SAll
'London Glow' (p)	SAll
'London Lovely' (p)	SAll
'London Poppet' (p)	ECtt SAll
'Lord Nuffield' (b)	SAll
lumnitzeri	XLum
'Lustre' (b)	SAll
'Maggie' (p)	LSRN
'Maisie Neal' (b) ♀^{H6}	SAll
'Mandy' (p)	SAll
'Manon des Sources' (pf)	CNMi
'Margaret Taylor' (p)	SAll
'Maria'	see *D.* 'Allen's Maria'
'Marian Allwood' (pf)	EMal
'Marilyn's Highlight' (pf)	CNMi
'Marjery Breeze' (p)	SAll
'Marmion' (M)	EMal SAll
'Ma's Choice' (p)	SAll
'Matthew' (p)	WHoo
'Maudie Hinds' (b)	SAll
'Maxine' (pf)	CNMi
'Maybole' (b)	SAll
'Maybush' (pf)	CNMi
MEMORIES ('WP11 Gwe04'^{PBR}) (Scent First Series) (p)	CMea CRos EBee ELan EPfP LBuc LRHS LSun MCot MHol MTis NRHS SPer SPoG WCot WWFP
MENDLESHAM MINX ('Russmin'^{PBR}) (p)	CRos EDAr ELan EPfP LRHS NRHS SAll SWvt
'Messines Pink' (p)	SAll WHer
microlepis	EDAr EPot LLHF NGdn NSla
- f. ***albus***	NSla
- ED 791562	NGdn
- 'Rivendell' (p)	WAbe
'Mike Briggs' (b)	SAll
'Miss Farrow' (p)	EWes LRHS SCob SPhx
'Miss Sinkins' (p)	CTri IFoB
* 'Misty Morn'	ECtt
MOJÁCAR ('Barjamocar'^{PBR}) (pf)	SAll
MOJITO ('Wp15 Pie41') (p)	MTis WTor
'Monica Wyatt' (p) ♀^{H6}	CBcs CRos ECtt ELan EPfP GJos LRHS NEgg NRHS SPoG
'Montrose Pink'	see *D.* 'Cockenzie Pink'
'Monty Allwood' (p)	ECtt SAll
'Monty's Pink' (pf)	EMal
'Moor Editha' (p)	CNMi
'Moor Simply Red' (b) **new**	SAll
MORNING STAR	see *D.* 'Devon Winnie'
'Morrissey' (pf)	CNMi
MOTHER OF PEARL ('Wp10 Ele04'^{PBR}) (Perfume Pinks Series) (p)	ELan
'Mottisfont Pink'	NWad
'Moulin Rouge' (p) ♀^{H6}	CMea CRos CTri ECtt ELan EPfP LRHS MTis NRHS SPhx SPoG
'Mrs Macbride' (p)	SAll
'Mrs Sinkins' (p)	Widely available
'Musgrave's Pink' (p)	CFis ECha MRav SAll WHer
'Musgrave's White'	see *D.* 'Musgrave's Pink'
myrtinervius	EDAr GPSL NGdn WAvo
'Mystic Dawn' (b)	SAll
§ MYSTIC STAR ('WP 05 Saphire') (p) ♀^{H6}	CMea ELan IPot MTis
'Mystic Sunset' (b) **new**	SAll
'Napoleon III' (p)	SAll
nardiformis	XLum
'Natalie Saunders' (b) ♀^{H6}	SAll
'Nautilus' (b)	SAll
neglectus misapplied	see *D. pavonius*
'Neon Star'^{PBR} (p) ♀^{H6}	CRos CTri EDAr ELan GKev LRHS MTis NCou NRHS SPoG SRot
'Night Star' (p) ♀^{H6}	CRos ELan EPfP GBin GKev GMaP GWyn LRHS MHol NCou NEgg NRHS SEND SRot WPtf
noeanus	see *D. petraeus* subsp. *noeanus*
'Nomie' (pf)	CNMi
'Northland' (pf)	CNMi EMal SAll
'Nyewoods Cream' (p)	CMea EPot GCrg GMaP MHer NGdn NWad SBch
'Oakwood Erin Mitchell' (p)	CNMi
'Oakwood Sweetheart' (p)	SAll
'Old Blush'	see *D.* 'Souvenir de la Malmaison'
'Old Clove Red' (b)	WHoo
'Old French Red' (pf)	EMal
'Old Man's Head' (p)	SBch
'Old Mother Hubbard' (p)	SBch
'Old Red Clove' (p)	ECtt GAbr MBel MCot MHol MPie NCou NSti SPer WCot
'Old Rose' (pf)	EMal
§ 'Old Square Eyes' (p)	MNrw SAll SHar WHer
'Old Velvet' (p)	SAll WHoo
'Oliver' (p)	SAll
'Oscar' (b)	CRos LRHS NRHS
'Owston Third Avenue' (p)	SAll
'Oxford Magic' (p)	SAll
'Painted Lady' (p)	SAll
'Paisley Gem' (p)	SAll
PASSION ('Wp Passion'^{PBR}) (Scent First Series) (p)	CRos EBee ECtt ELan EPfP LRHS LSou MBel MHol MPie MTis NNor NRHS SAko SBod SEND SPoG WCot
§ ***pavonius***	EBee EWes NGdn NSla WRHF
'Peach' (p)	SEND
'Pendle Doris Delight' (p)	SAll
'Pennine Reflections' (b)	SAll
'Peter Wood' (b) ♀^{H6}	SAll
§ ***petraeus***	EWes NGdn
§ - subsp. ***noeanus***	EPot LLHF MMuc WHal
'Petticoat Lace' (p)	SAll
'Pheasant's Eye' (p)	SAll WHer
* 'Picton's Propeller' (p)	GCal NWad
PIERROT ('Kobusa') (pf)	CNMi
'Pike's Pink' (p) ♀^{H6}	CRos CSpe CTri EDAr ELan EPfP EPot GCrg LRHS MAsh MCot MMuc NGdn NRHS SAll SEND
PINBALL WIZARD ('Wp15mow08') (p)	CRos LRHS MTis NRHS

pindicola	see *D. haematocalyx* subsp. *pindicola*
pinifolius	SBrt
'Pink Doris' (pf)	CNMi
'Pink Fantasy' (b)	SAll
PINK FIZZ ('Wp10 Xav04'PBR) (Scent First Series) (p)	CRos LRHS NRHS
'Pink Jewel' (p)	CMea CPBP ECha EDAr MAsh MCot MNHC SAll SBch XLum
PINK KISSES ('Kledg12163') (pt) **new**	LRHS NRHS SPoG
'Pink Mrs Sinkins' (p)	MHer SAll
'Pink Pearl' (b)	SAll
'Pink Peony' (Scents of Summer Series) (p) **new**	ETMg
'Pixie' (b)	EPot
'Pixie Star'PBR (p) 🏆H6	EPfP SPoG SRot
plumarius	SAll XLum
- 'Albiflorus' (p)	XLum
- subsp. ***praecox***	CPBP
pontederae	NDov
§ POP STAR ('Wp04 Esther'PBR) (p)	CRos LRHS MTis NRHS SGbt
'Pretty' (p)	ECtt SAll
PRETTY FLAMINGO	see *D.* 'Carmine Letitia Wyatt'
'Prince Charming' (p)	MAsh
'Princess of Wales' (M)	EMal SAll
'Priory Pink' (p)	SAll
§ 'Prudence' (p)	SAll
'Pudsey Prize' (p)	EPot WAbe
'Purple Frosted' (pf)	EMal
'Purple Jenny' (p)	ECtt SAll
'Queen of Hearts' (p)	SEND
§ 'Queen of Henri' (p)	CRos EBee LRHS NRHS
'Queen of Sheba' (p)	SAll WHer WHoo WKif
'Rachel' (p)	SAll
'Rainbow Loveliness' (p,a)	SAll WOut
'Raspberry Parfait' (p,a)	CRos LRHS NRHS
RASPBERRY SUNDAE	see *D.* 'Devon Yolande'
REBEKAH ('Wp09 Mar05'PBR) (Early Bird Series) (p)	CMea CRos ELan LRHS NRHS
'Red Dwarf'	see *D.* 'Red Star'
§ 'Red Star'PBR (p) 🏆H6	CRos ELan GAbr GJos LRHS MAsh NRHS SRot WTor
'Reine de Henri'	see *D.* 'Queen of Henri'
repens	GKev
'Richard Pollak' (b)	SAll
'Ringwood Belle' (pf)	CNMi
'Rizalene' (p)	CNMi
'Robert Allwood' (pf)	EMal SAll
'Robert Smith' (b)	SAll
'Robin Ritchie' (p)	WHoo
'Robin Thain' (b)	SAll
ROMANCE ('Wp09 Wen04'PBR) (Scent First Series) (p)	CRos ELan LCro LOPS LRHS LSou MTis NRHS
'Romsey' (pf)	CNMi
'Roodkapje' (p)	XLum
'Rose de Mai' (p)	CFis CNMi CSam SAll WHer WHoo
'Rose Joy' (p) 🏆H6	CBcs CRos EPfP ESps LRHS NRHS
ROSEBUD ('Wp08 Ros03'PBR) (Early Bird Series) (p)	CRos LRHS NRHS
'Rötkappchen' (p)	ELon
'Royal Crimson' (pf)	EMal
'Royal Fragrance' (pf)	EMal
'Royal Salmon' (pf)	EMal
'Ruby'	see *D.* 'Houndspool Ruby'

'Ruby Doris'	see *D.* 'Houndspool Ruby'
'Ruby Wedding' (p)	LSRN
rupicola	WCot
'Saint Nicholas' (p)	WThu
'Sam Barlow' (p)	SAll
'Santa Claus' (b)	SAll
'Seraphina' (pf)	CNMi
'Seren Wen' (p)	WAbe
serotinus	WCot
SHERBET ('Wp08 Ros03'PBR) (Early Bird Series) (p)	CRos ELan LRHS NRHS
§ SHOOTING STAR ('Wp04 Flores'PBR) (p)	ELan MTis SRms
'Shot Silk' (pf)	EMal SAll
'Show Aristocrat' (p)	SAll
'Show Beauty' (p)	SAll
SHOW GIRL ('Hilshow') (pt)	CRos LRHS
'Show Glory' (p)	SAll
'Show Harlequin' (p)	SAll
'Show Satin' (p)	SAll
SHOWGIRL ('Wp08 Uni02'PBR) (Scent First Series) (p)	ELan LSou
SILVER STAR ('Wp10 Hel01'PBR) (p)	CRos LRHS SEND
* 'Six Hills' (p)	NWad
SLAP 'N' TICKLE ('Wp 05 Pp 22'PBR) (Scent First Series) (p)	CRos EBee ECtt ELon LRHS LSRN LSou NRHS SPoG SRot
'Snowshill Manor' (p)	ECtt
'Solomon' (p)	SAll
'Somerset' (pf)	CNMi
'Sops-in-wine' (p)	CFis CSam ECha ECtt SAll
§ 'Souvenir de la Malmaison' (M)	EMal SAll
'Spangle' (b)	SAll
spiculifolius	CAby EPot MMuc
'Spinfield Joy' (b) 🏆H6	SAll
'Spring Star' (p)	ECtt SRot
'Square Eyes'	see *D.* 'Old Square Eyes'
squarrosus	CPBP EPot
- 'Nanus'	see *D.* 'Berlin Snow'
'Starburst'PBR (p)	CBod CMea CPla CRos LRHS MTis NRHS
STARGAZER ('Wp13 Gil05'PBR) (Whetman Stars Series) (p)	CRos LRHS MTis NRHS
STARLIGHT ('Hilstar') (pf)	CMea SRms
STARLIGHT ('Wp 06 Parnia'PBR) (p)	CSma
'Starry Eyes' (p) 🏆H6	CRos CSam ELan GCrg GMaP LRHS NRHS SRms SRot SWvt WTor
'Storm' (pf)	EMal SAll
'Strawberries and Cream' (p)	ECtt NEgg SPoG
strictus	WCot
* - subsp. ***pulchellus***	GEdr
subacaulis	EDAr IFoB NSla XLum
- subsp. ***brachyanthus***	EPot GJos
- - 'Murray Lyon' (p)	WThu
suendermannii	see *D. petraeus*
SUGAR PLUM ('Wp08 Ian04'PBR) (Scent First Series) (p)	CRos EBee ECtt ELan LRHS LSou MTis NRHS
'Summerfield Adam' (p)	SAll
'Summerfield Amy Francesca' (p)	SAll
'Summerfield Blaze' (p)	SAll
'Summerfield Blush' (p)	SAll

	'Summerfield Daniel' (b)	SAll
	'Summerfield Debbie' (p)	SAll
	'Summerfield Emma Louise' (p)	SAll
	'Summerfield Jo' (p)	CFis SAll
	'Summerfield Rebecca' (p)	SAll
	'Sunray' (b)	SAll
§	***superbus***	EPPr LRHS NNor SBch SHar SPhx WHer WMoo WWFP
	- 'Crimsonia' (p)	WOut
	SUPERNOVA ('Wp11Tyr04'^{PBR}) (pf)	MTis
	'Susan' (p)	SAll
	'Susannah' (p)	SAll
*	'Susan's Seedling' (p)	SAll
	'Sweet Cecille' (pf)	CNMi
	'Sweet Sue' (b)	SAll
	sylvestris	WOut
	'Tamsin Fifield' (b) ♀^{H6}	SAll
	'Tatra' (pf)	NQui
	'Tatra Blush' (p)	GCal
	'Tatra Fragrance' (p)	CCse GCal SAll
	'Tatra Ghost' (p)	SAll SDys
	'Tayside Red' (M)	EMal SAll
	THE WESSEX PINK ('Wp15val11') (p)	ECtt MTis NDov
	'Thora' (M)	EMal SAll
	'Thunderstorm' (pf)	CNMi
	TICKLED PINK ('Devon Pp 11'^{PBR}) (Scent First Series) (p)	CRos ECtt ELan ELon LRHS LSRN LSou NRHS SPoG
	'Tiny Rubies'	see *D. gratianopolitanus* 'Tiny Rubies'
	'Tony's Choice' (pf)	CNMi
	'Treasure' (p)	SAll
	'Trevor' (p)	SAll
	tristis	XLum
	'Tudor'	ELon MHCG MNrw
	'Tudor Rose' (b) **new**	MNrw
	turkestanicus	NNor WPtf
	'Uncle Teddy' (b) ♀^{H6}	SAll
	'Unique' (p)	SAll
	'Valda Wyatt' (p) ♀^{H6}	CBcs ELan EPfP GJos MCot NEgg NNor NSti SAll SEND SPoG SWvt WGwG
	'Velvet Pelargonium' (pf)	EMal
	'Vic Masters' (p)	SBch
	'Violet Clove' (b)	SAll
	'Violet Yates' (pf)	CNMi
	'W.A. Musgrave'	see *D.* 'Musgrave's Pink'
	'Waithman Beauty' (p)	CFis ECtt SAll WHoo
	'Waithman's Jubilee' (p)	ECtt SAll SBch WAvo
	'Warden Hybrid' (p)	CRos CTri ECtt GCrg LRHS MNHC NRHS NWad SPoG SWvt WAbe
	'Waterloo Sunset'^{PBR} (p)	CMea MTis
	'Weetwood Double' (p)	SBch WAvo
	'Welton Raspberry Ice' (p)	SAll
	'Wessex' (pf)	CNMi CRos LRHS NRHS
	weyrichii	EPot
	'Whatfield Anona' (p)	SAll
	'Whatfield Beauty' (p)	ECtt
	'Whatfield Cancan' (p) ♀^{H6}	CBod CMea CRos ECtt ELan EPot GMaP LRHS MHol MNHC NEgg NGdn NRHS NSla SAll SBch SPoG SWvt
	'Whatfield Cyclops' (p)	SAll
	'Whatfield Dorothy Mann' (p)	SAll
	'Whatfield Fuchsia Floss' (p)	SAll
	'Whatfield Gem' (p)	CFis ECtt ELan ELon EPfP GCrg MNHC NGdn SAll SWvt WHoo WTor
	'Whatfield Joy' (p)	CRos ECtt ELan EPfP GCrg GPSL LRHS NGdn NRHS SAll
	'Whatfield Magenta' (p) ♀^{H6}	CRos CSam ECtt ELan EPot EWTr GCrg LRHS NRHS SAll SBch SPoG WAbe
	'Whatfield Mini' (p)	SAll SBch
	'Whatfield Miss' (p)	SAll SBch
	'Whatfield Misty Morn' (p)	SAll
	'Whatfield Peach' (p)	SAll
	'Whatfield Ruby' (p)	ECtt ELan GJos SAll
	'Whatfield White' (p)	ECtt SAll
	'Whatfield Wisp' (p)	CPBP EPfP EPot MRav
	'White and Crimson' (p)	SAll
	'White Joy'^{PBR} (p) ♀^{H6}	MRav
	'White Ladies' (p)	MRav SAll
	'Widecombe Fair' (p) ♀^{H6}	CRos ELan EPfP LRHS MTis NRHS SAll SPoG
	'Yesterday, Today, Tomorrow' **new**	ETMg
	'Zebra' (b)	SAll

Diarrhena (*Poaceae*)

	japonica	MAvo MMoz
	obovata	EPPr

Diascia (*Scrophulariaceae*)

	'Andrew'	SBch
	APRICOT DELIGHT ('Codicot') (Sun Chimes Series)	EDAr
	barberae 'Belmore Beauty' (v)	EWes
	- 'Blackthorn Apricot' ♀^{H4}	CRos EBee ECha EPfP GBin GWyn LRHS LSRN NDov NLar NRHS SPer SPlb SPoG SRms SWvt XEll
	- JULIET LIGHT PINK ('Baljulink') **new**	WHlf
	- JULIET ORANGE ('Balajulor')	LSou
	- JULIET PINK WITH EYE ('Baljulpiney')	WHlf
§	- 'Ruby Field' ♀^{H4}	CRos EBee ECha EPfP GBin LRHS LSRN NRHS SPer SPoG SRms SWvt
	BLUE BONNET ('Hecbon')	SWvt
	'Bluebelle' (Maritana Series)	NDov NLar
	'Blush'	see *D. integerrima* 'Blush'
	(Breezee Series) BREEZEE APPLE BLOSSOM	CPla NLar
	- BREEZEE APRICOT ('Diaspritwo'^{PBR})	NLar
	- BREEZEE RED	NLar
	- BREEZEE SNOW ('Inndiabzsno'^{PBR})	NLar
	'Coldham'	LPla
	CORAL BELLE ('Hecbel'^{PBR}) ♀^{H3}	CRos LRHS LSou NRHS
	'Denim Blue'	EDAr
	elegans misapplied	see *D. fetcaniensis*, *D. vigilis*
	'Emma'	LPla NDov SMHy SWvt
	felthamii	see *D. fetcaniensis*
§	***fetcaniensis***	CMea CPrp CRos EBee EPfP LPla LRHS MCot MHer MMuc NEgg NLar SPer WHal WKif
	- 'Daydream'	LBuc MNrw MPie SBch WCFE WHrl
	flanaganii misapplied	see *D. vigilis*

	(Flying Colours Series) FLYING COLOURS ANTIQUE ROSE ('Diastu'PBR) **new**	SPoG
	- FLYING COLOURS APPLEBLOSSOM ('Diastara')	EPfP SPoG
	- FLYING COLOURS APRICOT ('Diastina')	EPfP SPoG
	- FLYING COLOURS DEEP SALMON IMPROVED ('Dala Depsam'PBR) **new**	SPoG
	- FLYING COLOURS RED ('Diastonia')	EPfP SPoG
	'Hector Harrison'	see *D.* 'Salmon Supreme'
§	'Hopleys'	CRos EPPr EWes LRHS MAvo MHCG MPie MSCN NRHS SMHy WFar WWtn
	ICE CRACKER ('Hecrack')	CMea CRos ELan LRHS NRHS SRms
	ICEBERG ('Hecice')	NDov SWvt
§	***integerrima*** ♀H4	CSam ECha MCot MHer
	- 'Alba'	see *D. integerrima* 'Blush'
§	- 'Blush'	CSpe NDov
	- 'Ivory Angel'	see *D. integerrima* 'Blush'
	integrifolia	see *D. integerrima*
	'Jacqueline's Joy'	CMea NPer
	'Joyce's Choice' ♀H3	CRos LRHS NRHS SRms
	JULIET WHITE ('Baljalite')	WHlf
	'Katherine Sharman' (v)	EWes
	'Lady Valerie' ♀H3	GPSL
	'Lilac Belle' ♀H3	CRos EDAr ELan LRHS NEgg NRHS SPlb SPoG SRms
	'Lilac Mist' ♀H3	NPer
	LITTLE DANCER ('Pendan'PBR)	ELan LSou NLar
	LITTLE DREAMER ('Pender'PBR)	NLar
	LITTLE DRIFTER ('Pendrif'PBR)	LSou NLar
	LITTLE MAIDEN ('Penmaid'PBR)	NLar
	LITTLE TANGO ('Pentang'PBR)	LSou NLar SRms
	'Peaches and Cream' (v)	CMea
	personata	CAby CBar CBod CHll CMea CPne CPrp CSam CSpe EBee ECtt EHoe EPfP GBin GMaP ITim LLHF LRHS MCot MHer MHol MMuc MNrw NDov SPer SPhx WCot WSHC WWFP
	- 'Hopleys'	see *D.* 'Hopleys'
	'Peter'	NDov
	PINK PANTHER ('Penther')	SWvt
	RED ACE ('Hecrace'PBR)	EPfP NPer SWvt
	REDSTART ('Hecstart')	SWvt
	rigescens ♀H3	CBod CCht CPne CPrp CRos CSpe CWCL ECtt ELan EPfP GWyn ILea LRHS NLar NPer SChF SPer SPlb SPoG SWvt WAvo WCFE WSHC WSpi
§	- 'Anne Rennie'	LRHS SWvt
	- pale-flowered	see *D. rigescens* 'Anne Rennie'
	'Ruby Field'	see *D. barberae* 'Ruby Field'
	'Rupert Lambert' ♀H3	NDov
§	'Salmon Supreme'	CRos LRHS NPer NRHS SPoG SRms
	(Sundiascia Series) SUNDIASCIA BLUSH PINK	LCro LOPS
	- SUNDIASCIA ORANGE	LSou
	- SUNDIASCIA ROSE PINK	LSou
	'Twinkle' ♀H3	CRos LRHS NPer NRHS SRms
§	***vigilis*** ♀H3	CExl CMea CRos EPot LRHS NBro NRHS SRms WHal

Dicentra ✿ (*Papaveraceae*)

	CC 4452	CExl
	'Adrian Bloom'	CExl ECtt EPfP MAsh MCot SPer SWvt WFar WMoo
	(Amore Series) 'Amore Pink'	CWGN NLar WHil
	- 'Amore Rose'PBR	CWGN NLar
	'Aurora'	CBod CRos EBee ECtt ELon EPfP EWTr GWyn IBoy LCro LOPS LRHS MRav NGdn NLar NRHS NSti SCob SPer SPoG SWvt WCAu WMoo
	'Boothman's Variety'	see *D.* 'Stuart Boothman'
	'Bountiful'	CMac ECtt EPau LRHS MRav NGdn NRHS SWvt WGwG
	'Burning Hearts'PBR	CBod CWCL CWGN ECtt EPot LRHS LSou MPnt SCob SPer SPoG
	canadensis	CAby EBee GKev LEdu MAvo MNrw NLar WAbe WHal
	'Candy Hearts'PBR	EBee ECtt ELan EWTr MHol SCob SGol
	cucullaria	CAby CElw CRos CTal CWCL EBee ELon EPPr EPot GAbr GEdr GKev ITim LEdu LRHS MNrw MRav NHpl NLar NRHS WAbe WFar XEll
	- 'Pink Punk'	CTal CWCL EBee ELon EPPr EPot LEdu MNrw NLar WFar
	- 'Pittsburg'	CAby EPPr MNrw WSpi
	eximia misapplied	see *D. formosa*
	eximia ambig.	CPla GKev GPSL MHol
	eximia (Ker Gawl.) Torr. 'Alba'	see *D. eximia* (Ker Gawl.) Torr. 'Snowdrift'
§	- 'Snowdrift'	CBod MCot SRms WFar WMoo
	'Filigree'	CSpe
	'Firecracker'	ECtt MPnt
§	***formosa***	CBcs CRos CSpe CTri ECha EHrv ELan EPfP GAbr GKev GMcL IFro LRHS NBro NGdn NRHS SPlb SRms WArt WMoo
	- f. ***alba***	CTri GAbr GLog SRms WCru WFar WKif
	- 'Bacchanal' ♀H5	Widely available
	- 'Cox's Dark Red'	CExl EHrv EWes GAbr GBin GKev LLHF NHpl
	- 'Langtrees' ♀H5	CMac CRos CSam ECha EPau LEdu LRHS MRav NBro NLar NRHS SRms SSut SWvt WCru WFar WMoo WSpi
	- subsp. ***oregana***	EPPr NChi WHal
	- - 'Rosea'	EPPr
	- SNOWFLAKES ('Fusd')	EWes MRav
	- 'Spring Gold'	CRos ECha ELon EPPr IBoy LRHS NLar NRHS SPad WMoo
	- 'Spring Magic'	CRos EBee ECtt EPPr GBin GWyn LRHS MRav NLar NRHS
	'Ivory Hearts'PBR	CWGN EBee ELan EPot GKev MAvo MCot MPnt NLar NPnk NSti SPer
§	'Katie'	EPPr
	'Katy'	see *D.* 'Katie'
	'King of Hearts'	Widely available
	'Luxuriant' ♀H5	CBcs CBod CRos CSBt ECtt ELan EPfP EShb GKev LPmr LRHS LSRN MAsh MCot MGos MHol MRav NRHS SCob SPer SPoG SRms SRot SWvt WCAu WMoo
	macrantha	see *Ichthyoselmis macrantha*
	'Pearl Drops'	CRos GLog GMaP GMcL GWyn LRHS MCot MHCG MMoz MMrt NBid NLar NRHS SRms WMoo
	peregrina	WAbe

	'Red Fountain'^{PBR}	ECtt EWTr MPnt NLar NPnk NSti SMad WHil
	'Rekka'^{PBR}	GEdr
	scandens	see *Dactylicapnos scandens*
	'Silver Beads'	ELon
	spectabilis	see *Lamprocapnos spectabilis*
	'Spring Morning'	CElw CSam CTal ECtt EPPr EPau LEdu NGdn WSpi
§	'Stuart Boothman' 🏆^{H5}	CMac CRos CWCL ECtt EPfP GMaP ILea LRHS MCot MHol MRav NBro NGdn NLar NRHS SPoG SRms SWvt WFar WKif WMoo
	thalictrifolia	see *D. scandens*
	ventii	see *Dactylicapnos ventii*

Dichelostemma (*Asparagaceae*)

§	***capitatum***	GKev
	congestum	CAvo GKev SDeJ WCot
§	***ida-maia***	CAvo CGrW CWCL EPot GKev SDeJ
	- 'Pink Diamond'	EBee GKev SDeJ
	pulchellum	see *D. capitatum*
	volubile	GKev
	- 'Pink Giant'	SDeJ

Dichondra (*Convolvulaceae*)

	argentea 'Silver Falls'	CPla EShb LSou NPri SCoo SPer SPoG
§	***micrantha***	EShb
	repens misapplied	see *D. micrantha*

Dichopogon (*Asparagaceae*)

	strictus	SBrt WSFF

Dichroa ✿ (*Hydrangeaceae*)

	from Guizhou, China **new**	WPGP
	cyanea NJM 13.104	WPGP
	febrifuga B&SWJ 9734	WCru
	- B&SWJ 9753	WCru
	- HWJK 2430	WSHC
	- NJM 10.042	WPGP
	- PAB 8639	LEdu
	hirsuta B&SWJ 8207 from Vietnam	WCru
	aff. ***hirsuta*** B&SWJ 8371 from Laos	WCru
	- NJM 10.051 **new**	WPGP
	aff. ***yunnanensis*** B&SWJ 9734	WCru

Dichroa × *Hydrangea* see × *Didrangea*

Dichromena see *Rhynchospora*

Dichrostachys (*Mimosaceae*)

	cinerea	SPlb

Dicksonia ✿ (*Dicksoniaceae*)

	antarctica 🏆^{H3}	Widely available
	arborescens	NLos
	fibrosa 🏆^{H3}	CDTJ CKel
	sellowiana	CDTJ CKel
	squarrosa 🏆^{H3}	CBdn CCCN CDTJ CKel NLos
	thyrsopteroides	NLos
	youngiae	CKel

Dicliptera (*Acanthaceae*)

§	***sericea***	CCCN CHll ECtt EShb MCot MSCN SBch SEND SRkn
	suberecta	see *D. sericea*

Dictamnus (*Rutaceae*)

	albus	CBcs CHll CRos CWCL EBee ECha ELan EPfP EWTr LEdu LRHS LSun MCot MNrw MRav NRHS SMHy SPer SPoG SWvt WCAu WSpi XAbr
	- var. ***albus*** 🏆^{H6}	IBoy SWvt WAul
§	- var. ***purpureus*** 🏆^{H6}	CPla CRav CRos ECha ELan EPfP IBoy ILea LRHS LSun MBel MNrw MRav NEgg NGBl NRHS SPer SPoG SRms SWvt WAul WKif WSpi
*	- var. ***roseus***	EWTr IMou
*	- ***turkestanicus***	GCal
	caucasicus	SBrt SMHy WSHC
	fraxinella	see *D. albus* var. *purpureus*

× *Didrangea* (*Hydrangeaceae*)

	B&SWJ 6605 from Thailand	WCru
	versicolor	CAbb CBcs CBot CExl CHll CMCN CRos EBee EPfP LRHS MGil SCob SPoG SWvt WPGP
	- B&SWJ 6565	WCru
	ytiensis B&SWJ 11790	WCru

Didymochlaena (*Dryopteridaceae*)

	lunulata	see *D. truncatula*
§	***truncatula***	EShb XBlo

Dierama ✿ (*Iridaceae*)

	CD&R 192	CElw
	adelphicum	LLHF
	ambiguum	CElw EBee GAbr NLos XLum
	argyreum	CBcs CBod CCCN CElw CMac CTsd CWCL EBee EPri ETMg GAbr GBin GEdr GKev GPSL ITim MMuc MWat NLar SPad SPoG SRot WGob WHil XLum
	atrum	EBee
	'Autumn Dazzler' **new**	CPla
	'Ballyrogan Red'	IBlr
	Barr hybrids	CBro MMuc
	'Black Knight'	CExl IBlr
	'Blackberry Bells'	CPla CRos CWCL CWGN ELon ETMg GBin GPSL GWyn LRHS MAvo MHol NLar NLos NRHS NWad SPer SPoG WHil WSpi
	BLUE BELLE ('Rowblu'^{PBR})	CBod CWCL EBee ECtt GBin GEdr IBal LRHS
	'Blush'	IBlr
	'Candy Stripe'	EBee IBal
	'Carmine'	CWCL
	'Cinnamon Fairy'	EBee EPfP IBal
	cooperi	CElw CPou
	'Coral Belle'	EBee IBal IRob LRHS
	'Coral Bells'	CKno GCal IBal
	'Cosmos'	CExl CPla CWCL EPri EUJe GAbr LRHS MHer MMrt NWad WFar WGob WHil
	'Delicacy'	IBlr
	'Desire'	IBlr
	'Donard Legacy'	IBlr
§	***dracomontanum***	Widely available
	dracomontanum × ***pulcherrimum***	SMad
	dubium	IBlr
	ensifolium	see *D. pendulum*
	erectum	CBcs CCCN CHid CMac CTsd CWCL EBee EPri GPSL NLar NLos SRot WGob
	formosum	EBee

galpinii CBod CCCN CPla CWCL EBee EPri LLHF MMuc NLos
grandiflorum CPou IBlr WSHC
'Guinevere' CAby CDor CExl CRos CTca CWCL CWGN EBee ECtt ELon GEdr GMaP GWyn IBal IBoy IRob LEdu LRHS MRav NChi NGdn SCob SPoG SVen WFar WGwG WHoo WSHC XEll
igneum Widely available
- CD&R 278 CExl CPou ELon
insigne CCCN CHid CRos CWCL EBee GAbr LRHS MMrt NLos NRHS NWad WCot WHil
'Iris' IBlr
jucundum CBod CWCL EBee LRHS
'Kilmurry White' **new** IBal
'Lancelot' CBcs CElw CExl CKno CRos EBee ECtt GMcL IBal IBlr IRob LRHS SWvt WFar WKif WSHC
latifolium CHid IBlr WGob
luteoalbidum GAbr
'Mandarin' IBlr MAvo
medium CRos ELon NRHS
'Milkmaid' CExl IBlr
'Miranda' CBod CKno CWCL EBee ECtt EPri GMcL IBal IRob LRHS LSRN NLar SPhx
mossii CBcs CBod CCCN CExl CHid CRos CWCL EPri GAbr LRHS NHpl NLar NLos NWad SPhx SPlb SPoG SRot SVen WGob WHil XLum
'Painted Lady' EBee EPfP IBal SLon
'Pale Pink' **new** CWCL
pallidum CExl
'Pamina' CExl CPrp IBlr
'Papagena' IBlr
'Papageno' IBlr
pauciflorum CCCN CExl CHid CPrp CRos CWCL EBee EPri GBin LRHS NLar NLos NSla SPhx SRot WGob WSHC
§ ***pendulum*** CBro CRos IBlr LRHS MRav SWvt WFar WGob
pictum IBlr
'Pink Rocket' CBod CPla CWCL MHer MWat NCou SPoG
Plant World hybrids ELon WFar
PLANT WORLD JEWELS CBct CWCL NLos NWad WFar
'Pretty Flamingo' CExl CPrp IBlr
'Puck' EBee GCal IBlr ITim MRav
pulcherrimum Widely available
- var. ***album*** CCCN CWCL GAbr IBlr MHer MNrw NLos WHil
- 'Blackbird' CBWd CBcs CBod CCCN CExl CPla CWCL ELan EPri EUJe GAbr GBin IBoy LRHS LSRN MAvo MBel MHer MMuc MWat NHpl NLar NLos SPer SPoG SWvt WFar WGob WHoo WPGP
- dark pink-flowered IBoy
- 'Falcon' IBlr
- 'Flamingo' IBlr
- 'Merlin' CDor CElw CExl CKno CPou CWCL EBee ECtt ELon GEdr GMcL IBal IBlr IBoy IRob LRHS SCob SPoG SVen SWvt WGwG
- pale-flowered ECha
- 'Peregrine' IBoy
- 'Porty' **new** CTca
- Slieve Donard hybrids CWCL NLos WFar WHil WHrl
pumilum misapplied see *D. dracomontanum*
'Queen of the Night' IBlr
reynoldsii CBcs CCCN CExl CHid CPla CTsd CWCL EPri GAbr GBin GEdr IBlr MBel MMuc NHpl NWad SBrt SPhx SPlb SRkn SVen WFar WKif WSpi
robustum CAbb CExl CPou CWCL EWes LRHS WPGP
'Sarastro' CExl IBlr
sertum EBee
'Snowgoose' CPla
'Spring Dancer' CPla CWCL EBee EHoe MHer NLos SPlb
'Tamino' IBlr
'Tiny Bells' EDAr GCal GKev IBal MMuc SMHy
'Titania' IBal IBlr
trichorhizum CCCN CElw CExl CWCL EPri GKev LPla WHil
'Tubular Bells' IBlr
tyrium LLHF
'Violet Ice' IBlr
'Westminster Chimes' IBlr
white-flowered MBel
Wildside cross **new** CTca

Diervilla ✿ (*Caprifoliaceae*)

middendorffiana see *Weigela middendorffiana*
rivularis HONEYBEE ('Diwibru01') **new** LCro LOPS NEoE SGol SPoG
- 'Troja Black' EPPr NLar SGol
§ ***sessilifolia*** CBcs CHGN CMac EBee EPPr MBlu MRav SLon WCot WFar WMoo
- 'Butterfly' CMac EPPr LCro LSou NLar SCob WMoo
- COOL SPLASH ('Lpdc Podaras'^PBR) (v) CBod CMac EBee ELan LRHS NEoE SPoG SWvt WCot
× ***splendens*** CExl CRos EBee EHoe ELan EPPr EPfP GAbr IDee LRHS MBNS MBlu MGil MSwo NLar SPer SPoG SWvt

Dietes (*Iridaceae*)

bicolor CAbb CAby CBod CExl CPbh CPrp CTca EBee EPri IBoy LEdu LRHS LSou SChr SPoG WSHC
grandiflora CAbb CAby CBod CExl CHll CPbh CPne SVen WCot
§ ***iridioides*** CPrp CSpe EPri IBoy LRHS WCot WGob XLum
robinsoniana WCot

Digitalis ✿ (*Plantaginaceae*)

'Albino' CRos EPfP LRHS NRHS
ambigua see *D. grandiflora*
apricot hybrids see *D. purpurea* 'Sutton's Apricot'
canariensis CAbb CBcs CBot CCCN CCht CDTJ CRHN CSpe CTsd EUJe GCal LRHS MGil MMrt SEND SEle SPad SPlb SVen WCFE
cariensis CBot
ciliata EPPr GKev NSti NWad
davisiana CExl GKev GLog LLHF MNHC WMoo
'Elsie Kelsey' ECtt SWvt
eriostachya see *D. lutea*
ferruginea ♀H7 CBWd CBot CDor CRos ECha ECtt ELan EPPr EPfP GKev IBoy IFoB LEdu LRHS MRav NBro NDov NGdn NRHS SCob SPav SPer SRms SVen WArt WBrk WCAu WKif WMoo

	Name	Suppliers
	- 'Gelber Herold'	CDor GBin GMaP LRHS WCot WFar WSpi
	- 'Gigantea'	CBod ECtt ELan EPfP EWTr LEdu MBNS SCob SHar SPlb WPGP WWtn
	'Foxtrot'	CRos EPfP LRHS NRHS
	'Glory of Roundway'	CBod CBot CDor ECtt IBoy LEdu MBel MHol MNrw MPie MSCN SPer STPC WCAu WCot
§	***grandiflora*** ♀H5	Widely available
	- 'Carillon'	CBod ELan EPfP GJos GPSL IFoB SCob SRot WHoo
	- 'Cream Bell'	EPfP LRHS MHol WHar
	- 'Temple Bells'	CBot
	aff. ***grandiflora***	IBoy
	heywoodii	see *D. purpurea* subsp. *heywoodii*
	Illumination Series	EPfP LRHS NRHS SCob
	- ILLUMINATION APRICOT	see *D.* × *valinii* 'Harkstead Apricot'
	- ILLUMINATION CHELSEA GOLD	see *D.* × *valinii* 'Harkstead Apricot'
	- ILLUMINATION CHERRY BRANDY	CRos EWTr LRHS NRHS
	- ILLUMINATION DARK PINK	CBod CRos LRHS NRHS
	isabelliana	CCCN CHll GCal
	'John Innes Tetra'	CBot EPPr MNrw SPtp WHoo
	kishinskyi	see *D. parviflora* Jacq.
	laevigata	CBod CBot LEdu NBro SBrt SEND SPav WArt WMoo
	- subsp. ***laevigata***	SPtp
	- white-flowered	MCot WCot
	lamarckii misapplied	see *D. lanata*
§	***lanata***	CBot CRos EBee ECtt ELan EPfP GKev IBoy LRHS MBNS MNHC NGdn NRHS NWad SPav SPlb SPtp SRms WGwG
	- 'Café Crème'	CBot CDor WHar WTor
	'Lucas' **new**	CBot WHlf
§	***lutea***	Widely available
§	- subsp. ***australis***	SBrt
	'Martina' **new**	CBot
	× ***mertonensis*** ♀H5	Widely available
	- 'Summer King'	CChe CDor ECtt ELan GJos LSRN LSun MHol MWat
	micrantha	see *D. lutea* subsp. *australis*
	minor	CBot SBee WAbe
	obscura	CBot CCCN EAJP IFoB SBee SBrt SEND SPlb SVen WCot WHer WHrl
*	- 'Dusky Maid'	WFar WHlf
	- 'Sunset'	CBod
	orientalis	see *D. grandiflora*
§	***parviflora*** Jacq.	CBot CRos CSam ECha ECtt ELan EPPr EPfP IBoy LCro LOPS LRHS MBNS MMuc NBro NChi SBrt SEND SPav WArt WHil WMoo WWtn
	- 'Milk Chocolate'	CAbb CBot CDor CSpe ECtt ELan EPfP GBin GKev IBoy LOPS LRHS LSRN MCot NEgg NLar NWad SCob SPtp WHar
	'Pink Chapel'	ECtt
	(Polkadot Series) 'Polkadot Pippa'	CBot CRos LRHS NRHS
	- 'Polkadot Polly'	CBot
	- 'Polkadot Princess'	CBot
	purpurea	CHab EBWF ELan ENfk EPfP ESps GPoy GQue LSun MHer MMuc MNHC NMir SCob SPlb SPoG WBrk WHar WMoo WOut WSFF
	- 'Alba'	see *D. purpurea* f. *albiflora*
§	- f. ***albiflora***	Widely available
	- - 'Anne Redetzky'[PBR]	CSpe LRHS
	- 'Apricot Delight'	EBee WHar
	- 'Bare Necessities' **new**	CNat
	- Camelot Series	SHar SVic
	- - 'Camelot Cream'	CBot CRos ELan EPfP ETMg LRHS SWvt
	- - 'Camelot Lavender'	CBot CRos ELan EPfP ESps ETMg LRHS SWvt
	- - 'Camelot Rose'	CBot CRos ELan EPfP ESps ETMg LRHS SWvt
	- - 'Camelot White'	ELan EPfP
*	- 'Campanulata Alba'	CBot
	- 'Candy Mountain'	CBod CBot
	- Dalmatian Series	ETMg LPmr
	- - 'Dalmatian Crème'	CBot CRos LCro LOPS LRHS MAsh NRHS
	- - 'Dalmatian Peach'	CBod CBot CRos ELan EPfP IBoy LCro LOPS LRHS MAsh NRHS
	- - 'Dalmatian Purple'	CBod CBot CRos ELan EPfP ESps LCro LOPS LRHS MAsh NRHS
	- - 'Dalmatian Rose'	CBod CBot ELan EPfP LCro LOPS MAsh MHol
	- - 'Dalmatian White'	CBod CRos ELan LCro LOPS LRHS LSou NRHS
	- Excelsior Group	CBcs CBot CDor CMac CRos CSBt CTri ECtt EHrv EPfP ESps GJos GMaP IBoy LCro LRHS MJak NMir NRHS SCob SPer SPoG SRms SVic SWvt WHar XLum
	- - (Suttons; Unwins) ♀H7	ECtt MRav
	- - white-flowered	CTri
	- Foxy Group	CBot CRos EPfP GMcL LPmr LRHS MJak MNHC NRHS SPoG WHar
	- - 'Foxy Apricot'	SPtp SWvt
	- - 'Foxy Pink'	CBod SPtp
	- Giant Spotted Group	CRos ECtt EPfP LRHS NRHS SPoG
	- Glittering Prizes Group	CBot
	- Gloxinioides Group	CBot LCro LOPS
	- - 'The Shirley' ♀H7	WMoo
§	- subsp. ***heywoodii***	CBot IBoy WMoo
	- - 'Silver Fox'	CBod LPmr WTor
	- 'Pam's Choice'	CBod CBot CChe CDor CExl CRos CSpe EAJP ECtt ELan EPPr EPfP GAbr IBoy IFro LCro LPmr LRHS LSRN MSCN MWat NEgg NLar NRHS SCob SPer SPtp SRGP WBor WMoo
	- 'Pam's Split'	CBot EBee GAbr MHol SCob WHil
	- 'Primrose Carousel'	CBod CBot NEgg NLar SCob STPC WHar
	- 'Serendipity'	CRos EPfP LRHS NRHS
	- 'Snow Thimble'	CBod CBot CDor CRos EAJP ELan EPfP GJos IBoy LRHS LSun MHol NLar NRHS STPC
	- 'Sugar Plum'	CBot ETMg
§	- 'Sutton's Apricot' ♀H7	Widely available
*	- 'Sutton's Giant Primrose'	CBot
	- (Virtuosa Series) 'Virtuosa Red'	GMcL
	- - 'Virtuosa Rose'	GMcL
	- - 'Virtuosa White'	GMcL
	- 'White Carousel' (Carousel Series) **new**	CBot
	'Red Skin'	NLar NWad
	sceptrum	CCCN CExl MGil SPlb SVen
	'Silver Cub'	GAbr
	'Spice Island'	CBod CDor CRos EBee ECtt IBoy LEdu LRHS LSou MNrw MSCN NLar

	NSti SCob SPer SPoG STPC WCot WSpi
* ***stewartii***	EWes MMrt NWad WMoo
'Strawberry Fayre'	GJos
thapsi	ELan EPPr EPfP
- 'Spanish Peaks'	CAbb CBod GJos IBoy WArt
trojana	CFis EAJP ECtt GKev IFoB SCob WWtn
- 'Helen of Troy'	SPtp WArt WHer WSpi
§ × ***valinii*** 'Harkstead Apricot'	ELan EPfP EWTr ILea LRHS MJak SEle
- 'Harkstead Flame'	CRos EWTr LRHS MCot MJak
- (Illumination Series) ILLUMINATION PINK ('Tmdgfp001'PBR)	CAbb CDor EBee ELan EPfP ETMg EWTr GBin GMaP LBuc LSou MAvo MCot MHol MJak MNrw MSCN NLar NPnk SCob SPoG STPC WCot
- - ILLUMINATION RASPBERRY ('Tmdg1204')	CBod CRos EBee EPfP ETMg GBin LBuc LRHS LSou MAvo MHol NCou NDov NLar NPnk SCob STPC
viridiflora	CExl CSam ECtt NBro

dill see *Anethum graveolens*

Dionaea ✿ (*Droseraceae*)

muscipula	EECP LOPS NLos SHmp SPlb WSSs
- 'Akai Ryu' ♀H3	NLos SHmp WSSs
- 'All Green'	EECP
- 'B52'	EECP WSSs
- 'Big Mouth'	EECP
- 'Bohemian Garnet'	EECP WSSs
- 'Darwin'	WSSs
- (Dentate Traps Group) 'Dentate Traps'	WSSs
* - f. ***heterodoxa***	NLos
- large clone	NLos
- long-toothed	NLos
- 'Mk1979'	WSSs
- 'Pink Venus'	NLos
- 'Royal Red'	NLos WSSs
- 'Sawtooth'	EECP NLos WSSs
- shark-toothed	EECP NLos
- Slack's red clone	NLos
- 'South West Giant' ♀H3	NLos WSSs
- 'Spider'	EECP NLos
- 'Tiger Fangs'	WSSs
- upright	NLos

Dionysia (*Primulaceae*)

'Annielle'	EPot WAbe
aretioides ♀H5	WAbe
- 'Alan Furness' **new**	EPot
- 'Bevere'	EPot WAbe
bryoides	WAbe
'Charlson Emma'	WAbe
'Charlson Gem'	EPot
'Charlson Jake'	WAbe
'Charlson Petite'	WAbe
'Charlson Pip'	WAbe
'Corona'	WAbe
curviflora	WAbe
'Eric Watson'	WAbe
'Ewesley Kappa'	WAbe
'Ewesley Theta'	WAbe
'Geist'	WAbe
janthina	WAbe
'Judith Bramley'	WAbe
'Lycaena'	WAbe
'Mike Bramley'	WAbe
'Monika'	WAbe
'Pascal'	WAbe
sarvestanica	WAbe
tapetodes	EPot WAbe
- 'Brimstone'	WAbe
- 'Peter Edwards'	WAbe
'Tess'	EPot WAbe
'Zdeněk Zvolánek'	WAbe

Dioon (*Zamiaceae*)

argenteum	CBrP
califanoi	CBrP
caputoi	CBrP
edule ♀H1b	CBrP SPlb
- var. ***angustifolium***	CBrP
merolae	CBrP
rzedowskii	CBrP
spinulosum	CBrP SBig

Dioscorea (*Dioscoreaceae*)

araucana	LSou
deltoidea	CExl
japonica	CAgr LEdu
polystachya	CAgr CRHN LEdu
quinqueloba	WCru
villosa	LEdu

Diosma (*Rutaceae*)

ericoides L.	SWvt
'Pink Fountain'	see *Coleonema pulchellum* 'Pink Fountain'
'Sunset Gold'	see *Coleonema* 'Sunset Gold'

Diosphaera (*Campanulaceae*)

asperuloides	see *Trachelium asperuloides*

Diospyros (*Ebenaceae*)

austroafricana	SPlb
glabra	SVen
* ***hyrcanum***	NLar
kaki (F)	CBcs CMCN IDee NLar NPla SAko WCot
- 'Fuyu' (F)	CAgr
- 'Hana Fuyu' (F)	MRai
- 'Kostata' (F)	CAgr
- 'Mazelii' (F)	CAgr WPGP
- 'Rojo Brillante' (F)	MRai
lotus	CAgr CBcs CMCN EBee GBin LEdu NLar SPlb
- FMWJ 13164 **new**	WCru
- PAB 10032	LEdu WPGP
- (f)	IDee LMaj
- 'Albert' (m) **new**	CAgr
- 'Browny' (f/F) **new**	CAgr
lycioides	CPbh SPlb
'Mount Goverla' (F) **new**	CAgr
'Nikita's Gift' (F)	CAgr
'Nikita's Russian' (F)	CAgr
'Nikshoo' (F)	CAgr
ramulosa	SPlb
rhombifolia	NLar
'Russian Beauty' (F)	CAgr
'Russian Red' (F)	CAgr
virginiana (F)	CBcs CMCN CRos NLar SPlb
- 'Morris Burton' (F)	CAgr
- 'Nc-10' (F)	CAgr

Diostea (*Verbenaceae*)

juncea	MGil

Dipcadi (*Asparagaceae*)

viride	CTal

Dipelta (*Caprifoliaceae*)

floribunda ♀H5	CBcs CBot CDul CExl CFil CJun CMCN CRos CTho ELan EPfP IDee LRHS MBlu NLar SWvt WPGP
ventricosa	CBcs CExl CFil CJun CRos ELan EPfP LRHS MBlu NLar SBrt SPoG WPGP
yunnanensis	CAby CBcs CBot CCCN CDul CExl CJun CTho EBee ELan EPfP IArd IDee LRHS MBNS NLar SPoG SWvt WPGP

Diphylleia (*Berberidaceae*)

cymosa	CAby CTal ECha GCal GEdr IRob LEdu MNrw MRav SPhx WCot WCru
grayi	GEdr LEdu WCru
sinensis	CExl WCru

Diplacus see *Mimulus*

Dipladenia see *Mandevilla*

Diplarrena (*Iridaceae*)

§ ***latifolia***	CNor GCal IBlr LRHS
moraea	CAby CElw CJun CMac CWCL EBee GAbr GCal IBlr IBoy LEdu MBel WSHC
- ***minor***	IBlr
- 'Slieve Donard'	CBot IBlr
- West Coast form	see *D. latifolia*

Diplazium (*Woodsiaceae*)

maximum	NLos

Diplopanax (*Cornaceae*)

stachyanthus B&SWJ 11803	WCru

Diplotaxis (*Brassicaceae*)

tenuifolia	CAgr ENfk MNHC SRms

Dipsacus (*Caprifoliaceae*)

asper PAB 8884	LEdu
§ ***fullonum***	CBod CHab EBWF ENfk EPfP LCro MHer MNHC NMir SEND SRms WHer WSFF XAbr
inermis	CBWd CSam ECha MMoz NBid
japonicus HWJ 695	SPhx WCru
pilosus	CBgR EBWF NDov
sativus	NLar
strigosus	SPhx
sylvestris	see *D. fullonum*

Dipteracanthus see *Ruellia*

Dipteronia (*Sapindaceae*)

sinensis	CBcs CMCN MBlu

Disa (*Orchidaceae*)

aurata	NDav
Bride's Dream gx	NDav
Child Safety Transvaal gx	NDav
- 'Sonia'	NDav
Colette Cywes gx 'Blush'	NDav
Constantia gx	NDav
Diores gx	NDav
- 'Inca City'	NDav
- 'Inca Gold'	NDav
- 'Inca Princess'	NDav
- 'Inca Warrior'	NDav
Diorosa gx	NDav
Foam gx	NDav
- 'Zoe'	NDav
Glasgow Orchid Conference gx	NDav
Ivan Watson gx	NDav
Kalahari Sands gx	NDav
- 'Tina'	NDav
Kewbett gx	NDav
- 'Pink Gem'	NDav
Kewdior gx	NDav
Kewensis gx 'Alice'	NDav
- 'Ann'	NDav
- 'May'	NDav
- 'Milkmaid'	NDav
- 'Ruth'	NDav
Reheat gx	NDav
Riette gx	NDav
Robert Parkinson gx	NDav
Sealord gx	NDav
Tracey Parkinson gx	NDav
tripetaloides	NDav
Unidiorosa gx 'Tracey'	NDav
uniflora	NDav SPlb
- carmine-flowered	NDav
- pink-flowered	NDav
- red-flowered	NDav
Unifoam gx	NDav
- 'Firebird'	NDav
Unilangley gx	NDav
Watsonii gx 'Bramley'	NDav
- 'Candy'	NDav
- 'Don'	NDav
- 'Sandra'	NDav

Disanthus (*Hamamelidaceae*)

cercidifolius ♀H5	CBcs CDul CMCN CMac CRos EPfP GBin GKin IArd IDee LRHS MBlu MPkF NLar SPoG WHor WPGP
- 'Ena-nishiki' (v)	MBlu NLar WPGP

Discaria (*Rhamnaceae*)

chacaye	LEdu

Diselma (*Cupressaceae*)

archeri	CAco CKen IDee SLim
- 'Read Dwarf'	CKen

Disepalum (*Annonaceae*)

petelotii B&SWJ 11690	WCru
- FMWJ 13375	WCru

Disporopsis (*Asparagaceae*)

B&SWJ 229 from Taiwan	WCru
B&SWJ 1864 from Taiwan	WCru
aspersa	CAvo CBro EBee EPPr EWld GEdr LEdu MAvo MNrw WCru WPGP
- tall	CBct CExl WCru
bodinieri KWJ 12277 **new**	WCru
fuscopicta	CAby CBct EBee EHrv EPPr LEdu MAvo MPie WCru
longifolia B&SWJ 5284	WCru
luzoniensis	IMou
- B&SWJ 3891	CBct CExl GEdr LEdu WCru
'Min Shan'	CExl CTal ELon
* ***nova***	EPPr MAvo
§ ***pernyi***	Widely available
- B&SWJ 1864	CBct EPPr GEdr

- 'Bill Baker'	CBct EBee EPPr LEdu MAvo WSHC
taiwanensis	EBee IMou LEdu
- B&SWJ 3388	CBct GEdr WCru
undulata	CBct CSpe EPPr ILea IMou LEdu MAvo NBid WCru WPGP

Disporum (*Colchicaceae*)

bodinieri	CBct CExl EPfP
- DJHC 765	WCru
- KWJ 12277 new	WCru
cantoniense	CBct CHid IMou LEdu LRHS WCru WFar
- B&L 12512	CExl
- B&SWJ 1424	WCru
- B&SWJ 9715	WCru
- DJHC 98485	LEdu MMoz WPGP
- PAB 8339	LEdu
I - 'Aureovariegata'	CBct EPfP LEdu MMoz WCot
- 'Blueberry Bere' new	LEdu
- var. ***cantoniense*** f. ***brunneum*** B&SWJ 5290	WCru
- 'Leigong'	WPGP
- var. ***multiflorum*** B&SWJ 11252	WCru
- - B&SWJ 11291	WCru
- 'Shirui Pink'	LEdu
- var. ***sikkimense*** B&SWJ 2337	WCru
- - B&SWJ 2358	LEdu WCru
- - PAB 13.1711	LEdu
- - PAB 4973	LEdu
- var. ***y-tiense*** HWJ 1045	WCru
hookeri	see *Prosartes hookeri*
kawakamii B&SWJ 350	WCru
- RWJ 10103	CBct WCru
lanuginosum	see *Prosartes lanuginosa*
leschenaultianum B&SWJ 9484	WCru
- B&SWJ 9505	WCru
leucanthum	CTal WCru
- B&SWJ 2389	WCru
longistylum	CBcs CTal EBee EHrv LEdu
- B&SWJ 2859	WCru
- BWJ 8128	WCru
- L 1564	CBct LEdu WCru
- 'Green Giant'	CBct CExl CTal EBee EPfP GEdr IDee IFoB ILea LEdu LPla LRHS MAvo MBel MSCN NLar WCot WFar WHil WPtf
- 'Night Heron'	CBct CExl CRos CTal IFoB IMou LEdu LPla LRHS NRHS SHar WCot WFar
- 'Night Heron' seedlings	CTal WPGP
aff. ***longistylum*** NJM 11.011 new	WPGP
lutescens	CTal WCru
maculatum	see *Prosartes maculata*
megalanthum	CBct CExl IFoB LEdu MMoz WCru WPGP
- CD&R 2412B	CExl CTal
menziesii	see *Prosartes smithii*
nantouense	CTal
- B&SWJ 359	LEdu WCru
- B&SWJ 6812	WCru
oreganum	see *Prosartes hookeri* var. *oregana*
sessile	EBee LEdu WCru
- B&SWJ 2824	WCru
I - 'Aureovariegatum' (v)	WCru
- 'Awa-no-tsuki' (v)	GEdr
- 'Ginsekai'	GEdr
- 'Kinga' (v)	CTal LEdu
- f. ***macrophyllum*** B&SWJ 4316	WCru
I - 'Robustum Variegatum' (v)	EBee
- 'Snow Stream' (v)	GEdr WFar
- 'Variegatum' (v)	CAby CExl CNor CRos CTal EBee ELan ELon EPPr EPfP GCal IMou LEdu LRHS MNrw NHpl NLar NQui NRHS SPhx WCru WFar WPGP WSHC
- var. ***yakushimense***	LEdu
shimadae B&SWJ 399	WCru
smilacinum	CTal EHrv NLar WCru
- B&SWJ 713	CBct WCru
* - 'Aureovariegatum' (v)	LEdu WCru
- pink-flowered	CBct LEdu WCot WCru WSHC
smithii	see *Prosartes smithii*
taiwanense	CAvo
- B&SWJ 1513	WCru
- B&SWJ 2018	WCru
tonkinense B&SWJ 11672	WCru
- B&SWJ 11814	WCru
- HWJ 882	WCru
trabeculatum	CBct WCru
- 'Nakafu'	EBee IMou LEdu WCru
trachycarpum	see *Prosartes trachycarpa*
uniflorum	CAby CBct CRos CTal EHrv EPPr EPfP GKev LEdu LRHS MHol MMrt MNrw NBid NRHS SMad WSHC
- B&SWJ 651	CBct LEdu WCru
- B&SWJ 872	WCru
- B&SWJ 4100	WCru
- MSF 800	LEdu
viridescens	CBct EBee EHrv EPPr LEdu MMoz WCru WPnP
- B&SWJ 4598	WCru

Distictis (*Bignoniaceae*)

buccinatoria	CHII

Distyliopsis (*Hamamelidaceae*)

tutcheri	CJun

Distylium (*Hamamelidaceae*)

myricoides	NLar
racemosum	CCCN CMac EBee EPfP MBlu NLar SSta WSHC

Dittrichia (*Asteraceae*)

viscosa	WCot

Diuranthera see *Chlorophytum*

Dizygotheca see *Schefflera*

Dodecatheon (*Primulaceae*)

alpinum	GKev
- subsp. ***alpinum***	EBee
'Aphrodite'PBR	ECtt LPmr MHol NLar WFar
austrofrigidum	EBee GEdr GKev SBrt
clevelandii	GEdr WAbe
- subsp. ***insulare***	LLHF
- subsp. ***patulum***	CRos LRHS NRHS
conjugens	GKev LLHF XEll
cusickii	see *D. pulchellum* subsp. *cusickii*
dentatum ♀H5	CPBP GEdr GKev LEdu SBrt WAbe WFar
frigidum	GEdr GKev WAbe
§ ***jeffreyi***	CRos ECtt EPPr EPfP GAbr GEdr GKev LEdu LRHS MBNS MNrw

	NLar NPnk NRHS NSum WAbe WFar
- subsp. ***pygmaeum***	GKev
§ ***meadia*** 🏆H5	Widely available
- from Cedar County	WAbe
- f. ***album*** 🏆H5	CBro CRos ELan EPfP EPot GKev IBoy LAma LEdu LRHS NHpl NPnk NRHS NSum SDir SPer SWvt WPnP WSpi
- 'Aphrodite'	EPfP WFar
* - 'Goliath'	GAbr GWyn NSum
- membranaceous	WAbe
- 'Purple Rose'	SPad
- 'Queen Victoria'	LEdu NLar WFar
- red shades	NSum
pauciflorum misapplied	see *D. pulchellum*
pauciflorum (Dur.) E. Greene	see *D. meadia*
poeticum	SPlb
§ ***pulchellum*** 🏆H5	CBro CRos EBee GEdr IBoy LLWG LRHS MNrw NRHS NRya WArt
§ - subsp. ***cusickii***	LEdu
- subsp. ***pulchellum*** 'Red Wings'	CRos ELan ELon EPot GWyn IBoy LLHF LRHS NHpl NLar NRHS
- ***radicatum***	see *D. pulchellum*
- 'Sooke Variety'	WAbe
radicatum	see *D. pulchellum*
tetrandrum	see *D. jeffreyi*

Dodonaea (*Sapindaceae*)

viscosa	SPlb
- 'Purpurea'	CBcs CCht CExl CHGN CTsd EBee EUJe LRHS SPoG SVen
- 'Red Wings' (f)	SRkn

Doellingeria (*Asteraceae*)

scabra	see *Aster scaber*
umbellata	CBWd CBre CKno EBee ECha EPPr LEdu MMuc MTis MWat NDov NLar WCot WOld WSpi
- 'Weisser Schirm'	MNrw

Dolichandra (*Bignoniaceae*)

§ ***unguis-cati*** 🏆H2	CCCN CRHN

Dolomiaea (*Asteraceae*)

forrestii new	GKev

Dombeya (*Malvaceae*)

wallichii	CCCN

Dondia see *Hacquetia*

Doodia ✿ (*Blechnaceae*)

§ ***caudata***	NBro
media	CAbb CAby CBct CBdn CRos EBee EShb EUJe LEdu LLWG LRHS NBro NHim NLos NRHS SPlb WCot
squarrosa	see *D. caudata*

Doronicum (*Asteraceae*)

austriacum	GKev NBid
- PAB 5641	LEdu
caucasicum	see *D. orientale*
§ ***columnae***	CBcs GKev
cordatum	see *D. columnae*
§ × ***excelsum*** 'Harpur Crewe'	EBee LEdu MRav NPer SHar
'Finesse'	CRos EPfP GCal GJos LRHS NRHS SRms
'Little Leo'	CBod CRos ELan ELon EPfP GJos GMaP LPmr LRHS LSRN NLar NRHS SPoG SRms
§ ***orientale***	EPed EPfP GJos MBel MMuc SEND SPoG
- 'Leonardo'	CRos GMcL LRHS NRHS WHar
- 'Leonardo Compact'	WTor
- 'Magnificum'	CRos CSBt EBee EPfP ESps GMaP LRHS MBNS NRHS SPoG SRms WHar
pardalianches	CFis CMea GCal GJos WBrk WHal WRHF
- 'Goldstrauss'	EBee
plantagineum	MMuc
- 'Excelsum'	see *D.* × *excelsum* 'Harpur Crewe'

Dorotheanthus (*Aizoaceae*)

bellidiformis	see *Cleretum bellidiforme*

Doryanthes (*Doryanthaceae*)

palmeri	CBrP CTsd

Dorycnium see *Lotus*

Doryopteris (*Pteridaceae*)

pedata var. ***palmata***	NLos

Douglasia see *Androsace*

vitaliana	see *Vitaliana primuliflora*

Dovyalis (*Salicaceae*)

caffra (F)	XBlo

Doxantha see *Macfadyena*

Draba (*Brassicaceae*)

acaulis	WAbe
aizoides	CRos GJos LRHS NRHS SPlb SRms
aizoon	see *D. lasiocarpa*
bertolonii Boiss.	see *D. loeseleurii*
bruniifolia subsp. ***heterocoma*** var. ***heterocoma*** new	NSla
- subsp. ***olympica***	GJos
'Buttermilk'	WAbe
* ***condensata***	GJos
cretica	GJos
cusickii	GKev
cuspidata	GJos
dedeana	EPot GJos WAbe
densifolia	IFoB
gilliesii	GJos
incana	GJos
'John Saxton'	WAbe
kotschyi	SPlb
§ ***lasiocarpa***	XLum
§ ***loeseleurii***	GJos
longisiliqua 🏆H4	GJos LLHF WAbe
mollissima	EPot SPlb WAbe
- 'Göteborg'	EPot
nivalis	SPlb
norvegica	GJos
oligosperma	EDAr GJos IFoB
ossetica	WAbe
parnassica	GJos
paysonii var. ***treleasei***	LLHF
polytricha	NSla
ramosissima	GJos
rigida var. ***bryoides*** compact	EPot WAbe

* - var. ***imbricata***	GCrg NRHS NSla
rosularis	EDAr EPot GJos WAbe
× ***salomonii***	EPot
scardica	see *D. lasiocarpa*
sphaeroides	SPlb
stellata	GJos
ventosa	WAbe
yunnanensis	WAbe

Dracaena ✿ (*Asparagaceae*)

cochinchinensis	SPlb
draco ♀H1c	CCCN CMCN EShb SPlb WCot XBlo
elliptica __new__	EShb
fragrans	EUJe
- (Compacta Group) 'Compacta'	XBlo
- Deremensis Group	XBlo
- - 'J.A. Truffaut'	XBlo
- - 'Lemon Lime' (v) ♀H1b	LOPS
- - 'Souvenir d'August de Schrijver' (v)	XBlo
indivisa	see *Cordyline indivisa*
'Lemon Lime Tips'	XBlo
marginata (v) ♀H1b	XBlo
- 'Tricolor' (v) ♀H1b	XBlo

Dracocephalum (*Lamiaceae*)

altaiense	see *D. imberbe*
argunense	CAby SPhx SRms
- 'Blue Carpet'	LEdu NLar
- 'Fuji Blue'	CExl CSma EDAr EWes SPoG
- 'Fuji White'	CExl SPhx SPoG
austriacum	SBrt
botryoides	EPot MMuc SPhx
calophyllum var. ***smithianum***	IMou
forrestii	GKev SBrt
grandiflorum	GBin MMrt SPhx WCot XLum
§ ***imberbe***	GBin
mairei	see *D. renatii*
moldavica	GBin XAbr
peregrinum	GBin
- 'Blue Dragon'	SPhx
prattii	see *Nepeta prattii*
§ ***renatii***	SPhx
rupestre	EBee SBee SPhx
ruyschiana	ELan MMrt SPhx XLum
sibiricum	see *Nepeta sibirica*
* ***tataricum***	CRos LRHS NRHS
virginicum	see *Physostegia virginiana*

Dracophyllum (*Ericaceae*)

prostratum	EPot

Dracunculus (*Araceae*)

canariensis	CBod GKev WCot
muscivorus	see *Helicodiceros muscivorus*
§ ***vulgaris***	CAby CHid CRos EBee EPfP EPot GKev LRHS MBNS NRHS SEND SPlb WCot WHil
- white-flowered	WCot

Dregea (*Apocynaceae*)

sinensis	CBcs CBot CCCN CHll CRHN CRos EBee ECre ELan EPfP EShb ETMg EWes LRHS MRav SEND SPoG SWvt WPGP WSHC
- 'Brockhill Silver'	CBot EPfP LRHS SPoG SWvt
- 'Variegata' (v)	EWes

Drepanostachyum (*Poaceae*)

falconeri J.J.N. Campbell. ex D. McClintock	see *Himalayacalamus falconeri* 'Damarapa'
hookerianum	see *Himalayacalamus hookerianus*
§ ***khasianum***	CExl

Drimiopsis (*Asparagaceae*)

maculata	EShb GKev LToo

Drimys (*Winteraceae*)

andina	CExl EPfP MGil MMuc WSHC
aromatica	see *Tasmannia lanceolata*
colorata	see *Pseudowintera colorata*
granadensis var. ***grandiflora*** B&SWJ 10777	WCru
winteri ♀H4	Widely available
§ - var. ***chilensis***	CBcs CExl EPfP LRHS WCru WPGP
- Latifolia Group	see *D. winteri* var. *chilensis*
- var. ***winteri***	SRms

Drosanthemum (*Aizoaceae*)

hispidum	CRos ELan EPot LRHS MAsh NRHS SPlb SPoG

Drosera ✿ (*Droseraceae*)

aliciae ♀H3	EECP NLos SHmp
binata	EECP SHmp
§ - subsp. ***dichotoma*** ♀H3	NLos SHmp
- 'Extrema'	NLos
- 'Giant'	NLos
capensis	LOPS NLos SHmp SPlb
- 'Albino' ♀H3	EECP NLos SHmp
dichotoma	see *D. binata* subsp. *dichotoma*
dichrosepala	EECP
filiformis	NLos
- var. ***filiformis***	EECP SHmp
- var. ***tracyi***	NLos
madagascariensis	NLos SHmp
nidiformis	NLos
paradoxa	NLos
rotundifolia	SHmp
scorpioides	EECP SHmp
slackii ♀H3	SPlb
spatulata	SHmp

Dryandra (*Proteaceae*)

formosa	CPbh SPlb
quercifolia	SPlb

Dryas (*Rosaceae*)

drummondii	LLHF
§ ***integrifolia***	CMea WAbe
- 'Greenland Green'	WAbe
octopetala ♀H5	CMea CPla CRos GKev LRHS NChi NRHS SPoG SRms SWvt WAbe
- subsp. ***hookeriana***	LLHF
§ - 'Minor' ♀H5	EPot WAbe
× ***suendermannii*** ♀H5	EPot GCrg GMaP LLHF NSla SBch WAbe
tenella misapplied	see *D. octopetala* 'Minor'
tenella Pursh	see *D. integrifolia*

Drynaria (*Polypodiaceae*)

baronii	WCot

Dryopteris ✿ (*Dryopteridaceae*)

from Kunming, China	NLos

	from Mount Zijin, China	NLos
	from Nanjing Botanical Garden, China	NLos
	aemula	CBdn EFer
§	***affinis*** ♀H5	CBdn CDor CKel CMac CRos CWCL ECha EPfP ERod ESps GMaP LBuc LRHS MCot MGos MMoz MMuc NPnk NRHS SCob SPer SPoG SRms WCot WFib WShi WSpi XLum
	- 'Angustata Crispa'	CBdn EBee SRms
	- subsp. ***cambrensis*** 'Insubrica'	EFer
	- 'Congesta'	CKel
	- 'Congesta Cristata'	CTal CWCL ECtt EFer GMaP SRot
	- Crispa Group	CBdn CBod CRos EPfP LRHS MMoz NRHS SCob
§	- 'Crispa Gracilis' ♀H5	CAby CBod CKel CRos ELan ERod MMoz NEgg NHim NLar
*	- 'Crispa Gracilis Congesta'	CKel LLWG MRav NGdn NWad WCot WFib
§	- 'Cristata' ♀H5	Widely available
	- 'Cristata Angustata' ♀H5	CKel CTal EFer ELan EPed EPfP LLWG MMoz NBid NBro NGdn WFib WMoo
	- 'Cristata The King'	see *D. affinis* 'Cristata'
	- 'Grandiceps Askew'	WFib
	- 'Pinderi'	CBdn EBee EPfP EUJe GBin GEdr LLWG LPla LSun MMoz MMuc MPie NCou NLar NRHS SCob WCot WRHF WSpi
	- Polydactyla Group	SPlb
	- - 'Polydactyla Dadds'	CBdn EBee LLHF NLar
	- - 'Polydactyla Mapplebeck' ♀H5	NBid WFib
	- 'Revolvens'	EFer
	atrata misapplied	see *D. cycadina*
	atrata (Wall. ex Kunze) Ching	CDTJ CRos CWCL LLWG LRHS NEgg NHim NLar NRHS SPoG XLum
	× ***australis***	CBdn EBee NLos
	austriaca	see *D. dilatata*
	buschiana	EBee EWTr MRav NLar WCot
	carthusiana	CBdn CKel EBee EFer MMoz NLar WSpi XLum
	- 'Cristata'	EFer
	celsa	EBee NLos
	championii	CBdn CCCN CRos EBee LRHS NBro NLar NRHS SRot
	aff. ***chrysocoma*** **new**	CBdn
	clintoniana	CKel CRos EBee ECtt EFer GBin GQue ITim LLWG LPla LRHS MMoz MPie NRHS WCot
	× ***complexa***	CBdn NLos
	- 'Stablerae' ♀H7	EFer WFib
	- 'Stablerae' crisped ♀H7	WFib
	coreanomontana	EBee NLar
	crassirhizoma ♀H6	CAby CBdn CBod CCCN CKel CRos EBee ECtt EPfP EUJe GAbr GBin LPla LRHS LSun MMoz MMuc NLar NRHS WCot WPtf WRHF WSpi
	cristata	CWCL EBee EPfP WMoo XLum
§	***cycadina*** ♀H4	CBcs CBdn CRos CTal EBee EFer ELan ERod EShb EUJe GBin LRHS MGos MMoz NBid NLos NRHS SCob SPtp WFib WMoo
	cystolepidota	EFer
	dickinsii	CBdn
§	***dilatata*** ♀H6	CRos ECha EFer ELan EPfP ERod ESps LRHS MMuc MRav NRHS WCot WFib WHal WShi
	- 'Crispa Whiteside' ♀H6	CBdn CDor CRos CWCL EBee EFer ELan EPfP ERod EShb EUJe GBin LRHS MMoz MRav NBro NEgg NLar NRHS SPlb SPoG WCot WFib WMoo
	- 'Cristata'	LSun
	- 'Grandiceps'	CMac EFer WFib
	- 'Jimmy Dyce'	CBdn CRos EBee GBin LRHS NRHS
	- 'Lepidota Crispa Cristata'	EBee NRHS SRot
	- 'Lepidota Cristata' ♀H6	CBdn CWCL ELan EMOT ERod NBro NLos WFib WMoo
*	- 'Recurvata'	LLHF NLar
	erythrosora ♀H4	Widely available
	- from Guizhou, China **new**	WPGP
	- 'Brilliance' ♀H5	CBct CBdn CCCN CRos CSpe EBee ECtt ELon EMFm EUJe GAbr GQue IRob LLWG LPla LRHS LSou MAvo MPie NCou NRHS SBod WCot WRHF
	- var. ***koidzumiana***	CBdn CRos LRHS NRHS WCot
	- var. ***prolifica***	CBdn CBod CKel CRos EBee ELan EPfP GBin GMaP LEdu LRHS MGos MMoz NEgg NLar NRHS SPoG SRot WFar WFib
	filix-mas ♀H7	Widely available
	- 'Barnesii'	CBdn CKel CRos CWCL EFer ELan EMOT ERod LRHS NEgg NLar NRHS SEND SPlb
	- 'Bollandiae'	EBee
	- 'Crispa'	CRos EPfP LRHS NRHS WFib
	- 'Crispa Congesta'	see *D. affinis* 'Crispa Gracilis'
	- 'Crispa Cristata' ♀H7	CChe CKel CRos CWCL EAJP EBee ECtt EFer ELan EPfP ERod ESps EUJe GBin GEdr GMaP GWyn LLWG LRHS NBid NBro NRHS SCob SPoG WFib XLum
	- 'Crispatissima'	EBee
	- 'Cristata' ♀H7	CTal EBee ECtt EFer ELan LCro LLWG LOPS MJak MMoz NBro SEND WMoo
	- Cristata Group	EFer
*	- - 'Cristata Grandiceps'	EFer
	- - 'Cristata Jackson'	SPlb
	- - 'Cristata Martindale'	CBdn EBee NBid WFib
	- - 'Fred Jackson'	WFib
	- 'Furcans'	CBdn CRos EBee ECtt LRHS NRHS WMoo
	- 'Grandiceps Wills' ♀H7	NBid WFib
	- 'Linearis'	CRos EFer ELan LRHS MCot MGos NRHS WFib
	- 'Linearis Polydactyla' ♀H7	CBdn CBod CDor CKel CMac CRos CWCL EFer ELan EMOT EPfP EShb EUJe EWTr GBin LRHS MMoz MMuc MRav NEgg NLar NLos SCob SEND SPoG SPtp WMoo WPnP XLum
	- 'Parsley'	CBdn EBee
*	- Polydactyla Group	ECha MRav NEgg NRHS SCob
I	- 'Revolvens'	WFib
	formosana	CBdn
	goldieana	CBod CDTJ CRos CTal EBee ECha ECtt EFer EMOT EWTr GMaP LLWG LRHS NBid NEgg NLar NRHS SRot WFar WFib WMoo WPnP WSpi XLum
	hirtipes misapplied	see *D. cycadina*
	intermedia	EBee
	labordei	CBdn CRos EBee GBin LRHS NRHS
	lepidopoda	CAby CBcs CBdn CBod CDor CRos ECtt EUJe GBin LPla LRHS MAvo

	MPie NBro NRHS WCot WPtf WRHF WSpi
ludoviciana	CRos LRHS NLar NRHS WSpi
magellanica new	EBee
marginalis	CDTJ CKel CRos EMOT LRHS MMoz NLar NRHS SCob WMoo
neorosthornii	NLos
oreades	WCot
pseudomas	see *D. affinis*
pulcherrima	CRos LRHS NRHS
× ***remota***	CBdn EBee EFer MMoz NLos
sichotensis	CBdn
sieboldii ♀H6	Widely available
stewartii	CBdn LLHF NBro
subarborea new	EBee
tokyoensis ♀H6	CDTJ CRos LRHS MMoz NLar NRHS WSpi
uniformis	EFer NLos
wallichiana ♀H5	Widely available
- from Yunnan, China	GCal
yigongensis	NLos

Duchesnea (*Rosaceae*)

chrysantha	see *D. indica*
§ ***indica***	GJos MRav SEND WMoo WOut XLum
§ - 'Harlequin' (v)	CExl
- 'Variegata'	see *D. indica* 'Harlequin'

Dudleya (*Crassulaceae*)

brittonii ♀H3	SMad
calcicola	SPlb
cymosa	SPlb
lanceolata	SPlb

Dugaldia (*Asteraceae*)

hoopesii	see *Hymenoxys hoopesii*

Dulichium (*Cyperaceae*)

arundinaceum	LLWG
- 'Tigress'	LLWG

Dunalia (*Solanaceae*)

australis	see *Iochroma australe*
- blue-flowered	see *Iochroma australe* 'Bill Evans'
- white-flowered	see *Iochroma australe* 'Andean Snow'

Duranta (*Verbenaceae*)

§ ***erecta***	CCCN CHll
§ - 'Geisha Girl'	CCCN EShb
- 'Sapphire Swirl'	see *D. erecta* 'Geisha Girl'
- 'Variegata' (v)	CCCN
- white-flowered	SVen
plumieri	see *D. erecta*
repens	see *D. erecta*
serratifolia	CCCN

Duvernoia see *Justicia*

Dyckia (*Bromeliaceae*)

brevifolia	WCot
'Burgundy Ice' new	WCot
'Cherry Coke'	WCot
frigida	WCot WGrn
goehringii	WCot
jonesiana	WCot
leptostachya	SEND SPlb WCot WGrn
marnier-lapostollei	CBlu SPlb WCot
'Morris Hobbs'	WCot
remotiflora	SChr
velascana	WCot

Dypsis (*Arecaceae*)

§ ***decaryi***	CBlu CCCN SPlb XBlo
lutescens ♀H1a	NLos XBlo

Dysosma see *Podophyllum*

E

Ecballium (*Cucurbitaceae*)

elaterium	CDTJ CFil LEdu WCot WPGP
- 'Lahij'	WPGP

Eccremocarpus (*Bignoniaceae*)

ruber	see *E. scaber* 'Ruber'
scaber	CBcs CKel CRos CWCL ELan EPfP LRHS MNHC NPer WArt
- 'Carmineus'	EPfP
- cream-flowered	NLar
- red-flowered	CWCL NLar
§ - 'Ruber'	GKev
- 'Tangerine'	CSpe
- Tresco Series	GKev

Echeandia (*Asparagaceae*)

formosa B&SWJ 9147	WCru

Echeveria ✿ (*Crassulaceae*)

affinis	CBod CDTJ MHer NEoE SRot
agavoides ♀H1c	CDTJ MRav
- 'Ebony'	WCot
- 'Lipstick'	WCot
albicans	SPlb
alpina	see *E. secunda*
ballsii	WCot
bicolor B&SWJ 14388 new	WCru
* 'Black Knight'	EUJe
* 'Black Prince'	CDTJ ELan NPer SPlb SRot WCot
'Blue Waves'	WCot
* ***cana***	CDTJ NCft SRot
cante ♀H2	SPlb
coccinea	ELan
'Corymbosa'	WCot
'Curly Locks'	ECtt EMFm WCot
derenbergii ♀H2	MHCG
× ***derosa***	CDTJ
'Duchess of Nuremberg'	CBod EUJe MCot SPlb SRot
elegans ♀H2	CBod CDTJ CRav EPfP EUJe LSun NCft NEoE NWad SEND SPlb
'Ghost Buster'	WPGP
* × ***gilva*** 'Red'	MHol WCot
glauca Baker	see *E. secunda* var. *glauca*
lilacina ♀H2	NCft SPlb SRot
'Mahogany'	WCot WGrn
'Mauna Loa'	WGrn
maxonii B&SWJ 10396	WCru
minima ♀H2	SPlb
montana B&SWJ 10277	WCru
nodulosa	WCot
peacockii	MHer SPlb
'Perle von Nürnberg' ♀H2	CAbb SMad SPhm
prolifica	SPlb
pulidonis ♀H1c	MHer
pulvinata ♀H1c	MHCG
I - 'Rubra'	SPlb

purpusorum	SPlb
rosea ♀H1c	MHer WCot
runyonii 'Topsy Turvy' ♀H2	CDTJ EUJe SRot WCot
§ ***secunda***	CAbb CCac CFil EUJe SPlb
§ - var. ***glauca***	CDTJ ELan EShb GAbr NCft SEND WPGP
- - 'Compton Carousel' ♀H1c	WCot
* - - 'Gigantea'	NPer
'Set-Oliver' × ***setosa***	WCot
setosa ♀H1c	CDTJ NCft
- var. ***ciliata***	EShb
shaviana ♀H2	CDTJ EUJe SPlb SRot WCot
subsessilis	WCot

Echinacea ✿ (*Asteraceae*)

'12th of July'	EBee
§ 'Adam Saul'	CRos LRHS NRHS
§ 'After Midnight'PBR (Big Sky Series)	EBee ECtt
'Aloha'PBR	LRHS NLar NRHS SPoG WCAu
'Amazing Dream'PBR	CAbb CWGN EBee ECtt IBoy LCro LRHS NRHS
angustifolia	ENfk EPfP GPoy LRHS SPhx XAbr
§ 'Art's Pride'PBR	LCro MJak SCob
'Big Kahuna'PBR	CAbb CWGN ECtt IPot SCob
'Buttercream'	EBee
'Butterfly Kisses'PBR (d)	CRos EBee LCro LRHS NRHS
'Caribbean Green'	EBee
'Champagne Bubbles' **new**	CRos
CHEYENNE SPIRIT, mixed	CBod CDor EAJP ETMg GMcL LCro LOPS LPla LPmr LRHS MHol SPhx WFar WTor
'Chiquita'PBR (Prairie Pixie Series)	CRos EBee LRHS NRHS
'Cleopatra'PBR	CWGN EBee
'Colorburst Orange' (Colorburst Series) (d)	CWGN
'Coral Reef'PBR	ECtt
'Coupe Soleil' (d)	EBee
'Cranberry Cupcake'PBR (d)	EBee ECtt
CRAZY PINK	see *E.* 'Adam Saul'
CRAZY WHITE	see *E.* 'Noam Saul'
'Daydream'PBR	CWCL CWGN ECtt LSou WSpi
'Delicious Candy' **new**	CWGN WCot
(Double Scoop Series) DOUBLE SCOOP BUBBLEGUM ('Balscblum'PBR) (d)	EBee LPmr MHol
- DOUBLE SCOOP LEMON CREME ('Balsclemc') (d) **new**	MHol
- DOUBLE SCOOP RASPBERRY ('Balsceras'PBR) (d)	EBee LPmr MHol
'Eccentric'PBR (d)	CRos CWCL CWGN EBee IPot LRHS NRHS SMad WNPC WTor
'Emily Saul'	see *E.* 'After Midnight'
'Evan Saul'	see *E.* 'Sundown'
'Evening Glow'	CBod CWGN EBee WSpi WWtn
'Ferris Wheel' (Carnival Series)	CWCL EBee SCob WSpi
'Flame Thrower'PBR	CWGN ECtt EWTr LSou NLar SCob
'Gemini Pink'	CRos EBee LRHS NRHS
'Golden Skipper'	CRos ECtt LRHS NRHS
'Green Envy'PBR	CBcs CRav CRos CWGN EBee ECtt ELan EPfP GMaP IBoy LCro LOPS LRHS MBNS MBel MNrw NLar NPnk NRHS SCob SMad WTor
'Greenline'PBR	EBee ECtt
'Guava Ice'PBR	CDor CWCL EBee LLHF WSpi
§ 'Harvest Moon'PBR (Big Sky Series)	CBcs CBod CRos CWCL EBee ECtt EPfP EWTr LCro LOPS LRHS SCob SPer SPoG SWvt
'Heavenly Dream'PBR	ECtt
'Hot Lava'PBR	CWGN EBee ECtt EWTr LCro LRHS NRHS SPoG
'Hot Papaya'PBR (d)	CBod CWCL CWGN ECtt EUJe IPot LCro LLHF LOPS SCob SMad SPoG SWvt
'Hot Summer'PBR	CBcs CBod CPar CRos CWCL CWGN EBee LEdu LRHS NLar NRHS SCob SGbt
'Indian Summer'	EBee
'Irresistible'PBR (d)	CWGN EBee IPot LCro LOPS
'Julia'PBR	ECtt
'Jupiter' (Big Sky Series)	ECtt SCob
'Katie Saul'	see *E.* 'Summer Sky'
'Leilani'PBR	CAbb MMrt
'Mac 'n' Cheese'PBR	EBee LCro LOPS LRHS SCob
'Mama Mia'PBR	CAbb CWCL CWGN EBee ECtt LCro LOPS LRHS NLar SGbt
MANGO MEADOWBRITE ('CBG Cone3')	CRos EPfP LRHS NRHS
'Marmalade'PBR	CBcs CBod CDor CWCL CWGN EBee EWTr LLHF SCob SPad WCAu
'Matthew Saul'	see *E.* 'Harvest Moon'
'Maui Sunshine'PBR	CAbb EBee ECtt NHpl
'Maya Raya'	WNPC
'Meditation'PBR	EBee WCot
'Meteor Red' (Meteor Series)	CRos ECtt LRHS NRHS
Moodz Shiny ('Hilmoooshin')	LRHS NRHS
'Mozzarella' (d)	EBee GBin
§ 'Noam Saul'	CRos EBee LRHS NRHS
'Now Cheesier'PBR	LCro LOPS SMad
ORANGE MEADOWBRITE	see *E.* 'Art's Pride'
'Orange Passion'	CBod CWGN EBee ECtt WCAu
'Orange Skipper' (Butterfly Series) **new**	CRos EWTr NRHS
'Pacific Summer'	CWGN EBee WSpi
pallida	CBWd CBod CKno CRos CSam CSpe EBee ELan EPfP EShb ESps GPoy LRHS MBel MGos NDov NGdn NRHS SPer SPhx SRms SWvt WHar WSpi XLum
- 'Hula Dancer'	CDor GWyn LRHS NGdn NRHS SPhx
paradoxa	CBod CHid CRos EHrv ELan EPfP GPoy IDee LPla LRHS MBel MCot NGdn NRHS NSti SPav SPer SPhx SPlb SPtp SWvt WHil XLum
- var. ***paradoxa***	SPtp
paradoxa × ***purpurea***	IBoy
'Piccolino'	CWGN EBee ECtt LRHS
'Pink Mist'PBR (Mistical Series)	EBee
PIXIE MEADOWBRITE ('CBG Cone 2')	CWGN EBee ECtt MNrw
'Purple Emperor'PBR	ECtt
§ ***purpurea***	Widely available
- 'Alaska'PBR	IBoy NGdn NLar
- 'Alba'	CBWd CBod CRos EPfP EWTr GMcL LRHS NRHS WCot XLum
- 'Amber Mist'PBR (Mistical Series)	EBee
- 'Augustkönigin'	CKno EBee LRHS MNrw NDov WCAu WCot
- 'Avalanche'PBR	CWGN EBee ELon
- 'Baby Swan Pink'	CRos GPSL LRHS NRHS

- 'Baby Swan White'	CRos EBee ELon GPSL LRHS NLar NRHS WFar
- Bradfield hybrids **new**	EHrv
- Bressingham hybrids	CBod CRos EShb LRHS MArl MRav MSpe NRHS SPer WGwG
- 'Catharina'PBR	CWGN EBee ECtt
- 'Coconut Lime'PBR	CWGN EPfP LCro LOPS LSou
- DOPPELGANGER	see *E. purpurea* 'Doubledecker'
§ - 'Doubledecker'	CNor CWCL EBee ELan EPfP ESps GWyn IBoy LLHF NGdn SGbt WHar XLum
- ELTON KNIGHT ('Elbrook'PBR) ♀H7	ECtt LCro LOPS LRHS NRHS STPC SWvt
- 'Fancy Frills'	ECtt
- 'Fatal Attraction'PBR	CBWd CBcs CPar CRos CWGN ECtt EHrv EPfP EWTr GMaP IBoy IPot LEdu LRHS LSRN LSou MBNS MBel MRav NLar NPnk NRHS SCob SPad SPer SPoG SWvt WCot
- 'Firebird'PBR	CWCL ECtt LEdu LRHS SCob SGbt SPoG
- 'Fragrant Angel'PBR	ECtt ELon EPfP IBoy LRHS MBel NLar SWvt WNPC
- 'Green Eyes'	EBee ECtt NLar
- 'Green Jewel'PBR	CBcs CBod CDor CPar CWGN EBee ECtt EPfP EUJe LCro LOPS LPla LRHS LSou MBel MCot MNrw NDov NLar NRHS NSti SCob SGbt SPad WCAu WCot
- 'Gum Drop'PBR	EBee LRHS
- 'Happy Star'	CDor CRos EBee EPed LRHS LSou NRHS WGwG
- 'Hope'PBR	CRos EBee ECtt LRHS MBel NLar NRHS WCAu
- 'Jade'	EBee LSRN MBNS NLar
- 'JS Purple Prairie'	IPot
- 'Kim's Knee High'PBR	CKno CRos ECtt EHrv ELan EPfP GMaP LRHS MBel MCot NGdn NLar NRHS SCob SPer SWvt
- 'Kim's Mop Head'	CRos ECtt EHrv ELan EPfP EWes LRHS MCot MRav NLar WCot
§ - 'Leuchtstern'	CKno CRos ELan EPfP LRHS NGdn NRHS XLum
- 'Lilliput'PBR	ECtt NLar
- 'Little Magnus'PBR	CKno ECtt ETMg LRHS NRHS SPoG
- 'Lucky Star'	CRos ELan EPfP LRHS NRHS SPhx
- 'Magnus'	Widely available
- 'Magnus Superior'	CBod CDor CMea CRos GBin LRHS LSou LSun MNrw NRHS SPhx SWvt WGwG WHoo
- 'Mars'	SCob
- 'Maxima'	CRos ECtt LRHS
- 'Meringue'PBR	IBoy SCob
- 'Merlot'PBR	ECtt LRHS
- 'Milkshake'PBR	CWCL CWGN EBee LLHF LRHS MBel WSpi
- 'Mistral'	CRos EBee LRHS NRHS
- 'Pica Bella'	CBod CRos CWGN ECtt EPfP LRHS NRHS SPad
- 'Pink Double Delight'PBR	MRav NGdn
- 'Pink Glow'	NDov
- 'Pink Poodle'PBR	EBee IBoy
- 'Pink Sorbet'PBR	IPot NLar
- (PowWow Series) POWWOW WHITE ('Pas709018')	CBod CRos LRHS NRHS SPoG WTor
- - POWWOW WILD BERRY ('Pas702917'PBR)	CRos IPot LRHS NRHS SCob SPoG WFar WTor
- 'Prairie Splendor'	CRos EHoe EPed EPfP GMcL LRHS NDov SPhx WHar
- 'Primadonna Deep Rose'	GPSL LEdu MHer NGBl SRot SVic
- 'Primadonna White'	LRHS MHer SRot
- 'Purity'PBR	ECtt LRHS SPoG
- 'Rainbow Marcella' **new**	CRos NRHS
- 'Razzmatazz'PBR (d)	CMac CWCL EBee ECtt EHrv ELan IBoy IRob MRav NGdn SPer SWvt WCot
- 'Red Baron'	EBee
- 'Robert Bloom'	SWvt WSpi
- 'Rubinglow'	ECtt IBoy LCro LOPS NDov NLar SWvt
- 'Rubinstern'	Widely available
- 'Ruby Giant' ♀H7	CDor CKno CRos ECtt EHrv ELan GMaP IBoy IRob LRHS LSRN LSou LSun MBel MNrw MTis NEgg NLar NRHS SGbt SPer WCot
- 'Sensation Pink'PBR	CPar CWGN EBee LRHS MNHC
- 'Southern Belle'PBR	CDor CWCL CWGN EBee IPot MBNS SMad WSpi
- 'Summer Salsa'PBR	CWCL CWGN EBee EUJe LLHF WCot
- 'The King'	CRos LRHS NGdn NLar NRHS WSpi
- 'Tom Thumb'	EBee
- 'Vanilla Cupcake'PBR (d) **new**	LRHS
- 'Verbesserter Leuchtstern'	NLar
- 'Vintage Wine'PBR	CBcs CKno CRos ECtt EHrv ELan EPfP LCro LOPS LRHS NEgg NLar NSti SCob SPer SPoG SWvt WCAu WCot
- 'Virgin'PBR	EBee IPot LCro LOPS MAvo MBel NDov NLar SCob
- 'White Double Delight'PBR (d) **new**	CWCL
- 'White Lustre'	ECha EPfP SRms
- WHITE NATALIE ('Norwhinat'PBR)	EBee
- 'White Swan'	Widely available
'Quills and Thrills'PBR (Prairie Pillars Series)	CWGN ECtt MMrt SCob
'Raspberry Tart'	ECtt
'Raspberry Truffle'PBR	EBee ECtt
(Secret Series) 'Secret Desire'PBR (d)	EBee NHpl SPoG
- 'Secret Joy'PBR (d)	NHpl
- 'Secret Love' (d)	CWGN SCob
- 'Secret Lust'PBR (d)	EBee ECtt
- 'Secret Passion'PBR (d)	CWGN EBee ECtt LRHS NHpl SGbt
- 'Secret Pride' (d)	SCob
- 'Secret Romance'PBR	LRHS NHpl NRHS
simulata	EWTr
'Solar Flare'PBR (Big Sky Series)	EBee ECtt
(Sombrero Series) SOMBRERO ADOBE ORANGE ('Balsomador') **new**	CBod
- SOMBRERO BAJA BURGUNDY ('Balsombabur') **new**	LSou MHol
- SOMBRERO BLANCO **new**	LSou MHol
- SOMBRERO FLAMENCO ORANGE ('Balsomenco'PBR)	LRHS NPnk
- SOMBRERO HOT CORAL ('Balsomcor'PBR)	EBee WFar
- SOMBRERO LEMON YELLOW ('Balsomemy'PBR) **new**	CBod
- SOMBRERO SALSA RED ('Balsomsed'PBR)	CBcs CBod LRHS NPnk WFar

- SOMBRERO SANDY YELLOW ('Balsomselo'PBR)	EBee MAsh WFar
'Spider'	EBee
'Starlight'	see *E. purpurea* 'Leuchtstern'
'Strawberry Shortcake'	EBee
'Summer Breeze'	EBee SCob
'Summer Cloud'	CBod CRos CWGN EBee LRHS LSou NRHS SCob SMad SPoG WTor
'Summer Cocktail'PBR	ELan LCro LOPS LRHS SCob SPoG WTor
'Summer Passion'	ELan
'Summer Samba' (d)	EBee
§ 'Summer Sky'PBR (Big Sky Series)	CRos ECtt EPfP LRHS NLar NPnk NRHS
'Summer Sun'PBR	LRHS NLar
§ 'Sundown'PBR (Big Sky Series)	CPar CRos EBee ECtt EHrv EPfP EWTr IBoy LOPS LRHS NLar NRHS NSti SCob SGbt SPoG SWvt WCAu
'Sunrise'PBR (Big Sky Series)	CRos EBee ECtt ELan EPed EPfP EWes GMaP LLHF LRHS MCot NEgg NRHS NSti SCob SGbt SPer SPoG SWvt WCAu WSpi
'Sunset'PBR (Big Sky Series)	CRav ECtt ELan EWes LLHF LSRN NEgg SWvt WSpi
'Supreme Cantaloupe' (d)	ECtt
'Supreme Elegance' (d)	EBee
'Tangerine Dream'PBR	EBee ECtt EPfP LRHS SCob WNPC
tennesseensis	SPhx
- 'Rocky Top'	CDor EPfP IBoy LRHS MBNS MGos
'Tiki Torch'PBR	CBcs CDor CMea CRos CWCL ECtt LCro LEdu LOPS LRHS MAvo NRHS SCob SPer SPoG SWvt WCot WTor
'Tomato Soup'PBR	Widely available
'Twilight'PBR (Big Sky Series)	LEdu LRHS
'White Meditation'	CBod CRos IRob LRHS NRHS
'White Mist'PBR (Mistical Series)	EBee
'White Spider'	MBel SCob
'Yellow Spider'	EBee EWTr SCob
'Zion' (Sunacea Series) **new**	EBee

Echinocereus (*Cactaceae*)

§ ***coccineus***	CCac
- SB 236	CCac
- from Belen, New Mexico	CCac
- from Jarilla Mountains, New Mexico	CCac
engelmannii var. ***variegatus*** LZ 867	CCac
reichenbachii ♀H2 HK 1228	CCac
- from Montemorelos, Mexico	CCac
- subsp. ***baileyi***	CCac
- subsp. ***caespitosus***	CCac
- - from Mason County, Texas	CCac
triglochidiatus	CCac
- SB 223	CCac
- from Sandoval County, New Mexico	CCac
- var. ***melanacanthus***	see *E. coccineus*
- var. ***mojavensis***	CCac
- - SB 686	CCac
viridiflorus DJF 713.1 from Larimer County, Colorado	CCac
- SB 137/18 from Sandia Mountains, New Mexico	CCac
- SB 876 from Chaffee County, Colorado	CCac
* - var. ***robustior*** HK 1007	CCac

Echinops (*Asteraceae*)

albus	see *E.* 'Nivalis'
§ ***bannaticus***	CBcs CMac CSBt NBid SCob WWtn
* - 'Albus'	WCAu
- 'Blue Globe'	CBod CRos EBee EHoe ELan EPed EPfP EUJe GBin GCal GMcL IBoy LRHS LSRN LSun MGos MHol NGdn NRHS SCob SPoG WCAu WFar
- 'Blue Glow' **new**	CBod
- 'Star Frost'	CBod CRos EBee ELan EPfP LRHS NLar NRHS SPhx
- 'Taplow Blue'	Widely available
maracandicus	WCot
§ 'Nivalis'	CBre CRos LRHS NRHS
* ***perringii***	GCal
ritro misapplied	see *E. bannaticus*
§ ***ritro*** L. ♀H7	Widely available
- 'Blue Cloud'	EBee
- subsp. ***ruthenicus*** ♀H7	MRav WCot
- - 'Platinum Blue'	CMea CRos ECtt ELan ELon LRHS NDov NEgg SPhx SRms WHar
- 'Veitch's Blue' misapplied	see *E. ritro* L.
- 'Veitch's Blue'	Widely available
sphaerocephalus	MSCN NDov SPlb
- 'Arctic Glow'	CBWd CBod CMac CPou CRos EBee ECha ECtt EHoe EHrv ELan EPfP ESps GMaP IBoy LRHS MMuc MTis NDov NGdn NLar NRHS SCob SPer SPlb SPoG SWvt WFar WHar WWtn
spinosissimus	EBee
tjanschanicus	CPla CRos EBee GPSL LRHS MMuc NLar NRHS SEND

Echium ✿ (*Boraginaceae*)

aculeatum	MEch
amoenum	MEch SPhx WArt
angustifolium Mill. **new**	MEch SPhx
asperrimum **new**	MEch
bethencourtianum	SVen
'Blue Steeple'	MEch NLos
boissieri	CCCN MEch
brevirame	MEch
candicans ♀H1c	CAbb CBcs CBod CCCN CHll CPbh CPne CTsd ECre ELan EUJe GKev IBoy MEch NLos SArc SCob SEND SVen
- 'Dwarf Blue'	CCCN
decaisnei subsp. ***decaisnei***	MEch SVen
gentianoides	MEch SPlb SVen
italicum	CCCN MEch
lusitanicum	CCCN
nervosum	MEch
onosmifolium	MEch SVen
pininana ♀H2	CAbb CBcs CBod CPbh CPla CRos CTsd ECre ELan EUJe GBin IBoy MEch NLos SArc SChr SCob SEND SPav SPhx SVen
- 'Snow Tower'	CBod CCCN CDTJ CPla ELan IBoy LRHS MEch NLos SVen
pininana × ***wildpretii***	MEch
'Pink Fountain'	CBod CCCN CDTJ CPla ELan LRHS MEch NLos
'Red Rocket' **new**	CCCN
rosulatum	CCCN

	russicum	CBod CCCN CFis CSpe EAJP ELan ESps EUJe GPSL IBoy LRHS MEch MNHC SPad SPav SPhx SPlb WArt XEll
	sabulicola **new**	MEch
	simplex ♀H1c	MEch
	strictum	CCCN MEch
	sventenii	SPlb
	tuberculatum	EWld MEch SPhx WMoo
	virescens	MEch SVen
	vulgare	CBod CCCN CHab CSpe CWld EBWF ELan ENfk IBoy LCro LEdu LOPS MEch MHer MNHC NLar NMir SBch SPhx WOut WSFF WTre
	- 'Blue Bedder' ♀H7	CSpe MEch SPhx WSFF
	- 'Pink Bedder' **new**	MEch
	- 'White Bedder' **new**	MEch
	webbii	MEch MMrt SVen
	wildpretii ♀H1c	CCCN CDTJ CPla CTsd ECre MEch NLos SPlb SVen
	- subsp. ***wildpretii***	MEch SPav

Ectotropis (*Aizoaceae*)

§	***alpina***	CRos EWes GEdr LRHS NRHS
	seanii-hoganii	CTal ECtt EPot EWes GCrg GEdr LLHF NSla WAbe

Edgeworthia (*Thymelaeaceae*)

§	***chrysantha***	CCCN CExl CHGN EBee ELan EPfP ETMg LCro LOPS LRHS MGos NLar SBig SPer SPoG SWeb WHlf
I	- 'Grandiflora'	CBcs EBee ELon GBin IDee LRHS MGos MPkF NLar SMad WPGP
§	- 'Red Dragon'	LOPS LRHS MPkF NLar SPer
	- f. ***rubra*** hort.	see *E. chrysantha* 'Red Dragon'
	- 'Winter Liebe' **new**	NLar
	papyrifera	see *E. chrysantha*

Edraianthus (*Campanulaceae*)

	croaticus	see *E. graminifolius*
	dalmaticus	GKev
	- ***albus***	GKev
	dinaricus	GKev
§	***graminifolius***	GKev
	- subsp. ***graminifolius***	GKev LLHF
	niveus	GKev
	owerinianus	LLHF
	pilosulus	WAbe
§	***pumilio*** ♀H5	EPot GEdr GKev NSla SRms WAbe
	serbicus	GKev
§	***serpyllifolius***	GKev
	sutjeskae **new**	GKev
	zogovicii	see *E. graminifolius*

Egeria (*Hydrocharitaceae*)

§	***densa***	CBen

Ehretia (*Boraginaceae*)

	anacua	CBcs
	rigida	SPlb

Elaeagnus (*Elaeagnaceae*)

	angustifolia	CAgr CArg CBcs CDul CTho EPfP ESps LMaj MCoo MGos NLar SCob SPer SRms
	- Caspica Group	see *E.* 'Quicksilver'
	argentea Pursh	see *E. commutata*
§	***commutata***	CBcs CDul CMac ECrN EHoe EPfP MBlu MCoo NLar SPer
	- 'Zempin'	EPfP LRHS
§	× ***ebbingei*** ♀H5	Widely available
	- 'Coastal Gold' (v)	CBcs CDul CRos EBee EPfP LRHS LSRN MAsh MGos SGol SLim SRms WAvo WFar WRHF
I	- 'Compacta'	CRos ECrN LRHS LSou MGos NRHS
	- 'Gilt Edge' (v) ♀H5	Widely available
	- GOLD SPLASH ('Lannou') (v)	CMac EPfP SGol SWvt
	- 'Limelight' (v)	Widely available
	- 'Moonlight'	CRos EPfP LRHS MAsh
	- 'Salcombe Seedling'	CCCN
	- 'Svelte Edge' **new**	NLar
	- 'Viveleg'PBR (v)	CCVT ELan EPfP LMaj LRHS NLar SCob SEWo
	macrophylla	EPfP LRHS
	multiflora	MBlu NLar SPer WPGP
	- 'Sweet Scarlet'	CAgr
	parvifolia	CCCN ELan
	pungens 'Argenteovariegata'	see *E. pungens* 'Variegata'
	- 'Aureovariegata'	see *E. pungens* 'Maculata'
	- 'Dicksonii' (v)	LRHS NLar SLon SPer SRms
	- 'Forest Gold' (v)	ELan EPfP LRHS MAsh
	- 'Frederici' (v)	CBcs CMac EBee EHoe ELan LRHS MAsh MRav NLar SCob SPer SWvt WAvo
	- 'Goldrim' (v)	ESps
	- 'Hosoba-fukurin' (v)	CRos EBee ELan EMil EPfP LRHS NLar SLon
§	- 'Maculata' (v)	Widely available
§	- 'Variegata' (v)	CBcs CMac GMcL SPer
§	'Quicksilver'	Widely available
	× ***submacrophylla***	see *E.* × *ebbingei*
	umbellata	CAco CBcs CDul CExl CTho EBee EPfP EWTr LEdu MBlu NLar SPer WSHC
	- 'Amber' (F)	CAgr
	- 'Big Red' (F)	CAgr CFGn
	- var. ***borealis*** 'Polar Lights'	NLar
	- 'Brilliant Rose' (F)	CAgr
	- 'Garnet' (F)	CAgr
	- 'Hidden Springs' (F)	CAgr
	- 'Jewel' (F)	CAgr
	- 'Late Scarlet' (F)	CAgr CFGn
	- 'Newgate' (F)	CAgr CFGn
	- 'Red Cascade' (F)	CAgr LEdu
	- var. ***rotundifolia*** CWJ 12835	WCru
	- 'Ruby' (F)	CAgr CFGn LEdu MCoo
	- 'Sweet 'n'Tart' (F)	CAgr LEdu MCoo

Elaeocarpus (*Elaeocarpaceae*)

	sylvestris var. ***ellipticus***	LEdu WPGP

elderberry see *Sambucus nigra*

Elegia (*Restionaceae*)

	capensis	CCCN CDTJ CExl CPbh LRHS MPkF NLos SPlb WPGP
	cuspidata	NLos
	elephantina	CBod CCht CPbh NLos
	equisetacea	CPbh NLos
	filacea	NLos
	grandis	SPlb
	macrocarpa	CCCN CPbh NLos SPlb
	mucronata	LRHS
	stipularis	LRHS
	tectorum ♀H2	CPbh LRHS NLos NRHS SPlb SPoG
	- dwarf	CPbh
	- 'Fish Hoek'	CPbh LRHS

Eleocharis (*Cyperaceae*)

acicularis	LLWG MSKA
palustris	EBWF LLWG
parvula	MSKA
vivipara	XBlo

Elettaria (*Zingiberaceae*)

cardamomum	GPoy LEdu SPre

Eleutherococcus ✿ (*Araliaceae*)

from Manipur	WPGP
divaricatus B&SWJ 5027	WCru
giraldii BWJ 8091	WCru
hypoleucus B&SWJ 5532	WCru
aff. ***leucorrhizus*** PAB 8119 **new**	WPGP
nodiflorus PAB 8119	LEdu
pictus	see *Kalopanax septemlobus*
senticosus	GPoy LEdu
- B&SWJ 4568	WCru
septemlobus	see *Kalopanax septemlobus*
sessiliflorus B&SWJ 4528	WCru
- B&SWJ 8457	WCru
- B&SWJ 8618	WCru
sieboldianus	MRav SEND
- 'Variegatus' (v)	CBod CCCN EBee EHoe ELan ELon EPfP EShb EUJe LRHS MGil MRav NLar SEND SPoG WCFE WHer WSHC WWFP
trifoliatus PAB 7113	LEdu
- RWJ 10108	WCru

Elingamita (*Primulaceae*)

johnsonii	CPla

Elisena (*Amaryllidaceae*)

longipetala	see *Ismene longipetala*

Ellisiophyllum (*Plantaginaceae*)

pinnatum	SBrt
- B&SWJ 197	EBee LEdu WCru

Elmera (*Saxifragaceae*)

racemosa	EWes

Elodea (*Hydrocharitaceae*)

canadensis	LLWG MSKA WMAq
densa	see *Egeria densa*

Elsholtzia (*Lamiaceae*)

flava PAB 13.012 **new**	WPGP
stauntonii	CBcs EBee ECha ELan GPoy LRHS MHer MNrw NLar SBrt SPer SPhx SRms SWvt WBor WHer WHil XLum

Elymus (*Poaceae*)

arenarius	see *Leymus arenarius*
canadensis	EHoe EPPr
glaucus misapplied	see *E. hispidus*
§ ***hispidus*** 🏆H6	CBod EPPr MBlu NDov SPer WCFE WCot
§ ***magellanicus***	Widely available
- 'Blue Sword'	CRos ELan LRHS MGos NRHS SRkn SRms
riparius	EPPr
sibiricus	EPPr
villosus	EPPr
- var. ***arkansanus***	EPPr
virginicus	EPPr

Embothrium ✿ (*Proteaceae*)

coccineum	CBcs CFil CMCN CPla CPne CRos CTri EPfP GBin GMcL LRHS LSou MGil NRHS SPlb WPGP
* - var. ***andina***	MGil
- Lanceolatum Group	CAby CBcs CEnd CHll CRos CTsd ELon EPfP EUJe LRHS MBlu MMuc MPkF SAko SArc SLim SPer SSta SWvt WAbe
- - 'Inca Flame'	CCCN CJun CRos EPfP LRHS MAsh SPoG SWvt
- Longifolium Group	CCCN EPfP IBlr WPGP

Emmenopterys (*Rubiaceae*)

henryi	CBcs CMCN EPfP IArd MBlu NLar WCot

Empetrum (*Ericaceae*)

nigrum	GPoy WThu
rubrum	MGil

Empodium (*Hypoxidaceae*)

namaquensis	NRog
plicatum	NRog

Encephalartos ✿ (*Zamiaceae*)

altensteinii	CBrP
ferox	CBrP
horridus	CBrP
lebomboensis	CBrP
lehmannii	CBrP
natalensis	CBrP
villosus	CBrP

endive see AGM Vegetables Section

Endymion see *Hyacinthoides*

Engelmannia (*Asteraceae*)

peristenia	GLog

Enkianthus ✿ (*Ericaceae*)

campanulatus 🏆H5	Widely available
- var. ***campanulatus*** f. ***albiflorus***	CBcs GKin NLar NPnk
I - 'Pagoda'	CBcs IArd IDee NLar NPnk SAko
- var. ***palibinii***	CBcs CRos EPfP GGGa GKin LRHS MAsh MMrt NLar
- 'Red Bells'	CBcs CDul CRos EPfP GKin LRHS MAsh NLar SGol SWvt WFar
- 'Red Velvet'	CBcs GKin NLar
- 'Ruby Glow'	CBcs NLar SAko
- 'Showy Lantern'	NLar
- var. ***sikokianus***	GGGa GKin NLar
- 'Sinsetu'	NLar
- 'Tokyo Masquerade' (v)	CRos LRHS MAsh SPoG
- 'Venus'	CBcs GKin NLar
- 'Victoria'	CBcs IArd NLar
- 'Wallaby'	CBcs CRos LRHS NLar
cernuus f. ***rubens*** 🏆H5	CBcs GGGa GKin ITim NLar
chinensis	CBcs CRos EPfP GGGa LRHS MAsh
deflexus	CRos GGGa IArd LRHS WPGP
I 'Pagoda Red'	LRHS
perulatus 🏆H5	CBcs CDul CRos LRHS MGos MMrt NLar SPer
serrulatus	GGGa

Ensete (*Musaceae*)

gilletii	XBlo

- from Malawi	XBlo
- from Mozambique	XBlo
glaucum	CDTJ
§ ***ventricosum*** 🏆H1c	CCCN CDTJ CHll NLos SEND XBlo
§ - 'Maurelii' 🏆H1c	CCCN CDTJ CSBt CSpe CTsd ETod EUJe LCro LOPS NLos NPlą SChr SEND SPhm WCot
- 'Rubrum'	see *E. ventricosum* 'Maurelii'
- 'Tandarra Red'	CAbb

Entelea (*Malvaceae*)

arborescens	EShb SPlb

Eomecon (*Papaveraceae*)

chionantha	CExl CSam CSpe EBee GAbr GCal GEdr IDee LEdu MAvo MRav NHpl NQui SBrt WCru WMoo WPGP XLum

Epacris (*Ericaceae*)

microphylla	ITim
serpyllifolia	WThu

Ephedra (*Ephedraceae*)

sp.	MPie SArc
andina	IMou
chilensis	MGil
distachya	GPoy
equisetina RCB/TQ K-1	WCot
fragilis	XSen
gerardiana	CRos LRHS
- var. ***sikkimensis***	GEdr WOld
§ ***major***	EBee XSen
monosperma	GEdr WThu
nebrodensis	see *E. major*
nevadensis	GPoy
sinica	GPoy
viridis	MGil

Epilobium (*Onagraceae*)

angustifolium	see *Chamaenerion angustifolium*
- f. ***leucanthum***	see *Chamaenerion angustifolium* 'Album'
californicum misapplied	see *Zauschneria californica*
canum	see *Zauschneria cana*
dodonaei	see *Chamaenerion dodonaei*
fleischeri	see *Chamaenerion fleischeri*
garrettii	see *Zauschneria californica* subsp. *garrettii*
glabellum misapplied	NRHS NSla WCFE
glabellum G. Forst.	CSpe MMuc WKif
hirsutum	EBWF
- 'Album'	EWTr
microphyllum	see *Zauschneria cana*
rosmarinifolium	see *Chamaenerion dodonaei*
septentrionale	see *Zauschneria septentrionalis*
villosum	see *Zauschneria californica* subsp. *mexicana*
'White Wonder Bells'PBR	GMcL GWyn

Epimedium ✿ (*Berberidaceae*)

sp.	ESps
from Jian Xi, China	GEdr
from Yunnan, China	IFoB WPGP
acuminatum	CAby CFil CSam CWCL ESMi GEdr LEdu MNrw NLar SCob WMoo WPGP WSHC
- CC 031207	XPou
- L 575	CElw CExl CFil EHrv
- 'Galaxy'	CExl CFil CJun CMil LEdu
- 'Night Mistress'	GPSL WPGP XPou
- 'Quinquin'	IMou
- yellow-flowered	WPGP
- - CC 011415	XPou
'Akakage'	CExl
'Akebono'	Widely available
ALABASTER ('Conalba')	ELan NDov NEgg
alpinum	CBod CFil CFis CMac CRos CWCL EBee EPot EWTr GBin GKev GLog IFro LEdu LRHS NChi NRHS SHar SPer WMoo XLum
'Amanogawa'	CAby CJun CMil EHrv GEdr IFoB LEdu XPou
'Amber Queen'PBR	Widely available
'Anju'	GEdr
'Arctic Wings'PBR	CSpe EBee EPfP GEdr NGdn SMHy SWvt
'Asiatic Hybrid'	CJun WHal
'Autumn Raspberry'	CJun
baojingense	XPou
'Beni-goromo'	GEdr
'Beni-kujaku'	CAby CJun EBee GEdr GPSL IFoB MHol NDov WFar
'Beni-yushima'	GEdr
'Bieke'	SMHy
'Black Sea'	CElw CFil CJun CMil CSpe EBee EPPr EPot ESMi EWTr GBin GPSL IFoB IMou LEdu MAvo MNrw MPnt NPnk SCob WHil WHoo XPou
borealiguizhouense CC 0207 **new**	XPou
brachyrrhizum	CAby CExl CJun GPSL NLar
- CPC 940447	XPou
- 'Elfin Magic'	IFoB
brevicornu	CFil GEdr WPGP
- Og 82.010	CAby CExl CFil CJun XPou
- Og 88.010	CJun XPou
'Buckland Spider'	CFis EBee EPPr GEdr IFoB MNrw WCot WPGP
campanulatum	CAby
- CC 002079	XPou
- Og 93.087	CExl CFil CJun EBee
× ***cantabrigiense***	CBro CDor CMac CRos CTal CWCL ECtt GEdr GKev GMaP GPSL ILea LRHS MRav NEgg NHpl NLar NRHS SRms XLum
chlorandrum	CAby EBee EHrv IFoB LEdu WPGP
- Og 94.003	EBee XPou
creeping yellow	EBee LSou MNrw WHil
cremeum	see *E. grandiflorum* subsp. *koreanum*
'Dark Secret' **new**	ESMi
'Darrell's Pink' **new**	EBee
davidii	CFil EBee EPPr ESMi GEdr LEdu MNrw NLar SCob WHal WHil WHoo WPGP WSHC
- CPC 960079	CExl EBee XPou
- EMR 4125	CElw CExl CJun EHrv XPou
- dwarf	CAby CExl
dewuense	XPou
diphyllum	CExl CFil CTsd EBee EHrv EPfP GEdr IFoB WHal WPGP XPou
- dwarf white	CSam
- pink-flowered	XPou
dolichostemon	CElw IFoB
- Og 81.010	CJun WPGP XPou
'Domino'	EBee GPSL WPGP XPou
ecalcaratum	CAby CMil EBee LEdu WPGP

- Og 93.082	CExl CJun XPou
- spurred	XPou
'Egret'	CAby CMil EBee LEdu SMHy
elongatum CC 012906 **new**	XPou
'Emperor'	see *E.* 'Phoenix'
'Enchantress'	CElw CJun CMil CTal EHrv ESMi EWTr EWld IFoB MBel MNrw NLar WHal WHoo
epsteinii	CAby CFil CMil CTal EBee EPPr ESMi GEdr IFoB LEdu MNrw SBrt WPGP WSHC
- CPC 940347	CElw CExl CJun XPou
fangii	CExl IFoB
- CC 022008	XPou
- Og **new**	XPou
fargesii	CAby CExl CFil EBee EHrv GEdr IFoB LEdu MAvo MNrw WCAu WPGP
- Og 93.057	CTal
- 'Pink Constellation'	CAby CExl CFil CJun EBee GEdr ITim LEdu MNrw SBch WPGP XPou
'Fire Dragon' PBR	CWCL EBee EPfP GEdr IFoB LLHF MBNS MNrw SPoG WFar
flavum	CFil EBee WPGP
- Og 92.036	CExl CJun EBee EHrv XPou
'Flowers of Sulphur' PBR	EBee EPfP GEdr IRob WFar
franchetii	CAby CElw CExl CTsd ELon GEdr IFoB
- 'Brimstone Butterfly'	CAby CExl CFis CJun EPPr EPot ESMi GEdr GPSL LEdu NLar WCot WPGP WSpi XPou
'Fukujuji'	GEdr
'Genpei'	GEdr
'Golden Eagle'	CExl CJun EBee EWes MNrw SMHy
§ ***grandiflorum*** ♀H5	CBcs CBod CElw CRos CTri CWCL ELan ELon EPfP EWTr GLog IBoy LRHS NHpl NLar NPnk SCob SPer WPnP
- 'Akagiza Kura'	XPou
- 'Beni-chidori'	CJun GEdr
- 'Bicolor Giant'	XPou
- 'Circe'	XPou
- var. ***coelestre***	XPou
- 'Cranberry Sparkle' **new**	EBee
- 'Crimson Beauty'	CAby CJun ECha NLar WHal WHoo WSHC
- 'Elfenkönigin'	CRos GPSL LRHS NLar
- 'French Braid' **new**	EBee
- 'Freya'	CExl EBee IFoB SMHy WSHC XPou
- 'Freya Mk II'	SMHy
§ - var. ***higoense***	CJun GEdr WHal WPGP
- - 'Bandit'	GEdr IFoB XPou
- - 'Saturn'	CMil EHrv XPou
- 'Jennie Maillard'	ELon WCot
- 'Koji'	EBee IFoB WHil WSHC
§ - subsp. ***koreanum***	ECha GEdr IFoB
- 'Kotobuki' **new**	XPou
- 'Kourin'	GEdr
- 'La Rocaille'	CAby CElw EBee EHrv XPou
- lilac-flowered	CAby WHal
- 'Lilafee'	Widely available
- 'Mount Kitadake'	WAbe XPou
- 'Mugawa-gen-pan'	XPou
- 'Nanum' ♀H5	CAby CJun EBee EPot ESMi EWTr GKev MNrw NEgg SMHy WAbe WPGP WTor XPou
- pink-flowered	EHrv MCot
- 'Princess Susan' **new**	XPou
- 'Purple Pixie' PBR	CBod CWCL ECtt EWTr MHol NEgg WCAu WFar WHil
- 'Purple Prince'	CExl CMil CTal EBee EHrv WPGP XPou
- purple-flowered	EHrv
- 'Queen Esta'	CAby CExl CJun CMil EBee IFoB LEdu MNrw MRav WPGP WSHC XPou
- 'Red Beauty'	CBod CMac CNor CRos CTal CWCL ECtt ELan ELon EPfP EUJe GEdr IFoB ILea LEdu LRHS LSou MAvo MCot MNrw NRHS SEle WFar WGrn WPGP WPnP
- 'Rose Queen' ♀H5	CAby CRos CSam CWCL EBee EHrv ELan ELon EPfP ESMi EWTr GBin IFoB LRHS MNrw MRav NEgg NRHS NSti SCob SWvt WFar WMoo WPGP
- 'Roseum'	CBod CMac CMil GMaP GPSL IFoB MMoz SWvt
- 'Rubinkrone'	CWCL GEdr GMaP IMou LRHS MNrw
- 'Sirius'	CAby CJun
- 'Tancho' **new**	XPou
- f. ***violaceum***	CElw CJun EBee EHrv WCFE
- 'White Beauty'	WSHC
- 'White Queen' ♀H5	CElw CJun EBee EHrv EPPr EWTr IFoB LLHF LRHS MBel SMHy WCot WHal XPou
- 'Wildside Red'	CJun
- 'Yellow Princess'	CAby CElw CJun EBee XPou
- 'Yubae'	GEdr IFoB
'Hagoromo'	GEdr
'Hakubai'	GEdr
'Harugasumi'	GEdr
'Heavenly Purple'	CJun
higoense	see *E. grandiflorum* var. *higoense*
'Hina Matsuri'	GEdr
hunanense	XPou
ilicifolium	CAby CFil CJun LEdu WPGP
- Og 93020 **new**	XPou
'Jean O'Neill'	CAby CMil EBee EPPr EPri LEdu WCot WPGP WSHC
'Jenny Pym'	EBee
'Jujisei'	XPou
'Kaguyahime'	CElw CJun CMil EHrv EPPr GPSL IFoB WSHC
'Kibana Genpei'	XPou
'King Prawn'	LEdu SMHy WPGP
'Knight Star' **new**	ESMi
'Kodai Murasaki'	XPou
'Koki'	GEdr
koreanum 'Harold Epstein'	XPou
'Korin'	XPou
'Kotobuki'	GEdr
latisepalum	CTal EBee EHrv GEdr IRob LEdu MNrw WCot
- Og 91.002	CJun
- Og 93.009 **new**	XPou
'Lemon Meringue Pie'	CJun
'Lemon Zest' **new**	EBee XPou
leptorrhizum	CAby CDor CElw CExl CFil CJun CWCL EBee EHrv ELon EPPr ESMi EWld GEdr IFoB LEdu MNrw NLar SBrt WCot WHal
- Og Y44	CExl WSHC XPou
- 'Mariko'	CAby CExl CJun CMil LEdu MNrw XPou
lishihchenii	CAby CExl CFil CJun CTal EBee EHrv GEdr WPGP
- CC 95007	XPou
- CC 96024 **new**	XPou

	'Little Shrimp'	CJun CRos CTal CTri EBee ELon GMaP GPSL LLHF LRHS MNrw NLar NRHS WSHC
	macranthum	see *E. grandiflorum*
	macrosepalum	CElw GEdr XPou
	'Mandarin Star'	CWCL GEdr GPSL
	'Marchant's Sulphur Queen'	SMHy
	'Marchant's Twin Set' **new**	SMHy
	membranaceum	CAby CFil CMil EBee ESMi GEdr LEdu LLHF WHal WPGP XEll XPou
	- Og 93.047	CExl CJun EBee EPPr GEdr
	mikinorii	CExl GEdr
	- CC 990001	WPGP XPou
	'Milky Way'	CAby MNrw
	'Mine-no-fubuki'	GEdr
	'Miyako' **new**	XPou
	'Moonlight' **new**	XPou
	'Myojo'	GEdr
	myrianthum	CAby CJun EBee GEdr LEdu WPGP XPou
	ogisui	CAby CElw CMil IFoB LEdu MRav WPGP XPou
	- Og 91.001	CExl CFil CJun EBee EHrv MNrw
	- 'Diane' **new**	XPou
§	× ***omeiense*** 'Akame'	CAby CExl CJun CMil EPPr GEdr XPou
	- 'Emei Shan'	see *E.* × *omeiense* 'Akame'
	- 'Myriad Years'	XPou
	- 'Pale Fire Sibling'	CJun GEdr
	- 'Stormcloud'	CAby CElw CExl CFil CJun CMil EBee EPPr LEdu MAvo XPou
	parvifolium	XPou
	'Pathfinder' **new**	ESMi
	pauciflorum	CFil EBee EPPr GEdr LEdu WPGP XPou
	- Og 92.123	CExl CJun
	× ***perralchicum***	CAby CBro CJun CTri ECha GKev IFro NLar WSHC
	- 'Fröhnleiten'	Widely available
	- 'Lichtenberg'	EWes
	- 'Wisley'	CDor CElw CJun CSam EHrv EWes
	perralderianum	CBod CMac CSam CTal CWCL EPot GMaP MBel MCot MNrw SRms WHal WPnP
	- 'Weihenstephan'	CRos CWCL LRHS MMoz NLar WPnP
	aff. ***perralderianum***	MPnt
	'Perrine's Pink' (Magique Elfes Series)	WCot
§	'Phoenix'	CAby CExl CMil WCot
	'Pink Champagne'	EPfP GEdr LEdu WCot WFar WPGP XPou
	'Pink Elf' PBR	CMil CWCL CWGN EPfP GBin GEdr GMcL IFoB LLHF MNrw MPie NGdn NLar NSti SCob SRms WCAu WFar
	pinnatum	EBee GMaP WHal XLum
§	- subsp. ***colchicum*** ♀H7	CJun CWCL ELan EPfP EWTr GLog GQue LEdu LRHS MCot MRav NGdn NLar SCob SPer WCot WFar WPnP WSpi XEll
	- - L 321	GEdr WPGP
	- - 'Thunderbolt' **new**	EBee
	- ***elegans***	see *E. pinnatum* subsp. *colchicum*
	platypetalum	CAby CFil SBrt WCot
	- Og 93.085 **new**	CExl CJun EBee XPou
	pubescens	CAby EHrv IFoB
	- CC 022556 from Shaanxi, China	XPou
	- Og 91.003	CExl CFil CJun EBee WPGP XPou

	pubigerum	CDor CJun CRos CSam CWCL EBee EHrv ESMi EWTr GAbr GLog IFro ILea LEdu LPla LRHS MMuc NEgg NHpl NLar SCob SEND SWvt WCAu WHal WSpi XEll
	qingchengshanense 03124	XPou
	'Red Maximum'	WPGP XPou
	reticulatum	GEdr
	rhizomatosum	CAby EPPr ESMi GEdr GMaP WPGP WSHC
	- Og 92.114	CJun EHrv WCot WPGP XPou
	× ***rubrum*** ♀H7	Widely available
	- 'Galadriel'	GBin
	- 'Sweetheart'	GEdr
	sagittatum 'Warlord'	WPGP XPou
	'Sakura-maru'	GEdr
	'Sasaki'	CWCL EPot GPSL IFoB NLar WHil XEll
	sempervirens	CAby CJun WHal
	- 'Creamsickle' (v)	GEdr
	- 'Mars' **new**	XPou
	- 'Okuda's White'	EBee XPou
	- 'Violet Queen'	XPou
	× ***setosum***	CJun EHrv ESMi NLar WHal
	'Shien' **new**	XPou
	'Shiho'	CWCL EBee GEdr GPSL NLar WHil
	shuichengense CC 030175	XPou
	'Sphinx Twinkler'	see *E.* 'Spine Tingler'
§	'Spine Tingler'	CAby CBod CMil CSpe CWCL EBee ECtt EUJe GBin GEdr GPSL LEdu LSou MBel MNrw MPie MSCN NLar SCob SMad SPad SPoG WCAu WCot WPGP XPou
	'Spinners'	EBee WCot
	'Starcloud'	WGrn
	stellulatum	GEdr
	- long-leaved	XPou
	- 'Wudang Star'	CExl CFil CJun CMil EBee EHrv EPot EWes IFoB IMou ITim MCot SCob WSHC XPou
	- 'Yukiko'	XPou
	'Sunshowers'	CFil EBee
	sutchuenense CC 990394	XPou
	'Suzuka'	GEdr LEdu
	'Tama-no-genpei'	CJun GEdr IFoB LEdu
	'Tanima-no-yuki'	GEdr
	'The Giant'	WCot WPGP XPou
	'Togen'	WCot XPou
	'Tokiwa-gozen'	GEdr
	'Totnes Turbo'	EBee
	trifoliolatobinatum CC 950046 **new**	XPou
	truncatum CC 030557	XPou
	× ***versicolor***	CExl EShb SCob SSut
	- 'Cherry Tart'	EBee XPou
	- 'Cupreum'	CFis CJun CRos CWCL LEdu LRHS NRHS WCAu
§	- 'Discolor'	CAby CElw CFis CTal ECha EHrv EPPr EWld SMHy WCot XPou
	- 'Neosulphureum'	CAby CBro CTal CWCL EHrv EPPr WFar WPGP WSHC WThu XPou
	- 'Sulphureum' ♀H7	Widely available
	- 'Versicolor'	see *E.* × *versicolor* 'Discolor'
	× ***warleyense***	Widely available
	- 'Orangekönigin'	Widely available
	'Wildside Ruby'	CMil
	'William Stearn'	CExl CJun EBee GEdr WCot XPou
	'Windfire' **new**	EBee
	wushanense	CAby CFil EBee EHrv EPPr ESMi GEdr LEdu XPou

- Og 93.019 **new**	CExl CJun WPGP XPou
- 'Caramel'	CAby CExl CJun EBee EHrv GEdr GPSL IFoB LEdu MAvo WCAu WCot WSHC XPou
- 'Sandy Claws' **new**	CFil
- spiny-leaved	WCot
- - CC 014631	WPGP XPou
'Yachimata-hime'	GEdr
'Yokihi'	GEdr XPou
× ***youngianum***	IFoB NEgg
- 'Be My Valentine' **new**	EBee
- 'Beni-kujaku'	NEgg WHil XPou
- 'Capella'	XPou
- 'Fairy Dust'	CFil EBee
- 'Grape Fizz' **new**	EBee
- 'Marchacos Sprite' **new**	EBee
- 'Merlin'	CDor CElw CJun CMil CWCL EBee EPfP ESMi EWTr GEdr GPSL IFoB NLar NSti WHal WSHC
- 'Niveum' ♀H5	Widely available
- 'Roseum'	Widely available
- 'Ruby Tuesday' **new**	EBee
- 'Shikinomai'	CExl CJun
- 'Tamabotan'	CAby CMil GEdr MNrw MRav XPou
§ - 'Typicum'	CElw WSHC
- 'Yenomoto'	CJun EHrv
- 'Youngianum'	see *E.* × *youngianum* 'Typicum'
zhushanense	CAby CTal EBee LEdu WCot WPGP
- CC 022403	XPou
- CC 02885 **new**	XPou

Epipactis (*Orchidaceae*)

Catalina gx	CJun CTal GEdr MNrw
gigantea	CAvo CBro CJun EBee ECha ELan EWld GBin GEdr GKev LRHS MHer MNrw MRav MWts NDav NRHS WPGP
- 'Serpentine Night'	CJun CTal
gigantea × ***palustris***	CJun NRHS
gigantea × ***veratrifolia***	see *E.* Lowland Legacy gx
helleborine	WHer
Lizzy Lou gx	CJun
§ **Lowland Legacy gx**	CJun GEdr
- 'Edelstein'	MNrw
- 'Frankfurt'	GEdr
palustris	GEdr LRHS MNrw NDav WHer WPnP
Passionata gx Light Royals Group	CJun GEdr
Renate gx	CJun
royleana	CAby CJun GEdr
Sabine gx	CAby CJun GEdr WHlf
- 'Frankfurt'	CTal MNrw

Epipremnum (*Araceae*)

pinnatum 'Marble Queen' (v)	XBlo

Episcia (*Gesneriaceae*)

dianthiflora	WCot WDib
'San Miguel'	WDib

Equisetum ✿ (*Equisetaceae*)

'Bandit' (v)	CNat EBee MAvo SMad WMoo
× ***bowmanii***	CNat
* ***camtschatcense***	EUJe EWat SArc SBig SMad SPlb XLum
fluviatile	CNat MSKA
giganteum	LLWG
hyemale	CBen CTsd EHoe EWat GQue LLWG LRHS MAvo MMuc MSCN MSKA NPer NSti SCob SPlb WCot WMoo WWtn XLum
§ - var. ***affine***	CBdn CNat EBee ELan EUJe LEdu MSKA SCob WMAq WPGP
- var. ***robustum***	see *E. hyemale* var. *affine*
ramosissimum var. ***japonicum***	LEdu NLos NPla SCob WPGP
robustum	SCob
scirpoides	EFer EHoe EWat LLWG MSKA MWts NPer NWad SPlb WMAq WMoo XLum
sylvaticum	CNat
telmateia	LEdu SMad
variegatum	EBee EFer

Eragrostis (*Poaceae*)

airoides ambig.	CBod WMoo
curvula	CBod CElw CKno CMea CRos CWCL ECha EHoe EPPr LRHS MAvo MBel MRav NGdn NWsh SEND SPhx WMoo XLum
- S&SH 10	CElw EPPr SMHy WPGP
- 'Totnes Burgundy'	CAby CExl CKno CRos EBee ECha EPPr EPfP EShb LRHS MAvo NRHS NWsh SPhx SPoG SRms WMoo WPGP
elliottii	CBod CKno ECha EPPr EShb LRHS MAvo SEND
- 'Wind Dancer'	EBee WHar XSen
prolifera	IMou
spectabilis	CBod CKno CSBt CTsd EAJP EBee ELan EPfP NGdn NLar NWsh WMoo XLum XSen
trichodes	CBod CKno EHoe LEdu NWsh SEND WCot

Eranthemum (*Acanthaceae*)

pulchellum ♀H1b	ECre

Eranthis (*Ranunculaceae*)

cilicica	see *E. hyemalis* Cilicica Group
§ ***hyemalis*** ♀H5	CArg CBro CMea CRav CRos CSpe CTca EBWF ELan ELon EPfP GKev LAma LCro LOPS LRHS NHpl NPri NRHS SCob SDeJ SDir SPhx SWvt WCot WHoo WShi
§ - Cilicica Group	CRos ELan ELon EPot GEdr GKev GMaP IRob LRHS NLar NPnk NRHS SCob SDeJ SDir SPer SPhx WBor WCot WShi
- 'Flore Pleno' (d)	EPot GEdr WCot
- 'Grünling'	CAvo GKev WCot
- 'Grünspecht'	GEdr
- 'Orange Glow'	CPla GEdr GKev
- 'Schwefelglanz'	CAvo CBro EPot GEdr GKev WCot
§ - Tubergenii Group	CBro EPot
- - 'Guinea Gold' ♀H5	CMea
pinnatifida	GEdr
× ***tubergenii***	see *E. hyemalis* Tubergenii Group

Ercilla (*Phytolaccaceae*)

volubilis	CBcs CBod CExl CFil CHll CRHN CWGN EPfP IArd IDee LRHS MGil SAko SEND SMad WCot WCru WSHC

Eremophila (*Scrophulariaceae*)

longifolia	SPlb

Eremurus (*Asphodelaceae*)

'Brutus'	EBee
bungei	see *E. stenophyllus* subsp. *stenophyllus*
'Emmy Ro'	EBee LAma LRHS NLar
'Foxtrot'	CMea GKev SDeJ
fuscus	EBee GKev LRHS
'Grace'	LAma
'Helena'	LAma LRHS SDir
himalaicus	EBee ELan EPot ERCP GBin GKev ILea LAma LRHS MHer NLar SCob SDeJ SDir SPer SPhx
'Image'	CRos LRHS NRHS
× ***isabellinus*** 'Cleopatra'	CBod CMea CRav CRos EBee EPfP EPot ERCP ETMg EUJe GKev GMaP LAma LCro LOPS LRHS MBNS MHer NLar SCob SDeJ SPad SPer SPhx SPoG WHar
- 'Obelisk'	EBee LAma LRHS
- 'Pinokkio'	CRos CWCL EBee EPot GKev LAma LCro LOPS LRHS NRHS SDeJ SPad SPer
- Ruiter hybrids	CMea CRos ELan EPfP GKev GMaP LAma LRHS MGos MNHC NLar NRHS SDeJ
- Shelford hybrids	CBcs CRos GKev LAma LRHS NRHS SDeJ SPer
'Jeanne-Claire'	LAma LRHS NLar SDir
'Joanna'	LAma LRHS NLar SDir SPhx
'Line Dance'	GKev LAma
'Moneymaker'	CWCL EBee EPot GKev LAma LRHS
'Oase'	EBee GKev LAma LRHS SDeJ
'Paradiso'	GKev
'Pink Sky'	EBee
'Rexona'	GKev LAma MBNS SDeJ
robustus ♀H7	CBcs CRos ELan EPot ERCP GBin GKev LAma LRHS NLar NRHS SDeJ SDir SPer SPhx SPlb
'Romance'	CBod EBee EPot ERCP GKev LAma MBNS NLar SCob SDeJ
'Rumba'	GKev LAma SDir
'Samba'	LAma NLar
'Sarah Cato'	EBee GKev SPhx
stenophyllus ♀H6	CBod CGar CRos CTri EPot ERCP GKev LCro LOPS LRHS NLar NRHS SDeJ SDir SPhx SPoG
§ - subsp. ***stenophyllus***	CBcs EBee EPfP EUJe GMaP IBoy MHer MNrw NPer SPer
'Tap Dance'	GKev LAma NLar SPhx
'White Beauty Favourite' PBR	ERCP EUJe GKev LCro LOPS SDeJ
'White Plume'	EBee
'White Sensation'	LRHS SDir
'Yellow Giant'	GKev
zenaidae JCA 0.444.409	WCot

Erepsia (*Aizoaceae*)

lacera	SPlb

Erianthus see *Saccharum*

Erica ✿ (*Ericaceae*)

aestiva	SPlb
alopecurus	SPlb
andevalensis f. ***albiflora***	CFst
arborea	CBcs SPlb XSen
- var. ***alpina*** ♀H5	CTri EPfP GAbr SCob SPer SWhi
§ - - f. ***aureifolia*** 'Albert's Gold' ♀H5	CFst CRos CSBt CTri ELan EPfP LRHS MGos MMrt NRHS SCob SCoo SPer SPoG SWhi
- 'Arbora Gold'	see *E. arborea* var. *alpina* f. *aureifolia* 'Albert's Gold'
- 'Arnold's Gold'	see *E. arborea* var. *alpina* f. *aureifolia* 'Albert's Gold'
- 'Estrella Gold' ♀H5	CBcs CFst CRos CSBt CTri ELan EPfP LRHS MMrt NRHS SCob SCoo SPer SPoG SWhi
- 'Golden Joy'	CFst
australis f. ***albiflora*** 'Mr Robert' ♀H2	CFst GCal
- 'Holehird'	CFst
- 'Riverslea' ♀H4	CFst CRos CTri GCal LRHS NRHS SCob SPer SPoG SWhi
- 'Trisha'	CFst
bauera	CPbh
caffra	CPbh SPlb
canaliculata ♀H2	CBcs
carnea	ESps
- 'Adrienne Duncan' ♀H7	SCoo SRms SWhi
- f. ***alba*** 'Golden Starlet' ♀H7	CFst CSBt CTri EPfP MAsh MJak SCoo SPer SRms SWhi
- - 'Ice Princess' ♀H7	ELan EPfP MAsh SCoo SRms SWhi
- - 'Isabell' ♀H7	CBcs CFst CSBt EPfP MAsh SCoo SRms SWhi
- - 'Rosalinde Schorn'	SRms
- - 'Schneekuppe'	SWhi
- - 'Schneesturm'	SRms
- - 'Snow Queen'	ETMg SRms SWhi
- - 'Springwood White' ♀H7	CFst CSBt CTri ELan EPfP ESps MAsh MMuc SEND SRms SWhi
- - 'Whitehall'	CFst LCro LOPS SCoo SRms SWhi
- - 'Winter Snow' ♀H7	CFst CSBt ELan SCoo SPer SRms SWhi
- 'Amy Doncaster'	see *E. carnea* 'Treasure Trove'
- 'Ann Sparkes' ♀H7	CBcs CSBt CTri ELan EPfP MAsh SCoo SRms SWhi
- 'Antje' **new**	SWhi
- 'Atrorubra'	SWhi
- f. ***aureifolia*** 'Aurea'	SCoo SRms SWhi
- - 'Barry Sellers'	SRms
§ - - 'Bell's Extra Special'	EPfP SRms SWhi
- - 'Foxhollow' ♀H7	CBcs CFst CTri EPfP IArd MAsh MJak SCoo SRms SWhi
- - 'Gelber Findling'	SRms
- - 'Hilletje'	SRms SWhi
- - 'January Sun'	SRms
- - 'Westwood Yellow' ♀H7	CSBt MAsh SRms SWhi
- 'Aztec Gold'	CFst SPer SWhi
- 'Beoley Pink'	SRms
- 'Branton Bamford' **new**	SWhi
- 'C.J. Backhouse'	SRms
- 'Challenger' ♀H7	ELan EPfP MAsh SCoo SLon SRms SWhi
- 'Clare Wilkinson'	SRms
- 'Claribelle'	CFst SWhi
- 'Corinna' PBR	SWhi
- 'December Red'	CFst ELan EPfP MAsh MMuc SCoo SEND SPer SRms SWhi
- 'Diana Young'	SCoo SWhi
- 'Dømmesmoen'	CFst SRms
- 'Dorset Sunshine'	CFst SWhi
- 'Early Red'	SRms
- 'Eileen Porter'	MMuc SEND
- 'Eva' ♀H7	CBcs CFst SRms SWhi
- 'Foxhollow Fairy'	SPer SRms
- 'Gracilis'	SRms
- 'Heathwood'	MAsh SRms SWhi
- 'James Backhouse'	CTri
- 'Jason Attwater'	SRms
- 'Jennifer Anne'	SRms

	– 'John Kampa'	SRms
	– 'John Pook'	SCoo SRms SWhi
	– 'Kathy'	SWhi
	– 'King George'	CFst CTri SRms SWhi
§	– 'Kramer's Rubin'	CFst SRms
	– 'Lena'	see *E.* × *darleyensis* 'Lena'
	– 'Lesley Sparkes'	CFst
	– 'Lohse's Rubin'	SRms SWhi
	– 'Loughrigg' ♀H7	CTri MAsh MJak SCoo SRms SWhi
	– 'March Seedling' ♀H7	CFst EPfP MAsh SCoo SPer SRms SWhi
	– 'Margaret Benson' **new**	SWhi
	– 'Margery Frearson'	SRms
I	– 'Martin'	SRms
	– 'Memory'	SWhi
	– 'Myretoun Ruby' ♀H7	CBcs CFst CSBt CTri EPfP ETMg LCro LOPS MAsh SCoo SPer SRms SWhi
	– 'Nadja' **new**	SWhi
	– 'Nathalie' ♀H7	CFst CSBt MAsh SCoo SRms SWhi
	– 'Pink Cloud'	CFst
	– 'Pink Mist'	SRms
	– 'Pink Spangles' ♀H7	CBcs CFst CSBt CTri MAsh MJak SCoo SPer SRms SWhi
	– 'Pirbright Rose'	SRms
	– 'Polden Pride'	SRms
	– 'Porter's Red'	SWhi
	– 'Praecox Rubra'	SCoo SRms SWhi
	– 'Queen Mary'	SRms
	– 'Queen of Spain'	SRms
	– 'R.B. Cooke'	EPfP MAsh MJak SCoo SRms SWhi
	– 'Robert Jan'	SRms
	– 'Rosalie' ♀H7	CFst EPfP IArd MAsh SCoo SRms SWhi
	– 'Rosantha'	CFst SRms
	– 'Rosea'	SPlb
	– 'Rosy Morn'	SRms
	– 'Rotes Juwel'	SRms
	– 'Rubens' Palette'	SWhi
	– 'Rubinette'	SWhi
	– 'Rubinteppich'	SRms
	– 'Ruby Glow'	SWhi
	– 'Saskia'	SWhi
	– 'Scatterley'	SRms
	– 'Schatzalp'	SRms
	– 'Sherwood Creeping'	SRms
	– 'Smart's Heath'	SRms
	– 'Springwood Pink'	CSBt CTri SRms SWhi
	– 'Tanja'	CFst SWhi
§	– 'Treasure Trove'	CFst SWhi
	– 'Viking'	MAsh
	– 'Vivellii' ♀H7	CFst CTri MAsh MJak SCoo SRms SWhi
	– 'Walter Reisert'	SRms
	– 'Wentwood Red'	SRms
	– WHISKY	see *E. carnea* f. *aureifolia* 'Bell's Extra Special'
	– 'Winter Beauty'	MJak SWhi
	– WINTER RUBIN	see *E. carnea* 'Kramer's Rubin'
	– 'Winterfreude'	SWhi
	– 'Wintersonne' ♀H7	CFst MMuc SRms SWhi
	cerinthoides	CPbh
	ciliaris 'Bretagne'	SWhi
	– 'Corfe Castle'	CFst
	– 'David McClintock'	CFst SWhi
	– 'Globosa'	SWhi
	cinerea	SWhi
	– f. ***alba*** 'Alba Major'	SWhi
	– – 'Alba Minor'	CFst MAsh SWhi
	– – 'Celebration'	SWhi

	– – 'Domino'	MAsh
	– 'Atrorubens'	CFst MJak
	– f. ***aureifolia*** 'Anne Berry'	SWhi
	– – 'Apricot Charm'	CSBt
	– – 'Fiddler's Gold'	MAsh SWhi
	– – 'Golden Drop'	CFst CSBt MAsh
	– – 'Golden Hue'	MAsh
	– – 'Golden Sport'	SWhi
	– – 'Goldilocks'	CFst
	– – 'Summer Gold'	SWhi
	– 'Bucklebury Red'	CFst
	– 'C.D. Eason' ♀H7	CFst CSBt CTri MAsh SCoo SWhi
	– 'Champs Hill'	CFst
	– 'Coccinea'	SWhi
	– 'Discovery'	CFst
	– 'Eden Valley'	CFst SCoo
	– 'John Ardron'	CFst
	– 'Joseph Murphy'	CFst
	– 'Joyce Burfitt'	CFst
	– 'Katinka'	CFst SWhi
	– 'Lilac Time'	CFst
	– 'Molly Rose' **new**	SWhi
	– 'Mrs E.A. Mitchell'	SPlb SWhi
	– 'My Love'	CFst SWhi
	– 'Ockham'	CFst
	– 'Pentreath'	SWhi
	– 'Pink Ice' ♀H7	CFst CTri EPfP MAsh SWhi
	– 'Providence'	CFst
	– 'Purple Beauty'	SWhi
	– 'Rosita'	CFst
	– 'Roter Kobold'	SWhi
	– 'Sandford Heritage'	CFst
	– 'Sandpit Hill'	CFst SWhi
	– 'Sherry'	SWhi
	– 'Stephen Davis' ♀H7	SCoo SWhi
	– 'Ted Oliver'	CFst
	– 'Velvet Night' ♀H7	CSBt MAsh SWhi
	– 'Vivienne Patricia'	CFst
	coccinea	CPbh
	cooperi	SPlb
	curviflora	SPlb
	× ***darleyensis***	ESps ETMg
	– 'Alba'	see *E.* × *darleyensis* f. *albiflora* 'Silberschmelze'
	– f. ***albiflora*** 'Ada S. Collings'	MAsh SRms
	– – 'Bing'	SCoo SWhi
	– – 'N.R. Webster'	SRms
§	– – 'Silberschmelze'	CSBt CTri EPfP MAsh MJak MMuc SCoo SRms SWhi
	– – 'White Glow'	CTri MAsh SRms SWhi
	– – 'White Perfection' ♀H6	CBcs CFst EPfP IArd MAsh MJak SCoo SPer SPoG SRms SWhi
	– 'Archie Graham'	SRms
	– 'Arthur Johnson' ♀H6	CFst CTri MAsh SRms
§	– f. ***aureifolia*** 'Eva Gold' PBR	CFst SWhi
	– – 'Jack H. Brummage'	CSBt CTri MAsh SRms SWhi
	– – 'Mary Helen'	CSBt EPfP MAsh SCoo SRms SWhi
	– – 'Moonshine'	CFst SRms SWhi
	– – 'Tweety'	CBcs CFst CSBt SRms SWhi
	– 'Aurélie Brégeon'	CFst SRms
	– 'Bert'	SCoo SWhi
	– 'Cherry Stevens'	see *E.* × *darleyensis* 'Furzey'
§	– 'Darley Dale'	CFst CSBt ELan EPfP ESps MAsh MJak MMuc SCoo SPoG SRms SWhi
	– 'Epe'	CFst SRms SWhi
	– 'Eva'	see *E.* × *darleyensis* f. *aureifolia* 'Eva Gold'
§	– 'Furzey' ♀H6	CSBt EPfP ESps LCro LOPS MAsh SCoo SRms SWhi
	– 'George Rendall'	CTri EPfP MAsh SCoo SRms SWhi

- 'Ghost Hills' ♀H6	CSBt EPfP ESps LCro LOPS MAsh MJak SCoo SPoG SRms SWhi
- 'Golden Perfect'	CFst SWhi
- 'Irish Treasure'	CFst
- 'J.W. Porter' ♀H6	EPfP ESps MJak MMuc SCoo SRms SWhi
- 'James Smith'	SRms
- 'Jenny Porter' ♀H6	ELan EPfP ESps SCoo SWhi
- 'Katia'PBR (Winter Belles Series)	CFst SWhi
- 'Kramer's Rote' ♀H6	CFst CSBt CTri ELan EPfP MJak SCoo SPer SPoG SRms SWhi XLum
§ - 'Lena'	CFst
- 'Lucie'PBR (Winter Belles Series)	CFst SWhi
- 'Margaret Porter'	CFst EPfP SCoo SWhi
- MOLTEN SILVER	see *E.* × *darleyensis* f. *albiflora* 'Silberschmelze'
- 'Phoebe'PBR (Winter Belles Series)	CFst SPer SWhi
- 'Pink Perfection'	see *E.* × *darleyensis* 'Darley Dale'
- 'Rubina'PBR	CFst SWhi
- 'Snow Surprise'	SWhi
- 'Spring Surprise'PBR ♀H6	CFst EPfP SCoo SWhi
- 'W.G. Pine'	SRms
- 'White Spring Surprise'	SWhi
- 'Winter Surprise'	CFst SWhi
- 'Winter Treasure'	CFst SWhi
discolor	CPbh
erigena f. ***alba*** 'W.T. Rackliff' ♀H5	CBcs CSBt EPfP MAsh SCoo SRms SWhi
- f. ***aureifolia*** 'Golden Lady'	CSBt MAsh SCoo SRms SWhi
- - 'Thing Nee'	CFst SRms SWhi
- 'Brightness'	CSBt EPfP SCoo SWhi
- 'Golden Jubilee'	SWhi
- 'Irish Dusk' ♀H5	CBcs CSBt CTri EPfP MAsh MMuc SCoo SEND SRms SWhi
- 'Irish Salmon'	SWhi
- 'Superba'	MAsh SRms
formosa	CPbh
glandulosa	CPbh
glauca var. ***glauca***	SPlb
× ***griffithsii*** 'Jacqueline'	SWhi
lusitanica ♀H2	CFst
- f. ***aureifolia*** 'George Hunt'	CFst CRos ELan EPfP LRHS SLon SPer
- GREAT STAR	see *E. lusitanica* 'La Vasterival'
§ - 'La Vasterival'	CFst
- 'Sheffield Park'	CFst EPfP SPer SPoG
mackayana f. ***eburnea*** 'Doctor Ronald Gray'	CFst
- - 'Shining Light'	CFst SWhi
- 'Errigal Dusk'	CFst
- f. ***multiplicata*** 'Plena' (d)	WHer
mammosa ♀H2	CPbh SPlb
- cream-flowered	CPbh
- pink-flowered	CPbh
- red-flowered	CPbh
- white-flowered	CPbh
mediterranea misapplied	see *E. erigena*
multiflora	XSen
× ***oldenburgensis*** 'Ammerland' ♀H6	SCoo SRms
patersonii	SPlb
perspicua	CPbh SPlb
platycodon	CFst
subsp. ***maderincola*** f. ***aureifolia*** 'Levada Gold'	
plukenetii	CPbh
scabriuscula	CPbh
sessiliflora	CPbh
spiculifolia 'Balkan Rose'	GCal
straussiana	SPlb
× ***stuartii*** 'Irish Lemon' ♀H5	CFst CSBt MJak SWhi
- 'Irish Orange'	CSBt MJak SWhi
tetralix	SWhi
- f. ***alba*** 'Alba Mollis' ♀H7	CFst CSBt MAsh SWhi
- 'Con Underwood'	CFst CSBt SWhi
- 'Riko'	CFst
- 'Samtpfötchen'	CFst
- 'Silver Bells'	CSBt
- f. ***stellata*** 'Pink Star' ♀H7	CFst SWhi
vagans f. ***alba*** 'Cornish Cream' ♀H6	EPfP SWhi
- - 'Diana's Gold'	SRms
- - 'Golden Triumph'	CFst
- - 'Lyonesse' ♀H6	MAsh MMuc SWhi
- f. ***aureifolia*** 'Valerie Proudley' ♀H6	CSBt MAsh
- - 'Yellow John'	CFst CSma SRms SWhi
- 'Birch Glow' ♀H6	CSma EPfP
- 'Keira'	CFst CSma SRms
- 'Mrs D.F. Maxwell' ♀H6	CBcs CFst CSBt MMuc SWhi
- 'Mrs Donaldson'	CFst
- 'Saint Keverne'	CFst CSBt IArd MMuc SWhi
- 'Summertime'	CFst
× ***veitchii*** 'Exeter' ♀H5	CFst CRos CSBt ELan EPfP LRHS MAsh NRHS SPer SWhi
- 'Gold Tips' ♀H5	CFst CSBt EPfP
versicolor	CPbh SPlb
verticillata	CPbh
× ***watsonii*** 'Claire Elise'	CFst
- 'Mary'	SWhi
- 'Pink Pacific'	CFst SWhi
× ***williamsii*** 'Ken Wilson'	CFst
'Winter Fire'	CPbh
woodii	SPlb

Erigeron (*Asteraceae*)

acris	EBWF
'Adria'	CRos EBee ECtt EUJe LLHF LRHS MMuc NRHS
§ ***alpinus***	CPla
annuus	CSpe MMuc MNrw NDov SPhx WBrk WSHC
aurantiacus	CBcs GKev IBoy NBro
aureus 'Canary Bird' ♀H4	CPBP ECtt EPot GCrg NRHS NSla WAbe
- 'The Giant'	WAbe
'Azure Beauty'	WHar
AZURE FAIRY	see *E.* 'Azurfee'
§ 'Azurfee'	CSBt ELan EPfP GKev GMaP LPmr MBNS MHol NLar SPer SPoG SWvt WArt WFar WMoo
BLACK SEA	see *E.* 'Schwarzes Meer'
'Blue Beauty'	CMac CRos EPfP LRHS NRHS
'Charity'	MHCG MRav NPnk
chrysopsidis	GKev
- 'Grand Ridge'	CRos LRHS NRHS WAbe
compositus	GKev SRms
§ - var. ***discoideus***	CMea CPBP NSla SPlb WHal WHoo WOld
- 'Rocky'	CBod MMuc
DARKEST OF ALL	see *E.* 'Dunkelste Aller'
'Dignity'	CBod ELan LLHF MBel MBrN MMuc MPie MRav SBod SPoG SWvt WBrk
'Dimity'	CRos ECha NBre NRHS WHal
'Dominator'	CWGN IRob MNrw WCot

I 'Dunkelste Aller' CAby CBcs CBod CRos CSam ELan EPfP GBin GLog GMaP LRHS LSou MBel MRav MSpe NLar NPnk NRHS SCob SGbt SPer SPoG SRms SWvt WCAu WCot WFar WHoo
* ***ereganus*** NBre
flettii CPla GKev
'Foersters Liebling' ♀H5 EBee MBel MNrw MTis
formosissimus GBin
'Four Winds' ECtt ELan EWes GKev LRHS NGdn NHpl WBrk
'Gaiety' NBre
glaucus CCCN CSBt GJos LRHS MMuc MRav NGdn SEND SMad WArt WBrk WFar
- 'Albus' ELon LRHS NLar WArt WBor WFar
- 'Elstead Pink' CTri ECtt ELan WFar
- large-flowered ELon LRHS
- 'Roger Raiche' CFis MRav
- 'Rose Purple' CFis
- 'Roseus' CBcs SEND
- 'Sea Breeze' CBod CCCN CPla CRos EBee ECtt ELon EPfP ETMg GBin GJos GMaP GMcL LOPS LRHS MBel MHol MPnt NLar NRHS SCob SGbt SMad SPoG SRms SWvt WBor WBrk WFar WHoo
- 'Sennen' MHCG WBrk
- 'Viewpoint Blue' ELon LRHS
§ ***karvinskianus*** ♀H4 Widely available
- 'Kew Profusion' CRos LRHS MHol NRHS
- 'Sea of Blossom' CBod GCal NCou WArt
- 'Stallone' LPmr LSun MHol NLar
leiomerus GEdr GKev LLHF
linearis ITim LLHF
'Mrs F.H. Beale' WCot
mucronatus see *E. karvinskianus*
multiradiatus GCal
'Nachthimmel' NBre NGdn NPnk
philadelphicus MNrw NBro WArt WHal
PINK JEWEL see *E.* 'Rosa Juwel'
PINK TRIUMPH see *E.* 'Rosa Triumph'
'Professor Korodi' (d) EBee
'Profusion' see *E. karvinskianus*
pulchellus **new** WBrk
pumilus MAvo
pygmaeus LLHF
pyrenaicus misapplied see *E. alpinus*
pyrenaicus Rouy see *Aster pyrenaeus*
'Quakeress' CAby CBod CMea ECtt EPri GMaP GQue MBel MMuc MNrw MRav MSpe NGdn NPnk SCob SPoG SWvt WBrk WFar WGwG
§ 'Rosa Juwel' CBod CRos CSBt ECtt ELan EPfP GBin GMaP LPmr LRHS MBNS MHol MRav NPnk NRHS SPer SPoG SRms SWvt WCAu WFar WHar WMoo
§ 'Rosa Triumph' EBee
'Rotes Meer' CMac EBee ELan MRav
rotundifolius 'Caerulescens' see *Bellis caerulescens*
salsuginosus misapplied see *Eurybia sibirica*
§ 'Schneewittchen' CBod CRos CSam EBee ELan EPPr EPfP LRHS MBNS MBel MPie MRav NGdn NPnk NRHS SRms SWvt WGwG
§ 'Schwarzes Meer' EBee ELon MSpe WCot
scopulinus ITim SBch WAbe WHal WOld
simplex CRos LRHS NRHS
'Sincerity' XLum
'Snow Queen' SWvt
SNOW WHITE see *E.* 'Schneewittchen'
'Sommerneuschnee' MTis NDov NPnk SCob SPhx WCAu
speciosus 'Grandiflora' CBod WArt
'Strahlenmeer' NBre
'Synehurst' WCot
trifidus see *E. compositus* var. *discoideus*
uniflorus LLHF SRms
'Wayne Roderick' CBod CRos ECtt ELan EPfP LRHS NRHS WTor
'White Quakeress' CFis CMea LLHF MHCG MRav WCot

Erinacea (*Papilionaceae*)

§ ***anthyllis*** ♀H5 WAbe WThu
pungens see *E. anthyllis*

Erinus (*Plantaginaceae*)

alpinus ♀H4 CTri ECtt EDAr GAbr GJos GKev NSla SBch SRms XLum
- var. ***albus*** GJos GMaP NSla SRms WHoo XLum
- 'Doktor Hähnle' EDAr GJos GMaP SRms WHoo XLum

Eriobotrya (*Rosaceae*)

sp. ETod LPra
'Coppertone' see × *Rhaphiobotrya* 'Coppertone'
japonica (F) ♀H3 CAbb CBcs CCCN CRos CTsd ELan EPfP ETod EUJe LPra LRHS MGos MMuc NLar NLos NPla SArc SCoo SEND SPer SPlb SPtp SSta SVic WHer WPGP
- 'Gold Nugget' (F) XBlo
- 'Oliver' (F) LRHS
- 'Rose-Anne' LRHS SGol

Eriocapitella see *Anemone*

Eriocephalus (*Asteraceae*)

africanus CBod SPlb

Eriogonum (*Polygonaceae*)

SDR 7201 **new** GKev
alleni 'Little Rascal' EBee ELan
cespitosum LLHF WAbe
fasciculatum EBee
ovalifolium GKev
- var. ***nivale*** WAbe
- Wellington form GKev
umbellatum EPot GKev
- var. ***humistratum*** WAbe
- var. ***porteri*** GKev
- var. ***torreyanum*** CMea

Eriophorum (*Cyperaceae*)

angustifolium CBen CWat EBWF EHoe LLWG MSKA MWts SPlb WMAq WPnP WWtn XLum
chamissonis MWts
latifolium LLWG MSKA MWts XLum
rousseauianum LLWG MSKA
vaginatum EHoe EWat LLWG MSKA XLum

Eriophyllum (*Asteraceae*)

lanatum EBee ECha ELan EPfP MMuc NBid NGBl SHar

Eriostemon (*Rutaceae*)

myoporoides see *Philotheca myoporoides*

Eritrichium (*Boraginaceae*)

aretioides	SPlb
villosum new	GKev

Erodium (*Geraniaceae*)

absinthoides	CRos LRHS NRHS XSen
- var. ***amanum***	see *E. amanum*
§ ***acaule***	EPPr
'Almodovar'	WCot
§ ***amanum***	CSpe ECtt EWes GMaP
balearicum	see *E.* × *variabile* 'Album'
'Caroline'	CMea WHoo
§ ***castellanum***	EBee LLHF NLar
- 'La Féline'	GCrg
celtibericum	EPot
'Cézembre'	WCot
chamaedryoides	see *E. reichardii*
- 'Roseum'	see *E.* × *variabile* 'Roseum'
cheilanthifolium 'David Crocker'	EPot WAbe
chrysanthum	CElw CSpe CTri EAJP ECha ECtt EDAr ELan EPfP EPot EWTr GJos ITim MMuc MPnt NChi NLar SEND SRot SWvt WSHC XLum XSen
- (f)	WFar
- (m)	NRya
- 'Arcadia'	CMea SPhx
- pink-flowered	CSpe ECtt EHrv EPot MMuc SEND SRot
- 'Special Rose'	CSpe
'County Park'	ECha EPPr SHar SRms XSen
daucoides misapplied	see *E. castellanum*
daucoides ambig.	GKev
'Fran's Delight'	CMea CSpe ECtt EPot GJos SBch WAbe WHoo
'Freedom'	IPot MAvo MHol SCob SMad WCot XEll
'Géant de Saint Cyr'	ECtt
'Gini's Choice'	WCot
glandulosum ♀H5	ELan EPfP MAsh MMuc NLar SBch SEND SPtp SRms SRot XLum
'Grey Blush'	SMHy WKif
gruinum	CHid SPhx
guttatum misapplied	see *E.* 'Katherine Joy'
guttatum (Desf.) Willd.	CWGN EPot EWTr GMaP SRms
hymenodes L'Hér.	see *E. trifolium*
'Julie Ritchie'	CSpe WHoo
§ 'Katherine Joy'	ECtt EPot EWes GCrg MHer NRya SRot
× ***kolbianum***	SMHy WAbe WCot WHoo
- 'Natasha'	ECtt EPPr EPot EWes MHer MMuc SEND SPoG WKif XSen
'Las Meninas'	ECtt WCot
× ***lindavicum***	GCrg NChi
macradenum	see *E. glandulosum*
manescavii	Widely available
'Marchants Mikado'	WKif
'Maryla'	CMea
'Merstham Pink'	ELon SRms XLum
'Mesquita'	CMea
'Milly'	CMea
'Pallidum'	CSam
pelargoniiflorum	CAby CHid CMea CRos CSpe ELan EPfP EWTr LRHS MCot NLar NRHS SAko SBee SEND SRms SWvt WFar WKif WTor
'Peter Vernon'	MHer
petraeum	EPot
subsp. ***petraeum***	
'Pickering Pink'	EBee
'Purple Haze'	ELan SRms SRot WFar
§ ***reichardii***	CRos CTri ECtt LRHS MBrN NRHS SPoG SRms WCFE
- 'Album'	CRos GCrg LRHS MAsh MHol MMuc MSCN NHpl NRHS SPoG WHoo
- 'Bianca'	ELan EPfP
- 'Jenny'	NHpl
- 'Rubrum'	CElw MAsh
'Robertino'	WAbe
rodiei	EWes
romanum	see *E. acaule*
§ ***rupestre***	SRms SRot
'Spanish Eyes'	CDor CSpe EBee ECtt EWTr GCrg LRHS LSou LSun MHol MPie NCou SMad SPoG SRot SWvt WCot WKif WRHF WWFP
'Stephanie'	ECtt ELan EPPr EWes MHer MMuc SEND XSen
supracanum	see *E. rupestre*
tordylioides	EWTr
trichomanifolium L'Hér.	EWes
§ ***trifolium***	CMea ELan MHer SBch SPhx
× ***variabile***	WFar
§ - 'Album'	CMea CRos EPfP EPot GCrg GMaP LRHS MHer NEgg NRHS SRms SRot SWvt WAbe WBrk WFar WTor
I - 'Bishop's Form'	CBod CMea CRos ECtt EPfP EPot GCrg GJos GMaP LRHS MAsh MHol MJak NEgg NQui NRHS NRya SPoG SRms SRot SWvt WAbe WBrk WCFE WFar WHoo
- 'Candy'	ECtt MHer NHpl SRot WBrk
- 'Derek'	SRGP
- 'Flore Pleno' (d)	CRos CTri ELan EPfP EWes GCrg ITim LRHS MHer NHpl NRHS SPoG SRms SRot WBrk WTor
- 'Red Rock'	CTri
§ - 'Roseum' ♀H4	CBod ECtt ELan MMuc NCou SEND SPlb SRms WBrk
- 'Timpany Seedling'	ITim

Erpetion see *Viola*

Eruca (*Brassicaceae*)

vesicaria	ENfk
- subsp. ***sativa***	CRav CSpe GPoy MHer MNHC SRms SVic

Eryngium (*Apiaceae*)

§ ***agavifolium***	Widely available
- giant	WPGP
alpinum	CBod CRav CSpe ECha ESps EWTr GKev GMaP GMcL IBoy MGos MSCN SCob SPer SPhx SRms SRot WCAu WFar WHar
- 'Amethyst'	CRos LRHS LSRN NRHS
- 'Blue Star'	CAby CBcs CBot CExl CSpe EBee ECtt EHrv ELan ELon GPSL IRob NDov NLar WBor WCFE WSpi
- 'Slieve Donard'	see *E.* × *zabelii* 'Donard Variety'
- 'Superbum'	CRos ECtt GAbr GCal GLog LRHS MNrw NRHS SRms
amethystinum	ELon EPri LRHS
'Blue Jackpot'	EBee ECtt EPfP EWes MBel MHol MNrw
'Blue Steel'	EBee LLHF
bourgatii	Widely available

– Graham Stuart Thomas's selection	CDor CEnd CExl CRos CSpe ECtt EHrv ELan EPPr EWes GAbr GMaP LRHS MBel MCot MHol NBid NEgg NLar NRHS SPad SPer SRms WCAu WCot WHoo WHrl WSpi
– 'Oxford Blue' ♀H5	LRHS MHer NLar NSla SWvt
– 'Picos Amethyst'	CBWd CBcs CMac CRos CWCL EBee EPfP IPot LCro LRHS LSRN MBel NRHS NSti SCob SCoo SRms WSHC
– 'Picos Blue'PBR	CAby CBcs CBct CBot CExl CRav CSpe ECtt EHrv ELan EPfP EShb EUJe IPot LRHS LSRN MBel MRav NDov NEgg NLar NRHS NSti SPhm SWvt WKif
bromeliifolium misapplied	see *E. agavifolium*, *E. eburneum*
bromeliifolium ambig.	CRos NRHS
'Cobalt Star'	GWyn IRob MRav SMHy WHoo
creticum	MNrw
cymosum B&SWJ 10267	WCru
decaisneanum misapplied	see *E. pandanifolium*
deppeanum	CFil CSpe
– F&M 54	WPGP
– NJM 05.031	LEdu
Dove Cottage hybrid	MAvo
ebracteatum	CSpe LEdu
– var. ***poterioides***	ELan LRHS NDov SMad SPhx
§ ***eburneum***	CBod ECha ELan EPfP EWes GMaP ILea LRHS SMad
aff. ***eburneum***	CMac
'Electric Haze'	CSam ECtt LSou MAvo
elegans var. ***elegans***	CFil
foetidum	XAbr
§ ***giganteum*** ♀H7	Widely available
– 'Silver Ghost' ♀H7	CAby CBod CExl CMac CSam CSpe ECtt GMaP LCro LOPS LRHS NChi NDov NGdn NLar NSti SPhx SWvt WAvo WCot WSpi
glaciale	GKev
– from Sierra Nevada, Spain **new**	SBrt
gracile B&SWJ 10351	WCru
– B&SWJ 10441	WCru
'Green Jade'	CRos LRHS NRHS
guatemalense B&SWJ 10397	WCru
horridum misapplied	see *E. eburneum*
horridum ambig.	EWes MNrw NLar NLos SArc
humboldtii B&SWJ 14342 **new**	WCru
aff. ***humboldtii*** B&SWJ 14367 **new**	WCru
humile B&SWJ 10464	WCru
'Indigo Star'	MAvo
'Lapis Blue'	IRob
leavenworthii	CRos LRHS NRHS
maritimum	CEls CPou EBWF GPoy MNHC SPhx SPlb SRms
Miss Willmott's ghost	see *E. giganteum*
× ***oliverianum*** ♀H6	CBod CDor CMea CTri CWCL ECtt ELan EPfP GAbr GKev IRob LRHS MAvo MCot MRav MTis NLar SPer SPoG SWvt WCot
§ ***pandanifolium*** ♀H3	CBot CKno ELan EUJe EWes GCal MNrw SArc SEND SMHy SPlb SWvt
– 'Physic Purple'	CAby CDor CSpe ELan GPSL MAvo
'Pen Blue'	CAby CSpe CWld EBee ECha ECtt EPfP IPot LRHS LSun MAvo MGos MHol MNrw MSCN SAko SCob SPoG WCAu WCot WTor
planum	Widely available
§ – 'Blauer Zwerg'	GMaP LRHS NLar
– 'Blaukappe'	CBod CExl CMea CRos EBee ELan ELon EPfP LRHS MMuc NLar NRHS SEND SPhx SRms
– BLUE DWARF	see *E. planum* 'Blauer Zwerg'
– 'Blue Glitter'	CBod CDor CRos EBee ELon GPSL LRHS LSun NLar NRHS SPhx SWvt
– 'Blue Hobbit'	Widely available
– 'Blue Ribbon'	CSam
– 'Flüela'	EPed EShb EWes GCal LRHS LSRN NEgg NRHS
– 'Jade Frost'PBR (v)	Widely available
– 'Naughty Jackpot' (v)	NLar
– 'Paradise Jackpot'PBR	SRms
– 'Seven Seas'	MBNS NEgg
– 'Silver Salentino'	CBod ELon GPSL
– 'Silver Stone'	SRms
– 'Tetra Petra'	LRHS SRms
– 'Tiny Jackpot'	CWGN GMaP IBoy NLar NPnk
– 'White Glitter'	CBod EBee ELan
proteiflorum	CBod EPfP LRHS NDov SBrt SMad SPlb WFar
serbicum	GCal
serra	CRos EWes LRHS NLos NRHS
tricuspidatum	CRos EBee ECtt LRHS NRHS
× ***tripartitum*** ♀H5	CBcs CBod CRos CTri ECha ECtt EHrv ELan EPfP GMaP LRHS LSRN MNrw MRav NBro NEgg NLar NRHS SRkn SWvt WAvo
* ***umbelliferum***	GCal MBNS
variifolium	Widely available
– 'Miss Marble'	EPfP LSun SRms WHar WWtn
venustum	CRos EBee LRHS NRHS SMad
yuccifolium	CBWd CBod CSpe EBee EPfP EWes GCal LEdu LRHS MAvo MSpe SMad SPhx SPlb SWvt XLum XSen
– 'Kershaw Blue' **new**	WPGP
× ***zabelii***	CDor ECha
– 'Big Blue'	Widely available
§ – 'Donard Variety'	ECtt EUJe GCal ILea LRHS MAvo MCot NLar
– 'Forncett Ultra'	IRob MNrw
– 'Jos Eijking'PBR	Widely available
– 'Neptune's Gold'	CAby CBcs CBct CWGN EBee ECtt EMFm EUJe GBin GMaP ILea LCro LOPS LRHS MJak NLar NPri NSti SCob SHar SMad SPer SPhm SPoG WHlf WWFP
– 'Violetta'	CBod MCot NLar SPoG WCAu

Erysimum ✿ (*Brassicaceae*)

alpinum Pers.	see *E. sylvestre*
* ***altaicum*** var. ***humillinum***	LLHF
'Andy's Oranges and Lemons' (v)	WCot
'Apricot Delight'	see *E.* 'Apricot Twist'
§ 'Apricot Twist'	CBcs CBod CMea CRos CSpe CWCL CWGN ECtt ELan ELon EPfP GBin GMaP LRHS MCot MHol NLar NRHS SCob SCoo SPer SPoG SRms SWvt WFar WHil WHoo
arenicola var. ***torulosum***	see *E. torulosum*
arkansanum	see *E. helveticum*
bicolor from La Gomera	WArt
'Bowles's Mauve' ♀H4	Widely available
'Bowles's Purple'	SRms SWvt
'Bowles's Yellow'	MHCG WCot
'Bredon'	CRos NPer NRHS WKif

'Butterscotch'	WHoo
'Canaries Yellow'	GMcL WHar
capitatum* var. *purshii	WAbe
cheiri	EBWF MHer
- 'Baden-Powell' (d)	GCal
- 'Blood Red'	CRav
- 'Bloody Warrior' (d)	CElw ECtt
- 'Fire King'	CRav LCro
- 'Harpur Crewe' (d)	NPer SRms WHer
- 'Vulcan' **new**	CRav
- 'White Dame'	CRav
'Constant Cheer'	CElw CMea CSBt CWCL EAJP ECtt ELan EPfP IFoB MAvo MCot MMuc MNHC NLar NPer SCob SEND SPoG SRGP SRkn SRms SWvt WHoo WKif WSpi
'Cotswold Gem' (v)	ELon GPSL LSou MHer MMuc NPer SEND SWvt
'Dawn Breaker'	ECtt
'Desert Island'	ECtt MAsh
'Dorothy Elmhirst'	see *E.* 'Mrs L.K. Elmhirst'
'Gogh's Gold'	WHlf
'Golden Gem'	EPfP
'Golden Jubilee'	ECtt EPPr LRHS SRms
§ ***helveticum***	SRms
'Jacob's Jacket'	ECha MBNS MHer NPer
'John Codrington'	GBin NPer WKif WSpi
'Joseph's Coat'	EWld MHCG
'Jubilee Gold'	CWCL
kotschyanum	ELon GCrg GEdr NRHS NSla SRms WHal
'Lemon Light'	WHoo
linifolium	SRms
§ - 'Variegatum' (v)	CCCN CSBt CWCL EAJP EBee ECtt ELan EPfP EUJe IBoy LRHS MHol NPer NPri SCob SPer SPoG SRot WHar WHer XLum
- 'Variegatum' peach-flowered (v)	NQui
'Moonlight'	GMaP MHer MRav SRms WHoo
§ 'Mrs L.K. Elmhirst'	NPer
mutabile	CTri EPfP WHal
'Orange Flame'	CMea ECha GCrg MHer NPer SEND WHoo
'Orange Zwerg'	MMuc
'Paintbox'	EBee WHlf
'Parish's'	CElw CFis CSpe CWld
'Parkwood Gold'	NHpl
'Pastel Patchwork'	CSpe ECtt WCot
Perry's hybrid	NPer
'Perry's Peculiar'	NPer
'Perry's Surprise'	NPer
'Perry's Variegated' (v)	NPer
'Plant World Lemon'	CDor CHGN CPla CRav ELon NLar
'Poem Lilac' **new**	WHlf
§ ***pulchellum***	ECha
pumilum DC.	see *E. helveticum*
'Purple Jep'	CRos LRHS NRHS
'Red Jep'	CRos EBee EPfP LRHS NRHS
rupestre	see *E. pulchellum*
'Ruston Royal'	ECha
RYSI BRONZE ('Innrysibro')	LRHS
RYSI COPPER **new**	SPoG
RYSI GOLD ('Innrysigol'[PBR])	LRHS NRHS SPoG
RYSI MOON	LRHS NPnk
RYSI STAR ('Inneryrysistar')	LRHS
scoparium	ECha ELon
'Sissinghurst Variegated'	see *E. linifolium* 'Variegatum'
'Spice Island'	ECtt
'Sprite'	CMea CTri NPer
'Stars and Stripes' (v)	CBod CRos ECtt LRHS LSou SRkn WCFE
SUGAR RUSH MIXED **new**	ETMg
SUNBURST ('Listrace')	CDor CMea CRos ECtt LSou NRHS WCot
'Sweet Sorbet'	CElw ELon MBNS NLar SRkn SWvt
§ ***sylvestre*** **new**	CPBP
§ ***torulosum***	GKev
WALBERTON'S FRAGRANT STAR ('Walfrastar'[PBR]) (v)	CRos EPfP LRHS NRHS SPoG SRms WTor
WALBERTON'S FRAGRANT SUNSHINE ('Walfrasun')	CBod CRos EBee EPfP LRHS NRHS SCoo SPoG
'Wenlock Beauty'	CFis SRms
'Winter Joy'	CRos EPfP LLHF LRHS MBNS NLar
'Winter Light' **new**	CBod
WINTER ORCHID	CRav CWGN NLar NPnk
'Winter Party'	CBod ETMg LSou NPnk
'Winter Passion' **new**	CBod CRos MBNS NRHS SPoG
WINTER ROUGE	CBod CMea
WINTER SORBET ('Inneryws'[PBR])	ECtt EPfP LRHS SPoG

Erythraea see *Centaurium*

Erythrina (*Papilionaceae*)

abyssinica	SPlb
amazonica	SPlb
arborescens	SPlb
× ***bidwillii***	CCCN LRHS
crista-galli ♀H3	CBcs CBlu CCCN CDTJ CHll CRos CSpe EBee ELan EPfP LRHS MGil MPie MPkF SPlb WCot WPGP
- 'Compacta'	LRHS
flabelliformis	SPlb
guatemalensis	SPlb
herbacea	SPlb
§ ***humeana***	SPlb
latissima	SPlb
lysistemon	SPlb
princeps	see *E. humeana*
rubrinervia	SPlb
speciosa	SPlb
vespertilio	SPlb

Erythronium ✿ (*Liliaceae*)

albidum	EPot GEdr GKev IBlr IRob LAma SDir
americanum	EPot GKev IBlr IRob LAma MNrw NRog SDir WAbe
'Apple Blossom'	IBlr
'Ballyrogan's Blaze'	IBlr
'Beechpark'	IBlr
'Blush'	IBlr
'Bronze Beauty'	IBlr
'Bryn Meifod'	WAbe
'Californian Star'	IBlr
'Californian Sunshine'	IBlr
californicum ♀H5	CRos EBee GKev IBlr LRHS MNrw NRHS NRog
- 'Ballyrogan Bronze Bounty'	IBlr
- 'Brimstone'	IBlr
- 'Brocklamont Inheritance'	IBlr
- 'Bronze Edge'	IBlr
- 'Dark Delight'	IBlr
- 'Harvington Snowgoose'	see *E.* 'Harvington Snowgoose'
- Plas Merdyn form	IBlr
- 'Stellar'	IBlr
- 'White Beauty' ♀H5	Widely available

	californicum* × *hendersonii	NRog
	'Carol Scott'	IBlr
	caucasicum	EPot NRog
	citrinum	LLHF NRog
	- var. ***roderickii***	NRog
	citrinum* × *hendersonii	IBlr NRog
	'Citronella'	GKev IBlr NRog
	cliftonii hort.	see *E. multiscapideum* Cliftonii Group
	'Craigton Beauty'	IBlr
	'Craigton Cover Girl'	IBlr
	'Craigton Cream'	IBlr
	'Delicacy'	IBlr
	dens-canis ♀H5	Widely available
	- 'Charmer'	GEdr MNrw NRog
	- 'Frans Hals'	EPot GEdr GKev MNrw NRog WAbe
	- large-flowered	IBlr
	- 'Lilac Wonder'	EBee EPot GEdr GKev GMaP LAma LEdu MNrw NRog NWad SDeJ
*	- 'Moerheimii' (d)	GEdr GKev IBlr NRog
	- var. ***niveum***	EPot GEdr GKev IBlr NRog
	- 'Old Aberdeen'	CAvo CRos CWCL EHrv IBlr LLHF LRHS NRHS NRog WAbe
	- 'Pink Perfection'	EBee GEdr GKev LEdu MNrw NRog SDeJ WAbe
	- 'Purple King'	EBee EPot GEdr GKev GMaP IRob LAma LEdu MAvo MNrw NHpl NPnk NRog NWad SDeJ WAbe WCot
	- 'Rose Queen'	EHrv EPot GEdr GKev GMaP IRob LAma LEdu MAvo MNrw NRog NWad SDeJ
*	- 'Semi-plenum' (d)	IBlr
	- 'Sheer Delight'	IRob
	- 'Snowflake'	CAvo CRos EPot GEdr GKev IRob LAma LEdu LRHS MNrw NHpl NRHS NRog NWad SDeJ WAbe
	- 'White Splendour'	EPot GEdr IBlr MNrw NRog
	'Eirene'	IBlr
	elegans	CWCL EBee NRog
	'Flaire'	IBlr
	'Flash'	IBlr
§	***grandiflorum***	NRog
	- subsp. ***chrysandrum***	see *E. grandiflorum*
§	'Harvington Snowgoose'	CBro CRos EBee EHrv IBlr LLHF LRHS NRHS
	helenae	GKev IBlr MNrw NRog
	hendersonii	CRos EBee EHrv IBlr LAma LRHS NRHS NRog SPlb WAbe XEll
	- 'Pacific Skies' **new**	IBlr
	- 'Pacific Sunshine' **new**	IBlr
	'Hidcote Beauty'	CRos LLHF LRHS NRHS
	howellii	EBee
	'Janice'	IBlr
	japonicum	EPot IRob LAma MNrw NRog
	'Jeanette Brickell'	IBlr
	'Jeannine'	IBlr WAbe
	'Joanna'	CTal GEdr IBlr MAvo MNrw NRog WAbe WCot
	'John Brookes'	IBlr
	'Kinfauns Pink'	CWCL ELon EPot GBin GEdr IBlr LAma LLHF NRog WCot
	'Kondo'	CRos CTri EPfP GKev GMaP IBlr LAma LRHS NLar NRHS NRog NWad SCob SPer WAbe WPnP
	'Lavender Eye'	IBlr
	'Margaret Mathew'	IBlr WAbe
	'Minnehaha'	IBlr
§	***multiscapideum***	CWCL GKev LLHF MNrw WSHC
§	- Cliftonii Group ♀H4	WAbe
	'Oregon Encore'	IBlr
	oregonum	CRos EBee ECha EHrv GEdr GKev IBlr LAma LLHF LRHS MNrw NRHS NRog
	- 'Ballyrogan Yellow'	IBlr
	- subsp. ***leucandrum*** 'The Giant'	IBlr
	oregonum* × *revolutum	IBlr
	'Pagoda' ♀H5	Widely available
	purdyi	see *E. multiscapideum*
	'Purple Heart'	IBlr
	revolutum ♀H5	CAvo CBro CRos CWCL ELon GBin GEdr GKev GMaP IBlr IRob LAma LCro LOPS LRHS MNrw NLar NRHS NRog SChF SRot WCru
	- from God's Valley, Oregon	IBlr MNrw
	- 'Ballyrogan White Blusher'	IBlr
	- 'Dark Dapple'	IBlr
	- 'Guincho Splendour'	IBlr
	- 'Inferno' **new**	IBlr
I	- 'Inshriach Form'	IBlr
	- Johnsonii Group	EBee EPot WAbe WCru
	- 'Knightshayes'	CRos EBee IBlr LRHS NRHS
	- 'Knightshayes Pink'	CWCL EHrv IBlr LAma LLHF WShi
	- 'Pink Beauty'	NRog
	- Plas Merdyn form	IBlr
	- 'Wild Salmon'	CRos EBee EHrv LLHF LRHS NRHS
	'Rippling Waters'	IBlr
	'Rosalind'	IBlr NRog WAbe
	sibiricum	CWCL LAma NHpl NRog
	'Spring Fresh'	IBlr
	'Sundisc'	CTal ECha GKev IBlr NRog WAbe
	'Sunshine'	IBlr
	'Susannah'	CRos IBlr LRHS NRHS
	tuolumnense ♀H5	CTal CWCL EHrv GEdr GKev GMaP IBlr IRob LAma MCot MMoz MNrw NHpl NRog NWad SDeJ WAbe
	- EBA clone 2	IBlr
	- EBA clone 3	IBlr
	- 'Edgar Klein'	CTal
	- Plas Merdyn form	IBlr
	- 'Spindlestone'	CRos CTal CWCL EBee GEdr IBlr LAma LLHF LRHS NRHS WAbe
	umbilicatum	EPot GEdr GKev IBlr NHpl
	'White Star'	IBlr
	'Winifred Loraine'	IBlr

Escallonia (Escalloniaceae)

	sp.	CPer
	'Alice'	SCob SPer
§	***alpina***	MGil
	'Apple Blossom' ♀H5	Widely available
§	***bifida*** ♀H4	CBot CDul CHGN CRos EBee ECre ELan LRHS NRHS SBrt WPGP
	'C.F. Ball'	CBcs CRos CTri ELan EPfP ESps GKin GMcL IArd LRHS MAsh MSwo NEgg SGol SRms
	'Cardinalis'	CRos LRHS NRHS
	'Compacta Coccinea'	LRHS
	'Donard Beauty'	SRms
	'Donard Brilliance'	SGol SRms
	'Donard Radiance' ♀H5	CBcs CDul CMac CRos CSBt EMOT EPfP EShb ESps LRHS NLar NWad SCob SGol SLim SPer SPoG SRms SWvt
	'Donard Seedling'	CBcs CCVT CDul CRos ECrN ELan EMOT EPfP ESps GKin GMcL LRHS MAsh MGos MMuc MSwo NEgg

	NPer NRHS SCob SGol SLim SPer SRms SWvt
'Donard Star'	EPfP NLar NWad WAvo WCFE WHar
'Donard White'	CBod EPfP NLar SPoG
'Edinensis'	EPfP NLar SLim SRms WSpi
'Everest'	CRos EPfP LRHS MMuc SLon
× ***exoniensis***	SRms
fonkii	see *E. alpina*
GOLDEN CARPET ('Alcaura')	CBod CRos GBin LRHS MAsh MJak MTin NEoE NRHS SCob SHar WFar
'Hopleys Gold'	see *E. laevis* 'Gold Brian'
illinita	CDul NLar
'Iveyi' 🏆^{H4}	Widely available
'Jamie'^{PBR}	EShb LLHF LSRN
§ ***laevis***	LRHS
§ - 'Gold Brian'^{PBR}	CDul CMac CRos EHoe EPfP ESps GMcL LRHS LSRN MAsh MGos MJak NLar NRHS SCob SGol SPer
- 'Gold Ellen' (v)	CRos CSBt CTri EHoe ELan EMOT EPau EPfP ESps EUJe GMcL LRHS LSRN MAsh MGos MRav MSwo NEgg NLar NRHS SCob SCoo SEND SLim SPer SPoG SRms SWvt WBor
- PINK ELLE ('Lades'^{PBR})	EPfP LCro LOPS LRHS MAsh MGos NRHS SCob
'Langleyensis' 🏆^{H5}	CMac CTri SCob SGol SRms WHar
mexicana	CBot
× ***mollis***	SBrt
montevidensis	see *E. bifida*
myrtilloides B&SWJ 14329 **new**	WCru
organensis	see *E. laevis*
'Peach Blossom' 🏆^{H5}	CBar CRos EBee ELan EPfP ESps GKin GMcL LRHS MAsh MMuc MSwo NEgg NRHS SCob SCoo SEND SGol SLim SPer SRms
'Pink Pyramid'	LRHS
'Pride of Donard' 🏆^{H5}	CAco CSBt EPfP ESps GKin MGos SCob SRms
punctata	see *E. rubra*
RED CARPET ('Loncar'^{PBR})	CBcs GBin LRHS SLon WNPC
'Red Dream'	CRos CSBt EPfP ESps GMcL LRHS MAsh MGos MSwo NLar NRHS SCob SCoo SPoG SRms SWvt WAvo WFar
'Red Elf'	CMac CRos EBee ELan EMOT EPfP ESps GKin GMcL LRHS MGos NEgg SBod SCob SPer SPlb SRms SWvt WFar
'Red Hedger'	CBod CSBt CTsd ECrN ELan EShb MRav SCob SRms
'Red Knight'	CRos LRHS MAsh NEgg NRHS WNPC
resinosa	CBod CExl CTsd SPlb SRms SVen
revoluta	CTri MGil
§ ***rubra***	GKev
- 'Crimson Spire' 🏆^{H5}	CBar CBcs CDul CRos CSBt CTri ECrN EMOT EPfP ESps GKin GMcL LRHS LSRN MAsh MGos MMuc MRav NEgg SCob SEND SGbt SLim SPer SPlb SRms
- 'Ingramii'	SEND
- var. ***macrantha***	CBar CBcs CBod CCVT CDul CMac CRos CSBt CTri ECrN ELan EPfP ESps GKin GMcL IArd LRHS MHed MJak NEgg NLar NRHS SCob SCoo SLim SPer SPoG SRms WAvo
* - - ***aurea***	NPla
- 'Pygmaea'	see *E. rubra* 'Woodside'
§ - 'Woodside'	CMCN LLHF NWad SGol SRms
'Silver Anniversary'	MSwo
'Slieve Donard'	CMac MRav SLim SRms
tucumanensis	SPlb
'Ventnor'	SPlb SVen
virgata	MGil

Eschscholzia (*Papaveraceae*)

californica	MBel
- 'Alba'	CSpe
- subsp. ***mexicana*** 'Sun Shades'	SPhx
- 'Mission Bells'	LCro
- 'Red Chief'	LRHS SPhx

Escobaria (*Cactaceae*)

missouriensis	CCac
vivipara SB 128 from Manzano, New Mexico	CCac

Espeletia (*Asteraceae*)

argentea B&SWJ 14322 **new**	WCru
killipii B&SWJ 14319 **new**	WCru
aff. ***killipii***	WCru
aff. ***lopezii*** B&SWJ 14374 **new**	WCru
aff. ***summapacis***	WCru
uribei B&SWJ 14339 **new**	WCru

Esterhuysenia (*Aizoaceae*)

alpina	CPBP SPlb

Eucalyptus ✿ (*Myrtaceae*)

sp.	LPra
aggregata	CBlu SArc SKin
alpina	SPlb
amygdalina	SPlb
approximans	SKin
archeri	CDTJ CDul CRos EPfP LRHS MGos MMuc NLar SKin WCot
caesia 🏆^{H2}	SPlb
camaldulensis	LMaj SPlb
camphora	CCCN CTsd EMOT SKin
cinerea	CTsd SBig SKin SPlb
citriodora	see *Corymbia citriodora*
coccifera	CBcs CSBt CTsd EPfP EUJe MMuc NPer SBig SKin SPlb
cordata	EBee SAko SKin WPGP
crenulata	SKin
crucis subsp. ***crucis***	SPlb
cypellocarpa	SPlb
dalrympleana 🏆^{H4}	CAbb CRos EPfP EUJe LRHS LSRN MGos MMuc NPer SBig SEND SKin SLim SPer SPlb WCot WPGP
debeuzevillei	see *E. pauciflora* subsp. *debeuzevillei*
delegatensis	NPer
divaricata	see *E. gunnii* subsp. *divaricata*
erythrocorys	SPlb
eximia	see *Corymbia eximia*
ficifolia	see *Corymbia ficifolia*
fraxinoides	SPlb
gamophylla	SPlb
glaucescens	CAbb CRos ELan EPfP LRHS SArc SEWo SKin SPer
globulus	CWCL LPra SPlb
§ ***gregsoniana***	EPfP EUJe SKin SPlb
gunnii 🏆^{H5}	Widely available
- AZURA ('Cagire'^{PBR})	LCro LOPS LRHS LSRN NLar SCob SEWo SLim SLon
§ - subsp. ***divaricata***	EPfP SKin

* - 'Silver Drop'	CBlu WFar
johnstonii	IDee SKin SPer
kitsoniana	SKin
kruseana	SPlb
kybeanensis	SKin WCot
leucoxylon	SPlb
subsp. ***megalocarpa***	
ligustrina	SKin
macrocarpa	SPlb
mitchelliana	SKin
moorei var. ***nana***	CDTJ
neglecta	SKin
nicholii	CAbb CBcs CRos CSpe ECre EPfP EWes LRHS MGos MMuc SCoo SKin SPoG WCot
niphophila	see *E. pauciflora* subsp. *niphophila*
nitens	CDTJ SBig SKin SPlb
§ ***nitida***	SKin
parviflora	SKin
parvula	CCCN EPfP MMuc MRav SEND
pauciflora	CCCN CTsd EMOT ESps EUJe SPer
§ - subsp. ***debeuzevillei*** 🏆H5	CAbb CBlu EPfP SArc SBig SKin
- var. ***nana***	see *E. gregsoniana*
§ - subsp. ***niphophila*** 🏆H5	Widely available
perriniana	CAco CBcs CRos ECrN EPfP EUJe LRHS MGos SAko SBig SKin SPer SPlb SPoG SWvt WFar
pulverulenta	SPlb
- 'Baby Blue'	CRos CTsd ELan LRHS NRHS SKin SPer SWvt
regnans	SKin
rossii	SPlb
rubida	CCCN GAbr IDee SKin
sideroxylon	SPlb
- 'Rosea'	SPlb
simmondsii	see *E. nitida*
stellulata	SKin
stricta	SKin
subcrenulata	ELan EPfP SKin
tetraptera	SPlb
torquata	SPlb
urnigera	CMCN
vernicosa	SKin
viminalis	SKin

Eucharis (*Amaryllidaceae*)

§ ***amazonica*** 🏆H1b	CCCN EShb LAma SDeJ SPav
grandiflora misapplied	see *E. amazonica*

Eucomis ✿ (*Asparagaceae*)

ALOHA	see *E.* 'Leia'
autumnalis misapplied	see *E. zambesiaca*
§ ***autumnalis*** (Mill.) Chitt. 🏆H3	CBlu CBod CBro CGar EPot ERCP GKev LAma LRHS SDeJ SDir SPav SPlb WCot
- subsp. ***autumnalis***	IBoy
bicolor 🏆H3	Widely available
- 'Alba'	CExl CTca EPot GKev LAma
- 'Stars and Stripes'	WCru WHil
§ ***comosa***	CAvo CBro CHll CPrp CRos CSam CTal CTca EBee ERCP EShb GKev LAma LRHS NRHS SDeJ SPav WCot
- 'Cherry Blossom' new	LAma
- 'Cornwood'	CAvo CTca
- 'Johannesburg'	EBee GKev
- 'Kilimanjaro'	CTca EBee
- 'Lotte'	CTca GKev
- 'Oakhurst'	CAby CChe CPla CRos ECtt GMcL LRHS NRHS SPad SPtp
- purple-leaved	CAvo EShb
- 'Sparkling Burgundy' 🏆H6	Widely available
- 'Sparkling Rosy'	ERCP GKev LAma SCob WFar
- var. ***striata***	CAby EBee
'Dark Star'	CAbb ECtt SPad WCot
'Freckles'	CAby CPla SPad SRms
'Glow Sticks'	CWGN ECtt WHil
humilis	XEll
- 'Twinkle Stars'	ERCP GKev LAma SCob SDeJ WFar
'John Treasure'	SMHy
'Joy's Purple'	CBro CPar CTca EPri
§ 'Leia'PBR	CBro CTca ERCP GKev LAma LRHS
montana	CBlu CBro CPrp CTca EBee EPot ERCP GKev LAma SDeJ WCot
pallidiflora 🏆H3	CAvo CTal LEdu WPGP
'Pink Gin'	CAvo
'Playa Blanca'	CTca EBee EShb GKev LAma
pole-evansii	CBro CExl CPar CPne CTal CTca ELan EPri EUJe GKev LAma MRav SDeJ SDir WCru WPtf
- dark	GKev
- pink-flowered	CPar
I - 'Purpurea'	CExl GCal
punctata	see *E. comosa*
regia JCA 3.230.709	WCot
undulata	see *E. autumnalis* (Mill.) Chitt.
vandermerwei 🏆H3	CAvo CBlu CBro CPne CTal CTca EBee EPot GKev LAma LEdu SDeJ SDir SPlb
- 'Octopus'	CCCN CExl CPrp CTca ELan EPfP GBin GKev LSou MHer SDir WCot WFar
§ ***zambesiaca***	CAvo CBro CTal CTca EBee GCal GKev LAma SMHy
- JCA 3.230.709	WCot
- JCA 3.231.010	WCot
- 'White Dwarf'	CBcs CBod SPer WGwG
'Zeal Bronze'	CTal CTca GCal WAvo

Eucommia (*Eucommiaceae*)

ulmoides	CDul CMCN EBtc EPfP NLar

Eucryphia ✿ (*Cunoniaceae*)

cordifolia	CMac IDee MBlu
§ ***cordifolia*** × ***lucida***	CCCN SSta
glutinosa 🏆H4	CCCN CRos EPfP GGGa GKev IDee LRHS MAsh NHim SAko
- 'Miniature'	CBct EBee EPfP SChF WPGP
× ***hillieri***	WSpi
- 'Winton'	CBct EBee WPGP
× ***intermedia***	CExl CMac CTsd NLar SPer SRms SSta
- 'Rostrevor' 🏆H4	CBcs CDul CExl CJun CMac CTho ELan EPfP GBin GCal GGGa LRHS LSRN MAsh MBlu NLar SAko SReu SSta WPGP WSHC
'Leatherwood Cream'	WSpi
lucida	CCCN CRos LLHF LRHS MMuc NLar NRHS WSpi
- 'Ballerina' 🏆H4	CBcs CBct CJun CMac CRos CTho EBee ELan ELon EPfP GKin LRHS MAsh MPkF SAko SChF SCoo WPGP
I - 'Chaplin's Variety'	CBct EBee SChF WPGP
- 'Dumpling'	CExl EBee SChF WPGP
- 'Gilt Edge' (v)	CBcs CRos GKin LLHF LRHS
- 'Leatherwood Cream' (v)	WHor
- 'Pink Cloud'	CBcs CDul CEnd CExl CJun CMac CRos CTho ELan EPfP GKin LRHS LSRN MBlu MGil MGos NLar SAko SWvt WPGP

- 'Spring Glow' (v)	CExl CRos ELan GCal LLHF LRHS MAsh SPoG
milliganii	CFil CHll CRos EPfP LRHS MBlu MRav SAko SPer SRms SSta WPGP WSpi
moorei	CBcs CCCN CExl CMac EBee IDee SAko WPGP
× ***nymansensis***	CHab SArc SRms WSpi
- 'George Graham'	GGGa
- 'Mount Usher'	CRos
- 'Nymans Silver' (v)	CBot CDul CJun CMac CRos ELan EMil GGGa LLHF LRHS MAsh SPer SPoG
- 'Nymansay' ♀H4	Widely available
'Penwith' misapplied	see *E. cordifolia* × *lucida*
'Penwith' ambig.	IDee MGos

Eugenia (*Myrtaceae*)

uniflora	CCCN

Eumorphia (*Asteraceae*)

sericea	CFis GBin

Eunomia see *Aethionema*

Euodia (*Rutaceae*)

daniellii	see *Tetradium daniellii*
hupehensis	see *Tetradium daniellii* Hupehense Group

Euonymus ✿ (*Celastraceae*)

sp.	LPra
B&L 12543	EWes
CC 4522	CExl
NJM 09.109	CRHN
NJM 10.106	WPGP
alatus	Widely available
- B&SWJ 8794	WCru
- var. ***apterus***	EPfP WGrn
- 'Blade Runner'	CRos EPfP LRHS MGos NRHS SGol
- CHICAGO FIRE	see *E. alatus* 'Timber Creek'
- 'Ciliodentatus'	see *E. alatus* f. *striatus*
- 'Compactus' ♀H5	Widely available
- 'Fastigiata'	CJun
§ - 'Fire Ball'	CJun
* - 'Macrophyllus'	CJun EPfP
- 'Rudy Haag'	CJun
- 'Select'	see *E. alatus* 'Fire Ball'
- 'Silver Cloud'	EPfP NLar
§ - f. ***striatus***	CJun
- - B&SWJ 11051	WCru
§ - 'Timber Creek'	CJun EPfP IDee LLHF MBlu NLar
americanus	EPfP MBlu NLar
- var. ***angustifolius*** B&SWJ 12905	WCru
- 'Evergreen'	EPfP
- narrow-leaved	EPfP
bungeanus	EPfP
- B&SWJ 8782 from South Korea	WCru
- 'Dart's Pride'	CJun EPfP NLar
- 'Fireflame'	CJun LRHS
* - var. ***mongolicus***	EPfP
- 'Pendulus'	MBlu
- var. ***semipersistens***	CJun WCru
§ ***carnosus***	CJun CMCN
- CWJ 12425	WCru
- 'Red Wine'	CJun ELon EPfP LEdu MBlu NLar WCot
chibae B&SWJ 11159	WCru
§ ***clivicola***	CJun EPfP WCru
'Copper Wire'	EHoe
cornutus	WPGP
- var. ***quinquecornutus*** ♀H5	CBot CJun CMCN ELan EPfP MBlu MGil SBrt WPGP
'Den Haag'	CJun EPfP LRHS NLar
echinatus	IArd IDee
europaeus	Widely available
- from Slovakia	WCru
- f. ***albus***	CTho EPfP LRHS NLar SPoG
- 'Atropurpureus'	CMCN CTho EPfP NLar
- 'Atrorubens'	CJun
- 'Aucubifolius' (v)	CMac
* - 'Aureus'	CNat
- 'Brilliant'	CJun EPfP LRHS NLar
* - f. ***bulgaricus***	EPfP
- 'Chrysophyllus'	EPfP MBlu
- 'Howard'	EPfP NLar
- var. ***intermedius***	CJun EPfP MBlu
- 'Miss Pinkie'	CEnd
- 'Red Cascade' ♀H5	Widely available
- 'Scarlet Wonder'	CJun EPfP IArd NLar
- 'Thornhayes'	CTho EPfP
farreri	see *E. nanus*
fimbriatus	CJun
fortunei	ESps
- BLONDY ('Interbolwi'PBR) (v)	CDul CRos CTri ELan EPfP ESps GMcL LRHS MAsh MGos MJak MMuc MSwo NEgg NLar NPri NRHS SCob SCoo SEND SGol SLim SPoG SRms WHar
- 'Canadale Gold' (v)	CRos EPfP ESps LRHS MAsh NRHS SLon WAvo
- 'Coloratus'	CMac ECrN EPfP MBlu MSwo
- 'Country Gold'	WFar
- DAN'S DELIGHT ('Dandel') (v)	EBee MGos SGol SPoG
- 'Dart's Blanket'	ELan EPfP GMcL MRav SCob SEND SGol
- 'Emerald Gaiety' (v) ♀H5	Widely available
- 'Emerald 'n' Gold' (v) ♀H5	Widely available
- 'Emerald Surprise' (v) ♀H5	SRGP
- 'Gaiety Silver'	IBoy
- 'Gold Spot'	see *E. fortunei* 'Sunspot'
- 'Gold Tip'	see *E. fortunei* 'Golden Prince'
- GOLDEN HARLEQUIN ('Hoogi'PBR) (v)	EPfP GMcL LRHS MAsh NRHS NWad SPoG SWvt
§ - 'Golden Pillar' (v)	GMcL
§ - 'Golden Prince' (v)	CMac EHoe MRav MSwo NLar SRms
- GOLDY ('Waldbolwi'PBR)	EPfP LRHS NLar NRHS SGol SPoG
- 'Harlequin' (v)	CBcs CMac CRos CSBt EHoe ELan ELon EPfP ESps ETMg LBuc LRHS LSRN MAsh MBlu MGos MJak MRav NRHS SGol SLim SPer SPoG SRms SWvt WFar
- 'Heins Silver'PBR	EBee MGos SGol
- 'Kewensis' ♀H5	CMac ELan EUJe GCal GEdr LRHS MSCN SArc SCob SPoG WCFE WCru
- 'Kewensis Variegatus' (v)	MRav
- 'Longwood'	LRHS
- 'Minimus'	CDul CTri EPPr MSwo SCob SMad WBor WPGP XLum
* - 'Minimus Variegatus' (v)	EPPr SPlb
- 'Prince John'	CSBt
- 'Sheridan Gold'	CTri MRav
- 'Silver Gem'	see *E. fortunei* 'Variegatus'
- 'Silver Queen' (v)	Widely available

- 'Silverstone'^{PBR} (v)	CRos EBee EMil EPfP LRHS NRHS SGol SPoG
- 'Sunshine' (v)	CRos ELan EPfP LRHS MAsh SLon SPoG WAvo
§ - 'Sunspot' (v)	CBcs CBod CMac EBee ELan ELon ESps MJak MMuc MSwo SEND SGol SRms WRHF
§ - 'Variegatus' (v)	ESps SRms
- 'Wolong Ghost' 🏆H5	CBot CExl CRos GKin LRHS MBlu MGos MMuc NLar NRHS SGol SWvt WCot
frigidus	EPfP
- KWJ 12275 **new**	WCru
- var. ***elongatus*** GWJ 9378	WCru
grandiflorus misapplied	see *E. carnosus*
§ ***grandiflorus*** Wall.	CJun EPfP IArd NLar SCoo
- f. ***salicifolius*** misapplied	see *E. grandiflorus* Wall.
- f. ***salicifolius*** Stapf. & F. Ballard	CJun EPfP
hamiltonianus	CMCN EBtc ECrN EPfP EWTr LRHS MMuc
- NJM 11.006	WPGP
- 'Fiesta'	CJun LRHS NLar
- subsp. ***hians***	see *E. hamiltonianus* subsp. *sieboldianus*
- 'Indian Summer'	CJun CRos ELon EMil EPfP LRHS MAsh NLar NOra SPoG
- 'Koi Boy'	CJun EPfP MAsh SPoG
- 'Miss Pinkie'	CJun EPfP NLar
- 'Pink Delight'	CJun
- 'Poort Bulten'	CJun
- 'Popcorn'	CJun EPfP
- 'Rainbow'	CJun EPfP
- 'Red Chief'	CJun EPfP
- 'Red Elf'	CJun NLar
- 'Rising Sun'	CJun EPfP NLar
§ - subsp. ***sieboldianus***	CExl CTho EPfP MRav
- - B&SWJ 10941	SAko WCru
- - PAB 5337	LEdu
- - 'Calocarpus'	CJun EPfP LRHS
- - 'Coral Charm'	CJun EPfP NLar
* - - var. *yedoensis* f. ***koehneanus***	EPfP
- 'Snow' (v)	WCot
- 'Winter Glory'	CJun LRHS MMrt
§ ***huangii***	CJun
- B&SWJ 3700	WCru
japonicus	CBcs CBod CDul CMac CTri ECrN EPfP ESps GMcL LMaj SArc SBod SCob SEND SEWo SPer
- 'Albomarginatus' (v)	CBcs CTri EHoe EPfP NPri SEND SRms
- 'Argenteovariegatus' (v)	ESps
§ - 'Aureomarginatus' (v)	CCVT GBin GMcL NPri
- 'Aureopictus'	see *E. japonicus* 'Aureus'
- 'Aureovariegatus'	see *E. japonicus* 'Ovatus Aureus'
§ - 'Aureus' (v)	CBcs CDul CSBt CTsd EPfP ESps GMcL LRHS NPri SCoo SEND SLon SPer
- 'Benkomasaki'	ECrN EPfP
- 'Bravo' (v)	CBar CCVT CDul CRos ECrN EHoe EPfP ESps GMcL LMaj LRHS MAsh MGos NLar NPri NRHS SArc SCob SCoo SEWo SLim SPer SPoG SWeb SWvt WCot WFar
- 'Carnival Candle' **new**	SEND
- 'Charles'^{PBR} **new**	SPoG
- 'Chollipo' (v) 🏆H5	CRos ELan EPfP LRHS NRHS SEND SPoG
- 'Compactus'	SCoo
- 'Duc d'Anjou' misapplied	see *E. japonicus* 'Viridivariegatus'
- 'Duc d'Anjou' Carrière (v)	EBee EHoe ELan EPfP EWes MRav SEND SPoG
- 'Elegantissimus Aureus'	see *E. japonicus* 'Aureomarginatus'
- EXSTASE ('Goldbolwi'^{PBR}) (v)	SPoG WCot
- 'Francien' (v)	EBee EPfP LRHS NLar NRHS
- 'Gold Queen'^{PBR}	CRos LRHS NLar
- 'Golden Maiden' (v)	CRos ELan EPfP LRHS MAsh SLim SLon SPoG SRms SWvt
- 'Golden Pillar'	see *E. fortunei* 'Golden Pillar'
- GREEN MILLENIUM ('Minmil'^{PBR})	LRHS
- 'Green Rocket'	CBod CCVT CRos EBee EPfP GBin LRHS MGos MRav NPnk NRHS SGol SLim SPoG WCot WFar
- 'Green Spider'	SPoG
- 'Green Spire'	CRos LRHS NLar NRHS
- 'Happiness'^{PBR}	NEoE
- 'Hibarimisaki' (v)	EPfP
- 'Kathy'^{PBR}	CRos ELan ELon EPfP ESps LRHS MAsh MJak NLar NRHS SCob SPoG SRGP
§ - 'Latifolius Albomarginatus' (v)	ELan EPfP ESps MRav MSwo SPer SWvt
- 'Luna'	see *E. japonicus* 'Aureus'
- 'Macrophyllus Albus'	see *E. japonicus* 'Latifolius Albomarginatus'
- 'Maiden's Gold'	CSBt
- 'Marieke'	see *E. japonicus* 'Ovatus Aureus'
- 'Microphyllus'	CMac MRav NEgg SBod SGol SRms
§ - 'Microphyllus Albovariegatus' (v)	CBcs CDul CMac CSBt CTri ELan EPfP ESps LRHS MGos SCob SEND SLim SRms SWvt WAvo WFar
§ - 'Microphyllus Aureovariegatus' (v)	CMac CRos CSBt ELan ELon EPfP ESps LRHS MAsh MMuc NLar NRHS WHar
- 'Microphyllus Aureus'	see *E. japonicus* 'Microphyllus Pulchellus'
§ - 'Microphyllus Pulchellus' (v)	CBcs CMac CRos CSBt EBee ECrN EPfP ESps LRHS MGos MMuc SEND SPoG SWvt
- 'Microphyllus Variegatus'	see *E. japonicus* 'Microphyllus Albovariegatus'
§ - 'Ovatus Aureus' (v) 🏆H5	CBar CDul CExl CMac CRos CSBt CTri ELon EPfP ESps GMcL LMaj LRHS MGos MRav NLar NRHS SCob SEND SGol SLim SPer SPlb SPoG SRms SWvt WFar
- PALOMA BLANCA ('Lankveld03'^{PBR})	CRos LCro LRHS NRHS SPoG
- 'Président Gauthier' (v)	CAco EBee ESps GMcL LRHS SCob SCoo SLim SPer SWvt WCFE
- 'Pulchellus Aureovariegatus'	see *E. japonicus* 'Microphyllus Aureovariegatus'
I - 'Pyramidatus'	EPfP
- 'Rokujo'	GEdr
- 'Silver King'	CMac
- 'Silver Krista' (v)	NLar
- 'Susan' (v) 🏆H5	CMac EShb MAsh SRGP
§ - 'Viridivariegatus' (v)	LRHS WAvo
kachinensis B&SWJ 11668	WCru
kiautschovicus 'Berry Hill'	NLar
- 'Manhattan'	NLar
latifolius	CJun CMCN CTho EPfP IMou LEdu WCru
§ ***laxiflorus*** GWJ 9351	WCru
- HWJ 890	WCru
lucidus	CBcs CExl CHll EBee

macropterus	CJun EPfP IArd
mexicanus	CFil
morrisonensis	see *E. huangii*
myrianthus	CJun ELan EPfP EWes MBlu MPkF NLar
aff. ***myrianthus*** slim-leaved NJM 11.016 new	WPGP
§ ***nanus***	NLar WSHC
- var. ***turkestanicus***	CRos GKin LRHS SBrt SLon SRms
occidentalis	SBrt
'Ogisu' new	GKev
oxyphyllus ♀H5	CDul CJun CMCN CTho EPfP LRHS MMuc NLar WCot WCru WHar
- 'Waasland'	CJun EPfP
phellomanus ♀H5	CBot CDul CTho EBee EPfP EWTr GKin IDee LRHS MBlu MGil MGos MPkF MRav MSCN NLar NOra SCoo SPer SPoG SWvt WPGP
- 'Silver Surprise' (v)	CJun ELon EPfP
PIERROLINO ('Heespierrolino'PBR)	LRHS MRav NLar SCoo
§ ***planipes***	CAby CBot CCVT CDul CExl CMCN CRos CTho CTri EBee ECrN ELan EPfP EWTr GKin LRHS MAsh MBlu MGil MMuc MRav NLar NPnk SAko SLim SMad SPer SPoG WCot WHor
- B&SWJ 8660	WCru
- 'Dart's August Flame'	CJun EPfP
- 'Sancho' ♀H5	CJun EPfP LRHS
porphyreus B&SWJ 13914 new	WCru
- GWJ 9377	WCru
quelpaertensis	CJun
'Rokojō Variegated' (v)	WCot
rongchuensis 'Cliuicolus'	see *E. clivicola*
rosmarinifolius	see *E. nanus*
rubescens	see *E. laxiflorus*
sachalinensis misapplied	see *E. planipes*
sachalinensis (F. Schmidt) Maxim.	EPfP WCot
- B&SWJ 10835	WCru
sacrosanctus	CJun MBlu
sanguineus	NLar
sieboldianus	WCru
var. ***sanguineus*** B&SWJ 11140	
- - B&SWJ 11386	WCru
spraguei CWJ 12446	WCru
tingens	CJun CMCN
trapococcus	EPfP
vagans Wall.	EPfP WCot
verrucosus	CJun NLar
vidalii	EPfP
wilsonii	LRHS NLar
yedoensis	see *E. hamiltonianus* subsp. *sieboldianus*

Eupatoriadelphus see *Eupatorium*

Eupatorium ✿ (*Asteraceae*)

B&SWJ 9052 from Guatemala	WCru
FMWJ 13428 from Northern Vietnam	WCru
album misapplied	see *Ageratina altissima*
album L.	NBid
altissimum	SRms
aromaticum	see *Ageratina aromatica*
atrorubens	see *Bartlettina sordida*
cannabinum	CBod CHab EBWF ELan EShb GLog GPoy IFoB LLWG MBNS MHer MMuc MNHC MWts NMir NPer SEND SPav WHer WSFF
- f. ***cannabinum*** 'Flore Pleno' (d)	CMac ECtt ELan ELon GBin IBoy MBel MHer MRav MSpe NGdn NLar WCot WFar WSFF WWtn XLum
- - 'Spraypaint' (v)	WSFF
capillifolium ♀H3	CAby EBee ECtt EWes LCro MBel MNrw MPie SHar SPad WCot
- 'Elegant Plume'	EBee IPot MNrw
coelestinum	see *Conoclinium coelestinum*
dubium 'Baby Joe'PBR	CBod CMea CRos CWGN ECtt ETMg IPot LRHS MBNS MNrw NEgg NLar NRHS SHar SPad WHar WNPC WSFF WWtn
- 'Little Joe'	EBee LEdu NDov WSFF
fistulosum	EBee
- f. ***albidum***	MMuc
- - 'Bartered Bride'	CKno EBee ECtt EWes GCal MBel WCot WSFF
- - 'Ivory Towers'	CRos EShb GJos LRHS LSun NRHS SPtp WCot WPtf WSFF
- - 'Massive White' ♀H6	EBee ELon GCal MNrw NSti WCAu
- 'Berggarten'	GCal WSFF
- 'Carin'	WSFF
fortunei 'Capri' (v)	WHil
- 'Fine Line' (v)	LSou WSFF
- 'Pink Elegance' (v)	CAby EBee ECtt EShb LLWG LRHS MNrw MPie NRHS SPoG SRms WWtn
- 'Pink Frost' (v)	CRos EWTr LRHS MWts NGdn NRHS
japonicum	GPoy
ligustrinum	see *Ageratina ligustrina*
lindleyanum	CKno EBee LEdu WSFF
- var. ***trisectifolium*** B&SWJ 12742	WCru
maculatum	NGdn NLar WHrl
- Atropurpureum Group	Widely available
- - 'Ankum's August'	IMou LPla
- - 'Gateway'	CBod CKno CRos EBee ECtt ELon GCal LEdu LRHS NBid NBre NLar NRHS SMad SWvt WSFF WWtn
- - 'Glutball'	CKno CRos ELon GCal IMou LRHS LSun MNrw NChi NRHS SMad WWtn
- - 'Little Red'	WSFF
- - 'Orchard Dene' ♀H6	LEdu MAvo SMHy
- - 'Phantom'PBR	CBot CRos EBee ECtt ELon GBin GQue LRHS MHol NLar NRHS SAko SMad SPoG WPtf
- - 'Purple Bush' ♀H6	CDor CKno EBee ECtt ELon EPPr GBin GCal GQue ILea LCro LOPS LRHS MTis NDov NEgg SPhx SWvt WCAu WSFF
- - 'Red Dwarf'	CBod ECtt ELon EShb GBin GQue ILea LEdu LLWG LRHS MBel MHol MPie NRHS SCob SHar SPoG SWvt WCAu WPGP
- - 'Riesenschirm' ♀H6	Widely available
- 'J.S. Humble'	IPot MNrw
- 'Snowball'PBR	CBot
makinoi var. ***oppositifolium*** B&SWJ 8449	WCru
'Mask'	IPot LRHS MNrw NLar NRHS
micranthum	see *Ageratina ligustrina*
perfoliatum	GPoy MNrw NBre NLar WSFF

purpureum	CBcs CHby CKno ECtt ELon GAbr GBin GMaP GMcL GPoy IFoB IFro LLWG MHer MNHC MWat NBro NChi NEgg NGdn SCob SPer SPlb SRms WCAu WHer WMoo WOld WSFF WWtn
- 'Album'	CTri MBel SWvt
rugosum	see *Ageratina altissima*
* 'Snowball'	LLWG NDov SCob
weinmannianum	see *Ageratina ligustrina*

Euphorbia ✿ (*Euphorbiaceae*)

'Abbey Dore'	SPhx WCot
ambovombensis	LToo
amygdaloides	ECtt SWvt WOut XSen
- 'Craigieburn'	CRos EWes LRHS MRav NRHS
§ - 'Purpurea'	Widely available
§ - var. ***robbiae***	Widely available
- - dwarf	EWes
- - 'Redbud'	EWes
- 'Rubra'	see *E. amygdaloides* 'Purpurea'
- RUBY GLOW ('Waleuphglo')	ETMg SWeb
atropurpurea	IBoy
baselicis	EWes
biglandulosa Desf.	see *E. rigida*
BLACKBIRD ('Nothowlee'PBR)	CBcs CExl CMac CWCL CWGN EAJP EBee ECtt ELan EPfP IBoy LCro LLHF LOPS LRHS MBel MGos MRav NLar NPnk NSti SCob SLim SWvt WSpi XEll XSen
'Blue Dome'	CSpe
'Blue Haze'	ECrN MAvo WCot WFar WRHF WSHC WSpi
capitulata	SBrt
cashmeriana CC&McK 607	EWes
ceratocarpa	CBod CFil CRav ECtt EWes GMaP LSou SEND SMad SPhx WAvo WCot WSHC WSpi XSen
characias	CAby CBcs CMac CRos ECtt EPfP IBoy LRHS LSun MCot MRav NPer NRHS SPer SRms SWvt WBrk WCot XSen
- 'Ascot Moonbeam' **new**	SPoG
- 'Black Pearl'	CAbb CBcs CBod CRos ECtt ELan EPfP ETMg GBin GMcL LRHS MAvo MBel MPnt NLar NPnk NRHS SGbt SGol SLim SPer SPoG SRkn SWvt WFar WSpi XSen
- 'Blue Wonder'	CExl CRos ECtt ELan EMFm EPfP EWes GMaP LRHS MAvo NEgg NLar NRHS WCot WRHF XSen
- 'BQ'	WCot
- subsp. ***characias***	NLar SEND
- - 'Blue Hills'	ECtt
- - 'Burrow Silver' (v)	CDor CRos MRav NEgg SWvt
- - 'Humpty Dumpty'	CBod CExl CRos EBee ECtt EHrv ELan EPfP ESps EWTr GMaP GWyn IBoy LRHS LSRN NGdn NLar NPer NRHS SCob SPer SRms SWvt
- - 'Joshua'	WCot
- 'Forescate'	EBee EPfP NRHS
- 'Glacier Blue'PBR (v)	CAby CBct CRos CSpe CWGN EBee ECha EHoe ELan EMFm EPfP EShb ETMg LRHS LSRN MAvo MBel MHol MNrw NHpl NLar NPri NRHS SCob SHeu SPoG WCot WNPC WRHF
- 'Goldbrook'	CWCL EPfP GBin LRHS MRav NRHS
- 'Kestrel' (v)	WCot
- 'Portuguese Velvet' ♀H5	CBod CExl CRos ECtt EHrv ELan EPed EPfP EUJe GWyn LRHS MBel MCot MRav NLar NRHS SArc SLim SPtp WCot XSen
- SILVER SWAN ('Wilcott'PBR) (v) ♀H2	Widely available
- 'Tasmanian Tiger'PBR (v)	CBct CRos CWGN ECtt EWTr EWes GMaP LRHS LSRN LSou MGos MHol MJak MPnt MSCN NHpl NLar NRHS SCob SEle SHeu SPad SPoG SRms SWvt WCot WHlf WNPC WSpi
- subsp. ***wulfenii***	Widely available
- - 'Bosahan'	CExl
- - 'Emmer Green' (v)	CExl CRos ECtt EWes GMaP MHol NSti WCot
- - 'Jayne's Golden Giant'	SMad
- - 'Jimmy Platt'	SRms WCot
§ - - 'John Tomlinson' ♀H5	EWes MRav WAvo WSpi
- - 'Joyce's Giant'	WKif
- - Kew form	see *E. characias* subsp. *wulfenii* 'John Tomlinson'
- - 'Lambrook Gold' ♀H4	CSam IRob MNrw MRav NLar NPer SCob SMad WCot WSpi
- - 'Lambrook Gold' seed-raised	see *E. characias* subsp. *wulfenii* Margery Fish Group
§ - - Margery Fish Group	CWCL LRHS MCot NRHS SBod SPer
- - 'Perry's Tangerine'	EWes NPer
§ - - 'Purple and Gold'	ECtt EWes MNrw SWvt
- - 'Purpurea'	see *E. characias* subsp. *wulfenii* 'Purple and Gold'
- - 'Shorty'	EBee ECtt EUJe GBin LRHS LSou NLar XSen
- - var. ***sibthorpii***	IBoy
- - 'Silver Shadow' (v)	EBee MAvo MHol WCot
- - 'Thelma's Giant'	MAvo
- - 'Westacre Giant'	EWes
clavarioides	WAbe
- var. ***truncata***	WCot
'Copton Ash'	CBcs CSpe EBee ECtt LRHS SPhx WCot WNPC XSen
corallioides	ECha GWyn LPla LSun NLar NPer NSti WHer XSen
§ ***cornigera*** ♀H6	CDor CRos EBee ECha EPfP LRHS MMuc NBid NGdn NLar NRHS NSti SEND SPhx WCru WFar
- 'Goldener Turm'	CSpe ECtt EPfP GBin GMcL IRob LCro LOPS LRHS LSou NRHS SCob SMHy SPer SPhx WCot
corollata	MNrw SBrt SPhx
cylindrifolia var. ***tubifera***	LToo
cyparissias	CBcs ECha ELan MRav NGdn NLar SBod SRms WBrk WFar XLum XSen
- 'Betten'	see *E. × gayeri* 'Betten'
- 'Clarice Howard'	see *E. cyparissias* 'Fens Ruby'
- clone 2	WCot
§ - 'Fens Ruby'	Widely available
- 'Orange Man'	CBcs CBod CRos ECtt EPfP EWes LRHS LSou NEgg NGdn NLar NRHS SPoG SVen SWvt WAul WBrk WFar
- 'Purpurea'	see *E. cyparissias* 'Fens Ruby'
- 'Red Devil'	CDor
- 'Tall Boy'	EWes
decaryi	LToo
deflexa	EBee EWes MAvo
dendroides	CKel LRHS
'Despina'PBR	CWCL LRHS
§ ***donii***	ECha EWes MAvo WSpi XEll
- HWJK 2405	WCru

- 'Amjillasa'	ECha LPla SMHy WWtn
dulcis	CBre IFro NBro
- 'Chameleon'	CDor CWCL ECtt EHoe EHrv ELan ELon EPfP GCal GWyn IBoy IFro MGos MRav NBid NLar NPer SCob SPlb SRot SWvt WArt WBrk WCot WFar WMoo WSpi
'Efanthia'PBR	CDor CEnd CRos ELon EWes GBin GMcL LPla LRHS LSou MAvo
enormis	LToo
§ ***epithymoides***	Widely available
- 'Bonfire'PBR	ECtt ETMg MAvo MBel SAko SPer SPoG WHil
§ - 'Candy'	CBod CWCL EBee ECha ELan EPfP LPla MNrw WFar
- 'First Blush' (v)	CBod EBee ECtt EMFm LSou MNrw NLar WCot WFar
- 'Geisha'	EWes
- 'Golden Fusion'	EPfP WFar
§ - 'Lacy' (v)	EWes NGdn WFar
§ - 'Major' ♀H6	CExl EBee WKif
- 'Midas'	MNrw SCob SMHy
- 'Senior'	CRos LRHS MAvo MNrw NLar NRHS
esculenta	LToo
EXCALIBUR ('Froeup'PBR)	CBod CExl CMac CWCL ELan ELon GBin LSRN MBNS MMoz MMuc MNrw MRav NLar NRHS NSti SEND SPtp SWvt
fischeriana B&SWJ 8575	WCru
§ × ***gayeri*** 'Betten'	EBee EWes GBin XSen
'Gloria'	LPmr
'Golden Foam'	see *E. stricta*
'Grey Hedgehog'	CBod WNPC
griffithii	CHll ESps IFoB NBro WFar WMoo WWtn
- 'Dixter' ♀H7	Widely available
- 'Dixter Flame'	IFoB
- 'Fern Cottage'	CElw EWes GBin
- 'Fireglow'	Widely available
- 'King's Caple'	EWes LRHS NLar SPoG WCru
- 'Wickstead'	CWCL GBin LRHS NLar WAvo
griseola	LToo
'Helena'PBR (v)	CExl LSRN NLar SWvt
heptagona **new**	SEND
horrida ♀H2	LToo SPlb
- f. ***cristata*** hort. miniature **new**	LToo
hypericifolia DIAMOND FROST ('Inneuphe'PBR)	CRav CSpe LSou SRkn WCot
- 'Diamond Star'	WCot
inermis	LToo
ingens	CAbb
jacquemontii	IFoB MRav NLar WCot
'Jade Dragon'	LRHS SWvt
'Jessie'	NLar
jolkinii	CExl
KALIPSO ('Innkalff')	CDor CRos EPfP LRHS NLar NRHS SPoG SRot
'Lambrook Silver'	SRkn
lathyris	CBre NLar NPer SRms SVic
longifolia misapplied	see *E. cornigera*
longifolia D. Don	see *E. donii*
longifolia Lam.	see *E. mellifera*
margalidiana	EWes
× ***martini***	Widely available
- 'Aperitif'	SPoG
- 'Ascot Rainbow'PBR (v)	Widely available
- 'Baby Charm'	CBod CRos CWCL EBee ECtt ELon EPed EPfP EUJe GBin GKin IPot LRHS LSRN MBel MGos NLar NRHS SPoG WFar WNPC
- 'Helen Robinson'	WCot
- HELENA'S BLUSH ('Inneuphhel') (v)	EPfP
- 'Kolibri'	EBee MPnt SWvt
- 'Little John'	CRos LRHS NRHS
- 'Rudolph'PBR	CBod ECtt EPfP EUJe NLar SPoG
- TINY TIM ('Waleutiny')	CBod CRos EBee ECtt EPfP ESps GBin LRHS LSRN LSou NRHS SWvt
- 'Walberton's Red Flush'	CRos EPfP LRHS NRHS
mauritanica **new**	EShb
§ ***mellifera*** ♀H2	Widely available
meloformis ♀H2	LToo
milii ♀H1b	EBak
* - 'Variegata' (v)	CBlu
moratii	LToo
muirii **new**	LToo
multifolia **new**	LToo
myrsinites ♀H4	Widely available
nereidum	EWes
nicaeensis	CSpe EBee GCal LRHS SPhx WCot XSen
- subsp. ***nicaeensis***	CBot
obesa ♀H2	LToo
oblongata	CRav LRHS NLar NPnk SEND WCot
officinarum subsp. ***echinus*** **new**	LToo
palustris ♀H7	Widely available
- 'Walenburg's Glorie'	CBot CWCL EBee ECha ELan ELon EWTr GBin IBoy IRob LCro LOPS MAvo MNrw MRav NLar NSti SMad WCot WKif
- 'Woodchippings'	WCot
- 'Zauberflöte'	ELon SRms
paralias	WHer
× ***pasteurii***	CBct CDTJ CKel EPfP EUJe EWes GBin GWyn LSou MNrw NLos SPhx WCot WPGP
- Brown's strain	CBod EBee EMFm LSun MNrw WCot
- 'John Phillips'	CBct CExl CFil EPfP LRHS MAvo SChF SMad WPGP
- 'Phrampton Phatty'	LRHS WCot WPGP
pentagona	SVen
pilosa 'Major'	see *E. epithymoides* 'Major'
pithyusa	CBot ECha ELan SEND SPlb WCot WSHC XSen
platyclada	LToo
polychroma	see *E. epithymoides*
- 'Purpurea'	see *E. epithymoides* 'Candy'
- 'Variegata'	see *E. epithymoides* 'Lacy'
portlandica	SVen WHer
pseudocactus 'Lyttoniana'	LToo
REDWING ('Charam'PBR) ♀H5	CBcs CBod CMac CWCL ECtt EHoe ELan EPfP GMcL GWyn LBuc LRHS LSou MAvo MBel MHol MNrw MRav NLar NSti SBod SGol SLim SPer SPoG SWvt WCot
reflexa	see *E. seguieriana* subsp. *niciciana*
restricta **new**	LToo
§ ***rigida*** ♀H6	CBod CBro CSpe EBee ELan EPfP EUJe EWes GCal SPhx WCot WSpi XSen
robbiae	see *E. amygdaloides* var. *robbiae*
'Roundway Titan'	CBot CFil EMil EPfP LRHS SAko SWvt
sarawschanica	ECha GBin GQue LPla LRHS SMad SPhx

schillingii ♀H5	Widely available
schoenlandii	SPlb
seguieriana	ECha EWes SPhx
§ - subsp. ***niciciana***	CSpe EWTr IMou LRHS SCob WHoo XSen
serrulata Thuill.	see *E. stricta*
sikkimensis ♀H5	CExl ECha ELan EWes GBin GCal GLog GMcL IMou LRHS MAvo NEgg NLar NPer NRHS SCob SRms WCru
- 'Crûg Contrast'	WCru
spinosa	SPlb XSen
stellata	LToo
stellispina	LToo
§ ***stricta***	CBgR CFil GWyn NWad WSpi
stygiana	CAbb CBod CCht CDTJ CExl CPla CPne CSam CSpe CWCL ELon EMFm EUJe EWes GBin IBoy LPla LRHS MCot MGil SAko SHar SPlb SPtp WCot WCru WPGP WSHC
- subsp. ***santamariae***	CDTJ CFil WPGP WSHC
- subsp. ***stygiana***	CFil WPGP
susannae	LToo
tirucalli	EShb
tortirama	LToo
umfoloziensis	LToo
valdevillosocarpa	GWyn NLar SPhx WFar
'Velvet Ruby'	GBin GWyn LSRN SWvt WNPC XSen
viguieri	LToo
- var. ***capuroniana*** **new**	LToo
villosa Waldst. & Kit. ex Willd.	GBin LEdu
§ ***virgata***	EWes
× ***waldsteinii***	see *E. virgata*
wallichii misapplied	see *E. donii*
wallichii Kohli	see *E. cornigera*
wallichii ambig.	CBod GBin MRav SCob
wallichii Hook. f.	CExl EPfP MNrw SPhx WCot
'Whistleberry Garnet'	CMac EBee ELan EPfP LLHF LRHS LSou MMuc NSti SCob SPhx SWvt WNPC

Euptelea (*Eupteleaceae*)

franchetii	see *E. pleiosperma*
§ ***pleiosperma***	NLar
polyandra	EPfP NLar SBrt WPGP

Eurya (*Pentaphylacaceae*)

japonica 'Variegata' misapplied	see *Cleyera japonica* 'Fortunei'

Eurybia (*Asteraceae*)

§ ***conspicua***	MAvo MWat
§ ***divaricata***	Widely available
§ - 'Eastern Star'	IBoy WCot WFar WOld WSpi
- Raiche form	see *E. divaricata* 'Eastern Star'
- 'Tradescant'	IMou MNrw SMad
§ ***furcata***	XLum
§ × ***herveyi***	CSam ECha ECtt ELan ELon EPPr EPed GLog IMou LCro LEdu LOPS LRHS MAvo MSpe MTis NDov NLar NSti NWsh SPer SPhx SPoG WCot WFar WOld WSHC XLum
§ ***macrophylla***	CFis CRos EBee ELan GQue LRHS MMuc MSpe NLar NRHS SPhx WArt WFar WOld WWtn
- 'Albus'	EPPr WFar WOld
- 'Twilight'	see *E.* × *herveyi*
§ ***radula***	CSam EPPr EWes IMou MAvo MNrw NLar NWsh WOld WSHC
- 'August Sky'	CBod CKno EBee EPPr ITim MBel MTis NDov SPhx WCot WFar WHoo WRHF
§ ***schreberi***	CDor EPPr EWes LEdu MNrw MPie MSpe MWat NWsh WCot WFar WHoo WOld WPGP WWtn
§ ***sibirica***	NLar WOld
§ ***spectabilis***	CRos EBee IMou LRHS WFar WOld
- 'JS Macho Blue'	MNrw

Euryops (*Asteraceae*)

abrotanifolius	CCCN SVen
§ ***acraeus*** ♀H4	CSBt ECtt ELan EPot EWes GCrg GEdr WAbe
brachypodus	SVen
§ ***chrysanthemoides***	CBcs CCCN EShb SEND SVen
- 'Sonnenschein'	SPtp
evansii Schltr.	see *E. acraeus*
lateriflorus	SPlb
pectinatus ♀H3	CBcs CBod CCCN CDTJ CExl CRos CTri CTsd ELan EPfP EShb LRHS MGil MSCN SEND SPtp SVen SWvt
tenuissimus	SVen
tysonii	ELon EWes GCal SPlb SVen
virgineus	CCCN CExl SPlb SVen

Euscaphis (*Staphyleaceae*)

japonica B&SWJ 11359	WCru
- B&SWJ 12739	WCru

Eustachys (*Poaceae*)

§ ***distichophylla***	NWsh

Eustephia (*Amaryllidaceae*)

coccinea	WCot

Eutrema (*Brassicaceae*)

§ ***japonicum***	CExl GPoy LEdu
- 'Monzen' **new**	GPoy

Eutrochium see *Eupatorium*

Ewartia (*Asteraceae*)

planchonii	NRHS SPlb WAbe

Exbucklandia (*Hamamelidaceae*)

tonkinensis KWJ 12209 **new**	WCru

Exochorda (*Rosaceae*)

alberti	see *E. korolkowii*
giraldii var. ***wilsonii***	CDul CExl EBee ELan EPfP LRHS MBlu MMuc MNHC MRav NLar SWvt WCFE
§ ***korolkowii***	LRHS MAsh
× ***macrantha***	LRHS
- 'Irish Pearl'	CExl
§ - 'Niagara' PBR	CBcs CMac EPfP EShb LCro LOPS LRHS LSRN MAsh MGos MPkF NLar NPnk NRHS SCob SEle SGol SPoG
- SNOW DAY SURPRISE	see *E.* × *macrantha* 'Niagara'
- 'The Bride' ♀H6	Widely available
MAGICAL SPRINGTIME ('Kolmaspirit') **new**	LRHS NLar
racemosa	EPfP NHim NLar SPer
serratifolia	CBcs ELan EPfP LRHS SPoG
- 'Snow White'	CJun EWes GKin IArd IDee IMou LRHS MAsh MBlu NLar SLon SWvt

F

Fabiana (*Solanaceae*)

foliosa 'Cliftonville Limelight'	WAbe
imbricata	CPbh CRos ELon LLHF LRHS MGil SLon SPlb
- 'Prostrata'	CRos CTsd ELan LRHS SVen WThu
- f. ***violacea*** ♀H4	CExl CMac CRos CSBt CTri EBee ELan EPfP LLHF LRHS MMuc SPad SPer SPoG SWvt WAvo WKif
- - dark-flowered	CBcs
nana	WAbe

Fagopyrum (*Polygonaceae*)

cymosum	see *F. dibotrys*
§ ***dibotrys***	CSpe ECha EWld LEdu MMuc XLum
I - 'Cally Form'	EMFm GCal

Fagraea (*Loganiaceae*)

ceilanica FMWJ 13099 new	WCru

Fagus ✿ (*Fagaceae*)

§ ***crenata***	CMCN CMen MBlu
- 'Mount Fuji'	CAco CMen LLHF NEgg SBir
engleriana	CExl SBir
grandifolia subsp. ***mexicana***	SBir WPGP
japonica	SBir
- var. ***multinervis***	SBir
longipetiolata	CExl CMCN EBee WPGP
- NJM 11.036 new	WPGP
lucida	CExl CMCN MBlu
orientalis	CMCN SBir
- 'Iskander'	CDul IArd IDee MBlu SGol
sieboldii	see *F. crenata*
sylvatica ♀H6	Widely available
- 'Aniek'	SGol
- 'Arcuata'	SBir
- 'Asterix'	LRHS MBlu
- Atropurpurea Group	Widely available
- - 'Purpurea Pendula'	CAco CBcs CCVT CEnd CMCN CMac CSBt CTri EBee ELan EPfP ESps GKin GMil IBoy MAsh MGos MJak NEgg SCoo SGol SLau SLim SPer WHar WTSh
- - 'Riversii' ♀H6	CBcs CDul CEnd CLnd CMCN CTho CTri EBee ECrN ELan EMOT EPfP ESps GKin LPra MAsh MGos SPer SPoG WHar
- 'Aurea Pendula'	CEnd CMCN MBlu SBir
- 'Bicolor Sartini'	MBlu
- 'Birr Zebra'	CEnd
- 'Black Swan'	CDul CLnd CMCN EBee ELan GMil LSRN MAsh MBlu MGos NEgg NOra SBig SBir SLon SMad SPoG
- 'Bornyensis'	MBlu
- 'Brathay Purple'	MBlu
- 'Cochleata'	CMCN
- 'Cockleshell'	MBlu SBir
- 'Cristata'	MBlu
§ - 'Dawyck' ♀H6	CBcs CDul CLnd CMac CTho ECrN ELan EPfP ESps LMaj LPra MGos NEgg NLar SBir SCob SGol SLau SPer
- 'Dawyck Gold' ♀H6	CBcs CDul CEnd CMCN CMac CSBt CTri EBee ELan EMOT ESps GKin GMil IBoy LPra MAsh MBlu MGos NEgg NLar NOra SBir SCob SGol SLau SPer WHar WMou
- 'Dawyck Purple' ♀H6	Widely available
- 'Eugen'	SBir
- 'Fastigiata' misapplied	see *F. sylvatica* 'Dawyck'
- 'Felderbach'	SBir
- 'Franken' (v)	CAco EBtc MBlu SBir
- 'Green Obelisk'	MBlu
- 'Greenwood'	LLHF MBlu NEgg
- var. ***heterophylla***	CLnd CTho
- - 'Aspleniifolia' ♀H6	CBcs CDul CEnd CMCN CMac EBee ECrN ELan EMOT EPfP ESps EWTr GKin LMaj MBlu MGos NEgg SBir SCoo SGol SLau SPer SPoG WMou
- - (Atropurpurea Group) 'Ansorgei'	CEnd MBlu
- - 'Incisa'	MBlu
- - f. ***laciniata***	ESps MBlu
- - 'Mercedes'	CAco CDul CMCN LLHF MBlu NEgg SMad WCot
- 'Horizontalis'	MBlu
- 'Luteovariegata' (v)	EBee
- 'Pendula' ♀H6	CAco CBcs CCVT CDul CEnd CMCN CMac CRos CSBt CTho ECrN ELan ESps GMil LPra MGos MSwo NEgg NOra SGol SLau SPer WHar WMou WTSh
- 'Prince George of Crete'	CDul
- 'Purple Fountain' ♀H6	CAco CDul CEnd CMCN EBee ELan ESps MAsh MBlu MGos NLar NOra SBir SLau
- Purple-leaved Group	see *F. sylvatica* Atropurpurea Group
§ - 'Purpurea Tricolor' (v)	CAco CDul CEnd CMCN CMac EBee GMil MBlu MGos NEgg NOra SBir SCoo WMou
- 'Red Obelisk'	see *F. sylvatica* 'Rohan Obelisk'
- 'Rohan Gold'	CEnd CMCN SGol
- 'Rohan Minaret'	SGol
§ - 'Rohan Obelisk'	CAco CDul CEnd CMCN ELan GMil IBoy LMaj MBlu NEgg NLar SBir SGol
I - 'Rohan Pyramidalis'	CEnd CMCN
- 'Rohan Trompenburg'	CMCN MBlu
- 'Rohan Weeping'	MBlu SBir
- 'Rohanii'	CBcs CDul CEnd CMCN CTri ELan EMOT EPfP ESps GKin MGil MGos NEgg SBir SLau SPer WHar
- 'Roseomarginata'	see *F. sylvatica* 'Purpurea Tricolor'
- 'Rotundifolia'	CDul LMaj MBlu NEgg SGol
- 'Spaethiana'	GKin
- 'Striata'	CAco NEgg
- f. ***tortuosa***	MPkF NEgg
- - 'Rot Süntel'	CDul GMil NEgg
- 'Tricolor' misapplied (v)	see *F. sylvatica* 'Purpurea Tricolor' (v)
- 'Tricolor' ambig. (v)	SLau
- 'Tricolor' (v)	CBcs CLnd ELan LLHF SGol
- 'Viridivariegata' (v)	CMCN
- 'Zlatia'	CBcs CDul CLnd CMCN ELan EPfP MBlu MGil MGos NLar SBir SGol SLau

Fallopia (*Polygonaceae*)

aubertii	see *F. baldschuanica*
§ ***baldschuanica***	Widely available

§	***japonica*** var. ***compacta***	WMoo XLum
	- - 'Fuji Snow'	see *F. japonica* var. *compacta* 'Milk Boy'
§	- - 'Milk Boy' (v)	EShb
	- - 'Variegata' misapplied	see *F. japonica* var. *compacta* 'Milk Boy'
§	***multiflora***	CBod LEdu WGwG
	- var. ***hypoleuca***	SCoo SPoG
	- - B&SWJ 120	WCru

Farfugium (*Asteraceae*)

§	***japonicum***	CTal
	- B&SWJ 884	WCru
	- 'Argenteum' (v)	SMad WCot
§	- 'Aureomaculatum' (v) ♀H3	ECtt EUJe LEdu
	- 'Bumpy Ride'	WCot
	- 'Crispatum'	CTal EUJe LEdu
	- double-flowered (d)	WCru
	- var. ***giganteum***	EUJe
	- 'Kaimon Dake'	WCot
	- 'Kinkan' (v)	WCot
	- 'Ryuto'	WCot
I	- 'Tsuwa-buki'	WCot
	'Last Dance'PBR	EBee ECtt NLar
	tussilagineum	see *F. japonicum*

Fargesia (*Poaceae*)

	from Jiuzhaigou, China	CBdn CDTJ EPfP ERod ETod EUJe GMcL MAvo MMoz MMuc MWht NLar SBig WPGP
	adpressa	CBdn MWht
	confusa	CDTJ
	denudata	CBdn CDTJ CFil ENBC ERod NLar SBig
	- L 1575	CExl MMoz MWht
	- Xian 1	CBdn CDTJ MMoz
	dracocephala	CBdn CExl CFil ERod MAvo MBrN MMuc MWht SBig WMoo
	- 'White Dragon'	CDTJ CExl CFil
§	***murielae*** ♀H4	CAgr CBdn CFil CRos ELan ENBC EPau EPfP ERod ESps ETMg ETod LCro LOPS LRHS MGos MJak MMoz MMuc MWht NLos SArc SCob SPlb WMoo
	- 'Bimbo'	CBdn CBod CRos CSBt EPfP ERod ESps ETod GCal LRHS MAvo MWht NLar NRHS SBig SCob SPoG SWvt WMoo
	- 'Dana Jumbo'	CRos LRHS NRHS
	- 'Dino' **new**	SBig
	- 'Grüne Hecke'	ERod MWht SBig
	- 'Harewood'	CFil GMcL MWht SWvt
	- 'Joy'	NLar WMoo
	- 'Jumbo'	CBod CRos CSBt ELon EPfP ERod ESps ETod EUJe GBin GMcL LRHS MAvo MGos MJak MMoz MWht NGdn NLar NRHS SBig SPer SRms SWvt
	- 'Mae'	CDTJ MWht
	- 'Panda'PBR **new**	CRos LRHS
	- 'Simba'	Widely available
	- 'Vampire'	ERod EUJe LRHS SBig
	murieliae 'Superjumbo'PBR	CBdn ETod
§	***nitida***	CAbb CBcs CDul CEnd CRos CSBt ELan EPfP ERod ESps IFro LRHS MAsh MGos MJak MMoz MWht NRHS SCob SPoG SRms SWvt WMoo WPGP
	- 'Black Pearl' **new**	ENBC SBig
	- 'Eisenach'	MMoz
	- 'Great Wall'	CBod CDTJ CSBt ELan ETod EUJe GBin MMuc MWht NLar SCob
	- Jiuzhaigou 1	see *F.* RED PANDA
	- 'Jiuzhaigou 4'	CDTJ CExl CFil WPGP
	- 'Jiuzhaigou 8'	CDTJ WPGP
	- 'Jiuzhaigou Genf'	CDTJ CFil NLar WPGP
	- 'Nymphenburg'	MMoz SBig
	- 'Pillar' **new**	SBig
	perlonga Yunnan 6	ERod MMoz WPGP
§	RED PANDA ('Jiu') ♀H4	CExl CFil CRos EBee LCro LOPS LRHS MPkF NRHS SPoG SWvt
	robusta ♀H4	CAbb CDTJ CRos CSBt ELan ENBC EPfP ERod ETod LRHS MAvo MBrN MMoz MMuc MWht NGdn NLos NRHS SBig SSut
	- 'Campbell'	CBdn MJak MMoz NLar SBig
	- 'Ming Yunnan'	LEdu WPGP
	- 'P. King'	ERod MWht
	- 'Pingwu'	CBdn CBod CDTJ ENBC ERod ETod EUJe GMcL MGos MJak MWht SBig
	- 'Red Sheath'	CDTJ CExl CJun ERod MMoz MWht WPGP
	- 'Wolong'	CBdn CExl ERod ETod MMoz MWht WPGP
	rufa ♀H4	Widely available
	similaris KR 4175 **new**	MWht
	spathacea misapplied	see *F. murielae*
	utilis	CBdn ERod ETod MMoz MMuc MWht SEND
	yulongshanensis	ERod MWht

Farsetia (*Brassicaceae*)

	clypeata	see *Fibigia clypeata*

Fascicularia (*Bromeliaceae*)

	andina	see *F. bicolor*
§	***bicolor***	Widely available
	- subsp. ***bicolor***	CBod CFil CMac CPne IBoy NLos SMad
	- subsp. ***canaliculata***	CFil GEdr IBlr LEdu MNrw SChr SPad WPGP
	kirchhoffiana	see *F. bicolor*
	litoralis	see *Ochagavia litoralis*
	pitcairniifolia misapplied	see *F. bicolor*
	pitcairniifolia (Verlot) Mez	see *Ochagavia litoralis*

× *Fatshedera* ✿ (*Araliaceae*)

	lizei ♀H3	CBcs CDul CMac CRos CTri EBee ECrN ELon EMOT EPfP ESps EUJe EWTr GBin LRHS MAsh MRav SArc SCob SEND SGol SPer SPlb SPoG SWvt WAvo
§	- 'Annemieke' (v) ♀H3	CBcs CBot CRos ELan ELon EMOT EPfP ESps EUJe LRHS MMuc MRav SCob SEND SEle SPoG WAvo
	- compact	EBee EMil EPfP
	- 'Lemon and Lime'	see × *F. lizei* 'Annemieke'
	- 'Maculata'	see × *F. lizei* 'Annemieke'
	- 'Variegata' (v) ♀H3	CRos EBee ELan ELon EMOT EPfP ESps EUJe LRHS SCob SEND SPer SWvt WAvo
	- 'Variegata' compact (v)	EMil SPoG

Fatsia ✿ (*Araliaceae*)

§	***japonica*** ♀H5	Widely available
	- 'Annelise' (v)	SEND SMad
	- 'Annemie' (v)	NLos
	- 'Moseri'	CExl ELan MBNS NGdn SWvt WCot
	- 'Murakumo-nishiki' (v)	CBot

	- 'Spider's Web' (v)	Widely available
	- 'Variegata' (v) $\mathbb{Y}^{H3}$	CAbb CBcs CBot CMac CRos EBee ELan EPfP ESps LRHS MAsh MGos MRav NLos SCob SEND SLim SLon SPer SPoG WCot WGrn WWFP
I	'Megafatsia' **new**	CDTJ
	papyrifera	see *Tetrapanax papyrifer*
	polycarpa	CBot CDTJ CExl CFil
	- B&SWJ 1776	WCru
	- B&SWJ 3467	WCru
	- B&SWJ 7144	CExl WCru
	- RWJ 10133	WCru
	- from Tregye	CFil
	- deeply cut leaf	WCot WPGP
	- - BWJ 12499	WCru
	- giant-leaved	CFil

Feijoa see *Acca*

Felicia (*Asteraceae*)

	aethiopica	CPbh
§	***amelloides***	CCCN SPlb
	- 'Santa Anita'	CTri SVen
§	- variegated (v)	CCCN ECtt MSCN NPer
§	***amoena***	CTri
	- 'Variegata' (v)	CCCN CTri
	capensis	see *F. amelloides*
	coelestis	see *F. amelloides*
	echinata	CCCN IDee
	FELICITARA BLUE ('Wigetablue'^{PBR})	CRos LRHS NRHS
	filifolia blue-flowered	SVen
	fruticosa	CHll
	natalensis	see *F. rosulata*
	pappei	see *F. amoena*
§	***petiolata***	CFis CTri EBee EWes MMuc MNrw
§	***rosulata***	CFis CSma GCrg GEdr MBrN MHol NBro NLar SBrt SRot WHal
	tenella **new**	WSpi
	uliginosa	EWes SBrt SPlb
	wrightii	GEdr

fennel see *Foeniculum vulgare*

fenugreek see *Trigonella foenum-graecum*

Ferraria (*Iridaceae*)

§	***crispa***	NRog
	- var. ***nortieri***	NRog
	divaricata	EBee NRog
	- subsp. ***arenosa***	NRog
	schaeferi	NRog
	undulata	see *F. crispa*

Ferula (*Apiaceae*)

	chiliantha	see *F. communis* subsp. *glauca*
§	***communis***	CAby CMea CRos CSpe ECha EHoe ELan EPPr EWes GBin IBoy LEdu LRHS NDov SEND SPav SPhx SPlb SPoG SPtp
	- 'Gigantea'	see *F. communis*
§	- subsp. ***glauca***	ECha EWes SMHy SSut WCot
	- - B&SWJ 12999	WCru
	- - NJM 13.001 **new**	WPGP
	'Giant Bronze'	see *Foeniculum vulgare* 'Giant Bronze'
	szowitsiana	NDov
	tingitana B&SWJ 14005	WCru
	- 'Cedric Morris'	ECha WCot

Ferulago (*Apiaceae*)

	cassia	WCot
	stellata	WCot
	sylvatica PAB 2875	LEdu WPGP

Festuca (*Poaceae*)

	actae	XLum
	amethystina	CBod CBot CKno EHoe EShb LCro LOPS LRHS MBel MMuc NGdn SCob SEND SPhx SRot WMoo XLum
	- 'Aprilgrün'	XLum
	arenaria	EBWF
	arundinacea	CHab EBWF MMuc SEND
	californica	CKno EPPr IMou
	coxii	CHid
	curvula subsp. ***crassifolia***	EShb
	durissima	XLum
	'Eisvogel'	EPPr
	elegans	EPPr XLum
	eskia	EHoe IMou XLum
	filiformis	CHab
	gamisansii	XLum
§	***gautieri***	EBee EUJe LRHS XLum
	- 'Hobbit'	CBod
	- 'Pic Carlit'	NLar XLum
	gigantea	CBod CHab MMuc SEND XLum
	glacialis	XLum
	- 'Czakor'	XLum
	glauca Vill.	CAco CBar CBcs CBod EShb ESps GMaP GWyn MBNS MGos MRav MSCN NGdn SLim SPer SPlb SRms XSen
I	- 'Auslese'	CExl EShb NGdn
	- 'Azurit'	EHoe EWes NLar NWad SPoG SRms
§	- 'Blaufuchs'	CRos CSBt ELan EPfP EWes GMaP LRHS MAsh MAvo MBlu MGos NLar NRHS NWad NWsh SLim SPer SPlb SWvt WFar XLum
§	- 'Blauglut'	CRos EBee LRHS MRav NRHS SRms
	- BLUE FOX	see *F. glauca* 'Blaufuchs'
	- BLUE GLOW	see *F. glauca* 'Blauglut'
	- 'Elijah Blue'	Widely available
	- 'Golden Toupee'	CRos CTsd ECha EHoe ELan EPfP ESps LRHS MBlu MGos NEgg NLar NRHS SLim SPer SPlb SWvt WAvo WHar XLum
	- 'Harz'	EHoe XLum
	- INTENSE BLUE ('Casblue'^{PBR})	CKno CRos EHoe EPfP EWes GBin GMcL GQue LCro LOPS LRHS LSRN MAsh MGos NRHS SMad SPoG SRms
*	- ***minima***	CCCN NWsh
	- 'Pallens'	see *F. longifolia*
	- SEA URCHIN	see *F. glauca* 'Seeigel'
§	- 'Seeigel'	CRos LRHS NRHS NWad
	- SELECT	see *F. glauca* 'Auslese'
	- 'Seven Seas'	see *F. valesiaca* 'Silbersee'
	- 'Silberreiher'	EPPr
	- 'Solling'	XLum
	- 'Uchte'	EPPr
	'Hogar'	EPPr
	idahoensis	EShb
	- 'Tomales Bay'	CKno
§	***longifolia***	EPPr
	mairei	CBod CKno ECha EHoe EPPr IMou LPla NWsh SPhx XLum
	ovina	CHab EBWF WSFF

	- var. ***gallica***	NWsh
*	- 'Tetra Gold'	SWvt
	paniculata	CKno EHoe XLum
	- subsp. ***spadicea***	XLum
	pratensis	CHab EBWF
	punctoria	MMuc
	rubra	CHab CKno EBWF WSFF XLum
	scoparia	see *F. gautieri*
	'Siskiyou Blue'	CKno
	tatrae	MBel MMuc SEND
	valesiaca	XLum
	- var. ***glaucantha***	NGdn XLum
§	- 'Silbersee'	EHoe SRms WFar
	- SILVER SEA	see *F. valesiaca* 'Silbersee'
	violacea	EPPr
	vivipara	EBWF EHoe LEdu NBid XLum
*	'Willow Green'	SPlb

Fibigia (*Brassicaceae*)

§	***clypeata***	GPSL
I	- 'Select'	CSpe

Ficaria (*Ranunculaceae*)

§	***verna***	EBWF GKev MMuc
	- Alba Group	CHid CSam LEdu NRya
	- anemone-centred	see *Ficaria verna* 'Collarette'
§	- Aurantiaca Group	CDor ECha GCrg NLar NRya SPhx
	- var. ***aurantiacus***	see *Ficaria verna* Aurantiaca Group
	- black-leaved	CHid
	- 'Bowles's Double'	see *Ficaria verna* 'Double Bronze', 'Picton's Double'
	- 'Brambling'	CHid EBee ECha LEdu NLar
	- 'Brazen Child'	SHar
	- 'Brazen Hussy'	CAby CBod CDor CExl CSam CTri EBee ECha EHoe ELan EPPr EPfP GBin GMaP IFro IRob LEdu LRHS NHpl NLar NRHS NSti NWad SEND SMad SPer WCot WHal WPnP XLum
	- subsp. ***bulbilifer***	see *Ficaria verna* subsp. *verna*
§	- subsp. ***chrysocephala***	CHid EBee ECha IFro MNrw WCot
§	- 'Collarette' (d)	CHid GCrg LEdu MHer NLar NRya
	- 'Coppernob'	CDor CHid WCot WPnP
	- 'Cracked Parchment' **new**	CNat
	- 'Cupreus'	see *Ficaria verna* Aurantiaca Group
	- 'Dahlem'	EPPr
	- 'Damerham' (d)	CHid
§	- 'Double Bronze' (d)	CHid LEdu MHer NLar NRya
§	- 'Double Mud' (d)	CHid EPPr EWTr GAbr IFro LEdu NLar NRya SHar WHal
	- double, cream-flowered	see *Ficaria verna* 'Double Mud'
	- - green-eyed (d)	CHid LEdu
	- - yellow-flowered	see *Ficaria verna* Flore Pleno Group
	- 'Dusky Maiden'	NLar NRya
	- 'E.A. Bowles'	see *Ficaria verna* 'Collarette'
	- 'Edna'	WOut
	- 'Elan' (d)	MMoz
§	- Flore Pleno Group (d)	CBod CDor CHid CMac CTri ECha ELan EPPr GAbr NRya SRms WCot WPnP
	- 'Green Petal'	CAby CHid EPPr MCot NRya WHal WHer
	- 'Green Rim' **new**	CNat
	- 'Hyde Hall'	CHid NLar WCot
	- 'Jake Perry'	MNrw
	- 'Jane's Dress'	CHid
	- 'Ken Aslet Double' (d)	EPPr LEdu MHer WHal
	- 'Lambrook Variegated' (v)	CFis
	- 'Lemon Queen'	CHid
	- 'Leo'	MNrw
	- subsp. ***major***	see *Ficaria verna* subsp. *chrysocephala*
	- 'Martin Gibbs' Progeny' **new**	CNat
	- 'Monksilver'	IFro
	- 'Montacute'	CDor CFis
	- 'Newton Abbot'	CBre
	- 'Old Master'	WCot
	- 'Orange Sorbet' (d)	LEdu MNrw NLar
	- 'Petrol Spillage'	CNat
§	- 'Picton's Double' (d)	MNrw
	- 'Primrose'	NRya
	- 'Primrose Elf'	EBee
	- 'Ragamuffin' (d)	EBee
	- 'Randall's White'	CAby CDor SHar
	- 'Richard and Val'	WCot
	- 'Rita Pirouet'	WCot
	- 'Salmon's White'	CBre EPPr NLar NRya SHar WHal
	- 'Sheldon Silver'	CHid
	- 'Silver Collar'	LEdu
	- 'Single Cream'	MNrw
	- 'Suffusion'	CNat
	- 'Tortoiseshell'	CHid EPPr
§	- subsp. ***verna***	CPla CTri WHer WOut WSFF WShi
	- - 'Chedglow'	WCot
	- 'Wisley Double'	see *Ficaria verna* 'Double Bronze'
	- 'Yaffle'	CHid

Ficinia (*Cyperaceae*)

§	***nodosa***	SPlb
	truncata **new**	GEdr WCot
	- 'Ice Crystal' (v)	EShb LRHS SPoG

Ficus (*Moraceae*)

	afghanistanica	ERea
	- 'Silver Lyre'	WPGP
	benjamina ♀H1c	EUJe
	- 'Exotica'	EUJe
	- 'Midnight Lady' PBR **new**	EUJe
	carica (F)	CCCN ESps ETod EUJe LMaj LPra SArc SEWo SLon SPad
	- 'Abicou' (F)	ERea
	- 'Adam' (F)	CCCN ERea LEdu MRai NLar SEND SMad
	- 'Alma' (F)	ERea
	- 'Angélique' (F)	ERea
I	- 'Bauern Feige' (F)	NLar SRms
	- 'Beall' (F)	CCCN
	- 'Bellone' (F)	CCCN
	- 'Black Ischia' (F)	CCCN ERea
	- 'Black Jack' (F)	ERea
	- 'Bornholm' (F)	CCCN LSRN SPre
	- 'Bourjassotte Grise' (F)	CAgr ERea SDea XSen
	- 'Brogiotto' (F)	CCCN
	- 'Brogiotto Bianco' (F)	EMOT
	- 'Brown Turkey' (F) ♀H4	Widely available
	- 'Brunswick' (F)	CAgr CCCN CHll CRHN CTri ELan ELon EPfP EPom ERea EShb EUJe LEdu LRHS NLar NRHS SEND SKee SLim SRms WCot WFar
	- 'Califfo Blue' (F)	SRms
	- 'Castle Kennedy' (F)	CCCN ERea
	- 'Celeste' (F)	CBcs CCCN ERea SRms
	- 'Col de Dame Blanc' (F)	ERea XSen
	- 'Col de Dame Noir' (F)	ERea
	- 'Colummaro Black Apulia' (F)	CCCN
	- 'Columnaro White Apulia' (F)	CCCN

	- 'Dalmatie' (F)	CAgr CCCN CFGn ELan EPfP ERea LRHS MGos MRai NPri SEND SRms WPGP XSen
§	- 'Desert King' (F)	ERea
I	- 'Digitata' (F)	MBlu
	- 'Digredo' (F)	CCCN
	- 'Dorée' (F)	EPom XSen
	- 'Dorée de Porquerolles' (F)	CCCN
	- 'Drap d'Or' (F)	ERea
	- 'Excel' (F)	ERea
	- 'Figue d'Or' (F)	ERea
	- 'Filacciano' (F)	CCCN
	- 'Flanders' (F)	CCCN
	- 'Gentile' (F)	MRai
	- 'Goutte d'Or' (F)	CAgr CCCN EPfP EPom ERea SDea
	- 'Green Ischia' (F)	CCCN ERea
	- 'Grise de Marseille' (F)	CCCN
	- 'Grise de Saint Jean' (F)	CCCN ERea XSen
	- 'Ice Crystal' (F) ♀H5	CRos ECrN ELan EMOT EMil EPfP ERea EShb EUJe LRHS MBlu SPoG SRms WCot WPGP
	- 'Jordan' (F)	CFGn EMOT LRHS
	- 'Kadota' (F)	CCCN EMOT ERea MRai
	- 'King'	see *F. carica* 'Desert King'
	- 'Lisa' (F)	ERea
	- 'Little Yellow Wonder' (F)	ERea
	- 'Longue d'Août' (F)	XSen
	- 'LSU Gold' (F)	ERea
	- 'LSU Purple' (F)	ERea
	- 'Madeleine des Deux Saisons' (F)	EPom ERea MRai SEND XSen
	- 'Marseillaise' (F)	EPfP SDea
	- 'Melanzana' (F)	CCCN
	- 'Morena' (F)	SRms
	- 'Moscatel' (F)	CCCN
	- 'Napolitana' (F)	ERea
	- 'Negrétte de Porquerolles' (F)	CCCN
	- 'Nero' (F)	SGol
	- 'Newlyn Harbour' (F)	ELon
	- 'Noire de Caromb' (F)	CAgr CCCN CFGn EPfP ERea LRHS SKee SRms
	- 'Noire de Provence'	see *F. carica* 'Reculver'
	- 'Orphan' (F)	ERea
	- 'Osborn's Prolific' (F)	EPfP SEND SGol SWeb SWvt
	- 'Panachée' (F)	CCCN EMOT EPom ERea LRHS SMad SRms
	- 'Pastilière' (F)	ERea
	- 'Peter's Honey' (F)	ERea
	- 'Petite Nigra' (F)	ERea
	- 'Pied de Boeuf' (F)	CCCN
	- 'Pingo de Mel' (F)	ERea
	- 'Précoce de Dalmatie' (F)	CCCN CTho ERea EShb LEdu NLar SRms
	- 'Précoce Ronde de Bordeaux' (F)	CCCN EPfP ERea SEND XSen
	- 'Quinta' (F)	CCCN
§	- 'Reculver' (F)	SEND
	- 'Rouge de Bordeaux' (F)	CCCN CTsd EMOT EPom ERea NPri SDea SPlb SRms SSta
	- 'Safi' (F)	CCCN
	- 'Saint Johns' (F)	ERea SDea
	- 'San Pedro Miro' (F)	ERea
	- 'Sugar 12' (F)	ERea
	- 'Sultane' (F)	CAgr EPom ERea XSen
	- 'Tena' (F)	ERea
	- 'Texas Everbearing' (F)	ERea
	- 'Verte d'Argenteuil' (F)	CCCN
	- 'Violette Dauphine' (F)	EPfP ERea EUJe LEdu MRai NLar SEND
	- 'Violette de Bordeaux' (F)	ERea
	- 'Violette de Sollies' (F)	ERea SVic
	- 'Violette Normande' (F)	SEND
	- 'Violette Sepor' (F)	ERea
	- 'White Adriatic' (F)	ERea MRai SRms
	- 'White Genoa'	see *F. carica* 'White Marseilles'
	- 'White Ischia' (F)	ERea
§	- 'White Marseilles' (F)	CAgr CCCN CMac CRHN CRos ECrN ERea LRHS SDea SEND SKee SRms WPGP
	- 'Zamoreica' (F) **new**	SEND
	- 'Zidi' (F)	CCCN
	elastica	XAbr
	- 'Abidjan' **new**	EUJe
	- 'Robusta'	LCro
	pubigera	CExl
	pumila ♀H1c	CBcs EShb
	- 'Nana' **new**	NWad
	- 'Sonny' (v)	NWad
	- 'Variegata' (v) ♀H1c	EShb
	tikoua	CFil

fig see *Ficus carica*

filbert see *Corylus maxima*

Filipendula (*Rosaceae*)

	alnifolia 'Variegata'	see *F. ulmaria* 'Variegata'
	camtschatica	ECha ELan IMou MMuc NBid NLar WPGP WWtn
	- B&SWJ 10987	WCru
	- RBS 0224	NLar
	- 'Rosea'	MRav
	digitata 'Nana'	see *F. multijuga*
	hexapetala	see *F. vulgaris*
	- 'Flore Pleno'	see *F. vulgaris* 'Multiplex'
	'Kahome'	CRos EAJP ELon EShb GLog GMaP IFoB IRob LLWG LRHS MHol NBid NGdn NLar NRHS NSti SCob SPer SPhx WMoo WPnP
	kiraishiensis	EBee
	- B&SWJ 1571	WCru
	koreana **new**	CRos LRHS NRHS
§	***multijuga***	EBee GCal IFoB NLar NWad WBor WMoo
	- B&SWJ 10950	WCru
	- 'Hjördis'	CBod EBee ELon MHol SPad
	- var. ***yezoensis*** B&SWJ 10828	IMou WCru
	palmata	CBWd CRos ECha IBlr LLWG LRHS NBre NRHS WMoo
	- 'Digitata Nana'	see *F. multijuga*
	- 'Elegantissima'	see *F. purpurea* 'Elegans'
	- 'Nana'	see *F. multijuga*
	- 'Rosea'	CMac LLWG MMoz
	- 'Rubra'	CRos EBee LRHS MRav NGdn NRHS
	purpurea	CKno ECha ELon GQue IBlr ILea LLWG MMuc SBod SEND SRms WCru WMoo
	- f. ***albiflora***	ILea LLWG WMoo
§	- 'Elegans'	CRos EBee ELon EWTr ILea IRob LLWG LRHS NBid NRHS NWad SCob SPer SRms WFar WMoo WPnP
	- 'Pink Dreamland'	SPhx
*	- 'Plena' (d)	NLar
	'Queen of the Prairies'	see *F. rubra*

§	***rubra***	GNew IRob WSFF
§	- 'Venusta' ♀H5	Widely available
	- 'Venusta Magnifica'	see *F. rubra* 'Venusta'
	rufinervis B&SWJ 8469	WCru
	- B&SWJ 8611	WCru
§	***ulmaria***	CBen CBod CHab CHby CWat CWld EBWF EBee ENfk GJos GMaP GPoy LOPS MCot MHer MMuc MNHC MWts NMir WHer WMoo WOut WPnP WSFF WShi XLum
	- 'Aurea'	CBod CDor CMac CNor CRos CTri CWCL EBee ECha ECtt EHoe ELan GMaP LEdu LLWG LRHS MRav NBid NLar NRHS SPer SRms WCot WFar WMoo WSHC
	- 'Corinne Tremaine' **new**	WHer
	- 'Flore Pleno' (d)	EBee LLWG LRHS MRav NBid SPer WCot WFar
	- 'Rosea'	CRos LLWG LRHS MHer NRHS
§	- 'Variegata' (v)	CRos CWCL EBee ECtt EHoe ELan GQue IFoB LLWG LRHS NBid NGdn NLar NRHS SPer SRms WBor WFar WHer WMoo
§	***vulgaris***	CDor CHab CWld EBWF GLog ILea MMuc MNHC NBro NMir NQui WHer
	- 'Flore Pleno'	see *F. vulgaris* 'Multiplex'
	- 'Grandiflora'	CBre
§	- 'Multiplex' (d)	CDor CMac CRos CSpe ECha ELan EWTr GMaP LLWG LRHS MHer MMuc MRav NBid NRHS NRya NSti SRms WFar WMoo XLum
	- 'Plena'	see *F. vulgaris* 'Multiplex'
	- 'Rosea'	NBre

Firmiana (*Malvaceae*)

simplex	CBcs EBee EShb EUJe MBlu SPad WPGP

Fitzroya (*Cupressaceae*)

cupressoides	CAco CBcs CDul IArd IDee SLim WThu
- 'Borde Hill' (f)	WThu
- 'Westonbirt' (m)	WThu

Flueggea (*Phyllanthaceae*)

suffruticosa	SBrt

Fockea (*Apocynaceae*)

edulis	LToo

Foeniculum (*Apiaceae*)

	vulgare	CAgr CHby EBWF ECha ECrN ELan ENfk EPfP ESps GPoy MGos MHer MJak MNHC NPnk NPri SCob SEND SPer SPhx SPlb SPoG SRms SVic SWvt
	- 'Bronze'	see *F. vulgare* 'Purpureum'
	- var. ***dulce***	ENfk
§	- 'Giant Bronze'	CBod EBee GWyn IBoy LCro LEdu LOPS LRHS SCob SPhx WCot WGrn XSen
	- 'Orion' ♀H2 **new**	EKin EMsh
§	- 'Purpureum'	Widely available
	- 'Smoky'	ECha MRav
	- 'Sweet Florence'	SVic
	- 'Zefa Fino' ♀H2 **new**	EKin MCtn NRob

Fontanesia (*Oleaceae*)

fortunei	EBtc

Fontinalis (*Fontinalaceae*)

antipyretica	XBlo

Forsythia (*Oleaceae*)

	'Arnold Dwarf'	ECrN SRms
	'Beatrix Farrand' ambig.	CTri SEND SRms
	'Beatrix Farrand' K. Sax	MMuc NLar
	'Fiesta' (v)	CRos ELon EPfP LRHS MAsh MRav MSwo NEgg NLar SPer WCot
	giraldiana	MSwo SRms
	GOLD TIDE	see *F.* MARÉE D'OR
	'Golden Nugget'	CMac ELan EPfP LBuc MAsh NLar SLon SPoG WCFE WFar
	'Golden Times' (v)	CMac GMcL LBuc LSRN MAsh MSwo NEoE SPoG SWvt WAvo
	'Goldstream' (v)	NWad
	× ***intermedia***	CAco EShb ESps IBoy WHar
	- 'Arnold Giant'	MBlu
	- 'Goldrausch'	CRos ELan ETMg GMcL LCro LOPS LRHS NLar NRHS SAko
	- 'Lynwood Variety' ♀H5	Widely available
	- MINIGOLD ('Flojor')	CMac CSBt ELan ESps MSwo NLar SRms
	- 'Nimbus'PBR	CRos LRHS NRHS
	- SHOW OFF ('Mindor'PBR)	CRos LBuc LRHS NRHS
	- 'Spectabilis'	CDul EPfP LBuc SCob SCoo SGol SLim WFar
	- 'Spectabilis Variegated' (v)	MBNS NEoE
	- 'Spring Glory'	MHer WAvo WSpi
	- 'Variegata' (v)	SRms
	- WEEK END ('Courtalyn'PBR) ♀H5	CBod CEnd CRos EPfP ESps LBuc LRHS MAsh MJak MMuc NLar NRHS SCob SEND SGol SLon SPlb WFar
	'Kanarek'	NLar
	× ***mandshurica***	CBcs IDee IMou SAko
§	MARÉE D'OR ('Courtasol'PBR) ♀H5	CRos ELon EPfP IRob LRHS MAsh MJak MRav NLar NRHS SLon SPer SPoG
	MÊLÉE D'OR ('Courtaneur')	SGol WBor
	'Northern Gold'	MBlu
	ovata 'Ottawa' **new**	WAvo
	'Paulina'	GEdr NLar WAbe
	suspensa	CMac CTri EPfP SPlb SRms WSpi
	- f. ***atrocaulis***	CDul WSpi
	- 'Nymans'	MRav NLar NSti SBrt SEND SPer
§	- 'Taff's Arnold' (v)	CExl WAvo WSpi
	- 'Variegata'	see *F. suspensa* 'Taff's Arnold'
	'Tremonia'	ECrN
	viridissima 'Bronxensis'	CMac CTal EPot GEdr LLHF MAsh NLar WAbe
	- CITRUS SWIZZLE ('Mckcitrine'PBR)	NLar
	- var. ***koreana*** 'Kumsom' (v)	CRos EBee IArd IDee LRHS NLar SAko SPoG
	- 'Weber's Bronx'	NLar

Fortunella see *Citrus*

× ***crassifolia***	see *Citrus japonica*
'Fukushu'	see *Citrus* × *obovata* 'Fukushu'
hindsii	see *Citrus japonica*
margarita	see *Citrus japonica*

Fothergilla (*Hamamelidaceae*)

gardenii	CBcs CJun CRos EPfP LRHS MBlu MGil MRav NLar SPer SWvt
- 'Blue Mist'	CCCN CEnd CExl CJun CRos EBee ELan ELon EPfP LRHS MAsh NLar SPer SPoG SSta WHor

	- 'Glaucophylla'	NLar
	- 'Suzanne'	CJun NLar
	- 'Zundert'	NLar
	× ***intermedia*** BEAVER CREEK ('Klmtwo')	NLar
	- 'Blue Shadow'	CBcs CCCN CJun CRos EPfP IDee IRob LRHS LSRN MGos MPkF MRav NLar NRHS SGol
	- 'Mount Airy' ♀H5	CJun CMCN CRos EPfP LRHS MPkF NLar SSta
	- 'Red Licorice'	CJun EPfP NLar
	- 'Sea Spray'	CJun NLar
	- 'Windy City'	CJun NLar
	major ♀H5	CBcs CDul CJun CRos EBee ELan EPfP ESps LCro LOPS LRHS LSRN MAsh MBlu MGil MGos MJak NEgg NLar SPer SReu SWvt WFar WHor WTSh
	- 'Bulkyard'	CJun
	- Monticola Group	CDul CEnd CJun CRos CTho EPfP LRHS MAsh MMuc SLim SPer SSta WHar
	- - 'Huntsman'	CCCN CJun CTho EPfP SPer SSta WHor

Fouquieria (*Fouquieriaceae*)

	columnaris	SPlb
	splendens	SPlb

Fragaria (*Rosaceae*)

	from Taiwan	WHer
	alpina 'Alba'	see *F. vesca* 'Semperflorens Alba'
	× ***ananassa*** 'Albion'PBR (F)	LCro LOPS LRHS LSRN NRHS
	- 'Alice'PBR (F) ♀H6	CAgr CMac EPom
	- 'Anablanca' (F)	LRHS
	- 'Aromel' (F)	CTri MMuc
	- 'Buddy'PBR (F)	CSBt EPom LCro LOPS LRHS NRHS SPer
	- 'Calypso' (F)	LBuc SDea SPer
	- 'Cambridge Favourite' (F) ♀H6	CAgr CMac CRav CRos CSBt CTri EMil EPfP EPom GAbr LBuc LCro LOPS LRHS MGos MJak MMuc NPri NRHS SDea SPlb WHar
	- 'Cambridge Vigour' (F)	LRHS NRHS
	- 'Christine' (F)	CAgr CRos EPom LRHS NRHS SDea
	- 'Cupid'PBR (F)	CArg LCro LOPS LRHS
	- 'Darselect'PBR (F)	EPom
	- 'Delia' (F)	CRos LRHS NRHS
	- 'Elan'PBR (F)	LRHS NRHS
	- 'Elegance'PBR (F)	EPom
	- 'Elsanta' (F)	CRos CSBt CTri EMil EPfP EPom IArd LBuc LEdu LRHS NEgg NPri NRHS SDea SPer WHar
	- 'Elvira' (F)	EPfP
*	- 'Emily' (F)	LEdu
	- 'Eros'PBR (F)	LBuc
	- 'Everest'PBR (F)	LRHS NRHS
	- 'Fenella'PBR (F)	CMac EMil EPom LCro LOPS
	- 'Finesse' (F)	CSBt LRHS NRHS
	- 'Flamenco'PBR (F)	CArg EPom LEdu NWad SDea
	- 'Florence'PBR (F)	CAgr CArg CRav CRos CSBt CTri EPfP EPom LBuc LEdu LRHS NRHS SDea SPer
	- 'Florian' (F)	LEdu
	- (Fragoo Series) FRAGOO DEEP ROSE ('Tarpan') (F)	LRHS NRHS
	- - FRAGOO PINK ('Pikan') (F)	LRHS NRHS
	- - FRAGOO WHITE ('Belton') (F)	LRHS NRHS
	- Fraise des Bois	see *F. vesca*
	- 'Framberry' (F)	EPom LEdu LRHS
	- 'Gariguette' (F)	EPom
	- 'Hapil' (F) ♀H6	CTri EMil EPfP EPom LBuc LEdu LRHS
	- 'Honeoye' (F) ♀H6	CAgr CRav CRos CSBt EMil EPfP EPom LBuc LCro LEdu LOPS LRHS MMuc NWad SPer WHar
	- 'Judibell'PBR (F)	LEdu
	- 'Korona'PBR (F)	CMac EPom
	- 'Leo Alba' (F)	CArg
	- 'Loran' (F)	CRos LRHS NRHS
	- 'Lucy'PBR (F)	LCro
	- 'Malling Centenary'PBR (F)	EPom LRHS
	- 'Malling Opal'PBR (F)	EPom
	- 'Malwina'PBR (F)	EPom SVic
	- 'Manille' (F)	EPom
	- 'Merlan'PBR (F)	LRHS NRHS
	- 'Monterey'PBR (F) **new**	LEdu
	- 'Pandora' (F)	LEdu
	- 'Pegasus'PBR (F) ♀H6	CAgr CRos CSBt EPfP EPom LRHS NRHS
	- pineberry (F)	LEdu
	- PINK PANDA ('Frel') (F)	CBod CMac CTri EBee ELan GMcL IRob LRHS MBel MRav NEgg NGdn NLar NRHS SPer SPoG WCAu
	- pink-flowered (F)	GAbr
	- 'Red Glory'PBR (F)	LRHS NRHS
	- 'Red Princess'PBR (F)	LRHS NRHS
	- RED RUBY	see *F. × ananassa* 'Samba'
	- 'Redgauntlet' (F)	CRos EPfP LBuc LRHS NRHS
	- 'Rhapsody' (F) ♀H6	CRos LRHS LSRN NRHS
	- 'Rosie'PBR (F)	SDea
	- 'Roman' (F)	LRHS
	- 'Royal Sovereign' (F)	CMac CTri EPom LEdu SDea SVic
§	- 'Samba'PBR (F)	CBod ELan GLog LEdu LRHS MBel MNrw NGdn NLar NRHS NWad
	- 'Senga Sengana' (F)	SVic
	- SNOW WHITE ('Hansawhit') (F)	EMil EPom LCro LOPS
	- 'Sonata'PBR (F)	ELan EPom NWad
	- 'Sophie'PBR (F)	LEdu NWad
	- 'Sweetheart' (F)	LCro LOPS LRHS
	- 'Symphony'PBR (F) ♀H6	CAgr CRos CSBt EPfP EPom LBuc LRHS LSRN NRHS
	- 'Temptation' (F)	CRos LRHS NRHS
§	- 'Variegata' (v)	EBee EHrv MRav SPer SPoG WMoo WOut
	- 'Vibrant'PBR (F)	CSBt EMil EPom
	- 'White Dream' (F)	LCro LOPS
	'Bowles's Double'	see *F. vesca* 'Multiplex'
	chiloensis (F)	IFro LEdu
	- 'Chaval' (F)	CHid ECha EPPr IMou MRav NChi WMoo
	- 'Variegata' misapplied	see *F. × ananassa* 'Variegata'
	indica	see *Duchesnea indica*
	'Lipstick'	EBee NLar WSpi
	moschata	CAgr
	nubicola	CAgr GPoy
	- 'Mount Omei'	EBee
	'Variegata'	see *F. × ananassa* 'Variegata'
§	***vesca*** (F)	CAgr CBcs CWld EBWF ELan EPfP GPoy GQue LCro LEdu LOPS MHer MNHC NMir NPri SPlb SRms SVic WGwG WOut WSFF WShi
	- 'Alexandra' (F)	ENfk ERea NLar WHar
	- 'Alpina Scarletta' (F)	ENfk
	- 'Baron Solemacher' (F)	ERea SPhx WHer

- 'Capron Royale' (F)	CAgr
- 'Flore Pleno'	see *F. vesca* 'Multiplex'
- 'Fructu Albo' (F)	CAgr CBre WMoo
- 'Golden Alexandra' (F)	ECha EWes NWad WHer
- 'Mara des Bois'[PBR] (F)	EPom LRHS SPer
- 'Monophylla' (F)	WHer
§ - 'Multiplex' (d)	EPPr WBor WHer WOut
§ - 'Muricata'	CBre LEdu
- 'Patchwork' **new**	CNat
- 'Pineapple Crush' (F)	WHer
- 'Plymouth Strawberry'	see *F. vesca* 'Muricata'
- 'Reine des Vallées' (F)	ERea
- 'Scarlet Beauty' (F)	EPom MCoo
§ - 'Semperflorens Alba' (F)	CAgr NWad
- 'Variegata' misapplied	see *F.* × *ananassa* 'Variegata'
- 'Variegata' ambig. (v)	EHoe
virginiana	CAgr
- subsp. ***glauca***	EPPr
viridis	CAgr

Francoa (*Francoaceae*)

appendiculata	GAbr ILea NWad WHer WMoo
Ballyrogan strain	IBlr
'Confetti'	CExl
* dwarf purple	CElw
'Purple Spike'	see *F. sonchifolia* Rogerson's form
ramosa	CTri GKev IBlr ILea NBro WKif WMoo
* - 'Alba'	CSpe SBee
sonchifolia	Widely available
- 'Alba'	EBee WMoo
- 'Cally Dwarf Purple'	MHer
- 'Culm View Lilac'	MSCN
- 'Molly Anderson'	MAvo
- 'Petite Bouquet'	CKno EWes GKev LRHS SHar
- 'Pink Bouquet'	CAbb CKno CMac CWGN EBee LRHS SHar SRkn WFar WHlf WOut
- 'Pink Giant'	CAby CBod CPla CWld GAbr GCal GEdr GKev IPot LRHS MBel MPie NRHS NWad WMoo
§ - Rogerson's form	CBWd CElw CTri CWld EHrv ELon EShb GBin IBoy IMou LRHS NChi SPad WFar WMoo

Frangula (*Rhamnaceae*)

§ ***alnus***	CArg CCVT CDul CHab CPer CTri ECrN EShb EWTr LBuc MBlu MGos SEWo WFar WMou WSFF WTSh
- 'Aspleniifolia'	CTho ELan EPfP LRHS MBlu MMuc MPkF MRav NLar WCFE WGrn
- 'Fine Line'	CRos ELan LRHS NLar NRHS SPoG
- 'Minaret'	MBlu
- 'Ron Williams'	MBlu
californica B&SWJ 14057 **new**	WCru

Frankenia (*Frankeniaceae*)

laevis	SRms XSen
thymifolia	CTri ECtt EPot MAsh MHer MMuc SPlb WHoo WOld WRHF XLum

Franklinia (*Theaceae*)

alatamaha	CBcs EBee IArd IDee LRHS MBlu MGil SAko WPGP

Frasera (*Gentianaceae*)

speciosa **new**	GKev

Fraxinus ✿ (*Oleaceae*)

americana	CDul
- 'Autumn Purple'	CDul CEnd EBee EPfP MAsh
angustifolia	LPra
- 'Raywood'	CCVT CDul CEnd CTri ECrN EPfP EWTr GBin LPra MAsh MGos MMuc MSwo SCob SEND SGol
chiisanensis B&SWJ 12719	WCru
chinensis	CDul
excelsior	CAco CCVT CDul CHab CTri ECrN EPfP LPra MAsh MGos MMuc SCob SEWo SGol
- 'Atlas'	LPra
- 'Aurea Pendula'	CDul CEnd EBee
- 'Crispa'	NLar
- f. ***diversifolia***	CDul
- 'Jaspidea'	CCVT CDul CEnd ECrN EMOT EPfP ERod LPra MAsh MGos MMuc MSwo SCob SGol
- 'Pendula'	CCVT CDul CEnd CTsd ECrN LPra SGol
- 'R.E. Davey'	CDul
- 'Westhof's Glorie'	CCVT CDul EMOT LPra
insularis var. ***henryana***	CDul
mariesii	see *F. sieboldiana*
nigra 'Fallgold'	CEnd
ornus	CCVT CDul CTri ECrN EPfP LPra MMuc MSwo SEND WTSh
- 'Arie Peters'	CDul
- 'Obelisk'	EBee MAsh
pennsylvanica	CDul
quadrangulata	CDul
§ ***sieboldiana***	CDul EPfP
sogdiana Potamophila Group	EBee
velutina	CDul
xanthoxyloides	CDul

Freesia (*Iridaceae*)

sp.	CRav
alba Watson	see *F. caryophyllacea*
alba (G.L. Mey.) Gumbl.	CPbh
'Blue Moon' **new**	LCro LOPS
§ ***caryophyllacea***	NRog
corymbosa	NRog
'Delta River'	SPoG
'Fragrant Sunburst'	SPoG
'Gold River'	SPoG
grandiflora	CExl CHll
§ ***laxa*** ♀H3	CExl CPbh CSpe CTal CTri EPri GKev LRHS NHpl NLos
- var. ***alba*** ♀H3	CExl CPbh CSpe EPri GKev
- 'Joan Evans'	CSpe LLHF SChF
- red-spotted	CExl
leichtlinii	NRog
PATIO PERFECTION MIXED **new**	ETMg
'Red River'	SPoG
refracta	CTal NRog
viridis	CExl CTal NRog
'White River'	SPoG
xanthospila	NRog WCot

Fremontodendron (*Malvaceae*)

'California Glory' ♀H4	CBcs CBod CDul CMac CRos EPfP ESps EUJe GMcL IDee LRHS LSRN MAsh MBlu MGil MGos NPla NPri NRHS SArc SBod SEle SGbt SGol SMad SPer SPoG SVen SWvt
californicum	CTri EBee ELan NLar SEND SLim SNig SPlb WFar
'Dara's Gold'	CRos LRHS NRHS

'Pacific Sunset'	CBcs EPfP LRHS MGos MRav SGol WHar
'Tequila Sunrise' ♀H4	CWGN LRHS WFar

Freylinia (*Scrophulariaceae*)

cestroides	see *F. lanceolata*
§ ***lanceolata***	CBcs CCCN EBee SPlb SVen
tropica	CHll MGil
visseri	SVen

Fritillaria ✿ (*Liliaceae*)

acmopetala ♀H4	CAvo CTal CWCL ELon EPot ERCP GKev ITim LAma MNrw SDeJ SDir WCot WSHC
- 'Brunette'	GKev
- subsp. ***wendelboi***	GKev LAma NPnk
affinis	GKev NHpl
§ - var. ***tristulis***	ELon
- 'Vancouver Island'	LAma
- yellow-flowered	CWCL
amana	CWCL ELon EPot ERCP GKev LLHF WCot
- 'Cambridge'	WCot
- 'Goksan Gold'	GKev
arabica	see *F. persica*
assyriaca	EPot IFro
aurea	LAma
- 'Golden Flag'	EPot LAma LLHF SDeJ
'Beethoven' (Rascal Series)	GKev WCot
biflora	GKev
- 'Martha Roderick'	SDeJ
§ ***bithynica***	ITim LAma
bucharica	EPot GKev LAma
camschatcensis	CRos CWCL ELon EPfP EPot ERCP GBin GEdr GKev GMaP LAma LRHS MMoz NHpl NRHS SDeJ SDir WAbe WCot WCru
- black-flowered	CAby
- double-flowered (d)	LAma
- f. ***flavescens***	GEdr LAma
- green-flowered	CAby
carduchorum	see *F. minuta*
carica	GKev
'Chopin' (Rascal Series)	CAvo GKev
citrina	see *F. bithynica*
conica	GKev
§ ***crassifolia*** subsp. ***kurdica***	EPot ITim
davisii	EPfP EPot GKev LAma LLHF SDeJ
eduardii	EPot GKev
- 'Castor'	GKev LAma
elwesii	CAvo EPot ERCP GKev ITim LAma LLHF SDeJ SDir WTor
* ***glauca*** 'Golden Flag'	GKev SDeJ
- 'Goldilocks'	LAma SDeJ
graeca	EPot LAma SDeJ
grandiflora	GKev
hispanica	see *F. lusitanica*
imperialis ♀H6	SDir
- 'April Flame'	LAma SDir
- 'Argenteovariegata' (v)	GKev LAma SDir
- 'Aureomarginata' (v)	GKev LAma SDir
- 'Aurora'	CRos EPot ERCP GKev GMcL LAma LRHS NChi NLar NPer NRHS SDeJ SDir WFar
- 'Early Fantasy'	GKev LAma
- 'Early Passion'	GKev LAma
- 'Garland Star'	CRos GKev LAma LRHS LSun NLar NRHS SDeJ SPhx
- 'Grenadier'	LAma
- var. ***inodora***	GKev LAma
- 'Inodora Purpurea'	LAma
- 'Lutea'	CAvo CRos ERCP GKev LAma LRHS NChi NRHS SPoG WFar
- 'Maxima'	see *F. imperialis* 'Rubra Maxima'
- 'Maxima Lutea' ♀H6	CRos CWld ELan EPfP EPot ERCP GKev GMcL LRHS LSun NLar NRHS SDeJ SPer SPhx SPoG
- 'Orange Beauty'	CRos GKev LAma LRHS NRHS
- 'Orange Brilliant'	LAma
- 'Pollux'	LAma
- 'Prolifera'	GKev LAma SDeJ
- 'Rubra'	CBod CRos EPfP ERCP GKev LAma LRHS NLar NRHS SPer WFar
§ - 'Rubra Maxima'	CRos ELan EPfP EPot ERCP GKev GMcL LRHS LSun NChi NRHS SDeJ
- 'Slagzwaard'	GKev LAma
- 'Striped Beauty'	EPot GKev LAma SDeJ
- 'Sulpherino'	GKev LAma SDir
- 'Sunset'	GKev LAma SDir
- 'The Premier'	GKev LAma SDeJ
- 'William Rex'	CAvo CRos CWCL EPot ERCP GKev LAma LBuc LRHS NRHS SPhx SPoG
involucrata	WCot
karadaghensis	see *F. crassifolia* subsp. ***kurdica***
kotschyana	GKev
lanceolata	see *F. affinis* var. ***tristulis***
latakiensis	EPot GKev
§ ***lusitanica***	ITim
'Mahler' (Rascal Series)	GKev
meleagris ♀H5	Widely available
- var. ***unicolor*** subvar. ***alba*** ♀H5	CAvo ERCP GKev IBoy IFro LCro LOPS MWat SCob SDeJ SPer SPhx WPnP WShi
- - - 'Aphrodite'	EPot WCot
michailovskyi	CHid CRos CWCL EPfP EPot ERCP GKev IFro LAma LRHS MNrw NHpl NPnk NRHS SDeJ SDir SRms WFar
- 'Multiflorum'	GKev IBoy
§ ***minuta***	EPot ERCP GKev LAma NPnk SDeJ
montana	GKev
nigra Mill.	see *F. pyrenaica*
olivieri	GKev
pallidiflora ♀H5	CAvo CWCL ELon EPot ERCP GKev LAma NHpl NPnk SDeJ SPhx WCot
- yellow-flowered **new**	ITim
§ ***persica***	ECha EPfP EPot ERCP GKev LAma LRHS NChi NPnk NRHS SCob SPhx WCot
- 'Adiyaman' ♀H4	ELan SDeJ
- 'Alba'	GKev SDeJ
- 'Bicolor' **new**	GKev
- 'Chocolate'	CWCL
- 'Ivory Bells'	EPot ERCP GKev LAma LRHS SDeJ
- 'Midnight Bells'	GKev
- 'Pastel'	GKev
* - 'Senkoy'	GKev
pinardii	LAma
pontica ♀H4	CAvo CWCL EPot ERCP GKev ITim LAma NHpl SDeJ WCot
pudica	LAma
- 'Giant'	EPot SDeJ
§ ***pyrenaica*** ♀H5	LAma LLHF
raddeana	CAvo ELon EPot ERCP GBin GKev LAma SDeJ SPhx WCot
reuteri	EPot GKev LAma
roylei 'Lowndes' Variety'	GKev
rubra major	see *F. imperialis* 'Rubra Maxima'
ruthenica	GKev
sewerzowii	EPot GKev LAma WCot
- 'Brown Eyes'	GKev

stenanthera	EPot GKev LAma
stribrnyi	GKev
thunbergii	CTal GKev LAma LLHF WCot
uva-vulpis	CAby CMea CRos CTca EAJP ECtt ELon EPfP EPot ERCP GKev GWyn LAma LRHS MNrw NPri NRHS SDeJ SDir WFar
verticillata	ECha LAma WCru
'Vivaldi' (Rascal Series)	GKev
whittallii	EPot GKev LAma

Fuchsia ✿ (*Onagraceae*)

'A.M. Larwick'	EBak SLBF
'A.W. Taylor'	EBak
'Aalt Hillie van de Veen'	WOth
'Abbé Farges' (d)	CLoc CRos CWVF EBak EPts LRHS MSmi NRHS SVic WOth
'Abigail' ambig.	CWVF
'Abundance'	EHDe
'Achievement' ♀H4	CLoc LCla MJac MSmi SVic
'Adinda' (T) ♀H1c	EPts LCla MHer WOth
'Adriaan van Bylant' (d)	WOth
'Adrienne' (d)	MSmi
'Ailsa Garnett' (d)	EBak
'Aintree'	CWVF
'Airedale'	CWVF
'Aladna's Sander' (d)	CWVF
'Alan Ayckbourn'	CWVF WOth
'Alan Titchmarsh' ♀H2	EPts ESps LCla MSmi SLBF
'Alaska' (d)	CLoc SVic
'Alberttina'	MSmi SVic WOth
'Albertus Schwab'	LCla
'Alde'	CWVF WOth
'Alderford'	SLBF
'Alexandra Meles'	WOth
'Alf Thornley' (d)	CWVF WOth
'Alfonso' (d)	SLBF
'Alice Ashton' (d)	EBak
'Alice Blue Gown' (d)	CWVF
'Alice Doran'	LCla
'Alice Hoffman' (d) ♀H4	Widely available
'Alice Sweetapple' (d)	CWVF
'Alicia Sellars'	SLBF
'Alison Ewart'	CLoc CWVF SPet SVic
'Alison Patricia' ♀H2	CWVF EBak LCla MJac MSmi SLBF SVic WOth
'Alison Reynolds' (d)	CWVF WOth
'Alison Ruth Griffin' (d)	MJac
'Alison Ryle' (d)	EBak
'Alison Sweetman' ♀H2	CWVF MJac
'Allan Taylor'	WOth
'Allen Jackson'	LCla SLBF WOth
'Allure' (d)	WOth
'Aloha'	WOth
'Aloys Hetterscheid'	WOth
alpestris	EBak GCal LCla SVic
'Alton Water' (d/v)	WOth
'Alwin' (d)	CWVF
'Alyce Larson' (d)	CWVF EBak MJac SVic
'Alyssa May Garcia' (d)	EPts MJac SLBF WOth
'Amaranth'	WOth
'Amata' **new**	SLBF
'Amazing Maisie' (d)	MSmi SLBF WOth
'Ambassador'	SVic WOth
'Amelia Rose'	SLBF
'Amelie Aubin'	CLoc CWVF EBak SVic
'America'	CWVF WOth
'Amerika' (d)	WOth
§ ***ampliata***	LCla
'Amy'	MJac
'Amy Lye'	CLoc EHDe SVic
'Amy Ruth'	CWVF
§ 'Andenken an Heinrich Henkel' (T)	CLoc CWVF EBak SVic WOth
'André Le Nostre' (d)	CWVF EBak SVic
'Andreas Schwab'	LCla
andrei	LCla
'Andrew Carnegie' (d)	CLoc
'Andrew Hadfield'	CWVF SVic WOth
'Andromeda' De Groot	WOth
'Angela' (d)	WOth
'Angela King'	WOth
'Angela Leslie' (d)	CLoc EBak SVic
'Angela Rippon'	CWVF
'Angel's Flight' (d)	EBak
'Angel's Kiss' (E)	SLBF WOth
'Angie'	MSmi
'Angie Baby'	WOth
'Anhaltiner'	WOth
'Anita'	CLoc CWVF EPts MJac MSmi SLBF SVic WOth
'Anjo' (v)	CWVF WOth
'Ann Allen'	SLBF
'Ann Howard Tripp'	CLoc CWVF EPts MJac SVic
'Ann Reid' **new**	NWms SLBF
'Anna of Longleat' (d)	CWVF SPet
'Anna Sunshine' (T)	EPts SLBF
'Annabel' (d) ♀H4	CCCN CLoc CTri CWVF EBak EPts ESps ETMg LCla MJac MSmi SLBF SPet SVic WOth
'Anneke de Keijzer'	LCla WOth
'Annie den Otter'	WOth
'Annie Earle'	EHDe WOth
'Annie M.G. Schmidt'	EPts LCla WOth
'Anniek Geerlings' (T)	WOth
'Ant and Dec' (d/v)	MJac MSmi
'Anthea' (d) **new**	MSmi
'Anthea Day' (d)	CLoc
'Antigone'	SLBF WOth
'Apart'	WOth
'Aphaia'	WOth
'Aphrodite' (d)	CLoc CWVF
'Applause' (d)	CLoc CWVF EBak EPts MSmi SLBF SPet SVic
aprica misapplied	see *F.* × *bacillaris*
aprica Lundell	see *F. microphylla* subsp. *aprica*
'Apricot Ice'	CLoc SVic
'Arabella'	CWVF
'Arabella Improved'	CWVF EHDe SVic
arborea	see *F. arborescens*
§ ***arborescens***	CBcs CBot CHll CLoc CWCL CWVF EBak ETMg EUJe EWld LCla MCot MHer SDys SVic
– B&SWJ 10475	WCru
'Arcadia Gold' (d)	CWVF WOth
'Arcady'	CLoc CWVF
'Arels Nina'	WOth
'Arels Tojo'	WOth
'Ariel' (E)	CRos LRHS NRHS SVic WOth
'Arkie'	MJac
'Arlendon' (d)	CWVF
'Army Nurse' (d) ♀H4	CLoc CRos CWCL CWVF ELan ELon EPfP EPts IRob LCro LRHS MGos MSmi NLar NRHS SGol SLBF SPet SVic WOth
'Ashley'	LCla
'Ashley and Isobel'	CWVF WOth
'Ashtede'	SLBF
'Ashville'	SLBF WOth
'Atahualpa'	WOth

'Atlantic Star'	CWVF MJac
'Atlantis' (d)	CWVF
'Atomic Glow' (d)	SVic
'Aubergine'	see *F.* 'Gerharda's Aubergine'
'Audrey Hepburn'	CWVF
'Auenland'	MJac
'Auntie Jinks' ♀H2	CWVF EBak MJac MSmi SPet SVic WOth
'Aurora Superba'	CLoc CWVF EBak SLBF
'Australia Fair' (d)	CWVF
'Autumnale' ♀H2	CLoc CWVF EBak EPts MSmi SLBF SPet SPoG SVic WOth
'Avalanche' ambig. (d)	CLoc EBak SLBF
'Avalanche' Henderson (d)	WOth
'Avocet'	CLoc
'Avon Celebration' (d/v)	CLoc WOth
'Avon Gem'	CLoc
'Avon Glow' (d)	CLoc
'Avon Gold'	CLoc
'Awake Sweet Love' (T)	EPts
ayavacensis	LCla
'Aylisa Rowan' (E)	SLBF
'Azure Sky' (d)	MJac WOth
'Baby Blue Eyes' ♀H4	CLoc CRos CWVF ELan ELon EPfP ESps LRHS LSRN MAsh NRHS SLBF SVic WOth
'Baby Bright'	CWVF LCla
'Baby Brooke'	WOth
'Baby Chang'	WOth
'Baby Pink' (d)	CWVF
'Baby Thumb' (v)	EPts
'Babyface' Tolley (d)	SVic
§ × ***bacillaris*** (E)	CAbb CChe CHGN EWes GCal LRHS SEle SLBF SPoG WHer XLum
§ – 'Cottinghamii' (E)	EWld ILea WOth WSHC
§ – 'Reflexa' (E)	CCCN LSou WOth
'Baden Powell' (E)	SVic
'Bagworthy Water'	CLoc
'Baker's Tri' (T)	EBak
'Balkonkönigin'	CLoc CWVF
'Ballerina Girl' (E)	SLBF
'Ballet Girl' (d) ♀H2	CLoc CWVF EBak MSmi SLBF
'Bambini'	CWVF EPts SLBF
'Barbara'	CLoc CWVF EBak EPts LCla MJac SPet SVic WOth
'Barbara Evans'	SLBF
'Barbara Pountain' (d)	CWVF
'Barbara Reynolds'	WOth
'Barbara Windsor'	CWVF MJac MSmi
'Barry's Queen'	see *F.* 'Golden Border Queen'
'Bashful' (d)	EPts LCla SPet SVic
'Beacon'	CLoc CMac CRos CWVF EBak EPfP EPts ESps ETMg LCla LRHS MJac MSmi NRHS SGol SLBF SPet SPoG SVic
'Beacon Rosa' ♀H4	CLoc CRos CWVF ELon EPfP EPts LCla LRHS MJac NRHS SLBF SPet SPoG SVic
'Bealings' (d)	CWVF SVic
'Beauty of Bath' (d)	CLoc
'Beauty of Clyffe Hall' Lye	EBak EHDe WOth
'Beauty of Exeter' (d)	CWVF EBak WOth
'Beauty of Prussia' (d)	CLoc CWVF WOth
'Beauty of Purbeck' (d)	WOth
'Beauty of Swanley'	EHDe
'Beauty of Trowbridge'	CWVF EHDe LCla WOth
'Beauty Queen' (d) **new**	ETMg
'Beckie Lou'PBR	EBee
'Beebop'	MSmi
'Belinda Jane'	WOth

'Bella Forbes' (d) ♀H2	MSmi
'Bella Rosella' (California Dreamers Series) (d) ♀H2	CLoc EPts ETMg MJac MSmi SCoo
'Belsay Beauty' (d)	CWVF
'Belvoir Beauty' (d)	CLoc
'Ben de Jong'	LCla SLBF
'Ben Jammin'	CLoc CWVF EPfP EPts MSmi SVic WOth
'Ben-Ben'	SLBF
'Beninkust'	WOth
'Berba's Happiness' (d)	CWVF
'Berba's Trio'	WOth
'Berliner Kind' (d)	CWVF EBak
'Bermuda' (d)	CWVF
'Bernadette' (d)	CWVF
'Bernie's Big-un' (d)	MJac SLBF
'Bernisser Hardy' ♀H4	EPts LCla NQui SAko SLBF SLim WOth XLum
'Bessie Kimberley' (T)	LCla
'Beth Robley' (d)	CWVF
'Betsy Huuskes'	SLBF
BETTY ('Shabetty'PBR) (Shadowdancer Series)	MSmi
'Beverley'	CWVF EBak EPts
'Beverley Hills' (d)	WOth
'Bianca' (d)	CWVF SVic
'Bicentennial' (d)	CLoc CWVF EBak EPts ETMg MJac MSmi SLBF SPet SVic
'Big Slim'	WOth
'Billy Green' (T) ♀H2	CLoc CWVF EBak EPts LCla MHer MJac MSmi SVic
'Bishop's Bells' (d)	CWVF SVic
'Bittersweet' (d)	SVic
'Black Beauty' (d)	CWVF
'Black Prince'	CWVF SVic WOth
'Black to the Future'	MSmi WOth
'Blackmore Vale' (d)	CWVF
'Blacky' (d)	CCCN EBak EUJe GBin MSmi SDys SEND SPet SVic
I 'Blanche Regina' (d)	CWVF MJac
'Bland's New Striped'	EBak EPts LSou MSmi SLBF SPoG WOth
§ 'Blauer Engel' (d)	MJac MSmi WOth
'Blaze Away' (d)	MJac
'Blowick'	CWVF MJac SPet WOth
BLUE ANGEL	see *F.* 'Blauer Engel'
'Blue Bush'	CWVF EPts MJac SVic WOth XLum
'Blue Butterfly' (d)	CWVF
'Blue Eyes' (d)	MSmi SPet
'Blue Gown' (d)	CLoc CWVF EBak MSmi SVic
'Blue Heaven' **new**	MSmi
'Blue Lace' (d)	SVic
'Blue Lagoon' ambig. (d)	CWVF
'Blue Lake' (d)	CWVF
'Blue Mirage' (d)	CLoc CWVF MSmi SVic
'Blue Pearl' (d)	CWVF EBak
'Blue Pinwheel'	CWVF EBak
'Blue Satin' (d)	MSmi WOth
'Blue Sleighbells'	WOth
'Blue Tit'	LCla
'Blue Veil' (d)	CLoc CWVF MJac MSmi SCoo SVic WOth
'Blue Waves' (d)	CLoc CSBt CWVF EBak SVic
'Blush o' Dawn' (d)	CLoc EBak MSmi SLBF SVic
'Bob Pacey'	CWVF
'Bobby Dazzler' (d)	CWVF
'Bobby Shaftoe' (d)	EBak
'Bobby Wingrove'	EBak
'Bobby's Girl'	EPts
'Bobolink' (d)	EBak

	'Bob's Best' (d)	CWVF EPts
	boliviana Britton	see *F. sanctae-rosae*
	boliviana ambig.	CBcs GCal MHer
§	***boliviana*** Carrière	CHll CLoc CWVF LCla WOth
§	- var. ***alba*** ♀H2	CHll CLoc EBak EPts LCla SVic WOth
	- var. ***boliviana***	CRHN SVic
	- var. ***luxurians*** 'Alba'	see *F. boliviana* Carrière var. *alba*
	- f. ***puberulenta*** Munz	see *F. boliviana* Carrière
	'Bon Accorde'	CLoc CWVF EBak EPts SLBF
	'Bon Bon' (d)	CWVF SVic
	'Bonita' (d)	CWVF SVic
	'Bonnie Lass' (d)	EBak
	'Boogie'	MSmi
I	'Boogie Woogie' (d) **new**	LCla MJac NWms SLBF
	'Bora Bora' (d)	CWVF SVic
	'Borde Hill' (d)	EPts
	'Border Princess'	EBak
	'Border Queen' ♀H4	CLoc CWVF EBak EPts MJac SLBF SVic WOth
	'Border Reiver'	CWVF SVic
	'Börnemann's Beste'	see *F.* 'Georg Börnemann'
	'Bouffant'	CLoc SVic
	'Bountiful' Munkner (d)	CLoc CWVF
	'Bouquet' (d)	SLBF
	'Bow Bells'	CLoc CWVF MJac SPet SVic WOth
	'Boy Marc' (T) ♀H1c	LCla
	'Brandt's 500 Club'	CLoc
	'Breckland'	EBak
	'Breeders' Delight'	CWVF
	'Breeder's Dream' (d)	EBak
	'Breevis Minimus'	SLBF
	'Brenda' (d)	CWVF
	'Brenda White'	CLoc CWVF EBak SVic WOth
	'Brian C. Morrison' (T)	LCla
	'Brian G. Soanes'	EBak
	'Brian Kimberley' (T)	LCla
	'Brian McFetridge' (d)	WOth
	'Bridesmaid' (d)	CWVF EBak SVic
	'Brighton Belle' (T)	CWVF
	'Brilliant' ambig.	CWVF EHDe
	'Brilliant' Bull, 1865	CLoc EBak LCla
	'British Jubilee' (d)	CWVF SVic WOth
	'British Sterling' (d)	WOth
	'Britney'PBR **new**	MSmi
	'Brixham Orpheus'	CWVF
	'Bromley Beauty'	MJac
	'Brookwood Belle' (d) ♀H3	CWVF EPts LCla MJac SLBF
	'Brookwood Joy' (d)	CWVF
	'Brutus' ♀H4	CLoc CRos CWVF EBak EPfP EPts LRHS MSmi NRHS SCoo SLBF SPet SVic WFar WOth
	'Bryan Breary' (E)	LCla WOth
	'Buddha' (d)	EBak
	'Bugle Boy'	LCla
	'Bunny' (d)	CWVF ESps SVic
	'Burgundy Velvet'	WOth
	'Buster' (d)	LCla
	'Buttercup'	CWVF SVic
	'Butterfly Dance'	SLBF WOth
	'C.J. Howlett'	EBak
	'Caesar' (d)	CWVF EBak
	'Caledonia'	WOth
	'Callaly Pink'	CWVF
	'Calverley'	WOth
	'Cambridge Louie'	CWVF EBak SPet WOth
	campos-portoi	CFil MGil WOth WPGP
	'Candle in the Wind' **new**	WOth
	'Candy Bells' (d)	CSBt
	canescens misapplied	see *F. ampliata*

'Canny Bob'	MJac WOth
'Canopy' (d)	CWVF
'Capri' (d)	CWVF
'Cara Mia' (d)	CLoc SPet
'Caradela' (d)	CLoc MJac
'Cardinal'	CLoc WOth
'Cardinal Farges' (d)	CLoc CWVF SLBF SVic
'Careless Whisper'	LCla SLBF WOth
'Carl Drude' (d)	SVic
'Carla Johnston' ♀H2	CLoc CWVF EPts MJac SVic WOth
'Carmel Blue'	CCCN CLoc CRos LCla LRHS MSmi NRHS SVic
'Carnoustie' (d)	EBak
'Carol Grace' (d)	CLoc
'Carol Nash' (d)	CLoc
'Caroline'	CLoc CWVF EBak EPts SVic WOth
'Caroline's Joy'	MJac SCoo SPet
'Cascade'	CLoc CWVF EPts ESps MJac MSmi SLBF SPet
'Caspar Hauser' (d)	CWVF SVic
'Catherine Bartlett'	CWVF
'Cecil Glass'	EHDe WOth
'Cecile' (d)	CCCN CWVF EPts ETMg LCla MJac MSmi SLBF SVic
'Celadore' (d)	CWVF
'Celebration' (d)	CLoc CWVF
'Celia Smedley' ♀H3	CLoc CRos CWVF EBak EPts LCla LRHS MJac NRHS SLBF SPet SVic WOth
'Celine'	WOth
'Centerpiece' (d)	EBak
'Ceri'	CLoc
'Cerrig'	SVic
'Chain Reaction' (d) **new**	WOth
'Champagne Celebration'	CLoc WOth
'Champion'	WOth XLum
'Chandleri'	CWVF SVic
'Chang' ♀H2	CLoc CWVF EBak LCla SLBF SVic WOth
'Chantelle Garcia' (d)	EPts LCla MJac SLBF WOth
'Chantry Park' (T)	LCla
'Chapel Rossan' (E)	SLBF
'Charisma'	SVic
'Charles Welch'	EPts
CHARLIE DIMMOCK ('Foncha'PBR) (d)	CLoc
'Charlie Gardiner'	CWVF EBak
'Charlie Girl' (d)	SVic
'Charming'	CLoc CRos CWVF EHDe EPfP LRHS MAsh MJac NRHS SVic WOth XLum
'Chartwell'	WOth
'Chatt's Delight'	SLBF
'Checkerboard' ♀H3	CLoc CWVF EBak EPts LCla MHer MJac MSmi SLBF SPet SVic WOth
'Cheers' (d)	CWVF
'Chelsea Louise'	EPts
'Cherry Lee'	SLBF WOth
'Cherry Pop' (E)	WOth
'Chessboard'	CLoc
'Chillerton Beauty' ♀H4	CLoc CRos CTri CWVF ELan ELon EPts LCla LRHS MJac MSmi NLar NRHS SEND SLBF SPer SPet SVic WOth
'Chilli Red'	CRos EPfP EPts LRHS MSmi NRHS
'China Doll' (d)	CWVF
'China Lantern'	CLoc CWVF MSmi SVic
'Chloe Christina' (E) **new**	WOth
'Chor Echo'	SLBF WOth
'Chris Bright'	MJac
'Chris Tarrant' (d)	EPts

	'Christina Becker'	SVic
	'Christine Bamford'	CWVF
	'Christmas Ribbons' (d)	MSmi
	'Churchtown'	CWVF
	cinerea	LCla WOth
	'Cinnabarina' (E)	CLoc SVic WOth
	'Cinvenu'	LCla
	'Cinvulca'	LCla
	'Circe' (d)	CWVF
	'Citation'	CLoc CWVF EBak SVic
	'City of Adelaide' (d)	CLoc
	'City of Leicester'	CWVF SPet
	'Clair de Lune'	CWVF EBak SLBF SVic
	'Claire Oram'	CLoc
	'Claire Simone' **new**	SLBF
	'Claudia' (d)	LCla MJac MSmi SLBF
	'Cliff's Hardy'	LCla MSmi SVic
	'Cliff's Own'	SVic
	'Cliff's Unique' (d)	CWVF EPts
	'Clifton Beauty' (d)	CWVF MJac
	'Clifton Belle' (d)	CWVF
	'Clifton Charm'	EPts LCla MJac SVic WOth
	'Clipper'	CWVF EHDe WOth
	'Cloth of Gold'	CLoc CWVF EBak MJac SLBF SPet SVic WOth
	'Cloverdale Jewel' (d)	CWVF MSmi SPet SVic WOth
	'Cloverdale Joy'	WOth
	'Cloverdale Pearl'	CWVF EBak MAsh MSmi SPet SPoG SVic WOth
	'Cloverdale Star'	WOth
	'Coachman' ♀H4	CLoc CWVF EBak EPts LCla MSmi SLBF SVic WOth
	coccinea	CTsd WOth
	'Codex' (d)	SLBF
	× ***colensoi***	LCla
*	- var. ***purpurascens***	WOth
	'Collingwood' (d)	CLoc CWVF WOth
	'Come Dancing' (d)	CWVF SPet SVic
	'Comet' Banks	CWVF
I	'Comet' Tiret (d)	CLoc
	'Connie' (d)	EBak SVic XLum
	'Connor's Cascade'	SLBF
	'Conspicua' ♀H4	CWVF LRHS SLBF SVic WOth
	'Constable Country' (d)	CWVF
	'Constance' (d)	CLoc CWVF LCla MJac MSmi SLBF SPet SVic WOth
	'Constance Comer'	MJac
	'Constellation' ambig.	CWVF
	'Constellation' Schnabel, 1957 (d)	CLoc EBak
	'Coquet Bell'	CWVF EBak
	'Coquet Dale' (d)	CWVF
	'Coral Baby' (E)	LCla SLBF
	'Coral Rose' (d)	SVic
	'Coralle' (T) ♀H1c	CCCN CLoc CWVF EBak EPts LCla MJac MSmi SLBF SVic WOth
	'Corallina' ♀H4	CLoc SEND SVic WOth
*	***cordata*** B&SWJ 9095	WCru
	- B&SWJ 10325	WCru
	cordifolia misapplied	see *F. splendens*
	'Core'ngrato' (d)	CLoc CWVF
	'Cornelia Smith' (T)	LCla
	'Cornish Blue'	CLoc
	'Cornwall Calls' (d)	EBak
	'Corsage' (d)	CWVF SVic
	'Corsair' (d)	EBak SVic
	corymbiflora misapplied	see *F. boliviana* Carrière
	corymbiflora Ruíz & Pav.	SVic
	'Costa Brava'	CLoc
	'Cotta Bright Star'	CWVF LCla

'Cotta Carousel'	LCla
'Cotta Christmas Tree'	LCla SLBF
'Cotta Fairy'	CWVF
'Cotta Vino'	SVic
'Cottinghamii'	see *F.* × *bacillaris* 'Cottinghamii'
'Cotton Candy' (d)	CLoc CWVF SVic WOth
'Countdown Carol' (d)	EPts
'Countess of Aberdeen'	CWVF EBak SLBF WOth
'Countess of Maritza' (d)	CLoc CWVF
'Court Jester' (d)	CLoc
'Cover Girl' (d)	EPts
'Coxeen'	EBak WOth
'Crackerjack'	CLoc
'Crescendo' (d)	CLoc CWVF
'Crinkley Bottom' (d)	EPts MJac SLBF
'Crosby Serendipity'	CLoc
'Crosby Soroptimist'	CWVF WOth
'Cross Check'	CWVF WOth
'Crusader' (d)	CWVF
'Crystal Blue'	EBak SVic
'Crystal Stars' (d)	SVic
'Cumbrian Lass'	WOth
'Cupid'	EBak
'Curly Q'	EBak SVic
'Curtain Call' (d)	CWVF EBak SVic
cylindracea misapplied	see *F.* × *bacillaris*
'Cymon' (d)	CWVF
'Cymru' (d)	SVic
'Dainty'	EBak
'Dainty Lady' (d)	EBak WOth
'Daisy Bell'	CLoc CWVF EBak LCla MJac SPet SVic WOth
'Dana Samantha'	EPts
'Dancing Bloom'	EPts
'Dancing Flame' (d) ♀H3	CLoc CWVF EBak EPts LCla MJac MSmi SLBF SVic
'Daniel Pfaller' (d)	MJac
'Danish Pastry'	CWVF SPet
'Danny Boy' (d)	CLoc CWVF EBak SVic
'Dark and Delicious' (Mojo Series)	MSmi WOth
'Dark Eyes' (d) ♀H4	CCCN CLoc CWVF EBak MJac MSmi SLBF SPer SPet SVic WOth
'Dark Mystery' (d)	WOth
'Dark Secret' (d)	EBak
'Daryn John Woods'	ECre LCla WOth
'David' ♀H4	CLoc CWVF ELon EPfP EPts LCla LSRN MJac SLBF SPoG WAvo WOth
'David Alston' (d)	CLoc CWVF
'David Lockyer' (d)	CLoc CWVF SVic
'David Savage' (d)	LCla
'Dawn Fantasia' (v)	CLoc EPts
'Dawn Redfern' (d)	CWVF
'Dawn Star' (d)	CLoc CWVF MSmi SVic WOth
'Dawn Thunder' (d)	SVic
'De Groot's Dream'	WOth
'De Groot's Floriant'	LCla
'De Groot's Vulkaan'	WOth
'Debby' (d)	EBak
'Deben Petite' (E)	LCla
'Deborah Jane'	SLBF WOth
'Deborah Street' (d)	CLoc
'DebRon's Beau Dean Richard'	WOth
'DebRon's Black Cherry'	SLBF WOth
'DebRon's Party Girls'	WOth
'DebRon's Snow Fairy'	WOth
'DebRon's Tonii Nicole' (d)	WOth
'DebRon's White Linen' (d)	WOth

'Dee Copley' (d)	EBak
'Deep Purple' (d)	CLoc EPts ETMg MJac MSmi SCoo SLBF
'Delia Smith' (d)	EPts
'Delicate Blue' **new**	WOth
'Delicate Purple'	EPts WOth
'Delicate White' **new**	WOth
'Delilah' (d)	CWVF
'Delphobe'	EPts WOth
'Delta's Bride'	SLBF
'Delta's Dream'	CWVF WOth
'Delta's Drop'	SVic
'Delta's Fellow'	WOth
'Delta's Groom'	LCla SLBF
'Delta's Ko' (d)	SVic
'Delta's Parade' (d)	WOth
'Delta's Sara'	CRos ELon EPfP EShb ETMg IRob LBuc LCro LOPS LRHS MJac NRHS SLim SLon SPoG WBor WFar WHar WOth
'Delta's Symphonie' (d)	CWVF
'Delta's Wonder'	SVic
§ ***denticulata*** ♀H2	CBot CLoc CRos CWVF EBak EPts LCla LRHS MHer NRHS SLBF SVic WOth
'Derby Imp'	CWVF
'Derrick's Folly'	WOth
'Desperate Daniel'	EPts
'Deutsche Perle'	WOth
'Devonshire Dumpling' (d) ♀H2	CCCN CLoc CWVF EBak EPts MJac MSmi SPet SVic
'Dharlah' (T)	SLBF WOth
'Diablo' (d)	EBak
'Diamond Celebration' (d)	WOth
'Diamond Wedding'	SVic WOth
'Diana Wills' (d)	CWVF
'Diana Wright'	WAvo
DIANA, PRINCESS OF WALES ('Fucdpw'PBR)	MSmi
'Diane Brown'	CWVF
§ 'Die Schöne Wilhelmine'	SVic
'Dilly-Dilly' (d)	CWVF
'Dipton Dainty' (d)	CLoc EBak SVic
'Display' ♀H4	CLoc CRos CWVF EBak EPfP EPts ETMg LCla LRHS MGos MJac NPer NRHS SGol SLBF SPet SPoG SVic WHar
'Diva'	WCot
'Doc'	EPts SPet SVic
'Docteur Topinard'	CLoc
'Doctor'	see *F.* 'The Doctor'
'Doctor Foster' ♀H4	CLoc CTri EBak MSmi SVic
'Doctor Mason'	CWVF
'Doctor Olson' (d)	CLoc
'Doctor Robert'	CWVF EPts MJac
'Dodo'	LCla SLBF
'Doffie'	WOth
§ 'Dollar Prinzessin' (d) ♀H4	CLoc CMac CRos CWVF EBak EPfP EPts EShb ETMg IRob LCla LRHS MAsh MGos MJac MSmi NPer NRHS SGol SLBF SLim SPet SPlb SVic WFar
'Dominyana'	EBak LCla
'Dopy' (d)	EPts SPet SVic
'Doray'	EPts WOth
'Doreen Redfern'	CLoc CWVF MJac SPet SVic
'Doreen Stroud' (d)	CWVF
'Doris Joan'	SLBF WOth
'Dorothea Flower'	CLoc CWVF EBak WOth
'Dorothy'	EPts LCla SLBF
'Dorothy Ann'	LCla SLBF
'Dorothy Cheal'	CWVF
'Dorothy Day' (d)	CLoc
'Dorothy Hanley' (d)	CCCN CLoc ELon EPts MJac MSmi SLBF SPet SVic WOth
'Dorothy Shields' (d)	CWVF MJac WOth
'Dorrian Brogdale' (T)	LCla
'Dorset Abigail'	CWVF
'Dorset Delight' (d)	CWVF
'Dragon Quest' **new**	WOth
'Drake 400' (d)	CLoc
'Drama Girl' (d)	CWVF
'Drame' (d)	CWVF EBak MSmi SVic
'Duchess of Albany'	CLoc EHDe WOth
'Duchess of Cornwall' (d)	EPts
'Duet' (d)	SVic
'Duke of Wellington' Haag, 1956 (d)	CLoc
'Dulcie Elizabeth' (d)	CWVF EBak MJac SPet
'Dunrobin Bedder'	SLBF
'Dusky Beauty'	CWVF SVic
'Dusky Rose' (d)	CLoc CWVF EBak MJac SVic
'Dutch Mill'	CLoc CWVF EBak
'Duyfken'	CWVF
'Dying Embers' ♀H4	CLoc MHer SVen WOth
'Dymph Werker van Groenland' (E)	LCla
'Earre Barré'	SLBF
'East Anglian'	CLoc WOth
'Easter Belle'	CRos LRHS NRHS
'Easter Bonnet' (d)	CLoc CWVF
'Ebb 'n' Flow'	EBak
'Ebbtide' (d)	CLoc
'Echo'	CWVF WOth
'Ed Largarde' (d)	EBak
'Edale'	MSmi
'Ede Staal'	WOth
'Eden Lady'	CLoc SPet
'Eden Princess'	CWVF MJac
'Eden Rock' (d)	CLoc MSmi WOth
'Edith' ambig.	EPts
'Edith' Brown (d)	LCla SLBF
'Edith Emery' (d)	SPet
'Edna May'	CWVF
'Edna W. Smith'	CWVF
'El Camino' (d)	CWVF MSmi
'El Cid'	CLoc EBak SVic WOth
'Elaine Ann'	EPts MJac
'Elaine Taylor' (d)	MJac
'Elburg's Minibel'	WOth
'Eleanor Clark'	WOth
'Eleanor Grace'	WOth
'Eleanor Leytham'	CWVF EBak SVic WOth
ELECTRIC LIGHTS ('Nufu1'PBR)	EPts
'Elfin Glade'	CLoc CWVF EBak SVic
'Elfrida' (d)	MSmi
'Elfriede Ott' (T) ♀H1c	CLoc EBak LCla
'Elizabeth' Whiteman, 1941	WOth
'Elizabeth Honnorine'	SVic
'Ellebel'PBR	MSmi
'Ellen Morgan' (d)	CWVF
'Ellie's Charm' **new**	NWms SLBF
'Elma'	LCla MJac
'Elsa' (d)	CWVF SVic
'Elsie Mitchell' (d)	CWVF SPet
§ 'Emile de Wildeman' (d)	CWVF SPet
'Emily'	WOth
'Emily Austen'	CWVF
'Emily Bright'	EHDe

'Emily Eve' (d)	MJac SLBF WOth
'Emma Alice' (d)	CWVF
'Emma Calvé' (d) **new**	WOth
'Empress of Prussia' ♀H4	CLoc CWVF EBak EPts MSmi SLBF SVic WOth
'Enchanted' (d)	CWVF
encliandra subsp. ***encliandra*** (E)	WOth
§ 'Enfant Prodigue' (d)	CLoc SLBF SPet SVic XLum
'English Rose' (d)	CWVF
'Enstone'	see *F. magellanica* var. *molinae* 'Enstone'
'Eppsii'	SLBF
'Eric's Majestic' (d)	MJac
'Erik'	WOth
'Erika Köth' (T)	WOth
'Ernest Rankin'	SVic
'Ernie' PBR	EPts SLBF
'Ernie Bromley'	CWVF WOth
'Ernie Wise' (d)	MSmi SCoo
'Eroica'	SVic
'Eruption'	CLoc MCot
'Estelle Marie'	CLoc CWVF EBak SPet SVic
'Eternal Flame' (d)	CWVF EBak EPts SVic
'Ethel May' (d)	MJac
'Eusebia' (d)	SVic
'Eva Boerg' ♀H4	CCCN CLoc CTri CWVF EBak EPts ESps MSmi SPet SVic WKif
'Eva Thwaites' (E) **new**	WOth
'Evelyn Stanley' (d)	CWVF
'Evensong'	CLoc CWVF EBak SVic WOth
'Evita' (Bella Series) **new**	ETMg MSmi
excorticata	CBcs CExl CTsd EBee MCot SPlb WBor
'Fabian Franck' (T)	LCla
'Falklands' (d)	EPts SLBF
'Falling Stars'	CLoc CWVF SVic
'Fancy Pants' (d)	CLoc CWVF SVic
'Fanfare'	LCla SVic
'Fascination'	see *F.* 'Emile de Wildeman'
'Feather Duster'	MSmi
'Felicity Kendal' (d)	SCoo
'Feltham's Pride'	CWVF
'Fenman'	CWVF SVic
'Festival Lights' (E)	SLBF
'Festoon'	WOth
'Fey' (d)	CWVF
'Ffion'	EPts WOth
'Fiery Spider'	EBak SVic
'Finn'	CWVF EPts
'Fiona'	CLoc CWVF EBak SVic WOth
'Fiona Pitt' (E)	WOth
'Fire Mountain' (d)	CLoc SVic
'Firecracker'	see *F.* 'John Ridding'
'Firefly'	SVic
'Firelite' (d)	EBak
'Firenza' (d)	CWVF
'First Kiss' (d)	CWVF WOth
'First Lady' (d)	CWVF
'First Lord'	CWVF
'First Success' (E)	CWVF LCla SVic WOth
'Flair' (d)	CLoc CWVF WOth
'Flamenco Dancer' (California Dreamers Series) (d)	CLoc
'Flamingo' (d)	SVic
'Flamingo Wings' (d)	EPts
'Flash' ♀H4	CLoc CTri CWVF ELan EPts LCla MJac MRav MSmi SLBF SPet SPoG SVic WOth

'Flashlight'	CWVF EWld LCla MAsh MJac MSmi SCoo WOth
'Flat Jack o' Lancashire' (d)	SLBF WOth
'Fleur de Picardie'	SLBF
'Flirtation Waltz' (d)	CLoc CWVF EBak MJac SVic
'Flocon de Neige'	SLBF
'Flogman'	EWld LCla
'Floral City' (d)	CLoc
'Florence Taylor' (d)	CWVF
'Florence Turner'	EBak MSmi WOth
'Florentina' (d)	CLoc CWVF EBak SVic
'Florrie's Gem' (d)	SLBF
'Flowerdream' (d)	CWVF
'Fluffy Frills' (d)	MSmi
'Fly-by-night' (d)	CWVF
'Flying Cloud' (d)	CLoc CWVF EBak MSmi SVic WOth
'Flying Scotsman' (d)	CLoc CWVF EBak EPts MSmi SCoo SVic WOth
'Fokko's Katrientje'	WOth
'Folk'	MSmi
'Foolke'	EBak
'Forget-me-not'	CLoc CWVF SVic WOth
'Formosissima'	WOth
'Fort Bragg' (d)	CWVF EBak
'Fountains Abbey' (d)	CWVF
'Four Farthings' (d)	EPts
'Foxgrove Wood' ♀H4	CWCL CWVF EBak EPts SLBF WOth
'Foxtrot' (d)	CWVF
'Foxy Lady' (d)	CWVF
'Frank Saunders'	CWVF LCla SLBF
'Frank Unsworth' (d)	CWVF EPts MJac SPet
'Frankfurt 2006'	MJac
'Frankie's Magnificent Seven' (d)	EPts
'Franz von Zon'	LCla
'Frau Hilde Rademacher' (d)	CWVF EBak EPts SLBF SVic
'Frauke'	SVic
'Fred Hansford' (v)	CWVF WOth
'Fred Swales' (T)	WOth
'Fred's First' (d)	SVic
'Friendly Fire' (d)	CLoc
'Frosted Flame'	CLoc CWVF LCla MJac MSmi SLBF SPet
'Frozen Tears'	EPts WOth
'Frühling' (d)	EBak
FUCHSIABERRY (F) **new**	ETMg
'Fuchsiade '88'	CLoc CWVF
'Fuchsiarama '91' (T) ♀H2	CWVF
'Fuji-san'	ELon EPts
'Fuksie Foetsie' (E)	WOth
fulgens (T) ♀H2	GCal LCla
* - 'Variegata' (T/v)	CLoc EPts LCla WOth
'Fulpila'	LCla SLBF
'Funk'	MSmi
'Gala' (d)	EBak
'Galadriel'	SAko WOth
'Garden News' (d) ♀H4	CLoc CRos CWVF ELon EPfP EPts LCla LRHS MAsh MJac MSmi NGBl NPer NRHS SGol SLBF SPer SPet SVic WFar WHar
'Garden Week' (d)	CWVF SVic
'Gartenmeister Bonstedt' (T) ♀H1c	CLoc CWVF EWld LCla SVic WOth
'Gary Rhodes' (d)	EBak MSmi SCoo
'Gay Anne' (d)	WOth
'Gay Fandango' (d)	CLoc CWVF
'Gay Señorita'	EBak
'Gay Spinner' (d)	CLoc

	Name	Suppliers
	'Gemma Fisher' (d)	EPts
	GENE ('Goetzgene'PBR) (Shadowdancer Series)	SCoo
	'Général Monk' (d)	CWVF EBak EPts MSmi SGol SVic WOth
	'General Wavell' (d)	SVic
	'Genii' ♀H4	Widely available
	'Geoff Amos' (d)	MSmi
	'Geoff Oke'	WOth
	'Geoffrey Smith' (d)	EPts
§	'Georg Börnemann' (T) ♀H2	CLoc EBak MJac WOth
	'George Allen White' (d)	CWVF
	'George Barr'	CRos LRHS NRHS
	'Georges Remy'	WOth
§	'Gerharda's Aubergine'	CLoc CWVF WOth
	'Gesaüseperle'	WOth
	'Gesneriana'	CLoc EBak
	'Giant Pink Enchanted' (d)	CLoc
	'Gilda' (d)	CWVF MJac SVic
	'Gill Chumbley' **new**	WOth
	'Gillian Althea' (d)	CWVF MSmi
	'Gilt Edge' (v)	CLoc
I	'Gina'	WOth
	'Gina Bowman' (E)	EPts LCla SLBF
	GINGER ('Goetzginger'PBR) (Shadowdancer Series)	SCoo
	'Gipsy Princess' (d)	CLoc
	'Girls' Brigade'	CWVF
	'Gladiator' (d)	CMac EBak SVic WOth
	'Gladys Lorimer'	CRos CWVF EPts LRHS NRHS WOth
	'Gladys Miller'	CLoc
	glazioviana ♀H2	CWVF EPts GCal LCla MHer SLBF SMHy SVen WOth
	'Glenby' (d)	CWVF
	'Glendale'	CWVF WOth
	'Glitters'	CWVF EBak
§	'Globosa'	CAgr WOth
	'Glow'	WOth
	'Glowing Embers'	EBak
	'Glowing Lilac' (d)	EPts MSmi
	'Gold Brocade'	ELan
	'Gold Leaf'	CWVF
	'Golden Anniversary' (d)	CLoc CWVF EBak MSmi SVic
	'Golden Arrow' (T)	LCla SVic
§	'Golden Border Queen'	CLoc EBak SPet
	'Golden Dawn'	CLoc CWVF SPet SVic
	'Golden Girl'	SLBF
	'Golden Herald'	SLBF
	'Golden la Campanella' (d/v)	CLoc
	'Golden Lena' (d/v)	CWVF
	'Golden Marinka' (v) ♀H2	CLoc EBak ESps SPet SVic
	'Golden Swingtime' (d)	MJac SPet SVic
	'Golden Treasure' (v)	CLoc CWVF MSmi
	'Golden Vergeer' (v)	SLBF
	'Golondrina'	CWVF
	'Good Girl'	WOth
	'Goody Goody'	SVic
	'Gordon's China Rose'	LCla
	'Göttingen' (T)	WOth
	'Governor Pat Brown' (d)	EBak
	'Grace Darling'	CWVF EBak
	gracilis	see *F. magellanica* var. *gracilis*
	'Graf Witte'	CWVF SPet SVic
	'Granada' (d)	WOth
	'Grand Duke' (T/d)	CWVF
	'Grand Prix' (d)	SVic
	'Grandad Fred' (d)	SLBF
	'Grandad Hobbs' (d)	LCla
	'Grandma Sinton' (d)	CLoc CWVF
	'Grandpa Jack' (d)	SLBF
	'Granny Charlton'	WCFE
	'Grasmere'	WOth
	'Grayrigg'	ELon EPts EShb LCla LSRN MSmi SLBF WOth
	'Great Ouse' (d)	EPts
	'Great Scott' (d)	CLoc
	'Green 'n' Gold'	EBak
	'Greenpeace'	SLBF SVic WOth
	'Grey Lady' (d)	MSmi SVic
	'Grietje' (E)	WOth
	'Gris'	WOth
	'Groene Kan's Glorie'	SVic
	'Grumpy'	CWVF EPts SPet SVic WOth
	'Gruss aus dem Bodethal'	CLoc CWVF EBak EPts SLBF
	'Guinevere'	CWVF
	'Gunar Reich' (d)	WOth
	'Gustave Doré' (d)	EBak
	'Gwen Dodge'	SVic
	'Gypsy Girl' (d)	CWVF
	'H.G. Brown'	EBak SLBF
	'Hampshire Blue'	CWVF WOth
	'Hanna' (d)	CRos LRHS NRHS WOth
	'Hanna Amelia Dowling' **new**	WOth
	'Hannah Amelia'	MJac
	'Hannah Louise' (d)	EPts
	'Hans Callaars'	LCla
	'Happiness' (d)	SVic
	'Happy'	CWVF EPts MSmi SPet SVic
	'Happy Anniversary'	CLoc SVic WOth
	'Happy Fellow'	CLoc EBak WOth
	'Happy Wedding Day' (d)	CLoc CWVF EPts EShb MJac MSmi SCoo SPet SVic
	'Hapsburgh'	EBak
	'Harbour Lites'	SLBF
	'Harlow Car'	CWVF EPts WOth
	'Harlow Perfection'	WOth
	'Harmony' Niederholzer, 1946	EBak WOth
	'Harriet Lye'	EHDe WOth
	'Harriett' (d)	WOth
	'Harry Gray' (d) ♀H2	CLoc CWVF EBak EPts MJac MSmi SPet SVic
	'Harry Lye'	WOth
	'Harry Taylor' (d)	EPts
	'Harry's Sunshine'	SLBF
	hartwegii	LCla MHer
	'Harvey's Reward'	SLBF WOth
	'Hathersage' (d)	EBak WOth
	hatschbachii ♀H2	CRos EPfP EShb EWes GCal LCla LRHS MCot MHer NRHS SBrt SCob SLon SMHy SPlb SVen WOth WPGP
	'Haute Cuisine' (d)	CLoc SVic
	'Hawaiian Sunset' (d)	CLoc CWVF EPts SLBF WOth
	'Hawkshead' ♀H4	Widely available
	'Hayley Jay' (d)	SLBF WOth
	'Hazel' (d)	CWVF SVic WOth
	'Heidi Ann' (d) ♀H4	CLoc CRos CWVF EBak EPts ESps LRHS MAsh MRav MSmi NRHS SLBF SPet SVic
	'Heidi Blue' (d)	SLBF
§	'Heidi Weiss' (d)	CLoc CWVF SPet
	'Heinrich Henkel'	see *F.* 'Andenken an Heinrich Henkel'
	'Helen Clare' (d)	CLoc CWVF
	'Helen Gair' (d)	CWVF
	'Helen Storer'	MJac

'Hellen Devine'	CWVF
'Hemsleyana'	see *F. microphylla* subsp. *hemsleyana*
'Hendrikje Stoffels' (d)	WOth
'Henkelly's Chloris'	WOth
'Henkelly's Gitano'	WOth
'Henkelly's Hermine'	WOth
'Henkelly's Trubia'	WOth
'Henkelly's Vitalia'	WOth
'Henning Becker' ♀H3	CWVF ELan
'Henri Poincaré'	EBak
'Henriette Ernst'	WOth
'Her Majesty's Crown' (T)	WOth
'Herald' ♀H4	CRos CWCL CWVF EPfP LRHS MGos SLBF SVic WOth
'Herbé de Jacques'	see *F.* 'Mr West'
'HeRi Asagi'	WOth
'HeRi Buffalo' (d)	WOth
'HeRi Orka' (d) **new**	WOth
'HeRi Trevally'	SLBF WOth
'Heritage' (d)	CLoc EBak
'Herman de Graaff' (d)	SLBF
'Hermiena'	CLoc CWVF EPts SLBF SVic WOth
'Herps Bazuin'	WOth
'Herps Buggy'	WOth
'Herps Conga' (d)	WOth
'Herps Kipkar'	WOth
'Herps Martina'	WOth
'Herps Mignon' (d)	WOth
'Herps Piccolo'	WOth
'Herps Pierement'	SLBF
'Herps Schalmei'	WOth
'Herps Serang' **new**	SLBF
'Herps Steekkar'	WOth
'Herps Tamboerijn'	WOth
'Herps Witkar' (d) **new**	WOth
'Hessett Festival' (d)	CWVF EBak
'Heston Blue' (d)	CWVF
'Heydon'	CWVF
'Hi Di' **new**	NWms SLBF
hidalgensis	see *F. microphylla* subsp. *hidalgensis*
'Hidcote Beauty' ♀H2	CLoc CWVF LCla SLBF SPet SVic WOth
'Highland Pipes'	LCla SVic
'Hilda May Salmon'	CWVF
'Hindu Belle'	EBak
'Hinnerike' (E)	CWVF LCla SVic
'Hiroshige' (T)	LCla
'Hobson's Choice' (d)	CWVF SLBF
'Holly's Beauty' (d)	CLoc EPts MSmi
'Horsforth Beauty'	WOth
'Horsforth in Bloom'	WOth
'Hot Coals'	CWVF EPts MJac SVic
'Howlett's Hardy' ♀H4	CLoc CWVF EBak MSmi SVic WOth
'Huet's Baraketh'	WOth
'Hula Girl' (d)	CWVF EBak MJac
'Hulshorst Longhorn' (d) **new**	WOth
'Huntsman' (d)	CCCN
'I Love You'	WOth
'Ian Storey'	CRos EPfP LRHS NRHS
'Ice Cool' (d)	MSmi
'Iceberg'	CWVF EBak SVic
'Icecap'	CWVF SVic
'Iced Champagne'	CLoc CWVF EBak MJac
'Ichiban' (d)	CLoc
'Ida' (d)	EBak
'Igloo Maid' (d)	CLoc CWVF EBak SVic
'Imogen Faye' (d)	LCla SLBF WOth
'Impala' (d)	CWVF
'Imperial Crown'	WOth
'Imperial Fantasy' (d)	CWVF
'Impudence'	CLoc CWVF EBak
'Impulse' (d)	CLoc WOth
'Independence' (d)	SVic
'Indian Maid' (d)	CWVF EBak
'Inekris'	WOth
'Insetta' (d)	WOth
'Insulinde' (T)	CWVF EPts LCla MHer MJac SLBF
'Iolanthe' (T)	CWVF
'Irene L. Peartree' (d)	CWVF LCla
'Irene Sinton' (d)	MJac
'Iris Amer' (d)	CLoc CWVF
'Irving Alexander' (d)	WOth
'Isis' Lemoine	WOth
'Isle of Purbeck'	SVic
'Italiano' (d)	CWVF MJac SVic
'Ivana van Amsterdam'	WOth
'Ixion'	WOth
'Izabela Cieszyńska' (d)	WOth
'Jack Acland'	CWVF WOth
'Jack Shahan' ♀H2	CCCN CLoc CWVF EBak EPts ESps LCla MJac WOth
'Jack Siverns'	WOth
'Jack Stanway' (v)	CWVF MSmi WOth
'Jackie Bull' (d)	CWVF
'Jackpot' (d)	EBak
'Jackqueline' (T)	CWVF
'Jadi Messingtetra'	WOth
'James Bamber'	WOth
'James Lye' (d)	CWVF EBak EHDe WOth
'James Travis' (E)	LCla
'Jan Baptist David'	WOth
'Jan Bremer'	SVic
'Jan Everett' (d)	WOth
'Jan van Erp'	WOth
'Jandel'	CWVF
'Jane Humber' (d)	CWVF
'Jane Lye'	EHDe
'Janice Perry's Gold' (v)	CLoc MJac
'Janie' (d)	CRos EPfP LBuc LRHS MAsh NRHS SVic
'Jap Vantveer' (T)	LCla
'Jasper Marnix'	WOth
'Jasper's Formidable' (T) **new**	SLBF
'Jasper's Lightning' (T) **new**	SLBF
'Jasper's Red Ruby'	SLBF
'Jasper's Unbelievable' **new**	WOth
'Jasper's Zuurstok'	WOth
'Jaunty Jack'	WOth
'Javelin'	WOth
'Jean Frisby'	CLoc WOth
'Jean Shelton' **new**	LCla
'Jean Smith' (d)	MSmi
'Jean Taylor'	EPts
'Jean Webb' (v)	WCot
'Jeeves' (d)	WOth
'Jennifer'	MJac
'Jennifer Ann'	SLBF WOth
'Jenny May'	CLoc EPts LCla WOth
'Jenny Sorensen' ♀H2	CWVF
'Jess'	LCla SLBF WOth
'Jessie Pearson'	CWVF
'Jessimae'	CWVF SPet
'Jester' Holmes (d)	CLoc
'Jet'	MJac
'Jezebel' (d)	SVic
'Jiddles' (E)	LCla WOth
'Jill Holloway' (T)	SLBF

	'Jim Coleman'	CWVF SVic
	'Jim Dodge' (d)	EPts
	'Jim Muncaster'	CWVF
	'Jim Watts'	WOth
	'Jimmy Cricket' (E)	WOth
	'Joan Barnes' (d)	CWVF
	'Joan Cooper'	CLoc CWVF SLBF SVic
	'Joan Goy'	CWVF MJac SVic
	'Joan Knight'	CLoc
	'Joan Margaret' (d)	MJac
	'Joan Morris'	SLBF
	'Joan Pacey'	CWVF
	'Joan Waters' (d)	CWVF
	'Joanna Lumley' (d)	EPts
	'Joanne'	WOth
	'Jo-Anne Fisher' (d)	EPts
	'Joanne Jackson'	MJac
	'Joan's Delight'	SVic
	'Joe Kusber' (d)	CWVF EBak
	'John Bartlett'	CLoc
	'John Galea' **new**	SLBF
	'John Grooms' (d)	CLoc SVic
	'John Hitchcock' (d)	SLBF
	'John Lockyer'	CLoc CWVF
	'John Maynard Scales' (T) ♀H2	CWVF LCla MJac WOth
	'John Nicholass'	SLBF WOth
§	'John Ridding'PBR (T/v) ♀H1c	CLoc SPoG
	'John Wright'	LCla
	'Johnny Boy'	SLBF
	'Jomam'	CWVF
	'Jon Oram'	CLoc CWVF
	'Jose's Joan' (d)	CWVF SVic
	'Jotu'	WOth
I	'Joy' **new**	NWms SLBF
	'Joy Patmore'	CLoc CWVF SLBF SPet WOth
	'Joyce'	WOth
	'Joyce Adey' (d)	CWVF
	'Joyce Sinton'	CLoc CWVF
	'Judith Coupland'	CWVF
	'Judith Louise'	WOth
	'Jules Daloges' (d)	EBak
	'Julie Marie' (d)	CWVF MJac WOth
	'June Gardner'	CWVF
	'June Marie Shaw'	MJac
	'Jungle'	LCla SLBF WOth
	juntasensis	WOth
	'Just Pink' (E)	WOth
	'Jülchen'	CWVF
	'Kaley Jackson'	MJac
	'Kames Bay'	WOth
	'Karen Isles' (E)	LCla SLBF
	'Karen Louise' (d)	CLoc
	'Kate Taylor' (d)	SLBF
	'Kath Barnes' (E) **new**	WOth
	'Kath van Hanegem'	CLoc SLBF WOth
	'Kathryn Maidment'	SVic
	'Katie'	WOth
	'Katie Rogers'	EPts
	'Katinka' (E)	CWVF LCla WOth
	'Katjan'	GBin LCla SLBF WOth
	'Katrina Thompsen'	CLoc CWVF EPts SLBF WOth
	'Katy Flynn'	CWVF WOth
	'Kegworth Carnival' (d)	CWVF
	'Ken Goldsmith' (T)	CWVF
	'Ken Jennings'	CWVF
	'Ken Tudor'	MJac
	'Kenny Holmes'	CWVF
	'Kenny Walkling' ♀H2	MJac SLBF

	'Ken's Pixie'	MJac
	'Kernan Robson' (d)	CWVF EBak
	'Keystone'	EBak
	'King's Ransom' (d)	CLoc CWVF EBak SPet SVic
	'Kirsten de Keijzer' (E)	WOth
	'Kiss 'n'Tell'	CWVF
	'Kit Oxtoby' (d)	CWVF MJac WOth
	'Kiwi' (d)	EBak
	'Klu' **new**	NWms
	'Knockout' (d)	CWVF SVic
	'Kobold'	SLBF
	'Kocarde'	WOth
	'Kolding Perle'	CWVF SLBF
	'Kuniko Atarashi' (d)	EPts
	'Kwintet'	CWVF EBak MJac SPet
	'La Bianca'	EBak
	'La Campanella' (d) ♀H2	CCCN CLoc CWVF EBak EPts ESps MJac SVic
	'La France' (d)	EBak
	'La Neige' ambig.	CWVF
	'La Porte' (d)	CLoc CWVF
	'La Rosita' (d)	EBak
I	'La Traviata' Blackwell (d)	EBak
	'Lace Petticoats' (d)	EBak SVic
	'Lady Beth' (d)	SVic
	'Lady Boothby' ♀H4	Widely available
	'Lady Framlingham' (d)	EPts
	'Lady Heytesbury'	WOth
	'Lady in Black' (d)	CBcs MCot SPoG
	'Lady in Grey' (d)	SVic
	'Lady Isobel Barnett'	CLoc CWVF EBak MJac SLBF SVic WOth
	'Lady Kathleen Spence'	CWVF SPet SVic
	'Lady Patricia Mountbatten'	CWVF SVic WOth
	'Lady Ramsey'	EBak
	'Lady Rebecca' (d)	CLoc
	'Lady Thumb' (d) ♀H3	Widely available
	'Laepines'	WOth
	'Laing's Hybrid'	CWVF EBak
	'Lakeland Princess'	EBak
	'Lambada'	CLoc
	'Lancashire Lad' (d)	MJac
	'Lancashire Lass'	CWVF WOth
	'Lancelot'	EBak
	'Land van Beveren'	WOth
	'Landgoed Hulshorst'	WOth
	'Lapshead White'	CExl
	'Larissa'	WOth
	'Lark' (T)	CWVF WOth
	'Lassie' (d)	CLoc CWVF EBak
	'Last Chance' (E)	SLBF
	'Laura' ambig.	CWVF SVic WOth
I	'Laura' (Dutch)	CLoc EPts LCla SLBF
I	'Laura' Martin (d)	WOth
	'Laura Cross' (E)	SLBF WOth
	'Lavender Kate' (d)	CWVF EBak
	'Lazy Lady' (d)	CWVF
	'Lechlade Apache'	LCla
	'Lechlade Bullet'	LCla
	'Lechlade Chinaman'	SVic
	'Lechlade Debutante'	WOth
	'Lechlade Gorgon'	CWVF LCla SLBF
	'Lechlade Magician'	EPts LCla SEND SLBF SPet WOth
	'Lechlade Maiden'	CWVF WOth
	'Lechlade Martianess'	SVic WOth
	'Lechlade Potentate'	LCla
	'Lechlade Tinkerbell' (E)	LCla
	'Lechlade Violet' (T)	LCla SVic
	lehmanii	LCla
	'Len Bielby' (T)	CWVF LCla

	'Lena' (d) ♀H2	CLoc CMac CTri CWVF EBak EPts MJac MSmi SLBF SPer SPlb SVic
	'Lena Dalton' (d)	CLoc CWVF EBak SVic
	'Leonhart von Fuchs'	WOth
	'Leonora'	CLoc CWVF SLBF SPet SVic
	'Lesley' (T)	CWVF LCla WOth
	'Lesley's Wonder'	MJac
	'Leslie Bowman' ♀H2	LCla SLBF
	'Lett's Delight' (d)	CWVF EPts
	'Letty Lye'	EBak EHDe WOth
	'Leverhulme'	see *F.* 'Leverkusen'
§	'Leverkusen' (T)	CLoc EBak LCla MJac WOth
	'Lidie Bartelink'	WOth
	'Liebriez' (d) ♀H4	EBak SVic
	'Liemers Lantaern'	CWVF
	'Likalin'	CWVF
	'Lilac Lustre' (d)	CLoc CWVF SPet SVic
	'Lilac Mist'	SLBF
	'Lilac Queen' (d)	EBak
	'Lilian'	WOth
	'Lillian Annetts' (d) ♀H2	CWVF MJac SLBF WOth
	'Lillibet' (d)	CLoc CWVF
	'Lime Lite' (d)	MJac
	'Lincoln Castle'	WOth
	'Linda Goulding'	CWVF EBak SVic
	'Linda Grace'	MJac WOth
	'Linda Hinchliffe'	EPts MJac
	'Lindisfarne' (d)	CLoc CWVF EBak MJac WOth
	'Lindsey Victoria' (d)	SVic
	'Lionel'	WOth
	'Lisa' (d)	EPts
	'Lisi'	WOth
	'Little Beauty'	CWVF SVic WOth
	'Little Boy Blue'	EPts
	'Little Brook Gem'	SLBF
	'Little Catbells' (E)	SLBF WOth
	'Little Fellow'	WOth
	'Little Gene'	EBak
	'Little Jessica' (E)	LCla MJac SLBF WOth
	'Little Jewel'	SPet
	'Little Nan'	SLBF
	'Little Ouse' (d)	CWVF
	'Little Tony'	SLBF
	'Lochinver' (d)	CWVF
	'Loeky'	CLoc CWVF SVic WOth
	'Logan Garden'	see *F. magellanica* 'Logan Woods'
	'Lolita' (d)	CWVF EBak
	'London 2000'	EPts LCla MJac SLBF WOth
	'London Eye'	WOth
	'London in Bloom'	LCla SLBF
	'Lonely Ballerina' (d)	CLoc CWVF
	'Long Distance' (T)	LCla
	'Long Wings'	LCla SVic WOth
I	'Longfellow' Lockerbie	WOth
	'Lord Byron'	CLoc
	'Lord Jim'	LCla
	'Lord Lonsdale'	CWVF EPts LCla SVic
	'Lord Roberts'	CLoc CWVF SLBF WOth
	'Lorna Swinbank'	CWVF SVic
	'Lorraine's Delight' (d)	SVic
	'Lottie Hobby' (E) ♀H3	CLoc CMac CMea CWVF EPfP EPts EShb EUJe LCla MSmi NWad SVic WCot
	'Louise Emershaw' (d)	CWVF EBak MJac SVic
	'Louise Nicholls'	MJac
	'Loulabel'	SVic
	'Loveliness'	CLoc CWVF EHDe SVic WOth
	'Lovely Linda'	SLBF
	'Love's Reward' ♀H2	CLoc CWVF MJac SLBF SVic
I	'Loxensis'	CWVF SVic

	loxensis misapplied	see *F.* 'Loxensis', *F.* 'Speciosa'
	'Loxhore Lullaby' (E)	LCla
	'Loxhore Minuet' (T)	LCla
	'Lucinda'	CWVF
	'Lucy Locket'	MJac WOth
	'Lustre'	CWVF SVic WOth
I	'Lycioides'	LCla
	lycioides misapplied	see *F.* 'Lycioides'
§	***lycioides*** Andrews	WOth
	'Lydia'	WOth
	'Lye's Elegance'	EHDe WOth
	'Lye's Excelsior'	EHDe
	'Lye's Favourite'	EHDe
	'Lye's Own'	EHDe SLBF SPet
	'Lye's Perfection'	EHDe
	'Lye's Unique' ♀H3	CLoc CWVF EBak EHDe EPts LCla MJac SLBF SPet SVic WOth
	'Lyndon'	MJac
	'Lynette' (d)	CLoc
	'Lynn Parnell' **new**	WOth
	'Lynne Marshall'	WOth
	'Lynne Patricia' (d)	EPts SLBF WOth
	'Mabel Greaves' (d)	CWVF
	'Machu Picchu'	CLoc CWVF EPts LCla SVic WOth
	macrophylla	WMoo
	'Madame Butterfly' (d)	CLoc
	'Madame Cornélissen' (d) ♀H4	CLoc CMac CRos CSBt CTri CWVF EBak EBee ELan EPfP EPts ESps LRHS MAsh MRav NLar NRHS SCob SCoo SEND SLBF SLim SPer SPet SVic WFar XLum
	'Madeleine Sweeney' (d)	MJac
	'Maetsuycker'	WOth
	'Magda Cerules' (d)	WOth
	magellanica ♀H4	CBcs CRos CTsd ESps MGil MMuc NPer SPer SVic WGwG WMoo WSpi
	- 'Alba'	see *F. magellanica* var. *molinae* 'Alba'
	- 'Alba Variegata' (v)	WFar
	- 'Folius Aureus'	WFar
§	- var. ***gracilis*** ♀H4	CAgr CLoc CRos CTri CWVF EPfP LRHS NBro NRHS SVic WMoo WOth
	- - 'Aurea' ♀H4	CBcs CMac CRos CTsd CWVF ELan ELon EPfP ESps LCla LRHS MHer MRav MSmi NRHS SCoo SLBF SPer SPet SRms SVic WMoo WOth XLum
	- - 'Purple Mountain'	CRos EPfP LRHS NRHS SPoG
	- - 'Variegata' (v) ♀H4	CRos CTsd EBak EPfP LRHS MGos MRav NRHS SPer SPet SVic
§	- - 'Versicolor' (v) ♀H4	Widely available
	- 'Lady Bacon'	CBot CRos ELon EPri EPts EWes GCal LRHS MCot MMuc NRHS SDys SEND SLBF SMHy SPoG WOth WPGP WSHC
§	- 'Logan Woods'	CAby EBee ELon EPfP GKin SLBF WPGP
	- var. ***magellanica***	SCob
	- var. ***molinae***	CDul CLoc CTri CWVF EBak EBee ECrN ELan EPfP EShb GBin GKin GWyn LCla LCro LOPS LRHS MBlu MNrw MSwo NBid NPer SCob SPer SPlb WArt WFar WMoo
§	- - 'Alba' ♀H4	EPts EUJe GMcL NLar SGol SHar SPet WGwG WSpi
I	- - 'Alba Aureovariegata' (v)	CBcs CMac EPfP SPer SVic WFar XLum
§	- - 'Enstone' (v)	ELon
	- - 'Golden Sharpitor' (v)	CCCN WFar
	- - 'Mr Knight's Blush'	WSpi

§	- - 'Sharpitor' (v) ♀H2	CTsd EBak ELan ELon EPfP LRHS MAsh NChi NPer SGol SPer SVic WFar WKif WMoo WOth WSHC
	- var. ***myrtifolia***	CTsd
	- 'Pumila'	CAby CMea ESps EWes GCal MAsh MHer SMHy SRot SVic WAbe WFar WHal WPGP
	- 'Red Mountain'	EWes
§	- 'Thompsonii' ♀H4	SMHy
	- 'Variegata Aurea' (v) **new**	SGol
	'Magenta Flush'	CWVF
	'Magic Flute'	CLoc CWVF MJac SVic
	'Major Heaphy'	CWVF EBak MHer MSmi WOth
	'Malibu Mist' (d)	CWVF
	'Mama Bleuss' (d)	EBak
	'Mancunian' (d)	CWVF
	'Mandarin Cream'	MSmi WOth
	'Mandi Oxtoby' (T)	LCla
	'Mantilla' (T)	CLoc CWVF LCla MJac MSmi SVic WOth
	'Maori Maid'	MSmi
	'Marble Crepe' (T)	WOth
	'Marbled Sky'	SVic
	'Marcia'PBR (Shadowdancer Series)	CLoc
	'Marcus Graham' (d)	CLoc CWVF EBak SCoo SVic
	'Marcus Hanton' (d)	CWVF
	'Margaret' (d) ♀H4	CDul CLoc CTri CWVF EBak EPts SEND SLBF SPet SVic WFar WOth
	'Margaret Bird'	LCla
	'Margaret Brown' ♀H4	CLoc CRos CTri CWVF LCla LRHS NRHS SLBF SPet SVic WOth
	'Margaret My Own'	EPts
	'Margaret Pilkington'	CWVF SVic WOth
	'Margaret Roe'	CWVF EBak MJac SPet
	'Margaret Susan'	EBak
	'Margaret Viscountess Thurso'	SLBF WOth
	'Margarite Dawson' (d)	SVic
	'Maria Landy'	CWVF MJac SLBF WOth
	'Maria Mathilde' (d)	SLBF
	'Maria Shaw'	EPts
	'Marilyn Jane'	WOth
	'Marilyn Olsen'	CWVF
	'Marin Glow' ♀H3	CLoc CWVF EBak SVic
	'Marina Kelly'	WOth
	'Marinka' ♀H2	CLoc CWVF EBak EPts ESps LCla MJac SPet SVic
	MARISKA ('Bf01') (Bella Series) **new**	ETMg MSmi
	'Mark Kirby' (d)	CWVF
	'Marlies de Keijzer' (E)	EPts LCla NWad SLBF SVen WOth
	'Martha Adcock' **new**	SLBF
	'Martin's Double Delicate' (d)	WOth
	'Martin's Inspiration'	LCla WOth
	'Martin's Yellow Surprise' (T)	LCla SLBF SVic
	'Marty' (d)	EBak
	'Martyn Smedley'	WOth
	'Mary' (T) ♀H1c	CLoc CWVF EPts LCla MSmi SLBF SVic WCot WOth
	'Mary Gwenda' (E) **new**	WOth
	'Mary Lockyer' (d)	CLoc EBak
	'Mary Poppins'	CWVF SVic
	'Mary Reynolds' (d)	CWVF WOth
	'Mary Thorne'	EBak
	'Mary's Beauty' (d)	MSmi
	'Mary's Millennium'	CWVF
	'Mauve Beauty' (d)	CWVF MSmi SLBF WOth
	'Mauve Wisp' (d)	SVic
	'Mavis Enderby'	MJac SLBF
	'Max Jaffa'	CWVF
I	'Maxima'	EPts LCla SLBF
	'Maxine's Smile'	SLBF
	'Mayblossom' (d)	CWVF
	'Mayfield'	CWVF
	'Mazda'	CWVF WOth
	'Meadowlark' (d)	CWVF
	'Meditation' (d)	CLoc
	'Melanie'	SVic WOth
	'Melissa Heavens'	CWVF
	'Melody'	SPet SVic
	'Melody Ann' (d)	EBak
	'Melting Moments' (d)	SCoo
	'Mendocino Mini' (E)	WOth
	'Mendocino Rose'	SVic
	'Mephisto' ♀H2	CWVF WOth
	'Mercurius' ♀H4	WOth XLum
	'Merlin'	LCla
	'Merry Mary' (d)	CWVF EBak
	'Mersty' (d)	SLBF WOth
I	'Mexicali Rose' Machado	CLoc
	'Michael' (d/v)	CWVF EPts WOth
	'Michael Wallis' (T)	SLBF WOth
	'Michelle Wallace'	SVic
	michoacanensis misapplied	see *F. microphylla* subsp. *aprica*
	michoacanensis Sessé & Moç. (E) B&SWJ 9027	WCru
	- B&SWJ 9148	WCru
	'Micky Goult' ♀H2	CLoc CWVF EPts MJac SLBF SVic WOth
	'Microchip' (E)	LCla
	microphylla (E)	CAby CBcs CElw CExl CLoc CRos CTsd CWVF EBak EBee ELon GBin GCal IDee LRHS MGil NRHS SMHy SVic WAbe
	- B&SWJ 10331	WCru
§	- subsp. ***aprica*** (E)	LCla
	- - B&SWJ 9101	WCru
	- - 'Dolly's Dress' (E)	WCru
§	- subsp. ***hemsleyana*** (E)	CExl SVic
	- - B&SWJ 10478	WCru
	- - 'Silver Lining' (E)	SCob SPoG WCot WCru WOth
§	- subsp. ***hidalgensis*** (E)	LCla
§	- subsp. ***minimiflora*** (E)	SVic
	- 'Variegata' (E/v)	EWes
	'Midas'	CWVF
	'Midwinter'	CWVF SVic
§	'Mieke Meursing' ♀H2	CLoc CWVF EBak MJac SPet SVic
	'Miep Aalhuizen'	LCla WOth
	'Mike Oxtoby' (T)	CWVF
	'Millennium'	CLoc EBak EPts MJac SCoo SVic
	'Millfield Alpha'	EPts
	'Millfield Bravo'	EPts
	'Millfield Charlie'	EPts
	'Millfield Delta'	EPts
	'Millfield Echo'	EPts
	'Millie Butler'	CWVF
	'Ming'	CLoc
	'Mini'	WOth
	'Miniature Jewels' (E)	SLBF
	minimiflora misapplied	see *F.* × *bacillaris*
	minimiflora Hemsl.	see *F. microphylla* subsp. *minimiflora*
	'Minipani'	SLBF
	'Minirose'	CWVF EPts SLBF WOth
	'Minnesota' (d)	EBak WOth

'Miramere'	EPts
'Mischief'	SVic
'Miss California' (d)	CLoc CWVF EBak ESps
'Miss Great Britain'	CWVF
'Miss Lye'	EHDe
'Miss Muffett' (d)	EPts
'Miss Vallejo' (d)	EBak WOth
'Mission Bells'	CLoc CWVF EBak EPts SPet SVic
'Misty Blue' (d)	SVic
'Misty Haze' (d)	CWVF SVic
'Moe Katelijne' **new**	WOth
'Molesworth' (d)	CWVF MJac
'Money Spinner'	CLoc
'Monsieur Thibaut' ♀H4	SPer
'Monte Rosa' (d)	CWVF
'Montevideo' (d)	CWVF
'Monty Python'	WOth
'Mood Indigo' (d)	CWVF MSmi SVic WOth
'Moody Blues'	WOth
'Moonbeam' (d)	CLoc
'Moonglow'	MJac WOth
'Moonlight Sonata'	CLoc CWVF SPet
'Moonraker' (d)	CWVF SVic
'More Applause' (d)	CLoc
'Morning Light' (d)	CLoc SVic
'Morrells' (d)	EBak
'Moth Blue' (d)	CWVF EBak
'Mountain Mist' (d)	CWVF SVic
'Moyra' (d)	CWVF WOth
'Mr A. Huggett'	CLoc CWVF EPts SLBF WOth
'Mr Blue Sky' **new**	ETMg
'Mr W. Rundle'	EBak SVic WOth
§ 'Mr West' (v)	ETMg LSou MCot SPet
'Mrs Churchill'	CLoc
'Mrs Grant' **new**	EHDe
'Mrs Hobhouse' (d)	EHDe
'Mrs J Bright' **new**	EHDe
'Mrs Lee Belton' (E)	LCla SLBF WOth
'Mrs Lovell Swisher' ♀H4	CWVF EBak LCla SVic WOth
'Mrs Marshall'	CWVF SLBF WOth
'Mrs Popple' ♀H4	Widely available
'Mrs W. Castle'	SVic
'Mrs W.P. Wood' ♀H4	CLoc CRos CWVF ELon LRHS MSCN SVic WOth
'Mrs W. Rundle'	CLoc CWVF SLBF WOth
'Mrs Wilks'	SLBF
'Multa'	WOth
'Muriel' (d)	CLoc CWVF WOth
'Musetta'	WOth
'My Delight'	CWVF
'My Fair Lady' (d)	CLoc CWVF EBak
'My Grandchildren'	SLBF
'My Honey'	WOth
'My Little Cracker'	MJac
'My Mum'	LCla SLBF WOth
'My Pat'	SLBF
'My Reward' (d)	CWVF
'Naaldwijk 800'	WOth
'Nancy Lou' (d)	CLoc CWVF MJac SLBF SPet SVic
'Nanny Ed' (d)	CWVF
'Napoléon'	WOth
'Natasha Lynn' (d)	WOth
'Natasha Sinton' (d)	CCCN CWVF MJac SPet
'Nathan Rhys'	EPts WOth
'Native Dancer' (d)	CWVF
'Neapolitan' (d)	SLBF
'Neck'	LCla
'Nell Gwyn'	CLoc CWVF SVic
'Nellie Nuttall' ♀H2	CLoc CWVF EBak EPts SPet SVic
'Neopolitan' (E)	CLoc EPts LCla SVic WOth

'Nephele'	EPts WOth
'Nettala'	SVic WOth
'Neue Welt'	CWVF
'New Millennium' (d)	EShb
'Nice 'n' Easy' (d)	MJac
'Nicki Fenwick-Raven' (E)	LCla
'Nicki's Findling'	CWVF EPts LCla MJac
'Nicola'	EBak
'Nicola Jane' (d)	CWVF EBak EPts LCla MJac SLBF SPet SVic
'Nicolette'	CWVF MJac
§ ***nigricans*** B&SWJ 10664	WCru
'Niula'	LCla
'Noblesse'	WOth
'Nonchalance' (T)	LCla
'Nora' (Bella Series) **new**	ETMg MSmi
'Nordseebrandung'	WOth
'Norman Welton'	MJac SLBF
'Normandy Bell'	EBak SVic
'Northern Jewel'	EPts SLBF
'Northern Pride' (d)	WOth
'Northilda'	SVic
'Northumbrian Pipes'	LCla WOth
'Northway'	CLoc CWVF MJac MSmi SPet SVic
'Norvell Gillespie' (d)	EBak
'Novella' (d)	CWVF
'Nuance'	LCla
'O Sole Mio'	SVic
'Obcylin' (E)	EPts LCla WOth
'Ocean Beach'	EPts WOth
'Oddfellow' (d)	WOth
'Oetnang' (d)	CTri SCoo
'Oh Carol' (E)	LCla WOth
'Old Somerset' (v)	CCCN SVic WOth
'Olga Storey'	CRos LRHS NRHS
'Olive Moon' (d)	WOth
'Olive Smith'	CWVF EPts LCla MJac
'Olive Suker' (d) **new**	WOth
'Olympia'	WOth
'Olympic Lass' (d)	WOth
'Olympic Sunset'	SVic WOth
'Oosje' (E)	LCla SVic
'Oostveens Thymen'	WOth
'Opalescent' (d)	CLoc CWVF SVic
'Orange Crush'	CLoc CWVF EBak SPet WOth
'Orange Crystal'	CWVF MJac SLBF SVic WOth
'Orange Drops'	CLoc CWVF EBak EPts SVic WOth
'Orange Flare'	CLoc CWVF EBak SLBF SVic
'Orange King' (d)	CLoc CWVF
'Orange Mirage'	CLoc CWVF SPet SVic
'Orange Star' (E)	LCla SLBF WOth
'Orangeblossom'	SLBF WOth
'Oranje van Os'	CWVF
'Orient Express' (T) ♀H1c	CLoc CWVF MJac SVic WOth
'Oriental Sunrise'	CWVF
'Ornamental Pearl' (v)	CLoc CWVF SLBF WOth
'Orwell' (d)	CWVF
'Oso Sweet'	CWVF
'Other Fellow'	CWVF EBak EPts LCla MJac SLBF SPet SVic WOth
'Oulton Empress' (E)	LCla SLBF
'Oulton Fairy' (E)	SLBF
'Oulton Hoya' (E)	WOth
'Oulton Red Imp' (E)	LCla SLBF
'Oulton Travellers Rest' (E)	SLBF WOth
'Oulton Tu-Fu' (E)	WOth
'Our Carol'	SLBF
'Our Darling'	CWVF
'Our Hilary'	SLBF WOth
'Our Nan' (d)	MJac

'Our Pamela'	MJac
'Our Spencer'	SLBF
'Our Ted' (T)	EBak EPts
'Overbecks'	see *F. magellanica* var. *molinae* 'Sharpitor'
'P.E. King' (d)	SLBF
'Pabbe's Belle'	WOth
'Pabbe's Kirrevaalk'	WOth
'Pabbe's Klompnoagel'	WOth
'Pabbe's Kopstubber' (d)	WOth
'Pacific Queen' (d)	EBak
'Pacquesa' (d)	CWVF EBak SPet SVic
'Padre Pio' (d)	CWVF EBak MJac
'Pam Plack'	LCla SLBF WOth
'Pamela Hutchinson'	WOth
'Pamela Knights' (d)	EBak
'Pam's People'	LCla
'Pan'	WOth
'Panache' (d)	LCla
paniculata (T) ♀^{H2}	CBot CCCN CRHN CWVF EBak EPts LCla MCot MHer SLBF WCot WCru
'Panique'	LCla
'Pantomine Dame' (d)	CWVF
'Panylla Prince'	LCla
'Papa Bleuss' (d)	CWVF EBak
'Papoose' (d)	EBak SLBF SVic
'Parkstone Centenary' (d)	CWVF
'Party Frock'	CLoc CWVF EBak SPet WOth
parviflora misapplied	see *F.* × ***bacillaris***
parviflora Lindl.	see *F. lycioides* Andrews
'Pat Meara'	CLoc EBak
'Pathétique' (d)	CLoc
'Patience' (d)	CWVF EBak SLBF
'Patio Princess' (d)	CLoc CWVF EPts
'Patty Evans' (d)	CWVF
'Paul Cambon' (d)	EBak
'Paul und Carola' (d)	WOth
'Paula Jane' (d) ♀^{H2}	CWVF MJac SLBF SVic
'Pauline Rawlins' (d)	CLoc
'Pavilion Princess'	WOth
'Peachy' (California Dreamers Series) (d)	CLoc SCoo SLBF
'Peachy Keen' (d)	EBak
'Peacock' (d)	CLoc
'Pearly Queen' (d)	WOth
'Peasholm'	WOth
'Pee Wee Rose'	EBak SVic WOth
'Peggy Burford' (T)	LCla
PEGGY ('Goetzpeg'^{PBR}) (Shadowdancer Series)	SCoo
'Peggy King'	EBak SPet
'Peloria' (d)	CLoc EBak
'Peper Harow'	EBak
'Pepi' (d)	CWVF EBak
'Peppermint Candy' (d)	CWVF MJac
'Peppermint Stick' (d)	CLoc CWVF EBak MSmi SPet SVic
'Perky Pink' (d)	EBak EPts
'Perry Park'	CWVF MJac SVic
'Perry's Jumbo'	NPer
perscandens	CBcs CExl LCla WOth
'Peter Bielby' (d)	CWVF
'Peter Crookes' (T)	CWVF
'Peter Meredith'	MJac WOth
'Peter Pan'	CWVF
petiolaris	LCla
- B&SWJ 10675	WCru
'Petit Four'	CWVF WOth
'Phaidra' (T)	LCla WOth
'Pharaoh'	CLoc
'Phénoménal' (d)	CWVF EBak MSmi
'Phryne' (d)	SVic WOth
'Phyllis' (d) ♀^{H4}	CLoc CRos CWVF EBak EPts LCla LRHS MJac MSmi NRHS SEND SLBF SPet SVic WOth
'Piet van der Sande'	LCla SLBF
'Piggelmee'	WOth
'Pinch Me' (d)	CWVF EBak SPet SVic
'Pink Aurora'	CLoc
'Pink Ballet Girl' (d)	CLoc SVic
'Pink Bon Accord'	CLoc CWVF SVic
'Pink Cloud'	CLoc EBak
'Pink Cornet'	LCla
'Pink Darling'	CLoc EBak
'Pink Dessert'	EBak
'Pink Elephant' (d) **new**	ETMg
'Pink Fairy' (d)	SPet
'Pink Fandango' (d)	CLoc
'Pink Fantasia' ♀^{H2}	CLoc CWVF EBak EPts LCla MJac SLBF SVic
'Pink Fizz' **new**	CRos ETMg LRHS NRHS
'Pink Galore' (d) ♀^{H2}	CLoc CWVF MJac SLBF SPet
'Pink Goon' (d)	MSmi SLBF SVic
'Pink Haze'	SVic
'Pink Jade'	CWVF
'Pink la Campanella'	CWVF EBak WOth
'Pink Lace' (d)	SPet
'Pink Marshmallow' (d) ♀^{H4}	CLoc CWVF EBak MJac SLBF SPet SVic
'Pink Profusion'	EBak
'Pink Quartet' (d)	CLoc CWVF EBak WCot
'Pink Rain'	CWVF MJac WOth
'Pink Slippers'	CLoc
'Pink Spangles'	see *F.* 'Mieke Meursing'
'Pink Sprite'	WOth
'Pink Temptation'	CLoc CWVF SVic
'Pinnochio' (T)	WOth
'Pinokkio Krom' (T) **new**	WOth
'Pinto de Blue' (d)	MSmi
'Pinwheel' (d)	CLoc EBak
'Piper' (d)	CWVF
'Piper's Vale' (T)	MJac SLBF WOth
'Pirbright'	CWVF
'Pixie'	CLoc CWVF EBak MJac SEND SLBF SPet SVic
'Playboy' (d)	SVic
'Playford'	CWVF EBak
'Pledle' (T)	WOth
'Plenty'	EBak SVic
'Plumb Bob' (d)	CWVF
'Polar'	WOth
'Pop Whitlock' (v)	CWVF SPet SVic
'Poppet'	CWVF WOth
'Popsie Girl' (v)	SLBF WOth
'Port Arthur' (d)	EBak
'Postiljon'	CWVF EBak
'Powder Puff' ambig.	CWVF
'Powder Puff' Hodges (d)	CLoc SVic
'Prelude' Blackwell	CLoc
'President'	CRos EBak LRHS NRHS
'President Barrie Nash'	CLoc WOth
'President George Bartlett' (d) ♀^{H2}	CLoc EPts MJac SLBF WOth
'President Jim Muil'	SLBF
'President Joan Morris' (d)	SLBF
'President John Porter'	MJac SLBF
'President Leo Boullemier'	CWVF MJac MSmi SPet SVic WOth
'President Margaret Slater'	CLoc CWVF SPet SVic WOth
'President Moir' (d)	SLBF WOth
'President Norman Hobbs'	CWVF WOth

	'President Peter Holloway' **new**	LCla MJac NWms SLBF WOth
	'President Stanley Wilson' (d)	EBak EPts WOth
	'President Wilf Sharp' (d)	SVic
	'Preston'	CMac
	'Preston Guild' 🏆H3	CLoc CWVF EBak NPer SDys SPet SRms SVic WOth
	'Prestonfield' (v)	WOth
	'Pride of the West'	EHDe
	'Prince George' **new**	ETMg
	'Prince of Orange'	CLoc SVic WOth
	'Prince Syray'	WOth
	'Princess Charlotte' **new**	ETMg
	'Princess Dollar'	see *F.* 'Dollar Prinzessin'
	'Princessita'	CWVF EBak SPet WOth
	procumbens	CAby CBcs CCCN CExl CLoc CWVF EBak EHDe ELon EPfP EPts EUJe LCla MCot MHer SBrt SLBF WAbe WOth
	- 'Argentea'	see *F. procumbens* 'Wirral'
	- grey-leaved **new**	SBrt
	- 'Variegata'	see *F. procumbens* 'Wirral'
§	- 'Wirral' (v)	CLoc CTsd EHDe EShb ITim WOth
	'Prodigy'	see *F.* 'Enfant Prodigue'
	'Profusion' ambig.	SVic
	'Prosperity' (d) 🏆H3	CLoc CRos CWVF EBak EPfP EPts LCla LRHS MAsh MJac MSmi NRHS SEND SLBF SPet SVic WOth
	'Pumila'	CExl CMac ELan EPfP LRHS SPet SVic WSHC
	'Purbeck Mist' (d)	CWVF
	'Purcellian Elegancy' (T) **new**	WOth
	'Purperklokje'	CWVF EBak SVic WOth
	'Purple Emperor' (d)	CLoc
	'Purple Heart' (d)	CLoc EBak
	'Purple Lace'	SVic
	'Purple Rain'	EPts
	'Pussy Cat' (T)	CLoc CWVF EBak SVic WOth
	'Putney Pride'	EPts
	'Put's Folly' 🏆H2	CWVF EBak MJac SPet WOth
	putumayensis	EBak
	'Quasar' (d)	CCCN CLoc CWVF EPts EShb MJac SLBF SVic
	'Queen Elizabeth'	WOth
	'Queen Ester'	WOth
	'Queen Mary'	CLoc EBak
	'Queen of Bath' (d)	SVic
	'Queen of Derby' (d)	CWVF
	'Queen of Hearts' Kennett (d)	SVic
	'Queen of Mercia'	MJac
	'Queen's Park' (d)	EBak
	'Query'	SVic WOth
	'R.A.F.' (d)	CLoc CWVF EBak EPts SPet SVic
	'Radings Gerda' (E)	LCla SLBF
	'Radings Magma'	WOth
	'Radings Mia' (T)	SLBF
	'Radings Michelle'	CWVF WOth
	'Ragtime'	MSmi
	'Rahnee'	CWVF
	'Rainbow'	CWVF MSmi
	'Ralph's Delight' (d)	CWVF
	'Rambling Rose' (d)	CLoc CWVF
	'Rams Royal' (d)	CWVF
	'Raspberry' (d)	CLoc CWVF EBak SVic
	'Raspberry Ripple' (d)	WOth
	'Raspberry Sweet' (d)	CWVF

	'Raspberry Twist'	WOth
	'Ratae Beauty'	CWVF
	'Ratatouille' (d)	WOth
	ravenii	WOth
	'Ray Redfern'	CWVF
	'Reading Ruby' **new**	LCla MJac NWms SLBF WOth
	'Reading Show' (d)	CWVF EPts SLBF
	'Rebecca Williamson' (d)	CWVF MJac
	'Rebeka Sinton' (v)	CLoc EBak
	'Red Ace' (d)	WOth
	'Red Jacket' (d)	CWVF EBak
	'Red Petticoat'	CWVF
	'Red Rain'	CWVF WOth
	'Red Rum' (d)	CRos SPet
	'Red Shadows' (d)	CLoc CWVF EBak
	'Red Spider'	CCCN CLoc CWVF EBak SCoo SPet SVic WOth
	'Red Wing'	CLoc
	'Reflexa'	see *F.* × *bacillaris* 'Reflexa'
	'Reg Gubler'	SLBF
	'Regal'	CLoc WOth
	regia subsp. ***regia***	LCla XLum
	- subsp. ***reitzii***	CDul LCla XLum
	- subsp. ***serrae***	WOth WPGP
	'Remember Carole Anne' (d)	SLBF WOth
	'Remember Eric'	WOth
	'Remembering Claire'	EPts WOth
	'Remembrance' (d)	EPts LCla MSmi SLBF
	'Remus' (d)	SVic
	'Rene Schwab'	LCla
	'Renée-Madeleine'	WOth
	'Requiem'	CLoc
	'Reverend Frank Pagden'	WOth
	'Rhapsody' ambig.	SVic
I	'Rhapsody' Blackwell (d)	CLoc
	'Riccartonii' 🏆H6	Widely available
	'Richard John' (v)	SVic
	'Ridestar' (d)	CLoc CWVF
	'Rigoletto'	SVic
	'Rijs 2001' (E)	SLBF WOth
	'Ringwood Gold'	SVic
	'Ringwood Market' (d)	CWVF EPts MJac SCoo SPet SVic
	'Rivendell'	EPts
	'Riverdancer Claire'	WOth
	'Riverdancer Liam'	WOth
	'Robert Lutters'	SVic
	'Rocket'	WOth
	'Rocket Fire' (California Dreamers Series) (d)	SVic
	'Roesse Arnold'	WOth
	'Roesse Duck'	WOth
	'Roesse Meton'	WOth
	'Roger de Cooker' (T)	CLoc EPts LCla MJac SVic WOth
	'Rohees Lava'	SLBF
	'Rohees Matar' (d)	WOth
	'Rohees New Millennium' (d)	SLBF
	'Rolla' (d)	CWVF EBak
	'Rolt's Bride' (d)	WOth
	'Rolt's Ruby' (d)	CWVF SVic WOth
	'Roman City' (d)	CLoc SVic
	'Romance' (d)	CWVF
	'Romany Rose'	CLoc
	'Ronald L. Lockerbie' (d)	CLoc CWVF SVic
	'Roos Breytenbach' (T)	CCCN LCla MJac WOth
	'Rosamunda' (d)	CLoc
	'Rose Aylett' (d)	EBak
	'Rose Bradwardine' (d)	EBak
	'Rose Churchill' (d)	MJac
	'Rose Fantasia' 🏆H2	CLoc CWVF EPts MJac SLBF

'Rose of Castile'	CLoc EBak EPts LCla MJac MSmi SLBF SVic
'Rose of Castile Improved' ♀H4	CWVF LCla MJac SLBF SPet WOth
'Rose of Denmark'	CCCN CLoc CWVF EBak MJac SCoo SLBF SPet WOth
'Rose Winston' (d)	SCoo
rosea misapplied	see *F.* 'Globosa'
rosea Ruíz & Pav.	see *F. lycioides* Andrews
'Rosecroft Beauty' (d/v)	CWVF EBak SVic WOth
'Rosemarie Higham' (v)	MJac SCoo WOth
'Rosemary Day'	CLoc
'Rosy Bows'	CWVF
'Rosy Frills' (d)	CWVF MJac SVic
'Rosy Morn' (d)	CLoc
'Rough Silk'	CLoc CWVF EBak
'Roy Castle' (d)	CWVF
'Roy Walker' (d)	CWVF
'Royal Academy' (d)	EPts
'Royal and Ancient'	CWVF
'Royal Mosaic' (California Dreamers Series) (d)	MJac
'Royal Purple' (d)	EBak WOth
'Royal Serenade' (d)	CWVF
'Royal Velvet' (d) ♀H2	CCCN CLoc CRos CWVF EBak EPts LRHS MJac SLBF SPet SVic
'Rubra Grandiflora'	CWVF LCla WOth
'Ruby Wedding' (d)	CWVF SLBF
'Ruddigore'	CWVF
'Ruffles' (d)	CWVF
'Rufus' ♀H4	CDul CLoc CMac CWVF EBak ELan EPts IRob LCla MJac MRav SLBF SPet SVic
'Ruth'	SVic WOth
'Ruth King' (d)	CWVF EBak
'Ryan'	SLBF
'S'Wonderful' (d)	CLoc EBak
'Sailor'	EPts SVic
'Salmon Cascade'	CWVF EPts LCla MJac SLBF
'Salmon Glow'	CWVF SVic
'Sam Sheppard'	SLBF
'Samantha Reynolds'	WOth
'San Diego' (d)	CWVF
'San Mateo' (d)	EBak
§ ***sanctae-rosae***	LCla
'Sandboy'	CWVF EBak
'Santa Cruz' (d)	CMac CWVF MSmi SLBF SVic WOth
'Santa Lucia' (d)	CLoc
'Santa Monica' (d)	EBak
'Sapphire' (d)	EBak
'Sappho Phaoon' (T)	EPts
'Sara Helen' (d)	CLoc EBak
'Sarah' (Bella Series) new	MSmi
'Sarah Brightman' (d)	CLoc
'Sarah Eliza' (d)	EShb MSmi SCoo
'Sarah Jane' (d)	EBak SVic
'Sarah Louise'	CWVF
'Satellite'	CLoc CWVF EBak SPet SVic
'Saturnus' ♀H4	CRos CWVF EBak LRHS SEND SPet SPoG
'Saxondale Sue'	SVic
scabriuscula	LCla
'Scarcity'	CWVF EBak EHDe MSmi SVic WOth
'Scarlet Jester'	EPts WOth
'Schneeball' (d)	EBak SVic
'Schneewitcher'	EPts
'Schöne Wilhelmine'	see *F.* 'Die Schöne Wilhelmine'
'Scotch Heather' (d)	CWVF
'Sea Shell' (d)	CWVF

'Sealand Prince'	CWVF LCla SVic WOth
'Seattle Blue' (T/d)	SLBF
'Sebastopol' (d)	CLoc
'Sensation'	WOth
serratifolia Ruíz & Pav.	see *F. denticulata*
'Seventh Heaven' (d)	CLoc CWVF MJac SCoo
'Shady Blue'	CWVF
'Shanley'	CWVF SVic WOth
'Sharon' (d)	WOth
'Sharpitor'	see *F. magellanica* var. *molinae* 'Sharpitor'
'Shatzie B'	SLBF
'Shawna Ree' (E)	WOth
'Sheila Crooks' (d)	CWVF EBak
'Sheila Kirby'	CWVF
'Sheila Steele' (d)	CWVF
'Shelford'	CLoc CWVF EBak EPts MJac SLBF SVic WOth
'Shell Pink'	SVic
'She's a Beauty'	MJac
'Shirley Halladay' (d)	LCla
'Shirley'PBR (Shadowdancer Series)	SCoo
'Shirley Teece'	EPts
'Showfire'	EBak
'Showtime' (d)	CWVF
'Shrimp Cocktail'	CLoc EShb ETMg SGol WFar
'Shuna Lindsay'	LCla WOth
'Shy Lady' (d)	SPet
'Siberoet' (E)	LCla SLBF WOth
'Sierra Blue' (d)	CLoc CWVF EBak
'Silver Anniversary' (d)	SVic
'Silver Dawn' (d)	WOth
'Silver Dollar'	SVic
'Silver Surfer'	LCla MJac SLBF WOth
'Silverdale'	EPts
'Simon J. Rowell'	LCla
simplicicaulis	EBak LCla
'Sincerity' (d)	CLoc SVic
'Siobhan'	CWVF
'Siobhan Evans' (d)	SLBF
'Sir Alfred Ramsey'	CWVF EBak
'Sir David Jason'	MJac
'Sir Matt Busby' (d)	EPts MJac
'Sister Ann Haley'	EPts
'Sister Sister' (d)	SLBF
'Skater's Waltz' (d)	CLoc
'Sleepy'	EPts SPet SVic
'Sleigh Bells'	CLoc CWVF EBak SVic WOth
'Small Pipes'	CWVF
'Smokey Mountain' (d)	SVic
'Sneezy'	EPts SVic
'Snow Burner' (California Dreamers Series) (d)	CLoc
'Snow White' (d)	SVic
'Snowbird' (d)	SLBF
§ 'Snowcap' (d) ♀H4	CCCN CChe CLoc CRos CWVF EBak ELon EPfP EPts ESps ETMg GKin LCla LRHS MAsh MGos MJac MSmi NPer NRHS SCoo SGol SLBF SLim SPet SPoG SVic WFar
'Snowdon' (d)	CWVF
'Snowdrift' Colville (d)	CLoc
'Snowdrift' Kennett (d)	EBak
'Snowfall'	CWVF
'Snowfire' (d)	CLoc CWVF SVic
'Snowflake' (E)	EPts WBor WOth
'Softpink Jubelteen'	WOth
'Soila' (Bella Series) new	MSmi

'Son of Thumb' ♀H4	CLoc CRos CWVF EPts ESps LRHS MJac NRHS SCob SGol SLBF SLim SPer SPet SVic WOth
'Sonata' (d)	CLoc CWVF SVic
'Sophia' **new**	ETMg MSmi
'Sophie Grace'	WOth
'Sophie Louise'	CWVF EPts SLBF WOth
'Sophisticated Lady' (d)	CWVF EBak EPts SVic
'South Gate' (d)	CLoc CWVF EBak EPts MSmi SPet SVic
'Space Shuttle'	CLoc LCla
'Sparky' (T)	CLoc CWVF EPts LCla WOth
'Speciana'	EPts
§ 'Speciosa'	EBak LCla
'Spion Kop' (d)	CCCN CWVF EShb SPet
§ ***splendens*** ♀H2	CBot CCCN CLoc EBak LCla MCot NPer SLBF WOth
- B&SWJ 10469	WCru
'Sporting Chance' **new**	NWms
'Spring Bells' (d)	CRos LRHS NRHS
'Squadron Leader' (d)	CWVF EBak EPts
'Squirtie'	SLBF
'Stan'	WOth
'Stanley Cash' (d)	CLoc CWVF SPet SVic
'Star Wars'	CLoc EPts MJac WOth
'Stardust'	CWVF WOth
'Steeley' (d)	SVic
'Stella Ann' (T)	CWVF EPts LCla
'Straat Cumberland'	LCla
'Straat Futami' (E)	EPts LCla
'Straat Kobe' (T)	LCla
'Straat La Plata'	LCla
'Straat Magelhaen'	WOth
'Straat of Plenty'	LCla WOth
'Strawberry Daiquiri' (d)	WOth
'Strawberry Delight' (d)	CLoc CWVF MJac SPet SVic
'Strawberry Sundae' (d)	CLoc CWVF EBak
'Strike the Viol' (T)	SLBF WOth
'String of Pearls'	CLoc CWVF MJac SLBF SPet SVic WOth
'Stuart Joe'	CWVF
'Stuart Lockyer' (d)	CLoc
'Sue'	SLBF WOth
'Suffolk Splendour' (d)	EPts
'Sugar Almond' (d)	CWVF
'Sunbeam Hillary' (Sunbeam Series)	WOth
'Sunday's Child' **new**	WOth
'Sunny Jim'	SVic
'Sunny Smiles'	CWVF
'Sunray' (v)	CLoc CPla CRos CWVF EBak ELon EPfP ESps LBuc LRHS MAsh MGos NEgg NRHS SCoo SLBF SLim SPoG SPtp SVen WCot WOth
'Sunset'	CLoc CWVF WOth
'Sunshine'	WOth
'Supersport' (d)	SVic
'Superstar'	CWVF SVic
'Susan' (d)	WOth
'Susan Ford' (d)	CWVF SPet
'Susan Green'	CWVF EBak MJac WOth
'Susan McMaster'	CLoc
'Susan Olcese' (d)	CWVF EBak
'Susan Travis'	CLoc CWVF EBak SVic
SUSANNA ('Bf02') **new**	MSmi
'Suzanna'	WOth
'Swanley Beauty'	EHDe WOth
'Swanley Gem' ♀H2	CLoc CWVF EBak SLBF SPet SVic
'Swanley Pendula'	CLoc WOth
'Swanley Yellow'	CWVF EBak SVic WOth

'Sweet Hollie'	SLBF
'Sweet Sarah' (E)	EPts WOth
I 'Sweetheart' van Wieringen	EBak
'Swingtime' (d) ♀H2	CCCN CLoc CWVF EBak EPts ESps LCla MJac SLBF SPet SVic
sylvatica misapplied	see *F. nigricans*
'Sylvia Barker' ♀H2	CWVF LCla SLBF WOth
'Sylvia Rose' (d)	CWVF
'Sylvia's Choice'	EBak
'Symphony'	CLoc CWVF
'Syreme' (d)	SLBF
'Szilvia Ócsai' (d)	WOth
''t Binnenland'	WOth
'T.I.S. Herentals'	SLBF
'T.S.J.' (E)	LCla
'Taco'	LCla WOth
'Taddle'	CWVF SLBF
'Taffeta Bow' (d)	CLoc SLBF SVic
'Tamworth'	CLoc CWVF EBak MJac SVic
'Tangerine'	CLoc CWVF SVic WOth
'Tanya Bridger' (d)	EBak WOth
'Tarra Valley'	LCla SVic WOth
'Task Force'	CWVF SVic
'Taudens Heil'	WOth
'Tausendschön' (d)	CLoc WOth
'Ted Perry' (d)	CWVF
'Temptation' ambig.	CWVF
'Temptation' Peterson	CLoc EBak WOth
'Tennessee Waltz' (d) ♀H2	CLoc CWVF EBak EPts SLBF SPer SPet SVic
'Tess'	EPts SLBF
tetradactyla misapplied	see *F.* × *bacillaris*
'Texas Longhorn' (d)	CLoc CWVF EBak MSmi SVic
'Thalia' (T) ♀H1c	CBot CCCN CLoc CWVF EBak EPts ESps EUJe LCla LSRN MCot MHer MJac MSmi NEgg SLBF SPlb SPoG SVic SWeb WOth
'Thamar'	CLoc CWVF EPts SVic WOth
'That's It' (d)	SVic
'The Aristocrat' (d)	CLoc EBak
§ 'The Doctor'	CLoc CWVF EBak WOth
'The Jester' (d)	EBak
'The Madame' (d)	CWVF
'The Tarns'	CWVF EBak SVic WOth
'Think Pink'	WOth
'Thistle Hill' (d)	WOth
'Thomas' (d)	EPts
'Thompsonii'	see *F. magellanica* 'Thompsonii'
'Thornley's Hardy'	SVic
'Three Cheers'	CLoc
'Three Counties'	EBak
'Thumbelina'	CRos LRHS NRHS
'Thunderbird' (d)	CLoc CWVF
thymifolia (E)	CRos CWVF LRHS MHer SDys SEND SMHy WKif WOth
- subsp. ***minimiflora*** (E)	CBot
- subsp. ***thymifolia*** (E)	SEle WOth
'Tiara' (d)	EBak
'Tillingbourne' (d)	SLBF
'Time After Time'	CLoc EShb SLBF
'Timlin Brened' (T)	CWVF EBak
'Timothy Titus' (T) ♀H1c	LCla
'Ting-a-ling'	CLoc CWVF EBak SPet SVic WOth
'Tinker Bell' Hodges	EBak SVic
'Tintern Abbey'	CWVF
'Tip Toes' **new**	SLBF
'Tjinegara'	LCla
'Toby Bridger' (d)	CLoc EBak
'Toby Foreman'	SLBF
'Toby S' (d)	SLBF WOth

'Tolling Bell'	CWVF EBak SPet
'Tom Goedeman'	LCla
'Tom Knights'	EBak SPet WOth
'Tom Thumb' ♀H4	Widely available
'Tom West' misapplied	see *F.* 'Mr West'
'Tom West' Meillez (v)	CChe CLoc CRos CSBt CWVF EBak EHoe EPfP EPts ESps LRHS MAsh MHer MJac MRav MSCN MSmi NRHS SGol SLBF SLim SPtp WAvo WFar WOth
'Tom Woods'	CWVF
'Tomarama' (E)	WOth
'Ton Ten Hove'	LCla
'Tony Talbot'	MJac
'Tony's Treat' (d)	EPts WOth
'Toos'	SVic
'Toosje Vantveer'	WOth
'Topper' (d)	CWVF
'Torch' (d)	CLoc CWVF EBak SVic
'Torchlight'	CWVF EPts LCla
'Torvill and Dean' (d)	CLoc CWVF EPts MJac SLBF SPet
'Tosca'	CWVF
'Touch the Lute' (T)	WOth
'Tracid' (d)	SVic
'Trail Blazer' (d)	CLoc CWVF MJac
'Trailing King'	WOth
'Trailing Queen'	MJac
'Trase' (d)	CWVF EBak SVic
'Traudchen Bonstedt' (T) ♀H1c	CLoc CWVF LCla SVic
'Traviata'	see *F.* 'La Traviata' Blackwell
'Treasure' (d)	EBak
'Tricolor'	see *F. magellanica* var. *gracilis* 'Versicolor'
'Trientje'	LCla SLBF WOth
triphylla (T)	CPla EBak MHer
'Trish's Triumph'	EPts
'Tristesse' (d)	CLoc CWVF EBak
'Troon'	CWVF
'Tropicana' (d)	CLoc CWVF SVic
'Troubador' Waltz (d)	CLoc
'Trudi Davro'	MJac SCoo
'Trudy'	CWVF EPts SVic
'Truly Treena' (d)	SLBF
'Trumpeter' ambig.	CWVF
'Trumpeter' Fry	SVic
'Trumpeter' Reiter (T)	CLoc EPts LCla MJac MSmi
'Tubular Bells' (T)	LCla WOth
'Tuonela' (d)	CLoc CWVF
'Turkish Delight'	WOth
'Tutti-frutti' (d)	CLoc
'Twinkling Stars'	CWVF MJac SVic WOth
'Twinny'	CWVF
'Twist and Shout'	WOth
'Two Tiers' (d)	CWVF
'U.F.O.'	CWVF SVic
'Ullswater' (d)	CWVF EBak WOth
'Uncle Charley' (d)	EBak MSmi SVic
'Uncle Jinks'	SPet
'Uncle Steve' (d)	SVic
'University of Liverpool'	CLoc MJac WOth
'Upward Look'	EBak
'Valda May' (d)	CWVF
'Vale of Belvoir'	SVic
'Valerie Ann' (d)	EBak SPet SVic
'Valerie Bradley'	EPts
'Vanessa Jackson'	CLoc CWVF MJac SVic
'Vanessa Wright'	CRos LRHS NRHS
'Vanity Fair' (d)	CLoc EBak
'Variegated Pixie' (v)	MSmi

'Variegated Procumbens'	see *F. procumbens* 'Wirral'
'Veenlust'	EBak MJac
'Velvet Crush'	EPts EShb
'Vendeta'	LCla WOth
'Venus Victrix'	EBak
venusta	EBak LCla
'Vera' (Bella Series) **new**	ETMg MSmi
'Vera Garcia'	EPts LCla MJac SLBF WOth
'Versicolor'	see *F. magellanica* var. *gracilis* 'Versicolor'
'Vicky Bradshaw'	SLBF
'Ville de Paris'	WOth
'Vincent van Gogh'	WOth
'Vintage Dovercourt'	LCla
'Violet Bassett-Burr' (d)	CLoc EBak
'Violet Gem' (d)	CLoc
'Violet Rosette' (d)	CWVF SVic
VIOLETTA ('Goetzviol') (Shadowdancer Series)	SCoo
'Viva Ireland'	EBak
'Vivien Colville'	CLoc SVic WOth
'Vobeglo'	CWVF
'Voodoo' (d)	CCCN CLoc CWVF EBak EPts EShb LCla SCoo SPet SVic
'Vyvian Miller'	CWVF
'Wagtails White Pixie'	EBak
'Wake the Harp'	WOth
'Waldis Grafin'	WOth
'Waldis Spezi'	LCla
'Walsingham' (d)	CWVF
'Walton Jewel'	EBak
'Walz Beiaard'	WOth
'Walz Bella'	LCla
'Walz Blauwkous' (d)	CWVF WOth
'Walz Bruintje'	WOth
'Walz Doedelzak'	WOth
'Walz Estafette' (d)	SVic
'Walz Fanclub'	WOth
'Walz Fanfare' (T) **new**	WOth
'Walz Fluit'	MJac
'Walz Freule'	CWVF MJac WOth
'Walz Harp'	CWVF WOth
'Walz Hoorn'	WOth
'Walz Jubelteen' ♀H2	CLoc CWVF ELon EPts LCla MJac SAdn SEle SLBF SVen SVic WOth
'Walz Lucifer'	CWVF LCla SLBF WOth
'Walz Mandoline' (d)	CWVF SVic WOth
'Walz Panfluit'	LCla
'Walz Parasol'	WOth
'Walz Polka'	LCla WOth
'Walz Sprietje'	WOth
'Walz Toeter'	WOth
'Walz Triangel' (d)	SVic
'Walz Trompet'	WOth
'Walz Tuba'	WOth
'Wapenveld 150'	LCla
'Wapenveld's Bloei'	EPts LCla SLBF
'War Paint' (d)	CLoc
'Warton Crag'	CWVF SVic
'Wassernymphe'	WOth
'Water Color'	SLBF
'Water Nymph'	CLoc MHer SLBF SVic
'Wattenpost'	SLBF WOth
'Wave of Life'	CWVF
'Waveney Gem'	CLoc CWVF EBak LCla MJac SLBF WOth
'Waveney Queen'	CWVF SVic WOth
'Waveney Sunrise'	CWVF MJac SVic WOth
'Waveney Unique'	CWVF
'Waveney Valley'	CWVF WOth

'Waveney Waltz'	CWVF EBak WOth
'Wedding Bells' ambig.	SVic
'Welsh Dragon' (d)	CLoc CWVF EBak WOth
'Wendy' Catt	see *F.* 'Snowcap'
'Wendy Bendy'	EPts
'Wendy Jane Webster'	EPts
'Wendy's Beauty' (d)	CLoc EBak EPts ETMg MJac
'Wentworth'	CWVF SVic WOth
'Wessex Belle' (d/v)	CWVF
'Westham'	LCla
'Westminster Chimes' (d)	CLoc CWVF SPet
'Wharfedale' ♀H4	ELon EPts MJac SLBF SVic WOth
'What's-it' (E)	SLBF
'Whickham Blue'	CWVF
'Whirlaway' (d)	CLoc CWVF SVic
'White Academy'	EPts
'White Ann'	see *F.* 'Heidi Weiss'
'White Bride' (d)	SVic
'White Clove'	SVic WOth
'White Galore' (d)	CWVF SVic
'White Joy'	EBak
'White King' (d)	CLoc CWVF EBak ETMg SVic
'White Pixie' ♀H4	EPts MJac MSmi SLBF SPet SVic
'White Queen' ambig.	CWVF EHDe
'White Queen' Doyle	WOth
'White Spider'	CLoc CWVF EBak SVic WOth
'White Veil' (d)	CWVF
'Whiteknights Amethyst'	WOth
'Whiteknights Blush'	CCse CExl EBee EWes GCal LRHS MSmi
'Whiteknights Cheeky' (T)	CWVF EBak EPts SVic
'Whiteknights Pearl' ♀H3	CBot CTsd CWVF ECha EPfP EPts LCla LCro MMuc SDys SEND SGol SLBF SVic WHar WOth
'Whiteknights Ruby' (T)	WOth
'Whitton Starburst'	LCla
'Whoopee' (d)	EPts MJac SLBF WOth
'Wicked Queen' (d)	SVic
'Widnes Wonder'	MJac SLBF WOth
'Widow Twanky' (d)	CWVF
'Wigan Peer' (d)	EPts MJac WOth
'Wight Magic' (d)	MJac
'Wild and Beautiful' (d)	CWVF SVic
'Wilf Langton'	WOth
'Wilhelmina Schwab'	LCla
'Willow Tinsdale'	SGol
'Willy Nijhuis' (T)	WOth
'Wilma van Druten'	LCla WOth
'Wilson's Colours'	EPts LCla
'Wilson's Joy'	MJac
'Wilson's Pearls' (d)	CWVF SLBF SPet
'Wilson's Sugar Pink'	EPts LCla MJac WOth
'Win and Walt' **new**	NWms SLBF
'Win Oxtoby' (d)	CWVF
'Windhapper'	LCla SLBF WOth
'Windmill'	CWVF
'Wine and Roses' (d)	EBak
'Wingrove's Mammoth' (d)	SVic
'Wings of Song' (d)	CWVF
'Winifred Glass' **new**	EHDe
'Winston Churchill' (d) ♀H2	CLoc CWVF EBak EPts ESps MJac SCoo SPet SVic
'Winter Hymn'	WOth
'Winter's Tale' **new**	NWms SLBF
'Witchipoo'	SLBF
'Woodnook' (d)	CWVF
'Woodside' (d)	SVic
'Wyre Light' (E)	SLBF WOth
'Yattendon Lady'	SLBF
'York Manor'	EShb MSmi
'Yvonne Schwab'	LCla
'Zara'	WOth
'Zeebrook'	SVic
'Zeeuwse Parel'	WOth
'Zellertal'	WOth
'Zeta'	WOth
'Ziegfield Girl' (d)	SVic
'Zifi'	SLBF
'Zolly' **new**	NWms
'Zulu King'	SVic WOth
'Zus Liebregts' (d)	WOth
'Zwarte Snor' (d)	CWVF

Fumaria (*Papaveraceae*)

capreolata	WSFF
lutea	see *Corydalis lutea*

Furcraea (*Asparagaceae*)

bedinghausii	see *F. parmentieri*
§ ***foetida***	CCCN CPla EUJe WCot
§ - var. ***mediopicta*** (v)	CPla
- 'Variegata'	see *F. foetida* var. *mediopicta*
gigantea	see *F. foetida*
longaeva misapplied	see *F. parmentieri*
macdougalii	SPlb
§ ***parmentieri***	CBcs CCCN CCht CDTJ CExl CFil CHGN CHll CTsd EBee GBin LEdu LRHS NLos SPlb SVen

G

Gahnia (*Cyperaceae*)

sieberiana	SPlb

Gaillardia (*Asteraceae*)

'African Sunset'	GMcL WFar
aristata misapplied	see *G.* × *grandiflora*
- 'Maxima Aurea'	EBee EPfP MSpe NBre SPhx
'Arizona Sun'	CRos EAJP ESps ETMg LRHS MNHC NRHS SCob SVic
'Bijou'	EBee ELon SWvt
'Celebration'	CMea CRos LRHS NRHS SPoG
'Dwarf Goblin'	NGBl
§ 'Fackelschein'	IBoy MSpe
'Fanfare'PBR	CBod CRos CWGN EBee LRHS SCoo
GOBLIN	see *G.* × *grandiflora* 'Kobold'
§ × ***grandiflora***	ESps
- 'Amber Wheels'	CDor EPfP MSpe
- 'Arizona Apricot'	CDor CRos LRHS NRHS
- 'Arizona Red Shades'	CRos EAJP LRHS NRHS WFar
- 'Burgunder'	CSBt CSpe EAJP ELan ELon EPfP LRHS LSou MSpe NGBl NRHS SCob SPer SPhx SPoG SWvt WHar
- 'Dazzler' ♀H5	CPla CRos CSBt EBee ELan EPfP LRHS NRHS SPer SPoG WHar
- 'Fanfare Blaze'	CRos GMcL LRHS NRHS
- 'Frenzy'PBR (Commotion Series)	SPad
- Gallo Series	NRHS
- - 'Gallo Dark Bicolor'	CBod CRos LRHS NRHS
- - 'Gallo Fire'	CRos LRHS NRHS
- - 'Gallo Peach'	CRos LRHS NRHS
- - GALLO YELLOW ('Klegalyel')	CRos LRHS NRHS
- - 'Gallo Yellow Trumpet'	CRos LRHS NRHS

§ - 'Kobold'	CBcs CDor CMac CRos CSBt CTsd EBee ELan ELon EPfP ESps ETMg GMaP GMcL IBoy LPmr LRHS NLar NRHS SPer SPlb SPoG SWvt WHar
- 'Mesa Yellow' (Mesa Series)	CBod
- 'Red Sun'PBR	CWGN NLar
- (Sunburst Series) SUNBURST BURGUNDY PICOTEE ('Granretip')	CRos GMcL LRHS NRHS
- - SUNBURST BURGUNDY	CRos LRHS NRHS
- - SUNBURST ORANGE ('Granoran')	CRos LRHS NRHS
- - SUNBURST YELLOW ('Granyel')	CBod CRos LRHS NRHS
- 'Sunset Cutie'	SPoG
- 'Sunset Snappy' **new**	ETMg SPad
- 'Tokajer'	CRos EBee ELan EPfP LRHS MSpe NBre NRHS SPhx
'Naomi Sunshine'	SHar
§ 'Oranges and Lemons'PBR	EBee SCob SHar
SAINT CLEMENTS	see *G.* 'Oranges and Lemons'
'Solar Flare'	SCob
TORCHLIGHT	see *G.* 'Fackelschein'

Galactites (*Asteraceae*)

tomentosa	CPla EHoe EWTr SPav WCot
- white-flowered	CPla

Galanthus ✿ (*Amaryllidaceae*)

'Ailwyn'	CAvo EHrv GEdr
'Alan's Treat'	CAvo GEdr
'Alison Hilary'	CAvo EHrv GEdr MAsh
× ***allenii***	CBro EHrv EPri GKev
alpinus var. ***bortkewitschianus***	GKev
'Anglesey Not Galatea'	EHrv
'Anne of Geierstein'	IFoB MHCG WCot
'Ann's Millennium Giant'	CBro GEdr
'Armine'	CElw CRos CTal GKev IFoB LRHS NRHS WCot
'Art Nouveau'	CAvo CElw EHrv
'Atkinsii' ♀H5	CAvo CBro CElw CMea CRos EHrv EPot GEdr GKev IFoB IRob LAma LRHS MAsh MRav MWat NPnk NRHS SDir WCot WFar WHoo WShi XEll
'Autumn Beauty'	CBro CRos LRHS NRHS
'Babraham Scented'	GEdr
'Backhouse Spectacles'	GEdr
'Ballerina' (d)	CAvo GEdr
'Barbara's Double' (d)	EWes GEdr MAsh
'Barbara's Hybrid'	EHrv
'Benhall Beauty'	CElw EHrv EWes GEdr
'Benton Magnet'	ITim
'Bertram Anderson' ♀H5	EHrv GEdr ITim MAsh MWat WCot
'Bess'	CElw CTal EHrv GEdr IFoB
'Big Eyes' **new**	CAvo
'Bill Bishop'	CAvo CBro CTal ECha EHrv GEdr IFoB MAsh WCot
'Bitton' ambig.	GEdr NPol
'Blewbury'	ECha EHrv IFoB ITim
'Brenda Troyle'	CBro CElw CRos ECha EPot EPri GEdr GKev LRHS MAsh MHom NPol NRHS WCot WFar
'Brigadier Mathias'	EHrv
'Byfield Special'	CAvo EHrv IFoB
byzantinus	see *G. plicatus* subsp. *byzantinus*
cabardensis	see *G. transcaucasicus*
'Caryl Baron'	CAvo
'Castlegar'	IFoB ITim
caucasicus misapplied	see *G. elwesii* var. *monostictus*
caucasicus ambig.	IFoB NPol
- 'Comet'	see *G. elwesii* 'Comet'
- var. ***hiemalis*** Stern	see *G. elwesii* Hiemalis Group
- 'John Tomlinson'	see *G. elwesii* 'John Tomlinson'
'Charlotte'	IRob LRHS
'Chequers'	GEdr
'Cicely Hall'	GEdr IFoB
'Clare Blakeway-Phillips'	CAvo
corcyrensis spring-flowering	see *G. reginae-olgae* subsp. *vernalis*
- winter-flowering	see *G. reginae-olgae* subsp. *reginae-olgae* Winter-flowering Group
'Cordelia' (d)	CElw GEdr IFoB MAsh
'Cornwood Gem'	CAvo IFoB
'Cowhouse Green'	CAvo CSna EHrv GEdr
'Curly'	EHrv EWes GEdr IFoB MAsh
'Daglingworth'	EPri GEdr
'David Baker'	CAvo GEdr
'Desdemona' (d)	CBro EHrv EPot GAbr GEdr GMaP IRob LLHF WCot WFar
'Ding Dong'	EHrv GEdr IFoB MHCG
'Dionysus' (d)	CBro CExl EHrv ELon EPot EWes GAbr GEdr GKev LLHF MHom NPnk WBrk WFar WShi XEll
'Dodo Norton' **new**	CSna GEdr
'Drummond's Giant'	IFoB
'Dymock'	CAvo
'Ecusson d'Or'	CAvo
'Eliot Hodgkin' **new**	GEdr
§ ***elwesii*** ♀H5	CBro CRos CTri CWld ELan EPfP EPot ERCP ETMg GWyn IFoB IRob LAma LCro LRHS MWat NPnk NPol NRHS SCob SDeJ SDir SEND SRms WCot WFar WHoo WShi
- 'Abington Green'	CSna IRob
- 'Bo Bette'	GEdr
- 'Bubble'	CAvo
- 'Cedric's Prolific'	ECha EHrv GEdr IFoB WFar
§ - 'Comet' ♀H5	CElw EHrv GEdr IFoB MAsh MAvo WFar
- 'Daphne's Scissors'	CElw EHrv GEdr
- 'David Shackleton'	CElw EHrv GEdr IFoB MAsh
- 'December Green Tip'	WCot
- 'Early Twin'	WCot
- 'Echoes'	WCot
- (Edward Whittall Group) 'Two Eyes'	EHrv GEdr
- 'Elmley Lovett'	CElw
- var. ***elwesii***	EHrv
- - 'Big Boy'	GEdr
- - 'Fenstead End'	GEdr
- - 'Fred's Giant'	GMaP
- - 'Kite'	EHrv GEdr
- - 'Maidwell L'	CBro CTal EHrv
- - 'Paradise Giant'	GEdr
- - 'Sibbertoft Magnet'	GEdr IFoB
- 'X Files'	EHrv
* - 'Flore Pleno' (d)	NPol
- 'Godfrey Owen'	CAvo GEdr IFoB
- 'Green Brush'	CBro EWes GKev IFoB IRob LAma LRHS
- 'Grumpy'	EHrv GEdr MAsh
§ - Hiemalis Group	CBro EHrv EPot EPri GKev MHom WCot XEll
- - from Broadleigh Gardens	EHrv
- - 'Barnes'	ECha EHrv GKev WCot
- - 'Donald Sims'	EHrv
- - 'Highdown' **new**	GKev

	- - 'Rainbow Farm Early'	EHrv
	- 'J. Haydn'	LAma
	- 'Jessica'	CAvo IFoB
§	- 'John Tomlinson'	GEdr
	- 'Jonathan' **new**	CAvo
	- 'Kyre Park'	GEdr MAsh
	- late-flowering **new**	GEdr
	- 'Long 'drop'	GEdr IFoB
	- 'Mandarin'	CElw EWes
	- 'Marielle'	EPPr
	- 'Marjorie Brown'	CFis ECha EHrv GEdr ITim
	- var. ***maximus***	see *G. elwesii* 'Yvonne Hay'
	- 'Milkwood'	see *G. elwesii* 'Mrs Macnamara'
	- 'Miss Mowcher'	WCot
§	- var. ***monostictus*** ♀H5	CAvo CBro CRos ECha EHrv GKev IFoB LLHF LRHS NPnk NRHS WBrk WFar WShi
	- - 'B. Britten'	LAma
	- - 'G. Handel'	IFoB LAma LLHF LRHS NPnk
	- - 'Grayswood'	GEdr
	- - 'Green Tips'	CAvo
	- - 'H. Purcell'	CTal GEdr IRob LAma LLHF LRHS NPnk
	- - 'Jimmy Platt' **new**	CAvo
	- - 'Lord Monostictus'	CAvo
	- - 'Miller's Late'	CAvo EHrv
	- - 'Mozart'	LAma
	- - 'Rogers Rough'	SDys
	- - 'Warwickshire Gemini'	CAvo MAvo MHCG
	- aff. var. ***monostictus***	WFar
	- 'Mr Omer'	WCot
	- 'Mr Peggotty'	WCot
§	- 'Mrs Macnamara'	CAvo CTal ECha EHrv ELon EPri GEdr IFoB MAsh MWat WFar
	- November-flowering	WCot
	- 'Penelope Ann'	ECha EHrv GEdr
	- 'Peter Gatehouse'	EHrv
§	- 'Ransom's Dwarf'	GEdr
	- 'Remember, Remember' **new**	GEdr
*	- 'Robustus Praecox'	GKev
	- 'Selborne Green Tips'	EHrv
	- 'Sickle'	CSna CTal EHrv
	- 'Sir Edward Elgar'	GKev LAma LLHF LRHS
	- 'Three Leaves'	IFoB
	- 'Washfield Colesbourne'	see *G.* 'Washfield Colesbourne'
	- 'Yashmak' **new**	CAvo
§	- 'Yvonne Hay'	EHrv GEdr
	- 'Zwanenburg'	EHrv
	'Epiphany'	CAvo EHrv
	'Ermine House' (d)	EHrv GEdr
	'Ermine Joyce' **new**	CRos NRHS
	'Erway'	MHom
I	'Excelsis'	CAvo
	'F63'	IFoB
	'Fake Pearls' **new**	CAvo
	'Falkland House'	CElw GEdr
	'Faringdon Double' (d)	EHrv EPri MAsh
	'Fieldgate Forte'	CAvo
	'Fieldgate Prelude'	CAvo EHrv GEdr
	'Fieldgate Superb'	CAvo EHrv IFoB
	'Fieldgate Tiffany'	CAvo
	'Flevo Cool' **new**	CAvo
	'Fly Fishing'	CAvo
	'Forge Double' (d) **new**	GEdr
	fosteri	CBro EHrv GEdr
	'Framlingham Double' (d)	EHrv
	'G71' (d)	IFoB
	'Gabriel'	CAvo GEdr
	'Galadriel'	CAvo GEdr
	'Galatea'	CBro EHrv EPot EPri EWes GAbr IRob ITim MAsh MHom SDys WFar
	'George Elwes'	CAvo GEdr
	'Gill Gregory'	GEdr
	'Ginns'	EHrv IFoB IRob
	'Gloria'	MAsh
	(Gold Group) 'Ronald Mackenzie' **new**	GEdr
§	***gracilis***	CBre CBro CExl CRos GEdr GKev NPol WCot
	- 'Highdown'	CElw EHrv GKev IFoB MAsh MHom
	- hybrid	CRos
	- Kew	CElw
	- 'Vic Horton'	CElw EHrv GEdr WThu
	graecus misapplied	see *G. gracilis*
	graecus Orph. ex Boiss.	see *G. elwesii*
	'Grande Juge'	IFoB
	'Gravity' **new**	CAvo
	'Grayling'	see *G. plicatus* 'Percy Picton'
	'Green Arrow'	CAvo
	'Green Comet' **new**	CAvo
	'Green Man'	EHrv GEdr IFoB WFar
	'Green Necklace'	CRos EWes GEdr LRHS NRHS
	'Greenfields'	CSna GEdr IFoB MAsh
	green-tipped double (d)	GEdr
	'Headbourne' **new**	ECha
	'Heffalump' (d)	EHrv EPri GEdr IFoB MAsh
	'Hercule'	CAvo
	'Hill Poë' (d)	CAvo CBro CElw EHrv EPot GEdr IFoB ITim LLHF MAsh MHom MWat
	'Hippolyta' (d)	CAvo CBro CElw ECha EHrv EPot GEdr GKev IFoB LAma LRHS MAsh MAvo MHom NPol SDir WCot
	'Hobson's Choice'	EHrv GEdr
	'Homersfield'	EHrv ELon EPri
	'Honeysuckle Cottage'	CAvo
	× ***hybridus*** 'Merlin' ♀H5	CBro CElw EHrv EPri GEdr IFoB WCot WFar WHoo
	- 'Robin Hood'	EHrv GAbr GEdr IFoB
	'Icicle'	GEdr
§	***ikariae*** Bak.	CRos EPfP GEdr LRHS NRHS
	- subsp. ***ikariae*** Butt's form	NPol
	- Latifolius Group	see *G. platyphyllus*
	- subsp. ***snogerupii***	see *G. ikariae* Bak.
	'Imbolc'	EHrv GEdr IFoB
	(Imperial Group) 'Shepton Merlin' **new**	CElw
	'Irish Green'	IFoB
	'Ivy Cottage Corporal'	EHrv GEdr
	'Ivy Cottage Green Tip'	EHrv
	'Jacquenetta' (d)	CBro CElw CSna EHrv EWes GEdr IFoB IRob ITim LAma MCot MHom
	'Jade'	CAvo
	'James Backhouse'	ECha EHrv WHoo WShi
	'John Gray'	CBro EHrv EPri EWes GEdr IFoB MAsh
	'Kersen'	CAvo
	'Ketton'	CBro CElw CSna CTal EHrv GEdr GKev IFoB LLHF NRya
	'Kew Green'	CAvo
	'Kildare'	CAvo CTal GEdr IFoB
	'Kingston Double' (d)	EHrv
	'Kinn McIntosh'	WCot
	'Lady Beatrix Stanley' (d) ♀H5	CAvo CBro CElw CRos ECha EHrv EPot GEdr GKev IFoB IRob ITim LRHS MAsh MHom NRHS WCot WFar
	lagodechianus	CBro GEdr GKev
	'Lapwing'	EHrv GEdr IFoB MAsh

latifolius Rupr.	see *G. platyphyllus*
'Lavinia' (d)	CElw EHrv EWes GEdr MAsh MHom WFar
'Lerinda'	EHrv IFoB
'Limetree'	CElw EHrv EPri EWes GEdr ITim MAvo MHom NPol WFar
'Little Ben'	CElw EHrv GEdr GMaP
'Little Dorrit'	GEdr
'Little John'	EHrv GEdr WBrk
'Little Magnet'	CAvo SDir
'Longstowe'	CTal MAsh
'Lord Lieutenant'	GEdr
'Louise Ann Bromley'	CAvo
lutescens	see *G. nivalis* Sandersii Group
'Lyn'	CBro EHrv GEdr
'Magnet' 🏆H5	CAvo CBro CElw CMea CRos CTal EHrv ELon EPfP EPot GEdr GKev IRob LAma LEdu LRHS MAsh MHom MWat NPol NRHS SDir WBrk WCot WFar WHoo WShi XEll
aff. 'Magnet'	GMaP SDir
'Maidwell'	GEdr IFoB
'Melanie Broughton'	CAvo GEdr IFoB
'Midwinter'	CAvo
'Mighty Atom'	CBro GAbr WBrk
'Mill House'	EHrv
'Moccas'	CElw CSna MHom
'Modern Art'	GEdr IFoB MAsh MHCG
'Mr Thompson' **new**	EHrv
'Mrs Backhouse No 12'	EHrv IFoB
'Mrs Thompson'	CAvo CElw ECha EHrv GEdr GKev IFoB MAsh
'Mrs Wrightson's Double' (d)	GEdr
'Natalie Garton'	CAvo EHrv GEdr IFoB
'Neill Fraser'	EHrv EPri GEdr IRob MHom
'Nerissa' (d)	GEdr
nivalis 🏆H5	Widely available
- 'Courteenhall' Wyatt **new**	EPri
- 'Anglesey Abbey'	CElw EHrv EWes GEdr IFoB MHom
- 'April Fool'	MHom
- 'Ballynahinch'	GEdr ITim
- 'Bitton'	EHrv GEdr
- 'Blonde Inge'	GEdr IFoB MAsh
- 'Chedworth'	CElw GEdr WBrk
- 'Cornwood'	GEdr
- 'Dreycott Greentip'	IFoB
- dwarf	ITim
- 'Elfin'	CAvo CElw EHrv EWes GEdr GKev IFoB MAsh WCot
- 'Fluff'	EHrv
- 'Gloucester Old Spot'	GEdr
- subsp. ***imperati***	CExl WBrk
- 'Lutescens'	see *G. nivalis* Sandersii Group
- 'Major Pam'	IFoB
- 'Margery Fish'	CSna
- 'Maximus'	WShi
- 'Melvillei'	MAsh
- f. ***pleniflorus*** (d)	GKev MAsh NPri SPoG
- - 'Bagpuize Virginia' (d)	GEdr
- - 'Blewbury Tart' (d)	CAvo CBro CElw CSna EHrv EPri EWes GEdr IFoB WBrk WCot WFar
- - 'Flore Pleno' (d) 🏆H5	CArg CBro CExl CRav CRos EPfP EPot ERCP ESps GWyn IFoB IRob LAma LCro LOPS LRHS MMuc NHpl NPnk NRya SCob SDeJ SEND SPer SRms WBrk WCot WHoo WShi
- - 'Lady Elphinstone' (d)	CAvo CBro CRos CSna EHrv GEdr IFoB LLHF LRHS MAsh MHom NPol NRHS NRya WCot
- - 'Octopussy' (d)	GEdr
- - 'Pusey Green Tips' (d)	CBro CElw EPot GAbr IFoB NPol WCot
- - Scharlockii Group double (d)	GKev
- - 'Walrus' (d)	EHrv ELon GEdr MAsh
§ - - 'Wonston Double' (d)	EHrv IFoB
- Poculiformis Group	CElw EHrv MAsh
- - 'Angelique'	CAvo
- - 'Henry's White Lady'	GEdr
- cf. Poculiformis Group	CElw
- 'Puck'	CAvo
- 'Rosemary Mitchell' **new**	MAvo
§ - Sandersii Group	CSna GEdr GMaP IFoB WFar
- - 'Norfolk Blonde' **new**	GEdr
§ - Scharlockii Group	CElw MAsh MHom WBrk
- 'Sibbertoft White'	EPri MAsh
- 'Tiny'	CRos GEdr IFoB LRHS MHom NRHS WFar
- 'Tiny Tim'	GEdr ITim MAsh WFar
- 'Tippy Green' **new**	GKev
- 'Virescens'	IFoB
- 'Viridapice'	CAvo CBro CElw CExl CRos CWld ECha EPot ERCP GKev GMaP IFoB LAma LRHS MAsh MWat NPnk NPol NRHS SDeJ WCot WFar WHoo WShi
- 'Warei'	EHrv EPri
- 'White Cloud' **new**	GKev
- 'White Dream'	GEdr IFoB
'Nothing Special'	GKev MAsh
'One Drop or Two'	CAvo
'Ophelia' (d)	CBro CRos EHrv EPot GEdr LRHS MAsh MHom MWat NPol NRHS WBrk WFar WHoo
'Peardrop'	EHrv GEdr
'Peg Sharples'	CRos EHrv GEdr IFoB LRHS MHom NRHS
peshmenii	LEdu
'Phantom' **new**	CAvo
'Philippe André Meyer'	CAvo
§ ***platyphyllus***	CExl CRos LRHS NRHS
plicatus 🏆H5	CAvo CBro CElw CRos EHrv GKev LRHS MCot MHom NPnk NPol NRHS WBrk WCot WHoo WShi
- from Coton Manor	EHrv MCot
- 'Augustus'	CBro CElw EHrv ELon EPot EWes GEdr IFoB MAsh MHom WCot WHoo
- 'Babraham Dwarf'	EHrv
- 'Baxendale's Late'	GEdr
- 'Beth Chatto'	EHrv
- 'Bill Clark'	IFoB
- 'Bolu Shades'	GKev IFoB
- 'Bowles's Large'	EHrv
§ - subsp. ***byzantinus***	CBro EHrv MHCG MHom WThu
- - 'Fox Farm'	EHrv
- 'Colossus'	CBro CRos CTal EHrv EWes GKev IFoB WCot
- 'Diggory'	CAvo EHrv EPri GEdr IFoB MAsh MHCG
- 'Duckie'	GEdr WFar
- 'E.A. Bowles'	GEdr
- 'Edinburgh Ketton'	EHrv
- 'Florence Baker'	CAvo EHrv GEdr
- 'Gerard Parker'	EHrv GEdr IFoB
- 'Green Hayes'	EHrv
- 'Green Teeth'	GEdr MAsh
- 'Henham No. 1'	EHrv
- 'John Long'	GEdr
- late flowering	GKev

- 'Madelaine'	CAvo MAsh
§ - 'Percy Picton'	CAvo EWes GEdr
- subsp. ***plicatus***	GKev
- 'Sally Pasmore'	CAvo GKev
- 'Sophie North'	CElw CTal GEdr IFoB LLHF
- 'The Pearl'	EHrv GEdr IFoB
- 'Three Ships'	CAvo EHrv GEdr IFoB MHom
- 'Trym'	CAvo CElw EPri GEdr IFoB NPol WFar
- 'Wandlebury Ring'	EHrv
- 'Warham'	CBro CElw EPot GKev IFoB ITim MHom NPnk WCot
- 'Warham Rectory'	EHrv
- 'Wendy's Gold' ♀H5	CAvo CBro CSna EHrv EPri GEdr IFoB IRob MAsh WFar
- 'Woodtown'	IMou
'Polar Bear' **new**	CAvo
'Pom-pom'	CAvo
'Porlock No 2'	EHrv
'Pride o' the Mill'	CAvo GEdr
'Primrose Warburg'	CRos EHrv GEdr IFoB LRHS MAsh NRHS WFar
'Ransom's Dwarf'	see *G. elwesii* 'Ransom's Dwarf'
reginae-olgae	EHrv GKev IFoB MHom
- 'B.Tickner' **new**	EHrv
- subsp. ***reginae-olgae*** ♀H3	EPot GKev
- - 'Cambridge'	EHrv MHom
- - 'Tilebarn Jamie'	MHom
§ - - Winter-flowering Group	CBro
§ - subsp. ***vernalis***	EPot IFoB LEdu WCot
- - 'Miss Adventure'	EHrv
'Reverend Hailstone'	CAvo EHrv GEdr IFoB
'Richard Ayres' (d)	CRos EHrv ELon EPri GEdr IFoB IRob LRHS NRHS
rizehensis	EHrv GKev IFoB MHom
- Baytop 34474	EHrv GEdr IFoB
'Rodmarton'	EHrv EPri GEdr IFoB
'Ruth Birchall'	EHrv
'S.Arnott' ♀H5	CAvo CBro CElw CExl CMea CRos ECha EHrv EPot ERCP GKev GMaP IFoB IRob LAma LCro LOPS LRHS MAsh MAvo MWat NPnk NPol NRHS NRya SDeJ WBrk WCot WFar WHoo
'Saint Anne's'	CAvo CElw CSna GEdr IFoB MHom
'Scharlockii'	see *G. nivalis* Scharlockii Group
'Seagull'	CElw EHrv GEdr
'Sentinel'	CAvo CElw EHrv GEdr
'Silverwells'	CTal EHrv GEdr IFoB
'Sir Herbert Maxwell'	GEdr ITim MAsh
'South Hayes' **new**	GEdr
'Spindlestone Surprise'	CAvo EHrv GEdr
'Sprite'	CAvo
'St Pancras'	CAvo EHrv
'Starling'	CAvo
§ 'Straffan' ♀H5	CAvo CBro CElw EHrv EPot EPri GEdr GKev IFoB IRob MHom NPol WBrk WCot WFar
'Sutton Courtenay'	CAvo CSna GEdr
'The Apothecary'	EHrv
'The Linns'	GEdr
'The O'Mahoney'	see *G.* 'Straffan'
'The Wizard'	CAvo
'Titania' (d)	EHrv GEdr IFoB MAsh MHom WShi
§ ***transcaucasicus***	GEdr
'Trotter's Merlin'	CElw
'Trumps'	CAvo EHrv GEdr
'Trymming'	CAvo
'Trympostor'	CAvo EHrv GEdr
'Tryzm' **new**	CAvo
'Tubby Merlin'	CElw EHrv IFoB
'Uncle Dick'	CAvo
× ***valentinei*** 'Compton Court'	CBro GEdr IFoB IRob ITim
'Vertigo'	CAvo
§ 'Washfield Colesbourne'	CElw ECha EHrv
'Washfield Warham'	CElw ECha EHrv EPri IRob ITim MAsh
'Wasp'	CAvo CRos EPri GEdr MAsh WCot
'Welshway'	CAvo GEdr
'White Dreams'	GEdr IFoB
'White Swan' Ballard (d)	CElw EWes GEdr ITim
'William Thomson'	CSna EWes
'Winifrede Mathias'	CElw EHrv MAsh
'Wisley Magnet'	EHrv
'Wonston Double'	see *G. nivalis* f. *pleniflorus* 'Wonston Double'
woronowii ♀H5	CArg CBro CElw CTca CTri EHrv EPfP EPot GAbr GKev IFoB IRob LAma LCro LEdu LRHS MHom MWat NPnk SCob SDeJ SPer WBrk WCot WFar WShi

Galatella (*Asteraceae*)

§ ***linosyris***	EBee EWes MAvo NLar SPer SPhx WFar WHer WOld XLum
- 'Goldilocks'	see *G. linosyris*
§ ***sedifolia***	CBod ECtt ELon EPPr GAbr LEdu LRHS MAvo NBid NEgg NRHS NSti SEND SPoG WCot WOld
- subsp. ***dracunculoides*** RCB AM 5 **new**	WCot
§ - 'Jean Polignier' **new**	LPla
- 'Nana'	CExl EBee GCal MRav NLar NWsh SPer WCot WFar WOld XLum
- 'Rosea'	IMou

Galax (*Diapensiaceae*)

aphylla	see *G. urceolata*
§ ***urceolata***	EBee GKev IBlr MNrw WSHC

Galega (*Papilionaceae*)

bicolor	SRms
'Duchess of Bedford'	ELon WCot
× ***hartlandii***	CExl GAbr
- 'Alba' ♀H7	ELon EWes GBin GNew IBlr LRHS MArl MCot MRav SHar SMHy WCot WHoo WSHC WWtn XEll
- 'Lady Wilson' ♀H7	CWld ECtt ELon EPPr EWes EWld GBin MArl MAvo MMrt MNrw SRms WCot WHrl WKif
'Her Majesty'	see *G.* 'His Majesty'
§ 'His Majesty'	EBee ELon EPPr IFro LEdu MAvo MCot MRav WCot
officinalis	Widely available
- 'Alba'	CBod ECtt ELan EPfP GMaP LEdu LSun MAvo MBel MBrN MHer MMuc SEND SPer SRms WCAu WHrl WKif WMoo WSpi
orientalis	EBee ECtt EWes LEdu MArl MAvo MCot MRav SBrt SPhx WMoo WPGP WSHC
- PAB 6771 **new**	WPGP

Galeobdolon see *Lamium*

Galeopsis (*Lamiaceae*)

tetrahit	WSFF

Galium (*Rubiaceae*)

	boreale	EBWF IMou
	cruciata	see *Cruciata laevipes*
	mollugo	CHab CWld EBWF
§	***odoratum***	Widely available
	palustre	EBWF
	verum	CHab CWld EBWF EBee ENfk GJos GPoy MHer MMuc MNHC NMir SEND SRms WFar

Galtonia (*Asparagaceae*)

candicans 🏆H4	Widely available
- 'Moonbeam' (d)	EBee GKev
princeps	CRos CSam ECha GBin IMou LRHS NRHS WPGP
regalis	CExl CTca WPGP
viridiflora	CAby CAvo CTca EBee ECha ELan EPot ERCP GBin GCal GKev IBoy LRHS MNrw NWad SDeJ SDir WHil XLum

Galvezia (*Plantaginaceae*)

speciosa	CCCN CHll CSpe LRHS MCot

Gamblea (*Araliaceae*)

innovans **new**	WCru
pseudoevodiifolia B&SWJ 11707	WCru

Garcinia (*Clusiaceae*)

mangostana	CCCN

Gardenia (*Rubiaceae*)

	augusta	see *G. jasminoides*
	'Crown Jewel' PBR	CBcs CRos EPfP ETMg LCro LOPS LRHS MPkF NRHS SEle SPoG
	florida L.	see *G. jasminoides*
	grandiflora	see *G. jasminoides*
§	***jasminoides*** 🏆H1c	CBcs CCCN EBak
	- 'Kleim's Hardy'	Widely available
	- SUMMER SNOW ('Bab1183') **new**	MPkF

garlic see *Allium sativum*; also AGM Vegetables Section

garlic, elephant see *Allium ampeloprasum* 'Elephant'

Garrya ✿ (*Garryaceae*)

sp.	ESps
elliptica	CBcs CDul CMac CRos EBee EPfP ESps ETMg LRHS LSRN MAsh MGos NPnk NPri NRHS SCob WHar
- (f)	MJak MSwo SWvt WSpi
- (m)	CAby CTri NLar SGol SLim WSpi
- 'James Roof' (m) 🏆H4	CBcs CDul CMac CRos CSBt EBee ELan EPfP ESps GMcL LCro LOPS LRHS LSRN MAsh MGil MGos NEgg NLar SCob SGbt SGol SLim SPer SPoG SRms SWvt WFar WHar
× ***issaquahensis*** 'Glasnevin Wine' (m) 🏆H4	CRos ELan EPfP IArd LRHS MAsh MGos SCob SCoo SPoG WSpi
- 'Pat Ballard' (m)	EPfP NLar WSpi
× ***thuretii***	CBcs EBee EUJe GMcL MJak MMuc NLar SGol SPer WFar

× *Gasteraloe* (*Asphodelaceae*)

'Flo' **new**	LToo

Gasteria ✿ (*Asphodelaceae*)

batesiana 🏆H2	SEND
bicolor var. ***liliputana*** 🏆H2	SPlb
carinata var. ***verrucosa***	EShb SEND SPlb
nitida var. ***nitida*** variegated (v)	WCot
'Smokey'	EShb

× *Gaulnettya* see *Gaultheria*

Gaultheria ✿ (*Ericaceae*)

	NJM 10.032	WPGP
	SDR 7025 **new**	GKev
	antarctica	WThu
	cardiosepala	WThu
	cuneata	CRos GEdr LRHS MAsh WThu
	aff. ***dumicola*** NJM 10.032 **new**	WPGP
	forrestii	CExl
	- BWJ 7809	WCru
	itoana	GEdr GJos GKev WThu
	'John Saxton'	WAbe
	miqueliana	GEdr NLar WThu
	mucronata	CRos EPfP ESps MAsh MJak WFar
	- (m)	CMac CSBt CTri ELan EPfP GMcL MGos MMuc NEgg NWad SPer SRms WFar
	- 'Alba' (f)	MJak
	- 'Bell's Seedling' (f/m) 🏆H6	CBcs CDul CRos CTri ELan EPfP ESps GMcL LRHS MAsh MMuc NEgg NLar SCob SGbt SPer SPoG
	- 'Cherry Ripe' (f)	CMac MMuc
	- 'Crimsonia' (f) 🏆H6	CBcs CMac EPfP SRms
	- 'Indian Lake'	NWad
	- 'Lilacina' (f)	CMac MAsh
	- 'Lilian' (f)	CSBt EPfP NWad
	- MOTHER OF PEARL	see *G. mucronata* 'Parelmoer'
	- 'Mulberry Wine' (f) 🏆H6	CBcs CSBt CTri ELan MMuc NEgg SPer
§	- 'Parelmoer' (f)	CSBt EBee SPer
	- 'Pink Pearl' (f) 🏆H6	SRms
	- pink-berried (f)	GMcL
	- red-berried (f)	GMcL MJak
	- 'Rosea' (f)	MJak
§	- 'Signaal' (f)	CBcs CRos ELan EPfP LRHS MAsh NEgg NLar NWad SCob SPer
	- SIGNAL	see *G. mucronata* 'Signaal'
§	- 'Sneeuwwitje' (f)	CBcs CDul CSBt ELan EPfP LRHS MAsh MMuc SPer
	- SNOW WHITE	see *G. mucronata* 'Sneeuwwitje'
	- 'Thymifolia' (m)	EPfP
	- 'White Pearl' (f)	ESps
	- white-berried (f)	GMcL
	- 'Wintertime' (f) 🏆H6	CMac SRms
§	***myrsinoides***	GKev WThu
	'Pearls'	EPot NWad WAbe WThu
	'Pink Champagne'	ITim
	procumbens 🏆H4	Widely available
	- 'Big Cherry' **new**	NRHS
	- 'Very Berry'	CBod EShb NWad
	prostrata	see *G. myrsinoides*
	schultesii	WThu
	shallon	CAgr CBcs CDul CSBt EPfP GMcL MCoo MJak NLar SPer SRms SWvt WFar
	sinensis lilac-berried	GEdr

tetramera	CExl
thymifolia	NWad
× ***wisleyensis***	CRos LRHS SLon SRms
- 'Pink Pixie'	CRos LRHS MAsh NLar
- 'Ruby'	CMac
- 'Wisley Pearl'	SCoo WFar
yunnanensis	CExl

Gaura (*Onagraceae*)

'Experimental Deep Rose'	CRos LRHS NRHS
§ GAUDI PINK ('Florgaucompi'^{PBR})	CRos EPfP LRHS NRHS
'Ice Cool Rosy'	EBee SHar
lindheimeri 🏆^{H4}	CAby CBar CMea CRos CSBt CSpe EBee ECha ELan EPfP ESps EWTr IFro LCro LOPS LRHS MCot MGos MHer NRHS SBch SPer SWvt WCAu WCFE WHar WHoo WOut XLum XSen
- 'Bargau' (Pink Panache) (v)	EBee SEle WTor
- Belleza Series	CRos CWCL EPau EPfP LRHS NRHS
- - BELLEZA DARK PINK ('Kleau04263')	EAJP LRHS NRHS
- - BELLEZA WHITE ('Kleau04264')	LRHS NRHS
- 'Blaze'^{PBR}	CRos LRHS NRHS
- CHERRY BRANDY ('Gauchebra'^{PBR})	CRos EAJP EBee ECtt ELan EPfP GWyn IPot LRHS NRHS SWvt WHar
- 'Chiffon'	SHar
- 'Corrie's Gold' (v)	CAby CRos EAJP EBee ECha ECtt EHoe ELan EPfP LRHS MHer NRHS SPer
- 'Crimson Butterflies'^{PBR}	CWGN ECtt ELan EPfP
- 'Ellura White' **new**	NRHS
- 'Freefolk Rosy' (v)	CRos EBee LCro LOPS LRHS NRHS SHar
- GAUDI RED ('Florgaured')	CRos EPfP LRHS NRHS
- GAUDI ROSE ('Florgaucomro'^{PBR}) **new**	CRos LRHS NRHS
- (Geyser Series) GEYSER PINK ('Gaudros'^{PBR})	EBee EPfP
- - GEYSER WHITE ('Gaudwwhi'^{PBR})	EBee EPfP
- 'Jo Adela' (v)	ECha EPfP
- KARALEE PETITE ('Gauka')	CWCL EPfP SEle
- KARALEE PETITE IMPROVED	see *G. lindheimeri* LILLIPOP PINK
- KARALEE WHITE ('Nugauwhite'^{PBR})	CKno CRav CRos CWCL ELan EPfP LRHS NLar NRHS SCoo SPer SPoG
§ - LILLIPOP PINK ('Redgapi'^{PBR})	CAby CWCL EPfP LRHS MBrN NLar NRHS SCob SPoG
- 'Little Janie' **new**	MHol
- 'My Melody'^{PBR} (v)	CWCL WTor
- 'Occitania' (v)	XLum
- PAPILLON ('Nugaupapil'^{PBR})	CRos CWCL LRHS NRHS SPer SPoG
- 'Passionate Blush'^{PBR}	CBcs CChe CRos ECtt EPfP LRHS LSou MGos NRHS SLon SPoG SRms
- 'Passionate Pink'	LRHS NRHS
- 'Passionate Rainbow'^{PBR} (v)	CRos CWCL EPfP LRHS NRHS SPad SPoG SRms
- 'Pink Dwarf'	EBee EPfP SAdn
- PINK FOUNTAIN ('Walgaupf')	CRos LRHS NRHS
- 'Pink Gin'	LSou NRHS SPoG
- ROSYJANE ('Harrosy'^{PBR})	CAby CBod CChe CMea CWCL EBee ECtt EPfP ETMg EWTr LCro LOPS LRHS LSRN LSou MNrw MRav NRHS SCob SHar SLon SMad SPer SPoG SRms SWvt WHil WSHC XSen
- RUBY RUBY ('Harruby'^{PBR})	SHar
- 'Siskiyou Pink'	CBar CBcs CRos CSBt CSpe CWCL EAJP EBee ECha ECtt EHoe ELan EPfP LCro LOPS LRHS MBel MWat NRHS SAdn SCob SMad SPer SPhm SWvt WCFE WGwG XLum XSen
- SNOW FOUNTAIN ('Walsnofou')	CRos LRHS NRHS
- 'Sparkle White'	CBod EAJP ETMg WFar
- 'Summer Breeze'	CBod CDor CRos CSpe LRHS LSun NGBl NRHS SPhx
- 'Summer Emotions'	CBod MNrw
- 'The Bride'	CBcs CRav CTri EBee ECtt EHrv ELan EPed EPfP LRHS LSRN MBel MNHC MRav MWat NRHS SAdn SBod SGbt SPav SPhm SWvt WGwG WSHC
- 'Tutti Frutti'	LSou SCob
- 'Val's Pink'	WAvo
- 'Vanilla'	CKno CWCL LRHS LSou SPoG
I - 'Variegata' (v)	CRos CWCL LRHS NRHS SRms
- 'Whirling Butterflies'	CBWd CKno CSpe CWCL ECtt ELan EPfP ESps IBoy LCro LOPS LRHS MWat SCob SMad SPer SPhm SWvt
- 'Whiskers Deep Rose' **new**	CBod LSou MHol
- 'White Dove'	CRos LRHS NRHS
- 'White Heron'	MNrw
'Rosy Shimmer'	EBee SHar
sinuata	CAby CFis SHar
STRATOSPHERE PINK PICOTEE	see *G.* GAUDI PINK

Gaylussacia (*Ericaceae*)

baccata (F)	CMac

Gazania (*Asteraceae*)

'Aztec' 🏆^{H2}	CCCN
'Bicton Orange'	CCCN CSam ECtt SCoo SVen
'Big Kiss White Flame' (Kiss Series)	LBuc
'Big Kiss Yellow Flame' (Kiss Series)	LBuc
'Blackberry Ripple'	CCCN CPla SCoo
'Blackcurrant Ice'	MCot
'Christopher'	SCoo
'Christopher Lloyd'	CCCN ECtt
'Cookei' 🏆^{H2}	CSpe
'Cornish Pixie'	CCCN
'Cream Beauty'	MCot
FROSTY KISS MIXED **new**	ETMg
krebsiana	CCCN
'Lemon Beauty'	ECtt
'Magic'	CCCN CPla SCoo
NAHUI ('Suga119') (Sunbathers Series)	CCCN
'Orange Beauty'	ELan
rigens 'Variegata' (v) 🏆^{H2}	CCCN ELan
RUMI ('Suga116') (Sunbathers Series)	CCCN
SHEPHERDS DELIGHT MIXED **new**	ETMg
Sunbathers Series **new**	CPla
- SUNSET JANE LEMON SPOT ('Sugajale')	CCCN
- SUNSET JANE ('Sugaja'^{PBR})	CCCN
'Talent'	SEND
TIGER EYE ('Gazte') (v)	CCCN

	TIGER STRIPES MIXED **new**	ETMg
	TOPTOKAI ('Suga407') (Sunbathers Series)	CCCN
	TOTONACA ('Suga212') (Sunbathers Series)	CCCN

Geissorhiza (*Iridaceae*)

	aspera	CPbh
	tulbaghensis	CPbh

Gelidocalamus (*Poaceae*)

	fangianus	see *Ampelocalamus mocrophyllum*

Gelsemium (*Gelsemiaceae*)

	rankinii	LRHS
	sempervirens ♀H1c	CAby CCCN CHll CRHN EBee EShb LRHS LSRN MGil SBrt SLim SPoG WCot

Genista (*Papilionaceae*)

	aetnensis ♀H5	ELan EPfP LRHS MGil MMrt SArc SBrt SEND SMad SPer SRms WSHC WSpi
§	***canariensis*** ♀H1c	CExl CSBt
	carinalis	GJos
	cinerea	WCFE
	decumbens	see *Cytisus decumbens*
	'Emerald Spreader'	see *G. pilosa* 'Yellow Spreader'
	fragrans	see *G. canariensis*
	hispanica	CBcs CDul CSBt ELan EPfP ESps GMcL MAsh MMuc SCob SPer SRms SWvt WCFE
	humifusa	see *G. pulchella*
	lydia ♀H5	Widely available
§	***maderensis***	CRos LRHS
	monosperma	see *Retama monosperma*
	pilosa	EPot MAsh
	- 'Goldilocks'	LRHS MMuc
	- 'Lemon Spreader'	see *G. pilosa* 'Yellow Spreader'
	- var. ***minor***	NLar WAbe
	- 'Procumbens' ♀H5	CMea GEdr SRot
	- 'Vancouver Gold'	CMac ELan EPfP MRav SPer SRms
§	- 'Yellow Spreader'	MAsh MSwo
§	'Porlock' ♀H3	CBcs CDul CExl CMac CRos CSBt CTri EPfP LRHS MAsh MMuc MRav NRHS SEND WHor
§	***pulchella***	CTri
	sagittalis	CTri GJos LRHS MMuc SBrt SPer WWFP
§	× ***spachiana*** ♀H1c	CEnd CTri SPoG
	tinctoria	CHab EBWF GJos GPoy MCot MMuc WHer WSFF
§	- 'Flore Pleno' (d) ♀H6	GEdr
	- 'Humifusa'	EPot GCrg GEdr
	- 'Moesiaca'	WAbe
	- 'Plena'	see *G. tinctoria* 'Flore Pleno'
	- 'Royal Gold' ♀H6	ESps MRav NWad SPer SPlb
	villarsii	see *G. pulchella*

Gennaria (*Orchidaceae*)

	diphylla	GKev

Gentiana ✿ (*Gentianaceae*)

§	***acaulis*** ♀H5	CRos EPfP EPot GKev GMaP LRHS MAsh NGdn NLar NRHS NSla SBch SPlb SRms WAbe
	- SDR 1323	GKev
	- f. ***alba***	EPot LLHF WThu
	- - 'Snowstorm'	GKev
	- 'Belvedere'	EPot
	- 'Coelestina'	WThu
	- 'Holzmannii'	WAbe
	- 'Krumrey'	EPot GEdr GKev
	- 'Luna'PBR	NLar
I	- 'Maxima Enzian'	EPot GEdr
	- 'Rannoch'	GEdr
	- 'Stumpy'	GEdr
	- 'Trotter's Variety'	WAbe
	- 'Undulatifolia'	EPot
	- 'Velkokvensis'	EPot
	'Alex Duguid'	CRos GCrg GEdr LRHS
	'Amethyst'	CRos EPot GEdr LRHS WAbe
	angulosa misapplied	see *G. verna* 'Angulosa' hort.
	angustifolia	WAbe XEll
	'Ann's Special'	GEdr
	asclepiadea ♀H5	CRos CSpe CTal CTri ELan GAbr GEdr GKev GMaP IRob LEdu LRHS MNrw NBid NLar NRHS NSti SPer SRms WBor WCAu WCFE WHoo WKif WSHC
	- 'Alba'	CRos CTal EBee GCal GEdr GKev GMaP IRob LEdu LRHS NBid NRHS SPer SRms WCFE WHoo
	- dark blue-flowered	GCal WPGP
	- 'Hoo House'	WHoo
	- 'Knightshayes'	EBee GKev LEdu
I	- 'Nana'	GKev
	- 'Phyllis'	GKev WHoo
	- 'Pink Swallow'	GEdr GQue IRob WArt
	- 'Rosea'	GEdr GKev MNrw
	- 'White Swallow'	GEdr
	- 'Whitethroat'	GKev
	'Balmoral'PBR	GMaP
	'Barbara Lyle'	WAbe
	bavarica var. ***subacaulis***	SPlb
	× ***bernardii***	see *G.* × *stevenagensis* 'Bernardii'
	'Berrybank Dome'	CRos GMaP LRHS
	'Berrybank Sky'	CRos GAbr GEdr GMaP LRHS
	'Berrybank Snowflakes'	GMaP
	'Berrybank Star'	CRos GEdr LRHS
	bisetaea	SRms
	'Blauer Diamant'	GEdr
	'Blauer Kobold'	GEdr
	'Blauer Zwerg'	GEdr
	'Blue Flame'	GEdr
	'Blue Heaven'	GEdr
	'Blue Magic'PBR	LRHS
	'Blue Sea'	CRos LRHS
	'Blue Silk' ♀H5	CRos CSma EPfP GCrg GEdr LRHS NRHS SPoG WAbe
	brachyphylla	WAbe
	'Braemar'PBR	GMaP
*	***burrowthii***	GEdr
	'Cairngorm'	CRos GEdr LRHS
	'Carmen'	GEdr
	× ***caroli***	WAbe
	'Compact Gem'	GEdr WAbe
§	***cruciata***	ELan GEdr NLar
§	***dahurica***	GEdr GLog MMuc NGdn NLar
	'Dark Hedgehog'	GEdr
	decumbens	GKev
	depressa	EPot GEdr WAbe
	'Devonhall'	GEdr NWad
	'Diana'PBR	EBee LRHS NLar
	dinarica 'Colonel Stitt'	GCrg GEdr WThu
	- 'Frocheneite'	EPot
	'Dumpy'	GEdr
	'Elehn'	GEdr
	'Elizabeth'	GEdr
	'Ettrick'	GEdr

	'Eugen's Allerbester' (d)	CRos CSma EWld GEdr GKev GMaP LRHS NLar NWad SPer WAbe
	farreri	WAbe
	- Silken Star Group	WAbe
	'Faszination'	GEdr
	fetissowii	see *G. macrophylla* var. *fetissowii*
	'Gellerhard'	GEdr
	'Gewahn'	GEdr
I	'Glamis Strain'	CRos GEdr LRHS
	'Glen Moy'	GEdr
	'Glendevon'	GEdr
§	***gracilipes***	GEdr GKev LLHF SPlb SRms
	- 'Yuatensis'	see *G. macrophylla* var. *fetissowii*
	'Henry'	GEdr
	hexaphylla	EPot
	Inshriach hybrids	CRos LRHS
	'Inverleith'	CRos GEdr LRHS SPlb
	'Joan Ward'	CRos LRHS SPer
	'John Aitken'	GEdr
	'Juwel'	GEdr
	'Kobold'	GEdr
	kochiana	see *G. acaulis*
	kurroo var. ***brevidens***	see *G. dahurica*
	lagodechiana	see *G. septemfida* var. *lagodechiana*
	ligustica	EPot GKev
	'Little Diamond'PBR	LRHS NLar
	'Lucerna'	CRos EPfP GCrg GEdr GKev LRHS
	lutea	GAbr GCal GKev GPoy LLHF SMad SRms WCAu
	× ***macaulayi***	CPla
	- 'Blue Bonnets'	GEdr
	- 'Elata'	NWad
	- 'Kidbrooke Seedling'	CRos GEdr GMaP LRHS WAbe
	- 'Kingfisher'	CPla CRos GEdr LRHS WAbe
§	***macrophylla*** var. ***fetissowii***	LLHF
	makinoi 'Marsha'PBR	CHll GEdr LRHS MMrt NHpl NLar SPoG
	- 'White Magic'PBR	GEdr
	'Margaret'	GEdr
	'Maryfield'	GEdr
	'Melanie'	GEdr
	microdonta	EPot LLHF
	'Multiflora'	CRos LRHS
	'Mystic'PBR	NLar
	'Oban'PBR **new**	GMaP
	occidentalis	EPot
	ornata	CRos LRHS
	'Orva'	CRos
	paradoxa ♀H5	EPot GKev LLHF NRHS SBrt WAbe
	phlogifolia	see *G. cruciata*
	pneumonanthe	LRHS NLar SPlb
	pumila subsp. ***delphinensis***	WAbe
	purdomii	see *G. gracilipes*
	robusta CC 7494	GKev
	'Sapphire Blue'	GEdr
	saxosa	GCrg GKev GWyn ITim LRHS NHpl NRHS NSla WAbe
	scabra	CRos LRHS
	- 'Royal Stripe'	ETMg
	- 'Zuikorindo'	NLar
	'Selektra'	GEdr
	septemfida ♀H5	CRos EPot LRHS MAsh MJak NHpl NRHS NSla SPlb SRms WHoo WKif
	- 'Alba'	GKev LLHF
	- var. ***kolakovskyi***	LLHF
§	- var. ***lagodechiana*** ♀H5	LLHF LRHS SRms XLum
	'Serenity'	CRos CSma GEdr LRHS NLar NWad WAbe
	'Shot Silk' ♀H5	CRos EPfP EWes GAbr GCrg GEdr GMaP LRHS MGos NHpl SPoG WAbe
	'Silken Giant'	GEdr WAbe
	'Silken Glow' **new**	WAbe
	'Silken Night'	GEdr WAbe
	'Silken Seas'	CSma GCrg GEdr NWad WAbe
	'Silken Skies' ♀H5	EPot GEdr WAbe
	'Silken Surprise'	WAbe
	sino-ornata ♀H5	CPla CSma EPfP GAbr GMaP LSRN MAsh NHpl SRms WAbe
	- SDR 5127	MGos
	- 'Alba'	CPla
	- 'Angel's Wings'	CRos GEdr LRHS
	- 'Bellatrix'	GEdr
	- 'Blautopf'	GEdr
	- 'Brin Form'	SRms
	- 'Downfield'	CRos GKev LRHS
	- 'Edith Sarah'	GEdr
	- 'Gorau Glas'	WAbe
	- 'Mary Lyle'	GEdr
	- 'Oha'	GEdr
	- 'Purity'	CRos GEdr LRHS WAbe
	- 'Starlight'	GEdr
	- 'Weisser Traum'	CRos GEdr LRHS NLar
	- 'White Wings'	GEdr
	'Sir Rupert'	GEdr
	'Sternschuppe'	GKev
	× ***stevenagensis***	CRos LRHS
§	- 'Bernardii'	GEdr
	- dark-flowered	WAbe
	straminea	EPot GKev
	'Strathmore' ♀H5	CRos CSma EWes EWld GAbr GEdr GKev GMaP LRHS SPer SPlb WAbe
	'Surprise'	GEdr
	syringea	WAbe
	szechenyii	LLHF
	ternifolia 'Cangshan'	EPot GEdr
	- 'Dali'	GEdr
	'The Caley'	CRos GEdr GMaP LRHS
	tibetica	GCal GPoy WCAu XLum
	- PAB 2357	LEdu WPGP
	Tough's form	GEdr
	triflora var. ***japonica***	NLar
	veitchiorum	GKev LLHF WAbe
	verna	CRos CSma EDAr EPfP EPot EWes GKev IRob LCro LOPS LRHS LSRN NHpl NRHS NSla SPlb SPoG WAbe WHoo
	- 'Alba'	GEdr NSla WAbe
§	- 'Angulosa' ♀H5	MAsh
	- subsp. ***balcanica***	CPBP
	'Violette'	CRos GEdr LRHS NWad
	waltonii	EWes
	wilsonii	GKev ITim
	wutaiensis	see *G. macrophylla* var. *fetissowii*
	zekuensis	WCot

Gentianopsis (*Gentianaceae*)

paludosa	GKev

Geranium ✿ (*Geraniaceae*)

sp.	ESps
CC 7067 **new**	MMoz
aconitifolium misapplied	see *G. palmatum*
aconitifolium L'Hér.	see *G. rivulare*
'Adam Moreland'	WOut
'Alan Mayes'	CBod CElw CMac ECtt EPPr GBin GKin LRHS LSou NGdn NRHS SBod SRGP WFar WPnP

'Alan's Blue'	EBee
albanum	CElw CPla EPPr GLog GPSL GWyn MMuc SRGP WMoo
anemonifolium	see *G. palmatum*
'Ann Folkard' 🏆^{H7}	Widely available
'Ann Folkard' × ***psilostemon***	GWyn LSRN
'Anne Thomson' 🏆^{H7}	Widely available
× ***antipodeum*** 'Chocolate Candy'^{PBR}	NRHS SPoG
- 'Pink Spice'^{PBR}	CWGN GKin GMcL LBuc LRHS NRHS SRms
- 'Purple Passion'^{PBR}	LBuc LRHS NRHS SPoG
- 'Sea Spray'	NBro
- 'Stanhoe'	MHCG
- (***sessiliflorum*** subsp. ***novae-zelandiae*** 'Nigricans' × ***traversii*** var. ***elegans***)	SRms
argenteum	NSla
aristatum	EPPr EWes GCal MNrw MRav SGbt SPhx SRGP WCru WMoo
armenum	see *G. psilostemon*
asphodeloides	CElw CRos IFro LRHS MBNS MNrw NBid NRHS SGbt SPav SRGP WBrk WFar WMoo
- subsp. ***asphodeloides*** white-flowered	CElw SRGP WMoo
- subsp. ***sintenisii***	EPPr
- 'Starlight'	GCal NBid
atlanticum Hook. f.	see *G. malviflorum*
'Azure Rush'	CDor CRos EBee ECtt EPfP EWTr ILea IPot IRob LRHS MHol NDov NRHS NSti SPoG SRms WCAu WFar WPnP
'Azurro'	EBee LRHS
'Baby Blue'	see *G. himalayense* 'Baby Blue'
'Bertie Crûg'	ECtt EHrv ELon GMcL GWyn LLHF NCou NLar SRms SRot SWvt
biuncinatum	IFro
'Blue Boy'	NLar
'Blue Cloud' 🏆^{H7}	CBod CElw CMea CSam EPPr EPed EPfP GCal GMaP LPla LRHS LSou MAvo MCot NBid NDov NLar NRHS NSti NWad SPhx SPoG SRGP WCAu WFar WGwG WHoo WMoo WPtf WWtn
'Blue Pearl'	EPPr MAvo NSti SRGP WMoo
§ BLUE SUNRISE ('Blogold'^{PBR}) 🏆^{H7}	CBod CRos EBee ECtt ELan ELon EPfP GMaP ILea LLWG LPla LRHS LSRN MAvo MHol MNrw MRav MTis NEgg NLar NRHS NSti SPer SPoG SRms SRot WCot WFib WPnP WSpi
'Blue Thunder'	EPPr
'Blushing Turtle'^{PBR}	CBod CRos EBee EPPr EPfP LBuc LRHS MAvo MHol NLar NRHS NSti SPoG WCAu
'Bob's Blunder'	CBod CRos ECtt EPfP IBoy LLWG LRHS MBNS MBel MHol MNrw SAko SPoG SRGP SRms SWvt WCot WFar WHoo
bohemicum	SRGP WHer
- 'Orchid Blue'	SWvt
'Brookside' 🏆^{H7}	Widely available
'Buckland Beauty'	CExl EBee EWes SBch
'Buxton's Blue'	see *G. wallichianum* 'Buxton's Variety'
caeruleatum	EBee GCal NLar SBrt
caffrum	SRGP
canariense	see *G. reuteri*
§ × ***cantabrigiense***	CMac CRos CSBt ECtt ESps GMcL LRHS MHer MNrw NBro NLar NPer NRHS NSti SRms WBor WCru WMoo
- 'Andrew Clarke'	WBrk
- 'Berggarten'	EBee EPPr NLar SAko SRGP WBrk WPtf
- 'Biokovo'	Widely available
- 'Cambridge'	CBod CRos EBee ECha ECtt EHrv ELan EPPr EPfP ESps GAbr GKin LRHS MCot MRav MSwo NRHS SCob SPer SPoG SRms SWvt WBrk WFar WFib WMoo WPnP
- CRYSTAL ROSE ('Abpp')	EBee EPPr NSti WCot
- 'Hanne'	CDor EBee ECtt EPPr EWes
- 'Harz'	CDor EPPr SAko WBrk
- 'Hilary Rendall'	EBee ECtt EPPr
- 'Karmina'	CBod CDor CRos EBee EPPr EPfP GBin IRob LRHS NLar NRHS SBod SRGP WFar WHoo WMoo WPnP XEll XLum
- 'Rosalina'	EPPr WBrk
- 'Show Time'	EPPr
- 'St Ola'	CBod CRos EBee ECtt EPPr EPfP GMaP ILea LRHS MNrw MRav MSpe NBro NChi NEgg NGdn NRHS NSti SAko SCob SRGP WCot WCru WFib WHoo WMoo WPnP WWtn
- 'Vorjura'	EBee EPPr SAko WBrk
- 'Westray'^{PBR}	CBod CMac EBee ECtt EPPr EPfP GLog LSou MBel MHol MMuc NGdn NLar NRya NSti SCob SEND SRms SWvt WFib WPnP
'Chantilly'	CBod CRos EBee ECtt EPPr EPfP EWTr LRHS MAvo MNrw NChi NLar NRHS WCru WFib WGwG WMoo WPtf
'Chipchase Castle'	NChi
christensenianum B&SWJ 8022	WCru
cinereum	NSla
- 'Album'	IBoy
- 'Apple Blossom'	see *G.* × *lindavicum* 'Apple Blossom'
- 'Elizabeth'	ECtt LSRN
- 'Sateene'^{PBR}	CAby CSma ECtt EPPr GMaP SRms
(Cinereum Group) 'Alice'^{PBR}	CSma EBee EPPr EWTr GMaP LSRN MBNS NLar SRms SRot WFar
- 'Ballerina' 🏆^{H5}	Widely available
- 'Carol'	CRos CSma CWGN ECtt EPPr EWes GKin LRHS LSRN LSou MBNS MRav NLar NRHS SWvt WFar
I - 'Heather'	CSma
- 'Janette'	NRHS
- JOLLY JEWEL NIGHT ('Noortnight') **new**	IPot NSti WHlf
- JOLLY JEWEL PURPLE ('Noortpur') **new**	WHlf
- JOLLY JEWEL RED **new**	MPnt
- JOLLY JEWEL SALMON ('Noortsal') **new**	IPot WHlf WTor
- 'Lambrook Helen'	CExl CFis
- 'Laurence Flatman'	CAby CBod CExl CKno CRos CSpe ECtt ELan EPfP EPri GCrg GMaP LRHS LSou MPnt NBid NChi NEgg NQui NRHS NSla SPoG SRms SRot WHoo

- 'Lizabeth'PBR	ECtt EPPr LSou NLar WCot
- 'Melody'PBR	CAby CSma
- 'Penny Lane'PBR	CSma
- 'Purple Pillow'	CWGN ECtt ELan EPPr EPot LSRN LSou MCot MHer MHol MRav NChi NSti SAko SCob SPer SRms SRot SWvt WFar
- RENÉ MACÉ ('Progera')	SRkn
- ROTHBURY GEM ('Gerfos'PBR) ♀H5	CBod CGar ECtt ELon MRav MSCN SWvt
- 'Signal'	ECtt EPPr EPot MPnt
- 'Sophie'PBR	CSma LSRN
§ - 'Thumbling Hearts'	CSma CWGN EBee ECtt LCro LLWG LOPS LPla MHol NCou NSti SAko SCob SMad WCot WHoo
- THUMPING HEART	see *G.* (Cinereum Group) 'Thumbling Hearts'
'Claridge Druce'	see *G.* × *oxonianum* 'Claridge Druce'
§ ***clarkei*** 'Kashmir White'	Widely available
- 'Mount Stewart'	CExl CHid EBee EPfP GCal WCru WPGP
- (Purple-flowered Group) 'Kashmir Purple'	Widely available
- Raina 82.83	MNrw
clarum B&SWJ 10246	WCru
collinum	EPPr SRGP WCru
'Color Carousel'	EBee GBin
'Coombland White'	CCht CExl CHid CRos ECtt EWTr GCal LRHS LSou MAvo MBel NLar NRHS SPer SPoG WCot WMoo
'Coquet Island'	EBee EPPr
'Criss Canning'	EBee EPPr
'Cyril's Fancy'	EPPr
dalmaticum ♀H5	Widely available
- 'Album'	CBod CMea CRos EBee ECtt EPPr EPfP EPot IRob LRHS MRav NHpl NRHS NRya SBch SRGP SRms WAbe
- 'Bressingham Pink'	EBee ECtt EPPr IRob
- 'Bridal Bouquet'	CPBP ECtt EPot GCrg LLHF NSla
- 'Stade's Hellrosa'	EPPr
dalmaticum* × *macrorrhizum	see *G.* × *cantabrigiense*
'Danny Boy' ♀H7	EBee
'Deep Purple' **new**	EBee
delavayi misapplied	see *G. sinense*
'Deux Fleurs'	GBin MAvo MNrw
'Devon Pride'	CElw EBee EPPr SRGP
'Dilys' ♀H7	CBod CElw CFis EBee ELan EPPr LPla MAvo MNrw MTis NChi NDov NGdn NLar SRGP WCru WFar WHal WMoo WPnP WSpi
'Distant Hills'	EBee EPPr SRGP
'Diva'	EBee ELan EPPr EPfP LLHF
'Double Jewel'	see *G. pratense* 'Double Jewel'
DRAGON HEART ('Bremdra'PBR)	ECtt EPfP IPot LCro LOPS LPla LRHS LSRN MAsh MNrw MPnt MSCN NDov NLar NRHS NSti SCob SMad STPC WCAu WFar WHil WPnP
DREAMLAND ('Bremdream'PBR)	CBod CDor CPou CWGN EBee ECtt ETMg ILea LCro LOPS LPla LSou LSun MAsh MAvo MBNS MHol NLar SAko SMad WCot WPnP
'Dusky Crûg'	CSBt CSam ECtt EHoe EHrv ELan ELon EPPr EPfP GKin GMcL MBel MHol MJak MPie NEgg NHpl NLar NSti SPoG SWvt WCot WFar WSpi
'Dusky Rose'	CAby CBod CDor CSpe ECtt GJos GKev GMcL GWyn LBuc NLar SHar SRot WFar
'Elke'	Widely available
'Elworthy Eyecatcher'	CDor CElw MAvo MNrw SRGP WPGP
'Elworthy Tiger'	CElw MAvo
'Emily'	SRGP
endressii ♀H7	CBod CBre CWCL ECha EPfP ESps GLog GMaP GMcL MBNS MCot MHer MMuc MSCN NBro NPer NPol SCob SEND SPlb SRGP SRms SWvt WHar WMoo XLum
- 'Album'	see *G.* 'Mary Mottram'
- 'Castle Drogo' ♀H7	EPPr
- 'Prestbury White'	see *G.* × *oxonianum* 'Prestbury Blush'
- 'Rose'	MAvo
- 'Wargrave Pink'	see *G.* × *oxonianum* 'Wargrave Pink'
erianthum	GLog GMaP IMou NLar SRGP WCru WMoo
- 'Axeltree'	WCot
- 'Blues in the Night' **new**	EBee
- 'Cally Pearl'	GCal
- 'Calm Sea'	WCru WMoo
- 'Neptune'	EBee WCru
- 'Pale Blue Yonder'	EBee EWes
eriostemon Fischer	see *G. platyanthum*
'Eureka Blue'	CPou CRos ECtt LPla LRHS LSun MAvo MHol MTis NLar NRHS NSti SPoG WCot WPnP WRHF
'Eva'	WPnP
'Expression'	see *G.* 'Tanya Rendall'
'Extravaganza'	EWes
'Farncombe Cerise Star'	CElw MAvo
§ ***farreri***	CExl CPBP CRos EPot LLHF LRHS NRHS
'Fay Anna'	CBct CBod EPPr GBin MPnt MSCN SCob SPoG WFar WHar
'Foundling'	MAvo
gracile	CFis CRos EBee GMaP LRHS LSou MNrw NRHS SRGP WBrk WCru WMoo
- 'Blanche'	CRos EPPr LRHS MNrw NRHS
- 'Blush'	CElw EPPr EWes
grandiflorum	see *G. himalayense*
'Grasmere'	ECtt
'Gwen Thompson'	WOut
gymnocaulon	CMac SRGP WCru
gymnocaulon* × *platypetalum	EBee
'Harmony'	EBee EPPr
harveyi	EWes SPhx SRGP WKif
§ ***hayatanum***	CRos LRHS NRHS
- B&SWJ 164	NLar WCru WMoo WPnP
'Hilary'	WWtn
§ ***himalayense***	CBcs CRos ECha ELan EPfP ESps EWTr LRHS MBNS MMuc MRav MWat NBro NRHS SBod SEND SPlb SRGP SRms SRot WFar WMoo XLum
- CC 1957 from Tibetan border	CExl EPPr
- ***alpinum***	see *G. himalayense* 'Gravetye'
§ - 'Baby Blue'	CElw CRos EBee ECtt ELon EPPr GBin GCal LRHS MAvo MNrw NGdn NLar NRHS NSti SPoG SRGP WBrk WCAu WCru WFib WMoo WPnP WPtf
- 'Birch Double'	see *G. himalayense* 'Plenum'
- 'Derrick Cook'	CElw EBee ECtt EPPr EPfP GCal MAsh MAvo MNrw MSpe MTis

		NLar NSti SAko STPC WBrk WCAu WHal WHil WHoo
	- 'Devil's Blue'	EPPr SRGP WPtf
§	- 'Gravetye'	Widely available
	- 'Irish Blue'	CBod CDor CElw CRos EBee EPPr GCal GMaP LRHS MSpe NLar NPol NRHS NSti SRGP WCru WFib WMoo WPnP WPtf
	- ***meeboldii***	see *G. himalayense*
	- 'Pale Irish Blue'	EBee EPPr GCal
§	- 'Plenum' (d)	Widely available
	- 'Spiti Valley'	WPtf
	himalayense × pratense	WFib
	'Hola Guapa'	GBin
	ibericum misapplied	see *G.* × *magnificum*
	ibericum ambig.	SRms WCAu
	ibericum Cav.	CRos CSBt CTri LRHS NBre NRHS SPav SRGP
§	- 'Ushguli Grijs'	EBee EPPr IMou NLar WCot
	- 'Black and Blue' **new**	EBee
	- 'Blue Springs'	ECtt SAll
	- subsp. ***ibericum***	CMac
	- subsp. ***jubatum***	EPPr MNrw SGbt SRms WCru
	- - 'White Zigana'	CAby CBod EBee ECtt EPed LSRN NLar NSti SRms WGwG WPnP WWtn
	- subsp. ***jubatum*** × ***renardii***	SWvt
	- var. ***platypetalum*** misapplied	see *G.* × *magnificum*
	- var. ***platypetalum*** Boiss.	see *G. platypetalum* Fisch. & C.A.Mey.
	ibericum × libani	EBee
	incanum	CAby CPla EBee ELon EWes GCal NHpl SBrt SRGP SVen WSpi
	- var. ***incanum***	SBch
	- white-flowered	SRGP
	'Ivan' ♀H7	CBod CElw CRos EBee ECtt EPPr LRHS NChi NLar NRHS SRGP WCru WFib WHoo WMoo
	'Jean Armour'	CBod ECtt LRHS MAvo NRHS SPoG SRGP WFar WGwG
	'Johnson's Blue'	Widely available
	'Jolly Bee'	see *G.* ROZANNE
	'Joy'	CBod CCht CDor CRos EBee ECtt EPPr GWyn LRHS LSou MAvo MBel MCot MRav NEgg NLar NRHS NSti NWad SBch SRGP SRms WCot WFib WGwG WMoo WPnP
§	'Kanahitobanawa'	EBee
	'Karen Wouters'	EPPr
	'Kashmir Blue'	CExl CRos ECtt ELan EPfP EWTr GMaP LRHS MAvo NLar NRHS SWvt WFar WKif
	'Kashmir Green'	ECtt EPfP LLHF WMoo
	'Kashmir Pink'	CBod CElw CExl CMac CRos ECha ECtt ELan EPfP EPri EWes GBin GKev GMaP LRHS MAvo MGos MMuc MNrw NBid NChi NLar NRHS NSti SPer WAvo WCAu WFar WPnP
§	'Khan'	CElw EPPr EWes LRHS MAvo NEoE SDys SMHy SRGP WCru
	'Kirsty'	EBee EWes NChi
	kishtvariense	GCal IMou MRav NSti WCru
	koraiense	CFis WMoo
	- B&SWJ 797	WCru
	- B&SWJ 878	CExl EBee WCru
	koreanum misapplied	see *G. hayatanum*
	koreanum ambig.	GCal LRHS NLar NRHS WMoo
	- B&SWJ 602	CExl WCru WHoo
	krameri	IMou NLar
	- B&SWJ 1142	CExl WCru
	'Lakwijk Star'	ECtt ILea NLar SPoG SRms WCAu
	lambertii 'Swansdown'	GCal
	'Larch Cottage Velvet'	MAvo
	libani	CDor ELon EPPr MCot NBid NSti WBrk WCot WSHC
	- RCB RL B-2	WCot
	- 'Kew Gardens' **new**	EPPr
	'Light Dilys'	EBee EPPr LCro LOPS NDov
	'Lilac Ice'	CBod CMil CWGN EBee ECtt EPfP GMaP LPla LRHS MAsh MNrw NDov NLar NRHS NSti SCob SPoG
§	× ***lindavicum*** 'Apple Blossom'	EBee EPot LRHS MAsh NSla WFar
	linearilobum subsp. ***transversale***	SRot
I	- - 'Laciniatum'	GKev WCot
	- - 'Rose Foundling'	SBrt
§	'Little David'	NLar
	'Little Devil'	see *G.* 'Little David'
	'Little Gem'	CMea CRos EBee LRHS MAvo NDov NRHS SBch WFar WHoo WMoo
	lucidum	WOut WPtf WSFF
	'Luscious Linda'	MAvo WSHC
	'Lydia'	SRGP
§	***macrorrhizum***	CBod CSBt ECrN EPed EPfP ESps GBin GJos GKev GKin GMcL GWyn IFro LEdu LOPS LSun MCot MRav MWat NBro SBod SRms WCAu WFar WHar XLum
	- AL & JS 90179YU	CHid EPPr
	- 'Album'	CBod CBre CElw CRos ECha EHrv EPPr GMaP LRHS MBel MSpe MSwo NBid NBro NChi NRHS SAko WBrk WCot WCru WFib WMoo
	- 'Bevan's Variety'	Widely available
	- 'Bulgaria'	EPPr WBrk
	- 'Cham-ce'	ECtt EPPr
	- 'Czakor'	CMac CRos EBee ECtt ELan ELon EPPr EPfP LRHS MCot MRav MSpe NEgg NGdn NLar NRHS SAko SRGP SRms SWvt WBrk WCot WCru WFar WMoo XLum
I	- 'De Bilt'	EPPr EWes WBrk
	- 'Freundorf'	EBee EPPr EWes GBin GCal SAko
	- 'Galgenveld' **new**	EBee
	- 'Glacier'	EPPr EWes
	- 'Ingwersen's Variety' ♀H7	Widely available
	- 'Lohfelden'	EPPr EWes GCal SRGP WBrk WCru
	- 'Mount Olympus'	see *G. macrorrhizum* 'White-Ness'
	- 'Mytikas'	EPPr WBrk WPtf
	- 'Olympos'	EBee EPPr NLar
	- 'Pindus'	CBod CRos CWCL EBee EPPr GAbr LRHS MWat NLar NRHS NSti SPoG SRGP WCru WFar WPnP WPtf
	- 'Prionia'	EBee EPPr GCal SAko WBrk
	- 'Purpurrot'	WBrk
	- 'Ridsko'	EPPr GCal SRGP WBrk WCru
	- ***roseum***	see *G. macrorrhizum*
	- 'Rotblut'	EPPr SRGP WBrk
	- 'Sandwijck'	EBee EPPr MAvo
	- 'Snow Sprite'	CMea EPPr LLHF MHer NEoE NLar WBrk WHrl WPnP WPtf WWFP XLum
	- 'Spessart'	CBar CRos EBee ECtt ELan ELon EPPr EPfP GBin GMaP GQue LRHS MMuc NLar NRHS SCob SEND SGbt SPer SPhx SPoG SWvt WFib WHar WRHF XLum

	- 'Variegatum' (v)	CFis CRos EBee EHrv ELan GMaP GMcL LEdu SRGP SRms WCot WFar
	- 'Velebit'	EPPr SRGP WBrk WCru XLum
§	- 'White-Ness' ♀H7	Widely available
	macrostylum	CDor WCot WCru
	- 'Leonidas'	EPPr
	- 'Talish'	EPPr
	- 'Uln Oag Triag'	EPPr
	maculatum	CFis CRos LRHS MAvo MCot MMrt MNrw MRav NLar NRHS NSti SRGP WCru WHal
	- from Kath Dryden	EPPr
	- f. ***albiflorum***	CElw CRos EBee ELan ELon EPPr EPfP EWTr GBin LRHS MBel MNrw MTis NChi NLar NRHS NSti SRGP SSut WBrk WCru WFar WMoo WPnP
	- 'Beth Chatto'	CBod CDor CElw CSam CSpe EBee ECha ECtt EHrv ELan ELon EPPr EPfP GCal GMaP IRob LEdu MBel MMuc MNrw MTis NBid NDov NLar NRHS WAul WFar WFib WPnP
	- 'Elizabeth Ann'PBR ♀H7	CSam CWGN EBee ECtt EHrv EPPr GBin LRHS LSou MBel MHol MNrw MTis NGdn NLar NSti NWad WCot WFar WFib WHil WMoo WPnP
	- 'Espresso'	Widely available
	- 'Putnam County'	EPPr
	- 'Shameface'	EPPr WMoo
	- 'Silver Buttons'	EBee
	- 'Smoky Mountain'	EPPr
	- 'Spring Purple'	CElw EBee EPPr NLar WFar
	- 'Sweetwater'	EPPr
	- 'Vickie Lynn'	EBee EPPr EWTr WCAu
	maderense ♀H3	CAbb CBcs CBod CCht CPbh CPla CRav CRos CSpe ECre ELan EUJe EWes GKev IBoy LRHS NLos NPer NRHS NSti SArc SPav SPhx SRGP SVen SWvt WFar
	- 'Guernsey White'	CBod CCCN CPla CRos NLos WOut
	- white-flowered	CSpe
§	× ***magnificum*** ♀H7	Widely available
	- 'Blue Blood'	CElw CRos EBee ECtt EMFm EPPr EPfP GAbr GCal GMcL LRHS LSou MBNS MCot MHol NGdn NRHS NSti SRms SWvt WCAu WCot WRHF
	- 'Ernst Pagels'	CBod GBin MHol WOut
	- 'Hylander'	EPPr
	- 'Peter Yeo'	EBee EPPr SRGP
	- 'Rosemoor'	CBod CElw CHid CRos CWCL ECtt EHrv ELan EPPr EPed EPfP GCal LCro LOPS LRHS NEoE NRHS SPer SPhm SPtp WFib WHoo XLum
	- 'Vital'	XLum
	magniflorum	EBee EWes GKev NBid NGdn
	'Maître Hugo'	EBee
§	***malviflorum***	CDor CFis ECha ELan EPPr NSti SBrt WCot WCru WHoo
	- from Spain	EWes
	- pink-flowered	EPPr WSHC
§	'Mary Mottram'	CElw
	'Mavis Simpson' ♀H4	Widely available
	'Maxwelton'	EBee
	'Melinda'PBR	CDor EBee ECtt LCro LOPS MMuc NLar NMir NSti WCot WFib WPnP WRHF
	'Memories'PBR	CSma ECtt LSRN MBNS SRms
	'Menna Bach'	MAvo WFar
	'Meryl Anne'	SRGP WPtf

	microphyllum	see *G. potentilloides*
	'Midnight Star'	EBee EPPr EWes
	molle	WSFF
	× ***monacense***	CBod CRos EBee ELan IFoB IMou LEdu LRHS MBNS MWat NRHS SRGP WCru WGwG WMoo WPnP WWtn
	- var. ***anglicum***	CRos ECtt EPPr EPfP LRHS NLar NRHS WMoo
	- 'Anne Stevens'	EBee
	- 'Claudine Dupont'	CElw EBee EPPr IFro NWad WCot WFib
	- dark-flowered	WMoo
	- 'Emma White'	EBee EPPr NChi
	- 'Jackie'	EBee EPPr
	- var. ***monacense*** 'Breckland Fever'	EBee EPPr SRGP
§	- - 'Muldoon'	EPPr EPfP SRGP WMoo WPnP
	- 'Spotted in the Pass' **new**	EBee
	'Mourning Widow'	see *G. phaeum* 'Lady in Mourning'
	'Mrs Jean Moss'	EBee EPPr EWes MAvo SRGP
	napuligerum misapplied	see *G. farreri*
	'Natalie'	CRos EBee EPPr LRHS LSRN MAsh MAvo NChi NRHS
	nepalense	SRGP SRms
	'Nicola'	CElw CRos EPPr EPfP IFro LRHS MAvo MNrw NLar NRHS SRGP
	'Nimbus' ♀H7	Widely available
	nodosum	Widely available
	- 'Blueberry Ice'	CElw MAvo
	- 'Clos de Coudray'	EBee EPPr EWTr ILea MAvo NLar NSti SBch SHar SPoG WCAu WFar WPnP
	- 'Dark Heart'	MCot
	- dark-flowered	see *G. nodosum* 'Swish Purple'
	- 'Darkleaf'	EBee
	- 'Hexham Big Eye'	CDor CElw EBee EWes MAvo WFar
	- 'Hexham Face Paint'	EBee EPPr
	- 'Hexham Feathers'	CElw
	- 'Hexham Freckles'	EBee EPPr
	- 'Hexham Lace'	CElw EPPr
	- 'Hexham Whitethroat' **new**	EBee
	- 'Julie's Velvet'	CElw LEdu SBch WHoo WPGP
	- pale-flowered	see *G. nodosum* 'Svelte Lilac'
	- 'Pascal'	EPPr
	- 'Saucy Charlie'	SBch
	- 'Silverwood'	CDor CElw CSpe EBee ECtt EPPr GBin GCal LPla LSou LSun MBel MTis NSti SAko SBch SPhx SPoG SRGP WCAu WCot WHoo WPnP WRHF WWFP
	- 'Simon'	MAvo SRGP
§	- 'Svelte Lilac'	CBod CElw CRos ECtt EPPr LPla LRHS LSou NBro NRHS SPhm SPhx SPoG SRGP WBrk WCAu WCru WFar WFib WMoo WPnP
§	- 'Swish Purple'	CElw CRos ELon EPPr LRHS MAvo NLar NRHS SRGP WCru WMoo
	- 'Tony's Talisman'	EBee MAvo
	- 'Whiteleaf'	CElw CFis CMac CMea CRos EPPr GBin GCal LRHS NChi NRHS SRGP WCru WFar WHal WMoo WPnP
	- 'Wreighburn House White'	EBee MAvo
	'Nunwood Purple'	EBee EPPr EWes MAvo
	ocellatum	IFro
	'Old Rose'	CRos LRHS NRHS SRGP WCru
§	***orientalitibeticum***	CExl CRos CSpe ECtt EPPr GAbr GKev IFro LRHS MCot MHer MMuc NBid NLar NRHS NRya SEND SMad SRGP WCot WMoo

	'Orion' ♀H7	Widely available
	'Orkney Blue'	CElw EPPr NChi WCru
	ORKNEY CHERRY ('Bremerry'PBR)	CMac EBee ECtt EPfP EWTr GBin LCro LLHF LOPS LRHS MBel SCob SRkn SRms
	'Orkney Dawn'	MAvo WPnP
	'Orkney Flame'	EBee EPPr
	'Orkney Mist'	EBee EPPr MAvo
	'Orkney Pink'	ECtt EPPr EPfP LRHS SRGP
	'Out of the Blue'	WOut
	× ***oxonianum***	WMoo
	- 'A.T. Johnson' ♀H7	CAby CBcs CRos CTri CWCL EBee ECtt ELan EPPr EPfP EShb ESps GKin GMaP LRHS MRav MWat NEgg NGdn NLar NRHS NSti SCob SPer SRGP SRms SWvt WCru WMoo WWtn
	- 'Alice' **new**	SRGP
	- 'Ankum's White'	EBee EPPr EWes
	- 'Anmore'	SRGP
	- 'Beholder's Eye' ♀H7	EPPr GWyn MMuc NLar SRGP WPnP
	- 'Breckland Sunset'	EBee EPPr NLar SRGP
	- 'Bregover Pearl'	CBre EPPr SRGP WMoo
	- 'Bressingham's Delight'	CRos LRHS NRHS SRGP
	- 'Buttercup'	SRGP
I	- 'Cally Seedling'	EBee EWes GCal
	- 'Cam Beauty' **new**	WHoo
	- 'Chocolate Strawberry'	EBee EPPr EWes
§	- 'Claridge Druce'	CBod CMac CRos CTri ECha ELan EPPr EPfP EShb ESps GKin GMaP LRHS MCot MRav MSwo MWat NGdn NLar NRHS SCob SPer SRms WAvo WFar WHar WMoo WWtn XLum
	- 'Coronet'	GCal SRGP WMoo
	- 'Cream Chocolate'	EBee EPPr
	- 'David Rowlinson'	CDor EBee EPPr
	- 'Dawn Time'	CDor
	- 'Diane's Treasure'	EBee
	- 'Ella'	CWGN
	- 'Elworthy Misty'	CElw CFis EPPr SRGP
	- 'Frank Lawley'	IRob NBid NChi SRGP WMoo
§	- 'Fran's Star' (d)	SRGP WCru
	- 'Frilly Gilly'	EBee
	- 'Glynis' **new**	SRGP
	- 'Hexham Pink'	EBee EPPr EWes SRGP
	- 'Hollywood'	ELan EPPr NLar NPer SAko SRGP SRms WMoo
	- 'Iced Green Tea'	EBee
	- 'Julie Brennan'	CRos EBee LRHS NRHS
	- 'Kate Moss'	EPPr EWes NSti SRGP
	- 'Katherine Adele'	CMea CSpe ECha ECtt EPPr EPfP EShb EWes GCal LSou MAsh MAvo MMuc MSpe NLar SEND SRGP SRms WFar WFib WHil
§	- 'Kingston'	EPPr
	- 'Königshof'	EPPr EWes
	- 'Kurt's Variegated'	see *G.* × *oxonianum* 'Spring Fling'
	- 'Lace Time'	CAby CBod CBre CRos EBee ECtt EPPr GKin LRHS LSRN MAsh MSpe NEgg NRHS SPer SPoG SRGP SRms WCAu WGwG WMoo
	- 'Lady Moore'	SRGP WMoo
	- 'Lambrook Gillian'	CFis EPPr SRGP WBrk
	- 'Lasting Impression'	EPPr SRGP
	- 'Laura Skelton'	CElw EBee
	- 'Little John'	EPPr EWes
	- 'Maid Marion'	EWes
	- 'Maurice Moka'	ECtt NLar
	- 'Miriam Rundle'	SRGP WCru WMoo
	- 'Moorland Jenny'	WMoo
	- 'Moorland Star'	WMoo
	- 'Mrs Leafe' **new**	SRGP
	- 'Mrs Molly Kisby'	EBee
	- 'Music from Big Pink'	EBee EPPr EWes
	- 'Pat Smallacombe'	EBee EPPr SRGP WMoo
	- 'Patricia Josephine'	WCAu
	- 'Pearl Boland'	EBee EPPr SRGP
	- 'Phantom'	EBee EPPr
	- 'Phoebe Noble'	CBre CRos EBee EPPr LRHS MNrw NLar NRHS SRGP WFib WMoo
	- 'Phoebe's Blush'	EPPr SRGP
§	- 'Prestbury Blush'	CElw EPPr SRGP
	- 'Prestbury White'	see *G.* × *oxonianum* 'Prestbury Blush'
	- 'Raspberry Ice'	EBee EWes
	- 'Rebecca Moss'	CBod CRos ECha ECtt ELan EPPr GAbr LRHS LSRN NChi NRHS NSti SAko SRGP WCru WFib WOut
	- 'Red Sceptre'	EBee
	- 'Rose Clair'	CRos ELan EPPr LRHS NLar NRHS SRGP WCAu WCru WHar WMoo
	- 'Rosenlicht'	CBod EBee EPPr GKin LRHS MAsh MRav NRHS SRGP WCru WMoo XLum
	- 'Rothbury Sarah'	EBee EPPr
	- 'Sandy'	EBee EPPr EWes
	- 'Something Special'	EBee EPPr
§	- 'Spring Fling' (v)	CDor CRos ECtt EWes MSpe NRHS NWad SRGP WFar
	- 'Stillingfleet Keira'	EBee EPPr NSti SRGP
	- 'Summer Surprise'	EBee EPPr EWes WCru
	- 'Susan'	EPPr EWes
	- 'Susie White'	EPPr SRGP WCru
	- 'Tess' **new**	ECtt MHol
§	- f. ***thurstonianum***	CAby CBod CBre CMac EBee ECtt EPPr EPfP EPri GAbr GBin IFro LRHS MNrw MRav MSpe NBid NBro NLar NRHS SCob SPoG SRms WBrk WCot WCru WFar WMoo WSpi XLum
	- - 'Armitageae'	EBee EPPr SRGP
	- - 'Breckland Brownie'	EBee EPPr EWes MAvo SRGP
	- - 'Crûg Star'	WCru
	- - 'David McClintock'	EBee EPPr SRGP WMoo
	- - 'Red Sputnik'	SRGP
	- - 'Robin's Ginger Nut'	EBee EWes
	- - 'Sherwood'	EPPr GCal MSpe NBro NSti SRGP WFar WMoo
	- - 'Southcombe Double' (d)	CBod ECtt ELan EPPr LSou MHol SRGP SRms WGwG WMoo
§	- - 'Southcombe Star'	EBee EPPr GAbr NBro NGdn SRGP WCru WMoo
	- - 'Sue Cox' (d)	EBee EPPr NLar
	- - 'White Stripes'	EBee EPPr
	- 'Trevor's White'	CDor CRos EBee EPPr LRHS NRHS SRGP WCru
	- 'Tyne Salmon'	EBee
	- 'Wageningen' ♀H7	CBod CBre CRos EBee EPPr GCal LRHS LSou NGdn NRHS SEND SRGP WCot WCru WGwG WHoo WMoo
	- 'Walter's Gift'	CBod CRos ECtt EPPr EPri EShb GBin LRHS LSou MAsh MAvo MRav NBro NChi NLar NPer NRHS SAko WCru WFar WHoo WMoo WPnP WWtn
§	- 'Wargrave Pink'	Widely available
	- 'Waystrode'	EBee EPPr SRGP

	- 'Westacre White'	ECha EPPr EWes
	- 'Whitehaven'	SRGP
	- 'Whiter Shade of Pale'	EBee EPPr
	- 'Winscombe'	EPfP GCal SRGP WMoo
§	***palmatum*** ♀H4	Widely available
	palustre	EBee EPPr GLog MMuc MNrw NLar SRGP WCot WMoo
	- 'Money Peniche'	XEll
	'Pastel Clouds'	GWyn WFar
	PATRICIA ('Brempat') ♀H7	Widely available
	peloponnesiacum	CElw EPPr EWes GQue NLar NWad WMoo
	'Perfect Storm'	ECtt LLHF
	phaeum	Widely available
	- 'Acorn Bank'	EBee EPPr
	- 'Advendo'	EBee EPPr
	- 'Album'	Widely available
	- 'Alec's Pink'	EBee EPPr WCAu WPnP
	- 'All Saints'	EBee EPPr LEdu SRGP
	- 'Angelina'	EBee EPPr
	- 'Ann Logan'	EBee
	- 'Aureum'	see *G. phaeum* 'Golden Spring'
	- 'Basket of Lavender'	EBee
	- 'Blauwvoet'	EPPr NChi
	- 'Blue Shadow'	CElw EBee EPPr LEdu SRGP
	- 'Brown Sugar' new	EBee
	- 'Calligrapher'	EPPr LLHF NChi SRGP WMoo
	- 'Chocolate Biscuit' new	EBee
	- 'Chocolate Chip'	EPPr
	- 'Conny Broe' (v)	CDor EShb WSHC
	- 'Dark Angel'	EBee
	- 'Dark Dream'	EBee
	- 'David Bromley'	WCru
	- 'David Martin'	EBee EPPr SRGP
	- 'Enid'	EPPr
	- 'Garage Door'	EBee
	- 'George Stone'	EPPr
	- 'Golden Samobor'	CElw EPPr
§	- 'Golden Spring'	EBee EPPr NEoE SRGP WFar
	- 'Green Ghost'	EBee
	- 'Hector's Lavender'	EBee SRGP WOut
	- var. ***hungaricum***	EBee EPPr SRGP
	- 'James Haunch'	EPPr
	- 'Judith's Blue'	EBee EPPr
	- 'Klepper'	EBee EPPr GBin
§	- 'Lady in Mourning'	CExl EBee EPPr GCal NChi SRGP SRms WCru WMoo WPnP
	- 'Lavender Pinwheel'	CBod CDor EBee EPfP MSpe SPer WCot WHar
*	- 'Lilacina'	ECha
	- 'Lily Lovell'	Widely available
	- 'Lisa' (v)	CDor CElw CFis EPPr MAvo MNrw SMHy WCot WFar
	- 'Little Boy'	EPPr
	- var. ***lividum***	CBre EPfP GMaP MRav SRGP SRms WFar WPnP XLum
	- - 'Joan Baker'	CDor CFis CSam EBee EPPr MNrw NChi NGdn NSti SDys SRGP WCru WFib WMoo WOut WPnP
	- - 'Majus'	CRos EBee ECtt ELan EPPr EPfP LRHS NRHS WFar WMoo
	- 'Lustige Witwe' (v)	WCot
	- 'Marchant's Ghost'	IFro SMHy
	- 'Margaret Wilson' (v)	CWGN EBee ECtt EPPr EWes GAbr GCal LEdu MAvo MSpe NEgg NGdn NLar NSti SRGP WCot WHil WMoo WSHC
	- 'Mierhausen'	EBee EPPr
	- 'Misty Samobor'	ECha
	- 'Mojito' (v)	WCot
	- 'Moorland Dylan'	WMoo WOut
	- 'Mottisfont Rose'	CDor CElw SBch
	- 'Mourning Widow'	see *G. phaeum* 'Lady in Mourning'
	- 'Mrs Charles Perrin'	CFis CRos
	- 'Mrs Withey Price'	WHil
	- 'Night Time'	EBee EPPr
	- 'Nightshade'	EBee EPPr
	- 'Our Pat' ♀H7	EBee EPPr NChi WCot
	- var. ***phaeum*** 'Langthorns Blue'	CRos CWCL EBee ELan EPPr EPfP EWes LEdu LRHS MNrw NRHS SRGP SWvt WPGP
	- - 'Samobor'	Widely available
	- 'Phantom of the Opera' (v)	EBee EPPr
	- 'Pink Palava'	LEdu
I	- 'Ploeger de Bilt'	EBee EPPr
	- 'Purple Moon'	EBee EPPr
	- 'Rachel's Rhapsody'	EBee EPPr MSpe SRGP
	- 'Raven'	CBod CRav EBee ECtt EPPr LRHS NChi NLar SCob SPer WCAu WFar WHar
	- 'Ray of Light'	EPPr
	- 'Rise Top Lilac'	EBee WPGP
	- 'Robin's Angel Eyes'	EBee EPPr
	- 'Rose Air'	EPPr SRGP WMoo WPnP
	- 'Rose Madder'	CElw EPPr GCal LEdu MNrw NChi NLar SPhx SRGP WCru WGwG WMoo WPnP
	- 'Rothbury Ruby'	EBee EPPr
	- 'Saturn'	EPPr
	- 'Séricourt'	WCot WFib
	- 'Shadowlight'	EBee ECtt EPPr NLar
	- 'Slatina'	EPPr
	- 'Springtime' PBR	CDor EBee EPPr LLHF MBNS MSpe NGdn NLar WFib
	- 'Stillingfleet Ghost'	EBee EPPr LEdu MNrw NChi NSti
	- 'Taff's Jester' (v)	MSpe WCot WHil
	- 'Trevor's Recall'	EBee
	- 'Tyne Mist'	EBee EPPr
§	- 'Variegatum' (v)	CBre CFis CMac EBee EHoe ELan EPPr GMaP IFro MSpe NBro SRGP WHer WMoo
	- 'Vintage Dave'	WOut
	- 'Walküre'	EPPr EWes NLar
	'Philippe Vapelle'	Widely available
	'Pink Delight'	CElw IRob MAvo SBch
	'Pink Penny'	CDor CRos EBee ECtt EPPr EPfP GBin LRHS MNrw NLar NRHS NSti SRGP WCAu WFar WMoo
§	***platyanthum***	EPPr MNrw SRGP WCru
	- var. ***reinii***	GCal WCru
	- 'Russian Giant'	EPPr
	platypetalum misapplied	see *G. × magnificum*
	platypetalum Franch.	see *G. sinense*
§	***platypetalum*** Fisch. & C.A. Mey.	CRos EBee EPPr LRHS NRHS SRGP WCru XLum
	- 'Georgia Blue'	WCru
	- 'Dark Side of the Moon'	EBee EPPr
	- 'Genyell'	EBee EPPr NChi
	- 'Turco'	EBee EPPr NLar
§	***pogonanthum***	CHid GLog
	polyanthes	EWes NChi
§	***potentilloides***	GCal SRGP WMoo
	pratense	CBre CHab CMac CWld EBWF EBee ELan EPPr ESps GJos GMaP MHer MNHC NMir SCob SPer SPlb SPoG SRGP SRms WCot WHar WMoo WPnP WSFF XLum
	- 'Akaton'	NLar
I	- 'Alboroseum'	EBee

	- 'Algera Double'	ECtt EUJe LLHF MHol MSCN WCAu WCot
	- 'Bittersweet'	EPPr
	- 'Blue Lagoon'	EBee EPPr
*	- 'Blue Skies'	LSou WFar
	- 'Blue Sky Thinking' **new**	EBee
	- 'Carrie's White' **new**	EBee
	- 'Cluden Sapphire'	EBee EPPr EWTr NEoE WCAu WCru
	- 'Delft Blue' **new**	CBod
§	- 'Double Jewel' (d)	CWGN EBee EPfP MBNS MHol NLar SPoG WBor WFar
	- 'Else Lacey' (d)	CElw EBee WCot
	- 'Flore Pleno'	see *G. pratense* 'Plenum Violaceum'
	- 'Hexham Spook' **new**	EBee
I	- 'Himalayanum'	NLar
	- 'Hocus Pocus'	CRos CWGN ECtt ELan EWTr LRHS MAvo MBNS MHol MNrw MSCN NBro NLar NRHS NSti SCob WFar
	- 'Hoo House' **new**	WHoo
	- 'Ilja'	EBee EPPr MNrw
	- 'Janet's Special'	WHoo
	- 'Marshmallow'	EBee ECtt MAvo MHol NSti SPoG WCAu WCot
	- 'Milou'	MAvo
	- 'Mrs Kendall Clark' ♀H7	Widely available
	- 'Okey Dokey'	EBee
	- 'Pink Splash'	WMoo
	- 'Plenum Caeruleum' (d)	ECtt EPPr MRav NBid NEgg NLar WSHC
§	- 'Plenum Violaceum' (d) ♀H7	Widely available
	- 'Pope's Purple'	see *G. pratense* (Victor Reiter Group) BLACK BEAUTY
	- var. ***pratense*** f. ***albiflorum***	CRos CSam EPPr EPfP GMaP IFro LRHS MNrw NBid NRHS SCob SGbt SPer WMoo WSpi
	- - - 'Galactic'	ECtt LRHS LSun MHol NEgg NLar SEND SPoG WCot WCru WFib WMoo WPnP
	- - - 'Laura'PBR (d)	CExl EBee EPPr EPfP EWes LSRN LSou MHol MSCN NGdn NLar NSti SCob WPnP
	- - - 'Plenum Album' (d)	CBot CWCL EBee ECtt ELan EPPr EPfP EWes GBin GWyn LLHF LRHS MBel MNrw MRav NEgg NGdn NLar SGbt SRms SWvt WCot WFar WGwG WSpi
	- - - 'Silver Queen'	CAby CPla CRos EBee ECtt EPed LRHS LSou NRHS SRGP WAvo WGwG WMoo WPnP
	- 'Purple Ghost'	CAbb CRos ECtt LRHS NEoE NRHS WHar
	- 'Rectum Album'	see *G. clarkei* 'Kashmir White'
	- 'Robin's Grey Beard'	EBee EPPr
§	- 'Rose Queen'	SGbt SRGP WCru
	- 'Roseum'	see *G. pratense* 'Rose Queen'
	- 'Southease Celestial'	SMHy
	- 'Splish-splash'	see *G. pratense* 'Striatum'
	- 'Stanton Mill'	NBid
	- var. ***stewartianum***	MRav
	- - 'Elizabeth Yeo'	CRos ECtt EPPr LRHS NRHS WCru
	- - (Purple Flowered Group) 'Raina'	EPPr
§	- 'Striatum'	Widely available
	- variegated, white-flowered (v)	WCot
§	- (Victor Reiter Group) BLACK BEAUTY ('Nodbeauty'PBR)	CAby CBcs CExl CRos CWCL CWGN EBee ECtt EPfP EUJe EWes LBuc LCro LOPS LRHS MGos MHol MPnt NHpl NLar NRHS SPoG SRkn SRot WFar WHoo WSpi

	- - 'Kaya' **new**	MHol
	- - 'Midnight Blues'	CWGN EBee SCob
	- - 'Midnight Clouds'	CWGN EBee ECtt EPfP LBuc MAsh NSti SCob SPoG WFar
	- - MIDNIGHT GHOST ('Midnightlyona') **new**	MSCN WHar
	- - 'Midnight Reiter'	CExl CWGN ELan EPfP EWTr GCal GWyn IBoy IFoB MAvo MHol NBro NChi NGdn NHpl NLar NQui SCob SDys SMad SWvt WFar WPnP
	- - 'New Dimension'	EBee WFib
	- - 'Purple Heron'	LSRN NRHS
	- - 'Purple-haze'	CPla GPSL GWyn SMad WMoo WSHC
§	- - 'Victor Reiter'	CSpe ELan EPPr LEdu NChi NGdn NHpl SRot WCot
	- 'Wisley Blue'	EPPr SRGP WHal
	- 'Yorkshire Queen'	EBee NGdn NSti WCru
	'Prelude'	CBre CDor CElw EBee ELon EPPr NEoE NLar SHar SRGP WCAu WFib WPtf
	'Prima Donna'	WCAu
	procurrens	CBre CElw CTri EPPr GAbr GCal WBrk WCru WMoo WPtf
§	***psilostemon*** ♀H7	Widely available
	- 'Bressingham Flair'	CDor CTri ECtt LRHS MRav NBid NChi NLar NRHS SRms WCAu WCru WFar WMoo WPnP
	- 'Catherine Deneuve'PBR	CWGN EBee EWTr EWes ILea SCob STPC WCAu
	- 'Coton Goliath'	EBee EPPr EWes MAvo
	- 'Jason Bloom'	CRos EBee EPPr LRHS NRHS
	- 'Madelon'	CElw MAvo NLar
	- 'Moorland Jack'	WMoo
	pulchrum	CDor CFil CSpe EWes GWyn SRGP
	punctatum hort.	see *G. × monacense* var. *monacense* 'Muldoon'
	- 'Variegatum'	see *G. phaeum* 'Variegatum'
	'Purple Rain'	EBee EPPr
	pylzowianum	NBid NRya WMoo
	pyrenaicum	EBWF GAbr NSti
	- f. ***albiflorum***	GAbr IFro MNrw SRGP WBrk WCot WFar
	- 'Barney Brighteye'	SRGP
	- 'Bill Wallis'	CRav CSpe EHrv ELan EPPr EPfP IFro IPot LRHS LSRN LSun MBrN MMuc MRav NDov NHpl NPer SEND SPhx SPtp SRGP SWvt WCFE WCot WFar WHoo WPnP WSpi
	- 'Isparta'	EPPr IFro LRHS MNrw SHar SPhx SRGP WBrk
	- 'Summer Sky'	SPav SRGP SWvt
	- 'Summer Snow'	GPSL GWyn
	'Rainbow'PBR	MBNS
	Rambling Robin Group	CSpe ECre EWes
*	- 'Silver Shadow'	SPhx
	rectum	EPPr NBre NLar WCru
	- 'Album'	see *G. clarkei* 'Kashmir White'
	'Red Admiral'	CBod CMea CSam ECtt EHoe EPPr GCal LRHS MAvo NDov NLar NQui NRHS NSti SPoG SRGP WCot WFar WGwG WHoo WPnP WWtn
	'Red Propellers'	CElw
	reflexum	CDor CRos EPfP LRHS NRHS WCru
	- 'Katara Pass'	NChi
	refractoides	WCot
	refractum	CExl
	regelii	GWyn WCru WMoo

renardii ♀H5	Widely available
- 'Beldo'	MAvo
- blue-flowered	see *G. renardii* 'Whiteknights'
- 'Rothbury Hills'	EBee EPPr
- 'Tcschelda'	CBod ECha ECtt EPPr EShb NLar SRms WFar WMoo
§ - 'Whiteknights'	EBee
- 'Zetterlund'	CBod CRos EBee ELan EPPr EPfP EPri EWTr IRob LRHS NEgg NQui NRHS WMoo
§ ***reuteri***	CHid CTsd EBee NLos SChr SRGP WCru
'Richard Nutt'	EBee
richardsonii	CBod CFis EBee EPPr GCal LEdu LRHS MCot MNrw NRHS NWad SBod SPoG SRGP WCru WGwG
- pink-flowered	MAvo
- white-flowered	NChi
× ***riversleaianum*** 'Russell Prichard' ♀H4	Widely available
§ ***rivulare***	GLog NLar
robertianum	EBWF ENfk EPPr SRms WSFF
§ - 'Album'	EPPr SHar SPhx SRGP SRms WHer
- f. ***bernettii***	see *G. robertianum* 'Album'
- 'Celtic White'	CBre EPPr GCal IFro MMuc SEND SPav SRGP
robustum	CFil EPri SPav SPlb SRGP WCFE WKif
'Rosetta'PBR	CBod ELon MSCN
'Rosie Crûg'	SWvt
rosthornii	WCru
'Rothbury Red'	EBee NChi
§ ROZANNE ('Gerwat'PBR) ♀H7	Widely available
rubescens	see *G. yeoi*
rubifolium	NWad WCru
ruprechtii (Grossh.) Woronow	EPPr MNrw SRGP
SABANI BLUE ('Bremigo'PBR)	CMac CSpe CWGN EBee ECtt EPPr EWTr EWes LCro LOPS MHol NLar NSti SMHy SPer WCot WSHC
'Salome'	CBcs CBod CDor EBee ECtt EHrv ELan GAbr GLog GWyn ILea MBel MCot NLar NSti SCob SPoG SRms SRot SWvt WCot WGwG WKif WMoo
'Sandrine'PBR	CBcs CRos CSam CWCL CWGN EBee EPfP IMou LLHF LRHS LSou MHol MNrw NSti SCob SPoG SRms WCot WHil WPnP
sanguineum	Widely available
- ALAN BLOOM ('Bloger'PBR)	CRos EBee EPPr IRob LRHS NRHS WFib
- 'Album' ♀H5	Widely available
- 'Alpenglow'	EBee EPPr SRGP WBrk
- 'Ankum's Pride' ♀H7	CDor CElw CRos EPPr EPfP LRHS LSou MAsh MTis NChi NDov NGdn NLar NRHS NSti SBch SRGP WBrk WCru WFib WMoo WPnP
- 'Apfelblüte'	CBod ELon EPPr GBin NLar WCAu
- 'Aviemore' ♀H7	CElw CFis EPPr GBin GCal GQue
- 'Barnsley'	EPPr NBro NEoE
- 'Belle of Herterton'	CElw EPPr MAvo NBid NChi NEoE WBrk WCru
- 'Bloody Graham'	CRos EPPr LRHS MAvo NRHS SPhx WBrk WMoo
- 'Canon Miles'	CElw ECtt EPPr EWTr IRob NLar SRGP SRms
- 'Catforth Carnival'	EPPr
- 'Cedric Morris'	CElw ECha ELon EPPr MAvo NBid SRGP WBrk WCru WPnP
- 'Compactum'	EPPr WMoo XLum
- dark purple	SSut
§ - 'Droplet'	SRGP
- dwarf	WAbe
- 'Elsbeth'	CElw CRos EBee ECha ECtt ELan ELon EPPr EPfP EWes GBin GCal LRHS MSpe NGdn NLar NRHS NSti SPoG SRGP WBrk WCAu WCru WFar WFib WHal WMoo WPnP XLum
- 'Feu d'Automne'	EBee ELon EPPr NLar WBrk
- 'Fran's Star'	see *G.* × *oxonianum* 'Fran's Star'
- 'Glenluce'	CBod CDor CElw ECtt ELon EPPr EPfP EShb GCal LRHS MRav MSpe MTis NChi NDov NLar NRHS NWad SPoG SRGP SRms WBrk WHal WPnP
- 'Hampshire Purple'	see *G. sanguineum* 'New Hampshire Purple'
- 'Hannelore' **new**	EBee
- 'Holden'	CElw ELon EPPr WBrk
- 'Inverness'	EBee EPPr XLum
- 'Joanna'	CFis ELon EPPr MAvo WBrk
- 'John Elsley'	EBee ECtt EHoe EPPr LRHS LSou MSpe NBro NGdn NRHS NSti SRGP WPnP
- 'John Innes'	EPPr
- 'Jubilee Pink'	GCal WCru
- 'Kristin Jacob'	EPPr
- var. ***lancastrense***	see *G. sanguineum* var. *striatum*
- 'Leeds Variety'	see *G. sanguineum* 'Rod Leeds'
§ - 'Little Bead' ♀H5	EPPr GCrg NHpl NWad SBch WBrk XLum
- 'Max Frei'	Widely available
- 'Minutum'	see *G. sanguineum* 'Droplet'
- 'Nanum'	see *G. sanguineum* 'Little Bead'
§ - 'New Hampshire Purple'	EBee ECtt ELon EPPr EPfP EWTr GLog IPot LRHS MAvo NBro NDov NLar SRms WBrk WFib WHar
- 'Nyewood'	EBee ECtt EPPr LRHS MAsh NRHS SEND SRGP WBrk WCru WFib
- 'Pink Pouffe'	CRos CWGN EBee ECtt ELon LRHS MAsh NRHS SCob
- 'Pink Summer' **new**	EBee
I - 'Plenum' (d)	EPPr
- 'Prado'	XLum
- var. ***prostratum*** (Cav.) Pers.	see *G. sanguineum* var. *striatum*
- 'Purple Flame'	see *G. sanguineum* 'New Hampshire Purple'
§ - 'Rod Leeds'	EBee SRGP
- 'Sandra'	SRGP
§ - 'Shepherd's Delight'	ECtt EPPr
- 'Shepherd's Warning' misapplied	see *G. sanguineum* 'Shepherd's Delight'
- 'Shepherd's Warning' ♀H7	CMea CTri ECtt GCal MMuc MRav NLar SEND SRGP WCru WFib WHoo WPnP
- 'Shooting Star'	EPPr
- 'South Nutfield'	CElw NChi
§ - var. ***striatum*** ♀H5	Widely available
- - deep pink-flowered	CSBt MSwo SWvt
- - 'Mottisfont'	SBch
- - 'Reginald Farrer'	WCru
- - 'Splendens' ♀H7	CRos EBee EPPr GCal LRHS NBid NChi NRHS SAko WCru
- 'Vision Light Pink'	CBod EPPr LPmr WFar
- 'Vision Violet'	CBod IFoB LPmr MAvo SRms SWvt WBrk WFar WHar WPnP
- 'Westacre Poppet'	EWes

'Sanne'	CBod EPPr EWes GKev LRHS MHol SCob STPC WCot WFib WPGP
saxatile	EPPr
* - var. ***candidum***	EBee
'Scapa Flow'	EBee EPPr GCal MAvo WSHC
schlechteri	EWes MMuc SEND WBrk
'Sea Spray'	CTri GMcL
sessiliflorum	GBin
- subsp. ***novae-zelandiae*** 'Mandy'	GBin
I - - 'Nigricans'	ECha GAbr SBch SCob SRGP WFar
§ - - 'Porters Pass'	EHoe EWes NHpl SBch SPlb WFar WHoo
- - red-leaved	see *G. sessiliflorum* subsp. *novae-zelandiae* 'Porters Pass'
shikokianum	GLog GWyn NLar SRGP WPnP
- var. ***kaimontanum***	WCru
- var. ***quelpaertense***	CFis EBee MAvo
- - 'Crûg's Cloak'	WCru
'Shocking Blue'	NLar NSti WFib
'Shouting Star'	see *G.* 'Kanahitobanawa'
'Simonside'	EBee
§ ***sinense***	CExl GCal LRHS MCot NRHS WGwG XLum
'Sirak' ♀^{H7}	Widely available
soboliferum	CBod CFis NDov NLar SPer SRGP WCru WMoo WSHC
- Cally strain	EBee EPPr GCal LPla MAvo WHoo
- var. ***kiusianum***	CElw
- 'Rothbury Star'	EBee
- 'Starman'	EBee ECtt NLar SCob STPC WMoo WSHC
'Solitaire'	CFil EBee WCot
'Southcombe Star'	see *G.* × *oxonianum* f. *thurstonianum* 'Southcombe Star'
'Spinners'	CBod CHid CMac CRos EBee ECtt EPPr EPfP GCal GMaP LRHS LSRN MAvo MRav NBid NGdn NLar NRHS NSti SPer WCru WFar WFib WMoo WPnP
stapfianum var. ***roseum***	see *G. orientalitibeticum*
'Stephanie'	CElw EPPr EPfP EWes LPla LRHS LSRN MAvo MBNS MNrw MRav MSpe NChi NGdn NLar NRHS NSti WBor WCAu WPnP WSHC
'Storm Chaser'	EBee IPot LRHS SCob
'Strawberry Frost'	LLHF
subcaulescens ♀^{H4}	CAby CMea CRos CWCL EBee ELan EPPr EPfP EWTr IBoy LRHS LSRN MCot MRav NBid NDov NEgg NRHS NRya SCob SPer SPoG SRms SWvt WAbe WCFE WFar WHar WHoo
- 'Giuseppii' ♀^{H5}	CBod CExl CGar CRos ECtt ELon EPPr EPfP EPot GAbr GCrg LRHS LSou MAsh MRav NDov NRHS SRGP SRot SWvt WSpi
- 'Splendens' ♀^{H5}	CRos CTri ECtt EPPr GCrg GMcL LRHS LSou MHer NEgg NRHS NSla SRms WFar
'Sue Crûg'	CRos EBee ECtt ELan EPfP LPla LRHS LSou NChi NEgg NRHS WCru WMoo
'Sue's Sister'	WCru
'Summer Cloud'	EPPr SRGP WOut
SUMMER SKIES ('Gernic'PBR) (d)	Widely available
suzukii B&SWJ 016	CExl WCru
'Sweet Heidy'PBR	CBod EBee ECtt EPfP IRob LLHF LPla MHol MNrw MSwo NLar NSti SCob SRGP WBor WCAu WFar WPnP

sylvaticum	EBWF NBid NGdn NMir WArt WFar WMoo WShi
- f. ***albiflorum***	CBre ELan NSti WCru
- - 'Cyril's Superb White'	EBee EPPr
- 'Album' ♀^{H7}	Widely available
- 'Amanda'	EBee
- 'Amy Doncaster'	CAby CDor CElw CExl CRos CSam CSpe EBee ECtt ELan EPPr EPfP LRHS MRav NEgg NLar NRHS NSti SPer SRGP WBor WCot WCru WFib WGwG WHoo WMoo WPnP
- 'Angulatum'	CElw EPPr WMoo
- 'Birch Lilac'	CElw EBee EPPr EPri GCal LRHS NLar NPnk WFib WMoo
- 'Coquetdale Lilac'	CDor EBee EPPr
- 'Greek Fire'	EBee EPPr MAvo
- 'Ice Blue'	EBee EPPr NChi
- 'Immaculée'	EPPr MRav
- 'Jonah P'	EBee
- 'Kanzlersgrund'	CElw EPPr
- 'Lilac Time'	EPPr
- 'Master Niall Lawson' **new**	EBee WFar
- 'Mayflower' ♀^{H7}	Widely available
- 'Meran'	EPPr
- 'Miss Connie Wilson'	EBee EPPr
- 'Nikita'	EPPr
- f. ***roseum***	NLar
- - 'Baker's Pink'	EBee EPPr MNrw MRav SBch SRGP WCru WFar WMoo
- 'Silva'	CElw MRav WCru
- subsp. ***sylvaticum*** var. ***wanneri***	WCru
§ 'Tanya Rendall'PBR	EBee ECtt EHrv ELan ELon GMcL IPot MHer NLar SPer SRms WCot WFar WFib WPnP
'Terre Franche'	EPPr MAvo NLar SPhx
§ ***thunbergii***	CHid EWes LSou SRGP WMoo XLum
- 'Jester's Jacket' (v)	CPla GMcL MNrw SRGP WFar WMoo WOut
- pink-flowered	EPPr SRGP
- white-flowered	EPPr SRGP
thurstonianum	see *G.* × *oxonianum* f. *thurstonianum*
'Tinpenny Mauve'	MAvo WHoo
'Tiny Monster'	Widely available
transbaicalicum	CFis EPPr XLum
traversii var. ***elegans***	CRos LRHS NRHS
tuberosum	CDor CElw CHid ECha ELan GEdr GKev IMou MRav NGdn NQui SPhx WFar
- subsp. ***linearifolium***	EPPr
- 'Richard Hobbs'	EPPr
- 'Rosie's Mauve'	EPPr MAvo
'Ushguli Grijs'	see *G. ibericum* Cav. 'Ushguli Grijs'
'Vectis'	CElw
'Verguld Saffier'	see *G.* BLUE SUNRISE
versicolor	CGar CMea EBWF EBee EPPr EPfP EWTr GAbr GCal GPSL MHer SRms WCAu WMoo WPnP XEll
- 'Kingston'	see *G.* × *oxonianum* 'Kingston'
§ - 'Snow White'	EPPr SEND SRGP WCru WFib WMoo
- 'White Lady'	see *G. versicolor* 'Snow White'
'Victor Reiter'	see *G. pratense* (Victor Reiter Group) 'Victor Reiter'
violareum	see *Pelargonium* 'Splendide'
viscosissimum	WFib

wallichianum	CFis CPou EBee IFro NChi NSti WMoo
§ - 'Buxton's Variety'	Widely available
- 'Chris'	EWes SRGP
- 'Crystal Lake'PBR	CWGN EBee ECtt EPfP IPot MBNS MHol MNrw MTis NDov NGdn NLar NSti SCob WCAu WFar WPnP
- 'Havana Blues'	CBod EBee ECha ECtt EPfP ETMg GBin IPot LCro LOPS LRHS MHol MMrt NLar NRHS NSti SCob WBrk WCot WFar
- pale-blue-flowered	CElw
- 'Pink Buxton'	EWes NLar
- pink-flowered	GCal WCru
- 'Rise and Shine'PBR	CBod CWGN EBee ECtt ELan LCro MHol NSti WCAu WCot
- 'Rosetta'	IMou
- 'Rosie'	SRGP
- 'Syabru'	CElw MNrw WArt WMoo
- 'Sylvia's Surprise'PBR	EBee ECtt IMou LRHS LSRN NLar SCob
'Wednesday's Child'	WFar
'White Doves'	NDov
wilfordii misapplied	see *G. thunbergii*
Wisley hybrid	see *G.* 'Khan'
wlassovianum	Widely available
- 'Blue Star'	EBee MRav NEoE SRGP WFar
- 'Martyn and Emma' **new**	SRGP
§ ***yeoi***	CSpe NSti SEND WCru WOut
yesoense	IFro NSti
- var. ***nipponicum***	WCru
yoshinoi misapplied	see *G. thunbergii*
yunnanense misapplied	see *G. pogonanthum*

Gerbera (*Asteraceae*)

sp.	ESps
(Garvinea Series) 'Fleurie'PBR	MBNS
- GARVINA SWEET DREAMS ('Gardreams') **new**	ETMg
- GARVINEA CATHERINE ('Garcatherine') **new**	MBNS
- GARVINEA LISA ('Garlisa'PBR)	MHol
- GARVINEA ORANGINA ('Orangina'PBR)	MBNS
- GARVINEA PAM ('Pam'PBR)	CPla MBNS
- GARVINEA RACHEL ('Garrachel'PBR)	MHol MNrw
- GARVINEA SWEET GLOW ('Garglow') **new**	ETMg MBNS
- GARVINEA SWEET HONEY ('Garhoney') **new**	ETMg
- GARVINEA SYLVANA ('Garsylvana'PBR)	MHol

Gesneria (*Gesneriaceae*)

cardinalis	see *Sinningia cardinalis*

Gethyum (*Alliaceae*)

atropurpureum	GKev

Geum ✿ (*Rosaceae*)

sp.	ESps
'Abbeydore Burnt Orange'	CElw
'Abendsonne'	CElw MAvo MNrw MRav MSpe NEoE
'Alabama Slammer' (Cocktails Series)	CRos CWCL EBee ECtt ELan GBin ILea LRHS MAvo MPnt MSpe NDov NEgg NLar NRHS SBri SCob SPad SRms WCAu WFar
alpinum	see *G. montanum*
'Apricot Beauty'	CWCL
'Apricot Crush' **new**	MNrw
'Apricot Delight'	LLHF NEoE NWad
'Baked Beans'	NEoE
'Banana Daiquiri' (Cocktails Series)	CMea CRos CWCL EBee ECtt ELan EPfP ETMg LLWG LRHS MAsh MSpe MTis NRHS SCob WFar WTor
'Beech House Apricot'	CDor CRos ECtt EPri ILea LRHS MAvo MNrw MRav NEoE NRHS NWad SBri WMoo XEll
'Beech's Double'	EWes
'Bell Bank'	Widely available
'Birkhead's Creamy Lemon'	EBee MHCG
'Blazing Sunset' (d)	Widely available
'Blood Orange'	ECtt EPed LRHS MAsh NEoE NRHS SPoG
'Borisii'	Widely available
'Bremner's Gold'	NEoE
'Bremner's Nectarine'	CElw MNrw MSpe NChi NEoE SHar
'Broomrigg Beauty'	NEoE
'Brown Sugar'	NEoE
bulgaricum	CElw EBee MRav NEoE NLar NRya WFar XLum
'Butterscotch'	EBee
calthifolium	EPPr
'Can-can' (d)	CDor CElw MAvo WHoo
'Cantamos'	NEoE
capense	NBre NEoE SPlb
'Centurion' **new**	NEoE
chiloense 'Red Dragon'	CElw GPSL LLHF SWvt WHrl
'Chipchase'	CElw NChi NPnk NWad WHoo
coccineum ambig.	GKev
coccineum Sibth. & Sm.	GLog WHoo
- 'Ann'	ECtt EPri
- 'Cooky'	CElw CRos EBee EPfP ESps GMcL GPSL LRHS MMuc NEoE NLar NRHS SPoG SRms SWvt WFar WWtn
- 'Eos'	CBcs CElw CSpe CWCL EBee ECtt ELon EWes GBin IBoy LEdu LRHS MHol MNrw MPnt MRav MSpe NEoE NGdn NLar SCob SPoG SRms WGwG WHrl WMoo
- 'Koi'	EBee ELon GBin GPSL GWyn ILea IRob LEdu NCou NEoE SPad WMoo
- 'Queen of Orange'	CBod GJos LSou NEoE SRms SRot
- 'Tango' **new**	CBod
- 'Werner Arends'	CElw ECtt GAbr GCal LRHS MNrw MRav WCot WFar WMoo
'Copper Pennies'	CElw NEoE
'Coppertone'	CElw CWCL ELan EPri LPla MRav NBro NChi SCob XEll
'Cosmopolitan' (Cocktails Series)	CRos CSpe CWCL EBee ELan GBin IBoy ILea LCro LOPS LRHS MAvo MPnt MSCN MSpe NDov NEoE NLar NRHS SBri SCob SPad WFar
'Cotton Candy'	NEoE
'Country Rock Star'	NEoE WFar
'Cream Crackers'	NEoE
'Cumbrian Candy'	NEoE
'Cumbrian Cheddar'	NEoE
'Cumbrian Cherrypie'	NEoE WFar
'Cumbrian Cream'	NEoE
'Custard Pie'	NEoE
'Custard Tart'	NEoE
'Dawn'	NEoE SBri SMHy
'Deano's Delight'	NEoE
'Diana'	MAvo MNrw NEoE NLar

	'Dingle Apricot'	ECtt GAbr GCal MNrw MRav
	'Dolly North' (d)	CElw CWCL EBee GWyn IRob MCot MRav NBro NGdn SHar WHal XEll
	'East of Eden'	NEoE
	'Eden Rising' **new**	NEoE
	'Eden Valley Angel'	MAvo NChi NEoE WWtn
	'Eden Valley Elf'	NEoE
	'El Wano'	NEoE
	'Elworthy Amber'	CElw
	'Emmylou' **new**	NEoE
	'Emory Quinn'	ECtt LLHF LRHS NEoE
	'Fancy Frills'	CElw ECtt MAvo WHoo
	'Farmer John Cross'	CAby CElw EBee ECtt ELon EPri GBin GJos IRob MTis NLar WHal WMoo WOut WWtn
	'Feuermeer'	CElw NEoE NLar
	'Fire Opal' (d) 🏆H7	CElw CWCL EAJP GWyn MAvo MNrw NEoE WMoo
	'Fire Storm'PBR	CBre CMea CWGN EBee ECtt IRob LRHS LSun MBel MNrw MPnt MTis NEgg NLar SBod SMad SPoG WCot WFar WGrn
	'Fireball'	CBod CWCL ECtt EShb ETMg GBin LRHS LSou MArl MAsh NLar NRHS SBee
	'Firefinch'	NEoE
	'Flame'	NEoE NLar
	'Flames of Passion'PBR	Widely available
	'Flower of Darkness'	NEoE
	'Furay's Fire'	NEoE
	'Georgenberg'	CBod CElw CRos ECtt EHrv EPfP EPri GMaP LRHS MBel MCot MNrw MRav NGdn NLar NRHS NWad SBod SPer SRms SWvt WCAu WGwG WMoo
	'Gimlet' (Cocktails Series)	CBod ECtt ELon GBin NLar SBri SCob
	'Golden Joy'	CDor CElw LLHF MAvo NEoE WHoo
	'Hannay's'	EBee MAvo MHCG MNrw MSpe NEoE SHar SPtp WOut
	'Harvest Moon'	NEoE
	'Hearts in Amber'	NEoE WFar
	'Herterton Lemon'	CElw WCot
	'Herterton Primrose'	CElw CWCL ECtt EPPr GCal LLHF LLWG MAvo MSpe NSti WBor WHal WHoo
	'Hilltop Beacon' (d)	CDor CElw EBee LLHF LPla MAvo MHCG NEoE WFar WHoo
	'Honeydew'	NEoE
*	***hybridum luteum***	NSti
	× ***intermedium***	CBre EPPr GPSL MAvo NEoE NGdn NLar WMoo
	- 'Diane'	MAvo NChi
	- 'Hofrennydd'	NWad
	'Jolly Roger'	EBee NEoE NWad
	'Karlskaer'	CBod CElw CRos CWCL ECtt EPri EWTr EWes GBin GQue LPla LRHS LSun MBel MCot MNrw NGdn NLar NRHS SPtp WFar WGwG WMoo WPtf WWtn
	'Lady Stratheden' (d) 🏆H7	Widely available
	'Lemon Delight'	CDor CElw MAvo
	'Lemon Drops'	Widely available
	'Lionel Cox'	CWCL EHrv ELan EPPr GAbr GCal GMaP MBNS MCot MRav NBro NChi NGdn NLar SBch SRGP SRms WFar
	'Lipstick Sunset'	NEoE
	'Lisanne'	CElw CSam CWCL GKev IPot IRob MAvo MNrw MSpe NDov SBri SHar SMHy SPtp WCAu
	'Little Lottie'	NEoE
	'Little Twister'	NEoE
	macrophyllum	EBee
	'Maddy Prior'	NEoE
	magellanicum	EWes LEdu NBre NLar
	- PAB 237	LEdu
	'Magic Toybox'	NEoE
	'Mai Tai'PBR	Widely available
	'Mandarin' (d)	CCse GCal IRob SHar
	'Mango'	EBee NDov
	'Mango Lassi'	CElw ECtt GBin MAvo MTis NEoE SHar WCAu
	'Marmalade'	ECtt EPri GAbr GJos LLWG LPla MNrw MRav MSpe NEoE NLar SMHy SSut WFar WHrl WKif WMoo WOut
	'McClure's Magic'	NEoE
§	***montanum*** 🏆H5	CRos EBee EDAr GLog LRHS MMuc NRHS NRya NSla SRms XLum
	'Moonlight Serenade'	CBod CWCL EBee ECtt EPed GCal LLHF LRHS LSou NEoE NRHS SBri
	'Moorland Sorbet'	NEoE SBri WFar WMoo
	'Mrs J. Bradshaw' (d) 🏆H7	Widely available
	'Mrs W. Moore'	CBre CElw CWCL EBee ECtt EPPr EShb GAbr GJos IPot MNrw MRav NChi NEoE NLar NPnk NQui SCob SRGP WMoo
	'Nordek'	CElw CRos ECha ECtt GAbr GCal GQue IRob LRHS MNrw MRav NEgg NGdn NRHS WPtf
	'Onslow Cream' **new**	LPla
	'Orangeman'	MNrw
	'Peachy Proud'	NEoE
	'Pear Drops'	NEoE
	pentapetalum	see *Sieversia pentapetala*
	'Pineapple Crush' **new**	MAvo
	'Pink Frills'	CElw CWCL ECtt EHrv EPri EWes GAbr GBin LEdu LLWG MAvo MPnt MRav NLar SGbt SMHy SPtp
	'Pink Petticoats' **new**	MAvo
	'Poco'	CBod CWCL EBee ECtt GBin GCal LLHF LRHS MAsh MAvo MNrw NEoE NRHS
	'Prairie Dancer'	NEoE
	'Present'	ECtt NBre NChi NEoE
	'Primrose'	GAbr GJos NEoE NGdn NLar
	'Primrose Cottage'	EBee
	'Prince of Orange' (d)	CElw CRos GAbr LRHS MNrw MRav NBre NRHS SWvt WFar WHrl
	'Prinses Juliana'	Widely available
	pseudococcineum	CRos LRHS NRHS
	pyrenaicum	EBee NBre
I	'Rearsby Hybrid'	CElw LLHF MRav NEoE SPlb WHoo
	'Red Wings' (d)	CElw CWCL GCal GMaP ILea LRHS MAsh MCot MNrw MRav NRHS SBri SHar WGwG
§	***reptans***	LLHF
	'Rijnstroom'	EPPr MNrw SHar WPtf
	'Rise and Shine'	NEoE
	rivale	CBen CBod CHab CRos CWld EAJP EBWF ELan EPfP IBoy MCot MHer MHol MMuc MNHC MWts NBro NMir NPer NRHS SPlb SRms WFar WHar WMAq WMoo WOut
	- 'Album'	Widely available
	- 'Barbra Lawton'	LEdu MSpe SHar
	- 'Cream Drop'	GJos LLWG MCot NChi NEoE SHar

- subsp. ***islandicum***	SBrt
- 'Leonard's Variety'	Widely available
- 'Marika'	CAby CHid EBee EPri GBin SRGP WMoo WWtn
- 'Marmalade'	CAby CBre CElw CWCL EBee IPot MPnt NChi NEoE SBri
- 'Salmon Bells'	XEll
- 'Snowflake'	CDor CElw MAvo MSpe NChi NEoE
'Roger's Rebellion'	NEoE WFar
'Rubin'	EBee IPot IRob NBro NDov NSti SBch
'Rusty Young'	CWCL ECtt EWes GCal LLHF LRHS LSou MAsh MBel MNrw NEoE NRHS
'Savanna Sunrise' **new**	MNrw
'Savanna Sunset'	CBod ECtt EPed EWes GCal LLHF LRHS MCot NEoE NRHS WAvo WHrl
'Sigiswang'	EWes LEdu MNrw MRav NEoE
'Son of Poco'	NEoE
'Spider Muffin'	NEoE
'Stacey's Sunrise'	CBod ECtt EWes GCal LLHF LRHS MAsh MAvo MHCG MNrw NEoE NRHS
'Star of Bethlehem'	NEoE
'Starker's Magnificum'	MAvo WCot
'Stevie Nicks'	NEoE
'Strawberries and Cream'	NEoE
'Sundrud Star'	NEoE
'Sunkissed Lime' **new**	ECtt
'Sunrise' (d)	CBod CRos EBee ECrN LRHS MHol NRHS
'Sweet Angel Dar'	NEoE
'Tangerine'	EPri MRav MSpe NEoE
'Tango Dream'	LRHS MAvo NEoE
'Tequila Sunrise'	CRos EBee ECtt ELan ILea LRHS MHol MNrw MSCN MSpe NDov NGdn NHpl NRHS SCob SPad
'Tinkerbell'	NEoE
'Tinpenny Orange'	CElw NEoE WHoo
× ***tirolense***	EBee NBre NEoE
'Toast of Cumbria'	NEoE
'Toffee Apples'	NEoE
'Totally Tangerine'PBR	Widely available
triflorum	CBod CElw EWes GEdr LEdu MHer MNrw NDov SHar SPhx
- SDR 8121	GKev
- var. ***campanulatum***	NEoE
- 'Peace Pipe'	MNrw
'Turbango'	NEoE
'Turbango Twister'	NEoE
'Turnpike Tales'	NEoE
'Turnpike Troubadour'	NEoE
'Tutti Frutti'	MAvo
urbanum	EBWF ENfk WHer WMoo
'Welcome Joy'	CElw
'Wyn's Wish'	NEoE

Gevuina (*Proteaceae*)

avellana	WPGP

Gilia (*Polemoniaceae*)

achilleifolia	CSpe SPhx

Gillenia (*Rosaceae*)

stipulata	IPot LEdu MNrw SHar SPhx WPGP
trifoliata ♀H7	Widely available
- 'Pink Profusion'	CAby CBct CBot CKno CSpe EBee ECtt EWTr GBin ILea IPot LLWG LPla LSou MAvo MBel MHol MNrw NDov NGBl NLar SAko SCob SPad SPer STPC WCAu WCot

Gilliesia (*Alliaceae*)

graminea	GKev

Ginkgo (*Ginkgoaceae*)

biloba	Widely available
- B&SWJ 8753	WCru
- 'Anny's Dwarf'	MAsh MBlu NLar SAko SBig
- 'Autumn Gold' (m) ♀H6	CBcs CDul CEnd CMCN ECrN EMOT MBlu MGos MPkF SBig SLim
- 'Barabits' Fastigiata'	MBlu SBig SMad
- 'Barabits' Nana'	MBlu SBig
- 'Beijing Gold'	MBlu MPkF SAko SBig SMad WPGP
- 'Blagon' **new**	SGol
- 'California Sunset'	MBlu NLar SBig
- 'Chase Manhattan'	MPkF
- 'Chotek'	SBig
- 'Chris' Dwarf'	LRHS NLar
- 'David'	SBig
- 'Eastern Star' (f)	CAgr
- 'Eiffel' **new**	SBig
- 'Elsie'	SBig
- 'Everton Broom'	CMac CMen GMil NEgg NLar SBig SBod
- 'Fairmount' (m)	MBlu NLar SBig
- 'Fastigiata' (m)	CAco CMCN EPfP LMaj MBlu SBig
- 'Finger'	SLim
- 'Globosa'	MBlu SBig
- 'Gnome'	LSRN MPkF SCob
- 'Golden Dragon'	MBlu
- 'Golden Globe'	MPkF SBig
- 'Gresham'	MPkF
- 'Horizontalis'	CAco MBlu SBig
- 'Jade Butterflies' ♀H6	MBlu MPkF NLar SBig SLim SMad
- 'Jehosaphat'	NLar SBig SMad
- 'Jerry Vercade'	MPkF
- 'King of Dongting' (f)	CAgr MBlu SBig
- 'Lakeview' (m)	MPkF NLar SBig SCob
- 'Little Joe' **new**	NLar
- 'Long March'	CAgr
- 'Magyar'	SBig
- 'Majestic Butterfly' **new**	NLar
- 'Mariken' ♀H6	CWGN ELan EPfP LMaj MPkF NLar SBig SCob SLim
- 'Mayfield' (m)	GMil NLar SBig SMad
- 'McFarland'	CAgr
- 'Menhir'PBR	CBcs EBee ELan EMOT EPfP MPkF
- 'Montezuma'	SBig
- 'Nelleke'	SBig
- 'Obelisk'	NLar SBig SLim
- Ohazuki Group (f)	CAgr SBig
- Pendula Group	CEnd CMCN EBee MBlu MPkF SBig SGol
- 'Pendula Gruga'	SBig
- 'Pixie'	SBig
- 'Pragense' **new**	SBig
- 'Princeton Sentry' (m) ♀H6	LRHS MBlu NLar SBig
- 'Pyramidalis' **new**	SBig
- 'Robbie's Twist'	MPkF NLar SBig
- 'Santa Cruz'	SBig
- 'Saratoga' (m) ♀H6	CAco CAgr CBcs CEnd CMCN EPfP MBlu MPkF NLar SAko SBig SCob SLim SMad
- 'Scotts Form' **new**	NLar
- 'Shangri-La' (m)	MBlu SBig SMad
- 'Sinclair'	MPkF
- 'Snowcloud' **new**	NLar
- 'Survivor'	SMad

- 'Thelma'	SLim
- 'Tit'	CEnd CMCN EPfP MBlu MPkF SBig SLim
- 'Tremonia'	CMCN EPfP MBlu MPkF SAko SBig
- 'Troll' 🏆^{H6}	LRHS MAsh MBlu NRHS SBig SCoo SLim SMad SPoG
- 'Tubifolia'	CMCN MBlu MPkF NLar SBig SCob SLim SMad WPGP
- 'Umbrella'	SBig SLim
- Variegata Group (v)	MPkF NLar SBig
- 'W.B.'	MPkF SBig
- 'Weeping Wonder' (f)	SBig
- 'Yellow Mellow'	LRHS NRHS

ginseng see *Panax ginseng*

Gladiolus (*Iridaceae*)

'Adi'	WCot
'Akuta' (M/E)	CGrW
alatus	NRog
'Alba' (N)	LRHS NRHS
'Alice' (Min)	ERCP
'Amanda Mahy' (N)	GKev LAma NRog
'Amsterdam' (G)	CGrW
angustus L.	CGrW CTal NRog
antakiensis	CPou
'Atom' (S/P)	CAvo CGrW GKev LAma NRog SDeJ SDir
aurantiacus	WCot
'Avalanche' (B)	SDeJ
'Bangladesh'^{PBR}	CRav
Barnard hybrids	CGrW
'Beautiful Angel'	CGrW
'Beauty Bride' (L)	CGrW
'Big Boss' (G)	CGrW
'Black Jack' (L)	SDeJ SDir
'Black Star'	CRav ERCP
'Blackbird' (S)	CGrW
'Blue Frost' (L)	SDeJ
'Bonfire' (G)	CGrW
byzantinus	see *G. communis* subsp. *byzantinus*
callianthus	see *G. murielae*
cardinalis	CPne CPrp GCal IBlr LEdu SBrt WCru
carinatus	CGrW NRog
carinatus* × *orchidiflorus	WCot
'Carine' (N)	GKev NRog SDeJ
carmineus	CGrW GKev WCot
carneus	CGrW CTal EPot GBin GKev NRog SDeJ
- 'Georgina'	CGrW
caucasicus	GKev
'Charm' (N/Tub)	GKev LEdu NRog SDeJ SDir
'Charming Beauty' (Tub)	GKev LAma LRHS NRog SDeJ
'Charming Lady' (Tub)	GKev NRog
citrinus	see *G. tribonemifolius*
'Claudia' (N)	CGrW
'Columbine' (P)	SDeJ
× ***colvillii***	IBlr
- 'Albus'	ERCP GKev
communis	WCot
§ - subsp. ***byzantinus*** 🏆^{H5}	Widely available
'Coral Lace' (L)	SDeJ
'Côte d'Azur' (G)	SDeJ
crassifolius	CPbh
'Cream Perfection' (L)	CGrW SDeJ
'Creamy Yellow' (S)	CGrW
cruentus	CGrW WCot
cunonius	CTal
§ ***dalenii***	CAby CExl CPbh CPou CSam GBin GCal IBlr LEdu SMad
- 'Apricot Delight' (v)	IBlr
- 'Boone'	WCot
- 'Citrone Spectrum' (v)	IBlr
§ - subsp. ***dalenii***	CPrp IBlr WCot
- - 'Spinners'	EBee IBlr
- green-flowered	IBlr
- 'Guardsman' (v)	IBlr
- red-flowered	GCal
* - f. ***rubra***	IBlr
'David Hills' (*papilio* hybrid)	CCse CDor CMea CPrp SBch SDys WCot WSHC
'Delirium'	CGrW
'Dion' (M)	CGrW
ecklonii	CPbh
'Elvira' (N)	GKev LAma NRog SDir
'Emerald Spring' (S)	WCot
'Esta Bonita' (G)	CGrW
'Extasy'^{PBR} (L)	CGrW
'Farandole' (S)	SDeJ
'Fidelio' (L)	SDeJ
'Fiona'	CGrW GKev
'Fiorentina' (L)	ERCP SDeJ
flanaganii	CAby CBro CExl CPBP CPbh CSpe EPot EPri GCal GEdr GKev LLHF NHpl NSla SBrt WAbe
'Flevo Bambino' (S)	EPri
'Flevo Dancer' (S)	CGrW
'Flevo Laguna' (S)	CAvo
'Flevo Souvenir'^{PBR} (L)	CGrW
'Flevo Spirit' (L)	CGrW
'Flevo Vito' (Min)	CAvo
floribundus Jacq.	NRog
- subsp. ***fasciatus***	CGrW
fourcadei	CGrW
'French Silk' (L)	CGrW
× ***gandavensis*** hort.	GBin WCot
garnieri	see *G. dalenii* subsp. *dalenii*
geardii	WCot
(Glamini Series) 'Glamini Luca' (Min)	WTor
- 'Glamini Thomas' (Min)	WTor
- 'Glamini Tom' (Min)	SPad WTor
'Gold Struck' (L)	CGrW
gracilis	CTal
grandis	see *G. liliaceus*
'Green Star' (L)	CGrW CRav ERCP LCro LOPS SDeJ
griseus	NRog
gueinzii	CGrW
'Guernsey Glory' (N)	GKev
'Halley' (N)	GKev NRog
'Hansnett'	WCot
'Happy Weekend' (L)	SDeJ
'Holland Pearl' (B)	SDeJ
'Huron Silk' (L)	CGrW
huttonii	CGrW NRog
huttonii* × *tristis	CPou
huttonii* × *tristis var. ***concolor***	WCot
'Ibadan'^{PBR} (L)	CGrW
illyricus	CSam GKev SPlb
imbricatus	EPot GKev MHer
'Imperialis'	IBlr
'Impressive' (N)	GKev LAma NRog SDeJ
'Indian Summer'^{PBR} (L)	ERCP
'Invitation' **new**	SDeJ
§ ***italicus***	CGrW CHid EPfP GKev LRHS
'Jacksonville Gold' (L)	SDeJ
'Jester' (L)	SDeJ

	Plant	Suppliers
	'Las Vegas' (P)	CGrW GKev NRog
	'Lemon Drop' (S)	CGrW
	leptosiphon	CGrW
§	***liliaceus***	CGrW NRog
	'Little Vintage'	GKev
	'Lynwood Pinkie'	CMea
	'Match Point' (L)	SDeJ
	meliusculus	NRog
	'Mexico' (L)	SDeJ
	miniatus	NRog WCot
	'Mirella' (N)	CAvo GKev LAma NRog SDir
	'Mon Amour'^{PBR} (L)	SDeJ
	'Monsieur Piquet' (P)	EPri WCot
§	***murielae*** 🏆^{H3}	CAby CAvo CBod CBro CGrW
		CMea CRos EAJP ERCP EShb GBin
		GKev GWyn LCro LOPS LRHS
		MCot MPie NPnk NRHS SCoo SDeJ
		SDir SPer SPhm SPlb SRms WArt
		WHal WHil
	natalensis	see *G. dalenii*
	'Natan'	WCot
	'Nathalie' (N)	GKev NRog SDeJ
	'Nova Lux' (L)	SDeJ
	'Nymph' (N)	CAvo GKev LAma LCro LEdu LOPS
		NRog SDeJ SDir WRHF
	'Oasis'^{PBR} (G)	CGrW
	ochroleucus	WHil
§	***oppositiflorus***	CPbh EBee IBlr LEdu SPlb
	- subsp. ***salmoneus***	see *G. oppositiflorus*
	orchidiflorus	CGrW
	'Oscar' (G)	ERCP SDeJ
	papilio	Widely available
§	- Purpureoauratus Group	CBro CSam IBlr SRms WSHC
	- yellow-flowered	CMea SMad
	'Passos'^{PBR} (S)	ERCP
	'Peach Blossom' (N)	IBlr WCot
	'Perseus' (P/Min)	ERCP
	'Peter Pears' (L)	ERCP SDeJ
	'Phyllis M' (L)	CGrW
	Pilbeam hybrids	CGrW WCot
	'Pink Lady' (L)	SDeJ
	'Plum Tart' (L)	ERCP LCro LOPS SDeJ
	'Pop Art'	SDeJ
	primulinus	see *G. dalenii*
	'Prins Claus' (N)	EShb GKev LAma NRog SDeJ SDir
	'Priscilla' (L)	SDeJ
	'Purple Flora'	CRav ERCP
	'Purple Mate'	LCro LOPS
	'Purple Prince' (M)	CGrW
	purpureoauratus	see *G. papilio* Purpureoauratus Group
	quadrangularis	CGrW
	recurvus	CGrW
	'Robinetta' (*recurvus* hybrid) 🏆^{H3}	CWCL GKev LAma LCro LOPS
		LRHS NRHS NRog SDeJ
	'Ruby' (*papilio* hybrid)	CAby CAvo CBro CDor CElw
		CExl CMea CPou CPrp CTal CTca
		ECha ELon EPri GKev IMou IPot
		LEdu LSRN MHer NChi NPnk
		SMad WAul WCFE WHoo WKif
		WPGP
	'Ruth Ann'	CGrW
	SANCERRE (B/L)	CRav
	saundersii	GCal LEdu
	scullyi from Ceres Karoo, South Africa	NRog
	segetum	see *G. italicus*
	'Shadows' **new**	CMea
	'Slick Chick' (S)	CGrW
	'Solveiga' (L/E)	CGrW
	'Sophie'^{PBR} (L)	CGrW
	'Sourire' (S) **new**	SDeJ
	'Spic and Span' (L)	SDeJ
	splendens	CGrW CTal NRog
	stefaniae	CGrW
	'Stiena' (L)	CGrW
	'Terry' (G)	CGrW
	'That's Love' (L)	SDeJ
	'The Bride'	CAvo CBro CRav CTca EBee GKev
		GWyn ITim LAma LCro LEdu LOPS
		LSRN SDeJ SDir
	'Trader Horn' (G)	CGrW SDir
§	***trichonemifolius***	CGrW GKev
	tristis	CAvo CBro CElw CGrW CMea
		CPne CPou CTal EHrv ELon GBin
		NRog
	- var. ***concolor***	CGrW CPbh CPou CPrp WCot
	undulatus	CGrW NRog WCot
	uysiae	CGrW CTal
	vandermerwei	CGrW
	venustus	CGrW CPbh NRog
	'Violetta' (M)	CGrW
	virescens	NRog
	'Volcano'	GKev IPot
	watermeyeri	CPbh
	watsonius	NRog
	'White Prosperity' (L)	ERCP LCro LOPS
	woodii	WCot
	'Zamora' (L)	CGrW
	'Ziporra' (S)	EPri
	'Zizanie' (L) **new**	SDeJ
	'Zorro'	CRav

Glandularia (*Verbenaceae*)

	Plant	Suppliers
	(Aztec Series) AZTEC PEARL ('Balazpearl'^{PBR})	SCoo
	- AZTEC RED ('Balazred')	SCoo
	- AZTEC SILVER MAGIC ('Balazsilma'^{PBR}) 🏆^{H2}	CRav NPri SCoo
	'Blue Prince'	CSpe
§	'Claret' 🏆^{H3}	CMac CSpe EAJP EBee ECtt ELan
		EPfP LRHS LSRN LSou NRHS SCoo
		SPhx SPoG
	'Corsage Peach' (Corsage Series)	LRHS NRHS
	corymbosa	CAby CHid CHll ECha LRHS SPer
		SPhx WMoo
	'Diamond Merci'	WHoo
	'Edith Eddleman'	CMac CWGN EPfP LRHS NRHS
		SPoG
	elegans	NDov
	gooddingii	EBee
	'Hammerstein Pink'	EBee EPfP
	'Homestead Purple'	CMac CRav CRos EAJP EBee ELan
		EPfP ESps GBin LCro LOPS LRHS
		MNrw NRHS SCob SRkn SRms
		SWvt
	'Jenny's Wine'	see *G.* 'Claret'
	'La France'	CHGN ECha EPfP LRHS NRHS
		SMHy SPhx SPoG
	LANAI ROYAL PURPLE WITH EYE ('Lan Roypureye'^{PBR}) (Lanai Series)	MCot
	'Little Annie'	MPnt
	'Lois' Ruby'	see *G.* 'Claret'
§	***peruviana***	LRHS NRHS SRms XLum
	'Pink Bouquet'	see *G.* 'Silver Anne'
	'Pink Parfait'	EPfP
	platensis	ELan

Quartz Series ♀H2	ETMg NPri
- 'Quartz Red Polka Dot'	ELan EPfP
SEABROOK'S LAVENDER ('Sealav'PBR)	EBee EPfP LRHS NRHS SCoo SHar SRkn SRms SWvt
§ 'Silver Anne' ♀H3	MCot
§ 'Sissinghurst' ♀H2	CRav CSam ECtt SRms
'Sparkle Purple Blues' new	NPri
'Strawberry Kiss'	EPfP SPoG
(Superbena Series) SUPERBENA BURGUNDY ('Usbenal5'PBR)	CAby
- SUPERBENA CORAL STAR	CPla NPri
(Tapien Series) TAPIEN SALMON ('Suntapiro'PBR) ♀H2	LSou
- TAPIEN SKY BLUE ('Suntapilabu'PBR) ♀H2	ESps
- TAPIEN VIOLET ('Sunvop'PBR)	LSou
- TAPIEN WHITE ('Suntapipurew'PBR)	ESps
TEMARI PEACHES AND CREAM ('Sunmaripeach'PBR) (Temari Series)	ETMg
'Tenerife'	see *G.* 'Sissinghurst'
(Vepita Series) VEPITA BLUE VIOLET ('Invebluvio'PBR)	CPla NPri
- VEPITA HOT PINK	NPri
- VEPITA WHITE new	CRav

Glaucidium (*Ranunculaceae*)

palmatum ♀H5	CExl EWld GEdr GKev WCru
- 'Album'	see *G. palmatum* var. *leucanthum*
§ - var. ***leucanthum***	GEdr GKev
- 'Mikado'	GEdr

Glaucium (*Papaveraceae*)

§ ***corniculatum***	CAby CRos CSpe LRHS NRHS SPhx
flavum	CRos CSpe EBee ECha LRHS MHer SPhx XSen
- ***aurantiacum***	see *G. flavum* f. *fulvum*
§ - f. ***fulvum***	ECha GJos MMuc MNrw SEND WHil
- orange-flowered	see *G. flavum* f. *fulvum*
- red-flowered	see *G. corniculatum*
grandiflorum	SPhx
phoenicium	see *G. corniculatum*

Glaucosciadium (*Apiaceae*)

cordifolium	CSpe WCot
- PAB 9003	LEdu
- from Hatay, Turkey	WCot

Glaux (*Primulaceae*)

maritima	EBWF

Glebionis (*Asteraceae*)

coronaria	MNHC SRms
§ ***segetum***	CHab EBWF

Glechoma (*Lamiaceae*)

hederacea	EBWF GPoy NMir WHer
§ - 'Variegata' (v)	EShb SPer XLum

Gleditsia (*Caesalpiniaceae*)

caspia	LEdu
- NJM 13.019	WPGP
japonica	ITim NLar
koraiensis	LEdu
- B&SWJ 12569	WCru
triacanthos	CDul ESps LEdu LPra SCob SPlb WTSh
- 'Calhoun'	CAgr
- 'Elegantissima' (v)	SPer
- 'Emerald Cascade'	CEnd NRHS
- 'Goofy'	SMad
- f. ***inermis***	LPra
- - 'Shademaster'	LPra
- - SPECTRUM ('Speczam')	EBee WHar
- - 'Sunburst'	Widely available
- 'Millwood'	CAgr
- 'Rubylace'	CCVT CDul CEnd CLnd CMCN CSBt EBee ECrN ELan EMOT EPfP EWTr LMaj LSRN MBlu MGos MRav MSwo SCob SGol SMad SPer WHar
- 'Skyline'	LMaj

Globba ✿ (*Zingiberaceae*)

racemosa var. ***hookeri*** HWJCM 471	WCru WSHC
radicalis new	WPGP

Globularia (*Plantaginaceae*)

alypum	IDee SBrt
bellidifolia	see *G. meridionalis*
cordifolia ♀H5	CPla CRos CSma EDAr EPot GCrg GEdr GKev LRHS NHpl NRHS NSla SBch
- RCB UA 30	SPad WCot
incanescens	CPBP CPla
§ ***meridionalis***	CBod CPBP EPot EWes GMaP WOld
- 'Blue Bonnets'	GCrg GEdr
- 'Hort's Variety'	CTri NSla WAbe
nana	see *G. repens*
nudicaulis	CMea GEdr GKev IMou
orientalis	GKev
punctata	SRms
pygmaea	see *G. meridionalis*
§ ***repens***	EPot GEdr LLHF WAbe
trichosantha	GEdr MMuc SRms XSen
valentina	GEdr LLHF
vulgaris	XSen

Gloriosa (*Colchicaceae*)

lutea	see *G. superba* 'Lutea'
§ ***modesta***	CPne CRHN GKev LAma
rothschildiana	see *G. superba* 'Rothschildiana'
superba ♀H1c	GKev SDeJ
- 'Carsonii'	GKev LAma SDeJ
- 'Greenii'	GKev LAma SDeJ
§ - 'Lutea'	GKev LAma SDeJ SDir
§ - 'Rothschildiana'	CBcs CGrW EUJe GKev LAma LCro LOPS SDeJ SRms
- 'Rothschildiana Orange'	GKev SDir
- 'Rothschildiana Salmon'	GKev SDir
- 'Sparkling Jip'	GKev
- 'Sparkling Striped'	GKev
- 'Tricolor'	GKev

Gloxinella (*Gesneriaceae*)

lindeniana new	WDib

Gloxinia (*Gesneriaceae*)

'Defiance' new	SDeJ
'Étoile de Feu' new	EShb
nematanthodes	SBrt
- 'Evita'	EShb WCot
sylvatica 'Bolivian Sunset'	WDib

Glumicalyx (*Scrophulariaceae*)

flanaganii	CPbh SPlb
goseloides	CPbh

Glyceria (*Poaceae*)

aquatica variegata	see *G. maxima* var. *variegata*
fluitans **new**	EBWF
maxima	EBWF MMuc MSKA NPer SEND SPlb
§ - var. ***variegata*** (v)	CRos CWat ECha EHoe ELan EPfP EShb EWat GMaP GMcL IBoy LLWG LRHS MMuc NGdn NRHS SCob SEND SPer SRms SVic WMAq WMoo XLum
notata	SVic
spectabilis 'Variegata'	see *G. maxima* var. *variegata*

Glycyrrhiza (*Papilionaceae*)

echinata	CAgr
§ ***glabra***	CAgr CBod CCCN CHby ENfk GPoy MHer MNHC SPlb SRms
glandulifera	see *G. glabra*
uralensis	ELan GPoy LRHS NRHS SPhx
yunnanensis	CSpe LPla SMHy

Glyptostrobus (*Cupressaceae*)

pensilis	CExl CFil SLim WPGP

Gmelina (*Lamiaceae*)

hystrix	CCCN

Gnaphalium (*Asteraceae*)

'Fairy Gold'	see *Helichrysum thianschanicum* 'Goldkind'
trinerve	see *Anaphalis trinervis*

Gomphocarpus ✿ (*Apocynaceae*)

§ ***fruticosus***	SVen

Gompholobium (*Papilionaceae*)

scabrum	SPlb

Gomphostigma (*Scrophulariaceae*)

virgatum	CBod CCCN CExl CFis CSpe EPPr EPfP EWld LLWG MHol MMuc MPie SMad SPhx SPlb WCFE WCot WRHF WTor
- 'White Candy'	GBin LRHS MGil MPkF SVen

Gomphrena (*Amaranthaceae*)

globosa	CCCN
pulchella	CSpe

Goniolimon (*Plumbaginaceae*)

incanum 'Blue Diamond'	NHpl WCot
§ ***tataricum***	GJos MMuc
§ - var. ***angustifolium***	SEND SRms

Goodia (*Papilionaceae*)

lotifolia	CCCN

gooseberry see *Ribes uva-crispa*

Gordonia (*Theaceae*)

axillaris	see *Polyspora axillaris*

Gorgonidium (*Araceae*)

intermedium	WCot

Gossypium (*Malvaceae*)

herbaceum	XAbr
hirsutum 'Flora'PBR **new**	NHim

granadilla see *Passiflora quadrangularis*

granadilla, purple see *Passiflora edulis*

granadilla, sweet see *Passiflora ligularis*

grape see *Vitis*

grapefruit see *Citrus* × *aurantium* Grapefruit Group

Graptopetalum (*Crassulaceae*)

filiferum	SPlb
§ ***paraguayense***	SVen

× *Graptosedum* (*Crassulaceae*)

'Darley Sunshine' **new**	NWad

× *Graptoveria* (*Crassulaceae*)

'Ghostly'	WCot

Gratiola (*Plantaginaceae*)

officinalis	CBod CRos LLWG LRHS MHer MSKA NRHS

Greenovia (*Crassulaceae*)

§ ***aurea***	NMen SPlb
diplocycla 'Gigantea'	SPlb
dodrentalis	SChr

Grevillea (*Proteaceae*)

* ***alba***	SEle
banksii 'Canberra Hybrid'	see *G.* 'Canberra Gem'
- var. ***forsteri***	SPlb
'Bronze Rambler'	CCCN
§ 'Canberra Gem' ♀H4	Widely available
'Clearview David'	CCCN CCht EUJe LRHS LSRN MMuc SEND SLim SVen
crithmifolia	SPlb
'Desert Flame'	see *G. rosmarinifolia* 'Desert Flame'
'Ivanhoe' **new**	CCCN
juniperina	CBcs CCCN CExl CMac EPfP SEle SLim SVen
- f. ***sulphurea***	CCCN CExl ELon EPfP MGil MMuc SEle SPer SPlb WSHC
lanigera 'Mount Tamboritha'	CBcs CCCN CExl CMac EBee EPfP EUJe SEle SLim SPoG SVen WFar
- prostrate	MAsh WAbe WGrn
lavandulacea 'Penola' **new**	CCCN
leucopteris	SPlb
'Murray Valley Queen' **new**	WPGP
'Olympic Flame'	CBcs CCCN CExl CRos CSBt CTsd ELon EPfP LEdu LRHS LSou MGos MMuc SAko SBod SEle SPoG SVen WBor WGrn
paniculata	SPlb
'Pink Lady'	CBcs CCCN ELon EPfP LRHS
'Poorinda Queen'	CCCN
robusta ♀H1c	SPlb
'Robyn Gordon'	CCCN
'Rondeau'	CCCN
rosmarinifolia ♀H4	CBcs CCCN CExl CMac CSBt CTri CTsd ELan EPfP GKin SArc SEle SLim SLon SPer SPlb WFar

§ – 'Desert Flame'	CBcs CExl
– 'Jenkinsii'	CCCN CExl CMac CSBt EPfP EUJe LSou SEle SLim
§ × ***semperflorens***	CRos EBee LRHS SPlb WGrn
'Spider Man'	CCCN
tolminsis	see *G.* × *semperflorens*
victoriae	CBcs CCCN CCht CJun CTsd EBee ECre EPfP LRHS SAko SChF SEle WGrn WPGP
– subsp. ***victoriae***	CExl
– yellow-flowered	LRHS
williamsonii	CBcs CTsd LRHS

Grewia (*Malvaceae*)

occidentalis	ECre LRHS

Greyia (*Melianthaceae*)

sutherlandii	SPlb

Grindelia (*Asteraceae*)

§ ***camporum***	SPlb
chiloensis	CAbb SMad
integrifolia	XLum
robusta	see *G. camporum*

Griselinia ✿ (*Griseliniaceae*)

littoralis ♀H4	Widely available
– 'Bantry Bay' (v)	CCCN ECrN EHoe ELan LRHS MAsh SPer SPoG SWvt WFar
– 'Brodick Gold'	CExl ELon GKin
– 'Dixon's Cream' (v)	CBcs CCCN CDul CMac CRos CSBt EBee EPfP LRHS MRav SGol SLon SRms SVen
– 'Green Favor'	EBee
– GREEN HORIZON ('Whenuapai'PBR)	ELan IBal LRHS SLim SPer
– 'Green Jewel' (v)	CCCN ECrN NLar
– 'Variegata' (v) ♀H4	Widely available
ruscifolia	LEdu
scandens	CCCN EUJe SEND

guava, common see *Psidium guajava*

guava, purple or strawberry see *Psidium littorale* var. *longipes*

Gueldenstaedtia (*Papilionaceae*)

himalaica	CPBP

Guichenotia (*Sterculiaceae*)

macrantha	SPlb

Gunnera ✿ (*Gunneraceae*)

chilensis	see *G. tinctoria*
cordifolia	LLWG
densiflora	GEdr
hamiltonii	ECha GAbr SRms XLum
killipiana B&SWJ 9009	WCru
magellanica	Widely available
– SDR 7035	GKev
– (f)	SRms
– 'Osorno'	MMoz
manicata	Widely available
monoica	GAbr
– bronze-leaved **new**	LLWG
perpensa	CBcs CBen CCCN EBee EWTr GBin IMou LLWG WFar
prorepens	CExl CMac CPla ECha GAbr ILea SRms WFar
scabra	see *G. tinctoria*
§ ***tinctoria***	CBod CCCN CExl CFGn CMac CRos ECha EPfP IBoy LLWG LRHS MMuc NLar NRHS SEND SRms SWvt WBor WFar

Gymnocarpium ✿ (*Woodsiaceae*)

dryopteris ♀H5	CKel EFer EShb GKev GMaP GWyn MMoz WAbe WFib WShi
– PAB 1757	LEdu
– PAB 8351	LEdu
– 'Plumosum' ♀H7	CBdn CBod CKel CWCL ERod GEdr LEdu LRHS NHim NLar NRHS WFib WHal WMoo
oyamense ♀H5	SPlb
robertianum	EFer EWld

Gymnocladus (*Caesalpiniaceae*)

chinensis	WPGP
dioica	CBcs CDul CMCN EBee ELan EPfP EUJe LEdu LPra MBlu SMad SPer WPGP WTSh

Gynandriris see *Moraea*

Gynerium (*Poaceae*)

argenteum	see *Cortaderia selloana*

Gynostemma (*Cucurbitaceae*)

pentaphyllum	CAgr LEdu
– B&SWJ 570	WCru

Gynura (*Asteraceae*)

§ ***aurantiaca*** 'Purple Passion' ♀H1c	EShb
sarmentosa misapplied	see *G. aurantiaca* 'Purple Passion'

Gypsophila (*Caryophyllaceae*)

aretioides	CRos EPot LRHS NRHS NSla
§ – 'Caucasica'	CPBP LLHF
– 'Compacta'	see *G. aretioides* 'Caucasica'
cerastioides	CMea CRos CTri ECtt EDAr EPfP EPot ETMg GAbr GCrg LRHS MHol NGdn NHpl NLar NRHS NSla SPlb SRms SWvt WAbe WHoo XLum
– 'Rosy Stripe'	GKev
– silver variegated (v)	MHol
dubia	see *G. repens* 'Dubia'
elegans	SVic
fastigiata 'Silverstar'	CRos LRHS NRHS
'Festival' (Festival Series)	SGbt
gracilescens	see *G. tenuifolia*
muralis 'Garden Bride'	SWvt
– 'Gypsy Deep Rose'	CRav CRos ELan EPfP LRHS NRHS
– 'Gypsy Pink' (d)	EPfP SWvt
nana 'Compacta'	CPBP
pacifica	WOut
paniculata	ESps MHol MRav SRms XLum
– 'Bristol Fairy' (d)	CRos CSBt CTri ECha ELan EPfP GMaP GMcL LRHS MBel MJak NLar SCob SHar SPoG SWvt WFar WHil XLum
– 'Compacta Plena' (d)	ECtt EPfP GMaP MRav NGdn SRms
– double white-flowered (d)	XLum
– FESTIVAL STAR ('Danfestar'PBR) (Festival Series)	GMcL
– 'Flamingo' (d)	CBcs CRos ECha LRHS MTis NLar NRHS SPer SWvt XLum
– 'Pacific Pink'	EBee
– 'Perfect Alba'	LRHS

	- 'Perfekta'	CBcs SPer
	- 'Pink Star' (d)	ECtt
§	- 'Schneeflocke' (d)	CBod CRos EPfP GMaP LRHS MBel MHol NRHS SRms
	- SNOWFLAKE	see *G. paniculata* 'Schneeflocke'
	- SUMMER SPARKLES ('Esm Chispa' PBR)	EBee NPnk
	- WHITE FIRE ('Dangypwhifa')	EBee
	'Pink Festival' (Festival Series) (d)	CDor CRos ECtt EPfP LRHS NRHS SPoG WTor
	repens 🏆H5	ECtt GBin GJos SCob SPlb SWvt WFar XLum
	- dark-pink-flowered	CPBP
	- 'Dorothy Teacher'	CMea CSma CTal ECtt GCrg SBch WFar
§	- 'Dubia'	ECha ECtt ELon EPot MHer NLar SRms
	- 'Filou Rose' **new**	EDAr NDov
	- 'Filou White'	NDov
	- 'Fratensis'	ECtt LLHF
	- PINK BEAUTY	see *G. repens* 'Rosa Schönheit'
§	- 'Rosa Schönheit'	CMea ECha ECtt EPot NDov SPer XLum
	- 'Rosea'	CTri EBee ECtt EDAr ELan EPfP GJos GMaP ITim MHol MMuc NGdn NHpl NSla SBch SCob SEND SPoG SRms SWvt WFar WHoo XLum
	- 'Silver Carpet' (v)	EBee ELan
	- white-flowered	CMea NGdn SWvt
§	'Rosenschleier' (d) 🏆H6	CBod CDor CMea EBee ECha ECtt ELan EPfP MBel MRav NDov NGdn SPer SRms SRot SWvt WCAu WHoo WSHC XLum
I	'Rosenschleier Variegata' (v)	EBee ELan EPfP
	'Rosy Veil'	see *G.* 'Rosenschleier'
§	***tenuifolia***	CMea CPBP EPot GMaP ITim NHpl
	VEIL OF ROSES	see *G.* 'Rosenschleier'
	'White Festival' PBR (Festival Series) (d)	CRos EPfP LRHS NRHS SPoG WTor

H

Haberlea (*Gesneriaceae*)

	ferdinandi-coburgii	GEdr
	- 'Connie Davidson'	EBee GEdr GKev
	rhodopensis 🏆H5	CElw CPla CTal EBee ELan EPPr GEdr IMou NHpl NRHS NSla SRms WAbe WCot WThu XLum
	- 'Virginalis'	CElw GEdr NSla WAbe WThu

Hablitzia (*Amaranthaceae*)

	tamnoides	CAgr LEdu MCoo

Habranthus (*Amaryllidaceae*)

	'Amazing Jumbo'	NRog
	andersonii	see *H. tubispathus*
	brachyandrus	CTal GKev NRog SRms
	caeruleus	NRog
	gracilifolius	NRog WAbe
	magnoi	NRog
	martinezii 🏆H2	CPBP CTal NRog
§	***robustus*** 🏆H2	CAby CCCN CExl CTal EPfP EPot GKev LAma NRog
	- 'Russell Manning'	NRog
§	***tubispathus*** 🏆H2	CTal GKev NRog SBrt WHil
	- var. ***roseus***	NRog

Hacquetia (*Apiaceae*)

	epipactis 🏆H5	CDor CElw CRos CSpe CTal EBee ECha EHrv EPfP EPot GAbr GEdr GKev GMaP GQue IRob LRHS MAvo MCot MMuc MNrw NBro NChi NRHS NRya NSum WCot WHoo WKif WSHC
	- 'Harry Foley' (v)	NWad
§	- 'Thor' (v)	ECha EHrv EWes GBin GEdr LLHF WAbe
	- 'Variegata'	see *H. epipactis* 'Thor'

Haemanthus (*Amaryllidaceae*)

	albiflos 🏆H2	CAvo CPne CPrp CTca ELan EPri EShb GKev LAma LToo NSti SRms
	amarylloides	WCot
	barkerae	WCot
	carneus	WCot
	coccineus 🏆H2	EPri WCot
	humilis	CPne WCot
	- subsp. ***hirsutus***	WCot
	kalbreyeri	see *Scadoxus multiflorus* subsp. *multiflorus*
	katherinae	see *Scadoxus multiflorus* subsp. *katherinae*
	natalensis	see *Scadoxus puniceus*
	nortieri	WCot
	pauculifolius	GKev
	pubescens	WCot
	sanguineus	WCot

Hagenia (*Rosaceae*)

	abyssinica	WPGP

Hakea (*Proteaceae*)

	baxteri	SPlb
§	***drupacea***	CPbh
	laurina	CPbh SPlb
§	***lissosperma***	CBcs EBee EPfP SPlb WPGP
	nodosa	CCCN
	oleifolia	CPbh
	platysperma	SPlb
§	***salicifolia***	CBcs CCCN SPlb
	saligna	see *H. salicifolia*
	sericea misapplied	see *H. lissosperma*
	- pink-flowered	SPlb
	suaveolens	see *H. drupacea*
	victoriae	SPlb

Hakonechloa ✿ (*Poaceae*)

	macra 🏆H7	Widely available
§	- 'Alboaurea' (v) 🏆H7	CBcs CExl CKno CRos CTsd ELan EPfP GMcL LCro LRHS LSRN MGos MMuc NPla NRHS SRms WOld
	- 'Albovariegata' (v)	CAbb CKno EBee EPPr EUJe GCal LCro LEdu LOPS LRHS MAvo SCob SPoG WAvo
§	- 'All Gold'	CAby CExl CFil CKno CWCL EBee ECha ECtt EPPr EShb EWes GQue IBoy ITim LEdu LRHS MAsh MAvo MGos MJak SCob SMad SPad WCot WPGP
	- 'Aureola' 🏆H7	Widely available
	- 'Beni-kaze'	EBee EShb MAvo SCob
	- 'Fubuki' (v) **new**	CKno
	- 'Mediovariegata' (v)	EBee ECha EPPr
	- 'Naomi' (v)	EBee SCob

	- 'Nicolas'	CExl CSam EBee ECtt EHoe EPfP EWes GMcL LCro LEdu LLHF LOPS LPla LSRN LSou MBel NQui NSti SCob
	- 'Ogon'	see *H. macra* 'All Gold'
	- 'Samurai' (v)	CKno CRos LRHS NRHS
	- 'Stripe It Rich' (v)	EBee ECtt EWes SGol
	- 'Variegata'	see *H. macra* 'Alboaurea'

Halenia (*Gentianaceae*)

	elliptica	GKev
	- SDR 7809	GKev

Halesia (*Styracaceae*)

§	***carolina***	Widely available
	- Monticola Group	CAco CBcs CCVT CMCN CRos EBee ELan EPfP LRHS LSRN MMuc NLar SWvt WHar
I	- - 'Variegata' (v)	MBlu NLar SSta
	- 'Uconn Wedding Bells'	CJun MBlu
	- Vestita Group ♀H5	CDul CJun CRos CTho EPfP EUJe LRHS MAsh MBlu MGil MGos MRav NLar SPer SSta
	- - 'Rosea'	CJun EPfP MBlu NLar
	diptera	CBcs MBlu
	- Magniflora Group	CJun EPfP LRHS MBlu SAko
	macgregorii	CMCN MBlu
	tetraptera	see *H. carolina*

× *Halimiocistus* (*Cistaceae*)

	algarvensis	see *Halimium ocymoides*
§	'Ingwersenii' ♀H4	ELan EWes SPer SPoG SRms XLum
	revolii misapplied	see × *H. sahucii*
§	***sahucii*** ♀H4	CBcs CBod CRos CSBt CTri ECha ELan EPfP ESps LRHS MAsh MBNS MRav MSwo NPri SCob SPer SPoG SRms SWvt WKif XLum
	- ICE DANCER ('Ebhals'PBR) (v)	EBee EPfP MAsh SCob SPer SWvt WFar
	'Susan'	see *Halimium* 'Susan'
§	***wintonensis*** ♀H4	CBcs CRos ELan EPfP LRHS MAsh MGil MMrt MMuc SCob SLon SPer SRms
§	- 'Merrist Wood Cream' ♀H4	CBcs CBod CBot CMac CRos CSBt EBee ELan EPfP EWTr LRHS LSRN MAsh MGil MRav MSwo SEle SLim SPer SPoG SRkn SWvt WFar WGrn

Halimium (*Cistaceae*)

§	***atriplicifolium***	CAby
§	***calycinum***	CBcs CBod CRos ELan EPfP LRHS MAsh MMuc NRHS SCoo SLim SPer SPoG SWvt WCFE WHar WKif
	commutatum	see *H. calycinum*
	halimifolium misapplied	see *H.* × *pauanum*
§	***lasianthum***	CMac CRos CSBt EPfP LRHS MRav SLim
	- 'Concolor' ♀H4	CRos LRHS MAsh MSwo SWvt
	- subsp. ***formosum*** 'Sandling' ♀H4	CRos ELan EPfP LRHS MAsh MMuc SLon SPoG SRms
	libanotis misapplied	see *H. calycinum*
§	***ocymoides***	MGil MSwo WKif
§	× ***pauanum***	CRos LRHS MMuc NRHS
§	'Susan' ♀H4	CRos EBee ELan EPfP LRHS NRHS SCoo SLim SPer WAbe
§	***umbellatum***	EPfP
	wintonense	see × *Halimiocistus wintonensis*

Halimodendron (*Papilionaceae*)

	halodendron	CBcs CDul MBlu SPer

Halleria (*Stilbaceae*)

	lucida	CBcs CCCN EBee SEle SPlb SVen

Haloragis (*Haloragaceae*)

	erecta	SPlb SVen XLum
	- 'Rubra'	WCot
	- 'Wellington Bronze'	CBod CExl CPla CSpe EHoe ELan EUJe LEdu SPtp WHer WMoo XLum

Hamamelis ✿ (*Hamamelidaceae*)

	'Amethyst'	CJun MBlu SGol
	'Brevipetala'	CEnd CJun LMaj
	'Danny'	CJun
	'Dishi'	CJun
	'Doerak'	CJun
	'Fire Blaze'	CJun MBlu NLar
	× ***intermedia***	CDul
	- 'Advent'	CJun NLar
	- 'Amanda' **new**	NLar
	- 'Andre' **new**	WPGP
	- 'Andrea'	NLar
	- 'Angelly' ♀H5	CEnd CJun CRos LRHS MBlu NLar NRHS
	- 'Anne'	CRos LRHS NLar NRHS
	- 'Aphrodite' ♀H5	CDul CJun CRos EPfP GMcL LRHS MBlu MGos MRav NLar NRHS SCob SPer
	- 'Arnold Promise' ♀H5	Widely available
	- 'Aurora' ♀H5	CJun CRos EPfP LRHS MBlu NLar WPGP
	- 'Barmstedt Gold' ♀H5	CJun CRos EPfP IArd LRHS LSRN MGos MRav NLar NRHS SAko SCob SPer SPoG SRms
	- 'Bernstein'	CJun
	- 'Carmine Red'	CJun CMac
	- 'Copper Beauty'	see *H.* × *intermedia* 'Jelena'
	- 'Cyrille'	MMuc
	- 'Diane' ♀H5	Widely available
§	- 'Feuerzauber'	CEnd CSBt CTri LBuc LMaj NLar SCob SPer SWvt
	- FIRE CRACKER	see *H.* × *intermedia* 'Feuerzauber'
	- 'Foxy Lady'	LRHS NRHS
	- 'Frederic' ♀H5	CJun CRos EPfP LRHS NRHS
	- 'Gingerbread'	CJun CRos EPfP LLHF LRHS NRHS
	- 'Glowing Embers'	CJun CRos LRHS
	- 'Harlow Carr'	CRos LRHS NLar NRHS
	- 'Harry' ♀H5	CJun CRos LRHS LSRN MAsh NLar
	- 'Heinrich Bruns'	CJun
§	- 'Jelena' ♀H5	Widely available
	- 'John'	LRHS LSRN
	- 'Kew Sunshine'	CRos LRHS NRHS
	- 'Limelight'	CJun MBlu MMuc
	- 'Livia'	CJun CRos EPfP LRHS NLar NRHS SCoo
	- MAGIC FIRE	see *H.* × *intermedia* 'Feuerzauber'
	- 'Moonlight'	CJun
	- 'Nina'	CRos EPfP LRHS NRHS
	- 'Ninotchka'	CJun
	- 'Old Copper'	NLar
	- 'Orange Beauty'	CBcs CDul CRos LRHS MBlu MGos NRHS SAko SCoo SGol SPer WPGP
	- 'Orange Peel'	CDul CJun CRos EPfP LCro LLHF LRHS NLar
	- 'Ostergold'	CJun NLar
	- 'Pallida' ♀H5	Widely available
	- 'Primavera'	CJun CLnd CRos LRHS NRHS
	- 'Ripe Corn'	CJun CRos EPfP LRHS
	- 'Robert' ♀H5	CJun CRos EPfP LRHS LSRN NRHS

- 'Rubin' ♀H5	CJun CRos EPfP GMcL LRHS MGos NLar NRHS SCoo SPer
- 'Rubinstar'	CJun
- 'Ruby Glow'	CBcs CRos LRHS LSRN MGos NEgg NLar NRHS SCoo SPer SPoG SWvt
- 'Savill Starlight'	CJun
- 'Spanish Spider'	CJun MBlu MMuc NLar
- 'Strawberries and Cream'	CJun
- 'Sunburst'	CJun CRos LRHS MBlu MGos NLar SGol
- 'Twilight'	CJun NLar
- 'Vesna' ♀H5	CJun CMac CRos EPfP LRHS MAsh MBlu NLar NRHS SCoo
- 'Westerstede'	CJun ESps GMcL LRHS LSRN MGos NLar NPla SCob SCoo SEWo SGol SLim WHor
- 'Wiero'	CJun NLar
- 'Zitronenjette'	CJun
japonica	LPra
- 'Pendula'	CJun MBlu
- 'Zuccariniana'	NLar
mollis	Widely available
- 'Boskoop'	CJun NLar
- 'Coombe Wood'	CJun LRHS
- 'Emily'	CRos LRHS NRHS
- 'Goldcrest'	CJun
- 'Imperialis'	CJun CRos LRHS MAsh NRHS
- 'Iwado'	CJun
- 'Jermyns Gold' ♀H5	CJun CRos EPfP LRHS MAsh NRHS
- 'Kort's Yellow'	CJun
- var. ***pallida***	SEWo SWvt
- 'Wisley Supreme' ♀H5	CJun CRos ELan EPfP LLHF LRHS MGos SGol
'Rochester'	CJun NLar
vernalis purple-flowered	MBlu
- 'Quasimodo'	NLar
- 'Sandra'	CBcs CMCN CRos EPfP LRHS MAsh MBlu MGos MRav NLar SLon
virginiana	CAgr CMCN GPoy GQue IDee MMuc
- 'Green Thumb' (v)	NLar
- 'Mohonk Red'	CJun
'Yamina'	NLar SGol

Hamelia (*Rubiaceae*)

patens	CCCN

Hanabusaya (*Campanulaceae*)

§ ***asiatica***	SBrt

Haplocarpha (*Asteraceae*)

rueppellii	NHpl SRms

Haplopappus (*Asteraceae*)

coronopifolius	see *H. glutinosus*
§ ***glutinosus***	ECha ECtt EDAr EPot MMuc SPlb SRms
prunelloides var. ***mustersii*** F&W 9384	WCot

Hardenbergia (*Papilionaceae*)

comptoniana ♀H3	CExl
violacea ♀H3	CCCN CHll CRHN ELan MHer MMuc SEND SLim SPer
- f. ***alba***	CHll SEND
- - 'White Wanderer'	CCCN
- 'Happy Wanderer'	CCCN
- f. ***rosea***	CCCN

Harpephyllum (*Anacardiaceae*)

caffrum (F)	XBlo

Hasteola (*Asteraceae*)

§ ***suaveolens***	LEdu

Hastingsia (*Asparagaceae*)

alba	WSHC

Haworthia ✿ (*Asphodelaceae*)

attenuata	EShb
'Big Band'	NLos
'Black Major'	LToo
'Black Prince'	EShb SBch
coarctata ♀H2	SEND
fasciata	SEND
- 'Concolor'	NLos
glabrata var. ***concolor***	EShb
limifolia	EShb
- SPIDER WHITE ('Lock01'PBR) **new**	LCro
- variegated **new**	LToo
maraisii	LToo
var. ***meiringii*** **new**	
margaritifera	NLos
pumila ♀H2	SEND
pygmaea	LToo
reinwardtii ♀H2	LToo
tesselata	see *H. venosa* subsp. ***tesselata***
truncata ♀H2	LToo
§ ***venosa***	SEND
subsp. ***tesselata*** ♀H2	

hazelnut see *Corylus*

Hebe ✿ (*Plantaginaceae*)

albicans ♀H4	CBcs CRos ELan EPfP ESps GKin GMcL LCro LOPS LRHS LSRN MGos MJak MRav NRHS SCob SCoo SLim SPer SRms SWvt WCFE WHar WOld WSpi XLum
- prostrate	see *H. albicans* 'Snow Cover'
* - 'Snow Carpet'	CCCN LRHS
§ - 'Snow Cover'	EWes
- 'Snow Drift'	see *H. albicans* 'Snow Cover'
§ 'Alicia Amherst'	CRos LRHS
'Amanda Cook' (v)	NPer
'Amethyst Mist'	GMcL
§ 'Amy'	ELon LRHS NPer SWvt WCot
'Amy' variegated (v)	LRHS
§ × ***andersonii*** 'Andersonii Variegata' (v)	ESps LRHS SRms
- 'Argenteovariegata'	see *H.* × ***andersonii*** 'Andersonii Variegata'
'Andressa Paula'	CCCN LRHS
anomala misapplied	see *H.* 'Imposter'
§ ***armstrongii***	MMuc SCob
'Autumn Glory'	CRos ELan EPfP ESps GMcL LCro LOPS LRHS LSRN MAsh MGos MJak MRav MSwo NRHS SCob SPer SPlb SPoG SVen SWvt XLum
'Autumn Joy'	SWvt
azurea	see *H. venustula*
'Azurens'	see *H.* 'Maori Gem'
'Baby Blush'PBR	LRHS
'Baby Boo' (v)	LRHS SCob SLon
'Baby Marie'	CRos CSBt ELan EPfP GKin GMcL LBuc LRHS LSRN MSwo NPer

		NRHS SCob SCoo SLim SPoG SRms
		SRot SWvt
	'Beverley Hills'PBR	CRos CSBt LRHS SCob
	'Bicolor Wand'	CCCN CTsd LRHS
	bishopiana	EPfP SCob
	'Black Beauty'	CRos EPfP GMcL LBuc LRHS MJak
		NRHS SCob
	'Black Panther'	ELon GMcL
	'Blue Clouds' 🏆H4	CRos EBee EPfP LLHF LRHS MSwo
		NRHS NWad SBod SCob SPer
		WCFE
	BLUE ELEGANCE	LRHS SLim
	('Lowgeko'PBR)	
	(Garden Beauty Series)	
§	'Blue Gem'	CMac GMcL SCob SLim
	BLUE HAZE ('Lowchi')	LRHS
	(Garden Beauty Series)	
	BLUE ICE ('Lowapb')	LRHS
	(Garden Beauty Series)	
	'Blue Shamrock'	SWvt
	BLUE STAR ('Vergeer 1'PBR)	CRos EPfP LBuc LRHS MAsh NRHS
		SLon SPoG SRms
	'Boscawenii'	WHer
	'Bouquet'PBR	LLHF
§	'Bowles's Hybrid'	CCCN LRHS MRav MSwo SCob
		SEND SRms
	brachysiphon	CTri SCob SEND SPer SRms SVen
	brevifolia	LRHS
	BRONZE GLOW ('Lowglo')	LBuc LRHS
	(Garden Beauty Series)	
	'Bronzy Baby'PBR (v)	SPoG
	buchananii	NPer
§	- 'Fenwickii'	WHoo
	- 'Minor' ambig.	EPot
	- 'Minor' Hort. NZ	GBin GCrg
	'Bullfinch'	LRHS
	buxifolia (Benth.) Andersen	see *H. odora*
§	'Caledonia' 🏆H4	CBcs CCCN CRos EPfP LCro LOPS
		LRHS LSRN MAsh MGos NPer
		NRHS SCob SCoo SLim SPoG SRms
		SWvt XLum
	'Carl Teschner'	see *H.* 'Youngii'
	'Carnea Variegata' (v)	CRos EPfP EShb ESps GMcL LRHS
		NRHS SPer SRms
	carnosula	SPer
	catarractae	see *Parahebe catarractae*
	'Celine'	CRos EBee EPfP LRHS NRHS
	'Champagne'	CCCN CRos EPfP LCro LOPS LRHS
		LSRN MBlu MJak NLar NRHS NWad
		SCob SCoo SLim SRms XLum
	CHAMPION	GMcL MSwo NLar SCob SCoo
	('Champseiont'PBR)	
	'Charming White'	CChe CRos LRHS LSRN SCob
	cheesemanii	WAbe
	'Christabel'	LRHS
	'Claret Crush' **new**	SPoG
	'Clear Skies'PBR	LLHF LRHS SRms
	'Conwy Knight'	SRms WAbe
	corstorphinensis	LRHS
	'County Park'	EWes GAbr GMcL
	'Cranleighensis'	CTsd LRHS
	cupressoides	GCal
	- 'Boughton Dome'	CTri GEdr MHer WAbe WCFE
		WHoo WOld
	darwiniana misapplied	see *H. glaucophylla*
	'Dazzler' (v)	MAsh
	decumbens	EWes GBin
	'Denise'	LRHS
	'Diamond'	LRHS LSRN SLon SRms

	dieffenbachii	SVen
	diosmifolia	CRos EPfP LRHS MAsh NRHS
	- 'Wairua Beauty'	LRHS
	'Dorothy Peach'	see *H.* 'Watson's Pink'
	'E.B. Anderson'	see *H.* 'Caledonia'
	'Edington'	SPer WCFE
	'Ellie'	LRHS
	elliptica 'Variegata'	see *H.* 'Silver Queen'
	'Emerald Dome'	see *H.* 'Emerald Gem'
§	'Emerald Gem' 🏆H4	CRos CSma CTri EPfP EShb GMcL
		GWyn LRHS LSRN MAsh MGos
		MHer MJak MMuc MSwo NRHS
		SArc SCob SPer SPlb SPoG WHar
	'Emerald Green'	see *H.* 'Emerald Gem'
§	'Eveline'	CRos CSBt CTri LRHS SLim WKif
	'Eversley Seedling'	see *H.* 'Bowles's Hybrid'
	'Eyecatcher' (v)	EBee MAsh MJak
	'Fairfieldii'	WAbe WAvo
	'First Light'PBR	CRos LRHS NRHS SCob SRms
	'Fragrant Jewel'	LRHS SEND SPhx
	× ***franciscana***	SBod
	- 'Blue Gem' ambig.	CDul CRos CTsd ELan EPfP LRHS
		MMuc MRav NPer NRHS SCob
		SEND SPer SPlb SPoG SRms WSpi
		XLum
	- 'Foreness Pink'	SEND
	- 'Lavender Queen'	LRHS
	- lime variegated (v)	SEND
	- 'Purple Tips' misapplied	see *H. speciosa* 'Variegata'
	- 'Variegata'	see *H.* 'Silver Queen'
I	- 'White Gem'	SRms
	'Frozen Flame' (v)	ELan LBuc LRHS MAsh NRHS SPoG
	(Garden Beauty Series)	LBuc LCro LOPS LRHS MAsh SLim
	GARDEN BEAUTY BLUE ('Cliv'PBR)	SRms
	- GARDEN BEAUTY PINK ('Lowink')	LRHS SLim SRms
	- GARDEN BEAUTY PURPLE	CRos LBuc LCro LOPS LRHS MAsh
	('Nold'PBR)	MJak MTin NRHS SLim
	- GARDEN BEAUTY WHITE ('Lowhi')	LRHS
	(Garden Elegance Series) 'Garden Elegance Blush'	LRHS
	- 'Garden Elegance Pink'	SLim
	- 'Garden Elegance Purple'	SLim
	- 'Garden Elegance Rose'	LRHS SLim
	'Gauntlettii'	see *H.* 'Eveline'
	'Gibby'	LRHS
§	***glaucophylla***	XLum
I	- 'Variegata' (v)	CRos CTri LRHS NRHS SCoo SLim
		SPer WKif
	'Gold Beauty' (v)	SRms
	'Gold Pixie'	LBuc
	GOLDEN ANNIVERSARY ('Lowag')	LRHS
	'Golden Glow' (v)	CRos EPfP LRHS NRHS
	'Golden Nugget'	LRHS
	'Goldrush'PBR (v)	SPoG
	gracillima	SCob SEle
	'Gran's Favourite'	LSRN
	'Great Orme' 🏆H4	CDul CRos ELan EPfP ESps GBin
		GLog LRHS LSRN MAsh MGos MJak
		MRav MSwo NPer NRHS SCob
		SEND SLim SPer SPlb SPoG SRms
		SWvt WCFE WSFF
	'Green Globe'	see *H.* 'Emerald Gem'
	'Greensleeves'	CRos LRHS
	'Grethe'	CRos LRHS NRHS SEND
	'Hadspen Pink'	LRHS
	'Hagley Park'	CRos LRHS

	'Hanne' **new**	CRos NRHS
§	'Hartii'	CRos LRHS MRav SCob
	'Havens Green'	GMcL
	'Heartbreaker'PBR (v)	CRos EBee ELan EPfP ESps GMcL LBuc LCro LOPS LRHS MAsh MGos MJak NHPl NPri NRHS SCob SCoo SLim SPoG SWvt
	HEBEDONNA JULIA ('Zelma'PBR)	EBee
	'High Voltage'PBR	MJak
	'Highdownensis'	LRHS
	'Highland Jubilee'	CRos GMcL LRHS NRHS
	'Hinderwell'	NPer
	hulkeana	LLHF LRHS MHer SCob WAbe WKif
§	'Imposter'	SRms
	'Inspiration'	CRos LRHS NWad SCob
	'James Stirling'	see *H. ochracea* 'James Stirling'
	'Jane Holden'	LRHS
	'Jewel of the Nile'PBR (v) **new**	SPoG
	'John Collier'	GAbr SEND
§	'Johny Day'	LRHS SCob
	'Judy'	LRHS
	'Karna'	ECrN
	'Karo Golden Esk'	EPfP
	'Kirkii'	CBar EPfP MSwo NLar SCob XLum
	'Knightshayes'	see *H.* 'Caledonia'
	'La Favorite'	CTsd
	'Lady Ann'PBR (v)	CRos CSBt EPfP ESps GMcL LBuc LRHS MAsh MJak NRHS SPoG
	'Lady Ardilaun'	see *H.* 'Amy'
	laevis	see *H. venustula*
	laingii	GCrg
	latifolia	see *H.* 'Blue Gem'
	'Lavender Spray'	see *H.* 'Hartii'
	leiophylla	SVen
	LEOPARD ('Lowand') (Garden Beauty Series)	LRHS
	'Lilac Fantasy'	LRHS
	'Lilac Wand'	CTsd
	'Linda'	SEND
	'Lindsayi'	LRHS
	'Lisa'	CRos NRHS
	'Liz'	LBuc LRHS SPoG
	lyallii	see *Parahebe lyallii*
	lycopodioides 'Aurea'	see *H. armstrongii*
	'Lynash'	LRHS
	mackenii	see *H.* 'Emerald Gem'
	macrantha ♀H4	CBod CRos GBin GMcL GWyn LRHS SRms WAbe
	macrocarpa	LRHS
	- var. ***latisepala***	LBuc LRHS
	'Magic Summer'PBR	LBuc LRHS MAsh MJak NRHS SPoG
§	'Maori Gem'	MRav
	'Margery Fish'	see *H.* 'Primley Gem'
	'Margret' ♀H4	CRos CSBt EBee ECrN EPfP ESps GMcL LRHS LSRN MAsh MBrN MGos MJak MRav NRHS SCob SCoo SLim SPer SPoG SRms
	'Maria'	CRos LRHS NRHS
	'Marie Antoinette'	CRos LRHS
	'Marilyn Monroe'PBR	LRHS
	'Marjorie'	CDul CMac CRos ECrN ELan EPfP GBin LRHS LSRN MJak MSwo NLar NPer NRHS SCob SPer SPoG SRms SWvt
	matthewsii 'Turkish Delight'PBR **new**	NEoE
	'Mauve Queen'	LRHS
	'McKean'	see *H.* 'Emerald Gem'

	MIDNIGHT SKY ('Lowten'PBR) (Garden Beauty Series)	LBuc LCro LOPS LRHS NPri SCoo SLim SPoG
	'Midsummer Beauty' ♀H4	CRos CWCL ECrN EPfP ESps GMcL IBoy LRHS LSRN MGos MJak MRav NRHS SCob SEND SLim SPer SPlb SPoG SRms SWvt WOut WSFF XLum
	'Milmont Emerald'	see *H.* 'Emerald Gem'
§	'Mohawk'PBR	CRos LRHS NRHS SPoG WSpi
*	'Moppets Hardy'	SPer
§	'Mrs Winder' ♀H4	CCCN CMac CRos ELan EPfP GMcL GWyn LRHS LSRN MAsh MCot MGos MJak MRav MSwo NLar NPer NRHS SCob SCoo SGbt SGol SLim SPer SPoG SWvt WHar
	'Nantyderry'	LRHS MGil
§	'Neil's Choice' ♀H4	CRos ELon LRHS
	'Neopolitan'	EBee
	'New Zealand'	GMcL GWyn XLum
	'Nicola's Blush' ♀H4	CMac CRos ELon EPfP EShb ESps GBin GMcL GWyn LRHS LSRN MCot MRav NLar NRHS SCob SEND SGol SPer SPoG SRGP SRms SWvt WKif
	ochracea	CRos EPfP LRHS NRHS
§	- 'James Stirling' ♀H4	CBcs CMac CRos CSBt ELan EPfP EShb ESps GKin LRHS LSRN MAsh MGos MMuc MSwo NLar NRHS NWad SCob SCoo SPer SPlb SPoG SWvt WHar WSpi
	'Oddity'	LRHS
§	***odora***	ELan LRHS SArc SCob SEND WSpi XLum
I	- 'Nana'	MMuc
	- 'New Zealand Gold'	CRos EPfP ESps LRHS MAsh MMuc NRHS NWad
	- 'Summer Frost'	LRHS
	'Oratia Beauty' ♀H4	CRos LRHS LSRN MMuc MRav SCob SEND
	'Orphan Annie' (v)	LSRN NLar
	'Pacific Paradise'PBR	SPoG
	parviflora misapplied	see *H.* 'Bowles's Hybrid'
	- var. ***angustifolia***	see *H. stenophylla*
	- 'Holdsworth'	CBod LRHS SEND
	'Pascal' ♀H4	CBod CRos ELan EPfP ESps GMcL LCro LOPS LRHS LSRN MAsh MGos NRHS SCoo SLim SLon SPer SPoG SRms SWvt WFar
	PASTEL ELEGANCE ('Lowjap'PBR) (Garden Beauty Series)	SLim
	'Patti Dossett'	see *H. speciosa* 'Patti Dossett'
	pauciramosa	GCal SRms
	'Pearl of Paradise'PBR	CRos NRHS NWad SPoG
	perfoliata	see *Parahebe perfoliata*
	'Perry's Rubyleaf'	NPer
	'Petra's Pink'	CCCN CRos LRHS
	'Pewter Dome' ♀H4	EPfP GMcL LRHS MGos MRav SCob SRms SWvt XLum
	pimeleoides	GMcL SCob
	- 'Glauca'	NPer
	- 'Quicksilver' ♀H4	CRos CSBt CTri ELan EPfP ESps LRHS LSRN MGil MGos MMuc MRav NPer NRHS SBod SCob SCoo SLim SPer SRms WAvo WHar WSpi XLum
	pinguifolia	NLar SPlb
	- 'Pagei' ♀H5	Widely available
	- 'Sutherlandii'	CBcs CDul CRos ESps GMcL LRHS LSRN MAsh MGos MJak NRHS SCob SCoo SWvt WFar XLum

	Name	Suppliers
	PINK ELEGANCE ('Lowuni')	LCro LOPS
	'Pink Elephant' (v) Υ^{H4}	CRos LBuc LRHS MAsh MJak NRHS SLim SPoG
	'Pink Fantasy'	LRHS NWad SCob SRGP
	'Pink Goddess'	CRos LRHS NRHS SEND
	'Pink Lady'^{PBR}	GMcL SPoG
	'Pink Paradise'^{PBR}	CRos ELan EPfP GMcL LBuc LRHS MJak NRHS NWad SPoG SRms
	'Pink Payne'	see *H.* 'Eveline'
	'Pink Pixie'	LBuc LRHS MAsh NRHS SCoo SPoG SRms
	'Pink Wand'	CTsd
	poppelwellii	NLar
	'Porlock Purple'	see *Parahebe catarractae* 'Delight'
§	'Primley Gem'	CRos LRHS
I	'Prostrata'	CSBt
	'Purple Emperor'	see *H.* 'Neil's Choice'
	'Purple Paradise'^{PBR}	GMcL SPoG
	'Purple Picture'	ELon
	'Purple Pixie'	see *H.* 'Mohawk'
	'Purple Princess'	CRos LRHS MJak NRHS
	'Purple Queen'	CRos EPfP EShb GMcL LRHS MCot MJak NRHS SCob
	PURPLE SHAMROCK ('Neprock'^{PBR}) (v)	CRos EPfP EUJe GMcL LRHS MAsh NEgg NLar NRHS SCoo SLim SPer SPoG SRms SWvt
	'Purple Tips' misapplied	see *H. speciosa* 'Variegata'
	'Rachel'	LRHS LSRN
§	***rakaiensis*** Υ^{H4}	Widely available
	- 'Golden Dome'	see *H. rakaiensis*
	ramosissima	GAbr GBin
	raoulii	SRms WAbe
	RASPBERRY RIPPLE ('Tullyraspb'^{PBR})	GMcL LBuc NEoE
	'Raven'	LRHS
	recurva	CSam CTri EMOT LRHS MCot SCob SRms
	- 'Boughton Silver' Υ^{H5}	CRos LRHS LSRN MMuc SLim
	'Red Edge' Υ^{H4}	Widely available
	'Red Moon'	SCob
	'Red Rum'	LBuc LRHS
	'Red Ruth'	see *H.* 'Eveline'
	'Rhubarb and Custard'	LBuc LRHS MAsh MMrt NRHS SCob SPoG
	rigidula	LRHS MMuc SEND
	'Rosie'^{PBR}	LBuc LRHS LSRN NRHS SCoo SPer SWvt
	'Royal Blue'	LRHS
	'Royal Purple'	see *H.* 'Alicia Amherst'
	salicifolia	CCCN CMac CRos CTca ELan EPfP LRHS MMuc MRav NRHS NWad SCob SEND SPlb SRms WSpi XLum
	- pale blue-flowered	SEND
	'Sandra Joy'	LRHS LSRN
	'Santa Monica'	GMcL MJak
	'Sapphire' Υ^{H4}	CRos EPfP GMcL LRHS MAsh MJak SCob SCoo SLim SRms SWvt
	'Sarana'	LRHS LSRN
	'Shiraz'	CRos LRHS
	'Silver Dollar' (v)	CCCN CMac CRos GBin GMcL LRHS MJak NEgg NRHS NWad SLim SPoG SRms
§	'Silver Queen' (v) Υ^{H3}	CBcs CRos CSBt ELan EShb GMcL LCro LOPS LRHS MAsh MMuc NLar NPer NRHS SCob SEND SPer SPoG SRms WOut
	'Silver Swallow'	CRos LRHS NRHS SPoG
	'Simon Délaux'	LRHS SEND SPer WOut
	'Sparkling Sapphires'	LBuc LRHS SPoG
	speciosa 'Johny Day'	see *H.* 'Johny Day'
	- 'La Séduisante'	CTri LRHS SEND WSpi
§	- 'Patti Dossett'	LRHS
	- 'Red Hugh' **new**	SEND
§	- 'Variegata' (v)	CRos ESps LRHS NPer NRHS
	'Spender's Seedling' misapplied	see *H. stenophylla*
	'Spender's Seedling' ambig.	MCot MMuc MSCN SCob
	'Spender's Seedling' Hort.	LRHS MRav SEND SPoG SRms
	'Spring Glory'	CRos LRHS NRHS
§	***stenophylla***	EShb EUJe LRHS LSRN NLar SArc SBod SPer SPlb
	stricta	LRHS SEND
	- var. ***egmontiana***	LRHS
	subalpina	CSBt
	'Summer Blue'	LRHS MBlu
	'Sunset Boulevard'^{PBR}	LLHF
	'Super Red'	CSBt
	'Sweet Dreams'	EBee LRHS
	'Sweet Kim' (v)	CMac CRos LBuc LRHS NRHS SLim SPoG
	topiaria Υ^{H4}	CAgr CMac CRos CSBt CSam EPfP ESps GMcL LRHS MBrN MMuc MRav MSwo NLar NWad SCob SCoo SEND SGbt SPer SPoG WRHF WSpi XLum
	- 'Doctor Favier'	LRHS SRms
	townsonii	LRHS SCob
	'Tricolor'	see *H. speciosa* 'Variegata'
	'Twisty'	LRHS
	'Valentino'^{PBR}	SCoo
	'Veitchii'	see *H.* 'Alicia Amherst'
§	***venustula***	LRHS MMuc
	vernicosa Υ^{H4}	CDul CRos EPfP ESps GMcL LRHS MGos MHer NWad SCob SCoo SEle SPer SPlb SPoG SRot SVen SWvt WSpi
	'Violet Wand'	LRHS
	'Vogue'	LRHS
	'Waikiki'	see *H.* 'Mrs Winder'
§	'Warley'	LRHS WSpi
	'Warley Pink'	CRos LRHS
	'Warleyensis'	see *H.* 'Warley'
§	'Watson's Pink'	SPer WKif
	'White Gem' (*brachysiphon* hybrid) Υ^{H4}	GMcL GWyn LRHS NPer SEND SPer
	'White Heather'	CRos EPfP LRHS NRHS SCob
	'White Paradise'^{PBR}	SPoG
	'Wild Romance'	LBuc LRHS MAsh NRHS SPoG
	'Willcoxii'	see *H. buchananii* 'Fenwickii'
	'Wingletye' Υ^{H4}	CCCN CRos IRob LRHS XLum
	'Winter Glow'	CCCN LRHS
	'Wiri Blush'	LRHS SLim SWvt
	'Wiri Charm'	CBcs CMac CRos CSBt EPfP LRHS MSwo NLar NRHS SCob SEND SLim SPer
	'Wiri Cloud' Υ^{H4}	CBcs CMac CRos EPfP LRHS MMuc MSCN MSwo NRHS SCob SEND SEle SRms
	'Wiri Dawn' Υ^{H4}	CRos ELan EPfP ESps LBuc LRHS NRHS SLim SRms SWvt XLum
	'Wiri Desire'	CCCN CRos LRHS
	'Wiri Gem'	SCob
	'Wiri Image'	CBcs CRos CSBt EPfP LRHS MRav NRHS SEND
	'Wiri Joy'	CRos LRHS NRHS
	'Wiri Mist'	CBcs CRos ELan EPfP LRHS NRHS SCob XLum
	'Wiri Prince'	CRos LRHS
	'Wiri Splash'	CRos EPfP LRHS NRHS SGol
	'Wiri Vision'	CRos CSBt LRHS SEND
	'Wiri Vogue'	LRHS

§ 'Youngii' 🏆H4 — CBcs CMac CRos CSBt CTri ELan EPfP GBin GKin LCro LOPS LRHS MAsh MHer MJak MMuc MRav NRHS SEND SLim SPer SPlb SPoG SRms SWvt WCFE WHoo

Hebenstretia (*Scrophulariaceae*)

dura — WAbe

Hechtia (*Bromeliaceae*)

sp. — WCot

Hedeoma (*Lamiaceae*)

ciliolata — WAbe

Hedera ✿ (*Araliaceae*)

sp. — ESps SCob
§ ***algeriensis*** — SArc WFib
- 'Bellecour' — WFib XLum
§ - 'Gloire de Marengo' (v) 🏆H5 — Widely available
- 'Gloire de Marengo' arborescent (v) — GMcL
- 'Marginomaculata' (v) — CRos EPfP EShb LRHS MAsh SMad SPoG WFib
- 'Montgomery' — CRos LRHS LSRN NRHS
- 'Ravensholst' 🏆H4 — CMac EShb MRav SCob SGol WFib
§ ***azorica*** — EShb WFib
- 'Pico' — WFib
canariensis misapplied — see *H. algeriensis*
- 'Variegata' — see *H. algeriensis* 'Gloire de Marengo'
canariensis Willd. — SEND
- var. ***azorica*** — see *H. azorica*
- 'Cantabrian' — see *H. maroccana* 'Spanish Canary'
chinensis — see *H. nepalensis* var. *sinensis*
- typica — see *H. nepalensis* var. *sinensis*
§ ***colchica*** — CDul SPer WCFE WFib
- 'Arborescens' — see *H. colchica* 'Dendroides'
- 'Batumi' — MBNS WFib
§ - 'Dendroides' — EWTr
- 'Dentata' 🏆H5 — ESps MRav SGol WFar WFib
- 'Dentata Aurea' — see *H. colchica* 'Dentata Variegata'
§ - 'Dentata Variegata' (v) 🏆H5 — Widely available
- 'My Heart' — see *H. colchica*
- 'Paddy's Pride' — see *H. colchica* 'Sulphur Heart'
§ - 'Sulphur Heart' (v) 🏆H5 — Widely available
- 'Variegata' — see *H. colchica* 'Dentata Variegata'
cristata — see *H. helix* 'Parsley Crested'
§ ***cypria*** — WFib
helix — CCVT CMac CTri EBWF ESps SCob WSFF XLum
- 'Adam' (v) — LSRN WFib
- 'Amberwaves' — WFib
- 'Angularis Aurea' 🏆H5 — WFib
- 'Anita' — GBin WFib
§ - 'Anna Marie' (v) — WFib
- 'Anne Borch' — see *H. helix* 'Anna Marie'
- 'Arborescens' — EShb WSFF
- 'Ardingly' (v) — WFib
- 'Atropurpurea' — ELan GBin MMuc SEND WFib
- var. ***baltica*** — WFib
- 'Bill Archer' — GBin WFib
- 'Bird's Foot' — see *H. helix* 'Pedata'
- 'Boskoop' — WFib
- 'Bredon' — MRav
- 'Brimstone' (v) — WFib
§ - 'Brokamp' — WFib
- 'Buttercup' 🏆H5 — CBcs CDul CMac CRos CTri EHoe ELan EPfP ESps GMcL GQue LRHS LSRN MAsh MGos MMuc NBid NLar NPri NRHS SEND SPer SPoG SRms SWvt WCFE WFib
- 'Caecilia' (v) 🏆H5 — EPfP MSwo SWvt WFib
- 'Caenwoodiana' — see *H. helix* 'Pedata'
- 'Caenwoodiana Aurea' — WFib
- 'Calico' (v) — WFib
- 'Calypso' — WFib
- 'Carolina Crinkle' — GBin
- 'Cathedral Wall' — WFib
§ - 'Cavendishii' (v) — SRms WFib
- 'Cavendishii Latina' (v) — WCot
§ - 'Ceridwen' (v) 🏆H5 — SPlb WFib
- 'Cheeky' — WFib
- 'Cheltenham Blizzard' (v) — CNat
- 'Chester' (v) — CKel CRos LRHS WFib
- 'Chicago' — WFib
- 'Chicago Variegated' (v) — WFib
- 'Chrysophylla' — MSwo
- 'Clotted Cream' (v) — CRos ELon ESps GMcL LRHS MAsh WFib
- 'Cockle Shell' — WFib
- 'Colin' — GBin
§ - 'Congesta' 🏆H5 — CMac SRms WFib
- 'Conglomerata' — ELan MMoz SRms WFib
- 'Courage' — WFib
- 'Crenata' — WFib
- 'Crispa' — MRav
- 'Cristata' — see *H. helix* 'Parsley Crested'
- 'Curleylocks' — see *H. helix* 'Manda's Crested'
- 'Curley-Q' — see *H. helix* 'Dragon Claw'
- 'Curvaceous' (v) — WFib
- 'Cyprus' — see *H. cypria*
§ - 'Dealbata' (v) — CMac SRms WFib
- 'Deltoidea' — see *H. hibernica* 'Deltoidea'
- 'Diny' **new** — SMad
- 'Discolor' — see *H. helix* 'Dealbata', *H. helix* 'Minor Marmorata'
§ - 'Donerailensis' — MBlu WFib
- 'Don's Papillon' — CNat
§ - 'Dragon Claw' — WFib
- 'Duckfoot' 🏆H5 — EShb GBin WCot WFib
- 'Dyinnii' — GEdr NLar WCot
- 'Eileen' (v) — WFib
- 'Elfenbein' (v) — WCot WFib
- 'Erecta' — CDul CRos EPPr EPfP GAbr GCal IDee LRHS MBlu NWad SMad SPer SPlb SPoG WCFE WFib XLum
- 'Ester' (v) — SRGP WHar
§ - 'Eva' (v) — WFib
- 'Fantasia' (v) — WFib
- 'Feenfinger' — WFib
- 'Filigran' — WFib
- 'Flashback' (v) — WFib
- 'Flavescens' — WFib
- 'Fluffy Ruffles' — WFib
I - 'Francis Ivy' — WFib
- 'Frosty' (v) — WFib
- 'Garland' — WFib
- 'Gavotte' — WFib
- 'Gilded Hawke' — WFib
- 'Glache' (v) — MRav WFib
- 'Glacier' (v) 🏆H5 — CArg CBcs CDul CRos CTri ELan EMOT EPfP ESps GMcL LCro LOPS LRHS MAsh MGos MJak MMuc MRav MSwo NRHS SCob SEND SGol SLim SPer SPoG SRms SWvt WFar WFib
- 'Glymii' — ELan GBin GCal WFib
- 'Gold Harald' — see *H. helix* 'Goldchild'
- 'Gold Ripple' — NLar SEND

§	– 'Goldchild' (v) ♀H5	CBcs CKel CMac EBee ELon EMOT EPfP EShb ESps EUJe GMcL LCro LOPS LRHS MAsh MGos MMuc MRav MSwo NRHS SCob SLim SPer SPoG SWvt WFib WHar
	– 'Golden Ann'	see *H. helix* 'Ceridwen'
*	– 'Golden Arrow'	CRos LRHS MAsh
	– 'Golden Curl' (v)	CMac CRos EPfP LRHS
	– 'Golden Ester'	see *H. helix* 'Ceridwen'
	– 'Golden Girl'	WFib
	– 'Golden Ingot' (v) ♀H5	ELan WFib
	– 'Golden Jytte' (v)	WFib
	– 'Golden Kolibri'	see *H. helix* 'Midas Touch'
	– 'Goldfinch'	WFib
	– 'Goldfinger'	WFib
	– 'Goldheart'	see *H. helix* 'Oro di Bogliasco'
	– 'Goldstern' (v)	MRav WFib
	– 'Gracilis'	see *H. hibernica* 'Gracilis'
	– 'Green Finger'	see *H. helix* 'Très Coupé'
	– 'Green Man'	WFib
	– 'Green Ripple'	CBcs CRos CTri ELan EPfP ESps GMcL LRHS MBlu MGos MJak MMuc MSwo MWht NRHS SCob SEND SLim SPer SPlb SRms SWvt WFib
	– 'Halebob'	WFib
	– 'Hamilton'	see *H. hibernica* 'Hamilton'
	– 'Harald' (v)	CTri WFib
*	– 'Hazel' (v)	WFib
	– 'Heise' (v)	WFib
	– 'Heise Denmark' (v)	WFib
	– 'Helvig'	see *H. helix* 'White Knight'
	– 'Henriette'	WFib
	– 'Hispanica'	see *H. iberica*
	– 'Hite's Miniature'	see *H. helix* 'Merion Beauty'
	– 'Holly'	see *H. helix* 'Parsley Crested'
	– 'Hullavington'	CNat
	– 'Humpty Dumpty'	CExl
	– 'Ice Cream'	LRHS
	– 'Imp'	see *H. helix* 'Brokamp'
	– 'Ingelise' (v)	GMcL
	– 'Ingrid' (v)	SRms
	– 'Ivalace'	CBcs EShb MSwo SRms WFib XLum
	– 'Jake'	WFib
	– 'Jara' (arboreal) **new**	WCot
	– 'Jasper'	WFib
	– 'Jersey Doris' (v)	WFib
	– 'Jerusalem'	see *H. helix* 'Schäfer Three'
	– 'Jubilee' (v)	WFar WFib
	– 'Kaleidoscope'	WFib
	– 'Kevin'	WFib
	– 'Kolibri' (v)	WFib
	– 'Königer's Auslese'	WFib
	– 'Lalla Rookh'	MRav WFib WRHF
	– 'Leo Swicegood'	WFib
	– 'Light Fingers'	CRos ELon EPfP LRHS NRHS WFib
	– 'Little Diamond' (v)	CMac CRos CTri ELan GMcL LRHS SLon SRms SWvt WFib
	– 'Little Luzii'	WFib
	– 'Liz'	see *H. helix* 'Eva'
	– 'Luzii' (v)	WFib
	– 'Maculata'	see *H. helix* 'Minor Marmorata'
§	– 'Manda's Crested' ♀H5	ELan NLar WFib
	– 'Maple Leaf' ♀H5	EShb GBin WFib
	– 'Marginata Elegantissima'	see *H. helix* 'Tricolor'
	– 'Marginata Minor'	see *H. helix* 'Cavendishii'
I	– 'Marmorata' Fibrex	WFib
	– 'Mathilde' (v)	CKel WFib
	– 'Melanie'	WCot WFib
	– 'Meon'	WFib
§	– 'Merion Beauty'	EUJe WFib
§	– 'Midas Touch' (v) ♀H5	EPfP GMcL WFib
	– 'Minikin' (v)	WCot
	– 'Minima' misapplied	see *H. helix* 'Spetchley'
	– 'Minima' Hibberd	see *H. helix* 'Donerailensis'
	– 'Minima' M.Young	see *H. helix* 'Congesta'
§	– 'Minor Marmorata' (v)	XLum
	– 'Minty' (v)	WFib
	– 'Misty' (v)	WFib
	– 'Needlepoint'	XLum
	– 'Niagara Falls'	CRos LRHS SPoG
	– 'Nigra Aurea' (v)	WFib
	– 'Obovata'	WFib
	– 'Oro di Bogliasco' (v)	CArg CDul CMac CRos CTri EBee EMOT EPfP ETMg GMcL LRHS MJak MMuc MRav MSwo NLar NRHS NWad SCob SEND SLim SPer SPlb SRms SWvt WFar WFib
	– 'Ovata'	WFib
§	– 'Parsley Crested' ♀H5	ELan EPfP SGol WFib
	– 'Patent Leather'	WFib
	– 'Pedata'	CDul MSwo SRms WFib
	– 'Perkeo'	EUJe WFib
	– 'Peter' (v)	WFib
	– 'Pink 'n' Curly'	WCot WFib
	– 'Pink 'n' Very Curly'	WCot
§	– 'Pittsburgh'	WFib
	– 'Plume d'Or'	WFib
§	– f. ***poetarum***	GCal MBlu WCot WFib
	– – 'Poetica Arborea'	EShb
	– 'Poetica'	see *H. helix* f. *poetarum*
	– 'Raleigh Delight' (v)	WCot
	– 'Ray's Supreme'	see *H. helix* 'Pittsburgh'
	– subsp. ***rhizomatifera***	WFib
	– 'Richard John'	WFib
	– 'Ritterkreuz'	WFib
	– 'Romanze' (v)	WCot WFib
	– 'Russelliana'	WFib
	– 'Sagittifolia' misapplied	see *H. helix* 'Pedata'
	– 'Sagittifolia' Hibberd	CTri EPfP
	– 'Sagittifolia' ambig.	LRHS MAsh MBlu SPoG
	– 'Sagittifolia Variegata' (v)	WFib WRHF
	– 'Saint Agnes'	CRos LRHS
	– 'Sally' (v)	WFib
	– 'Salt and Pepper'	see *H. helix* 'Minor Marmorata'
§	– 'Schäfer Three' (v)	WFib
	– 'Seabreeze'	WFib
	– 'Shamrock' ♀H5	EPfP WFib
	– 'Shannon'	WFib
	– 'Silver Ferny'	WFib
	– 'Silver King' (v)	WFib
	– 'Silver Queen'	see *H. helix* 'Tricolor'
§	– 'Spetchley' ♀H5	CMac GEdr GKev MRav NLar NPer NWad WCot WFib
	– 'Splashes'	WFib
	– 'Sunrise'	WFib
	– 'Suzanne'	see *H. nepalensis* 'Suzanne'
	– 'Tanja'	WFib
	– 'Teardrop'	WFib
	– 'Telecurl'	WFib
	– 'Temptation' (v)	WFib
	– 'Tenerife' (v)	WFib
	– 'Topazolite' (v)	WFib
§	– 'Très Coupé'	CRos LRHS MMuc SArc SEND
§	– 'Tricolor' (v)	CTri EPfP LRHS WCFE WFib
	– 'Trinity' (v)	WFib
	– 'Tripod'	WFib
	– 'Triton'	WFib
	– 'Troll'	WFib
	– 'Ursula' (v)	WFib

	- 'Very Merry'	WFib
*	- 'Vitifolium'	WFib
§	- 'White Knight' (v) ♀H5	WFib
	- 'White Mein Herz' (v)	WFib
	- 'White Ripple' (v)	WFib
	- 'White Wonder'	SPoG
	- 'Williamsiana' (v)	WFib
	- 'Winter Purple Vein'	CNat
	- 'Woerneri'	NLar WFib
	- 'Yellow Ripple'	EShb WFib
	- 'Zebra' (v)	WFib
	hibernica	CCVT CDul CSBt EPfP ESps ETMg EWTr GMcL LBuc LRHS MJak MRav MSwo SCob SEWo SGol SPer SWvt WFib
	- 'Anna Marie'	see *H. helix* 'Anna Marie'
	- 'Betty Allen'	WFib
§	- 'Deltoidea' ♀H5	MWht WCFE WFib
I	- 'Digitata Crûg Gold'	WCru
	- 'Ebony'	WFib
	- 'Glengariff'	WFib
§	- 'Gracilis'	WFib
§	- 'Hamilton'	WFib
	- 'Lobata Major'	SRms
	- 'Palmata'	WFib
	- 'Rona'	WFib
	- 'Sulphurea' (v)	WFib
	- 'Variegata' (v)	WFib
§	***iberica***	WFib
	maderensis	WFib
	maroccana 'Morocco'	WFib
§	- 'Spanish Canary'	WFib
	nepalensis	WFib
	- 'Marble Dragon'	see *H. nepalensis* var. *sinensis* 'Marble Dragon'
§	- var. ***sinensis***	WFib
	- - KWJ 12345	WCru
§	- - 'Marble Dragon'	WFib
§	- 'Suzanne'	WFib
	pastuchovii	EShb WFib
	- from Troödos, Cyprus	see *H. cypria*
	- 'Ann Ala' ♀H5	CFil EUJe MBlu WAvo WCot WFib
	- 'Lagocetti'	WFib
§	***rhombea***	WCot WFib
	- 'Japonica'	see *H. rhombea*
	- var. ***rhombea*** 'Variegata' (v)	WFib

Hedychium ✿ (*Zingiberaceae*)

	'Anne Bishop'	NLos SEND
	aurantiacum	CBcs CBct CCCN CDTJ CTsd GKev LAma LEdu NLos SBig XLum
	brevicaule B&SWJ 7171	WCru
	'C.P. Raffill'	see *H.* × *moorei* 'Raffillii'
	chrysoleucum	CCCN
*	'Clarkei'	CCCN CTsd
	coccineum	CDTJ CTsd GKev MNrw SBig
	- B&SWJ 5238	WCru
	- var. ***angustifolium***	CFil WPGP
	- 'Disney'	CDTJ
	- 'Hungphung Stripe'	LEdu WPGP
	- 'Khangkhui Tall Boy'	LEdu WPGP
	- 'Khonoma Silver'	LEdu WPGP
I	- 'Mishmi Form'	GCal
	- 'Shillong Ghost'	LEdu WPGP
	coronarium ♀H1c	CAbb CAvo CBct CCCN CDTJ CExl CFil CTsd ETod EUJe GKev LLWG NLos NRHS SBig SPer WPGP XBlo XLum
	- B&SWJ 3745	WCru
	- 'Gold Spot'	CCCN CTsd EUJe GKev NLos
	- var. ***urophyllum***	see *H. flavum* Roxb.
	densiflorum	CAbb CCCN CDTJ CExl CTsd ECha EUJe GKev IBlr LCro LEdu LOPS NLos SRms WCot WCru WPGP XLum
	- EN 562	CExl CFil
	- LS&H 17393	CExl CFil WPGP
	- 'Assam Orange'	CAvo CBlu CCCN CExl CPla CPne CSam CTsd EUJe GCal IBlr LEdu MNrw SBig SChr SEND SMad SPlb WCru WPGP
	- pale-flowered	GCal
	- 'Sorung'	CDTJ CExl CFil LEdu SChr WPGP
	- 'Stephen'	CAvo CBct CCCN CDTJ CExl CFil CPne EBee EUJe LEdu MNrw SChr SPlb WPGP
	'Devon Cream'	CCCN CDTJ CExl LRHS SChr
	'Doctor Moy' (v)	CDTJ EUJe
	'Elizabeth'	EUJe
	ellipticum	CAbb CCCN CDTJ CTsd EUJe GKev LAma MPie NLos SBig XLum
	- B&SWJ 8354	WCru
	- PAB 7867	LEdu WPGP
	'Filigree'	CExl
§	***flavescens***	CBct CCCN CDTJ CTsd EBee EUJe GKev LAma LCro LOPS NLos
	flavum misapplied	see *H. flavescens*
§	***flavum*** Roxb.	CAbb CBcs IBlr XLum
	- HWJ 604	WCru
	forrestii misapplied	see *H.* 'Helen Dillon'
	forrestii Diels	WCru
	KWJ 12314 **new**	
	gardnerianum ♀H2	CAbb CDTJ CExl CPne CTsd ETod EUJe GKev LAma LCro LEdu LOPS LRHS MNrw NLos NRHS SArc SChr SDeJ SDir SPer SPlb WCru XLum
	- B&SWJ 12533	WCru
	'Gold Flame'	EBee
	gracile	NLos WCru
	greenii	CBcs CBct CCCN CDTJ CPne CTsd EUJe GKev LEdu MNrw MPie NLos SBig SDir SPlb WBor WCru XLum
	- 'Mhui Fang'	LEdu WPGP
	griffithianum	CCCN CDTJ CTsd SBig XLum
	- white-flowered	CCCN
§	'Helen Dillon'	CCCN CCse CDTJ CExl ETod EUJe IBlr SArc SPlb WCru WPGP
	'Keneggy'	SVen
	'Luna Moth'	CFil NLos WPGP
	luteum	CTsd
	maximum	CDTJ CFil NLos SChr WPGP
	- B&SWJ 8261A	WCru
	- HWJ 810	WCru
§	× ***moorei*** 'Raffillii'	SBig WCru
	'Orange Glow'	CPne
	'Pink V'	NLos
	'Samsheri'	CCCN SChr
	spicatum	CAbb CAvo CCCN CDTJ CExl CTsd EUJe GCal GKev GPoy IBlr LEdu MNrw MRav NLos SMHy WPGP
	- B&SWJ 7231	WCru
	- CC 1705	CExl
	- P. Bon. 57188	CExl CFil WPGP
	- PAB 13.0718	LEdu
	- from Ciaojiang	SBrt
	- from Salween Valley, China	CExl
	- 'Himalayan Lipstick'	GKev
	- 'Huani'	LEdu
	- 'Liberty'	WCru

- 'Shirui Steps'	LEdu
- 'Singalila'	LEdu WCru
'St Martin's'	CCCN
stenopetalum B&SWJ 7155	WCru
'Tahitian Flame' (v)	EUJe NLos
'Tai Pink Princess' (Tai Series)	CTsd
'Tara' ♀H4	CAvo CBct CBlu CDTJ CExl CPne CSam EUJe IBlr LEdu LRHS MNrw SArc SMHy SPlb WCru WPGP
tengchongense 'Trum Trom'	WCru
thyrsiforme	CDTJ CTsd EUJe GKev SBig WCru XLum
villosum	CDTJ GCal
- var. ***tenuiflorum***	WPGP
- - KWJ 12305	WCru
wardii	CDTJ CExl CFil CTsd EUJe WCru WPGP
yunnanense	LEdu SBig SBrt SPlb WPGP
- B&SWJ 9717	WCru
- BWJ 7900	WCru
- L 633	CExl IBlr
- from Cally Gardens	GCal

Hedysarum (*Papilionaceae*)

coronarium	CBod CSpe ELan IBoy SPoG WKif WOut
hedysaroides	GJos SPhx WCot
multijugum	MBlu WSHC

Heimia (*Lythraceae*)

salicifolia	IMou MGil SBrt

Helenium ✿ (*Asteraceae*)

'Adios'	WFar
'Amber'	EBee ECtt ILea MAvo MSpe WFar
autumnale	CExl CSBt CTri ESps LSRN MMuc NChi SWvt WFar WHar WMoo WPtf WWtn XLum
- 'All Gold'	SWvt
- 'Bandera' **new**	ECtt
- 'Fuego' PBR (Mariachi Series)	CBod CWGN EBee ECtt LCro LOPS LRHS LSou MAvo MNrw MSCN NRHS SRms WCAu WHil
§ - Helena Series	SWvt WHar
§ - - 'Helena Gold'	CBod EPfP IBoy NBre
- - 'Helena Rote Töne'	CBod CChe CRos EAJP EPed EPfP LPmr LRHS LSun MHol NRHS
- - 'Helena Yellow'	CRos LRHS NRHS
- 'Salsa' PBR (Mariachi Series)	CKno CRos EBee IBoy ILea LCro LOPS LRHS MAvo SPad SRms WHil WWtn
- 'Short and Sassy' **new**	CKno LCro LOPS SPoG WHil
- 'Siesta' PBR (Mariachi Series)	LRHS MAvo NRHS
- 'Sombrero' PBR (Mariachi Series)	CKno ECtt LCro LOPS LRHS LSou NEoE NRHS WWtn
'Baronin Linden'	MAvo
'Baudirektor Linne' ♀H7	CRos ILea LEdu LRHS MTis NRHS SHar
'Betty'	CBod ECtt
'Biedermeier'	CWCL ECtt LCro LOPS MNrw MSpe SAko
bigelovii	XLum
'Blütentisch' misapplied	see *H.* 'Riverton Beauty'
'Blütentisch' Foerster ♀H7	CMea CRos GMaP LRHS MAvo MTis NLar NRHS
'Bressingham Gold'	CRos LRHS MHCG MNrw MSpe NRHS WAvo WHrl
'Bruno'	CRos LRHS MArl NRHS SHar

'Butterpat' ♀H7	CDor CRos ECtt EHrv GMaP IRob LRHS MArl MNrw MRav NRHS WMoo
'Can Can'	CRos ECtt ELon EPfP LPmr LRHS LSou MAsh MAvo MHer MNrw MTis NGdn NRHS SPer SRms WCAu WFar WMoo
'Carmen' (UFO Series) **new**	MSpe
'Chelsey'	ECtt ELan EPfP GQue IRob LCro LOPS LPla LRHS LSRN MNrw MPie MRav MSpe NLar NSti SPoG SRms WBor
'Chipperfield Orange'	CSam EBee ECtt GMaP MArl NGdn WOld
'Coppelia'	CRos ECtt LRHS MHol MTis NGdn NRHS WFar
COPPER SPRAY	see *H.* 'Kupfersprudel'
DARK BEAUTY	see *H.* 'Dunkle Pracht'
'Dauerbrenner'	LEdu MAvo MTis SHar
'Die Blonde'	SMHy
'Double Trouble' PBR	CRos EBee ECtt ETMg GBin GMaP GPSL IBoy LLHF LPmr LRHS MBNS MHol MSCN MSpe NGdn NHpl NRHS SGbt SPer SRms WCot WFar
§ 'Dunkle Pracht' ♀H7	CRos EBee ECtt EHrv ILea LSRN MSpe NLar WFar WOld
'El Dorado'	CBWd CRos EBee ECtt ELon IBoy LEdu LRHS MAvo MBel MSpe MTis NRHS NSti SRms WCot WFar
'Fata Morgana'	CRav ECtt LLHF MSpe MTis NBre SCob
'Festival'	ECtt
'Feuersiegel' ♀H7	CRos ECtt EHrv LRHS MAvo MSpe NRHS SAko WOld
'Fiesta'	ECtt MAvo MSpe MTis WFar
'Flamenco' **new**	WFar
'Flammendes Käthchen'	CRos EBee ECtt EHoe LRHS MAvo MSpe NRHS SHar SPhx
'Flammenrad'	CAby CSam EBee SAko
'Flammenspiel'	CRos ECtt LRHS MNrw NRHS
flexuosum	SPhx
'Gartensonne' ♀H7	CSam LPla
'Gay-go-round'	CSam
'Gelbe Waltraut'	MAvo
'Gold Doubloons'	EBee
GOLD FOX	see *H.* 'Goldfuchs'
'Gold Intoxication'	see *H.* 'Goldrausch'
GOLDEN YOUTH	see *H.* 'Goldene Jugend'
§ 'Goldene Jugend'	ECtt ELon MTis WCot
§ 'Goldfuchs'	WCot
'Goldkogel'	EBee
§ 'Goldlackzwerg'	CRos GBin LRHS NRHS
§ 'Goldrausch'	CAby EBee ECtt EPfP GBin MNrw MSpe MTis MWat NGdn SAko WFar WMoo WOld
'Goldriese'	MSpe
'Hartmut Rieger'	CSam MSpe
'Helena' misapplied	see *H. autumnale* Helena Series 'Helena Gold'
'Herbstgold'	MSpe
hoopesii	see *Hymenoxys hoopesii*
'Hot Lava'	EBee ECtt GPSL LOPS MBel MNrw MSpe SCob
'Hot Luv'	MSpe WCot
'Indianersommer'	CDor CWCL ECtt EHrv GMaP GWyn ILea LRHS MNrw MSpe NLar SSut WCFE WWtn
'Jam Tarts'	WCot
'Julisamt'	LEdu

	'Kanaria'	CAby CDor CRos EBee ECtt EPfP GBin GKev GWyn ILea LRHS MAvo MBel MRav MSpe MTis NEgg NLar NRHS WCAu
	'Karneol' ♀^{H7}	CRos EBee LRHS NRHS
	'Kleine Aprikose'	MTis
	'Kleiner Fuchs'	EHrv
	'Kokarde'	MAvo
	'Königstiger'	CRos ECtt GBin ILea LRHS MAvo MHCG MNrw MTis NRHS SAko WFar
	'Kugelsonne'	CSam EHrv GBin ILea NBre SAko
§	'Kupfersprudel'	MAvo MTis SAko
	'Kupferzwerg'	CWCL EAJP ELan IPot NBre SAko
	'Lambada'	EBee SMHy
	'Louise Beacock'	MSpe
	'Loysder Wieck'	CKno EBee ECtt EPed MAvo MSpe MTis NGdn WCAu
	'Luc'	ELon MSpe MTis WCot WWtn
§	'Mahagoni'	LEdu SHar
	MAHOGANY	see *H.* 'Mahagoni'
	'Mahogany'	see *H.* 'Goldlackzwerg'
	'Mardi Gras'	CRos ECtt LRHS LSou MAvo MBel MSpe MTis NRHS SPoG SRms WCAu WMoo WWtn
	'Margot'	CAby MTis NBre
	'Marion Nickig'	MAvo WFar
	'Meranti'	CMea MAsh MAvo WCot
	'Moerheim Beauty' ♀^{H7}	Widely available
	'Moth'	MTis NEgg
	'Oldenburg'	WCot
	'Pat's Promise' **new**	CMea
	'Patsy'	MAvo
	PIPSQUEAK ('Blopip')	LLHF LRHS NBre SRms WHar
	'Potter's Wheel'	CBod EBee ECtt EPed LCro LOPS MSCN SHar SRms WWtn
	puberulum	CRos EBee EPfP LRHS NRHS
	'Pumilum Magnificum'	CRos EHrv ELan EPfP GQue IBoy LEdu LRHS MSpe NRHS SMad WFar XLum
	'Ragamuffin'	CSam ECtt GQue MTis WCot
	'Rauchtopas'	CAby CBWd EBee GQue GWyn ILea IPot LCro LEdu LOPS LPla MAvo MBel MSpe MTis SAko WPGP
	RED AND GOLD	see *H.* 'Rotgold' Foerster
	'Red Army'	CRos ECtt ELan ELon LEdu LRHS LSou MAvo MSpe NGdn NLar NRHS SRkn SWvt WWtn
	'Red Glory'	MTis
	'Red Jewel'	CMea CRos EBee ECtt ELan ELon IBoy IRob LLHF LRHS MAvo MBel MHol MMuc MNrw MPie NGdn NLar NRHS SAko SCob WCFE WCot WHoo WMoo WPGP
	'Ring of Fire' ♀^{H7}	SMHy
§	'Riverton Beauty'	CSam ECtt LCro LLHF MNrw MSpe NChi WCot WHoo WWtn
	'Riverton Gem'	CSam ECtt GQue LLHF MHCG
	'Rotgold' misapplied	see *H. autumnale* Helena Series
§	'Rotgold' Foerster	EBee ECtt SRms WMoo
	'Rouge Foncé'	WCot
	'Rubinzwerg' ♀^{H7}	Widely available
	'Ruby Charm'	EBee ECtt EPfP LSou MHol MSpe WCot WFar
§	'Ruby Thuesday'	Widely available
	'Ruby Tuesday'	see *H.* 'Ruby Thuesday'
	'Sahin's Early Flowerer' ♀^{H7}	Widely available
	'Samtjuwel'	MTis
	'Septemberfuchs'	LEdu MCot MTis SPhx
	'Sonnenwunder'	CSam NBre
	'Sophie zur Linden'	ECtt MTis WCot
	'Sunshine Superman'	MSpe
	'The Bishop'	CBod CRos EBee ECtt EPfP LCro LOPS LRHS MRav NRHS SCob SGbt SPer SWvt WFar WHar WMoo
	'Tie Dye'	CBod EBee ECtt EPfP MAvo MHol NGdn SPoG WFar WTor
	'Tijuana Brass'	ECtt NLar
	'Tip Top'	LRHS
	'Two-faced Fan' **new**	CSam MTis
	(UFO Series) 'UFO Betty' **new**	WHlf
	- 'UFO Carmen' **new**	WHlf
	- 'UFO Tom' **new**	ELon WHlf
	'Vicky'	MAvo MSpe SHar
	'Vivace'	ELon LEdu MSpe WCot
	'Wagon Wheel'	ECtt WCot
	'Waldhorn'	MTis
	'Waltraut' ♀^{H7}	Widely available
	'Wesergold' ♀^{H7}	CRos EBee ELon LLHF LPla LRHS MAvo NDov NLar NRHS NSti SPoG
	'Wonnadonga'	EBee GBin MTis
	'Wyndley'	CAby CBcs CDor CMea CRos ECtt EHoe EHrv ELan EPfP EShb GMaP LRHS MHer MRav MSpe MTis NGdn NLar NRHS SCob SPer SRms WCAu WFar WHar WHoo
	'Zimbelstern'	CCse ECtt EWTr MCot MPie MTis NLar SPhx WCot WFar WPGP
	'Zonnedam'	ECtt

Heliamphora (*Sarraceniaceae*)

	heterodoxa	NLos
	× ***nutans*** ♀^{H1b}	
	nutans	SHmp

Helianthella (*Asteraceae*)

§	***quinquenervis***	CBod CRos EBee GCal LLHF LRHS NLar NRHS

Helianthemum (*Cistaceae*)

	'Alice Howorth'	ECtt
	'Amabile Plenum' (d)	EWTr GAbr GBin GCal GCrg
	'Amy Baring' ♀^{H4}	CRos CTri ECtt GCrg LRHS NRHS NWad SRms WHoo
	'Annabel' (d)	CRos ECtt GBin LRHS NRHS
	apenninum	EPPr LLHF SRms WArt XSen
	'Apricot'	CTri ECtt
	'Apricot Blush'	WAbe
	'Baby Buttercup'	CMea
	'Beech Park Red'	CSma CTri ECtt EPot GCrg WAbe WFar WHoo WKif
	'Ben Afflick'	CRos ECtt LRHS NRHS SRms
	'Ben Alder'	ECtt GAbr
	'Ben Dearg'	CMea ECtt SRms
	'Ben Fhada'	CBcs CBod CMea CRos CTri ECtt ELan EPfP GAbr GCrg GJos GMaP LBee LRHS MAsh NEgg NHpl NRHS SEND SPoG SRms SRot WAbe WHoo XLum XSen
	'Ben Heckla'	CRos ECtt GAbr GCrg LRHS NRHS SRms XLum
	'Ben Hope'	CRos CTri ECtt ELan EPfP LRHS MJak NRHS SRGP SRms XLum
§	'Ben Ledi'	CBcs ECtt ELan ELon GAbr GCrg GMaP MAsh SEND SGbt SPoG SRms SRot WAbe
	'Ben More'	CBcs CRos ECtt ELan EPfP GAbr GJos GMaP LRHS MAsh MRav MSwo NHpl NRHS SEND SPoG SRGP SRms SRot WHoo

	'Ben Nevis'	CTri ECtt GAbr SRms
	'Ben Vane'	CRos ECtt LRHS NRHS SRms
	'Boughton Double Primrose' (d)	ECtt WAbe WHoo WSHC
	'Bronzeteppich'	CRav EAJP
	'Broughty Beacon'	ECtt
	'Broughty Sunset'	ECtt GAbr
	'Bunbury'	CRos ECtt ELon EPfP GCrg GJos LRHS NRHS SPoG SRms WFar
I	'Butter and Eggs'	SRms
	canum subsp. ***balcanicum***	WAbe
	'Captivation'	ECtt GAbr
	'Cerise Queen' (d)	ECha ECtt EPfP ESps GKev MHol MSwo SEND SPer SRms XSen
	chamaecistus	see *H. nummularium*
	'Cheviot'	ECtt GAbr WHoo WSHC XLum
	'Chocolate Blotch'	CRos ECtt LRHS NRHS NWad SEND SRms XSen
	'Cornish Cream'	ECtt LBee SRms
	croceum	LLHF
	cupreum	ECtt GAbr GKev
	'David Ritchie'	WHoo
	'Diana'	CMea ECtt
	'Everton Ruby'	see *H.* 'Ben Ledi'
	'Fairy'	ELan EPfP
§	'Fire Dragon' $\mathbb{Y}^{H4}$	CMea CRos ECtt ELan EPfP GAbr GCrg GMaP LRHS NRHS SGbt SRms WAbe XLum XSen
	'Fireball'	see *H.* 'Mrs C.W. Earle'
	'Georgeham'	CMea CSam CSma EAJP ECtt ELon GAbr GCrg SPhx SRms WHoo WRHF XLum
§	'Golden Queen'	ECtt EPfP GAbr MAsh MHol MSwo SRms
	'Hampstead Orange'	CTri
	'Hartswood Ruby'	CRos GMaP LLHF LRHS MBNS NRHS SAko SRms
	'Henfield Brilliant' $\mathbb{Y}^{H4}$	CExl CRos CSam CSpe ECtt ELan ELon EPfP GAbr GCrg LRHS MHol MRav NRHS NSla SMad SPoG SRms WCot WHil WHoo XLum
	'Highdown'	SRms
	'Highdown Apricot'	CRos ECtt ELon GCrg LLHF LRHS NHpl NRHS SPoG SRms
	'Honeymoon'	ECtt EPfP GAbr GCrg NWad
	'Jubilee' (d) $\mathbb{Y}^{H4}$	CTri ECtt ELan ELon EShb GJos MAsh MBNS NChi SPoG SRms WKif
	'Karen's Silver'	WAbe
	'Kathleen Druce' (d)	ECtt NWad WHoo
	'Kathleen Mary'	CMea
	'Lawrenson's Pink'	CRos CSma ECtt GAbr GCrg GJos IBoy LRHS MHol NRHS SAko SRGP SRms
	'Lemon Queen'	ECtt GCrg IBoy WHar
	'Lucy Elizabeth'	ECtt
	lunulatum	CMea CRos LLHF LRHS NRHS NWad SRms WAbe
	'Mead Sunset'	CMea ECtt
§	'Mrs C.W. Earle' (d) $\mathbb{Y}^{H4}$	CRos CTri ECtt ELan EPfP LRHS MBNS NRHS NSla SRms
	'Mrs Clay'	see *H.* 'Fire Dragon'
	'Mrs Croft'	SRms
	'Mrs Hays'	ECtt
	'Mrs Lake'	GAbr
	'Mrs Moules'	SRms
	mutabile	SPlb SVic
	'New Moon'	CSma
§	***nummularium***	EBWF ENfk GPoy MHer MNHC NMir SRms SVic WAbe WSFF
	- subsp. ***grandiflorum***	LLHF
	oelandicum	NSla NWad SRms WAbe
	- subsp. ***italicum*** new	ITim
	- subsp. ***piloselloides***	WAbe
	'Old Gold'	ECtt SRms WAbe
	'Orange Phoenix' (d)	ECtt GCrg MBNS NWad
	'Ovum Supreme'	ECtt
	'Peachy Keen' (d) new	ETMg
	'Pink Angel' (d)	CSma ECtt GCrg MBNS SRms WAbe WFar
	'Pink Glow'	GAbr
	'Praecox'	CMea CTri ECtt SRms WHoo
	'Prima Donna'	ELan EPfP
	'Prostrate Orange'	SRms
	'Raspberry Ripple'	CRos CSma ECtt ELan ELon EPfP EPot GCrg LRHS NRHS SPoG SRms XSen
	'Razzle Dazzle' (v)	CBod ECtt NHpl SRms
	'Red Dragon'	EPot GCrg NHpl WAbe
	'Red Orient'	see *H.* 'Supreme'
	'Regenbogen' (d)	ECtt GAbr GCal SEND
§	'Rhodanthe Carneum' $\mathbb{Y}^{H4}$	CMea CRos ECha ECtt ELan EPfP EWTr GCrg GKev GMaP LRHS MAsh MRav MSwo NHpl NRHS SEND SPer SPhx SPoG SRms SRot WAbe WKif WSHC
§	'Rosakönigin'	ECtt GAbr SEND WAbe
	'Rose of Leeswood' (d)	CBod ECtt NEgg SPoG SRms WHoo WKif WSHC XLum
	ROSE QUEEN	see *H.* 'Rosakönigin'
	'Roxburgh Gold'	SRms
	'Ruth'	SEND
	'Saint John's College Yellow'	CRos CSam LRHS NRHS SRms
	salicifolium new	CRos
	'Salmon Queen'	CRos ECtt GAbr LRHS NRHS SEND SRms
*	***scardicum***	CMea
	'Shot Silk'	CSma ECtt EWes SRms
	'Snow Carpet' new	CMea
	'Snow Queen'	see *H.* 'The Bride'
	'Sterntaler'	GAbr LLHF SAko SRms WFar
	'Strawberry Fields'	ECtt NSla
	'Sudbury Gem'	CRos CTri ECha ECtt GAbr LRHS NRHS SRms
	'Sulphur Moon'	CRos LRHS NRHS SRms
	'Sulphureum Plenum' (d)	ECtt
	'Sunbeam'	ECtt SRms
§	'Supreme'	ECtt ELan EPfP EWes LPla MHol SAko SRms XSen
	'Tangerine'	ECtt
§	'The Bride' $\mathbb{Y}^{H4}$	CBar CBcs CBod CMea CRos ECha ECtt ELan EPfP ESps GJos GMaP LRHS LSRN MAsh MHol NLar NRHS SEND SPer SPoG SRms SRot WAbe WFar WHoo WKif WTor XLum
	'Tigrinum Plenum' (d)	EWes
	'Tomato Red'	ECtt NSla
	umbellatum	see *Halimium umbellatum*
	'Voltaire'	ECtt LLHF NWad
	'Welsh Flame'	ECtt WAbe
	'Whenday'	CMea
	'Wisley Pink'	see *H.* 'Rhodanthe Carneum'
	'Wisley Primrose' $\mathbb{Y}^{H4}$	Widely available
	'Wisley Rose'	CRos LRHS NRHS
	'Wisley White'	CTri ECha ECtt ELan EPfP SHar
	'Wisley Yellow'	ECtt
	'Yellow Queen'	see *H.* 'Golden Queen'

Helianthus (*Asteraceae*)

	'Anne'	ELon NDov
	annuus 'Claret' $\mathbb{Y}^{H7}$ new	CRav

atrorubens	MRav MSpe NBro
'Bitter Chocolate'	LEdu MAvo MSpe WBor WCot WPGP
'Capenoch Star' ♀H7	CElw CRos ECtt GMaP IBoy IRob LEdu LRHS MArl MRav MSpe MTis NBro NLar NRHS SWvt
'Capenoch Supreme'	CRos ECtt LRHS NRHS
'Carine'	ELon MNrw MTis NLar SMHy WCot WFar WOld
debilis 'Vanilla Ice' **new**	LCro LOPS
decapetalus MORNING SUN	see *H.* 'Morgensonne'
'Dorian Roxburgh'	ECtt MAvo MTis WCot
'Double Whammy' (d)	ECtt
giganteus	SHar
- 'Sheila's Sunshine'	CElw CRos EWes GBin ILea LRHS MNrw NDov NRHS SAko SHar SMHy SPhx WFar WOld
grosseserratus	MPie
'Gullick's Variety' ♀H7	CBre ECtt NBro NChi NLar SPhx SWvt WFar WOld WWFP XLum
'Happy Days'	CAby CRos CSam EBee ECtt EWes GBin IRob LSou MBel MHol MSpe MTis NGBl NSti SPoG WCot WFar WHoo WMoo WOld WRHF
'Hazel's Gold'	CRos LRHS NRHS
'Inca Gold' **new**	ETMg
× ***kellermanii***	EBee MAvo MTis SPhx
§ × ***laetiflorus***	GPSL MMuc NLar
- 'Daniel Dewar'	MMuc
- var. ***rigidus***	see *H. pauciflorus*
§ 'Lemon Queen' ♀H7	Widely available
'Limelight'	see *H.* 'Lemon Queen'
'Loddon Gold' ♀H7	CRos ECtt ELan EPfP EShb LRHS MArl MBel MRav MSpe MTis NRHS SMad SWvt WBor WCot
§ ***maximiliani***	CBod ELan ELon MMuc SPhx SPtp
microcephalus	CSam EBee ELon IMou MMuc NDov
'Miss Mellish' ♀H7	EBee ECtt GCal LEdu MSpe WBor WBrk WCot WFar WHoo
mollis	CSam MMuc SBrt SPav SPhx WFar
'Monarch' ♀H4	CMea CSam EBee ECtt LEdu MBel MMuc MRav NLar SMad WCot WFar WHal WOld
§ 'Morgensonne'	MTis WBor WCot
× ***multiflorus*** 'Meteor'	CRos LRHS NBre NRHS
'O Sole Mio'	WCot WFar
occidentalis	SMad SPhx
orgyalis	see *H. salicifolius*
§ ***pauciflorus***	EBee
quinquenervis	see *Helianthella quinquenervis*
'Razzmatazz'	SAko
rigidus misapplied	see *H.* × *laetiflorus*
rigidus (Cass.) Desf.	see *H. pauciflorus*
§ ***salicifolius***	CAby CBWd EBee ECtt ELan ELon EPPr GBin LEdu LRHS LSun MBel MCot MHol MMuc MPie MSpe NRHS NSti SAko SEND SMad SPad SWvt WAul WCot WHil WMoo WPGP XLum
- 'Low Down'PBR	SWvt
- 'Table Mountain'PBR	LRHS SWvt
- very fine-leaved	WCot
scaberrimus	see *H.* × *laetiflorus*
'Soleil d'Or'	ECtt SRms WFar WHal
strumosus	WCot
'Triomphe de Gand'	LEdu MTis MWat NDov WFar
tuberosus	EBee GPoy SVic
- 'Bleu Patate'	LEdu
- 'Drago'	LEdu
- 'Dwarf'	LEdu
- 'Fuseau'	LCro LOPS SVic
- 'Garnet'	LEdu
- 'Sakahlinski'	LEdu
- 'Sugarball'	LEdu

Helichrysum (*Asteraceae*)

adenocarpum	SPlb
alveolatum	see *H. splendidum*
amorginum 'Pink Bud'	MMuc
- 'Pink Sapphire'PBR	EBee
- RUBY CLUSTER ('Blorub'PBR)	CRos LPla LRHS NRHS SMad WCot
angustifolium from Crete	see *H. microphyllum* (Willd.) Cambess.
§ ***arwae***	WAbe
bellidioides	see *Anaphalioides bellidioides*
bracteatum	see *Xerochrysum bracteatum*
'Coco'	see *Xerochrysum bracteatum* 'Coco'
coralloides	see *Ozothamnus coralloides*
'County Park Silver'	see *Ozothamnus* 'County Park Silver'
'Dargan Hill Monarch'	see *Xerochrysum bracteatum* 'Dargan Hill Monarch'
'Elmstead'	see *H. stoechas* 'White Barn'
frigidum	WAbe
hookeri	see *Ozothamnus hookeri*
'Icicles'	GBin
italicum	CBod ECha ECrN ENfk EPfP GBin GMaP GPoy GWyn MHer MMuc MNHC SArc SEND SPoG SRms SVen SVic WHer XLum XSen
- 'Dartington'	CBod ENfk GBin SRms
- 'Korma'PBR	CBod CRos EHoe ELan EPfP ESps GBin LRHS MAsh NRHS SLon SPoG SRms
- subsp. ***microphyllum***	see *H. microphyllum* (Willd.) Cambess.
- 'Nanum'	see *H. microphyllum* (Willd.) Cambess.
§ - subsp. ***serotinum***	CBcs CRos ECrN EHoe EPfP GPoy LRHS MRav SLim SPer SRms SWvt WRHF
lanatum	see *H. thianschanicum*
ledifolium	see *Ozothamnus ledifolius*
marginatum misapplied	see *H. milfordiae*
microphyllum ambig.	MMuc SPer SRms
§ ***microphyllum*** (Willd.) Cambess.	ENfk MNHC SEND
§ ***milfordiae*** ♀H4	EPot ITim NRHS SPlb SRms WAbe
orientale	EPot XSen
pagophilum	CPBP WAbe
petiolare ♀H3	EBak ECtt MCot SPer SPoG
- 'Aureum'	see *H. petiolare* 'Limelight'
- 'Goring Silver' ♀H3	SPoG
§ - 'Limelight' ♀H3	ECtt MCot NPri SPer SPoG
- 'Variegatum' (v) ♀H3	ECtt MCot SPoG
rosmarinifolium	see *Ozothamnus rosmarinifolius*
§ 'Schwefellicht'	EBee ECha EPfP MRav SPer WSHC
selago	see *Ozothamnus selago*
serotinum	see *H. italicum* subsp. *serotinum*
sessilioides	EPot WAbe
§ ***splendidum*** ♀H5	LRHS NBro SLon XSen
stoechas	XSen
§ - 'White Barn'	CSpe MAvo WCot XLum
SULPHUR LIGHT	see *H.* 'Schwefellicht'
§ ***thianschanicum***	SRms XLum
- GOLDEN BABY	see *H. thianschanicum* 'Goldkind'
§ - 'Goldkind'	XLum

- 'White Wonder'	CRos LRHS NRHS SArc
trilineatum misapplied	see *H. splendidum*
tumidum	see *Ozothamnus selago* var. *tumidus*
woodii	see *H. arwae*

Helicodiceros (*Araceae*)

§ ***muscivorus***	CHid WCot

Heliconia ✿ (*Heliconiaceae*)

caribaea 'Burgundy'	see *H. caribaea* 'Purpurea'
§ - 'Purpurea'	XBlo
'Golden Torch'	XBlo
indica 'Spectabilis'	XBlo
latispatha 'Orange Gyro'	XBlo
* - 'Red Gyro'	XBlo
metallica	XBlo
psittacorum	CCCN
rostrata	CCCN XBlo
schiedeana	CHll

Helictotrichon (*Poaceae*)

pratense	CHab EHoe
§ ***sempervirens*** 🏆^{H7}	Widely available
I - 'Pendulum'	CBod EUJe GBin MSpe XSen
- 'Saphirsprudel'	CCse CRos EBee EPfP LRHS MJak NRHS NSti WCot WPGP XSen

Heliophila (*Brassicaceae*)

coronopifolia	CSpe

Heliopsis (*Asteraceae*)

GOLDEN PLUME	see *H. helianthoides* var. *scabra* 'Goldgefieder'
helianthoides	CRos EBee LRHS NBre WFar WWtn
- 'Limelight'	see *Helianthus* 'Lemon Queen'
- LORAINE SUNSHINE ('Helhan'PBR) (v)	CWGN ECtt GMcL LLWG LSou MHol MMrt MSCN NCou NWsh SMad WCot WFar WRHF
- var. ***scabra***	SPer SRot WHar
- - 'Asahi'	CBod ECtt GMaP MSCN MSpe
- - BALLERINA	see *H. helianthoides* var. *scabra* 'Spitzentänzerin'
- - 'Benzinggold' 🏆^{H5}	CRos LRHS LSou MRav NRHS
- - 'Bressingham Doubloon' (d)	ECtt
- - GOLDEN PLUME	see *H. helianthoides* var. *scabra* 'Goldgefieder'
§ - - 'Goldgefieder' 🏆^{H5}	EBee MSpe NBre WFar
- - 'Hohlspiegel'	GBin
- - 'Light of Loddon' 🏆^{H5}	CRos LRHS NRHS
- - 'Mars'	EBee WFar
- - 'Patula'	EBee ECtt
- - 'Prairie Sunset'PBR	EBee ECtt MSCN SAko
§ - - 'Sommersonne'	CRos CSBt ECtt ELan EPfP GMcL LRHS NGBl NPer NRHS SCob SRms
§ - - 'Spitzentänzerin' 🏆^{H5}	ECtt MSpe
- - 'Summer Nights'	EBee ELan EPfP IBoy LCro LOPS MBel MNrw MSpe NSti SPhx WHil
- - SUMMER SUN	see *H. helianthoides* var. *scabra* 'Sommersonne'
- - 'Sunburst' (v)	SPav
- - 'Venus'	CBod CRos ECtt LRHS MBel MSCN NRHS SRms
- - 'Waterperry Gold'	MWat
- 'Summer Pink' (v)	CWGN MHol SMad SPoG WCot WFar WRHF
- 'Sunstruck'	ECtt
- 'Tuscan Sun'PBR	CRos EBee ECtt LRHS NCou NRHS SCob

Heliotropium ✿ (*Boraginaceae*)

§ ***amplexicaule***	SDys
anchusifolium	see *H. amplexicaule*
§ ***arborescens***	ENfk EPfP EShb MCot MHom
- 'Chatsworth' 🏆^{H1c}	CAby CCCN CSpe ECre ECtt MHom
- 'Dame Alice de Hales'	ECtt MHom
- dark-flowered **new**	CSam
- 'Gatton Park'	ECtt MHom
- 'Lord Roberts'	ECtt MHom
- 'Mary Fox'	ECtt MHom
* - 'Midnight'	CRav
- 'Mrs J.W. Lowther'	ECtt MHom
- 'Netherhall Lilac'	EBee
- pale lilac-flowered	CSam
- 'President Garfield'	ECtt MHom
- 'Princess Marina' 🏆^{H1c}	EPfP LCro LOPS NLar
- 'Reva'	ECtt MHom
- 'The Speaker'	ECtt MHom
- 'White Lady'	CCCN CSpe ECtt MHom
- 'White Queen'	ECtt MHom
- 'Woodcote'	ECtt MHom
'Butterfly Kisses'	SPoG
peruvianum	see *H. arborescens*

Helipterum see *Syncarpha*

anthemoides	see *Rhodanthe anthemoides*

Helleborus ✿ (*Ranunculaceae*)

abruzzicus	CBot MAsh
- WM 0227	MPhe
abschasicus	see *H. orientalis* Lam. subsp. *abchasicus*
'Angel Glow'	LRHS SCob SPoG WHil
§ ***argutifolius*** 🏆^{H5}	Widely available
- 'Red Riding Hood'	LRHS
- 'Silver Lace'	CMil CRos ELan ELon EPfP GKev IBoy LRHS LSRN MHol NLar NPnk NRHS NWad SPer SPoG SPtp WMoo
- variegated (v)	GKev
atrorubens misapplied	see *H. orientalis* Lam. subsp. *abchasicus* Early Purple Group
atrorubens ambig.	CBot EHrv EWTr MAsh SCob
atrorubens Waldst. & Kit.	MRav XEll
- WM 9028 from Slovenia	MPhe
- WM 9805 from Croatia	MPhe
- spotted form	MPhe
× ***ballardiae***	EPfP GKev
- 'Candy Love'PBR	CRos EPfP LRHS MAvo MHol NLar NRHS SCob
- HGC CAMELOT ('Coseh 940'PBR)	CRos ECtt EPfP LRHS NLar NRHS
- HGC CHAMPION ('Coseh 730'PBR)	CRos LRHS NRHS
- HGC JOKER ('Coseh 740'PBR)	CRos LRHS NRHS SPoG
- HGC MAESTRO ('Coseh 890'PBR)	CRos LRHS NRHS
- HGC MERLIN ('Coseh 810'PBR)	CRos EBee LRHS NLar NRHS SPoG
- HGC SNOW DANCE ('Coseh 800'PBR)	CRos EBee LRHS NRHS SPoG
'Blue Moon'	IBoy
§ ***bocconei***	CBot MAsh
- WM 1332 from Sicily	MPhe
- WM 1334 from Calabria, Italy	MPhe
- WM 9719 from Italy	MPhe

- WM 9905 from Sicily	MPhe
- subsp. ***bocconei***	see *H. bocconei*
colchicus	see *H. orientalis* Lam. subsp. *abchasicus*
corsicus	see *H. argutifolius*
croaticus	MAsh
- WM 9810	MPhe
dumetorum	CBot GCal GKev MAsh
- WM 1306 from Hungary	MPhe
- WM 1309 from Slovenia	MPhe
- WM 9209	MPhe
- WM 9627 from Croatia	MPhe
§ × ***ericsmithii***	CExl ECha ELon EPfP LLHF LRHS LSRN LSou MAsh NLar SCob WHoo WPGP WSpi
- 'Bob's Best'	CExl ECtt EPfP MBNS MHol SEND SRms SWvt
- HGC MARLON CREAM ('Coseh 980'PBR)	LRHS NRHS
- HGC MONTE CRISTO ('Coseh 860'PBR)	CRos LRHS NRHS
- HGC SHOOTING STAR ('Coseh 790'PBR)	CRos EBee ECre LRHS NRHS
- 'HGC Silvermoon'PBR	IBoy LRHS NLar
- 'Molly's White' **new**	CRos NRHS
- 'Pirouette'PBR	ECre EPfP LCro LOPS LRHS MAsh NRHS SCob
- 'Ruby Glow'	ECre EPfP LRHS NPnk NRHS SCob SPoG WHil
- 'Snow Love'PBR	CRos EPfP LBuc LRHS NLar NRHS SCob
- 'Winter Moonbeam'PBR	CEnd CRos ECtt EHrv EPfP LBuc LRHS LSRN LSun MAsh MCot MHol MJak NRHS SCob SLon SPoG SRms WCot WHil
- 'Winter Sunshine'PBR	CRos EHrv EPfP ESps LBuc LRHS NPnk NRHS SCob SPoG SRms WHil
foetidus ♀H7	Widely available
- from Italy	IFoB
- 'Chedglow'	CNat
- 'Chedglow Variegated' (v)	CNat
- 'Gold Bullion'	MAsh
- 'Green Giant'	SEND
- 'Harvington Pewter'	LRHS NRHS
- 'Miss Jekyll'	EBee SVic
- 'Ruth'	MAsh SCob
- 'Sienna'	SCob
- 'Vogezen'	SCob
- Wester Flisk Group	CAby CBod CExl CMea ECtt EPfP EUJe GBin GWyn IFoB MAsh NPer NPnk SCob SEND SPer WHar WPGP WSpi WWtn
- Wilgenbroek selection	SCob
- 'Yellow Wilgenbroek'	MAsh SCob
Gold Collection	see *Helleborus* with names starting HGC
'Harvington Black'	LRHS NRHS
'Harvington Blush Picotee'	LRHS NRHS SRms
'Harvington Chocolate'	LRHS NRHS
'Harvington Petticoat'	LRHS NRHS
'Harvington Rebekah'PBR	CRos LRHS NRHS
HGC CINNAMON SNOW ('Coseh 700'PBR)	ECre LRHS NLar NRHS
HGC MADAME LEMONNIER ('Lem 100') **new**	CRos NRHS
HGC PINK FROST ('Coseh 710'PBR)	CRos ECtt LRHS NLar NRHS SPoG
Hillier hybrids anemone-centred, spotted pink	CRos LRHS NRHS

- - yellow	CBod CRos LRHS NRHS
× ***hybridus***	Widely available
- anemone-centred	CBot CHid IFoB LEdu MNrw WFar
- 'Apple Blossom'	IFoB WFar
- 'Apricot Blush' (Winter Jewels Series)	CWGN NPnk
- apricot-flowered	CTal IFoB WFar
- 'Ashwood Blushing Bride'	MAsh
- 'Ashwood Elegance Pearl'	MAsh
- 'Ashwood Fascination'	MAsh
- Ashwood Garden hybrids	ELan EPfP MAsh MRav SRms
- - anemone-centred	MAsh
- - double-flowered (d)	MAsh
- 'Ashwood Glade'	MAsh
- 'Ashwood Lunar Neon'	MAsh
- 'Ashwood Meadow'	MAsh
- 'Ashwood Moonlight' (d)	MAsh
- 'Ashwood Neon Star'	MAsh
- Ballard's Group	CRos IBoy LRHS NRHS WFar WPnP
- Barnhaven hybrids, anemone-centred	XBar
- - apricot	XBar
- - dark purple	XBar
- - picotee	XBar
- - pink	XBar
- - red and green	XBar
- - slate	XBar
- - spotted	XBar
- - white	XBar
- - yellow	XBar
- 'Black Beauty'	IFoB WSpi
- black-flowered	GMaP IFoB WFar
- 'Black Knight'	IFoB
- 'Black Swan' **new**	ETMg
- 'Blue Lady' (Lady Series)	CBcs GAbr IFoB LRHS MBNS NCou NGdn SPer
- 'Blue Metallic Lady' (Lady Series)	CBod CExl CTsd EPed EPfP IBoy IFoB LCro LRHS MBNS MHol NEgg NGdn NPnk NRHS SPer WSpi
- Bradfield hybrids	EHrv MCot
- - anemone-centred	EHrv MCot
- - double-flowered (d)	EHrv MCot
- - picotee	EHrv MCot
- Bradfield Star Group	EHrv
- 'Burgundy'	CBod CBot EWTr
- 'Cherry Blossom' (Winter Jewels Series)	CWGN NPnk
- 'Cherry Frost'	MAsh
- 'Cinderella'PBR (d)	LRHS
- 'Clare's Purple'	CBod
- 'Cosmos'	CTal MBNS
- cream-flowered	IFro WFar
- Credale strain, double-flowered (d)	WCFE
- dark picotee	WFar
- dark purple-flowered	IFoB WFar
- dark red-flowered	IFoB WFar
- dark-flowered	WFar
- deep red-flowered	MHol WFar
- double (d)	IFoB MNrw WFar WHar
- - black-flowered (d)	CBot CExl IFoB LEdu WFar
- - pink-flowered (d)	CBot IFoB WFar
- - white picotee (d)	CBod CBot LRHS NRHS WHlf
- - yellow, cream-speckled (d)	CRos LRHS NRHS
- - dark purple-flowered (d)	SMad WFar
- - green-flowered (d)	IFoB WFar
- - picotee (d)	CBod CBot GEdr WFar
- - purple-flowered (d)	GEdr WFar
- - red-flowered (d)	CExl WFar

- - white-flowered (d)	CExl GEdr IBoy IFoB WFar
- - yellow-flowered (d)	CBot CExl CWCL IBoy IFoB IFro WFar
- 'Double Bicolor' (d) **new**	CBot
- 'Double Black' (d) **new**	CBot
- 'Double Ellen Green' (d) **new**	LOPS
- 'Double Ellen Picotee' (d)	CWGN LOPS NPnk
- 'Double Ellen Pink' (d)	CRos LCro LOPS LRHS NPnk NRHS
- 'Double Ellen Purple' (d)	CRos LCro LOPS LRHS NRHS
- 'Double Ellen Red' (d)	CRos LCro LOPS LRHS NPnk NRHS
- 'Double Ellen White' (d)	CRos CWGN EPfP LCro LOPS LRHS NPnk NRHS
- 'Double Ellen Yellow' (d) **new**	EWTr
- Double Ladies, mixed (d)	GAbr WCot
- Elizabeth Town anemone-centred	IFro
- - double-flowered (d)	IFro
- 'Enchantment'	MAsh
- Farmyard anemone-centred	WFar
- - apricot	WFar
- - black	WFar
- - cream	WFar
- - - spotted	WFar
- - dark pink	WFar
- - double apricot (d)	WFar
- - - black (d)	WFar
- - - cream (d)	WFar
- - - - spotted (d)	WFar
- - - pink (d)	WFar
- - - - spotted (d)	WFar
- - - primrose (d)	WFar
- - - - spotted (d)	WFar
- - - red (d)	WFar
- - - slate-grey (d)	WFar
- - - white (d)	WFar
- - - - spotted (d)	WFar
- - green	WFar
- - - spotted	WFar
- - picotee	WFar
- - pink	WFar
- - - spotted	WFar
- - plum	WFar
- - primrose	WFar
- - - dark-eyed	WFar
- - - spotted	WFar
- - red	WFar
- - slate spotted	WFar
- - slate-grey	WFar
- - white	WFar
- - - dark-eyed	WFar
- - - splash	WFar
- - - spotted	WFar
- 'Farmyard Appleblossom'	WFar
- 'Farmyard Woodland'	WFar
- Field of Blooms hybrids	IFoB
- - anemone-centred	IFoB
- - double-flowered (d)	IFoB
- - picotee	IFoB
- 'Gold Red Star' **new**	CBot
- 'Golden Lotus' (d)	CWGN NPnk
- 'Green Ripple'	WFar
- green-flowered	IFoB WFar
- Harvington apricot	LCro LRHS NLar NRHS SLon
- - double apricot (d)	CRos LRHS NRHS SHeu
- - - chocolate (d)	CRos LCro LRHS NRHS SHeu
- - - dark purple (d)	CRos LRHS NRHS
- - - pink (d)	CRos LCro LOPS LRHS NRHS SHeu SLon SPoG
- - - - speckled (d)	CRos GAbr LCro LRHS NRHS SHeu SPoG
- - - purple (d)	CRos GAbr LRHS NLar NRHS SHeu SPoG
- - - - cascade (d)	CRos LRHS NRHS SHeu
- - - red (d)	CRos LCro LOPS LRHS NLar NRHS SLon SPoG
- - - speckled (d)	LCro LOPS LRHS NRHS
- - - white (d)	CRos LCro LRHS NLar NRHS SHeu SLon SPoG
- - - yellow (d)	CRos LRHS NLar NRHS SHeu SLon SPoG
- - - - speckled (d)	SHeu SPoG
- - - lime-green (d)	LCro LOPS SHeu
- - dusky	CRos LRHS NRHS
- - lime	CRos LCro LOPS LRHS NRHS
- - picotee	CRos LCro LRHS NLar NRHS SHeu SLon SPoG
- - pink	CRos LRHS NLar NRHS SHeu SLon SPoG
- - - speckled	LCro NLar SHeu SLon SPoG
- - red	CRos LCro LOPS LRHS NLar NRHS SLon SPoG
- - speckled	CRos LRHS NRHS SHeu SLon
- - white	CRos LCro LOPS LRHS NLar NRHS SLon SPoG
- - - speckled	LCro LOPS SHeu SLon SPoG
- - yellow	CRos LRHS NLar NRHS SHeu SLon SPoG
- - - speckled	CRos LCro LRHS NLar NRHS SHeu SLon SPoG
- 'Harvington Shades of the Night'	CRos LCro LRHS NLar NRHS SHeu SLon SPoG
- 'Harvington Smokey Blues'	LCro SHeu SLon
- 'Harvington Smokey Double' (d)	SHeu
- 'Helen Ballard'	SVic
- Hillier hybrids burgundy	CRos LEdu LRHS NRHS SMad
- - clear white	CRos LRHS NRHS
- - pink and white	CRos NRHS
- - purple	CRos NRHS
- - slate	CRos LRHS NRHS
- - spotted, double yellow (d)	CRos EPfP LRHS NRHS
- - - - pink (d)	CRos EPfP LRHS NRHS
- - - green	CRos NRHS
- - - pink	CRos LRHS NRHS
- - - white	CRos LRHS NRHS
- - - yellow	CRos LRHS NRHS
- 'John Hopkins'	CRos LRHS NRHS
- 'Kingston Cardinal'	LRHS MAsh
- 'Lady in Red'	IBoy
- Lady Series	EPau IFoB NSum
- large, pink-flowered	IFoB IFro
- maroon-flowered	WFar
- mauve freckled, double (d)	IFro WFar
- 'Mrs Betty Ranicar' (d)	CBro EPfP IFoB ILea SCob SRms
- nearly black-flowered	WFar
- 'Onyx Odyssey'	CWGN NPnk
- 'Orion'	CTal
- pale-pink-flowered	WFar
- 'Pamina'	IFoB
§ - Party Dress Group (d)	CBod CHid ELon GBin IFoB LSRN NLar SCob WFar
- - 'Party Dress Pink' (d)	CBod
- - 'Party Dress Primrose' (d)	CBod
- 'Pebworth White'	CTal
- 'Philip Ballard'	CTal
- Picotee Group	NLar WFar WHoo
- 'Picotee'	IFoB WFar
- pink freckled, double (d)	IFro WFar

- 'Pink Lady' (Lady Series)	CBcs CBod CSBt EPau EPfP GMcL GQue IFoB LCro LOPS LRHS NCou NEgg NGdn NRHS SPer WHar
- 'Pink Lady Spotted' (Lady Series) **new**	CRav
- 'Pink Upstart'	IFoB
- pink-flowered	MBNS SDeJ WHoo
- pink-red-flowered	WFar
- plum-flowered	CRos MMuc SEND
- 'Pluto'	CTal WFar
- 'Pretty Ellen Pink'	CRos GBin LCro LOPS LRHS NRHS
- 'Pretty Ellen Purple'	CRos LRHS NRHS
- 'Pretty Ellen Red'	CRav LCro LOPS
- 'Pretty Ellen White'	LCro LOPS
- 'Primrose Picotee'	WFar
- primrose-flowered	ELan MCot
- 'Purity'	MAsh
- purple-flowered	WFar
- Queen Series, dark red-flowered	GBin
- - double white-flowered (d)	GBin
- - - yellow-flowered (d)	GBin
- - picotee	GBin
- - pink-flowered	GBin
- - 'Queen of the Night'	CExl EPfP WSpi
- - white-flowered	GBin
- - yellow-flowered	GBin
- red and purple	CBod
- 'Red Lady' (Lady Series)	CBcs CBod CExl CMea CRos CSBt EPed EPfP GAbr IFoB LCro LOPS LRHS LSRN MBNS NEgg NRHS SPer
- 'Red Picotee' **new**	CBot
- 'Red Star' **new**	CBod
- 'Red Upstart'	IFoB
- red-flowered	CBod LEdu WFar WHoo
- 'Sirius'	CTal
- slaty blue-flowered	CBod IFoB LEdu SEND
- 'Smokey Blue'	CRos ELan IFoB LRHS NRHS
- smokey purple-flowered	LSRN MAsh SGbt
- SP Anja Oudolf (Spring Promise Series) **new**	CRos LRHS NRHS
- SP Charlotte ('Hlr 140'PBR) (Spring Promise Series)	CRos LRHS NRHS
- SP Elly ('Hlr 190'PBR) (Spring Promise Series) (d)	CRos LRHS NRHS
- 'Speckled Draco'	CExl
§ - spotted	EPfP IFoB NEgg WCot WFar WHoo
- - cream	CBod IFoB WFar
- - double, pink (d)	GEdr WFar
- - - white (d)	IFoB WFar
- - - yellow (d)	IFoB SMad WFar
- - green	WFar
- - ivory	WFar
- - light purple	WFar
- - pink	CBod IFro LRHS MBNS NRHS SEND WFar WHoo
- - primrose	ELan SGbt WFar
- - white	CBot IFro MMuc SEND WBor WFar
- - yellow	CBot WFar
- 'Stained Glass'	MAsh
- 'Titania'	CTal
- 'Tricastin'	IBoy
- 'Tutu'PBR	CRos EHrv EPfP LBuc LRHS NRHS SCob SPer SPoG SRms WHil
- 'Ushba'	IFoB
- Washfield double-flowered (d)	CMea EPau EPfP LEdu MBel SPer SRkn WBor WHil WRHF
- - - white (d)	IFoB
- 'White Lady' (Lady Series)	CBcs CBod CExl CMea GAbr IFoB MBNS NCou NEgg SPer
- 'White Lady Spotted' (Lady Series)	CBod ELon EPed EPfP LCro LOPS LRHS MHol NEgg NRHS SPer
- white-flowered	GMaP IFoB WCFE WFar WHoo
- white-veined	WFar
- Wilgenbroek hybrids anemone-centred, red	SCob
- - - white freckled	SCob
- - apricot	SCob
- - aubergine with white edge	SCob
- - black	SCob
- - dark	SCob
- - double red (d)	SCob
- - - picotee (d)	SCob
- - - slaty blue (d)	SCob
- - - white (d)	SCob
- - - - spotted (d)	SCob
- - green	SCob
- - picotee	SCob
- - red	SCob
- - slaty blue	SCob
- - spotted, apricot	SCob
- - - aubergine	SCob
- - - pink	SCob
- - - red	SCob
- - - yellow	SCob
- - white	SCob
- - - with pink edge	SCob
- yellow freckled, double (d)	IFro
- yellow-flowered	GMaP IFoB MCot SEND WFar WHoo
- 'Yellow Lady' (Lady Series)	CBcs CBod CBro CRos CTsd EPed GAbr GMcL LRHS MBNS MBel NEgg NRHS SPer
- Zodiac Group	CBod MBNS
'Ice Dance'	LRHS
§ 'Ivory Prince'PBR	CRos EPfP LBuc LRHS MAsh NRHS SPoG
liguricus	CBot MAsh
- WM 0230	MPhe
lividus	CBar CRos CSpe EPfP EWes GKev IFoB LRHS MBel NRHS SDeJ SRms WAbe
- subsp. ***corsicus***	see *H. argutifolius*
- 'Green Marble'	ELan NPnk
- 'Pink Marble'	EBee ELan
- 'Purple Ear'	EBee LRHS
- 'Purple Marble'	NPnk
- 'Purple Rose'	SRms
- 'Silver Edge'	EPfP
- 'White Marble'	EBee GKev LRHS MAsh
- white-flowered	GKev
lividus × niger	GKev
'Lucy Black'	LRHS NRHS
'Marshmallow'	NPnk WCot
'Moonshine'PBR	CMil EBee MHol NLar NWad SLon WMoo
multifidus	CBot IFoB
- WM 1316	MPhe
- subsp. ***hercegovinus***	CTal SCob XEll
- - WM 0020	CBot MPhe
- - WM 0622	MPhe
- subsp. ***istriacus***	CBot CBro MAsh WCot
- - WM 9322	MPhe
- - WM 9324	MPhe
- subsp. ***multifidus***	MAsh
- - WM 9529	MPhe
- - from Croatia WM 9833	MPhe

niger	Widely available
- Ashwood marble leaf	MAsh
- Ashwood strain	MAsh
- Blackthorn Group	NLar
- 'Christmas Carol'	CRos GMcL LRHS NRHS
- 'Double Fashion'PBR (d)	EPfP SCob
- double-flowered (d)	CDor MAsh
- Harvington hybrids (d)	CRos LRHS MAsh NRHS
- Harvington hybrids double-flowered (d)	CRos LCro LOPS NRHS SPoG
- 'HGC Jacob'PBR	LBuc LSRN SRms
- 'HGC Jacob Royal'	CRos LRHS NRHS
- HGC JOEL ('Coseh 210'PBR)	CRos ECtt LRHS NRHS
- HGC JONAS ('Coseh 220'PBR)	CRos ECtt LRHS NRHS
- 'HGC Josef Lemper'PBR	LRHS LSRN NLar SRms
- 'HGC Joshua'PBR	CRos LRHS NRHS
- HGC SNOW FRILLS ('Coseh 230'PBR)	ECtt
- HGC WINTERGOLD ('Coseh 2010'PBR)	CRos ECtt LRHS NRHS
- 'Ivory Prince'	see *H.* 'Ivory Prince'
- marbled leaves	SCob
- 'Marion' (d)	IFoB
- 'Mini Blanc' **new**	CRos NRHS
- pink-flowered	MAsh
- 'Potter's Wheel'	CRos EPfP LRHS NRHS SCob
- 'Praecox'	CRos ELon EWes LRHS NRHS
- Sunset Group	SCob
- 'Wilgenbroek Select'	EPfP SCob
× ***nigercors***	ECha ECtt SCob
- double-flowered (d)	LSou
- 'Emma'PBR	CEnd CMil CRos ECtt EPfP LRHS LSun MAvo MHol NRHS SCob SPoG WCot
- 'HGC Green Corsican'	CRos LRHS NRHS
- HGC ICE BREAKER FANCY ('Hlr 820')	CRos LRHS NRHS
- HGC ICE BREAKER MAX ('Coseh 750'PBR)	CRos EPfP LRHS MAsh NRHS
- HGC ICE BREAKER PICO ('Coseh 840')	ECre EPfP
- 'Morning's Pride'PBR	CRos LRHS NRHS
- 'Pink Beauty'	NLar SCob
× ***nigristern***	see *H.* × ***ericsmithii***
odorus	CBro GCal IFoB MAsh MPhe SCob XEll XLum
- WM 0312 from Bosnia	MPhe
- WM 9415	MPhe
- WM 9728 from Hungary	MPhe
- subsp. ***cyclophyllus***	CBot MAsh MPhe SCob
orientalis misapplied	see *H.* × *hybridus*
orientalis ambig.	CBar CTsd CWCL GKev GMcL MSCN MWat NPri SCob WHar WHil WPtf
orientalis Lam.	CBcs CRav CRos EWes LRHS MPhe MSwo NRHS XLum
§ - subsp. ***abchasicus*** (A. Braun) B. Mathew	CBro GKev MAsh WSpi
§ - - Early Purple Group	CTri GCal MRav SRms
- subsp. ***guttatus*** misapplied	see *H.* × *hybridus* spotted
- subsp. ***guttatus*** (A. Braun & Sauer) B. Mathew	SRkn
'Pink Beauty'PBR	CBcs CEnd EPfP LRHS NLar SLon SPoG WCot
purpurascens	CBot CBro GMaP IFoB LCro LOPS MAsh MRav MSCN XEll
- WM 0815 from Romania	MPhe
- WM 9211 from Hungary	MPhe
- WM 9412	MPhe
(Rodney Davey Marbled Group) 'Anna's Red'	CBcs CRos EBee ECtt EPfP GBin LCro LOPS LRHS MAsh MHol NRHS SPoG WCot
- 'Penny's Pink'	CBcs CMil CRos ECtt EPfP GBin LRHS LSRN LSun MAsh MHol MJak NPnk NRHS SCob SPoG WCot WHil
× ***sahinii*** 'Winterbells'PBR	EBee LCro LOPS LRHS NRHS SPoG SRms
'Silver Dollar'	EBee EPfP GKev LCro LOPS LRHS LSRN NPnk SPer SPoG SRms
'Snow White'	LBuc
(Spring Promise Series) SP CONNY ('Hlr 160'PBR)	CRos EPfP LRHS NRHS
- SP MARY LOU ('Hlr 150'PBR)	CRos LRHS NRHS
- SP RACHEL	CRos LRHS NRHS
- SP TIFFANY	CRos LRHS NRHS
× ***sternii***	CBcs CBod CRos CSpe CTri ELan EPed EPfP EWTr GKev GMaP LCro LRHS MMoz MNrw MWat NEgg NLar NRHS SCob SPoG WBrk WMoo WWtn
- Aberconwy strain	MAsh
- 'Ashwood Silver'	MAsh
- Ashwood strain	MAsh NLar
- Blackthorn Group	CRos ECre EHrv ELon EPfP EUJe IFoB LRHS NPnk NRHS SWvt
- 'Boughton Beauty'	CMea EHrv ELan IRob NPnk SCob WSpi
- pewter-flowered	CSpe
- 'Tom'	SCob
- 'Wilgenbroek'	SCob
thibetanus	CBro CExl EHrv EWes GKev LAma LLHF MAsh MPhe WPnP
torquatus	CBot CBro CTal MAsh MPhe XEll
- WM 0609 from Montenegro	MPhe
- WM 0617 from Serbia	MPhe
- WM 9106 from Montenegro	MPhe
- WM 9820 from Bosnia	MPhe
- 'Dido' (d)	CExl WFar
- double-flowered, from Montenegro (d) WM 0621	MPhe
- hybrids	CTal IFoB
- Party Dress Group	see *H.* × *hybridus* Party Dress Group
'Verboom Beauty'	CRos LRHS NRHS
vesicarius	MAsh
viridis	CBot CFis CRos GCal IFoB LRHS MAsh MHer SCob SRms XEll XLum
- WM 0444	MPhe
- WM 0444 from Italy	MPhe
- WM 1303 from Slovenia	MPhe
- WM 9723 from Italy	MPhe
- subsp. ***occidentalis***	CBot CBro MAsh
- - WM 1340 from Germany	MPhe
- - WM 1344 from Spain	MPhe
- - WM 9501 from Wales	MPhe
WALBERTON'S ROSEMARY ('Walhero'PBR)	CRos EPfP LRHS MAsh NRHS SHar SPoG WSpi
'Washfield Queen' (Queen Series)	CWCL
'White Beauty'PBR	EPfP LRHS NLar NRHS SCob SPoG WHil

Helminthotheca (*Asteraceae*)

§ ***echioides***	EBWF WHer

Helonias (*Melanthiaceae*)

bullata	EBee

Heloniopsis (*Melanthiaceae*)

acutifolia B&SWJ 218	WCru
- B&SWJ 6817	WCru
- B&SWJ 6836	WCru
japonica	see *H. orientalis*
§ ***kawanoi***	EBee GKev IMou WCot WCru
koreana B&SWJ 4173	WCru
leucantha B&SWJ 11148	WCru
§ ***orientalis***	CTal GCal GKev LLHF WCru
- B&SWJ 6278	WCru
- B&SWJ 6327	WCru
- B&SWJ 6380 from Japan	WCru
- from Korea	EPfP SChF
- var. ***breviscapa***	EPfP GEdr LEdu SChF SMad WCru
- - B&SWJ 5635	WCru
- - B&SWJ 5873	WCru
- - B&SWJ 5938	WCru
- - 'A-so'	LEdu WCru
- 'Dark Single'	GEdr
- var. ***flavida*** B&SWJ 11400	CTal WCru
- - 'Snow White'	GEdr
- variegated (v)	WCru
- var. ***yakusimensis***	see *H. kawanoi*
tubiflora B&SWJ 822	WCot WCru
- 'Temple Blue'	EBee WCru
umbellata	CTal EBee EPfP WMoo WSHC
- B&SWJ 1839	WCru
- B&SWJ 3732	CBct MAvo WCru
- B&SWJ 6836	WCru
- B&SWJ 6846	WCru
- B&SWJ 7117	WCru

Helwingia (*Helwingiaceae*)

chinensis	CBcs CBod CCCN CTsd EUJe EWTr EWld GBin LEdu MGil MPie NLar SBrt SEND SMad SPoG WBor WPGP
- broad-leaved	EBee NLar WPGP
himalaica	CExl CFil SBrt
japonica	CHGN EWld NLar
- broad-leaved	WPGP

Helxine see *Soleirolia*

Hemerocallis ✿ (*Hemerocallidaceae*)

'A Groovy Kind of Love' **new**	EStr
'A Lady Named Hank' **new**	EStr
'Aabachee'	CBgR EStr
'Absolute Treasure'	EStr
'Absolute Zero'	SDay SPol
'Adah'	SDay
'Addie Branch Smith'	CWel SDay
'Adoration'	SPer
'Aerial Display'	EStr
'Africa'	SPol
'African Chant'	ELan
'Age of Miracles'	SPol
'Ageless Beauty'	ELon EStr
'Agnes Elpers'	WAul
'Ahoy Matey'	EStr
'Ahoya'	CBgR SPol
'Airs and Graces'	SDay
'Alabama Jubilee'	WNHG
'Alabama Slammer'	EStr
'Alan'	CRos LRHS MRav NRHS
'Alaqua'	MBNS
'Alec Allen'	SDay
'Alexander the Great'	WHrl
'Alien DNA' **new**	EStr
'Alien Encounter'	SPol
'Aliens in the Garden' **new**	EStr
'All American Baby'	EStr SPol
'All American Chief' 🏆H6	EStr
'All American Eagle'	SPol
'All American Magic'	SPol
'All American Plum'	CWCL IBoy MSpe SPol WAul WHrl
'All American Tiger'	SDay
'All American Windmill'	CBgR EStr
'All Fired Up'	EStr SDay SPol
'All the Magic'	SDay
'Allegiance'	WNHG
'Alli Sheldon'	ECha
'Alluring Peach'	EStr
'Almost Paradise'	SPol
'Alpine Mist'	SDay
'Alpine Rhapsody'	SPol
altissima	MNrw SPhx XLum XSen
'Always Afternoon' 🏆H6	CBgR EPfP EStr MNrw SPol WHrl XSen
'Amadeus'	EStr SCob
'Amazon Amethyst'	WCAu
'Ambassador'	CBgR
'Amber Classic'	ELon
'American Revolution'	CBgR CBod CPar CRos CSpe EHrv ELon EStr GBin LRHS LSun MBNS MHol MWat NChi NRHS SDys SPoG SPol WAul WCot WHrl WMoo WOut WPnP WSpi XLum XSen
'Amerstone Amethyst Jewel'	EStr SPol
'Amy Michelle' (d)	EStr
'Amy's Rainbow'	EStr
'Andrew Christian'	SPol
'Andy Candy'	CWel
'Angel Artistry'	SDay
'Angel Rodgers'	EStr
'Angels Gather Around'	CWel
'Angelus Runaway'	EStr
'Anna Warner'	ELon MMuc SEND
'Annabelle's Ghost'	CBgR SPol
'Annie Welch'	ELon EPfP NBre
'Antarctica'	SPol
'Antique Lavender'	WCAu
'Antique Rose'	EStr
'Anzac'	CBro CRos CTsd ECha ECtt EHrv IBoy LRHS NGdn NRHS SWvt WMoo
'Apollo'	XSen
'Apollodorus'	WNHG
'Apple Court Chablis'	EStr SPol
'Apple Court Champagne'	SPol
'Apple Court Damson'	EStr SPol
'Apple Court Ruby'	ELon SPol
'Apple Swirl'	EStr SPol
'Applique'	EStr
'Après Moi'	NLar
'Apricot Beauty' (d)	EWTr WSpi
'Apricot Velvet'	CBgR
'April Fools'	EStr
'Aquadisiac'	CWel
'Aquarelle'	EStr
'Arabian Magic'	EStr
'Arctic Lace'	CWel
'Arctic Snow' 🏆H6	CBgR CBod CBro CMac CRos ECrc ECtt ELon EStr GKev LRHS MNrw NRHS SCob SDay SPol WAul WPnP

'Arms to Heaven'	CWel
'Arpeggio'	EStr SDay
'Art Gallery Curly-Q' **new**	EStr
'Art Gallery Quilling'	EStr
'Arthur Moore'	SDay
'Artificial Evolution' **new**	EStr
'Asheville Pink Lady' **new**	EStr
'Asian Artistry'	WNHG
'Asiatic Pheasant'	SPol
'Asterisk' ♀H6	EStr SDay
'Astolat'	EBee
'Aten'	CBgR CRos SDay
'Atlanta Bouquet'	SDay
'Atlanta Cover Girl'	SDay
'Atlanta Fringe Benefit'	SDay
'Atlas'	ETMg WGwG
'Augenstern'	EStr
'August Frost' ♀H6	EStr SDay SPol
'August Morn'	CBgR
'Authur Vincent'	SPol
'Autumn Jewels'	CWel SPol
'Autumn Red'	CBcs CBgR EStr GKin MMuc MNrw SEND SPol WCot
'Avant Garde'	LMea SPol WCAu
'Avon Crystal Rose'	WNHG
'Awakening Dream'	SDay
'Awash With Color'	EStr SDay
'Awesome Blossom'	CWel EStr LSou MBNS MNrw SPol
'Aztec Furnace'	EStr SDay
'Aztec Gold'	EStr
'Baby Betsy'	EStr
'Baby Blues'	SDay SPol
'Baby Darling'	SDay
'Baby Red Eyes'	EStr WFar
'Baja'	WFar
'Bakabana'	CRos LRHS NRHS
'Bald Eagle'	EStr MNrw
'Bali Hai'	CRos EStr LRHS NRHS SRms WHrl WSpi
'Bali Watercolor'	EStr
'Bama Bound'	EStr
'Bamboo Blackie'	CBgR SPol XSen
'Banana Cream Beauty'	SDeJ WSpi
'Banana Man'	EStr
'Banbury Cinnamon'	MBNS
'Bandit Man'	EStr SDay
'Barbara Alsop' **new**	EStr
'Barbara Dittmer'	SPol
'Barbara Mitchell'	EStr EWTr SDeJ WCAu WNHG XSen
'Barbaresco'	SPol
'Barbary Corsair'	CWel EStr SDay
'Barn Owl'	CWel
'Baronet's Badge'	SPol
'Baroni'	ECha
'Bas Relief'	EStr
'Bat Masterson'	CWel
'Bat Signal'	SPol
'Batgirl' **new**	EStr
'Bathsheba'	SPol
'Bayou Bride'	SDay
'Bea'	EStr
'Beat the Barons'	SPol
'Beautiful Design'	EStr
'Beautiful Edgings'	EStr SPol
'Beauty to Behold' ♀H6	CWel SDay
'Becky Lynn'	CWel ECtt EStr
'Bed of Nails' **new**	EStr
'Bed of Roses'	EStr
'Bedarra Island'	SDay
'Before You Accuse Me' **new**	EStr
'Beijing'	SDay
'Bela Lugosi'	CBgR CMac CRos ECrc ELon EPfP EStr GQue LRHS LSRN LSun MBNS MCot MNrw NBro NChi NEgg NQui NRHS SCob SDay SMad SPer SPol WHrl WNHG
'Believe It'	WNHG
'Belly Button Slipknots'	EStr
'Beloved Deceiver'	SDay
'Ben Adams'	SDay
'Ben Bachman'	EStr
'Benchmark'	SDay WHrl
'Bengal Fire'	WNHG
'Berlin Oxblood'	WAul
'Berlin Red'	CWCL CWel ECha ELon MNrw SDay WFar
'Berlin Tallboy'	CWel SDay WAul
'Berliner Premiere'	EStr
'Berry Blitz'	EStr
'Berry Patch' **new**	EStr
'Berrylicious'	EPfP EStr
'Bertie Ferris'	CWel EStr NLar SDay
'Bess Ross'	XSen
'Best Kept Secret'	SPol
'Best Seller'	CBod LMea
'Bette Davis Eyes'	CBgR CWat EStr SDay SPol
'Betts Allen'	EStr
'Betty Jenkins'	EStr
'Bettylen'	EStr
'Beyond Borders'	CWel
'Beyond Riches' **new**	EStr
'Bi-colored Blues' **new**	EStr
'Big Apple'	EStr SDay SPol
'Big Beautiful Babe' **new**	EStr
'Big Bird'	CWel EStr SDay
'Big Blue'	EStr SDay
'Big City Eye'	CWel MBNS
'Big Honking Bahama Richie' **new**	EStr
'Big Kiss' (d)	SPol
'Big Ogeeche'	EStr
'Big Smile'	MBNS MNrw SDeJ
'Big Snowbird'	SDay
'Big Time Happy'	CRos LRHS NRHS SCob SPoG STPC WHar
'Big World'	CBgR
'Bill Norris'	SPol
'Bird Bath Pink'	SPol
'Birdwing Butterfly'	CWel SPol
'Bitsy'	ELon SCob WRHF
'Black Adder'	SDay
'Black Ambrosia'	CWel EStr SDay SPol
'Black Arrowhead'	EStr LLWG SPol
'Black Emanuelle'	CExl LSun MNrw NLar
'Black Eye'	SDay WNHG
'Black Eyed Stella'	WSpi
'Black Eyed Susan'	CBod ECtt EStr
'Black Friday' **new**	EStr
'Black Ice'	SDay SPol
'Black Knight'	NLar SRms
'Black Magic'	CBro CTri ECtt ELan EPfP EUJe GBin GKin GMaP LRHS LSRN MHer MRav NEgg NGdn NRHS SPer WHer WHrl WMoo WNHG
'Black Plush'	SPol
'Black Prince'	CBgR EShb IBoy MBNS NBre NBro WAul
'Black Stockings'	EBee ELon EStr EWes LMea SCob SDeJ
'Blackberries and Cream'	EStr

'Blackberry Candy'	CSam ECtt EStr GKin MNrw MSpe NWad
'Blackberry Sherbert'	WFar
'Blacky'	EStr
'Blazing Lamp Sticks'	CWel
'Blessed Again'	SDay
'Blessing'	EStr SPol
'Blizzard Bay'	EStr SDay SPol WFar
'Blizzard Blast' **new**	EStr
'Blonde is Beautiful'	SDay
'Blood Spot'	SDay
'Blue Haired Girl'	CWel
'Blue Oasis'	CWel
'Blue Sheen'	CBgR CMac CRos ECtt GMaP MBNS WFar WMoo WRHF WSpi
'Blue Stardust' **new**	EStr
'Blueberry Breakfast'	WNHG
'Blueberry Candy'	ECtt EStr IBoy ILea
'Blueberry Cream'	CWCL ELon MMrt MNrw
'Blueberry Frost'	CBgR
'Blueberry Sundae'	CWat
'Blue-eyed Butterfly'	SPol
'Bluethroat' **new**	EStr
'Blufftop Volunteer' **new**	EStr
'Blushing Belle'	NBro NEgg
'Bobby's Lavender Eyes'	EStr
'Bobo Anne'	EStr
'Bogie and Becall'	SPol
'Bohemian Rhapsody'	EStr
'Bold Courtier'	CBgR
'Bold One'	SPol
'Bold Ruler'	SPol
'Bonanza'	CBcs CBgR CBro CRos CTri ECha ECtt EPfP ESps EStr EUJe GMcL IRob LEdu LRHS MJak MRav MSpe NBro NGdn NLar NRHS SCob SEND SPer SRot SWvt WCot WFar WMoo
'Bone China'	WNHG
'Boney Maroney'	CBgR
'Bonibrae Blue-eyed Baby'	EStr
'Bonnie Boy'	XLum XSen
'Booger'	SDay
'Booroobin Magic'	EStr
'Border Baby'	ECtt
'Border Lord'	EStr
'Border Music'	EStr
'Borgia Queen'	SDay
'Boss Hogg' **new**	EStr
'Both Sides Now'	ECtt
'Boulderbrook Serenity'	SDay
'Bourbon Kings'	GNew MSpe SDeJ WHrl WWtn
'Bowl of Cream'	EStr
'Bowl of Roses'	EStr
'Bradley Bernard'	SPol
'Brass Buckles'	see *H.* 'Puddin'
'Brasstown'	SPol
'Brazilian Orange'	XSen
'Breath of Blue Air'	EStr
'Breathless Charm' **new**	EStr
'Breed Apart'	SPol
'Brenda Newbold'	EStr SDay SPol
'Bridget'	ELan
'Bright Beacon'	CWel SPol
'Bright Island'	XSen
'Bright Side'	CBgR
'Bright Spangles'	MSpe SDay WAul
'Brilliant Circle'	ECtt
'Broadway Bold Eyes'	SPol
'Broadway Valentine'	XSen
'Brocaded Gown'	ELan SDay
'Brooklyn Twist'	EStr
'Brown-Eyed Girl'	SPol
'Browns Ferry Royalty'	EStr
'Bruce'	EStr
'Brushed with Bronze'	SPol
'Brutus'	WHrl
'Bubbling Brown Sugar'	EStr MSpe SDay
'Bubbly'	SDay
'Bud Producer'	CBgR SPol
'Buddy's Wild and Wonderful' **new**	EStr
'Buenos Aires'	XSen
'Buffys Doll'	SDay
'Bumble Bee'	ECtt EStr NBre SDay
'Burgundy Love'	EStr LLWG
'Burlesque'	SDay SPol WCot
'Burning Daylight' ♀H7	CAby CBgR CRos EBee ECtt EPfP LRHS MNrw MRav NEgg NRHS SCob SPer SRms WAul WCAu WCot WFar WPtf
'Burning Inheritance'	SDay
'Burnished Ruffles'	EStr
'Bus Stop'	SPol
'Butterfly Charm'	SDay
'Butterpat'	SDay
'Butterscotch'	WFar
'Butterscotch Ruffles'	SDay
'Buzz Bomb'	CRos ECrc ECtt EStr GKin LRHS LSRN MCot NEgg NGdn NRHS SPer WFar
'By Myself'	XSen
'Byzantine Emperor'	CRos LRHS NRHS
'Caballero'	EStr
'Cabbage Flower'	SDay XSen
'Cabriolet'	XSen
'Cajun Gambler'	EStr
'Calgary Stampede'	EStr
'Calico Jack'	EStr SPad
'Calico Spider'	EStr SPol XSen
'California Sunshine'	SPol
'Caliph's Robes'	SDay
'Call Girl'	SDay
'Calligraphy' **new**	EStr
'Camden Ballerina'	SDay
'Camden Gold Dollar'	SDay
'Camelot Green'	WNHG
'Cameroons'	SPol
'Campfire Embers'	EStr
'Canadian Border Patrol'	EStr MNrw NLar SPer SPol WHrl
'Canary Chaos'	EStr
'Canary Glow'	CTri IBoy WFar
'Canary Wings'	CBgR
'Candide'	SDay
'Canopy of Heaven'	SPol
'Can't Fault Ya' **new**	EStr
'Cantique'	SDay SPol
'Cape Breton'	EBee EStr
'Capernaum Cocktail'	SPol
'Cara Mia'	CBgR EStr MBNS SPol WFar
'Caramba'	CBgR
'Caramel Taffy' **new**	WHrl
'Caribbean Frank League'	SDay
'Caribbean Purple Spires'	EStr
'Carlotta'	SDay
'Carmen Marie'	XSen
'Carmine Monarch'	EStr
'Carolicolossal'	ELon SDay SPol
'Carolina Cool Down'	EStr
'Carolina Cranberry'	ELan

'Carolina Dynamite'	EStr
'Carolina Lemon Squeezer'	EStr
'Caroline Taylor'	WHrl
'Carousel Princess'	CRos LRHS NRHS
'Carrick Wildon'	EBee WFar
'Carrot'	SDay
'Cartwheels'	ECha EHrv EPfP EShb EStr GKin GMaP LRHS MRav NBro NRHS SPer SRms SSut WCAu WFar WMoo
'Casino Gold'	SDay
'Castile'	SDay
'Castle Strawberry Delight'	SPol
'Cat Dancer' 🏆H6	EStr
'Catawampus' **new**	EStr
'Catherine Neal'	EStr SPol
'Catherine Woodbery'	Widely available
'Cathy's Sunset'	CSam ECtt GKin LRHS LSRN MBNS MSpe NBro NGdn NRHS NWad SRGP
'Cause for Pause'	EStr
'Caviar'	SDay
'Cayenne' 🏆H6	SPol
'Cedar Waxwing'	MNrw
'Celebration of Angels'	EStr SPol
'Celtic Christmas'	SPol
'Cerulean Star'	CWel SPol
'Cerulean Warbler'	EStr
'Chamonix'	XSen
'Chance Encounter'	EStr LRHS NRHS SPol
'Changing Latitudes'	SPol WHrl
'Chantilly'	EStr
'Charlene Moore'	SPol
'Charles Johnston'	CBgR EPfP EStr SDay
'Charlie Pierce Memorial'	EStr SPol
'Charon the Ferryman'	SPol
'Chasing Shadows'	CWel
'Checkerboard Curls'	EStr
'Cheerful Note'	WNHG
'Cheese and Wine' **new**	EStr MHol
'Cherokee Patterns'	SPol
'Cherokee Star'	EStr
'Cherry Cheeks'	CRos CWel ECtt ELan ELon EStr LRHS MHol MNrw MRav NRHS SPol WCAu WCot WFar WMoo WWtn
'Cherry Eyed Pumpkin' 🏆H6	EStr SDay SPol WCAu
'Cherry Grove Beach' **new**	EStr
'Cherry Lace'	XSen
'Cherry Peacock' **new**	EStr
'Cherry Tiger'	EStr
'Cherry Valentine'	CWel ELon GWyn SPad
'Cherrystone'	EStr
'Chesapeake Crablegs'	EStr
'Chesières Lunar Moth'	CBgR ELon SPol
'Chester Cyclone'	SDay
'Chestnut Mountain'	SDay
'Chevron Spider'	EStr
'Chicago Antique Tapestry'	SDay
'Chicago Apache'	CWel EBee ELon EPfP EStr LLWG MBNS MBel SDay SPer SPol WSpi
'Chicago Aztec'	ELon
'Chicago Blackout'	ECtt WAul WCot
'Chicago Cherry'	WNHG
'Chicago Fire'	CBod EBee EPfP SDay
'Chicago Firecracker'	XLum XSen
'Chicago Heirloom'	WCAu
'Chicago Jewel'	ELon NSti
'Chicago Knobby'	EBee EStr MNrw SDay
'Chicago Knockout'	ELan EPfP WAul
'Chicago Mist'	WNHG
'Chicago Petticoats'	WFar
'Chicago Picotee Memories'	EBee
'Chicago Picotee Promise'	WNHG
'Chicago Queen'	SDay WNHG
'Chicago Rainbow'	CBgR
'Chicago Royal Blue' **new**	CTri
'Chicago Royal Crown'	CWld ECtt
'Chicago Royal Robe'	CWCL ELon GNew MBNS NBid SDay SPer SRms WCot WWtn
'Chicago Silver'	SDay WAul
'Chicago Star'	WNHG
'Chicago Sugarplum'	SDay
'Chicago Sunrise'	CBgR CRos ELon GMaP IBoy IRob LRHS MRav NGdn NRHS SDay SPol SWvt WAvo WCot
'Chick Flick'	EStr
'Chick Magnet' **new**	EStr
'Chicken Coop Madonna'	EStr
'Chief Sequoia'	EStr
'Children's Festival'	CMac CRos ECtt EStr GMaP LRHS MBNS MRav NLar SWvt WFar WMoo
'China Bride'	EStr SCob SPol
'China Lake'	SDay
'Chinese Autumn'	CWel EStr
'Chinese Cloisonne'	EStr
'Chinese Imp'	NLar SDay
'Chinese New Year'	EStr
'Chinese Temple Flower'	SDay
'Chocolate Candy'	CWGN EPfP EStr
'Chocolate Splash'	SDay
'Chokecherry Mountain'	CBod EStr MSCN
'Chorus Line'	SDay SPol WNHG
'Chorus Line Kid'	SPol
'Chosen Ruler'	CWel
'Christina's Pink Parasol'	EStr
'Christine Lynn'	WNHG
'Christmas Is'	CBgR CMac CPar CWGN CWel EBee ECtt ELon EStr GBin GKin GMcL LRHS LSou MBel NRHS SPol WAul WCot WHrl XSen
'Christmas Ornament'	EStr
'Christmas Wishes'	EStr
'Château Lafite'	SPol
'Ciarra Vonnie'	SDay
'Cimarron Knight'	CBgR SPol
'Cindy's Eye'	EStr WCot
'Cindy's Tie Dye'	CWel
'Cinnamon Stick' **new**	EStr
'Cinnamon Sunrise'	EStr
'Circle of Beauty'	SPol
'Circles and Stripes'	CWel
citrina 🏆H6	CBgR CExl CHid CMac CRos EBee EStr GKev GNew IBoy IMou LRHS MCot WCot WHrl WRHF XLum XSen
citrina × (× ***ochroleuca***)	WCot
'Civil Law'	SDay
'Civil Rights'	SDay
'Classic Caper'	WNHG
'Classic Edge'	SDay
'Claudine'	ELon
'Claudine's Charm'	CWel
'Clearly a Thrill' **new**	EStr
'Cleo'	WHrl
'Cleopatra'	ELon SPol
'Clothed in Glory'	CWel EStr MBNS WCot
'Cocktail Party'	EStr
'Colonel Mustard' **new**	EStr
'Comanche Eyes'	SDay

'Comet Flash'	SPol
'Coming Up Roses'	CBod CPar CWld ELon
'Condilla' (d) ♀H6	CWel EStr SDay SPol
'Conspicua'	CBgR SMHy SPol
'Contessa'	CBro CRos IRob LRHS NRHS
'Conway Red Light' **new**	EStr
'Cool It'	CWel MPie NLar SCob SDeJ WHrl
'Cool Jazz'	EStr SDay SPol
'Cool Summer Breeze'	SPol
'Cooler Than Me' **new**	EStr
'Copper Dawn'	EStr NChi SPol
'Copper Windmill'	CBgR ELon EStr SDay SPol
'Copperhead'	EStr SPol
'Coral Majority' **new**	EStr
'Coral Mist'	ECrc NBre
'Coral Sparkler'	WNHG
'Coral Spider'	SPol
'Corky'	CAby CBro CRos ECha ELan EPfP GBin GCal GMaP GMcL GWyn IRob LRHS LSRN MBel MNrw MSpe NEgg NGdn NLar NRHS SCob SPer SPhx SSut WAul WFar WSpi XLum XSen
'Cornwall'	EStr
'Corryton Pink'	SPol
'Cosmic Blast' **new**	EStr
'Cosmic Hummingbird'	ECtt EStr LRHS NRHS SDay
'Cosmopolitan'	ILea
'Country Club'	EBee GMaP SPol
'Country Melody'	SDay
'Court Magician'	EStr SDay
'Court Troubadour'	SPol
'Coyote Moon'	EStr SDay
'Cranberry Baby'	CWel ECtt EStr WHoo WNHG
'Cranberry Coulis'	CWat
'Crawleycrow'	XSen
'Crazy Larry'	EStr
'Crazy Mr Jim'	EStr
'Crazy Pierre'	SPol WHrl XSen
'Cream Drop'	CRos ECtt EPPr GMaP GQue IBoy LRHS MCot MRav MWat NBro NGdn NLar NRHS NSti SCob SPer WAul WCot WFar WHrl WMoo
'Crimson Edgings'	CWel
'Crimson Icon'	SDay
'Crimson Pirate'	Widely available
'Crimson Wind'	EStr
'Crintonic Shadowlands'	SPol
'Cripple Creek'	EStr
'Croesus'	SRms
'Crown Royal' **new**	SDay
'Cruise Control'	SPol
'Crystal Cupid'	XSen
'Crystal Pinot'	CWel ELon EStr
'Cumulus Sunset' **new**	EStr
'Cupid's Gold'	SDay
'Curls'	CBgR MBNS SDay
'Curly Brick Road'	SPol
'Curly Cinnamon Windmill' ♀H6	EStr SDay SPol
'Curly Rosy Posy'	SDay
'Custard Candy' ♀H6	CRos CWCL CWGN ECtt EPfP EStr GKin LRHS MBNS MBel NRHS WCAu WNHG
'Cute As Can Be'	EStr
'Cyclone Twister' **new**	EStr
'Cynthia Lucius' **new**	EStr
'Cynthia Mary'	ECtt GKin SRGP
'Cypriana'	EBee XSen
'Czarina'	EStr
'Daddeeo Segrest'	EStr
'Daddy's Catfish Stew' **new**	EStr
'Dad's Best White'	EStr
'Daggy'	CWel
'Daily Dollar'	MBNS NGdn
'Dainty Pink'	WWtn
'Dallas Spider Time'	SDay
'Dallas Star'	EStr SDay SPol WHrl
'Dan Mahony'	EStr
'Dan Tau'	SDay
'Dance Ballerina Dance'	EBee SDay
'Dance with Somebody'	EStr
'Dancing Crab'	CBgR SPol
'Dancing Dreams' **new**	EStr
'Dancing Elf' **new**	EStr
'Dancing in the Rain'	EStr
'Dancing on Ice'	EStr
'Dancing Shiva'	SDay SPol
'Dancing Summerbird'	ELon EStr SDay SPol
'Daring Deception'	CRos CWel ECtt ELon EPfP LRHS MNrw NRHS SCob SDeJ
'Daring Dilemma'	EStr SPol
'Daring Reflection'	SDay
'Darius'	WNHG
'Dark Angel'	NRHS
'Dark Elf'	SDay
'Dark Magician'	EStr
'Dark Monkey' **new**	EStr
'Darker Shade'	EStr
'Darla Anita'	LMea
'Darrell'	SDay
'David Holman'	WNHG
'David Kirchhoff'	EStr SDay
'Davidson Update'	WNHG
'Daylight' **new**	WNHG
'Days of Joy'	CWel
'De Colores'	EStr
'Debary Canary'	CWel
'Debussy'	EStr
'Decatur Ballerina'	WNHG
'Decatur Captivation'	WNHG
'Decatur Dictator'	WNHG
'Decatur Imp'	SDay WHrl
'Decatur Jewel'	WNHG
'Decatur Piecrust'	EStr
'Decatur Rhythm'	WNHG
'Decatur Supreme'	WNHG
'Decatur Treasure Chest'	WNHG
'Decidedly Happy' **new**	EStr
'Delicate Design'	SDay SPol
'Deloris Gould'	SDay
'Demetrius'	CWat EStr
'Derrick Cane'	SPol
'Desdemona'	EStr SPol XLum
'Desert Dreams'	WCot
'Desert Icicle'	CWel EStr SPol
'Designer Gown'	EStr SDay
'Designer Jeans'	EStr SDay SPol
'Designer Rhythm'	EStr
'Desirable Duchess'	EStr
'Destination Y'	XSen
'Destined to See'	CBcs CBro CPar CWel ECtt EHrv ELon EStr LMea LSou MHol MNrw NBro NEgg SPad SPer SPol WAvo WCot WHrl
'Devil's Footprint'	SPol
'Devon Cream'	SPer
'Devonshire'	SDay
'Diamond Dust'	CKel ECtt NLar SPer WSpi
'Diamonds for Divas'	CWel

'Diana Grenfell'	CBgR
'Dick Kitchingman'	CBgR SPol
'Dipped in Ink'	EStr SPol
'Discarded Beauty' **new**	EStr
'Distant Galaxy'	EStr
'Diva Bride' **new**	EStr
'Diva's Choice'	EStr MHol SCob
'Divertissment'	CBgR ELon SDay WHrl
'Dizzy Miss Lizzy'	EStr
'Doc Holliday'	EStr
'Doctor Freckles Mr Hyde' **new**	EStr
'Dominic'	CBgR CPar IBoy MBNS MSpe SDay SPol WCot WMoo
'Don Stevens'	WHrl
'Don's Wild Heather'	EStr
'Don't Leave Empty-handed' **new**	EStr
'Dorethe Louise'	CBgR SDay SPol
'Dorothy McDade'	MNrw
'Dot Paul'	ELan
'Double Action' (d)	SDay SPol
'Double Bold One' (d)	CWel SPol
'Double Charm' (d)	XSen
'Double Coffee' (d)	SPol
'Double Corsage' (d)	SPol
'Double Cream' (d)	WCot
'Double Cutie' (d)	EStr NLar SDay SRms
'Double Delicious' (d)	WCot
'Double Doubloon' (d)	XLum
'Double Dream' (d)	EStr WHrl
'Double Firecracker' (d)	EBee MBNS MSpe NBro NLar XSen
'Double Gardenia' (d)	EStr WNHG
'Double Glitter' (d)	XSen
'Double Honey' (d)	EStr
'Double Oh Seven' (d)	ELon SPol
'Double Pink Treasure' (d)	SDay
'Double Pompon' (d)	EStr
'Double Pop Art' (d)	XSen
'Double Red Royal' (d)	EPfP EStr XSen
'Double River Wye' (d)	CBgR CRos CWel ECtt EShb EStr IBoy LRHS MBNS MHer MNrw NGdn NRHS SPol WAul WBrk WCot WFar WHoo WHrl
'Dowager Queen'	WNHG
'Dragon Dreams'	CWel SPol
'Dragon King'	SPol
'Dragon Lore'	EPfP EStr
'Dragon Seeker' **new**	EStr
'Dragon's Eye'	CWel SDay SPol WNHG
'Dragon's Orb'	SDay
'Dream Baby'	NBre
'Dresden Doll'	SPer
'Driving Me Wild'	SDay
'Droopy Drawers'	SPol
'Drop Cloth'	EStr
'Duke of Durham'	MSpe
'Duke of Earl'	CBgR
dumortieri	CAgr CBro EBee ECha EHrv ELan MCoo MCot MMuc MRav NBid NSti SCob SEND SPer WCot WHrl WWtn XSen
- B&SWJ 1283	WCru
'Dumpy'	EStr
'Dune Buggy'	XSen
'Dune Needlepoint'	EStr SPol WHrl
'Duplex' (d)	XSen
'Dutch Art'	SDay
'Dutch Artist' (d)	EStr
'Dutch Beauty'	WFar

	'Dutch Gold'	MHCG MNrw
	'Earl of Warwick'	CBgR SPol
	'Earlianna'	EStr SPol
	'Earnest Yearwood'	SDay
	'Earth Angel'	SPol
	'Easy Ned'	ELon SPol
	'Easy Street'	SDay
	'Eat Our Wake Pintaheads'	EStr
	'Ed Kirchhoff'	XLum
	'Ed Murray'	EStr SBee SDay WAul WCAu WHrl
	'Edgar Brown'	MBNS SPol WCot
	'Edge Ahead'	CMac ECtt GKin GMcL LRHS NRHS SDay WHrl
	'Edge of Darkness'	CKel CWGN EPfP MBNS NSti SDay WFar
	'Edith Vaughan'	EStr
	'Edna Spalding'	CRos LRHS NRHS SDay
	'Eenie Allegro'	CBro ECtt SPer
	'Eenie Weenie'	CBro ECtt ELon EStr GKev IBoy NBro SRms WOut WWtn
	'Eenie Weenie Non-stop'	ECha EPPr
	'Eggplant Escapade' ♀H6	CBgR EStr MSpe SDay SPol WHrl
	'Egyptian Ibis'	MSpe SPol WNHG
	'Egyptian Queen'	CBgR
	'Eight Miles High'	EStr
	'Eighteen Karat'	EStr
	'El Desperado'	CBgR CPar CRos CSam ECtt ELon EPfP EStr GQue ILea LRHS LSun MBNS MHol MNrw NEgg NRHS SPav SPol WAvo WCAu WCot
	'El Glorioso'	CWat EStr
	'Elaine Farrant'	SDay
	'Elaine Strutt'	MNrw SDay SWvt WCot WSpi
	'Electric Lemonade'	CWel
	'Elegant Candy' ♀H6	CBgR CMac CWel EPfP EStr
I	'Elegantissima'	SPol
	'Eleonor'	EBee EPfP WFar
	'Elfin Daydream'	SPol
	'Elfin Illusion'	EStr
	'Elijah Sain'	SPol
	'Elizabeth Salter'	CWCL CWel EStr NLar SPol
	'Eloquent Silence'	SDay
	'Elva White Grow'	SDay
	'Elves' Watermark'	SPol
	'Emerald Dew'	SDay
	'Emerald Eye'	SDay
	'Emerald Lady'	SPol
	'Emerald Starburst' **new**	EStr
	'Emily Anne'	SPol
	'Emperor's Choice'	SDay
	'Emperor's Dragon'	EStr SDay
	'Enchanted April'	SPol
	'Enchanted Forest'	EStr WCAu
	'Enchanter's Spell'	SDay
	'Enchanting Blessing'	EStr SDay
	'English Cameo'	SPol
	'Enigma Variations'	SPol
	'Entrapment'	ECtt EStr IBoy SDeJ WFar
	'Entwined in the Vine' **new**	EStr
	'Envoyé Spécial'	XSen
	'Envy Me'	SPol
	'Erica Nichole Gonzales'	SDay
	'Erin Prairie'	EStr SPol
	esculenta	SMad
	'Etched Eyes'	CWel SPol
	'Eternal Blessing'	SPol
	'Eternity Road'	EStr
	'Etruscan Tomb'	EStr SPol
	'Evelyn Claar'	CMac
	'Evelyn Lela Stout'	SDay

'Even Stephen'	SPol
'Evening Enchantment'	EStr SDay
'Evening Gown'	SPol
'Ever So Ruffled'	EStr SDay
'Excellent'	EStr
'Exotic Candy'	SPol
'Exotic Love'	SDay
'Exotic Spider' **new**	EStr
'Exotic Star'	EStr
'Exotic Treasure'	CWel EStr
'Exploded Pumpkin'	EBee EStr
'Exploding Galaxy' **new**	EStr
'Explosion in the Paint Factory' **new**	EStr
'Eye of the Hurricane'	EStr
'Eye on America'	CWel EBee ELon
'Eyes are Mosaics' **new**	EStr
'Eyes Wide Shut'	CWel
'Eye-yi-yi'	SPol
'Ezekiel'	CWel SPol XSen
'Fabergé'	SDay
'Fabergé Easter'	CWel
'Fairest Love'	EBee MBNS MNrw
'Fairest of Them'	CBgR CWel
'Fairy Charm'	SDay
'Fairy Firecracker'	SPol
'Fairy Summerbird'	SDay SPol
'Fairy Tale Pink'	EStr SDay SPol
'Faith Nabor'	SPol
'Falcon'	SPol
'Fall Farewell'	WNHG
'Fall Guy'	SDay
'Fama'	EStr
'Fan Club'	CWel
'Fandango'	SPer
'Farmer's Daughter'	CBgR
'Fat Lady Sings'	SPol
'Father James Foster'	EStr
'Feather Down'	SPol
'Fellow'	EStr SPol
'Femme Osage'	EStr SDay
'Feria'	XSen
'Festive Art'	CWel SPol
'Fetish'	CWel
'Fiestaville'	EStr
'Final Touch'	CBgR EBee EStr LLWG MSwo NBro SPol
'Finders Keepers'	EBee EStr LMea
'Fire and Fog'	EStr
'Fire Bird Suite'	CWel
'Fire Dance'	ELon
'Fire from Heaven'	WHrl
'Fire Tree'	CBgR ELon EStr SPol
'Firestorm'	EStr SPol
'First Formal'	SPer
'First Knight'	CWel EStr SDay
'Flaming Firebird'	EStr
'Flaming Frolic'	SPol
'Flaming Sword'	WBrk WRHF
'Flamingo Parade' **new**	EStr
flava	see *H. lilioasphodelus*
'Fleeting Fancy'	SDay
'Flip Fiasco' **new**	EStr
'Florentine Silk'	EStr
'Florida Sunshine' (d)	XSen
'Florissant Miss'	EStr
'Flower Basket' (d)	EStr
'Flower Pavilion'	SDay SPol
'Floyd Cove'	SDay
'Fly Catcher'	CBgR SDay
'Flyaway Home'	SPol
'Fooled Me' ♀H6	CRos CWel EBee ECtt EPfP EStr LRHS MSpe NRHS SDay SPad SPol
'Forest Phantom'	EStr
'Forestlake Ragamuffin'	SPol
'Forever Red'	EStr
'Forgotten Dreams'	EBee MSpe
forrestii	CExl GKev
'Forsooth'	CBgR
'Forsyth Ace of Hearts'	CBgR
'Forsyth Evening Glow'	EStr
'Forsyth Frostbound'	SPol
'Forsyth Mint Condition'	CWel
'Forsyth Summer Snow'	CWel
'Forsyth White Buds'	EStr
'Forty Second Street'	MBNS
'Fragrant Bouquet'	EStr
'Fragrant Pastel Cheers'	SDay
'Fragrant Returns'	ECtt LEdu SPoG
'Fragrant Treasure'	CWld
'Frances Fay'	SPol
'Frances Joiner'	CWel
'Frank Gladney'	SPol XSen
'Frankly Scarlet' **new**	EStr
'Frans Hals'	Widely available
'Fred Ham'	XSen
'Free Wheelin''	EPfP EStr SCob
'French Connection'	SDay
'French Lingerie'	EStr
'French Pavilion'	SDay
'French Porcelain'	SDay
'Frequent Flyer' **new**	EStr
'Fresh Air'	MNrw
'Fried Green Tomatoes' **new**	EStr
'Friends with Benefits' **new**	EStr
'Fritz Schroer'	CBgR
'Frosted Encore'	SDay
'Frosted Pink Ice'	SPol
'Frosted Vintage Ruffles'	EBee EStr MNrw WCAu
'Frozen Jade'	EBee SDay
'Fuchsia Beauty'	SPol
'Fuchsia Four'	SPol
'Full Grown'	EStr
fulva	CTri ELan GPSL MMuc SCob SEND SPol SRms WBrk WHrl XSen
- B&SWJ 8647	WCru
- 'Flore Pleno' (d)	CAvo CMac CTri ECtt ELan GBin MHer MJak MRav MSpe NBro NGdn NSti SMad SPav SPer SRms WBrk WCAu WMoo XSen
- 'Green Kwanso' (d)	CBgR CExl CRos EBee ECha ITim LRHS MMoz NRHS WFar WPnP WWtn
- var. ***kwanso***	WWtn
- - B&SWJ 6328	WCru
- 'Kwanso' ambig. (d)	CRos LRHS NRHS
- var. ***littorea***	CMac XLum XSen
- var. ***rosea***	LPla SPol WCot XSen
§ - 'Variegated Kwanso' (d/v)	CBro EBee MRav SCob SMad WBor WCot WFar WHer WHoo WHrl
- yellow-variegated (v)	WCot
'Fun Fling'	EStr SPol
'Funicular' **new**	EStr
'Funky Blues'	CWel
'Funky Fuchsia'	SPol
'Gadsden Goliath'	SPol
'Gadsden Light'	EStr SDay SPol
'Gala Greetings'	XSen
'Gale Storm'	SPol WNHG
'Galileo' **new**	EStr

'Garden Crawler'	CBgR
'Garden Portrait'	SDay SPol
'Garrett Allen'	EStr
'Gary Colby' new	EStr
'Gay Octopus'	CBgR EStr SPol WHrl
'Gay Rapture'	SPer
'Gemini'	SDay
'Geneva Firetruck'	CWel EStr
'Gentle Country Breeze'	SDay SPol
'Gentle Rose'	EStr SDay
'Gentle Shepherd'	Widely available
'George Cunningham'	CRos ECtt EHrv ELan LRHS MRav NRHS SDay SPol WFar
'George David'	WHrl
'George Jets On'	SPol
'Georgette Belden'	CRos ECtt GKin LRHS MSpe NRHS SPol
'Georgia Cream' (d)	NLar
'Gerda Brooker' new	EStr
'German Ballerina'	SPol
'Get All Excited'	ELon SPol
'Giant Moon'	CBgR CRos ECtt ELan EStr LRHS NRHS SPer SRms WHal
'Giddy Go Round'	SDay SPol
'Ginger Twist'	EStr
'Gingerbread Man'	MSpe
'Girouette'	XSen
'Give Me Eight'	SPol
'Glacier Bay'	CBgR
'Glazed Heather Plum'	EStr
'Gleber's Top Cream'	EStr
'Gleeman Song'	CBgR
'Glittering Treasure'	XLum
'Glowing Heart'	SDay
'Gnarly Gnome' new	SPol
'God's Handicraft'	EStr
'Going Bananas'[PBR]	WCot
'Gold Elephant'	SDay
'Gold Imperial'	NBre
'Golden Bell'	NGdn
'Golden Chimes'	Widely available
'Golden Compass'	CWel EStr
'Golden Firefly' new	SDay
'Golden Ginkgo'	WAvo WNHG
'Golden Prize'	NGdn SDay WAvo WCot XSen
'Golden Scroll'	SDay
GOLDEN ZEBRA ('Malja'[PBR]) (v)	CWGN CWel ELan EPfP IBoy MAvo MRav NSti SRms
'Golliwog'	CBgR EStr
'Gorgeous Smile'	EStr
'Got Milk' new	EStr
'Gothic Butterfly' new	EStr
'Gothic Window'	SDay
'Graal'	XSen
'Grace and Favour'	SDay SPol
'Graceful Eye'	SDay
'Graceland'	SDay WHrl
'Grand Masterpiece'	EStr NGdn SDay WFar
'Grand Palais'	CWel SDay
'Grandma Kissed Me'	SPol
'Granite City Towhead'	ELon
'Grape Arbor'	WNHG
'Grape Harvest'	WNHG
'Grape Magic'	MSpe WCot
'Grape Velvet'	CSpe CWel EStr ILea IRob MHer NSti SDay SPol SRms WCAu WNHG WWtn
'Grapes of Wrath'	EStr
'Green Canary'	SPol
'Green Dolphin Street'	SDay SPol
'Green Dragon'	SDay SPol
'Green Eyes Wink'	MHol
'Green Flutter'	CBgR EBee EStr GCal GQue LSRN NGdn NSti SPhx SPol WAvo WSpi
'Green Fringe'	SDay
'Green Goddess'	XLum
'Green Lines'	EStr
'Green Mystique'	EBee EStr SDay
'Green Nautilus'	EStr
'Green Spider'	CBgR SDay
'Green Widow'	SDay
'Greenland'	EBee ECtt EStr
'Grey Witch' ♀H6	SPol
'Greywoods Cowgirl Casanova' new	EStr
'Greywoods Nautical Nellie'	EStr
'Groovy Green'	CWel SDay
'Grumbly'	ELan WPnP
'Gryphon Prague Gothic'	EStr
'Guardian Angel'	WCFE
'Gwen Leman'	EStr
'Gypsy Cranberry'	SPol
'Gypsy Sweetheart'	WNHG
'Hail Mary'	SDay
'Halloween Masquerade'	CWel
'Halloween Trick'	CWel
'Hamlet'	SDay WNHG
'Happy Apache'	EStr
'Happy Medium' new	EStr
'Happy Returns'	CBgR CHid CRos CSBt CTri ECha ELan EPfP EStr GBin LRHS LSRN MBel NGdn NRHS SRGP SRms WCAu XLum
'Harbor Blue'	CWel MSpe SDay
'Harrods'	EStr
'Harry Barras'	XLum
'Having Fun'	EStr
'Hawaiian Nights'	WNHG
'Hawk'	ELon SDay SPol
'Hazel'	EStr
'Heady Wine'	EStr SDay
'Heart Wishes' new	EStr
'Heart's Glee'	XSen
'Heavenly Angel Ice'	ELon EPfP EStr SPol
'Heavenly Beginnings'	EStr
'Heavenly Curls'	EStr SDay SPol
'Heavenly Flight of Angels'	EStr
'Heavenly Pink Butterfly'	EStr
'Heavenly Pink Fang'	EStr
'Heavenly Starfire'	SPol
'Heavenly Thunderbird' new	EStr
'Heavenly Treasure'	SPol
'Heavenly United We Stand' new	EStr
'Heidi Eidelweiss'	CExl
'Heirloom Lace'	SDay WCAu
'Helen Sever' new	EStr
'Helen Shooter'	EStr
'Helena Seabird'	EStr
'Helix'	EStr SDay
'Helle Berlinerin'	SDay SPol
'Hello Screamer'	EStr
'Helter Skelter'	SDay SPol
'Heman' new	EStr
'Henry D. Allnutt'	EStr
'Her Majesty's Wizard'	CBgR ELan ELon SPol
'Here Lies Butch' new	EStr
'Hermitage Newton'	SDay
'Hexagon'	EStr
'High Profile'	EStr

'High Tor'	ELon EStr SDay SPol WHrl
'Highland Lord' (d)	SDay WCAu XSen
'Hint of Blue'	SPol
'Hold Your Horses' **new**	SDay
'Holiday Mood'	ELan
'Holly Dancer' ♀H6	EStr SPol
'Homeward Bound'	SDay
'Honey Jubilee'	SPol
'Honey Redhead'	SPol
'Honeysuckle Rose'	EStr
'Honor Flight'	EStr
'Hooked on Romance' **new**	EStr
'Hope Diamond'	SDay
'Hoping for Hugs' **new**	EStr
'Hornby Castle'	CBro CRos LRHS NRHS
'Hot Cakes'	EStr
'Hot Chocolate'^{PBR}	EBee GKev
'Hot Pink Fury'	EStr
'Hot Tamales and Red Hots'	EStr
'Hot Town'	CWel ELan
'Hot Wheels'	CBgR
'Hot Wire'	SDay
'Houdini'	MSpe
'House Music'	XSen
'House of Bluelights'	SPol
'House of Orange'	EStr SPol
'Huckleberry Candy'	SPol
'Humdinger'	EStr SDay WCot
'Hummingbird'	EStr
'Hybridizer's Truffle' **new**	EStr
'Hymn'	SDay
'Hyperion'	CBgR CFGn CMac CTri ECha ECtt ELon EShb EStr GKin GMcL IRob LEdu MHol MMuc MRav MSpe NBid NGdn SDay SEND SPer SWvt WCot WWtn
'Ice Carnival'	ELon EStr MBNS NGdn NLar SCob SPol SWvt WSpi
'Ice Castles'	CTri SDay
'Icecap'	CBgR WMoo
'Icy Lemon'	EStr SDay
'Ida Duke Miles'	SDay
'Ida's Magic'	EStr
'Iditarod'	EStr
'Ikebana Star'	EStr
'Iktomi' **new**	EStr
'Illini Jackpot'	SDay
'Impromptu'	SDay
'In Depth' (d)	MBNS NBro NLar WCot WHrl
'In Her Shoes'	EStr
'In Strawberry Time'	WNHG
'Inca Puzzle' **new**	SDay
'Inchon'	EStr
'Increased Complexity' **new**	EStr
'Indian Giver'	SPol
'Indian Paintbrush'	ELon SPol WNHG
'Indigo Moon'	SPol XSen
'Indy Heart Stopper' **new**	EStr
'Inky Fingers'	SPol
'Inner View'	ECtt EStr SDay
'Innocent Blush'	EStr
'Inspired Word'	SDay
'Instant Zéro'	XSen
'Iowa Greenery'	SPol
'Iridescent Jewel'	SDay
'Irish Elf'	EBee ELon GBin SDay SHar
'Irish Veil'	EStr
'Iron Gate Glacier'	EBee EStr MBNS SDay XLum
'Irresistible Charm'	EPfP LMea
'Isaac'	EStr

'Isabelle Rose'	SDay
'Isle of Dreams'	SDay SPol
'Isolde'	CBgR EStr
'It's a Zinger'	CWel
'It's Soul Time' **new**	EStr
'Itsy Bitsy Spider'	CBgR
'Itza Mirage' **new**	EStr
'Ivelyn Brown'	EStr SDay SPol
'Ivory Cloud' (d)	EStr
'Ivory Coast'	SDay
'J.T. Davis'	EStr
'Jabo'	SPol
'Jamaican Jammin''	SPol
'Jamaican Me Crazy' ♀H6	CWel
'Jamaican Midnight'	CWel
'James Marsh'	CBgR EWes MNrw MSpe NSti WCAu WCot WFar WNHG
'Jane Trimmer'	CWel
'Jane's Prism' **new**	EStr
'Janet Gordon'	SPol
'Janice Brown'	CWCL ECtt EStr LRHS LSou NLar NRHS SDay SPol WHrl
'Janie Wilson'	WNHG
'Jan's Twister'	EStr MNrw SDay SPol WHrl
'Jason Salter'	EStr SDay WAul
'Jay Turman'	SDay
'Jean'	SDay
'Jean Swann'	EStr
'Jedi Dot Pierce'	EStr SDay
'Jelly Dancer'	SPol
'Jellyfish Jealousy' ♀H6	EStr SDay
'Jenny Wren'	EPPr NBro SRGP WAul
'Jersey Breeze'	EStr
'Jersey Jim'	SPol
'Jersey Spider'	SDay SPol
'Jerusalem'	SDay
'Jesse James'	SPol
'Jeu de Piste'	XSen
'Jeune Tom'	CBgR
'Jewel Case'	WNHG
'Jim McKinney'	EStr
'Joan Derifield'	EStr
'Joan Senior'	Widely available
'Job Creator' **new**	EStr
'Jockey Club' (d)	ECtt WHrl
'Joe Marinello'	SPol
'Jogolor'	EStr
'Johnny Come Lately'	EStr SPol
'Jolyene Nichole'	SDay
'Jordan'	LSRN SWvt
'Jordan's Jazz' **new**	EStr
'Josephine Marina'	EStr
'Journey's End'	SDay
'Jovial'	EStr SDay
'Joyful Participation'	EStr
'Judah'	SPol
'Judge Roy Bean'	EStr SDay SPol
'Julie Newmar' ♀H6	CWel
'June Melody'	WNHG
'June Rose'	EStr
'Jungle Beauty'	CBgR SDay SPol
'Just Fabulous'	CWel
'Just Kiss Me'	CWel SPol
'Just My Size'	EStr
'Just Whistle'	EStr
'Justin Brent'	XSen
'Justin George'	SDay SPol
'Kaleidoscopic Intrigue' **new**	EStr
'Kangaroo Pouch'	CWel

'Karen's Curls' ♀H6	SDay SPol
'Kasia'	WHrl
'Kate Carpenter'	EStr SDay SPol
'Kathleen Salter'	EStr SDay
'Katie Elizabeth Miller'	SDay
'Kazuq'	SDay
'Kelly's Girl'	SPol
'Kempion'	CBgR
'Kevin Michael Coyne'	SPol
'Key to my Heart'	CBgR
'Kharma Police' **new**	EStr
'Killer' ♀H6 **new**	EStr
'Killer Purple'	EStr
'Kimberly Sue'	EStr
'Kindly Light'	SPol
'King George'	EStr
'King Kahuna' (d)	EStr
'King of Anything'	EStr
'King's Gold'	EStr
'King's Throne'	WNHG
'Kirsten My Love'	EStr
'Kiss the Sky' **new**	EStr
'Knight Returns'	CWel
'Knights in White Satin'	EStr SPol
'Kristal Sunset'	CWel
'Kwanso Flore Pleno'	see *H. fulva* 'Green Kwanso'
'Kwanso Flore Pleno Variegata'	see *H. fulva* 'Variegated Kwanso'
'La Fenice'	EStr
'La Peche'	SDay
'Lacy Doily'	EStr LLHF LMea WCAu
'Lacy Marionette'	SDay SPol
'Lady Betty Fretz'	EBee EStr
'Lady Fingers'	CBgR SPol
'Lady Grace'	CWel
'Lady Inara'	EStr
'Lady Liz'	SDay SPol WNHG
'Lady Mischief'	EStr SDay
'Lady Neva' ♀H6	CBgR ELon
'Lady Tiger'	WNHG
'Ladybug's Two Moons' (d)	EStr
'Ladykin'	CWel ELon SPol
'Lake Norman Spider'	SPol
'Lambada'	EStr
'Lamplighter's Circle' **new**	EStr
'Land of Cotton'	XSen
'Land's End'	EStr
'Lark Song'	CRos LRHS NRHS WFar WHrl
'Larry's Candy Stripe Swizzle' **new**	EStr
'Last Song'	CWel
'Late Summer Rose' **new**	WNHG
'Laughing Giraffe'	EStr WCot
'Laughton Tower'	SMHy
'Laura Harwood' **new**	SPol
'Laura Lambert'	SPol
'Lauradell'	SDay
'Lauren Leah'	SDay
'Laurena'	SPol
'Lavender Blue Baby'	CRos CWel EPfP LRHS NRHS
'Lavender Bonanza'	SDay
'Lavender Deal'	MNrw WNHG
'Lavender Handlebars'	SDay
'Lavender Illusion'	CWel
'Lavender Memories'	EStr SDay
'Lavender Plicata'	SPol
'Lavender Showstopper'	WCAu
'Lavender Silver Cords'	SPol
'Lavender Spider'	CBgR SPol
'Lavender Tonic'	SPol WNHG

	'Lavender Tutu'	ECtt EStr
	'Layers of Gold' (d)	XSen
	'Lazy Hazy Days'	EStr
	'Ledgewood's Gabrielle'	CWel
	'Ledgewood's Irish Spirit' **new**	EStr
	'Ledgewood's Sunday Dessert'	EStr
	'Lee Reinke'	SPol
	'Leila Mantle'	CBgR
	'Lemon Bells'	CWat CWel ECha EPfP EStr GKev GKin GMaP LEdu LRHS NBro NRHS SHar WCAu WSpi
	'Lemon Custard'	EStr
	'Lemon Dessert'	ELon
	'Lemon Madeline'	EStr
	'Lemon Mint'	ELon
	'Lemonora'	SDay
	'Lenox'	SDay
	'Leonard Bernstein'	EStr SPol
	'Leslie Renee'	CWel
	'Let it Rip'	SPol
	'Let Loose'	EStr
	'Let Love Rejoice' **new**	EStr
	'Lexington Avenue'	SPol
	'Licorice Candy'	CWel SPol
	'Licorice Twist'	CWel
	'Light the Way'	CBod CRos GBin LLWG LRHS MHol MSCN NRHS SPoG WCot
	'Light Years Away'	ELon MBNS MNrw
	'Lilac Wine'	SCob
§	***lilioasphodelus***	Widely available
	'Lilly Dache'	EStr
	'Lilting Belle'	SPol
	'Lilting Lady'	EStr SPol
	'Lilting Lavender'	ELon SPol WCAu
	'Lily Munster' **new**	EStr
	'Lime Frost' ♀H6	CBgR CWel EStr SPol
	'Lime Painted Lady'	CBgR
	'Limetree'	CBgR EStr
	'Linda'	MRav
	'Linda the Green Eyed Lady' **new**	EStr
	'Litchfield Plantation'	EStr
	'Little Anna Rosa' **new**	EStr
	'Little Audrey'	EStr
	'Little Bee'	NBre
	'Little Big Man'	SDay
	'Little Bugger'	ELon MBNS
	'Little Bumble Bee'	CRos LRHS MBNS NRHS WWtn
	'Little Business'	SDay SPol
	'Little Cadet'	XLum
	'Little Cranberry Cove'	GBin
	'Little Dart'	ECha
	'Little Deeke'	CWel SDay WHrl
	'Little Fantastic'	CRos ELon LRHS NRHS SDay WWtn
	'Little Fat Cat'	EStr
	'Little Fat Dazzler'	SPol
	'Little Fellow'	EStr MBNS
	'Little Girl'	ELon
	'Little Grapette'	ELon EPfP EStr GQue LLWG NLar NSti WAul WCAu WHar
	'Little Greenie'	CWel SDay
	'Little Gypsy Vagabond'	CBgR CWat EStr SPol
	'Little Heavenly Angel'	EStr SPol
	'Little Isaac'	EStr
	'Little Judy'	SPol
	'Little Kiki'	SDay
	'Little Lassie'	CBgR

'Little Maggie'	SDay SPol
'Little Men'	WCAu
'Little Miss Lucy' **new**	EStr
'Little Miss Manners'	EStr NLar
'Little Missy'	CBgR EPfP SDay WHoo WNHG
'Little Monica'	SDay
'Little Music Maker' (d)	EStr
'Little Paul'	EStr
'Little Red Hen'	CSam GKin LRHS MSpe NBro NEgg NGdn NRHS SDay WFar
'Little Sea Sprite'	CWel
'Little Show Stopper'	NBro NLar
'Little Showoff'	SDay
'Little Swain'	SDay
'Little Sweet Talk'	ELon
'Little Tawny'	CRos ELon LRHS NRHS
'Little Toddler'	SDay
'Little Violet Lace'	SDay
'Little Wart'	CBgR SDay WHrl
'Little Wine Cup'	CMac CRos CSam ECrc ECtt ELon EPfP EStr GKin GMaP LRHS MRav NEgg NGdn NRHS SPer SPol SRms WAul WMoo WOut
'Little Women'	SDay
'Little Zinger'	SDay
'Littlest Angel'	SDay
'Littlest Clown'	SDay
'Living in Amsterdam'	EBee EStr
'Lobo Lucy'	ELon EStr
'Loch Ness Monster' **new**	EStr
'Lochinvar'	CSam MRav
'Loco Bo'	EStr
'Lois Burns'	SDay SPol
'Lonely Heart' **new**	EStr
'Lonesome Dove'	SPol
'Long John Silver'	ELon EStr
'Long Stocking'	EStr SPol WCot
'Long Tall Sally'	EStr
'Longfields × Factor'	EStr
'Longfields Glory'	CRos LRHS MBNS MSpe NBre NRHS
'Longfields Maxim' (d)	EStr MHol SDeJ
'Longfields Pearl'	EStr
'Longfields Pride'	EStr IBoy MBNS SRms WBor
'Longfields Purple Eye'	NLar
'Longfields Think Pink'	EStr
'Longfields Twins'	MBNS WCot WFar
'Longfields Whoopy'	ELon EPfP MNrw SCob
'Longfields Woodpecker' **new**	EStr
longituba AIK 284	WCot
– B&SWJ 4576	WCru
'Look at Me'	ELan
'Lost in the Toy Store' **new**	EStr
'Loth Lorien'	EBee
'Lots of Hoopla'	EStr
'Lotus Land'	SDay
'Louis Burnes'	SPol
'Louis McHargue'	SDay
'Lourice Abdallah'	EStr
'Love Those Eyes'	EStr
'Lovely Rita'	EStr
'Loverboy' **new**	EStr
'Loving Memories'	SDay
'Lowcountry Gem'	EStr
'Lucille Lennington'	WNHG
'Lullaby Baby'	CWel ELan GCal NLar SDay SPol WNHG
'Luna'	SPol
'Lupita Vindaz' **new**	EStr
'Luscious Honeydew'	WNHG
'Lusty Lealand'	MBNS SDay
'Luxury Lace'	CAgr EBee ECtt ELan EPfP EStr GBin GKin LSRN NGdn NWad SPer SPol WFar WHrl WMoo WWtn XLum XSen
'Lycean'	CWel
'Lydia Bechtold'	EStr SDay
'Lynn Hall'	NLar WSpi
'Mabel Fuller'	CBgR MRav SPer WHrl
'Mabel Nolen'	EStr
'Mable Lewis Nelson'	EStr
'Macbeth'	EStr MBNS MNrw
'Mad Max'	EStr SDay SPol
'Madeline Nettles Eyes'	ELon EStr
'Maestro Puccini'	SDay
'Maggie Fynboe'	CBgR SPol
'Magic Amethyst'	CBgR
'Magic Carpet Ride'	EStr SPol
'Magic Dancer'	EStr
'Magic Lace'	EStr
'Magic Masquerade'	SDay
'Magic of Oz'	CWel
'Magical Messenger'	EStr
'Magnificent Eyes'	SPol
'Magnificent Rainbow'	CBcs
'Mahogany Magic' ♀H6	ELon
'Majestic Dark Eyes'	EStr
'Malachite Prism'	EStr
'Malaysian Monarch'	EStr SDay WNHG
'Malaysian Spice'	WNHG
'Maleny Chantilly Lace'	EStr
'Maleny Debutante'	EStr
'Maleny Kiwi Dazzler'	EStr
'Maleny Think Big'	CWel
'Mallard'	CAby CBgR ECtt EHrv EStr LLWG MRav SPer WCot
'Malmaison Plum'	EStr SDay
'Mama Sophia'	EStr
'Mama's Pajamas' **new**	EStr
'Mambo Maid'	XSen
'Man on Fire'	WNHG
'Manchurian Apricot'	SDay
'Marble Faun'	SDay
'Margaret McWhorter'	SPol
'Margaret Perry'	MNrw NLar
'Margaret Seawright'	EStr
'Margaret's Blue Diamond'	CWel
'Margo Reed Indeed'	SPol
'Marietta Charmer'	SDay SPol
'Marietta Delight'	EStr
'Marilyn Lee Bock'	CWel EStr
'Marion Caldwell'	SPol
'Marion Vaughn'	ECtt EHrv ELan EPfP GKin GMaP LLWG MBel MRav NSti SPer SRGP SWvt WCAu WCot WFar WHar WHoo WPtf WSHC
'Mariska'	EStr SDay WNHG
'Marked by Lydia'	ELon SPol
'Marmalade'	EPfP
'Marse Connell'	MSpe
'Martha Adams'	SDay
'Martina Verhaert'	CWGN CWel EBee EStr
'Mary Alice Stokes'	EStr
'Mary Ethel Anderson'	EStr
'Mary Todd'	EBee GMcL MBNS XSen
'Mary's Gold' ♀H6	SDay SPol
'Masada'	WNHG
'Mata Hari'	SDay SPol
'Matisse'	SPol
'Maude's Valentine' **new**	SDay

'Mauna Loa'	CSBt ELon EStr GQue MNrw NLar SDeJ SWvt WAul WCot
'May May'	CBgR SPol
'Mayan Poppy'	EStr
'Meadow Mist'	CBgR ELon WWtn
'Meadow Sprite'	WCot
'Meadowsweet'	EStr
'Mean Mister Mustard' **new**	EStr
'Medieval Guild'	EStr
'Mema's Dingaling'	EStr
'MeMe's Guilty Pleasure'	EStr
'MeMe's Lovin' the Limelight' **new**	EStr
'MeMe's Tuitti Fruitti' **new**	EStr
'Mephistopheles'	CWel
'Merry Moppet'	EStr
'Merry Witch'	EStr
'Metaphor'	ECtt SDay XSen
'Michael Poliga' **new**	EStr
'Michael's Sword' **new**	EStr
'Michele Coe'	ECtt GKin NBro NEgg NGdn SDay SRGP WCAu WHrl WMoo
'Mico'	ELon
middendorffii	CMac GMaP MCoo NSti WHrl WSpi WThu
'Midnight Magic'	SDay
'Midnight Mantis'	SPol
'Midnight Rambler'	SDay
'Midnight Rendezvous'	EStr
'Mikado'	CBgR CMac
'Mike Reed'	EStr
'Milady Greensleeves'	EStr SDay SPol WHrl
'Milanese Mango'	EStr
'Mildred Mitchell'	CBgR ELon EStr NLar SPol
'Military School'	EStr
'Millie Schlumpf'	CWel SPol
'Mimosa Umbrella'	EStr SPol
'Mind that Bird' **new**	EStr
'Ming Porcelain'	SPol WCAu WNHG
'Mini Pearl'	CRos ECtt ELon EStr LRHS NRHS SDay SPer
'Mini Stella'	CBro ECtt SDay SHar WFar
miniature hybrids	SRms
'Minnie Wildfire'	EStr SPol
minor	CBro CRos EBee EDAr EPPr LRHS NRHS SPhx SRms XSen
- B&SWJ 8841	WCru
'Mint Octopus'	CWel
'Miracle Maid'	WNHG
'Miss Jessie'	EStr SPol WHrl
'Missenden'	CBgR MNrw
'Mississippi Blues'	CWel
'Missouri Beauty'	IBoy SPol SWvt
'Missouri Memories'	SPol
'Mister Lucky'	CWel
'Mojave Sunset' **new**	EStr
'Moment of Truth'	NBre
'Monica Marie'	EStr SDay
'Mont Royal Demitasse'	ELon SPol
'Moon Music'	CWel
'Moon Snow'	SDay
'Moon Witch'	EStr SDay SPol
'Moonlight Masquerade'	CBgR ECtt MMuc NLar SRms WOut
'Moonlight Mist'	SDay SPol
'Moonlight Orchid'	WHrl
'Moonlit Caress'	CBgR EBee ECtt NBro
'Moonlit Crystal'	EStr SPol
'Moonlit Masquerade' ♀H6	CPar CWGN CWel EStr MBNS MNrw SEND SHar SPol WHrl
'Moonlit Summerbird'	EStr SDay SPol

'Moontraveller'	WCot
'Morgen le Fay'	EStr SPol
'Mormon Spider'	EStr SPol
'Morning Face' **new**	EStr
'Morning Sun'	MBNS WCot
'Morocco'	SPol
'Morocco Red'	CBro CCse ELan MHCG
'Morrie Otte'	SPol
'Mosel'	SDay
'Moses' Fire'	ECtt EPfP EStr MHol NLar WFar
'Mossy Glade'	CBgR
'Mount Joy'	EStr
'Mountain Laurel'	CRos ECtt EStr GKin LRHS MRav NEgg NRHS SPol WFar WGwG
'Moussaka'	CWGN EStr WFar
'Move Over Moon'	EStr SDay
'Mrs David Hall'	CCse
'Mrs Hugh Johnson'	CChe EShb WHrl
* 'Mrs Lester'	SDay
'Much Ado About Magic'	CWel
'Muffet's Little Friend'	SPol
multiflora	XSen
'Muriel Rhem'	EStr
'Murphy's Law'	EStr
'Muscle Man'	EStr XSen
'My Belle'	SDay
'My Darling Clementine'	EStr SDay
'My Gal Sal'	CWel
'My Heart Belongs to Daddy'	EStr
'My Hope'	SPol
'My Melinda'	SDay
'Mynelle's Starfish'	CPar SPol WHrl
'Mystical Rainbow'	SDay
'Nabis'	SDay
'Nacogdoches Lady'	SWvt
* 'Nana Wallich'	EStr
'Nanuq'	CWel ELon SDay
'Naomi Ruth'	CWel EStr MBNS
'Nashville'	CBro ELan WHrl
'Nashville Lights'	CBgR EStr SPol
'National Memento' **new**	EStr
'Native Reflection' **new**	EStr
'Natural Born Charmer'	CWel
'Natural Veil'	SPol
'Nature's Crown' (d)	CWel
'Naughty Red' **new**	EStr
'Navajo Jewel'	EStr
'Navajo Pony' **new**	EStr
'Navajo Princess'	EBee MNrw SPol
'Neal Berrey'	EStr SDay SPol
'Nefertiti'	CBgR ELon WAul WCAu
'Neon Sunshine'	EStr
'Neon Yellow'	EStr
'Never Ending Fantasy'	EStr
'Never Get Away'	EStr
'New Paradigm'	CWel
'New York Follies'	EStr
'Neyron Rose'	GKin LRHS NEgg NGdn NRHS WMoo WWtn XLum
'Nick's Faith'	WHrl
'Nicole Joyce'	SPol
'Night Beacon'	CBgR ECtt ELon EStr EWes GKin LLWG MNrw MPie NLar SCob SDay SDeJ SPol WCAu WHrl
'Night Embers'	ECtt IPot LMea NLar
'Night Raider'	CBgR EStr SDay WNHG
'Night Whispers'	LCro LOPS SPer
'Night Wings'	CWel
'Nile Crane'	CBgR CWel ELon EStr MNrw SDay SPer WAul

'Nile Plum'	EStr SDay SPol
'Nina Winegar'	EStr
'Nob Hill'	CCse ELon EStr SPol WHrl XLum
'Nona's Garnet Spider'	ELon SPol
'Nordic Night'	CBgR SDay SPol
'North Wind Drifter' **new**	EStr
'Norton Beauté'	WCot
'Norton Eyed Seedling'	WNHG
'Norton Orange'	EStr
'Nosferatu'	SPol
'Not Forgotten'	WNHG
'Nothing is Easy' **new**	EStr
'Nouveau Riche'	SPol
'Nova'	ELon SDay
'Now and Zen'	CWel
'Nowhere to Hide'	EStr
'Nuit Parisienne'	EStr
'Nuka'	XLum
'Nutmeg Elf'	CBgR SDay SPol
'Oakes Love'	MNrw
'Ocean Rain'	EStr SDay SPol WNHG
'Ocean Spirit' **new**	EStr SPol
'Octopus Hugs'	SPol
'Official Curse'	SPol
'Oke-She-Moke-She-Pop'	EStr
'Oklahoma Kicking Bird'	SDay
'Old San Juan'	EStr
'Old Tangiers' ♀H6	EStr WNHG
'Olive Bailey Langdon'	EStr SDay SPol WCot
'Olive's Odd One'	EStr
'Oloroso'	CBgR
'Olympic Gold'	EStr XSen
'Olympic Showcase'	EStr
'Omomuki'	CWel SDay
'On and On'	EStr GBin GQue
'On Silken Thread'	SPol
'One Fire'	XSen
'Oodles'	WHrl
'Open Hearth'	EStr SPol WHrl
'Open my Eyes'	EStr
'Optical Art'	CWel
'Orange Dream'	SDay
'Orange Empire'	SDay
'Orange Exotica'	CBgR
'Orange Nassau'	WFar
'Orange Prelude'	XSen
'Orange Velvet'	SPol
'Orangeman' misapplied	MBNS NGdn
'Orchid Beauty'	WMoo
'Orchid Candy'	EStr GMcL MBNS SPol
'Orchid Corsage'	ELon EStr SPol
'Oriental Ruby'	SDay
'Orphée'	XSen
'Osterized'	EStr
'Ostrich Plume'	EStr SDay
'Ouachita Beauty'	CBgR SPol
'Our Kirsten'	EStr SDay
'Outrageous'	CBgR EStr SDay SPol WNHG
'Outrageous Ramona'	WNHG
'Oy Vey'	EStr
'Paige's Pinata'	EStr
'Painted Lady'	WNHG
'Painted Peach'	SPol
'Painted Pink'	SDay
'Palace Pagoda'	WNHG
'Panda Bear'	CWel
'Pandora's Box'	CExl CRos CTri CWat ECtt EHrv ELan EStr LLWG LRHS MMuc MNrw NGdn NLar NRHS SDeJ SPol SWvt WBor WCAu WHoo WMoo
'Panther Eyes'	CWel
'Pantherette'	SPol
'Papa Goose'	EStr
'Paper Butterfly'	EStr SDay SPol
'Papilion'	EStr
'Papoose'	XLum
'Paprika Flame'	EStr MHol
'Parade of Peacocks'	CBgR
'Paradise Bar and Grill' **new**	EStr
'Paradise Lost' **new**	EStr
'Pardon Me'	CBro CRos CWel CWld ECtt ELan ELon EStr GKin GMaP IRob LRHS NGdn NRHS SDeJ SMad SPol SRGP SWvt WAul WBor WCAu WFar
'Pardon Me Boy'	SPol
'Parfait'	CBgR EStr SPol WHrl
'Parrot Tattoo'	EStr
'Parson's Robe'	SDay
'Part-time Princess' **new**	EStr
'Party Queen'	SDay
'Pastel Ballerina'	SDay
'Pastel Classic'	SPol
'Pastilline'	SPol
'Pat Mercer'	SDay XSen
'Patchwork Puzzle'	EStr SPol
'Patricia Fay'	XSen
'Patriotic Flavor'	EStr
'Patsy Jane'	SPol
'Patterns'	SPol
'Patti Neyland'	EStr
'Paul Sain's Prize'	CWel
'Paula Nettles'	CWel EStr
'Pawn of Prophecy'	EStr
'Peach Jubilee'	EStr SPol
'Peach Magnolia' (d)	EStr
'Peach Whisper'	SDay
'Peacock Maiden'	EStr SPol WHrl XSen
'Pear Ornament'	SDay
'Pearl Anniversary' **new**	EStr
'Pearl Jam'	SDay
'Pearl Lewis'	EStr SDay SPol
'Peggy Jeffcoat'	EStr
'Penelope Vestey'	CBgR EStr SPol SRGP
'Penny's Worth'	CRos LEdu LRHS MBNS WAul WCot WFar XLum
'Peppermint Ice' **new**	EStr
'Persian Melon Plus'	WCAu
'Persian Ruby'	CWel EStr SDay SPol
'Persian Shrine'	SPol
'Persimmone'	SPol
'Petite Ballerina'	SDay
'Phyllis Cantini'	SPol
'Piano Man'	CWel EStr MBNS WAul WNHG
'Piccadilly Princess'	CWel EStr
'Pickin' and Grinnin''	EStr
'Piece of the Action' **new**	EStr
'Pigment of Imagination' **new**	EStr
'Pinhill Navajo Beauty' **new**	EStr
'Pink Ambrosia'	ECtt EStr
'Pink Ballerina'	WWtn
'Pink Charm'	CMac CRos ECha ECtt EPPr GKin GMaP LRHS NBro NRHS SPol
'Pink Circle'	SDay
'Pink Cotton Candy'	SDay SPol
'Pink Damask' ♀H7	Widely available
'Pink Dazzler'	WNHG
'Pink Delight'	MPie
'Pink Dream'	CBgR NBre SPol
'Pink Flirt'	SDay

'Pink Grace'	SPol
'Pink Lady'	MNrw MRav SRms
'Pink Monday'	SDay WNHG
'Pink Prelude'	MSpe
'Pink Puff'	NBre NLar
'Pink Rain Dance'	SPol
'Pink Spider'	SDay
'Pink Stripes'	EStr
'Pink Sundae'	SBee WHrl
'Pink Super Spider'	SDay SPol
'Pink Windmill'	ELon SPol
'Pinocchio'	SMHy
'Piquante'	SCob
'Pirate Treasure'	EStr MBNS
'Pirate's Patch'	SDay SPol WCot
'Pixie Parasol'	WNHG WSpi
'Pixie Pinwheel Party'	CWel
'Pixie Pipestone'	SPol
'Pixie Princess'	EStr
'Pizza'	SDay
'Pleated Petticoats' **new**	EStr
'Plum Beautiful'	EStr
'Plum Beauty'	NLar
'Plumburst'	EPfP
'Poinsettia'	EStr
'Point of View'	EStr
'Pojo'	EStr SDay
'Polka Dot Bikini' **new**	EStr
'Pony'	ELon GNew SPol
'Porcelain Pleasure'	SDay
'Possum in a Sack'	CBgR
'Post Time'	EStr
'Prague Spring'	CWel EStr MSpe SDay SPol WHrl
'Prairie Belle'	GKev NLar SPol
'Prairie Blue Eyes'	EStr IBoy ILea SDay SPlb SPol WCot WHrl WWtn
'Prairie Charmer'	MMuc SEND WHrl
'Prairie Moonlight'	EWTr
'Prankster' **new**	EStr
'Precious Candy'	CWel
'Precious d'Oro'	GQue
'Pretty Face Nice Legs' **new**	EStr
'Pretty Miss'	ECtt EStr LRHS NRHS WGwG
'Preview Party'	WNHG
'Primal Scream' ♀H6	EStr GAbr LSun MHol SDay SPoG SPol WCot
'Prince of Midnight'	SDay
'Prince of Purple'	ELon
'Prince Poppycock'	EStr
'Prince Redbird'	SDay
'Princess Blue Eyes'	SPol
'Princess Charming' **new**	EStr
'Princeton Eye Glow'	MSpe SDay
'Princeton Silky'	ELon
'Priscilla's Wish'	SPol
'Prisoner of Time'	CWel
'Prissy Frills'	SPol
'Prize Picotee Deluxe'	SDay SPol
'Prize Picotee Elite'	SDay SPol
'Protocol'	MSpe SDay SPol
'Proud Mary'	SDay
'Ptarmigan'	CBgR EStr
'Pterodactyl Eye'	EStr SDay
§ 'Puddin'	SDay
'Pueblo Dancer'	EStr
'Pug Yarborough'	EStr SDay SPol
'Pullin' Strings'	EStr
'Pumpkin Kid'	CWel SDay SPol
'Pumpkin Pie Spice'	SPol
'Punxsutawney Phil'	EStr

'Puppet Show'	SDay
'Pure and Simple'	SPol
'Purple Arachne'	SPol
'Purple Avenger' **new**	SDay
'Purple Bicolor'	WHrl
'Purple Flame' **new**	EStr
'Purple Many Faces'	SPol
'Purple Oddity'	SPol
'Purple Pinwheel'	SPol
'Purple Rain'	CWat MBNS MPie SDay SPol SWvt
'Purple Rain Dance'	SPol
'Purple Waters'	EStr MJak SPol WPnP
'Purpleicious'	NLar
'Pursuit of Excellence'	SDay
'Putting on the Ritz' **new**	EStr
'Pygmy Plum'	SDay XSen
'Pyrotechnics'	EStr
'Quality of Mercy'	SDay
'Quartzitic Scintillation' **new**	EStr
'Queen Charlotte'	EStr
'Queen Empress'	WNHG
'Queen Lily'	WNHG
'Queen of Green' **new**	EStr
'Queen of May'	MNrw WCot
'Quick Results'	SDay
'Quietly Awesome'	SDay
'Quilt Patch'	EStr SPol
'Quinn Buck'	SDay
'Ra Hansen'	CWel EStr
'Rachael My Love' (d)	XSen
'Radiant Greetings'	XSen
'Radiant Moonbeam' ♀H6	CBgR EStr
'Radiation Biohazard'	SPol
'Raging Tiger'	SDay WHrl
'Rain Dance'	EStr
'Rainbow Candy'	CWGN LLHF
'Rainbow Gold'	XSen
'Rainbow Maker' **new**	EStr
'Rajah'	CBgR CMac EStr MSpe NBro SCob SPer WHrl
'Randall Moore'	SPol
'Raspberry Candy'	CBro EStr IBoy MNrw SRms WHrl
'Raspberry Pixie'	SPol
'Raspberry Star'	EStr
'Raspberry Wine'	ECha
'Raspberry Winter'	EStr
'Razzle'	EStr
'Real Life Drama'	EStr
'Real Wind'	EStr SPol
'Red Admiral'	CRos LRHS NRHS
'Red Butterfly'	SPol
'Red Grace'	EStr
'Red Pennant'	SDay
'Red Precious' ♀H7	MNrw SMHy WCot
'Red Rain'	EStr WHrl XSen
'Red Ribbons'	ELon SDay SPol
'Red Rum'	CBgR CBod EUJe LRHS MSpe MSwo NBro NRHS WMoo
'Red Suspenders'	ECtt EStr MBNS
'Red Tallboy'	EStr
'Red Thrill'	WHrl
'Red Twister'	ELon EStr SPol
'Red Volunteer'	EStr SDay SPol
'Redheaded Hussy'	EStr
'Regal Giant'	EStr
'Regency Dandy'	SDay SPol XSen
'Regency Heights'	EStr
'Renee'	MNrw
'Respighi'	EStr
'Return Trip'	SPol

'Revolute'	SDay
'Rhubarb Wine'	EStr
'Rhythm of Love'	EStr
'Ribbonette'	EBee EStr
'Ricky Rose'	SDay XSen
'Rigamarole'	SPol
'Riley Barron'	SDay
'Rise of the Phoenix'	EStr
'Rocket Booster'	EStr
'Rocket City'	ELan EStr SPol WNHG
'Roger Grounds'	CBgR SPol
'Roll Up Candy'	CWel
'Roman Toga'	CBgR SDay
* 'Romantic Rose'	MBNS NLar WHrl
'Romeo is Bleeding'	EStr
'Romulan Defector'	CWel
'Ron Azzanni' **new**	EStr
'Ron Rousseau'	SPol
'Root Beer'	GQue WCAu WHrl
'Rose'	SDay
'Rose Emily'	CBgR EStr SDay SPol
'Rose F. Kennedy' **new**	EStr
'Rose for Charlotte'	SPol
'Rose Tattoo'	EStr
'Roses in Snow'	IBoy SDay SPol
'Rosewood Rainbow End'	CWel
'Roswitha'	EStr SPol
'Rosy Lights'	SPol
'Rosy Polyphemus'	EStr
'Rosy Returns'	CRos EPfP LRHS NLar NRHS
'Round Midnight'	SPol
'Roy Likes Em Hot' **new**	EStr
'Royal Braid'	NLar SPer WCot
'Royal Celebration'	WCot
'Royal Eventide'	XSen
'Royal Heritage'	EBee EStr SDay
'Royal Robe'	CTri
'Royal Saracen'	SDay
'Royal Thornbird'	CBgR
'Royal Trophy'	WNHG
'Ruby Corsage'	EStr
'Ruby Sentinel'	SDay
'Ruby Spider' ♀H6	CWel ELon EStr SPol
'Rue Madelaine'	SPol
'Ruffled Apricot'	SDay WNHG
'Ruffled Carousel'	WNHG
'Ruffled Dude'	EStr
'Ruffled Ivory'	SDay
'Ruffled Lemon Lace'	EStr
'Ruffled Magic'	SDay
'Ruffled Perfection'	EStr
'Rumble Seat Romance'	WNHG
'Running for the Border' **new**	EStr
'Russian Easter'	EStr
'Russian Ragtime'	EStr
'Russian Rhapsody' ♀H6	SDay SPol
'Ruth Oliver'	EStr
'Sabie'	EStr
'Sabine Baur'	CRos EStr LRHS MNrw NRHS WFar
'Sabra Salina'	EStr SDay SPol
'Sacred Drummer'	SDay
'Saffron Glow'	SDay
'Sahara Sand Storm'	CWel EStr
'Sahara Song'	EStr
'Sallie Brown'	EStr SDay
'Salmon Sheen'	SPer
'Sammy'	EStr SDay WHrl
'Sammy Russell'	Widely available
'San Luis Halloween'	CWel

'Sandra Walker'	WWtn
'Sandy Beckman' **new**	EStr
'Santiago'	SPol
'Saratoga Belle'	EStr
'Saratoga Pinwheel'	SPol
'Sariah'	SDay
'Satin Glass'	CRos LRHS NRHS
'Satin Glow'	ECha
'Scandinavia' **new**	SPol
'Scarlet Butterfly'	SPol
'Scarlet Flame'	ECha WMoo
'Scarlet Orbit'	SPol
'Scarlet Prince'	WNHG
'Scarlet Ribbons'	EStr SPol
'Scatterbrain'	SPol
'Schnickel Fritz'	EBee
'School Girl'	CRos LRHS NRHS
'Scorchio'	EStr
'Scorpio'	CBgR MSpe SDay SPol WHrl
'Screaming Demon'	EStr SPol WCot
'Sea Swept Dreams'	SDay
'Seal of Approval'	EBee EStr
'Seal the Deal' **new**	EStr
'Sebastian'	SDay
'Secret Splendor'	SPol
'Seductive Fairy Tale'	EStr
'Selma Longlegs' ♀H6	EStr SDay SPol
'Seminole Blood'	SPol
'Seminole Wind'	SDay SPol
'Semiramide'	CBgR WNHG
'Serena Lady'	SDay
'Serena Sunburst' ♀H6	CWel EStr SPol
'Serene Madonna'	ELan ILea
'Serenity Morgan'	CBgR
'Serge Rigaud'	WHrl
'Shadowed Pink'	WNHG
'Shady Lady'	SDay SPol
'Shaman' Gates	SDay SPol
'Shark Attack' **new**	EStr
'She Devil'	EStr
'Shelly Victoria'	SDay
'Sherry Lane Carr'	EStr SDay SPol
'Sherwood Gladiator'	WNHG
'Shibui Splendor'	SPol
'Shimek September Morning'	EStr SPol
'Shinto Etching'	EStr
'Shinto Shrine'	WNHG
'Shotgun'	EStr SPol
'Sigudilla'	WNHG
'Silent Sentry'	EStr
'Silken Fairy'	CBgR SDay WWtn
'Silken Touch'	CBgR EStr SDay SPol
'Silly Whimsey'	CWel
'Siloam Amazing Grace'	SDay
'Siloam Angel Blush'	SDay
'Siloam Baby Doll'	SDay
'Siloam Baby Talk'	ELon EStr SDay WAul WMoo WPnP
'Siloam Bo Peep'	SDay
'Siloam Button Box'	WHrl
'Siloam Bye Lo'	SDay
'Siloam Cinderella'	SDay SPol
'Siloam David Kirchhoff'	EBee SDay XSen
'Siloam Doodlebug'	CBgR
'Siloam Double Classic' (d)	EStr SDay SPol
'Siloam Dream Baby'	ELon
'Siloam Edith Sholar'	CWel
'Siloam Ethel Smith'	SDay SPol
'Siloam Fairy Tale'	SDay
'Siloam Flower Girl'	SDay

'Siloam French Doll'	MBNS NLar
'Siloam French Marble'	SDay
'Siloam Frosted Mint'	SDay SPol
'Siloam Gold Coin'	SDay
'Siloam Grace Stamile'	MBNS
'Siloam Helpmate'	WNHG
'Siloam John Yonski'	SDay
'Siloam June Bug'	CBgR ELan WCot
'Siloam Justine Lee'	MBNS
'Siloam Little Angel'	SPol
'Siloam Little Girl'	CWel ECtt EStr SDay
'Siloam Mama'	SDay
'Siloam Merle Kent'	CWel SDay SPol WAul
'Siloam Nugget'	EStr
'Siloam Orchid Jewel'	SDay
'Siloam Paul Watts'	EStr GMcL SPol
'Siloam Peewee'	CRos ELon LRHS NRHS
'Siloam Pink Glow'	SDay
'Siloam Plum Tree'	SPol
'Siloam Pocket Size'	SDay
'Siloam Queen's Toy'	SPol
'Siloam Red Toy'	SMHy
'Siloam Ribbon Candy'	SDay WNHG
'Siloam Rose Dawn'	SPol
'Siloam Rose Queen'	SDay
'Siloam Ruffled Infant'	SDay
'Siloam Shocker'	EStr
'Siloam Show Girl'	CWGN CWel EStr GKin
'Siloam Space Age'	WNHG
'Siloam Spizz'	EStr SDay
'Siloam Sugar Time'	ELon
'Siloam Tee Tiny'	WAul WWtn
'Siloam Tiny Mite'	SDay WHrl
'Siloam Toddler'	EStr
'Siloam Tom Thumb'	CBgR EStr MBNS
'Siloam Ury Winniford'	CBro CMac GMcL NLar WHoo WPnP
'Siloam Virginia Henson'	EStr WWtn
'Silver Ice'	SDay SPol
'Silver Lance'	EStr SDay SPol
'Silver Quasar'	SDay SPol
'Silver Veil'	SDay
'Simmons Overture'	ECtt EStr
'Sinbad Sailor'	NLar
'Sink Into Your Eyes'	EStr WHrl
'Sir Blackstem'	GCal SDay
'Sir Knight'	SPol
'Sir Modred' ♀H6	EStr SDay SPol WHrl WNHG
'Sister Grace' **new**	SDay
'Sitting on a Rainbow'	EStr
'Sixth Sense'	ELon MBNS
'Slapstick'	ELon EStr SDay SPol
'Sleepy'	ECha
'Sleepy Hollow'	EStr
'Slender Lady'	ELon XSen
'Slipping Into the Abyss'	EStr
'Smith Brothers'	SPol
'Smoke Scream'	EStr
'Smoky Mountain Autumn'	SPol WHrl
'Smooch Hollow'	CBgR EStr
'Smuggler's Gold'	ECtt EStr SDay
'Smuggler's Temptation'	SPol
'Snaggle Tooth'	EStr
'Snow Wonder'	CWel
'Snowy Apparition'	CRos EBee ECrc ECtt GBin GKin LRHS NRHS NWad SPol SWvt
'Snowy Eyes'	CHid GKin WHrl
'So Excited'	SDay
'So Lovely'	XLum
'So Many Stars'	SPol

'Soft Cashmere'	XLum
'Solid Geometry'	EStr
'Solid Scarlet'	EStr
'Solomon's Robes'	SDay
'Sombrero Way'	SDay
'Someone Special'	EStr SDay SPol
'Somerset Fandango'	CBgR
'Song Sparrow'	CBro IRob
'Soraya Seline'	CBgR
'Sound of Color'	EStr
'South Carolina Peach' **new**	EStr
'South Seas'	EStr
'Southern Cotton' **new**	EStr
'Sovereign Queen'	WNHG
'Spacecoast Devil's Eye'	CWel
'Spacecoast Dream Catcher' **new**	EStr
'Spacecoast Freaky Tiki'	EStr
'Spacecoast Gone Bulldoggin''	CWel
'Spacecoast Scrambled'	CWel NLar
'Spacecoast Starburst'	EStr WCot
'Spanish Fandango'	EStr SPol
'Spanish Glow'	SPol
'Sparkling Dawn'	EStr
'Sparkling Orange'	SDay
'Special Candy'	CWel
'Spellbound Secret'	CWel
'Spider Breeder'	CBgR ELon EStr
'Spider Man' ♀H6	ELon EStr SDay SPol WCAu XSen
'Spider Miracle'	SDay SPol
'Spider Red'	CWGN EWTr
'Spider Web'	EStr
'Spilled Milk'	SPol
'Spin Master'	EStr
'Spindazzle'	CBgR SDay SPol
'Spinne in Lachs'	EStr SPol
'Spinneret'	EStr
'Spiny Sea Urchin'	CWel
'Spiral Charmer'	SPol
'Spiral Nebula'	EStr
'Spirit Folk' **new**	EStr
'Spirited Butterfly'	CWel
'Splatter' **new**	EStr
'Splittin' Hairs'	EStr
'Spooner'	CBgR
'Spoons for Escargot'	EStr
'Spotted Fever' **new**	EStr
'Spring Willow Song'	EStr SDay
'Springfield Clan'	EStr
'Springmaid Beach' **new**	EStr
'Spunky Monkey' **new**	EStr
'Stafford' ♀H7	Widely available
'Staghorn Sumac'	GKin LEdu WCAu
'Star Asterisk'	SPol
'Star of India'	SPol
'Star Poly'	EStr
'Star Spangled'	SPol
'Stargate Corridor'	SPol
'Starling'	CPar GNew NChi WSpi WWtn
'Starman's Quest'	EStr SPol
'Starstruck'	WNHG
'Startle'	ELon EStr MNrw WCot WHrl
'Steely Blue Eyes'	EStr
'Stella de Oro'	Widely available
'Stella in Purple'	EPfP
'Stella in Red'	EPfP ETMg
'Stenciled Impressions'	CWel
'Steve Trimmer'	SPol

'Stoke Poges' CBgR CBro EBee ELon EPPr EPfP EShb EStr GBin IRob MMuc SPer WHrl
'Stop the Insanity' **new** EStr
'Stoplight' CBgR ELon EStr LRHS NRHS SMHy SPol WHrl
'Storm of the Century' CBod EStr
'Strasbourg' CMac
'Strawberry Candy' ♀H6 CBgR CMac CRos CSBt CWel ECtt ELon EPfP EStr IBoy ILea LLWG LRHS MPie NGdn NLar NRHS SCob SDay SPer WAul WCAu WHrl WMoo WNHG WSpi
'Strawberry Fields Forever' SPol
I 'Streaker' B. Brown (v) XSen
'Street Urchin' SPol
'Strider Spider' EStr
'String Bikini' EStr
'Strutter's Ball' CBod EStr MJak NGdn SPer SPol WAul WAvo WCAu WHar WHrl
'Stupidville USA' EStr
'Stu's Old Pink Spider' CBgR
'Suburban Golden Eagle' EStr
'Sue Strickfaden' **new** EStr
'Sugar Cookie' SDay SPol
'Summer Dragon' EStr MBNS
'Summer Interlude' WMoo
'Summer Star' EStr
'Summer Wine' Widely available
'Sunday Gloves' MBNS SPol WNHG
'Sunday Morning' SDay
'Sungold Candy' CWel EStr
'Sunset Lagoon' EStr SPol
'Superlative' EStr SPol
'Susan Pritchard Petit' CWel LMea
'Susan Weber' CWel SPol
'Suzy Cream Cheese' SPol
'Svengali' SDay SPol
'Swallow Tail Kite' SPol
'Swan Dance' EStr SDay
'Swashbuckler Bay Boy' CWel
'Sweet Charlotte' SPol
'Sweet Country Luvin'' EStr
'Sweet Home Louisiana' **new** EStr
'Sweet Hot Chocolate' LRHS
'Sweet Pea' EStr
'Sweet Sugar Candy' ECtt SDeJ
'Swirling Spider' CBgR SPol
'Taj Mahal' ELon GQue SDay
'Tang' CHid MBNS
'Tangerine Twist' EStr SPol
'Tango Noturno' SPol
'Tani' SDay
'Taos' EStr
'Tar and Feather' CWel EStr
'Tarantula' ELon SPol
'Taruga' SDay
'Tasmania' SPer
'Tchao Pantin' XSen
'Techny Peach Lace' EStr SPol
'Techny Spider' EStr SPol
'Teenie Girl' EStr
'Tejas' CElw ELon SPer
'Témoin' XSen
'Tennessee Flycatcher' SPol
'Tennessee Williams' SPol
'Tequila and Lime' EStr
'Tet Set' WNHG
'Tetraploid Siloam Red Toy' SDay
'Tetraploid Stella de Oro' SDay
'Tetrina's Daughter' CBgR EPfP LRHS
'Thank Your Lucky Stars' EStr
'Thanks a Bunch' SPol
'The Bird is the Word' **new** EStr
'The Ghosts of Boyfriends Past' **new** EStr
'The New Normal' **new** EStr
'Thelma Douglas' EStr
'Thelma Perry' LEdu
'Thermal Overload' EStr
'Thin Man' EStr
'Think Pink' EPfP
'Thomas Tew' CWel
'Thousand Voices' EStr
'Three Diamonds' SPol
'Three Times a Lady' EStr
'Thrill Ride' SPol
'Thumbelina' ECha WMoo XLum
§ ***thunbergii*** ECha GCal MCoo XLum
– 'Ovation' MBNS
'Thunder and Lightning' EStr
'Thundering Ovation' CWGN
'Thy True Love' SDay
'Tiger Blood' EStr
'Tigereye Spider' EStr
'Tigerling' CWel EStr SPol
'Tigger' EStr SDeJ SPad SPol
'Till I Turn Purple' EStr
'Time Lord' SDay XSen
'Time of Angels' **new** EStr
'Time to Believe' SPol
'Time Together' EStr
'Time Window' EStr
'Tiny Temptress' SDay
'Tip of the Iceberg' **new** EStr
'Tirade' EStr
'Tis Midnight' WNHG
'Titanic Tower' CWel
'Tixie' EStr
'Tom Barnes' **new** EStr
'Tom Collins' SDay
'Tom Wise' EStr SPol
'Tomorrow's Song' SPol
'Tone Poem' WNHG
'Tonia Gay' SDay SPol
'Tooth' EStr
'Toothpick' SPol WHrl
'Tootsie' SDay
'Tootsie Rose' SDay SPol
'Top Honors' SPol
'Topaz Gem' SPol
'Topguns Aztec Vision' **new** EStr
'Topguns Bandit's Bandana' EStr
'Topguns Cactus Jack' EStr
'Torpoint' CBgR MRav NEgg
'Touch of Magic' EStr
'Towhead' MRav SDay WCot
'Toyland' NGdn NLar SPol
'Trahlyta' CBgR EStr SDay SPol WHrl
'Tramps Like Us' **new** EStr
'Trance' **new** EStr
'Treasure That I Seek' **new** EStr
'Tribute to Joe' EStr
'Trickster' **new** EStr
'Trog' EStr
'Trond' SDay
'Tropical Hot Flash' EStr
'Tropical Passion' EStr LMea
'Tropical Toy' SDay
'True Gertrude Demarest' WHrl

'Trump Card' **new**	EStr
'Tune the Harp'	EStr SPol
'Tuolumne Fairy Tale'	SPol
'Tupac Amaru' **new**	EStr
'Turkish Tapestry'	CBgR
'Turkish Turban'	SDay SPol
'Turn the Other Cheek'	EStr
'Turtle Island'	EStr
'Tuscawilla Blackout'	SPol XSen
'Tuscawilla Pink Joe'	CWel
'Tuscawilla Princess'	EStr
'Tuscawilla Tigress'	CWel EStr GKin MNrw MSpe SDay SPol WAul WHrl
'Tutankhamun'	EStr SDay
'Tuxedo'	SPol
'Tuxedo Junction' ♀^{H6}	EStr
'Tuxedo Whiskers'	EStr
'Twenty Third Psalm'	WHal
'Twilight Swan'	WNHG
'Twist of Lemon'	SDay
'Two Faces of Love'	SPol
'Two Part Harmony'	WHrl
'Tylwyth Teg'	SPol
'Ultra Persuasion' **new**	SDay
'Umbrella Parade'	EStr
'Unique Purple'	SPol
'Uniquely Different'	SPol
'Unlock Your Dreams' **new**	EStr
'Up the Wazoo' **new**	EStr
'Upper Class Peach'	EStr
'Uptown Girl'	CWel EStr
'Valiant'	MBNS WHrl
'Valley Monster'	SPol
'Valley Sprite'	EStr
'Vanessa Arden'	SPol
'Vanilla Fluff'	EStr
'Varsity'	CExl CRos LRHS NRHS SPer
'Vectis Jean Merritt' **new**	EStr
'Vectis Jean Peirce' **new**	EStr
'Veins of Truth'	CBgR EStr LMea WCAu
'Velvet Eyes'	EStr
'Velvet Shadows'	CBgR SDay
'Velvet Web' **new**	EStr
'Vendetta'	WNHG
'Venusian Mirage'	EStr
'Vera Biaglow'	EStr MSpe SDay SPol
'Vermilion Flycatcher'	CWel
'Very Berry Ice'	EStr SPol
'Vespers'	WPnP
vespertina	see *H. thunbergii*
'Vesuvian'	SDay
'Veuve Joyeuse'	XSen
'Vi Simmons'	EStr
'Vicountess Byng'	WWtn
'Victoria Aden'	CBro
'Victoria Elizabeth Barnes'	WNHG
'Victorian Ribbons'	SPol
'Victorian Violet'	SDay
'Video'	SDay
'Vie en Rose'	EStr
'Viewpoint'	SDay
'Vino di Notte'	EStr
'Vintage Bordeaux'	ELan SDay
'Vintage Burgundy'	CBgR WNHG
'Vintage Passion'	EStr
'Vintage Wine'	WNHG
'Violent Thunder'	EStr
'Violet Cuckoo' **new**	EStr
'Violet Hour'	EStr SDay
'Viracocha'	WNHG

'Virgin's Blush'	SPer
'Vohann'	SDay
'Volcano Queen'	EPfP EStr WFar
'Voodoo Dancer'	CWel EStr SCob
'Waiting in the Wings'	SDay
'Walking on Sunshine'	EStr WCot
'Walnut Hill'	EStr
'Walt Disney'	GKin
'Wanda Evans' **new**	EStr
'War Paint'	EStr SDay
'Warp Drive'	SDay
'Watch Tower'	CBgR
'Watchyl Dancing Spider'	EStr SPol
'Water Witch'	CWat CWel SDay
'Watermelon Man'	CBgR
'Waxen Splendor'	EStr
'Wayne Johnson'	WNHG
'Wayside Green Imp'	MNrw
'Weaver's Art'	SPol
'Web Browser'	EStr
'Web Dancer'	SPol
'Webster's Aggie' **new**	EStr
'Webster's Pink Wonder'	EStr SPol
'Wee Willie Winkie'	WNHG
'Welchkins'	CWel SDay WAul
'Welfo White Diamond'	SPol
'Wesley Lee Kirby' **new**	EStr
'When I Dream'	EStr
'When You Get to Asheville' **new**	EStr
'Which Way Jim'	SDay
'Whichford'	CAby CBgR CBro CMea CRos CSam ECha ECtt ELan EPfP GCal GKin IRob LRHS NRHS SPer SPhx WGwG WHrl
'Whip City Fancy Free'	EStr
'Whirling Fury'	ELon
'White Behemoth' **new**	SPol
'White Coral'	LRHS LSRN NBro NRHS
'White Edged Madonna'	WHrl
'White Ensign'	SDay
'White Magician'	EStr
'White Pansy'	SDay
'White Temptation'	EPfP IBoy LRHS NGdn SDay WAul WHoo WNHG XSen
'White Tie Affair'	CWel
'White Zone'	SDay
'Whooperee'	SDay
'Whoopie'	CHid SPad
'Wideyed'	XLum
'Wiggle Butt' **new**	EStr
'Wigglesworth' **new**	EStr
'Wild about Sherry'	SPol
'Wild and Wonderful'	EPfP EStr LLWG LSun SDay WFar
'Wild Horses'	CRos CWel EPfP EWes LRHS MNrw NLar NRHS SCob SMad SPol WHrl
'Wild Mustang'	EStr MSpe
'Wild Wookie'	SDay
'William Milo Spalding'	EStr
'Willy Nilly'	SPol
'Wilson Spider'	EStr SPol
'Wind Frills'	NQui SPol XSen
'Wind Song'	ELon SDay
'Wind Storm' **new**	EStr
'Windmill Yellow'	SDay
'Window Dressing'	SDay
'Wineberry Candy'	EStr MBNS NLar SDay
'Wings of Chance'	SPol
'Wings on High'	SPol
'Winnie'	EStr

'Winnie the Pooh'	SDay
'Winsome Lady'	ECha ECtt GKin WHrl
'Winter Wolf'	EStr
'Winyah Eye' **new**	EStr
'Wired' **new**	EStr
'Wisest of Wizards'	SPol WHrl
'Wishful Dreaming' **new**	EStr
'Wishing Well'	WCot
'Witch Hazel'	WCAu WWtn
'Witch Stitchery'	EStr SDay
'Witches Brew'	CBgR
'Without Warning'	CBgR
'Womanizer'	EStr
'Wonder of it All' **new**	EStr
'Woodbury'	CBod
'Woodland Spider'	SDay
'Woodside Ruby'	WNHG
'Working with Green'	CWel
'Wyoming Wildfire'	CBgR
'Xia Xiang'	SDay
'Xochimilco'	WNHG
'Yabba Dabba Doo'	EStr SPol
'Yankee Pinstripes' **new**	EStr
'Yazoo Wild Violet'	EStr
'Yellow Angel'	ELon SPol WCot
'Yellow Lollipop'	SDay
'Yellow Rain'	WCot
'Yellow Ribbon'	EStr SPol
'Yellow Submarine'	EPfP
'Yes Man' **new**	EStr
'Yesterday Memories'	SDay
'Yesterday, Today and Tomorrow' **new**	SDay
yezoensis	EBtc
'Yum Yum Plum'	EStr SDay
'Yuma'	WNHG
'Zagora'	EStr WCAu
'Zampa'	CBgR EStr SDay
'Zara'	EStr SPer
'Zenobia'	EStr
'Zip Boom Bah'	EStr
'Zuni Mountains'	WNHG

Hepatica ✿ (*Ranunculaceae*)

acutiloba	EPot GEdr GKev IRob MBel MMoz WPnP XEll
- blue-flowered	MAsh
- white-flowered	MAsh
acutiloba × nobilis	SPer
americana	ELan GKev MAsh
- 'Ashwood Marble'	MAsh
angulosa	see *H. transsilvanica*
(Forest Series) 'Forest Blue'	EBee EHrv
- 'Forest Pink'	CWCL EBee EHrv ELan EWTr GBin GKev IRob XEll
- 'Forest Purple'	CWCL EBee ELan EWTr GBin GKev LCro LOPS XEll
- 'Forest Red'	CWCL EBee EHrv ELan GBin GKev LCro LOPS XEll
- 'Forest White'	CWCL EBee EHrv ELan GBin GKev LCro LOPS XEll
henryi	GEdr GKev MAsh
insularis	MAsh
maxima	GEdr LLHF MAsh WAbe
× ***media*** 'Ballardii'	GEdr LLHF MAsh
- 'Harvington Beauty'	GEdr IBlr IFoB MAsh WSHC
- 'Millstream Merlin'	GEdr
- 'Violett Prinz'	MAsh
§ ***nobilis*** ♀H5	Widely available
- var. ***asiatica***	MAsh
- - pink-flowered	MAsh
- - purple-flowered	MAsh
- - white-flowered	MAsh NPnk
- 'Bibo' **new**	EWld
- blue-flowered	IFoB MAsh NSla WAbe WHoo
- 'Cobalt'	GEdr NSla
- compact evergreen	MAsh
- 'Cremar'	GEdr MAsh
- dark-blue-flowered	ITim
- dwarf white-flowered	IFoB
- 'Elkofener Heidi'	GEdr
- 'Gold Band' (v)	GEdr
- var. ***japonica***	EPfP EWes GEdr IFoB MAsh NSla
- - 'Aikawa' (5/d) **new**	GEdr
- - 'Akabuku' (1)	GEdr
- - 'Akafuku' (1)	GEdr
- - 'Akane' (1)	GEdr
- - 'Akanezora' (6/d)	GEdr
- - 'Akebono' (9/d)	GEdr
- - 'Anjyu' (9/d)	GEdr
- - 'Aozora' (1) **new**	GEdr
- - 'Asahi' (7/d)	GEdr
- - 'Asahizuru' (6/d)	GEdr
- - 'Benifusya' (1) **new**	GEdr
- - 'Benihagure' (9/d) **new**	GEdr
- - 'Benikanzan' (1)	GEdr
- - 'Benikujyaku' (7/d)	GEdr
- - 'Benioiran' (3)	GEdr
- - 'Beniokesa' (9/d)	GEdr
- - 'Benishinjyu' (6/d)	GEdr
- - 'Benisuzume' (1)	GEdr
- - 'Benitaiko' (9/d)	GEdr
- - 'Bojyou' (5A/d)	GEdr
- - 'Daishihou' (9/d)	GEdr
- - 'Dewa' (9/d)	GEdr
- - 'Ebisu-no-hana' (5A/d) **new**	GEdr
- - 'Echigobijin' (1)	GEdr
- - 'Fukujyu' (9/d)	GEdr
- - 'Getsurin' (5A/d)	GEdr
- - 'Gosho-zakura' (5A/d)	GEdr
- - 'Gyousei' (1)	GEdr
- - 'Hakuji' (1)	GEdr
- - 'Hakurin' (6/d)	GEdr
- - 'Hakusetsu' (9/d)	GEdr
- - 'Hanagoromo' (9/d) **new**	GEdr
- - 'Haruka' (2)	GEdr
- - 'Harukaze' (5A/d)	GEdr
- - 'Harumo-no-gatari' (8/d) **new**	GEdr
- - 'Haruno-awajuki' (9/d)	GEdr
- - 'Hatsune' (5/d)	GEdr
- - 'Hidamari' (5/d) **new**	GEdr
- - 'Hohobeni' (9/d)	GEdr
- - 'Hokutosei' (7/d)	GEdr
- - 'Hoshizora' (2) **new**	GEdr
- - 'Hosyun' (1)	GEdr
- - 'Houkan' (9/d)	GEdr
- - 'Isaribi' (1)	GEdr
- - 'Junissen' (6/d)	GEdr
- - 'Kagura' (5A/d)	GEdr
- - 'Kasumino' (1)	GEdr
- - 'Kiko' (9/d)	GEdr
- - 'Kimon' (9/d)	GEdr
- - 'Koshi-no-maboroshi' (7/d)	GEdr
- - 'Kotobuki-hime' (5A/d) **new**	GEdr
- - 'Kouen' (6/d) **new**	GEdr
- - 'Kougyoku' (9/d)	GEdr

	- - 'Kousei' (9/d)	GEdr
	- - 'Kuetsu' (9/d)	GEdr
	- - 'Kuukai' (8/d)	GEdr
	- - f. ***magna***	MAsh
	- - 'Manazuru' (9/d)	GEdr
	- - 'Minamo' (5/d) **new**	GEdr
	- - 'Miwaku' (1)	GEdr
	- - 'Miyoshino' (1)	GEdr
	- - 'Miyuki' (9/d)	GEdr
	- - 'Murasaki-sakama' (9/d)	GEdr
	- - 'Murasaki-shikibu' (9/d)	GEdr
	- - 'Nanakubo' (1) **new**	GEdr
	- - 'Noumurasaki' (1)	GEdr
	- - 'Oboryo' (1)	GEdr
	- - 'Odoriko' (9/d)	GEdr
	- - 'Okesabayashi' **new**	GEdr
	- - 'Okina' (9/d)	GEdr
	- - 'Ō-murasaki' (1)	GEdr
	- - 'Orihime' (9/d)	GEdr
	- - 'Reeka' (1)	GEdr
	- - 'Reika' (5/d) **new**	GEdr
	- - 'Ryokurei' (5A/d)	GEdr
	- - 'Ryokusetsu' (9/d)	GEdr
	- - 'Ryokuun' (9/d)	GEdr
	- - 'Ryougetsu' (1)	GEdr
	- - 'Sadobeni' (1)	GEdr
	- - 'Saichou' (7/d)	GEdr
	- - Sandan Group (7/d)	GEdr
	- - 'Satsuma' (5A/d) **new**	GEdr
	- - 'Sawanemidori' (6/d)	GEdr
	- - 'Sayaka' (1)	GEdr
	- - 'Seikai' (5A/d)	GEdr
	- - 'Seizan' (9/d)	GEdr
	- - 'Senhime' (9/d)	GEdr
	- - 'Sen-nin' (6/d) **new**	GEdr
	- - 'Sennin-buraku' (8/d) **new**	GEdr
	- - 'Setsudu' (7/d)	GEdr
	- - 'Shihou' (9/d)	GEdr
	- - 'Shikouden' (9/d)	GEdr
	- - 'Shikouryuu' (9/d)	GEdr
	- - 'Shio' (9/d) **new**	GEdr
	- - 'Shirayuki' (9/d)	GEdr
	- - 'Shirin' (9/d)	GEdr
	- - 'Shiun' (9/d)	GEdr
	- - 'Shoujyouno-homare' (9/d)	GEdr
	- - 'Sougetsu' (6/d)	GEdr
	- - 'Souhou' (1) **new**	GEdr
	- - 'Soushyunka' (9/d)	GEdr
	- - 'Subaru' (9/d)	GEdr
	- - 'Suien' (9/d)	GEdr
	- - 'Syouchikubai' (7/d) **new**	GEdr
	- - 'Syunryuu' (9/d) **new**	GEdr
	- - 'Tae' (5A/d)	GEdr
	- - 'Taeka' (9/d)	GEdr
	- - 'Takumi' (9/d)	GEdr
	- - 'Tamahime' (8/d)	GEdr
	- - 'Tamakujyaku' (6/d)	GEdr
	- - 'Tamamushi' (9/d)	GEdr
	- - 'Tamao' (1)	GEdr
	- - 'Tamasaburou' (1)	GEdr
	- - 'Tenjinbai' (1)	GEdr
	- - 'Tenjin-ume' (1) **new**	GEdr
	- - 'Tennyonomai' (6A/d)	GEdr
	- - 'Tenzan' (7/d)	GEdr
	- - 'Toki' (9/d)	GEdr
	- - 'Touen' (9/d)	GEdr
	- - 'Touhou' (9/d)	GEdr
	- - 'Touryoku' (9/d)	GEdr
	- - 'Toyama-chiyo-iwai' (7/d)	GEdr
	- - 'Umezono' (1)	GEdr
	- - 'Unabara' (9/d)	GEdr
	- - 'Usugesyou' (9/d)	GEdr
	- - 'Usui' **new**	GEdr
	- - 'Utyuu' (1)	GEdr
	- - 'Wakakusa' (9/d)	GEdr
	- - 'Wakana' (1)	GEdr
	- - 'Yaegoromo' (6/d)	GEdr
	- - 'Yahiko' (5/d)	GEdr
	- - 'Yahikomurasaki' (1)	GEdr
	- - 'Yamahibiki' (9/d)	GEdr
	- - 'Yukishino' (2)	GEdr
	- - 'Yumes' (7/d) **new**	GEdr
	- - 'Yuunagi' (9/d)	GEdr
	- - 'Yuunami' (1)	GEdr
	- - 'Yuuzen' (5/d) **new**	GEdr
	- - 'Yuzuru' (9/d)	GEdr
	- large, pale blue-flowered	NSla
	- 'Lilac Picotee'	NSla
	- patterned leaf	NSla
	- pink-flowered	GAbr MAsh MMoz WHoo
	- var. ***pubescens***	MAsh
*	- var. ***pyrenaica***	LEdu MAsh NSla WThu
*	- - 'Apple Blossom'	WAbe
	- var. ***rubra***	NSla
	- 'Rubra Plena' (d)	CElw GEdr IRob MAsh NSla
	- violet-flowered	GAbr MAsh
	- 'White Sands'	ELan GBin GEdr
	- white-flowered	EHrv GAbr MAsh MMoz WHoo XEll
	'Noubeni'	GEdr
	× ***schlyteri*** Ashwood hybrids	MAsh
	- 'The Bride'	MAsh
	'Stained Glass'	EWld
§	***transsilvanica*** ♀H5	CBro EHrv MAsh MAvo MCot MMoz NPnk WCot WThu
	- 'Ada Scott'	GEdr MAsh
	- 'Blue Eyes'	GEdr GKev
	- 'Blue Jewel'	CWCL EBee ELan EPot GBin GEdr GKev IRob MCot MHol WPnP
	- blue-flowered	IBlr IFoB MAsh
	- 'Buis'	ECha GEdr IFoB ILea MAsh NLar
	- 'Connie Greenfield'	NSla
	- 'Eisvogel'	GEdr
	- 'Elison Spence' (d)	GEdr IBlr LLHF MAvo MCot
	- 'Lilacina'	GEdr MAsh
	- 'Loddon Blue'	GEdr IBlr MAsh
	- pink-flowered	MAsh
	- 'Sieben Bergen'	IBlr
	- 'Supernova'	MAsh
	- white-flowered	EWld GEdr MAsh
	triloba	see *H. nobilis*
	yamatutai	GEdr GKev
	aff. ***yamatutai***	MAsh

Heptacodium (*Caprifoliaceae*)

	jasminoides	see *H. miconioides*
§	***miconioides*** ♀H5	Widely available
	- TIANSHAN ('Minhep') **new**	SGol WCot

Heptapleurum see *Schefflera*

Heptaptera (*Apiaceae*)

	triquetra W&B BGA-2	CSpe WCot

Heracleum (*Apiaceae*)

	dulce	EBee
	sphondylium	WSFF
	stevenii	MHol WCot

Herbertia (*Iridaceae*)

§ ***lahue*** GKev

Hereroa (*Aizoaceae*)

glenensis CRos CSma EDAr LRHS NHpl NRHS SPlb

Hermannia (*Malvaceae*)

erodioides CPBP
flammea SPlb
stricta CPBP WAbe

Hermodactylus see *Iris*

Herniaria (*Caryophyllaceae*)

glabra GPoy

Hertia (*Asteraceae*)

§ ***cheirifolia*** CCCN CMea EWes SEND XLum

Hesperaloe (*Asparagaceae*)

campanulata WCot
engelmannii WCot
funifera white-flowered WCot
'Lynn's Pink' WCot
malacophylla CFil EBee
'Mamulique' WCot
'New Blue' WCot
parviflora CAco EBee LEdu SBig SChr SPlb XSen
– creamy yellow-flowered WCot
– 'Rubra' LRHS MPkF

Hesperantha ✿ (*Iridaceae*)

§ ***baurii*** CPbh GBin GKev LLHF NHpl WThu
coccinea CMac CPla CPrp CTri CTsd EBee EHoe ELan EPfP EUJe GKev IBlr LLWG MSCN MWts NChi NEgg NGdn NLar NPnk SBod SCob SDeJ SRot WCot WFar WMAq XLum
– f. ***alba*** CBro CExl CMea CPne CPrp CTri CTsd CWCL EBee ECha ELan EPfP GKev GMcL IRob ITim LRHS MRav NGdn NLar NRHS SCob SDeJ SPlb SRms SWvt WFar WMoo WPnP
– 'Anne' NLar
– 'Autumn's Dawn' **new** WFar
– 'Ballyrogan Giant' CPrp ECtt IBlr WFar WHer WSHC
– 'Big Moma' CPrp WFar
– 'Cardinal' WFar WMoo
– 'Caroline' CPrp WFar
– 'Cindy Towe' CAbb CKno EAJP IRob LLHF LSou WFar
– 'Countesse de Vere' EBee
– 'Elburton Glow' CPla WFar
– 'Eric's Early' CPrp
– 'Fenland Daybreak' CBcs CBod CChe CDor CKno CPrp CRos CWCL EAJP EBee ECtt ELan ELon EPfP GWyn LRHS LSou MGos MHol NEgg NLar NRHS SPoG SRms SRot SWvt WFar WHil WHoo WMoo
– 'Gigantea' see *H. coccinea* 'Major'
– 'Good White' CWCL SMHy
– 'Grandiflora' see *H. coccinea* 'Major'
– 'Hilary Gould' CMea CPrp ECtt WHal
– 'Ice Maiden' CAbb CBWd LSou SPoG
– 'Jack Frost' EBee WFar WMoo
– 'Jennifer' 🏆^{H4} CBro CDor CElw CPrp CTri EBee ECha ECtt ELon EPfP GAbr LRHS LSou MCot MMuc MRav NLar NRHS SRms SWvt WAvo WFar WMoo WPnP
– 'Maiden's Blush' ECtt EHrv ELan LEdu LRHS LSou MCot NLar SRms WFar
§ – 'Major' 🏆^{H4} Widely available
– 'Marietta' WFar
– 'Mollie Gould' CAvo CPrp ECtt EHrv ELon LLWG LRHS LSou MAvo MHer MNrw MPie NPnk NRHS SCoo SRms WAvo WFar WMoo
– 'Mrs Hegarty' CMac CPrp CSam ECtt ELan EPfP GAbr GMaP GMcL GWyn IBoy LRHS MGos MHer MRav MWts NBid NLar NRHS SDeJ SPer SPlb SRms SWvt WFar WHar
– 'November Cheer' CMac IBlr NLar
– 'Oregon Sunset' CBod CPrp LLHF LSou WFar WHil
– 'Pallida' CPrp CSam ECtt EHrv ELan MRav WFar
– 'Pink Marg' CPrp ITim WFar
– 'Pink Princess' see *H. coccinea* 'Wilfred H. Bryant'
– pink-flowered CPne MBel
– 'Professor Barnard' CCCN CSpe EBee ECtt ELon EPfP EPri GAbr GWyn MBNS MNrw NLar SRot WFar WRHF
– 'Red Arrow' EWes
– 'Red Dragon' ECtt IRob
– red-flowered **new** NRHS
I – 'Rosea' GKev SDeJ WFar
– 'Ruth' **new** WFar
– 'Salmon Charm' ECtt LRHS NRHS WFar WHar WMoo
– 'Salmon's Leap' **new** WFar
– 'Salome' CPrp WFar
– 'Scarlet Queen' **new** WFar
– 'Silver Pink' IBlr
– 'Snow Maiden' CWCL EBee EWTr GAbr LLHF LRHS WFar
– 'Strawberry' CPrp WFar
§ – 'Sunrise' 🏆^{H4} CBcs CBro CExl CPrp CSBt CSam CWCL EBee ECha EHoe ELan EPfP EPri GAbr GKev IBlr IRob LRHS LSou MCot MHer MRav NGdn NRHS NWad SWvt WHoo WKif WMoo
– 'Sunset' see *H. coccinea* 'Sunrise'
– 'Tambara' CPou CPrp CSam ECtt EHrv GAbr WFar XLum
– 'Vibrant Scarlet' WFar
– 'Viscountess Byng' CFis CPrp CTri CWCL EBee MNrw SPer
§ – 'Wilfred H. Bryant' 🏆^{H4} Widely available
– 'Zeal Salmon' CBro CElw CPou ECha ECtt GAbr WFar
cucullata CPbh NRog
huttonii GEdr ITim LLHF WFar
mossii see *H. baurii*
pauciflora CPbh
vaginata CPbh

Hesperis (*Brassicaceae*)

matronalis Widely available
– ***alba*** see *H. matronalis* var. *albiflora*
§ – var. ***albiflora*** CRav CSpe ELan EPfP GMaP LCro LOPS LRHS MCot MNHC NGdn NPnk SPer SPhx SPoG WBrk WMoo
– – 'Alba Plena' (d) CRos EBee IBoy LRHS LSun MCot SBod WCAu WCot
– 'Cally Dwarf' (d) GCal
I – 'Variegata' (v) WBor

nivea	LEdu
steveniana	SPhx

× *Hesperotropsis* see × *Cuprocyparis*

leylandii	see × *Cuprocyparis leylandii*

Heteromeles (*Rosaceae*)

arbutifolia	see *H. salicifolia*
§ ***salicifolia***	LEdu

Heteromorpha (*Apiaceae*)

arborescens	CExl SPlb SVen

Heteropolygonatum (*Asparagaceae*)

'Mikinori Ogisu'	EBee
roseolum	CAby
urceolatum new	WCru

Heterotheca (*Asteraceae*)

subaxillaris	WCot

Heuchera ✿ (*Saxifragaceae*)

'Alan Davidson'	MPnt
'Alison'	MPnt
'Amber Waves'PBR	CExl CRos ELan ESps LRHS MJak MPnt NRHS SCob SWvt WHar
§ ***americana***	MRav SHeu SWvt WGwG
- var. ***americana***	MPnt
- Dale's strain	GPSL IBoy IFoB LSun MPnt NLar SHeu SPlb SWvt WRHF
- 'Harry Hay'	EBee EPPr EPri LEdu LPla MPnt SHeu WPGP WSHC
- 'Marvellous Marble'	MPnt
- 'Ring of Fire'	MPnt SHeu SRms SWvt
'Amethyst Myst'	ECtt EPfP ESps EUJe GKev LSRN MCot MPnt NPla SCob SHeu SPer WAvo
'Apple Crisp'PBR	ECtt MPnt MTin SCob SHeu SWvt WNPC
'Apple Souffle'	MPnt SHeu
'Apricot'	CWGN MPnt
'Apricot Muscat'	WCot
'Autumn Glow' (Seasonal Selection Series)	LRHS MPnt NRHS SHeu
'Autumn Haze'PBR	MPnt SHeu
'Autumn Leaves'PBR	CPla ECtt ELan ESps EUJe LCro LOPS MBel MPnt NHpl SHeu SPoG SWvt
'Baby's Breath'	MPnt
'Bardot'	MPnt
'Beaujolais'PBR	CRos LRHS MBNS MNrw MPnt NRHS SHeu WCot WNPC
'Beauty Colour'	CRos ECha ELan EPfP GMaP LRHS LSRN MJak MRav NGdn NRHS NWad SHeu SWvt
'Belle Notte'	EBee ECtt MPnt SHeu WNPC
'Berry Marmalade'PBR	EBee ECtt EPfP LSou MAsh MPnt NHpl NWad SCob SHeu SPer SWvt WHar WNPC
'Berry Smoothie'PBR	Widely available
(Big Top Series) 'Big Top Bronze'	EBee SHeu
- 'Big Top Burgundy'	SHeu
- 'Big Top Gold'	CWGN MNrw SHeu
'Binoche'PBR	CRos EBee ECtt LRHS MPnt NRHS SCob SHeu WCot WTor
'Birkin'	MPnt
'Black Sea' new	MPnt
'Black Taffeta'PBR	CWGN EBee EPfP LBuc MPnt SHeu SPad
'Blackberry Crisp'PBR	EBee MPnt SHeu WNPC
'Blackberry Jam'	CRos ECha ELan ELon EUJe GMcL LRHS MPnt NPnk NRHS SHeu SWvt WFar
'Blackbird'	ESps GBin MPnt SHeu SWvt WFar WSpi
'Blackout'	ECtt MNrw MPnt NLar SHeu
'Blondie in Lime' (Little Cutie Series) new	MPnt
'Blondie'PBR (Little Cutie Series)	CBod CRos CWGN EBee ECtt GBin LRHS MPnt NPnk NRHS SCob SHeu SPoG WCot WHlf WNPC
'Blood Red'	MPnt SHeu WNPC
'Blood Vein'	MPnt SHeu
'Blushing Down'	MAsh MPnt
'Bouquet'	MPnt SHeu
'Boysenberry' (Indian Summer Series) new	EBee
bracteata	MPnt XLum
'Bressingham Glow'	MPnt SHeu
Bressingham hybrids	CSBt GJos IFoB SRms
'Bressingham Spire'	MPnt
'Bright and Breezy' (Seasonal Selection Series)	CRos LRHS MPnt NRHS SCob SHeu WNPC
'Bronze Beauty'	CMil ECtt MPnt SAko SHeu WBrk WCot
'Brown Sugar'	ECtt MPnt SHeu
'Brownfinch'	CElw MAvo MPnt SHeu WCot
'Brownies'	ECtt MPnt SHeu WHrl WPtf WWtn
'Burgundy Frost'	MPnt SHeu WBrk
'Café Olé'	ECtt MPnt NLar SCob SHeu WHer
'Cajun Fire'PBR	CWGN EBee ECtt MPnt SCob SHeu WNPC
'Can-can' ♀H6	CRos CTri ELon EPfP ESps GKev LRHS MNrw MPnt NLar NRHS SCob SHeu SRot SWvt WSpi
'Canyon Duet'	MPnt SHeu
'Cappuccino'	EBee ELan EPfP ESps IBoy MPnt MRav SCob SHeu SRGP SWvt
'Caramel'PBR	CBod CMac CRos CWGN EBee ECtt ELan ESps GAbr GMaP LLHF LRHS LSou MNrw NRHS NSti SBod SCob SGbt SHeu SPer SPoG SWvt WAul WBrk WCot WPnP
'Carmen'	MPnt SHeu
(Carnival Series) CARNIVAL COCOMINT ('Balcarcint'PBR)	SHeu
- CARNIVAL LIMEADE ('Balcarmade'PBR)	SHeu
- CARNIVAL PEACH PARFAIT ('Balcarpait'PBR)	SHeu
- CARNIVAL PLUM CRAZY ('Balcarulm'PBR)	SHeu
- CARNIVAL ROSE GRANITA	SHeu
'Cascade Dawn'	EBee MPnt SWvt
'Cassis'	CWGN LSun MPnt SCob SHeu WCot
'Cézanne' (Master Painters Series)	MPnt SHeu
'Champagne' new	MPnt
'Champagne Bubbles'	MPnt SHeu
CHARLES BLOOM ('Chablo')	CRos EBee LRHS MPnt NRHS SHeu
'Chatterbox'	MPnt SHeu
'Checkers'	see *H.* 'Quilter's Joy'
'Cherries Jubilee'PBR	EPfP GMaP MPnt SHeu SLim
'Cherry Cola'PBR	CBcs CBod CPla CRos CSBt EBee ECtt EPfP GBin LRHS MAsh MAvo MCot MJak MPnt NHpl NLar NPri

	NRHS NSti SCob SHeu SPad SPoG SRkn WFar WNPC WTor
'Chiqui'	MPnt
chlorantha	MPnt
- 'Burnt Sienna'	GCal
'Chocolate Ruffles'PBR	Widely available
'Chocolate Veil'	MPnt
'Christa'	ECtt MPnt SHeu
'Cinnabar Silver'PBR	ECtt MPnt SCob SHeu WHar WNPC
'Circus'PBR	CWGN ECtt MPnt SCob SHeu WNPC
'Citronelle'	CRos CWGN ECtt EPfP LRHS MPnt NRHS SCob SHeu SWvt WCot WPnP
'City Lights'	SHeu
'Coco'PBR (Little Cutie Series)	CRos EBee ECtt EPfP GBin LRHS MPnt NRHS SHeu WCot WNPC
'Color Dream'PBR	MPnt SHeu
coral bells	see *H. sanguinea*
'Coral Bouquet'	MPnt SHeu
'Coral Cloud'	MPnt SHeu
'Corallion'	MPnt
CRÈME BRÛLÉE ('Tnheu041') (Dolce Series)	CBcs CExl CRos ECtt EHoe ELan EPau EPfP EShb ESps GMaP LLHF LRHS MGos NHpl NLar NPla NRHS SCob SHeu SLim SPer SPoG SRot SWvt
'Crème Caramel'	CExl IFoB MPnt
'Creole Nights'PBR	ECtt MPnt SHeu WNPC
'Crimson Curls'	CRos ECtt EPfP LBuc LRHS LSou MPnt NRHS SCob SHeu SRms SWvt WNPC
'Crispy Curly'	MPnt SHeu
cylindrica	EPfP GKev GWyn LRHS MPnt NChi SHeu
- var. ***alpina***	GKev LLHF
- 'Cream'	MPnt
- 'Francis'	MPnt
- 'Greenfinch'	ELan EWTr GKev GLog GMaP GWyn LRHS MPnt MRav SHeu SWvt XLum
- 'Hyperion'	CRos LRHS MPnt NRHS SHeu
'Da Vinci' (Master Painters Series)	MPnt SHeu
'Damask'	CRos LRHS MPnt NRHS SHeu
'Dark Beauty'PBR	CRos ECtt LRHS MJak NHpl NRHS NWad SCob SHeu WNPC
'Dark Secret'PBR	EBee MPnt SHeu
'Dark Storm' (Seasonal Selection Series)	LRHS MPnt NRHS SCob SHeu WNPC
'David'	MPnt SHeu WBrk
'Delta Dawn'PBR	CSBt CWGN EBee ECtt LRHS LSou MPnt SCob SHeu SPoG SWvt WHoo WNPC
'Dennis Davidson'	see *H.* 'Huntsman'
'Earth Angel'	MPnt SHeu
EBONY AND IVORY ('E and I'PBR)	CRos EBee EHoe EShb ESps GMaP LRHS LSRN MPnt NRHS NWad SCob SRms SRot SWvt WSpi
'Eden's Aurora'	MPnt
'Eden's Mystery'	NLar
'Electra'PBR	CMea CSpe EBee ECtt EUJe GMcL MBNS MPnt SCob SHeu SWvt
'Electric Lime'	ECtt EHoe ELan GBin MPnt NHpl NLar SHeu SPoG WNPC
'Elworthy Rusty'	CElw
'Emperor's Cloak'	GLog LEdu SHeu SPad SWvt WHrl WMoo
'Encore'PBR	ECtt MPnt SHeu
'Fairy Dance'	MPnt
'Fantasia'	SHeu
'Fire Alarm'PBR	CWGN EBee ECtt LBuc MPnt SHeu WNPC WTor
'Fire Chief'PBR	CBod CRos CWGN EBee ECtt EPfP EShb ESps EUJe GMcL LRHS LSou MAvo MPnt NHpl NLar NRHS SCob SHeu SPer SPoG SRkn SRot SWvt
'Firebird'	CRos LRHS MPnt NRHS
FIREFLY	see *H.* 'Leuchtkäfer'
'Fireworks'PBR ♀H6	CRos ECtt GBin LRHS MBNS MPnt MRav NLar NRHS SHeu SRot
'Florist's Choice'	SHeu
'Forever Purple'	CBod CRos CWGN EBee LBuc LRHS MPnt NLar NPnk NRHS SHeu SPoG WNPC
'French Quarter'	MPnt SHeu
'Frost' (Little Cutie Series)	ECtt MPnt SHeu WCot WNPC
'Frosted Violet'	see *H.* 'Frosted Violet Dream'
§ 'Frosted Violet Dream'PBR	CBod ECtt LSRN MPnt SCob SHeu SWvt WNPC
'Galaxy'PBR	CWGN ECtt GBin MPnt SHeu
'Gauguin' (Master Painters Series)	ECtt MPnt SCob SHeu
'Georgia Peach'PBR	CWGN EBee ECtt ELan EPfP ESps MNrw MPnt NHpl NLar NPla SHeu SPer SWvt WFar WHar
'Georgia Plum'	CWGN EBee ECtt MPnt SHeu WNPC
'Ginger Ale'PBR	CBod CRos CWGN EBee ECha ECtt ELan ELon EPfP ESps EWes GMcL LRHS LSou MBNS MJak MPnt NHpl NLar NPnk NSti NWad SCob SHeu SPer SPoG SWvt WHar
'Ginger Peach'PBR	ECtt LSou MPnt SCob SHeu WNPC
'Ginger Snap'PBR (Little Cutie Series)	CRos LSou MAsh MPnt NRHS SHeu WCot WNPC WTor
glabra	MPnt SHeu
glauca	see *H. americana*
'Glitter'PBR	CRos EBee ECtt LRHS MPnt NRHS SHeu WNPC
'Gloire d'Orléans'	MPnt XLum
'Gloriana'	CRos LRHS NRHS
'Gojiberry' (Indian Summer Series) **new**	EBee
'Gotham'PBR	CRos EBee ECtt LRHS MPnt NRHS SCob SHeu WNPC
'Grape Soda' (Soda Series)	CWGN MPnt SHeu WNPC
'Green Ivory'	MPnt SHeu XLum
'Green Sashay'	MPnt SHeu
'Green Spice'	CBod CRos EBee ECtt ELan EPed EPfP EShb ESps LRHS MJak MPnt NPla NRHS SCob SHeu SPer SPoG SWeb SWvt
grossulariifolia	GMaP
'Guacamole' **new**	MPnt
'Guardian Angel'	MPnt SHeu SRGP
'Gypsy Dancer'PBR (Dancer Series)	MPnt SHeu
'Hailstorm' (v)	MPnt
hallii	MPnt SPlb
HARVEST BURGUNDY ('Balheubur')	MPnt SHeu
HARVEST SILVER ('Balheusil')	EBee EPfP MPnt SHeu
'Havana'PBR	ECtt MPnt SHeu
'Helen Dillon' (v)	GMaP MPnt SHeu SRGP SWvt
'Hercules'PBR	ECtt LRHS MAsh MPnt SCob SHeu
hispida	MPnt

'Hocus Pocus'	SHeu
'Hollywood'PBR	EBee ECtt EPfP GMcL MGos MPnt NLar SCob SHeu SPoG SRot
'Hot Stuff'	SHeu
§ 'Huntsman'	CRos LRHS MPnt MRav NRHS SHeu
'Iron Maiden'	SHeu
'Jade Gloss'PBR	CRos EPfP GBin LRHS MPnt NRHS SHeu SWvt WNPC
'June Bride'	MPnt
'Kadastra'	MPnt SHeu
'Kassandra'PBR	EBee ECtt MPnt SCob SHeu SWvt
KEY LIME PIE ('Tnheu042'PBR) (Dolce Series)	CExl CRos CWGN ECtt EPfP ESps EUJe LRHS MGos NHpl NRHS SCob SHeu SRms SWvt WFar
'King Kong'	MPnt
Kira Series	MPnt
- 'Kira Alpine Forest'	CRos LRHS NRHS
- 'Kira Arizona'	CRos LRHS NRHS
- 'Kira Green Tea'	CRos LRHS NRHS
- 'KiraPurple Rain Forest'	SHeu
- 'Kira Rockies'	CRos LRHS NRHS
'Lady in Red'	NBre
'Lady Romney'	GCal XLum
'Lemon Chiffon'PBR	ECtt MAsh MPnt NHpl SHeu
§ 'Leuchtkäfer'	CBWd CWat EPfP EShb GMaP GWyn MHer MMuc MPnt MRav NMir SHeu SPlb SRms WMoo XLum
LICORICE ('Tnheu044'PBR) (Dolce Series)	CBod CRos ECtt ESps EUJe GBin GMcL LRHS MBNS MGos MPnt NHpl NLar NRHS SHeu SLim SPoG SRot SWvt WFar
'Lime Marmalade'	CBcs CBod CMea CRos CWGN EBee ECtt ELan ELon EPfP GMcL LRHS LSou MBNS MGos MJak MPnt NHpl NLar NPnk NPri NRHS SCob SHeu SPer SPoG WFar
'Lime Rickey'PBR	CWGN ECtt EPfP ESps ETod LRHS MGos NSti SCob SHeu SWvt WCot
'Lime Ruffles'PBR	MPnt SHeu WNPC
'Lipstick'PBR	CWGN MPnt SHeu SWvt WNPC
'Little Tinker'	MPnt SHeu
'Lune Rousse'	MPnt SHeu
'Magic Wand' 🏆H6	SHeu
'Magnum'	CMil CWGN IBoy MPnt SHeu WCot
'Mahogany'PBR	CBod CRos EPfP EUJe LRHS LSou MJak MPnt NHpl NPri NRHS SCob SHeu SLim SWvt WHoo
'Malachite'	CRos EPfP LRHS MPnt NRHS SHeu
'Mango'	ECtt MPnt SHeu
'Mardi Gras' (v) **new**	WCAu
'Marmalade'PBR	Widely available
'Maroon Blush'PBR	SHeu
'Mars'	CRos EPfP LRHS MPnt NRHS SHeu
'Mary Rose'	MPnt SHeu
maxima	MPnt
'Mega Caramel'	MPnt SHeu
'Mega Citronelle'	MPnt
'Melting Fire'	CChe CRos GJos GMcL GPSL LRHS MPnt NRHS SHeu WHar
'Mercury'	SHeu
'Metallic Shimmer' (Fox Series)	MPnt WNPC
'Metallica'	SHeu WMoo
micans	see *H. rubescens*
micrantha	GCal MPnt SHeu SRms
- var. ***diversifolia*** misapplied	see *H. villosa*
- 'Martha's Compact'	MPnt
§ - 'Ruffles'	ECha MPnt SHeu
'Midas Touch'	CWGN EBee MPnt NLar SHeu
'Midnight Bayou'	CBod CPla EBee ECtt ELan EPfP GBin GMcL MPnt NHpl NLar NPer SHeu SWvt WNPC
'Midnight Rose'	Widely available
'Midnight Rose Select'	ECtt MPnt NWad SHeu
'Midnight Ruffles'PBR	MPnt SHeu WFar WNPC
'Milan'PBR	MPnt SCob SHeu WNPC
'Mini Caramel'	MPnt
'Mini Mouse'	MPnt SHeu
'Mint Frost'PBR	CRos ECtt ELan LRHS MPnt SHeu SWvt
'Mint Julep'PBR	ECtt MPnt SHeu
'Miracle'PBR	ECtt EPfP MPnt SHeu WNPC
'Mocha'PBR	ECtt MNrw MPnt SHeu SWvt
'Molly Bush' 🏆H6	EBee MPnt SHeu
'Morello'	MPnt SCob SHeu WNPC
'Mother of Pearl'	MPnt SHeu
'Muscat'	ECtt MPnt SHeu
'Mysteria'PBR	MPnt SHeu
'Mystic Angel'	ECtt MPnt SHeu
'Neptune'	EShb MAsh MBel MPnt SHeu
'Oakington Jewel'	MPnt
'Obsidian'PBR	Widely available
'Orange Dream' **new**	MPnt
'Orphée'	MPnt NChi
'Paprika'PBR	CMea CRos CWGN EBee ECtt LRHS LSun MBNS MPnt MSCN NRHS SHeu WCot WFar WNPC
'Paris'PBR	CRos EBee ECtt EPfP LRHS LSRN LSou MBel MGos MPnt NRHS SCob SHeu SPoG WNPC
parishii NNS 93384	MPnt
parvifolia var. ***nivalis***	MPnt
- var. ***utahensis***	MPnt
'Pauline' (Fox Series)	MPnt WNPC
'Peach Crisp'PBR	CWGN EBee ECtt LSou NEoE SCob SHeu SPoG SRkn WNPC
'Peach Flambé'PBR	CBcs CBod CRos CWGN ECtt ELan EPfP EShb ESps IRob LRHS LSou MBNS MGos MJak NDov NEgg NHpl NLar NPla NPri NRHS NSti SCob SHeu SLim SPoG SWvt WHar WHer
'Peach Melba'	ESps MPnt
'Peach Pie'	MPnt
'Peachy Keen'	SHeu
'Pear Crisp'PBR	ECtt MPnt SCob SHeu WNPC
'Penelope'	CRos LRHS MPnt NRHS SHeu
'Peppermint' (Little Cutie Series)	CRos ECtt GBin LRHS LSun MPnt NRHS SHeu WCot WNPC
'Peppermint Spice'PBR (21st Century Collection Series)	MPnt SHeu
'Persian Carpet'	CRos LRHS MPnt NRHS SHeu SWvt
(Petite Series) 'Petite Marbled Burgundy'	EHoe LLHF MPnt SHeu SWvt
- 'Petite Pearl Fairy'	EHoe MPnt SHeu SWvt
- 'Petite Pink Bouquet'	MPnt SHeu
'Pewter Moon'	CRos ELan GMaP MPnt SHeu WFar
'Pewter Veil'	MPnt SHeu
'Phoebe's Blush' (Fox Series)	MPnt WAvo WNPC
'Picasso' (Master Painters Series)	ECtt MPnt SHeu
'Pilley Pink'	SHeu
'Pilley Pumpkin'	SHeu
pilosissima	XLum
'Pink Pearls'	CRos EBee LRHS MPnt NRHS SCob SHeu WCot WNPC
'Pinot Bianco'	MPnt SHeu

	'Pinot Gris'^{PBR}	CWGN EBee ECtt MAsh MNrw MPnt SHeu WCot WNPC WTor
	'Pinot Noir'	MPnt SHeu WNPC
	'Pistache'	ECtt MPnt SHeu WCot WNPC
§	'Pluie de Feu'	CRos LRHS MPnt MRav SHeu XLum
	'Plum Pudding'^{PBR}	Widely available
	'Plum Royale'^{PBR}	CRos ELan EPfP GBin LRHS MCot MGos MPnt NRHS NWad SHeu SWvt
	'Pretty Perinne'^{PBR}	EBee MPnt SHeu
	'Pretty Polly'	CRos LRHS MPnt NRHS SHeu
	'Pride of Pilley'	SHeu
	'Prince'	CRos ELan LRHS MBNS MPnt NRHS SHeu SWvt
	'Prince of Orange'	SHeu
	'Prince of Silver'	CRos ETMg LRHS MPnt NRHS SHeu
	pringlei	see *H. rubescens*
	pubescens	MPnt SHeu XLum
	- 'Alba'	MPnt
	pulchella	EDAr GCal GKev GLog LLHF MHer MPnt NLar SHeu SPlb SRms
	'Purple Mountain Majesty'	ECtt
	'Purple Petticoats' ♀H6	CBcs ELan LRHS LSou MGos MPnt NLar SHeu SLim SPoG SRot
	'Quick Silver'	CRos LRHS MPnt NRHS SWvt
§	'Quilter's Joy'	MPnt
	'Rachel'	CMea CRos EBee ELan EPfP GMaP IFoB LRHS LSRN MPnt MRav NGdn NRHS SHeu SRGP SWvt XLum
	RAIN OF FIRE	see *H.* 'Pluie de Feu'
	'Raspberry' (Fox Series)	MPnt
	'Raspberry Ice'^{PBR}	MPnt SHeu
	'Raspberry Regal' ♀H6	MPnt MRav SHeu SWvt WCot WSHC
	'Rave On'^{PBR}	CRos CWGN EBee ECtt ELan GBin LRHS MPnt NEgg NLar NRHS NWad SCob SHeu SRot SWvt
	'Red Dress'	MPnt SHeu
	'Red Lightning' **new**	MPnt
	'Red Pearls' **new**	MPnt
	'Red Sea' **new**	LSun MPnt WCot
	'Red Spangles'	CRos LRHS MPnt NRHS SHeu
	'Regina' ♀H6	CRos ECtt EPfP MPnt NRHS SCob SHeu SWvt
	'Renoir' (Master Painters Series)	MPnt SHeu
	'Rhapsody'	CRos LRHS NRHS
	richardsonii	EBee MPnt SHeu XLum
	'Rickard'	MPnt
	'Rio'^{PBR}	CWGN ECtt LBuc MPnt SCob SHeu WHlf WNPC
	'Robert'	MPnt
	'Root Beer'^{PBR}	CRos ECtt EPfP LRHS LSou MPnt NHpl NRHS SHeu WNPC
	ROSEMARY BLOOM ('Heuros'^{PBR})	CRos EBee LRHS NRHS SHeu
§	***rubescens***	NBro WThu
	- var. ***versicolor***	GKev
	'Ruffles'	see *H. micrantha* 'Ruffles'
	'Sanbrot'	MPnt
§	***sanguinea***	CMac ESps MMrt MPnt MRav
	- 'Alba'	MPnt SMHy
	- 'Frosty'	CRos LRHS NRHS
	- 'Geisha's Fan'	ECtt MPnt SHeu SWvt WNPC
	- 'Monet' (v)	EBee ECtt MPnt SHeu
	- 'Ruby Bells'	CBod CRos CSBt ESps GMcL LRHS LSRN MPnt MSCN NLar NRHS SHeu SRms WHoo
	- 'Sioux Falls'	GPSL SHeu
	- 'Snow Storm' (v)	ELan MPnt SHeu SRms
	- 'Splendens'	MPnt XLum
	- 'Taff's Joy' (v)	MPnt
	- 'White Cloud' (v)	CBod EBee EPfP EShb MPnt MWat NBre SHeu SRms XLum
	'Sashay' ♀H6	GBin IBoy LSou MPnt SHeu WNPC
	'Saturn'	MPnt SHeu SWvt
	'Schneewittchen'	MPnt MRav SCob SHeu
	'Scintillation' ♀H6	MPnt
	'September Morn' (Seasonal Selection Series)	CRos LRHS MPnt NRHS SHeu WNPC
	'Shanghai'^{PBR}	CRos EBee ECtt EPfP LRHS LSRN MPnt NRHS SHeu SWvt WFar WNPC WTor
	'Shenandoah Mountain'	MPnt
	'Shere Variety'	CRos LRHS MPnt NRHS
	'Silver Celebration' (Fox Series) **new**	MPnt WNPC
	'Silver Dollar'	CWGN EBee MPnt WCot
	'Silver Heart'	EBee MPnt
	'Silver Indiana'	MPnt SHeu
	'Silver Light'^{PBR}	MPnt SHeu
	'Silver Lode'^{PBR}	MPnt SHeu
	'Silver Scrolls'^{PBR}	Widely available
	'Silver Shadows'	MPnt SHeu
	'Silver Streak'	see × *Heucherella* 'Silver Streak'
	'Sioux Falls'	MPnt
	'Slater's Pink' (Fox Series)	MPnt WNPC
	'Snow Angel'	CRos CWGN ECtt LRHS LSou MPnt NRHS SHeu SPoG WCot WNPC
	'Snowfire' (v)	MPnt SHeu
	'Southern Comfort'^{PBR}	CRos CWGN EBee ECtt LRHS MBNS MPnt NHpl NLar NPer NRHS SHeu SLim SPoG SWvt
	'Sparkler'	MPnt
	'Sparkling Burgundy'	ECtt ELan MPnt NHpl SHeu SWvt
	'Spellbound'^{PBR}	CRos CWGN EBee ECtt EPfP LRHS MPnt NRHS NSti SCob SHeu SPoG SRkn WNPC WPnP
	'Spotlight' **new**	CRos
	'Starry Night'	MPnt
	'Steel City'	MPnt SHeu
	'Stormy Seas'	CDor CRos EBee ELan EPed EPfP LRHS MPnt MRav NRHS SCob SHeu SWvt
	'Strawberries and Cream' (v)	EHrv MPnt SHeu
	'Strawberry Candy'^{PBR}	CWGN MPnt NLar NWad SHeu SLim WNPC WWtn
	'Strawberry Swirl'	CBod CElw EPfP EWTr GMaP MPnt MRav SCob SHeu SWvt WCAu WNPC
	'Sugar Berry'^{PBR} (Little Cutie Series)	CRos ECtt LRHS MPnt NRHS SCob SHeu WCot WNPC
	SUGAR FROSTING ('Pwheu0104'^{PBR})	CBod CRos EHoe EPau GKev LRHS LSRN MGos MPnt NCou NPri NRHS SHeu SRot SWvt
	'Sugar Plum'^{PBR}	CRos CWGN ECtt EPfP GMcL LBuc LRHS LSRN MBNS MPnt NHpl NPri NRHS SCob SHeu SRot WHoo WNPC
	'Sunrise' (Seasonal Selection Series)	MPnt SCob SHeu WNPC
	'Sweet Berry'	MPnt
	'Sweet Tart'^{PBR} (Little Cutie Series)	CBod CRos GBin LRHS MPnt NRHS SHeu WCot WNPC
	'Swirling Fantasy'^{PBR}	EShb MAsh MPnt SHeu WFar
	'Tangerine Wave' (Fox Series)	MPnt SHeu WAvo WNPC
	'Tara'	ECtt MPnt SHeu
	'Thomas' (Fox Series)	GBin MPnt SHeu WNPC
	'Tiramisu'^{PBR}	CRos CWGN ECtt ESps IBoy LRHS MBNS MJak MPnt NRHS SHeu SWvt

'Tresahor White' MPnt
'Van Gogh' (Master Painters Series) ECtt MPnt SCob SHeu
'Vanilla Spice' MPnt SHeu
'Veil of Passion' NBre
'Velvet Night' EPfP ESps LSou MPnt SHeu SPlb
'Venus' CWGN ECtt MBel MHol MMuc MNrw MPnt NSti SHeu SPer WBrk WCFE WCot WHoo
'Vesuvius' MPnt SHeu WNPC
'Vienna'PBR (City Series) GBin MPnt SHeu WNPC
§ ***villosa*** CSam GKev LEdu MPnt MRav SVic XLum
- 'Autumn Bride' MPnt SHeu SMHy
- BRESSINGHAM BRONZE ('Absi'PBR) CRos LRHS MPnt NRHS SHeu
- 'Chantilly' MPnt SHeu
- var. ***macrorhiza*** EShb MPnt NBre XLum
- 'Palace Purple' Widely available
- 'Palace Purple Select' CMac CTri ETod EUJe IBoy LSun MCot MJak SLim SWvt WHar WSpi
'Virginale' MPnt
'Walnut' (Fox Series) GBin MPnt SHeu WAvo WNPC
'White Marble' MPnt SHeu
'White Spires' CRos LRHS MPnt NRHS SHeu
'White Swirls' MPnt
'William How' MPnt
'Winter Joy' (Seasonal Selection Series) LRHS MPnt NRHS SCob SHeu WNPC
'Winter Red' CRos LRHS MPnt NRHS SHeu
'XXL' MPnt SCob SHeu
'Zabeliana' MPnt
'Zipper'PBR CWGN ECtt LBuc MJak MPnt SHeu WNPC

× *Heucherella* ✿ (*Saxifragaceae*)

'Alabama Sunrise'PBR CBod CHid CRos ECtt ELan EPfP GMcL LRHS MPnt NPer NRHS SCob SHeu SPad SPoG SRot SWvt WFar WTor WWFP
alba 'Bridget Bloom' CRos ECha ELan EPfP GMaP LRHS MPnt MRav NRHS SHeu SPer SRms WCAu WFar XLum
§ - 'Rosalie' CRos ECha GMcL LRHS MPnt MRav SHeu SPlb WSHC
'Art Deco' MPnt SHeu
'Art Nouveau' **new** CRos MPnt NRHS
'Autumn Cascade' **new** MPnt
'Berry Fizz' LBuc MPnt NPnk SHeu SWvt WNPC
'Birthday Cake' MPnt SHeu
'Blue Ridge' MPnt WTor
'Brass Lantern'PBR CBod CRos CSBt CSpe CWGN ECtt EPfP LRHS LSou MAsh MAvo MBel MJak MPnt NDov NLar NRHS NSti SCob SHeu SRot SWvt WNPC
'Burnished Bronze'PBR CRos ECtt EPfP GBin LRHS MPnt NBro NLar NPla NPnk NRHS NWad SCob SHeu SRot SWvt
'Buttered Rum'PBR EBee MPnt SHeu WNPC
'Chocolate Lace'PBR MPnt SHeu
'Cinnamon Bear' MPnt SHeu
'Citrus Shock' MPnt SHeu
'Copper Cascade' (Cascade Series) MPnt NPnk SHeu WNPC
'Cracked Ice'PBR CBod MAvo MPnt SHeu
'Dayglow Pink'PBR CDor ECtt GMaP LSRN MPnt NLar SCob SHeu
'Fan Dancer' MPnt SHeu
'Fire Frost' MPnt SHeu
'Glacier Falls' (Falls Series) NPnk SHeu WNPC
'Gold Cascade' (Cascade Series) MPnt WNPC
GOLD STRIKE ('Hertn041'PBR) ECtt MBNS MPnt SHeu
'Golden Zebra'PBR CRos CWGN EBee ELan LRHS MBNS MJak MNrw MPnt NLar NRHS SHeu SWvt
'Great Smokies' MPnt SHeu
'Gunsmoke'PBR ECtt LSou MAvo MBel MPnt NWad SCob SHeu SWvt WFar WNPC
'Heart of Darkness'PBR MPnt SHeu
'Honey Rose' EBee MPnt SHeu WNPC WTor
'Hot Spot' **new** MPnt
'Infinity' SHeu
'Kimono'PBR ♀H6 CBod CMac CRos ECtt EHoe ELan EPed EPfP EShb GBin GKev GMaP GMcL GWyn LRHS LSRN LSou MBel MJak MPnt NLar NRHS NWad SCob SHeu SPoG
'Mojito' MPnt SHeu WNPC
'Ninja' see *Tiarella* 'Ninja'
'Party Time'PBR SHeu
PINK WHISPERS ('Hertn042'PBR) MPnt SHeu
'Quicksilver' CBcs EPfP GMaP MPnt SHeu SWvt
'Redstone Falls'PBR CRos CWGN ECtt GBin LRHS LSou MJak MNrw MPnt NLar NPnk NRHS NSti NWad SHeu SPer SPoG SWvt WCot WNPC
'Ring of Fire' SWvt
§ 'Silver Streak' MPnt NBro SHeu SWvt
'Solar Eclipse' CRos EBee ECtt EShb IBoy LCro LOPS LRHS MAvo MJak MPnt NLar NRHS NSti NWad SCob SHeu SPad SPer SPoG SWvt WNPC
'Solar Power'PBR CRos CWGN ECtt EPfP EUJe LRHS MAsh MPnt NLar NRHS NWad SCob SHeu SWvt WFar WNPC
'Stoplight'PBR CMac CRos CWGN ECha EPau EPfP GBin GMaP MGos MJak MPnt MRav NBro NEgg NPla NSti SCob SHeu SPer SRkn SRot SWvt WFar
'Sunrise Falls'PBR (Falls Series) CWGN EBee MJak MNrw MPnt NWad SHeu SWvt WNPC
'Sunspot'PBR (v) NBro SHeu SRms WHer
'Sweet Tea'PBR Widely available
'Tapestry'PBR CBod CDor CHid CRos ECtt ELan EPfP GMaP GMcL LRHS MAvo MBNS MPnt NDov NPnk NRHS NSti NWad SCob SHeu SPer SPoG SRkn SRms SRot SWvt WFar
tiarelloides ♀H6 CMac EPfP SRms
'Twilight' MJak MPnt NPnk SHeu WNPC
§ 'Viking Ship' CBWd CRos ECtt MPnt SHeu
'Yellowstone Falls'PBR CRos CWGN GBin GMcL LRHS LSou MJak MMoz MPnt NCou NHpl NPnk NRHS NWad SCob SHeu SWvt WAvo WNPC

Hexastylis see *Asarum*

Hibanobambusa (*Poaceae*)

tranquillans CBdn ERod MBrN MMuc MWht SEND
- 'Shiroshima' (v) CAbb CBdn CBod CDTJ CRos ENBC EPfP ERod EUJe MBrN MJak MMoz MMuc MWht SBig SEND

Hibbertia (*Dilleniaceae*)

aspera	CAbb CBcs CCCN CTsd LRHS WCFE WCot WKif WSHC
§ ***cuneiformis***	CCCN
pedunculata	WAbe
procumbens	GEdr WAbe
§ ***scandens*** ♀H1c	CBcs CCCN CHll CRHN ELan
'Spring Sunshine'	SEle
tetrandra	see *H. cuneiformis*
volubilis	see *H. scandens*

Hibiscus ✿ (*Malvaceae*)

aculeatus	SBrt
coccineus	SBrt SPlb
- white-flowered	SBrt
'Eruption'	EBee ELon EPfP
'Fireball'PBR	SPoG
FULL BLAST	see *H.* 'Resi'
hamabo	CCCN
huegelii	see *Alyogyne huegelii*
'Jazzberry Jam'PBR	MNrw SPoG
'Kopper King'PBR	MBNS MNrw SPoG
militaris	SBrt
moscheutos	EBee SBrt SVic XLum
- 'Carrousel Pink Candy' **new**	SPad
- 'Cranberry Crush'	MNrw
'Newbiscus Pink'	CCCN
'Newbiscus Red'	CCCN
'Newbiscus White'	CCCN
paramutabilis	EWes
§ 'Resi'PBR	NPri
rosa-sinensis	EBak SPre
- 'Apple Blossom'	WFib
- 'Arcadian Spring'	WFib
- 'Blues Man'	WFib
- 'Byron Metts'	WFib
- 'Cajun Cocktail'	see *H. rosa-sinensis* 'Jambalaya'
- 'Candy Floss' (d)	WFib
- 'Carmen Keene'	WFib
- 'China Town'	WFib
- 'Cloud Nine'PBR	WFib
- 'Cockatoo'	WFib
- 'Cooperi' (v) ♀H1b	WFib
- 'Courier Mail'	WFib
- 'Dorothy Brady'	WFib
- 'Enid Lewis' (d)	WFib
- 'Expo'	WFib
- 'Fifth Dimension'	WFib
- 'Gabriel'	WFib
- 'Georgia Peach'	WFib
- 'Gwen Mary'	WFib
- 'Helene'	LSRN
- 'Holly's Pride'	WFib
- 'Hot Bikini'	WFib
§ - 'Jambalaya'	WFib
- 'Jayella'	WFib
- 'June's Joy'	WFib
- 'Key West Thunderhead' (d)	WFib
- 'Lady Flo'	WFib
- 'Lemon Chiffon'	WFib
- 'Linda Pear' (d)	WFib
- 'Madame Dupont'	WFib
- 'Me Oh My Oh'	WFib
- 'Mrs Andreasen' (d)	WFib
- 'Rhinestone'	WFib
- 'Roman Candle'	WFib
- 'Rose Flake'	WFib
- 'Rum Runner'	WFib
- 'Soft Shoulders'	WFib
- 'Spanish Lady'	WFib
- 'Sprinkle Rain'	WFib
- (Sunny City Series) 'Sunny Bary'	CCCN
- - 'Sunny Bordeaux'	CCCN
- - SUNNY CANCUN ('Hican'PBR)	CCCN
- - SUNNY TORINO ('Hirio'PBR)	CCCN
- 'Susan Schlueter'	WFib
- 'Tahitian Christmas'	WFib
- 'Tahitian Desert Sands'	WFib
- 'Tarantella'	WFib
- 'The Path'	WFib
- 'Vermillion Queen'	WFib
- 'Weekend'	WFib
- 'White Swan'	WFib
ROSE MOON ('Walhirosmo') **new**	CRos NRHS SPoG
schizopetalus ♀H1b	WFib
sinosyriacus 'Autumn Surprise'	CRos
- 'Lilac Queen'	CExl CRos LRHS WPGP
- 'Ruby Glow'	CExl LRHS LSRN WPGP
'Summer Storm'PBR	SPad
'Sunny Premiere'	CCCN
syriacus	CCCN ESps LMaj SWeb
§ - 'America Irene Scott'PBR	SPoG
- 'Aphrodite'	CRos LRHS MAsh
- 'Ardens' (d)	CEnd EBee SPer SPoG WFar
- BLUE BIRD	see *H. syriacus* 'Oiseau Bleu'
- BLUE CHIFFON ('Notwood3'PBR) (d) ♀H5	CSBt LCro LOPS LRHS SPoG WHlf
- CHINA CHIFFON ('Bricutts') (d)	CRos LRHS MMuc SEND SGol SPoG
- 'Coelestis'	SPer
- 'Diana' ♀H5	CDul CRos ELon EPfP EUJe EWTr LRHS LSRN MAsh NRHS SCoo SLon SPer
- 'Dorothy Crane'	CRos EMil LRHS
- 'Duc de Brabant' (d)	CCCN CSBt MBlu SPer
- 'Elegantissimus'	see *H. syriacus* 'Lady Stanley'
- 'Gandini van Aart' **new**	SGol
- 'Hamabo' ♀H5	CBot CDul CRos CSBt CTri EBee ELan ELon EPfP ESps LRHS LSRN MAsh MGos MMuc NLar NPri NRHS SBod SCoo SEND SGol SLim SPer SPoG SWvt WFar WHar
- 'Helene'	ELan LSRN MBlu
- 'Jeanne d'Arc' (d)	SGol
§ - 'Lady Stanley' (d)	CCCN CMac CSBt LSou SCoo SPer
- LAVENDER CHIFFON ('Notwoodone'PBR) (d) ♀H5	CRos CSBt ELan ELon EPfP EWes LCro LOPS LRHS LSRN MGos MMuc NRHS SCoo SEND SGol SPer SPoG
- 'Marina'	CBod CCCN ELon EPfP EUJe LRHS LSou MBlu MRav SGol WFar
- 'Meehanii' misapplied	see *H. syriacus* 'Purpureus Variegatus'
- 'Meehanii' (v) ♀H5	CDul CEnd CRos EBee EPfP LRHS SCoo SPer SPoG
- 'Monstrosus'	EBee MGos NLar
§ - 'Oiseau Bleu' ♀H5	Widely available
- PINK CHIFFON ('Jwnwood4'PBR) (d)	LCro LOPS LRHS WHlf
- PINK GIANT ('Flogi')	CDul CMac CRos ELan EPfP LRHS SPer

- 'Pinky Spot'	LRHS
- PURPLE PILLAR ('Gandini Santiago'PBR)	LRHS SGol
- PURPLE RUFFLES ('Sanchoyo') (d)	CRos EPfP ETMg LRHS SPoG
§ - 'Purpureus Variegatus' (v)	CBot CMac CRos LRHS
- 'Red Heart' ♀H5	CAco CBod CDul CEnd CMac CRos CSBt CTri ELan EPfP ESps LRHS MAsh MGos MMuc NRHS SEND SLim SPer SPoG SRms SWvt WCFE XSen
- ROSALBANE ('Minrosa')	SGol
- RUSSIAN VIOLET ('Floru')	CEnd CRos EPfP LRHS
I - 'Speciosus' (d)	EBee SPoG WFar
- SUGAR TIP	see *H. syriacus* 'America Irene Scott'
- 'Totus Albus'	CMac EBee
- ULTRAMARINE ('Minultra'PBR)	EPfP LRHS NPri
- 'Variegatus'	see *H. syriacus* 'Purpureus Variegatus'
- 'Violet Clair Double' (d)	CMac
- WHITE CHIFFON ('Notwoodtwo'PBR) (d) ♀H5	CRos CSBt EPfP EWes LCro LOPS LRHS LSRN MAsh MGos MRav SCoo SPer SPoG WHlf
- 'William R. Smith' ♀H5	CRos LRHS MSwo SPer
- 'Woodbridge' ♀H5	Widely available
trionum	CSpe EBtc WKif
- 'Sunny Day'	ELan

hickory, shagbark see *Carya ovata*

Hieracium (*Asteraceae*)

sp.	EBWF
aurantiacum	see *Pilosella aurantiaca*
brunneocroceum	see *Pilosella aurantiaca* subsp. *carpathicola*
laevigatum subsp. ***nivale***	MMuc
§ ***lanatum***	NWad
maculatum Sm.	see *H. spilophaeum*
pilosella	see *Pilosella officinarum*
scullyi	EPPr
§ ***spilophaeum***	EHoe MMuc NBid NPer NSti WOut
- 'Blue Leaf'	WCot
- 'Leopard'	GJos GPSL NDov
umbellatum	WOut
villosum	EHoe GJos WHer
welwitschii	see *H. lanatum*

Hierochloe (*Poaceae*)

odorata	CBod EAJP EBWF ELon EPPr GPoy LEdu MBNS XLum

Himalayacalamus (*Poaceae*)

asper	CBdn CDTJ ERod
cupreus	CBdn
§ ***falconeri*** 'Damarapa'	EPfP
§ ***hookerianus***	CBdn CExl EPfP IMou
- 'Himalaya Blue'	CDTJ

× *Hippeasprekelia* (*Amaryllidaceae*)

'Durga Pradhan'	WCot
'Red Beauty'	WCot
'Red Star'	CCCN

Hippeastrum ✿ (*Amaryllidaceae*)

× ***acramannii*** ♀H2	CPne GCal WCot
advenum	see *Rhodophiala advena*
'Amputo'	LAma
'Apple Blossom' ♀H2	LAma LCro LOPS SDeJ
'Baby Star'	SDeJ
bifidum	see *Rhodophiala bifida*
'Black Beauty'	LAma
'Black Pearl'	EPfP LCro LOPS
'Bogota'	LCro LOPS
'Bolero'	LAma
'Christmas Gift'	LAma LCro LOPS
'Clown'	LAma SDeJ
(Colibri Group) 'Rapido' **new**	LCro LOPS
- 'Veneto' **new**	SDeJ
(Diamond Group) 'Bianca'	LAma
- 'Charisma' ♀H2	LAma SDeJ
- 'Fairytale'	LCro LOPS SDeJ
- 'Green Magic' ♀H2	CRav LAma
- 'Lemon Lime'	CRav LAma
- 'Picotee'	LAma LCro LOPS SDeJ
(Double Diamond Group) 'Alfresco'PBR (d)	LAma SDeJ
(Double Galaxy Group) 'Blossom Peacock' (d)	LAma
- 'Dancing Queen' (d)	LAma LCro
- 'Double Dragon'PBR (d)	LAma
- 'Lady Jane' (d)	LAma SDeJ
'Double Record' (d)	SDeJ
'Fantasy'	LAma
'Ferrari'	LAma
'Flaming Peacock'	LAma
(Galaxy Group) 'Benfica' ♀H2	CSpe
- 'Flamenco Queen'	LAma
- 'Hercules'	CRav SDeJ
- 'Lagoon'PBR **new**	LCro LOPS
- 'Limona'PBR	LCro LOPS
- 'Purple Rain' **new**	LCro LOPS
- 'Red Lion' ♀H2	LAma
- 'Rilona'	LAma SDeJ
- 'Susan' **new**	SDeJ
'Grand Diva'	LAma
'Grandeur'	LAma
'Inca'	LAma
'Jewel' (d)	LAma
× ***johnsonii*** hort. ♀H2	CExl WCot
'Liberty'	CRav SDeJ
'Marilyn'PBR (d)	LAma
'Minerva'	SDeJ
'Misty'	LAma
'Mont Blanc'	CRav SDeJ
'Naughty Lady'	LAma
papilio ♀H1c	CRav LAma LCro LOPS MMrt SDeJ
'Pink Floyd'	LAma
'Red Peacock' (d)	LAma SDeJ
'Rosario'	LAma
'Royal Velvet'	CRav LAma
'San Antonio Rose'	WCot
'Santiago'	CRav LAma
'Snow Queen'	LCro LOPS
'Sonatini Valentino'	WCot
(Spider Group) 'Emerald'	LAma WCot
- 'Evergreen' ♀H2	EPfP LCro LOPS
- 'Lima'	LAma
- 'Sumatra'PBR	LCro LOPS
striatum	WCot
'Swan Lake'PBR	SDeJ
'Sweet Surrender'	LAma
'Toughie'	CTal EBee
vittatum	LAma
'White Dazzler'	LAma
yungacense 'Kiara'	XTur

Hippocrepis (*Papilionaceae*)

§ ***comosa***	EBWF EDAr SPhx WAbe
§ ***emerus***	CBcs CCCN CExl CMac ELan EPfP MAsh MGil MGos MMuc SBod SEND SNig SVen WSHC WSpi

Hippophae (*Elaeagnaceae*)

rhamnoides	Widely available
- (m)	EPom
- 'Askola' (f/F)	CAgr
- 'Dorana' (f/F)	CAgr
- 'Frugna' (f/F)	CAgr NLar
- 'Hergo' (f/F)	CAgr MCoo NLar
- 'Hikul' (m)	CAgr NLar WHor
- 'Juliet' (f/F)	CAgr
- 'Leikora' (f/F) ♀H7	CAgr CDul ELan MBlu MCoo NLar SPer
- ORANGE ENERGY ('Habego'PBR) (f/F)	CAgr EPfP MCoo
- 'Pollmix' (m) ♀H7	CAgr ELan MBlu MCoo NLar SPer
- 'Pollmix 3' (m)	MCoo
- 'Sirola' (f/F)	CAgr MCoo
salicifolia	CAgr
- GWJ 9221	WCru
sinensis LS&E 15724 **new**	WPGP

Hippuris (*Plantaginaceae*)

vulgaris	CBen CWat EWat LLWG MSKA NPer WMAq XLum

Hirpicium (*Asteraceae*)

armerioides	SPlb

Histiopteris (*Dennstaedtiaceae*)

incisa	CBdn

Hoheria ✿ (*Malvaceae*)

'Ace of Spades'	CAbb CBod CRos ELan ELon EPfP LRHS MGil NLar SEND SMad SPer SWvt WPGP
§ ***angustifolia***	CBcs EBee EPfP IDee SVen WPGP
angustifolia × ***sexstylosa***	WPGP
'Borde Hill'	CAbb CBcs CDul CJun CMac CRos CTho EBee ELan ELon EPfP GCal LRHS MAsh MGil SEND SLim SPer SWvt WCFE WPGP WSpi
glabrata	CMac EPfP GBin IDee WPGP
'Glory of Amlwch' ♀H4	CAbb CAby CBcs CDul CJun CTho ELan EPfP GGGa LRHS LSRN SChF SPer SWvt WKif WPGP WSpi
'Hill House'	CHll
§ ***lyallii*** ♀H4	CCCN CExl CTho ELan LRHS LSRN SPer SVen
microphylla	see *H. angustifolia*
populnea	CBcs CCCN CTsd
- 'Holbrook'	CSam
- 'Moonlight'	SPoG
sexstylosa	CAbb CBcs CBot CDul CHid CTho CTri ELan EPfP LRHS LSRN MGos NEgg SPer SPlb SVen SWvt WSpi
- 'Crataegifolia'	EBee EWTr MGil NLar
- 'Pendula'	CMac
- 'Stardust' ♀H4	CAby CBcs CCCN CDul CEnd CJun CMCN CRos CSBt CTho EBee ELan ELon EPfP EUJe LRHS LSRN MAsh MBlu MGil MGos MMuc NLar SEND SPer SPoG SWvt WPGP WSHC
'Snow White'	EUJe LRHS SLim SPoG

Holboellia (*Lardizabalaceae*)

angustifolia	NLar WCot WCru
- subsp. ***angustifolia***	LRHS WCru
- subsp. ***linearifolia*** BWJ 8004	WCru
- subsp. ***obtusa*** DJHC 506	WCru
brachyandra HWJ 1023	WCru
aff. ***chapaensis*** B&SWJ 7250	WCru
coriacea	CBcs CCCN CHll CKel CRHN CRos CTsd EBee ELan EPfP EShb IDee LEdu LRHS MGil MRav NLar SEND SPer WCFE WCru
- B&SWJ 2818	WCru
latifolia	CBcs CBot CCCN CHll CMac CRHN CRos CTri EBee ELan EPfP EUJe LEdu LRHS MGil NLar SAdn SArc SEle SLim SPer SPoG SWvt WBor WCFE WCru WPGP WSHC
- DJHC 98442	WCru
- HWJCM 008	WCru
- HWJK 2014	WCru
- HWJK 2213	WCru
- SF 95134	EPfP
- subsp. ***chartacea*** dark-flowered HWJK 2213D **new**	WCru
- - pale-flowered HWJK 2213C **new**	WCru
- dark-flowered HWJK 2213	WCru
- lanceolate-leaved HWJK 2419	WCru
- pale-flowered HWJK 2213C	WCru

Holcus (*Poaceae*)

lanatus	EBWF WSFF
mollis 'Albovariegatus' (v)	CWCL ECha EHoe ELan EMOT EPPr EPfP ESps GMaP GWyn NBid NBro NPer NSti SPlb SRms XLum
- 'White Fog' (v)	CBod CRos EAJP EBee EPPr MMuc NWad

Holmskioldia (*Lamiaceae*)

* ***lutea***	CCCN
sanguinea	CCCN

Holodiscus (*Rosaceae*)

discolor	CBcs CBod CDul CRos CWld EBee ELan EPfP EWes GCal LEdu LRHS MBlu MGil MMuc MRav NLar NRHS SLon SPer SPlb WBor
- var. ***ariifolius***	WSHC

Homalocladium (*Polygonaceae*)

§ ***platycladum***	EShb

Homeria (*Iridaceae*)

breyniana var. ***aurantiaca***	see *Moraea collina*

Homoglossum see *Gladiolus*

Hordeum (*Poaceae*)

jubatum	CDor CKno CSpe CWCL EAJP EHoe EWes LEdu NGdn SPhx
- 'Early Pink'	NDov
secalinum	CHab

Horminum (*Lamiaceae*)

pyrenaicum	IMou IRob MMuc SEND SRms WMoo

I - f. ***alboviolaceum***	GCal SBrt
- dark-flowered	GCal SBrt WSHC

Hornungia (*Brassicaceae*)

alpina	GCrg NSla XLum

horseradish see *Armoracia rusticana*

Hosta ✿ (*Asparagaceae*)

AGSJ 302	WCot
'A Many-Splendored Thing'	EMic IBal
'Abana' (v)	IBal
'Abba Dabba Do' (v)	CDor ECtt ELon EMic IBal NEgg NSue
'Abba Showtime'	IBal
'Abby' (v)	CBdn EHoe EMic IBal NSue WFar
'Abiqua Ariel'	CBdn EMic
'Abiqua Blue Crinkles'	IBal
'Abiqua Blue Edger'	IBal
'Abiqua Blue Madonna'	IBal
'Abiqua Delight' (v)	EMic
'Abiqua Drinking Gourd' ♀H7	CBdn CBod CDor ECtt ELon EMic GMaP IBal IFoB NEgg NLar NSue
'Abiqua Elephant Ears'	IBal
'Abiqua Ground Cover'	IBal
'Abiqua Moonbeam' (v)	EMic IBal NGdn
'Abiqua Recluse'	EMic IBal
'Abiqua Trumpet'	EMic IBal LRHS NGdn NLar NNor
'Abraham Lincoln'	IBal
'Academy Flora' **new**	IBal
'Academy Mavrodaphne'	EMic
'Ada Reed'	IBal
'Adorable'	CBdn IBal
aequinoctiiantha	EMic IBal
'Aksarben'	EMic
'Alabama Gold'	EMic
'Alakazaam' (v)	CBdn EMic IBal NSue WFar
'Alan Titchmarsh'	IBal
albomarginata	see *H.* 'Paxton's Original' (*sieboldii*)
§ 'Albomarginata' (*fortunei*) (v)	CBcs CMac ETMg GNew IFoB MNrw NGdn SWvt WFar WMoo
'Alex Summers'	EMic IBal WFar
'All That Jazz' (v)	EMic IBal
'Allan P. McConnell' (v)	EMic IBal LRHS MNrw NSue WHal
'Allegan Emperor' (v)	IBal
'Allegan Fog' (v) ♀H7	EMic EShb IBal IFoB LRHS NHpl NSue
'Alligator Alley' (v)	EMic IBal
'Alligator Shoes' (v) ♀H7	EMic IBal
'Alpine Aire'	EMic IBal
'Alpine Dream'	IBal
'Alternative'	IBal
'Alvatine Taylor' (v)	EMic IBal NGdn
'Amalia' (v) **new**	IBal
'Amanuma'	EMic IBal NSue
'Amazing Grace' (v)	EMic IBal
'Amber Tiara'	EMic IBal
'American Dream' (v)	EMic IBal LRHS
'American Gothic' (v)	IBal
'American Great Expectations' (v)	IFoB
'American Halo'	CBdn EMic IBal NEgg NLar NSti
'American Icon'	EMic IBal
'American Sweetheart'^{PBR}	EMic IBal
'Americana' (v)	IBal
'Amethyst Gem'	IBal NSue
'Amos'	IBal
'Amy Elizabeth' (v)	EMic IBal
'Andorian'	IBal NSue
'Andrew'	EMic
'Angel Feathers' (v)	IBal
'Anglo Saxon' (v)	IBal
'Ani Machi' (v) ♀H7	NSue
'Ann Kulpa' (v)	EMic GNew IBal NGdn
'Annabel Lee'	IBal
'Anne' (v)	IBal LSRN NSue
'Ansly' (v)	IBal
'Antioch' (*fortunei*) (v)	EMic EUJe GLog IBal MRav NLar
'Aoba Tsugaru'	IBal
'Aoki' (*fortunei*)	EMic IBal
'Aphrodite' (*plantaginea*) (d)	EMic EPfP EWTr
'Apollo'	NNor
'Apple Candy' (v)	IBal NSue
'Apple Green'	CBdn EMic GKev IBal
'Apple Pie'	CBdn IBal
'Appletini' **new**	NSue
'Aqua Velva'	IBal
'Arc de Triomphe'	ECtt EMic IBal NLar
'Arch Duke'	IBal
'Arctic Blast'	EMic IBal
'Arctic Circle' (v)	EMic
'Argentea Variegata' (*undulata*)	see *H. undulata* var. *undulata*
'Aristocrat' (Tardiana Group) (v)	EMic IBal NEgg NGdn WFar
'Asian Pearl' (v)	IBal
'Aspen Gold' (*tokudama* hybrid)	EMic
'Astral Bliss'	IBal
'Atlantis'^{PBR} (v) ♀H7	EMic IBal NGdn NSue
'Atom Smasher'	NSue
'Atomic Elvis'	IBal NSue
'August Beauty'	EMic IBal
'August Moon'	Widely available
'Aureafolia'	see *H.* 'Starker Yellow Leaf'
'Aureoalba' (*fortunei*)	see *H.* 'Spinners'
'Aureomaculata' (*fortunei*)	see *H. fortunei* var. *albopicta*
'Aureomarginata' ambig. (v)	ESps SCoo
'Aureomarginata' (*montana*) (v) ♀H7	CMac CRos EHoe ELan EMic GCal GMaP IBal LRHS MMuc NEgg NGdn NLar NRHS NSue WFar
§ 'Aureomarginata' (*ventricosa*) (v) ♀H7	EMic IBal NGdn WFar
'Aureostriata' (*tardiva*)	see *H.* 'Inaho'
'Austin Dickinson' (v)	ECtt EMic IBal LRHS NEgg
'Autumn Frost' (v)	EMic IBal NSue
'Avocado'	ELon EMic IBal NLar NSue
'Awakening Angel'	EMic
'Azure Snow'	IBal
'Azuretini'	IBal
'Babbling Brook'	IBal NSue
'Baby Blue' (Tardiana Group)	EMic
'Baby Blue Eyes'	EMic IBal NSue
'Baby Booties' (v)	IBal
'Baby Bunting' ♀H7	EMic IBal IFoB NBro NLar NNor NSue
'Baby Doll' (v)	IBal
'Baby Kim' **new**	EMic
'Backyard Monster' (v) **new**	IBal
'Bailey's Cream' (v)	IBal
'Baja White'	IBal
'Bali-Hai'	IBal
'Ballerina'	IBal LRHS NSue
'Bam Bam Blue'	IBal
'Banana Muffins'	IBal
'Band of Gold'	EMic IBal
'Banyai's Dancing Girl'	CBdn EMic IBal
'Barbara Ann' (v) ♀H7	EBee EMic IBal NGdn
'Barbara May'	IBal
'Barbara White'	IBal

'Barney Fife'	IBal
'Battle Star' (v)	EMic IBal
'Beach Boy' (v)	CBdn IBal MNrw NLar NSue
'Bea's Colossus'	IBal
'Beauty Little Blue'	IBal NSue
'Beauty Substance'	EMic IBal NNor
'Beckoning'	EMic IBal NSue
'Bedazzled' (v)	IBal
'Bedford Bashful' **new**	NSue
'Bedford Blue'	EMic IBal
'Bedford Rise and Shine' (v)	IBal LRHS
'Bedford Wakey-Wakey'	IBal
'Behemoth'	IBal NSue
'Bell Bottom Blues'	IBal
bella	see *H. crassifolia*
'Bells of Edinburgh'	IBal
'Ben Vernooij' (v)	CBdn EMic GNew IBal
'Bennie McRae'	IBal
'Best of Twenty'	IBal NSue
'Betcher's Blue'	EMic IBal
'Betsy King'	CMac MRav NLar
'Bette Davis Eyes'	IBal
'Betty'	IBal NSue
'Biddy's Blue'	IBal
'Big Boy' (*montana*)	IBal LRHS NSue
'Big Daddy' (*sieboldiana* hybrid) (v) ϒH7	Widely available
'Big John' (*sieboldiana*)	IBal
'Big Mama'	EMic IBal MBNS MNrw NGdn NSue
'Big Top'	IBal
'Bigfoot'	IBal
'Biggie'	IBal
'Bill Brinka' (v)	EMic IBal
'Bill Dress's Blue'	EMic NSue
'Birchwood Blue Beauty'	IBal
'Birchwood Gem'	IBal
§ 'Birchwood Parky's Gold'	EBee ECtt EMic EPfP GMaP IBal MBNS NGdn NLar NNor SCob
'Birchwood Ruffled Queen'	EMic
'Bishop George Bell' **new**	CBdn
'Bitsy Gold'	EMic
'Bix Blues'	IBal
'Bizarre'	EMic IBal
'Black Beauty'	IBal
'Black Hills'	EMic IBal
'Blackfoot'	EMic IBal
'Blackjack' (*sieboldiana*)	IBal WFar
'Blaue Venus'	IBal
'Blaugold' **new**	CBdn
'Blaze of Glory'	IBal
'Blazing Saddles' (v)	EMic IBal
'Blonde Elf'	EHoe EMic IBal MPnt NEgg NGdn NNor
'Blue Angel' misapplied	see *H. sieboldiana* var. *elegans*
'Blue Angel' (*sieboldiana*) ϒH7	Widely available
'Blue Arrow' ϒH7	IBal LRHS MHol NNor NSue
'Blue Baron'	EMic IBal
'Blue Belle' (Tardiana Group)	EMic IBal NEoE NGdn
'Blue Blush' (Tardiana Group)	EMic IBal NGdn
'Blue Boy'	EMic EWes IBal NNor
'Blue Cadet'	CBdn CMac CRos EBee EHoe EMic EPed EShb GBin GQue IBoy IFoB LRHS NGdn NLar NRHS NSue NWad SBod WAvo WFar
'Blue Canoe'	IBal
'Blue Cascade'	EMic IBal NSue
'Blue Chip'	EMic IBal
'Blue Circle'PBR	EMic IBal

'Blue Clown'	IBal
'Blue Cup' (*sieboldiana*)	EMic MRav SRms
'Blue Danube' (Tardiana Group)	EMic IBal NEgg
'Blue Diamond' (Tardiana Group)	EMic LRHS NNor NSue WFar
'Blue Dimples' (Tardiana Group)	ECtt EMic IBal
'Blue Dolphin'	IBal
'Blue Edger'	IBal
'Blue Eyes'	EMic
'Blue Flame'	ECtt EMic IBal
'Blue Frost'	IBal
'Blue Haired Lady'	IBal
'Blue Hawaii'	CBdn EMic IBal NSue
'Blue Heart' (*sieboldiana*)	CBdn ECha EMic IBal
'Blue Ice' (Tardiana Group)	EMic NSue
'Blue Impression'	EMic
'Blue Ivory' (v)	CBdn EBee ECtt ELon NSue SPad
'Blue Jay' (Tardiana Group)	EMic
'Blue Lady'	EMic IBal
'Blue Mammoth' (*sieboldiana*)	CBdn EMic EUJe IBal NEgg NLar NSue
'Blue Maui'	IBal
'Blue Monday'	EMic
'Blue Moon' (Tardiana Group)	EMic ESps GKev IBal NGdn NLar NNor
'Blue Mountains'	IBal LBuc
'Blue Mouse Ears' ϒH7	Widely available
'Blue River' (v)	EMic IBal
'Blue Seer' (*sieboldiana*)	EMic
'Blue Shadows' (*tokudama*) (v)	EMic GMcL NLar WFar
'Blue Skies' (Tardiana Group)	IBal
'Blue Splendor' (Tardiana Group)	IBal
'Blue Umbrellas' (*sieboldiana* hybrid)	ECtt ELan EMic EPfP GMaP GNew IBal LRHS NGdn NLar NNor
'Blue Vision'	IBal
'Blue Wedgwood' (Tardiana Group)	ELan EMic GQue IBal LRHS MHol NGdn
'Blue Wonder'	IBal
'Blue Wu'	IBal
'Blueberry à la Mode'	IBal
'Blueberry Cobbler'	IBal
'Blueberry Muffin'	CBdn EMic NSue
'Blueberry Tart'	IBal
'Bluetooth'	IBal
'Bob Deane' (v)	EMic IBal
'Bob Olson' (v)	IBal WFar
'Bobbie Sue' (v)	IBal
'Bobcat'	IBal
'Bogie and Bacall' (v)	IBal
'Bold Edger' (v)	EMic IBal
'Bold Intrigue' (v)	IBal
'Bold Ribbons' (v)	CBdn EMic GAbr
'Bolt out of the Blue'	EMic
'Bonanza'	EMic
'Boracay'	IBal
'Border Bandit' (v)	EMic IBal LRHS NRHS
'Border Favorite'	EMic
§ 'Borwick Beauty' (*sieboldiana*) (v)	ELon EMic IBal NGdn SPer
'Bottom Line' (v)	IBal
'Bountiful'	EMic IBal NSue
'Boyz Toy'	EMic IBal NSue
'Brandywine'	IBal
'Brave Amherst' (v)	IBal
'Brenda's Beauty' (v)	EMic IBal

'Bressingham Blue'	CAby CRos ECtt ELon GQue IBal LRHS MRav NLar NNor SPer SWvt WFar WMoo
'Bridal Falls'PBR (v)	CBdn IBal NSue
'Bridal Veil'	EMic IBal
'Bridegroom'	EMic IBal
'Bridgeville'	IBal
'Brigadier'	IBal
'Brigham Blue'	IBal
'Bright Glow' (Tardiana Group)	EMic IBal
'Bright Lights' (*tokudama*) (v)	EMic NGdn WFar
'Bright Star' (v)	IBal
'Brim Cup' (v)	CAby CDor CRos ECtt ELon EPfP EShb GMcL IRob LRHS LSou MBNS NBro NGdn NNor NRHS SPer
'Broadband' (v) **new**	IBal
'Broadway' (v)	EMic IBal
'Bronx Bomber' (v)	IBal NSue
'Brooke'	CBdn EMic IBal
'Brother Ronald' (Tardiana Group)	EMic IBal LRHS NEgg
'Brother Stefan'	CBdn EMic IBal
'Brutus'	IBal
'Buckshaw Blue'	EMic IBal NEoE NGdn WHrl
'Bulletproof'	IBal
'Bunchoko'	IBal NNor
'Burke's Dwarf'	IBal
'Cadillac' (v)	EMic
* 'Caerula' (*ventricosa*)	IFoB
'Cally Atom'	EBee GCal IBal
'Cally Colossus'	GCal IBal
I 'Cally Strain' (*nigrescens*)	MHer
'Cally White' (*nigrescens*)	EBee GCal IBal
'Calypso' (v)	EMic IBal MNrw NGdn WFar
'Camelot' (Tardiana Group)	IBal LRHS NGdn
'Cameo'	NSue
'Camouflage'	EMic IBal
'Canadian Blue'	ECtt EMic IBal LLWG LSou MSCN NLar NSue WFar
'Candle Wax'	IBal
'Candy Dish'	CBdn IBal NSue
'Candy Hearts'	CSam EMic IBal NNor
capitata	NNor
- B&SWJ 588	WCru
'Captain Kirk' (v) ♀H7	CBdn EMic IBal NGdn NSue WFar
'Captain's Adventure' (v)	CBdn EMic IBal NSue WFar
caput-avis	see *H. kikutii* var. *caput-avis*
'Carder Blue'	EMic IBal
'Carnival' (v)	EMic IBal IFoB LRHS NEgg NGdn NHpl SPoG
'Carol' (*fortunei*) (v)	CBdn IBal NEgg NGdn NLar NNor NSue
'Carolina Blue'	CBdn IBal
'Carousel' (v)	EMic IBal
'Carrie' (*sieboldii*) (v)	EMic
'Cascades' (v)	EMic IBal NGdn
'Cathedral Windows' (v) ♀H7	EMic IBal NSue
'Catherine'	ELon EMic IBal LSun NLar NSue WFar
'Cat's Eyes' (*venusta*) (v)	ITim NNor
'Cavalcade' (v)	EMic
'Celebration' (v)	ELan EMic IBal
'Celestial'	IBal
'Celtic Dancer'	EMic IBal
'Celtic Uplands'	EMic IBal
'Center of Attention'	EMic IBal NGdn
'Centerfold'	NSue
'Cha Cha Cha'	IBal

'Chabo-unazuki' (*kikutii* var. *caput-avis*)	EMic
'Chain Lightning' (v)	EMic IBal NSue
'Challenger'	EMic
'Chameleon' (v)	EMic
'Champagne Toast' (v)	IBal NSue
'Change of Tradition' (*lancifolia*) (v)	EMic
'Chantilly Lace' (v)	EMic IBal
'Chariots of Fire' (v)	IBal
'Chartreuse Waves'	IBal
'Chartreuse Wiggles' (*sieboldii*)	EMic IBal
'Cheatin' Heart'	EMic IBal NSue WFar
'Chelsea Babe' (*fortunei*) (v)	IBal
'Cherish' ♀H7	NGdn NHpl WFar
'Cherokee' (v) **new**	IBal
'Cherry Berry' (v)	CRos CWGN ECtt EMic EShb GEdr IBal IFoB LRHS MBNS MHol MNrw NBro NEgg NEoE NGdn NLar NRHS NSue NWad SCob SHar SPoG WFar WWtn
'Cherry Tart'	IBal NSue
'Cherub' (v)	EMic IBal LRHS
'Chesapeake Bay'	EMic IBal NSue
'Chesterland Gold'	IBal
'Chief Sitting Bull'	IBal
'Childhood Sweetheart' (v)	IBal
'China Girl'	EMic IBal
'Chinese Gold'	IBal
'Chinese Sunrise' (v) ♀H7	CWCL EMic GBin GMcL GWyn IBal NNor SRms
'Chionea' (v)	IBal
'Chiquita'	IBal
'Chi-town Classic' (v)	IBal
'Chodai Ginba'	IBal
§ 'Chōkō-nishiki' (*montana*) (v)	EMic IBal LRHS NGdn NNor NRHS
'Choo Choo Train'	EMic
'Chopsticks'	EMic
'Christmas Candy'PBR	CBdn ECtt EMic IBal IRob NSue
'Christmas Charm' (v)	IBal
'Christmas Cookies'	IBal
'Christmas Pageant' (v)	EMic IBal
'Christmas Tree' (v) ♀H7	CRos ECtt EMic IBal IFoB LRHS NEgg NGdn NLar NRHS NSue WMoo
'Church Mouse'	CBdn IBal NSue
'Cinderella'	EMic IBal
'Cinnamon Sticks'	EMic IBal NSue
'Citation' (v)	IBal
'City Lights'	ECtt EMic NEgg
'City Slicker' (v)	IBal
'Claudia'	IBal
clausa	EMic
- var. ***normalis***	IBal NGdn NLar
'Clear Fork River Valley'	EMic IBal
'Clifford's Forest Fire'	CBdn CRos ECtt EMic EUJe IBal LRHS NLar NRHS WFar
'Clifford's Stingray' (v)	CBdn EMic GNew IBal NSue
'Climax' (v) ♀H7	CBdn EMic EPfP IBal IBoy
'Cloudburst'	EMic IBal
'Clovelly'	IBal
'Clown's Collar' (v)	CBdn EMic IBal
'Coal Miner'	IBal
'Coconut Custard'	EMic NSue
'Cody'	IBal NSue
'Cold Heart'	EMic IBal
'Collector's Banner'	IBal
'Collector's Choice'	IBal NSue

'Color à la Mode' (v)	IBal
'Color Festival' (v)	CBod CDor ELon EMic IBal LLWG NLar NSue WFar
'Color Glory'	see *H.* 'Borwick Beauty'
'Colored Hulk' (v)	IBal
'Colossal'	EMic IBal
'Columbus Circle' (v)	EMic IBal
'Con Te Partiro' (v)	NSue WFar
'Confused Angel' (v)	IBal
'Cookie Crumbs' (v)	EMic IBal
'Cool as a Cucumber' (v) **new**	CBdn
'Coquette' (v)	EMic GAbr IBal
'Corkscrew'	EMic NSue
'Corn Belt' (v)	EMic IBal
'Corn Muffins'	EMic
'Corona' (v)	EMic
'Corryvreckan'	IBal
'Cotillion' (v)	CBdn EMic GEdr IBal NSue
'Count Your Blessings' (v)	EMic IBal
'Country Mouse' (v)	EMic IBal NHpl NSue SPoG WFar WTor
'County Park'	EMic IBal
'Cowrie' (v)	IBal
'Cracker Crumbs' (v) ♀H7	CBdn EHoe EMic GEdr IBal ITim LRHS MNrw NHpl NNor NSla NSue WCot WFar
'Craig's Temptation'	IBal NSue
'Cranberry Wine'	IBal
§ ***crassifolia***	EMic IBal LRHS XLum
'Cream Cheese' (v)	IBal
'Cream Delight' (*undulata*)	see *H. undulata* var. *undulata*
'Crepe Soul' (v)	IBal
'Crepe Suzette' (v)	EMic IBal NNor
'Crested Reef'	EMic
'Crested Surf' (v)	EMic IBal
'Crinoline Petticoats'	IBal
§ ***crispula*** (v)	CRos EMic EPfP IBal LRHS MCot MRav NChi NRHS
'Crocodile Socks' (v)	IBal
'Crown Prince' (v)	IBal NGdn
'Crown Royalty'	EMic IBal
§ 'Crowned Imperial' (*fortunei*) (v)	EMic IBal
'Crumb Cake'	NSue
'Crumples' (*sieboldiana*)	IBal
'Crusader' (v) ♀H7	ELon EMic IBal LRHS WFar
'Crystal Chimes'	IBal
'Crystal Dixie'	EMic IBal NSue WFar
'Cumulonimbus'	IBal
'Curlew' (Tardiana Group)	EMic IBal
'Curls'	EMic IBal
'Curly Fries'	CBdn EMic IBal NSue
'Curtain Call'	IBal
'Cutting Edge'	EMic IBal
'Cuyahoga' (v)	IBal
'Dab a Green'	IBal
'Dance with Me' (v)	EMic IBal
'Dancing in the Rain' (v)	CWGN EMic GMcL NBro WFar
'Dancing Mouse' (v)	IBal NSue WFar
'Dancing Queen'	EMic IBal NSue
'Dark Shadows'	EMic IBal NGdn NSti WFar
'Dark Star' (v)	EMic IBal NGdn
'Dark Victory'	EMic
'Dartmoor Forest'	CBdn IBal
'Dawn'	EMic IBal NSue
'Dawn's Early Light'	EMic IBal
'Dax'	IBal
'Daybreak' ♀H7	CRos EMic IBal NBro
'Day's End' (v)	EMic IBal
'Deane's Dream'	EMic GNew IBal
'Decorata'	EMic
decorata var. ***normalis***	EMic
'Deep Blue Sea' ♀H7	EMic IBal NSue
'Deep Pockets'	IBal
'Dee's Golden Jewel'	EMic
'Déjà Blu' (v)	EMic IBal
'Deliverance'	EMic IBal NSue
'Delta Dawn' (v)	EMic IBal NGdn
'Delta Desire'	IBal
'Desert Mouse' PBR (v)	IBal NSue
'Designer Genes'	EMic IBal WFar
'Devil's Advocate'	IBal
'Devon Blue' (Tardiana Group)	EMic IBal LRHS NNor
'Devon Desire' (*montana*)	IBal NLar
'Devon Discovery'	IBal
'Devon Giant'	EMic NNor
'Devon Gold'	EMic GAbr IBal
'Devon Green' ♀H7	Widely available
'Devon Mist'	IBal NNor
'Devon Tor'	IBal
'Dew Drop' (v)	EMic
'Dewed Steel'	IBal
'Diamond Tiara' (v)	EMic IBal LRHS NGdn WWtn
'Diamonds are Forever' (v)	CBdn IBal
'Diana Remembered'	CBdn EMic IBal NGdn NSue WFar
'Dick Ward'	EMic IBal
'Dilithium Crystal'	IBal NSue WFar
'Dillie Perkeo'	IBal
'Dilys'	EMic MNrw
'Dimple'	EMic
'Dinky Donna' (v)	EMic IBal NHpl NSue
'Dinner Jacket' (v)	CBdn ELan IBal LRHS
'Dino' (v) **new**	IBal
'Dixie Chick' (v)	EMic IBal LRHS NHpl NNor NSue
'Dixie Chickadee' (v)	NSue
'Dixieland Heat'	IBal
'Doctor Fu Manchu'	IBal
'Domaine de Courson'	EMic IBal NSue WFar
'Don Stevens' (v)	IBal LRHS
'Dorothy'	CBdn EMic
'Dorset Blue' (Tardiana Group)	EMic IBal LRHS
'Dorset Charm' (Tardiana Group)	EMic
'Dorset Flair' (Tardiana Group)	EMic IBal
'Doubled Up'	IBal
'Doubloons'	EMic
'Dragon Tails' ♀H7	EMic IBal NHpl NSue
'Dragon Warrior' (v)	IBal
'Drake's Tail'	IBal NLar
'Dream Queen' (v)	CBdn ECtt EMic EUJe IBal IPot NLar
'Dream Weaver' (v) ♀H7	CBdn ELon EMic EUJe IBal IFoB IPot LRHS MNrw NBro NEgg NGdn NSue SPoG WFar
'Dress Blues'	CMac EMic IBal
'Drummer Boy'	EMic IBal
'Duchess' (*nakaiana*) (v)	EMic
'Duke of Cornwall' (v)	CBdn IBal
'DuPage Delight' (*sieboldiana*) (v)	EMic IBal NGdn NLar
'Dust Devil' (*fortunei*) (v)	IBal
'Dusty Waters'	IBal
'Eagle's Nest' (v)	IBal
'Early Times'	IBal
'Earth Angel' PBR (v) ♀H7	CBdn EMic IBal NGdn NSue WHar
'Ebony Towers'	EMic IBal
'Edge of Night'	EMic IBal

'Edwin Bibby'	EMic
'El Capitan' (v)	CRos EMic IBal IFoB LRHS NRHS
'El Niño'PBR (Tardiana Group) (v) ♀H7	CBdn CDor CWGN EMic EPfP IBal LRHS MNrw NBro NGdn NLar NSue SPoG WFar WHoo
§ 'Elata'	EMic
'Elatior' (*nigrescens*)	IBal LRHS
'Elbridge Gerry' (v)	IBal
'Eldorado'	see *H.* 'Frances Williams'
'Eleanor Lachman' (v)	EMic IBal NSue
'Eleanor Roosevelt'	IBal
'Electrocution' (v)	CBdn IBal NSue
'Elegans'	see *H. sieboldiana* var. *elegans*
'Elephant Burgers'	EMic
'Elisabeth'	EMic IBal LSRN
'Elizabeth Campbell' (*fortunei*) (v)	EMic
'Elkheart Lake'	EMic IBal
'Ellen'	EMic
'Ellerbroek' (*fortunei*) (v)	EMic
'Elsley Runner'	IBal NSue
'Elvis Lives'	EMic IBal LRHS NEgg NEoE NGdn NLar NNor NSue
'Embroidery' (v)	EMic
'Emerald Carpet'	IBal NSue
'Emerald Charger' (v)	IBal
'Emerald Crown'	EMic IBal
'Emerald Emperor'	IBal
'Emerald Necklace' (v)	EMic IBal
'Emerald Paisley'	IBal
'Emerald Ruff Cut'	EMic IBal
'Emerald Tiara' (v)	CRos EMic IBal LRHS NLar NRHS NSue WFar
'Emeralds and Rubies'	EMic IBal NSue
'Emily Dickinson' (v)	ECtt EMic IBal LRHS NNor
'Empress Wu'PBR	CAby CBdn CBod CDor EBee ECtt EMic EUJe GBin IBal IBoy ITim LPla LRHS LSun MBel MHol MNrw MSCN NGdn NSue SPoG WCot WFar
'Encore'	IBal
'English Sunrise' (Tardiana Group)	IBal
'Enterprise' (v)	EBee EMic IBal NGdn NSue
'Eola Sapphire'	EMic IBal
'Eos'	IBal NLar
'Eric Smith' (Tardiana Group)	EMic IBal SHar WFar
'Eric Smith Gold'	GKev
'Eric's Gold'	IBal
'Erie Magic' (v)	EMic IBal
'Eskimo Pie' (v)	GEdr NSue WFar
'Essence of Summer'	EMic IBal
'Eternal Flame'	NSue
'Everlasting Love' (v)	IBal
'Excitation'	EMic IBal
'Exotic Presentation' (v)	EMic IBal
'Extasy' (v)	EMic IBal NGdn NSue WFar
'Eye Candy' (v)	IBal
'Eye Catcher'	EMic
'Eye Declare' (v)	IBal
'Fair Maiden' (v)	NHpl
'Faith'	EMic
'Faithful Heart' (v)	EMic IBal NSue
'Fall Dazzler' (v)	IBal
'Fall Emerald'	EMic
'Fan Dance' (v)	IBal
'Fantabulous' (v)	IBal
'Fantasy Island' (v)	CBdn EMic IBal NSue WFar
'Fat Boy'	IBal
'Fatal Attraction'	IBal
'Feather Boa'	EMic IBal IFoB LRHS NSue WFar
'Feng Shui'	IBal
'Fenman's Fascination'	EMic
'Fiesta' (v)	IBal
'Final Summation' (v)	EMic IBal NSue
'Final Victory' (v)	IBal
'Finlandia'	IBal
'Fire and Ice' (v) ♀H7	Widely available
'Fire Island' ♀H7	CBdn ECtt ELan EMic EPfP GBin GEdr IBal LRHS MNrw NLar NSue SPoG WCot
'Fire Opal' (v)	IBal
'Firefly' (v)	IBal
'Fireplace' (v) **new**	IBal
'Fireworks' (v) ♀H7	ECtt EMic EPfP GBin GEdr GMcL LSun MBNS MHol MNrw NBro NCou NGdn SMad WCot
'Firn Line' (v)	CBdn IBal
'First Frost' (v) ♀H7	CBdn CRos ECtt ELon EMic EPfP IBal LRHS MNrw NGdn NLar NRHS NSue SPoG
'First Love' (*montana*)	EMic IBal
'First Mate' (v)	EMic IBal NSue
'Five O'Clock Shadow' (v)	IBal
'Five O'Clock Somewhere' (v)	IBal
'Flapjack' (v)	IBal
'Fleet Week'	EMic IBal
'Flemish Angel' (v)	IBal NSue
'Flemish Gold'	IBal
'Flemish Master' (v)	IBal
'Flemish Sky'	EMic IBal IFoB NGdn NLar
'Flemish Steel' **new**	IBal
'Floradora'	EMic IBal NSue
'Floratini' **new**	NSue
'Flower Power'	CBdn IBal NNor
'Fluted Fountain'	EMic
'Fog Light'	IBal
'Fool's Gold' (*fortunei*)	EMic IBal
'Forbidden Fruit'PBR (v)	CBdn CBod IBal NSue
'Forest Fireworks' (v)	IBal
'Forest Shadows'	IBal
'Formal Attire' (*sieboldiana* hybrid) (v) ♀H7	EMic IBal LRHS
'Forncett Frances' (v)	IBal
'Fortis'	see *H. undulata* var. *erromena*
fortunei	EMic ESps GKev GMcL GWyn NNor WFar
§ - var. ***albopicta*** (v)	CRos CSam ECha EHoe ELan EMic EPed EPfP ESps EUJe GMaP GWyn IFoB LCro LOPS LRHS MJak MRav NEgg NLar NNor NRHS SPer SRms WBrk WFar WHoo WMoo
- - f. ***aurea***	CMac ECha EHoe EMic GMcL MMuc NEgg NLar SRms WFar WHal
- - - dwarf	EMic
- - f. ***viridis***	NNor
§ - var. ***aureomarginata*** (v) ♀H7	CBdn CRos CSam CTri ECha EHoe ELan ELon EMic EPfP EShb ESps ETMg GMaP GMcL GNew IBal LRHS MMuc NGdn NLar NNor NRHS SEND SPer SPlb WFar
- var. ***gigantea***	see *H. montana*
- var. ***hyacinthina***	EMic EPfP ESps GNew IBal IBoy LRHS MRav NGdn NLar XLum
- - variegated	see *H.* 'Crowned Imperial'
- var. ***stenantha***	EMic
'Fountain'	CBdn
'Fountain of Youth' (*kikutii*)	IBal

	'Fourteen Carats'	EMic IBal
	'Fourth of July'	CBdn NSue
	'Foxfire Palm Sunday' (v)	IBal
	'Fragrant Blue'	ELon EMic ETMg IBal LBuc LRHS NBro NGdn NHpl SPoG XLum
	'Fragrant Blue Ribbons' (v)	EMic IBal
	'Fragrant Bouquet' (v) ♀H7	CBdn CRos ECtt ELan EMic GNew IBal LRHS LSRN NEgg NGdn NLar NSue WFar WHar
	'Fragrant Dream'	CBdn EMic GBin IBal LRHS NLar NRHS
	'Fragrant Fire'	CBdn EMic IBal
	'Fragrant Gold'	EMic
	'Fragrant King'	IBal
	'Fragrant Queen'PBR (v)	CBdn IBal NSue
	'Fragrant Star'	EMic IBal
	'Fran Godfrey'	EMic IBal
	'Francee' (*fortunei*) (v) ♀H7	Widely available
§	'Frances Williams' (*sieboldiana*) (v) ♀H7	Widely available
	'Frances Williams Improved' (*sieboldiana*) (v)	EPfP IFoB
	'Francheska' (v)	EMic IBal
	'Frank Lloyd Wright'	IBal
	'Free Jazz' (v)	IBal
	'Fresh' (v)	EMic IBal NSue
	'Fried Bananas'	CBdn EMic GNew IBal ITim WWtn
	'Fried Green Tomatoes'	CBdn EMic GNew IBal NLar NNor
	'Friends' (v)	EMic
	'Fringe Benefit' (v)	EMic
	'Frisian Pride'	CBdn EMic IBal
	'Frisian Waving Steel'	CBdn EMic IBal
	'Frosted Dimples'	EMic GNew IBal
	'Frosted Frolic' (v)	CBdn EMic IBal WFar
	'Frosted Jade' (v) ♀H7	EMic EPfP IBal LRHS MMuc NEgg NLar
	'Frosted June'	CBdn EMic IBal
	'Frosted Mini Hearts'	IBal NSue
	'Frosted Mouse Ears'PBR	CBdn EMic IBal NHpl NSue
	'Frozen Margarita'	EMic IBal NLar
	'Fruit Punch'	EMic IBal IFoB
	'Fujibotan' (v)	EMic IBal IFoB
	'Fukurin-Fu' (*venusta*) (v)	GEdr
	'Fulda'	EMic IBal
	'Full Moon'	EMic
	'Funky Monkey'	EMic IBal
	'Funny Frolic' (v)	IBal
	'Funny Mouse' (v)	CBdn EMic IBal NHpl NSue WFar
	'Futura' (v)	IBal
	'Gaiety' (v)	ECtt EMic IBal LRHS NRHS
	'Gaijin' (v)	EMic IBal NSue
	'Garden Party' (v)	IBal
	'Garnet Prince'	IBal
	'Gay Blade' (v)	IBal
	'Gay Feather' (v)	EMic IFoB
	'Gay Search' (v)	IBal
	'Geisha' (v)	EMic IBal LRHS NEoE NGdn NNor NSue
	'Geisha Satin Ripples'	IBal
	'Gemstone'	NSue
	'Gene's Joy'	EMic
	'Gentle Giant'	IBal
	'Gentle Spirit' (v)	IBal
	'George M. Dallas' (v)	IBal
	'George Smith' (*sieboldiana*)	EMic IBal
	'Georgia Sweetheart' (v)	IBal
	'Ghost Spirit'	CBdn IBal NSue WFar
	'Ghostmaster' (v)	IBal WFar
	'Giantland Mouse Cheese'	IBal NSue
	'Giantland Sunny Mouse Ears'	IBal NSue
	'Gig Harbor'	IBal
	'Gigantea' (*sieboldiana*)	see *H.* 'Elata'
	'Gilt by Association'	EMic IBal
	'Gilt Edge' (*sieboldiana*) (v)	EMic
	'Gin and Tonic' (v)	EMic NSue
	'Gingee'	EMic IBal
	'Ginko Craig' (v) ♀H7	CMac CRos ECha EHoe ELan EMic EPfP GKev GMaP IBal IFoB LRHS MRav NEgg NGdn NLar NNor NRHS NSti SPer SPoG WFar
	'Ginrei'	IBal
	'Ginsu Knife' (v)	EMic IBal
	'Glacial Towers' (v)	IBal
	'Glad Rags' (v)	IBal
	'Glad Tidings'	IBal
	'Glamour'	CBdn EMic IBal NSue
	'Glass Hearts'	EMic IBal
	glauca	see *H. sieboldiana* var. *elegans*
	'Glitter'	EMic IBal
	'Glockenspiel'	EMic IBal
I	'Gloriosa' (*fortunei*) (v)	IBal IFoB LRHS NSue
	'Glory'	IBal
	'Glory Hallelujah'	EMic IBal
	'Goddess of Athena' (*decorata*) (v)	IBal
	'Gold Drop' (*venusta* hybrid)	EMic IBal NSue
	'Gold Edger'	CDor CMac CRos EHoe ELan EMic EPfP EShb GMaP IBal LRHS MRav NGdn NLar NNor NRHS NSti WFar
	'Gold Edger Surprise' (v)	EMic
	'Gold Flush' (*ventricosa*)	EMic
§	'Gold Haze' (*fortunei*)	EMic IBal
	'Gold Leaf' (*fortunei*)	IBal
	'Gold Pressed Latinum'	IBal
	'Gold Regal'	EBee EMic IBal IFoB LRHS NRHS WFar
	'Gold Rush'	EMic IBal
	'Gold Standard' (*fortunei*) (v) ♀H7	Widely available
	'Goldbrook' (v)	EMic IBal
	'Goldbrook Galleon'	IBal
	'Goldbrook Gaynor'	IBal
	'Goldbrook Genie'	CBdn IBal
	'Goldbrook Glamour' (v)	IBal
	'Goldbrook Gleam' (v)	IBal
	'Goldbrook Glimmer' (Tardiana Group) (v)	IBal LRHS
	'Goldbrook Glory'	EMic IBal
	'Goldbrook Gold'	IBal
	'Goldbrook Good Gracious' (v)	IBal
	'Goldbrook Grace'	IBal
	'Goldbrook Gratis' (v)	CBdn IBal
	'Goldbrook Grayling'	EMic IBal LRHS NRHS
	'Goldbrook Grebe'	IBal
	'Goldbrook Greengage' (v)	IBal
	'Goldbrook Greenheart'	IBal
	'Golden Age'	see *H.* 'Gold Haze'
	'Golden Fountain'	EMic
	'Golden Gate'	IBal
	'Golden Goal'	IBal
	'Golden Guernsey' (v)	EMic
	'Golden Isle'	EMic IBal NSue
	'Golden Meadows'PBR (*sieboldiana*)	CDor ECtt EMic IBal NGdn NSue WFar
	'Golden Medallion' (*tokudama*)	CRos ECtt EMic LRHS NEgg NGdn NRHS WFar

'Golden Nakaiana'	see *H.* 'Birchwood Parky's Gold'
'Golden' (*nakaiana*)	see *H.* 'Birchwood Parky's Gold'
'Golden Needles' (v)	NSue
'Golden Oriole'	EMic LRHS NNor
'Golden Prayers' (*tokudama*)	ECtt EHoe ELan GMcL MRav NBro NEgg NGdn NLar WFar WHal WSHC
'Golden Scepter'	EMic IBal LRHS NNor SRms WFar
'Golden Sculpture' (*sieboldiana*)	EMic
'Golden Spades'	EMic NSue
'Golden Spider'	EMic
'Golden Sunburst' (*sieboldiana*)	ECtt NEgg NGdn NLar XLum
'Golden Sweetie'	EMic
'Golden Tiara' (v) ♀H7	Widely available
'Golden Tusk'	IBal
'Golden Waffles'	ECtt EMic NEgg
'Goldsmith'	EMic
'Gone Fishin'' (v)	IBal
'Gone with the Wind' (v)	CBdn IBal
'Goober'	IBal
'Good as Gold'	EMic
'Goodness Gracious' (v)	CBdn EMic IBal NSue
'Gorgeous George'	IBal
'Gosan' (*tardiva*)	EMic
'Gosan Gold Midget'	EMic
'Gosan Leather Strap'	IBal
'Gosan Mina'	EMic
'Gosan Shining'	EMic
gracillima	IBal NRya
'Grand Canyon'	CBdn EMic
'Grand Finale'	IBal
'Grand Marquee' (v)	EMic IBal NGdn NLar WFar
'Grand Master'	IBal
'Grand Prize' (v)	EMic IBal NSue
'Grand Rapids'	IBal
'Grand Slam'	IBal
'Grand Tiara' (v)	EMic IBal LRHS NGdn NRHS
'Grand Total'	IBal
'Grant Park'	EMic IBal
'Grape Fizz'	IBal
'Gray Cole' (*sieboldiana*)	EMic IBal ITim
'Great Arrival'	EMic IBal
'Great Escape'^{PBR} (v)	EMic IBal
'Great Expectations' (*sieboldiana*) (v)	CDor CHid CMac CNor CRos EMic EPfP IBal IBoy IFoB LPmr LRHS LSRN MBNS MHer MNrw NBro NGdn NHpl NNor NRHS SPoG
'Great Lakes Gold'	IBal
'Green Acres' (*montana*)	CBdn EMic GNew IBal LEdu WFar
'Green Angel' (*sieboldiana*)	IBal
'Green Cheese' **new**	EMic
'Green Dwarf'	WFar
'Green Eyes' (*sieboldii*) (v)	EMic IBal NSue WFar
'Green Fountain' (*kikutii*)	EMic IBal
'Green Gold' (*fortunei*) (v)	EMic
'Green Lama'	EMic IBal
'Green Mouse Ears'	CBdn EMic IBal NHpl NSue WFar
'Green Piecrust'	EMic NNor
'Green Platter'	EMic
'Green Sheen'	EMic
'Green Velveteen'	IBal
'Green with Envy' (v) ♀H7	EMic IBal LLHF NNor NSue NWad
'Greenie Weenie Bikini'	NSue
'Greensleeves' (v)	IBal
'Grey Ghost'	EMic IBal
'Grey Goose' (Tardiana Group)	EMic
'Groo Bloo'	IBal
'Ground Master' (v)	CMac CRos EBee ECtt ELan EPfP GMaP IBal IFoB MRav NBro NGdn NLar NNor NSti WFar WMoo
'Ground Sulphur'	EMic IBal NSue
'Grover Cleveland'	IBal
'Grunspecht' (Tardiana Group)	IBal
'Grünherz'	IBal
'Guacamole' (v) ♀H7	CAby CBcs CBdn CDor CRos ECha ECtt EHoe ELon EMic EPfP GBin GNew IBal LRHS NGdn NLar NNor NRHS SCob SPoG WFar WHar
'Guardian Angel' (*sieboldiana*) ♀H7	CBdn EMic NSue
'Gum Drop'	EMic NNor
'Gun Metal Blue'	IBal
'Gunther's Prize' (v)	IBal
'Gunther's Rim' (v)	IBal
'Gypsy Rose' ♀H7	CBdn EMic IBal IPot NGdn NLar NSue WFar
'Hacksaw'	EMic IBal NSue
'Hadspen Blue' (Tardiana Group) ♀H7	CAby CRos CSBt CWCL EBee ELan EMic EPfP ESps GMaP IBal IBoy IRob LRHS MBrN MGos MRav NBro NEgg NGdn NLar NNor NRHS SPer SPoG WSpi
'Hadspen Hawk' (Tardiana Group)	IBal
'Hadspen Heron' (Tardiana Group)	EMic IBal XLum
'Hadspen Honey'	CRos LRHS NRHS
'Hadspen Nymphaea'	IBal
'Hadspen Rainbow'	CBdn EMic IBal
'Hadspen Samphire'	EMic IBal NBro
'Hadspen White' (*fortunei*)	EMic IBal NLar
'Haku-chu-han' (*sieboldii*) (v)	EMic NHpl
'Hakujima' (*sieboldii*)	IBal NSue
'Hakumuo' (v)	IBal
§ 'Halcyon' (Tardiana Group) ♀H7	Widely available
'Halcyon Gold'	ESps LSun
'Half and Half'	EMic IBal NSue
'Hampshire County' (v)	EMic IBal
'Hands Up'^{PBR} (v)	CBdn EMic IBal NSue
'Hanky Panky' (v)	CBdn IBal NGdn NSti NSue WFar
'Hannibal Hamlin' (v)	IBal
'Happily Ever After' (v)	IBal
'Happiness' (Tardiana Group)	EHoe EMic IBal MRav
'Happy Camper' (v)	IBal
'Happy Dayz' (v)	IBal
'Happy Hearts'	EMic
'Happy Valley' (v)	IBal
'Harmony' (Tardiana Group)	EMic
'Harpoon' (v)	EMic
'Harriette Ward'	IBal
'Harry van de Laar'	CBdn EMic IBal
'Harry van Trier'	EMic GBin GWyn
'Hart's Tongue'	IBal
'Harvest Delight'	EMic
'Harvest Glow'	IBal
'Hawkeye' (v)	IBal
'Hazel'	EMic IBal
'Heart and Soul' (v)	EMic IBal
'Heart Broken'	IBal
'Heart of Chan'	IBal
'Heart Throb'	CBdn EMic
'Heartache'	IBal
'Heartleaf'	EMic
'Heart's Content' (v)	IBal

'Heartsong' (v)	CBdn EMic IBal LRHS
'Heat Wave'PBR (v)	CBdn EMic IBal
'Heavenly Beginnings' (v)	IBal
'Heavy Duty'	IBal
'Heideturm'	IBal
'Helen Doriot' (*sieboldiana*)	EMic IBal
'Helen Field Fischer' (*fortunei*)	IBal NLar
helonioides f. ***albopicta*** misapplied	see *H. rohdeifolia*
'Herifu' (v)	EMic
'Herkules'	CBdn
'Hertha' (v)	EMic
'Hida-no-hana' (*montana*) (v)	IBal
'Hidden Cove' (v)	IBal NSue
'Hidden Treasure' (v)	IBal
'Hideout' (v)	IBal NSue
'High Kicker'	IBal
'High Society' (v)	ELan EPfP IBal IFoB MNrw NHpl NNor NSue
'High Tide'	IBal
'Hi-ho Silver' (v)	EMic IBal NSue
'Hilda Wassman' (v)	CBdn IBal
'Hillbilly Blues' (v)	NSue
'Hippodrome' (v)	EMic IBal
'Hirao Elite'	EMic IBal
'Hirao Majesty'	IBal
'Hirao Splendor'	GNew
'Hirao Supreme'	EMic IBal
'His Honor' (v)	EMic IBal
'Hoarfrost'	EMic
'Hollywood Lights' (v)	EMic EPfP IBal NGdn NSue
'Holstein'	see *H.* 'Halcyon'
'Holy Molé' (v)	EMic IBal
'Holy Mouse Ears'PBR	CBdn EMic IBal NSue
'Honey Moon'	EMic IBal NNor
'Honeybells'	CBcs CMac EBee ECha ELan EMic EPfP GBin GNew IBal LEdu MCot MRav NBid NGdn NNor NSti SPer XLum
'Honeysong' (v)	EMic IBal NNor
'Hoosier Dome'	EMic
'Hoosier Harmony' (v)	EMic
'Hope' (v)	NLar NSue
'Hot Air Balloon'	IBal
'Hotcakes'	IBal
'Hotspur' (v)	EMic
'Hudson Bay' (v)	CBdn EMic IBal
'Humpback Whale'	CBdn IBal
'Hush Puppie'	EMic IBal MNrw NHpl NSue WFar
'Hyacintha Variegata' (*fortunei*) (v)	CMac NNor
'Hydon Gleam'	EMic IBal NSue
'Hydon Sunset'	CBdn CNor CRos EBee ECtt EMic GEdr IBal IRob LRHS MNrw NLar NNor NRHS NRya NSti NSue WHal
hypoleuca	EMic IBal
'Hyuga-urajiro' (v)	EMic IBal NSue WFar
'Ice Cream' (*cathayana*) (v)	IBal LRHS NGdn NRHS
'Ice Cube' (v)	CBdn IBal NSue
'Ice Prancer'	EMic IBal
'Iced Lemon' (v)	EMic GNew IBal NHpl NNor NSue WFar
'Illicit Affair'	EMic IBal NHpl NSue
'Imp' (v)	EMic IBal
§ 'Inaho'	LRHS NSue
'Inca Gold'	IBal NSue
'Incoming'	IBal
'Independence' (v)	EBee EMic IBal NBro NSue SPoG WFar
'Independence Day' (v)	EMic
'Inniswood' (v)	CDor CWCL ECtt EMic IBal MBNS NBro NGdn NLar NSti WFar
'Invincible'	CDor ECtt EMic IBal NBid NEgg NGdn NLar NNor WFar
'Invincible Spirit'	IBal
'Iona' (*fortunei*)	CBdn EMic IBal NNor
'Irische See' (Tardiana Group)	IBal
'Irish Eyes' (v)	EMic IBal
'Irish Luck'	EMic IBal NSue
'Iron Gate Delight' (v)	NNor
'Iron Gate Special' (v)	EMic
'Iron Gate Supreme' (v)	EMic
'Iron Sky' **new**	IBal
'Island Charm' (v) ♀H7	CRos GBin IBal LRHS NHpl NLar NRHS NSue SCob WFar
'Itty Gold'	IBal
'Ivory Coast' (v)	CBdn ECtt EMic IBal IPot MHol
'Ivory Necklace' (v)	EMic IBal
'Ivory Queen' (v)	EMic IBal NSue
'Iwa Yara Moto'	IBal
'Jack of Diamonds'	IBal
'Jade Beauty'	CBdn
'Jade Cascade'	EMic GBin IBal NEgg NLar WFar WHal
'Jade Scepter' (*nakaiana*)	EMic
'Janet Day' (v)	EMic
'Janet' (*fortunei*) (v)	EMic NGdn NNor
'Janet's Green Sox'	EMic
'Jason and Katie' (v)	EMic IBal
'Jaws'	CBdn EMic IBal NSue
'Jaz'	IBal
'Jennifer' (v)	IBal
'Jerry Landwehr'	EMic IBal
'Jewel of the Nile' (v)	EMic IBal
'Jimmy Crack Corn'	EMic IBal NEgg NGdn
'Jingle Bells'	IBal
'John Wargo'	IBal
'Johnny Angel'	EMic
'Joker' (*fortunei*) (v)	NNor
'Jolly Green Giant' (*sieboldiana* hybrid)	EMic
'Joseph'	EMic IBal
'Josephine' (v)	NNor
'Journeyman'	EMic IBal
'Journey's End' (v)	CBdn EMic IBal
'Joyce Trott' (v)	EMic
'Joyful' (v)	IBal
'Jubilee' (v)	EMic IBal
'Judy Rocco'	IBal
'Juha' (v)	EMic
'Jules'	IBal
'Julia' (v)	EMic IBal NSue
'Julie Morss'	EMic GMaP IBal NEgg
'June'PBR (Tardiana Group) (v) ♀H7	Widely available
'June Fever'PBR (Tardiana Group)	CBdn EMic GBin IBal NBro NGdn NLar NSue SPoG WFar
'June Spirit' (v)	CBdn IBal NSue
'Junka'	SMHy
'Jurassic Park'	CBdn EMic EUJe GMcL IBal LLWG LRHS MNrw NLar NSue
'Just So' (v)	EMic IBal
'Justine'PBR	EMic IBal NSue
'Kabitan'	see *H. sieboldii* var. *sieboldii* f. *kabitan*
'Kabuki'	IBal
'Kalamazoo' (v)	EMic IBal
'Kaleidochrome' (v)	IBal NSue

'Karin'	EMic IBal
'Katherine Lewis' (Tardiana Group) (v)	EMic IBal LRHS LSRN
'Kath's Gold'	EMic
'Katie Q' (v)	EMic IBal
'Katsuragawa-beni' (v)	EMic IBal
'Kelly'	EMic
'Kelsey'	EMic
'Kenzie' (v)	EMic IBal
'Key Lime Pie'	EMic IBal
'Key West'	EMic
'Kifukurin' (*kikutii*)	see *H.* 'Kifukurin-hyuga'
§ 'Kifukurin-hyuga' (v)	IBal
'Kifukurin-kiyosumi'	IBal
'Kifukurin-ko-mame' (*gracillima*) (v)	EMic NSue
'Kifukurin-otome' (*venusta*) (v)	EMic NSue
'Kifukurin-ubatake' (*pulchella*) (v)	EMic IBal
kikutii	CBdn EMic IBal IMou LRHS
§ - var. ***caput-avis***	EMic
§ - var. ***yakusimensis***	EMic GEdr IBal SMad
'Ki-nakafu-otome' (*venusta*)	EMic IBal NSue
'Kinbotan' (*venusta*) (v)	EMic GEdr
'Kinbuchi Tachi' (*rectifolia*) (v)	IBal
'King James'	IBal
'King of Spades'	IBal
'King Tut'	EMic
'Kingfisher' (Tardiana Group)	LRHS
'Kingsize'	IBal
§ 'Kirishima'	EMic NHpl NSue NWad
'Kisuji'	see *H.* 'Mediopicta'
'Kitty Cat'	EMic IBal WFar
'Kiwi Black Magic'	IBal
'Kiwi Blue Baby'	EMic IBal
'Kiwi Blue Ruffles'	IBal
'Kiwi Blue Sky'	IBal
'Kiwi Canoe'	IBal
'Kiwi Cream Edge' (v)	EMic
'Kiwi Forest'	IBal
'Kiwi Full Monty' (v)	CBdn CDor EMic GNew IBal NSue
'Kiwi Hippo'	IBal
'Kiwi Jordan'	IBal
'Kiwi Kaniere Gold'	IBal
'Kiwi Minnie Gold'	IBal ITim
'Kiwi Parasol'	IBal
'Kiwi Skyscraper'	IBal
'Kiwi Spearmint'	CBdn WFar
'Kiwi Sunshine'	IBal
kiyosumiensis	IBal
'Klopping Variegated' (v)	EMic
'Knight's Journey'	IBal
'Knockout' (v)	MBNS MRav NBro NEgg NGdn NLar NNor
'Komodo Dragon'	EMic GNew IBal
'Konkubine'	EMic
'Korean Snow'	IBal
'Koriyama' (*sieboldiana*) (v)	EMic
'Krossa Cream Edge' (*sieboldii*) (v)	IBal
'Krossa Regal' ♀H7	Widely available
'La Donna'	IBal
'Lacy Belle' (v)	CDor CSBt EBee EMic EPfP IBal LRHS NBro NEoE NGdn NSue
'Lady Godiva'	IBal
'Lady Guineverre'	EMic IBal IRob
'Lady Helen'	EMic
'Lady in Red'	IBal
'Lady Isobel Barnett' (v) ♀H7	IBal
laevigata	IBal
'Lake Hitchcock'	IBal
'Lake Superior'	IBal
'Lake Tekapo' (v) **new**	IBal
'Lakeside Accolade'	IBal
'Lakeside Alex Andra' (v)	IBal
'Lakeside April Snow' (v)	EMic IBal NGdn
'Lakeside Baby Face' (v)	EMic IBal NHpl NSue WFar
'Lakeside Banana Bay' (v)	IBal NGdn
'Lakeside Beach Bum'	IBal
'Lakeside Beach Captain' (v)	EMic
'Lakeside Black Satin'	EMic WFar
'Lakeside Blue Cherub'	EMic IBal
'Lakeside Breaking News' (v)	EMic IBal
'Lakeside Butter Ball'	IBal
'Lakeside Cha Cha' (v)	CBdn EMic IBal WFar
'Lakeside Cindy Cee' (v)	IBal
'Lakeside Circle O' (v)	IBal
'Lakeside Coal Miner'	EMic NGdn NLar
'Lakeside Color Blue'	IBal
'Lakeside Contender'	IBal
'Lakeside Cupcake' (v)	EMic IBal NGdn NSue
'Lakeside Cupid's Cup' (v)	IBal
'Lakeside Dimpled Darling' (v)	NSue
'Lakeside Dividing Line' (v)	IBal
'Lakeside Doodad' (v)	IBal NSue
'Lakeside Down Sized' (v)	CBdn EMic IBal MNrw NSue WFar
'Lakeside Dragonfly' (v)	ECtt ELon EMic EPfP EShb IBal LLWG MNrw NGdn NLar NSue WFar
'Lakeside Elfin Fire'	EMic NSue
'Lakeside Fancy Pants' (v)	IBal
'Lakeside Feather Light' (v)	IBal
'Lakeside Foaming Sea'	IBal
'Lakeside Full Tide'	IBal
'Lakeside Hazy Morn' (v)	IBal
'Lakeside Hoola Hoop' (v)	IBal
'Lakeside Iron Man'	IBal
'Lakeside Jazzy Jane' (v)	IBal
'Lakeside Kaleidoscope'	EMic IBal NGdn
'Lakeside Keepsake' (v)	IBal
'Lakeside Khum Kaw'	IBal
'Lakeside Legal Tender'	IBal
'Lakeside Lime Time'	IBal
'Lakeside Little Gem'	IBal NSue
'Lakeside Little Tuft' (v)	EMic IBal NLar NSue
'Lakeside Lollipop'	EMic IBal
'Lakeside Looking Glass'	EMic
'Lakeside Love Affaire'	EMic IBal WFar
'Lakeside Maestro'	IBal NLar
'Lakeside Maverick'	IBal
'Lakeside Meadow Ice' (v)	IBal
'Lakeside Meter Maid' (v)	IBal NSue
'Lakeside Midnight Miss'	IBal
'Lakeside Miss Muffett' (v)	EMic NSue
'Lakeside Missy Little' (v)	IBal
'Lakeside Neat Petite'	IBal NSue
'Lakeside Ninita' (v)	EMic IBal LRHS NRHS NSue
'Lakeside Old Smokey'	IBal
'Lakeside Paisley Print' (v)	ECtt EMic IBal MHol NSue SPad WFar
'Lakeside Pebbles'	IBal
'Lakeside Premier'	EMic IBal
'Lakeside Prissy Miss' (v)	NSue

'Lakeside Prophecy'	IBal
'Lakeside Prophecy Fulfilled' (v)	IBal
'Lakeside Rhapsody' (v)	EMic IBal
'Lakeside Ring Master' (v)	IBal
'Lakeside Ripples'	IBal
'Lakeside Rocky Top' (v)	IBal WFar
'Lakeside Roy El' (v)	IBal
'Lakeside Sapphire Pleats'	EMic
'Lakeside Sassy Sally'	IBal
'Lakeside Scamp' (v)	CBdn EMic NSue SPoG
'Lakeside Shadows' (v)	IBal
'Lakeside Shoremaster' (v)	CBdn IBal
'Lakeside Slick Chick' (v)	IBal
'Lakeside Small Fry' (v)	NSue
'Lakeside Sophistication' (v)	IBal
'Lakeside Sparkle Plenty' (v)	IBal
'Lakeside Spellbinder' (v)	IBal LRHS
'Lakeside Spruce Goose' (v)	EMic IBal
'Lakeside Storm Watch'	EMic IBal NSue
'Lakeside Swan Pon' (v)	IBal
'Lakeside Symphony' (v)	EMic
'Lakeside Tee Ki' (v)	IBal
'Lakeside Whizzit' (v)	IBal NSue
'Lakeside Zesty Zeno' (v)	IBal
'Lakeside Zinger' (v)	EMic IBal NSue
lancifolia	CMac EBee ELan EMic GMaP IBal MRav NGdn NSti SBod SPer SRms WKif WSHC WThu
'Last Dance' (v)	IBal
'Laura Lanier'	EMic IBal
'Laura Z'	IBal
'Lavender Doll'	IBal
'Leading Lady' 🏆H7	IBal
'Leather Sheen'	EHoe EMic
'Leatherneck'	IBal
'Lederhosen'	EMic
'Lemon Delight'	CBdn EMic IBal LRHS NNor NSue WFar
'Lemon Frost'	EMic IBal
'Lemon Lime'	CBdn EMic EWld IBal MNrw NEgg NEoE NNor NSue WCot
'Lemon Meringue'	EMic
'Lemonade'	GBin IBal
'Leola Fraim' (v)	EMic IBal LRHS
'Let Me Entertain You'	EMic
'Leviathan'	EMic
'Lewis and Clark'	IBal
'Libby'	EMic IBal NSue
'Liberty'PBR (v) 🏆H7	CBdn CBod CDor CWGN EMic EPfP GMcL IBal IRob NBro NGdn NLar NNor NSue SPer
'Light of Zetar'	IBal
'Li'l Abner' (v)	IBal
* ***lilacina***	WFar
'Lily Blue Eyes'	EMic
'Lime Fizz'	EMic IBal NHpl NSue WFar
'Lime Shag' (*sieboldii* f. *spathulata*)	GNew IBal NSue
'Limey Lisa'	EMic IBal NSue
'Linda Sue' (v)	EMic IBal
'Lionheart' (v)	EMic IBal NSue
'Little Aurora' (*tokudama* hybrid)	EMic IBal NSue WFar
'Little Bit'	IBal NSue
'Little Black Scape'	EMic IBal LSRN NEgg NGdn NLar NWad
'Little Blue' (*ventricosa*)	EMic
'Little Bo Beep' (v)	IBal WFar
'Little Boy'	IBal

'Little Caesar' (v)	EMic IBal LRHS NGdn NSue WFar
'Little Devil'	EMic NSue
'Little Doll' (v)	IBal
'Little Jay' (v)	IBal NSue
'Little Maddie'	EMic NSue
'Little Miss Magic'	IBal NSue
'Little Miss Muffett'	NSue
'Little Miss Sunshine'	IBal
'Little Prayer' **new**	WFar
'Little Razor'	NSue
'Little Red Joy'	EMic IBal NSue
'Little Red Rooster'	EMic GEdr IBal NGdn NHpl NLar NNor NSue WFar
'Little Star Struck' **new**	NSue
'Little Stiffy'	EMic IBal
'Little Sunspot' (v)	EMic NSue
'Little Treasure' (v)	EMic IBal NSue WFar
'Little White Lines' (v)	EBee EHoe EMic GKev IBal LRHS NRHS NSue
'Little Willie' (v)	NSue
'Little Wonder' (v) 🏆H7	EMic NSue
'Living Water'	EMic
'Lizard Lick'	EMic IBal NSue
'Lollapalooza' (v)	IBal
'London Fog' (v)	IBal NSue
'Long Fellow' (v)	IBal
longipes B&SWJ 10806	WCru
longissima var. ***brevifolia***	NSue
'Lost World'	EMic IBal
'Lothar the Giant'	IBal
'Love Pat' 🏆H7	ECtt EMic EPfP IBal LSRN MRav NGdn NLar NNor NSue
'Love Song'	IBal
'Loyalist'PBR (v)	EMic IBal LRHS NGdn NLar SPoG WFar
'Lucky Mouse'PBR (v)	CBdn EMic IBal NSue
'Lucy Vitols' (v)	EMic IBal
'Lullabye'	EMic
'Luna Moth'	CBdn IBal
'Lunar Eclipse' (v)	EMic NEgg
'Machete'	IBal
'Mack the Knife'	EMic IBal NLar WFar
'Maekawa'	EMic IBal
'Magic Fire'PBR (v)	CBdn ECtt EMic EPfP IBal MNrw
'Magic Island'	IBal NSue
'Magica'	IBal
'Majesty'	EMic IBal MNrw NGdn
'Major Tom'	IBal
'Majordomo'	EMic
'Malabar' (v)	EMic IBal
'Mama Mia' (v)	EMic EPfP IBal MBNS NBro NGdn NWad WFar
'Mango Salsa'	IBal
'Mango Tango' (v)	EMic IBal
'Manhattan'	EMic
'Maple Leaf' (*sieboldiana*) (v)	EMic
'Maraschino Cherry'	EMic IBal LPla NEgg NGdn
'Mardi Gras' (v)	EMic IBal
'Marge' (*sieboldiana* hybrid)	EMic
'Margie's Angel' (v)	NSue
'Margin of Error' (v)	IBal
'Marginata Alba' misapplied	see *H.* 'Albomarginata' (*fortunei*), *H. crispula*
'Marginata Alba' ambig. (v)	NNor
'Marilyn'	EMic IBal NSue
'Marilyn Monroe'	EMic IBal NSue
'Marmalade on Toast'	EMic
'Marquis' (*nakaiana* hybrid)	CBdn IBal
'Marrakech'	EMic IBal LRHS NSue

'Mary Joe'	EMic
'Mary Marie Ann' (*fortunei*) (v)	EMic IBal
'Masquerade' (v)	EMic LLHF NRya NSue SMHy WFar WHal WThu
'Maui Buttercups'	EMic
'May'	EMic IBal
'Maya' (*fortunei*) (v)	EMic IBal
'Medieval Age' (v)	IBal
§ 'Mediopicta' (*sieboldii*)	EMic IBal
'Mediovariegata' (*undulata*)	see *H. undulata* var. *undulata*
'Medusa' (v)	NGdn NSue
'Memories of Dorothy'	EMic IBal
'Mesa Fringe' (*montana*)	EMic NLar
'Mid Afternoon'	IBal
'Midas Touch'	NEgg NLar NNor
'Middle Ridge'	EMic
'Midnight at the Oasis' (v)	CBdn EMic IBal NSue
'Midnight Ride'	IBal
'Midwest Magic' (v)	EMic IBal NLar
'Mighty Mite'	IBal
'Mikawa-no-yuki'	IBal
'Mike Shadrack' (v)	EMic IBal
'Miki'	IBal
'Mildred Seaver' (v)	EMic IBal LRHS
'Millennium'	CBdn ECtt EMic IBal
'Mini Skirt' **new**	NSue
I 'Minima Aurea'	IBal
'Minnesota Wild' (v)	IBal
'Minnie Bell' (v)	IBal
'Minnie Klopping'	EMic
minor misapplied f. ***alba***	see *H. sieboldii* var. *alba*
§ ***minor*** Maekawa	GEdr ITim NWad WFar XLum
- B&SWJ 1209 from Korea	WCru
- B&SWJ 8775 from Korea	WCru
- B&SWJ 11103 from Japan	WCru
- from Japan	EMic
- from Korea	IBal NSue
'Minor' (*ventricosa*)	see *H. minor* Maekawa
'Mint Julep' (v)	IBal
'Minuet' (v)	IBal
'Minuteman' (*fortunei*) (v) ♀H7	CBcs CDor CRos ECtt ELon EMic EPfP GNew IBal LPmr LRHS MBNS MMuc NGdn NHpl NLar NNor NRHS SEND SPoG WFar
'Minutini'	NSue
'Miracle Lemony' **new**	CBdn NSue
'Miss Linda Smith'	EMic IBal
'Miss Ruby'	CBdn EMic IBal
'Miss Saigon' (v)	IBal
'Miss Susie'	IBal
'Miss Tokyo' (v)	EMic IBal
'Mississippi Delta'	EMic
'Mister Watson'	EMic IBal
'Misty Waters' (*sieboldiana*)	EMic
'Moerheim' (*fortunei*) (v)	EMic IBal LRHS WFar WHal
'Mohegan'	EMic
'Mohrchen' **new**	EMic
'Moi Marleen'	EMic
'Monster Ears'	EUJe IBal NSue
montana	EMic WFar
- B&SWJ 4796	WCru
- B&SWJ 5585	WCru
- f. ***macrophylla***	IBal NSue
aff. ***montana***	WFar
'Moody Blues' (Tardiana Group)	EMic
'Moon Dance' (v)	IBal
'Moon Lily'	EMic
'Moon River' (v)	EMic IBal
'Moon Split' (v)	EMic EPfP IBal NGdn
'Moonbeam'	CBdn EMic EShb
'Moongate Flying Saucer'	EMic
'Moonlight' (*fortunei*) (v)	EMic GMaP IBal IRob LRHS NEgg NNor
'Moonlight Sonata'	EMic IBal
'Moonstruck'PBR (v)	ECtt EMic IBal NSue
'Morning Light'	CBdn ECtt EMic EPfP ESps GBin GMcL IBal LLWG MBNS NBro NGdn NLar SRkn WFar
'Morning Star' (v)	EMic IBal NSue WFar
'Moscow Blue'	EMic
'Moulin Rouge'	IBal NSue
'Mount Everest'	EMic IBal
'Mount Fuji' (*montana*)	CBdn IBal
'Mount Kirishima' (*sieboldii*)	see *H.* 'Kirishima'
'Mount Tom' (v)	EMic IBal
'Mountain Snow' (*montana*) (v)	CRos EMic LRHS NRHS
'Mourning Dove' (v)	EMic IBal
'Mr Big'	IBal NGdn WCot
'Mr Blue'	NSue
'Mrs Minky'	CBdn CRos EMic LRHS NRHS
'Muffie' (v)	EMic
'Munchkin' (*sieboldii*)	LLHF WFar
'My Claire' (v)	IBal
'My Cup of Tea'	IBal
'My Precious' (v)	IBal NSue
'Mystic Mouse'	IBal
'Mystic Star'	IBal NSue
nakaiana	EBee EMic
'Nakaimo'	CBdn GBin IBal
'Nana' (*ventricosa*)	see *H. minor* Maekawa
'Nancy'	EMic
§ 'Nancy Lindsay' (*fortunei*)	CBdn CDor EMic IBal NGdn NLar
'Nancy Minks'	EMic IBal
'Neat and Tidy'	IBal
'Neat Splash' (v)	CWCL
'Neelix'	IBal
'Nemesis' (v)	IBal
'Neptune'	EMic IBal
'Nesmith's Giant'	EMic
'Niagara Falls' ♀H7	EMic IBal NEgg NGdn NSue
'Nicola'	EMic IBal NSue
'Night before Christmas' (v) ♀H7	CHid EMic EWTr IBal LRHS MBNS MNrw NBro NEgg NGdn NNor WHar WHoo
'Night Life'	EMic IBal
nigrescens	CBdn EMic IBal LRHS NChi NEgg
'Niko' (v)	IBal
'Nippers'	EMic IBal NSue
'Nokogiryama'	EMic
'None Lovelier' (v)	EMic IBal
'North Hills' (*fortunei*) (v)	EMic IBal NGdn SWvt WFar
'Northern Exposure' (*sieboldiana*) (v)	CBdn EMic NGdn NLar SPoG WFar WHar
'Northern Halo' (*sieboldiana*) (v)	CDor EMic
'Norwalk Chartreuse'	IBal
'Nutty Professor' (v)	IBal
'Oberon'	NSue
'Obscura Marginata' (*fortunei*)	see *H. fortunei* var. *aureomarginata*
'Ocean Isle' (v)	IBal
'October Sky'	EMic IBal
'Oder'	EMic IBal
'Ogon Tachi' (*rectifolia*) (v)	EMic IBal
'Ogon-chirifu-hime'	EMic IBal
'Ogon-hime-tokudama'	IBal
'Ogon-koba'	IBal

'Oh Cindy' (v)	EMic IBal
'O'Harra'	EMic NSue
'Old Faithful'	EMic IBal LRHS
'Old Glory'PBR (v)	ECtt EMic IBal
'Olga's Shiny Leaf'	EMic
'Olive Bailey Langdon' (*sieboldiana*) (v)	CDor EMic IBal
'Olive Branch' (v)	EMic IBal
'Olympic Edger'	EMic IBal
'Olympic Glacier' (v)	EMic IBal
'Olympic Gold Medal'	EMic IBal
'Olympic Silver Medal'	EMic IBal
'Olympic Sunrise' (v)	EMic IBal
'Olympic Twilight'	EMic IBal
'On Stage'	see *H.* 'Chōkō-nishiki'
'On the Border' (v)	IBal
'On the Move' **new**	EMic
'One Iota' (v)	IBal
'One Man's Treasure' ♀H7	EMic IBal MBel NEgg NGdn
'Ooh La La' (v)	IBal
'Ophir'	EMic IBal
opipara	NEgg
'Ops' (v)	EMic IBal NSue
'Orange Crush' (v)	IBal
'Orange Marmalade' (v) ♀H7	CAbb CBdn CBod CRos CWGN ECtt EMic EPfP GNew IBal LRHS MBNS MNrw NGdn NLar NRHS NSue SCob SPoG WFar
'Orange Star'PBR (v)	CBdn EMic IBal NSue
'Oriana' (*fortunei*)	CBdn EMic
'Orion's Belt' (v)	IBal
'Osprey' (Tardiana Group)	IRob
'Over the Waves'	IBal NSue
'Oxheart'	EMic IBal
'Oze' (v)	EMic IBal NSue
pachyscapa	EMic
'Pacific Blue Edger'	CBdn EMic NNor WAul WFar
'Pamela Lee' (v)	IBal NGdn
'Pandora's Box' (v)	EMic GEdr NHpl NSue WCot WFar WTor
'Papa' (v)	IBal
'Paradigm' (v)	EMic IBal LRHS NGdn NLar
'Paradise Backstage' (v)	EMic IBal
'Paradise Beach'	EMic IBal WFar
'Paradise Blue Sky'	IBal
'Paradise Expectations' (*sieboldiana*) (v)	EMic IBal
'Paradise Glory'	EMic IBal
'Paradise Gold Line' (*ventricosa*) (v)	IBal
'Paradise Island'PBR (*sieboldiana*) (v)	CBdn ECtt EMic EPfP IBal NGdn NSue WFar
'Paradise Joyce'PBR	EMic GMcL IBal LRHS NEgg NNor
'Paradise Ocean'	EMic IBal
'Paradise on Fire' (v)	EMic IBal NSue
'Paradise Parade' (v)	EMic IBal
'Paradise Passion' (v)	IBal
'Paradise Power'PBR	CBdn EMic
'Paradise Puppet' (*venusta*) ♀H7	EBee EMic GKev IBal NNor NSue
'Paradise Red Delight' (*pycnophylla*)	EMic IBal
'Paradise Sandstorm'	IBal
'Paradise Standard' (d)	CBdn EMic IBal
'Paradise Sunset'	CBdn EMic IBal NHpl NSue WFar
'Paradise Sunshine'	EMic IBal
'Paradise Surprise' (v)	IBal
'Paradise Tritone' (v)	EMic IBal
'Parhelion'	EMic
'Parky's Prize' (v)	IBal
'Party Popper' (v) **new**	CBdn
'Pastures Green'	IBal
'Pastures New'	EMic NEgg
'Pathfinder' (v)	EMic IBal WFar
'Patricia'	EMic
'Patrician' (v)	EMic IBal
'Patriot' (v) ♀H7	Widely available
'Patriot's Fire' (v)	CRos IBal LRHS NRHS
'Patriot's Green Pride'	IBal
'Paul Revere' (v)	CBdn
'Paul's Glory' (v) ♀H7	CBdn CDor CRos EMic EPfP GLog GMaP IBal LRHS NGdn NNor NSue SPoG WFar
§ 'Paxton's Original' (*sieboldii*) (v)	ESps IFoB
'Peace' (v)	EMic IBal LRHS
'Peacock Strut'	IBal
'Peanut'	IBal NSue
'Pearl Lake'	EMic IBal NEgg NGdn NLar NNor
'Peedee Absinth'	EMic
'Peedee Elfin Bells' (*ventricosa*)	IBal
'Pelham Blue Tump'	EMic
'Peppermint Ice' (v)	EMic IBal NGdn
'Percy'	EMic
'Permanent Wave'	IBal
'Perry's True Blue'	CBdn EMic IBal
'Peter Pan'	EMic IBal NEgg
'Pete's Dark Satellite'	EMic IBal NSue
'Pewterware'	EMic IBal
'Phantom'	IBal
'Philadelphia'	EMic IBal
'Phoenix'	EMic IBal NLar
'Photo Finish' (v)	EMic IBal
'Phyllis Campbell' (*fortunei*)	see *H.* 'Sharmon'
'Picta' (*fortunei*)	see *H. fortunei* var. *albopicta*
'Piecrust Power'	IBal
'Piedmont Gold'	CHid CRos EHoe EMic GBin IBal LRHS NRHS
'Pilgrim' (v)	CDor CRos EMic IBal LRHS MMuc NBro NEgg NGdn NHpl NRHS SEND WFar
'Pineapple Poll'	CBdn EMic NNor WFar WHoo
'Pineapple Upside Down Cake' (v)	EMic IBal NBro NLar
'Pinky'	IBal
'Pin-up' (v)	CBdn IBal NSue
'Pistache' (v)	EMic IBal NSue
'Pixie Vamp' (v)	EMic IBal
'Pizzazz' (v)	EMic IBal LRHS NGdn NLar WFar
plantaginea	EMic LEdu LRHS WFar WSpi WWtn
- var. ***grandiflora***	see *H. plantaginea* var. *japonica*
§ - var. ***japonica*** ♀H7	CAby CBot EBee ECha EHrv LRHS MNrw MRav SMHy SMad SPer SPhx WCFE WFar WSpi
'Platinum Tiara' (v)	EMic IBal NSue
'Playmate' (v) **new**	IBal
'Plug Nickel'	EMic IBal NSue
'Pocketful of Sunshine' (v)	IBal NSue
'Poker'	IBal
'Polar Moon' (v)	IBal
'Pole Cat' (v)	IBal
'Pooh Bear' (v)	EMic NSue
'Popcorn'	IBal NSue
'Popo' ♀H7	EMic IBal NHpl NSue
'Porter' (*venusta*)	EMic IBal
'Pot of Gold'	EMic
'Potomac Pride'	CRos EMic LRHS NEgg NRHS
'Powder Blue' (v)	IBal
'Powder Keg' (v)	IBal

'Prairie Sky'	ECtt EMic GMcL IBal NGdn NLar WFar
'Prairie Sunset' (v)	NSue
'Praying Hands' (v) ♀H7	Widely available
'Precious Metal'	IBal
'Prestige and Promise' (v)	IBal
'Pretty Flamingo'	EMic
'Prima Donna'	EMic
'Prince of Wales'	CRos EMic IBal LPla LRHS NNor NRHS SPoG
'Private Dancer'	IBal
'Prom Queen' (v)	EMic IBal
'Proud Sentry'	CBdn EMic IBal
'Punk Rock'	IBal
'Punky' (v)	EMic IBal
'Purple Boots'	EMic IBal
'Purple Dwarf'	EHoe EMic IBal MBNS NLar NSue WCru WHal
'Purple Glory'	EMic
'Purple Haze'	EMic IBal NGdn WFar
'Purple Heart'	CAby CBcs CRos EBee ECtt GNew IBal IRob LCro LPla LRHS NEoE NHpl NRHS NSti NSue NWad SCob SPoG WNPC
'Purple Passion'	EMic IBal NSue
'Purple Profusion'	EMic IBal
'Purple Python'	IBal
'Quarter Note' (v)	IBal
'Queen Josephine' (v)	CRos ECtt EMic EPfP GMcL IBal LRHS MBNS NEgg NGdn NHpl SRGP WFar
'Queen of the Seas'	EMic IBal NSue
'Quill'	EMic NSue
'Quilting Bee'	EMic IBal NSue
'Radiant Edger' (v)	EMic IBal LRHS NRHS NSue
'Rain Dancer'	EMic IBal
'Rain Forest'	EMic IBal
'Rainbow's End' (v)	CBdn EBee ECtt EMic IBal NLar NSue
'Rainforest Sunrise' (v)	CBod ELon EMic IBal LSou NGdn NSue WFar
'Randy Rachel' (v)	LRHS
'Rare Breed' (v)	EMic IBal
'Rascal' (v)	EMic
'Raspberries and Cream' (v)	IBal
'Raspberry Sorbet'	EMic IBal LRHS NRHS NSue
'Raspberry Sundae' (v)	CBdn CWGN ECtt EMic IBal MHol NGdn NHpl NSue NWad SCob SPoG WNPC
'Rebel Heart' (v)	IBal
rectifolia	NNor
'Red Cadet'	EMic IBal NSue WFar
'Red Dog'	EMic NSue
'Red Dragon'	EMic IBal
'Red Hot Flash' (v)	EMic IBal
'Red Hot Poker'	IBal
'Red Neck Heaven' (*kikutii* var. *caput-avis*)	IBal
'Red October'	CRos ECtt EMic EPfP EUJe EWTr GAbr GQue IBal IBoy IRob LEdu LRHS LSou MBNS MHol MPie NEgg NGdn NHpl NLar NRHS WCot WFar
'Red Salamander'	EMic GNew IBal
'Red Sox'	IBal
'Red Stepper'	CBdn EMic IBal WFar
'Red Stilts'	IBal
'Red Tubes' (*venusta*)	IBal
'Regal Rhubarb'	EMic IBal
'Regal Splendor' (v) ♀H7	CBdn CDor CRos ECtt ELan ELon EMic GBin GNew IBal LRHS NBro NGdn NNor NRHS NSue SPoG WFar WHoo

'Regal Supreme' (v)	CBdn IBal NSue
'Regal Tot'	NSue
'Reginald Kaye'	CBdn EMic
'Rembrandt Blue'	EMic IBal
'Remember Me' PBR ♀H7	CWCL ELan EMic GMcL IBal LSRN MBNS MPnt NEgg NNor NSue NWad WFar
'Reptilian'	EMic IBal
'Resonance' (v)	IBal NGdn NLar
'Restless Sea'	EMic NSue
'Reverend Mac'	IBal IRob
'Reversed' (*sieboldiana*) (v)	EMic IBal LRHS NBro NGdn NNor WFar WHal
'Revolution' PBR (v) ♀H7	CBdn CRos EMic IBal LSRN NBro NEgg NGdn NLar NRHS NSue WFar
'Rhapsody' (*fortunei*) (v)	EMic IBal
'Rhein' (*tardiana*)	EMic IBal
'Rhinestone Cowboy' (v)	IBal
'Rhino Hide' (v)	EMic IBal NSue
'Rhythm and Blues'	IBal NSue
'Rich Uncle'	IBal
'Richland Gold' (*fortunei*)	CBdn EMic
'Rim Rock'	EMic IBal
'Ringtail'	EMic GNew IBal
'Ripple Effect' (v)	CBdn IBal NSue
'Rippled Honey'	ELan EMic IBal NEoE
'Rippling Waves'	EMic
'Riptide'	EMic NGdn
'Risa'	IBal
'Risky Business' PBR (v)	CWGN EMic IBal NLar NSue
'Robert Frost' (v)	EMic IBal
'Robin Hood'	EMic IBal
'Robin of Loxley'	EMic IBal
'Robusta' (*fortunei*)	see *H. sieboldiana* var. *elegans*
'Robyn's Choice' (v)	IBal
'Rock and Roll'	EMic IBal
'Rock Island Line' (v)	EMic IBal NSue WFar
'Rock Princess'	IBal LLHF
'Rocket's Red Glare'	IBal
§ ***rohdeifolia*** (v) B&SWJ 10862	WCru
- f. ***albopicta***	ELan
'Roller Coaster Ride'	IBal
'Ron Damant'	IBal
'Rootin'-Tootin'' (v)	IBal
'Roseann Walter' (v)	EMic IBal
'Rosedale Knox'	IBal
'Rosedale Lost Dutchman'	IBal
'Rosedale Melody of Summer' (v)	IBal
'Rosedale Misty Magic' (v)	IBal
'Rosedale Richie Valens'	IBal
'Rosemoor'	IBal NSue
'Roxsanne'	EMic
'Roy Klehm' (v)	EMic IBal
'Royal Charm'	IBal
'Royal Charmer' (v)	IBal
'Royal Flush' (v)	IBal
'Royal Golden Jubilee'	EMic IBal
§ 'Royal Standard' ♀H7	Widely available
'Royal Tapestry' (v)	IBal
'Royal Tiara' (*nakaiana*) (v)	IBal
'Royalty'	IBal NSue
'Rubies and Ruffles' (v)	IBal
'Ruffled Mouse Ears'	IBal NSue
'Rufus Rider'	IBal
rupifraga	IBal
'Rusty Bee'	GNew IBal

	'Ryan's Big One'	EUJe IBal
§	'Sagae' (v) ♀H7	CRos EMic EUJe GNew IBal IRob LRHS MNrw NGdn NNor NRHS WAul WFar WHoo
	'Saint Elmo's Fire' (v)	EMic IBal LRHS
	'Saint Fiacre'	EMic
	'Saint John'	IBal
	'Saint Paul'	EMic IBal MNrw NSue
	'Saishu-jima' (*sieboldii* f. *spathulata*)	EMic GEdr ITim WCru
	'Saishu-yahato-sito' (v)	IBal NSue
	'Salute' (Tardiana Group)	EMic
	'Samurai' (*sieboldiana*) (v)	EMic MRav NBro NEgg NGdn NLar NNor NSue
	'Sandhill Crane' (v)	LSou
	'Sarah Kennedy' (v)	IBal
	'Sara's Sensation' (v)	IBal
	'Satisfaction' (v) ♀H7	EMic IBal
	'Sazanami' (*crispula*)	see *H. crispula*
	'Scallion Pancakes'	EMic
	'Scarlet Ribbons' (v)	EMic IBal
	'Schwan'	GBin
	'Sea Current'	IBal
	'Sea Dream' (v)	CBdn EMic LRHS NEgg NGdn NNor
	'Sea Fire'	IBal
	'Sea Gulf Stream'	EMic
	'Sea Lotus Leaf'	EMic NLar NNor
	'Sea Monster'	IBal
	'Sea Nymph'	EMic
	'Sea Thunder' (v)	EMic IBal LRHS
	'Sea Yellow Sunrise'	EMic IBal
	'Searing Flame' (v)	IBal
	'Second Wind' (*fortunei*) (v)	EMic
	'Secret Ambition'^{PBR} (v)	EMic IBal
	'Secret Love'	EMic IBal
	'Secret Treasure'^{PBR} (v)	IBal
	'Seducer' (v)	EMic IBal
	'See Saw' (*undulata*)	EMic IBal
	'Semperaurea' (*sieboldiana*)	IBal
	'September Sun' (v)	EMic IBal LRHS NNor
	'Serena' (Tardiana Group)	IBal
	'Serendipity'	CBdn EMic IBal
	'Shade Beauty' (v)	EMic IBal
	'Shade Fanfare' (v)	CDor CRos ECtt EHoe ELan ELon EMic EPfP GQue IBal LRHS MBNS MRav NGdn NLar NRHS NSti SPer WFar
	'Shade Finale' (v)	IBal
	'Shade Master'	EMic
	'Shade Parade' (v)	EMic IBal
	'Shady Affair'	EMic
§	'Sharmon' (*fortunei*) (v)	CBdn ELon EMic MBNS NEgg NLar
	'Sharp Dressed Man'	IBal WCAu
	'Shazaam'	IBal
	'Sheila West'	EMic
	'Shelleys' (v)	IBal
	'Sherborne Profusion' (Tardiana Group)	EMic IBal
	'Sherborne Songbird' (Tardiana Group)	IBal
	'Sherborne Swallow' (Tardiana Group)	EMic IBal
	'Sherborne Swan' (Tardiana Group)	IBal
	'Sherborne Swift' (Tardiana Group)	EMic IBal LRHS NRHS
	'Shere Khan' (v)	EMic IBal
	'Shimmy Shake'	EMic
	'Shining Tot' ♀H7	IBal LLHF NSue
	'Shiny Penny' (v)	EMic IBal NSue
	'Shiny Sonata' **new**	IBal
	'Shirley Levy'	IBal
	'Showboat' (v)	EMic LRHS
	sieboldiana	CAgr CMac CSBt CWat ECha ELan EMic ESps GMaP IRob MRav MSwo NChi SPlb SRms WMoo XLum
§	- var. ***elegans*** ♀H7	Widely available
	- var. ***mira***	EMic
	- var. ***sieboldiana***	NGdn
	sieboldiana* × *venusta	NGdn
	sieboldii	GBin MRav
§	- var. ***alba***	IBal
§	- var. ***sieboldii*** f. ***kabitan*** (v)	EMic IBal NGdn NSue
	- - f. ***shiro-kabitan*** (v)	EMic LRHS
	- f. ***spathulata***	EMic
	'Silberpfeil'	EMic NSue
	'Silk Road' (v)	IBal
	'Silver Bay' ♀H7	EMic
	'Silver Crown'	see *H.* 'Albomarginata'
	'Silver Halo' (v)	EMic
	'Silver Lance' (v)	EMic IBal
	'Silver Lode' (v)	IBal
	'Silver Mine' **new**	NSue
	'Silver Moon'	EMic IBal
	'Silver Serenity'	IBal
	'Silver Shadow' (v)	CHid EMic GBin IBal NGdn NLar NNor NWad
	'Silver Spray' (v)	IBal
	'Silver Star' (v)	IBal
	'Silver Threads and Gold Needles' (v)	IBal NHpl NSue
	'Silverado' (v)	IBal
	'Silvery Slugproof' (Tardiana Group)	IBal LRHS
	'Simply Sharon' (v)	IBal
	'Singin' the Blues'	IBal
	'Singing in the Rain' (v)	IBal NSue
	'Sitting Pretty' (v)	IBal
	'Sizzle'	EMic IBal
	'Sky Dancer'	ECtt EMic IBal NSue
	'Sleeping Beauty'	CWGN ECtt EMic IBal NGdn
	'Sleeping Star'^{PBR} (v)	IBal
	'Slick Willie'	EMic
	'Slim and Trim'	EMic IBal MHom NHpl NSue
	'Small Parts'	CBdn EMic IBal NSue
	'Small Sum'	IBal
	'Smash Hit' (v)	IBal
	'Smiley Face'	NSue
	'Smiling Mouse' **new**	NSue
	'Smoke Signals'	IBal
	'Snake Eyes' (v)	CBdn ELon EMic IBal NSue SCob
	'Snow Boy' (v)	EMic IBal NSue
	'Snow Cap' (v)	CDor ECtt EMic IBal NEoE NGdn NNor WFar
	'Snow Crust' (v)	EMic
	'Snow Flakes' (*sieboldii*)	CMac NBro NEoE NGdn NLar
	'Snow Mouse' (v)	EMic IBal NHpl NSue WFar
	'Snowden' ♀H7	CBdn ECha EMic GMaP IBal LRHS MWat NGdn NNor NRHS SPhx WCru
	'So Sweet' (v)	CBdn CRos EBee ECtt EHoe ELan ELon EMic EPfP ESps GBin GEdr GLog LRHS LSun MSwo NBro NGdn NNor NRHS SPoG WAvo WFar WHar
	'Something Blue'	EMic IBal
	'Something Else'	EMic
	'Southern Gold'	EMic
	'Space Odyssey'	IBal NSue

	'Sparkler' (v)	CBdn IBal
	'Sparkling Burgundy'	EMic LRHS
	'Sparky' (v)	IBal
	'Spartacus' (v)	CBdn EMic IBal NSue
	'Spartan Arrow'	CBdn NSue
	'Spartan Glory' (v)	IBal
	'Special Blend' (v)	IBal
	'Special Gift'	EMic IBal
	'Spellbound' (v)	IBal
	'Spilt Milk' (*tokudama*) (v) ♀H7	EMic IBal SPoG WHoo
	'Spinach Souffle' (v)	IBal
§	'Spinners' (*fortunei*) (v)	ECha EMic IBal NNor
	'Split Decision'	EMic
	'Spock's Ears'	IBal
	'Spring Break' (v)	EMic
	'Spring Fling'	EMic IBal
	'Spring Love' **new**	IBal
	'Spritzer' (v)	CBdn EMic MNrw NSue
	'Squash Casserole'	IBal NSue
	'Stained Glass' (v) ♀H7	CAby CBcs CDor CRos ECtt ELon EMic EPfP GBin IBal IRob LRHS NEgg NGdn NNor NRHS NSue WFar
	'Stand by Me' (v)	CBdn EMic IBal NSue
	'Stand Corrected' (v)	IBal
	'Star Kissed'	IBal
	'Star Light Star Bright'	EMic IBal
	'Starburst' stable (v)	IBal
	'Stardust'	IBal
	'Stargate'	IBal
§	'Starker Yellow Leaf'	EMic
	'Starship' (v)	EMic IBal
	'Steffi' (v)	IBal
	'Step Sister'	EMic IBal
	'Stepping Out' (v)	EMic IBal
	'Stetson' (v)	EMic IBal
	'Stiletto' (v)	CBdn EHoe EHrv ELon EMic GBin GEdr GKev IBal LRHS MBNS MNrw NBro NEoE NGdn NHpl NLar NNor NSue SPoG SWvt WFar WSHC
	'Stimulation'	IBal
	'Sting' (v) **new**	CBdn
	'Stirfry'	EMic SCob
	'Stone's Valentine' **new**	EMic
	'Strawberry Surprise' (v)	EMic IBal
	'Strawberry Yoghurt'	CBdn NSue
	'Striker' (v)	IBal NSue
	'Striptease' (*fortunei*) (v) ♀H7	CMac EMic EPfP GLog IBal LRHS MBNS MNrw NEgg NGdn NLar NSue WFar
	'Stuck in Time'	IBal
	'Sugar and Cream' (v)	CBdn EMic IBal LRHS NGdn NNor
	'Sugar and Spice' (v)	CBod ELon EMic EPfP GNew IBal
	'Sugar Daddy'	EMic IBal
	'Sultana' (v)	EMic IBal
	'Sum and Substance' ♀H7	Widely available
	'Sum and Subtle' (v)	EMic IBal
	'Sum Cup-o-Joe' (v)	EMic
	'Sum it Up' (v)	EMic
	'Sum of All' (v)	EMic EUJe NSue
	'Summer Breeze' (v)	EMic IBal NGdn NSue
	'Summer Dress' **new**	NSue
	'Summer Fragrance'	EBee ECtt EMic GBin IBal LRHS
	'Summer Gold'	EMic
	'Summer Lovin'' (v)	IBal
	'Summer Music' (v) ♀H7	CWCL EMic IBal
	'Summer Serenade' (v)	EMic NGdn
	'Summer Squall'	IBal
	'Sumsational'	IBal
	'Sun Catcher'	EMic
	'Sun Power'	CRos EBee ELon EMic LRHS MBNS NBro NLar
	'Sun Worshipper'	IBal
	'Sundance' (v)	IBal
	'Sunlight Child'	EMic IBal NSue
	'Sunny Smiles' (v)	EMic
	'Sunset Grooves' (v)	CBdn IBal
	'Sunshine Glory'	EMic IBal
	'Super Bowl'	IBal
	'Super Nova' (v)	CBdn EMic IBal
	'Super Sagae'	CDor EMic EUJe IBal WFar
	'Surfer Girl'	NSue
	'Surprised by Joy' (v)	CBdn EMic IBal NHpl NNor NSue
	'Susy'	IBal
	'Sutter's Mill'	IBal
	'Suzuki Thumbnail'	EMic
	'Swamp Thing' (v)	IBal
	'Sweet Bo Beep'	EMic IBal LRHS
	'Sweet Bouquet'	EMic
	'Sweet Home Chicago' (v)	EMic IBal LRHS NRHS
	'Sweet Innocence' (v)	EMic IBal
	'Sweet Marjorie'	IBal
	'Sweet Sunshine'	EMic
	'Sweet Susan'	CBdn CRos EMic LRHS LSRN MBNS NRHS SPer SWvt
	'Sweet Tater Pie'	EMic IBal
	'Sweetheart'	EMic
	'Sweetie' (v)	EMic IBal LRHS
	'Sweetness'	IBal
	'Swirling Hearts'	IBal NSue
	'Swizzle Sticks'	EMic
	'T-Dawg' (v) **new**	CBdn
	'T. Rex'	ELon EMic EUJe IBal NSue WFar
	'Tall Boy'	CBdn GBin IBal NNor
	'Tamborine' (v)	CBdn EMic IBal LRHS
	'Tango'	EMic IBal
	'Tappen Zee' (v)	EMic IBal
	Tardiana Group	GWyn NGdn
	tardiflora	CExl CFil IBal LRHS
	tardiva	EMic NLar
	'Tattle Tails'	CBdn EMic IBal NHpl NSue
	'Tattoo'PBR (v)	CWGN EMic LSRN MBNS NLar
	'Tea at Bettys' ♀H7	CBdn EMic IBal NSue
	'Teacher's Pride'	NSue
	'Tears of Joy'	NSue
	'Teaspoon'	EMic IBal NHpl NNor NSue
	'Teatime' (v)	EMic IBal
	'Teeny-weeny Bikini' (v)	NSue WFar
	'Templar Gold'	IBal
	'Temple Bells'	IBal
	'Temptation'	EMic IBal
	'Tequila Sunrise'	IBal
	'Terpsichore'	EMic
	'Terracotta'	MCri
	'Terry Wogan'	IBal NNor
	'Tet-a-Poo'	IBal
	'The King' (v)	IBal NSue
	'The Leading Edge' (v)	IBal SDay
	'The Queen' (v)	IBal
	'The Razor's Edge'	IBal
	'The Right One' (v)	IBal
	'The Shining'	IBal
	'The Twister'	EMic
	'Theo's Blue'	EMic IBal
	'Theo's Red'	IBal
	'Thomas Hogg'	see *H. undulata* var. *albomarginata*
	'Thumb Nail'	EMic IBal NNor NSue
	'Thumbelina'	EMic IBal NGdn

'Thunderbolt'PBR (*sieboldiana*)	EMic EUJe IBal MBNS NGdn NLar WFar
tibae	IBal
'Tick Tock' (v)	ECtt EMic IBal NSue
'Tickle Me Pink'	EMic IBal NSue WFar
'Tidewater'	IBal
'Tilt-a-Whirl' **new**	IBal
'Time Tunnel' (*sieboldiana*) (v)	EMic IBal
'Timeless Beauty' (v)	CBdn IBal NSue WFar
'Tiny Tears'	GAbr IFoB NSue
'Titanic'PBR	CBdn EMic IBal NSue
'Titanium'	IBal
'Toasted Waffles'	WFar
tokudama	CRos EMic IBal LRHS NGdn NNor NRHS WFar XLum
§ - f. ***aureo-nebulosa*** (v)	EMic IBal NGdn SRms
- f. ***flavocircinalis*** (v) ♀H7	CBod ELon EMic EPfP GMaP IBal NBro WFar WHoo
'Tokudama Blue'	IBoy
'Tokyo Smog' (v)	NSue
'Toledo'	IBal
'Tom Schmid' (v)	CBdn EMic IBal NSue
'Tom Thumb'	EMic IBal NSue
'Tongue Twister'	IBal
'Topaz'	IBal
'Topscore'	NNor
'Torchlight' (v) ♀H7	CBdn IBal LRHS NSue
tortifrons	EMic IBal
'Tortilla Chip'	EMic IBal
'Tot Tot'	EMic IBal NSue
'Totally Twisted'	EMic IBal
'Touch of Class'PBR (v) ♀H7	CBdn CDor EBee ECtt EMic GMcL GNew IBal NGdn NNor NSue WFar
'Touchstone' (v)	CRos SWvt
'Toy Soldier'	EMic IBal NGdn NLar NSue
'Trail's End'	EMic
'Tranquility' (v)	EMic
'Tremors'	EMic IBal
'Trixi' (v)	IBal
'Tropical Dancer'	IBal
'Tropical Storm' (v)	IBal
'True Blue'	CBdn ECtt EMic
'Tsugaru Komachi'	EMic
'Tsugaru Komachi Kifukurin' (v)	IBal
'Turnabout' (v)	IBal
'Turning Point'	IBal LRHS
'Twiggie'	EMic
'Twilight' (*fortunei*) (v)	CAby CRos ECtt EMic EShb IBal LRHS MBNS MHol NEgg NGdn NLar NRHS NSue SWvt WFar WHar
'Twilight Time'	IBal LRHS
'Twinkle Toes'	EMic IBal NSue
'Twist of Lemon'	NEgg
'Twist of Lime' (v)	EMic GKev IBal LRHS NGdn NNor NSue WCot
'Twitter'	IBal
'UFO'	EMic IBal NSue WFar
'Ultramarine'	IBal
'Ultraviolet Light'	IBal
'Ulysses S. Grant'	IBal
'Unchained Melody'	IBal
undulata (v)	NNor WFar
§ - var. ***albomarginata*** (v)	CMac CRos CSam EMic EPfP ESps GMaP IBoy LRHS LSRN MRav NBid NGdn NLar NRHS SCob SPer SRms SWvt WFar XLum
§ - var. ***erromena***	CRos EMic GMaP LRHS NNor NRHS WHrl XLum
§ - var. ***undulata*** (v) ♀H7	CRos EBee ESps GMaP IBal LRHS MCot MRav NEgg NGdn NLar NNor NRHS SCob SPer WHar
- var. ***univittata*** (v)	ECha EHrv EMic GKev NEoE NRHS SRms WFar WMoo
'Unforgettable'	EMic IBal
'Upper Crust' (v)	IBal
'Uprising' (v)	IBal
'Urajiro' (*hypoleuca*)	IBal
'Urajiro-hachijo' (*longipes* var. *latifolia*)	IBal
'Valentine Lace'	EMic GKev IBal
'Valley's Blue Curaçao'	IBal
'Valley's Cathedral'	IBal
'Valley's Chute the Chute'	EMic IBal
'Valley's Glacier' (v)	EMic IBal WFar
'Valley's Paparazzi' (v)	IBal
'Valley's Vanilla Sticks'	EMic IBal
'Van Wade' (v)	EMic IBal
'Vanilla Cream' (*cathayana*)	EMic IBal LRHS NRHS NSue WFar
'Variegata' (*gracillima*)	see *H.* 'Vera Verde'
'Variegata' (*tokudama*)	see *H. tokudama* f. *aureo-nebulosa*
'Variegata' (*undulata*)	see *H. undulata* var. *undulata*
'Variegata' (*ventricosa*)	see *H.* 'Aureomarginata' (*ventricosa*)
'Variegated' (*fluctuans*)	see *H.* 'Sagae'
'Velvet Moon' (v)	EMic IBal
ventricosa ♀H7	CMac EMic GMcL IBal WFar XLum
- BWJ 8160 from Sichuan	WCru
- var. ***aureomaculata***	EMic NNor WFar
'Venus' (d)	CAby ECtt EMic ITim LEdu MHol NGdn NSue WCot WFar
'Venus Star'	EMic
venusta ♀H7	CRos EBee EMic EWld GCal GEdr IBal LRHS MRav NBid NNor NRHS NRya SRot WFar WRHF
- B&SWJ 4389	WCru
- dwarf	IBal
- ***yakusimensis***	see *H. kikutii* var. *yakusimensis*
§ 'Vera Verde' (v)	NSue
'Verdi Valentine'	EMic IBal
'Verkade's One'	IBal
'Vermont Frost' (v)	IBal NSue
'Verna Jean' (v)	EMic IBal LRHS NRHS NSue
'Veronica Lake' (v)	ECtt EMic IBal LRHS NNor NRHS NSue WHal
'Victor'	IBal
'Victory' ♀H7	IBal
'Viking Ship'	IBal
'Vilmoriniana'	EMic
'Vim and Vigor'	EMic IBal
'Vina'	IBal
'Virginia Reel' (v)	IBal
'Viridis Marginata'	see *H. sieboldii* var. *sieboldii* f. *kabitan*
'Volcano Island'PBR (v)	CBdn IBal NSue
'Vulcan' (v)	CBdn EMic IBal
'Wagtail' (Tardiana Group)	EMic IBal
'Wahoo' (*tokudama*) (v)	IBal
'War Paint' ♀H7	CBdn CBod EMic IBal ITim NSue WFar
'Warwick Comet' (v)	EMic IBal
'Warwick Curtsey' (v)	CBdn EMic IBal
'Warwick Edge' (v)	EMic IBal NEgg
'Warwick Essence'	EMic IBal
'Warwick Sheen'	IBal
'Watermark' (v)	EMic
'Waukon Glass'	EMic IBal
'Waukon Thin Ice'	EMic IBal
'Waukon Water'	EMic IBal
'Waving Winds' (v)	IBal

'Waving Wuffles'	EMic
'Wayne' (v)	EMic
'Wayside Blue'	EMic
'Wayside Perfection'	see *H.* 'Royal Standard'
'Weihenstephan' (*sieboldii*)	EMic IBal
'Well Shaked' (v)	IBal
'Weser'	IBal
'Wheaton Blue'	EMic LRHS
'Wheaton Thunder' (v)	EMic
'Wheee!'	IBal NSue
'Whirligig' (v)	EMic
'Whirling Dervish' (v)	IBal
'Whirlwind' (*fortunei*) (v) 𝕐H7	CBdn EBee EMic EPfP GBin GNew IBal IRob LRHS MNrw MRav NBro NEgg NGdn NLar NNor NSue SPoG SPtp WAul WBor WFar WHoo
'Whirlwind Tour' (v)	IBal
'Whiskey Sour'	IBal
'White Bikini' (v)	IBal NSue
'White Ceiling'	IBal
'White Christmas' (*fortunei*) (v)	NGdn
'White Christmas' (*undulata*) (v)	EMic
'White Dove' (v)	EMic IBal
'White Edger'	EMic
'White Elephant' (v)	IBal
'White Fairy' (*plantaginea*) (d)	EMic
'White Feather' (*undulata*)	CHid CWGN EBee ELan EPfP LCro LOPS MNrw NEoE NGdn NLar NNor SMad SPoG WFar
'White Gold'	EMic
'White Jewel' (v) **new**	IBal
'White Knight'	IBal
'White On' (*montana*)	EMic
'White Triumphator' (*rectifolia*)	EMic IBal
'White Trumpets'	EMic
'Wide Brim' (v) 𝕐H7	Widely available
'William Lachman' (v)	IBal NLar
'Willy Nilly' **new**	CBdn
'Wily Willy'	IBal
'Wind River Gold'	EMic
'Windsor Gold'	see *H.* 'Nancy Lindsay'
'Winfield Blue'	EMic IBal
'Winfield Gold'	EMic
'Winfield Mist' (v)	IBal
'Winsome' (v)	IBal LRHS NSue
'Winter Lightning' (v)	NNor
'Winter Snow' (v)	CBdn CDor EMic EUJe IBal IRob LRHS NSue WFar
'Winter Warrior' (v)	EMic IBal
'Wogon' (*sieboldii*)	EMic GKev GMaP ITim
'Wogon's Boy'	EMic LRHS WAvo
'Wolverine' (v) 𝕐H7	CBod CRos EBee ECtt EHoe EMic LRHS MBNS NGdn NQui NRHS NSue SPad SPoG SWvt WFar
'Woodland Elf' (v)	IBal NSue
'Woolly Mammoth' (v)	IBal
'Woop Woop' (v)	EMic IBal NSue
'World Cup'	IBal
'Worldly Treasure'	IBal
'Wrinkles and Crinkles'	EMic
'Wylde Green Cream'	IBal NGdn
'Xanadu' (v)	IBal
'X-ray' (v)	NSue
'Yakushima-mizu' (*gracillima*)	EMic IBal NSue
'Yankee Blue'	IBal
'Yellow Boa'	EMic IBal NSue
'Yellow Edge' (*fortunei*)	see *H. fortunei* var. *aureomarginata*
'Yellow Edge' (*sieboldiana*)	see *H.* 'Frances Williams'
'Yellow Polka Dot Bikini' (v)	CBdn EMic NSue
'Yellow River' (v)	CBdn CRos EBee EMic GNew IBal LRHS NGdn NNor NRHS NSue WFar
'Yellow Splash' (v)	EMic LRHS NNor
'Yellow Splash Rim' (v)	EMic
'Yesterday's Memories' (v)	EMic IBal
'Yin' (v)	EMic IBal
yingeri	CFil WPGP WSHC
- B&SWJ 546	LEdu WCru
'Yucca Ducka Do' (v)	EMic IBal
'Zager Blue'	EMic
'Zager Green'	EMic
'Zager White Edge' (*fortunei*) (v)	EMic IBal
'Zebra Stripes' (v)	IBal
'Zion's Hope'	EMic
'Zodiac' (*fortunei*) (v)	IBal
'Zorro'	IBal
'Zounds'	CBdn CRos EBee ECtt EMic EPfP EShb IBal LRHS MRav NGdn NLar NRHS SRms WFar

Hottonia (*Primulaceae*)

palustris	LCro LLWG LOPS MSKA MWts NPer

Houstonia (*Rubiaceae*)

caerulea L.	SPlb SRot
- var. ***alba***	EWes SPlb SRot
michauxii 'Fred Mullard'	EWes GCrg

Houttuynia (*Saururaceae*)

cordata	CAgr ESps GPoy LEdu LLWG WFar WWtn XLum
§ - 'Boo-Boo' (v)	CMac
§ - 'Chameleon' (v)	Widely available
- 'Fantasy' (v)	LLWG
- 'Flame' (v)	CMac CPla EBee GMcL LLWG MHol NPla WFar
- 'Flore Pleno' (d)	CBen CMac CPla CWat ECha EPfP EWld LLWG MRav MSCN NPer SPer SPlb SRms XLum
- 'Joker's Gold'	CMac ECtt ELan EPPr EPfP WFar
- 'Pied Piper' (v)	ELan SPtp
- 'Terry Clarke'	see *H. cordata* 'Boo-Boo'
- 'Tricolor'	see *H. cordata* 'Chameleon'
- Variegata Group (v)	LLWG NBro

Hovea (*Papilionaceae*)

celsii	see *H. elliptica*
§ ***elliptica***	SPlb
montana	SPlb

Hovenia (*Rhamnaceae*)

dulcis	CAgr CBcs EPfP LEdu MBlu NLar
- B&SWJ 11024	WCru
- NJM 11.003	WPGP

Howea (*Arecaceae*)

§ ***belmoreana*** 𝕐H1b	XBlo
§ ***forsteriana*** 𝕐H1b	CCCN ETod EUJe LCro NLos NPla SPlb XBlo

Hoya (*Apocynaceae*)

bella	see *H. lanceolata* subsp. *bella*
carnosa 𝕐H2	EBak EOHP WWFP

	- 'Compacta Regalis' (v)	NPer
	- 'Krinkle 8'	NPer
	- 'Tricolor' (v)	CCCN NPer
	- 'Variegata' (v)	EShb
*	***compacta*** 'Tricolor'	NPer
	gracilis	CCCN
	lacunosa	CCCN
§	***lanceolata***	CCCN EShb
	subsp. ***bella*** ♀H1c	

Huernia (*Apocynaceae*)

	aspera* × *piersii new	LToo
	leachii	LToo
	longituba	LToo
	schneideriana	LToo

Hugueninia (*Brassicaceae*)

	tanacetifolia	SBrt
	subsp. ***suffruticosa***	

Humata (*Davalliaceae*)

	tyermannii	CCCN CMen EShb NLos SBrt SPlb WCot WFib
	- 'Bunny'	CCCN LOPS
	- 'Selcka'	CMen

Humulus ✿ (*Cannabaceae*)

	japonicus 'Variegatus' (v)	SGol
	lupulus	CBcs EBWF EPfP GPoy NLar NMir SCob SRms WHer WSpi
	- 'Aureus' ♀H6	Widely available
	- 'Aureus' (f)	CRHN ELon GCal GKev MJak SPoG WCot
	- 'Aureus' (m)	MJak
*	- ***compactus***	GPoy
	- 'Fuggle'	CAgr GPoy SDea
	- 'Golden Tassels' (f)	CKel CRos ECrN ELon LRHS MGos MJak MMuc MNHC NLar SEND SGol SNig SPer SPoG WBor WFar
	- (Goldings Group) 'Cobbs'	SDea
	- - 'Mathons'	SDea
	- 'Hallertauer'	SDea
	- 'Northern Brewer'	EBee IPot
	- 'Prima Donna'	CAgr CMac LEdu MCoo MMuc NLar SPer SPoG SWvt
	- 'Taff's Variegated' (v)	EWes
	- 'Wye Challenger'	CAgr GPoy MHer
	- 'Wye Northdown'	CAgr SDea

Hunnemannia (*Papaveraceae*)

	fumariifolia	CSpe SBrt

Huodendron (*Styracaceae*)

	tibeticum	CFil

Hutchinsia see *Hornungia*

	rotundifolia	see *Thlaspi cepaeifolium* subsp. *rotundifolium*

Hyacinthella (*Asparagaceae*)

	lazulina	GKev
	leucophaea	GKev

Hyacinthoides (*Asparagaceae*)

	aristidis	WCot
	'Bakkum Blue'	GKev SDir
	ciliolata	CBro EPot GKev NRog SBch WCot
§	***hispanica***	GKev SEND WCot
	- 'Alba'	CRos LRHS NRHS
	- subsp. ***algeriensis***	WCot
	- 'Dainty Maid'	GKev WCot
	- 'Excelsior'	GKev
	- 'Miss World'	GKev WCot
	- 'Queen of the Pinks'	GKev WCot
	- 'Rose'	SEND
	- 'Rose Queen'	GKev
	- 'White City'	GKev WCot
§	***italica*** ♀H4	GKev WCot WShi
§	***lingulata***	LLHF WCot
§	***non-scripta***	Widely available
	- 'Alba'	CAvo GKev LRHS MMuc SDir SEND
	- 'Backkum's Blue'	SDir
	- 'Bracteata'	CNat WCot
	- cleistogamous	CNat
	- long-bracteate, white-flowered	WCot
	- 'Rosea'	GKev ILea
	- 'Wavertree'	GKev
	reverchonii	WCot
	- from Spain	WCot
§	***vincentina***	GKev

Hyacinthus ✿ (*Asparagaceae*)

	sp.	ESps
	amethystinus	see *Brimeura amethystina*
	azureus	see *Muscari azureum*
	comosus 'Plumosus'	see *Muscari comosum* 'Plumosum'
	orientalis 'Aiolos'	GKev SDeJ SDir
	- 'Anastasia'	CAvo CRav
	- 'Anna Liza'	SDeJ
	- 'Anna Marie' ♀H4	LAma SDeJ SDir
	- 'Apricot Passion'	ERCP GKev SDeJ SDir
	- 'Blue Eyes'	ERCP SDeJ
	- 'Blue Festival' ♀H4	GKev SDeJ SDir
	- 'Blue Giant'	LAma MJak SDeJ SDir
	- 'Blue Jacket' ♀H4	GKev LAma SCob SDeJ
	- 'Blue Magic'	SDeJ
	- 'Blue Pearl' PBR	GKev LCro LOPS SDeJ
	- 'Blue Star'	LAma SDeJ SDir
	- 'Carnegie'	CArg CAvo ERCP GKev LAma LCro LOPS MJak
	- 'Chestnut Flower' (d)	SDeJ SDir
	- 'China Pink'	CRav CRos GKev LRHS NRHS SDeJ
	- 'City of Haarlem' ♀H4	CArg CRos GKev LAma LRHS MJak NRHS SDeJ SDir
	- 'Crystal Palace' (d)	LAma SDeJ SDir
	- 'Dark Dimension'	LAma SDir
	- 'Delft Blue' ♀H4	CArg CAvo CRos EPfP GKev LAma LCro LOPS LRHS NRHS SCob SDeJ SPer WShi
§	- 'Fairly' PBR ♀H4	SDir
	- FAIRY WHITE	see *H. orientalis* 'Fairly'
	- 'Fondant'	CArg CRos LAma LRHS NRHS SDeJ
	- 'General Köhler' (d)	LAma SDeJ
	- 'Gipsy Princess'	LAma
	- 'Gipsy Queen' ♀H4	CAvo GKev LAma SCob SDeJ SDir WCot
	- 'Gypsy Princess'	SDir
	- 'Hollyhock' (d) ♀H4	LAma SCob SDeJ SDir WHil
	- 'Ibis'	SCob
	- 'Jan Bos' ♀H4	CArg CRos GKev LAma LCro LOPS LRHS NRHS SCob SDeJ SDir
	- 'Lady Derby'	SDeJ
	- 'L'Innocence' ♀H4	SCob
	- 'Madame Sophie' (d)	SDeJ SDir
	- 'Marie'	EPfP SPer
	- 'Midnight Mystique' new	ETMg
	- 'Miss Saigon' ♀H4	CAvo ERCP SDeJ SDir

- multi-flowered	ERCP SDeJ
- 'Odysseus'	LAma MJak SDeJ SDir
- 'Ostara' ♀H4	LAma
- 'Pacific Ocean'	LAma
- 'Paul Hermann' ♀H4	GKev SDeJ
- 'Peter Stuyvesant'	ERCP LAma LCro LOPS MJak SDeJ SDir
- 'Pink Festival' ♀H4	GKev SDeJ
- 'Pink Pearl'	CAvo CRos EPfP GKev LAma LCro LOPS LRHS NRHS SDeJ SDir
- 'Pink Royal' (d)	LAma
- 'Purple Sensation'PBR	GKev SDeJ SDir
- 'Purple Star' **new**	LCro LOPS
- 'Red Magic'	SDeJ SDir
- 'Rosette' (d)	LAma SDeJ
- 'Royal Navy' (d) ♀H4	ERCP SDeJ
- 'Sky Jacket'	GKev LCro LOPS SCob
- 'Snow Crystal' (d)	ERCP SDir
- 'Splendid Cornelia'	ERCP GKev SDeJ
- 'Spring Field' **new**	CRav
- 'White Festival' ♀H4	GKev IRob SDeJ
- 'White Pearl'	CAvo CRav CRos EPfP GKev LAma LCro LOPS LRHS NRHS SCob SDeJ SDir SPer
- 'Woodstock'	CAvo CRav EPfP ERCP GKev LAma LCro LOPS SCob SDeJ SDir WCot
- 'Yellowstone' **new**	SDeJ

Hydrangea ✿ (*Hydrangeaceae*)

angustipetala	see *H. scandens* subsp. *chinensis* f. *angustipetala*
anomala subsp. ***anomala*** BWJ 8052 from China	WCru
- - HWJK 2065 from Nepal	WCru
§ - - 'Winter Glow'	EBee MRav SGol WCru WFar
- subsp. ***glabra*** B&SWJ 6804	WCru
- - 'Crûg Coral'	SPoG WCru
§ - subsp. ***petiolaris*** ♀H5	Widely available
- - B&SWJ 5996	WCru
- - B&SWJ 6337	WCru
- - from Yakushima	CFil
§ - - var. ***cordifolia***	NBro NLar
- - - B&SWJ 6081	WCru
- - - B&SWJ 11487	WCru
§ - - - 'Brookside Littleleaf'	IDee NBro NLar WFar
- - dwarf	see *H. anomala* subsp. *petiolaris* var. *cordifolia*
- - 'Early Light' (v)	SGbt
- - var. ***megaphylla*** B&SWJ 4400	WCru
- - - B&SWJ 8497	WCru
* - - var. ***minor*** B&SWJ 5991	GEdr WCru
- - 'Mirranda' (v)	CBcs ELan EPfP GCal MGos MNHC NBro NLar SGol SPoG SRms SWvt WBor WGrn
§ - - var. ***ovalifolia***	CRHN LRHS
- - - B&SWJ 8799	WCru
- - - B&SWJ 8846	WCru
- - 'Silver Lining'PBR	CRos EBee EPfP LCro LOPS LRHS NRHS SMad SPoG
- - 'Summer Snow' (v)	CRos LLHF LRHS NRHS SPoG
- - var. ***tiliifolia***	see *H. anomala* subsp. *petiolaris* var. *ovalifolia*
I - - 'Tricolor' **new**	SMad
- - 'Yakushima'	WCru
- subsp. ***quelpartensis***	see *H. anomala* subsp. *petiolaris* var. *ovalifolia*
- 'Winter Surprise'	see *H. anomala* subsp. *anomala* 'Winter Glow'
§ ***arborescens***	CExl MRav WPGP
- 'Annabelle' ♀H6	Widely available
- 'Bounty'	MAsh SGol
§ - subsp. ***discolor***	GBin LEdu
- - 'Sterilis'	CFil GGGa SHyH WPGP
- 'Eco Pink Puff'	WPGP
- 'Emerald Lace'	MBlu
- 'Grandiflora'	CBcs ESps IBoy IRob NBro NEgg WPGP
- 'Hayes Starburst'PBR	CBot CMil CRos CWGN EMil LEdu LLHF LRHS MMrt MPkF SAko SGol SHyH SPoG SWvt WPGP
- 'Hills of Snow'	NLar
- INCREDIBALL ('Abetwo'PBR)	CBcs CRos ELan EPfP ETMg GBin LCro LRHS LSRN MBlu NLar NRHS SGol SLon SPoG
§ - INVINCIBELLE SPIRIT ('Ncha1'PBR)	CAby CBcs CBot CRos ECre ELan EPfP GMcL IRob LCro LLHF LOPS LRHS LSRN MBlu MPkF NLar NRHS SCob SGol SHyH SLon SMad SPer SPoG SWvt WSpi
- 'Invincible Spirit'	see *H. arborescens* INVINCIBELLE SPIRIT
- LIME RICKEY ('Smnhalr') **new**	SGol
- 'Picadilly'	NLar
- 'Pink Annabelle'	see *H. arborescens* INVINCIBELLE SPIRIT
- 'Pink Pincushion'	NBro NLar
- 'Puffed Green'	NLar
- subsp. ***radiata***	CRos LRHS MRav SGol WPGP
- - 'Samantha'	EPfP LLHF LRHS SCob SPoG WPGP
- 'Ryan Gainey'	EUJe LEdu
- 'Sheep Cloud'	MBlu
- 'Vasterival'	NLar
- 'Visitation'	MMrt
- WHITE DOME ('Dardom'PBR)	NBro
aspera	CMac CTri SHyH SLon SSta WCru WHar WKif WPGP
- HWJCM 452	WCru
- from Gongshan, China	CExl CFil CMil WPGP
- 'Anthony Bullivant' ♀H5	CBot IArd IDee LRHS MAsh NLar SAko SGol SHyH SWvt WKif
- 'Bellevue'	WPGP
- 'Cardinal' **new**	SGol
- 'Dark Chocolate' **new**	CRos
- Farrell form	CFil
- HOT CHOCOLATE ('Hpopr012')	CAbb CAby CMil ELan ETMg EUJe LCro LOPS LRHS MBlu MGos SCob SGol SHyH SPoG WGrn
- Kawakamii Group	CBot CExl CSpe LRHS NLar SGol SHyH SWvt WCru WPGP
- - B&SWJ 3456	WCru
- - B&SWJ 3527	WCru
- - B&SWJ 6702	WCru
- - B&SWJ 6714	WCru
- - B&SWJ 6827	WCru
- - B&SWJ 6996	WCru
- - B&SWJ 7101	WCru
- - 'August Abundance'	WCru
- - 'Formosa'	WCru
- - 'Maurice Mason'	CExl CFil
- - 'September Splendour'	WCru
- Kawakamii Group × ***involucrata***	CFil WPGP
- 'Koki'	CRos LRHS NRHS WPGP
- 'Macrophylla' ♀H5	CBot CFil EPfP ESps ETMg GCal GKin MGil MGos MRav NLar SHyH SPer SWvt WCru WPGP WSpi

	- 'Mauvette'	CBot CMil CRos EPfP GKin LRHS MBlu NBro NLar SCob SGol SHyH SPer WCru
	- 'Peter Chappell' ♀H5	CExl CMac CMil LRHS NLar SHyH SWvt
	- 'Pink Cloud'	CFil
§	- subsp. ***robusta***	CExl LRHS WPGP WSpi
	- - B&SWJ 13999	WCru
	- - GWJ 9430	WCru
	- - WWJ 11888	WCru
	- 'Rocklon'	NLar SGol
	- 'Rosthornii'	see *H. aspera* subsp. *robusta*
	- 'Sam MacDonald'	CExl CMil CRos EPfP LRHS NLar WPGP WSpi
§	- subsp. ***sargentiana***	Widely available
	- - 'La Fosse'	WPGP
	- - large-leaved	CExl CFil WCru
	- 'Spinners'	NLar
	- subsp. ***strigosa***	CDul CExl CRos EPfP LRHS SHyH SMad SWvt WCru WPGP
	- - B&SWJ 8201	WCru
	- - KWJ 12151 from northern Vietnam	WCru
	- - from Gong Shan, China	CExl
	- - 'Gongshan'	WPGP
	- aff. subsp. ***strigosa***	CFil
	- 'Taiwan Pink'	EPfP IArd NLar SGol
	- 'The Ditch'	NLar
	- 'Trelissick Blue Skies'	CFil
§	- Villosa Group	Widely available
	- - 'Trelissick'	CFil WPGP
	- - 'Velvet and Lace' ♀H5	CRos EPfP GMcL LRHS MGos NLar
	asterolasia B&SWJ 10481	WCru
§	'Blue Deckle' (L)	CAbb CMac LRHS MAsh MGos MRav NBro NLar SDys SGol SHyH WBor
	cinerea	see *H. arborescens* subsp. *discolor*
	davidii B&SWJ 8307	WCru
	- B&SWJ 11692	WCru
	- B&SWJ 11717	WCru
	- f. ***purpurascens*** KWJ 12233B	WCru
	'Dharuma'	CRos GKin LRHS SAko SGol
	EARLY SENSATION ('Bulk'[PBR])	CBcs CBot EPfP EShb ESps GBin GKin LRHS MSwo NRHS SGol SHyH SPoG WFar WGrn WMoo
	'Garden House Glory'	CExl CFil CMil SAko WPGP
	glabrifolia	see *H. scandens* subsp. *chinensis*
	glandulosa B&SWJ 4031	WCru
	'Glyn Church'	EBee EPfP SAko SChF WPGP
	aff. ***gracilis*** B&SWJ 3942	WCru
§	***heteromalla***	CMCN CPne NBro WPGP
	- B&SWJ 2142 from India	WCru
	- B&SWJ 2602 from Sikkim	WCru
	- BWJ 7657 from China	WCru
	- GWJ 9337 from Sikkim	WCru
	- HWJ 526	WCru
	- HWJ 938 from Vietnam	WCru
	- HWJCM 180	WCru
	- HWJK 2127 from Nepal	WCru
	- KR 9913 from India	WPGP
	- SBEC	GGGa
	- Bretschneideri Group	EBee EPfP GKin SHyH WCru
	- 'Fan Si Pan'	WCru
	- 'June Pink'	NLar
	- 'Long White'	NLar
	- 'Morrey's Form'	NLar WCru
	- 'Nepal Beauty'	EBee EPfP MMrt NLar SGol WPGP
	- 'Snowcap'	EPfP ESps IArd LRHS NLar SBrt SHyH

	- f. ***xanthoneura***	CBot
	- - NJM 11.009	WPGP
	- - 'Wilsonii'	WCru WKif
	- 'Yalung Ridge'	WCru
	aff. ***heteromalla***	SGol WSpi
	'Hidcote Pink'	see *H. macrophylla* 'Juno'
	hirta	MBlu
	- B&SWJ 5000	WCru
	- B&SWJ 11022	WCru
	indochinensis	CExl
	- B&SWJ 8307	WCru
	- WWJ 11609	WCru
	integerrima	see *H. serratifolia*
	integrifolia B&SWJ 022	WCru
	- B&SWJ 6967	NLar WCru
	involucrata	CRos LLHF LRHS MMrt SBrt SGol SHyH WSpi
	- B&SWJ 4790	WCru
	- B&SWJ 11578	WCru
	- dwarf	CExl CFil WCru
	- 'Hortensis' (d)	CBot CDul CMil MRav NLar SMad WCru WKif WPGP WSHC
	- var. ***idzuensis***	WCru
	- 'Mihara-kokonoe'	SGol WPGP
	- 'Multiplex'	CBot MBlu WCru
	- 'Oshima'	WPGP
	- 'Plena' (d)	LRHS MRav NLar SHyH WPGP WSpi
	- 'Plenissima' (d)	WCru
	- 'Sterilis'	CMil WCru
	- 'Tokada Yama'	CMil IArd NLar
	- 'Viridescens' ♀H4	LLHF LRHS NLar SHyH WCru WPGP
	- 'Yohraku-tama' ♀H4	CFil NLar SGol WPGP
	- 'Yokudanka' (d)	CBot CMil IArd IDee NLar WPGP
	- 'Yoraku' (d)	WCru
	kawagoeana	WCru
	var. ***grosseserrata*** B&SWJ 11500	
	- - B&SWJ 11511	WCru
	lobbii	see *H. scandens* subsp. *chinensis*
	longifolia CWJ 12413	WCru
	longipes	CExl WCru
	- var. ***fulvescens*** B&SWJ 8188	WCru
	- var. ***longipes***	CExl CFil
	luteovenosa	WCru
	- B&SWJ 5647	WCru
	- B&SWJ 5929	WCru
	- B&SWJ 6220	WCru
	- B&SWJ 6317	WCru
	macrophylla (H)	LRHS
	- 'AB Green Shadow'[PBR] (H)	MMrt SCob SGol
	- 'Adria' (H)	NLar SGol
	- 'Aduarda'	see *H. macrophylla* 'Mousmée'
	- 'All Summer Beauty' (H)	CBod ELon EUJe GBin GGGa MAsh SHyH
	- ALPEN GLOW	see *H. macrophylla* 'Alpenglühen'
§	- 'Alpenglühen' (H)	CBcs CExl CSBt LRHS MJak SHyH SLim
	- 'Altona' (H) ♀H5	CBcs CCVT CRos EPfP GMcL IArd LCro LOPS LRHS MAsh MGos MRav NLar SHyH SPer SRms
	- 'Amethyst' (H/d)	LRHS
	- 'Ami Pasquier' (H)	CBcs CMac CRos CSBt CTri ELan EPfP ESps LRHS LSRN MRav MSwo NEgg NRHS SAko SCob SCoo SHyH SLim SPoG SRms SWvt
	- 'Amor' (H)	SCob SGol
*	- 'Aureomarginata' (v)	WCot
	- 'Ave Maria' (H)	GGGa MAsh

§ - 'Ayesha' (H) Widely available
- 'Bachstelze' (Teller Series) (L) MAsh WPGP
- 'Bavaria' (H) GKin SGol WFar
- 'Beauté Vendômoise' (L) CFil CMil LRHS NLar SHyH
- 'Bela'[PBR] (H) LRHS MAsh SCob
- 'Benelux' (H) CBcs
- 'Bergfink' (Teller Series) (L) NLar
- BERLIN ('Rabe'[PBR]) (City-line Series) (H) MAsh SGol
- 'Bichon' (H) SGol
- 'Bicolor' see *H. macrophylla* 'Harlequin'
- Black Steel Series (H) LRHS NRHS
- - 'Black Steel Zambia' (H) EPfP LCro SGol WCot
- - 'Black Steel Zaza' (H) EPfP
- - 'Black Steel Zebra' (H) EPfP LBuc SGol
- 'Blanc Bleu' (L) ECrN EPfP LRHS LSRN SLim WFar
§ - 'Blauer Prinz' (H) SHyH SRms
§ - 'Bläuling' (Teller Series) (L) 🏆H5 GKin LRHS LSRN MAsh SCob SGol SLim
§ - 'Blaumeise' (Teller Series) (L) 🏆H5 CCht CFil CSBt EBee ELon GGGa GMcL LRHS MAsh MGos MRav NLar SCob SCoo SGol SHyH SLim SLon SPoG SWvt WFar WPGP
- BLOOMSTRUCK ('Piihm-II') (Endless Summer Series) (H) **new** ETMg SPoG
- 'Blue Bonnet' (H) CDul EPfP LRHS LSRN MRav SHyH
- BLUE BUTTERFLY see *H. macrophylla* 'Bläuling'
- 'Blue Danube' (H) **new** ETMg
- BLUE PRINCE see *H. macrophylla* 'Blauer Prinz'
- BLUE SKY see *H. macrophylla* 'Blaumeise'
- BLUE TIT see *H. macrophylla* 'Blaumeise'
- 'Blue Wave' see *H. macrophylla* 'Mariesii Perfecta'
- BLUEBIRD see *H. macrophylla* 'Bläuling'
- 'Bluebird' misapplied see *H. serrata* 'Bluebird'
§ - 'Blushing Bride'[PBR] (H) ETMg LCro LOPS
- 'Bodensee' (H) CCVT MAsh MJak SCob
- 'Bottstein' (H) CCVT
- 'Bouquet Rose' (H) ECtt ESps MJak MMuc NLar SEND SHyH
- 'Brestenburg' (H) MAsh
- 'Brügg' (H) LRHS MAsh SAko SGol SHyH SLim SPer
- 'Cameroun' (H) MAsh SGol
- 'Camilla'[PBR] (H) SGol WFar
- 'Camino' (L) EPfP
- CARDINAL see *H. macrophylla* 'Kardinal' (Teller Series)
§ - 'Cardinal Red' (H) ECre WFar
- 'Cendrillon' (H) CRos EBee LLHF LRHS
- CHIQUE ('Hbachi'[PBR]) (H) LRHS NRHS
- 'Choco Chic' (L) MAsh SGol
- CLARISSA ('Hba 208901'[PBR]) (H) LRHS
- 'Cocktail' (H) SGol
- 'Coco' (Beautensia Series) (H) EWTr LRHS NRHS
- 'Coco Blanc' (H/d) SCob SGol
- COLOR FANTASY (H) MBrN
- 'Cordata' see *H. arborescens*
- 'Cotton Candy Two' (L) CRos EPfP LRHS NRHS
§ - 'Dancing Snow' (L/d) SGol
- 'Dark Angel' (L) EBee LCro LOPS LRHS NRHS SGol
- 'Dark Angel Purple' (L) LCro LOPS
- 'Dart's Romance' (L) SHyH
- 'Deep Purple' (L) CRos LRHS NRHS
- 'Deutschland' (H) CTri
- 'Doctor Jean Varnier' (L) CDul EMil EPfP SHyH
- DOLCE FARFALLE ('Dolfarf') (H) WCot
- DOLCE GIPSY ('Dolgip'[PBR]) (L) CRos EPfP LRHS MGos NRHS
- DOLCE KISS ('Dolkis'[PBR]) (L) CRos EPfP LRHS MGos NRHS SGol
- 'Domotoi' see *H. macrophylla* 'Setsuka-yae'
§ - 'Doppio Bianco' see *H. macrophylla* 'Dancing Snow'
- 'Doris' (H) SCob SGol SHyH
- DOUBLE DELIGHTS see *H. macrophylla* 'Perfection'
- DRAGONFLY see *H. macrophylla* 'Libelle'
- EARLY BLUE ('Hba 202911'[PBR]) (H) CRos LRHS MAsh NRHS SCob SGol SPoG
§ - 'Early Sensation' (Forever & Ever Series) (H) CMac GKin LBuc LLHF MHol
§ - 'Eisvogel' (L) SHyH
- 'Eldorado' (H) MNHC SHyH
- 'Elégance' (L) MAsh SGol
- ENDLESS SUMMER ('Bailmer') (H) ELan EPfP SPoG
- ENDLESS SUMMER BLUSHING BRIDE see *H. macrophylla* 'Blushing Bride'
§ - 'Enziandom' (H) CBcs CExl CFil CSBt MAsh
- ETERNITY ('Youmetwo'[PBR]) (H/d) MAsh WCot
- 'Etoile Violette' (L) LRHS
- 'Europa' (H) 🏆H5 CBcs CExl NLar SHyH
- EXPRESSION ('Youmesix') (H/d) SGol
- 'Fanfare' (H) SGol
§ - 'Fasan' (Teller Series) (L) MAsh NBro SGol WFar WHar
- FIRELIGHT see *H. macrophylla* 'Leuchtfeuer'
- FIREWORKS see *H. macrophylla* 'Hanabi'
- FIREWORKS BLUE see *H. macrophylla* 'Jōgasaki'
- FIREWORKS PINK see *H. macrophylla* 'Jōgasaki'
- FIREWORKS WHITE see *H. macrophylla* 'Hanabi'
- FOREVER AND EVER see *H. macrophylla* 'Early Sensation'
- (Forever & Ever Series) FOREVER & EVER PEPPERMINT ('Rie 13'[PBR]) **new** LCro LOPS
- - FOREVER & EVER TOGETHER ('Rie 05') (H/d) CSBt SGol
- 'Forever Pink' (H) GGGa MAsh NLar SGol
- FOREVER ('Youmeone'[PBR]) (H/d) **new** CSBt LRHS NRHS
§ - 'Frau Fujiyo' (Lady Series) (H) CExl
§ - 'Frau Katsuko' (Lady Series) (H) SPer
§ - 'Frau Mariko' (Lady Series) (H) MRav
§ - 'Frau Taiko' (Lady Series) (H) SPer
- 'French Cancan' (Rendez-vous Series) (L) SGol
- 'Frillibet' (H) MRav NLar
- 'Ganku Bo Chokens' (H) WCot
- 'Gartenbaudirektor Kühnert' (H) SHyH
§ - 'Générale Vicomtesse de Vibraye' (H) 🏆H5 CBcs CChe CDul CEnd CRos CTri EBee ELan ELon EPfP GBin LRHS MAsh NRHS SCob SHyH SLim SPer SPoG WBor
- GENTIAN DOME see *H. macrophylla* 'Enziandom'
- 'Geoffrey Chadbund' see *H. macrophylla* 'Möwe'
- 'Gerda Steiniger' (H) GMcL SHyH

- 'Gertrud Glahn' (H) — SHyH
- 'Gimpel' (Teller Series) (L) — MAsh
§ - GLAM ROCK ('Horwack'[PBR]) (H) — EBee LCro LOPS MCot SGol
- 'Glowing Embers' (H) — ETMg IArd
- GOLDRUSH ('Nehyosh') (L/v) — CDul ESps GMcL SRms WCot
- 'Goliath' (H) — ELon
- 'Gräfin Cosel' (H) — SGol
§ - 'Grant's Choice' (L) — NBro
- GREAT STAR — see *H. macrophylla* 'Blanc Bleu'
- 'Grünes Gewölbe' (H) — SGol
- 'Hamburg' (H) — CBcs CTri ECtt EPfP GMcL LRHS SCob SHyH SLim WFar
§ - 'Hanabi' (L/d) ♕H5 — ECre MBlu MGil NLar SGol SHyH
§ - 'Harlequin' (H) — CMac WCot
- 'Hatfield Rose' (H) — SHyH
- 'Hatsu-shime' (L) — CMil NLar
- 'Heinrich Seidel' (H) — CBcs CTri SHyH WMoo
- 'Hercule Poirot' (H) — SGol
- 'Hobella'[PBR] (Hovaria Series) (L) — CBcs NPnk WCot WFar
- 'Hobergine'[PBR] (Hovaria Series) (H) — EBee SGol
- 'Holehird Purple' (H) — MAsh
- 'Homigo'[PBR] (Hovaria Series) (H) — SGol
- 'Hopaline'[PBR] (Hovaria Series) (H) — WPGP
- 'Hopcorn'[PBR] (H) — SGol
- HOT RED ('Hba 206901'[PBR]) (H) — CRos LRHS NRHS
- 'Hot Red Violet' (H) — EBee LCro LOPS MJak SPoG
- 'Izu-no-hana' (L/d) — CAbb CBcs CFil CMil ELon EPfP GBin MBlu NLar SGol SHyH SPoG WBor WSpi
- 'James Grant' — see *H. macrophylla* 'Grant's Choice'
- 'Jofloma' (H) — NLar
§ - 'Jōgasaki' (L/d) — CBcs CExl CMil CRos LRHS MAsh MBlu NLar SDys SHyH WPGP
- 'Joseph Banks' (H) — CBcs CTri EWld SHyH
§ - 'Juno' (L) — EMil SHyH
- 'Kardinal' — see *H. macrophylla* 'Cardinal Red' (H)
§ - 'Kardinal' (Teller Series) (L) ♕H5 — MAsh SCob SGol SHyH SPoG
- 'Kardinal Violet' (L) **new** — LCro
- 'King George' (H) — Widely available
- KINGFISHER — see *H. macrophylla* 'Eisvogel'
§ - 'Klaveren' (L) ♕H5 — CMil GGGa LRHS MAsh NBro SHyH
- 'Kluis Superba' (H) — CTri SHyH
- 'Koria'[PBR] (L) — LRHS NPnk NRHS SPoG
§ - 'Kumico' (H) — SGol
- 'L.A. Dreamin' (H) **new** — SGol
- 'La France' (H) — CCht CRos CTri LRHS SCob SHyH SLim SPoG
- 'La Vie en Rose' (H) — SGol
- 'Lady Fujiyo' — see *H. macrophylla* 'Frau Fujiyo'
- 'Lady in Red' (L) — CMil CRos EBee EPfP LRHS NRHS SPoG
- LADY KATSUKO — see *H. macrophylla* 'Frau Katsuko'
- 'Lady Mariko' — see *H. macrophylla* 'Frau Mariko'
- 'Lady Oshie' (Teller Series) (L) — SGol
- 'Lady Taiko Blue' — see *H. macrophylla* 'Frau Taiko'
- 'Lady Taiko Pink' — see *H. macrophylla* 'Frau Taiko'
- 'Lanarth White' (L) ♕H5 — Widely available
- 'Lemon Wave' (L/v) — NLar
§ - 'Leuchtfeuer' (H) — CRos ELon GMcL LRHS SGol SHyH WMoo
§ - 'Libelle' (Teller Series) (L) ♕H5 — CBcs CMac CRos ELan ELon EPfP GMcL LRHS MGos MMuc MRav NLar NRHS SCob SEND SGol SHyH SLim SPer SPoG
- 'Libertin'[PBR] (H) **new** — EBee
- 'Lilacina' — see *H. macrophylla* 'Mariesii Lilacina'
- LITTLE LIME — see *H. paniculata* 'Jane'
- 'Love You Kiss'[PBR] (Hovaria Series) (L) ♕H5 — CBcs CRos ELon LRHS NLar NRHS SCoo SGol SPoG WCot
- LOVE ('Youme H1917') (H/d) — LCro LOPS LRHS NRHS SGol SPer SPoG
- 'Lutin'[PBR] (L) **new** — EBee
§ - 'Maculata' (L/v) — ESps WGwG
- 'Madame A. Riverain' (H) — EPfP NLar SHyH
- 'Madame Emile Mouillère' (H) ♕H5 — Widely available
- 'Madame Plumecocq' (H) — LRHS
- MAGICAL AMETHYST ('Hokomathyst'[PBR]) (H) — SGol
- MAGICAL CORAL ('Hokomac'[PBR]) (H) — SGol
- MAGICAL GREENFIRE ('Qufu') (H) — SGol
- MAGICAL HARMONY ('Hortmahar'[PBR]) (H) — NLar
- MAGICAL JADE ('Hortmaja'[PBR]) (H) — EPfP MBlu WCot
- MAGICAL NOBLESSE ('Hokomano'[PBR]) (H) — SGol
- MAGICAL OCEAN ('Hortmoc'[PBR]) (H) — NLar
- MAGICAL REVOLUTION ('Hokomarevo') (H) — SGol
- 'Maréchal Foch' (H) — CTri LRHS NLar
- 'Mariesii' (L) — CRos CTri ECrN ELan GBin LRHS MSwo NLar SHyH SPer
§ - 'Mariesii Grandiflora' (L) — CRos EPfP LRHS MMuc NBro SGol SHyH SPer SRms WMoo
§ - 'Mariesii Lilacina' (L) ♕H5 — MMuc SEND SHyH SPer WMoo WSpi
§ - 'Mariesii Perfecta' (L) — Widely available
- 'Masja' (H) — CBar CBcs CCVT ELon GKin IArd MAsh MGos MMuc MRav MSwo NBro NLar SAko SCob SGol SHyH SLim WBor WMoo
- 'Mathilde Gütges' (H) — CCVT
- 'Max Löbner' (H) — SHyH
- 'Merveille' (H) — NBro
- 'Merveille Sanguine' (H) — Widely available
- 'Messalina' (L) — SCob SHyH
- 'Mini Penny'[PBR] (H) — SGol
- MINTY ICE ('Es11') (Flair and Flavour Series) (H) — SGol
- 'Mirai'[PBR] (H) — CBcs LRHS NRHS WCot WPGP
- 'Miss Belgium' (H) — CMac CTri GKin GMcL
§ - 'Mousmée' (L) — SHyH
- 'Mousseline' (H) — CFil CMil LRHS MAsh
§ - 'Möwe' (Teller Series) (L) ♕H5 — CBcs CCht CEnd CExl CMil ECtt ELon EPfP GBin MAsh MMuc SCob SCoo SEND SGol SHyH SLim SPer SRms SSta WSpi
- MRS KUMICO — see *H. macrophylla* 'Kumico'
- 'Mrs W.J. Hepburn' (H) — CSBt SPer
§ - 'Nachtigall' (Teller Series) (L) ♕H5 — EPfP MAsh SHyH WPGP
- 'Nadeshiko-gaku' (L) — SHyH

- 'Nanping'^{PBR} (Sturdy Series) (L)	NPnk SPoG
- 'Niedersachsen' (H)	CTri MRav SHyH
- NIGHTINGALE	see *H. macrophylla* 'Nachtigall'
- 'Nigra' (H)	CAby CBcs CExl CFil CMac CRav CRos CTsd ELan ELon EPfP EWTr GBin IFoB LRHS MGos MMuc MNHC MRav NBro NLar NRHS SAdn SBod SEND SHyH SLim SPer WGrn WGwG
- 'Nikko Blue' (H)	CBcs CRos EBee ESps EUJe GKin LRHS MJak NLar SHyH
- NIZZA ('Ranice'^{PBR}) (City-line Series) (H)	SCob
- var. ***normalis*** (L)	CExl
§ - 'Nymphe' (H)	SCob SHyH
- 'Oregon Pride' (H)	CFil GGGa MAsh WFar
- 'Otaksa' (H)	CMil NLar
- 'Papagei' (Teller Series) (L)	SPer
- PASSION ('Youmefour') (L)	WCot
- 'Pax'	see *H. macrophylla* 'Nymphe'
§ - 'Perfection' (H/d) **new**	CRos NRHS
- 'Pfau' (Teller Series) (L) 🏆^{H5}	CMil ELon GBin MAsh SHyH WSpi
- PHEASANT	see *H. macrophylla* 'Fasan'
- 'Pia' (H)	CExl CMac CMil CPla CRos EShb GBin LRHS MRav SCob SMad SPer SRms WSpi
- PIGEON	see *H. macrophylla* 'Taube'
- 'Pink Lollipop' (Flair and Flavour Series) (H)	SGol
- 'Pirate's Gold' (v)	EHoe WMoo
- 'Prinses Beatrix' (H)	SHyH
- 'Quadricolor' (L/v) 🏆^{H5}	CExl CHll CMac CMil CTsd EHoe GCal MGos MHol MRav SAdn SHyH SLim SPer SPlb SRms WCot WSHC
- 'Queen Elizabeth' (H)	GKin
- 'R.F. Felton' (H)	CBcs SHyH
- 'Radiant' (H) **new**	SRms
- 'Red Angel' (H)	LRHS NRHS SGol
- 'Red Baron'	see *H. macrophylla* 'Schöne Bautznerin'
- 'Red Beauty'^{PBR} (H)	LRHS
- 'Red Red' (H)	MAsh
- 'Red Romance' (H) **new**	CRos NRHS
- REDBREAST	see *H. macrophylla* 'Rotkehlchen'
- 'Regula' (H)	SHyH
- 'Renate Steiniger' (H)	CBod EBee MRav SCob SGol SHyH SLim WMoo WSpi
- ROMANCE ('Youmenine'^{PBR}) (H/d)	CRos EWTr GMcL LRHS MAsh NRHS SCob SGol SPoG WCot
- 'Rosa Zwerg' (H) **new**	CRos NRHS
- 'Rosita' (H)	CCht EBee MAsh SCob SGol
- 'Rotdrossel' (Teller Series) (L)	GBin
§ - 'Rotkehlchen' (Teller Series) (L)	NLar SGol SLim SPlb SWvt
- 'Rotschwanz' (Teller Series) (L) 🏆^{H5}	CFil CMil GBin LLHF LRHS MAsh NLar SHyH WBor WPGP
- 'Rouge Baiser' (H)	SGol
- 'Royal Red' (H)	LRHS
- 'Sabrina' (H)	CBcs CBod CChe CRos CTsd LLHF LRHS MAsh NRHS SCob SGol SHyH SRkn
- 'Saint Claire' (H)	CBcs
- 'Salsa' (H)	CRos LLHF LRHS MAsh NRHS SGol SHyH
- 'Sandra' (Dutch Ladies Series) (L)	CBcs LRHS NRHS
- 'Saskia' (Dutch Ladies Series) (H)	SGol
- SCHLOSS WACKERBARTH	see *H. macrophylla* GLAM ROCK
- 'Schneeball' (H)	CCVT MAsh SCob SGol
§ - 'Schöne Bautznerin' (H)	CCVT LRHS SAdn SCob SHyH SLim
- 'Sea Foam' (L)	NLar
- 'Selina' (Dutch Ladies Series) (L)	CBcs CRos EPfP LLHF LRHS LSRN NRHS SCoo SGol
- 'Selma'^{PBR} (Dutch Ladies Series) (L)	CBcs SGol SHyH
- 'Semperflorens' (H)	LRHS
§ - 'Setsuka-yae' (L/d)	CMil
- 'Shakira' (H)	LLHF SGol
- 'Shamrock' (L)	SHyH
- 'Sheila' (Dutch Ladies Series) (L)	CBcs EPfP LCro LOPS LSRN
- 'Shin-ozaki' (H)	NLar
- 'Shooting Star'^{PBR} (L)	LRHS
- 'Sibilla' (H)	MJak SGol SHyH SPlb WFar
- 'Sidashar' (Dutch Ladies Series) (H)	CRos LRHS NRHS
- 'Sindarella' (H)	GBin
- SISTER THERESE	see *H. macrophylla* 'Soeur Thérèse'
- 'Sita' (L)	LLHF SHyH
§ - 'Soeur Thérèse' (H)	CBar CBcs CSBt EPfP ESps MAsh MMuc NLar SGol SWvt WGwG
- 'Spike'^{PBR} (H)	LRHS NRHS
- subsp. ***stylosa***	WCru WPGP
- - MF 942115 **new**	WPGP
* - 'Sunset' (L)	CBcs
- 'Superba' (H)	SCob
- 'Sweet Fantasy' (Hovaria Series) (H)	ELan EPfP SGol
§ - 'Taube' (Teller Series) (L)	CBcs CDul CExl EBee MAsh SGol SHyH SLim SWvt
- 'Teller Pink'	see *H. macrophylla* 'Taube'
- 'Teller Red'	see *H. macrophylla* 'Rotkehlchen'
- Teller variegated	see *H. macrophylla* 'Tricolor'
- Teller Weiss	see *H. macrophylla* 'Libelle'
- 'Tivoli' (H)	EBee LRHS NRHS SCob WFar
- 'Tokyo Delight' (L) 🏆^{H5}	CExl CMac LRHS MAsh SDys SHyH
- 'Tovelit' (H)	SGol
§ - 'Tricolor' (L/v)	CBcs CTri CTsd EBee ELan EShb LRHS MGos NLar SHyH SLon SPer WAvo WFar WMoo
- TWIST-N-SHOUT ('Piihm-I') (Endless Summer Series) (L)	EPfP SPoG
- 'Variegata'	see *H. macrophylla* 'Maculata'
- 'Veitchii' (L) 🏆^{H5}	CBcs CDul CExl CMil CRos CSBt ECre EPfP LRHS MGos MRav MSwo SHyH SPer
- 'Vicomte de Vibraye'	see *H. macrophylla* 'Générale Vicomtesse de Vibraye'
- 'Warabe'	see *H. serrata* 'Warabe'
- 'Wedding Gown'	see *H. macrophylla* 'Dancing Snow'
- 'Weisse Königin' (H)	SHyH
- 'Westfalen' (H) 🏆^{H5}	CMac IArd
- 'White Wave'	see *H. macrophylla* 'Mariesii Grandiflora'
- 'Wudu'^{PBR} (H)	SGol
- 'Xian'^{PBR} (Sturdy Series) (H)	SGol
- 'Yola' (H)	NBro WFar
- YOU & ME TOGETHER ('Youmefive'^{PBR}) (H/d) **new**	MAsh
- 'Zebra'^{PBR} (H)	ELan EWTr LCro LOPS MHol SCob WCot
- 'Zhuni Hito' (L)	NLar

- 'Zorro'PBR (L) ♀H5	CBcs CCht CRos CWGN EMOT EPfP GGGa GKin GMcL LRHS MAsh MGos NRHS SCob SCoo SHyH SLim SLon SPer SPoG WCot WHlf
- 'Zurichsee'	SHyH
aff. ***mangshanensis*** BWJ 8120	WCru
MISS SAORI ('H20-2') (H/d)	CBcs CRos LCro LOPS LRHS NRHS
paniculata	CMCN ESps
- B&SWJ 3556 from Taiwan	WCru WFar
- B&SWJ 5413 from Japan	WCru
- B&SWJ 8894 from Japan	WCru
- 'Ammarin'	NLar
- ANGEL'S BLUSH	see *H. paniculata* 'Ruby'
- BABY LACE ('Piihp-1')	SGol
- 'Big Ben' ♀H5	CMil CRos EPfP GGGa LRHS NRHS
- BOBO ('Ilvobo'PBR)	CRos LRHS MGos MPkF NRHS SCob SGol
- 'Bombshell'PBR	EMil LCro LOPS NLar SCob SGol SHyH
- 'Brussels Lace'	CAbb CDul CMil CRos EPfP GBin GWyn LRHS LSRN MRav NLar NRHS SCob SGol SHyH SLon SSta
- 'Burgundy Lace'	MBlu NLar
- CANDLELIGHT ('Hpopr013'PBR)	SGol
- 'Chantilly Lace'	CMil CRos GBin LRHS NRHS SCob
- CONFETTI ('Vlasveld02')	LCro LOPS SGol
- DART'S LITTLE DOT ('Darlido'PBR)	GBin LLHF LSRN NLar SLim WFar WPGP
- DIAMANT ROUGE ('Rendia'PBR)	LCro LOPS LRHS MPkF SGol
- DIAMANTINO ('Ren101')	SGol
- 'Dolly'	CRos EPfP LRHS LSRN SHyH
- 'Everest'	CRos EPfP LEdu LRHS MMrt MNHC NLar SHyH SPoG
- 'Floribunda'	CRos ELan EPfP LRHS NRHS WFar
- FRAISE MELBA ('Renba') **new**	SGol
- 'Grandiflora'	Widely available
- 'Great Escape'	NLar
- GREAT STAR	see *H. paniculata* 'Le Vasterival'
- 'Greenspire'	CRos EPfP LRHS MBlu MRav NRHS SHyH WFar
- 'Harry's Souvenir'	NLar
§ - 'Jane'PBR	EMOT EMil ETMg LCro LOPS LRHS MMrt NLar NRHS SGol
- 'Kyushu'	Widely available
§ - 'Le Vasterival'PBR **new**	WSpi
- 'Levana'PBR	CMil SGol SHyH WFar
- 'Limelight'PBR ♀H5	Widely available
- MAGICAL CANDLE ('Bokraflame'PBR)	EPfP SGol WCot WHar
- MAGICAL FIRE ('Bokraplume'PBR)	LRHS NLar NRHS SCob SGol
- MAGICAL FLAME ('Bokratorch'PBR) **new**	WHar
- MAGICAL HIMALAYA ('Kolmahima')	EBee MGos SGol
- MAGICAL MONT BLANC ('Kolmamon') **new**	EBee
- MAGICAL MOONLIGHT ('Kolmagimo'PBR)	ECrN SGol
- MAGICAL STARLIGHT	see *H. paniculata* PERLE D'AUTOMNE
- MAGICAL VESUVIO ('Kolmavesu')	EBee MGos SGol
- 'Mathilde'	NLar
- MEGA MINDY ('Ilvomindy'PBR)	CBcs SCob SGol
- 'Mega Pearl'	LSRN NLar
- 'Melody'	NLar
- 'Mount Aso'	NBro SGol
- 'October Bride'	CEnd NLar WPGP
- 'Papillon'	WPGP
- 'Pee Wee'	LLHF NLar
§ - PERLE D'AUTOMNE ('Degustar')	SGol
- 'Phantom' ♀H5	Widely available
- 'Pink Beauty'PBR (H)	CTri LSRN
- PINK DIAMOND ('Interhydia') ♀H5	Widely available
- 'Pink Jewel'	LLHF
- 'Pink Lady'	NBro SCob SGol SHyH
- PINKY-WINKY ('Dvppinky'PBR) ♀H5	CBot CDul CRos CWGN ECrN EPfP ETMg GKin GMcL IArd LBuc LCro LLHF LOPS LRHS MBlu MGos MPkF NLar NPnk NRHS SCob SCoo SGol SHyH SLim SPoG SSta
- POLAR BEAR ('Wrhpbb2')	SCob SGol SHyH
- 'Praecox'	MRav WCru
- PRIM'WHITE ('Dolprim')	CRos LRHS NRHS
- 'Rosy Morn'	CRos LRHS
§ - 'Ruby'	CBcs LSRN NLar SGol
- 'Saville Lace'	CMil LSvl
- 'Silver Dollar' ♀H5	CMil CRos EPfP IArd LCro LOPS LRHS LSRN NRHS SCob SGol SHyH SPoG SWvt WFar
- 'Starlight Fantasy'	see *H. paniculata* PERLE D'AUTOMNE
- SUNDAE FRAISE ('Rensun'PBR)	CBod CChe CMil CRos CTsd CWGN EBee EPfP EShb GGGa IBoy LRHS MAsh MGos MPkF NRHS SGol WGrn
- 'Tardiva'	CBcs CRos CTho EBee GKin IRob LCro LRHS MGos MRav NBro SCob SGol SHyH SPer SRms SWvt WFar WPGP
- 'Tender Rose'	NLar
- 'Unique'	CBcs CDul CRos CTho ELan EPfP IRob LRHS LSRN MAsh MRav MSwo NBro NLar NRHS SCob SCoo SGol SHyH SPer SSta WAvo WCru WFar WHar WKif WPGP
- VANILLE FRAISE ('Renhy'PBR)	Widely available
- 'White Goliath'	NLar
- 'White Lace'	NLar
- 'White Lady'	CBcs LRHS NRHS SGol
- 'White Moth'	GGGa LEdu LLHF LRHS NBro NLar SAdn SHyH
- 'Wim's Red'PBR	CBcs CMil ELan EPfP IRob LCro LOPS MMrt NLar SCob SGol
- 'Yuan-Yang'	WCru
peruviana var. ***oerstedii*** B&SWJ 10750 **new**	WCru
peruviana × ***seemannii***	CEnd GKin IArd MJak SSta
petiolaris	see *H. anomala* subsp. *petiolaris*
'Preziosa' ♀H4	Widely available
quercifolia	Widely available
- 'Alice'	CJun EBee ELan EPfP LRHS LSRN MAsh NLar SCob SGol SHyH WPGP
- 'Alison'	SGol
I - 'Amethyst' Dirr	CJun NLar SGol
- 'Applause'	CRos ELan EPfP LRHS NLar SGol
- 'Back Porch'	NLar SGol
- 'Burgundy'	CBcs CJun CMil EBee EPfP IArd LRHS MBlu NLar SGol WPGP WSpi

- 'Flore Pleno'	see *H. quercifolia* SNOWFLAKE
- 'Harmony'	CJun CMil CRos EBee ELan EPfP LRHS MGos NLar NRHS SHyH SSta WPGP
- ICE CRYSTAL ('Hqopr010'[PBR])	CMil EBee ELan EPfP LRHS MMrt NLar SCob SGol SHyH WAvo WPGP WSpi
- 'Lady Anne'	WPGP
- 'Little Honey'[PBR]	SGol
- LITTLE HONEY ('Brihon')	CRos LRHS MAsh SGol
- 'Munchkin' **new**	SGol
- 'Pee Wee'	CBcs CJun CRos EBee ELan EPfP LRHS MAsh MPkF SAko SGol SHyH SLon SPoG SSta SWvt WPGP
- 'Ruby Slippers' **new**	SGol
- 'Sike's Dwarf'	CJun ELan MPkF MRav NLar SCob SGol WCFE
- 'Snow Giant'	CJun
- SNOW QUEEN ('Flemygea') ♀H5	CBcs CRos CTri ELan ELon EPfP EThi EWTr LCro LOPS LRHS LSRN MAsh MGos MPkF MRav MSwo NLar SCob SGol SHyH SLim SPer SPoG SWvt WFar WGrn WPGP WSpi
- 'Snowdrift'	CJun CMil
§ - SNOWFLAKE ('Brido') (d) ♀H5	CBcs CEnd CMac CMil CRos CWGN ELan EPfP LCro LOPS LRHS MAsh MGos MPkF MRav NLar SGol SHyH SLon SPer SPoG WCFE WPGP WSpi
- 'Tennessee Clone'	CJun LRHS NLar
'Renatea' **new**	CSBt
sargentiana	see *H. aspera* subsp. *sargentiana*
scandens	CFil NBro
- B&SWJ 5448	WCru
- B&SWJ 5481	WCru
- B&SWJ 5496	WCru
- B&SWJ 5523	WCru
- B&SWJ 5602	WCru
- B&SWJ 5725	WCru
- B&SWJ 5893	WCru
- B&SWJ 6159	WCru
- B&SWJ 6317	WCru
§ - subsp. ***chinensis***	CExl
- - B&SWJ 1488	WCru
- - B&SWJ 3214	WCru
- - B&SWJ 3410 from Taiwan	WCru
- - B&SWJ 3420	WCru
- - B&SWJ 3423 from Taiwan	WCru
- - B&SWJ 3487 from Taiwan	WCru
- - B&SWJ 3869	WCru
- - BWJ 8000 from Sichuan	WCru
- - BWJ 8035	WCru
- - NJM 11.090 **new**	WPGP
§ - - f. ***angustipetala***	WPGP
- - - B&SWJ 3454	WCru
- - - B&SWJ 3553	WCru
- - - B&SWJ 3667	WCru
- - - B&SWJ 3733	WCru
- - - B&SWJ 3814	WCru
- - - B&SWJ 6038 from Yakushima	WCru
- - - B&SWJ 6041 from Yakushima	WCru
- - - B&SWJ 6056 from Yakushima	WCru
- - - B&SWJ 6787	WCru
- - - B&SWJ 6802	WCru
- - - B&SWJ 7121	WCru
- - - B&SWJ 7128	WCru
§ - - - 'Golden Crane'	SCob WCru WPGP
- - - 'Monlongshou'	see *H. scandens* subsp. *chinensis* f. *angustipetala* 'Golden Crane'
- - 'Big White' **new**	EBee WPGP
- - f. ***formosana***	SBrt
- - - B&SWJ 1488	WCru
- - - B&SWJ 7058	NLar
- - - B&SWJ 7097	NLar WCru
- - f. ***macrosepala*** B&SWJ 3423	WCru
- - - B&SWJ 3476	WCru
- - - CWJ 12441	WCru
- - f. ***obovatifolia*** B&SWJ 3487b	WCru
- - - B&SWJ 3683	WCru
- - - B&SWJ 3869 from the Philippines	WCru
- - - B&SWJ 7121	WCru
- subsp. ***liukiuensis***	WCru
- - B&SWJ 11471	WCru
- - B&SWJ 6022	WCru
- 'Splash' (v)	CMil
seemannii	Widely available
- 'Roger Grounds' (v)	WCot
aff. ***seemannii***	CBod ESps GKin WSpi
SEMIOLA ('Inovalaur'[PBR])	CRos EBee EPfP LLHF LRHS SGol SLim
serrata	CExl CTri ESps WKif
- B&SWJ 6184	WCru
- B&SWJ 6241	WCru
- PAB 4757	LEdu
- 'Acuminata'	see *H. serrata* 'Bluebird'
- 'Aigaku' (L)	CExl CFil CMil
- 'Akabe-yama'	NBro NLar
- 'Akishino-temari'	EBee WPGP
- Amacha Group	SGol
- - 'Amagi-amacha' (L)	CMil NBro NLar
- - 'Ō-amacha' (L)	CMil WPGP
- 'Amagyana' (L)	CExl
- subsp. ***angustata***	WCru
- 'Ao-yama'	WPGP
- AVELROZ ('Dolmyf'[PBR])	CRos EPfP LRHS SGol
- 'Belladonna'	NBro
- 'Belle Deckle'	see *H.* 'Blue Deckle'
- 'Beni-gaku' (L)	CExl CFil CMil CRos ECre LRHS MAsh NBro NLar NRHS SCob SGol SHyH
- 'Beni-temari'	NBro
- 'Beni-yama' (L) ♀H5	CFil CMil
- 'Besshi-temari'	CFil
- 'Bleuet'	LRHS
- 'Blue Billow' (L)	NBro NLar
- BLUEBERRY CHEESECAKE	see *H. serrata* TUFF STUFF
§ - 'Bluebird' (L) ♀H5	Widely available
- 'Cap Sizun'	LRHS SChF SGol WPGP
- 'Chiba Cherry-lips'	WCru
- 'Chiri-san Sue' (d)	CFil WCru
- COTTON CANDY	see *H. serrata* TUFF STUFF
- 'Crûg Bicolor' (L)	WCru
- 'Crûg Caerulean'	WCru
- 'Crûg Cobalt' (L)	GGGa WCru
- 'Crûg Sō Cool' (L)	WCru
- 'Diadem' (L) ♀H5	CAbb CBot CExl CMil ELon EPfP LRHS NBro SHyH
- 'Forget Me Not'	LRHS NBro
- 'Fuji Snowstorm' (v)	CMil
- 'Fuji Waterfall'	see *H. serrata* 'Fuji-no-taki'
§ - 'Fuji-no-taki' (L/d) ♀H5	CBot CMil LLHF NLar WPGP WWFP
- 'Gaka'	LRHS
- 'Golden Showers' (L)	NBro
- 'Golden Sunlight'[PBR] (L)	SGol SWvt

- 'Graciosa' (L)	LLHF LRHS
- 'Grayswood' (L) ♀H5	CBcs CDul CExl CMac CRos CSBt ELan EPfP LRHS MAsh MRav NBro SCob SGol SHyH SLim SPer WKif WPGP
- 'Hakucho' (L/d)	CMil NBro WPGP
- 'Hallasan' misapplied	see *H. serrata* 'Maiko', 'Spreading Beauty'
- 'Hallasan' R. & J. de Belder (L)	CMil WPGP
- 'Hime-benigaku' (L)	CMil MAsh WFar
- 'Impératrice Eugénie' (L)	NLar
- 'Intermedia' (L)	CExl NBro
- 'Kiyosumi' (L) ♀H5	CEnd CExl CFil CMil ECre ELon EPfP LRHS NLar SBrt SHyH WBor WCot WCru WPGP
- 'Klaveren'	see *H. macrophylla* 'Klaveren'
- 'Koreana' (L)	SAko
- 'Kurenai' (L)	CMil NBro NLar SChF WPGP
- 'Kurohime' (L)	EBee NBro WPGP
- 'Macrosepala' (L)	WPGP
§ - 'Maiko' (L)	IArd
- 'Midori' (L)	CExl
- 'Mikata Yae'	CMil WPGP
- 'Miranda' (L) ♀H5	CExl CMil CRos EPfP LRHS MAsh NBro NLar SDys SGol SHyH WFar
- 'Miyama-yae-murasaki' (L/d) ♀H5	CExl CFil CMil SGol SRms WPGP
- 'Momo-beni-yama'	CMil NBro
- 'Mont Aso'	CBot CMil IArd NLar
- 'Niji' (L)	EBee WPGP
- 'Odoriko-amacha'	CMil EBee LRHS SChF WPGP
- 'Otsu-hime'	NLar
- 'Panachée' (L/v)	SHyH
- 'Pretty Maiden'	see *H. serrata* 'Shichidanka'
§ - 'Prolifera' (L/d)	CMil LLHF
- 'Pulchella'	see *H. serrata* 'Prolifera'
- 'Ramis Pictis' (L)	CBcs NBro NLar SHyH
- 'Rosalba' (L) ♀H5	CExl ECre NBro
- 'Santiago'PBR (L)	EPfP SGol WCot
- 'Sekka'	WPGP
§ - 'Shichidanka' (L/d)	CBot CFil EPfP LLHF LRHS NBro SHyH
- 'Shichidanka-nishiki' (L/d/v)	CExl ECre
- 'Shinonome' (L/d)	CExl CMil
- 'Shirahuzi' (L/d)	SGol
- 'Shirofuji' (L/d) ♀H5	CFil CMil LLHF MAsh
- 'Shiro-gaku' (L)	CMil MAsh NBro NLar
- 'Shiro-maiko'	CFil WPGP
- 'Shirotae' (L/d)	CExl CFil SGol
- 'Shōjō' ♀H5	CMil EBee LRHS NBro SGol SHyH WPGP
§ - 'Spreading Beauty' (L)	CMil WPGP
- 'Suzukayama-yama'	CMil SChF WPGP
* - var. ***thunbergii*** 'Plena' (L/d)	WCru
- 'Tiara' (L) ♀H5	CAbb CDul CExl CFil CMil CRos EBee EPfP GGGa LRHS LSRN MAsh NBro NLar SDys SGol SHyH SLim SPoG WPGP
- 'Tosa-no-akatsuki'	CFil
§ - TUFF STUFF ('Mak 20'PBR) (L)	CRos EPfP LCro LLHF LOPS LRHS MPkF NRHS SCob SGol SPoG
- 'Veerle' (L)	NBro NLar SGol
- 'Vicomte de Kerlot'	LRHS
§ - 'Warabe'	SGol
- 'Yae-no-amacha' (L/d)	CBcs CExl NBro NLar
- subsp. ***yezoensis***	CMil NLar SGol
- - 'Hime-gaku'	CMil
§ ***serratifolia***	CExl IArd IDee SSta WPGP
- HCM 98056	WCru
sikokiana B&SWJ 5035	WCru
- B&SWJ 5855	WCru
- B&SWJ 11174	WCru
- B&SWJ 11381	WCru
'Silver Slipper'	see *H. macrophylla* 'Ayesha'
steyermarkii B&SWJ 10501 new	WCru
tiliifolia	see *H. anomala* subsp. *petiolaris* var. *ovalifolia*
'Victoria'	GMcL
villosa	see *H. aspera* Villosa Group
xanthoneura	see *H. heteromalla*
aff. ***zhewanensis*** MF 93117	WCru

Hydrastis (*Ranunculaceae*)

canadensis	GPoy LEdu

Hydrocharis (*Hydrocharitaceae*)

morsus-ranae	CBen CHab CWat EWat LLWG MSKA MWts NPer WPnP

Hydrocleys (*Alismataceae*)

nymphoides	LLWG XBlo

Hydrocotyle (*Araliaceae*)

asiatica	see *Centella asiatica*
sibthorpioides 'Crystal Confetti' (v)	LLWG
vulgaris	CWat EBWF

Hydrophyllum (*Boraginaceae*)

canadense	IMou
virginianum	LEdu WHal

Hylomecon (*Papaveraceae*)

hylomeconoides	EWld WCru
§ ***japonica***	CAby CRos EBee ELan EWld GEdr GKev GLog IMou LEdu LRHS MAvo NHpl NQui NRHS NRya WCot WCru WPGP WThu

Hylotelephium see *Sedum*

Hymenanthera see *Melicytus*

Hymenocallis (*Amaryllidaceae*)

'Advance'	see *Ismene* 'Advance'
× ***festalis***	see *Ismene* × *deflexa*
harrisiana	CCCN GKev SDeJ
longipetala	see *Ismene longipetala*
'Sulphur Queen'	see *Ismene* 'Sulphur Queen'

Hymenolepis (*Asteraceae*)

parviflora	see *Athanasia parviflora*

Hymenosporum (*Pittosporaceae*)

flavum	EShb EUJe

Hymenoxys (*Asteraceae*)

grandiflora	see *Tetraneuris grandiflora*
§ ***hoopesii***	CBod CMac CRos EPfP GMaP GMcL GWyn LRHS MPie NLar NRHS SCob SPer SRms WCot WFar WHar XLum

Hyoscyamus (*Solanaceae*)

niger	GPoy WSFF XAbr

Hypericum ✿ (*Hypericaceae*)

	sp.	ESps
	CC 4131	CExl
	CC 4544	CExl
	aegypticum	CPBP CTri MHer SPlb WAbe WThu
	androsaemum	ECha ELan MHer MMuc MSwo NPer SEND WFar WMoo WOut
§	- 'Albury Purple'	ELan EShb NLar WMoo XLum
	- 'Autumn Blaze'	CBcs
	- 'Excellent Flair'	NLar
§	- f. ***variegatum*** 'Mrs Gladis Brabazon' (v)	EShb WCot
	'Archibald'	EWes NWad
	athoum	WThu
	balearicum	MMuc SBrt XSen
	bellum	GCal
	buckleyi	WAbe
	calycinum	CBcs CBod CDul CMac CTri ECrN ELan ELon EPfP ESps GMcL LBuc MGos MRav SCob SEND SGol SPer SRms SWvt WFar WMoo XLum
	- 'Brigadoon' ♀H5	MAsh SGol
	- CARNIVAL ('Crowthyp') (v)	NEoE SPad
	cerastioides	CSma CTri EDAr EWes MMuc NGdn SRms WAbe
	coris	EWes SRms
	cuneatum	see *H. pallens*
	× ***cyathiflorum*** 'Gold Cup'	CMac LRHS MAsh
	× ***dummeri*** 'Peter Dummer'	NLar WSpi
	'Eastleigh Gold'	CMac
	'Elite Baby Green'	EPfP
	'Elite Mayor'	EPfP
	'Elite Sweet Lion'	EPfP
	ellipticum new	EBWF
	elodes	CWat LLWG
	'Fancy Pants'	LEdu
	forrestii ♀H5	MMuc SEND
	fosteri new	CFil
	fragile misapplied	see *H. olympicum* f. *minus*
	GOLDEN BEACON ('Wilhyp'PBR) ♀H5	CBod CEnd CRos CSpe EBee EMOT GMcL LRHS LSou MMuc MNrw NEgg NRHS NWad SEND SPad SPoG WCot
	grandiflorum	see *H. kouytchense*
	grandifolium	EDAr GCal
	henryi L 753	SRms
	- subsp. ***hancockii*** NJM 10.092	WPGP
	'Hidcote'	see *H.* × *hidcoteense* 'Hidcote'
	× ***hidcoteense***	ESps
§	- 'Hidcote' ♀H5	Widely available
	- 'Hidcote Variegated' (v)	MAsh SLim SRms
	hirsutum	CHab EBWF NMir
	(Hypearls Series) HYPEARLS ANNELIES	CRos LRHS NRHS
	- HYPEARLS ELLA	CRos LRHS NRHS
	- HYPEARLS JACQUELINE	CRos LRHS NRHS
	imbricatum	LLHF
	× ***inodorum*** 'Albury Purple'	see *H. androsaemum* 'Albury Purple'
	- 'Autumn Surprise'PBR	ELon NEgg NEoE NWad
	- 'Dream'	NLar
	- 'Elstead'	ECtt ELan EPfP MRav NLar NWad WSpi
	- MAGICAL CHERRY ('Kolmcherrip'PBR)	ELan EPfP SCob
	- MAGICAL LIMELIGHT ('Kolmalimeli'PBR)	ELan
	- MAGICAL PUMPKIN ('Kolmapuki'PBR)	NEoE SPer
	- MAGICAL SUNSHINE ('Kolmasun'PBR)	CRos LRHS NEoE NRHS SPer
	- MAGICAL UNIVERSE ('Kolmuni')	NEoE SCob
	- MAGICAL WHITE ('Kolmawhi'PBR)	ELan EPfP NEoE SCob SPoG
	- MAGICAL WHITE FALL ('Kolmwhifa'PBR)	SCob
	- 'Rheingold'	MAsh NLar
	- 'Ysella'	MRav
	kalmianum	SBrt
	kamtschaticum	XLum
	kazdaghense	EWes
§	***kouytchense*** ♀H5	CDul CRos EBee EPfP EWes LRHS MAsh MMuc MRav SEND SPoG SWvt WCFE WSpi
	lancasteri	CRos EPfP LRHS MAsh SPoG
	leschenaultii misapplied	see *H.* 'Rowallane'
	'Little Misstery'	CRos EMOT IBoy LBuc LRHS NEoE NRHS SPoG
	maclarenii	EWes
	MAGICAL BEAUTY ('Kolmbeau'PBR)	CBod CRos ELon EPfP LRHS MJak MMrt NEoE NLar NRHS SCob SPer SPoG
	MAGICAL DREAM ('Kolmdream'PBR)	SCob
	MAGICAL FALL ('Kolmfa'PBR)	SCob
	MAGICAL FLAME ('Kolmagif')	SCob
	MAGICAL PINK ('Kolmpin')	SCob
	MAGICAL RED ('Kolmred')	EPfP MJak NEoE NLar SCob SPoG
	MAGICAL RED FLAME ('Kolmaref') new	MMrt
	MAGICAL RED STAR ('Kolmarest'PBR)	SCob
	MAGICAL SWEETHEART ('Kolmsweet')	SCob
	MIRACLE ATTRACTION ('Alldiablo'PBR)	CRos LRHS NLar SRms
	MIRACLE BLIZZ ('Allblizz')	CRos EBee LRHS NRHS
	MIRACLE BLOSSOM ('Allblossom'PBR)	CRos LRHS NRHS
	MIRACLE FANTASY ('Hymirfan')	NLar
	MIRACLE SUMMER ('Hymirsum')	CRos EPfP LRHS NEoE NLar
	MIRACLE WONDER ('Hymirwon')	CRos LRHS NLar
	× ***moserianum*** ♀H5	CDul CMac CRos EMOT EPfP EWes LRHS MJak NPer SCob SLon SPer SRms WFar
	- 'Daybreak'	LRHS MAsh NEoE SGol SPoG WRHF
§	- 'Tricolor' (v)	Widely available
	- 'Variegatum'	see *H.* × *moserianum* 'Tricolor'
	'Mr Bojangles' new	EMOT
	'Mrs Brabazon'	see *H. androsaemum* f. *variegatum* 'Mrs Gladis Brabazon'
	oblongifolium	CExl
	olympicum ♀H5	CRos CTri EBee ECha ELan GJos LRHS NEoE NRHS SCob SEND SPer SRms SWvt XLum XSen
	- 'Grandiflorum'	see *H. olympicum* f. *uniflorum*
§	- f. ***minus***	CSma CTri ECtt NGdn NHpl SPlb SRms WHrl
§	- - 'Sulphureum'	CBod CChe CRos ELon EWTr EWes GMaP LRHS NRHS SPer SRms SWvt WCFE

- - 'Variegatum' (v)	EWes SWvt
§ - f. ***uniflorum***	MMuc NBro
- - 'Citrinum' 🏆H5	CMea CSpe ECha ECtt EPfP MMuc MRav NLar SEND WAbe WCot WHoo WHrl WKif WSHC XSen
orientale	EWes GLog
§ ***pallens***	WAbe
perforatum	CBod CHab CHby EBWF ENfk EPfP GPoy IRos MHer MNHC NLar NMir SEND SRms WHer WMoo WSFF XAbr
polyphyllum misapplied	see *H. olympicum* f. *minus*
- 'Citrinum'	see *H. olympicum* f. *minus* 'Sulphureum'
- 'Grandiflorum'	see *H. olympicum* f. *uniflorum*
prolificum	MMrt WCFE
quadrangulum L.	see *H. tetrapterum*
reptans misapplied	see *H. olympicum* f. *minus*
reptans Hook.f. & Thomson ex Dyer	EWes GCrg NWad SBrt
revolutum PAB 3861	LEdu WPGP
§ 'Rowallane' 🏆H4	CBot CDul CTri GCal LRHS NLar SWvt
subsessile	CExl
'Sungold'	see *H. kouytchense*
'Sweet Lion'	CMac
§ ***tetrapterum***	CBod EBWF LLWG MMuc
trichocaulon	EWes ITim
uralum HWJ 520	WCru
- NJM 10.097 new	WPGP

Hypocalyptus (*Papilionaceae*)

sophoroides	SPlb

Hypochaeris (*Asteraceae*)

radicata	CHab EBWF NMir

Hypocyrta see *Nematanthus*

Hypoestes (*Acanthaceae*)

aristata	CExl EShb SVen

Hypolepis (*Dennstaedtiaceae*)

millefolium	EBee LEdu LRHS

Hypoxis (*Hypoxidaceae*)

hirsuta	CCCN GKev
hygrometrica	WThu
parvula	CAby XLum
§ - var. ***albiflora*** 'Hebron Farm Biscuit'	CCCN CTal EWes GEdr IRob NWad SRot WAbe WFar

Hypoxis × *Rhodohypoxis* see × *Rhodoxis*

H. parvula × ***R. baurii***	see × *Rhodoxis hybrida*

Hypsela (*Campanulaceae*)

longiflora	see *H. reniformis*
§ ***reniformis***	CMea CPla GCrg ITim LLWG MSCN NHpl

Hyssopus ✿ (*Lamiaceae*)

from Georgia	EWes
officinalis	CBod CHby CMea ECha ELan ENfk EPfP ESps ETMg GAbr GMaP GPoy MHer MJak MNHC MRav NPri SEND SPer SPlb SPoG SRms SVic XLum
- f. ***albus***	ECha ENfk EPfP GPoy MHer MNHC SPlb SRms WArt WHer XLum XSen
- subsp. ***aristatus***	CBod EBee ENfk EPfP GPoy IMou MHer MNHC SPoG WHoo XLum XSen
- 'Caeruleus'	WArt
- subsp. ***officinalis***	XSen
- 'Roseus'	CBod ECha ENfk EPfP ESps GPoy MHer MHol MNHC SPer SPoG WArt WHer XLum XSen
- white-flowered	CBod

Hystrix (*Poaceae*)

patula	CBod EHoe EPPr EShb ESps MMoz MNrw SPlb XLum

Iberis (*Brassicaceae*)

ABSOLUTELY AMETHYST ('Ib2401')	CRos ELan GBin LRHS MCot NRHS SPoG
candolleana	see *I. pruitii* Candolleana Group
commutata	see *I. sempervirens*
gibraltarica	CSpe SRms
- 'Betty Swainson' 🏆H4	CSpe ELan NWad SPhx
- 'Lavish' new	MHol
jordanii	see *I. pruitii*
'Masterpiece' PBR	CRos ECrN ECtt ELan GMaP LRHS NRHS SPoG WCot WFar
'Pink Ice'	CRos ETMg LRHS MCot NRHS WFar WTor
§ ***pruitii***	CTal NSla SPlb WAbe
§ - Candolleana Group	GEdr
saxatilis	CRos ITim LRHS NRHS WThu
semperflorens	WAvo WCFE
§ ***sempervirens***	CMea CTri ELan EPfP ESps IFoB IRob MAsh MCot MMuc NBro SEND SHar SRms WCFE WHar
- 'Appen-Etz'	CRos EPfP LRHS NRHS NWad SRms
- 'Elfenreigen'	GCal
- 'Fischbeck'	CRos SRms SRot
- 'Golden Candy'	CSma CTri ECtt EHoe NHpl SPoG SRms
- 'Little Gem'	see *I. sempervirens* 'Weisser Zwerg'
- 'Pygmaea'	CTal WHil
- SCHNEEFLOCKE	see *I. sempervirens* 'Snowflake'
- 'Snow Cushion'	EPfP LSun WRHF
§ - 'Snowflake' 🏆H5	CBod EPfP EPot ESps GBin GMaP IFoB MCot SPer SPoG SRms SRot SWvt XLum
§ - 'Weisser Zwerg'	CMea ECha ECtt ELan GCrg GMaP MRav SRms WHoo WThu
'Snowball'	MHol
umbellata	ECrN

Ichthyoselmis (*Papaveraceae*)

§ ***macrantha***	EPfP EPot IMou WCru WSHC

Idesia (*Salicaceae*)

polycarpa	CBcs CDul CMCN EBee EPfP SBrt SChF WPGP
- CWJ 12837	WCru

Ilex ✿ (*Aquifoliaceae*)

sp.	LPra
§ × ***altaclerensis*** 'Belgica Aurea' (f/v) 🏆H6	CBcs CJun CTho EPfP MSwo NEgg NLar WAvo
- 'Camelliifolia' (f) 🏆H6	CBcs CTho MBlu NEgg SGol SPer WSpi

	- 'Camelliifolia Variegata' (f/v)	CMac
	- 'Golden King' (f/v) 🏆H6	Widely available
	- 'Hendersonii' (f)	NEgg
	- 'Hodginsii' (m)	CTri
	- 'Howick' (f/v)	CJun
	- 'James G. Esson' (f)	CRos LRHS
	- 'Lawsoniana' (f/v) 🏆H6	CCVT CJun CMac CRos CSBt CTri EHoe ELan EPfP ESps LRHS MAsh MBlu MJak MMuc NEgg NRHS SCob SEND SGol SLim SLon SPer SPoG SRms WAvo WHar
	- 'Purple Shaft' (f)	CMCN MRav
	- 'Ripley Gold' (f/v)	CJun CMac CRos LRHS MAsh MRav WAvo
	- 'Silver Sentinel'	see *I.* × *altaclerensis* 'Belgica Aurea'
	- 'W.J. Bean' (f)	CJun
	- 'Wilsonii' (f)	NEgg NLar
	aquifolium 🏆H6	Widely available
	- 'Alaska' (f)	CCCN CCVT CDul CJun CMCN CRos EPfP GMcL IBoy IRob LBuc LMaj LRHS MAsh MJak NLar NOra NRHS SGol SWvt WAvo WFar
	- 'Amber' (f) 🏆H6	CJun CTri NLar
	- 'Angustifolia' (f)	CJun ESps WCFE
	- 'Angustifolia' (m or f)	EPfP LRHS MAsh SPoG
§	- 'Argentea Marginata' (f/v) 🏆H6	Widely available
§	- 'Argentea Marginata Pendula' (f/v)	CMac CRos CTri ELan EPfP LRHS MAsh SRms WCot WFar
	- 'Argentea Pendula'	see *I. aquifolium* 'Argentea Marginata Pendula'
	- 'Argentea Variegata'	see *I. aquifolium* 'Argentea Marginata'
	- 'Atlas' (m)	CBcs LBuc SWvt
	- 'Aurea Marginata' (f/v)	CMac EPfP ESps LMaj MGos NOra SCob SEWo WAvo WCFE WHar
	- 'Aurea Regina'	see *I. aquifolium* 'Golden Queen'
	- 'Aureomaculata'	NEgg
	- 'Aurifodina' (f)	CJun NEgg WAvo
	- 'Bacciflava' (f)	CBcs CJun CMac CTho CTri EBee ELan ELon EPfP IArd MBlu MGos MJak MRav NEgg NLar SLim SPer SRms SWvt WCFE WFar
	- 'Elegantissima' (m/v)	CJun
	- 'Fastigiata Sartori'	NLar
	- 'Ferox' (m)	CJun CRos ELan EPfP LRHS NEgg
	- 'Ferox Argentea' (m/v) 🏆H6	Widely available
	- 'Ferox Aurea' (m/v)	CJun CRos ELan ELon LRHS MAsh NEgg
§	- 'Flavescens' (f)	MBlu NEgg
	- 'Fructu Luteo' (f)	WHar
	- 'Glanzzwerg'	SAko
	- 'Gold Flash' (f/v)	CJun LRHS NLar
	- 'Golden Milkboy' (m/v)	CJun CMac ESps MAsh SGol WAvo WCot
§	- 'Golden Queen' (m/v) 🏆H6	IBoy SRms
	- 'Golden Tears' (f/v)	CJun
	- 'Golden van Tol' (f/v)	CBcs CJun CSBt CTri EBee ELan ELon EPfP ESps ETod GMcL IBoy LRHS MAsh MBlu MGos MJak MSwo NEgg NLar SCoo SGol SPer SRms WFar WHar
	- 'Green Minaret'	SAko
§	- 'Green Pillar' (f)	CRos LRHS NRHS
	- 'Green Spire'	see *I. aquifolium* 'Green Pillar'
	- 'Handsworth New Silver' (f/v) 🏆H6	Widely available
	- 'Harpune' (f)	IArd SAko
	- 'Hastata' (m)	IArd IDee
	- HECKENZWERG ('Hachzwerg'PBR)	SAko
	- 'Ingramii' (m/v)	CJun LRHS
	- 'J.C. van Tol' (f) 🏆H6	Widely available
	- 'Latispina' (f)	CJun
	- 'Lichtenthalii' (f)	CJun IArd NEgg
	- 'Madame Briot' (f/v) 🏆H6	CDul CJun CMac CRos CTri EBee EHoe ELan EMOT EPfP ESps GMcL IRob LBuc LRHS MAsh MRav MSwo NEgg NPri NRHS SEND SGol SPer SPoG SRms SWvt WFar WHar
	- 'Marijo'	CRos LRHS NRHS
	- 'Monstrosa' (m)	CJun
	- moonlight holly	see *I. aquifolium* 'Flavescens'
	- 'Myrtifolia' (f)	NEgg SWvt
	- 'Myrtifolia' (m)	CJun CMac ELan EPfP NLar SMad
	- 'Myrtifolia Aurea' (m/v)	SWvt
	- 'Myrtifolia Aurea Maculata' (m/v)	CJun CRos CTri ELan LRHS MAsh MRav NEgg SPoG SWvt WCot
	- 'Northern Lights' (v)	EPfP MSwo
	- 'Pendula' (f)	MRav
	- 'Pyramidalis' (f) 🏆H6	CBcs CDul CJun CMac CRos CTri ELan GMcL LPra LRHS MAsh MGos MJak NLar SCob SGol SPer SRms WFar
	- 'Pyramidalis Aureomarginata' (f/v)	NLar
	- 'Pyramidalis Fructu Luteo' (f) 🏆H6	MAsh
	- 'Recurva' (m)	CJun CMac
	- RED TIPS ('Spek 02') (m) **new**	EBee
	- 'Rubricaulis Aurea' (f/v)	CJun GMcL NEgg NLar
	- 'Scotica' (f)	CJun
	- SIBERIA ('Limsi'PBR) (f)	LPra
	- 'Silver King'	see *I. aquifolium* 'Silver Queen'
	- 'Silver Lining' (f/v)	CJun
	- 'Silver Milkboy' (f/v)	EPfP MBlu WFar
	- 'Silver Milkmaid' (f/v)	CJun CRos ESps LRHS MAsh MJak MMuc NEgg NRHS SLim SWvt
§	- 'Silver Queen' (m/v) 🏆H6	CBar CBcs CCVT CDul CEnd CRos EHoe EPfP ESps IRob LRHS MAsh MGos MJak MRav MSwo NEgg NLar NOra NPri SAko SLim SLon SPer SPoG SRGP SWvt WHar
	- 'Silver Sentinel'	see *I.* × *altaclerensis* 'Belgica Aurea'
	- 'Silver van Tol' (f/v)	CJun EBee ELan EPfP GMcL MAsh NEgg NLar NPer SPer WHar
	- 'Somerset Cream' (f/v)	CJun CTri
*	- 'Variegata' (v)	SArc SWeb
	- 'Victoria' (m)	CJun
	- 'White Cream' (m/v)	SAko
	- 'Zig Zag' (f)	CJun
	× ***aquipernyi*** DRAGON LADY ('Meschick') (f) 🏆H6	CJun CTho IArd LMaj NEgg NLar
	- 'San Jose' (f)	CJun
	× ***attenuata*** 'Sunny Foster' (f/v)	CMCN EPfP MAsh SAko
	× ***beanii***	CJun
§	***bioritsensis***	CMCN CTri
	'Brilliant' (f)	NEgg
	cassine L.	CMCN
	chapaensis HWJ 946 **new**	WCru
	'Clusterberry' (f)	CJun NEgg
	colchica	CMCN
	cornuta	EPfP
	- B&SWJ 8756	WCru

	- 'Anicet Delcambre' (f)	CJun
	- 'Burfordii' (f)	NLar
§	- 'Dazzler' (f)	CJun
	- 'Ira S. Nelson' (f)	CJun IArd SAko
	- 'Mercury' (f)	CJun
	- 'O. Spring' (f/v)	CJun WSpi
	crenata	CAco CMCN CTal CTri EPfP MGos SArc SCob STrG SVic SWeb WFar
*	- 'Akagi'	WFar
	- 'Aureovariegata'	see *I. crenata* 'Variegata'
	- 'Blondie'PBR (f)	SWeb
	- 'Carolina Upright' (m)	EBee
	- 'Convexa' (f) 🏆H6	CDul CJun CTho EPfP ESps GMcL LRHS MAsh MRav NEgg SCob SPer WMoo
	- 'Convexed Gold' (f/v)	CRos EPfP LRHS NLar NRHS NWad SPoG WFar WHar
	- DARK GREEN ('Icoprins11'PBR)	EPfP IBoy LBuc LCro LOPS LRHS LSRN SMad SPer SVic
	- 'Dwarf Pagoda' (f)	SAko
	- Fastigiata Group	SCob
	- - 'Fastigiata' (f) 🏆H6	CAco CRos EPfP LRHS LSRN MAsh MGos NLar SPer SPoG
	- - 'Sky Pencil' (f)	CMCN
	- 'Fructu Luteo'	see *I. crenata* f. *watanabeana*
*	- 'Glory Gem' (f)	CBcs LSRN
	- 'Golden Gem' (f/v) 🏆H6	CJun CMac CRos CSBt CTri EBee ELan ELon EPfP ESps GMcL LRHS MAsh MGos MSwo NLar NWad SAko SGol SPer SPoG SWvt WFar WThu
	- 'Green Hedger' 🏆H6	CPer EPfP MGos
	- 'Green Lustre' (f)	LSRN
	- 'Hetzii' (f)	CBod WMoo
	- 'Kinme'	SWeb
	- 'Luteovariegata'	see *I. crenata* 'Variegata'
	- 'Mariesii' (f)	CMac MBlu
I	- 'Pyramidalis' (f)	CMac MRav
§	- 'Shiro-fukurin' (f/v)	CMCN CRos ELan EPfP LRHS NRHS SLon SPoG
	- 'Snowflake'	see *I. crenata* 'Shiro-fukurin'
	- 'Stokes' (m)	CBod MSwo NLar NWad WMoo
§	- 'Variegata' (v)	CMCN CMac CRos EPfP LRHS NLar NRHS
§	- f. ***watanabeana*** (f)	WGwG
	cyrtura **new**	WPGP
	'Dazzler'	see *I. cornuta* 'Dazzler'
	dimorphophylla	CMac
	- 'Somerset Pixie' (f)	CJun
	dipyrena	SAko
	'Doctor Kassab' (f)	CMCN
	'Elegance' (f)	MBlu WFar
	excelsa	CMCN
	aff. ***gagnepainiana*** FMWJ 13168	WCru
	glabra	CJun
	- f. ***leucocarpa*** 'Snow White' (f)	CJun
	'Good Taste' (f)	CJun WFar
	'Hohman'	CJun
	'Indian Chief' (f)	CJun
	× ***koehneana***	CCVT CDul
	- 'Chestnut Leaf' (f) 🏆H5	CBcs CCVT CJun CLnd CMCN CTho EWTr LRHS MRav NEgg NLar SSta WFar WGrn
	laevigata	CMCN
	latifolia	CJun CMCN NLar
	'Leonardo'	EBee
*	'Little Diamond'	LSRN
	'Lydia Morris' (f)	CSam

'Mary Nell' (f)	CJun IArd
× ***meserveae***	LPra
- BLUE ANGEL ('Conang') (f)	CCCN CDul CMac CTho EBee ELan EPfP ESps EUJe GMcL IFoB LRHS MRav NEgg NLar SPer SPoG SRms WAvo WFar
- 'Blue Girl' (f)	CTri
- BLUE MAID ('Mesid') (f)	CCCN LCro LOPS LRHS MGos NEgg NLar NRHS
- BLUE PRINCE ('Conablu') (m) 🏆H6	CBcs CCCN CDul CMCN CMac CRos ELan ESps GMcL LBuc LPra LRHS MBlu MJak MMuc NEgg NLar SCob SLim SPer WFar
- BLUE PRINCESS ('Conapri') (f) 🏆H6	CBcs CCVT CMCN CMac CPer CTho ELan EPfP GMcL LBuc LPra MBlu MGos MJak MRav NEgg NLar SCob SCoo SLim SPer WFar
- CASTLE SPIRE ('Hachfee'PBR)	SLim WFar
- CASTLE WALL ('Hecken Star'PBR)	NLar SLim WFar
- 'Heckenpracht'PBR	EBee WFar
- LITTLE RASCAL ('Mondo') (m)	EBee EPfP LRHS
- 'Little Sensation'	LRHS SPoG
myrtifolia	MAsh MRav
'Nellie R. Stevens' (f)	CAco CCVT CJun CTho EBee ECrN ELan EPfP ESps LMaj LPra NLar NPri SCob SEWo WAvo
opaca	CMCN
pedunculosa	NLar
perado	NEgg
- subsp. ***azorica***	CFil WPGP
- - B&SWJ 12526	WCru
- subsp. ***platyphylla***	CMCN MBlu
pernyi	CJun CMCN CMac CTri MAsh
- var. ***veitchii***	see *I. bioritsensis*
rotunda	LEdu
rugosa	CMCN
'September Gem' (f)	CJun CMCN NEgg
serrata	CMac CMen
- 'Koshobai'	CMen
- 'Leucocarpa'	CMac CMen
spinigera	CBcs
suaveolens	CMCN
sugerokii	WCru
var. ***longipedunculata*** B&SWJ 10856	
'Tanager' (f)	CJun
triflora var. ***kanehirae***	CDul NLar
verticillata	CMCN EBee LRHS WFar
- (f)	CBcs EBtc ELon EPfP MMrt NLar
- (m)	EBtc ELon EPfP MMrt NLar
- f. ***chrysocarpa*** (f)	NLar
- 'Maryland Beauty' (f)	CJun NLar
- 'Southern Gentleman' (m)	CJun MBlu NLar
- 'Winter Gold' (f)	CJun MBlu
- 'Winter Red' (f)	CJun CMCN MBlu
vomitoria	CMCN EBtc
'Washington' (f)	IArd
'William Cowgill' (f)	CJun
yunnanensis	EBee IArd IDee

Iliamna see *Sphaeralcea*

Illicium (*Schisandraceae*)

anisatum	CBcs CCCN CExl CFil CMac EBee EPfP LEdu NLar WPGP WSHC
- B&SWJ 8411 **new**	WCru
floridanum	CBcs CCCN SBrt SSta

- 'Halley's Comet'	CExl CFil NLar
aff. ***griffithii*** WWJ 11911	WCru
- WWJ 11971	WCru
- WWJ 11974	WCru
henryi	CExl EBee EPfP LRHS NLar WPGP WSHC
aff. ***henryi***	CBcs
lanceolatum	CExl CFil
- KWJ 12245	WCru
macranthum B&SWJ 11809 **new**	WCru
majus	CFil
- WWJ 11919	WCru
aff. ***majus***	WCru
- WWJ 12017	WCru
merrillianum HWJ 1015 **new**	WCru
mexicanum	CExl CFil
oligandrum	CExl CFil WPGP
parviflorum	CFil
philippinense CWJ 12466 **new**	WCru
simonsii	CExl CFil MBlu WPGP
- BWJ 8024	WCru
'Woodland Ruby'	NLar WPGP

Ilysanthes see *Lindernia*

Impatiens (*Balsaminaceae*)

CC 4980	CExl
P1961	GCal
Accent Series **new**	ETMg
apiculata	EBee
arguta	CExl CSam CSpe EShb EWld GCal SBrt WBor WPGP
- 'Alba'	CExl CSpe MPie SBee
auricoma × ***bicaudata***	MPie WDib
bicaudata	CSpe SPlb
congolensis	CCCN
aff. ***corchorifolia*** B&SWJ 13927 **new**	WCru
ernstii	CExl
flanaganae	CFil WPGP
gomphophylla	CDTJ CFil
(Harmony Series) HARMONY ORANGE STAR ('Danhar305'[PBR]) (NG)	ESps
- HARMONY RADIANCE LILAC (NG)	ESps
hawkeri Divine Series	ETMg
insignis	EBee GCal
keilii	WDib
kerriae B&SWJ 7219	WCru
kilimanjari subsp. ***kilimanjari***	CSpe MPie WCot
kilimanjari × ***pseudoviola***	CSpe MPie WDib
kilimanjari × ***pseudoviola*** pale pink-flowered	MPie
langbianensis HWJ 1054	WCru
'Little Brother Montgomery'	CHll
macrophylla	SBrt
- B&SWJ 10157	WCru
MARGENTA ('Danharmgta') (Harmony Series) (NG)	ESps
namchabarwensis	CCCN CSpe MPie
niamniamensis 🏆H1b	CHll EBak EShb WDib
- 'Congo Cockatoo'	CDTJ NPer SRms
- 'Golden Cockatoo' (v)	CDTJ CHll EBak EShb
noli-tangere	WSFF
omeiana	CCCN CSam CSpe EBee EPPr EWld GCal GEdr GWyn ILea LEdu MNrw MSCN NLar WCru WFar WHil WPGP WPtf
- DJHC 98492	WCru
- 'Ice Storm'	CDTJ EBee GCal GEdr LEdu NLar WCot WCru WFar WPGP
- 'Pink Nerves'	EBee LEdu
- 'Red Leaf'	GCal
- 'Sango'	LEdu
- variegated (v)	GEdr
oxyanthera 'Milo' **new**	SBrt
parasitica	WDib
PASSION (Harmony Series) (NG)	ESps
platypetala B&SWJ 9722	WCru
pritzelii 'Sichuan Gold'	EBee GCal WFar
puberula HWJK 2063	EBee SBrt WCru WPGP
qingchengshanica 'Emei Dawn'	CExl EBee GCal WCru WPGP
repens 🏆H1c	WDib
rothii	CFil GCal WCot
scabrida	CSpe
§ 'Secret Love'	CCCN
sodenii 🏆H1c	CDTJ CSpe EShb GCal WDib
- 'Madonna'	CSpe
- 'Robert the Red'	CSpe
stenantha	SBrt
Sun Harmony Series **new**	ETMg
tinctoria	CAby CDTJ CExl CFil CHll CSpe EBee GCal SBrt
- from Cherangani, Kenya	EBee GCal
tuberosa	WDib
ugandensis	GCal
uniflora	SBrt
VELVETEA	see *I.* 'Secret Love'
walleriana DeZire Series	NPri

Imperata (*Poaceae*)

cylindrica	CMen XLum
- 'Red Baron'	see *I. cylindrica* 'Rubra'
§ - 'Rubra'	Widely available

Incarvillea (*Bignoniaceae*)

arguta	GKev XLum
brevipes	see *I. mairei*
compacta	EBee GKev LLHF
- BWJ 7620	WCru
delavayi	CAby CBcs CBod CRos CSBt CTsd ECha ELan EPfP ESps GKev IBoy LRHS MGos MSCN NRHS SDeJ SPad SPer SRms SVen SWvt WFar XLum
- 'Alba'	see *I. delavayi* 'Snowtop'
- 'Bees' Pink'	CAby CRos EPfP LPla LRHS SBee
- 'Rose'	CRos LRHS NRHS
§ - 'Snowtop'	CAby CBod CRos EBee ELan EPfP GBin IBoy LRHS MHol NRHS SDeJ SPer SWvt WCot WFar
cf. ***delavayi***	GMcL MHol
grandiflora	EBee GKev
himalayensis 'Frank Ludlow'	EBee GKev
lutea	EBee GKev
§ ***mairei***	CRos EWld GKev GWyn LRHS NRHS SRms
- var. ***mairei*** f. ***multifoliata***	see *I. zhongdianensis*
- white-flowered	GKev
olgae	EPfP GKev
sinensis var. ***przewalskii***	GKev

'Snowdrop' MSCN
younghusbandii EBee EPot GKev
§ ***zhongdianensis*** CFis EBee EPot GKev LLHF SBrt
- BWJ 7692 WCru
- BWJ 7978 WCru

Indigofera (*Papilionaceae*)

amblyantha CBcs CCCN CExl CRos EPfP LRHS MAsh MBlu NLar NRHS SEND SPlb WCFE WSHC WSpi
aff. ***amblyantha*** LSou
balfouriana Craib BWJ 7851 WCru
cassioides WCru
'Claret Cascade' ♀H5 WSHC
dielsiana CCCN CRos ELan EPfP LRHS WSpi
'Dosua' MMuc SEND
frutescens CPbh
gerardiana see *I. heterantha*
hancockii CExl CRos EBee EPfP LRHS NRHS SChF WPGP WSHC
hebepetala CHid EPfP SBrt WPGP WSHC
§ ***heterantha*** ♀H5 CBcs CCCN CDul CExl CMCN CRos CSpe CWGN EBee ELan EPfP IDee LRHS MBlu MGil MMuc NLar NRHS NSti SAko SEND SLon SPer SPoG SWvt WCFE WFar WPGP WSHC WSpi
heterophylla CCCN
himachalensis H&M 1818 new WPGP
himalayensis CExl EBee
- Yu 10941 CExl WPGP
- 'Silk Road' CCCN CDul CRos ELan EPfP GKev LCro LRHS MBlu MGos NLar NRHS SPoG WSpi
howellii CExl CHid EBee SChF WCru WPGP
- 'Reginald Cory' ♀H5 EPfP
kirilowii CRos ELan EPfP LRHS MBlu NLar WPGP WSHC WSpi
- var. ***alba*** EPfP LRHS WSHC
§ ***pendula*** CCCN CExl CRos CSpe CWGN EBee ELan EPfP GKev LRHS MGil SPoG WKif WPGP WSHC
- B&SWJ 7741 WCru
- 'Shangri-La' ♀H5 CBot
pendula × potaninii ambig. WSpi
potaninii misapplied see *I. howellii* & 'Reginald Cory', *I. amblyantha*, *I.* 'Claret Cascade', *I. pendula*
potaninii ambig. CBcs CExl CMac WHer
pseudotinctoria CCCN SRms
aff. ***pseudotinctoria*** CCCN
subverticillata LRHS WSHC
szechuensis LRHS SMad WSpi
tinctoria CCCN

Indocalamus (*Poaceae*)

latifolius ERod EUJe MMoz MMuc MWht
solidus see *Bonia solida*
§ ***tessellatus*** ♀H4 CAbb CBdn CBod ELon ENBC ERod MMoz MWht NGdn SMad WMoo
- f. ***hamadae*** CBdn ERod MMoz MWht

Indosasa (*Poaceae*)

gigantea ERod

Inula (*Asteraceae*)

acaulis CMea WCot
barbata GCal
conyzae GJos WHer
dysenterica see *Pulicaria dysenterica*
ensifolia CBcs EBee ELan EPfP EUJe EWTr GAbr LRHS MBel MNHC WHoo XLum
- 'Compacta' GCal
- 'Gold Star' EBee MBNS MRav NBid WAvo WFar
glandulosa see *I. orientalis*
helenium CBod CHab CHby EBWF ENfk GAbr GPoy IBoy LCro LEdu LOPS MHer MNHC NBid NLar SRms WGwG WHer WMoo XAbr
hirta XLum
hookeri CBWd CChe CMea CSam ECha ELan GBin GCal GJos GMaP GNew GWyn IBoy IFro ILea LEdu LLWG MBel MHol MMuc NBid NChi NDov NPer NSti SEND WBrk WOld WTre WWtn
- GWJ 9033 WCru
macrocephala misapplied see *I. royleana*
magnifica Widely available
- 'Sonnenstrahl' ♀H7 EPPr LEdu NLar SPhx
oculus-christi EBee EWes WCot WMoo
§ ***orientalis*** CRos EBee EPfP GAbr GJos LRHS LSun NGBl NLar NRHS SPad SPer SRms XLum
racemosa CRos EBee EPPr EWes GBin GCal LRHS MNrw NRHS SPlb SRms WBor
- 'Sonnenspeer' NBid NLar WPtf
§ ***royleana*** GCal IRob MNrw MRav

Inulanthera (*Asteraceae*)

calva WCot

Iochroma (*Solanaceae*)

§ ***australe*** ♀H3 CBlu CCCN CExl CHll CSpe EBee ELan LSRN MGil SEND SPlb SPoG SPtp SVen WPGP
§ - 'Andean Snow' CCCN CHll EShb MGil WHil WPGP
§ - 'Bill Evans' EShb
cyaneum CCCN CHll ECre SPlb SVen
- purple-flowered CCCN CHll
gesnerioides 'Coccineum' CCCN CHll
§ ***grandiflorum*** CCCN CHll SEND
warscewiczii see *I. grandiflorum*

Ipheion (*Alliaceae*)

'Alberto Castillo' ♀H4 Widely available
'Alice' new WCot
'Diana' new WCot
'Jessie' CAby CBro CMea CPrp CRos EBee ECha EPot EWes GKev LAma LLHF LRHS NHpl NPnk NRHS SCob SDeJ WBor WBrk WHoo WRHF WTor
'Judy' WCot
'Rolf Fiedler' ♀H3 CAvo CBro CPrp CRos CTri EBee ELan EPPr EPfP EPot ERCP EWes GKev LAma LRHS NPnk NRHS NRya SCob SDeJ SDir SRms WAul WFar WHil
sellowianum CAby WCot
'Tessa'PBR EBee EWes LLHF NHpl
§ ***uniflorum*** CBro CFis CTri ECha GKev ITim LAma MMoz MNrw SEND SRms WBrk WCot XLum
- f. ***album*** CBro CPrp EBee ECha EPPr EWes LEdu LRHS NRHS SCob WCot WHil

- 'Charlotte Bishop'	CAvo CBro CPne CPrp CRos EBee ECha ELon EPPr EPot ERCP EWes GKev LAma LLHF LRHS MNrw NHpl NPnk NRHS NRya SCob SDeJ SDir SRms WArt WAul WCot WHil WHoo
- 'Froyle Mill' ♀H5	CAvo CBro CPrp CRos ELon EPPr EPot ERCP EWes GKev LRHS MNrw NHpl NPnk NRHS SBch SCob SDeJ SDir SRms WCot WHoo WWFP
- subsp. ***tandiliense***	EBee EPPr
- f. ***violaceum***	SCob
- 'Wisley Blue' ♀H5	CBro CExl CPrp CRos CTri EAJP ECha ELan ELon EPPr EPfP EPot ERCP GKev LAma LRHS MRav NPnk NRHS NRya SCob SDeJ SDir SRms WCot WHoo
- 'Wisley Star' **new**	GKev

Ipomoea (*Convolvulaceae*)

acuminata	see *I. indica*
alba	CCCN EShb
batatas	CCCN
- (Bright Ideas Series) BRIGHT IDEAS BLACK	EShb
- - BRIGHT IDEAS LIME ('Fripalligr')	EShb
- (Sweet Caroline Series) 'Sweet Caroline Light Green'PBR	EUJe
- - 'Sweet Caroline Purple'PBR	EUJe
- - 'Sweet Caroline Sweetheart Light Green'PBR	CRav
cairica	WCot
carnea	CCCN
coccinea var. ***hederifolia***	see *I. hederifolia*
§ ***hederifolia***	CCCN
× ***imperialis*** 'Sunrise Serenade'	CCCN
§ ***indica*** ♀H1c	CCCN CHll CRHN ECre EShb SPer
learii	see *I. indica*
§ ***lobata*** ♀H1c	CRav CSpe LSou
mauritiana	CCCN
'Milky Way'	CCCN
muellerii	CCCN
× ***multifida***	CSpe
purpurea 'Grandpa Otts'	LCro
- 'Kniola's Black Night'	CSpe
quamoclit	CSpe EBee
tricolor 'Heavenly Blue' ♀H1c **new**	LCro LOPS
versicolor	see *I. lobata*

Iresine (*Amaranthaceae*)

BLAZIN' LIME	see *I.* 'Lime'
BLAZIN' ROSE	see *I.* 'Rose'
§ 'Lime'	EUJe
§ 'Rose'	EUJe

Iris ✿ (*Iridaceae*)

sp.	ETod
AGSJ **new**	EPPr
KR 3739 **new**	GEdr
'Abbey Chant' (IB)	WCAu XSen
'Abbondanza' (TB)	WCAu
'Abbracciami' (SDB)	SIri
'Ablaze' (MDB)	CTal
'About Town' (TB)	WCAu
'Action Front' (TB)	CBWd CBod CKel CRos CWld EIri EPfP ESgI EShb LRHS MGos NRHS SDeJ WCAu WGwG
'Actress' (TB)	CKel CRos EPfP LRHS LSRN LSou MGos NRHS WGwG
acutiloba subsp. ***lineolata***	CTal
'Adobe Rose' (TB)	SIri XSen
'Adventuress' (TB)	XSen
'Afternoon in Rio' (TB)	WCAu
'Agatha Christie' (IB)	WCAu
'Aggressively Forward' (TB)	WCAu
'Aglow Again' (MTB)	SDys
'Agnes James' (CH)	CBro MAvo
'Ahwahnee Princess' (SDB)	ELon
'Aichi-no-kagayaki' (SpH)	WCot XLum
'Alabaster Unicorn' (TB)	ESgI
albicans ♀H5	CBro CMea CTal EPot GKev LEdu
- 'Blue Pygmy'	CKel CTal
'Alcazar' (TB)	GMcL LSRN
'Aldo Ratti' (TB)	ESgI
'Alene's New Love' (SDB)	CTal
'Alene's Other Love' (SDB)	WCAu
'Alexia' (TB)	CKel
'Alice Harding' (TB)	ESgI
'Alida' (Reticulata)	EBee EPot ERCP GKev LAma LCro LLHF LOPS LRHS NRHS SAdu SDeJ WBrk WRHF XEll
'Alien Mist' (TB)	CIri
'Alizes' (TB) ♀H7	CKel CPar ESgI LRHS WViv XSen
'Allegiance' (TB)	WCAu
'Ally Oops' (SpH) **new**	WCAu
'Alpenview' (TB) **new**	LMea
'Amadora' (TB)	CKel EIri
'Amber Queen' (DB)	CKel CTal ECtt ELan LRHS LSou NRHS SDeJ SPer
'Ambroisie' (TB) ♀H7	ESgI
'American Patriot' (IB)	CKel WCAu
'Amethyst Flame' (TB)	SRms WCAu
'Amherst Blue' (IB)	EIri
'Amherst Bluebeard' (SDB)	ESgI
'Amherst Caper' (SDB)	EIri ESgI
'Amherst Glacier' (IB)	WCAu
'Amphora' (SDB)	CBro
'Ancient Echoes' (TB)	ESgI
'Andalou' (TB) ♀H7	CWCL WViv XSen
'Angel Unawares' (TB)	WCAu
'Angel Wings' (TB)	CIri
'Angel's Touch' (TB)	ESgI
anglica	see *I. latifolia*
'Ann Chowning' (La) **new**	LCro LOPS
'Ann Dasch' (Sib)	WAul
'Annabel Jane' (TB)	CKel ELon WCAu
'Anne Elizabeth' (SDB)	CBro
'Annemarie Troeger' (Sib) ♀H7	ELon
'Annick' (Sib)	CRos EBee LRHS MMrt NRHS XSen
'Annikins' (IB)	CKel
'Antarctique' (IB)	ESgI
'Aphrodisiac' (TB)	XSen
aphylla	GBin SBrt WAbe WThu
- 'Slick'	SDys
'Apollo' (Dut)	CAvo
'Appointer' (SpH)	NChi WWtn
'Apricorange' (TB)	CKel SRms WCot
'Apricot Blaze' (TB)	ESgI
'Apricot Drops' (MTB) ♀H7	ESgI WCAu
'Apricot Frosty' (BB)	WCAu XSen
'Apricot Silk' (IB)	CCCN CKel IBoy NQui WCot
'Apricot Topping' (BB)	WCAu
'Aquamarine'	MHol

	'Arab Chief' (TB)	CKel
*	'Arabic Night' (IB)	WCAu
	'Archie Owen' (Spuria)	WCAu
	'Arctic Age' (TB)	WCAu
	'Arctic Fancy' (IB)	CKel
	'Arctic Fox' (TB)	WCAu
	'Arctic Sunrise' (TB)	ESgI
	'Arctic Wind' (IB)	WCAu
	arenaria	see *I. humilis*
	'Argus Pheasant' (TB)	ESgI
	'Arms Wide Open' (TB)	CIri
	'Around Midnight' (TB)	CRos LRHS NRHS
	'Arpège' (TB)	GWyn XSen
	'Art Deco' (TB)	SIri XSen
	'Art School Angel' (TB)	CIri
	'As de Coeur' (TB)	XSen
	'As You Were' (TB)	CIri
	'Ascension Crown' (TB)	ESgI
	'Ask Alma' (IB)	XSen
	'Astrid Cayeux' (TB)	ESgI
	'Astro Flash' (TB)	ESgI
	'Athaenos' (IB)	CIri
	'Atlantic Crossing' (Sib)	SIri WAul
	'Attention Please' (TB)	CKel
	attica	CBro CPBP GEdr GKev LLHF WThu
	- blue-flowered	GKev
	- lemon-flowered	EPot GKev SBrt WThu
	'Attitude' (IB)	WCAu
§	***aucheri*** ♀H4	EPot GKev LLHF
	- indigo-flowered	GKev
	- 'Snow White'	GKev
	aucheri × bucharica	EWTr
	'Aunt Josephine' (TB)	ESgI
	'Aunty Ruth' (CH) new	MAvo
	'Aurélie' (TB)	WViv
	'Austrian Sky' (SDB)	CAby CKel CMac ECtt ELon EPfP LRHS NRHS SDeJ WAul WCot
	'Autumn Circus' (TB)	WCAu
	'Autumn Echo' (TB)	ESgI XSen
	'Autumn Encore' (TB)	CKel GMcL SRms
	'Autumn Leaves' (TB)	WCAu
	'Autumn Princess' (Dut)	CAvo GKev SDeJ
	'Autumn Riesling' (TB)	WCAu
	'Autumn Tryst' (TB)	ESgI WCAu
	'Autumn Wine' (BB)	CIri
	'Avalon Sunset' (TB)	EIri
	'Awesome Blossom' (TB)	ESgI
	'Az Ap' (IB)	ELon WCAu
	babadagica	WAbe
	'Babbling Brook' (TB)	CKel GWyn XSen
	'Baby Bengal' (BB)	XSen
	'Baby Blessed' (SDB)	CBro WCAu
	'Baby Prince' (SDB)	ESgI
	'Baby Sister' (Sib)	CRos EBee ELon GBin GMcL LRHS LSRN NBro NRHS WFar
	'Bach Toccata' (MTB)	SDys
	'Back in Black' (TB)	CKel
	'Badlands' (TB)	WCAu
	'Baie Rose' (IB)	SIri
	'Bal Masqué' (TB)	EBee ESgI WViv XSen
	'Ballerina Pink' (BB)	WCAu
	'Ballistic' (SDB)	WCAu
	'Ballyhoo' (TB)	WCAu XSen
	'Baltic Star' (TB)	WCAu
	'Banbury Beauty' (CH) ♀H4	MAvo NLar
	'Banbury Gem' (CH)	NLar
	'Banbury Melody' (CH)	MAvo
	'Banbury Ruffles' (SDB)	ESgI LRHS NLar WCAu
	'Bandera Waltz' (TB)	WCAu
	'Bang' (TB)	CKel

'Bangles' (MTB) ♀H7	SDys WCAu
'Banish Misfortune' (Sib)	EPri WAul
'Banker Dave' (TB)	CIri
'Bar de Nuit' (TB)	ESgI
'Barbara May' (TB)	WCAu
'Barbara My Love' (TB)	WCAu
barbatula BWJ 7663	WCru
'Baria' (SDB)	CTal
'Batik' (BB)	SIri WCot XSen
'Battle Star' (TB)	CIri
'Battlestar Atlantis' (TB)	CIri
'Bayberry Candle' (TB)	WCAu
'Be Mine' (TB)	CIri
'Be My Baby' (BB)	WCAu
'Bedtime Story' (IB)	XSen
'Bee Wings' (MDB)	CTal
'Bee's Knees' (SDB) ♀H7	SIri
'Before the Storm' (TB)	CKel ELon ESgI LRHS SBee WCAu XSen
'Being Busy' (SDB)	ESgI
'Bel Azur' (IB)	ESgI LRHS
'Belgian Princess' (TB)	WCAu
'Belle de Nuit' (TB)	WViv
'Ben a Factor' (MTB)	ESgI
'Benbow' (TB)	WMil
'Benton Ankarat' (TB) new	NRHS
'Benton Apollo' (TB)	ECha EMal LRHS NRHS
'Benton Argent' new	NRHS
'Benton Arundel' (TB)	EMal LRHS NRHS
'Benton Bluejohn' (TB)	EMal LRHS NRHS
'Benton Caramel' (TB)	ECha EMal LRHS NRHS
'Benton Cordelia' (TB)	EMal LRHS NRHS
'Benton Daphne' (TB)	EMal LRHS NRHS
'Benton Dierdre' (TB)	CKel ECha ECtt ELon EMal LRHS NRHS SRms
'Benton Duff' (TB) new	NRHS
'Benton Evora' (TB)	EMal LRHS NRHS
'Benton Farewell' (TB)	LRHS NRHS
'Benton Judith' (TB) new	NRHS
'Benton Lorna' (TB)	ECha EMal LRHS NRHS
'Benton Menace' (TB)	EMal LRHS NRHS
'Benton Nigel' (TB)	ECha ECtt EMal IPot LRHS NRHS WAul WCAu WGwG
'Benton Nutkin' (TB)	EMal LRHS NRHS
'Benton Olive' (TB)	EMal LRHS NRHS
'Benton Opal' (TB)	EMal LRHS NRHS
'Benton Pearl' (TB)	ECha EMal LRHS NRHS
'Benton Primrose' (TB)	EMal LRHS NRHS
'Benton Sheila' (TB)	ECha ELon
'Benton Susan' (TB)	ECha ECtt EMal IPot LRHS NRHS WGwG
'Beotie' (TB)	SBee
'Berkeley Gold' (TB)	CKel CRos CSBt ECtt ELan EWes LRHS NRHS SCob SDeJ SPer WGwG
'Berlin Bluebird' (Sib)	SMHy
'Berlin Purple Wine' (Sib)	EPri
'Berlin Ruffles' (Sib) ♀H7	CKel EWes WAul
'Berlin Sky' (Sib)	ESgI EWes
'Berlin Tiger' (SpH) ♀H7	CKel EBee EPPr EWTr LCro LLWG LOPS MWts NLar SCob SMHy WCAu WMoo
'Bermuda Triangle' (BB)	SDys
'Best Bet' (TB)	ESgI WCAu
'Bethany Claire' (TB)	ESgI WCAu
'Betty Cooper' (Spuria)	WCAu
'Betty Simon' (TB)	CWCL XSen
'Beverly Sills' (TB)	CAby CKel CRos CWld EIri EPfP LCro LRHS LSou MHer MRav NRHS SCob SDeJ SRGP WCAu WGwG XSen

'Bewilderbeast' (TB)	XSen
'Bianco' (TB)	GWyn WCAu WHil
'Bibury' (SDB) ♀H7	WCAu
bicapitata new	CBot CPBP
'Bickley Cape' (Sib)	GBin
'Big Blue' (Sib)	WFar
'Big Heart' (Sib)	EIri
'Big Squeeze' (TB)	WCAu
biglumis	see *I. lactea*
biliottii	CBro
'Bishop's Robe' (TB)	ESgI LRHS
'Black as Night' (TB)	XSen
'Black Aura'	NWad
'Black Bull' (BB)	CIri
'Black Cherry Delight' (SDB)	ESgI
'Black Dragon' (TB)	CCCN CKel CRos GMcL GWyn LRHS NRHS XSen
'Black Flag' (TB)	XSen
'Black Gamecock' (La)	CBod CRos CWCL EBee ECtt LCro LLWG LOPS MNrw MSCN MWts NLar WFar WHar WMAq WWtn
'Black Hope' (TB)	CIri
'Black is Back'	WCAu
'Black Knight' (TB)	LRHS MJak MRav NLar NQui WKif WSpi
'Black Night' (IB)	NEgg SRGP
'Black Prince' (IB)	SCob
'Black Stallion' (MDB)	ESgI
'Black Swan' (TB)	CAby CBWd CKel CMac ECha ECtt ELan EPfP ESgI EShb EUJe EWTr GCal LCro LOPS LRHS LSRN MAvo MNrw NQui NRHS SCob SPer SPoG SRms WCot XSen
'Black Tie Affair' (TB)	CBod CKel CWld ELan EPfP ESgI IPot LRHS MAsh MAvo NRHS WCAu XSen
'Black Watch' (IB)	CKel GWyn
'Blackbeard' (BB) ♀H7	WCAu
'Blackbeard's Ghost' (AB)	WCAu
'Blackberry Tease' (TB)	WCAu
'Blackberry Towers' (TB)	ESgI
'Blackcurrant' (IB)	WCAu
'Blackout' (TB)	ESgI
'Blast' (IB)	CKel
'Blatant' (TB)	ESgI WCAu XSen
'Blaue Milchstrasse' (Sib)	GBin GWyn MMrt
'Blaues Schweben' (Sib)	GBin
'Blazing Light' (TB)	XSen
'Blazing Sunrise' (TB)	LMea
'Blenheim Royal' (TB)	ESgI WCAu XSen
'Blitzen' (IB)	WCAu
bloudowii	WAbe
'Blowing Bubbles' (TB)	CIri
'Blue Admiral' (TB)	GBin
'Blue Bird' (Sib)	ECtt LLWG SPoG WFar
'Blue Burgee' (Sib)	ECha
I 'Blue Butterfly' (Sib)	EBee EPfP NGdn
'Blue Denim' (SDB)	CRos ECtt ELon EPfP GMaP MHol MRav NLar WCAu WCot
'Blue Eyed Brunette' (TB)	WCAu
'Blue Giant' ambig. (Dut)	LLWG
'Blue Hendred' (SDB)	WCAu
'Blue Hill' (Reticulata)	LAma
'Blue Hour' (TB)	WCAu
'Blue King' (Sib)	CDor CHid ELan EPfP GMaP ILea LRHS MRav NBro NGdn SCob SPer WMoo
'Blue Meadow Fly' (Sino-Sib)	LLHF
'Blue Mere' (Sib)	MCot
'Blue Moon' (Sib)	ELon IMou MJak WFar
'Blue Mystery' (J)	LLHF
'Blue Note Blues' (TB)	CRos NRHS WCAu
'Blue Note' (Reticulata)	EPfP EPot ERCP GKev LAma LLHF LRHS MWat SAdu
'Blue Pigmy' (SDB)	CTal CWat ECtt EPfP LRHS LSou MRav MTin NLar NRHS SDeJ SPer
'Blue Reverie' (Sib)	ELon ESgI
'Blue Rhythm' (TB)	CKel CRos ELan ELon EPfP EUJe GBin GMaP GMcL GPSL LCro LOPS LRHS MAvo MRav NRHS SCoo SDeJ SPer SPhm WCAu
'Blue Sapphire' (TB)	CKel ESgI WCAu
'Blue Sapphire' (Dut)	MHol
'Blue Sceptre' (Sib)	IBlr
'Blue Shimmer' (TB)	CMac CRos CSBt EBee ECha ELan EPfP ESgI EShb LRHS LSRN LSou MWat NRHS SDeJ SPer SPhm WCAu WGwG
'Blue Splash' (IB)	WCAu
'Blue Staccato' (TB)	WCAu XSen
'Blue Suede Shoes' (TB)	ESgI LSRN XSen
'Blue Trill' (TB)	WCAu
'Bluebeard's Ghost' (SDB) ♀H7	WCAu
'Bluebird Wine' (TB)	CKel MNHC WCAu
'Blue-eyed Susan' (TB)	CIri
'Blushing Pink' (TB)	CKel
'Bob's Fancy'	SDeJ
'Bockingford' (MTB)	SIri
'Bohemian' (TB)	CWCL
'Bold Encounter' (TB)	WCAu
'Bold Pretender' (La)	ECtt ELon EPfP LLWG MBNS NLar WHil
'Bold Print' (IB)	CBod CKel CRos EBee ELon IPot LRHS LSRN MAvo MGos MHer MWat NRHS SPoG WCAu
'Bollinger'	see *I.* 'Hornpipe'
'Bonnie Davenport' (TB)	CIri
'Boo' (SDB)	CPBP CTal WCAu XSen
'Border Guard' (BB)	WCAu
'Border Happy' (TB)	WCAu
'Border Town' (Spuria)	WCAu
'Bottled Sunshine' (IB)	LRHS
'Bound for Glory' (La)	LLWG
'Bournemouth Ball Gown' (Sib)	WAul
'Bournemouth Beauty' (Sib) ♀H7	WAul
'Bouzy Bouzy' (TB)	ESgI XSen
'Bracknell' (Sib)	WAul
bracteata	EBee
'Braggin' Rights' (TB)	CIri
'Braithwaite' (TB)	CAby CKel CRos CWGN ELan EPfP ESgI EShb LRHS NRHS SDeJ SPer SRms WCAu WGwG
'Brandaris' (TB)	ESgI
'Brannigan' (SDB)	NRHS NSti
'Brassie' (SDB)	CBro MBNS XSen
'Brave New World' (TB) ♀H7	CIri
'Breakers' (TB) ♀H7	CKel WCAu
'Breezy Blue' (SDB)	WCAu
'Brenchley' (IB)	SIri
'Bridal Icing' (TB)	WCAu
'Bride's Halo' (TB)	LSRN WCAu XSen
'Bright Button' (SDB)	CKel ESgI
'Bright Spring' (DB)	CTal
'Bright Vision' (SDB)	ESgI
'Bright White' (MDB)	CBro CKel
'Bright Yellow' (DB)	MRav
'Brighteyes' (IB)	SRms

'Brindisi' (TB)	XSen
'Brise de Mer' (TB)	XSen
'Bristo Magic' (TB)	XSen
'Bristol Gem' (TB)	XSen
'Broad Shoulders' (TB)	WCAu
'Broadleigh Angela' (CH)	CBro
'Broadleigh Carolyn' (CH) $\mathbb{Y}^{H5}$	CBro CElw WSHC
'Broadleigh Lavinia' (CH)	CBro
'Broadleigh Mitre' (CH)	CBro
'Broadleigh Nancy' (CH)	CBro
'Broadleigh Peacock' (CH)	CElw MAvo NLar WSHC
'Broadleigh Penny' (CH)	CBro NLar
'Broadleigh Rose' (CH)	CBro CElw EPri MBrN WSHC
'Broadway Baby' (IB)	ESgI
'Broadway Star' (TB)	CKel CRos LRHS NRHS
'Bronzaire' (IB)	CKel EIri WCAu WGwG
'Bronze Beauty' (Dut)	ERCP
'Bronze Beauty' (TB)	SDeJ
'Bronze Beauty' van Tubergen (*boogiana* hybrid)	SDeJ
'Brother Carl' (TB)	XSen
'Brown Chocolate' (TB)	WCAu
'Bruce' (TB)	WCAu
'Brummit's Mauve' (TB)	WCAu
'Bruno' (TB)	LSRN NLar WMil
'Brussels' (TB)	ESgI
bucharica misapplied	see *I. orchioides* Carrière
bucharica ambig.	CAvo ELon GKev LSun MNrw NHpl SDeJ
§ ***bucharica*** Foster $\mathbb{Y}^{H5}$	CBro EPfP EPot LAma
* - 'Top Gold'	GKev
'Buckwheat' (TB)	CKel SIri
'Buisson de Roses' (TB)	XSen
bulleyana	CBro GKev SRms WArt
- BWJ 7912	WCru
- from Dali, Yunnan, China	SBrt
- black-flowered	CExl GKev
- - SDR 1792	EBee
'Bumblebee Deelite' (MTB) $\mathbb{Y}^{H7}$	CKel CTal WCAu
'Bundle of Joy' (Sib) <u>**new**</u>	ECtt
'Bundle of Love' (BB)	WCAu
'Burgermeister' (TB)	XSen
'Burgundy Party' (TB)	XSen
'Burka' (TB)	ESgI LMea
'Burmese Dawn' (TB)	CKel
'Burnt Toffee' (TB)	ESgI SIri XSen
'Burst' (TB)	CKel WCAu
'Butter and Sugar' (Sib) $\mathbb{Y}^{H7}$	Widely available
'Buttermere' (TB)	SRms
'Butterpat' (IB)	ESgI
'Butterscotch Carpet' (SDB)	WCAu
'Butterscotch Kiss' (TB)	CKel CMac CRos CWld ELan ELon EPfP GMaP IRob LRHS MGos MRav NLar NRHS SDeJ SPer SPhm WHoo
'Buzzword' (SDB)	WCAu
'Bye Bye Blues' (TB)	ESgI XSen
'Cabaret Royale' (TB)	ESgI XSen
'Cable Car' (TB)	CKel CWCL ESgI
'Cache of Gold' (SDB)	CTal
'Caesar' (Sib)	IBoy SDys SRms
'Caesar's Brother' (Sib)	CHid CKel CRos ELan EPfP GWyn LCro LOPS LRHS MGos NLar NRHS SPer WFar WHar WHoo WWtn
'Cajun Rhythm' (TB)	CKel XSen
'Calgary' (TB)	WCAu
'Caliente' (TB)	MRav WCAu XSen
'California Style' (IB)	XSen
§ Californian hybrids	CElw CMac CPBP WCot
'Calm Stream' (TB)	WCAu
'Calypso Mood' (TB)	XSen
'Cambridge' (Sib) $\mathbb{Y}^{H7}$	CAvo CKel CRos CWld EHoe EIri EPfP IMou IRob LRHS NGdn NRHS WAul WFar WHoo
'Camelot Rose' (TB)	WCAu XSen
'Cameo Blush' (BB)	XSen
'Cameo Queen' (SDB) $\mathbb{Y}^{H7}$	CIri
'Cameo Wine' (TB)	ESgI MNrw XSen
'Cameroun' (TB)	ESgI
canadensis	see *I. hookeri*
'Canadian Kisses' (SDB)	ESgI
'Canadian Streaker' (TB/v)	WCot
'Canary Bird' (TB)	ESgI
'Candy Rock' (IB)	CIri WCAu
'Cannington Ochre' (SDB)	CBro
'Canonbury Belle' (Sib)	WAul
'Can't Touch This' (TB)	WCAu
'Cantab' (Reticulata)	CRos EPot ERCP GKev LAma LRHS NRHS SAdu SCob SDeJ
'Capricious Candles' (TB)	CIri
'Captain Indigo' (IB)	ESgI WCAu
'Captive Sun' (SDB)	CKel CTal EPfP LRHS MAsh NRHS SIri WTor
'Caramel' (TB)	XSen
'Cardinal' (TB)	WMil
'Care to Dance' (TB)	WCAu
'Careless Sally' (Sib)	WAul WCAu
'Carfax' (TB)	WMil
'Caribbean Dream' (TB)	CKel XSen
'Carnaby' (TB)	CKel CRos CWld ELon EPfP ESgI EShb LRHS MRav MSCN NRHS SDeJ WCAu WGwG XSen
'Carnival Time' (TB)	CBod CKel CMac CRos CWGN ECtt EPfP LRHS MCot NRHS SHar SPer XSen
'Carolina' (Reticulata)	CRos GKev LAma LLHF LRHS NRHS
'Carolina Gold' (TB)	XSen
* 'Caronte' (IB)	ESgI
'Carriage Trade' (TB)	LRHS
'Carriwitched' (IB)	CKel
'Casbah' (TB)	XSen
'Cascade Rhythm' (TB)	WCAu
'Cascade Springs' (TB)	XSen
'Cascade Sprite' (SDB)	SRms
'Casino Cruiser' (TB)	CIri
'Casual Joy' (TB)	CIri
'Catalyst' (TB)	XSen
'Cat's Eye' (SDB)	CTal ESgI SIri WCAu
'Catwalk Idol' (La)	LLWG
caucasica	CMac
'Cause for Pause' (TB)	CIri
'Cayenne Capers' (TB)	ESgI
* 'Cedric Morris'	EWes
'Cee Tee'	XSen
'Celebration Song' (TB)	ESgI SIri WCAu XSen
'Celestial Glory' (TB)	XSen
'Cerdagne' (TB)	XSen
'Chalkhill' (SDB)	WCAu
chamaeiris	see *I. lutescens* subsp. *lutescens*
'Champagne Elegance' (TB)	CKel EIri EPfP XSen
'Champagne Encore' (IB)	ELon
'Champagne Frost' (TB)	XSen
'Champagne Waltz' (TB)	SIri XSen
'Chance Beauty' (SpH) $\mathbb{Y}^{H7}$	WCAu
'Chandler's Choice' (Sib)	EWes
'Change of Pace' (TB)	ESgI WCAu XSen

	'Chanted' (SDB)	WCAu XSen
	'Chantilly' (TB)	CBod CHid CKel CRos EBee ELan EUJe LRHS MRav MSCN NGdn NLar NRHS SPer
	'Chapeau' (TB)	ESgI WCAu
	'Charlotte's Tutu' (La)	LLWG
	'Charmaine' (TB)	XSen
	'Chartreuse Bounty' (Sib)	ECtt ELan EPri EWTr EWes GAbr GMaP MHol NLar NSti WFar
	'Chasing Rainbows' (TB)	SDys WCAu
	'Cheap Frills' (TB)	WCAu
	'Cher' (TB)	LSRN
	'Cherished One' (La)	LLWG
	'Cherry Blossom Song' (TB)	SIri
	'Cherry Blossom Special' (TB)	CIri
	'Cherry Garden' (SDB)	CAby CBro CKel CPBP CRos CTal CWat ECtt EHrv ELan ELon EPfP EShb EWes GMaP LEdu LRHS LSou MBNS MRav MTin NGdn NLar NRHS SDeJ WAul WCot WWFP
	'Cherry Twist' (La)	LLWG
	'Cherub's Smile' (TB)	XSen
	'Chicken Little' (MDB)	CBro
	'Chief Moses' (TB)	WCAu
I	'Chieftain' (SDB)	MRav
	'Childhood Sweetheart' (La)	LLWG
	'Chilled Wine' (Sib)	ELan ELon IRob
	'China Dragon' (TB)	XSen
	'Chinese Coral' (TB)	XSen
	'Chinese Treasure' (TB)	XSen
	'Chinook Winds' (TB)	ESgI WCAu
	'Chivalry' (TB)	ESgI
	'Christine Mullins' (Sib)	WBor
	'Christmas Angel' (TB)	WCAu
	Chrysofor Group	CAby
	chrysographes ♀H7	CBWd CBod CBro CDor CHid CKel CMac CRos CTsd CWCL EHoe EPfP EPri GJos GKev IBoy LRHS MBel MHer MRav NRHS NSti SCob SPoG
	- BWJ 7930	WCru
I	- 'Black Beauty'	EPfP
	- 'Black Gold'	EPri MHol NLar
I	- 'Black Knight'	CBot CCse CExl EPfP GBin GCal MCot NChi NLar SMad WPnP
I	- 'Black Velvet'	GEdr NPnk WSpi
	- black-flowered	Widely available
	- dark-flowered	GKev GMcL IBoy MSCN WFar
	- 'Goldvein'	CMac
	- hybrid	WFar
	- 'Inshriach'	IMou LEdu WAbe
	- 'Kew Black'	CExl GKev LEdu WHil
	- 'Mandarin Purple'	GCal GQue SPer
	- yellow-flowered	WFar
	'Château d'Auvers-sur-Oise' (TB)	SIri WViv
	'Chubby Cheeks' (SDB)	CKel WCAu
	'Church Stoke' (SDB)	WCAu
	'Ciel et Mer' (TB)	WViv
	'Cimarron Rose' (SDB)	ESgI
	'Cimarron Strip' (TB)	CKel EPfP WCot XSen
	'Cinque Terre' (TB)	WCAu
	'Circle of Light' (TB)	WCAu
	'Circle Round' (Sib)	CSpe
	'Circus Stripes' (TB)	XSen
	'Cirrus Veil' (SDB)	WCAu
	'Citoyen' (TB)	XSen
	'Citronnade' (TB)	ESgI
	'City' (SDB)	SIri
	'City of Paradise' (TB)	ESgI
	'Clairette' (Reticulata)	CRos EPot GKev LAma LRHS MWat NRHS SAdu SCob SDeJ
	'Clara Garland' (IB)	WCAu
	'Clarence' (TB)	ESgI WCAu XSen
	clarkei B&SWJ 2122	WCru
	- CC 2751	CExl
	- SDR 3819	GKev
	'Class Ring' (TB)	WCAu
	'Classic Look' (TB)	ESgI SIri
	'Classic Navy' (BB)	ESgI
	'Clee Hills' (Sib)	WAul
	'Cleedownton' (Sib)	WAul
	'Clematis' (TB)	CIri WMil
	'Cleo' (TB)	NSti
	'Cleo Murrell' (TB)	ESgI
	'Cleve Dodge' (Sib)	EPri ESgI SIri XLum
	'Cliffs of Dover' (TB)	CKel EIri ESgI GCal MCot SCob SRms
	'Cloudcap' (TB)	SRms
	'Clownerie' (TB)	WViv
	'Clyde Redmond' (La) ♀H5	WMAq
	'Coal Face' (TB)	WCAu
	'Coal Seams' (TB)	WCAu
	'Coalignition' (TB)	WCAu
	'Codicil' (TB)	EIri XSen
	colchica	LEdu
	'Colette Thurillet' (TB)	CKel WViv XSen
	'Colin's Pale Blue' (Sib)	SMHy
	'Collingwood Ingram'	WThu
	'Color Carnival' (TB)	ESgI
	'Color Glory' (TB)	SIri
	'Color Me Blue' (TB)	WCAu
	'Color Splash' (TB)	XSen
	'Color Strokes' (TB)	WCAu
	'Colortart' (TB)	XSen
	'Come to Me' (TB)	CIri
	'Coming Up Roses' (TB)	XSen
	'Con Fuoco' (TB)	XSen
	'Concertina' (IB)	CIri WCAu
	'Concord Crush' (Sib)	IPot MHol WHar WHil WTor WWtn
	confusa ♀H4	SArc SBig SMad XSen
§	- 'Martyn Rix'	CAbb CAby CBct CHid CMac CPou CRos ELon EPfP GCal IDee LRHS MMoz MPie SBrt SEND SRms WGwG
	confusa × japonica	WWFP
	'Conjuration' (TB)	CKel LMea SIri
	'Connection' (TB)	WCAu
	'Constant Wattez' (IB)	CKel ESgI NLar
	'Constantine Bay' (TB)	ESgI
	'Consummation' (MTB)	CRos
	'Contrast in Styles' (Sib)	CBod ECtt EPri LSou MNrw MSCN NQui WFar WGob WWtn
	'Cool Satin' (SDB)	CIri
	'Copatonic' (TB)	ESgI WCAu
	'Copper Capers' (TB)	ESgI
	'Copper Classic' (TB)	ELon ESgI LSRN WCAu
	'Coquet Waters' (Sib)	NBid WAul
	'Coral Point' (TB)	WCAu
	'Coral Splendor' (TB)	WCAu
	'Coral Sunset' (TB)	XSen
	'Cordoba' (TB)	WCAu XSen
	'Coronation Anthem' (Sib)	EPri WAul
	'Côte d'Or' (TB)	XSen
	'Counting Sheep' (SDB)	SIri
	'Country Kisses' (TB)	WCAu
	'County Town Red' (TB)	SIri
	'Cozy Calico' (TB)	WCAu
	'Cracklin' Burgundy' (TB)	XSen
	'Crackling Caldera' (TB)	MMrt

'Craithie' (TB)	EMal
'Cranapple' (BB) ♀H7	ESgI SBee WCAu
'Cranberry Ice' (TB)	ELon XSen
'Cranberry Sauce' (TB)	SIri WCAu
'Cranbrook' (IB) ♀H7	SIri
'Cream Beauty' (Dut)	GKev LCro LOPS SDeJ
'Cream Pixie' (SDB)	WCAu
'Creative Artistry' (La)	LLWG
'Crème Chantilly' (Sib)	NEoE
cretensis	see *I. unguicularis* subsp. *cretensis*
'Crinoline' (TB)	CKel XSen
'Crispette' (TB)	WCAu
cristata	EPot GEdr GKev NHpl SMad
- 'Abbey's Violet'	EBee
- 'Alba'	CPBP EBee GEdr WAbe WThu
crocea ♀H7	EBee GBin GKev
'Croftway Lemon' (TB)	ELon
'Cross Current' (TB)	WCAu
'Crowned Heads' (TB)	WCAu XSen
'Crow's Feet' (BB)	WCAu
'Crushed Ice' (La)	LLWG
'Crystal Fountain' (TB)	CIri
'Crystal Gazer' (TB)	ESgI
'Crystal Glitters' (TB)	ESgI
'Cumulus' (TB)	SIri
cuniculiformis	WCot
'Cup Race' (TB)	WCAu XSen
'Curlew' (IB)	WCAu
'Cutie' (IB)	ESgI WCAu
'Cyanea' (DB)	GKev
'Cyclamint' (La)	LLWG
cycloglossa	GKev
'Daedalus' (Rc) **new**	GKev
'Daemon Imp' (MTB)	WCAu
'Dahdah' (TB)	WCAu
'Dainty Lace' (La)	LLWG
'Dale Dennis' (DB)	XSen
'Dame de Coeur' (TB) **new**	SIri
'Dance Ballerina Dance' (Sib)	CHid EBee EPfP EPri GWyn MRav NLar WFar WGob WHlf
'Dance for Joy' (TB)	XSen
'Dance On' (Reticulata)	LAma
'Dance the Night Away' (TB)	WCAu
'Dancer's Veil' (TB)	CKel CMac EBee ECtt ELon ESgI LRHS MRav NRHS SPer WArt WCAu WHoo
'Dancing Lilacs' (MTB)	ESgI
'Dancing Nanou' (Sib)	ECtt
danfordiae	CRos EPfP EPot GKev IRob LAma LCro LOPS LRHS NHpl NRHS SAdu SCob SDeJ
'Dardanus' (Rc)	EPot ERCP GKev SDeJ WCot
'Dark Circle' (Sib)	WFar
'Dark Crystal' (SDB)	CTal ESgI
'Dark Desire' (Sib)	MRav
'Dark Drama' (TB)	WCAu
'Dark Spark' (SDB)	WCAu
'Dark Vader' (SDB)	CTal ESgI
'Darkness' (IB)	SIri
'Darkside' (TB)	XSen
'Darts' (IB)	CIri
'Dauber's Delight'	CIri
'Dauber's Surprise' (TB)	CIri
'Daughter of Stars' (TB)	ELon ESgI
'Dauntless' (TB)	ESgI
'Dawn of Fall' (TB)	ESgI
'Dawn Waltz' (Sib)	EBee EWTr LLWG WCAu WFar WGob WHlf
'Dawning' (TB) ♀H7	ESgI
'Dazzle Time' (TB)	CIri

'Dazzling' (IB)	WCAu
'Dazzling Gold' (TB)	ESgI XSen
'Dear Currier' (Sib)	WAul
'Dear Delight' (Sib)	ELon ILea LLHF MSCN NLar WFar
'Death by Chocolate' (SDB)	CTal ESgI
'Decadence' (TB)	WCAu
§ ***decora***	CTal LLHF WAbe
'Deep Black' (TB)	CKel CPar CRos CSpe CWGN EBee EHrv ELan EPfP ESgI EUJe GMaP LRHS LSRN MBNS MCot MRav MSCN MWat NLar NRHS NWad SDeJ SPer SPoG WGwG
'Deep Pacific' (TB)	WCAu
'Deep Sea Quest' (La)	LLWG
'Deepening Shadows' (CH)	MAvo
'Deft Touch' (TB)	XSen
delavayi ♀H7	EWes GMaP
- SDR 50	CExl GKev
- 'Didcot'	CRos LRHS NRHS
'Delirium' (IB)	WCAu
'Delta Blues' (TB)	SIri
'Delta Butterfly' (La)	WMAq
'Demon' (SDB)	XSen
'Demure Illini' (Sib)	MNrw
'Denys Humphry' (TB)	WCAu
'Derwentwater' (TB)	SRms WCAu
'Desert Echo' (TB)	GMcL XSen
'Desert Jewel' (La)	LLWG
'Desert Lullaby' (TB)	EBee
'Desi Brouwer' (IB)	SIri
'Desiris' (TB)	WCAu
'Devil David' (TB)	CIri
'Devil May Care' (IB)	ESgI
'Devilry' (SDB)	CTal
'Devil's Spoon' (TB)	CIri
'Devonshire Cream' (TB)	WCAu
'Devoted' (SDB)	WCAu
'Dewful' (Sib)	WFar
'Diabolique' (TB) ♀H7	XSen
'Diamond Ring' (TB)	SDys
§ ***dichotoma***	SBrt
'Disco Jewel' (MTB)	ESgI
'Discovered Treasure' (TB)	WCAu
'Discovery'PBR (Dut) **new**	SDeJ
'Disguise' (TB)	WCAu
'Distant Chimes' (TB) **new**	CKel
'Distant Music' (La)	LLWG
'Ditzy' (SDB)	SIri
'Diversion' (TB)	ESgI
'Dividing Line' (MTB)	WCAu
'Dixie Darling' (TB)	ESgI XSen
'Dixie Pixie' (SDB)	WCAu
'Doctor No' (TB)	CIri
'Dolce' (SpH)	WCAu
'Doll Ribbons' (MTB)	EPfP
'Dolly Madison' (TB)	ESgI
§ ***domestica***	CBlu CBro CHll CRos EPfP LRHS SPav SPlb SRms WSHC
- 'Crûg Colossal'	WCru
- 'Freckle Face'	CWCL LSou MHol
'Dominion' (TB)	WMil
'Doohicky' (IB)	CIri
'Dot Com' (SDB) **new**	CTal
'Dotted Swiss' (TB)	XSen
'Double Byte' (SDB)	XSen
'Double Espoir' (TB)	XSen
'Double Lament' (SDB)	CBro
'Double Standards' (Sib)	EBee EPri IPot NLar WFar WGob WHil
'Double Vision' (TB)	XSen

	douglasiana	GCal GKev
	'Dover Beach' (TB)	SIri
	'Dover Castle' (BB) ♀H7	SIri
	'Downtown Brown' (TB)	WCAu
	'Draco' (TB)	ESgI XSen
	'Drama Queen' (TB)	WCAu
	'Dream Indigo' (IB)	WCAu XSen
	'Dreaming Green' (Sib)	EBee
	'Dreaming Late' (Sib) **new**	WCAu
	'Dreaming Orange' (Sib)	ECtt EPri
	'Dreaming Rainbows' (TB)	WCAu
	'Dreaming Spires' (Sib)	ESgI GBin
	'Dreaming Yellow' (Sib)	CAby CAvo CBar CBre CKel CRos CSam CWld ECha EPfP EPri EShb GBin GKin LEdu LRHS MRav NGdn NRHS SPer WAul WCAu WGwG WMoo WWtn
	'Dresden Candleglow' (IB)	WCAu
	'Drive Me Wild' (TB)	WCAu
	'Dualtone' (TB)	CKel
	'Dude Ranch' (TB)	WCAu
	'Duded Up' (TB)	CIri
	'Duke of Bedford' (TB)	WMil
	'Dunkler Wein' (Sib)	EWes
	'Dunlin' (MDB)	CBro CRos CTal NRHS
	'Dural White Butterfly' (La)	CBod CHid EPfP WWtn
	'Durham Dream' (TB)	CIri
	'Dusky Challenger' (TB)	CKel EBee ESgI LCro SBee SRms WCAu WTor XSen
	'Dusky Evening' (TB)	XSen
	'Dutch Chocolate' (TB)	CKel EWes LCro XSen
	DYNAMIC DUET MIXED (Dut)	GKev
	'Dynamite' (TB)	ESgI XSen
	'Dyonisos' (TB)	SIri
	'Eagle's Flight' (TB)	XSen
	'Earl of Essex' (TB)	WCAu XSen
	'Early Frost' (IB)	CKel
	'Early Light' (TB) ♀H7	ESgI WCAu
	'Easter' (SDB)	SIri
	'Eastertime' (TB)	ESgI
	'Eastman Winds' (La)	LLWG
	'Easy' (MTB)	EIri SIri
	'Echo de France' (TB)	CKel ESgI SRms XSen
	'Eden's Paradise Blue' (Sib)	ELon WHar
	'Edge of Winter' (TB)	CKel XSen
	'Edith Wolford' (TB)	CCCN CKel GMcL GWyn MMrt SCob SRGP XSen
	'Edna Grace' (La)	LLWG
	'Ed's Blue' (DB)	ELan
	'Edward' (Reticulata)	EPot GKev LAma SAdu SDeJ
	'Edward of Windsor' (TB)	ELan GMaP LRHS NLar SCob SRGP
	'Ego' (Sib)	CHid ECha ELon EPfP EPri WFar WMoo
	'Eileen Louise' (TB) ♀H7	WCAu
	'Eleanor's Pride' (TB)	ESgI SRms WCAu
	'Electrique' (TB)	WCAu
	'Eliminator' (TB)	CIri
	'Elizabeth of England' (TB)	GKev
	'Elizabeth Poldark' (TB)	ESgI XSen
	'Ellesmere' (Sib)	WAul
	'Elsa Sass' (TB)	ESgI
	'Elsie Petty' (IB)	SIri
	'Elvinhall'	CBro
	'Emperor' (Sib)	CWat NSti
	'Empress of India' (TB)	EWTr
	'Encre Bleue' (IB)	ESgI
	'Endless Love' (TB)	EIri
	'Enfant Prodige' (SpH)	WCAu
	'English Charm' (TB)	ESgI WCAu XSen
	'English Cottage' (TB)	CKel CRos CTsd ELon GCal LSRN MHer MWat NLar SRms WCAu XSen
	'Ennerdale' (TB)	SRms
	'Enriched' (MTB) ♀H7	WCAu
§	***ensata***	CBcs CBod CBro CRos CTri ELan EPfP GKev LRHS LSun MJak MMuc MNrw NLar NRHS SPlb SRms WBor WPnP WWtn
	- 'Activity'	SHar WFar
	- 'Agrippine'	XSen
	- 'Alba'	ECha MMuc
I	- 'Amethyst'	IPot XSen
	- 'Angel Mountain' **new**	LMea WFar
	- 'Angelic Choir' **new**	LLWG
	- 'Aquamarin'	IPot XSen
	- 'Asian Warrior'	WFar
	- 'August Emperor'	MBel
	- 'Azuma-kagami'	EBee ELan MNrw
	- 'Azure'	WFar WMoo
	- 'Blue Spritz' **new**	LLWG
	- 'Caprician Butterfly' ♀H7	EPfP NLar
	- 'Carnival Prince'	WFar WMoo
	- 'Cascade Crest'	WFar
	- 'Celestial Emperor' **new**	LLWG
*	- 'Charm'	CRos LRHS NRHS
	- 'Christina's Gown' **new**	WFar
	- 'Crepe Paper'	WFar
	- 'Cry of Rejoice'	EBee ECtt GMcL WCAu
	- 'Crystal Halo' ♀H7	EBee LMea LSun WWtn
I	- 'Darling'	EPfP WFar WMoo
	- 'Diamant'	XSen
	- 'Dramatic Moment'	WFar WSpi
I	- 'Dresden China'	EBee WFar
	- 'Eden's Blush'	EBee
	- 'Eden's Charm'	CRos EPfP
	- 'Eden's Delight'	CRos
	- 'Eden's Paintbrush'	EShb SPer
	- 'Eden's Purple Glory'	CHid
	- 'Electric Rays'	EBee IPot LLWG WFar WGob
I	- 'Emotion'	CMac CRos WFar
I	- 'Fortune'	CBod EBee EHrv GBin LMea WGob WHar WWtn
	- 'Freckled Geisha'	CMac EBee ECtt ELon EPfP IPot NQui SRms WFar
	- 'Frilled Enchantment' ♀H7	IPot IRob WFar
	- 'Galatea Marx'	CBod CExl EBee LEdu WFar
	- 'Gipsy'	CMac EBee LRHS
	- 'Gold Bound'	ECtt IRob LMea
	- 'Gracieuse'	CRos CTsd LRHS NLar
	- 'Greywoods Catrina' **new**	LLWG WFar
	- 'Gusto'	CMac EBee ELon EPfP IPot IRob MNrw SRms WFar
	- 'Harlequinesque'	ECtt WFar
	- 'Harpswell Chantey'	IPot
	- 'Hercule'	CExl CHid WFar
	- Higo white	SPer
	- 'Hoshi-akari'	WFar
	- hybrids	GWyn
	- 'Imperial Velvet'	WFar
	- 'Indigo Delight'	LLWG
*	- 'Innocence'	EHrv NLar SRms WFar WMoo
	- 'Iso-no-nami'	EBee WFar
	- 'Jocasta'	EPfP WFar
	- 'Jodlesong'	WFar
	- 'Kalamazoo'	WFar
	- 'Katy Mendez' ♀H7	IPot NLar
*	- 'Kiyo-zuru'	EPfP
	- 'Kogesho'	EPfP NLar
	- 'Koh Dom'	SPer

	- 'Kongo-san'	NLar WFar
	- 'Kuma-funjin'	CExl EBee
	- 'Kumo-no-obi'	CExl EBee GBin LRHS MCot NRHS SPtp WFar
	- 'Lady in Waiting'	EBee ECtt EPfP IRob WGob
	- 'Laughing Lion'	ECtt WCAu WFar WMoo
	- 'Light at Dawn'	MBel WMoo
	- 'Lilac Blotch'	SPer
	- 'Loyalty'	CExl CRos LMea LRHS SHar WFar
	- 'Momogasumi'	ECtt IRob LLWG MNrw NQui WGob WHil
	- 'Momozomo'	LLHF
§	- 'Moonlight Waves'	CExl CHid CMac CRos EBee ELan EPfP GBin GKin GMaP IPot IRob LLWG LRHS MCot MHer MRav NGdn NRHS SRms WFar WSpi WWtn
	- 'Oase'	ECtt
	- 'Ocean Mist'	CHid EBee ECtt WHar
	- 'Oku-banri'	CExl EBee WFar
	- 'Oriental Eyes'	NGdn
	- 'Pin Stripe'	EBee WMoo
	- 'Pink Frost'	EBee EPfP WFar
	- 'Pleasant Earlybird'	WFar
	- 'Pleasant Journey'	ECtt EHrv
	- 'Prairie Frost'	EBee NLar
	- 'Prairie Noble'	EBee
	- 'Purple Parasol'	LLWG LMea
	- purple-flowered	SPer
	- 'Queen's Tiara'	ECtt ELon EWTr IPot WBor
	- 'Rakka-no-utage'	EBee NLar
	- 'Rivulets of Wine'	LLWG
§	- 'Rose Queen' ♀H7	CExl CMac CRos CSam ECha ELan EPfP EWTr GBin GKin GMaP IRob LRHS MCot MRav MWts NGdn NRHS SPer SRms WFar WHar WMoo XLum
	- 'Rowden'	CRoa
	- 'Rowden King'	NChi
	- 'Rowden Mikado'	MAvo NChi
I	- 'Royal Banner'	EBee ECtt LRHS WFar
	- 'Royal Crown'	XLum
I	- 'Ruby King'	LEdu LRHS
	- 'Ruffled Dimity'	EBee IPot
I	- 'Sensation'	CWCL ECtt GBin IPot MWts NLar SRms WWtn
	- 'Snowy Hills'	XLum
	- 'Sorcerer's Triumph'	WFar
	- var. ***spontanea*** B&SWJ 1103	WCru
	- - B&SWJ 8699	WCru
	- 'Stippled Ripples'	IPot
	- 'Summer Storm' ♀H7	SPer
	- 'Taketori-hime' (v)	XLum
	- 'Topas' **new**	EBee WFar XSen
	- 'Umi-kaze'	NLar
	- 'Variegata' (v) ♀H7	Widely available
	- 'Velvety Queen'	ECtt WCAu
	- 'Wave Action' **new**	EWTr
I	- 'White Ladies'	CSBt LRHS WSpi
	- 'Wine Ruffles'	LSRN
	- 'Yako-no-tama'	WFar WMoo
	- 'Yedo-yeman'	EBee IMou WFar
	'Épée Violette' (TB)	ESgI
	'Epicenter' (TB)	XSen
	'Eramosa Miss' (BB)	WCAu
	'Eramosa Skies' (SDB)	WCAu
	'Erect' (IB)	CKel
	'Eric the Red' (Sib)	ELon
	'Erste Sahne' (Sib)	GBin
	'Eternal Bliss' (TB)	SIri
	'Evadne' (TB)	WMil
	'Evening Drama' (TB)	WCAu
	'Evening Gown' (TB)	XSen
	'Ever After' (TB)	LCro XSen
	'Ever Again' (Sib)	ELon
	'Everything Plus' (TB)	ESgI XSen
	'Ewen' (Sib)	CDor CHid CPou GKin GLog GMaP ILea LEdu NGdn WAul WCot
	'Exotic Isle' (TB)	EPPr ESgI XSen
	'Exotic Star' (TB)	CKel
	'Experiment' (SDB) **new**	EIri
	'Expose' (TB)	WCAu
	'Extra' (BB)	CPBP LLHF
	'Extra Dazzle' (La)	LLWG
	'Eye Catcher' (Reticulata) **new**	EPot ERCP LAma
	'Eye Magic' (IB)	CKel XSen
	'Eye of Tiger'	see *I*. 'Tigereye'
	'Eye Shadow' (SDB)	WCAu
	'Eyebright' (SDB) ♀H7	CBro WCAu
	'Fabiola' (Reticulata)	CRos EPot ERCP LAma LLHF LRHS NRHS SDeJ
	'Fabuleux' (TB)	SIri
	'Face of an Angel' (TB)	WCAu
	'Faenelia Hicks' (La)	WMAq
	'Falconeer' (TB)	CIri
	'Fall Fiesta' (TB)	XSen
	'Fanciful Whimsy' (IB)	WCAu
	'Fancy Brass' (TB)	SIri
	'Fanfaron' (TB)	ESgI XSen
	'Farleigh Damson' (SDB)	SIri
	'Fashion Holiday' (IB)	SIri
	'Fashion Lady' (MDB)	CBro CTal
	'Fathom' (IB)	WCAu
	'Feather and Fan' (La)	LLWG
	'Feminine Charm' (TB)	MRav WCAu
	'Festive Skirt' (TB)	CKel WCAu
	'Feu du Ciel' (TB) ♀H7	CKel ESgI XSen
	'Few Are Chosen' (La)	LLWG
	'Fiddlin' Around' (TB)	WCAu
	'Fiesta Time' (TB)	CWCL XSen
	'Film Festival' (TB)	ESgI
	'Finalist' (TB)	WCAu XSen
	'Fire in the Sky' (IB)	WCAu
	'Firebeard' (TB)	CIri
	'Firebird' (TB)	CRos LRHS NRHS
	'Firebreather' (TB)	EPfP MHol
	'Firebug' (IB)	ESgI XSen
	'Firecracker' (TB)	MRav WCAu
	'First Interstate' (TB)	ESgI XSen
	'First Movement' (TB)	ESgI
	'First Romance' (SDB)	LSRN
	'First Violet' (TB)	ESgI
	'Five Star Admiral' (TB)	XSen
	'Flaming Dragon' (TB)	XSen
	'Flaming Victory' (TB)	XSen
	flavescens	ESgI WCAu XSen
	'Flavours' (BB)	WCAu
	'Fleece of White' (BB)	WCAu
	'Flibbertigibbet' (SDB) **new**	SIri
	'Flight of Butterflies' (Sib)	Widely available
	'Flirting Again' (SDB) ♀H7	CTal SIri
	'Floorshow' (TB)	XSen
	'Florence Dayton' (TB) **new**	LMea
§	'Florentina' (IB/TB) ♀H7	CBod CBro CHby CKel ESgI GCal GPoy LRHS MRav NBid SEND WCAu XAbr XSen
	'Florentine Silk' (TB)	WCAu

'Fluffy Pillows' (TB)	CIri
'Flumadiddle' (IB)	CBro CTal
'Flying Solo' (IB)	CIri
'Flûte Enchantée' (TB)	CIri XSen
'Focus' (TB)	XSen
foetidissima ♀H5	Widely available
- 'Aurea'	WCot
- ***chinensis***	see *I. foetidissima* var. *citrina*
§ - var. ***citrina***	CBre EPri EWld GAbr GKev LEdu NLar SChr WGwG
- var. ***lutescens***	CHid
- 'Variegata' (v) ♀H5	CElw ESps NPer WAvo
'Fogbound' (TB)	WCAu
'Foggy Dew' (TB)	CRos EPfP LRHS NRHS SDeJ
'Fond Kiss' (Sib)	WCAu
'Fondation Van Gogh' (TB)	XSen
'Foolish Fancy' (TB)	SIri
'Footloose' (TB)	SIri XSen
'For Clive' (TB)	CIri
'For Richard' (TB)	CIri
'Fordwich' (SDB)	SIri
'Forecasting Rain' (SDB)	CTal SIri
'Foreign Legion' (TB)	WCAu
'Foreigner' (TB)	WCAu
'Forest Light' (SDB)	CBro ESgI
'Forever Blue' (SDB)	WCAu
'Forever Gold' (TB)	XSen
'Forge Fire' (TB)	ESgI
formosana B&SWJ 3076	WCru
'Forrest Hills' (TB)	EPfP GPSL LRHS NRHS
forrestii ♀H7	CAby CBro CExl CHid CMac EHoe EPfP GAbr GCal GKev GLog LRHS SPtp SRot WAbe
- SDR 5802	GKev
- SDR 7871	GKev
'Fort Apache' (TB)	EWes
'Fortunata' (TB)	XSen
'Fortunate Son' (TB)	WCAu
'Fortune Teller' (TB)	CKel
'Fourfold Blue' (SpH)	GBin
'Fourfold Lavender' (Sib)	EWes NLar WCAu
'Fourfold White' (Sib)	ESgI
'Framboise' (TB)	XSen
'Francina' (TB)	WMil
'Frank Elder' (Reticulata)	CRos EPot ERCP GKev LAma LLHF LRHS NRHS SDeJ WAbe
'Frappe' (TB) **new**	CKel
'Freedom Flight' (TB)	CIri
'French Can Can' (TB)	CKel GWyn LMea SIri
'French Horn' (TB)	CIri
'French Rose' (TB)	WCAu
'Fresno Calypso' (TB)	CKel ESgI WCAu XSen
'Frimousee' (TB)	WViv
'Frison-roche' (TB)	CWCL WViv
'Frisounette' (TB)	ESgI
'Fritillary Flight' (IB) ♀H7	CKel
'From this Moment' (La)	LLWG
'Frontier Marshall' (TB)	XSen
'Frost and Flame' (TB)	CKel CRos EBee ECtt ELan GBin LCro LRHS MAsh MRav NLar NRHS SDeJ SPer SPoG WGwG
'Frosted Angel' (SDB)	CBro
'Frosted Velvet' (MTB)	WCAu
'Frosty Jewels' (TB)	XSen
'Frosty Moonscape' (TB)	CIri
'Fruit Cocktail' (IB)	XSen
fulva ♀H5	CKel CSpe EBee EPri EWat GCal MMrt NSti SBrt WCot
- 'Marvell Gold' (La)	CRoa EBee
× ***fulvala*** ♀H5	EWes NSti
- 'Violacea'	CRos LRHS NRHS
'Furnaceman' (SDB)	CBro CTal
'Futuriste' (TB)	SIri
'Gai Luron' (TB)	CKel
'Gallant Moment' (TB)	SIri XSen
'Galway' (IB)	SIri XSen
'Game Plan' (TB)	WCAu
'Gandalf the Grey' (TB)	ESgI
'Garnet Storm Dancer' (La)	LLWG
'Gelbe Mantel' (Sino-Sib)	CHid GKin MSpe NSti
'Gemstone Walls' (TB)	ESgI
'George' (Reticulata) ♀H7	CAby CAvo CRav CRos EPfP EPot ERCP GKev IRob LAma LRHS NRHS SAdu SDeJ WBor WBrk WCot WHoo XEll
'Gerald Darby'	see *I.* × *robusta* 'Gerald Darby'
§ ***germanica***	CBot ESps MMuc SEND WCAu WCot WGwG
- var. ***florentina***	see *I.* 'Florentina'
§ - 'Nepalensis'	WCAu
- 'The King'	see *I. germanica* 'Nepalensis'
'Ghost Train' (TB)	CKel SIri
'Gingerbread Castle' (TB)	WCAu
'Gingerbread Man' (SDB)	CBro CMea CTal EHrv ESgI GEdr MBrN WCAu
'Girly Girl' (TB)	WCAu
'Glacier Gold' (TB)	XSen
'Glacier Point' (TB)	CIri
'Glad Rags' (TB)	XSen
'Gladiator's Gift' (La)	LLWG
'Gladys Austin' (TB)	XSen
'Glas-y-Dorlan' (Sib)	GCal
'Glenthorn' (TB)	SIri
'Glowing Embers' (TB)	ESgI
'Gnu' (TB)	XSen
'Go Between' (TB)	WCAu
'Godfrey Owen' (TB)	WCAu
'Godsend' (TB)	CIri
'Going Home' (TB) ♀H7	SIri
'Going My Way' (TB)	ESgI LSou SIri WCAu XSen
'Gold Burst' (TB)	XSen
'Gold Country' (TB)	XSen
'Gold Galore' (TB)	SIri
'Gold of Autumn' (TB)	CKel WArt
'Goldberry' (IB)	WCAu
'Golden Alps' (TB)	SRms WCAu
'Golden Beauty'	GKev SDeJ
'Golden Child' (SDB)	XSen
'Golden Edge' (Sib)	ELon GBin GQue LLWG NLar WCAu WFar WGob
'Golden Encore' (TB)	CKel WCAu
'Golden Fireworks' (La)	LLWG
'Golden Folly' (SDB)	CIri
'Golden Panther' (TB)	WCAu
'Golden Violet' (SDB)	ESgI
'Good Looking' (TB)	ESgI WCAu
'Good Show' (TB)	ESgI WCAu XSen
'Good Vibrations' (TB)	XSen
'Goodbye Heart' (TB)	LSRN
'Gordon' (Reticulata)	CAvo CRos EPfP EPot ERCP GKev LAma LRHS NRHS SAdu SCob
gormanii	see *I. tenax*
'Gossip' (SDB)	CBro
'Got the Melody' (TB)	WCAu
'Goudhurst' (SDB)	SIri
'Gracchus' (TB)	WCAu
'Grace Sturtevant' (TB)	WMil
gracilipes	GEdr SBrt
- 'Alba'	GEdr
gracilipes* × *lacustris	GEdr

	Name	Suppliers
	aff. ***gracilipes*** purple and gold-flowered from Gongga Shan, China **new**	SBrt
	graeberiana	EPot GKev SDeJ
	graminea ♀H7	CAvo CBro CHid CMac EHrv EIri ELan EPfP EPri GKev IFro NChi NSti WCot XEll
	- var. ***pseudocyperus***	GBin GCal SDys
	graminifolia	see *I. kerneriana*
	'Granaat' (Sib)	EBee
	'Granada Gold' (TB)	SRms XSen
	'Grand Amiral' (TB)	WViv
	'Grand Waltz' (TB)	XSen
	'Grandis' (Sib)	GBin
	'Granny Jean' (Sib)	CKel
	'Grapelet' (MDB)	CPBP CTal WCAu
	'Great Gatsby' (TB)	CKel
	'Great Lakes' (TB)	ESgI
	'Grecian Skies' (TB)	ESgI
	'Green Eyed Lady' (TB)	ESgI
	'Green Ice' (TB)	LRHS MRav
	'Green Prophecy' (TB)	CKel
	'Green Spot' (SDB) ♀H7	CBod CBro CKel CRos CTal ECha ECtt EHrv LRHS MRav NLar NRHS SDeJ SPer WAul WCAu
	'Greenstuff' (SDB)	CTal
	'Grenade' (TB)	SIri WViv
	grey-flowered (Sib)	ELon
	'Gringo' (TB)	WCAu
	'Grooving' (BB)	ESgI
	'Grosser Wein' (Sib)	GBin
	'Guatemala' (TB)	WCAu
	'Guess Who I Am' (TB)	WCAu
	'Gull's Wing' (Sib)	EPfP LEdu LLWG MHol NLar NSti SPoG WGob
	'Gurkha's Dance' (SDB)	SIri
	'Gypsy Beauty' (Dut)	CAvo ELan GKev LCro LOPS SDeJ
	'Gypsy Jewels' (TB)	CKel ESgI XSen
	'Gypsy Romance' (TB) ♀H7	EIri ESgI SIri WCAu
	'Gypsy Tart' (SDB)	SIri
	'Habit' (TB)	WCAu
	'Hakuna Matata' (AB)	SDys
	'Halloween Halo' (TB)	WCAu
	halophila	see *I. spuria* subsp. *halophila*
	'Happenstance' (TB)	WCAu
	'Happy Mood' (IB)	EIri WCAu
	'Harbor Blue' (TB)	CKel CRos CTsd MWat WCAu
	'Harlow Gold' (IB)	ESgI
	'Harmony' ambig.	SCob SPer
	'Harmony' (IB)	CRos
	'Harmony' (Reticulata)	CAby CAvo CRav EPfP EPot GKev IRob LAma LCro LOPS LRHS MJak MWat NRHS SAdu SCob SDeJ WArt WBrk
	'Harpswell Happiness' (Sib) ♀H7	CKel EBee ELon EPfP EPri GBin ILea IRob SBch SPer WAul WGob WHlf WMoo
	'Harpswell Haze' (Sib)	ECha
	'Harpswell Velvet' (Sib)	GBin
	'Harriette Halloway' (TB)	CRos CWGN EPfP EShb LRHS LSRN NLar NRHS SHar SRGP WCot
	'Harvest King' (TB)	XSen
	'Harvest of Memories' (TB)	CKel ESgI GMcL GWyn SPoG
	'Haute Couture' (TB)	XSen
	'Haviland' (TB)	XSen
	'Headcorn' (MTB) ♀H7	SIri
	'Headline Banner' (BB)	WCAu
	'Headway' (Spuria)	WCAu
	'Heartbeat Away' (TB)	CIri
	'Heart's Radiance' (MTB)	SDys
	'Heather Carpet' (SDB)	WCAu
	'Heather Stream' (La)	ELon
	'Heavenly Blue' (Sib)	MWat SPer
	'Heavenly Days' (TB)	WCAu
	'Heavenly Horns' (TB)	CIri
	'Helen Astor' (Sib)	CDor CTri MRav
	'Helen Collingwood' (TB)	ESgI
	'Helen Dawn' (TB) ♀H7	SIri
	'Helen Proctor' (IB)	ESgI WCot XSen
	'Helen Traubel' (TB)	WCAu
	'Helena Terry' (TB)	ESgI
	'Helene C.' (TB)	WViv XSen
	'Hellcat' (IB)	WCAu
	'Hello Darkness' (TB) ♀H7	ESgI WCAu WCot XSen
	'Hell's Fire' (TB)	ELan ELon WCAu
	'Hemstitched' (TB)	MHol
	'Here Be Dragons' (Sib) **new**	WCAu
	'Here Comes The Sun' (TB)	WCAu
	'Hey True Blue' (TB)	WCAu
	'High Blue Sky' (TB)	WCAu
	'High Command' (TB)	CKel WCAu
	'High Impact' (TB)	CIri
	'High Peak' (TB)	WCAu
	'Highland Mist' (La)	LLWG
	'Hildegarde' (Dut)	SDeJ
	'Hindenburg' (TB)	CKel
	'Hippolyta' (Rc) **new**	GKev
	'His Royal Highness' (TB)	WCAu
	'Hissy-Fit' (IB)	CKel
	histrio	EPot
	- subsp. ***aintabensis***	GKev
	histrioides	GKev
	- 'Finola'	ERCP GKev LAma
	- 'Halkis' (Reticulata)	EBee EPot ERCP GKev LAma SDeJ
	- 'Lady Beatrix Stanley'	CAvo CMea CRos EPot ERCP GKev LAma LLHF LRHS NRHS SAdu SDeJ WBrk WHoo
	- 'Major'	GKev LAma
	- var. ***sophenensis***	EPot GKev LAma
	'Hoar Edge' (Sib)	EPri NChi WAul
	'Hocus Pocus' (SDB)	CAby CKel CTal CWGN EPfP LRHS LSou NRHS WAul
	'Hohe Warte' (Sib) ♀H7	GBin WAul WCAu
	'Holden Clough' (SpH) ♀H7	CBod CExl EBee ELan EPfP GBin GMaP GMcL LEdu MMuc MNrw MRav MSpe NChi NGdn NSti NWad WBrk WCAu WFar WSHC
	'Holden's Child'	LLWG WCAu
	'Holidaze' (IB) ♀H7	CKel EIri
	'Holtentol'	WCAu
	'Holy Night' (TB)	CKel SRms
	'Honey Glazed' (IB)	ELon ESgI WCAu
	'Honey Stars' (La)	LLWG
	'Honeylove' (SDB)	SDys
	'Honeyplic' (IB) ♀H7	ESgI SIri
	'Honington' (SDB)	WCAu
	'Honky Tonk Blues' (TB)	ESgI LSRN
	'Honorabile' (MTB)	ESgI WCAu
	hoogiana ♀H4	GKev
I	- 'Amazon'	GKev
I	- 'Amphion'	GKev
I	- 'Antiope'	GKev
	- 'Purpurea'	GKev
§	***hookeri***	CBod CFis CPBP CRos CSma CTal GEdr GKev GMaP IBoy MHol NSla SBrt WAbe WThu
	- SDR 2202	GKev
	'Hopelessly Devoted' (La)	LLWG
	'Hoptoit' (TB)	CIri
§	'Hornpipe' (TB)	WCAu

'Hortensia Rose' (TB)	SIri
'Hot' (SDB) **new**	CTal
'Hot and Spicy' (La)	LLWG
'Hot Spiced Wine' (TB)	SIri
'Hot to Trot' (TB)	ESgI
'Hottentot' (SDB)	WCAu
'Howler' (TB)	WCAu
'Hubbard' (Sib)	EPri LLWG MBel MNrw SPoG WFar WGob WHlf
'Huckleberry Fudge' (TB)	XSen
'Hugh Miller' (TB)	WCAu
'Hula Hands' (IB)	CIri
§ ***humilis***	GCrg
'Hypnotizer' (TB)	CIri
hyrcana	GKev WCot
'I Feel Good' (TB)	WCAu
'I Pink I Can' (TB)	WCAu
'I Repeat' (TB)	XSen
'I Seek You' (TB)	ESgI
'Ice'	WCAu
'Ice and Indigo' (SDB)	WCAu
'Ice Cave' (TB)	WCAu
'Ice Dancer' (TB) 🏆H7	CKel
'Ice Etching' (SDB)	WCAu
'Ice for Brice' (TB)	CIri
'Ice Wings' (BB)	WCAu
'Ida' (Reticulata)	LAma
'Ila Crawford' (Spuria) 🏆H7	XSen
'Illini Charm' (Sib)	CHid EBee WFar WMoo
illyrica	see *I. pallida*
'I'm Back' (TB)	WCAu
'Immortality' (TB)	CKel CRos CWGN EPfP GKev GMcL GWyn LRHS SCob WCAu XSen
'Imperative' (IB)	SIri WCAu
'Imperial Opal' (Sib)	ECtt NGdn WFar
I 'Imperial Velvet' (Sib)	ELon WFar
'Impersonator' (TB)	CIri
'Imprimis' (TB)	XSen
'In a Flash' (IB)	WCAu
'In Love' (TB)	XSen
'In Town' (TB)	XSen
'In Your Dreams' (TB)	CIri
'Incognito Too' (TB)	CIri
* 'Incoscente' (TB)	ESgI
'Indeed' (IB)	ESgI
'Indian Chief' (TB)	CBod CCCN CRos CWCL EPfP ESgI IBoy MCot MHer MRav WCAu
'Indian Idyll' (IB)	CKel
'Indiana Sunset' (TB)	CKel
'Indigo Princess' (TB)	XSen
'Infanta' (SDB)	WCAu
'Ink Patterns' (TB)	WCAu
'Inner Show'	WCAu
'Innocent Devil' (TB)	CIri
'Innocent Pink' (TB)	ESgI
innominata	CRos GKev LRHS NBro NRHS SRms
- yellow-flowered	NRya
'Inside Job' (TB)	WCAu
'Inspired' (TB)	WCAu
'Instant Hit' (TB)	WCAu
'Intermediary' (IB)	WCAu
'Interpol' (TB)	ESgI XSen
'Invicta Daybreak' (IB)	SIri
'Invicta Garnet' (SDB)	SIri
'Invicta Gold' (SDB)	SIri
'Invicta Reprieve' (IB)	SIri
'Irene' (TB)	WCAu
'Iriade' (TB)	WCAu
'Iris Bohnsack' (BB)	WCAu
'Irisades' (TB)	WCAu
'Irish Chant' (SDB)	WCAu
'Irish Gold' (TB)	WCAu
'Irish Harp' (SDB)	ESgI
'Irish Jig' (TB)	WCAu
'Irish Squire' (TB)	WCAu
'Irish Tune' (TB)	ESgI
'Iron Eagle' (TB)	CIri
'Isabelle' (Sib)	LSRN XSen
'Island Sun' (SDB)	SIri
'Island Sunset' (TB)	SIri
'Isobel Rose' (TB) **new**	SIri
'Isoline' (TB)	ESgI
'It Happens' (TB)	WCAu
'Italian Ice' (TB)	EIri
'Italian Velvet' (TB)	WCAu
'It's Amazing' (IB)	WCAu
'I've Got Rhythm' (TB) **new**	CKel
'J.S. Dijt' (Reticulata)	CAvo CRos EPot ERCP GKev LAma LCro LOPS LRHS MGos NRHS SAdu SDeJ
'Jack Attack' (La)	CBod SPoG WHar WMoo WWtn
'Jac-y-do' (Sib)	EWes
'Jamie Roo' (TB) **new**	SIri
'Jane Phillips' (TB) 🏆H7	Widely available
'Janet Lane' (BB)	CKel
'Japanese Pinwheel'	IPot
'Japanesque' (MTB)	CIri
japonica 🏆H4	CExl NLar NPer SPlb WCot XLum XSen
- B&SWJ 8921	WCru
- 'Bourne Graceful'	CExl
- 'Ledger'	CAby CExl CHll CMac ECha EHrv MRav SEND SMad WWFP
- 'Monty'	WWFP
- 'Rudolph Spring'	GCal WSHC WWFP
§ - 'Variegata' (v) 🏆H4	CAby CBcs CBro ECha ELan NPer NSti SArc WAvo WWFP XSen
'Jasper Gem' (MDB)	EPot
'Jazz Festival' (TB)	SIri WCAu XSen
'Jazz Hot' (La)	LLWG
'Jazzed Up' (TB)	XSen
'Jean Cayeux' (TB)	ESgI
'Jean Guymer' (TB)	ESgI
'Jeanne Price' (TB)	ESgI LSRN WCAu
'Jeremy Brian' (SDB)	WCAu
'Jeremy Jets On' (TB)	CIri
'Jesse's Song' (TB)	ESgI WCAu XSen
'Jet-Setter' (TB)	CIri
'Jeunesse' (TB)	ESgI
'Jewel Baby' (SDB)	CBro
'Jeweler's Art' (SDB)	ESgI
'Jiansada' (SDB)	CBro CTal
'Jigsaw' (TB)	XSen
'Jitterbug' (TB)	EHrv WCAu
'Joanna' (TB)	LSRN NLar
'John' (IB)	CKel LSRN
'Joyce' (Reticulata)	CRos EPfP EPot GKev LAma LRHS NRHS SAdu SDeJ
'Joyce Cole' (Sib) **new**	WCAu
'Joyful Skies' (TB)	WCAu
'Jubilant Spirit' (Spuria)	EWes
'Jubilee Gem' (TB)	CKel WCAu
'Judy Mogil' (TB)	CIri
'Juliet' (TB)	ESgI
'Jump for Joy' (TB)	CIri
'Jump Start' (IB)	WCAu
'Jumping Jupiter' (TB)	CIri
'June Prom' (IB)	CKel IRob LRHS NRHS SRGP
'June Rose' (IB)	CKel

'Jungle Fires' (TB)	WCAu
'Jungle Shadows' (BB)	ESgI MRav WCAu
'Jurassic Park' (TB)	CKel ESgI LMea WCAu XSen
'Just Imagine' (La)	LLWG
'Just Jennifer' (BB)	WCAu
'Kabluey' (Sib)	EBee ECtt IPot MWts WFar
'Kaboom' (Sib)	MHol
kaempferi	see *I. ensata*
'Kahuna' (IB)	WCAu
'Kaint Hardly Believe' (TB)	CIri
'Karen' (TB)	LSRN
'Kasim' (J) **new**	GKev
'Katharine Hodgkin' (Reticulata) ♀H7	CAby CAvo CMea CRos CTca EBee ECha EPfP EPot ERCP GAbr GKev LAma LCro LOPS LRHS MNrw MRav MWat NHpl NLar NRHS SAdu SCob SDeJ WBrk WCot WFar WHoo
'Katharine Hodgkin' dark-flowered (Reticulata)	EPot
'Kathleen Mary' (Sib)	CKel
'Katie-Koo' (IB) ♀H7	CKel
'Katy Petts' (SDB)	ESgI
'Keeping up Appearances' (TB)	WCAu
kemaonensis PAB 8473	LEdu
'Kent Arrival' (Sib)	SIri
'Kent Blackguard' (IB)	SIri
'Kent Compote' (IB)	SIri
'Kent Pride' (TB)	CAby CBWd CBod CKel CRos CSBt ECha ECtt EPfP ESgI EUJe GBin LRHS MCot MRav MSCN NRHS SCob SPer SPoG SRms WCAu WHoo
Kenta No Se129 (Sib)	EPri
'Kentish Icon' (SDB)	SIri
'Kentish Lad' (IB)	SIri
'Kentucky Derby' (TB)	XSen
§ ***kerneriana*** ♀H4	CBro EHoe GKev
'Kęstutis Genys' (Sib)	WAul
'Kildonan' (TB)	WCAu
'Kingfisher' (Sib)	WAul
'Kirkstone' (TB)	WCAu
kirkwoodii	GKev
'Kiss of Summer' (TB) ♀H7	ESgI SDys
'Kiss the Girl' (Sib) **new**	WCAu
'Kissing Circle' (TB)	ESgI
'Kita-no-seiza' (Sib)	LLWG NGdn WFar
'Kiwi Slices' (SDB)	CWat
'Knick Knack' (MDB)	CBro CKel CPBP CRos CTal ELan ELon EPfP GMaP LRHS MRav MTin NRHS SDeJ SPoG
korolkowii	CTal GKev
'Kuh-e-Abr'	GKev LAma
'La Meije' (TB)	SIri WViv
'La Senda' (Spuria)	WCot
'Lace Legacy' (TB)	LSRN
'Laced Cotton' (TB)	WCAu XSen
§ ***lactea***	SBrt SMHy XEll XSen
- CC 7174	GKev
lacustris	CPBP MAvo WAbe WCot XSen
- 'Captain Collingwood' **new**	WAbe
'Lacy Snowflake' (TB)	LRHS
'Lad'	WCAu
'Lady Belle' (MTB)	ESgI
'Lady Byng' (TB)	WMil
'Lady Essex' (TB)	WCAu
'Lady Friend' (TB)	WCAu XSen
'Lady in Red' (SDB)	ESgI WCAu
'Lady Mohr' (AB)	WCAu
'Lady of the Night' (BB)	WCAu
'Lady Vanessa' (Sib)	CPou EBee ELon MRav NSti
laevigata	CRoa CRos CWat EPfP EWat ITim MRav NBro NPer SPer SRms WFar WMAq WMoo WShi
- var. ***alba***	LLWG SRms WAbe WMoo
- 'Atropurpurea'	LLWG
- blue-flowered	LLWG
- 'Colchesterensis'	CWat EWat NGdn NPer WMAq WMoo
I - 'Dorothy'	NGdn
- 'Dorothy Robinson'	EPfP MRav
I - 'Elegante'	EWat
* - 'Elgar'	WMAq
- 'Liam Johns'	LLWG
- 'Monstrosa'	EWat
- 'Richard Greaney'	EWat LLWG
- 'Rose Queen'	see *I. ensata* 'Rose Queen'
- 'Rowden Starlight'	LLWG
- 'Royal Cartwheel' **new**	LLWG
I - 'Snowdrift'	CWat EWat LCro LLWG LOPS MJak NGdn NLar NPer WFar WMAq WMoo
- 'Variegata' (v) ♀H7	CBen CBot CRoa CWat ECha EHoe ELan ELon EPfP EWat LLWG MWts NBro NGdn NPer SPer WMAq WMoo WPnP WWtn
- 'Violet Garth'	EWat
- 'Weymouth'	see *I. laevigata* 'Weymouth Blue'
§ - 'Weymouth Blue'	EWat LLWG
- 'Weymouth Purity'	EWat
laevigata × versicolor Tamberg hybrid	LLWG
§ 'Lake Niklas' (Sib)	ELon MHol
'Lambourn Hills' (TB)	WCAu
'Lamia' (TB)	CIri
'Langport Chapter' (IB)	CKel ESgI
'Langport Chief' (IB)	CKel
'Langport Claret' (IB)	CKel ESgI
'Langport Curlew' (IB)	CKel ESgI
'Langport Duchess' (IB)	ESgI
'Langport Fairy' (IB)	CKel
'Langport Flame' (IB)	CKel ESgI WArt
'Langport Hope' (IB)	CKel
'Langport Jane' (IB)	CKel
'Langport Lady' (IB)	CKel
'Langport Lord' (IB)	ESgI
'Langport Minstrel' (IB)	CKel ESgI
'Langport Pearl' (IB)	CKel
'Langport Pinnacle' (IB)	CKel
'Langport Smoke' (IB)	CKel
'Langport Star' (IB)	CKel ESgI
'Langport Storm' (IB)	CKel ELon EPfP LRHS MRav NRHS SDeJ WHoo
'Langport Sun' (IB)	ESgI
'Langport Sylvia' (IB)	CKel
'Langport Violet' (IB)	CKel ESgI
'Langport Vista' (IB)	CKel
'Langport Wren' (IB) ♀H7	CAby CBWd CBro CKel CRos CWld ELon EPfP EPri ESgI EShb GCal IRob LRHS MBel NGdn NRHS WAul
'Langthorns Pink' (Sib)	ELan MRav WAul WCAu
'Lark Rise' (TB) ♀H7	CKel
'Larry Gaulter' (TB)	WCAu
'Larue Boswell' (TB)	EPfP
'Late Liftoff' (TB)	CIri
§ ***latifolia***	GKev WShi
- ***alba***	WCot
- 'Duchess of York'	EBee

- 'Isabella'	GKev SDeJ
- 'King of the Blues'	CAvo EBee GKev SDeJ
- 'Mansfield'	MNrw
- 'Montblanc'	CAvo GKev SDeJ
- 'Queen of the Blues' (Eng)	GKev SDeJ
- wild-collected	GCal
'Latin Lark' (TB)	ESgI
'Latin Rock' (TB)	WCAu
'Latino' (IB)	WCAu
'Laura Louise' (La)	LLWG
'Laurenbuhl' (Sib)	CExl
'Lavanesque' (TB)	WCAu
'Lavender Bounty' (Sib)	CHid GBin
'Lavender Fair' (Sib)	WCAu
'Lavender Light' (Sib)	WAul
lazica ♀H5	CBct CBod CBot CBro CMac CSpe EIri EPPr EPfP EPot EPri GKev IBlr LRHS MMrt MRav NChi NSti SBrt SEND SPer SPlb SRms WAul WGwG WHil
- 'Joy Bishop'	CJun
* - 'Richard Nutt'	CJun ELon WCot WSHC
- 'Turkish Blue'	IBlr
'Lazuline'	GKev
'Legato' (TB)	ESgI
'Lemon Brocade' (TB)	WCAu
'Lemon Flare' (SDB)	MRav SRms
'Lemon Ice' (TB)	CKel ECha EPfP GBin LRHS NRHS SDeJ SPer
'Lemon Lyric' (TB)	ESgI
'Lemon on Ice' (SDB)	WCAu
'Lemon Pop' (IB)	WCAu
'Lemon Puff' (MDB)	CBro LLHF WCAu
'Lemon Tree' (TB)	WCAu
'Lemon Veil' (Sib)	EBee MNrw WCAu
'Lena' (SDB)	CBro
'Lenora Pearl' (BB)	XSen
'Lent A. Williamson' (TB)	GMaP
'Lenten Prayer' (TB)	WCAu
'Leo Hewitt' (Sib)	ELon
'Leprechaun's Purse' (SDB)	WCAu
leptophylla **new**	GKev
'Let's Elope' (IB)	ESgI WCAu
'Licorice Stick' (TB)	XSen
'Light Beam' (TB)	XSen
'Light Cavalry' (IB)	ESgI
'Light Laughter' (IB)	WCAu
'Lilli-white' (SDB)	CAby CKel CRos CWat EHrv ELon EPfP LRHS MRav NRHS SPoG
'Lilting' (TB)	XSen
'Limbo' (SpH)	LLWG
'Lime Fizz' (TB)	XSen
'Limeheart' (Sib)	CPou LLHF
'Limelight' (TB)	SRms
'Linda's Child' (TB)	WCAu
lineata **new**	GKev
'Ling' **new**	CRos
'Lingering Love' (TB)	WCAu
'Lion King' (Dut)	LCro LOPS MMrt
'Little Black Belt' (SDB)	LRHS
'Little Blackfoot' (SDB)	CTal ESgI WCAu WCot
'Little Blue-eyes' (SDB)	ESgI WCAu
'Little Bluets' (SDB)	ESgI
'Little Dream' (SDB)	WCAu
'Little Episode' (SDB)	CBro ELon
'Little Firecracker' (SDB)	WCAu
'Little Freak' (BB)	CIri
'Little Nutkin' (La)	LLWG
'Little Paul' (MTB)	ESgI
'Little Rosy Wings' (SDB)	CBro CPBP
'Little Shadow' (IB)	MRav SRms
'Little Sheba' (AB)	WCAu
'Little Showoff' (SDB)	ESgI
'Little Tilgates' (CH)	WCot WSHC
'Living Waters' (TB)	ESgI
'Local Color' (TB)	ESgI SIri XSen
'Local Hero' (IB)	WCAu
'Lodore' (TB)	SRms
'Logo' (IB)	WCAu
'Lollipop' (SDB)	ESgI SIri
longipetala	EPPr
'Looking Forward' (TB)	ESgI
'Loop the Loop' (TB)	CKel CMac CRos CTsd SPoG WCAu
'Loose Valley' (MTB) ♀H7	SIri
'Lord Warden' (TB)	CKel CRos ECtt EPfP LRHS NRHS WGwG
'Lorilee' (TB)	ESgI WCAu
'Lost in Love' (TB)	WCAu
'Lost in Space' (BB)	CIri
'Lottie Lou' (TB)	SIri
'Lotus Land' (TB)	WCAu
'Louisa's Song' (TB)	WCAu
Louisiana hybrids	ELan SDir
'Louvois' (TB)	CKel ESgI NLar
'Love Power' (BB)	WCAu
'Love the Sun' (TB)	ESgI XSen
'Lovely Again' (TB)	CKel CRos GKev LRHS MRav NRHS WCAu
'Lovely Leilani' (TB)	ESgI
'Lovely Señorita' (TB)	WCAu
'Love's Tune' (IB)	CKel CRos EBee LRHS NRHS SRGP WTor
'Low Ho Silver' (IB)	WCAu
'Loyalist' (TB)	CPar SBee SIri
'Lucy's Gift' (MTB) ♀H7	EAJP SRGP
'Lugano' (TB)	ESgI
'Luli-Ann' (SDB)	CKel
'Lullaby of Spring' (TB)	CKel
'Lullingstone Castle' (Kent Castles Series) (IB)	SIri
'Lumarco' (TB)	WViv
'Lumière d'Automne' (TB)	XSen
'Lunar Fire' (TB)	CRos LRHS NRHS
'Lure of Gold' (IB)	WCAu
'Lurline' (TB)	WMil
lutescens ♀H7	EPot GKev WAbe
§ - subsp. ***lutescens***	XSen
- subsp. ***subbiflora***	EPot
'Ma Mie' (IB)	WViv
'Mabel Coday' (Sib)	EBee EPri
'Mad Magenta' (Sib)	GBin
'Madeira Belle' (TB)	CAby CKel EPfP ESgI LRHS NRHS WCAu WGwG
'Magharee' (TB)	ESgI
'Magic Man' (TB)	XSen
'Magic Masquerade' (TB)	WCAu
'Magical Encounter' (TB)	SIri
magnifica ♀H5	GKev
- 'Agalik'	GKev
- 'Alba'	GKev
* 'Mahogany Mix' (Dut)	GKev
'Maisie Lowe' (TB)	ESgI
'Majestic' (TB)	WMil
'Majestic Overtures' (Sib) **new**	LLWG WCAu
'Majestic Ruler' (TB)	WCAu
'Make a Wish' (TB)	CIri
'Making Eyes' (SDB)	ELon WCAu
'Mambo Italiano' (TB)	WCAu

	'Man About Town' (TB)	WCAu
	'Mandarin Purple' (Sino-Sib)	NEgg
	'Mandela' (TB) **new**	LMea
	mandshurica	CPBP
	'Mango Entree' (TB)	WCAu
	'Mango Smoothy' (BB)	ESgI
	'Man's Best Friend' (IB) **new**	SIri
	'Marcel Turbat' (TB)	SBee
	'Marden Beech' (IB)	SIri
	'Marden Meadow' (MTB)	SIri
	'Margot Holmes' (Cal-Sib)	WFar
	'Margrave' (TB)	XSen
	'Marguérite' (Reticulata/v)	WCAu
	'Marilyn Holmes' (Sib)	GLog GQue WCot
	'Mariposa Autumn' (TB)	SIri
	'Marjaneh' (J) **new**	GKev
	'Marjorie' (TB) **new**	SRms
	'Marmalade Skies' (BB)	WCAu
	'Marsh Marigold' (TB)	WMil
	'Martyn Rix'	see *I. confusa* 'Martyn Rix'
	'Mary Frances' (TB)	CKel ESgI WCAu XSen
	'Mary McIlroy' (SDB) 🏆H7	CBro
	'Marybill' (TB)	SIri
	'Master Touch' (TB)	CKel ELon XSen
	'Masterwork' (TB)	CIri
	'Mastery' (TB)	LMea
	'Material Girl' (TB)	WCAu
	'Matinata' (TB)	CKel XSen
	'Maui Moonlight' (IB) 🏆H7	CKel ESgI NLar WCAu
	'May Melody' (TB)	WCAu
	'Maya Mint' (MDB)	LLHF
	'Meadow Court' (SDB)	CBro CKel CTal WCAu
	'Medici Prince' (TB)	WCAu
	'Medway Valley' (MTB) 🏆H7	SIri WCAu
	'Megglethorp' (IB)	WCAu
	'Meg's Mantle' (TB)	CKel
	'Melbreak' (TB)	ESgI
	mellita	see *I. suaveolens*
	'Melon Honey' (SDB)	CKel ELon WCAu
	'Melted Butter' (TB)	WCAu
§	'Melton Red Flare' (Sib)	CRos EAJP EBee GBin LRHS LSou MBNS MSpe NRHS WAvo
	'Memphis Memory' (Sib)	ELan ELon MHol NLar SPer WCAu WFar WGob
	'Men in Black' (TB)	WCAu
	'Mer du Sud' (TB) 🏆H7	EIri ESgI LCro LRHS WViv XSen
*	'Merebrook Blue Lagoon' (La)	WMAq
	'Merebrook Jemma J' (La)	WMAq
	'Merebrook Purpla' (La)	WMAq
	'Merebrook Rum 'n' Raisin' (La)	WMAq
*	'Merebrook Rusty Red' (La)	WMAq
*	'Merebrook Snowflake' (La)	WMAq
	'Merebrook Sunnyside Up' (La)	WMAq
	'Merebrook Symphony' (La)	WMAq
	'Mescal' (TB)	WCAu
	'Mesmerizer' (TB)	EBee
	mesopotamica	see *I. germanica*
	'Messire Pierre' (BB)	CIri
	'Messy Jessi' (TB)	CIri
	METALLIC MIXED **new**	ETMg
	'Metaphor' (TB)	WCAu
	'Mezza Cartuccia' (IB)	ESgI
	'Miami Beach' (TB)	WCAu
	'Midas Mite' (MDB)	LLHF
	'Midhurst White' (TB)	SIri
I	'Midnight Blue' (MDB)	CBro
	'Midnight Caller' (TB)	ESgI XSen
	'Midnight Thunder' (TB)	CIri
	'Midnight Treat' (TB)	WCAu
	'Midsummer Night's Dream' (IB)	ESgI
	'Mighty Mouse' (MDB)	ELon
	'Mighty Warrior' (TB)	CIri
	milesii 🏆H3	CExl EPri GBin GKev SBrt WSHC
	- CC 6839	GKev
	'Millennium Sunrise' (TB)	WCAu
	'Mini Big Horn' (IB)	CIri
	'Mini-Agnes' (SDB)	CBro
	'Minidragon' (SDB)	SIri
	'Minisa' (TB)	ESgI
	'Miss Nellie' (BB)	CKel
	'Mission Ridge' (TB)	MHol
	missouriensis	CMac GKev
	'Mist on the Mountain' (TB) **new**	CKel
	'Mister Roberts' (SDB)	ESgI
	'Mistress of Camelot' (TB)	SDys
	'Mme Chéreau' (TB)	ESgI WCAu
	'Mon Prince' (BB)	CIri
	'Monsieur-Monsieur' (TB)	ESgI
	Monspur Group	WCot
	'Moon Silk' (Sib)	CBro ECtt ELon EPri LLHF MAvo SCob WCot WFar WGob
	'Moonlight Waves'	see *I. ensata* 'Moonlight Waves'
	'Moonlit Water' (TB)	WCAu
	'Morwell' (TB)	WMil
	'Morwenna' (TB) 🏆H7	ESgI
	'Mother Earth' (TB)	ESgI
	'Mountain Lake' (Sib)	EPfP EShb GBin LRHS NRHS SPtp WFar WSpi
	'Mrs Nate Rudolph' (SDB)	WCAu
	'Mrs Rowe' (Sib)	CPou EIri EPri MRav MWat WAul WFar
	'Mrs Tait' (Spuria)	NChi
	'Mrs Valerie West' (TB)	WMil
	'Mrs Wright's Pink'	WCAu
	'Muggles' (SDB)	CTal SIri
	'Mukaddam' (TB)	CIri
	'Murder Mystery' (TB)	WCAu
	'Murmuring Morn' (TB)	WCAu
	'Music' (SDB)	CTal SIri
	'Must Unite' (TB)	WCAu
	'My First Kiss' (Sib)	WAul
	'My Kayla' (SDB)	ESgI
	'My Love' (Sib)	IMou WAul
	'My Seedling' (MDB)	CBro
	'Myra' (SDB)	XSen
	'Mysterieux' (TB)	SIri
	'Mystic' (TB)	WMil
	'Mystic Beauty' (Dut)	GKev SDeJ
	'Mystic Dragon' (TB)	CIri SDys
	'Nada'	WCot
	'Naivasha' (TB)	CKel
	'Nancy Hardy' (MDB)	CBro
	'Naples' (TB)	WCAu
	'Natascha' (Reticulata)	EPot GKev LAma SAdu SCob SDeJ
	'Natchez Trace' (TB)	CKel EPri LRHS XSen
	'Navajo Code' (TB)	CIri
	'Navajo Jewel' (TB)	ESgI WCAu XSen
	'Navy Brass' (Sib)	EPri WAul
	'Needlecraft' (TB)	XSen
	'Needlepoint' (TB)	ESgI
	'Negro Modelo' (SDB)	WCAu
	'Neige de Mai' (TB)	ESgI
*	'Nel Jupe' (TB)	CRos LRHS NLar NRHS
	nepalensis	see *I. decora*

	'Neutron Dance' (TB)	WCAu
	'New Argument' (J)	LLHF
	'New Centurion' (TB)	XSen
	'New Face' (TB)	WCAu
	'New Flame' (TB)	ESgI
	'New Idea' (MTB)	CBro ESgI WCAu
	'New Leaf' (TB)	WCAu
	'New Perspective' (TB)	CIri
	'New Snow' (TB)	WCAu
	'Nibelungen' (TB)	CBro ESgI WCAu XSen
	'Night Breeze' (Sib)	EPri
	'Night Edition' (TB)	CKel ESgI XSen
	'Night Game' (TB)	XSen
	'Night Owl' (TB)	CKel ELon ESgI GMcL MHer SPoG
	'Night Ruler' (TB)	WCAu
	'Nights of Gladness' (TB)	ESgI
	'Nine Lives' (SDB)	WCAu
	'No Down Payment' (TB)	WCAu
	'Noble Lady' (TB)	CIri
	'Noctambule' (TB)	SIri WViv
	'Noon Siesta' (TB)	ESgI
	'Nordica' (TB)	ESgI
§	× ***norrisii***	EBee
	– 'Butterfly Magic'	EBee
	'North Downs' (BB)	SIri
	'Northern Jewel' (IB)	SIri
	'Northumberland Piper' (TB)	SIri
	'Nottingham Lace' (Sib)	LLHF
	'Nouveau Riche' (TB)	WCAu
	'Now and Forever' (La)	LLWG
	'Oasis Fuzzy Wuzzy' (TB)	CIri
	'Oasis Sydney' (TB)	CIri
	'Obligato' (IB)	CKel
	'Obsidian' (TB)	WCAu
	'Ochre Doll' (SDB)	CBro CKel CTal
	ochroleuca	see *I. orientalis* Mill.
	'O'Cool' (IB)	CKel
	'October' (TB)	ESgI
	'October Storm' (IB)	CIri
	'Oh Happy Day' (La)	LLWG
	'Oh Jamaica' (TB)	WCAu XSen
	'Oh So Cool' (MTB)	ESgI
	'Oklahoma Centennial' (TB)	WCAu
	'Oktoberfest' (TB)	XSen
	'Ola Kalá' (TB)	CAby CBod CKel CRos GMaP GMcL LRHS MCot MGos NLar NRHS SPer WAul WCAu XSen
	'Old Black Magic' (TB)	ESgI XSen
	'Old Flame' (TB)	XSen
	'Olympiad' (TB)	ESgI XSen
	'Olympic Challenge' (TB)	ESgI MRav WCAu
	'Olympic Torch' (TB)	WCAu
	'Ominous Stranger' (TB)	ESgI MMrt WCAu
	'Once Again' (TB)	XSen
	'One Desire' (TB)	XSen
	'Open Arms' (TB)	CIri
	'Open Sky' (SDB)	CTal LRHS SIri XSen
	'Opposing Forces' (TB)	WCAu
	'Orageux' (IB)	SIri
	'Orange Caper' (SDB)	CKel CMac CRos CTal ECtt EPfP ESgI LRHS LSou MRav MTin NRHS WCot
	'Orange Harvest' (TB)	ESgI XSen
	'Orange Order' (TB)	WCAu
	'Orange Thunder' (TB) <u>**new**</u>	CKel
	'Orbison' (TB)	CIri
	'Orchidarium' (TB)	CKel
	orchioides misapplied	see *I. bucharica* Foster
§	***orchioides*** Carrière	CAby ELan
	'Oregon Skies' (TB)	ESgI
	'Oriental Beauty' (Dut)	GKev LCro LOPS
	'Oriental Beauty' (TB)	SDeJ
	orientalis ambig.	CAvo EWes MNrw
§	***orientalis*** Mill. ♀H7	GBin GCal GKev MMuc SEND WCot WCru XSen
	'Orinoco Flow' (BB) ♀H7	CKel ESgI WCAu
	'Orloff' (TB)	ESgI
	'Oro Antico' (TB)	CIri
	'Orville Fay' (Sib)	GWyn WBor WCot
	'Osay Canuc' (TB)	CIri
	'Osborne's Grey' (Sib)	WAul
	'Ostrogoth' (TB)	CIri
	'Ottawa' (Sib)	CPou CRos CWat LRHS MMuc NRHS WFar
	'Oulo' (TB)	ESgI XSen
	'Our House' (TB)	ESgI
	'Our Marcus' (TB)	SIri
	'Out of the Dark' (TB)	WCAu
	'Out Yonder' (TB)	WCAu
	'Outrage' (SDB)	CIri
	'Outset' (Sib)	ELon
	'Over Easy' (SDB)	CKel
	'Overjoyed' (TB)	WCAu XSen
	'O'What' (SDB)	ESgI
	'Owyhee Desert' (TB)	WCAu
	'Ozark Maid' (MTB)	SDys
	Pacific Coast hybrids	see *I.* Californian hybrids
	'Pacific Mist' (TB)	WCAu
	'Pacific Panorama' (TB)	XSen
	'Pagan Dance' (TB)	WCAu
	'Pagan Pink' (TB)	XSen
	'Pagan Princess' (TB)	WCAu
I	'Pageant' (Sib)	WCot
	'Paint It Black' (TB)	XSen
	'Pale Shades' (IB)	CBro CKel
§	***pallida***	CBWd CBro CMac EHrv ESgI ESps GMaP MRav SCob SEND SRms WCAu WTor XSen
§	– 'Argentea Variegata' (TB/v)	Widely available
	– 'Aurea'	see *I. pallida* 'Variegata' Hort.
	– 'Aurea Variegata'	see *I. pallida* 'Variegata' Hort.
	– subsp. ***cengialtii***	XSen
	– var. ***dalmatica***	see *I. pallida* subsp. *pallida*
§	– subsp. ***pallida***	CExl CKel CRos ECha ELan EPfP GCal LRHS NRHS SPer
	– 'Variegata' misapplied	see *I. pallida* 'Argentea Variegata'
§	– 'Variegata' Hort. (v) ♀H7	CBcs CBot CBro CKel CMac CRos CWat ECha ELan EPfP ESgI ESps LRHS MAsh MHol MRav MWat NRHS SPer SPlb SPoG SRms SRot SWvt WAbe XSen
	'Palm Springs' (IB)	EPot GKev SDeJ
	'Palm Springs' (Reticulata)	LAma SDeJ
	'Palomino' (TB)	WCAu
	'Pamplemousse' (IB)	SIri
	'Pane e Vino' (TB)	ESgI
	'Pansy Purple' (Sib)	MNrw WHil
	'Panther' (SDB)	WCAu
	'Papillon' (Sib)	CRos CTri ECtt ELan ELon EPri GWyn IRob LRHS MBel NGdn NRHS NSti SCob SDeJ SPer WAul WFar
	'Paprika Fono's' (TB)	WCAu
	'Paradise' (TB)	CKel
	paradoxa	GKev
	'Paris Lights' (TB)	XSen
	'Parisian Dawn' (TB)	WCAu
	'Parisien' (TB)	EIri
	'Parts Plus' (IB)	CIri

	'Party Dress' (TB)	CBod CKel CMac CRos EBee ELan EPfP EShb LRHS MRav NLar NRHS NWad SPer SPoG SRms WGwG
	'Party's Over' (TB)	WCAu
	'Passionate Embrace' (TB)	WCAu
	'Pastel Accent' (La) **new**	LLWG
	'Patina' (TB)	EIri LRHS WCAu
	'Patricia Elizabeth Linnegar' (TB)	WCAu
	'Paul Black' (TB) $\mathbb{Y}^{H7}$	WCAu
	'Pauline' (Reticulata)	CAvo CRos EPfP EPot ERCP GKev LAma LCro LRHS MWat NRHS SAdu SCob
	'Pauline' (TB) **new**	WRHF
	'Pause' (SDB)	WCAu
	'Peaceful Waters' (TB)	XSen
	'Peach Eyes' (SDB)	CBro CKel CTal
	'Peach Picotee' (TB)	ESgI XSen
	'Peaches in Wine' (La)	LLWG
	'Peachy Face' (IB)	ESgI XSen
	'Pearl Queen' (Sib)	MCot
	'Pearls of Autumn' (TB)	WCAu
	'Pearly Dawn' (TB)	ECtt SRGP
*	'Pêche Melba' (TB)	XSen
	'Peebee and Jay' (MTB)	WCAu
	'Pelion Hills'	LRHS
	'Penny a Pinch' (TB)	CKel
	'Percheron' (Sib)	EBee EPri ESgI MNrw
	'Peresh' (AB)	CTal
	'Perfect Interlude' (TB)	EIri XSen
	'Perfect Vision' (Sib) $\mathbb{Y}^{H7}$	MHCG
	'Performer' (MTB)	EIri
	'Perry's Blue' (Sib)	Widely available
I	'Perry's Favourite' (Sib)	WAul
	'Perry's Pigmy' (Sib)	ELon
	'Persian Berry' (TB)	WCAu XSen
	'Persimmon' misapplied	see *I.* 'Tycoon'
	'Persimmon' ambig. (Sib)	CAby CHid CKel CRos ECtt GKin GQue LRHS NRHS SPtp WFar WMoo
	'Petal Pushers' (TB)	CIri
	'Peter Hewitt' (Sib) $\mathbb{Y}^{H7}$	EPri WAul WCAu
	'Petit Tigre' (IB)	SIri
	'Petite Monet' (MTB)	ESgI
	'Petite Polka' (SDB)	NLar
	'Picadee'	CTal EPfP
	'Picasso Moon' (TB)	WCAu
	'Pigeon' (SDB)	XSen
	'Pinewood Amethyst' (CH)	MAvo
	'Pinewood Charmer' (CH)	CElw
	'Pink Attraction' (TB)	ESgI XSen
	'Pink Blink' (MDB) **new**	CTal
	'Pink Bubbles' (BB)	XSen
	'Pink Charm' (TB)	CKel CRos EPfP LRHS NRHS SDeJ SPlb SPoG
	'Pink Confetti' (TB)	XSen
	'Pink Haze' (Sib)	CDor CKel EBee EPfP ESgI
	'Pink Horizon' (TB)	XSen
	'Pink Kitten' (IB)	WCAu WGwG XSen
	'Pink Lavender' (TB)	ELon SRms
	'Pink Parfait' (Sib)	MBNS MHol NGdn WFar WHar WTor WWtn
	'Pink Pele' (IB)	ESgI
	'Pink Quartz' (TB)	ESgI
	'Pink Swan' (TB)	XSen
	'Pink Taffeta' (TB)	XSen
	'Pinnacle' (TB)	CKel GCal
	'Pioneer' (TB)	WMil
	'Pipes of Pan' (TB)	ESgI MRav WCAu
	'Pirate Prince' (Sib)	NPer
	'Pirate's Quest' (TB)	ELon ESgI XSen
	'Piroska' (TB)	ESgI XSen
*	'Piu Blue' (TB)	ESgI
	'Pixie' (DB)	CRos GKev
	'Pixie' (Reticulata) $\mathbb{Y}^{H7}$	ELan EPot ERCP LAma LRHS SAdu SDeJ XEll
	'Pleasures of May' (Sib)	EBee ELon WCAu WGob
	'Pledge Allegiance' (TB)	ESgI WCAu
	'Plickadee' (SDB)	CBro
	'Plissée' (Sib) $\mathbb{Y}^{H7}$	GBin GWyn
	'Plum Lucky' (SDB)	SIri
	'Plum Wine' (SDB)	CKel
	'Poem of Ecstasy' (TB)	WCAu
	'Poesie' (TB)	WViv
	'Pogo' (SDB)	CKel CMac CRos CTal ECtt ELon EPfP EShb GMaP LRHS LSou MRav MTin NRHS SDeJ SRms
	'Polvere di Stelle' (TB)	ESgI
	'Popsicle' (SDB)	WCAu
	'Pounsley Purple' (Sib)	CPou EPri
	'Powder Blue Cadillac' (TB)	WCAu
	'Power Point' (TB)	CIri WCAu
	'Prairie Thunder' (AB)	WCAu
	'Presby's Crown Jewel' (TB)	WCAu
	'Presence' (TB)	SIri
	'Pretender' (TB)	WCAu
	PRETTY IN BLUE mixed (Dut)	GKev SDeJ
	'Pretty Please' (TB)	ESgI
	'Primrose Cream' (Sib)	WCot
	'Primrose Drift' (TB)	ESgI
	'Prince Indigo' (TB)	MRav
	'Prince of Burgundy' (IB)	WCAu
	'Princess Beatrice' (TB)	WCAu
	'Princess Bride' (BB) $\mathbb{Y}^{H7}$	WCAu
	'Princess Diana' (SDB)	SIri
	'Princess Osra' (TB)	WMil
	'Princesse Caroline de Monaco' (TB)	CKel ESgI WViv
	prismatica	GKev
	'Private Eye' (TB)	WCAu
	'Professor Blaauw' (Dut) $\mathbb{Y}^{H5}$	CAvo CWCL
	'Props' (SDB)	CIri
	'Prosper Laugier' (IB)	WCAu
	'Protocol' (IB)	CKel
	'Proud Tradition' (TB)	ESgI SIri WCAu XSen
	'Provençal' (TB)	CKel CPar ELon ESgI WCAu XSen
	'Prussian Blue' (Sib) $\mathbb{Y}^{H7}$	GBin SMHy
	pseudacorus	Widely available
	- B&SWJ 5018 from Japan	WCru
	- 'Alba'	MSKA NGdn SRms
	- var. ***bastardii***	CBen CRoa CWat ECha ELon EPfP EWat LLWG MSKA NPer SLon SPer WBrk WFar WMoo WPnP WWtn XLum
	- 'Clotted Cream'	GLog
	- 'Come in Spinner'	LLWG
	- 'Crème de la Crème'	CKel ELon EPfP LLWG NLar NSti NWad WFar
	- 'Dragonfly Dance'	LLWG
	- 'Flore Pleno' (d)	CBen LLWG MSKA NLar NPer WBrk WCot WFar WPnP WWtn
	- giant	CRoa
I	- 'Golden Fleece'	SPer
	- 'Golden Queen'	CRoa EWat LLWG
	- 'Ivory'	LLWG
	- 'Kelis Choice'	LLWG
	- 'Krill'	EBee LLWG

- 'Mandchurica'	XBlo
- 'Mini Mart'	LLWG
- 'Rowden Brimstone'	CRoa
- 'Roy Davidson' 🏆H7	CBre CBro GCal LLWG MWts NLar WCot WFar WHil WWtn
- 'Spartacus'	EBee
- 'Sulphur Queen'	GBin LLWG NLar WCot
- 'Sun Cascade'	GBin
- 'Tiger Brother'	CBro LLWG WBrk
- 'Turnipseed'	WCot
- 'Variegata' (v) 🏆H7	Widely available
pseudopumila	CBot
'Puddy Tat' (SDB)	WCAu
'Pulse Rate' (SDB)	CBro
pumila	CBot CRos ITim LRHS MCot NRHS
- f. ***atroviolacea***	CKel WAbe
* - 'Gelber Mantel'	WFar
- 'Violacea' (DB)	CRos NRHS SRms
- yellow-flowered	WAbe
'Pumpin' Iron' (SDB) 🏆H7	CKel CTal ESgI
'Punk' (MDB)	CIri
'Pure As Gold' (TB)	CWCL ESgI WCot XSen
'Purple Gem' (Reticulata)	CAby CRos EPfP LAma LRHS NRHS SAdu
'Purple Hill' (Reticulata)	GKev LAma
PURPLE LAVENDER MIXED (Dut)	GKev
'Purple Mere' (Sib)	MHCG
'Purple Pepper' (TB)	WCAu
'Purple Ritz' (TB)	WCAu
'Purple Sensation' (Dut)	SDeJ
'Purple Study' (MTB)	WCAu
'Purr for Mints' (TB)	CIri
'Pussycat Pink' (SDB)	ESgI WCAu
'Quaker Lady' (TB)	ESgI SBee SIri WCAu
'Quantum Leap' (TB)	CIri
'Quark' (SDB)	CBro CKel
'Quechee' (TB)	CBWd CKel CWld EBee EPPr EPfP ESgI GMaP LBuc LRHS MAvo MCot MRav MWat NLar NRHS NWad SCob SDeJ SPer WGwG
'Queen in Calico' (TB)	ESgI WCAu
'Queen Jeanne' (La)	LLWG
'Queen of Angels' (TB)	WCAu
'Queen of Hearts' (TB)	XSen
'Queen's Circle' (TB) 🏆H7	WCAu
'Queen's Prize' (SDB)	SIri
'Rabbit's Foot' (SDB)	CTal SIri
'Radiant Apogee' (TB)	EIri
'Radiant Burst' (IB)	SIri
'Rain Dance' (SDB) 🏆H7	ESgI
'Rainbow Candy' (TB)	WCAu
'Rainbow Etude' (TB)	WCAu
RAINBOW GRAND MIXTURE	SDeJ
'Rainbow High' (TB)	WCAu
'Rainbow Rim' (SDB)	ESgI WCAu
'Rainbow Selection' (TB)	CIri WCAu
'Rainbow Sky' (TB)	WCAu
'Rainbow Tour' (TB)	WCAu
'Rajah' (TB)	CAby CBod CKel CRos EHrv ELan ELon EPfP EUJe GMaP LRHS LSRN MHer MNrw MRav NRHS SDeJ SPer SPhm SPoG WBor
'Rameses' (TB)	ESgI
ramsayi **new**	GCal
'Rancho Rose' (TB)	XSen
'Rare Edition' (IB)	CKel WArt XSen
'Rare Quality' (TB)	XSen
'Rare Treat' (TB)	XSen
'Raspberry Acres' (IB)	MRav WCAu
'Raspberry Blush' (IB) 🏆H7	CBod CKel CRos CWld EIri EPfP GBin LRHS LSou MAvo MRav NRHS SDeJ WAul WGwG WHoo WTor XSen
'Raspberry Tiger' (SDB)	WCAu
'Razoo' (SDB)	CKel CPBP
'Re La Blanche' (TB)	SIri
'Real Coquette' (SDB)	CTal SIri
'Rebecca Perret' (TB)	WCAu
'Recurring Delight' (TB)	WCAu
'Red Canyon Glow' (TB)	CIri
'Red Dazzler' (La)	CIri
'Red Echo' (La)	CIri
'Red Ember' (Dut)	CAvo ERCP GKev LCro LOPS MMrt WHil WRHF
'Red Flare' (TB)	WFar
'Red Flash' (TB)	ESgI
'Red Heart' (SDB)	ELon ESgI MRav XSen
'Red Orchid' (IB)	ELan ESgI LRHS SRms WCAu
'Red Revival' (TB)	MRav WCAu
'Red Rum' (TB)	EWes
'Red Zinger' (IB)	CMac ESgI LRHS
'Redelta' (TB)	XSen
'Reflets Safran' (TB)	SIri XSen
'Regal' (Reticulata) **new**	LAma
'Regal Surprise' (SpH) 🏆H7	CRoa EWat LLWG WWtn
'Regality' (Sib)	EBee MHer MMuc
'Regards' (SDB)	CBro XSen
'Regency Buck' (Sib)	WFar
§ ***reichenbachii***	GKev LLHF WAbe
'Reincarnation' (TB)	CIri
'Rendez-Vous' (Dut) **new**	SDeJ
'Repartee' (TB)	XSen
reticulata	ELan GKev SAdu SDeJ SPer
- var. ***bakeriana***	GKev LAma LLHF XEll
'Return to Elegance' (TB)	WCAu
'Rhapsody' (Reticulata)	CRos EPot ERCP GKev LAma LLHF LRHS NRHS SDeJ
'Rheingauperle' (TB)	ESgI
'Rhett' (La)	EBee
'Rigamarole' (Sib)	MWts SCob WFar WGob
'Rikugi-sakura' (Sib)	EBee ELon EPri LLHF NLar WCot WGob
'Ringo' (TB)	LSRN MRav WCAu
'Rings of Saturn' (TB)	CIri
'Rio Rojo' (TB)	WCAu
'Rip City' (TB)	ESgI SBee
'Rising Moon' (TB)	SIri
'Rive Gauche' (TB)	ESgI
'River Avon' (TB)	WCAu
'Riverbuds' (SDB)	SIri WCAu
'Roanoke's Choice' (Sib)	CBro CElw ELon EWes MNrw WFar WGob
'Roaring Jelly' (Sib)	EPri EWes NLar WCAu WCot
'Rob Cornell' (TB)	ESgI
§ × ***robusta*** 'Dark Aura' 🏆H7	LLWG MAvo MWts SIri WCot
§ - 'Gerald Darby'	CBod CRos CSpe CWat EBee EHrv ELan EPPr EPfP IBoy LRHS MCot MHer MHol MNrw NGdn NLar NRHS NSti SCob WBrk WCAu WHil WMoo WOut WPnP WSpi WWtn
- 'Mountain Brook'	CRoa LLWG
* - 'Purple Fan'	LLWG
'Robusto' (TB) **new**	CKel
'Rochester Castle' (Kent Castles Series) (IB)	SIri
§ 'Rocket' (TB)	EPfP GMaP LBuc LRHS MCot MRav NRHS SDeJ SPer
'Rocket Master' (TB)	ESgI
'Rocket Randy' (TB)	CIri

	'Rodeo Arena' (TB)	CIri
	'Roku Oji' (Sib)	CIri
	'Romantic Evening' (TB)	EIri WCAu XSen
	'Romney Marsh' (IB)	SIri
	'Romola' (TB)	WMil
	'Roryu' (SpH) **new**	LLWG
	'Rosalie Figge' (TB)	CMac ESgI WCAu WCot
	'Rosé' (TB)	LSRN
	'Rose Queen'	see *I. ensata* 'Rose Queen'
	'Rose Violet' (TB)	WCAu
	'Rosebud Melody' (Sib)	GBin GWyn
	'Roseplic' (TB)	LRHS
	'Rosette Wine' (TB)	ESgI
	'Rosselline' (Sib)	WAul
	'Rosy Bows' (Sib)	EBee WFar
	'Rosy Veil' (TB)	ESgI
	'Rosy Wings' (TB)	ESgI
	'Roucoulade' (TB)	SIri
	'Rouge Gorge' (TB)	SIri WViv
	'Roussette' (IB) **new**	SIri
	'Rowden Aurelius' (Sib)	WAul
I	'Royal Blue' (Sib)	EBee ECha
	'Royal Crusader' (TB)	CCse WCAu XSen
	'Royal Elegance' (TB)	SIri
	'Royal Intrigue' (TB)	SIri
	'Royal Satin' (TB)	CHid
	'Royal Tapestry' (TB)	MAvo
	'Roy's Repeater'	WCAu
	'Rubacuori' (TB)	ESgI
	'Ruby' (Reticulata) **new**	LAma
	'Ruby Chimes' (IB)	ESgI WCAu
	'Ruby Contrast' (TB)	WCAu
	'Ruby Eruption' (SDB)	CTal EIri WCAu
	'Ruby Morn' (TB)	WCAu
	'Ruby Wine' (Sib)	EPri LEdu
	rudskyi	see *I. variegata*
	'Ruffled Velvet' (Sib) ♀H7	CBcs CDor CElw CHid CKel ECtt ELan EPfP EPri GBin GLog GMaP GMcL ILea IMou LRHS MCot MHol MRav MSpe NChi NLar SCob SPer WAul WCAu WFar WHar WWtn
	'Ruffles and Flourishes' (Sib) **new**	LLWG WCAu
	'Ruffles Plus' (Sib)	EPri
	'Russet Crown' (TB)	CKel
	'Rustic Cedar' (TB)	ESgI
	'Rustle of Spring' (TB)	WCAu
	'Rustler' (TB)	WCAu
	'Rusty Beauty' (Dut)	SDeJ
	'Ruth Margaret' (TB)	CKel
	'Ruth Rowlands' (TB)	ESgI
	ruthenica	WHil
	- var. ***nana***	CExl GEdr GKev
	'Sable' (TB)	CKel CRos EHrv ELan EPfP ESgI GMaP LRHS MCot MRav MWat NLar NRHS SCob SDeJ SPer WAul WCAu WGwG
	'Sable Night' (TB)	CKel ESgI
	'Safari Sunset' (TB)	WCAu
	'Sailor' (IB)	WCAu
	'Sailor's Dream' (MTB)	WCAu
	'Saint Crispin' (TB)	CRos EBee EPfP GMaP IRob LRHS MRav NRHS SPer SPoG WGwG
	'Salamander Crossing' (Sib) ♀H7	WAul WCAu
	'Sally Jane' (TB)	WCAu
	'Salonique' (TB)	ESgI NLar WCAu
	'Saltwood' (SDB)	CBro ESgI
	'Saltwood Castle' (Kent Castles Series) (IB)	SIri
	'Salzburg Echo' (TB)	WCAu
	'Sam Carne' (TB)	WCAu
	'Samarcande' (TB)	ESgI
	× ***sambucina***	XSen
	'San Diego' (TB)	ESgI
	'San Francisco' (TB)	ESgI
	'Sandling Sunset' (TB)	SIri
	'Sandy Caper' (IB)	WCAu
	'Sangreal' (IB)	CRos LRHS NRHS
§	***sanguinea*** 'Snow Queen'	CAvo CBcs CKel CRos EBee EHoe ELan EPfP EPri GBin GWyn IBoy IMou LRHS MMuc NBid NLar NQui NRHS NSti SCob SPer WAul WCAu WCot WFar WHar WMoo
	'Sapphire Beauty' (Dut)	GKev SDeJ
	'Sapphire Gem' (SDB)	CKel ESgI LSRN WCAu
	'Sapphire Hills' (TB)	LRHS WCAu XSen
	sari	CTal
	'Sasha Borisovich' (TB)	ESgI
	'Savoir Faire' (Sib)	ECha
	'Scandinavian Girl'	WCAu
	'Scent Sational' (Reticulata)	LAma
	'Scented Wonder' (TB)	WCAu
	'Scentillating Scentinel' (TB) **new**	LMea
	schachtii purple-flowered	WAbe
	'Scholar' (SDB) **new**	CTal
	'Scottish Warrior' (TB)	CIri
	'Scramble' (Sib)	GMcL NEgg WCot WFar
	'Scribe' (MDB)	CBro
	'Sea Breeze' (Reticulata) **new**	LAma
	'Sea Fret' (SDB)	CBro
	'Sea Green' (Reticulata) **new**	LAma
	'Sea of Joy' (TB)	CKel XSen
	'Sea Power' (TB)	SIri
	'Sea Shadows' (Sib)	EPri ESgI WCAu
	'Seafire' (SDB)	WCAu
	'Seakist' (TB)	WCAu
	'Season Ticket' (IB)	XSen
	'Seastone' (SDB)	WCAu
	'Second Look' (TB)	XSen
	'Second Wind' (TB)	WCAu
	'Secret Melody' (TB)	XSen
	'Self Evident' (MDB)	LLHF
	'Semiramis' (TB) **new**	CKel
	'Semola' (SDB)	ESgI
	'Senlac' (TB)	NLar WMil
	'Señor Frog' (SDB)	ESgI
	'Sensation' (TB) **new**	WHar
	serbica	see *I. reichenbachii*
	'Serene Moment' (TB)	SIri
	'Serenity Prayer' (SDB)	WCAu
	setosa ♀H7	CFis CMac CRos CTri CWCL EAJP GAbr GBin GKev LRHS MNrw NHpl NRHS WOld
	- ***alba***	NLar
	- var. ***arctica***	GKev LEdu
I	- 'Baby Blue'	CRos EPfP LRHS MBNS MJak NRHS
	- subsp. ***canadensis***	see *I. hookeri*
	- dark violet-flowered	EPri
	- var. ***nana***	see *I. hookeri*
	'Seven Hills' (TB)	ESgI
	'Shaker's Prayer' (Sib) ♀H7	EWes GBin MBrN MNrw SBch WGob
	'Shakespeare's Sonnet' (SDB)	ESgI
	'Shall We Dance' (Sib) ♀H7	CIri EWes
	'Shampoo' (IB)	SIri WCAu
	'Share the Spirit' (TB)	WCAu

'Sharp Dressed Man' (TB)	WCAu
'Sharrie Carrie' (TB) **new**	SIri
'Sheila Ann Germaney' (Reticulata)	CRos EPot ERCP GKev LAma LLHF LRHS NRHS SAdu WBrk
'Shelby Lynne' (TB)	CIri
'Shelford Giant' (Spuria) 🏆H7	NEgg
'Sherbet Lemon' (IB) 🏆H7	WCAu
'Shifnal'	WCAu
'Shirley Chandler' (IB) 🏆H7	SIri
'Shirley Pope' (Sib) 🏆H7	EWTr EWes GBin GWyn LRHS MAvo NSti WFar WMoo WPnP
'Shirley's Choice' (Sib)	EBee EPri SIri
'Short Distance' (IB)	SIri
'Showdown' (Sib)	CRos ECtt GMaP LRHS NRHS
'Shrawley' (Sib)	WAul
shrevei	see *I. virginica* var. *shrevei*
'Shurton Demon' (TB)	CKel
'Shurton Inn' (TB)	CKel SRms WCAu
'Shurton Princess' (TB)	CKel
sibirica	CAvo CTri CTsd ESps GAbr GBin GKev MCot MMuc NChi SCob SPlb SRot WArt WBrk WCFE WFar WGwG WHer WMoo WShi
- PAB 6119	LEdu
- 'Niklas Sea'	see *I.* 'Lake Niklas'
- 'Redflare'	see *I.* 'Melton Red Flare'
- 'Snow Queen'	see *I. sanguinea* 'Snow Queen'
'Sibirica Alba'	ECha EPfP EPri SRms WBrk WFar
sichuanensis	CExl SPlb
'Side Effect'	WCAu
'Sidney Linnegar' (TB)	WCAu
'Sidney Unknown'	WCAu
'Sierra Blue' (TB)	ESgI
'Sierra Grande' (TB)	SIri XSen
'Sierra Nevada' (Spuria)	XSen
'Sign of Leo' (TB)	CKel XSen
'Silkirim' (TB)	CKel
'Silver Edge' (Sib) 🏆H7	Widely available
'Silverado' (TB)	CKel ESgI GBin LRHS WCAu
'Silvery Beauty' (Dut)	CAvo ELan GKev LCro LOPS SDeJ
'Silvery Princess' (Dut) **new**	SDeJ
sindjarensis	see *I. aucheri*
'Sinfonietta' (La)	LLWG WCot
'Sing to Me' (TB)	WCAu
'Sinister Desire' (IB)	SIri
sintenisii 🏆H5	CBot CBro CPBP GKev LLHF SBrt WAbe WArt XSen
'Sir Michael' (TB)	ESgI
'Siva Siva' (TB)	MRav
'Sixtine C' (TB)	SIri
'Skating Party' (TB)	CKel ESgI XSen
'Skiers' Delight' (TB)	LRHS
'Sky Beauty' (Dut)	SDeJ
'Sky Hooks' (TB)	XSen
'Sky Tracery' (MTB)	SDys
'Sky Wings' (Sib)	CSam ECha GQue MArl WMoo
'Skydancer' (SDB)	WCAu
'Skyfire' (TB)	ESgI
'Skylark's Song' (TB)	EIri
'Small Sky' (SDB)	CBro
'Smart' (SDB)	WCAu
'Smart Aleck' (TB)	ESgI
'Smart Girl' (TB)	EIri
'Smart Move' (TB)	ESgI
'Smiling Faces' (TB)	WCAu
'Smith Named Keith' (TB)	CIri
'Smitten Kitten' (IB)	LSRN WCAu
'Smokey Salmon' (TB)	CKel
'Smooth' (SDB)	SDys
'Snow Prince' (Sib)	EPri
'Snow Season' (SDB)	ESgI
'Snow Shoes' (TB)	CIri
'Snow Tracery' (TB)	LRHS NRHS
'Snow Troll' (SDB)	WCAu
'Snowcrest' (Sib)	CBre GBin LRHS MRav MSpe NRHS WAul WHoo
'Snowmound' (TB)	CCCN CKel ESgI WCAu
'Snowy Owl' (TB)	CKel WCAu
'Snugglebug' (SDB)	CTal WCAu
'Social Event' (TB)	ESgI XSen
'Soft Blue' (Sib) 🏆H7	EPri WAul WCAu
'Soft Rain' (TB)	CIri
'Solar Fire' (TB)	CIri
'Solid Mahogany' (TB)	MRav
'Soligo' (MDB)	ESgI
'Solo Flight' (TB)	SDys
'Somerset Blue' (TB)	CKel
'Somerton Dance' (SDB)	CKel
'Song of Norway' (TB)	EIri XSen
'Sonoran Sands' (IB)	SDys
'Sopra il Vulcano' (BB)	ESgI
'Sorbonne' (TB)	WCAu
'Sordid Lives' (TB)	WCAu
'Sostenique' (TB)	ESgI
'Southcombe White' (Sib)	SMHy
'Souvenir de Madame Gaudichau' (TB)	ESgI
'Spanish Angel' (TB)	CIri
'Sparkletts' (MDB) **new**	CTal
'Sparkling Rose' (Sib)	Widely available
'Sparkling Waters' (TB)	ESgI
'Speck So' (MTB)	WCAu
I 'Speckles' (Sib)	EPPr
'Spellbreaker' (TB)	SIri
'Spice Lord' (TB)	WCAu
'Spiced Custard' (TB)	EIri ESgI WCAu
'Spiced Lemon' (TB)	WCAu
'Spiced Tiger' (TB)	ESgI
'Spicy Cajun' (La)	WHil
'Spinning Wheel' (TB)	SIri
'Spirit of Memphis' (TB)	XSen
'Splashacata' (TB)	WCAu XSen
'Splat' (IB)	CIri
'Spot of Tea' (MDB)	LLHF
'Spot On' (Reticulata)	LAma LLHF
'Spreckles' (TB)	CKel ESgI
'Spree' (SDB)	WCAu
'Spring Blush' (MTB) 🏆H7	SIri
'Spring Festival' (TB)	WCAu
'Spring Kiss' (TB)	SIri
'Spring Madness' (TB)	WCAu
'Spring Time' (Reticulata)	LAma SDeJ
'Springtime Madonna' (TB)	EBee
spuria	CMac CPou
§ - subsp. ***halophila***	GKev
- subsp. ***notha*** CC 725	WCot
- subsp. ***ochroleuca***	see *I. orientalis* Mill.
'Spy' (BB)	WCAu
'Square Dance Skirt' (TB)	SDys
'St Louis Blues' (TB)	ESgI XSen
'Stairway to Heaven' (TB)	ESgI WCAu
'Stapleford' (SDB)	CBro
'Staplehurst' (MTB) 🏆H7	SIri
'Star Cluster' (Sib)	WFar
'Star in the Night' (TB)	WCAu
'Star Shine' (TB)	ESgI WCAu
'Stardate' (SDB)	CKel
'Starheart' (IB)	WCAu
'Starship' (TB)	XSen

'Starwoman' (IB) ♀H7	SDys
'Staten Island' (TB)	ESgI SRms WCAu
'Stella Polaris' (TB)	ELon
'Stellar Lights' (TB)	EIri WCAu
'Stephen Wilcox' (Sib)	CIri EPri WAul
'Stepping Dancer' (TB) **new**	CRos
'Stepping Out' (TB) ♀H7	CAby CKel CMac CPar EPfP ESgI GBin IRob LRHS NRHS SCob SDeJ WCAu WTor
'Steve' (Sib)	CPar EWes
'Steve Varner' (Sib)	EPri EWTr
'Stilo Libero'	WCAu
'Stinger' (SDB) ♀H7	CIri
'Stingray' (TB)	ESgI
'Stitch in Time' (TB)	EIri WCAu
'Stockholm' (SDB)	CKel
stolonifera	GKev
- 'Augustus' (Rc) **new**	GKev
- 'Morning Coffee' (Rc) **new**	GKev
- 'Zwanenburg Beauty' (Rc)	GKev
'Stop the Music' (TB)	XSen
'Storm' (Reticulata) **new**	LAma
'Storm Center' (TB)	CKel
'Stormy Circle' (SDB)	WCAu
'Storrington' (TB)	ECtt EMal LRHS NRHS
'Strange Brew' (TB)	WCAu
'Strathmore' (TB)	EMal LRHS NRHS
'Strawberry Fair' (Sib) ♀H7	WCAu
'Strictly Jazz' (TB)	WCAu
'Strike it Rich' (TB)	ESgI
'Strozzapreti' (TB)	ESgI
'Strut' (TB)	WCAu
'Strut your Stuff' (TB)	WCAu
'Study In Black' (TB)	XSen
stylosa	see *I. unguicularis*
§ ***suaveolens***	CPBP CPou GEdr NHpl NWad
- var. ***flavescens***	see *I. suaveolens* yellow-flowered
§ - purple-flowered	GCrg GEdr GKev WAbe
- var. ***violacea***	see *I. suaveolens* purple-flowered
§ - yellow-flowered	GKev WAbe
'Succès Fou' (TB)	SIri WViv
'Sugar' (IB)	NSti WCAu
'Sugar Magnolia' (TB)	SIri
'Sultan's Palace' (TB)	CKel EBee ESgI LCro LRHS NLar WCAu WSpi XSen
'Sultry Mood' (TB)	CKel
'Summer Holidays' (TB)	XSen
'Summer Revels' (Sib)	EPri
'Summer Sky' (Sib)	CBre CSpe LEdu MHCG WAul WCot
'Sun Doll' (SDB) ♀H7	CTal
'Sunblaze' (TB)	WCAu
'Sunday Brunch' (TB) **new**	MNHC
'Sunlit Shores' (La)	LLWG
'Sunny Dawn' (IB)	CKel
'Sunny Disposition' (TB)	XSen
'Sunnyside Delight' (TB)	WCAu
'Sunnyside Up' (TB)	GKev
'Sunset Skies' (TB)	CWCL
'Sunshine' (Reticulata) **new**	EPot LAma
'Superba' (Sib)	WWtn
'Superstition' (TB) ♀H7	CKel EIri ELan ESgI EWes LCro LRHS MRav SCob WCAu XSen
'Supreme Sultan' (TB)	CKel CWCL ESgI LCro SBee SCob WCAu XSen
'Susan Bliss' (TB)	CKel ELan EPfP ESgI WCAu WMil
'Sutton Valence' (Sib)	SIri
'Swain' (TB)	ESgI
'Swan Ballet' (TB)	ESgI
'Swank' (Sib)	WAul
'Swans in Flight' (Sib) **new**	WCAu
'Swazi Princess' (TB)	ELon ESgI SRms
'Sweet Kate' (SDB)	WCAu
'Sweet Lavender' (TB)	WMil
'Sweet Lena' (TB)	ESgI
'Sweet Musette' (TB)	SRms WCAu
'Sweet Surrender' (Sib)	EPri
'Sweeter than Wine' (TB)	MRav
'Swingtown' (TB)	WCAu
'Swirling Waters' (La)	LLWG
'Swish' (SDB) **new**	CTal
'Swiss Majesty' (TB)	WCAu
'Swizzle' (IB)	XSen
'Sybil' (TB)	GBin
'Sylvan' (TB)	XSen
'Sylvia Murray' (TB)	WCAu
'Symphony' (Dut)	SDeJ
'Symphony of Light' (TB)	CIri
'Syncopation' (TB)	ELon ESgI WCAu XSen
'Syrian Hills' (TB)	WCAu
'Tact' (IB)	SIri
'Take Me Away' (TB)	SDys
'Tall Chief' (TB)	WCAu
'Tamberg' (Sib)	CKel EBee
'Tan Tingo' (IB)	XSen
'Tantara' (SDB)	XSen
'Tantrum' (IB)	WCAu XSen
'Tanz Nochmal' (Sib)	GBin
'Tanzanian Tangerine' (TB)	WCAu
taochia	CPBP
'Tarn Hows' (TB)	ESgI SRms
'Taubenblau' (Sib)	SAko
'Teal Velvet' (Sib)	CKel ECha ELon EPfP EPri GLog LRHS MCot SCob WFar
'Tealwood' (Sib)	GBin
'Teapot Tempest' (BB)	WCAu
'Teasaucer Hill' (MTB) ♀H7	SIri
tectorum	CCse GKev LRHS SChr WCot XLum XSen
- BWJ 8191	WCru
- 'Alba'	GKev WThu XSen
- 'Cruella'	EPfP
- 'Variegata' misapplied	see *I. japonica* 'Variegata'
- 'Variegata' (v)	SRms
'Tell Fibs' (SDB)	CBro CTal
'Teller of Tales' (La)	LLWG
'Temper Tantrum' (Sib)	LRHS WCAu WHar
'Temple Gold' (TB)	CKel NPer
'Temple Meads' (IB)	ESgI WCAu
'Templecloud' (IB) ♀H7	CKel
'Tempting Fate' (TB)	SIri WCAu
§ ***tenax***	CRos EBee LRHS NRHS
'Tenebrae' (TB)	WMil
'Tennison Ridge' (TB)	WCAu
'Teverlae' (Sib)	CRos EBee LRHS NRHS
'Thaïs' (TB)	ESgI
'The Citadel' (TB)	ELon
'The Red Douglas' (TB)	ESgI
'The Rocket'	see *I.* 'Rocket'
'Thelma Perry' (Sib)	EPfP
'Theseus' (AB)	GKev
'Third Charm' (SDB)	CBro
'Third World' (SDB)	CBro
'This and That' (IB)	WCAu
'Thornbird' (TB) ♀H7	EIri ESgI LMea SRms WCAu
'Three Cherries' (MDB)	CTal
'Three Oaks' (TB)	SBee
'Three Quarters' (Sib)	ELon NChi
'Thriller' (TB)	ESgI WCAu XSen
'Thunder Echo' (TB)	SIri
'Thundering Ovation' (TB)	WCAu

TIGER MIXED (Dut)	GKev
§ 'Tigereye' (Dut)	ERCP GAbr GBin GKev LCro LOPS SDeJ
tigridia	CExl
'Time to Shine' (SDB)	WCAu
'Time Traveler' (TB)	CIri
'Time Zone' (TB)	WCAu
'Tinkerbell' (SDB)	CBod CPBP CTal EBee EPfP GMaP LRHS NRHS SDeJ WTor
'Titan's Glory' (TB) 𝕐H7	CKel CMac ESgI LEdu MRav SRms WCot WHoo
'To the Point' (TB)	CIri
'Tollong'	ILea IMou
'Tom Tit' (TB)	WCAu WMil
'Top Flight' (TB)	CKel ELan LRHS MAvo NRHS SPer SRms
'Top Gun' (TB)	ESgI
'Topaz Jewel' (TB)	MHol
'Topolino' (TB)	CKel
'Torero' (TB)	SIri
'Toro Blanco' (IB)	CIri
'Total Eclipse' (TB)	SRms
'Total Recall' (TB)	WCAu
'Totally Cool' (SDB)	CTal LSRN SIri
'Touch of Mahogany' (TB)	WCAu
'Town Flirt' (TB)	WCAu
'Trajectory' (SDB)	WCAu
'Trapel' (TB)	ESgI
'Trencavel' (TB)	ESgI
'Trenwith' (TB)	ESgI
'Trillion' (TB)	CIri
'Trim the Velvet' (Sib)	WAul
'Triple Whammy' (TB)	ESgI XSen
'Tripod' (IB)	CIri
'Tristan'	CKel
'Tristram' (TB)	WMil
'Tropic Night' (Sib)	CBWd CKel CRos CSam CTri EBee ECtt EHrv EIri ELan EPfP EPri GBin GKin LCro LRHS MBel MCot MRav MWts NRHS NRya NSti SPer SSut WAul WAvo WFar WWtn
'Tropical Delight' (TB)	CIri
tuberosa	CAby CAvo CBro CHid CTri CWCL ECha ERCP LAma MHer MPie SDeJ WShi
- MS 76	WCot
- MS 964	WCot
- PB	WCot
'Tulip Festival' (TB)	CRos
'Tumble Bug' (Sib) **new**	LLWG
'Tut's Gold' (TB)	ESgI WCAu
'Tuxedo' (TB)	XSen
'Twist of Twilight' (La)	LLWG
'Two Sided Coin' (TB)	WCAu
§ 'Tycoon' (Sib)	CRos EShb GBin LRHS NChi NRHS SPer
'Tyland Blue' (TB)	SIri
typhifolia	GKev
'Tyrian Dream' (IB)	WCAu
'UFO' (TB)	CIri
'Ultimate' (SDB)	WCAu
'Uncle Charlie' (TB)	WCAu
'Undercurrent' (TB)	LMea WCAu
'Unfinished Business' (TB)	CIri WCAu
§ ***unguicularis***	Widely available
- from Karpathos, Greece	GKev
- 'Abington Purple'	CJun EIri
- 'Alba'	CAvo CExl XEll XSen
- subsp. ***angustifolia*** **new**	WSHC
§ - subsp. ***cretensis***	GKev
- - white-flowered	WSHC
- 'Diana Clare'	CJun
- 'Kilbroney Marble'	EPri
- 'Marondera'	CAvo CJun
- 'Mary Barnard' 𝕐H5	CAvo CBro CJun CPou CRos EHrv LRHS MHer NRHS WHoo
- 'Peloponnese Snow' **new**	LLHF
§ - 'Walter Butt'	CAvo CJun CMea XEll
'Unicorn' (TB)	CIri
'Vague à l'Ame' (TB)	ESgI
'Valda' (Sib)	EBee ELon
'Valerie Joyce'	WCAu
'Vamp' (IB)	CKel GBin XSen
'Vanilla Mist' (La)	LLWG
'Vanilla Skies' (TB)	WCAu
'Vanity' (TB)	XSen
'Vanity's Child' (TB)	WCAu XSen
§ ***variegata*** 𝕐H7	CBot CMea GBin GKev XSen
- from Podyjí, Moravia	SBrt
'Vegas Heat' (BB)	CIri
'Velvet King' (TB)	ESgI
'Velvet Purple'	XBlo
'Velvet Smile' (Reticulata)	LAma
'Venita Faye' (TB)	WCAu
'Verity Blamey' (TB)	CKel
versicolor	CBen CRoa CWat GBin GKev GMaP GMcL GPoy MMuc MNHC MWts SEND SPlb SRms WBrk WFar WMAq WMoo WPnP WShi WWtn
- 'Algonquin'	LLWG
- 'Between the Lines'	LLWG
- 'Candystriper'	LLWG
- 'China West Lake'	CRoa LLWG
- 'Claret Cup'	CPou ILea
- 'Kermesina'	CWat ECha ELan ESgI LCro LLWG LOPS MMuc MWts NPer NSti SRms WFar WMAq WMoo WPnP
- 'Mint Fresh'	LLWG
- 'Mysterious Monique'	CCse CWat EBee LLWG MWts
- purple-flowered	EWat
- 'Rosea'	EWat
- 'Rowden Cadenza'	EWat LLWG
- 'Rowden Cantata'	LLWG
- 'Rowden Concerto'	LLWG
- 'Rowden Electro' **new**	LLWG
- 'Rowden Lyric'	LLWG
- 'Rowden Melody'	LLWG
- 'Rowden Pastorale'	LLWG
- 'Rowden Sonata'	CRoa LLWG
- 'Rowden Waltz'	LLWG
'Very Victorian' (Sib) **new**	WCAu
'Vi Luihn' (Sib)	ECha ELon SAko WMoo
'Vibrations' (TB)	ESgI WCAu
'Victoria Falls' (TB)	CKel ESgI MHol
'Victorian Secret' (Sib)	EBee ELon WCAu
'Viel Schnee' (Sib)	ELon
'Vigilante' (TB)	LMea
'Vin Nouveau' (TB)	XSen
'Vinho Verde' (IB)	CKel
'Vino Rosso' (SDB)	ESgI
'Violet Beauty' (Reticulata)	CRos GKev LAma LRHS NRHS
'Violet Classic' (TB)	WCAu
'Violet Harmony' (TB)	ESgI
'Violet Icing' (TB)	CKel
'Violet Rings' (TB)	WCAu
'Violet Turner' (TB)	MHol
'Viper' (IB)	CIri
virginica	LLWG

– 'De Luxe'	see *I.* × *robusta* 'Dark Aura'
– 'Lavender Lustre'	LLWG
– 'Orchid Purple'	LLWG
– 'Pale Lavender'	LLWG
– 'Pink Perfection'	LLWG
– 'Pond Crown Point'	CRoa
§ – var. ***shrevei***	LLWG
– 'Slightly Daft'	LLWG
'Vitafire' (TB)	CRos ESgI LRHS NRHS
'Vitality' (IB)	ELon ESgI
'Vizier' (TB)	WCAu
'Voilà' (IB)	CMea ESgI
'Volts' (SDB)	XSen
'Volute' (TB)	ESgI
'Voyage' (SDB)	XSen
'Wabash' (TB)	WCAu XSen
'Waihi Wedding' (La)	LLWG
'Walmer Castle' (Kent Castles Series) (IB)	SIri
'Walter Butt'	see *I. unguicularis* 'Walter Butt'
'War Chief' (TB)	EPfP ESgI MRav WCAu
'War Sails' (TB)	SIri WCAu
warleyensis	EPot GKev
'Warlsind' (J)	GKev
wattii	CExl GCal WGwG
– KWJ 12172	WCru
'Way to Go' (TB)	CIri
'Wealden Butterfly' (Sib) ♀H7	SIri WAul
'Wealden Carousel' (Sib)	SIri WAul
'Wealden Mystery' (Sib)	EPri SIri WAul
'Wealden Skies' (Sib)	SIri WAul
'Wealden Spires' (Sib)	WAul
'Wealden Summer' (Sib)	WAul
'Wearing Rubies' (TB)	ESgI WCAu
'Webelos' (SDB)	MRav NRHS
'Wedding Vow' (TB)	CKel EIri
* 'Wedgwood Blue' (Sino-Sib)	GBin
'Weisse Etagen' (Sib)	ELon
'Welch's Reward' (MTB)	ESgI
'Welcome Discovery' (TB)	WCAu
'Welcome Return' (Sib)	CElw LLWG LRHS MMuc WGob WMoo
'Welfenfürstin' (Sib)	GBin SAko
'Welfenprinz' (Sib) ♀H7	SMHy WAul
'Well Suited' (SDB)	CTal
'Wench' (TB)	WCAu
'Westar' (SDB)	CKel CTal
'Westpointer' (TB)	CIri
'Westwell' (SDB)	WCAu
'What a Mixture' (TB)	CIri
'What Again' (SDB)	XSen
'What's New' (TB)	WCAu
'Whee' (SDB)	WCAu
'Whispering Spirits' (TB)	WCAu
'White Amber' (Sib) **new**	WCAu
'White Caucasus' (Reticulata)	EPot ERCP LAma LLHF XEll
'White City' (TB)	CKel CRos EPfP ESgI GMaP LRHS MCot MRav MWat NPer NRHS SCob SDeJ SPer SRms WCAu
'White Gem' (SDB)	ESgI
'White Knight' (TB)	EBee EPfP ESgI WSpi
I 'White Queen' (Sib)	ESgI
'White Reprise' (TB)	ESgI XSen
I 'White Swan' (Sib)	EPri
'White Swirl' (Sib)	Widely available
'White Triangles' (Sib)	ELon
'White Umbrella' (La)	ECtt LLWG
'White van Vliet' (Dut)	SDeJ
'White Wine' (MTB)	WCAu
'White-Wave' (TB)	XBlo
'Widow's Veil' (SDB)	ESgI
'Wild Jasmine' (TB)	WCAu
'Wild Wings' (TB)	LRHS MCot SGbt WCAu
wilsonii ♀H7	CExl EBee GKev SBrt WGob
'Windjammer Seas' (TB)	SDys
'Winemaster' (TB)	SIri
'Winesap' (TB)	ESgI
'Winged Angel' (IB)	CIri
winogradowii ♀H7	CBro CRos EPot ERCP GKev LAma LLHF LRHS NRHS WAbe XEll
– white-flowered **new**	GKev
'Winter Olympics' (TB)	CBod CKel CRos ELan EPfP LRHS MRav NRHS SPer WGwG
'Wintry Sky' (TB)	WCAu
'Wise' (SDB)	CTal WCAu
'Wish Upon a Star' (SDB)	WCAu
'Wishful Thinking' (TB)	SIri
'Wisley White' (Sib)	IRob
'Wisteria Sachet' (IB)	WCAu
'Witching' (TB)	LMea
'Witch's Wand' (TB)	ESgI
'Wizard's Return' (SDB)	SIri
'Wonders Never Cease' (TB)	WCAu
'Wondrous' (TB)	ESgI
'Word of Warning' (La)	LLWG
'Wrangler' (IB)	SIri
'Wrights' Flights' (IB)	CIri
xiphioides	see *I. latifolia*
xiphium var. ***lusitanica***	GKev
'Yankee Consul' (Sib)	EPri
'Yaquina Blue' (TB)	WCAu
'Yarai' (SpH) **new**	LLWG
'Yasha' (SpH) **new**	LLWG
'Yellow Flirt' (MTB)	WCAu
'Yeoman' (TB)	WMil
'Yes' (TB)	ESgI LMea
'Yippy Skippy' (SDB)	WCAu
'Zakopane' (Sib)	EBee EWes WAul
'Zantha' (TB)	XSen
'Zero' (SDB)	CKel
'Zinger' (BB) **new**	WSpi
'Zipper' (MDB)	CTal
'Zweites Hundert' (Sib)	WFar

Isatis (*Brassicaceae*)

glauca	GJos
tinctoria	CBod CHab CHby EBWF ENfk GJos GPoy MHer MNHC SPav SRms WTre

Ismelia (*Asteraceae*)

carinata 'Sunset'	LRHS NRHS

Ismene (*Amaryllidaceae*)

§ 'Advance'	GKev LAma
§ × ***deflexa*** ♀H1c	CCCN EShb ETMg GKev LAma LCro LOPS SDeJ SPav WCot
§ – 'Zwanenburg'	CGrW GKev
§ ***longipetala***	GKev
§ 'Sulphur Queen' ♀H1c	CGrW GKev SDeJ SPav

Isodon (*Lamiaceae*)

calycinus	SPlb
effusus	WPGP
excisus	EBee IMou SBrt WPGP
longitubus	SBrt
– B&SWJ 11027	WCru
rubescens	IMou SBrt WCot

Isolepis (*Cyperaceae*)

§ ***cernua***	CBen CWat EShb LLWG LRHS MSKA MWts SCoo WArt WCot WMAq
nodosa (Rottb.) R. Br.	see *Ficinia nodosa*

Isoloma see *Kohleria*

Isomeris see *Cleome*

Isoplexis see *Digitalis*

Isopogon (*Proteaceae*)

anemonifolius	CCCN SPlb
anethifolius	SPlb
formosus	LRHS MPkF

Isopyrum (*Ranunculaceae*)

biternatum	LEdu
hallii new	EBee
nipponicum	WCru WPGP
stoloniferum	WCru
thalictroides	EBee GEdr IMou LEdu LLHF SDys WCot

Isotoma (*Campanulaceae*)

sp.	ESps SWvt
§ ***axillaris***	CSpe NPer SCoo SPer
- 'Fairy Carpet'	CBod NCou NHpl SRms
- 'Indigo Stars' new	ETMg
fluviatilis	NLar

Itea (*Iteaceae*)

chinensis	CExl
ilicifolia 🏆H5	Widely available
* - 'Rubrifolia'	CRos ELan LRHS SLon
virginica	CBcs CMCN ELon LRHS MRav SLim SLon
§ - 'Henry's Garnet' 🏆H5	CDul CEnd CMCN CMac CRos CSBt EBee ECrN EPfP EUJe GBin LEdu LRHS MGil MGos NLar NRHS SBod SCob SEle SGol SLim SPer SPoG SRms SWvt WPGP
- LITTLE HENRY ('Sprich'PBR)	CHGN CMac CRos CSBt EBee EPfP LRHS LSRN NLar NRHS SCob
- 'Long Spire'	NLar
- 'Merlot'	MBlu NLar SGol
- 'Sarah Eve'	CMCN NLar
- 'Saturnalia'	NLar
- Swarthmore form	see *I. virginica* 'Henry's Garnet'
yunnanensis	CExl MBlu NLar WSHC

Itoa (*Salicaceae*)

orientalis	SVen
- var. ***glabrescens*** new	CMCN

Ixeris (*Asteraceae*)

stolonifera	XLum

Ixia (*Iridaceae*)

'Blue Bird'	GKev LAma NRog SDeJ
'Castor'	CAvo NRog
'Giant'	GKev SDeJ WHil
'Hogarth'	CWld GKev LAma NRog WHil
'Holland Glory'	NRog
'Jesse'	GKev WHil
latifolia new	CPbh
'Mabel'	CAvo CWCL GKev NRog WCot WHil
'Marquette'	GKev WHil
paniculata 'Eos'	GKev
'Panorama'	NRog
polystachya	CPbh
'Rose Emperor'	GKev LAma NRog SDeJ WHil
scillaris	CPbh
'Spotlight'	CAvo GKev NRog WHil
thomasiae	WCot
'Venus'	CTca CWCL CWld ERCP GKev LAma NRog SDeJ WHil
viridiflora	NRog
'Vulcan'	NRog
'Yellow Emperor'	CTca GKev NRog SDeJ WHil

Ixiolirion (*Ixioliriaceae*)

pallasii	see *I. tataricum*
§ ***tataricum***	EBee GKev LAma SDeJ

J

Jaborosa (*Solanaceae*)

integrifolia	CExl LEdu SVen XLum

Jacaranda (*Bignoniaceae*)

acutifolia misapplied	see *J. mimosifolia*
§ ***mimosifolia*** 🏆H1c	CBcs CCCN SPlb

Jacobaea (*Asteraceae*)

§ ***aquatica***	LLWG
§ ***maritima***	ESps SEND
- 'Ramparts'	ECre
- 'Silver Dust' 🏆H4	EPfP ESps

Jacobinia see *Justicia*

Jamesbrittenia (*Scrophulariaceae*)

§ ***microphylla***	CPBP

Jamesia (*Hydrangeaceae*)

americana	CBcs CJun CMCN LLHF NLar SBrt WCru WSHC

Jasione (*Campanulaceae*)

§ ***heldreichii***	SRms
jankae	see *J. heldreichii*
§ ***laevis***	EPfP EPot GAbr SRms WMoo
§ - 'Blaulicht'	CRos EAJP ECha EPfP LPmr LRHS NEgg NRHS SPlb WMoo
- BLUE LIGHT	see *J. laevis* 'Blaulicht'
montana	EBWF MNHC SRms
perennis	see *J. laevis*

Jasminum ✿ (*Oleaceae*)

CC 4728	CExl
CW&T 6374	CMCN
affine	see *J. officinale* f. *affine*
angulare 🏆H2	CExl CHll CRHN WFib
azoricum 🏆H2	CBcs CCCN CHll CRHN CTsd CWCL EPfP EShb SEND SPre WFib
beesianum	Widely available
bignoniaceum	WSHC
blinii	see *J. polyanthum*
dispermum	CRHN NLar
farreri	see *J. humile* f. *farreri*
§ ***floridum***	EWes
fruticans	CMac EBee ELon LRHS SBrt SEND WCru XSen

	- RCB UA 22	WCot
	giraldii misapplied	see *J. humile* f. *farreri*
	giraldii Diels	see *J. floridum*
	grandiflorum misapplied	see *J. officinale* f. *affine*
	grandiflorum L. 'De Grasse' ♀H2	CRHN EShb WFib
	humile	CExl MGil SEND WKif
§	- f. ***farreri*** Farrer 867 **new**	WPGP
	- var. ***glabrum***	see *J. humile* f. *wallichianum*
§	- 'Revolutum' ♀H5	CAby CBcs CDul CMac CRHN CRos CSBt CWCL EBee ECrN EPfP EShb ESps ETMg GCal GMcL LRHS MGos MRav NLar SEND SGbt SLon SPer SPoG SRms SWvt WHar WSHC
§	- f. ***wallichianum*** B&SWJ 2559	WCru
	- - PAB 2534	LEdu
	- - PAB 9962	LEdu
	humile × ***parkeri***	SEle
§	***mesnyi*** ♀H3	CBcs CCCN CExl CHll CMac CRHN CTri EBak EMOT EPfP LRHS SBch SEND SGol SPer SVen WSHC
	multiflorum	CCCN
	multipartitum	CHll
	- bushy	CSpe
§	***nudiflorum*** ♀H5	Widely available
	- 'Argenteum'	see *J. nudiflorum* 'Mystique'
	- 'Aureum'	CKel CMac CRos ELan LRHS MAsh MBNS MRav NLar SPer SPoG SRms
§	- 'Mystique' (v)	CRos ELan LRHS MRav NRHS SLon SPoG
	odoratissimum	WFib
	officinale	Widely available
	- CC 1709	WMoo
§	- f. ***affine***	CBcs CCCN CRHN CRos CTri CWCL ELan EPfP LRHS MAsh MRav NRHS SCoo SLim SRms WHar
§	- 'Argenteovariegatum' (v) ♀H5	CDul CKel CMac CRos CWGN EHoe ELan EMOT EPfP ESps LRHS LSRN MAsh MGos MHer MJak MMuc MRav SEND SLim SPer SPoG SWvt WCFE WHar WSHC
	- 'Aureovariegatum'	see *J. officinale* 'Aureum'
§	- 'Aureum' (v)	CBcs CKel CMac CRos CTsd CWCL ELan EPfP IBoy LRHS MAsh MHer MJak NPri SCoo SLim SLon SPer SRms
	- 'Clotted Cream'	see *J. officinale* 'Devon Cream'
	- 'Crûg's Collection'	WCru
§	- 'Devon Cream'PBR	Widely available
	- FIONA SUNRISE ('Frojas'PBR) ♀H5	Widely available
	- 'Grandiflorum'	see *J. officinale* f. *affine*
	- 'Inverleith' ♀H5	CCCN CKel CMac CRos CWCL EBee ECtt ELan EPfP EWTr LRHS MAsh MBNS MGos MRav NRHS SCoo SLim SMad SNig SPad SPer SPoG WGrn WSHC
	- 'Sunbeam'	CRos EBee LRHS NRHS SNig
	- 'Variegatum'	see *J. officinale* 'Argenteovariegatum'
	parkeri	CBcs CCCN CJun CMac CRos CTri EBee ELon EPfP EPot GEdr GMaP LRHS MBNS MGil NLar SEle WThu XEll
	- 'Bychan'	WAbe
§	***polyanthum*** ♀H2	CBcs CExl CKel CRHN CSBt CTri EBak ELan EPfP ETho LCro SEND SLim SPer SPre SRms WHar
	- dark-red-leaved	CCCN CExl ELan EPfP
	primulinum	see *J. mesnyi*
	reevesii hort.	see *J. humile* 'Revolutum'
	sambac ♀H2	CBcs CCCN CHll CRHN ELan SPre WFib
	- 'Grand Duke of Tuscany' (d)	CCCN SPre
	- 'Maid of Orleans' (d)	CCCN EShb SPre
	sieboldianum	see *J. nudiflorum*
§	***simplicifolium*** subsp. ***suavissimum***	CHll CRHN
	stenalobium	WCot WFib
	× ***stephanense***	Widely available
	suavissimum	see *J. simplicifolium* subsp. *suavissimum*

Jatropha (*Euphorbiaceae*)

cinerea	SPlb
integerrima	CCCN
multifida	SPlb
podagrica ♀H1a	LToo

Jeffersonia (*Berberidaceae*)

diphylla	CRos EBee EPPr EPot EPri GKev LAma LEdu LRHS MBel MMoz MNrw NChi NPnk NRHS WAbe WCru WPGP WPnP WThu
dubia	CAby CRos EPot EWes EWld GKev LEdu LLHF LRHS MNrw NPnk NRHS WAbe WCot WCru WPGP WThu XEll
- 'Sunago-fu' (v)	GEdr

jostaberry see *Ribes* × *nidigrolaria*

Jovellana (*Calceolariaceae*)

punctata	CBcs CCCN CExl CTsd EBee GCal IArd IBlr SPlb
- var. ***coerulea***	IBlr
sinclairii	CExl CHll LLHF
violacea ♀H2	CAbb CBcs CBot CCCN CExl CMac CPla CPne CRos CTsd EPfP GCal GMcL IBlr IDee IMou LRHS MGil SEle SVen WPGP

Jovibarba ✿ (*Crassulaceae*)

§	***allionii***	CBod CMea CTri EDAr EPot MHer MSCN NHpl NMen WHal WHoo
	- 'Oki'	CRos LRHS NMen NRHS SRms
	allionii × ***hirta***	CTal MSCN SDys SPlb
§	***arenaria***	GAbr NMen XLum
*	***echiniformis***	XLum
§	***heuffelii***	CRos LRHS NHpl NMen NRHS XLum
	- 'Almkroon'	NWad
	- 'Anabokonak'	NMen
	- 'Angel Wings'	NMen SRms WHoo
	- 'Aquarius'	NMen
	- 'Be Mine'	NMen
	- 'Beacon Hill'	NMen
	- 'Belcore'	NMen XLum
	- 'Benjamin'	NMen
	- 'Big Red'	NWad
	- 'Blaze'	NMen
	- 'Bolero'	NMen
	- 'Bora'	NWad
	- 'Brandaris'	SDys
	- 'Brocade'	MSCN NWad
	- 'Bronze Ingot'	NMen
§	- 'Cherry Glow'	NMen
	- 'Chocoleto'	NMen

I	– 'Compacta'	NMen
	– 'Copper King'	NMen
	– 'Elmo's Fire'	NMen
	– 'Eos Moment'	NMen
	– 'Fan Joy'	NMen
	– 'Gento'	NMen
	– 'Geronimo'	NMen
	– 'Giuseppi Spiny'	NMen SPlb
	– var. ***glabra***	WHoo
	– – from Anaba Kanak, Bulgaria	NWad
	– – from Haila, Montenegro/ Kosovo	NMen
	– – from Jakupica, Macedonia	NMen
	– – from Kapaenianum	NMen
	– – from Ljuboten, Balkans	NMen
	– – from Ošljak, Albania	NMen
	– – from Treska Gorge, Macedonia	NMen SRms
	– 'Gladiator'	NMen
	– 'Grand Slam'	NMen
	– 'Green Land'	NMen
	– 'Greenstone'	NMen
	– 'Henry Correvon'	NMen
	– var. ***heuffelii***	NMen
	– 'Idylle'	NMen
	– 'Inferno'	NMen
§	– 'Inge'	NMen
	– 'Ithaca'	NWad
	– 'Iuno'	NWad
	– 'Jade'	NMen
I	– 'Jovi King'	NMen
	– 'King Sunny'	NMen
	– var. ***kopaonikensis***	NMen
	– 'Lucky Bell'	NMen
	– 'Mary Ann'	NMen
	– 'Miller's Violet'	NMen
	– 'Mink'	NMen
	– 'Minuta'	NMen
	– 'Mystique'	CMea NMen WHoo
	– 'Nannette'	NMen
	– 'Orion'	CMea CTal NMen XLum
	– 'Passat'	NWad
	– var. ***patens***	NMen
	– 'Pink Skies'	NMen
	– 'Pink Star'	NMen NWad
	– 'Prisma'	NMen
	– 'Purple Haze'	XLum
	– 'Purple Heide'	NMen
	– 'Serenade'	NMen SRms
	– 'Silex'	NMen
	– 'Springael's Choice'	NMen
	– 'Sundancer'	NMen
	– 'Sungold'	NWad
	– 'Suntan'	NWad
	– 'Sylvan Memory'	NMen
	– 'Tan'	NMen
	– 'Tancredi'	NMen
	– 'Torrid Zone'	MBrN NMen
	– 'Tuxedo'	NHpl NMen
	– 'Violet'	NMen SDys
	– 'Xanthoheuff'	NMen
	– 'Yodelheuff'	NMen
§	***hirta***	EDAr GAbr GKev NMen XLum
	– from Wintergraben, Austria	SPlb SRms
	– 'Belansky Tatra'	NMen SRms
	– subsp. ***glabrescens*** from High Tatra, Slovakia/Poland	XLum
	– – from Smeryouka, southern Carpathians	NMen
	– var. ***neilreichii***	CRos LRHS NRHS SRms
	– 'Purpurea'	XLum
	preissiana	NMen
§	***sobolifera***	EDAr EPot GKev NMen SPlb WHal XLum
	– 'Green Globe'	CRos CTal LRHS NMen NRHS SDys
	– 'Miss Lorraine'	XLum

Jubaea (*Arecaceae*)

	sp.	ETod
§	***chilensis***	CPHo ETod EUJe SArc SBig SPlb WHor
	spectabilis	see *J. chilensis*

Juglans ✿ (*Juglandaceae*)

§	***ailanthifolia***	CBcs CMCN
	– B&SWJ 11026	WCru
	– var. ***cordiformis***	MRai
	– – 'Brock' (F)	CAgr
	– – 'Campbell Cw3' (F)	CAgr
	– – 'Fodermaier' seedling (F)	CAgr
	– – 'Imshu' (F) new	CAgr
	– – 'Rhodes' (F)	CAgr
	– – 'Simcoe' (F)	CAgr
	ailanthifolia* × *cinerea	see *J.* × *bixbyi*
§	× ***bixbyi***	CAgr
	cinerea (F)	CBcs LMaj
	– 'Beckwith' (F)	CAgr
	– 'Booth' (F)	CAgr
	– 'Booth' seedling (F)	CAgr
	– 'Craxezy' (F)	CAgr
	– 'Kenworthy' seedling (F)	CAgr
	– 'Myjoy' (F)	CAgr
	mandshurica (F)	CBcs
	– BWJ 8097 from China	WCru
	– B&SWJ 12550 from Korea	WCru
	– RWJ 9905 from Taiwan	WCru
	microcarpa	CMCN
	microcarpa* × *nigra	EMOT
	nigra (F) 🏆^{H6}	CAco CBcs CCVT CDul CFGn CHab CLnd CMCN CMac CPer CSBt CTho EBee ECrN ELan EPfP LCro LPra MAsh MGos MMuc NOra SDea SEND SGol SPer WTSh
	– 'Bicentennial' (F)	CAgr
	– 'Emma Kay' (F)	CAgr
	– 'Laciniata'	EPfP MBlu
	– 'Potsdam' (F)	CAgr
	– 'Thomas' (F)	CAgr
	– 'Weschke' (F)	CAgr
	regia (F)	Widely available
	– 'Axel' (F)	CAgr MCoo
	– 'Broadview' (F) 🏆^{H6}	CAgr CArg CDul CEnd CFGn CTho ELan EMOT EPom ERea LBuc LRHS MBlu MCoo MGos NOra SCoo SDea SEWo SKee SPer SPoG SSFT SVic WHar
	– 'Buccaneer' (F) 🏆^{H6}	CAgr CArg CDul CFGn CTho ELan EMOT EPom NOra SDea SKee WHar
	– 'Chandler' (F)	CAgr
	– 'Corne du Périgord' (F)	CAgr
	– 'Excelsior of Taynton' (F)	MCoo
	– 'Ferjean' (F)	CAgr
	– 'Fernette'^{PBR} (F)	CAgr NOra WHar
	– 'Fernor' (F)	CAgr WHar
	– 'Franquette' (F)	CAgr EMOT MCoo NOra WHar
	– 'Hansen' (F)	CAgr
	– 'Hartley' (F)	CAgr
	– 'Laciniata' 🏆^{H6}	CDul CMCN ERea

	- 'Lara' (F)	NOra
	- 'Mayette' (F)	CAgr
	- 'Meylannaise' (F)	CAgr
	- number 16 (F)	WHar
	- 'Parisienne' (F)	CAgr SGol
	- 'Plovdivski' (F)	EMOT WHar
	- 'Proslavski' (F)	CDul WHar
	- 'Purpurea'	CMCN ERea MBlu
	- 'Rita' (F)	EMOT LBuc
	- 'Ronde de Montignac' (F)	CAgr
	- 'Sychrov' (F)	EMOT
	sieboldiana	see *J. ailanthifolia*
	sigillata	LEdu

jujube see *Ziziphus jujuba*

Juncus (*Juncaceae*)

	acutiflorus	EBWF
	acutus	EBWF
	articulatus	EBWF LLWG XLum
	bulbosus	CNat EBWF
	conglomeratus	EBWF
	'Curly Gold Strike' (v)	MSKA
§	***decipiens*** 'Curly-wurly'	CRos EPfP LRHS NRHS NWad
	- 'Spiralis'	see *J. decipiens* 'Curly-wurly'
	effusus	CBen CWat EBWF LRHS MSKA NPer WMAq XLum
	- 'Carman's Japanese'	NSti
	- 'Gold Strike' (v)	EPPr LLWG
§	- f. ***spiralis***	CBen CRos CSpe CWat EHoe EPfP LRHS MAsh MJak MWts NRHS SPlb SVic WMAq XLum
	ensifolius	CBen CWat EHoe EWat EWes LLWG MMrt MSKA MWts NPer NSti
	gerardii	EBWF
	inflexus	CBen CWat EBWF LLWG MSKA XLum
	- 'Afro'	NBro NWsh SPlb
	maritimus new	EBWF
	pallidus	EPPr GCal
	patens 'Carman's Gray'	CKno CRos CWCL GCal LRHS MMoz MMuc NRHS NWad
	- 'Elk Blue'	CKno
	subnodulosus	LLWG
	'Swarm of Hedgehogs'	NWsh
	xiphioides	EHoe

Junellia (*Verbenaceae*)

	azorelloides	WAbe
	congesta	WAbe
	erinacea	WAbe
§	***micrantha***	WAbe
	odonnellii	WAbe
§	***succulentifolia***	WAbe
	thymifolia	WAbe

Juniperus ✿ (*Cupressaceae*)

	sp.	LPra
	chinensis	CMen
	- 'Aurea' ♀H6	CBcs ESps SEND
§	- 'Blaauw' ♀H6	CMac CMen ETMg SGol SLim
	- 'Blue Alps' ♀H6	CAco EMOT ESps GMil LRHS MGos MMuc NEgg NRHS SCob SCoo SEND SGol SLim
	- 'Echiniformis'	CKen EPot
	- 'Expansa Aureospicata' (v)	CMac EMOT EPfP ESps NRHS SEND SPoG SRms
§	- 'Expansa Variegata' (v)	EMOT NRHS SLim
	- 'Itoigawa'	CMen
§	- 'Kaizuka' ♀H6	SGol
	- 'Kaizuka Variegata'	see *J. chinensis* 'Variegated Kaizuka'
	- 'Kuriwao Gold'	see *J.* × *pfitzeriana* 'Kuriwao Gold'
	- 'Obelisk'	GMil
§	- 'Parsonsii'	WCFE
	- 'Plumosa Aurea' ♀H6	ESps LRHS
	- 'Plumosa Aureovariegata' (v)	CKen
	- 'Pyramidalis' ♀H6	EMOT EPfP ESps GMcL GMil MAsh NRHS SCoo
	- 'Pyramidalis Variegata'	see *J. chinensis* 'Variegata'
	- 'San José'	CMen
§	- var. ***sargentii***	CMen
	- 'Shimpaku'	CKen CMen
	- 'Stricta'	CAco CSBt LRHS NRHS SGol SLim
	- 'Stricta Variegata'	see *J. chinensis* 'Variegata'
	- 'Sulphur Spray'	see *J.* × *pfitzeriana* 'Sulphur Spray'
	- 'Torulosa'	see *J. chinensis* 'Kaizuka'
§	- 'Variegata' (v)	ESps
§	- 'Variegated Kaizuka' (v)	EMOT SCoo SLim
	communis	CAco CDul CFGn CHab CPer ESps GPoy WTSh
	- 'Arnold'	NLar
	- 'Arnold Sentinel'	CKen
	- 'Barton'	NLar NWad
	- 'Barton Gem'	NWad
	- 'Brien'	CKen
	- 'Brynhyfryd Gold'	CKen SLim
§	- var. ***communis***	GMil
	- 'Compressa' ♀H7	CBcs CKen CMac CSBt CTri EMOT EPfP EPot ESps EUJe GEdr GMcL LBee LRHS MAsh MGos MJak NEgg NRHS SLim SPer SPoG
	- 'Corielagan'	CKen
	- 'Cracovia'	CKen
	- var. ***depressa***	GPoy SEND SGol
	- 'Depressa Aurea'	CKen CSBt EMOT ESps GMcL LBee
	- 'Depressed Star'	EMOT SPoG
	- 'Effusa'	CKen
	- 'Gelb'	see *J. communis* 'Schneverdingen Goldmachangel'
	- 'Gold Cone'	CKen ELan EMOT EPfP ESps EUJe LBee MAsh MGos SLim SPoG
	- 'Golden Showers'	see *J. communis* 'Schneverdingen Goldmachangel'
	- 'Goldschatz'	CKen EPfP GMil LRHS SLim SPoG
	- 'Green Carpet' ♀H7	CAco CKen ELan EMOT EPfP GKin GMcL GMil LBuc LRHS MAsh MGos NLar NRHS SCoo SLim SPoG WCFE
	- 'Haverbeck'	CKen
	- var. ***hemispherica***	see *J. communis* var. *communis*
	- 'Hibernica' ♀H7	CDul CSBt ELan EMOT EPfP ESps GMcL GMil LRHS MGos MJak SLim SPer SPoG
	- 'Hibernica Aurea'	CMac
	- 'Hornibrookii'	SRms
	- 'Kenwith Castle'	CKen
	- 'Meyer'	GMil
	- 'Pyramidalis'	SPlb
	- 'Repanda' ♀H7	CAco CBcs CMac CSBt EMOT EPfP ESps GMcL GMil LRHS MGos NLar NRHS SCoo SGol SLim SPer SPoG
§	- 'Schneverdingen Goldmachangel'	GMil IBoy MAsh
	- 'Sentinel'	ESps WCFE
	- 'Sieben Steinhauser'	CKen
	- 'Silver Mist'	CKen
	- (Suecica Group) 'Suecica Aurea'	GMcL
	- 'Zeal'	CKen

	conferta	see *J. rigida* subsp. *conferta*
	- 'Blue Lagoon' **new**	CAco
	- var. ***maritima***	see *J. taxifolia*
	davurica 'Expansa'	see *J. chinensis* 'Parsonsii'
	- 'Expansa Albopicta'	see *J. chinensis* 'Expansa Variegata'
	- 'Expansa Variegata'	see *J. chinensis* 'Expansa Variegata'
	- 'Leningrad'	NLar
	× ***gracilis*** 'Blaauw'	see *J. chinensis* 'Blaauw'
	'Grey Owl' ♀H7	CAco ELan EMOT ESps LRHS MMuc SEND SGol SLim SRms
	horizontalis	ESps
§	- 'Andorra Compact'	EPfP
I	- 'Andorra Variegata' (v)	EMOT SCoo
	- 'Bar Harbor'	CMac
§	- 'Blue Chip'	CAco ELan EPfP ESps GMcL GMil LBee MGos MJak SCoo SPer SPoG
	- 'Blue Moon'	see *J. horizontalis* 'Blue Chip'
	- 'Blue Rug'	see *J. horizontalis* 'Wiltonii'
	- 'Emerald Spreader'	ELan EMOT GMil
	- 'Glacier'	LRHS
	- 'Glauca'	ESps
	- 'Golden Carpet' ♀H7	ELan GMil LBuc LCro LOPS NLar
	- 'Grey Pearl'	CKen
	- 'Hughes'	CAco LBee MRav NRHS
	- ICEE BLUE ('Monber') ♀H7	CKen EPfP GKin GMil LRHS NLar SPoG
	- 'Jade River'	CAco
	- 'Limeglow' ♀H7	CAco ELan EMOT EPfP EUJe GMcL GMil MGos NLar SCoo SPoG
	- 'Mother Lode'	CKen
	- 'Neumann'	CKen
	- 'Pancake'	NLar
	- 'Plumosa Compacta'	see *J. horizontalis* 'Andorra Compact'
	- 'Prince of Wales'	GMil MAsh NRHS
	- 'Prostrata'	IBoy
	- var. ***saxatilis*** E. Murray	see *J. communis* var. *communis*
	- 'Turquoise Spreader'	CSBt NRHS SGol
	- 'Villa Marie'	CKen SPoG
§	- 'Wiltonii'	CDul
	- 'Youngstown'	GMil NRHS
	- 'Yukon Belle'	CKen
	× ***media***	see *J.* × *pfitzeriana*
	oxycedrus	XSen
	- subsp. ***macrocarpa*** **new**	GMil
§	× ***pfitzeriana***	CDul CMac ESps GMcL SCob SGol
	- 'Arctic'	NLar
	- 'Blaauw'	see *J. chinensis* 'Blaauw'
	- 'Blue and Gold' (v)	CKen SPoG
	- 'Blue Cloud'	see *J. virginiana* 'Blue Cloud'
§	- 'Carbery Gold' ♀H7	CBcs CMac CSBt EPfP ESps GKin GMil LRHS MGos NRHS SCoo SLim SPoG
	- 'Gold Coast'	CKen CSBt ESps LBee MGos SGol
	- GOLD SOVEREIGN ('Blound')	ESps LBee
	- 'Gold Star'	LRHS
	- 'Goldkissen'	NRHS
	- 'Hetzii'	NLar
	- 'King of Spring'	SLim
§	- 'Kuriwao Gold'	EMOT GKin GMcL SEND SGol
	- 'Mint Julep'	CAco CSBt EPfP ESps GMcL LOPS MJak NRHS SCob SCoo SGol SLim
	- 'Old Gold' ♀H7	EMOT EPfP ESps GKin GMcL GMil LBee LCro LOPS LRHS MGos MJak MMuc NEgg NRHS SCoo SEND SGol SPlb WCFE WHar
	- 'Old Gold Carbery'	see *J.* × *pfitzeriana* 'Carbery Gold'
	- 'Pfitzeriana Aurea'	CMac EMOT ESps LRHS SCob SGol
	- 'Pfitzeriana Glauca'	CAco ESps
§	- 'Sulphur Spray' ♀H7	CDul ESps GMil LRHS MMuc SEND SLim
	phoenicea	XSen
§	***pingii*** 'Glassell'	NLar
	- 'Hulsdonk Yellow'PBR	LRHS NLar SLim SPoG
§	- 'Loderi' **new**	GMil
§	- var. ***wilsonii***	CKen
	procumbens 'Kishiogima'	LRHS NLar
	- 'Lighting Spot'	NLar
	- 'Nana' ♀H7	CKen CMac CSBt EPfP GMcL LBee LRHS MAsh MGos MJak NEgg NLar NRHS SCoo SLim SPoG WCFE
	recurva 'Castlewellan'	NLar WHor
	- var. ***coxii***	CMac NLar SRms WCFE
§	- 'Densa'	CKen
	- 'Nana'	see *J. recurva* 'Densa'
	rigida	CMen
§	- subsp. ***conferta***	CMac EMOT NRHS SEND SGol
	- - 'All Gold' ♀H6	LRHS NRHS SLim SPoG
*	- - 'Blue Ice'	CKen GMil NRHS
	- - 'Blue Pacific'	CKen EMOT LRHS NRHS SGol SPoG
	- - 'Blue Tosho'	CDul NLar
	- - 'Silver Mist'	CKen
	sabina 'Skandia'	CKen
	- 'Tamariscifolia'	CBcs ESps GKin GMcL LBee LRHS MAsh MGos MJak SEND SGol SLim SPer SPoG WCFE
	sargentii	see *J. chinensis* var. *sargentii*
	scopulorum 'Blue Arrow' ♀H7	Widely available
	- 'Blue Banff'	CKen
	- 'Skyrocket'	CBcs CCVT CDul CMac CSBt ECrN EMOT EPfP ESps GMil LMaj LPra MGos MJak MRav SCob SGol SRms SWeb WCFE WHar WMou
	- 'Springbank'	WCFE
	- 'Wichita Blue'	CCVT EPfP
	squamata 'Blue Carpet' ♀H7	CAco CBcs CDul CKen CMac CSBt EPfP ESps GMcL GMil LBuc LRHS MAsh MGos MJak NEgg NLar NRHS SCob SEND SGol SLim SPer SPoG WCFE WFar WHar
	- 'Blue Spider'	LRHS
	- 'Blue Star' ♀H7	CJun CKen CMac CSBt ELan EMOT EPfP ESps GMcL GMil IBoy LBee LCro LOPS LRHS MAsh MGos MJak NEgg NLar NRHS SGol SLim SPer SPoG WCFE WFar
	- 'Blue Star Variegated'	see *J. squamata* 'Golden Flame'
	- 'Blue Swede'	see *J. squamata* 'Hunnetorp'
	- 'Dream Joy'	CKen NLar NWad
	- 'Filborna'	LBee
	- 'Floreant'	SLim SPoG
	- 'Glassell'	see *J. pingii* 'Glassell'
§	- 'Golden Flame' (v)	CKen
	- 'Holger' ♀H7	CMac EPfP ESps GMcL GMil LBee LRHS MAsh MGos MJak NLar NRHS SCoo SLim SPoG
§	- 'Hunnetorp'	GMil LRHS
	- 'Loderi'	see *J. pingii* 'Loderi'
	- 'Meyeri'	ESps GMcL GMil SGol
	- 'Tropical Blue' **new**	SPoG
	- 'Wilsonii'	see *J. pingii* var. *wilsonii*
§	***taxifolia***	CSBt
	virginiana	CAco LPra
§	- 'Blue Cloud'	SLim
	- 'Frosty Morn'	CKen
	- 'Golden Spring'	CKen

- SILVER SPREADER ('Mona') CKen
- 'Sulphur Spray' see *J.* × *pfitzeriana* 'Sulphur Spray'

Jurinea (*Asteraceae*)

ledebourii SPhx
mollis SPhx

Jurinella see *Jurinea*

Jussiaea see *Ludwigia*

Justicia (*Acanthaceae*)

americana LLWG
aurea EShb
§ **brandegeeana** ♀H1b CCCN EShb
- 'Lutea' see *J. brandegeeana* 'Yellow Queen'
- variegated (v) EShb
§ - 'Yellow Queen' EShb
- yellow-flowered EShb
§ **carnea** CHll EShb
- 'Alba' CCCN EShb
- dark-leaved CHll EShb
guttata see *J. brandegeeana*
'Penrhosiensis' EShb
pohliana see *J. carnea*
rizzinii ♀H1b CBcs CCCN CHll EUJe SEle SRot
spicigera CCCN EShb
suberecta see *Dicliptera sericea*

K

Kadsura (*Schisandraceae*)

coccinea B&SWJ 11793 WCru
- FMWJ 13489 WCru
heteroclita FMWJ 13385 WCru
- WWJ 11947 WCru
japonica CBcs
- B&SWJ 1027 WCru
- B&SWJ 4463 from Korea WCru
- B&SWJ 11109 from Japan WCru
- from Japan EPfP WSHC
- 'Fukurin' (v) IDee NLar
- 'Variegata' (v) CCCN CRos EBee EPfP LRHS WSHC
- white fruit NLar

Kaempferia ✿ (*Zingiberaceae*)

rotunda CCCN LAma SDir

Kageneckia (*Rosaceae*)

oblonga SPlb

Kalanchoe (*Crassulaceae*)

beharensis ♀H1b CCCN CDTJ ELan EShb WCot
- 'Fang' ♀H1b CDTJ ELan EShb
- 'Rusty' CDTJ CSpe
daigremontiana EShb
§ **delagoensis** CCCN EShb
fedtschenkoi EShb
- 'Variegata' (v) WCot
hildebrandtii EShb
humilis EShb WCot
laciniata EShb
'Oak Leaf' new EShb
orgyalis EShb
pinnata EShb
pubescens EShb
pumila ♀H1b EShb SAll SBch
serrata EShb
sexangularis EShb
'Tessa' ♀H1b WCot
thyrsiflora EShb
- 'Bronze Sculpture' CAbb EUJe
- 'Variegata' (v) EShb
tomentosa ♀H1b EShb SAll WCot XAbr
tubiflora see *K. delagoensis*

kale, curly see AGM Vegetables Section

Kalimeris (*Asteraceae*)

altaica new EPPr
§ **incisa** MMuc WBor
- 'Alba' ECha ELon NLar WFar
- 'Blue Star' ECha ECtt ELon GMaP GQue IRob MNrw MSpe NLar NPnk SCob SPoG WCAu WFar WPtf WSHC
- 'Charlotte' EWes LPla MNrw MSpe MTis NBre NDov NPnk SAko SPoG WFar
- 'Madiva' CSam EBee ELon IMou LPla NDov NPnk SAko WTor
- 'Nana Blue' EBee NDov SPoG
integrifolia MMuc
'Mon Jardin' WCot
§ **mongolica** CAby CMac ECha MMuc SAko WFar WRHF WSHC
- 'Antonia' EBee IRob NDov WCot
§ **pinnatifida** CRos LRHS NRHS
- 'Hortensis' EBee MNrw
§ **yomena** 'Shogun' (v) CBod ECha ECtt EHoe ELan EPfP LEdu MNrw MPie MSpe NSti SPer SRms WFar XLum
- 'Variegata' see *K. yomena* 'Shogun'

Kalmia ✿ (*Ericaceae*)

angustifolia ♀H4 GKev WSpi
- f. **rubra** ♀H6 CBcs CCCN CDul CRos ELan EPfP ETMg LRHS MAsh NLar SPer WSpi
I - 'Rubra Nana' CMac
latifolia CBcs ELan EPfP LRHS SPer SWvt WHar
- 'Alpine Pink' WSpi
- 'Bandeau' GGGa
- 'Bay State' LRHS
- 'Bridesmaid' NLar
- 'Bullseye' LRHS SAko SPoG
- 'Carousel' CBcs CCCN NLar
- 'Clementine Churchill' CMac
- 'Eskimo' GGGa
- 'Freckles' ♀H6 LRHS SPoG
- 'Galaxy' GGGa LRHS NLar SAko
- 'Ginkona' GGGa LRHS SAko
- 'Heart's Desire' LRHS
- 'Kaleidoscope' GGGa LSRN NLar
- 'Minuet' CBcs CCCN CRos GGGa GMcL LRHS MAsh MGil MLea NLar SPoG SWvt
- 'Mitternacht' GGGa
- 'Moyland' GGGa LSRN
- f. **myrtifolia** CRos LRHS MLea
- - 'Elf' CRos LRHS NLar
- 'Nani' GGGa
- 'Nipmuck' CMac
- 'Olympic Fire' ♀H6 CBcs CRos GGGa GMcL LRHS MGil NLar SAko SWvt WSpi WTSh

- 'Olympic Wedding' SPoG
- 'Ostbo Red' CBcs CDul CMac CRos LRHS LSRN MGil MLea MMuc SAko SPoG SWvt
- 'Peppermint' GGGa LRHS NLar
- 'Pink Charm' 🏆^{H6} SAko
- 'Pinkobello' GGGa
- 'Pinwheel' LRHS MGil MJak NLar SAko SPoG
- 'Quinnipiac' MJak
- 'Sarah' CRos LRHS MLea
- 'Snowdrift' LRHS NLar
- 'Starbust' LRHS
- 'Tad' LRHS
- 'You Can' LRHS

polifolia CCCN LCro LOPS LRHS SPer WThu
- f. ***leucantha*** WThu

Kalmiopsis (*Ericaceae*)
leachiana 'Glendoick' LRHS

× *Kalmiothamnus* (*Ericaceae*)
'Haytor' ITim
'Sindelberg' ITim

Kalopanax ✿ (*Araliaceae*)
pictus see *K. septemlobus*
§ ***septemlobus*** CBcs EPfP MMuc NLar SEND SPtp
- var. ***magnificus*** B&SWJ 10900 WCru
- f. ***maximowiczii*** CDul EPfP MBlu NLar

Keckiella (*Plantaginaceae*)
corymbosa B&SWJ 14096 **new** WCru

Keiskea (*Lamiaceae*)
japonica pink-flowered SBrt

Kelseya (*Rosaceae*)
uniflora WAbe

Kennedia (*Papilionaceae*)
coccinea CCCN
macrophylla CRHN
nigricans CCCN
prostrata SBrt SPlb
rubicunda CCCN CRHN

Kentia (*Arecaceae*)
belmoreana see *Howea belmoreana*
forsteriana see *Howea forsteriana*

Kentranthus see *Centranthus*

Kerria (*Rosaceae*)
japonica misapplied single see *K. japonica* 'Simplex'
japonica (L.) DC. CTho ESps
- (d) see *K. japonica* 'Pleniflora'
- 'Albescens' CBot NLar WCot
- 'Buttercup' NLar
- 'Golden Guinea' 🏆^{H5} CBot CExl CMac CRos ELan EPfP ESps ETMg GMcL IFro LRHS MAsh MGos MRav NRHS SCob SCoo SPer SRms SWvt WFar
- 'Honshu' IArd
§ - 'Picta' (v) CDul CMac CTho EBee ELan MGos MRav MSwo SCob SGol SLim SLon SRms WAvo WFar
§ - 'Pleniflora' (d) 🏆^{H5} Widely available
§ - 'Simplex' CDul CExl CMac SRms
- 'Variegata' see *K. japonica* 'Picta'

Keteleeria (*Pinaceae*)
evelyniana **new** CAco

Khadia (*Aizoaceae*)
acutipetala CCCN

Kiggelaria (*Flacourtiaceae*)
africana SVen

Kirengeshoma (*Hydrangeaceae*)
palmata Widely available
- 'Black Style' EBee
- dwarf WCot
- Koreana Group 🏆^{H7} Widely available

Kitagawia (*Apiaceae*)
§ ***litoralis*** EBee

Kitaibela (*Malvaceae*)
vitifolia CExl CSpe ELan EPPr NBid NSti SEND SPav SPlb WAvo WFar WHer WOut

Kitchingia see *Kalanchoe*

kiwi fruit see *Actinidia deliciosa*

Klasea (*Asteraceae*)
§ ***bulgarica*** MAvo NDov
§ ***coronata*** subsp. ***insularis*** B&SWJ 8698 WCru
§ ***radiata*** subsp. ***gmelinii*** EPPr LRHS NRHS
§ ***lycopifolia*** WCot

Kleinia (*Asteraceae*)
articulata see *Curio articulata*
§ ***grantii*** CSpe SBch WCot
neriifolia WCot
repens see *Curio repens*

Knautia (*Caprifoliaceae*)
§ ***arvensis*** CBod CElw CHab CWld EBWF EBee EPfP GCal LCro MHer MNHC NLar NMir SPer SPhx SRms WHer WMoo WOut WSFF
- white-flowered SPhx WSHC
dipsacifolia LPla SHar
'Jardin d'en Face' CBod EPfP LRHS
§ ***macedonica*** Widely available
- 'Crimson Cushion' CSpe ECtt LSou
- dark-flowered IFro
- 'Macedonia Lilac' IRob
- 'Mars Midget' CBod CExl CHll CRos CSpe EBee ELan ELon EPfP ESps GCal IBoy LRHS LSou MGos MSpe NLar NRHS SCob SPhx SPoG SWvt WArt WFar WHar WHoo WSHC
- Melton pastels CBod CChe CDor CExl CRos EBee ELan EPPr EPfP ESps GJos GMaP IBoy LRHS MGos NLar NPer NRHS SPhx SPoG SRkn SRms SRot SWvt WFar WHar
- pink-flowered CSam SRms
- 'Red Baron' **new** CChe
- 'Red Cherries' **new** CBod
- 'Red Knight' CDor CRos EBee EPfP ESps GWyn LRHS MBNS NRHS WCAu
- short ECtt
- tall, pale-flowered SPhx

- 'Thunder and Lightning'PBR (v)	CBct CBod CDor CRos CWGN EBee ECtt EPfP EWes ILea LBuc LRHS MAsh MHol MNrw MRav NLar NRHS SPad SPer SPoG SRms WCot
sarajevensis	MAvo

Knightia (*Proteaceae*)

excelsa	CBcs

Kniphofia ✿ (*Asphodelaceae*)

'Ada'	ELon EWes
albescens	NLos SPlb
'Alcazar'	CBcs CPrp ECtt ELon EPfP EUJe GMcL IBoy IRob LCro LOPS MAvo MHer SCob SPer SWvt WCFE WFar WHar WSpi
'Ample Dwarf'	ECtt WCot
'Amsterdam'	MWat
angustifolia	SPlb
'Apricot'	CRos LRHS NRHS
'Apricot Souffle'	EPri WCot
'Atlanta'	CRos LRHS NRHS
'Barton Fever' ♀H6	WCot
baurii	CExl SPlb
'Bees' Jubilee'	MAvo NChi
'Bees' Lemon'	Widely available
§ 'Bees' Sunset' ♀H5	CAvo CBWd CPrp CRos CSam EBee ECha ECtt EPfP EUJe LRHS MMuc MWat NRHS SEND SMHy SPoG SWvt WAul WSHC
'Bees' Yellow'	SBch WAvo
'Border Ballet'	CRos LRHS NGdn NLar NRHS WHar XLum
brachystachya	ELon SBrt SPlb
'Bressingham Comet'	CRos ECtt GKev LRHS NRHS SRms
BRESSINGHAM SUNBEAM ('Bresun')	CRos EBee ECtt LRHS NRHS
'Bressingham Yellow'	ECtt EUJe
'Brimstone' Bloom ♀H5	CDor CPrp CRos ECtt EPfP EPri LEdu LRHS MMuc MSpe NPnk NRHS SEND SPtp SWvt WFar WGwG
bruceae	SPlb SVen
'Buttercup' ♀H5	CAvo LCro LOPS LSRN
'Butterfly'	EBee
'C.M. Prichard' misapplied	see *K. rooperi*
'C.M. Prichard' Prichard	WCot
'Candlelight'	EBee ECtt EPri MAvo WSHC
'Candy Apple' **new**	EBee
caulescens	Widely available
- LEG 053	GKev
- 'Coral Breakers'	CExl CPrp ECtt ELon GAbr GBin LRHS MAvo MHol NEgg NLos NRHS SEND SPer WCot
- early-flowering	WSpi
- 'John May'	CAby CBod CBot CTsd EBee ECtt EMFm LEdu MAvo MHer SCob SWvt WCot
- short	ECha
- 'Tiny Girl'	ECtt
'Champagne' **new**	WCot
'Chichi'	WCot
'Christmas Cheer'	EBee
citrina	CBod GKev GLog IBoy MBrN NGBl WCot WHar XLum
'Cobra'	CDor CRos ECtt GMaP LRHS NRHS WAul WCot
'Coral Flame' ♀H5	CRos LRHS NRHS
'Coral Sceptre'	WCot
'Creamsicle'PBR (Popsicle Series)	ECtt SCob WCot
'Dingaan'	EBee ECtt GBin GMcL MNrw MTis NLar WCot
'Dorset Sentry'	CAbb CAby EBee ECtt ELon EPfP LRHS MBel MGos MNrw NEgg NLar SPhx WCot WFar
'Drummore Apricot'	CPrp CRos ECha ECtt ELan EPfP GBin IBoy LRHS LSRN MAvo MPie NEgg NRHS SPtp WCot WFar WGwG
'Early Buttercup'	WFar
'Early Orange' **new**	CSBt
'Early Red' **new**	CSBt
'Early Yellow'	CSBt
'Elvira'PBR	CBWd CPne CRos EBee ECtt EUJe GBin LRHS MBNS NRHS SAko WCot
EMBER GLOW ('Tneg'PBR) (Glow Series)	CAbb CPne EBee ECtt LCro LOPS
ensifolia	CTca ECtt NGdn SVen XLum
'Erecta'	CPne CTal
'Ernest Mitchell'	WCot
Express hybrids	XLum
'Fiery Fred' ♀H6	CPrp CRos EBee ECtt ELon EPfP LRHS MAvo MMuc MSpe NRHS SBod SPhm SPtp WAul WCot WSpi
FIRE GLOW ('Tnfg'PBR) (Glow Series)	NLar
'First Sunrise'PBR	ECtt LRHS MJak NPnk
'Flamenco'	CRos ELon LPmr LRHS NGdn NRHS SCob WFar
'Flaming Torch'	EBee ECtt
'Florence Bedecked'	WCot
fluviatilis	GKev
foliosa Hochst.	LEdu
'Frances Victoria'	WCot
galpinii misapplied	see *K. triangularis* subsp. *triangularis*
galpinii Baker ♀H4	CPne MAvo MMuc
'Gilt Bronze'	WCot
'Gladness'	MAvo WCot
'Goldelse'	CRos EBee LRHS NRHS
'Goldfinch'	CCse CSam
gracilis	LEdu
'Grandiflora'	CMac WHar
'Green and Cream'	MHCG
'Green Jade'	CAby CBcs CCse CExl CRos EBee ECha ECtt ELan EPfP EUJe GBin LRHS MBel MCot MNrw MRav NGBl NLar NRHS NSti SEND SGbt SPer SRms WCAu WCot WFar
'Green Jewel'	LRHS
'H.E. Beale'	WCot
'Hen and Chickens'	ECtt MAvo WCot
hirsuta	CRos EBee LRHS NLos NRHS SRms WSHC
- 'Fire Dance'	CRos ETMg LRHS LSun NRHS WFar
- 'Traffic Lights'	GMcL MAvo WHar
'Ice Queen'	CAvo CDor CPrp EBee ECha ECtt ELon EPPr EPri GBin GKev MAvo MHer MNrw MRav MTis NChi NLar SEND SGol SRms SWvt WCot WFar
ichopensis	LEdu NLos SVen WPGP
'Incandesce' ♀H5	EBee MBNS MNrw NCou SPoG WCot
'Innocence' ♀H4	CRos EPfP LRHS MAvo NRHS
'Jane Henry'	EBee LEdu
'Jenny Bloom'	CRos ECtt ELan ELon EPfP EUJe GCal GMaP LEdu LRHS MRav NLar

		NRHS NSti SEND SPtp SRms WAul WCAu WCot WFar
	'Jess's Delight'	WCot
	'John Benary'	CBod CPrp CRos ECtt EPPr GLog GMaP LLWG LRHS MBel NEgg NGdn NLar NRHS SEND SPtp SRms WCot WGwG WKif
	'Jonathan' ♀H5	WCot
	laxiflora	EPri NLos WPGP
	'Lemon Popsicle'PBR (Popsicle Series)	CAbb CBct CMea CRos CWCL CWGN LRHS NRHS SCob SRms WFar
	'Light of the World'	see *K. triangularis* subsp. *triangularis* 'Light of the World'
	'Limelight'	EBee ECtt EUJe
	linearifolia	CBlu CExl CPrp EBee NLos SPlb WCot XLum
	'Little Elf'	CDor XLum
	'Little Maid'	Widely available
	'Lord Roberts'	MAvo MRav SMad WCot WPGP
	'Luna'	WCot
	macowanii	see *K. triangularis* subsp. *triangularis*
	'Mango Popsicle'PBR (Popsicle Series)	CAbb CPne CRos EBee ECtt EWTr GMcL LRHS LSou MAvo MBel MNrw MPnt NLar NRHS NSti SCob SMad SPoG SRms WCot WFar WHoo WWFP
	'Mermaiden'	CRos ECtt MAvo MMuc MNrw SEND WCot
	'Minister Verschuur'	CRos EBee ECtt LRHS NRHS
	'Modesta'	WSHC
	'Molten Lava'	EBee
	'Moonstone' ♀H5	CPrp CSam EBee ECtt ELon EUJe GBin LLHF LSun MNrw MTis NLar NSti SEND SPoG WCot WSpi
	'Mount Etna'	WAvo
	multiflora	NLos
	- cream-flowered	NLos
	- 'November Glory'	WCot
	- yellow/orange-flowered	NLos
	'Nancy's Red'	Widely available
	nelsonii Mast.	see *K. triangularis* subsp. *triangularis*
	'New Sensation'	WCot
	'No Rhyme Nor Reason' **new**	WCot
§	'Nobilis' ♀H6	CAby CExl CRos ECha ECtt ELan ELon EUJe GAbr GBin GMaP LCro LOPS LRHS LSRN MBel MHol MMuc MNrw NGdn SArc SEND SPer SRms SWvt WCot
	northiae ♀H4	CBod CBot CCht CExl CHid CPla CTsd EBee ELan ELon EPfP EPri EUJe EWes GCal LEdu MAvo MNrw NLos SArc SEND SMad SPlb SPtp SWvt WCot WCru WPGP WSpi XLum
	'Orange Vanilla Popsicle'PBR (Popsicle Series)	CAbb CBct CPla CRos CSBt ECtt LRHS MAvo MPnt NRHS SCob SPad SPoG WTor
§	'Painted Lady'	CDor CSam CTri EBee ECtt GMaP IRob MAvo MHol MNrw NLar SEND SMHy SWvt WCot
	'Papaya Popsicle'PBR (Popsicle Series)	CBct CRos CWGN EBee ECtt ELon LRHS LSou MAvo MNrw NLar NRHS SCob SPoG SRms WFar WSpi
	parviflora	XLum
	pauciflora	CPbh WCot

	'Penny Rockets' ♀H6	EBee LRHS NRHS
	'Percy's Pride'	Widely available
	'Pfitzeri'	SRms
	'Pineapple Popsicle'PBR (Popsicle Series)	CAbb CRos CWGN ECtt LRHS NLar NRHS SCob SRms
	× ***praecox***	NLos
	'Primrose Upward' ♀H6	WCot
I	'Primulina' Bloom	CRos LRHS NRHS
	'Prince Igor' misapplied	see *K.* 'Nobilis'
	'Prince Igor' Prichard	ECtt
	'Red Rocket'PBR	EBee GMcL IBoy LRHS MNrw WCot
	'Redhot Popsicle'PBR (Popsicle Series)	CBod CRos CWGN IRob LRHS MAvo MHol MNrw NRHS SPoG WCot
	'Rich Echoes' ♀H5	CAby CAvo CWGN EBee ECtt ELon GBin IRob LEdu LLHF MAvo MHol MNrw MTis NLar WCot WRHF
	ritualis	CExl
§	***rooperi*** ♀H5	Widely available
I	- 'Torchlight'	CPne
	'Royal Castle'	CExl CRos GMaP LRHS MJak NGdn NRHS SCob SEND WFar XLum
	'Royal Standard' ♀H5	CBcs CBod CPrp CRos ECtt ELan ELon EPfP EUJe GMaP ILea LCro LOPS LRHS NLar NRHS SCob SPer SPoG SPtp SWvt WCAu WFar WGwG WHar WSpi
	rufa Baker	LEdu MAvo WPGP
	'Safranvogel' ♀H4	ECtt WCot
	'Samuel's Sensation' misapplied	see *K.* 'Painted Lady'
	'Samuel's Sensation' Samuel ♀H5	CRos EBee ECtt EPPr LRHS NLar NRHS SRGP SWvt WCot
	sarmentosa	CExl NLos SPlb SVen WCot
	'Saturn'	MAvo
	'Sherbet Lemon'	MNrw WCot
	'Shining Sceptre' misapplied	see *K.* 'Bees' Sunset'
	'Slush Puppy' **new**	ECtt
	'Springtime'	WCot
	'Star of Baden-Baden'	MAvo MMuc SEND SMad WCot
	Stark's early perpetual-flowering hybrids	XLum
	'Strawberries and Cream'	CBcs CPrp CTsd EBee ECha ECtt ELon EWld NLar SGbt SWvt
	stricta	XLum
	'Sunningdale Yellow' ♀H6	CCse ECha ECtt EHrv EUJe GMaP ILea MAvo SMHy SRms WHar WSpi
	'Tawny King' ♀H5	Widely available
	'Tetbury Torch'PBR	CBod CExl CPrp CRos CWGN EBee ECtt GBin LRHS MAvo MCot NRHS SEND SPtp SWvt WAul
	thomsonii	CExl NGdn
	- 'Kichocheo'	EBee GCal LEdu MAvo WCot
	- var. ***snowdenii*** misapplied	see *K. thomsonii* var. *thomsonii*
	- var. ***snowdenii*** ambig.	CExl WPGP XLum
§	- var. ***thomsonii***	SMHy WSHC
	- - 'Stern's Trip' ♀H4	EBee
	'Timothy' ♀H5	Widely available
	'Toffee Nosed' ♀H5	CBod CPrp CRos ECtt ELon EPPr EPed EPfP EPri GBin IPot IRob LRHS MRav MSpe MWat NEgg NGdn NLar NRHS SCob SEND SPer SPtp SRkn SWvt WAul WCAu WCot WSHC
	'Torchbearer'	WCot
	triangularis	GKev WFar XLum
§	- subsp. ***triangularis***	CRos EPfP LRHS NRHS SCob SMad SRms SVen XLum

§	- - 'Light of the World'	CAby CDor CMac CPrp ECtt GAbr IRob LRHS MHer NLar NRHS SCob SPer SPtp SWvt WCot WFar
	'Tuckii' misapplied	SRms
	typhoides	NLos SPlb
	tysonii	SPlb XLum
	- subsp. ***tysonii***	NLos
	uvaria	CPrp CRos EBee GKev LCro LRHS NLos NRHS SCob SPer SRms SVic WCAu WCot XLum XSen
	'Vanilla'	LRHS MMuc NLar SEND SMad
	'Vesta'	CRos EBee LRHS NRHS
	'Vincent Lepage'	NLar
	'Wol's Red Seedling'	CAby CSam ECtt ELon GAbr MCot MNrw SBch SEND SMHy WCot WGwG WHoo
	'Wrexham Buttercup' 🏆H6	CDor CSam EBee ECtt ELan EUJe GMaP IRob LSRN MAvo MCot MHol MNrw MTis SCob SEND SMad WCot WFar WHal WSpi
	'Yellow Cheer'	WCot
	'Yellow Hammer' Slieve Donard	CSam ECha ELon MMuc SEND

Knowltonia (*Ranunculaceae*)

	filia	CExl

Koeleria (*Poaceae*)

	cristata misapplied	see *K. macrantha*
	glauca	CBod CRos ECha EHoe EPfP EShb ESps GMaP GMcL LRHS MBNS MJak NGdn NRHS NWsh SCob SLim SPlb SWvt WFar WHar XSen
§	***macrantha***	EBWF
	vallesiana	EHoe

Koelreuteria (*Sapindaceae*)

	bipinnata	IDee LRHS
	elegans subsp. ***formosana***	CMCN
	paniculata	CAco CCVT CDul CLnd CMCN CMac CMen CTri ECrN ELan EMOT EPfP ESps LEdu LMaj LPra MGos MMuc SEND SGol SLim SPer SPlb WFar WHar WHor WTSh
	- 'Beachmaster'	NLar
	- 'Coral Sun' PBR 🏆H5	CExl ELan EPfP EUJe LRHS MBlu MGos NOra SLim SPoG WCot WMou
	- 'Fastigiata'	CDul EBee EPfP MBlu SCoo WHar WHor
	- 'Rosseels'	EMOT NLar
	- 'September'	EPfP MBlu

Kohleria (*Gesneriaceae*)

	'Ampallang'	WDib
	'An's Nagging Macaws'	WDib
	'Brazil Gem'	WDib
	'Bristol's Evil Storm' **new**	WDib
	'Cybele'	WDib
	'Dark Velvet'	WDib
	eriantha 🏆H1c	CTsd WDib
	'Flashdance'	WDib
	'Hcy's Jardin de Monet'	WDib
	'Heartland's Blackberry Butterfly'	WDib
	hirsuta	WDib
	'Jester' 🏆H1c	WDib
	'Lilla Gubben' **new**	WDib
	'Manchu'	WDib
	'Marquis de Sade'	WDib
	'Queen Victoria'	WDib
I	***sciadotydaea***	WDib
	'Silver Feather'	WDib
§	'Sunrise'	WDib
	'Sunshine'	see *K.* 'Sunrise'
	'Texas Rainbow'	WDib
	warszewiczii 🏆H1c	WDib
	'Yf's Emma' **new**	WDib
	'Yf's Josse' **new**	WDib

kohlrabi see AGM Vegetables Section

Kolkwitzia (*Caprifoliaceae*)

	amabilis	CExl CSBt CTri ELan EPfP ESps ETMg GBin GMcL IRob NEgg SCob SGol SPlb SRms WCFE WHar WMoo WRHF WSHC
	- DREAM CATCHER ('Maradco')	CMac EPfP MAsh MRav NEoE NLar SCob SGol WSpi
	- 'Pink Cloud' 🏆H5	Widely available

Kosteletzkya (*Malvaceae*)

	virginica	MHol SBrt WArt

kumquat see *Citrus japonica*

Kunzea (*Myrtaceae*)

	ambigua	EBee IDee SPlb
	- pink-flowered	SEle
	'Badja Carpet'	SAko SEle
	baxteri	CPbh CTsd
	ericifolia	SPlb
§	***ericoides***	CTsd GPoy
	parvifolia	SPlb
	pauciflora	SPlb

L

Lablab (*Papilionaceae*)

	purpureus 'Ruby Moon'	CSpe

+ *Laburnocytisus* (*Papilionaceae*)

	'Adamii'	CDul CMac EBee ELan EPfP LSRN MGil MGos NLar SPer

Laburnum ✿ (*Papilionaceae*)

	alpinum	SPlb
	- 'Pendulum'	CAco CCVT CDul CLnd ELan EMOT ESps LCro LSRN MAsh MGos MRav SGol SPer SPoG
§	***anagyroides***	CAco CDul ESps ETMg LPra MMuc SEND SRms WMou
	'Famous Walk'	see *L.* × *watereri* 'Vossii'
	vulgare	see *L. anagyroides*
	× ***watereri***	IBoy LPra
§	- 'Vossii' 🏆H6	Widely available
*	- 'Vossii Pendulum'	CCVT

Lachenalia ✿ (*Asparagaceae*)

§	***aloides***	CGrW CPbh CPne CTal NRog SDeJ
	- var. ***aurea***	see *L. flava*
	- var. ***luteola***	see *L. flava*
	- var. ***quadricolor***	see *L. quadricolor*
	- var. ***vanzyliae***	see *L. vanzyliae*
	arbuthnotiae	CTal
	bachmanii	CTal NRog
	bifolia	see *L. bulbifera*

	bolusii	CTal
	bowkeri	CTal
§	***bulbifera*** ♀H2	CPne GKev WCot
	- 'George' ♀H2	CTal WCot
	contaminata ♀H2	CGrW CPbh CTal NRog
§	***corymbosa*** ♀H2	CTal NRog
	elegans var. ***suaveolens***	NRog
	ensifolia	LLHF NRog WCot
	fistulosa	CTal
§	***flava*** ♀H2	CPbh NRog SBch WCot
	juncifolia	NRog
	kliprandensis	NRog
	latimerae	CPne WCot
	liliiflora	CGrW CTal NRog
§	***longituba*** ♀H3	CPBP CTal NRog
	mathewsii	NRog
	mediana	NRog
	'Namakwa' (African Beauty Series) ♀H1c	GKev NRog
	namaquensis	NRog
	'Nelsonii'	SBch WCot
	nervosa	WCot
	obscura	WCot
	orchioides var. ***glaucina***	NRog WCot
	orthopetala	CTal NRog WCot
	pallida	NRog
I	'Pearsonii'	CTal NRog SPlb
	pendula	see *L. bulbifera*
	pustulata ♀H2	NRog
	- blue-flowered	CGrW NRog
	- yellow-flowered	NRog
§	***pygmaea***	CPBP
§	***quadricolor*** ♀H2	CGrW CPrp CTsd NRog WCot
	reflexa	NRog
	'Romaud' (African Beauty Series)	GKev NRog SDeJ WCot
	'Romelia' (African Beauty Series)	WCot
	'Ronina' (African Beauty Series)	GKev NRog WCot
	'Rosabeth' (African Beauty Series)	GKev NRog WCot
	rosea	NRog
	'Rupert' (African Beauty Series) ♀H2	GKev NRog SDeJ WCot
	tricolor	see *L. aloides*
	unicolor	NRog WCot
	unifolia	NRog
§	***vanzyliae*** ♀H2	NRog WCot
	viridiflora ♀H2	NRog
	zeyheri	NRog WCot

Lactuca (*Asteraceae*)

	alpina	see *Cicerbita alpina*
	perennis	EPPr EWld WHer

Lagarostrobos ✿ (*Podocarpaceae*)

§	***franklinii***	CBcs IDee WPGP
	- 'Fota' (f)	WThu
	- 'Picton Castle' (m)	WThu

Lagenaria (*Cucurbitaceae*)

	siceraria 'Speckled Swan'	SVic

Lagerstroemia (*Lythraceae*)

	indica ♀H1c	CBod CCCN EPfP MGil SEND SEle SPlb SVen WFar WSHC
	- B&SWJ 12660	WCru
	- DYNAMITE ('Whit II')	IDee
	- 'Nivea' **new**	EBee
	- PETITE PINKIE ('Monkie')	IDee
	- PETITE RED IMP ('Monimp') **new**	EBee
	- 'Red Imperator'	CBcs
	- RHAPSODY IN PINK ('Whit VIII')	CBcs LRHS
	- 'Rosea'	CBcs LRHS SEND
	- 'Rubra'	LRHS
	- 'Superviolacea' **new**	EUJe
	STRAWBERRY DAZZLE ('Piilag-II') **new**	LRHS
	subcostata CWJ 12352	WCru
	'Tuscarora'	WPGP
	'Tuskegee'	WPGP

Lagotis (*Plantaginaceae*)

	glauca	GEdr
	takedana	GEdr

Lagunaria (*Malvaceae*)

	patersonii	CHll LRHS WPGP

Lagurus (*Poaceae*)

	ovatus	EBWF SAdn

Lamiastrum see *Lamium*

Lamium (*Lamiaceae*)

	album	CHab EBWF NMir
	- 'Friday' (v)	WHer
	armenum	WAbe
	- subsp. ***sintenisii***	WAbe
	flexuosum	EPPr
§	***galeobdolon***	CTri CWld EBWF EShb MHer SPhx SRms WHer WWtn XSen
§	- 'Florentinum' (v)	CMac ECha ELan MMuc MRav SPer WCAu WFar
	- 'Hermann's Pride'	CRos EBee EHoe ELan ELon EPfP GKev GMaP LRHS NMir NRHS SPer SRms SWvt WAul WHoo WMoo XLum
	- 'Kirkcudbright Dwarf'	EBee EPPr EWes GBin NBre XLum
§	- 'Silberteppich'	ECha MRav XLum
	- 'Silver Angel'	XLum
	- SILVER CARPET	see *L. galeobdolon* 'Silberteppich'
	- 'Variegatum'	see *L. galeobdolon* 'Florentinum'
	garganicum subsp. ***garganicum***	CCse EWes WHoo
	- subsp. ***pictum***	see *L. garganicum* subsp. *striatum*
	- subsp. ***reniforme***	see *L. garganicum* subsp. *striatum*
§	- subsp. ***striatum***	CDor WAbe
	(Lami Series) LAMI BLUSH	CRos LRHS NRHS
	- LAMI DARK PURPLE	LRHS NRHS
	- LAMI PINK	CRos LRHS NRHS
	luteum	see *L. galeobdolon*
	maculatum	GWyn MMuc SRms WCot WWtn
	- 'Album'	ELan EPfP SPer SRms WWtn
	- 'Anne Greenaway' (v)	EWes SCob SPoG WMoo
§	- 'Aureum'	ECtt EHoe ELan ESps SWvt WFar XLum
	- 'Beacon Silver'	CMac CRos EBee ECha ECtt EHrv ELan EPfP EShb ESps GMcL GWyn LCro LRHS MGos MJak MMuc MSCN NRHS SCob SPer SPlb SPoG SRGP SRms SWvt WFar WHar XLum
	- 'Brightstone Pearl'	ELon EWes EWld SHar
	- 'Cannon's Gold'	ECtt EWes SWvt WMoo
	- 'Chequers' ambig.	EBee
	- 'Dingle Candy'	MHCG
	- 'Elisabeth de Haas' (v)	EWes NBre

- 'Forncett Lustre' EWes
- 'Ghost' ECtt ELon EPPr LBuc LRHS SRms
- 'Gold Leaf' see *L. maculatum* 'Aureum'
- GOLDEN ANNIVERSARY ('Dellam'PBR) (v) CBod CRos ELan LSRN NBro NRHS SWvt
- 'Golden Nuggets' see *L. maculatum* 'Aureum'
- 'Golden Wedding' SRms
- LAMI MEGA PURPLE (Lami Series) EBee
- 'Margery Fish' SRms
- 'Orchid Frost' CHid EBee EHoe ELon GQue
- PINK CHABLIS ('Checkin'PBR) CBod CRos ELon LRHS MHol MRav NCou NLar NRHS SPer
- 'Pink Nancy' SWvt
- 'Pink Pearls' CSBt NLar SHar WMoo
- 'Pink Pewter' CRos EBee ECha ECtt EHoe ELan EPfP EShb ETMg GMaP GWyn LRHS NRHS SCob SPer SPlb SPoG SRms WWtn
- 'Purple Dragon' **new** IPot
- 'Red Nancy' CBod CRos ELan EPfP LRHS NLar NRHS SWvt XLum

§ - 'Roseum' EBee ELan GWyn MRav SPer WMoo XLum
- 'Shell Pink' see *L. maculatum* 'Roseum'
- 'Silver Shield' EWes
- 'Sterling Silver' CSam
- 'White Nancy' CBod CRav CRos CSBt EBee ECha ECtt EHoe EHrv ELan ELon EPfP ESps GMaP GWyn LRHS LSRN MCot MRav NRHS SCob SPer SPoG SRGP SRms SWvt WCAu WHar WMoo
- 'Wootton Pink' CRos MHCG NRHS SWvt

'Marshmallow' ELon

orvala Widely available
- 'Album' CDor CExl CRos EBee EHrv ELan EPPr IPot LEdu LPla LRHS MBel NLar SEND SHar SMad WCAu WHer
- pink-flowered CSpe
- 'Silva' CExl CRos EPPr EPfP IPot LEdu LRHS WCot WSHC

purpureum GJos

sandrasicum WAbe

Lamium × *Stachys* (*Lamiaceae*)

'Lilac Falls' **new** CBod

Lampranthus (*Aizoaceae*)

aberdeenensis see *Delosperma aberdeenense*

apricot-flowered CRos LRHS NRHS

aurantiacus CBcs

blandus CBcs CCCN

'Blousey Pink' SVen

§ ***brownii*** CBcs CCCN CRos ELan EPfP LRHS NRHS SPlb

coccineus CPla

deltoides see *Oscularia deltoides*

edulis see *Carpobrotus edulis*

'Exposure' CCCN

glaucus SEND

multiradiatus SEND

oscularis see *Oscularia deltoides*

'Pink' CPla ELan SPlb

purple-flowered CBlu CBod SPlb

roseus CCCN CRos CSma LRHS NRHS

'Salmon Pink' SPlb

'Shanklin' SPlb SVen

spectabilis CBWd CBcs CCCN CTri
- orange-flowered CBod WFar
- purple-flowered CPla SPlb
- 'Tresco Apricot' CCCN
- 'Tresco Brilliant' CBod CCCN ELon MSCN
- 'Tresco Fire' CAbb CCCN CExl CSma ELon SPlb SRms SVen
- 'Tresco Orange' CCCN CPla
- 'Tresco Peach' CCCN
- 'Tresco Purple' ELan
- 'Tresco Red' CBlu CCCN CPla ELon EUJe SEND
- white-flowered GKev SPlb SVen WFar
- yellow-flowered CPla EUJe SVen WFar

stipulaceus SPlb

'Tresco Pearl' CPla

Lamprocapnos (*Papaveraceae*)

§ ***spectabilis*** ♀H7 Widely available
- 'Alba' ♀H7 Widely available
- 'Gold Heart'PBR CAby CBcs CBod CRos CWCL CWGN EBee ECha ECtt EHoe ELon EPfP GMcL IBoy IRob LPmr LRHS MAsh MGos MHol MRav NHpl NLar NSti SCob SPoG WCot WFar WHil WSpi
- 'Love Hearts' MHol
- 'Valentine' Widely available
- 'White Heart' GJos

Lamprothyrsus (*Poaceae*)

hieronymi CBod
- RCB RA K2-2 CAby EBee ELon MAvo WCot WPGP

Lancea (*Phrymaceae*)

tibetica GEdr

Lantana ✿ (*Verbenaceae*)

'Calippo Tutti Frutti' CRav EUJe LSou

camara ELan EShb SEle SPhx
- (Lucky Series) LUCKY PEACH ('Balucpea') SPoG
- - LUCKY PURE GOLD ('Balucpure'PBR) SPoG
- - LUCKY RED FLAME ('Balandimfla') SPoG
- - LUCKY SUNRISE ROSE ('Balandrise'PBR) EPfP SPoG
- - LUCKY WHITE ('Balucwite'PBR) EPfP SPoG
- 'Mine d'Or' EUJe
- orange-flowered CCCN
- pink-flowered CCCN
- red-flowered CCCN
- white-flowered CCCN

'Chapel Hill Gold'PBR EMdy SPhm

'Chapel Hill Yellow'PBR **new** SPhm

'Dallas Red' EMdy

'Miss Huff' EBee EMdy

§ ***montevidensis*** CSam EShb

* - ***alba*** EShb

'Pink Caprice' EMdy

sellowiana see *L. montevidensis*

'Spreading Sunset' EMdy

'Sunny Side Up'PBR EMdy SPhm

Lapageria ✿ (*Philesiaceae*)

rosea ♀H3 CCCN CExl CPne CRHN CTsd SAdn SChF SWvt WPGP
- var. ***albiflora*** ♀H3 CRHN SChF
- - 'Hugletts Blush' **new** SChF
- 'Beatrix Anderson' CRHN

- 'Flesh Pink'	CExl CRHN
- 'Pink Panther'	CRHN
- 'Tierra del Fuego'	CRHN

Lapeirousia (*Iridaceae*)

cruenta	see *Freesia laxa*
laxa	see *Freesia laxa*

Lapsana (*Asteraceae*)

communis 'Inky'	CNat

Lardizabala (*Lardizabalaceae*)

biternata	see *L. funaria*
§ ***funaria***	CFil SBrt WCru

Larix ✿ (*Pinaceae*)

decidua	CAco CCVT CDul CMen CPer ECrN ELan EMOT EPfP ESps EWTr GMcL IBoy LPra MGos MMuc NEgg SEND SMad SPlb WHar WTSh
- 'Corley'	CKen
§ - var. ***decidua***	MJak
- 'Horstmann Recurved'	NLar
- 'Krejci'	NLar
- 'Little Bogle'	CKen MBlu NEgg NLar SLim
- 'Lucek'	NLar SLim
- 'Oberförster Karsten'	CKen NLar
- 'Pendula'	CMen
- 'Puli' ♀H7	LRHS MBlu NLar NOra SPer SPoG
- 'Raohuil'	NLar
- 'Roman'	NLar
× ***eurolepis***	see *L.* × *marschlinsii*
europaea DC.	see *L. decidua* var. *decidua*
gmelinii var. ***gmelinii***	CMen
- 'Tharandt'	CKen
§ ***kaempferi***	CAco CCVT CDul CMen CPer ELan EPfP ESps GMil LBuc LMaj LPra LRHS NEgg SCoo SEWo WTSh
- 'Bambino'	CKen SLim
- 'Bingman'	CKen
- 'Blue Ball'	CKen NLar
- 'Blue Dwarf' ♀H7	LRHS MAsh SLim
- 'Blue Rabbit'	CKen NEgg
- 'Cruwys Morchard'	CKen
- 'Diana'	CEnd CKen CMen LRHS NEgg SLim
- 'Elizabeth Rehder'	CKen
- 'Grant Haddow'	CKen
- 'Grey Pearl'	CKen LRHS SLim
- 'Hobbit'	CKen NEgg
- 'Jakobsen'	NLar
- 'Jakobsen's Pyramid'	CMen MAsh SPoG
- 'Lobby Dosser'	CMen NEgg
I - 'Nana'	CKen CMen GMil NEgg
I - 'Nana Prostrata'	CKen
- 'Pendula'	CEnd EPfP LPra SPoG
- 'Pulii'	EBee
- 'Stiff Weeper' ♀H7	LRHS NEgg NLar NRHS
- 'Varley'	CKen
- 'Wehlen'	CKen
- 'Wolterdingen'	CKen LRHS NLar
laricina 'Arethusa Bog'	CKen
- 'Bear Swamp'	CKen
- 'Bingman'	CKen
- 'Blue Sparkler'	NLar
- 'Hartwig Pine'	CKen
- 'Iron Red' **new**	NLar
- 'Michigan Tower' **new**	NLar
- 'Newport Beauty'	CKen
- 'Stubby'	CKen NLar
leptolepis	see *L. kaempferi*
§ × ***marschlinsii***	CCVT MMuc
- 'Domino'	CKen CMen GMil
- 'Gail'	CKen
- 'Julie'	CKen

Laser (*Apiaceae*)

trilobum	GEdr SPhx
- PAB 3382	LEdu WPGP

Laserpitium (*Apiaceae*)

halleri	SPhx
latifolium	EBee SPhx
§ ***siler***	CSpe IMou MAvo MNrw NDov SPhx SPlb WSHC WSpi

Lasiagrostis see *Stipa*

Lasiospermum (*Asteraceae*)

bipinnatum	SPlb

Lathraea (*Orobanchaceae*)

clandestina	CAvo

Lathyrus ✿ (*Papilionaceae*)

§ ***articulatus***	CSpe
§ ***aureus***	CDor CHid CSpe EBee GCal IFro IRob MCot MHer MNrw NBid SBrt SPhx WAul WCAu WFar WHal
- 'Cally Variegated' (v)	GCal
chilensis	GWyn WSHC
chloranthus	SPav
cirrhosus	SBrt WSHC
clymenum articulatus	see *L. articulatus*
cyaneus misapplied	see *L. vernus*
davidii	CFis LEdu SBrt WBor WCot
eucosmus	EBee
fremontii hort.	see *L. laxiflorus*
gmelinii	SBrt
grandiflorus ♀H7	CTri EBee NChi NHpl WCot
heterophyllus	EBee
hookeri **new**	GJos
incurvus	SPhx
inermis	see *L. laxiflorus*
japonicus	CEls
- subsp. ***maritimus***	GJos SPhx WCot
latifolius ♀H7	CAgr CRHN EBWF EPfP ESps GMcL MHol NPer SRms SVic WBrk WCot WFar WHer XLum
§ - 'Albus' ♀H7	CFlo CTri SPav SRms WKif XLum
- pale pink-flowered	MBel
- PINK PEARL	see *L. latifolius* 'Rosa Perle'
- 'Red Pearl'	CBcs CFlo CKel CRos CWGN EBee EPfP GAbr LBuc LRHS LSRN NLar NRHS SEND SPav SPer SPlb SPoG SRms SWvt WFar
§ - 'Rosa Perle' ♀H7	CBcs CFlo CKel CRos CTri EBee ECha ESps ETMg GJos LCro LOPS LRHS LSRN MHer MRav NLar NPer NRHS SBod SPer SPoG SWvt WBor WMoo XLum
- 'Rose Queen'	GJos
- WEISSE PERLE	see *L. latifolius* 'White Pearl'
- 'White Pearl' misapplied	see *L. latifolius* 'Albus'
§ - 'White Pearl' ♀H7	CBcs CKel CRos CWGN EBee ECha EPfP ESps GAbr LBuc LCro LOPS LRHS LSRN MBel MHer MRav NLar NPer NRHS SPer SPoG SRms SWvt WBor WFar XLum
§ ***laxiflorus***	EWld MCot WMoo WOut WSHC
- white-flowered	SBrt

	linifolius	EBee NLar SBrt
	magellanicus	CPla
	montanus	GPoy
	nervosus	CSpe EBee MCot SBee SRms
	neurolobus	SBrt
	niger	CFis CSpe EBee GJos LEdu LSou MCot MHer MMrt
	nissolia	WSFF
	odoratus	SVic
	- 'Almost Black' **new**	CRav
	- 'Anniversary'	CRav MCot
	- 'Barry Dare' **new**	CRav
	- 'Beaujolais' **new**	LCro LOPS
	- 'Beth Chatto'	MCot
	- 'Betty Maiden'	MCot
	- 'Black Knight'	CRav
	- 'Blue Medley'	MCot
	- 'Blue Velvet'	CRav
	- 'Bobby's Girl' 🏆H2 **new**	LCro LOPS
	- BOUNCE MIXED **new**	ETMg
	- 'Burnished Bronze'	MCot
	- 'Cathy' 🏆H2 **new**	EPfP
	- 'Charlie's Angel' 🏆H2	LCro LOPS MCot
	- 'Cupani'	CRav LCro LOPS MNHC SPhx
	- 'Cupid Pink' **new**	CRav
	- 'Daphne' **new**	LCro LOPS
	- 'Dark Passion'	MCot
	- 'Dawn'	MCot
	- 'Ethel Grace'	MCot
	- 'Evening Glow' 🏆H2	MCot
	- 'Flora Norton' **new**	CRav
	- 'Frances Kate' **new**	CRav
	- 'George Priestley'	MCot
I	- 'Gwendoline' 🏆H2	LCro LOPS
	- 'High Scent' 🏆H2	CRav LCro LOPS
	- 'Honey Pink'	MCot
	- 'Honeymoon'	MCot
	- 'Jilly' 🏆H2	MCot
	- 'Karen Louise'	LCro LOPS
	- 'King Edward VII' 🏆H2 **new**	CRav
	- 'Leamington' **new**	LCro LOPS
	- 'Linda C'	LCro LOPS
	- 'Lord Nelson'	CRav SPhx
	- 'Marion'	MCot
	- 'Marti Caine'	MCot
	- 'Matucana' 🏆H2	CRav CSpe LCro LOPS
	- 'Memorial Flight' **new**	CRav
	- 'Memories' **new**	CRav
	- 'Midnight'	LCro LOPS SPhx
	- 'Milly'	MCot
	- 'Misty Mountain'	MCot
	- 'Mollie Rilstone'	LCro LOPS MCot
	- 'Mrs Bernard Jones' 🏆H2	LCro LOPS MCot
	- 'Mrs Collier'	CRav SPhx
	- 'Noel Sutton' 🏆H2 **new**	CRav
	- 'Oxford Blue' **new**	LCro LOPS
	- 'Painted Lady'	CRav LCro LOPS
	- 'Pluto' **new**	LCro LOPS
	- 'Prince Edward of York' **new**	CRav
	- 'Promise'	MCot
	- 'Restormel'	LCro LOPS MCot
	- 'Richard and Judy'	MCot
	- 'Royal Wedding' **new**	LCro LOPS
	- SCENT INFUSION mixed **new**	ETMg
	- SUGAR 'N' SPICE mixed **new**	ETMg
	- SWEET DREAMS mixed **new**	ETMg
	- 'Tara' **new**	LCro LOPS
	- 'Wedding Day' 🏆H2	MCot
	- 'White Frills'	LCro LOPS
	palustris	EBWF EBee LLWG MMuc SPlb
	pisiformis	EBee
	pratensis	CHab EBWF EBee NMir WSFF
	pubescens	EBee
	roseus	EBee GCal WSHC
	rotundifolius 🏆H7	CHid GLog SPhx WSHC
	- 'Tillyperone' 🏆H7	EBee GNew SPhx WSHC
	sativus	CHid CSpe ELan MCot
	splendens	SBrt
	subandinus	SPlb
	sylvestris	EBee GJos WBrk
	- 'Hidcote' **new**	SBrt
	transsylvanicus	GBin SBrt SPhx
	tuberosus	CHid EBee LEdu WCot WSHC
	- 'Baby Pink' **new**	WCot
	'Tubro'	EBee
	venetus	EBee EWes MNrw SPhx WSHC
§	***vernus*** 🏆H5	Widely available
	- 'Albiflorus'	MNrw XEll
	- 'Alboroseus' 🏆H5	CDor ELan EPfP EWTr GCal IFro ILea IRob MNrw NChi NLar NPnk SPhx SPoG SWvt WCot WFar WHoo
	- var. ***albus***	CMea MNrw NChi SRms WCot
	- ***aurantiacus***	see *L. aureus*
	- 'Caeruleus'	WHoo
*	- 'Cyaneus'	CDor SHar WCot
	- 'Dama Emily'	SHar
	- 'Dama Violetta'	SHar
I	- 'Filifolius'	CSpe
	- 'Flaccidus'	CAby MNrw WCot
*	- 'Gracilis'	EBee LEdu NLar SHar WPGP
	- 'Little Elf'	SHar
	- 'Madelaine'	WCot
I	- 'Pendulus'	SHar
	- purple-flowered	CRos LRHS MMuc NRHS SEND
	- 'Rainbow'	CRos EPfP LRHS MPie NRHS
	- 'Rosenelfe'	CBcs CRos GJos GNew LEdu MHer SHar SPhx WCot WHal WSHC
	- f. ***roseus***	CRos ECha LRHS MMuc MRav NRHS SEND SRms WBrk WCot
	- 'Spring Melody'	EBee EHrv MRav SHar WCot
	- 'Subtle Hints'	SHar WCot
	- 'Winter Blush'	SHar

Laurelia (*Atherospermataceae*)

§	***sempervirens***	WPGP
	serrata	see *L. sempervirens*

Laureliopsis (*Atherospermataceae*)

	philippiana	CBcs CMCN EBee IDee NLar WPGP

Laurentia see *Isotoma*

Laurus (*Lauraceae*)

§	***azorica***	CBcs
	canariensis	see *L. azorica*
	nobilis 🏆H4	Widely available
	- f. ***angustifolia*** 🏆H4	CJun CMac CTsd LRHS MBlu MHer MMuc MRav NLar SArc SCob SEND SPoG WAvo
	- 'Aurea' 🏆H4	CBcs CMac ELan ELon EPfP ESps MHer MMuc NLar SCob SEND SLon SMad SWvt WMoo
	- clipped pyramid	LSRN
	- 'Crispa'	MRav
	- variegated (v)	CMac SRms
	rotundifolia	CAco

Lavandula ✿ (*Lamiaceae*)

'After Midnight'	see *L.* 'Avonview'
'Alba'	see *L. angustifolia* 'Alba', *L.* × *intermedia* 'Alba'
'Alba' ambig.	SPer
§ ***angustifolia***	CCVT CDor CRos EBee ENfk EPfP ESps GMcL GPoy LCro LOPS LRHS LSRN MGos MHer MHol NGdn NLar NPer NPri NRHS SCob SDow SLim SPlb SPoG SVic XAbr XLum XSen
- 'Alba' misapplied	see *L. angustifolia* 'Blue Mountain White'
§ - 'Alba'	ELan EPfP GPoy MHer MRav MSwo SCob SLon SPlb SVen WAvo WGwG WSpi XSen
- 'Alba Nana'	see *L. angustifolia* 'Nana Alba'
- 'Arctic Snow'	CBcs CRos EPfP LCro LOPS LRHS MHer MSwo NGdn NRHS SDow SFai SGol SPoG SRms WSpi XSen
- AROMATICO BLUE ('Lablusa'PBR)	CRos LRHS NRHS
- AROMATICO FORTE BLUE ('Laa20001')	CRos LRHS NRHS SPoG
- AROMATICO SILVER ('Lasila')	CRos GMcL LRHS NRHS
- 'Ashdown Forest'	ELan ENfk MHer MNHC SAdn SBch SCob SDow SFai SPer SRGP SRms WSpi XSen
- 'Babelle'	XSen
- 'Backhouse Purple'	SDow
- 'Beechwood Blue' Υ^{H5}	SCob SDow
- 'Betty's Blue'	SDow
- BLUE CUSHION ('Lavandula Schola'PBR)	LCro LOPS LSRN MAsh SFai SPoG SRms
- BLUE ICE ('Dow3'PBR)	SDow SFai SGol SLim XSen
- 'Blue Lance'	MHol
- 'Blue Mountain'	XSen
§ - 'Blue Mountain White'	CRos LRHS SDow XSen
- 'Blue Rider'	LRHS NRHS WGwG
- 'Blue River'	CBod
- BLUE SCENT ('Syngablusc')	LRHS
§ - 'Bowles's Early'	WGwG
- 'Bowles's Grey'	see *L. angustifolia* 'Bowles's Early'
- 'Bowles's Variety'	see *L. angustifolia* 'Bowles's Early'
- 'Cedar Blue'	ELan ENfk MHer MHol SDow SRms WGwG XSen
- 'Coconut Ice'	EMOT WSpi XSen
- 'Compacta'	SDow
- 'Crystal Lights'	EMOT
- 'Dwarf Blue'	CBod CRos ENfk ESps LSRN MHed SRms WFar XSen
- 'Elizabeth'	LCro LSRN SCob SDow SFai SPoG XSen
- (Ellagance Series) 'Ellagance Ice'	GMcL SRms
- - 'Ellagance Purple'	CRos LRHS NRHS SRms
- - 'Ellagance Sky'	CBod CRos LRHS MHol NRHS SRms
- 'Essence Purple'	CBod
- 'Felice'PBR	LRHS
- 'Folgate' Υ^{H5}	CBod ECtt ENfk MHer MNHC NGdn SDow SRms WAvo WHoo WSpi XSen
- GARDEN BEAUTY ('Lowmar'PBR) (v)	LBuc MAsh SPoG XSen
- GRANNY'S BOUQUET ('Lavang38')	EMOT GWyn WSpi XSen
- 'Havana'	MAsh SPoG XSen
§ - 'Hidcote' Υ^{H5}	Widely available
- 'Hidcote Pink'	ESps IRob LSou MHer MNHC MRav NGdn SCob SDow SPer SRms XSen
- 'Hidcote Superior'	NGdn
- 'Imperial Gem' Υ^{H5}	Widely available
- 'Jean Davis'	see *L. angustifolia* 'Rosea'
- 'Lady'	NPer WSpi
- 'Lady Ann'	SDow
- 'Lavenite Petite'PBR	CRos LRHS LSRN NLar SFai SPoG WSpi XSen
- LITTLE LADY ('Batlad') Υ^{H5}	CGar CMea ECtt GMcL LCro LOPS LRHS LSRN MAsh MNHC MPie MSwo NLar NRHS SFai SGol SPoG SRms SWvt WHoo WSpi XSen
- LITTLE LOTTIE ('Clarmo') Υ^{H5}	ELon LSRN MHer SDow XSen
- 'Loddon Blue'	CRos EPfP LRHS MAsh NRHS SDow SFai SRms WSpi XSen
§ - 'Loddon Pink'	CRos ELan EPfP ESps GMaP LRHS MAsh MMuc MRav NGdn NRHS SEND SFai SRms WAvo XSen
- 'Luberon'	XSen
- 'Lullaby Blue'	SDow
- 'Maillette'	EWTr MHed NGdn SDow SRms XSen
- 'Matheronne'	XSen
- 'Melissa'	MHol XSen
- MELISSA LILAC ('Dow4'PBR)	CBcs CSBt ECrN ENfk LCro LOPS LRHS LSRN MAsh MGos MHer MNHC NRHS SDow SFai SRkn SRms XSen
- 'Middachten'	XSen
- 'Miss Dawnderry'	SDow
- 'Miss Donnington'	see *L. angustifolia* 'Bowles's Early'
- 'Miss Katherine'PBR Υ^{H5}	CRos ECtt ELan EPfP ESps LRHS MAsh SDow SPoG XSen
- MISS MUFFET ('Scholmis') Υ^{H5}	SBch SDow SRms XSen
- 'Mont Ventoux'	XSen
- 'Montagne de Lure'	XSen
- 'Munstead'	Widely available
§ - 'Nana Alba' Υ^{H5}	CMea CRos ELan ENfk EPfP GMaP GPoy LRHS MAsh MHer SBch SDow SPer SRms SWvt WSpi XSen
- 'Nana Atropurpurea'	SDow XSen
- 'Nikita'	XSen
- 'No 9'	SDow
- 'Pacific Blue'	CRos LRHS NRHS XSen
- 'Peter Pan'	ECtt ELan ESps LSRN MAsh MHer MNHC SDow XSen
- PLATINUM BLONDE ('Momparler'PBR)	LSou SFai SPad SPoG
- 'Princess Blue'	CRos LRHS
- 'Purity' **new**	SDow
§ - 'Rosea'	Widely available
- 'Royal Blue'	LRHS
- 'Royal Purple'	ESps EWes NGdn SDow SWvt XSen
- 'Royal Velvet'	SDow
- 'Saint Jean'	SDow
- 'Siesta'	XSen
- 'Silver Blue'	XSen
- 'Silver Lining' **new**	CRos NRHS
- 'Silver Mist'	CBod CMea EPfP GMcL SRms WHer XSen
- 'Sophie'	XSen
- 'SuperBlue' **new**	LSou
- 'Thumbelina Leigh'PBR	MAsh SFai SRms WSpi XSen
- 'Twickel Purple'	CBar CBcs CRos EBee ELan ENfk EPfP ESps LRHS LSRN MAsh MHed

		MHol MNHC SCob SDow SFai SPer SRms SWvt WGwG WSpi XSen
	- 'Walberton's Silver Edge'	see *L.* × *intermedia* WALBERTON'S SILVER EDGE
	aristibracteata	MHer
§	'Avonview'	MHer WHoo
	'Ballerina' ♀^{H4}	SDow
§	'Bee Brilliant'^{PBR}	ENfk
§	'Bee Cool'^{PBR}	ENfk
§	'Bee Happy'	ENfk
§	'Bee Pretty'	ENfk
	'Bella Zealand' (Bella Series)	CRos LRHS NRHS
	'Blue Star'	CRos EPfP GMcL LRHS MNHC
	'Bouquet of Roses'	CRos LRHS NRHS
	buchii var. ***buchii***	SDow SVen
	canariensis	MHer SDow SVen
	× ***chaytoriae*** 'Bridehead Blue' **new**	SDow
	- 'Gorgeous'	SDow
	- 'Helen'	SDow
	- 'Joan Head'	XSen
	- 'Molton Silver'	XSen
	- 'Richard Gray' ♀^{H4}	LRHS LSRN MHed MHer MNHC NLar SDow SRms WAvo XSen
§	- 'Sawyers' ♀^{H4}	CBod CRos EPfP EShb ESps ETod GMaP LRHS LSRN MAsh MCot MHed MHer MNHC MRav NEgg NPer NRHS SCob SDow SEND SGol SPer SPhx SPoG SRms WGwG XSen
	- 'Silver Sands'	CRos EPfP LRHS LSou MCot NRHS SFai SPoG XSen
	× ***christiana***	CRos LRHS SDow SFai SVen
	'Cornard Blue'	see *L.* × *chaytoriae* 'Sawyers'
	CRÈME BRÛLÉE ('Lavsts10')	CRos LRHS NRHS
	dentata	ENfk MNHC SEND SRms XAbr XSen
§	- var. ***candicans***	MHer MNHC SDow SRms XSen
	- var. ***dentata*** 'Dusky Maiden'	SDow
	- - 'Ploughman's Blue'	SVen WGwG
	- - f. ***rosea***	SDow
	- - SERENITY ('Lavden123'^{PBR})	CRos LRHS NRHS
	- 'Harmony'	CRos LRHS NRHS
	- silver-leaved	see *L. dentata* var. *candicans*
	'Devonshire Compact'	CSBt EAJP MHol SRms
	'Fathead'	CBcs CBod CChe CRos EBee ECtt ELan EMOT EPfP ESps ETMg LRHS LSRN MAsh MGos MHer MNHC NGdn NLar SCob SCoo SDow SFai SGol SPoG WAvo
	'Flaming Purple'	SDow
	× ***ginginsii*** 'Goodwin Creek Grey' ♀^{H4}	MHer SDow SGol SRms WGwG
	'Hazel'	CRos EPfP LRHS NRHS
	'Heavenly Blue'	EPfP
	'Helmsdale'^{PBR}	CEnd CRos CSBt ELan EPfP ESps GMaP GMcL LCro LRHS LSRN MAsh MRav NGdn NLar SCob SCoo SFai SGol SLim SPer
	× ***heterophylla*** (Gaston Allard Group) 'African Pride'	SVen
	'Hidcote Blue'	see *L. angustifolia* 'Hidcote'
	× ***intermedia*** 'Abrialii'	SDow
§	- 'Alba' ♀^{H5}	CBot CMea MHed MHer MNHC SCob SEND SVen XSen
	- 'Anniversary Bouquet' **new**	SDow
	- 'Arabian Night'	see *L.* × *intermedia* 'Impress Purple', 'Sussex'
	- 'Arabian Night' ambig.	SRms
§	- Dutch Group	CBod CRos CSBt ENfk EPfP ESps LRHS MAsh MNHC MRav MSwo SArc SCoo SDow SFai SLim SPer SRms XSen
	- 'Edelweiss'	CBod CRos CSBt ENfk EPfP ESps LRHS MNHC MRav NEgg NGdn NLar NRHS SCob SDow SFai SGol SPoG SRms SWvt WSpi XSen
§	- 'Enigma'	CBar
	- 'Fragrant Memories'	SDow XSen
	- 'Fred Boutin'	WSpi
	- GOLDBURG ('Burgoldeen') (v)	SGol
	- 'Grappenhall' misapplied	see *L.* × *intermedia* 'Enigma', 'Pale Pretender'
	- 'Grappenhall' ambig.	WSpi XSen
	- 'Grey Hedge'	SRms
	- 'Gros Bleu'	SDow SFai XSen
	- 'Grosso'	Widely available
	- (Heavenly Series) 'Heavenly Angel'	SDow SFai XSen
	- - 'Heavenly Night'	LSRN SDow SFai
	- - 'Heavenly Scent'	SDow SFai XSen
	- 'Hidcote Giant' ♀^{H5}	CRos EPfP GCal LRHS NPer NRHS SDow WKif WSpi XSen
§	- 'Impress Purple'	SDow WAvo XSen
	- 'Lullingstone Castle'	ENfk SDow SRms WAvo
	- 'Old English' misapplied	see *L.* × *intermedia* 'Seal'
	- 'Old English'	CBod ENfk SDow SRms
	- Old English Group	MMuc MNHC SEND WHoo XSen
	- 'Olympia'	SDow XSen
§	- 'Pale Pretender'	CSBt MHer MSwo SPer SRms
	- 'Provence'	EBee SDow SFai XSen
	- PURE PLATINUM ('Niko'^{PBR})	LSRN SFai
§	- 'Seal'	ENfk GMaP MNHC SCob SDow SRms XSen
§	- 'Sussex' ♀^{H5}	CBod CFis CRos EPfP LRHS NRHS SDow
	- 'Twickel Purple'	ELan EWes NLar SGol
§	- WALBERTON'S SILVER EDGE ('Walvera') (v)	CRos EBee EMOT EPfP ESps LBuc LRHS MGos NRHS SCoo SDow SFai SRms XSen
	'Jean Davis'	see *L. angustifolia* 'Rosea'
	lanata ♀^{H3}	ECha SRms XSen
§	***latifolia***	XAbr XSen
I	'Lavender Lace'	LSRN
	'Loddon Pink'	see *L. angustifolia* 'Loddon Pink'
	'Madrid Blue'	see *L.* 'Bee Happy'
	'Madrid Pink'	see *L.* 'Bee Pretty'
	'Madrid Purple'	see *L.* 'Bee Brilliant'
	'Madrid White'	see *L.* 'Bee Cool'
	'Marshwood'	CTri
	minutolii	SDow
	multifida	MHer
	- 'Spanish Eyes' **new**	CRav
	officinalis	see *L. angustifolia*
	PASSIONNÉ ('Lavsts 08'^{PBR}) ♀^{H4}	EMOT
	pedunculata	EBee XSen
	- subsp. ***lusitanica***	CRos EPfP LRHS NRHS SPoG
	- - LUSI PINK ('Wijs02')	SFai
	- - 'Lusi Purple'	SFai SPoG
§	- subsp. ***pedunculata***	CAby CBar CBod CRos ECha ECrN EPau EPfP ETMg LCro LOPS LRHS LSRN MAsh MGos MJak MNHC MSwo NGdn NRHS SCob SDow SFai SGol SPer SRms WAvo WSpi
	- - 'James Compton' ♀^{H3}	CRos ECha LRHS MAsh NGdn

- subsp. ***sampaiana*** 'Purple Emperor'	CRos EPfP LRHS NRHS
pinnata	CRos ENfk EPfP LRHS MHol MNHC SDow
'Pretty Polly' 𝕐H4	CBcs CRos ELan EPfP LRHS MAsh NRHS SDow SFai SRkn
'Pukehou'	CRos EPfP LRHS NRHS SCoo
'Regal Splendour'[PBR]	CRos CSBt ECrN ELan EMOT EPfP ESps LRHS LSRN MAsh MGos MHer MNHC NPri NRHS SCob SCoo SDow SFai SGol SLim SPoG SRms
ROCKY ROAD ('Fair09'[PBR])	SFai
'Rosea'	see *L. angustifolia* 'Rosea'
rotundifolia	SDow
'Silver Edge'	see *L.* × *intermedia* WALBERTON'S SILVER EDGE
SILVER SANDS ('Fair 14'[PBR])	ENfk
spica nom. rejic.	see *L. angustifolia*, *L. latifolia*
- 'Hidcote Purple'	see *L. angustifolia* 'Hidcote'
stoechas	CBcs CBod CRav CRos CSBt ECha ELan EPfP ESps GMaP GPoy LRHS LSRN MJak MNHC MSwo NRHS SCob SDow SPer SPlb SWvt WArt WHar
- var. ***albiflora***	see *L. stoechas* subsp. *stoechas* f. *leucantha*
- 'Anouk'[PBR]	EBee ELan EPfP ESps LRHS SPoG
- 'Antibes' (Provençal Series)	SRms
- 'Bandera' **new**	CBod
- (Bella Series) BELLA LAVENDER ('Bellav')	CRos LRHS NRHS
- - BELLA PEACH	CRos LRHS
- - BELLA ROSE ('Belros')	CRos LRHS NRHS
- - BELLA ROUGE ('Belrou')	CRos LRHS NRHS
- 'Boysenberry Ruffles'[PBR] (Ruffles Series)	ENfk
- CASTILLIANO VIOLET	GMcL
- (Coco Series) COCO DEEP PINK	LRHS NRHS
- - COCO PURPLE ('Cocpur')	CRos LRHS NRHS
- - COCO ROSE	CRos LRHS NRHS
- - COCO WHITE ON BLUE ('Cocwob') **new**	CRos LRHS NRHS
- (Javelin Series) JAVELIN BLUE ('Jin Bulle')	CRos GMcL LRHS NRHS
- - JAVELIN COMPACT ROSE ('Labz0001'[PBR])	GMcL
- - JAVELIN UPRIGHT WHITE BLUSH ('Labz0002'[PBR])	GMcL
- 'Lace'	LSRN
- (Little Bee Series) LITTLE BEE DEEP PURPLE ('Florvendula Deep Purple')	CRos GMcL LRHS NRHS
- - LITTLE BEE DEEP ROSE ('Florvendula Deep Rose')	CRos LRHS
- - LITTLE BEE LILAC ('Florvendula Lilac')	CRos LRHS
- 'Night of Passion'	SDow
- 'Papillon'	see *L. pedunculata* subsp. *pedunculata*
- subsp. ***pedunculata***	see *L. pedunculata* subsp. *pedunculata*
- 'Pink Angels'	ELan
- 'Purley'	SRms
- Ruffles Series	ENfk
- 'Silver Anouk'[PBR]	CBod EPfP LRHS
- 'Spring-break Princess' **new**	CRos NRHS
§ - subsp. ***stoechas*** f. ***leucantha***	CRos EPfP LRHS MSwo NRHS SCob SDow
- - - 'Snowman'	CBcs CRos CSBt EPfP LCro LRHS MAsh MHer NRHS SCob SCoo SFai SPoG SWvt
- - LILAC WINGS ('Prolil'[PBR])	EPfP LRHS NLar NRHS SCoo SDow SFai
- - 'Provençal'	CRos LRHS NRHS SCob SCoo
- - 'Purple Wings'	CRos ELan EPfP LRHS MAsh MGos NRHS SLim
- - f. ***rosea*** 'Kew Red'	CBcs CTri EAJP ENfk LCro LOPS LRHS MGos MHer MNHC SDow SFai SRms SWvt WHar
- 'Sugarberry Ruffles'[PBR] (Ruffles Series)	ENfk
- 'Victory'	CRos LRHS NRHS SPoG
- 'With Love'[PBR]	SDow
TIARA ('Fair 10'[PBR])	CAby CRos CSBt ENfk LCro LOPS LRHS LSRN MGos NEoE NLar NRHS SCoo SFai SRms
'Van Gogh'	SDow
vera misapplied	see *L.* × *intermedia* Dutch Group
vera DC.	see *L. angustifolia*
viridis	CRos ELan EPfP LRHS MHer NPer NRHS SDow SRms WAbe
'Whero Iti'	SDow
'Willow Vale' 𝕐H3	CRos EPfP LCro LRHS MAsh MHer NRHS SDow SWvt WAvo

Lavatera (*Malvaceae*)

arborea	SChr SEND WHer
- 'Rosea'	see *L.* × *clementii* 'Rosea'
- 'Variegata' (v)	ELan NPer SEND WCot
bicolor	see *L. maritima*
cachemiriana	NPer
CHAMALLOW ('Inovera'[PBR])	CRos LRHS LSRN
× ***clementii*** 'Barnsley'	Widely available
- 'Barnsley Baby'	CBod CRos EBee ELan ETMg GMcL LBuc LRHS NGdn NLar NPer NPri SChF SEle SPer SRkn SWvt WBor WFar
- 'Blushing Bride'	CBod CRos EPfP ESps LRHS LSRN MGos NLar SWvt
- 'Bredon Springs' 𝕐H5	CBod CDul CRos CSBt EBee ECha ELon EPfP ESps GMcL LRHS LSRN MAsh MGos MMuc MSwo NGdn NRHS SEND SGol SLim SPer SWvt WAvo XLum
- 'Burgundy Wine' 𝕐H5	CBcs CMac CRos EBee ECrN ELan EPfP ESps EUJe LRHS MAsh MGos MJak MNHC MSwo NEgg NLar NPer NPri NRHS SGbt SGol SLim SLon SPer SPoG SWvt WAvo WFar
- 'Candy Floss' 𝕐H5	ESps GMcL LRHS NLar NPer SGol
- 'Eye Catcher'	LRHS MSwo NLar SPer WHar
- 'Kew Rose'	CBod ESps MMuc MSwo NLar NPer SEND SLim SRms XLum
- 'Lavender Lady'	NPer SEND
- 'Lisanne'	CRos ESps LRHS MMuc MSwo SGol
- 'Mary Hope' 𝕐H5	CRos EPfP LRHS MAsh NPri NRHS SEle SPoG SWvt
- MEMORIES ('Stelav')	CRos LRHS LSRN
- 'Pavlova'	CExl
§ - 'Pink Frills'	ESps SWvt WCot WFar
- RED RUM ('Rigrum'[PBR]) 𝕐H5	CBod CMac CRos CSBt EBee EPfP LBuc LLHF LRHS LSRN MAsh MGos MHol NEgg NLar NPri NRHS SCob SEND SLim SPoG SWvt WFar

§ - 'Rosea' ♀H5 — CBcs CDul CMac CRos EBee ECrN EPfP ESps GMcL LCro LOPS LRHS LSRN MAsh MGos NEgg NPri NRHS SBod SCob SGbt SGol SLon SPer SPoG SWvt WHar
- 'Ruby Star' — CRos LRHS MTin NRHS SCob
- 'Songbird' — SCob
§ - 'Wembdon Variegated' (v) — NPer
'Frederique' — CRos CSBt LBuc LRHS NLar SWvt WKif
'Grey Beauty' — CRos LRHS NRHS SMad
'Magenta Magic'[PBR] — EBee NLar SPoG
§ ***maritima*** ♀H3 — CBod CExl CMac CRos ELan EPfP ESps LRHS SEND SEle SPer SRkn SRms SWvt WFar WKif WOut
- 'Princesse de Lignes' — XLum
olbia — SPlb SRms WFar
- 'Lilac Lady' — ECha ECrN ELan MGos MMuc NLar SGol WFar WKif
'Peppermint Ice' — see *L. thuringiaca* 'Ice Cool'
'Pink Frills' — see *L.* × *clementii* 'Pink Frills'
'Rosea' — see *L.* × *clementii* 'Rosea'
'Sweet Dreams'[PBR] — LSou
thuringiaca — GCal LPla
- 'First Light' — SPhx
§ - 'Ice Cool' — NLar SCob SWvt WKif
'Variegata' — see *L.* × *clementii* 'Wembdon Variegated'
'White Angel'[PBR] — NLar

Lawsonia (*Lythraceae*)

inermis — WSFF

Ledebouria (*Asparagaceae*)

adlamii — see *L. cooperi*
concolor misapplied — see *L. socialis*
§ ***cooperi*** — CTal EAJP EPri EShb GKev LEdu LRHS MPie NRHS SBch WBor WHil WPGP XLum
§ ***socialis*** — EUJe GKev LEdu LToo MCot MPie SBch WCot
violacea — see *L. socialis*

Ledum see *Rhododendron*

leek see AGM Vegetables Section

Leiophyllum (*Ericaceae*)

buxifolium ♀H5 — EPfP NLar WThu

Lembotropis see *Cytisus*

Lemna (*Araceae*)

gibba — NPer
minor — CWat MSKA NPer
polyrrhiza — see *Spirodela polyrrhiza*
trisulca — CWat EWat MSKA NPer

lemon see *Citrus* × *limon*

lemon balm see *Melissa officinalis*

lemon grass see *Cymbopogon citratus*

lemon, rough see *Citrus* × *taitensis*

lemon verbena see *Aloysia citrodora*

Leonotis (*Lamiaceae*)

leonitis — see *L. ocymifolia*
leonurus — CBcs CCCN CDTJ CHGN CHll ECre EShb EWes LRHS MSCN SLim SMad SPav SPlb XLum
- var. ***albiflora*** — CCCN
nepetifolia — CHll
- var. ***nepetifolia*** 'Staircase' — CCCN SPav
§ ***ocymifolia*** — CCCN CExl LSou
- var. ***raineriana*** — CHll

Leontochir (*Alstroemeriaceae*)

ovallei — CCCN

Leontodon (*Asteraceae*)

autumnalis — CHab CWld EBWF NMir
hispidus — CHab EBWF NMir
§ ***rigens*** — CSpe CTal ELan GEdr MHer MMuc NBid WFar WMoo
- B&SWJ 12527 — WCru WSHC
- 'Girandole' — see *L. rigens*

Leontopodium (*Asteraceae*)

alpinum — see *L. nivale* subsp. *alpinum*
- subsp. ***nivale*** — see *L. nivale* subsp. *nivale*
conglobatum new — GKev
coreanum — GKev
discolor — EPot
haastioides — WAbe
jacotianum — GKev
kurilense — SPlb
nanum — CPBP SPlb
§ ***nivale*** subsp. ***alpinum*** — CTri ELan EPfP ESps MAsh NHpl SPlb SPoG SRms XLum
- 'Everest' — EDAr
- 'Matterhorn' — GEdr GMaP NLar
- 'Mignon' — EPfP EWes GMaP WAbe
§ - subsp. ***nivale*** — EPot GKev WAbe
§ ***ochroleucum*** var. ***campestre*** — NLar XLum
palibinianum — see *L. ochroleucum* var. *campestre*
pusillum — WAbe
souliei — SRot XLum
stracheyi — GKev

Leonurus (*Lamiaceae*)

cardiaca — CBod EBWF GPoy MHer MNHC SRms
- 'Grobbebol' — EBee EPPr WCot WHer
sibiricus L. — GCal

Leopoldia (*Asparagaceae*)

caucasica new — GKev
comosa — see *Muscari comosum*
spreitzenhoferi — see *Muscari spreitzenhoferi*
tenuiflora — see *Muscari tenuiflorum*
weissii new — GKev

Lepechinia (*Lamiaceae*)

bella — CSpe SDys
chamaedryoides — CExl
hastata — CCse CFil CSpe MSpe SPlb WOut
salviae — WHer

Lepidium (*Brassicaceae*)

campestre — CHab
latifolium — ENfk LEdu

Lepidothamnus (*Podocarpaceae*)

§ ***laxifolius*** — WThu

Lepidozamia (*Zamiaceae*)

peroffskyana	CBrP

Leptinella (*Asteraceae*)

atrata subsp. ***luteola***	ELan
'County Park'	EDAr
dendyi	EBee ECtt EWes GEdr MHer NSla
dioica	GBin
hispida	see *Cotula hispida* (DC.) Harv.
§ ***minor***	WMoo
§ ***pectinata***	ITim
§ ***potentillina***	CTal CTri ECha EHoe GEdr MBNS MSCN NLar SRms WMoo WPtf XLum
§ ***pyrethrifolia***	EDAr
reptans	see *L. scariosa*
§ ***scariosa***	GAbr
§ ***squalida***	ECha GBin NLar NSti WMoo
§ - 'Platt's Black'	CBcs CTal EBee ECha ECtt EDAr EHoe ESps EWes GAbr GBin GCrg IBoy MHer NHpl NLar SBch SPtp SWvt WFar WGwG WMoo XLum

Leptocodon (*Campanulaceae*)

gracilis	EWld

Leptodermis (*Rubiaceae*)

oblonga 'Summer Stars'	LRHS

Leptopus (*Euphorbiaceae*)

§ ***chinensis***	EWTr WCot

Leptospermum ✿ (*Myrtaceae*)

citratum	see *L. petersonii*
'Copper Sheen'	CBcs
'County Park Blush'	ELon
cunninghamii	see *L. myrtifolium*
'Electric Red' (Galaxy Series)	CAbb GMcL LRHS SEle
ericoides	see *Kunzea ericoides*
flavescens misapplied	see *L. glaucescens*
flavescens Sm.	see *L. polygalifolium*
§ ***glaucescens***	SPlb
§ ***grandiflorum***	ELan EPfP SVen WSHC
grandifolium	LRHS
'Havering Hardy'	SEle
humifusum	see *L. rupestre*
juniperinum	SPlb
laevigatum	SVen
§ ***lanigerum***	CExl CTri CTsd EPfP SPlb SVen
- 'Cunninghamii'	see *L. myrtifolium*
liversidgei	SPlb
§ ***myrtifolium***	CMac CTri CTsd EWes
nitidum	SPlb
obovatum	CTsd
§ ***petersonii***	MHer XAbr
phylicoides	see *Kunzea ericoides*
'Pink Cascade'	CBcs CMac CTri SEle
§ ***polygalifolium***	SPlb
prostratum	see *L. rupestre*
pubescens	see *L. lanigerum*
'Red Cascade'	SWvt
rodwayanum	see *L. grandiflorum*
rotundifolium	SPlb
§ ***rupestre***	CTri SPlb SVen WKif WSHC
scoparium	CTsd GPoy SPlb SVen
- 'Adrianne'	CRos EPfP LRHS MRav NRHS
- 'Appleblossom' 🏆H3	CBcs CEnd EPfP GMcL SAko SEle SGol
- 'Blossom' (d)	CBcs CMac
- 'Burgundy Queen' (d)	CBcs CMac CSBt EBee EUJe
- 'Chapmanii'	WPGP
- 'Charmer'	EBee
- 'Coral Candy'	CBcs CCht CEnd
- 'Crimson Glory' (d)	CSBt
- 'Elizabeth Jane'	MMuc WFar
- 'Gaiety Girl' (d)	CSBt
- 'Jubilee' (d)	CCCN CMac
- 'Lambethii'	EBee
- 'Leonard Wilson' (d)	CTri
- 'Martini'	CAbb CBcs CCCN CMac CRos CSBt EPfP LRHS MMuc NRHS SGol SPoG
- (Nanum Group) 'Kea'	CBcs MHer MRav
- - 'Kiwi' 🏆H3	CAbb CBcs CCCN CRos CSBt EPfP EUJe LRHS MAsh MMuc SEle SLim SLon SPoG WFar
- - 'Nanum'	CCCN ITim
- - 'Pipit'	ITim
- - 'Tui'	CMac CSBt
- 'Nichollsii' 🏆H3	CBcs SVen
- 'Nichollsii Nanum' 🏆H3	WAbe WThu
- 'Pink Damask'	SWvt
- var. ***prostratum*** misapplied	see *L. rupestre*
- 'Red Damask' (d) 🏆H3	CAbb CBcs CCCN CDul CExl CMac CRos CTri EBee EHoe ELan EPfP ESps GMcL LRHS LSRN MAsh MMuc MRav NRHS SAko SBod SEle SGol SLim SPlb SPoG SVen SWvt WFar
- 'Red Ensign'	SPoG
- 'Red Falls'	CExl
* - 'Ruby Wedding'	CRos ELan EPfP LRHS LSRN MAsh SLon
- 'Snow Flurry'	CBcs CRos EPfP LRHS NRHS SGol SVen
- 'Sunraysia'	CTsd
- 'Winter Cheer' (d)	CBcs CRos EPfP LRHS NRHS SGol
- 'Wiri Joan' (d)	CBcs
- 'Wiri Kerry' (d)	MPkF
- 'Wiri Linda'	CBcs CMac
'Silver Sheen' 🏆H3	CAbb CBcs CCCN CCht CEnd CRos ELan EPfP LRHS MAsh NLar SPer SPoG SVen WPGP

Lespedeza (*Papilionaceae*)

bicolor	CAgr CCCN LRHS MMrt MMuc WCFE WFar WSHC
- 'Yakushima'	NLar
buergeri	CRos LRHS MMrt NLar WSHC
japonica	SPlb
thunbergii 🏆H5	CBcs CBot CHll CRos EBee ELan EPfP IDee LRHS MAsh MBlu MGil NRHS SLon SMad SPer SPoG SSta WCFE WPGP WSHC
- subsp. ***formosa***	EBee MMrt
- 'Gibraltar'	WPGP
- 'Summer Beauty'	CBcs
- subsp. ***thunbergii*** 'Albiflora'	ELan LRHS SMad WPGP
- - 'Edo-shibori'	ELan NLar SPer WPGP
- - 'White Fountain'	CRos EPfP LRHS MAsh NRHS SPoG WSHC
tiliifolia	see *Desmodium elegans*

Lesquerella (*Brassicaceae*)

arctica	WCFE
- var. ***purshii***	GKev

lettuce see AGM Vegetables Section

Leucadendron (*Proteaceae*)

argenteum	CBlu CCCN CPbh SPlb
'Burgundy Sweet' **new**	CBcs
conicum	CPbh
'Cream Delight'	CCCN
daphnoides	SPlb
'Deacon Red'	MPkF
discolor	SPlb
eucalyptifolium	CPbh SPlb
galpinii	CPbh
- 'Purple Haze'	LRHS
gandogeri	CPbh
'Highlights'	CCCN
'Inca Gold' ℽH1c	CBcs CPbh
'Jack Harre'	LRHS MPkF
laureolum	CCCN CPbh
modestum 'Strawberry Fair'	CCCN
'Pisa'	LRHS MPkF
'Red Dwarf'	CPbh
'Royal Ruby'	LRHS
'Safari Magic'	CCCN
'Safari Sunset' ℽH1c	CBcs CCCN CPbh LRHS MPkF
'Safari Sunshine'	CPbh
salicifolium	SPlb
salignum	CCCN CPbh
- 'Fireglow'	LRHS
sessile	CPbh
strobilinum	CPbh
'Sundance'	LRHS
tinctum	CPbh

Leucaena (*Mimosaceae*)

leucocephala	SPlb

Leucanthemella (*Asteraceae*)

§ ***serotina*** ℽH7	Widely available
- 'Herbststern'	IMou NLar

Leucanthemopsis (*Asteraceae*)

§ ***alpina***	NSla
hosmariensis	see *Rhodanthemum hosmariense*

Leucanthemum ✿ (*Asteraceae*)

'Angel'	CBod ELon NCou NLar WArt
atlanticum	see *Rhodanthemum atlanticum*
catananche	see *Rhodanthemum catananche*
graminifolium	EPfP
hosmariense	see *Rhodanthemum hosmariense*
mawii	see *Rhodanthemum gayanum*
maximum misapplied	see *L.* × *superbum*
§ ***maximum*** (Ramond) DC.	NBro NPer
- ***uliginosum***	see *Leucanthemella serotina*
nipponicum	see *Nipponanthemum nipponicum*
'Osiris Neige'	ECtt ILea MAvo XLum
paludosum 'Snowland'	LRHS NRHS
'Real Charmer'	CBod CRos LRHS MHol NEoE NRHS SEle SRms WAvo
'Sante'	CRos EBee LCro LOPS LRHS MHol NRHS
'Sunshine Peach'	CRos EBee LRHS NRHS SRot
§ × ***superbum***	CMac ESps GAbr IBoy IRob MMuc SEND WBrk
- 'Aglaia' (d)	Widely available
- 'Alaska'	CAni CExl CRos CTsd EBee ELan EWTr GBin IBoy LRHS LSun MCot NLar NRHS SCob SPer SWvt WRHF XLum
- 'Amelia'	CRos EBee LRHS NBre NRHS
- 'Andernach'	CAni
- 'Anita Allen' (d)	CAni ECtt WCot
- 'Anna Camilla'	CAni
- 'Antwerp Star'	NBre NLar WBrk
- 'Banana Cream'	CBcs CBod CPla CRos CWGN EAJP EBee ECtt ELon EUJe LCro LRHS MAsh MHol MSCN NLar NRHS SCob SEle SPoG STPC WHoo WTor
- 'Banwell'	CAni
- 'Barbara Bush' (v/d)	SWvt
§ - 'Beauté Nivelloise'	CAni CElw CRos EBee ECtt EPfP GWyn IPot LCro LOPS LRHS MBel MSpe NRHS SRms WSpi
- 'Becky'	CCse CElw CMac CRos EBee ECha ELan ELon EWTr EWes GBin GWyn IPot LLHF LRHS LSRN LSou NEoE NLar NRHS WCAu WSpi
- 'Bishopstone'	CAni EBee ECtt ELan LEdu LLHF MSpe
- 'Bridal Bouquet'^{PBR}	CRos EBee ECtt LRHS NRHS SPhm
- 'Brightside'	CRos EBee ELan ELon LRHS MWat NRHS WFar WMoo
- BROADWAY LIGHTS ('Leumayel'^{PBR})	CRos EBee EPfP EWTr GBin GMcL IBoy IRob LRHS MRav NRHS SCob WAvo WCAu WFar WGrn WSpi WTor
- 'Christine Hagemann'	CAni CElw EBee ECtt EWTr EWes ILea IPot MAvo MNrw MRav SHar WBrk WCFE
- 'Cobham Gold' (d)	CWCL NBre
- 'Colwall'	CAni
- 'Crazy Daisy'	CAni CBod CChe CRos CTri EAJP ECtt GNew GWyn LRHS NRHS SRot SWvt WFar
- 'Devon Mist'	CAni
- 'Droitwich Beauty'	CAni ECtt LLHF WAvo WHil WHoo
- 'Duchess of Abercorn'	CAni
- 'Dwarf Snow Lady'	NBre NLar
- 'Easton Lady'	CAni
- 'Eclipse'	CAni
- 'Edgebrook Giant'	CAni WBrk WHil
- 'Edward VII'	CAni
- 'Eisstern'	EBee LEdu MAvo SHar
- 'Elworthy Sparkler'	CElw MAvo WBrk
- 'Engelina'^{PBR}	EBee NLar SPoG WCAu
- 'Esther Read' (d)	CRos EBee ECtt ELan EPau EPfP GBin GMaP LRHS LSRN NBro NChi NEgg NLar NRHS SRms SWvt WBrk WCot WFar
§ - 'Everest'	CAni SRms
- 'Exhibition'	CRos EBee LRHS NRHS
- 'Fair Lady' **new**	ETMg
- 'Fiona Coghill' (d)	CAni CBod CElw CWGN ECtt EPfP GBin IBoy LRHS MBel MNrw MSCN MSpe NEgg NGdn NLar NPnk NRHS STPC WCot WHoo
- 'Firnglanz'	CAni GBin
- 'Flore Pleno' (d)	MMuc SEND SPlb
- FREAK! ('Leuz0001'^{PBR})	CBcs CRos EBee EPfP GBin LRHS NRHS SPoG
- 'Goldfinch'^{PBR}	CBcs CMea CWCL CWGN EBee ECtt EUJe ILea LLHF LRHS MBel MTis NGBl NHpl NPnk NPri SPoG WCot WHil WTor
- 'Goldrausch'^{PBR}	CRos EBee ECtt EHrv ELan EPfP IBoy LLHF LRHS LSou MBel MCot MRav NEgg NGdn NRHS SCob SGbt SRms SWvt WFar
- 'Gruppenstolz'	CAni SAko
- 'H. Seibert'	CAni MArl

- 'Harry' CAni
- 'Highland White Dream'PBR CRos LRHS NRHS
- 'Horace Read' (d) CAni CDor CElw CMea ECtt SWvt
- 'Ice Star' EBee
- 'Jennifer Read' CAni
§ - 'John Murray' (d) CAni EWes NWsh WFar
- 'Lacrosse' CRos EBee EPfP LRHS NPnk NRHS SCob WCAu WFar
- 'Laspider' CRos EBee LRHS NPnk NRHS SRot
- 'Little Miss Muffet' CRos CSBt CWGN EBee ECtt LEdu LLHF LRHS LSou MBNS NRHS
- 'Little Princess' see *L.* × *superbum* 'Silberprinzesschen'
- 'Luna' **new** WTor
- 'Majestic' CAni
- 'Manhattan' CAni CCse CDor EBee EWes GBin
- 'Margaretchen' CAni
- 'Marion Bilsland' CAni MSpe NChi WBrk
- 'Mayfield Giant' CAni
- 'Mount Everest' see *L.* × *superbum* 'Everest'
- 'Octopus' CAni
- 'Old Court' see *L.* × *superbum* 'Beauté Nivelloise'
- 'Paladin'PBR EBee ECtt GBin IPot NLar SPoG
- 'Phyllis Smith' CAni CRos EBee ECtt ELan ELon GBin GNew GWyn LCro LSRN MAvo MCot MHer MPie MRav MSpe NGdn SCob SMad WBrk WCAu WCot WMoo
- 'Polaris' CRos EBee LRHS NBre NRHS WMoo XLum
- 'Rags and Tatters' CAni ECtt EWes
- 'Real Dream' EBee ETMg LSou MTis NEoE WFar
- 'Real Galaxy'PBR CMea CRos LBuc LRHS LSou MTis NEoE NRHS
- 'Real Glory' ECtt ILea LRHS MHol MTis NHpl WCAu WFar
- 'Real Neat' CAby CRos EBee ECtt ETMg LRHS LSou MAsh MAvo MHol MTis NEoE NHpl NRHS SCob SHar STPC WAvo
- 'Schwabengruss' CAni
- 'Shaggy' see *L.* × *superbum* 'Beauté Nivelloise'
- 'Shapcott Gossamer' CAby CAni CBod CPou EBee ECtt MNrw MTis NGBl SCob WCot
- 'Shapcott Ruffles' CAni CBod EBee ECtt EUJe MTis WCot
- 'Shapcott Summer Clouds' CAni CBod CDor CElw EBee ECtt ELon MBNS MBel MHol MTis SMad SPoG WCot
§ - 'Silberprinzesschen' CAni CRos CSBt ELon EPfP GJos GMaP GWyn IRob LRHS NRHS SPlb SRms WHar WMoo XLum
- 'Silver Spoon' CRos EPfP LRHS NRHS
- 'Snehurka' CAni CRos LLHF LRHS MAvo NRHS WCot WHoo
- 'Snow Lady' CBod CChe CRos EBee EPfP ESps GMcL GWyn LRHS NPer NRHS SRms WFar WHar
- 'Snow Queen' GWyn
- 'Snowbound' **new** NEoE
- 'Snowcap' CHid CRos ECha EPfP ESps LRHS MBel MRav NRHS SPer SWvt WGwG
- 'Snowdrift' CAni CRos LRHS MWat NBre NLar NRHS WBrk WCot WFar WMoo
- 'Snowstorm' MAvo
§ - 'Sonnenschein' CBod CDor CRos EBee ECha ECtt ELan EPfP GMaP GQue LRHS LSRN LSou MArl MCot MHol MRav NEgg NGdn NRHS NWsh SPer SRms WCAu
- 'Starburst' (d) CRos EBee ELan LRHS NRHS SRms
- 'Stina' EBee GBin XLum
- 'Summer Snowball' see *L.* × *superbum* 'John Murray'
- 'Sunny Side Up'PBR CBod CRos CWCL EBee ECtt LRHS MSCN MWat NLar NPnk NRHS SCob SRot WAul WFar
- SUNSHINE see *L.* × *superbum* 'Sonnenschein'
- 'T.E. Killin' (d) ♀H4 CBod CRos EBee ECha ECtt ELan EPau EPfP EUJe GBin IRob LCro LRHS LSou MRav.MWat NRHS SPtp WFar WHoo
- 'Victorian Secret'PBR CBod CRos ECtt GBin IRob LBuc LRHS MBel MNrw NEoE NRHS SCob SMad WCot WHil WHoo WTor
- WESTERN STAR LEO ('Leuz0002'PBR) CRos LRHS NRHS
- 'White Iceberg' (d) CAni
- WHITE MOUNTAIN ('Gfleuwhmtn'PBR) CRos LRHS NRHS
- 'Wirral Pride' CAni CRos EPfP WBrk
- 'Wirral Supreme' (d) ♀H5 Widely available

§ ***vulgare*** CBod CHab CMac CWld EBWF ENfk EPfP EShb GBin GJos GQue LCro LOPS MHer MMuc MNHC NMir SEND SPhx WFar WHer WMoo WOut WSFF WShi XLum XSen
- 'Filigran' CRos LRHS NRHS WFar
§ - 'Maikönigin' CRos GQue GWyn LRHS MJak NRHS XLum
- MAY QUEEN see *L. vulgare* 'Maikönigin'
- 'Sunny' CBre

'White Knight' CBod CRos GMcL LRHS NRHS

Leucocoryne (*Alliaceae*)

'Andes' ♀H3 CCCN GKev NRog SDeJ
'Dione' GKev NRog SDeJ
'Double Fantasy' NRog
hybrids CGrW
* ***ixioides alba*** NRog
- 'Blue Ocean' GKev NRog SDeJ
pauciflora NRog
purpurea ♀H3 CGrW NRog
'Spotlight' GKev NRog
vittata NRog
'White Dream' GKev NRog SDeJ

Leucogenes (*Asteraceae*)

grandiceps WAbe
leontopodium EPot NRHS NSla WAbe
tarahaoa EPot

Leucogenes × *Raoulia* see × *Leucoraoulia*

Leucojum ✿ (*Amaryllidaceae*)

aestivum CAby CBcs CDor CTri EBee GKev LAma MCot MJak MMuc NChi NEgg SDeJ SDir SEND SRms WCFE WCot WFar WHil WRHF WShi
- 'Gravetye Giant' ♀H7 Widely available
- var. ***pulchellum*** CElw
autumnale see *Acis autumnalis*
roseum see *Acis rosea*
tingitanum see *Acis tingitana*
trichophyllum see *Acis trichophylla*
valentinum see *Acis valentina*
vernum ♀H5 Widely available

- var. ***carpathicum*** EPri
- var. ***vagneri*** ECha SDys WSHC

Leucophysalis (*Solanaceae*)

sinense BWJ 8093 WCru

Leucophyta (*Asteraceae*)

§ ***brownii*** CCht GMcL
- 'Silver Sand' LSou

Leucopogon (*Ericaceae*)

§ ***colensoi*** WThu
ericoides GKev
§ ***fraseri*** WThu

× *Leucoraoulia* (*Asteraceae*)

§ ***loganii*** WAbe

Leucosceptrum (*Lamiaceae*)

canum CExl
- GWJ 9424 WCru
japonicum B&SWJ 10804 WCru
- B&SWJ 10981 WCru
- 'Silver Angel' (v) WCot
stellipilum var. ***formosanum*** IMou
- - B&SWJ 1926 WCru
- - RWJ 9907 SBrt WCru
- var. ***tosaense*** B&SWJ 8892 WCru

Leucospermum (*Proteaceae*)

(Carnival Series) 'Carnival Red' CCCN
- 'Carnival Copper' CCCN
cordifolium CCCN CPbh
'Fountain' LRHS
glabrum SPlb
'Scarlet Ribbon' CCCN
'Succession' CCCN
'Tango' CPbh
'Vulkano' CCCN

Leucostegia (*Davalliaceae*)

immersa PAB 7836 LEdu WPGP

Leucothoe (*Ericaceae*)

axillaris 'Curly Red'PBR CBod CMac CRos EBee ELan EPfP ESps ETMg LRHS MAsh MGos MJak MPkF NLar NRHS SGol SLim SLon SPoG SWvt WFar
- TWISTING RED ('Opstal20'PBR) IBoy MBlu SLim
CARINELLA ('Zebekot') CRos LRHS NLar NRHS SPoG
davisiae NLar
§ ***fontanesiana*** CMac
- 'Makijaz'PBR (v) CRos EPfP LRHS NLar SPoG
- 'Rainbow' (v) CBcs CDul CMac CRos EBee ELan EPfP ESps GMcL LRHS LSou MGos NLar SGbt SGol SLim SPer SPoG SRms SSta SWvt WFar WHar WMoo
- 'Rollissonii' ♀H6 MRav SRms
- WHITEWATER ('Howw'PBR) (v) CMac CRos CSBt LRHS MPkF NLar NRHS
keiskei BURNING LOVE ('Opstal50'PBR) **new** NLar
- HALLOWEEN ('Opstal16') EBee
- 'Royal Ruby' CRos ESps GMcL LRHS LSou MGos MJak MPkF NEgg NLar NRHS SGbt SGol SPoG WFar WMoo
'Little Flames'PBR **new** SPad
LOVITA ('Zebonard') GMcL MRav NLar SCoo
RED LIPS ('Lipsbolwi'PBR) EPfP GMcL
SCARLETTA ('Zeblid') ♀H6 CBcs CDul CMac CRos CSBt CTri EPfP ESps GMcL LCro LOPS LRHS MGos MJak MRav NEgg NLar NRHS NWad SGol SLim SPad SPer SPoG SWvt WFar WHar
walteri see *L. fontanesiana*

Leuzea (*Asteraceae*)

centaureoides see *Rhaponticum centaureoides*
rhaponticoides see *Rhaponticum exaltata*

Levisticum (*Apiaceae*)

officinale CAgr CBod CHby ENfk EPfP GAbr GPoy LEdu MHer MMuc MNHC NPri SEND SPlb SRms SVic WHer

Lewisia ✿ (*Portulacaceae*)

'Archangel' NRya
Ashwood Carousel hybrids CPBP CTri MAsh NRya
Birch strain CBcs ELan
brachycalyx ♀H4 EWes GCrg LLHF
Brynhyfryd hybrids pink-flowered GKev
- white-flowered GKev
- yellow-flowered GKev
cantelovii CWCL MAsh
columbiana CTal MAsh NHpl
- 'Alba' GKev NRHS NRya NSla
- 'Rosea' GKev MAsh
- subsp. ***rupicola*** ITim MAsh NSla
- subsp. ***wallowensis*** MAsh
congdonii MAsh
cotyledon ♀H4 CRos CWCL EPot GKev GMaP ITim LLHF LRHS NHpl NRHS NSla
- f. ***alba*** CWCL
- - 'Snowstorm' LLHF
- 'Ashwood Ruby' MAsh
- Ashwood strain CRos EPfP EWes LRHS MAsh NHpl SRms WOld
- 'Brannan Bar' MAsh
- 'Bright Eyes' GKev
- var. ***cotyledon*** LLHF
- double-flowered (d) GKev
- ELISE MIXED **new** ETMg
- var. ***heckneri*** MAsh
- var. ***howellii*** LLHF
- hybrid GKev NRya SPoG
- 'John's Special' MAsh
- magenta-flowered CWCL
- orange-flowered CWCL
§ - 'Regenbogen' ETMg LRHS MHer MHol
- rose-pink-flowered CWCL
- (Safira Series) 'Safira Orange' **new** ETMg
- - 'Safira Pink' **new** ETMg
- - 'Safira Purple' **new** ETMg
- salmon-flowered CWCL
- Sunset Group ♀H4 CGar ELon EPfP GCrg IRob NHpl NLar WHar WRHF
- 'White Splendour' MAsh
'George Henley' CPBP EWes LLHF MAsh NRya WAbe
glandulosa NSla
leeana MAsh
'Little Mango' CSma EDAr GCrg NSla
'Little Peach' CSma ECtt EDAr GBin GKev MAsh NHpl NRya NSla

'Little Plum'	CMea CPBP CSma ECtt EDAr GBin GCrg GEdr GKev LRHS MAsh NHpl NLar NRya NSla WThu
LITTLE TUTTI FRUTTI MIXED	CSma
longipetala 'Little Raspberry'	EDAr
§ ***nevadensis***	CRos EPot GKev ITim LRHS NRHS NRya WThu
I - 'Alba'	GKev NHpl
- ***bernardina***	see *L. nevadensis*
- 'Rosea'	NHpl NRya NSla
oppositifolia	LLHF MAsh
- 'Richeyi'	EPot
'Pinkie'	GCrg MAsh NHpl
pygmaea	CRos EWes GEdr GKev ITim LRHS MAsh MHer NRHS NRya NSla SPlb XLum
- carmine-flowered	GKev
pygmaea* × *rediviva	LLHF
Rainbow mixture	see *L. cotyledon* 'Regenbogen'
'Rawreth'	LLHF
rediviva	GKev LLHF MAsh NHpl
- dark pink-flowered	GKev
- white-flowered	GKev
serrata	MAsh
'Trevosia'	MAsh
tweedyi 𝕐[H4]	CPBP CRos EPot GKev LRHS MAsh NHpl NRHS NRya SPlb WAbe
- 'Alba'	MAsh WAbe
- 'Elliott's Variety'	MAsh
- 'Rosea'	CRos EPot LRHS MAsh NRHS WAbe
- yellow-flowered	GKev

Leycesteria (*Caprifoliaceae*)

crocothyrsos	CBcs NLar SPoG WFar
formosa	Widely available
- from Longstock	SLon
- brown-stemmed	IFoB
- 'Gold Leaf'	GAbr MHer SPad WBor WFar WPtf
- GOLDEN LANTERNS ('Notbruce'[PBR]) 𝕐[H4]	Widely available
- 'Golden Pheasant' (v)	EHoe
- 'Lydia'	LRHS
- 'Purple Rain'	CRos EBee EPfP EWes IBoy LRHS MAsh MGos NLar NRHS

Leymus (*Poaceae*)

from Falkland Islands	ELon EPPr
§ ***arenarius***	CAby CBod CElw CKno CSpe EBWF ECha EHoe ELan EPPr EShb GBin GMaP IBoy LRHS MMuc NBid NBro SEND SGbt SGol SPlb SRms WFar WMoo WWtn XLum XSen
cinereus	WCot
hispidus	see *Elymus hispidus*

Lhotzkya see *Calytrix*

Liatris (*Asteraceae*)

aspera	SPhx
cylindracea	SPhx
elegans	EPfP GKev SPlb
ligulistylis	EBee NDov SPhx
mucronata	NLar
pycnostachya	EBee NLar SAko SRms
scariosa	SPhx
- 'Alba'	CBcs SAko SPhx
§ ***spicata***	Widely available
- 'Alba'	CBWd CBod CMac CSBt EAJP ECha ELan EPfP ESps GBin LEdu LSRN MSCN NGdn NLar NPri SCob SPer SPlb WHar XLum
- ***callilepis***	see *L. spicata*
- 'Floristan Violett'	CMea CRos CTri EBee EPfP GMaP GMcL LRHS MHer MJak MSpe MWat NDov NEgg NLar NRHS SCob SCoo SPlb SPoG SWvt WFar WGwG WMoo WWtn XLum
- 'Floristan Weiss'	CExl CRos CTri EPPr EPfP ERCP GMaP GMcL LRHS MBel MHer MJak MRav NLar NRHS SDeJ SPoG SWvt WFar WMoo WWtn
- GOBLIN	see *L. spicata* 'Kobold'
§ - 'Kobold'	CMac CRos EBee ELan EPfP ESps GBin GMcL IBoy LCro LPmr LRHS MBel MRav NEgg NGdn NLar NRHS SGbt SPad SPtp SRms STPC SWvt WCAu WFar WMoo XLum
squarrosa	SPhx

Libanotis see *Seseli*

montana	see *Seseli libanotis*

Libertia ✿ (*Iridaceae*)

'Amazing Grace'	EBee GCal
breunioides	see *L. cranwelliae*
chilensis 𝕐[H3]	Widely available
- brown-stemmed	IFoB
- Elegans Group	CExl EBee WCru
§ - Formosa Group	CBcs CBod CBro CElw CExl CHid CRos CTri ELan ESps GCal GKev LRHS MMuc NChi NRHS NSti SArc SCob SPer SPtp SRms SWvt WHer
- Procera Group	CSpe EBee EPfP GBin GCal GLog LEdu LRHS SMad SPlb SPtp WPGP WSHC
§ ***cranwelliae***	CExl WPGP
formosa	see *L. chilensis* Formosa Group
grandiflora ambig.	CBWd CCht WHlf
'Grasshopper'	GBin
ixioides	CBcs ECha ILea LEdu MMuc SPtp WPGP
- 'Goldfinger' (v)	CBcs CBct CExl CKno CMac CRos CWCL EBee ELan ELon EPfP EShb ESps GMcL IBoy LEdu LLWG LRHS MHol MJak MPkF NRHS SLon SPoG SWvt WCot WGrn WHer WMoo
- 'Highlander'	ELon LRHS MHol
- 'Taupo Blaze'	CMac EBee EPfP LRHS MRav SLon SPoG
- 'Taupo Sunset'[PBR]	CBcs CCCN CExl CRos ELon EPfP LRHS MBNS MPkF SWvt
- 'Tricolor'	ECha GEdr MRav WMoo
'Nelson Dwarf'	GCal
paniculata	CExl EBee
peregrinans	CAbb CBod CExl CKno CSpe EBee ECha EHoe ELan EPri GCal GKev IBoy IFro ILea LEdu LRHS MMuc MRav NRHS SEND SPer SPtp SRkn SWvt WPGP
- 'Gold Leaf'	CBcs CCCN CRos CTri CTsd ELan EPfP GMcL LRHS MMoz NRHS SMad SWvt WFar
- 'Gold Stripe'	CPla CSpe ELan SPad SWvt
pulchella misapplied	LRHS NRHS
pulchella ambig. blue-flowered **new**	GKev
sessiliflora	CExl

	- 'Ballyrogan Blue'	EBee GKev
	- 'Caerulescens'	CBcs CCCN CExl CMac EPfP LRHS NGBl SMad SPer SPtp WMoo
	'Sunset Strain'	IBoy
	tricocca misapplied	see *L. umbellata*
§	***umbellata*** HCM 98.089	WPGP

Libocedrus (*Cupressaceae*)

chilensis	see *Austrocedrus chilensis*
decurrens	see *Calocedrus decurrens*
plumosa	CBrP

Libonia see *Justicia*

Licuala (*Arecaceae*)

dasyantha	CBlu
mattanensis 'Mapu'	CBlu

Ligularia (*Asteraceae*)

	amplexicaulis	GCal
	aff. ***atkinsonii*** WJC 13663 new	WCru
	'Bottle Rocket'PBR	NLar
	'Britt Marie Crawford'PBR 🏆H6	Widely available
	calthifolia	EBee
	clivorum	see *L. dentata*
§	***dentata***	ECtt NBro SRms
	- 'Dark Beauty'	IBoy MBNS
	- 'Desdemona'	Widely available
	- 'Enkelrig'	EBee WHar
	- 'Franz Feldweber'	EBee
	- 'Midnight Lady'	EAJP ELan ETMg GPSL GWyn MHol NLar
	- 'Orange Princess'	NPer
	- 'Osiris Café Dark'PBR	SCob
	- 'Osiris Fantaisie' (v)	CDor CExl ECtt EPfP EWes GMcL GWyn ILea LLHF MAvo MBel MHol MNrw MWts NLar NPnk NSti SPoG WBor WCot WFar WPnP
	- 'Othello'	CBod CRos EBee ECtt EPed EPfP ESps GMcL LPmr LRHS NBid NEgg NGdn NRHS NWad SCob SWvt WCAu WHar
	- 'Sommergold'	ECha IRob WFar
	- 'Twilight'	CBct ECtt MBNS
	dictyoneura	GKev
§	***fischeri***	ECha
	- B&SWJ 2570	WCru
	- B&SWJ 4381	WCru
	- B&SWJ 4478	WCru
	- B&SWJ 5653	WCru
	- B&SWJ 8802	WCru
	- var. ***megalorhiza*** 'Cheju Charmer'	ELon WCru
	'Franz Marc'	GCal
	'Garden Confetti'	ECtt MSCN
	'Gold Torch'	ECtt NLar
§	'Gregynog Gold' 🏆H6	CRos ECha ECtt ELan GMaP LRHS MRav NBro NLar
	× ***hessei***	CRos GMaP LRHS MMuc NRHS WWtn
	hodgsonii	EPPr MRav
	- B&SWJ 10855	WCru
	intermedia B&SWJ 606a	WCru WSHC
	japonica	CDor CRos ECha LEdu LRHS NLar NRHS WWtn
	- B&SWJ 2883	WCru
	- 'Rising Sun'	CExl NLar WCot WCru
	'Laternchen'PBR	ECtt SAko
	'Little Rocket'PBR	CBct CBod CExl EBee ECtt ELon EPfP IRob MBNS MSCN MWts NBro NGdn NLar NRHS SCob SPoG WFar WHil
	'Osiris Café Noir'	CBod ECtt ILea NLar SCob WFar WMoo WWtn
	'Osiris Pistache' (v)	EBee ECtt
	× ***palmatiloba***	see *L.* × *yoshizoeana* 'Palmatiloba'
§	***przewalskii***	Widely available
	- SSSE 176	WCot
	- 'Dragon Wings'	CAby EWTr GBin MHol NEoE NLar SCob
	- 'Dragon's Breath'	CAby ECtt EUJe GBin MHol SCob
	'Savill Spire' new	LSvl
	sibirica	CSam MMuc NLar WArt WMoo
	- B&SWJ 4383	WCru
	- B&SWJ 5841	WCru
	- var. ***speciosa***	see *L. fischeri*
	smithii	see *Senecio smithii*
	speciosa	see *L. fischeri*
	stenocephala	EBee NBro NLar SCob WWtn XLum
	'Sungold'	CMac CRos CSam ECtt LRHS NGdn NRHS
	tangutica	see *Sinacalia tangutica*
	'The Rocket' 🏆H5	Widely available
	tussilaginea	see *Farfugium japonicum*
	- 'Aureo-maculata'	see *Farfugium japonicum* 'Aureomaculatum'
	veitchiana	CBod CSam GCal WWtn
	vorobievii	GCal NLar
	'Weihenstephan'	CRos GCal LRHS NRHS
	wilsoniana	CRos GAbr LLWG LRHS MMuc MRav NRHS SEND WFar WWtn
	- B&SWJ 14195 new	WCru
§	× ***yoshizoeana*** 'Palmatiloba'	CRos ELan ELon EWes GCal LRHS MRav NRHS SPhx WFar WWtn
	'Zepter'	CBct CBod CRos ECtt EShb EUJe GCal LRHS MMuc NEgg NLar NRHS NWad WCot WWtn

Ligusticum (*Apiaceae*)

	lucidum	EBee EPfP EUJe LEdu MAvo NSti SPhx SPtp WBor WCot WPGP
	- subsp. ***lucidum***	CSpe
	mutellina	LPla
§	***scoticum***	CBod CHid EBWF EBee EWes GBin GLog GPoy LEdu LRHS MAvo MHer SPhx SPtp SRms WFar WOut WPGP WPtf
	- variegated (v)	LEdu WCot

Ligustrum ✿ (*Oleaceae*)

	B&L 12261	WPGP
	chenaultii	see *L. compactum*
§	***compactum***	ETod
§	***delavayanum***	EBtc EShb GKev SGol STrG SWeb WCFE WPGP
	- B&L 12083	CExl
	ibota	EBtc NLar
	- MUSLI ('Muster'PBR) (v)	LRHS MSCN SPoG WCot
	ionandrum	see *L. delavayanum*
	japonicum	CLnd CRos EBar ECrN LMaj LPra LRHS LSRN SEND SGol SPer
I	- 'Aureum'	EMOT
	- 'Coriaceum'	see *L. japonicum* 'Rotundifolium'
	- GREEN CENTURY ('Melgreen'PBR)	EBee LRHS
	- 'Korea Dwarf'	NLar

– 'Macrophyllum'	EPfP
§ – 'Rotundifolium'	CBcs CDul CExl CRos EBee ELan EPfP LRHS MAsh MMrt MRav NLar SPer SPoG WCFE WCot WFar
§ – 'Silver Star' (v)	NLar SGol
§ – 'Texanum'	ECrN EPfP LMaj NLar SArc SWeb WCFE
– 'Texanum Argenteum'	see *L. japonicum* 'Silver Star'
– 'Variegatum' (v)	SGol
lucidum ♀H5	CCVT CDul CSBt CTri ELan ESps EUJe EWTr GCal IDee LPra LRHS MRav NLar SArc SCob SEND SGol SPer SWvt
– Guiz 296	CExl
– 'Curly Wurly'	CRos LRHS NRHS SPoG
– 'Excelsum Superbum' (v) ♀H5	CCVT CJun CLnd CMac CRos EBar ECrN ELan EPfP ESps LMaj LPra LRHS LSRN MGos SGol SPoG WCot
– 'Golden Wax'	CJun MRav
– 'Tricolor' (v) ♀H5	CJun CRos ELan EPfP LRHS MAsh MGos SPer SPoG SWvt
obtusifolium var. ***regelianum***	MMuc NLar
ovalifolium	Widely available
§ – 'Argenteum' (v)	CBcs CCVT CDul CMac CTri ECrN EHoe ELan EMOT EShb ESps GAbr GMcL MMuc MRav NEgg SEND SGol SLim SPer SPoG SWvt
– 'Aureomarginatum'	see *L. ovalifolium* 'Aureum'
§ – 'Aureum' (v) ♀H5	Widely available
– 'Lemon and Lime' (v)	CBod CRos EBee EHoe ELan EPfP LSRN MAsh SCob SCoo SRms SWvt WCot
– 'Variegatum'	see *L. ovalifolium* 'Argenteum'
– 'Vicaryi'	CRos ELan EPfP GBin MGos NEoE NRHS NWad SCob SGol SPer WFar
quihoui	CBot CRos CTri EBee ECre ELan EPfP IDee LRHS MBlu NLar SEND SLon SPer SPoG
sempervirens	EPfP
sinense	CMCN MRav
– 'Multiflorum'	WFar
– 'Sunshine' **new**	CRos NRHS
– 'Variegatum' (v)	MRav SPer
strongylophyllum	CExl
texanum	see *L. japonicum* 'Texanum'
tschonoskii	MBlu
undulatum 'Lemon Lime and Clippers'	CRos EShb LRHS MBNS NLar NRHS SCob SPoG WMoo
vulgare	CArg CBcs CCVT CDul CHab CMac CPer CTri EBWF ECrN EPfP ESps LBuc MMuc MSwo SCob SEND SEWo SWvt WMou WSFF WTSh
– 'Lodense'	EBtc

Lilium ✿ (*Liliaceae*)

'4 You' (Ia-b/b)	CRos LRHS NRHS
'Abbeville's Pride' (Ia/b)	SDeJ
'Acapulco' (VII-/d)	SDeJ
§ 'Acoustic' (Colour Carpet Series) (VIIa/b-c)	CRos ETMg LRHS NRHS
'Adonis' (Ic/d)	GEdr
African Queen Group (VI-/a) ♀H6	CRos ERCP GKev LAma LCro LOPS NRHS SCoo SRms
– 'African Queen' (VIb-c/a)	CBro MCri SDeJ
'All Time' (Ia-b/b) **new**	CRos NRHS
'Altari' (VIIIa-b/b)	SDeJ
amabile var. ***luteum*** (IXc/d)	MCri
'Ambergate'	SDeJ
'Anastasia' (VIIIb-c/b-d)	EPfP GKev LAma LCro LOPS SDeJ SDir
'Annemarie's Dream' (Ia/c)	SDeJ SDir
'Apeldoorn' (Ia/b)	MCri
APOLLO (Ia-b)	see *L.* 'Blizzard'
'Arabian Knight' (IIc/d)	GKev LAma LRHS SDeJ SDir WFar
'Arena' (VIIa/b)	SCoo
Asiatic hybrids (I)	LRHS NGdn NRHS
auratum 'Gold Band'	see *L. auratum* var. *platyphyllum*
§ – var. ***platyphyllum*** (IXb/c)	MCri SDeJ
– – B&SWJ 4824	WCru
– – B&SWJ 5041	WCru
– var. ***virginale*** (IXb/c)	GKev MCri SDeJ
Backhouse hybrids	see *L.* × *dalhansonii* Backhouse Group
'Baferrari' (VIIa/b)	SDeJ
'Bamako' (VIIa-b/b) **new**	SDeJ
'Barbara North' (Ic/d)	GEdr
'Barbaresco' (VIIa-b/b)	SCoo
'Beijing Moon' (VIb-c/a) **new**	SDeJ
'Belgrado'^{PBR} (VIIa/b-c)	SDeJ SDir
'Belladonna'^{PBR} (VIIIb-a/b)	SDeJ
'Belle Epoque' (VIIb/b-c)	SDeJ
Bellingham Group (IVc/d)	GEdr
'Bergamo' (VIIb/b)	SCoo SDeJ
'Beverly Dreams' (VIIIa/a)	ERCP
'Beverly Hills'^{PBR} (VIIIa-b/b) **new**	SDeJ SDir
'Black Beauty' (VIIIb-c/d)	CTsd GKev LAma LCro LOPS MCri SDeJ SDir
'Black Dragon'	see *L. leucanthum* var. *centifolium* 'Black Dragon'
'Blazing Dwarf' (Ia/b)	CRos NRHS
§ 'Blizzard' (Ia/b)	SDeJ
'Bonbini' (VIIIa-b/b)	CRos LRHS NRHS
'Boogie Woogie' (VIIIa-b/b)	SDeJ
'Bowmore'^{PBR} (VIIIa/b) **new**	SDir
'Bracelet' (VIIIa-b/b)	SDeJ
'Brasil'^{PBR} (Ia/b)	GKev
BRASILIA ('Zora') (VIIa/b-c)	SDeJ
'Bright Diamond'^{PBR} (VIIIa/b)	GKev
BRIGHT PIXIE ('Ceb Bright') (Ia/b)	GKev SDeJ
'Bright Star' (VIb-c/c)	LAma MCri
'Broken Heart' (VIIb-a/c) **new**	SDeJ
bulbiferum var. ***croceum*** (IXa/b)	XEll
'Butter Pixie'^{PBR} (Ia/b)	CBod CRos GMcL NRHS SDeJ
§ ***canadense*** (IXc/a)	GEdr LAma WCot WCru XEll
– var. ***flavum***	see *L. canadense*
'Cancun' (Ia/b-c)	SDeJ
candidum (IXb/a)	CAvo CBcs CTca CTri CWCL EBee ECha EHrv ELan EPot ERCP GKev LAma NRog SDeJ SDir SRms WSpi WWFP
'Candy Blossom' (Ia/b) **new**	SDeJ
'Casa Blanca' (VIIb/b-c) ♀H6	CAvo CBro CRav EPfP GKev LAma LCro LOPS SCoo SDeJ SDir
'Ceb Latte' (Ia/b)	GKev
'Cecil' (VIIIa/b)	SDeJ
cernuum (IXc/d)	LAma SDeJ
* – 'Album'	SDeJ
'Chameleon' (II)	CAvo GKev LAma
'Chill Out' (VIIa/b)	LCro LOPS
§ 'Chocolate Canary' (Ic/-)	GKev SDeJ
Citronella Group (Ic/d)	SDeJ

'Claude Shride' (IIc/d)	CAvo CBro GEdr GKev LAma LRHS SDeJ SDir
'Cocktail Twins' (Ia/b)	CRos LRHS NRHS SDeJ
§ 'Coldplay' (Colour Carpet Series) (VIIa-b/b-c)	CRos ETMg LBuc LRHS NRHS
columbianum (IXc/d) B&SWJ 9564	WCru
'Con Amore' (VIIb/b)	SCoo
'Conca d'Or'[PBR] (VIIIb/b)	CRos LRHS NRHS SDeJ
'Connecticut King' (Ia/b)	MCri
'Corcovado'[PBR] (VIIIa/b) **new**	SDir
'Creation' (VIa/b)	SDeJ
'Crimson Pixie' (Ia/b)	CBod CRos GKev GMcL LCro LOPS NRHS SDeJ
'Crossover' (Ia/b-c)	CRos GMcL LRHS NRHS
× ***dalhansonii*** (IIc/d)	CAby
§ - Backhouse Group (IIc/d)	WFar
- 'Guinea Gold' (II)	GKev LAma
- 'Mrs R.O. Backhouse' (IIc/d)	GEdr SDeJ
- 'Sutton Court' (II)	GEdr
- Terrace City Group (II)	GKev LAma SDeJ
'Dark Romance' (Romance Series) (VIIb/b)	CRos LRHS NRHS
dauricum var. ***alpinum*** (IXa/b)	MCri
davidii (IXc/d)	CExl LAma MCri SDeJ WCru
§ - var. ***willmottiae*** (IXc/d)	MCri WCru
DAZZLER ('Maru') (Colour Carpet Series) (VIIa/b)	CRos ETMg LBuc LRHS NRHS
'Debby' (VIIIa-b/b-c)	SDeJ
'Delicate Joy' (Ia/b)	CRos LRHS NRHS
'Dimension' (Ia/b-c)	LAma LCro LOPS
DISCO	see *L.* 'Discoteca'
§ 'Discoteca' (Ia)	ETMg SDeJ
distichum (IXb-c/d) B&SWJ 794	WCru
- B&SWJ 4465	WCru
'Dizzy' (VIIa-b/b-c)	CBod CTsd ETMg SDeJ
'Dot to Dot'	CRos LRHS NRHS
duchartrei (IXc/d)	CAby CExl LAma WCru
'Electric' (Ia/b-c)	MCri
'Electric Yellow'	see *L.* 'Yellow Electric'
'Elgrado' (Ia/b) **new**	SDeJ
'Elodie'[PBR] (Ia/b)	CAvo LAma SDeJ SDir
'Elusive' (VIIIb/b-d)	GKev SDeJ
'Enchantment' (Ia/b)	SDeJ
'Eros' (Ic/d)	GEdr
'Esta Bonita'[PBR] (VIIIa-b/b)	SDir
'Eurydike' (Ic/d)	GEdr
'Exotic Sun'[PBR] (VIIIb-a/b) **new**	ETMg
'Expression' (VII)	SDeJ
'Eyeliner'[PBR] (VIIIa/b)	LAma SDir
fargesii (IXc/d)	CExl
'Fata Morgana' (Ia/b) ♀[H6]	LAma SCoo SDeJ SDir
'Fifty Fifty' (VIIIa/b-c)	GKev SDir
'Fine Romance' (Romance Series) (VII)	CRos LRHS NRHS
'Fire King' (Ib/d)	SCoo SDeJ SRms
'First Romance' (Romance Series) (VIIa /b)	CRos ETMg LRHS NRHS
'Fopapo' (Ia-b/c)	SDeJ
'Forever Marjolein' (Ia/b)	GKev
'Forever Marjon' (Ib-a/b-c)	GKev
'Forever Susan' (Ia/b)	GKev IPot SDeJ
formosanum short, from high altitude (IXb/a) RWJ 10005	WCru
- var. ***formosanum*** (IXb/a) B&SWJ 1589	WCru
- var. ***pricei*** (IXb/a)	CRos EAJP EDAr ELan EPot GBin GEdr LEdu LRHS MHer NRHS SRms
- - 'Snow Queen' (Vb/a)	EShb SDeJ
'Foxtrot' (Ia/b) **new**	SDeJ
'Friso' (VIIIb/b)	EPfP GKev SDeJ
'Garden Party' (VIIb/b) ♀[H6]	GKev SDeJ SDir
'Gaybird' (IIc/c)	GKev LRHS
'Gironde' (Ia/b)	SDeJ
GLIMMER	see *L.* 'Acoustic'
'Gluhwein'[PBR] (VIIIa-b/b)	CRos LRHS NRHS
'Gold Band' (VII) **new**	SDeJ
'Gold Class' (VIIIb-a/b-c) **new**	SDeJ
'Golden Romance' (Romance Series) (VIIa/b) **new**	ETMg
Golden Splendor Group (VIb-c/a) ♀[H6]	GKev IRob LAma MCri SCoo SDeJ
'Golden Stone' (VIIIa-b/b)	SDeJ
'Gran Paradiso' (Ia/b)	MCri
'Grand Cru' (Ia/b)	MCri SDeJ
'Hannah North' (Ic/d)	GEdr
hansonii (IXb-c/d)	CWCL ECha GBin IRob LAma MCri SDeJ SDir
- B&SWJ 4309	WCru
- B&SWJ 8506	WCru
- B&SWJ 8528	WCru
- B&SWJ 4756 from Aomori, Japan	WCru
hansonii × ***martagon*** (II)	ERCP SDeJ
henryi (IXc/d) ♀[H6]	CAvo CBro EBee GKev LAma MCri SCob SDeJ SDir WCru
'Hit Parade' (VII)	SDeJ
'Honeymoon' (VIIIa-b/b)	CBro SDeJ
'Hot Spot' (VII)	CRos LRHS NRHS
'Hotline' (VIIa/b)	LCro LOPS
humboldtii (IXc/d)	CWCL EBee
'Ice Pixie' (Ia/b)	SDeJ
'Inuvik' (Ia/b)	SDeJ
'Ivory Pixie' (Ia/b)	NRHS SDeJ
'João Pessoa' (Ia/b-c) **new**	SDeJ
'Jo's Choice' (VIa-b/a)	SDeJ
'Josephine' (VIIa/b)	GKev SDeJ SDir
'Joy'	see *L.* 'Le Rêve'
'Karen North' (Ic/d)	GEdr
§ ***kelleyanum*** (IXc/d)	EBee
kelloggii (IXc/d)	EBee GBin
'King Pete' (Ib/b-c)	SDeJ
'Kingdom'[PBR] (VIIIa/b-c)	SDeJ
'Kushi Maya'[PBR] (VIIIc/b-c) **new**	SDeJ SDir
'Lady Alice' (VI-/d)	GKev SDeJ SDir
'Ladylike' (Ia/b)	GMcL
'Lake Tulare' (IVc/c-d)	GEdr
§ ***lancifolium*** (IXc/d)	CHid CPne CRos EPot GBin NRHS XAbr XLum
- B&SWJ 4352	WCru
- var. ***flaviflorum*** (IXc/d)	EBee IBoy MCri SDeJ
- 'Flore Pleno' (IXc/d)	CRos EPPr GCal GKev GQue LRHS MHer NRHS SDeJ WCot WCru XLum
* - var. ***forrestii*** (IX)	MCri
- var. ***fortunei*** (IXc/d)	EPPr GBin GCal
- - B&SWJ 539	WCru
- pink-flowered	SDeJ
- 'Splendens' (IXc/d)	EBee EPfP GBin GKev IRob MCri NBid SDeJ SDir WCot
'Landini'[PBR] (Ia/b)	CRav SDeJ
'Lankon' (VIIIc/a)	ERCP

	lankongense (IXc/d)	CWCL EPot GBin GGGa GKev LAma LRHS SDir WCru
	- BWJ 7554	WCru
	- BWJ 7691	WCru
	'Late Morning' (VIIIb/c) **new**	SDeJ
	'Latvia' (Ia/b)	MCri SDeJ
	'Lazy Lady'	see *L.* 'Chocolate Canary'
§	'Le Rêve' (VIIa-b/b)	SDeJ
	leichtlinii (IXc/d)	CAby CAvo EBee EPot GBin GEdr GKev IMou LLHF MCri SDeJ WOld
	- 'Iwashimiza' (IXc/d)	MCri
	'Lemon Pixie' (Ia/b)	NRHS
	'Leslie Woodriff' (VIIIb-c/d)	IPot
	leucanthum (IXb-c/a)	LAma
	- var. ***centifolium*** (IXb-c/a)	MCri WCru
	- - BWJ 8130	WCru
§	- - 'Black Dragon' (IXb-c/a)	MCri
	lijiangense (IXc/d)	GEdr MCri XEll
I	'Linda' (Ia/b)	SDeJ
	'Little John' (VIIa-b/b)	CBod SDeJ
	'Little Kiss' (Ia/d)	SDeJ
	LOLLYPOP ('Holebibi') (Ia/b)	GMcL NRHS SCoo SDeJ
	'Londrina' (Ia/b) **new**	SDeJ
	longiflorum (IXb/a)	CTsd EBee MCri SCoo SDir XLum
	- B&SWJ 11376	WCru
	- 'Foliis Variegatis' (Vb/a/v)	MAvo
	- 'Rose'	SDeJ
§	- 'White American' (Vb/a)	CRos NRHS
	- 'White Heaven'[PBR] (Vb/a)	EPfP LCro LOPS
	'Lovely Girl' (VII-/b)	SDeJ
	'Luxor' (Ia/b)	CTsd
	'Luzia' (VIIa-b/c)	CRos LRHS NRHS
	mackliniae (IXc/a) ♀[H5]	CPne CWCL EWes GCal GGGa GKev ITim WAbe WHal WPGP
	- PAB 9327	LEdu WPGP
	- PAB 9668	LEdu WPGP
	- from Nagaland, India	CPne GGGa
	- deep pink-flowered	GGGa
	'Magic Star'[PBR] (VIIa-b/b)	SDeJ
	'Manitoba Morning' (IIc/c)	GKev LAma LRHS SDeJ SDir
	'Mapira' (VIIIb/b)	CHid GKev SDeJ
	'Marco Polo' ambig.	SCoo SDeJ
	'Marie North' (Ic/d)	GEdr
	'Maroon King' (II)	GKev LRHS WFar
	martagon (IXc/d) ♀[H7]	CAvo CBro CWCL EBee ECha EHrv ELan EPot ERCP GEdr GKev GPoy IRob ITim LAma LCro LOPS LRHS NChi SDeJ SRms WCot WPnP WShi WSpi
	- var. ***albiflorum*** (IXc/d)	EHrv LAma LRHS
	- var. ***album*** (IXc/d)	CAvo CBro CWCL ELan EPot GBin GKev LAma LRHS NChi NRHS SDeJ SRms WShi
	- var. ***cattaniae*** (IXc/d)	EPot GEdr MCri
	- 'Fairy Morning' (IIc/c)	GKev WFar
	- var. ***hirsutum*** (IXc/d)	GEdr
*	- var. ***rubrum***	CBro
	- 'Slate's Morning' (IIc/c)	GKev
	'Mascara' (Ia-b/b)	GKev
	'Matrix' (Ia-b/b) **new**	CBod
	medeoloides (IXc/d) B&SWJ 4184	WCru
	- B&SWJ 4363	WCru
	'Miss Feya' (VIIIb/c)	CAby LAma SDeJ SDir
	'Miss France' (VIIb/b-c)	SDeJ
I	'Miss Lily' (VIIIb/b-c)	SDeJ
	'Miss Lucy'[PBR] (VIIa-b/b-c)	CHid LAma SDeJ
	MISS RIO	see *L.* 'Rio'
	'Mister Job' (VIIIa/c)	SDeJ
	'Modern Romance' (Romance Series) (VIIa-b/b) **new**	ETMg
	'Mona Lisa' (VIIb/b-c)	CRos LAma LRHS MCri NGdn NRHS SDeJ
	monadelphum (IXc/d)	LAma SDeJ XEll
	'Mont Blanc' (Ia/b-c)	SDeJ
	'Monte Negro' (Ia/b)	MCri
	'Montezuma'[PBR] (VIIa-b/b)	SDeJ
	'Montreux' (Ia/b-c)	SDeJ
	'Mount Cook' (VIIa/b) **new**	SDeJ
	'Mountain Joy' (Ia/b)	CRos LRHS NRHS
	'Muscadet'[PBR] (VIIa-b/b)	CRav GKev LAma SDeJ
	'Must See' (Ia/b)	GKev
§	***nanum*** (IXc/b)	WAbe WHal
	'Navona' (Ia/b)	GKev SDeJ
	nepalense (IXc/a)	CAby CBcs CBro CExl CHid CWCL EPfP EPot ERCP GBin GEdr GKev LAma LCro LOPS LRHS MCri SDeJ SDir WCot WCru WPnP XLum
	- B&SWJ 2985	SDir WCru
	'Nerone' (Ia/b)	CHid CRav
	'Netty's Pride' (Ia/b-c)	CAvo CHid ERCP IPot SDeJ
	'New Wave' (Ia/b)	CBod GMcL SDeJ
	'Night Flyer' (Ib-c/b-c)	GKev SDeJ
	'Nove Cento' (Ia/b)	MCri SDeJ
	Olympic Group (VI-/a)	MCri
	'Orange County' (Ia/b)	SDeJ
	'Orange Electric' (Ia/b)	SDeJ SDir
	'Orange Marmalade' (IIb/c-d)	CBro GKev LAma LRHS SDeJ SDir
	'Orange Pixie' (Ia/b)	CBod CRos MCri NRHS SCoo
	'Orange Planet' (VIa/a)	SDeJ
	'Orange Twinkle' (Ib-c/b)	SDeJ
	'Orange Twins' (Ia-b)	CRos LRHS NRHS
	'Orania'[PBR] (VIIIb/b)	GKev SDeJ
	oriental hybrids (VII)	SDeJ
*	Oriental Superb Group	NGdn
§	***oxypetalum*** (IXb-c/b)	CPne
	- var. ***insigne*** (IXb-c/b)	EPot GBin NHpl SDir WAbe WHal
	'Pan' (Ic/d)	GEdr
	pardalinum (IXc/d) ♀[H6]	CBro CWCL EBee ERCP GKev WCot WCru
	- var. ***giganteum*** (IXc/d)	EPfP MCri MNrw
	- subsp. ***pardalinum*** (IXc/d)	SDeJ
§	- subsp. ***vollmeri*** (IXc/d)	WCru
§	- subsp. ***wigginsii*** (IXc/d)	WCru
	× ***parkmanii*** 'Journey's End' (VIIb/c)	LAma
	- 'Rosy Dimple' (VIIa/b)	SDeJ
	parryi (IXb-c/a)	SDir
	'Passion Moon' (VIIb-c/a) **new**	SDeJ
	'Patricia's Pride' (Ia-b/b-c)	SDeJ SDir
	'Peach Butterflies' (Ic/d)	SDeJ
	'Peach Dwarf' (Ia/b-c)	SDeJ
	'Peach Pixie' (Ia/b)	SCoo
	'Pearl Carolina' (Ic/c)	GKev SDir
	'Pearl Jennifer' (Ib-a/c)	GKev SDeJ SDir
	'Pearl Jessica' (Ib-c/b-c)	GKev SDeJ SDir
	'Pearl Justien' (Ia-b/c)	GKev SDeJ
	'Pearl Loraine' (Ib-c/b-c)	GKev SDeJ
	'Pearl Melanie' (Ib/c)	GKev SDeJ
	'Pearl Sonja' (Ib/b)	SDeJ
	'Pearl Stacey' (Ib-c/c)	GKev SDeJ
	'Peggy North' (Ic/d)	GEdr
	'Penthouse' (VIIa/b)	CRos LRHS NRHS
	'Pepard Gold' (IIc/d)	GEdr GKev LAma LRHS
	philippinense (IXa-b/a)	LAma WPGP
	'Pieton' (Ia/b-c) **new**	SDeJ

'Pimento' (VIIa/b)	SDeJ
'Pink Blossom' (Ia/b)	CRos LRHS NRHS
'Pink Expression' (VII)	CRos LRHS NRHS
'Pink Flavour' (Ic/c)	CAvo CRav GKev SDeJ
'Pink Heart'	LBuc
'Pink Morning' (IIc/c)	LRHS SDir
Pink Perfection Group (VIb/a) ♀H6	CRos ERCP GKev IRob LAma LCro LOPS MCri NRHS SCoo SDeJ
'Pink Pixie'^{PBR} (Ia/b)	CBod GMcL NRHS SDeJ
'Pink Romance' (Romance Series) (VIIa/b)	CRos ETMg LRHS NRHS
poilanei misapplied	see *L. primulinum*
poilanei Gagnep.	see *L. primulinum* var. *poilanei*
'Polar Star' (VIIa-b/b) **new**	SDeJ
'Precious Joy' (Ia/b)	CRos LRHS NRHS
§ ***primulinum*** (IXc/a)	GKev
- HWJ 681	WCru
- WWJ 11679	WCru
- var. ***ochraceum*** (IXc/a)	WCru
§ - var. ***poilanei***	EBee
aff. ***primulinum*** var. ***ochraceum*** (IXc/a) KWJ 12064	WCru
'Proud Bride' (VIIa/b)	CBod
§ ***pumilum*** (IXc/d)	EBee EPot GKev LAma SDeJ SDir
'Purple Eye' (Ia-b/b)	ERCP SDeJ
'Purple Prince' (VIIIa-b/a-b)	SDeJ
'Push Off' (Ia-b/b)	CRos LRHS NRHS
pyrenaicum (IXc/d)	CAby IFro WShi XEll
'Red Carpet' (Ia/b)	MCri SDeJ
'Red County' (Ia/c-b)	SDeJ
'Red Electric' (Ia/b)	SDeJ
'Red Eyes' (VIIa/-)	CRos LRHS NRHS
'Red Flavour' (Ic/b-c)	CRav GKev SDeJ
'Red Hot' (VIIIc-d/b)	SDeJ
'Red Morning' (VIIIa-b/b)	GKev
'Red Twinkle'	SDeJ
'Red Velvet' (Ic/d)	CAvo SDeJ SDir
regale (IXb/a) ♀H6	CAvo CBro CRos CWCL EBee ECha ELan EPfP ERCP GBin GKev LAma LCro LOPS LRHS MCri NRHS SCob SDeJ SDir SPer SRms
- 'Album' (IXb/a)	CAvo CRav EBee ERCP GBin GKev IMou LAma LCro LOPS LRHS MCri SCob SCoo SDeJ SDir
§ - 'Royal Gold' (IXb/a)	MCri
'Reinesse' (Ia/b)	CRos NRHS SDeJ
'Releeze'	CRos LRHS NRHS
§ 'Rio' (VIIb/b-c)	SCoo
RIO NEGRO ('Corvara'^{PBR}) (VIIa-b/b-c) **new**	SDeJ
'Robert Swanson' (VIIIb-c/b)	GKev LAma SDeJ
'Robina' (VIIIa-b/b-c)	WCot WWFP
'Rose Arch Fox' (IIc/c-d)	GKev LAma SDir
'Rosella's Dream' (Ia/b)	SDeJ
'Rosemary North' (Ic/d)	GEdr
'Rosselini' (VIIIa-b/b)	SDeJ
rosthornii (IXc/d)	CExl EBee LAma WCru
'Royal Gold'	see *L. regale* 'Royal Gold'
'Russian Morning' (IIc/c)	GKev LRHS SDir
'Russian Red' (IIc/d)	LAma
sachalinense (IXa/b) RBS 0235	EPPr
'Salinas' (VIIa/b)	SDeJ
'Salmon Flavour' (Ic/b-c)	CAvo GKev
'Salmon Party' (VIIb/b)	GKev
'Salmon Tiger'	SDeJ SDir
'Salmon Twinkle' (Ib-c/c)	SDeJ
sargentiae (IXb-c/a)	GCal GEdr
'Satisfaction' (VIIIa-b/-)	SDeJ
'Scarlet Delight' (VIIb-c/c-d)	SDeJ SDir
'Scheherazade' (VIIIc/d)	GKev LAma MCri SDeJ SDir
'Serrada'^{PBR} (VIIIa-b/b)	ILea
'Set Point' (VIIb/b)	SDeJ
shastense	see *L. kelleyanum*
'Showwinner' (VIIa/b-c)	CRos LRHS NRHS
'Slate's Select' (II)	LAma
'Smoky Mountain' (VIIIc/d)	SDeJ
'Souvenir'^{PBR} (VIIa-b/b)	SDeJ
SPARKLER	see *L.* 'Coldplay'
speciosum (IXb-c/d) B&SWJ 4847	WCru
- B&SWJ 4924	WCru
- var. ***album*** (IXb-c/d)	GKev SDeJ
- var. ***rubrum*** (IXb-c/d)	ECha EPfP LAma LCro LOPS MCri SDeJ SDir SRms
§ - - 'Uchida' (IXb-c/d)	CExl CRav GKev SDeJ
- 'Uchida' (IX) **new**	SDeJ
'Sphinx' (Ia/d)	WCot
'Spring Pink' (Ia/-)	CAvo SDeJ SDir
'Spring Romance' (Romance Series) (VIIa/b)	CRos LRHS NRHS
'Stainless Steel' (Ia/b)	SDeJ
'Star Gazer' (VIIa/c)	CRos EPfP GKev LAma LRHS NRHS SCob SCoo SDeJ SDir
'Star Romance' (Romance Series) (VIIa-b/b) **new**	ETMg
'Starfighter' (VIIa-b/c)	SDeJ
'Sterling Star' (Ia/b)	MCri
'Sunny Morning' (IIc/d)	CBro GKev LAma LRHS
superbum (IXc/d)	EBee GKev LAma WCru WPGP
'Sweet Lord' (Ia/b)	GKev SDeJ
'Sweet Surrender' (Ib-c/c-d)	MCri SDeJ
'Tailor Made' (Ia/b)	SDeJ
taliense (IXc/d)	WCru
'Tarragona'^{PBR} (VIIIb/b)	SDeJ
tenuifolium	see *L. pumilum*
Tiger Babies Group (VIIIb-c/c-d)	CAvo GKev SDeJ
'Tigeredition' (VIIa-b/b-c)	LCro LOPS
'Tigerwoods' (VIIa/c)	LCro LOPS
tigrinum	see *L. lancifolium*
'Tiny Dino'^{PBR} (Ia-b/b)	MAsh
'Tiny Ghost'^{PBR} (Ia-b/b-c)	MAsh
'Tiny Invader'^{PBR} (Ia-b/b-c)	MAsh
'Tiny Nanny'^{PBR} (Ia-b/b-c)	MAsh
'Tiny Skyline'^{PBR} (Ia-b/b)	MAsh
'Tom Pouce' (VIIa/b)	SDeJ
'Toronto' (Ia-b/b)	SDeJ
'Toscane' (Ia/b-c)	SDeJ
TRIUMPHATOR ('Zanlophator'^{PBR}) (VIIIb/a-b)	ILea SDeJ
'True Romance' (Romance Series) (VIIa/b) **new**	ETMg
tsingtauense (IXa/c)	GKev LAma MCri SDeJ
- B&SWJ 4263	WCru
- B&SWJ 4698	WCru
- B&SWJ 519	WCru
'Uchida Kanoka'	see *L. speciosum* var. *rubrum* 'Uchida'
'Urandi' (VIIIc/b)	GKev SDeJ
'Val Di Sole'^{PBR} (Ia/b)	SDeJ
'Venezuela' (VIIa-b/b-c)	SDeJ SDir
'Venture' (Ia/b)	NNor
'Visaversa' (VIIIa-b/b)	SDeJ
'Vivaldi' (Ia/b)	SDeJ
vollmeri	see *L. pardalinum* subsp. *vollmeri*

wallichianum (IXb/a)	GKev LAma SDeJ XLum
wardii (IXc/d)	CExl
washingtonianum (IXb/a)	EBee GBin
'Whistler' (Ia-c) **new**	SDeJ
'White American'	see *L. longiflorum* 'White American'
'White Paradise' (V)	SCoo
'White Pixels' (Ia/b) **new**	SDeJ
'White Present' (Vb/a)	GKev SDeJ
'White Twinkle' (Ia-b/b)	SDeJ
wigginsii	see *L. pardalinum* subsp. *wigginsii*
'Wild Romance' (Romance Series) (VIIa/b) **new**	SDir
willmottiae	see *L. davidii* var. *willmottiae*
'Wine Electric' (Ia/c)	SDeJ
xanthellum var. ***luteum*** (IXb-c/d)	WCru
'Yellow Cocotte' (Ia/c)	GKev
'Yellow County' (Ia/b-c)	GKev SDeJ
§ 'Yellow Electric' (Ia/b-c)	SDeJ
'Yellow Eye' (Ia/b)	SDeJ
'Yeti' (Ia/b)	SDeJ

lime see *Citrus* × *aurantiifolia*

lime, Philippine see *Citrus* × *microcarpa*

limequat see *Citrus* × *floridana*

Limnanthes (*Limnanthaceae*)

douglasii ♀H7	EPfP IRob LCro LOPS MNHC
- subsp. ***rosea***	CSpe

Limoniastrum (*Plumbaginaceae*)

monopetalum	XSen

Limonium (*Plumbaginaceae*)

sp.	ESps
bellidifolium	CFis CMea CPla EDAr ESps
binervosum	EBWF
cosyrense	CMea MHer
dumosum	see *Goniolimon tataricum* var. *angustifolium*
gmelinii	SPlb
* - subsp. ***hungaricum***	XLum
latifolium	see *L. platyphyllum*
perezii	SPhx
§ ***platyphyllum***	CBod CBot CMea EPfP GMaP LRHS LSun MHer MMuc MWat NRHS SCob SEND SPer SPhm SRms WHar WHoo XSen
- 'Blue Cloud' **new**	SRms
- 'Robert Butler'	CBod ECtt GCal GQue MRav
- 'Violetta'	CBod CTri EBee ECtt ELan EPfP GBin GMcL LRHS MBel MPie NRHS SPer SPoG WAul WHoo
'Salt Lake' **new**	NRHS
sinuatum	SVic
tataricum	see *Goniolimon tataricum*
vulgare	EBWF LRHS WHer XSen

Linaria (*Plantaginaceae*)

aeruginea	CMea CPBP CPla
- 'Lindeza Violet'	CSpe
- 'Neon Lights'	CSpe EDAr NGdn SPoG WFar
- subsp. ***nevadensis*** 'Gemstones'	SBch
alpina	CSpe GJos NRya NSla SRms WHoo
anticaria 'Antique Silver'	CExl MRav
cymbalaria	see *Cymbalaria muralis*
§ ***dalmatica***	ELan EPPr MMuc MPie NBid NGBl NSti SBee SPad SPhx WCot WMoo WWFP
dalmatica × ***purpurea***	WCot
'Dartmoor Sunset' **new**	LLHF
'Dial Park'	MAvo WCot
× ***dominii*** 'Yuppie Surprise'	CHid
'Florence Lily Sophia Brown'	WCot
genistifolia	WCot
- W&B BGB-6	WCot
- subsp. ***dalmatica***	see *L. dalmatica*
hepaticifolia	see *Cymbalaria hepaticifolia*
* ***lobata alba***	SPlb
origanifolia	see *Chaenorhinum origanifolium*
pallida	see *Cymbalaria pallida*
'Peachy'	CAby CDor CSpe EBee ECtt MHol MTis SBod SMHy SPad SPoG WCot WFar WHlf WHrl WOut WRHF WWFP
pilosa	see *Cymbalaria pilosa*
'Pink Kisses'	WCot
purpurea	CBod CDor CTri EBWF EHoe ELan EPfP ESps IFoB MHer MNHC NBro NPer NPol SEND SPhx SRms WCAu WCot WFar WMoo WSFF WTor
- 'Alba'	see *L. purpurea* 'Springside White'
- 'Brown's White Strain'	CBre CSpe EPPr IBoy WCot
- 'Canon Went'	CBod CBre CDor CRos CSpe CTri EBee ELan EPfP ESps GJos LCro LOPS LPmr LRHS MNHC NPol NRHS SGbt SPer SPhx SRms SWvt WCAu WCot WFar WHer WKif WMoo
- 'Freefolk Piccolo'	SHar
- pink-flowered	CSpe
- 'Poached Egg'	CMea MAvo
- 'Radcliffe Innocence'	see *L. purpurea* 'Springside White'
§ - 'Springside White'	CBod CDor GJos LRHS NGdn SBch SBee SPhx WFar
- 'Vainglorious'	CNat
repens	WCot WHer
× ***sepium***	WCot
triornithophora	SPlb WKif WMoo WWFP
- 'Pink Budgies'	LLHF LSou
- purple-flowered	WMoo
- 'Rosea'	CSpe
vulgaris	CHab CWld EBWF EPfP MHer MMuc MNHC NMir SRms WHer WMoo
- f. ***peloria***	CPBP

Lindelofia (*Boraginaceae*)

anchusoides misapplied	see *L. longiflora*
anchusoides (Lindl.) Lehm.	EPPr NBid
§ ***longiflora***	GCal GPSL SBee WSHC

Lindera (*Lauraceae*)

aggregata	CBcs WPGP
angustifolia	NLar
- FMWJ 13156	WCru
assamica B&SWJ 13984 **new**	WCru
benzoin	CBcs CRos EPfP LRHS MBlu NLar
erythrocarpa	EPfP
- B&SWJ 6271	WCru

	- B&SWJ 8730	WCru
	metcalfiana var. ***dictyophylla*** KWJ 12312	WCru
	obtusiloba ♀^{H5}	CBcs MBlu NLar WPGP
	- B&SWJ 8723	WCru
	- B&SWJ 11054	WCru
	- B&SWJ 12555 from Korea	WCru
	praecox	NLar
	- B&SWJ 10802	WCru
	- B&SWJ 10953 from north Japan	WCru
	- B&SWJ 11125 from south Japan	WCru
	reflexa	NLar
	sericea B&SWJ 11123	WCru
	- B&SWJ 11141	WCru
	- var. ***lancea*** B&SWJ 11071	WCru
	- - B&SWJ 11118	WCru
	strychnifolia	EPfP
	tonkinensis FMWJ 13123	WCru
	triloba B&SWJ 5570	WCru
	- B&SWJ 11121	WCru
	- B&SWJ 11466	WCru
	umbellata B&SWJ 10881	WCru
	- var. ***membranacea*** B&SWJ 6227	WCru
	- - B&SWJ 10837	WCru

Lindernia (*Linderniaceae*)

grandiflora	CBod LLWG WTor

Linnaea (*Caprifoliaceae*)

borealis	CExl EPot NSla WAbe XEll

Linum (*Linaceae*)

	arboreum ♀^{H4}	GKev LLHF WThu
	boissieri	LLHF
	campanulatum	WThu
	flavum	XSen
	- 'Compactum'	CMea LLHF NSla SRms
	'Gemmell's Hybrid' ♀^{H4}	EPot EWes GCrg WAbe WThu
	grandiflorum 'Bright Eyes'	CSpe
	- 'Rubrum'	CSpe
	hypericifolium	SPhx
	- from Lagonaki, Caucasus **new**	SBrt
	kingii var. ***sedoides***	WAbe
	monogynum	LLHF
	narbonense	CCse SPhx WArt
§	***perenne***	CBod ECha ELan ENfk EPfP ESps GMaP MHer MNHC SCob SPer SPoG WSHC XAbr
	- 'Album'	EBee ECha ELan EPfP
	- subsp. ***alpinum*** 'Alice Blue'	WAbe
§	- 'Blau Saphir'	MBel WRHF
	- BLUE SAPPHIRE	see *L. perenne* 'Blau Saphir'
	- 'Diamant'	SPoG
	- 'Nanum Sapphire'	see *L. perenne* 'Blau Saphir'
	rigidum	CPla
	sibiricum	see *L. perenne*
	suffruticosum from Teruel, Spain **new**	SBrt
	- from the French Alps **new**	SBrt
	- subsp. ***salsoloides***	SBrt
	- - 'Nanum'	WThu
	- 'Spanish Sun'	SBrt
	uninerve	WAbe

Lippia (*Verbenaceae*)

sp.	SWvt
canescens	see *Phyla nodiflora* var. *canescens*
chamaedrifolia	see *Verbena peruviana*
citriodora	see *Aloysia citrodora*
dulcis	ENfk
nodiflora	see *Phyla nodiflora*
repens	see *Phyla nodiflora*

Liquidambar ✿ (*Hamamelidaceae*)

	acalycina	CBcs CDul CJun EBee ELan EMOT EPfP NLar NOra SBir SCoo SGol SLim SSta WPGP
	- 'Burgundy Flush' ♀^{H6}	CJun NLar SBir SSta
	- 'Spinners'	CRos ELan EMil LRHS SBir
	formosana	CDul CMCN CMac IArd SBir SGol SSta WPGP
	- 'Afterglow'	CJun NLar
	- 'Ellen'	CJun NLar
	- Monticola Group	CJun SLim SSta
	orientalis	CDul CJun CLnd CMCN EBtc EPfP IDee SBir SSta
	- 'M. Foster'	NLar
	styraciflua	Widely available
	- 'Andrew Hewson'	CJun CLnd CRos EBee EPfP LRHS MAsh MBlu SBir SSta
	- 'Anja'	CJun MBlu SBir SSta
	- 'Anneke'	CJun SBir SSta
	- 'Aurea'	see *L. styraciflua* 'Variegata' Overeynder
	- 'Aurea Variegata'	see *L. styraciflua* 'Variegata' Overeynder
	- 'Aurora'	CJun SBir
	- 'Black Beauty' **new**	SBig
	- 'Burgundy'	CJun CLnd LLHF MBlu SBir SSta
I	- 'Corky'	SSta
	- 'Emerald Sentinel'	CJun SSta
	- 'Festeri'	CEnd SBir SSta
	- 'Festival'	CJun CLnd MBlu SGol
	- 'Frosty' (v)	CJun SBir SSta
	- 'Globe'	see *L. styraciflua* 'Gum Ball'
	- 'Gold Beacon'	NLar
	- 'Golden Sun'[PBR]	NLar
	- 'Golden Treasure' (v)	CDul CJun CLnd CMCN CRos LRHS MAsh MGos SBir SGol SReu SSta
	- 'Goldmember'	CJun SSta
	- 'Granary Sunset'	SBir SSta
§	- 'Gum Ball'	CCVT CEnd CJun CLnd CMCN EBee ELon EPfP EWes LLHF NLar SBir SCob SLim SPoG SSta SWvt
	- HAPPIDAZE ('Hapdell')	CJun SBir
	- 'Jennifer Carol'	NLar SBir SSta
	- 'Kia'	CEnd CJun SBir
	- 'Lane Roberts' ♀^{H6}	CDul CLnd CMCN CMac CSBt CTho EBee ELan EMOT EPfP ESps IArd LRHS LSRN MAsh MBlu MGos NLar NOra SBir SCob SCoo SPer SSta SWvt WCFE WMou
	- 'Lynn'	SBir SSta
	- 'Manon' (v)	CJun
	- 'Midwest Sunset'	CJun EBee MBlu NLar SBir
	- 'Moonbeam' (v)	CJun SBir SCob SLim SSta
	- 'Moraine'	CJun
	- 'Naree'	CJun NLar SSta
	- 'Nina'	SSta
	- 'Nyewood'	SBir
	- 'Oconee'	CEnd LLHF MAsh SSta
	- 'Paarl' (v)	CJun CLnd EMOT SGol

- 'Palo Alto' 🏆H6	CEnd CJun EMOT LLHF MAsh MBlu SBir SCoo SLim SMad SSta WMou WPGP
- 'Parasol'	CAco CEnd CJun CLnd EBtc SBir SSta
- 'Pendula'	CJun CLnd MBlu SBir SSta
- 'Penwood' 🏆H6	CJun NLar SBir SSta
- 'Red Sunset'	SSta
- 'Rotundiloba'	CJun CMCN EPfP LLHF LRHS MAsh MBlu SSta WPGP
- 'Savill Torch'	CJun LSvl SBir SSta
- 'Schock's Gold'	CJun NLar SSta
§ - 'Silver King' (v)	CJun CLnd CMCN CMac EBee MAsh MGos NLar SCoo SGol SLim SPer SReu SSta
- 'Simone'	SBir SGol SSta
- 'Slender Silhouette' 🏆H6	CCVT CDul CJun CLnd CRos CTho EBee EMOT EPfP EUJe LCro LLHF LRHS LSRN MAsh MBlu MSwo NLar NOra NRHS SBir SCoo SGol SLim SPer SPoG SSta WHor WMou
- 'Stared'	CDul CEnd CJun CLnd EMOT EPfP GQue MBlu MGos NHim NOra SBir SCoo SLim SPoG SSta WMou WPGP
- 'Thea'	CJun CLnd CRos EBee EMOT EPfP LRHS MAsh MBlu SBir SSta
- 'Variegata' misapplied	see *L. styraciflua* 'Silver King'
§ - 'Variegata' Overeynder (v)	CJun CMac CRos EBee ELan EMOT ESps LRHS SBir SLim SSta
- 'White Star' (v)	CJun
- 'Woorby Rose'	CJun NLar SBir
- 'Worplesdon' 🏆H6	Widely available

Liriodendron (*Magnoliaceae*)

chinense 🏆H6	CBcs CDul CMCN EBee EPfP MBlu SGol WPGP
× ***sinoamericanum***	WPGP
- 'Chapel Hill'	MBlu NHim NLar
- 'Doc Deforce's Delight'	MBlu NLar
tulipifera 🏆H6	Widely available
- 'Aureomarginatum' (v) 🏆H6	CBcs CCVT CDul CEnd CMCN CTho ECrN ELan EMOT EPfP ESps EWTr IDee LLHF MBlu MGos MSwo NEgg NLar SCob SGol SPer SPoG SSta WHar
- 'Fascination' **new**	SBig
- 'Fastigiatum'	CDul CEnd CLnd CMCN CTho EBee ECrN ELan EMOT EPfP ESps LMaj LPra MAsh MBlu MGos NHim NLar SGol SPer
- 'Glen Gold'	CEnd MBlu NLar
- 'Purgatory'	MBlu
- 'Roodhaan'	MBlu NLar
- 'Rotundiloba'	MBlu
- 'Snow Bird' (v)	EBee SPoG

Liriope ✿ (*Asparagaceae*)

'Big Blue'	see *L. muscari* 'Big Blue'
§ ***exiliflora***	CHll
- 'Ariaka-janshige' (v)	CRos LRHS NRHS
- SILVERY SUNPROOF misapplied	see *L. spicata* 'Gin-ryu', *L. muscari* 'Variegata'
graminifolia misapplied	see *L. muscari*
hyacinthifolia	see *Reineckea carnea*
'Majestic'	CBct MHer WHoo
minor	CMac
§ ***muscari*** 🏆H5	Widely available
- B&SWJ 561	WCru
- 'Alba'	see *L. muscari* 'Monroe White'
- AMETHYST ('Liptp')	CBod WMoo
§ - 'Big Blue'	Widely available
- 'Big Pink' **new**	CBod
- 'Christmas Tree'	EPPr WHoo WMoo
- 'Gold-banded' (v)	CBct EBee EPfP EUJe GWyn LRHS SCob WFar
- 'Goldfinger'	CExl EBee SMad
- 'Ingwersen'	CBod CExl CKno CRos EBee ELon EPPr EPfP EWTr NRHS SCob XLum
- ISABELLA ('Lirf')	EBee EPPr
- 'John Burch' (v)	CBct CExl ELon NLar WGob WGrn
- 'Lilac Wonder'	EPPr LRHS SCob
- 'Majestic' misapplied	see *L. exiliflora*
- 'Moneymaker'	CBod EPPr MNrw SCob XEll
§ - 'Monroe White'	CBct CExl CMac EBee EHrv ELan EPfP EShb LCro LOPS MJak MRav NBid NLar SCob SPer SWvt
- 'Okina' (v)	CAby CBro EBee ELon LLWG MBNS MBel MNrw MSCN NGBl NLar NSti SMad SPer SPoG WCot
- 'Purple Passion'	SCob
- 'Royal Purple'	CBct EAJP EBee ECtt ELon EPfP LRHS MMoz NLar NRHS SCob SMad SPer WGrn WHoo WMoo
- 'Silver Ribbon'	CBro EPfP LSRN MGos
§ - 'Variegata' (v)	CBod CExl CRos EBee EHrv ELan EWes LEdu LRHS MAvo MJak NRHS SPer SWvt WMoo
- 'Webster Wideleaf'	EBee WCot
platyphylla	see *L. muscari*
spicata	CBod EBee GCal XLum
- B&SWJ 8821	WCru
- 'Alba'	MRav
§ - 'Gin-ryu' (v)	CBct CExl CMac ELan EPfP EShb EWes MRav SCob SGol SPer WMoo XLum
- 'Silver Dragon'	see *L. spicata* 'Gin-ryu'

Listera (*Orchidaceae*)

ovata	WHer

Litchi (*Sapindaceae*)

chinensis	CCCN

Lithocarpus ✿ (*Fagaceae*)

densiflorus var. ***echinoides***	CMCN
edulis	CExl CFil EBee SArc
§ ***glaber***	CFil

Lithodora (*Boraginaceae*)

§ ***diffusa***	SGol SRot
- 'Alba'	CSma CWCL NCou SPoG
- 'Compacta'	CSma SRot WAbe
§ - 'Grace Ward' 🏆H5	CBod CRos ECtt ELan EPfP MHol MMuc NWad
§ - 'Heavenly Blue' 🏆H5	Widely available
- 'Pete's Favourite'	NWad
- 'Picos'	EPot NLar NSla NWad SBrt WAbe WThu
- 'Star' PBR	CRos CWCL ELan EPfP GKev LRHS MHol NHpl NLar NRHS SCoo SPer SPoG SRot SWvt WFar
× ***intermedia***	see *Moltkia* × *intermedia*
§ ***oleifolia*** 🏆H4	CRos LLHF LRHS NRHS WHil
rosmarinifolia	CRos EBee LRHS NRHS WCFE
zahnii	CRos EPot EWld LLHF LRHS NRHS SVen
- 'Azure-ness'	MCot SBch SChF WAbe

Lithophragma (*Saxifragaceae*)

parviflorum	CAby

Lithospermum (*Boraginaceae*)

diffusum	see *Lithodora diffusa*
doerfleri	see *Moltkia doerfleri*
'Grace Ward'	see *Lithodora diffusa* 'Grace Ward'
'Heavenly Blue'	see *Lithodora diffusa* 'Heavenly Blue'
officinale	EBWF GPoy NMir XAbr
oleifolium	see *Lithodora oleifolia*
purpureocaeruleum	see *Buglossoides purpurocaerulea*

Litsea (*Lauraceae*)

PAB 13.047	WPGP
glauca	see *Neolitsea sericea*
japonica	SVen

Littonia (*Colchicaceae*)

modesta	see *Gloriosa modesta*

Livistona (*Arecaceae*)

chinensis ♀H1c	CPHo NLos SBig
jenkinsiana	NLos
rotundifolia	NLos

Loasa (*Loasaceae*)

acanthifolia	GCal
triphylla var. ***volcanica***	EBee EWes WSHC

Lobelia ✿ (*Campanulaceae*)

	angustifolia	SBee
	'Bordervale'	WBor
	bridgesii	CDTJ CExl CFil CRos EBee ECtt EWes GCal LRHS SPlb WKif WMoo WPGP
§	***cardinalis*** ♀H3	CMac CPla ELon GMaP LCro LOPS NGBl NLar NPer SPlb SRms SWvt WFar WMAq
	- 'Bee's Flame'	CNor CRos CWGN ECtt LRHS MArl MRav MSpe NEgg NGdn NRHS SPtp SRkn WOut WWtn
	- 'Black Truffle'	CAbb EBee ECtt SPad SRms
	- 'Chocolate Truffle' **new**	SMad
§	- 'Elmfeuer'	CWCL ECtt EHoe IBoy NLar SPlb SPoG SWvt WHar XLum
§	- 'Queen Victoria' ♀H3	Widely available
	- 'Russian Princess' misapplied	CBot CRos CWCL CWld EPfP ESps IBoy LLWG LRHS MHol MSCN NGdn NRHS SPoG SRkn SWvt WFar WHar WOut
	- salmon-pink-flowered **new**	WWtn
	chinensis	LLWG
	'Cinnabar Deep Red'	see *L.* × *speciosa* (Fan Series) 'Fan Tiefrot'
	'Cinnabar Rose'	see *L.* × *speciosa* (Fan Series) 'Fan Zinnoberrosa'
	COMPLIMENT BLUE	see *L.* × *speciosa* (Fan Series) 'Kompliment Blau'
	COMPLIMENT DEEP RED	see *L.* × *speciosa* (Fan Series) 'Kompliment Tiefrot'
	COMPLIMENT PURPLE	see *L.* × *speciosa* (Fan Series) 'Kompliment Purpur'
	COMPLIMENT SCARLET	see *L.* × *speciosa* (Fan Series) 'Kompliment Scharlach'
	'Compton Pink'	CBod CBot ECtt ELan EShb EWes IPot LBuc LRHS MSCN MSpe NGBl NRHS SCob WOut
	davidii PAB 8547	LEdu
	Elizabeth Strangman selection	CSpe NDov
	erinus 'Cambridge Blue' ♀H2	ESps
	- CASCADE IMPROVED MIXED **new**	ETMg
	- 'Crystal Palace' ♀H2	ESps NPri
	- (Fountain Series) 'Fountain Blue'	ESps NPri
	- - 'Fountain White'	ESps NPri
	- 'Kathleen Mallard' (d)	CCCN
	- 'Monsoon' **new**	ETMg
	- PURPLE STAR ('Wespurstar' PBR) ♀H2	LSou
	- Riviera Series	NPri
	- 'Sapphire'	ESps NPri
	- 'String of Pearls' ♀H2	ESps
	- SUPER STAR ('Weslosu' PBR) (Star Series)	LSou
	- WATERFALL BLUE ICE (Waterfall Series) **new**	ETMg
	excelsa	GCal SBrt SEND
	FAN DEEP RED	see *L.* × *speciosa* (Fan Series) 'Fan Tiefrot'
	FAN DEEP ROSE	see *L.* × *speciosa* (Fan Series) 'Fan Orchidrosa'
	FAN SALMON	see *L.* × *speciosa* (Fan Series) 'Fan Lachs'
	'Flamingo'	see *L.* × *speciosa* (Fan Series) 'Pink Flamingo'
	fulgens	see *L. cardinalis*
	- SAINT ELMO'S FIRE	see *L. cardinalis* 'Elmfeuer'
	× ***gerardii***	see *L.* × *speciosa*
	gibberoa	CDTJ
	'Gladys Lindley'	LRHS
	'Grape Knee-Hi'	ECtt LLHF SPad SPhm
	'Hadspen Purple'	see *L.* × *speciosa* 'Hadspen Purple'
	inflata	GPoy
	(Laguna Series) LAGUNA TRAILING BLUE ('Lob Bule')	ESps
	- LAGUNA TRAILING DARK BLUE ('Loblamoubl' PBR)	ESps
	- LAGUNA TRAILING VIOLET ('Tec Travio')	ESps
	- LAGUNA TRAILING WHITE ('Lobtrawi')	ESps
	- LAGUNA WHITE ('Lobwhi' PBR)	ESps
	laxiflora	CBot CFis CHll
	- var. ***angustifolia***	CAby CDTJ CPbh CWCL EWld GCal LRHS SBee SBrt SMHy SRms WCot
	linnaeoides	SPlb
§	***montana***	EWld
	- B&SWJ 8220	WCru
	pedunculata	see *Pratia pedunculata*
	polyphylla	SBrt
	'Queen Victoria'	see *L. cardinalis* 'Queen Victoria'
	sessilifolia	CExl LLWG WArt
	- B&SWJ 8875	WCru
	siphilitica	CBcs CBod CExl CMac CRos CSam ELan ELon EPfP GCal IBoy ILea IRob LEdu LRHS MHer MMuc MSpe NEgg NGdn NRHS SBod SPer SPlb SRms SWvt WFar WHoo WMoo XLum
	- f. ***albiflora***	ECtt LEdu

	- - 'Alba'	CSam EPfP SBch SRms SWvt WArt WBor WFar WHrl WMoo WShi
	- blue-flowered	CSpe SWvt
	- 'Rosea'	MNrw
§	× ***speciosa***	ESps SVic WMoo XLum
	- 'Butterfly Blue'	CNor SGbt
	- 'Butterfly Rose'	SRot
	- 'Cherry Ripe'	LLHF
	- 'Cranberry Crush'	CAbb ECtt LRHS SPhm
	- CRIMSON PRINCESS ('Gencrim'^{PBR}) (Princess Series)	CAbb CRos LRHS MJak NRHS SPoG
	- 'Dark Crusader'	CRos EBee ECtt ELan EPfP LRHS MSpe NRHS
	- Fan Series	MRav
	- - 'Fan Blau'	CBod CRos EPfP IRob LRHS MCot MHol NRHS SCob WFar WHar WMoo WTor
	- - 'Fan Burgundy'	CRos EPfP ESps LRHS MCot MHer MHol NGdn NLar NRHS SCob
§	- - 'Fan Lachs'	CBod CRos CWld EPfP LRHS MHer MHol MSCN NRHS WFar WMoo WTor
§	- - 'Fan Orchidrosa' 🏆^{H5}	CRos EPfP LRHS NRHS SRot
	- - 'Fan Scharlach' 🏆^{H5}	CRos CWld EPfP LRHS NLar NRHS SPoG SRot SWvt WFar WTor
§	- - 'Fan Tiefrot' 🏆^{H5}	CRos LRHS NRHS SRms SWvt WBor WMoo
§	- - 'Fan Zinnoberrosa' 🏆^{H5}	SRms SRot SWvt WMoo
§	- 'Hadspen Purple'^{PBR}	Widely available
	- 'Kimbridge Beet'	CMac LRHS
§	- (Kompliment Series) 'Kompliment Blau'	SWvt
§	- - 'Kompliment Purpur'	MMuc SWvt
§	- - 'Kompliment Scharlach' 🏆^{H5}	CWat EPfP MNrw NPer SWvt
§	- - 'Kompliment Tiefrot'	EPfP LRHS MMuc MNrw SWvt
	- 'Monet Moment'	CBod CWCL EBee ECtt EWes ILea NLar SBee SWvt
	- 'Pauline'	ECtt
	- 'Pink Elephant' 🏆^{H3}	ECtt LLHF SHar WCFE
§	- 'Pink Flamingo'	LRHS WMoo
	- ROSE PRINCESS ('Genross'^{PBR}) (Princess Series)	CRos EWTr LCro LOPS LRHS MJak NRHS SPoG
	- 'Ruby Slippers'	EBee EPfP
	- 'Russian Princess' purple-flowered	CBod ECtt EHoe ELan ELon EWTr IBoy LSou MBel MCot MHer MPie MSpe NDov NGBl NPnk SPer SPtp WFar WHar WKif WMoo
	- SCARLET PRINCESS ('Genlet') (Princess Series)	CAbb CRos LCro LOPS LRHS NRHS
	- 'Sparkling Burgundy'	LRHS
	- 'Sparkling Ruby'	CBod CWld EPfP EWTr LBuc MCot NRHS SWvt WMoo
	- 'Starship Deep Rose' **new**	MHol
	- 'Starship Scarlet'	CRos LRHS MHol NRHS SPoG
	- 'Tania'	Widely available
§	- 'Vedrariensis'	CBod CMac CSam CSpe EAJP ECtt ELan EPfP LRHS MBel MCot MHer MMuc MNrw NGBl NRHS SPer SRms SWvt WCFE WFar WHoo XLum
	- 'Will Scarlet'	CRos LRHS NRHS
	'Tania's Sister'	WCot WFar
	treadwellii	see *Pratia angulata* 'Treadwellii'
	tupa	Widely available
	- JCA 12527	IBlr
	- Archibald's form	CExl IRob WPGP
	urens	CFil
	valida	SBee SWvt
	- 'Delft Blue'	CRos LRHS NRHS
	- 'True Blue'	SWvt
	vedrariensis	see *L.* × *speciosa* 'Vedrariensis'
	wollastonii	SPlb

Lobostemon (*Boraginaceae*)

belliformis	CPbh

Lobularia (*Brassicaceae*)

maritima Easter Bonnet Series 🏆^{H3}	NPri
- 'Snow Crystals'	NPri
- WHITE STREAM ('Dlobu21'^{PBR}) **new**	CRav
SNOW PRINCESS ('Inlbusnopr'^{PBR})	NPri

Loeselia (*Polemoniaceae*)

mexicana	CHll

loganberry see *Rubus* × *loganobaccus*

Lomandra (*Asparagaceae*)

filiformis SAVANNA BLUE ('Lmf500')	LSou
hystrix	SPlb
longifolia	GCal LEdu SPlb
- TANIKA ('Lm300'^{PBR})	GBin

Lomaria see *Blechnum*

Lomatia (*Proteaceae*)

	dentata	CRos LRHS MRav
	ferruginea	CBcs CCCN CDTJ CExl CTsd MPkF SArc WCru WPGP
	fraseri	CCCN CRos EBee EPfP LRHS NLar SPoG
	longifolia	see *L. myricoides*
§	***myricoides***	CBcs CCCN CExl CRos CTsd EBee ELan EPfP LRHS NLar SLon SPer
	silaifolia	CRos LRHS
	tinctoria	CBcs CExl CPbh CRos EPfP LRHS

Lomatium (*Apiaceae*)

grayi	SPhx

Lonicera ✿ (*Caprifoliaceae*)

	sp.	CMen ESps
	KR 291	ELon
	KR 10106	WPGP
§	***acuminata***	CMCN
	- B&SWJ 3480	WCru
	- B&SWJ 6743	CRHN WCru
	- B&SWJ 6815	WCru
	- var. ***acuminata***	WCot
	aff. ***acuminata*** NJM 11.033	WPGP
	albertii	EPfP MBNS NLar
	alseuosmoides	CBcs CDul CRHN EBee EWTr LEdu LRHS MMuc NLar SEND SLon SPoG WCru WPGP WSHC
	× ***americana*** misapplied	see *L.* × *italica*
	americana ambig.	ESps MSCN
§	***americana*** (Mill.) K. Koch	CBcs CFlo EPfP ETho LEdu MJak MSwo NLar SEND SLim SRms WBor WSHC
§	× ***brownii*** 'Dropmore Scarlet'	Widely available
	- 'Fuchsioides' misapplied	see *L.* × *brownii* 'Dropmore Scarlet'

caerulea	CRos EPom EWTr IDee LRHS MRav SCob SDea SRms SVic WBor WHar
- var. ***altaica***	LEdu
- 'Atut'	NLar
- 'Duet'	NLar
- var. ***edulis***	CAgr EPfP LBuc LEdu MCoo MMuc NLar SDea SEle
- var. ***kamtschatica***	EPom LCro LOPS NLar WPGP
- - 'Balalaika' (F)	CAgr MCoo
- - 'Borealis' (F) **new**	CAgr SBig
- - 'Eisbar' (F)	CAgr
- - 'Fialka'^{PBR} (F)	NLar
- - 'Honey Bee' (F) **new**	CAgr
- - 'Indigo Gem' (F) **new**	CAgr
- - 'Kalinka' (F)	CAgr
- - 'Larisa' (F)	LEdu WPGP
- - 'Maistar' (F) **new**	XAbr
- - 'Maries' (F)	LEdu WPGP
- - 'Morena'^{PBR} (F)	EPom SPoG
- - 'Rebecca' (F)	LEdu WPGP
- - 'Ruth' (F)	LEdu WPGP
- - 'Sinoglaska' (F)	GCal NLar
- - 'Vicky' (F) **new**	LEdu WPGP
- - 'Wojtek' (F)	NLar
- 'Kirke'	NLar
* - var. ***longifolia***	NLar
§ ***caprifolium***	CFlo CRHN CRos ECrN ELan EPfP LRHS NLar WCot
- 'Anna Fletcher'	CRHN WCFE
- 'Cornish Cream'	SGol
- f. ***pauciflora***	see *L.* × *italica*
- 'Spring Bouquet'	CRos LRHS
CAPRILIA EVER ('Inov42'^{PBR})	CKel EBee MJak
'Celestial'^{PBR}	CRos EPfP LCro LOPS LRHS
chaetocarpa	CEnd SBrt WSHC
ciliosa	CRHN
'Clavey's Dwarf'	EPPr GKin LLHF
crassifolia	GEdr NLar SBrt WSHC
- 'Little Honey'	EBee EPPr MBNS MMrt MPie MRav NLar NPnk SPoG
deflexicalyx	CMCN EPfP NLar
demissa	EPfP
'Early Cream'	see *L. caprifolium*
'Elegant'	LBuc SArc SCob
elisae	CBcs CBot CMac CRos CWld EBee EPfP EWTr GBin IMou LLHF LRHS MMuc NLar SEle SMad SPoG SSta WCot
etrusca	MRav XSen
- 'Donald Waterer'	CFlo CRHN CRos EPfP LRHS LSRN NLar WFar
- 'Michael Rosse'	CBot ELan IArd LRHS MBNS NLar
- 'Superba' 🏆^{H5}	CFlo CRHN CRos EBee ELan EPfP EWTr LEdu LRHS NLar SEND SLim SNig SPer WSHC
'Fire Cracker'	NLar SLon
flexuosa	see *L. japonica* var. *repens*
fragrantissima	Widely available
giraldii misapplied	see *L. acuminata*
giraldii Rehder	CBot CRHN EBee WSHC
glabrata	NLar SCoo
- B&SWJ 2150	WCru
'Golden Trumpet'	CWGN EPfP LSRN SPer
grata	see *L.* × *americana* (Mill.) K. Koch
× ***heckrottii***	CRHN CSBt NLar SNig
§ - 'American Beauty'	CKel EBee
- 'Gold Flame' misapplied	see *L.* × *heckrottii* 'American Beauty'
- 'Gold Flame' ambig.	CFlo ESps GKin LSRN NLar SCob
- 'Gold Flame' hort. 🏆^{H5}	CArg CDul CMac CRos EBee ELan EMOT EPfP ETho LBuc LCro LOPS LRHS MAsh MJak MMuc NRHS SEND SLim SNig SPer SPoG SRms SWvt WFar WMoo WSHC
hemsleyana	CBot
§ ***henryi***	Widely available
- B&SWJ 8109	WCru
- 'Copper Beauty'^{PBR}	Widely available
- var. ***subcoriacea***	see *L. henryi*
hildebrandiana 🏆^{H2}	CCCN CExl CFil CRHN
hirsuta	EBee SBrt
hispidula	SBrt
'Honey Baby'^{PBR}	ELon EPfP NWad
implexa	CMCN CRHN
insularis	see *L. morrowii*
involucrata	CExl CHll CMCN EBee EPPr MBNS MBlu MMuc NChi SEND SPer WCFE
- var. ***ledebourii***	CBcs CRos ELan EPfP LLHF LRHS MGil MMrt NLar
- - 'Vian'	NLar
§ × ***italica***	CRHN CRos CTri EBee ECrN LRHS MBNS MSwo NPer SCoo SPer
§ - HARLEQUIN ('Sherlite'^{PBR}) (v)	CKel CMac CRos EPfP ESps GMcL LRHS MJak SLim SPlb SRms SWvt
japonica	CMen ESps IBoy WFar
§ - 'Aureoreticulata' (v) 🏆^{H5}	CDul CMac CRos ECrN EHoe ELan EMOT EPfP EShb LRHS MJak MRav NPer SGol SPer SRms WFar
- 'Cream Cascade'	MSwo NLar SCoo SGol
- 'Dart's Acumen'	CRHN
- 'Dart's World'	CArg CKel CSBt CWld EBee NLar
- 'Halliana'	Widely available
- 'Hall's Prolific' 🏆^{H5}	CDul CKel CRos CSBt EBee ECrN ELan EPfP ESps LBuc LCro LOPS LRHS LSRN MAsh MBlu MGos MRav MSwo NRHS SCob SGol SLim SNig SPad SPoG SWvt WFar WHar
§ - 'Horwood Gem' (v)	ECtt NLar SCoo SLim
- 'Maskerade' (v)	LLHF NBro NLar
- 'Mint Crisp'^{PBR} (v)	Widely available
- 'Peter Adams'	see *L. japonica* 'Horwood Gem'
- 'Princess Kate'	ELan NLar NPri SRms
§ - var. ***repens*** 🏆^{H5}	CDul CKel CMac CRos CSBt CTri ECrN ECtt ELan EPfP EShb LRHS MRav MSwo NLar NRHS SCoo SGol SLim SLon SNig SPad SPer SPoG SRms WMoo
- 'Variegata'	see *L. japonica* 'Aureoreticulata'
korolkowii	CBot CFil EPPr EWTr LLHF MBNS MMuc NLar WAvo WCFE WCot WSHC
- 'Blue Velvet'	CAgr MCoo NLar
- 'Mayberry Farm'	MCoo
- var. ***zabelii*** misapplied	see *L. tatarica* 'Zabelii'
lanceolata BWJ 7935	WCru
'Lemon Beauty' (v)	CBcs CBot CMac EBee ECrN EHoe EMOT EPPr EPfP EShb ESps GMcL LRHS LSRN MAsh MBNS MGos NLar NRHS NWad SCob SGol SPer SPoG SRms SWvt WAvo WFar WHar WMoo
maackii	CBot CHll CMCN CRos EPPr EPfP LRHS MRav NLar NRHS WCFE
* ***macgregorii***	CMCN
macrantha B&SWJ 11687	WCru
- WWJ 11606	WCru
'Mandarin' 🏆^{H5}	CRHN ELan LCro LOPS MBlu MJak NLar SCoo SGol SWvt WCot WSHC

	maximowiczii var. ***sachalinensis***	NLar
§	***morrowii***	SBrt
	- 'Ullung do'	CMCN
	myrtillus	NLar
	nitida	CAco CArg CBar CBcs CCVT CDul CMac CMen CPer CSBt CTri ECrN ELan EPfP ESps GMcL SCob SEND SEWo SGol SPer WTSh XSen
	- 'Baggesen's Gold' ♀^{H5}	Widely available
	- EDMÉE GOLD ('Briloni')	MAsh WCot
	- 'Ernest Wilson'	EPPr
	- 'Golden Glow'^{PBR}	NEoE
	- 'Lemon Queen'	ELan MMuc MSwo
§	- 'Maigrün'	CBar CBcs CCVT CDul CRos EBee ELan EMOT EPfP EShb GMcL LRHS MSwo NEoE NRHS SCob SPer SWvt WFar
	- MAYGREEN	see *L. nitida* 'Maigrün'
	- 'Red Tips'	EHoe EShb NLar SCob SCoo SRms WMoo
	- 'Silver Beauty' (v)	CDul CMac ECrN EHoe ESps GMcL MGos MSwo SCob SPer SPlb SPoG SRms SWvt WFar WMoo
	- 'Tidy Tips'	MTin NEoE SCob
	- 'Twiggy' (v)	CSBt EDAr EHoe EUJe GMcL LRHS MAsh NLar NWad SPoG WAvo WFar
	periclymenum	CCVT CDul CPer CTri CWld EBWF ESps GJos GPoy MHer MRav NMir SCob SPlb WSFF XSen
	- 'Belgica' misapplied	see *L.* × *italica*
	- 'Belgica'	Widely available
	- CHIC ET CHOC ('Inov205'^{PBR})	LRHS WCot
*	- 'Cream Cascade'	GMcL
	- 'Florida'	see *L. periclymenum* 'Serotina'
	- 'Fragrant Cloud'	ETho LBuc LRHS NRHS
	- 'Graham Thomas' ♀^{H5}	Widely available
	- 'Harlequin'	see *L.* × *italica* HARLEQUIN
	- 'Heaven Scent'	CFlo ETho LBuc LCro LOPS LSRN NLar WFar
	- 'Honeybush'	CJun CWGN MAsh MGos NWad SLim WFar WMoo
	- 'Munster'	WSHC
	- 'Purple Queen'	CChe
	- 'Red Gables'	CRHN CRos ELon LSRN MBNS MNHC NLar SCoo SEND SLim SWvt WCot WKif
	- 'Rhubarb and Custard'	LCro LOPS
	- 'Scentsation'^{PBR}	CFlo CKel CMac CRos CSBt CWCL CWGN ELan EPfP ETMg EUJe GBin LRHS MAsh MJak NLar NRHS SCoo SLon SPoG SRkn
	- 'Serotina' ♀^{H5}	Widely available
	- 'Sweet Sue'	CFlo CKel CRHN CRos CTsd ELan ELon EPfP LRHS LSRN MAsh MBNS MGos MSwo NEgg NLar NRHS SCoo SNig SPoG SWvt WFar WMoo
	- 'Winchester'	SRms
	pileata	Widely available
	- 'Moss Green'	CBod EShb
	- 'Silver Lining' (v)	WCFE
	pilosa Maxim.	see *L. strophiophora*
	pilosa (Kunth) Willd. ex Kunth	CRHN EWld
	- F&M 207	CFil WPGP
	- F&M 256	CFil WPGP
	prolifera	CRHN NLar
	× ***purpusii***	CHll CMac CRHN CTri EBee ECrN ESps LMaj MBNS SCob SRms WCFE WFar
	- 'Spring Romance'	CMac
	- 'Winter Beauty' ♀^{H5}	Widely available
	quinquelocularis	CMCN
	ramosissima	NLar
	reticulata 'Silver'	NLar
	saccata	EPfP
	sempervirens	CBot CRHN CSBt IDee MBNS MRav WHar WSHC
	- 'Cedar Lane'	CRHN CRos LRHS SBrt
	- 'Dropmore Scarlet'	see *L.* × *brownii* 'Dropmore Scarlet'
	- 'Leo'	CWGN
	- f. ***sulphurea***	CBot WSHC
	- - 'John Clayton'	CRos EPfP LRHS
	setifera 'Daphnis'	CJun
	similis var. ***delavayi*** ♀^{H5}	CBot CFlo CKel CRHN CRos CWGN ELan EMOT EPfP ESps ETho GMcL LRHS MAsh MRav NEgg NLar NRHS SEND SRms SWvt WCot WCru WSHC
	'Simonet'	CWCL CWld EBee NLar WCot
	'Spring Purple'	LOPS NLar
	standishii	CTri WFar
	- var. ***lancifolia*** 'Budapest'	CBot CRos ELan ELon EPfP IArd IDee LLHF LRHS MAsh MBlu MRav NLar SRms WFar
§	***strophiophora***	WAvo WCot
	subaequalis	CFil CRHN
	- Og 93.329	CExl WPGP WSHC
	SWEET ISABEL ('Genbel'^{PBR})	EPfP
	syringantha	CBcs CRHN CTho CWld ECrN ELan EPfP EWTr IDee LRHS MMuc MNrw MRav NEgg NEoE NLar NWad SBod SEND SEle SPer WCFE WFar WSHC
	- 'Grandiflora'	CBot
	tangutica	NWad
	tatarica	CBot CHll CMCN MRav
	- 'Alba'	EPPr
	- 'Arnold Red'	CBcs ELan EPPr EPfP MBlu MHer NLar SBig SEND
	- 'Hack's Red'	CAby CBot CMCN EBee EPPr EPfP EWTr LEdu LRHS NLar SCoo SPer SVen SWvt WBor WGrn
	- 'Rosea'	EPPr
§	- 'Zabelii'	MNrw
	× ***tellmanniana*** ♀^{H5}	Widely available
	- 'Joan Sayers'	SCoo WCFE
	- 'Pharaoh's Trumpet'	CRos LRHS SLon
	thibetica	CBot MBlu
	tomentella B&SWJ 2654	WCru
	tragophylla ♀^{H5}	CBot CKel CRos CSBt ELan EWTr GCal IMou LRHS MBNS MRav NLar SCoo SLim SPer SWvt WSHC
	- 'Maurice Foster'	CRHN EBee EWTr NLar
	turczaninowii	LLHF
	× ***xylosteoides***	NLar
	xylosteum	EBtc EPPr MMuc NLar SSta

Lophomyrtus ✿ (*Myrtaceae*)

§	***bullata*** ♀^{H2}	CDTJ GMcL SPer
	- 'Matai Bay'	LRHS
	× ***ralphii*** 'Black Pearl'	CMac CRos EShb ESps LRHS SCoo SEle SGbt SLim SPoG WFar WGrn
	- 'Gloriosa' (v)	CCCN IBoy
	- 'Kathryn'	CBcs LRHS NLar SRGP
	- 'Krinkly'	SVen

- 'Little Star' (v)	CBcs CRos LRHS SEle
- Logan's form (v)	CBcs LRHS MGil NLar NRHS WAvo
- 'Magic Dragon'^{PBR} (v)	CRos ELan LCro LOPS LRHS NRHS SEle SGbt SPoG
- 'Multicolor' (v)	CBcs EBee ELan EPfP LRHS MRav SLim SVen
- 'Pixie'	CBcs LRHS MAsh SEle SLim SPoG SVen
- 'Red Dragon'	CBcs CMac ELan ESps LRHS LSou MAsh MGos NRHS SLim WFar
- 'Wild Cherry'	LRHS

Lophosoria ✿ (*Dicksoniaceae*)

quadripinnata	CBdn CDTJ NLos SBig

Lophospermum (*Plantaginaceae*)

'Cream Delight'	CCCN
§ ***erubescens*** $\mathbb{Y}^{H2}$	CRHN SBch
- 'Bridal Bouquet'	CPla
LOFOS WINE RED ('Sun-asaro') (Lofos Series)	EShb
§ 'Magic Dragon'	CPla SEND SLim WBor WHil
§ 'Red Dragon'	CCCN CPla CRos SBch
§ ***scandens***	CCCN

loquat see *Eriobotrya japonica*

Loropetalum (*Hamamelidaceae*)

chinense	SEle
§ - 'Chang Nian Hong'	LCro LRHS
- EVER RED	see *L. chinense* 'Chang Nian Hong'
- HOT SPICE **new**	SEle
- 'Ming Dynasty'	MAsh SEle SSta WFar
- var. ***rubrum***	CExl
- - 'Blush'	CBcs GMcL SEle SGol
- - 'Daybreak's Flame'	CBcs MGil SEle SGol SSta WCot
- - 'Fire Dance'	CBcs CBct CCCN CExl CHll CRos CTsd EPfP EShb EUJe LCro LOPS LRHS MAsh MGos MMuc NRHS SEle SPad SPoG SRkn SWvt WCot WFar
- - 'Fire Glow'	CRos LRHS
- 'Tang Dynasty'	CBct EBee WFar

Lotus (*Papilionaceae*)

berthelotii	CCCN CDTJ CRav ECtt MCot
- deep red-flowered $\mathbb{Y}^{H1c}$	CPla SWvt
berthelotii* × *maculatus $\mathbb{Y}^{H1c}$	CCCN MSCN
corniculatus	CHab CWld EBWF GJos LCro LOPS MCoo MHer MMuc MNHC NMir SEND SRms WSFF
creticus	SPhx
glaber **new**	EBWF
hirsutus $\mathbb{Y}^{H4}$	CBod CExl CMea CRos ECha EHoe ELan EPfP MAsh MCot MRav NSti SEND SLon SPer SPhx SPlb SPoG SWvt WSHC XLum XSen
- 'Brimstone' (v)	MRav SPer SPoG SWvt
- LITTLE BOY BLUE ('Lisbob'^{PBR})	CSBt EPfP LRHS NRHS
- 'Lois'	LRHS SPoG WAvo WCot
jacobaeus	MCot
maritimus	XLum
mearnsii	SPlb
pedunculatus	CHab EBWF MCoo NMir SPhx WSFF
pentaphyllus	XSen
tetragonolobus	SPhx SVic WSFF

lovage see *Levisticum officinale*

Loxostigma (*Gesneriaceae*)

kurzii GWJ 9342	WCru

Ludwigia (*Onagraceae*)

natans	XBlo
palustris	LLWG

Luetkea (*Rosaceae*)

pectinata	GEdr

Luffa (*Cucurbitaceae*)

aegyptiaca	SVic

Luma ✿ (*Myrtaceae*)

§ ***apiculata*** $\mathbb{Y}^{H4}$	Widely available
§ - 'Glanleam Gold' (v)	Widely available
- 'Nana'	LEdu
- 'Rainbow's Gold' (v)	EShb
- 'Saint Hilary' (v)	CBcs CRos EPfP LRHS NRHS
- 'Variegata' (v)	CTri WFar
§ ***chequen***	CBcs CBod CSBt EShb LEdu NLar WPGP

Lunaria (*Brassicaceae*)

§ ***annua***	GJos LCro LOPS MNHC WCot WSFF
- var. ***albiflora*** $\mathbb{Y}^{H7}$	LSun SEND WCot
I - - 'Alba Variegata' (v) $\mathbb{Y}^{H7}$	CSpe IBoy NPnk WBor WBrk
- 'Chedglow'	CNat LEdu LRHS SPhx WCot WSHC
- 'Corfu Blue'	CMea CSpe EWes SPhx SPtp WCot
- 'Cynthia'	CNat
- 'Munstead Purple' $\mathbb{Y}^{H7}$	CSpe
- 'Nettleton'	CNat
- purple-leaved	CMea WBor
- 'Rosemary Verey' **new**	WCot
- 'Ruth'	LEdu WCot
- 'The Optimist'	CNat
- 'Variegata' (v)	CNat GJos WBor WCot
biennis	see *L. annua*
rediviva $\mathbb{Y}^{H7}$	Widely available
- 'Partway White' (v)	CFis CMil WCot

Lupinus ✿ (*Papilionaceae*)

albifrons	EBee
arboreus $\mathbb{Y}^{H4}$	CBcs CRos CSBt CTri CWCL ELan EPfP IBoy LPmr LRHS MAsh MCoo MHer MNHC MNrw MRav NLar NRHS SCob SEle SPer SPlb SPoG SRms SVic WFar
- blue and white-flowered	SCob WFar
- 'Blue Boy'	ELan LRHS LSRN SWvt
- blue-flowered	CRos CWCL CWld GPSL LRHS NLar NRHS SCob SPer SPlb SPoG SRms SWvt WFar WOut
- 'Chelsea Blue'	CRos EPfP LRHS NRHS
- cream-flowered	SCob
- 'Lavender Spires' **new**	LCro LOPS
- prostrate	WAvo
- 'Snow Queen'	CPla CWCL SCob SPoG SWvt
- 'Sulphur Yellow'	SWvt
- white-flowered	CSpe MMrt SCob SPlb
- yellow and blue-flowered	IBoy SRkn WFar
- yellow-flowered	ELan IBoy MGil SCob SWvt
arcticus	EBee
argenteus	GKev
Band of Nobles Series	GJos
'Beefeater'	CRos CWCL ELan IBoy IRob LBuc LLHF LRHS NPri NRHS SPoG

'Bishop's Tipple'	EWes
'Blossom'PBR	CRos CWCL CWGN IBoy LLHF LRHS LSRN NPri NRHS SPoG
caespitosus	see *L. lepidus* var. *utahensis*
(Camelot Series) 'Camelot Blue'	EPfP GMcL WTor
- 'Camelot Red'	WTor
- 'Camelot Rose'	GMcL
- 'Camelot White'	GMcL WTor
- 'Camelot Yellow'	GMcL
'Cashmere Cream'	CRos CWCL EBee IRob LRHS NPri NRHS SPoG
'Chameleon'	CRos LBuc LRHS NRHS
chamissonis	CRos CSpe CWCL ELan EWes LRHS NRHS SPer WKif
'Chandelier' (Band of Nobles Series)	Widely available
'Desert Sun'PBR	CRos CWCL IRob LRHS NRHS SPoG
Dwarf Gallery hybrids	IBoy
'Dwarf Lulu'	see *L.* 'Lulu'
Gallery Series	CBod CSBt IBoy IRob LPmr SCoo SPlb WFar
- 'Gallery Blue'	CRav CRos ECtt ELan EPfP IBoy LBuc LCro LOPS LRHS LSRN MHol NLar NPri NRHS SCoo SPer SPoG WFar
- 'Gallery Pink'	CRos ELan EPfP ESps IBoy LCro LOPS LRHS MHol NLar NPri NRHS SCoo SPer SPoG WFar
- 'Gallery Red'	CRos ECtt ELan EPfP IBoy LCro LOPS LRHS MHol NLar NPri NRHS SCoo SPer SPoG WFar
- 'Gallery Rose'	IBoy LSRN NRHS SPoG WFar
- 'Gallery White'	CRos ELan EPfP IBoy LCro LOPS LRHS MHol NLar NPri NRHS SCoo SPer SPoG WFar
- 'Gallery Yellow'	CRos ECtt ELan EPfP ESps IBoy LCro LOPS LRHS MHol NLar NPri NRHS SPer SPoG WFar
'Gladiator'PBR	CRos CWCL EBee ECtt EPfP EWes IBoy LLHF LRHS LSou MJak MNrw NRHS SPoG
'Heathcliffe Blue'	WOut
'Judy Harper'	ECtt ELan GBin LRHS
'Jupiter'	CRos CWCL EBee GBin LRHS NLar NRHS SPoG
'King Canute'	CRos CWCL LRHS NPri NRHS
latifolius	EBee
subsp. ***parishii***	
'Le Gentilhomme' (Band of Nobles Series)	MCot
lepidus	CPbh
§ - var. ***utahensis***	SPlb
§ 'Lulu'	CRos EPfP IBoy LRHS NRHS SGbt SPer SPoG SWvt WHar
'Magic Lantern'	CRos CWCL LRHS NRHS
'Manhattan Lights'PBR	CBcs CChe CRos CWCL CWGN EPfP EWes IBoy ILea IPot LLHF LPmr LRHS MJak NLar NPri NRHS SPoG
'Masterpiece'PBR	CRos CWCL GBin IBoy ILea IRob LCro LLHF LOPS LRHS LSRN LSou MCot NPri NRHS SPoG
Minarette Group	CRos LRHS MNrw NRHS SRms
'Morello Cherry'	CWCL
mutabilis 'Sunrise'	LPmr
'My Castle' (Band of Nobles Series)	CBcs CBot CRos CSBt CTri ECtt EHrv ELan EPfP ESps GAbr GMaP GMcL IBoy LRHS LSRN MGos MJak MWat NGBl NLar NRHS SGbt SPer SPoG SWvt WFar WHar WMoo
nanus	LCro LOPS
'Neptune'	CWCL
'Noble Maiden' (Band of Nobles Series)	Widely available
nootkatensis	GLog
'Pam Ayres'	ECtt GBin LRHS
perennis	CBod
'Persian Slipper'PBR	CChe CEnd CRos CWCL CWGN ECtt EPfP EWes IBoy IPot IRob LBuc LCro LLHF LOPS LRHS LSRN MCot NPri NRHS
'Polar Princess'	CRos CWCL ECtt ELan EWes GBin LRHS NPri NRHS SPoG
polyphyllus var. ***burkei***	EBee
- 'Witchet' **new**	IPot
'Purple Swirl'	CRos CWCL EBee ECtt EPfP LRHS NRHS SPoG
'Rachel de Thame'	CChe CRos CWCL CWGN EBee LPmr LRHS NPri NRHS SPoG
'Red Rum'PBR	CEnd CRos CWCL CWGN IRob LBuc LRHS LSRN NLar NPri NRHS SPoG
'Rote Flamme'	ELon EWes SCob WOut
Russell hybrids	CPla CSBt EPfP ETMg GMcL IBoy IRob MHer SPlb SRms SVic SWvt WFar WHar
'Saffron'PBR	CEnd CRos CWCL IBoy IRob LBuc LRHS LSRN NPri NRHS SPoG
'Salmon Star'PBR	CRos CWCL IBoy LRHS NLar NRHS SPoG
'Sand Pink'	EWes
sericatus	EBee
'Silver Fleece'	CCCN CWld WFar
'Snow White'	IRob
'Sundown'	IRob
'Tequila Flame'PBR	CRos CWCL IRob LBuc LLHF LRHS LSou NRHS SPoG
'Terracotta'	CRos CWCL IBoy LRHS LSou NPri NRHS SPoG
texensis	CSpe
'The Chatelaine' (Band of Nobles Series)	Widely available
'The Governor' (Band of Nobles Series)	Widely available
'The Page' (Band of Nobles Series)	Widely available
'Thundercloud'	EBee
'Towering Inferno'	CEnd CRos CWCL ECtt EPfP EWes IBoy LBuc LRHS NLar NPri NRHS SPoG
'Tutti Frutti'	CBot IBoy WHar
Woodfield hybrids	LRHS

Luzula (*Juncaceae*)

alpinopilosa	EPPr
× ***borreri*** 'Botany Bay' (v)	CRos GBin LRHS NRHS
campestris	EBWF
'Engel'	EPPr EWes
forsteri	IMou
luzuloides 'Schneehäschen'	WSHC
maxima	see *L. sylvatica*
multiflora	EBWF
nivalis	GAbr
nivea	Widely available
pilosa	EBWF GCal
- 'Grünfink'	EBee
- 'Igel'	CBod CKno EBee EShb LEdu NBid SCob WHar

§ ***sylvatica***	CRos EBWF ELan EPPr GBin GMcL GQue LRHS MMoz MMuc MRav NBro NLar NMir NPol NRHS SCob SEND SPer WShi XLum
- from Tatra Mountains, Slovakia	EPPr
- 'A. Rutherford'	see *L. sylvatica* 'Taggart's Cream'
- 'Aurea'	CAby CBot CKno CRos ECha ELon EPPr LRHS MJak MMoz MMuc MRav NRHS NSti NWsh SEND WCot WFar WGrn WMoo WPtf
- 'Aureomarginata'	see *L. sylvatica* 'Marginata'
I - 'Auslese'	EPPr EPfP WMoo
- 'Bromel'	EPPr
- 'Hohe Tatra'	CBod CSpe EHoe EPPr EWes GBin GMaP GQue LEdu MBNS NGdn SCob SPer SPoG
§ - 'Marginata' (v)	CKno EBee ECha EHoe ELon EPPr EUJe GBin GMaP LRHS LSun MAvo MBNS MMoz MMuc MRav NBid NGdn NLar NSti SArc SCob SEND WCot WHoo WMoo
- 'Mariusz'	EPPr
* - f. ***nova***	ELon EPPr
- 'Onderbos'	EBee
- 'Solar Flair'	EUJe GBin
- 'Starmaker'	CBod
§ - 'Taggart's Cream' (v)	CRos EHoe GCal LRHS NBid NRHS NWad WMoo
- 'Tauernpass'	EPPr GCal LRHS SPhx
- 'Thierry's Cream' (v)	SPoG WCot
- 'Wäldler'	EBee EPPr
- 'Wintergold'	EPPr
ulophylla	GCrg GEdr SPlb WAbe WThu

Luzuriaga (*Luzuriagaceae*)

polyphylla	CTal
- HCM 98202	WCru
radicans	CCCN CRHN CTsd GEdr WCru WSHC
- RH 0602	WCru

Lychnis (*Caryophyllaceae*)

alpina	CMac EDAr LPmr NGdn WFar XLum
- 'Snow Flurry'	EDAr GKev
§ × ***arkwrightii***	ECha LRHS NRHS
- 'Orange Zwerg'	CRos SGbt
- 'Vesuvius'	CBcs CMac EBee SPer SRms WGwG
'Bull's Blood' new	SPhm
chalcedonica ♀H7	Widely available
- var. ***albiflora***	EPfP MBel NBro WCAu WHrl WMoo
- 'Carnea'	CRos EBee EPPr LRHS MBNS NGdn NRHS SPhx
- 'Dusky Salmon'	WHrl WOut
- 'Flore Pleno' (d)	EShb GCal WCot
- 'Pinkie'	MMuc NLar NWad
- 'Rauhreif'	NLar SPhx WHer
- 'Rosea'	EPfP ESps WHrl WMoo
* - 'Salmonea'	EPPr GPSL SRms
cognata	CTal GJos
- B&SWJ 4234	WCru
§ ***coronaria*** ♀H7	Widely available
- MESE 356	MAvo SPhx
- 'Abbotswood Rose'	see *L.* × *walkeri* 'Abbotswood Rose'
- 'Alba' ♀H7	Widely available
- 'Angel's Blush'	NLar SPav SRkn
- Atrosanguinea Group	CBre CRos EPfP ESps GMaP GMcL IBlr LRHS MBel MHol MRav MSpe MWat NEgg NGdn NRHS NSti NWad SPer WGwG WTor
- 'Blood Red'	CSpe EBee LEdu LRHS SBee
- 'Cerise'	MArl
- dark-red-flowered	MAvo
- GARDENERS' WORLD ('Blych') (d)	CBod CRos CSpe EBee ECha ECtt ELan ELon EMFm EWes IPot LCro LOPS LRHS LSou MBNS MBel MHol MPie NRHS NSti SPer SRkn WBrk WCot
- Oculata Group	CBod CSpe CTsd EBee ELan EPPr EPfP GQue LEdu SPav SPlb WFar WKif WMoo
coronata	CTsd
§ - var. ***sieboldii***	SBrt SPhx
dioica	see *Silene dioica*
flos-cuculi	Widely available
- var. ***albiflora***	CBre CElw CSam MSKA NBro NLar WHer WMoo
- var. ***congesta***	CMea
- JENNY ('Lychjen'PBR) (d)	CDor CRos EBee ECtt ELan EPfP LEdu LLWG LRHS MBNS MBel MHol MNrw NRHS NSti SCob SPoG SRkn WCAu WCot
- 'Little Robin'	LLWG
- 'Nana'	MHol NGdn NLar SPad WTor
- 'Petite Jenny' (d)	ECtt LRHS MBNS SPoG WCot WHlf WTor
- 'White Robin'	Widely available
flos-jovis ♀H5	CRos ECha EPfP GJos LRHS NRHS SRms WMoo XLum
- 'Hort's Variety'	CRos EBee LRHS NRHS
- 'Minor'	see *L. flos-jovis* 'Nana'
§ - 'Nana'	SBch
- 'Peggy'	CRos EBee LRHS NBre NGdn NLar
× ***haageana***	MPie SRms
- 'Lengai Red'	GMcL
- 'Lumina Bronze Leaf Red'	CRos LRHS NRHS
'Hill Grounds'	CElw EBee ECha ECtt WCot WSHC
miqueliana	WMoo
'Molten Lava'	CBod CRos EPfP LRHS NRHS SRms WHar
nivalis	WAbe
§ ***viscaria***	CWld EBWF ECha GJos GPSL WMoo
- 'Alba'	ECha NBre XLum
- ***alpina***	see *L. viscaria*
§ - subsp. ***atropurpurea***	EWes GJos LRHS MMuc MPie SHar SRms WArt WMoo
- 'Feuer'	EWes GJos NGBl WMoo
- 'Firebird'	EWes
- 'Plena' (d)	IPot SRkn WHil
- 'Schnee'	GJos NGBl NLar
- 'Snowbird'	CTsd EPPr
- 'Splendens'	MBel WFar XLum
- 'Splendens Plena' (d) ♀H5	XLum
§ × ***walkeri*** 'Abbotswood Rose' ♀H7	IBlr MAvo MJak
wilfordii	GKev
§ ***yunnanensis***	EBee NSti SPhx
- ***alba***	see *L. yunnanensis*

Lycianthes (*Solanaceae*)

biflora FMWJ 13059	WCru
§ ***rantonnetii*** ♀H1c	CBcs CCCN CHll ELan EUJe SEND SPoG WBor WKif
- 'Variegata' (v)	CHll MSCN WCot

Lycium (*Solanaceae*)

afrum	SVen

barbarum	CAgr CBcs CCCN CDul CSBt EPom LCro LEdu LOPS MCoo MGil NLar SCob SDea SEND SPre SVic SWvt WHar
- 'Big Lifeberry'	CAgr LEdu SBig
- 'Number 1 Lifeberry'	CAgr
- 'Sweet Lifeberry'	CAgr LEdu SBig
chinense	IBoy NQui

Lycopodium (*Lycopodiaceae*)

clavatum	GPoy

Lycopsis see *Anchusa*

Lycopus (*Lamiaceae*)

europaeus	CHab EBWF EBee GPoy LLWG MMuc WGwG WSFF XAbr

Lycoris (*Amaryllidaceae*)

albiflora	NRog
aurea	CAby CPne GKev LAma NRog SDeJ
caldwellii	NRog
chinensis	NRog
haywardii	NRog
houdyshelii	NRog
longituba	NRog
radiata	CAby CCCN CPne GKev LAma SDeJ
rosea	NRog
sanguinea	NRog
sprengeri	NRog

Lygeum (*Poaceae*)

spartum	XSen

Lygodium (*Lygodiaceae*)

articulatum new	WCot
japonicum	WFib

Lygos see *Retama*

Lyonothamnus (*Rosaceae*)

floribundus subsp. ***aspleniifolius***	CCCN CExl EBee EUJe SArc WPGP

Lysichiton (*Araceae*)

camtschatcensis 🏆H7	CBcs CBen CRos CTsd CWat ECha EPfP EUJe GBin IRob LLWG LRHS NLar NPer NRHS SMad SWvt WPnP WShi XLum
× ***hortensis***	ECha

Lysiloma (*Mimosaceae*)

watsonii	SPlb

Lysimachia (*Primulaceae*)

albescens	CExl XLum
§ ***atropurpurea***	CRos CSpe EBee EHoe ELan EPfP GJos GPSL LRHS NRHS SPer
- 'Beaujolais'	CBWd CChe CExl CRav CRos CWld GJos IBoy IPot LCro LEdu LPmr LRHS LSRN MGos MHol MWat NGBl NRHS SCob SPoG SPtp STPC WHar WHil
- 'Geronimo'	CSpe
barystachys 🏆H7	CSam LEdu MArl MBel MRav SHar WCot WOut XLum
- PAB 8755	LEdu
- 'Huntingbrook'	LEdu MAvo WPGP WWtn
CANDELA ('Innlyscand')	CBod CSpe ECtt GWyn LRHS LSou MHer MHol MMuc NPnk NRHS SPoG WCot WGwG WMoo WTor WWtn
candida	WCot
ciliata	CMac CRos ECha GMaP LRHS MNrw NGdn NLar NRHS
§ - 'Firecracker' 🏆H7	Widely available
- 'Purpurea'	see *L. ciliata* 'Firecracker'
clethroides 🏆H7	Widely available
- 'Geisha' (v)	EBee WCot
- 'Lady Jane'	CRos MAvo MNrw SRms
- 'Leigong Storm'	WPGP
§ ***congestiflora***	NPer
- 'Midnight Sun'PBR	CCCN ECtt
- 'Outback Sunset'PBR (v)	ECtt
- 'Persian Carpet'	WCot
- 'Persian Chocolate'	WCot WFar
ephemerum 🏆H6	Widely available
fortunei	WFar XEll XLum
japonica var. ***minutissima***	SRot
lichiangensis	CExl CRos GKev GPSL IMou LRHS NRHS WMoo
lyssii	see *L. congestiflora*
minoricensis	GKev WSpi XLum
nemorum	CWld EBWF IMou
- 'Lola Playle'PBR	WCot
- 'Pale Star'	CBre EBee
nummularia	CSBt CWat EBWF EPfP GPoy MJak WBrk
- 'Aurea' 🏆H5	CMac CSBt ECha ECtt EHoe EPfP ESps GAbr GQue MHer MJak MMuc MRav NBid NBro NLar NMir SEND SPer SPoG SRms SWvt WMoo WWtn XLum
paridiformis var. ***paridiformis*** NJM 11.067 new	WPGP
- var. ***stenophylla***	CExl GBin SPtp
punctata misapplied	see *L. verticillaris*
punctata L.	CBod CSBt ECha EPfP ESps GMaP LPmr MHer MMuc MRav NBro NMir NPer SCob SPer SPlb SRms WBrk WCAu WFar WHar WMAq WMoo
§ - 'Alexander' (v)	Widely available
- 'Gaulthier Brousse'	EBee MHCG WCot
- GOLDEN ALEXANDER ('Walgoldalex'PBR) (v)	CBod CChe CExl CRos LRHS MBNS NLar NPnk NRHS WMoo
- 'Golden Glory' (v)	WCot
- 'Hometown Hero'	EBee NLar
- 'Ivy Maclean' (v)	SWvt
- 'Variegata'	see *L. punctata* 'Alexander'
- ***verticillata***	see *L. verticillaris*
'Purpurea'	see *L. atropurpurea*
SNOW CANDLES ('L9902')	EBee NPnk WFar
thyrsiflora	CWat EBee EWat LLWG NPer WCot WMAq
§ ***verticillaris***	CTri WCot
vulgaris	CHab EBWF LLWG MSKA WMoo
- subsp. ***davurica***	WCot
- - B&SWJ 8632	WCru

Lysionotus (*Gesneriaceae*)

gamosepalus B&SWJ 7241	WCru
kwangsiensis HWJ 625	WCru
pauciflorus	WAbe
- B&SWJ 303	WCru
- B&SWJ 335	WCru
- HWJ 643 from Vietnam	WCru

- HWJ 811 from Vietnam	WCru
- dwarf B&SWJ 189	WCru
'Lady Lavender'	EBee MBNS
serratus HWJK 2426	WCru

Lythrum (*Lythraceae*)

alatum	NDov
anceps	NBre NLar
'Rose Dream'	NWad
salicaria	CBen CHab CWat CWld EBWF ENfk GJos LLWG MCot MHer MMuc MNHC MWts NBro SEND SPlb SRms WBrk WHer WMoo WPnP WSFF WShi WWtn XLum
- 'Augenweide'	XLum
- 'Blush' 🏆H7	Widely available
§ - 'Feuerkerze' 🏆H7	CAby CBWd CBod CMea CRos CSam EBee ECtt ELan ELon EPed EPfP GBin IRob LRHS LSou MArl MBel MCot MRav MSpe NEgg NRHS NSti SCob SPer WFar WWtn
- FIRECANDLE	see *L. salicaria* 'Feuerkerze'
- 'Happy'	ELon
- 'Lady Sackville'	EBee ECtt ELon GMaP IPot MCot MTis NLar WSHC
- 'Little Robert'	ECtt IBoy SPhm WFar
- 'Morden Pink'	CTri EBee MMuc NLar SEND SPhx WFar XLum
- 'Red Beauty'	LSun
- 'Robert'	Widely available
- 'Robin'	CRos ECtt ETMg GJos IRob LLHF LRHS MHol NDov NPri NRHS SGbt SRot SWvt
- 'Rose'	ELan SWvt
- 'Stichflamme'	ELon SBee
- 'Swirl'	ECtt ELon EPfP ILea LLWG LRHS MTis NDov NLar NRHS NSti SHar WHoo
- 'The Beacon'	EBee NLar SRms
- 'Zigeunerblut'	ECtt ELon LRHS MRav NLar NRHS XLum
virgatum	ESps SMHy SPhx WCFE WMoo WOut WSHC
- 'Dropmore Purple'	Widely available
- 'Helene'	IMou NDov
- pale-flowered **new**	NDov
- 'Rose Queen'	ECtt ESps IPot MRav SMHy
- 'Rosy Gem'	CRos EBee EPfP ESps GJos GMaP IBoy LRHS MWat NBro NRHS SRms SWvt WHar
- 'The Rocket'	CAby CBod CTri EPfP EShb GCal LRHS MPie MRav NBro NDov NRHS SWvt WFar WPnP

M

Maackia (*Papilionaceae*)

amurensis	CBcs CDul CHGN CMCN EPfP NLar
hupehensis	MBlu

Macadamia (*Proteaceae*)

integrifolia (F) **new**	XBlo

mace, English see *Achillea ageratum*

Macfadyena (*Bignoniaceae*)

unguis-cati	see *Dolichandra unguis-cati*

Machaerina (*Cyperaceae*)

rubiginosa **new**	LLWG
- 'Variegata' (v)	EWat LLWG

Machilus see *Persea*

Mackaya (*Acanthaceae*)

§ ***bella*** 🏆H1b	CHll EShb

Macleaya (*Papaveraceae*)

cordata misapplied	see *M.* × *kewensis*
§ ***cordata*** (Willd.) R. Br. 🏆H6	CRos EBee LRHS LSun MHol NRHS SPer SPlb SRms WMoo XLum
- NJM 11.002 **new**	WPGP
§ × ***kewensis***	EBee SCob
- 'Flamingo' 🏆H6	CExl EBee ECha ECtt GBin GWyn LRHS MBNS MPie NRHS SPer SWvt WCot WWtn
§ ***microcarpa***	GJos IBoy MHol
- 'Kelway's Coral Plume' 🏆H6	CBWd CBcs CBod CExl CMac CRos EBee ECtt ELan EPed EPfP GAbr GBin GMaP GMcL LCro LRHS LSRN MAvo MRav NBid NBro NEgg NLar NRHS SPhm SPoG SWvt WBor WWtn
- 'Spetchley Ruby'	CExl EBee GBin LRHS MRav NLar SPhx WCot XLum

Maclura (*Moraceae*)

pomifera	CBcs CMCN IDee LEdu MBlu SBrt SPlb
- 'Cannonball'	SAko
- var. ***inermis*** **new**	IArd
- 'Naughty Boy'	NLar
- 'Pretty Woman'	NLar
tricuspidata B&SWJ 12755	WCru
- 'Parthenos' **new**	CAgr

Macrodiervilla see *Weigela*

Macrothelypteris (*Thelypteridaceae*)

torresiana **new**	CBdn

Macrozamia (*Zamiaceae*)

communis	CBrP
dyeri	see *M. riedlei*
lucida	CBrP
moorei	CBrP
§ ***riedlei***	CBrP

Maddenia (*Rosaceae*)

hypoleuca	IDee MBlu NLar SAko

Maesa (*Primulaceae*)

japonica	CExl
- CWJ 12371	WCru
montana	CExl

Magnolia ✿ (*Magnoliaceae*)

sp.	CAco LPra
acuminata	CBcs CDul CMCN LMaj
- 'Blue Opal'	CBcs CJun
* - 'Kinju'	CEnd CJun
- 'Koban Dori'	CBcs CJun
- 'Moegi Dori'	NLar
- 'Patriot'	CMCN
- 'Patriot' × (× ***brooklynensis*** 'Yellow Bird')	MAsh

- 'Seiju'	CJun
- var. ***subcordata*** 'Miss Honeybee'	CBcs CJun
- - 'Mister Yellowjacket'	CJun
acuminata × 'Elizabeth'	ERea
'Advance'	CBcs CJun
'Albatross'	CBcs CEnd EBee ERea WPGP
'Alex'	CJun
'Alixeed'	CJun
'Amber'	CJun
'Ambrosia'	CJun
'Amethyst Flame' **new**	SBig
amoena	CBcs CTho
'Angelica'	CJun
'Anilou'	CJun
'Ann'	CExl
'Anna'	CJun
'Anne Rosse'	WPGP
'Anticipation'	CBcs CEnd CJun WPGP
'Apollo'	CBcs CJun LSRN SAko WPGP
'Archangel'	CJun
ashei	see *M. macrophylla* subsp. *ashei*
'Asian Artistry'	CJun
'Athene' ♀^{H5}	CBcs CEnd CJun LMil SAko WPGP
'Atlas'	CBcs CEnd CJun CTho ERea SAko WPGP
'Aurora'	CBcs CJun LMil SBig
'Banana Split'	LMil LRHS MAsh SBig
'Betty'	CBcs CDul CMac ELon EMOT ESps LRHS LSRN LSou MBlu MGos NLar NPla SLim SSta
'Big Dude'	CBcs CEnd CJun EPfP ERea IDee SBig SCob
biondii	CBcs MBlu NLar
'Black Beauty'	CBcs CJun LRHS SBig WHor
'Black Swan'	WPGP
BLACK TULIP ('Jurmag1'^{PBR})	CBcs CDul CRos CTho EBee ELan EPfP ERea GGGa LBuc LCro LMil LRHS MAsh MGos NHim NLar SBig SCoo SLon SPer SPoG WHor WPGP
'Blackbird'	LRHS SBig
'Blushing Belle'	CJun SAko
'Brenda'	CJun
'Brixton Belle'	CBcs WPGP
× ***brooklynensis*** 'Evamaria'	CTho LRHS
- 'Golden Joy'	CJun LRHS
- 'Hattie Carthan'	CBcs CJun LRHS
- 'Woodsman'	CBcs NHim NLar NOra
- 'Yellow Bird'	CBcs CDul CEnd CJun CMCN CRos CTho EPfP ERea IArd LMil LRHS LSRN MAsh MBlu MGos NLar NPri NRHS SCob SPoG
BURGUNDY STAR ('Jurmag4')	ERea LCro LOPS SPer SWeb
'Butterbowl'	CJun
'Butterflies'	CBcs CDul CJun CRos CTho CTsd ELan EMOT EPfP LMil LRHS LSRN MBlu MGos NLar NOra NRHS SBig SGol SPer SRms SSta WSpi
'Caerhays Belle' ♀^{H5}	CBcs CJun LMil LRHS NLar SAko SPoG WPGP
'Caerhays Surprise' ♀^{H5}	CBcs CEnd CJun LRHS WPGP
campbellii	CBcs CMCN EPfP LRHS
- Alba Group	WPGP
- - 'Chyverton'	WPGP
- - 'Sir Harold Hillier'	CJun WPGP
- - 'Strybing White'	WPGP
- 'Ambrose Congreve'	WPGP
- 'Betty Jessel'	CBcs CJun WPGP
- 'Darjeeling' ♀^{H4}	CBcs CJun LRHS WPGP
- 'Lionel de Rothschild'	WPGP
- subsp. ***mollicomata***	EPfP
- - 'Lanarth'	CBcs WPGP
- - 'Peter Borlase'	WPGP
- - 'Werrington'	CBcs
- 'Queen Caroline'	LRHS WPGP
- (Raffillii Group) 'Charles Raffill'	CDul ELan EPfP LRHS SPoG WHor
- - 'Kew's Surprise'	CBcs WPGP
- 'Sidbury'	CTho WHor
campbellii × ***sprengeri***	WPGP
'Candy Cane'	CJun ERea
'Carlos'	CBcs CJun
cathcartii B&SWJ 11802	WCru
- HWJ 874	WCru
cavaleriei var. ***platypetala***	CExl
caveana	LEdu
- NJM 13.037 **new**	WPGP
- NJM 13.044	WPGP
CHAMELEON	see *M.* 'Chang Hua'
§ 'Chang Hua'	CJun
'Charles Coates'	CJun EPfP NLar WPGP
'Charming Lady'	CJun
chevalieri	CBcs
- B&SWJ 11802	WCru
- DJHV 06037	WCru
- HWJ 621	WCru
CHINA TOWN ('Jing Ning')	CJun
'Columnar Pink'	NLar
compressa	CBcs
'Coral Lake'	CJun LMil LRHS
'Cornish Chough'	WPGP
crassifolia hort.	see *M. fansipanensis*
'Crescendo'	CJun
'Crystal Chalice'	CJun
'Cup Cake'	CJun
'Curlew'	WPGP
cylindrica misapplied	see *M.* 'Pegasus'
cylindrica ambig.	CBcs CMCN
cylindrica E.H.Wilson 'Bjuv'	CJun
'Daphne' ♀^{H6}	CBcs CDul CEnd CJun EPfP ERea GGGa LMil LRHS LSRN MAsh SCob SPoG WPGP
'Darrell Dean'	CJun ERea
'David Clulow' ♀^{H5}	CBcs CJun ERea LMaj WPGP
dawsoniana	CBcs CTho IDee IMou WSpi
- 'Barbara Cook'	CJun
- 'Chyverton Red'	CBcs WPGP
- 'Valley Splendour'	CJun
'Daybreak' ♀^{H6}	CBcs CJun CTho ELan ERea LMil LRHS MBlu MRav NOra SGol SSta WPGP
dealbata	see *M. macrophylla* subsp. *dealbata*
'Deborah'	CJun
decidua	CBcs
delavayi	CBcs CBrP CDul CFil CMCN CTho EBee EPfP ERea EUJe LRHS SArc SBig SEND WPGP
'Delia Williams'	EBee WPGP
§ ***denudata*** ♀^{H6}	CBcs CDul CMCN CTho EPfP LMil MBlu
- 'Double Diamond'	CJun SAko
- FESTIROSE ('Minfor')	LRHS
- 'Forrest's Pink'	CBcs LMaj LRHS
- FRAGRANT CLOUD ('Dan Xin')	CBcs CJun WHar
- 'Gere'	CBcs CJun

	- 'Ghost Ship'	CJun
	- late-flowered	see *M. denudata* 'Sleeping Beauty'
§	- 'Sleeping Beauty'	ERea
	- YELLOW RIVER ('Fei Huang')	CBcs CEnd CJun LMaj MJak NOra WHor
	doltsopa	CAby CBcs CCCN CExl LRHS SSta WPGP
	- B&SWJ 13996 **new**	WCru
	- NJM 12.028	WPGP
	- NJM 12.047	WPGP
	- 'Silver Cloud'	CExl
	'Double Trouble' **new**	SBig
	'Early Rose'	CJun
	'Eleanor May'	CJun
	'Elegance'	CJun
	'Elisa Odenwald'	CJun LRHS
	'Elizabeth' 🏆^{H6}	CBcs CDul CJun CMCN CRos CTho ELan EPfP ERea ESps LMil LRHS LSRN MAsh MBlu MGos NHim NLar NRHS SPer SPoG SRms SWvt
	'Emma Cook' **new**	CJun
§	***ernestii***	CExl WPGP
	'Eskimo'	CJun
	'Eternal Flames'	NLar
	'F.J. Williams'	CBcs WPGP
	FAIRY BLUSH ('Micjur01'^{PBR})	CBcs EPfP LCro LOPS MGos
	FAIRY CREAM ('Micjur02')	CBcs CCCN LCro LOPS LRHS SBig
	FAIRY MAGNOLIA WHITE ('Micjur05')	CBcs CCCN LCro LOPS LRHS SBig SPoG
§	***fansipanensis*** FMWJ 13054	WCru
	- FMWJ 13163	WCru
	'Felicity'	CJun
	FELIX JURY ('Jurmag2'^{PBR})	CBcs ELan EPfP ERea LCro LOPS SAko
	figo	CBcs CCCN CExl CFil CHll CRos CTsd EBee ELan EPfP EShb LRHS NRHS SMad SSta WPGP
	'Fireglow'	CJun CTho
	'Flamingo'	CJun
	floribunda NJM 09.179	WPGP
	- FMWJ 13384 from Tonkin, Vietnam **new**	WCru
	- WWJ 11874	WCru
	- WWJ 11982 from Tonkin, Vietnam **new**	WCru
	- WWJ 11996	WCru
	- WWJ 12003	WCru
	- WWJ 12011	WCru
	- 'Fansipan Furry' **new**	WCru
	- 'Furry Uok'	WPGP
	× ***foggii*** 'Jack Fogg'	SBig
	fordiana	CExl
§	***foveolata*** B&SWJ 11749	WCru
	- DJHV 06105 **new**	WCru
	- WWJ 11900 **new**	WCru
	- WWJ 11929	WCru
	- WWJ 11955	WCru
	'Frank Gladney'	CJun ERea
	'Frank's Masterpiece'	CJun ERea
	'Galaxy' 🏆^{H6}	CBcs CDul CEnd CJun CMac ELon EPfP ERea IArd IDee LMaj LMil LRHS MAsh MGos MMuc NHim NLar SAko SLim SPoG SSta WMou
	'Genie'^{PBR}	CBcs CRos LMaj LMil LRHS NLar NRHS SCob SPoG SWeb WPGP
	'George Henry Kern' 🏆^{H6}	CBcs CDul CLnd CRos CTho EMOT EPfP ETMg LRHS MGos MJak MMuc NEgg NLar NPri SEND
	'Gladys Carlson'	CJun
	globosa	CExl LEdu LRHS
	'Gold Crown'	CJun LMil LRHS SPoG
	'Gold Star' 🏆^{H6}	CBcs CDul CEnd CJun CRos CTho EPfP LMil LRHS MGos NLar NOra NRHS SAko SPoG SSta WPGP
	'Golden Endeavour'	CJun
	'Golden Gala'	CJun
	'Golden Gift'	CJun EBee LMil LRHS MAsh WPGP
	'Golden Pond'	CJun LRHS SPoG
	'Golden Rain'	CJun
	'Golden Sun'	CJun IArd
	'Goldfinch'	CJun
I	× ***gotoburgensis*** Chollipo clone	WPGP
	grandiflora	CMCN EBee EMOT EPfP ESps ETod LCro LEdu LOPS LPra LSRN MGos MMuc MRav NEgg NLar NPri SArc SCob SEND SEWo WTSh
	- ALTA ('Tmgh'^{PBR})	LRHS
	- 'Blanchard'	CBcs CJun LRHS NLar
	- 'Bracken's Brown Beauty'	CRos LMil NRHS
	- 'Charles Dickens'	CJun SVen
	- 'Edith Bogue'	CBcs EUJe LRHS NEgg NLar SSta
	- 'Exmouth'	Widely available
	- 'Ferruginea'	CBcs CJun EPfP NLar SGol
	- 'Flore Pleno' (d)	SGol
	- 'François Treyve'	EMOT EPfP LRHS LSRN
	- 'Galissonnière'	CAco CBcs CCVT CRos ECrN EPfP ERea ESps ETod EUJe LMaj LPra LRHS MGos NPri SCob SGol SWvt
	- 'Goliath'	CBcs ELan EMOT EPfP LMaj LRHS NPri SEWo SPer SSta
	- 'Harold Poole'	CJun
	- 'Kay Parris' 🏆^{H5}	CJun CRos EPfP LMil LRHS MAsh NRHS SPoG
	- 'Little Gem'	CBcs CJun CRos ELan ELon EMOT EPfP EUJe LCro LOPS LRHS LSRN NLar SGol SPer SPoG SSta
	- 'Mainstreet'	CJun LRHS
	- 'Monlia'	CJun
	- 'Nannetensis'	CRos LRHS
	- 'November Fox'	LRHS
	- 'Overton'	CJun
	- 'Praecox'	LPra
	- 'Russet'	CJun
	- 'Saint Mary'	CJun
	- 'Samuel Sommer'	CJun SBig
	- 'Symmes Select'	CJun
	- 'Treyvei'	CJun
	- 'Victoria' 🏆^{H5}	CJun CRos CTho ELan ELon EPfP LMil LRHS LSRN MAsh MBlu MGos NLar NRHS SPer SReu SSta
	'Green Bee'	CBcs CJun LRHS
	'Hawk'	CBcs EBee WPGP
	'Heaven Scent' 🏆^{H5}	Widely available
	'Helen Fogg'	CJun
	heptapeta	see *M. denudata*
	'Honey Belle' **new**	CJun
	'Honey Flower'	CJun SBig
	'Honey Liz'	LRHS SPoG
	HONEY TULIP ('Jurmag5')	CBcs LOPS SBig SPer SPoG SWeb
§	'Hong Yun'	CJun
	'Hot Flash'	CBcs CJun
	'Hot Lips'	CJun SBig
	hypoleuca	see *M. obovata* Thunb.
	'Ian's Red'	CBcs CJun EBee LMaj LRHS SCob WPGP
§	***insignis***	CBcs CExl EBee LEdu WPGP
	- B&SWJ 11810	WCru
	- NJM 12.040	WPGP
	- WWJ 11854	WCru

	insignis* × *yuyuanensis	WPGP
	'Iolanthe'	CBcs CEnd CJun CMCN CTho EPfP ERea MAsh MGos WPGP
	'Iufer'	CJun
	'J.C. Williams'	CBcs CJun CTho LRHS SSta WPGP
	'Jane'	CBcs CJun CMac CRos ELan EPfP LMil LRHS MAsh MGos MRav NRHS
	'Jersey Belle'	CJun
	'Joe McDaniel'	CBcs CJun ERea IArd NLar SAko
	'John Bond'	SSta
	'John Congreve'	WPGP
	'Joli Pompom'	CBcs CJun
	'Judy Zuk'	CBcs CJun ERea LRHS SBig
	× ***kewensis*** 'Wada's Memory'	see *M. salicifolia* 'Wada's Memory'
	kobus	CBcs CCVT CDul CLnd CMCN CRos CTho CTsd EPfP ERea ESps GKin LMaj LPra MBlu NLar SCob SEWo WMou
	- B&SWJ 12751	WCru
	- 'Esveld Select'	CJun
	- 'Janaki Ammal'	CJun SAko
§	- 'Norman Gould'	CJun CMCN EPfP
	- 'Octopus'	CJun
	- pink-flowered	CBcs CJun
	- 'White Elegance'	CJun
	'Kunming'	LRHS
	laevifolia	CExl CHid CJun CMCN CTho EBee EPfP LRHS SChF WPGP WSHC
	- 'Dali Velvet'	CExl
	- 'Gail's Favourite'	CRos EPfP LMil LRHS MAsh NRHS SArc
	- 'Kh-Achteraan'	LRHS
	- 'Mini Mouse'	CRos LMil LRHS MAsh NRHS
	'Laura Saylor'	CJun
	'Leda'	CBcs CJun ERea SSta WPGP
	'Legacy'	CJun WPGP
	'Legend'	CJun SBig
	'Lemon Star'	SBig
	'Lennarth Jonsson'	CJun
§	***liliiflora***	LPra
	- 'Darkest Purple'	CJun
§	- 'Nigra' ♀H6	Widely available
	- 'Raven'	EBee LMil LRHS WPGP
*	'Limelight'	CBcs CJun EBee EPfP NHim NLar NOra WPGP
	× ***loebneri***	LPra
	- 'Ballerina'	CBcs
	- 'Donna' ♀H6	CBcs CJun EPfP LMil LRHS LSRN MAsh
	- 'Encore'	CJun
	- 'Green Mist'	CJun CRos LRHS NRHS
	- 'Leonard Messel' ♀H6	Widely available
	- 'Lesley Jane'	CJun
	- 'Mag's Pirouette' ♀H6	CAby CBcs CJun EBee EPfP LLHF LMil LRHS SAko SPoG SSta
	- 'Merrill' ♀H6	CBcs CDul CJun CLnd CMCN CMac CRos CTho ELan EMOT EPfP ERea ESps LMaj LMil LPra LRHS MAsh MGos MMuc MRav NEgg NHim NLar NRHS SGol SPer SReu SSta
	- 'Neil McEacharn'	CJun
	- 'Pink Cloud'	CJun
	- 'Powder Puff'	CBcs CJun
	- 'Raspberry Fun'	CJun IArd
	- 'Snowdrift'	CJun LMaj SBig
	- 'Star Bright'	CJun
	- 'White Stardust'	CJun
	- 'Wildcat' ♀H6	CBcs CJun LRHS NLar SAko SBig SSta

	- 'Willow Wood'	CJun
	'Lois' ♀H6	CBcs CEnd CJun CRos EPfP ERea GGGa LMil LRHS LSRN NRHS WPGP
	'Lombardy Rose'	NLar
	'Longsleeper'	LRHS
	lotungensis	WPGP
	'Lotus'	CBcs CJun WPGP
	'Lucy Carlson'	CJun
	macrophylla	CBcs CBrP CFil CMac CRos EPfP IDee LRHS MBlu MPkF NLar NRHS WPGP
§	- subsp. ***ashei***	CBcs CFil CMCN WPGP
	- subsp. ***ashei*** × ***virginiana***	CJun WPGP
	- subsp. ***ashei*** × subsp. ***dealbata*** new	WPGP
§	- subsp. ***dealbata***	CFil
	- 'Julian Hill' new	CMCN
	macrophylla* × *sieboldii	CJun
	'Malin'	CJun
	'Manchu Fan'	CBcs CJun EPfP IArd LRHS LSRN WPGP
§	'March Til Frost'	CBcs CJun LMil WPGP
	'Margaret Helen'	CBcs CJun WPGP
	'Marj Gossler'	CJun
	'Marjorie Congreve'	WPGP
	martinii	CBcs
	'Mary Nell'	CJun
	'Maryland'	CJun GGGa
	maudiae	CBcs CExl NLar
	'Maxine Merrill'	CBcs CJun
	'May to Frost'	see *M.* 'March Til Frost'
	'Milky Way' ♀H5	CDul CJun CTho EPfP ERea LMil MGos WPGP
	'Mister Yellowjacket'	CJun
	'Moondance'	CJun
	'Nimbus'	CJun CRos ERea LRHS NRHS WPGP
	nitida	CBcs CExl CFil
	obovata Diels	see *M. officinalis*
§	***obovata*** Thunb.	CBcs CDul CJun CMCN CTho EPfP NLar SBig WMou WPGP
	- B&SWJ 10821	WCru
	- B&SWJ 12626	WCru
	- pink-flowered	WPGP
	obovata* × *sargentiana var. ***robusta***	WPGP
§	***officinalis***	EPfP NLar
	- var. ***biloba***	CBcs MBlu NLar WPGP
	'Old Port'	CBcs
	'Olivia'	CJun WPGP
	'Ossie's Yellow' new	SBig
	'Paul Cook'	CEnd
	'Peaches 'n' Cream'	CBcs CJun
	'Peachy'	CBcs CJun LRHS SBig
§	'Pegasus' ♀H6	CBcs CEnd CJun LMil LRHS SSta
	'Peppermint Stick'	CTsd LRHS
	'Peter Dummer'	LMil
	'Peter Smithers'	CJun
	'Petit Chicon'	CBcs EBee
	'Phelan Bright'	CBcs CJun SAko WPGP
	'Phillip Tregunna'	CBcs CTho EBee WPGP
	'Phil's Masterpiece'	CJun
	'Pickard's Garnet'	CBcs
	'Pickard's Stardust'	EPfP
	'Pickard's Sundew'	see *M.* × *soulangeana* 'Sundew'
	'Piet van Veen'	CJun
	'Pink Delight'	CJun
	'Pink Goblet'	CRos LRHS NRHS
	'Pink Surprise'	CJun

	'Pinkie'	CJun
	'Porcelain Dove'	CBcs CJun LMil LRHS WPGP
	'Premier Cru' **new**	LRHS
	'Princess Margaret'	CBcs CJun LMil
	'Pristine'	EPfP LMil LRHS
	× ***proctoriana***	CBcs CRos EBee LMil LRHS MMuc NRHS WPGP
	- 'Robert's Dream'	CJun CRos LRHS MAsh NRHS SBig SSta
	- 'Slavin's No 44'	CJun
	'Purple Breeze'	MBlu NLar SAko
	'Purple Cracker' **new**	SBig
	'Purple Globe'	CEnd CJun
	'Purple Platter'	CBcs
	'Purple Sensation'	CBcs CJun WPGP
	quinquepeta	see *M. liliiflora*
	'Randy'	CBcs
	'Raspberry Ice'	CBcs CMac CRos CTho EPfP LMil LRHS MAsh NRHS SRms
	'Raspberry Ripple' **new**	SBig
	'Raspberry Swirl'	SSta
	'Red as Red'	CBcs LRHS
	'Red Baron'	CJun
	'Red Lion'	CJun
	'Ricki'	CBcs CJun LSRN MBlu
	'Roseanne'	CJun
	rostrata	CBcs CExl CFil EBee IArd WPGP
	'Rouged Alabaster'	CBcs
	'Royal Crown'	CDul EMil EPfP IArd LRHS
	'Royal Flush'	NEgg
	'Ruby'	CJun
	'Ruth'	CBcs
	salicifolia	CBcs CMCN MMuc WSpi
	- var. ***concolor***	CJun
	- 'Garden House Upright'	EBee
	- 'Jermyns'	CJun
	- 'Louisa Fete'	CJun
	- 'Miss Jack' **new**	CMCN
*	- 'Rosea'	CJun
	- upright	WPGP
	- 'Van Veen'	CJun WPGP
§	- 'Wada's Memory' ♀H6	CDul CExl CJun CMCN CRos CTho ELan EMil EPfP ERea LMaj LMil LRHS MAsh MBlu MMuc NPri NRHS SPer SSta WFar
	- 'Windsor Beauty'	CJun ERea LSvl SSta
	sapaensis FMWJ 13315	WCru
	- FMWJ 13330	WCru
	- HWJ 533	WCru
	- NJM 09.168	WPGP
	sargentiana	SSta
	- 'Broadleas'	CJun
	- var. ***robusta***	CBcs CMCN CTsd EPfP MMuc
	- - 'Blood Moon'	CBcs CJun EBee WPGP
	- - 'Multipetal'	WPGP
	- - 'Trengwainton Glory'	ERea
	'Satisfaction'	LCro LOPS NLar
	'Sayonara' ♀H5	CBcs CJun ERea LMaj
	'Schmetterling'	see *M.* × *soulangeana* 'Pickard's Schmetterling'
	'Serene'	CBcs CEnd CJun EPfP LMil
	SHIRAZZ ('Vulden')	CBcs CJun EPfP IArd LMil LRHS NLar SCob SPoG WPGP
	sieboldii	Widely available
	- B&SWJ 4127	WCru
	- 'Colossus' ♀H6	CJun IArd MBlu SAko WPGP
	- 'Genesis'	CJun NLar
	- 'Genesis' × ***tripetala***	CJun
	- 'Genesis' × ***virginiana***	CJun SBig
	- 'Michiko Renge' (d)	CJun
	- 'Min Pyong-gal'	CJun
	- 'Pride of Norway'	CJun
	- subsp. ***sieboldii*** B&SWJ 12553 from Korea	WCru
	- subsp. ***sinensis***	CBcs CJun CMCN CTho ELan WPGP
I	- - 'Grandiflora'	CJun WPGP
	- 'White Flounces' (d)	NLar
	'Sir Harold Hillier'	CBcs WPGP
	'Snow Goose'	CJun
	'Solar Flair'	CBcs CJun IArd NLar SBig
	× ***soulangeana***	Widely available
	- 'Alba Superba'	CBcs CBot CTri EMOT EPfP ESps LCro LMil LOPS LRHS MBlu MRav NLar SLim SPer SPoG WFar WSpi
	- 'Alexandrina'	CBcs EPfP MBlu NLar
	- 'André Leroy'	EPfP LRHS
	- 'Beugnon'	IArd
	- 'Brozzonii' ♀H5	CMac EPfP LMil LRHS SSta
	- 'Cleopatra' PBR	CBcs
	- 'Fukuju'	CJun
	- 'Just Jean'	EBee
	- 'Lennei'	CBcs CMCN CMac CRos CSBt CTho EMOT EPfP ESps IArd LRHS MGos MRav NRHS SPer SPoG SRms WFar
	- 'Lennei Alba'	CMCN CMac ELan IArd MBlu NOra WFar WSpi
	- 'Nigra'	see *M. liliiflora* 'Nigra'
	- 'Pickard's Opal'	CMCN
	- 'Pickard's Ruby'	CBcs
§	- 'Pickard's Schmetterling' ♀H5	CBcs EPfP LMil MAsh
	- 'Pickard's Snow Queen'	CJun
	- 'Pickard's Sundew'	see *M.* × *soulangeana* 'Sundew'
	- 'Picture'	CMac CTri
	- 'Purpliana'	NPri
	- RED LUCKY	see *M.* 'Hong Yun'
	- 'Rubra' misapplied	see *M.* × *soulangeana* 'Rustica Rubra'
§	- 'Rustica Rubra'	CBcs CDul CLnd CMCN CMac CRos CTri ELan EPfP LMil LRHS LSRN MAsh NLar NRHS SGol SPer SRms WHar
	- 'San José'	CJun LMil LRHS MAsh
	- 'Speciosa'	SSta
§	- 'Sundew'	EPfP ERea GMcL NLar
	- 'Superba'	CMac LRHS
	- 'Verbanica'	EPfP LMil LRHS MAsh
	'Spectrum' ♀H6	CBcs CEnd CJun EPfP ERea IArd IDee IMou LMil LRHS MBlu MGos SPoG SSta
	sprengeri	CTsd
	- from Guizhou, China	WPGP
	- var. ***diva***	CBcs CEnd CExl WPGP
	- - 'Burncoose' ♀H6	CBcs
	- - 'Copeland Court' ♀H6	CJun LMil LRHS WPGP
	- - 'Dark Diva'	CJun
	- - 'Diva'	LRHS WPGP
	- - 'Eric Savill' ♀H6	CBcs CJun ERea WPGP
	- - 'Lanhydrock'	CJun LRHS WPGP
	- - 'Marwood Spring'	ERea LMil WPGP
	- - 'Westonbirt'	WPGP
	'Spring Rite'	CBcs CJun
	'Star Wars' ♀H5	CBcs CCVT CDul CEnd CExl CJun CRos CTho ECrN ELan EPfP ERea GGGa LMil LRHS MAsh MGos NHim NLar NOra NRHS SAko SBig SEWo SPoG SSta WPGP
	'Stellar Acclaim'	CJun LMil

stellata	Widely available
- 'Centennial' ♀H6	CJun CTho LMil
- 'Chrysanthemumiflora'	CJun ERea
- 'Dawn'	CJun
- 'Jane Platt' ♀H6	CBcs CJun CRos ELan EPfP ERea LMil LRHS MGos NRHS SPoG SSta WPGP
- f. ***keiskei***	CEnd CJun MGos
- 'Kikuzaki'	CJun
- 'King Rose'	CBcs CJun CTsd EPfP SPer
- 'Massey'	CJun
- 'Norman Gould'	see *M. kobus* 'Norman Gould'
- 'Rosea'	CJun CMCN CTho ELan ELon EPfP ESps GMcL IRob LMaj LMil MGos MRav MSwo NEgg NLar NPri SCob SWeb WFar
- 'Rosea Massey'	CJun
- 'Royal Star' ♀H6	Widely available
- 'Scented Silver'	CJun LRHS
- 'Shi-banchi Rosea'	CJun
- 'Water Lily'	CBcs CBot CJun CMCN CRos CTho ELan ELon EPfP LMil LRHS LSRN MAsh MBlu MGos NEgg NRHS SPer SPoG SSta WHor WPGP
- 'Wisley Stardust'	LRHS
'Summer Solstice'	CBcs CJun LMil WPGP
'Sun Ray'	CJun
'Sunburst'	CBcs CJun SRms
'Sundance'	CBcs CJun IArd MBlu NLar
'Sunrise'	CBcs CDul ETMg LRHS NLar SAko
'Sunsation'	CBcs CJun ELan ERea SBig
'Sunset Swirl'	CJun
'Sunspire'	CJun ERea NLar
'Suntown'	CJun
'Susan' ♀H6	Widely available
'Susanna van Veen'	CBcs CEnd CJun WPGP
'Swedish Star'	CJun
'Sweet Merlot'	CBcs CJun LRHS
'Sweet Valentine'	CBcs CJun GMcL WPGP
'Sweetheart' ♀H5	CBcs CJun
'Sybille'	CMCN WPGP
tamaulipana new	CFil
'Theodora'	CBcs LRHS
× ***thompsoniana***	CBcs CMCN
- 'Olmenhof'	IArd
'Thousand Butterflies'	CJun
'Tina Durio'	LRHS
'Todd Gresham'	CJun
'Todd's Forty Niner'	CJun
'Tranquility'	CBcs CJun
tripetala	CBcs CExl CMCN CTho ELan EPfP IDee LMaj LRHS MBlu NLar SBig SMad SSta
- 'Bloomfield'	CJun
'Ultimate Yellow'	CJun NLar
× ***veitchii***	CBcs
- 'Columbus'	CJun ERea LRHS WPGP
- 'Peter Veitch'	CRos CTho
virginiana	CBcs CJun CMCN LMaj SBig
- var. ***australis*** 'Green Shadow'	SGol
- - 'Henry Hicks'	LRHS SBig
- - 'Satellite'	NLar
- 'Havener'	SBig
§ - 'Jim Wilson'	CBcs CJun EPfP MBlu
- MOONGLOW	see *M. virginiana* 'Jim Wilson'
- 'Pink Halo'	SBig
'Vulcan'	CBcs CEnd CJun CMCN ELan EPfP IArd LRHS NHim NLar SBig SCoo
× ***watsonii***	see *M.* × *wieseneri*
'Wedding Vows'	CJun
'White Mystery'	CJun
§ × ***wieseneri***	CBcs CJun CMCN CRos EBee EPfP ERea LRHS MBlu NLar SPoG WPGP
- 'Aashild Kalleberg'	CBcs CJun WPGP
wilsonii ♀H6	CBcs CCVT CDul CExl CJun CMCN CRos CTho CTri ELan EPfP IArd IDee IRob LCro LOPS LRHS MBlu MGos MMuc MNrw SEND SMad WHar WPGP WSHC
- 'Gwen Baker'	CEnd CJun
- 'Highdownensis'	EBee
'Yaeko'	CBcs
'Yellow Fever'	CBcs CJun CTho EBee WPGP
'Yellow Garland'	CJun
'Yellow Lantern' ♀H6	CBcs CEnd CJun CRos EBee ELan EPfP GGGa LMaj LMil LRHS LSRN MAsh MBlu NLar NRHS SPoG SSta WPGP
'Yellow Sea'	CJun LRHS
Yuchelia No. 1	CBcs WPGP
yunnanensis	CBcs CCCN MPkF
zenii	CBcs CMCN IArd IDee
- 'Pink Parchment'	CJun

× *Mahoberberis* (*Berberidaceae*)

aquisargentii	CBcs CMac CRos EBee EMil EPfP LRHS MMuc MRav NLar SCob SEND WFar
'Dart's Desire'	NLar
miethkeana	SRms
§ ***neubertii***	NLar

Mahonia ✿ (*Berberidaceae*)

§ ***aquifolium***	CAco CAgr CBcs CDul CPer ECrN ESps ETMg GMcL GPoy MGos MMuc MRav SCob SEND SGol SPer SPlb SWvt WHar
- 'Apollo' ♀H5	CBcs CRos CSBt EBee ELan ELon EPfP ESps GMcL LCro LOPS LRHS LSRN MAsh MBlu MGos MJak MRav NLar SCob SCoo SPoG SRms SWvt WFar
- 'Atropurpurea'	CMac CRos CSBt CTsd ELan EPfP LRHS MRav NLar SPer
- 'Fascicularis'	see *M.* × *wagneri* 'Pinnacle'
- 'Smaragd'	CMac CRos ELan EPfP LRHS LSRN MBlu MGos MRav NLar SCob
- 'Versicolor'	MBlu
'Arthur Menzies'	LRHS NRHS
§ ***bealei***	CBcs CBod CDul CFil CSBt CTho ELan ELon EPfP ESps GMcL LRHS MAsh MGos MRav MSwo NEgg NLar NPer SCob SCoo SGol SLim SWvt
BLACKFOOT ('Bokrafoot'^{PBR})	ELan EPfP LRHS MAsh SLon
bodinieri	WPGP
- Og 93.033	WPGP
chochoco	CExl CFil
conferta	CFil
§ ***duclouxiana***	CFil
- KR 7692 new	WPGP
eurybracteata	CExl CFil LRHS WCru WPGP
- subsp. ***ganpinensis***	WPGP
- - 'Soft Caress'	CBcs CBod CHid CRos CTsd EBee ELan EPfP EUJe IDee LCro LOPS LRHS MGos MJak MPkF NLar NLos NRHS SCob SCoo SGol SMad SPoG SWvt
- 'Minganpi'^{PBR}	LSRN

- 'Sweet Winter'	LRHS MAsh MMrt SWvt
eutriphylla misapplied	see *M. trifolia*
fargesii	see *M. sheridaniana*
fortunei	CBcs CFil
- 'Winter Prince'	NLar
fremontii	SBrt SPhx
gracilipes	CExl CFil EPfP EWes GCal IDee IMou MBlu NLar SMad WAvo WCru WPGP
gracilis	CFil
haematocarpa	WPGP
hartwegii	CFil
huiliensis	see *M. sheridaniana*
japonica ♀H5	CAco CBar CBcs CMac CRos CTri EBee ECrN ELan EPfP ESps LRHS MAsh MGos MMuc MRav MSwo NLar NRHS SCob SEND SGbt SPer SPoG SRms SSta WCFE WHar
- 'Gold Dust'	CMac MBlu
lanceolata	CFil EBee WPGP
leschenaultii B&SWJ 9535	WCru
× ***lindsayae***	CFil WPGP
- 'Cantab' ♀H4	CFil EPfP SChF SMad WPGP
lomariifolia	see *M. oiwakensis* subsp. *lomariifolia*
longibracteata	GKin
mairei	see *M. duclouxiana*
× ***media***	ESps
- 'Buckland' ♀H4	CBcs CDul CMac CRos CTho EPfP ESps SCob SRms
- 'Charity'	Widely available
- 'Lionel Fortescue' ♀H4	CBcs CMac CRos CSBt CTho EBee ELan EMOT EPfP ESps GKin LRHS MAsh NEgg NRHS SCob SPer SWvt WHor
- 'Winter Sun' ♀H4	Widely available
moranensis	CExl CFil EBee
- T 292	WPGP
napaulensis	CFil NLar
- 'Maharajah'	IArd IDee IMou NLar
nervosa	CBcs CMac EPfP MBlu NLar WCru WPGP
- B&SWJ 9562	WCru
- B&SWJ 13580	WCru
neubertii	see × *Mahoberberis neubertii*
nevinii	SBrt
nitens	EBee WCru WPGP
- 'Cabaret'PBR ♀H4	CBcs CRos EBee EPfP LCro LOPS LRHS MAsh MBlu MGos MJak NRHS SCob SPoG SWvt
oiwakensis	NLar WPGP
- B&SWJ 371	WCru
- B&SWJ 3660	WCru
- PBR 371 from Hong Kong **new**	WCru
§ - subsp. ***lomariifolia*** ♀H4	CExl CFil CRos EPfP EWes LRHS SArc
- - var. ***tenuifoliola***	CFil
pallida	CExl CFil WPGP
- from Tamazunchale, Mexico	CFil
- from Zimapan, Mexico	CFil
'Pan's Peculiar'	WPGP
pinnata misapplied	see *M.* × *wagneri* 'Pinnacle'
pinnata (Lag.) Fedde 'Ken S. Howard'	NLar WPGP
- subsp. ***insularis*** 'Schnilemoon' **new**	WPGP
repens	NLar
- 'Rotundifolia'	SPlb
russellii	CFil
× ***savilliana***	CFil NLar WPGP
§ ***sheridaniana***	CFil
- Og 93033 **new**	WPGP
SIOUX ('Bokrasio'PBR)	CRos LRHS MAsh NRHS SPoG
§ ***trifolia***	CFil GCal LRHS
- EKB 4618	WPGP
trifoliolata var. ***glauca***	CEnd CFil
× ***wagneri***	SWvt
- 'Aldenhamensis'	NLar
- 'Fireflame'	GCal
- 'Hastings' Elegant'	NLar
§ - 'Pinnacle' ♀H5	CRos ELan EPfP LRHS MAsh MBlu NLar SPoG SWvt
- 'Sunset'	MBlu NLar
- 'Undulata'	MBlu NLar
- 'Vicaryi'	NLar

Maianthemum (*Asparagaceae*)

amoenum B&SWJ 10390	WCru
atropurpureum	WCru
bicolor	CTal LEdu
bifolium	CAvo CBct CHid CTal GLog GMaP LEdu MAvo MBel MMoz MNrw NBro NPnk SRms WCru WThu XLum
§ - subsp. ***kamtschaticum***	CAvo ECha EHrv EPPr LEdu MAvo NLar NRya WCot WPGP
- - B&SWJ 4360	WCru
- - CD&R 2300	WCru
- - var. ***pumilum***	EBee GCal LEdu WCru
canadense	CTal EAJP EBee EPot GCal GKev LEdu MNrw NBid WCru
chasmanthum	see *M. bifolium* subsp. *kamtschaticum*
comaltepecense B&SWJ 10215	WCru
dilatatum	see *M. bifolium* subsp. *kamtschaticum*
flexuosum	LEdu
- B&SWJ 9069	WCru
- B&SWJ 9079	WCru
- B&SWJ 9150	WCru
aff. ***flexuosum*** B&SWJ 9026	WCru
- B&SWJ 9055	WCru
formosanum B&SWJ 349	EPPr WCru
forrestii	WCru
fuscum	GEdr WCot WCru
- var. ***cordatum***	WCru
- 'Tangkhul Giant' **new**	LEdu
gigas B&SWJ 10470	WCru
henryi	EHrv GEdr LEdu WCru WPGP
- B&SWJ 4714 **new**	EHrv
- BWJ 7616	WCru
japonicum	CTal EHrv LEdu
- B&SWJ 1179	WCru
- B&SWJ 4714	WCru
- B&SWJ 7306	WCru
oleraceum	CBct CExl GEdr IRob LEdu LRHS WFar
- B&SWJ 2148	WCru
- purple-flowered	GEdr
paniculatum	EBee LEdu SHar
- B&SWJ 9137	WCru
- B&SWJ 9140	WCru
- purple-flowered B&SWJ 9139	WCru
pendent B&SWJ 10305 from Guatemala	WCru
purpureum	GEdr LEdu
- G-W&P 150	EPPr

racemosum 🏆H7	Widely available
- subsp. ***amplexicaule***	CAvo GCal ILea
- - 'Emily Moody'	CBct CExl CPou EBee EPPr EPfP SChF WCot WPGP
- 'Major'	CRos LRHS NRHS
aff. ***salvinii***	CBct CTal
- B&SWJ 9000	WCru
- B&SWJ 9088	WCru
- B&SWJ 10402	WCru
scilloideum	CTal
- B&SWJ 10407	WCru
* - var. ***roseum*** B&SWJ 10335	CBct WCru
stellatum	CBct CSam CTal EBee ECha EPPr EPfP GQue ILea LEdu LRHS MBel NChi NLar NPnk NRHS WCru WFar XLum
szechuanicum	WCru
tatsienense	CBct CExl EHrv GEdr LEdu WCru

Maihuenia (*Cactaceae*)

poeppigii	CCac SPlb
- F&W 9670	WCot
- JCA 2.575.600	WCot

Maihueniopsis (*Cactaceae*)

darwinii	SPlb
- LB 347	CCac
§ ***glomerata*** TG 63	CCac

Malope (*Malvaceae*)

trifida 'Alba' **new**	CRav
- 'Vulcan'	CRav

Malotigena (*Aizoaceae*)

§ ***frantiskae-niederlovae***	CCCN CSma CTal EDAr EPot GCrg GEdr GKev NHpl SMad WAbe WHal XLum
- 'Album'	see *M. frantiskae-niederlovae* 'White Nugget'
- 'Gold Nugget' 🏆H3	CRos ESps LRHS NRHS
§ - 'White Nugget'	CCCN CRos CSma CTal EDAr EPot EWes GEdr LRHS NHpl NRHS WAbe

Malus ✿ (*Rosaceae*)

sp.	LPra
§ 'Adirondack' 🏆H6	CLnd CSBt EBee EMOT EPfP EWTr MAsh MMuc NLar NOra SCoo SPoG WJas
'Admiration'	see *M.* 'Adirondack'
× ***adstringens*** 'Hopa'	CAgr CDul CLnd
- 'Simcoe'	EBee EMOT
'Aldenhamensis'	see *M.* × *purpurea* 'Aldenhamensis'
'Amberina'	CLnd
baccata	CDul CLnd CMCN CTho SCoo SEND SPlb
- var. ***mandshurica***	CTho
- 'Street Parade'	EWTr LMaj
(Ballerina Series) 'Ballerina Bolero' (D)	EMOT SDea
- 'Ballerina Polka' (D)	EMOT
- 'Ballerina Samba' (D)	LCro
§ ***bhutanica***	CDul CLnd
- 'Mandarin'	SCoo
'Bramley 20' (C)	CSBt
brevipes	CLnd LRHS SCoo
- 'Wedding Bouquet' 🏆H6	EBee EMOT EPfP ERea LBuc LCro LSRN MAsh NLar NOra SPer WMou
'Butterball' 🏆H6	CDul CLnd CSBt CTho EBee ECrN EMOT EPfP ERea ESps LMaj LRHS NOra SCoo SLim SPer SPoG SRms SVic WHar WJas WMou WWct
'Candymint Sargent'	CLnd ERea NOra SLim SPoG
'Cave Hill'	CLnd
'Cheal's Scarlet'	CHab
* 'Cheal's Weeping'	CAco CLnd CMac EMOT EWTr MJak NEgg SRms WMou
COCCINELLA ('Courtarou')	LMaj SGol
'Comtesse de Paris' 🏆H6	CDul CLnd EBee EPfP LRHS MAsh MBlu NLar NOra
CORALBURST ('Coralcole')	ERea MAsh NOra
coronaria var. ***dasycalyx*** 'Charlottae' (d)	CCVT CDul CLnd EWTr LPra SPer
- 'Elk River'	EPfP MAsh NOra SCoo
'Cowichan'	CLnd ECrN
'Crimson Brilliant'	CLnd
'Crittenden'	EPfP MAsh MRav
'Dartmouth'	CDul CHab CLnd CSBt CTri
'Directeur Moerlands'	CArg CCVT CSBt ECrN EMOT EPfP LMaj LRHS NOra SCoo SEND SPer SWvt WHar
domestica 'Acklam Russet' (D)	CHab SKee
- 'Acme' (D)	ECrN SDea
- 'Adams's Pearmain' (D)	CHab CLnd CTho CTri ECrN ERea MAsh NOra SCob SDea SKee WHar WWct
- 'Admiral'[PBR] (D)	ECrN ERea
- 'Akane' (D)	SDea
- 'Akerö' (D)	SKee
- 'Alfriston' (C)	CAgr CHab SKee
§ - 'Alkmene' (D) 🏆H6	CAgr ECrN NOra SDea
- 'All Doer' (C/D/Cider)	EMOT
- 'Allen's Everlasting' (D)	SDea SKee
- 'Allington Pippin' (D)	CHab CSBt CTho CTri ECrN ERea MGos NOra SDea SKee WHar
- AMBASSY ('Dalil'[PBR]) (D)	EBee
- 'American Mother'	see *M. domestica* 'Mother'
- 'Ananas Reinette' (D)	CHab ECrN SKee
- 'Anna Boelens' (D)	SDea
- 'Annie Elizabeth' (C)	CAgr CDul CHab ECrN EMOT ERea ESps IArd MGos MRai NOra SDea SKee SVic WHar WJas WWct
- 'Anniversary' (D)	SDea
- 'Antonovka' (C)	SKee
- 'Api' (D)	EMOT ERea LSRN NOra NPri SCob SKee WHar
- 'Ard Cairn Russet' (D)	ECrN IArd SDea
- 'Arkansas' (D)	SKee
- 'Arthur Turner' (C) 🏆H6	CCVT CHab CLnd CTri ECrN EMOT EPom ERea ESps IRob LBuc MWat NOra SDea SKee WHar WJas
- 'Ashmead's Kernel' (D) 🏆H6	Widely available
- 'Ashton Bitter' (Cider)	CHab CTri
- 'Askham Pippin' (F)	MCoo
- 'Autumn Pearmain' (D)	SDea WHar
- 'Baker's Delicious' (D)	EBee ECrN ERea NOra SDea SKee WHar
- 'Ballyvaughan Seedling' (D)	IArd
- 'Balsam'	see *M. domestica* 'Green Balsam'
- 'Banana Pippin' (F)	CEnd
- 'Banns' (D)	ECrN ERea
- 'Bardsey' (D)	CAgr CArg CHab EPom ERea NOra SKee WGwG WHar
- 'Barnack Beauty' (D)	CHab LEdu NOra SKee
- 'Baron Ward' (C)	CHab
- 'Bascombe's Mystery' (D)	SKee
- 'Baxter's Pearmain' (D)	ECrN SDea

- 'Beauty of Bath' (D)	CAgr CArg CCVT CDul CHab CLnd CTho CTri ECrN ELan EMOT EPom ERea ESps LBuc MRav NOra SDea SKee SPer WHar WJas WWct
- 'Beauty of Hants' (C/D)	ECrN SKee
- 'Beauty of Kent' (C)	SDea SKee
- 'Beauty of Moray' (C)	SKee
- 'Beeley Pippin' (D)	SDea SKee
- 'Bell Apple' (Cider/C)	CTho
- 'Belle de Boskoop' (C/D) 🏆^{H6}	CAgr CHab ECrN MCoo NOra SCob SDea SKee
- 'Belvoir Seedling' (C/D)	MRai
- 'Bembridge Beauty' (F)	CHab SDea
- 'Benenden Early' (D)	SKee
- 'Ben's Red' (D)	CAgr CEnd CFGn CTho SKee
- 'Bess Pool' (D)	CHab MCoo SDea
- 'Bewley Down Pippin'	see *M. domestica* 'Crimson King' (Cider/C)
- 'Bickington Grey' (Cider)	CTho
- 'Billy Down Pippin' (F)	CTho
- 'Black Dabinett' (Cider)	CEnd CTho ERea
- 'Blenheim Orange' (C/D) 🏆^{H6}	Widely available
- 'Blood of the Boyne' (D)	IArd
- 'Bloody Ploughman' (D)	CHab ECrN ERea ESps NOra SKee SLon WHar
- 'Blue Moon' (D)	LRHS SPoG
- 'Blue Pearmain' (D)	SDea SKee
- BOLERO	see *M. domestica* 'Tuscan'
- 'Boston Russet'	see *M. domestica* 'Roxbury Russet'
- 'Bountiful' (C)	CAgr CDul CLnd CMac CSBt CTri ECrN EMOT EPom ESps LRHS LSRN MAsh MRav NOra SDea SKee SSFT WHar WWct
- 'Bow Hill Pippin' (C)	SKee
- 'Box Apple' (D)	SKee
- 'Braeburn' (D)	CAgr CDul CLnd CSBt CTri ECrN EMOT EPom ERea ESps LBuc LEdu LRHS MWat NOra SCob SDea SEND SEWo SKee SPer WHar WJas
- 'Braeburn Hillwell' (D)	EPom NOra
- 'Braintree Seedling' (D)	ECrN
- 'Bramley's Seedling' (C) 🏆^{H6}	Widely available
- 'Bramley's Seedling' clone 20 (F)	CFGn CTsd ERea LSRN MAsh MNHC MWat NLar NOra SCoo SDea SKee SLim SPoG WHar WWct
- 'Bread Fruit' (C/D)	CEnd CFGn
- 'Brenchley Pippin' (D)	SKee
- 'Bridgwater Pippin' (C)	SKee
- 'Bright Future' (D)	EPom NOra WWct
- 'Brith Mawr' (C)	WGwG
- 'Broad-eyed Pippin' (C)	SKee
- 'Broadholme Beauty' (C)	EPom MAsh NOra WHar
- 'Brookes's' (D)	SKee WHar
- 'Brown Crofton' (D)	IArd
- 'Brown Snout' (Cider)	CTho
- 'Brownlee's Russet' (D)	CAgr CHab CTho CTri MCoo NEgg NOra SDea SKee WHar
- 'Brown's Apple' (Cider)	CAgr CHab CTri ECrN ERea MRai NOra
- 'Burr Knot' (C)	SKee
- 'Bushey Grove' (C)	SDea
- 'Byfleet Seedling' (C)	SKee
- 'Calville Blanc d'Hiver' (D)	NOra SKee
- 'Cambusnethan Pippin' (D)	SKee
- 'Camelot' (Cider/C)	EMOT
§ - 'Captain Broad' (Cider/D)	CEnd CTho

- 'Captain Kidd' (D)	EPom ERea NOra SKee WHar
- 'Carlisle Codlin' (C)	NLar NOra SDea
- 'Caroline' (D)	ECrN ERea
- 'Carswell's Honeydew' (D)	SKee
- 'Catherine' (C)	ECrN
- 'Catshead' (C)	CAgr CHab CTri ECrN IArd NOra SDea SKee WHar WWct
- 'Cellini' (C)	NOra SDea SKee
- 'Cevaal' (D)	WWct
- 'Channel Beauty' (D)	WGwG
- 'Charles Ross' (C/D) 🏆^{H6}	Widely available
- 'Charlotte'^{PBR} (C)	ECrN EMOT SDea
- 'Cheddar Cross' (D)	CAgr CCVT CTri ECrN SKee
- 'Chelmsford Wonder' (C)	ECrN SKee
- 'Chisel Jersey' (Cider)	CAgr CTri MRai NOra SKee
- 'Chivers Delight' (D)	CAgr ECrN EMOT EPom ERea LRHS MCoo NOra SDea SKee WHar WJas
- 'Christmas Pearmain' (D)	CAgr CTho ECrN MRai SDea SKee
- 'Christmas Pippin'^{PBR} (D)	CArg CRos CTri EPom ERea LBuc LCro LRHS MCoo MWat NLar NOra NRHS
- 'Cider Lady's Finger' (Cider)	SKee
- 'Cissy' (D)	WGwG
- 'Claygate Pearmain' (D)	CAgr CHab CTho CTri ECrN ERea MCoo NOra SDea SKee SVic WHar
- 'Clopton Red' (D)	ECrN SKee
- 'Cobra' (F)	CAgr LBuc MAsh MCoo NOra NPri SKee WHar WJas
- 'Cockett's Red' (D) **new**	SKee
- 'Cockle Pippin' (D)	CAgr MRai SDea
- 'Cockpit' (C)	CHab
- 'Coleman's Seedling' (Cider)	CTho
- 'Collogett Pippin' (C/Cider)	CEnd CTho CTsd
- 'Colonel Vaughan' (C/D)	SKee
- 'Colonel Yate' (D)	SKee
- 'Core Blimey' (D) **new**	LRHS
- 'Cornish Aromatic' (D)	CAgr CDul CFGn CTho CTri CTsd NOra SDea SKee WHar
- 'Cornish Gilliflower' (D)	CAgr CEnd CHab CTho EBee ECrN MCoo NOra SDea SKee WHar
- 'Cornish Honeypin' (D)	CEnd SKee
- 'Cornish Longstem' (D)	CAgr CEnd
- 'Cornish Mother' (D)	CEnd CFGn CTho CTsd
- 'Cornish Pine' (D)	CEnd SDea
- 'Coronation' (D)	CHab SDea
- 'Cortland' (D)	SKee
- 'Costard' (C)	CHab SKee
- 'Cottenham Seedling' (C)	SKee
- 'Coul Blush' (D)	SKee
- 'Court of Wick' (D)	CAgr CDul CHab CTho CTri ECrN NOra SVic WHar
- 'Court Pendu Plat' (D)	CAgr CArg CHab GQue LEdu MAsh MWat NOra SDea SKee SSFT WHar WJas WWct
- 'Court Royal' (Cider)	SKee
- 'Cox Cymraeg' (D)	WGwG
- 'Cox's Orange Pippin' (D)	Widely available
- 'Cox's Pomona' (C)	SDea SKee WHar
- 'Cox's Rouge de Flandres' (D)	SKee
- 'Cox's Selfing' (D)	CDul CMac CSBt CTri EPfP ESps LBuc MAsh MGos MNHC NLar SDea SKee SPer SPoG WHar WJas WWct
- 'Crawley Beauty' (C)	CAgr CHab SDea SSFT WHar
- 'Crawley Reinette' (D)	CHab

	- 'Crimson Beauty of Bath' (D)	CAgr
	- 'Crimson Bramley' (C)	IArd IRob
	- 'Crimson Cox' (D)	SDea
§	- 'Crimson King' (Cider/C)	CAgr MRai
	- 'Crimson King' (D)	CAgr CHab CTri
	- 'Crimson Peasgood' (C)	ECrN
	- 'Crimson Queening' (D)	SKee WHar
	- 'Crimson Victoria' (Cider)	CTho
	- CRISPIN	see *M. domestica* 'Mutsu'
	- 'Croen Mochyn' (D)	WGwG
§	- 'Crowngold' (D)	EPom
	- 'Curl Tail' (D)	SKee
	- 'Cutler Grieve' (D)	SDea
	- 'Dabinett' (Cider)	CAgr CArg CHab CTho CTri EMOT EPom ERea LBuc LRHS MRai NOra SDea SKee WHar WWct
	- 'D'Arcy Spice' (D)	CAgr ECrN EPfP ERea GQue MCoo MWat NOra SDea SKee WHar WWct
	- 'Deacon's Blushing Beauty' (C/D)	SDea
	- 'Deacon's Millennium' (D)	SDea
	- 'Decio' (D)	SKee
	- 'Devon Crimson Queen' (D)	CTho
	- 'Devonshire Buckland' (C)	CEnd CTho
	- 'Devonshire Crimson Queen' (D)	SDea
	- 'Devonshire Quarrenden' (D)	CAgr CDul CHab CTho CTsd ERea NOra SDea SKee SVic WHar
	- 'Diamond' (D)	WGwG
	- 'Diamond Jubilee' (D)	SKee
	- 'Discovery' (D) ♀H6	Widely available
	- 'Doctor Harvey' (C)	ECrN ERea SKee
	- 'Doctor Kidd's Orange Red'	see *M. domestica* 'Kidd's Orange Red'
	- 'Doddin' (D)	WWct
	- 'Domino' (C)	MCoo
	- 'Don's Delight' (C)	CTho
	- 'Downton Pippin' (D)	CHab WHar
	- 'Dredge's Fame' (D)	SKee
	- 'Duchess of Oldenburg' (C)	NOra SKee
	- 'Duchess's Favourite' (D)	SKee
	- 'Duke of Cornwall' (C)	CTho
	- 'Duke of Devonshire' (D)	CSBt CTri SDea SKee
	- 'Dumeller's Seedling'	see *M. domestica* 'Dummellor's Seedling'
§	- 'Dummellor's Seedling' (C) ♀H6	CHab CTri MCoo NOra SDea SKee WHar
	- 'Dunkerton Late Sweet' (Cider)	CCVT CHab EMOT LBuc
	- 'Dunn's Seedling' (D)	SDea
§	- 'Dutch Codlin' (C)	MRai
	- 'Early Blenheim' (D/C)	CEnd
	- 'Early Bower' (D)	CEnd
	- 'Early Julyan' (C)	SKee
	- 'Early Victoria'	see *M. domestica* 'Emneth Early'
	- EARLY WINDSOR	see *M. domestica* 'Alkmene'
	- 'Early Worcester'	see *M. domestica* 'Tydeman's Early Worcester'
	- 'Easter Orange' (D)	SKee
	- 'Eccleston Pippin' (D)	SKee
	- 'Ecklinville' (C)	SDea
	- 'Edith Hopwood' (D)	ECrN SKee
	- 'Edward VII' (C) ♀H6	CHab EMOT NOra SDea SKee WHar WWct
	- 'Egremont Russet' (D) ♀H6	Widely available
	- 'Ellis' Bitter' (Cider)	EMOT SKee SVic

	- 'Ellison's Orange' (D) ♀H6	CAgr CDul CHab CMac CSBt CTri ECrN EMOT EPfP EPom ESps LBuc MMuc MWat NOra SCob SDea SEND SKee SLon SPer SVic WHar WJas WWct
	- 'Elstar' (D) ♀H6	CCVT CLnd ECrN EMOT EPom NOra SDea SKee WHar
	- 'Elton Beauty' (D)	SDea
§	- 'Emneth Early' (C) ♀H6	CAgr CHab ECrN ERea NOra SDea SKee WJas WWct
	- 'Empire' (D)	NOra SDea SKee
	- 'Encore' (C)	SDea
	- 'English Codlin' (C)	CTho CTri ERea
	- 'Epicure'	see *M. domestica* 'Laxton's Epicure'
	- 'Ernie's Russet' (D)	SDea
	- 'Eros' (D)	ECrN
	- 'Essex Pippin' (D)	ECrN
	- 'Evening Gold' (C)	SDea
	- 'Eve's Delight' (D)	SDea
	- 'Excelsior' (C)	ECrN
	- 'Exeter Cross' (D)	CSBt ECrN SDea
	- 'Fair Maid of Devon' (Cider)	CAgr CDul CEnd CTho
	- 'Fall Pippin' (D)	SKee
	- 'Falstaff'PBR (D)	CAgr CDul CTri ECrN EPfP EPom ESps LSRN MGos NOra SCob SCoo SDea SPer WHar
	- 'Fameuse' (D)	NOra SKee
	- 'Farmer's Glory' (D)	CAgr CTho
	- 'Fiesta'PBR (D) ♀H6	Widely available
	- 'Fillbarrel' (Cider)	CHab
	- 'Fillingham Pippin' (C)	CHab SKee
	- 'Firedance' (D)	LRHS SPoG
	- 'Firmgold' (D)	SDea
	- 'First and Last' (D)	NOra
	- 'Flame' (D)	ECrN SKee
	- 'Flamenco'	see *M. domestica* 'Obelisk'
§	- 'Flower of Kent' (C)	CHab EPom MAsh NOra SDea SKee
	- 'Flower of the Town' (D)	CHab
	- 'Forge' (D)	CAgr CHab SDea SKee
	- 'Fortune'	see *M. domestica* 'Laxton's Fortune'
	- 'Foster's Seedling' (D)	SKee
	- 'Foxwhelp' (Cider)	CHab SKee
	- 'Francis' (D)	ECrN
	- 'French Codlin'	see *M. domestica* 'Dutch Codlin'
	- 'French Crab' (C)	SDea
	- 'Freyberg' (D)	NOra SKee
	- 'Fuji' (D)	LMaj NOra SDea SKee
	- 'Gala' (D)	CSBt CTri EBee EPom ESps NOra SCob SCoo SDea SKee WHar
	- 'Galaxy'PBR (D)	NOra
	- 'Galloway Pippin' (C)	NLar NOra SKee
	- 'Garden Fountain' (D)	LRHS
	- 'Gascoyne's Scarlet' (C/D)	SDea SKee WHar
	- 'Gavin' (D)	CAgr SDea
	- 'Genesis II' (C/D)	SDea
	- 'Genet Moyle' (C/Cider)	CTri MCoo WHar
	- 'George Carpenter' (D)	CTri SDea
	- 'George Cave' (D)	CDul CTho ECrN EMOT ESps IArd MCoo NOra SDea SKee WHar WJas
	- 'George Neal' (C)	CAgr SDea SKee
	- 'Gibbon's Russet' (D)	IArd
	- 'Gladstone' (D)	CAgr NOra SKee WHar WWct
	- 'Glansevin' (D)	WGwG
§	- 'Glass Apple' (C/D)	CEnd CTho
	- 'Glockenapfel' (C)	SKee
	- 'Gloria Mundi' (C)	SDea
	- 'Gloster '69' (D)	CLnd SDea SKee
	- 'Gloucester Cross' (D)	SKee
	- 'Golden Ball' (Cider)	CTho

	- 'Golden Bittersweet' (D)	CAgr CTho
	- 'Golden Delicious' (D) ♀^{H6}	CCVT CDul CMac CSBt EBee ECrN ELan EMOT EPom ESps LBuc MJak NOra NPri SCob SDea SEWo SKee SVic WHar
	- 'Golden Gate' (D)	SPoG
	- 'Golden Glow' (C)	SDea
	- 'Golden Harvey' (D)	CAgr SKee
	- 'Golden Jubilee' (F)	CEnd
	- 'Golden Knob' (D)	CTri SKee
	- 'Golden Noble' (C) ♀^{H6}	CAgr CTri ECrN EMOT ERea IArd MCoo NOra SDea SKee
	- 'Golden Nugget' (D)	CAgr SKee
	- 'Golden Pippin' (C)	CAgr NOra WHar
	- 'Golden Reinette' (D)	SKee
	- 'Golden Russet' (D)	CAgr ECrN NOra SDea SKee WHar
	- 'Golden Spire' (C)	CHab MCoo NOra SDea SKee WHar
	- 'Gooseberry' (C)	SKee
	- 'Grandpa Ailes' (D)	CTho
	- 'Grandpa Buxton' (C)	CHab
	- 'Granny Smith' (D)	CBcs CDul ECrN EMOT ESps IBoy LMaj LSRN NOra SDea SKee SPer SVic WHar
	- 'Gravenstein' (D)	CHab NOra SDea SKee
§	- 'Green Balsam' (D)	CHab CTri
	- 'Green Roland' (C/D)	ECrN ERea
	- 'Greenfinch' (D)	LRHS
	- 'Greensleeves'^{PBR} (D) ♀^{H6}	CAgr CDul CMac CTri EBee ECrN EMOT EPfP EPom ESps MAsh MGos MMuc NLar NOra SCob SDea SEND SKee SLim SPer SSFT WHar WJas WWct
	- 'Greenup's Pippin' (D)	CHab SKee
	- 'Grenadier' (C) ♀^{H6}	CAgr CHab CLnd CTri ECrN EMOT EPom IBoy IRob MGos MJak MMuc NLar NOra SCob SDea SEND SKee SLon SPer SSFT WHar WJas
	- 'Guillevic' (Cider)	CHab
	- 'Gwell Na Mil' (D)	WGwG
	- 'Halstow Natural' (Cider)	CAgr
	- 'Hambledon Deux Ans' (C)	SDea
	- 'Hambling's Seedling' (C)	SKee
	- 'Harling Hero' (D)	ECrN
§	- 'Harry Master's Jersey' (Cider)	CAgr CFGn CTho CTri EPom NOra SDea SKee WHar WWct
	- 'Harvey' (C)	SDea SKee
	- 'Hawthornden' (C)	CHab SKee
	- 'Hereford Cross' (D)	SKee
	- 'Herefordshire Beefing' (C)	SKee
	- 'Herefordshire Redstreak' (Cider)	CAgr CArg EMOT EPom LBuc NOra WHar
	- 'Herefordshire Russet'^{PBR} (D)	CDul CFGn EMOT EPom ERea LBuc LRHS MAsh MCoo NLar NOra NRHS SKee SPer WHar WJas WWct
	- 'Herring's Pippin' (C/D)	CDul CTri SDea SKee
	- 'Hibernal' (C)	SKee
	- 'High View Pippin' (D)	SKee
	- 'Histon Favourite' (D/C)	SKee
	- 'Hoary Morning' (C)	CTho ECrN SDea SKee
	- 'Hocking's Green' (C/D)	CAgr CEnd CTho CTsd
	- 'Holland Pippin' (C)	SKee WHar
	- 'Hollow Core' (C)	CAgr
	- 'Holstein' (D)	LMaj NOra SDea SKee WHar
	- 'Honey Pippin' (D)	ECrN SKee
§	- 'Honeygold' (D)	CEnd
	- 'Hormead Pearmain' (C)	SKee
	- 'Horsford Prolific' (D)	ECrN
	- 'Howgate Wonder' (C) ♀^{H6}	CAgr CCVT CDul CHab CLnd CSBt CTri EBee ECrN EMOT EPfP EPom ESps LBuc MAsh MMuc MWat NOra SDea SKee SPer SVic WHar WJas WWct
	- 'Hubbard's Pearmain' (D)	ECrN SKee
	- 'Hunter's Majestic' (D/C)	ECrN
	- 'Huntingdon Codlin' (D)	SKee
	- 'Idared' (D)	ECrN NOra SDea SKee SVic WHar
	- 'Improved Dove' (Cider)	MRai
	- 'Improved Keswick' (C/D)	CEnd
	- 'Improved Lambrook Pippin' (Cider)	CTri
	- 'Ingall's Pippin' (D)	SKee
	- 'Ingall's Red' (D)	SKee
	- 'Ingrid Marie' (D)	SDea SKee
	- 'Irish Peach' (D)	CAgr CFGn CHab CTri ECrN ERea ESps IArd MCoo NOra SDea SKee WHar
	- 'Isaac Newton's Tree'	see *M. domestica* 'Flower of Kent'
	- 'Isle of Wight Pippin' (D)	SDea
	- 'Isle of Wight Russet' (D)	SDea
	- 'Jackson's'	see *M. domestica* 'Crimson King' (Cider/C)
	- 'James Grieve' (D) ♀^{H6}	Widely available
	- 'Jerseymac' (D)	SDea
	- 'Jester' (D)	ECrN SDea SKee
	- 'Joaneting' (D)	CAgr CHab
	- 'John Broad'	see *M. domestica* 'Captain Broad'
	- 'John Standish' (D)	CAgr CTri ERea SDea SKee
	- 'John Toucher's'	see *M. domestica* 'Crimson King' (Cider/C)
	- 'Johnny Andrews' (Cider)	CAgr
	- 'Johnny Voun' (D)	CEnd CTho
	- 'Jonagold' (D) ♀^{H6}	CLnd CTri ECrN ELan EMOT EPom ESps IArd IBoy NLar NOra SDea SKee SPer WWct
	- 'Jonagold Crowngold'	see *M. domestica* 'Crowngold'
§	- 'Jonagored'^{PBR} (D)	NOra SDea WHar
	- 'Jonathan' (D)	NOra SDea SKee
	- 'Jordan's Weeping' (C)	SDea
	- 'Josephine' (D)	SDea
	- 'Joybells' (D)	SKee
	- 'Jubilee'	see *M. domestica* 'Royal Jubilee'
	- 'Julie's Late Golden' (F)	CTri
	- 'Jumbo' (C/D)	CFGn CLnd EMOT MAsh MCoo NOra SKee WHar WJas
	- 'Jupiter'^{PBR} (D) ♀^{H6}	CAgr CDul CSBt CTri ECrN EMOT ESps LSRN MJak MRav NLar NOra SDea SKee SLon WHar WJas
	- 'Kapai Red Jonathan' (D)	SDea
	- 'Karmijn de Sonnaville' (D)	MRai NOra SDea SKee
§	- 'Katja' (D)	Widely available
	- KATY	see *M. domestica* 'Katja'
	- 'Kemp' (F)	SDea
	- 'Kenneth' (D)	WGwG
	- 'Kent' (D) ♀^{H6}	ECrN SDea SKee
	- 'Kentish Fillbasket' (C)	SKee
	- 'Kerry Pippin' (D)	IArd IRob SKee
	- 'Keswick Codlin' (C)	CHab CRos ECrN ERea GQue MCoo NEgg NLar NOra SDea SKee WHar WJas
§	- 'Kidd's Orange Red' (D) ♀^{H6}	CAgr CDul CMac CRos CTri ECrN EMOT EPfP EPom ESps LBuc LRHS MWat NOra SDea SKee SLon WHar WWct
	- 'King Byerd' (C/D)	CEnd CTho
	- 'King Charles' Pearmain' (D)	SKee

- 'King Coffee' (D)	WHar
- 'King Luscious' (D)	SDea
§ - 'King of the Pippins' (D) ♀H6	CFGn CHab CLnd CTri ECrN EPom ESps MCoo NOra SDea SKee SVic WHar
- 'King of Tompkins County' (D)	SKee
- 'King Russet' (D) ♀H6	SDea
- 'King's Acre Pippin' (D)	NOra SDea SKee WHar
- 'Kingston Bitter' (Cider)	CTho
- 'Kingston Black' (Cider/C)	CAgr CArg CDul CEnd CHab CTho CTri EMOT EPom LBuc MGos NOra SDea SKee
- 'Knobby Russet' (D)	SKee
- 'Lady Henniker' (C)	CDul CEnd CHab ECrN SDea SKee WHar
- 'Lady Isabel' (D)	SKee
- 'Lady Lambourne' (C/D)	CHab
- 'Lady of the Wemyss' (C)	SKee
- 'Lady Sudeley' (D)	CEnd CHab SDea SKee
- 'Lady's Finger' (C/D)	CEnd
- 'Lady's Finger of Lancaster' (C/D)	CHab SKee
- 'Lady's Finger of Offaly' (D)	IArd SDea
- 'Lamb Abbey Pearmain' (D)	SKee
- 'Lambourne Pippin' (F)	CTho
- 'Lane's Prince Albert' (C) ♀H6	CAgr CHab CLnd CSBt CTri ECrN EMOT EPfP MGos MRav MWat NOra SCoo SDea SKee SVic WHar WJas
- 'Langley Pippin' (D)	SDea
- 'Lass o' Gowrie' (C)	SKee
§ - 'Laxton's Epicure' (D) ♀H6	CAgr CHab CTri ECrN EMOT ESps SDea SKee WHar
§ - 'Laxton's Fortune' (D) ♀H6	CArg CDul CHab CMac CSBt CTri ECrN ESps IArd IRob NOra SDea SKee WHar WJas WWct
- 'Laxton's Pearmain' (D)	MCoo
- 'Laxton's Royalty' (D)	SDea
§ - 'Laxton's Superb' (D)	CBcs CCVT CDul CHab CLnd CMac CSBt CTri ECrN EMOT EPom ERea ESps GKin IBoy LBuc MCoo NOra NPri SCob SDea SEWo SKee SPer SVic WHar WJas WWct
- 'Leicester Burton'	see *M. domestica* 'Dutch Codlin'
- 'Lemon Pippin' (C)	EBee ECrN ELan NOra SDea SKee WHar
- 'Liberty' (D)	SDea
- 'Limelight' (D) ♀H6	EBee EMOT ERea ESps MAsh MCoo NLar NOra SCoo SKee SSFT WHar
- 'Linda' (D)	SKee
- 'Link Wonder' (F)	CEnd
- 'Little Pax' (D)	EPom LCro LOPS MCoo NLar NOra
- 'Llwyd Hanner Goch' (D) **new**	WGwG
- 'Lodgemore Nonpareil' (D)	SKee
- 'Lodi' (C)	SDea
- 'London Pearmain' (D)	ECrN
- 'London Pippin' (C)	CAgr SKee
- 'Longkeeper' (D)	CAgr CEnd
- 'Lord Burghley' (D)	SDea
- 'Lord Derby' (C)	CAgr CDul CHab CLnd CMac CTho ECrN EMOT EPom ESps IRob MRav NOra SDea SEND SKee SPer SSFT SVic WHar WWct
- 'Lord Grosvenor' (C)	WHar
- 'Lord Hindlip' (D)	CHab NOra SDea SKee WWct
- 'Lord Lambourne' (D) ♀H6	CAgr CDul CHab CLnd CMac CSBt CTri ECrN ELan EMOT EPom ESps LSRN MAsh MCoo MGos MWat NLar NOra SDea SKee SLon SPer WHar WJas WWct
- 'Lord of the Isles' (Cider)	CAgr
- 'Lord Stradbroke' (C)	ECrN
- 'Lord Suffield' (C)	CTri ECrN
- 'Lough Tree of Wexford' (D)	IArd
- 'Lucombe's Pine' (D)	CAgr CEnd CTho ECrN SVic
- 'Lucombe's Seedling' (D)	CTho
- 'Lynn's Pippin' (D)	ECrN SKee
- 'Mabbott's Pearmain' (D)	SDea
- 'Machen' (D)	WGwG
- 'Maclean's Favourite' (D)	ECrN
- 'Madresfield Court' (D)	SDea SKee WWct
- 'Major' (Cider)	CAgr MRai
- 'Maldon Wonder' (D)	ECrN
- 'Malling Kent' (D)	SDea
- 'Maltster' (D)	MCoo SKee
- 'Manaccan Primrose' (C/D)	CEnd CFGn
- 'Mank's Codlin' (C)	SKee
- 'Marged Nicolas' (D)	WGwG
- 'Margil' (D)	SDea SKee WHar
- 'Markham Pippin' (D)	MCoo
- 'Marriage-maker' (D)	MRai SKee
- 'Martin's Custard' (C)	MRai
- 'Mary's Apple' (F)	SDea
- 'Maxton' (D)	ECrN
- 'May Queen' (D)	SDea SKee WWct
- 'Maypole'PBR (D)	SDea
- 'McIntosh' (D)	NOra SKee
- 'Médaille d'Or' (Cider)	SKee
- 'Melon' (D)	SDea
- 'Melrose' (D)	ECrN
- 'Merchant Apple' (D)	CTri
- 'Mère de Ménage' (C)	SDea SKee WHar
- 'Meridian'PBR (D)	CAgr ECrN LSRN MCoo NOra SDea
- 'Merton Charm' (D)	SKee
- 'Merton Knave' (D)	SDea
- 'Merton Russet' (D)	SCob SDea SKee
- 'Merton Worcester' (D)	ECrN SDea SKee
- 'Michaelmas Red' (D)	SKee
- 'Michelin' (Cider)	CAgr CTri MGos MRai NOra SDea SKee WHar WWct
- MIEL D'OR	see *M. domestica* 'Honeygold'
- 'Miller's Seedling' (D)	NOra SKee
- 'Millicent Barnes' (D)	SDea
- 'Mingan' (D)	MRai
- 'Mollie's Delicious' (D)	SKee
- 'Monarch' (C)	CAgr CTri ECrN EPom SDea SKee
- 'Monmouthshire Green' (D)	WGwG
- 'Montfort' (D)	ECrN
- 'Morgan's Sweet' (C/Cider)	CEnd CHab CTho CTri NOra SDea SKee
- 'Moss Orchard' (D) **new**	LPra
- 'Moss's Seedling' (D)	SDea
§ - 'Mother' (D) ♀H6	CAgr CEnd CLnd CTri ECrN MRai SDea SKee
§ - 'Mutsu' (C/D)	CLnd CTri ECrN EMOT MRav NOra SDea SKee
- 'Mylor Pike' (D)	CEnd
- 'Nancy Jackson' (C)	CHab SKee
- 'Nant Gwrtheyrn' (D)	WGwG
- 'Nettlestone Pippin' (D)	SDea
- 'Newton Wonder' (C)	CAgr CDul CHab CSBt CTho CTri ECrN EMOT EPom ERea ESps MCoo

MGos NOra SDea SKee WHar WJas WWct

- 'Newtown Pippin' (D) SDea
- 'Nine Square' (D) CTho
- 'Nittany Red' (D) SDea
- 'Nolan Pippin' (D) ECrN
- 'Nonpareil' (D) SKee WHar
- 'Norfolk Beauty' (C) ECrN ERea SKee
- 'Norfolk Beefing' (C) CHab ECrN ERea NOra SDea SKee
- 'Norfolk Royal' (D) ECrN ERea NOra SDea SKee
- 'Norfolk Royal Russet' (D) ECrN ERea NOra SKee
- 'Norfolk Summer Broadend' (C) ECrN
- 'Norfolk Winter Coleman' (C) ERea
- 'Northern Greening' (C) WHar
- § 'Northwood' (Cider) CTho
- 'Nutmeg Pippin' (D) ECrN SDea
- NUVAR CHEERFULL GOLD (D) SKee
- NUVAR FRECKLES (D) SKee
- NUVAR GOLDEN HILLS (D) SKee
- 'Oaken Pin' (D) CEnd CTho
- § 'Obelisk'^{PBR} (D) EMOT MAsh NOra SDea SKee
- 'Old Pearmain' (D) SDea WHar
- 'Old Somerset Russet' (D) CTho
- 'Onibury Pippin' (D) WHar
- 'Opalescent' (D) CEnd SKee
- 'Orin' (D) SKee
- 'Orleans Reinette' (D) CAgr CTri ECrN EMOT EPom ESps LBuc LRHS MWat NOra SDea SKee WHar WJas WWct
- 'Oslin' (D) SKee
- 'Otava'^{PBR} (C/D) SKee
- 'Owen Thomas' (D) SKee
- 'Paignton Marigold' (Cider) CTho
- 'Palmer's Rosey' (D) SKee
- 'Payhembury' (C/Cider) CAgr CTri
- 'Peacemaker' (D) SKee
- 'Pear Apple' (D) CAgr CEnd CTho MRai
- 'Pearl' (D) NOra SDea
- 'Peasgood's Nonsuch' (C) ♀^{H6} CAgr CHab ECrN EPom ERea IArd LRHS LSRN MAsh NOra SDea SKee SLon
- 'Pendragon' (D) CEnd CTho
- 'Peter Lock' (C/D) CAgr CEnd CTho
- 'Peter's Pippin' (D) SDea
- 'Peter's Seedling' (D) SDea
- 'Pethyre' (Cider) CCVT
- 'Pig Aderyn' (C) CHab WGwG
- 'Pig y Colomen' (C) WGwG
- 'Pig's Nose Pippin' (D) CEnd CTsd SKee
- 'Pig's Nose Pippin' Type III (D) CAgr
- 'Pig's Snout' (Cider/C/D) CEnd MRai
- 'Pine Apple Russet of Devon' (D) CEnd
- 'Pine Golden Pippin' (D) SKee
- 'Pineapple Russet' (C/D) CAgr ERea MAsh
- 'Pinova'^{PBR} (D) CAgr EPom WHar
- 'Pitmaston Pine Apple' (D) CArg CHab CTho CTri ECrN EMOT ERea ESps MCoo MWat NOra SCob SDea SKee SLon WHar WWct
- 'Pitmaston Russet Nonpareil' (D) SKee
- 'Pixie' (D) ♀^{H6} CSBt EMOT EPom MWat NOra SCob SDea SKee SLon WHar WWct
- 'Plum Vite' (D) CAgr CTri
- 'Plympton Pippin' (C) CEnd CTho CTri
- POLKA ('Trajan'^{PBR}) (D) NOra SDea SKee
- 'Polly' (C/D) MRai
- 'Polly Prosser' (D) SKee
- 'Polly Whitehair' (C/D) SDea
- 'Pomeroy of Somerset' (D) CHab CTho CTri SKee
- 'Ponsford' (C) CAgr CTho
- 'Port Wine' see *M. domestica* 'Harry Master's Jersey'
- 'Porter's Perfection' (Cider) CTri NOra
- 'Pott's Seedling' (C) SKee
- 'Prince Charles' (D) MRai
- 'Princesse' (F) CLnd ECrN SDea SKee
- 'Profit' (F) CTho
- 'Purpurroter Cousinot' (D) SKee
- 'Quarry Apple' (C) CTho
- 'Queen' (C) CAgr ECrN SDea SKee WHar
- 'Queen Caroline' (C) SKee
- 'Queen Cox' (D) CLnd CTri ECrN EPom ERea LSRN NOra SDea SKee SLon SWvt WHar WTSh
- 'Queens' (D) CEnd
- 'Rajka'^{PBR} (D) GQue NOra SKee WWct
- 'Red Alkmene' see *M. domestica* 'Red Windsor'
- 'Red Belle de Boskoop' (D) CAgr
- 'Red Bramley' (C) CDul ECrN
- 'Red Charles Ross' (C/D) SDea
- 'Red Delicious' see *M. domestica* 'Starking'
- 'Red Devil' (D) CAgr CLnd CMac CSBt CTri ECrN EMOT EPom ESps LRHS MRav MWat NLar NOra NPri NRHS SCob SCoo SDea SEWo SKee SLim SLon SSFT WHar WJas WWct
- 'Red Ellison' (D) CTri ECrN ERea SDea
- 'Red Falstaff'^{PBR} (D) ♀^{H6} CAgr CCVT CDul CMac CTri EBee ECrN EMOT EPfP ERea ESps GKin LBuc LRHS LSRN MAsh MCoo NLar NOra NRHS SKee SLim SLon SPer SPoG SSFT WHar WWct
- 'Red Fuji' (D) SDea
- 'Red James Grieve' (D) LSRN SDea SKee
- 'Red Joaneting' (D) SKee WHar
- 'Red Jonagold' see *M. domestica* 'Jonagored'
- 'Red Jonathan' (D) SDea
- 'Red Miller's seedling' (D) ECrN SDea
- 'Red Pixie' (D) GQue MCoo
- 'Red Rattler' (D) CTri
- 'Red Sauce' (C) SKee
- § 'Red Windsor' (D) CArg CDul CLnd CMac CRos CTri EBee EMOT EPom ERea ESps LBuc LRHS NLar NOra SCoo SDea SKee SLim SPoG WHar WJas
- 'Redcoat Grieve' (D) SDea
- 'Redsleeves' (D) CAgr CLnd ECrN EMOT NOra SDea SKee
- 'Reine de Pommes' (Cider) MRai
- 'Reine des Reinettes' see *M. domestica* 'King of the Pippins'
- 'Reinette Descardre' (D) SVic
- 'Reinette Rouge Etoilée' (D) SDea
- 'Resi'^{PBR} (C/D) WWct
- 'Reverend Greeves' (C) SDea
- 'Reverend McCormick' (D) CTho
- 'Reverend W. Wilks' (C) CAgr CHab CSBt CTri ECrN EMOT EPom ESps NOra SDea SKee WHar WJas WWct

	- 'Ribston Pippin' (D) $\mathbb{Y}^{H6}$	CDul CTho CTri ECrN EMOT ERea ESps LBuc MCoo MRav MWat NOra SDea SKee SLon WHar WJas WWct
	- 'Rival' (D)	CAgr SDea SKee
	- 'Rivers' Nonsuch' (D)	CHab
	- 'Rome Beauty' (D)	SDea
	- 'Rosemary Russet' (D) $\mathbb{Y}^{H6}$	CAgr CHab CTho EBee ERea ESps MCoo NOra SDea SKee SLon WHar WWct
	- 'Rosette' (D)	CRos EPom LBuc LRHS MAsh NLar NOra
	- 'Ross Nonpareil' (D)	CAgr IArd NOra SDea WHar
	- 'Rosy Blenheim' (D)	ECrN
	- 'Roter Ananas' (D)	SKee
	- 'Rough Pippin' (D)	CEnd
	- 'Roundway Magnum Bonum' (C/D)	CAgr CTho SDea SKee
§	- 'Roxbury Russet' (D)	SKee
	- 'Royal Gala' (D)	CMac ECrN EMOT EPom LBuc LRHS MRav SCob SDea SLon
§	- 'Royal Jubilee' (C)	SKee
	- 'Royal Russet' (C)	CAgr CEnd CTri ECrN SDea
	- 'Royal Somerset' (C/Cider)	CTho CTri
	- RUBINETTE ('Rafzubin') (D)	ECrN NOra SDea SKee
	- RUBINETTE ROSSO ('Rafzubex'^{PBR}) (D)	NOra
	- 'Rubinola'^{PBR} (D)	SKee WWct
	- 'Ruby Thorrington (D)	ECrN
	- 'Saint Cecilia' (D)	CHab SDea WGwG
§	- 'Saint Edmund's Pippin' (D) $\mathbb{Y}^{H6}$	CHab CTho ECrN ELan EPfP ERea MCoo NOra SDea SKee
	- 'Saint Edmund's Russet'	see *M. domestica* 'Saint Edmund's Pippin'
	- 'Saint Everard' (D)	SKee
	- 'Saint Magdalen' (D)	SKee
	- 'Saltcote Pippin' (D)	SKee
	- 'Sam Young' (D)	CAgr SKee
	- 'Samba' (C/D)	LCro LOPS
	- 'Sandlands' (D)	SDea
	- 'Sandlin Duchess' (D)	NOra
	- 'Sandringham' (C)	ECrN SKee
	- 'Sanspareil' (D)	CAgr SKee
	- 'Santana'^{PBR} (D)	NOra
	- 'Saturn' (D)	CAgr CCVT CTri ERea ESps MRai NOra SDea SKee WHar WWct
	- 'Saw Pits' (D)	CAgr CEnd MRai
	- 'Scarlet Crofton' (D)	IArd SKee
	- 'Scarlet Nonpareil' (D)	SDea SKee
	- 'Scarlet Pimpernel' (D)	SKee
	- 'Scotch Bridget' (C)	CArg CHab GQue NBid NOra SKee WHar WWct
	- 'Scotch Dumpling' (C)	GBin GKin GQue MCoo NOra SKee WHar
	- 'Scrumptious'^{PBR} (D) $\mathbb{Y}^{H6}$	Widely available
	- 'Sheep's Nose' (C)	CHab IArd SDea SKee
	- 'Shenandoah' (C)	SKee
	- 'Sidney Strake' (C)	CAgr CEnd
	- 'Sir Isaac Newton's'	see *M. domestica* 'Flower of Kent'
	- 'Sir John Thornycroft' (D)	SDea
	- 'Sisson's Worksop Newtown' (D)	MCoo
	- 'Slack Ma Girdle' (Cider)	NOra SKee
	- 'Smart's Prince Arthur' (C)	CHab SDea
	- 'Snell's Glass Apple'	see *M. domestica* 'Glass Apple'
	- 'Somerset Lasting' (C)	CTri
	- 'Somerset Redstreak' (Cider)	CAgr CHab CTri NOra WHar
	- 'Sops in Wine' (Cider/D)	CTho CTsd ECrN NOra SKee SVic
	- 'Sour Bay' (Cider)	CAgr
	- 'Spartan' (D)	CCVT CDul CLnd CMac CSBt CTri EBee ECrN ELan EMOT EPom ESps GKin LRHS MAsh MCoo MGos MJak MRav MWat NOra SCob SDea SKee SPer SSFT SVic WHar WJas WWct
	- 'Spencer' (D)	CTri ECrN
	- 'Spotted Dick' (Cider)	CTho
	- 'Stamford Pippin' (D)	SDea
	- 'Stanway Seedling' (C)	ECrN
	- 'Star of Devon' (D)	CEnd SDea
	- 'Stark' (D)	SDea
§	- 'Starking' (D)	ECrN LMaj NOra SKee
	- 'Stark's Earliest' (D)	SVic
	- 'Stembridge Cluster' (Cider)	CTri
	- 'Steyne Seedling' (D)	SDea
	- 'Stibbert' (D)	SKee
	- 'Stirling Castle' (C)	CAgr GQue NOra SKee
	- 'Stobo Castle' (C)	SKee
	- 'Stoke Edith Pippin' (D)	WHar
	- 'Stoke Red' (Cider)	NOra
	- 'Strawberry Pippin' (D)	CDul
	- 'Striped Beefing' (C)	ECrN ERea
	- 'Sturmer Pippin' (D)	CSBt CTri ECrN MWat NOra SDea SKee WHar WWct
	- 'Summerred' (D)	ECrN SDea
	- 'Sunburn' (D)	ECrN
	- 'Sunnydale' (D/C)	SDea
	- 'Sunrise'^{PBR} (D)	EMOT ESps NOra SCob SKee WHar
	- 'Sunset' (D) $\mathbb{Y}^{H6}$	Widely available
	- 'Suntan' (D)	ECrN ESps MWat NOra SDea SKee
	- 'Superb'	see *M. domestica* 'Laxton's Superb'
	- 'Sussex Mother' (C/D)	CHab
	- 'Sweet Alford' (Cider)	CTho WWct
	- 'Sweet Bay' (Cider)	CAgr
	- 'Sweet Caroline' (D)	SDea
	- 'Sweet Cleave' (Cider)	CTho
	- 'Sweet Coppin' (Cider)	CTri MRai
	- 'Sweet Lilibet'	see *M. domestica* 'Red Windsor'
	- 'Sweet Pethyre' (C)	EMOT
	- 'Sweet Sixteen' (D)	MRai
	- 'Sweet Society' (D)	EMOT LRHS MAsh NOra SKee WHar WJas
	- 'Sweetings'	MRai
	- 'Sylvia' (D)	MRai
	- 'Tamar Beauty' (D)	CEnd
	- 'Tan Harvey' (Cider)	CEnd
	- 'Taunton Cross' (D)	CAgr
	- 'Taylor's' (Cider)	CAgr SDea
	- 'Ten Commandments' (Cider/D)	SDea WWct
	- TENTATION ('Delblush'^{PBR}) (D)	SDea
	- 'The Rattler' (Cider)	CEnd
	- 'Thomas Rivers' (C)	SDea
	- 'Thorle Pippin' (D)	SKee
	- TICKLED PINK ('Baya Marisa') (C/D)	EPom ERea LRHS NLar NOra SPer SPoG
	- 'Tidicombe Seedling' (D)	CTho
	- 'Tom Putt' (C)	CAgr CArg CCVT CDul CHab CSBt CTho CTri ESps LBuc NOra SDea SKee WHar WJas WWct
	- 'Tommy Knight' (D)	CAgr CEnd
	- 'Topaz'^{PBR} (D)	SKee
	- 'Totnes Apple' (D)	CTho
	- 'Tower of Glamis' (C)	CHab GQue SKee
	- 'Tregonna King' (C/D)	CTho CTsd

	- 'Tremlett's Bitter' (Cider)	CAgr CHab CTho MRai NOra SDea SKee SVic
	- 'Trwyn Mochyn' (C)	WGwG
§	- 'Tuscan'^{PBR} (D)	EMOT SDea SKee
§	- 'Tydeman's Early Worcester' (D)	CAgr CHab CLnd ECrN SDea SKee WWct
	- 'Tydeman's Late Orange' (D)	CHab CTri ECrN ESps EWTr MCoo NOra SDea SKee WHar
	- 'Tyler's Kernel' (C)	SKee
	- 'Upton Pyne' (C/D)	CTho SDea
	- 'Veitch's Perfection' (C/D)	CTho
	- 'Venus Pippin' (C/D)	CEnd
	- 'Vicary's Late Keeper' (C)	CTho
	- 'Vickey's Delight' (D)	SDea
	- 'Vileberie' (Cider)	CTri
	- 'Vista-bella' (D)	ECrN EMOT SDea SKee
	- 'Wagener' (D)	ECrN SDea
	- WALTZ ('Telamon'^{PBR}) (D)	EMOT SDea
	- 'Warner's King' (C) Υ^{H6}	CTri NOra SDea SKee WHar
	- 'Warrior' (F)	CTho
	- 'Wealthy' (D)	SDea
	- 'Wellington' (C)	see *M. domestica* 'Dummellor's Seedling'
	- 'Wellington' (Cider)	CAgr
	- 'Welsh Russet' (D)	SDea
	- 'Werrington Wonder' (F)	CEnd
	- 'West View Seedling' (D)	ECrN
	- 'Wheeler's Russet' (D)	SKee
	- 'White Melrose' (C)	GQue NOra SDea SKee
	- 'White Transparent' (C/D)	SDea SKee
	- 'White Winter Pearmain' (D) **new**	SDea
	- 'Whitpot Sweet' (Cider)	CEnd
	- 'William Crump' (D)	CDul CHab CTho ECrN NOra SDea WHar WWct
	- 'Willoughby' (D)	MCoo
	- 'Winston' (D) Υ^{H6}	CAgr CCVT CMac CTri ECrN ESps MCoo SDea SKee SVic WHar WWct
	- 'Winter Banana' (D)	CHab ECrN GQue NOra SDea SVic WHar
	- 'Winter Gem' (D)	CAgr CArg CCVT CDul CLnd ECrN EPom ERea ESps LBuc NOra SCob SDea SKee WHar WJas
	- 'Winter Majetin' (C)	SKee
	- 'Winter Peach' (D/C)	CAgr ECrN
	- 'Winter Pearmain' (D)	WHar
	- 'Winter Quarrenden' (D)	SDea
	- 'Winter Queening' (D/C)	SDea
	- 'Winter Red' (F)	CEnd
	- 'Woodbine'	see *M. domestica* 'Northwood'
	- 'Woodford' (C)	ECrN
	- 'Woolbrook Pippin' (D)	CAgr CEnd CTho
	- 'Woolbrook Russet' (C)	CEnd ECrN
	- 'Worcester Pearmain' (D) Υ^{H6}	Widely available
	- 'Wormsley Pippin' (D)	ECrN
	- 'Wyken Pippin' (D)	ECrN SDea SKee WWct
	- 'Yarlington Mill' (Cider)	CAgr CHab CTri MRai NOra SDea SKee SVic WWct
	- 'Yellow Ingestrie' (D)	CHab ERea MCoo NOra SKee WHar WWct
	- 'Yorkshire Greening' (C)	CHab NOra SKee WHar
	- 'Zabergäu Renette' (D)	NOra
	'Donald Wyman'	CLnd EPfP LMaj MAsh NLar NOra SCoo
§	'Echtermeyer'	CTri SDea
	'Evelyn'	CLnd NOra
§	'Evereste' Υ^{H6}	Widely available
	florentina	CTho EPfP
	- 'Rosemoor'	CLnd
	- 'Skopje'	EPfP
	floribunda Υ^{H6}	Widely available
	fusca	CLnd
	'Gardener's Gold'	CEnd CTho SRms
	× ***gloriosa*** 'Oekonomierat Echtermeyer'	see *M.* 'Echtermeyer'
	'Golden Gem'	CLnd EMOT EPfP GQue MAsh NOra SEWo SKee
	'Golden Hornet'	see *M.* × *zumi* 'Golden Hornet'
	'Gorgeous'	CDul CLnd CMac CSBt CTho EBee ECrN EMOT EPfP ESps EUJe LBuc LMaj LRHS LSRN MAsh MRav MSwo NOra SCoo SEWo SKee SLim SPer SPoG WHar WJas WMou WWct
	'Harry Baker'	CCVT CDul CEnd CLnd CMac CSBt ECrN EMOT EMil EPfP EPom ERea LSRN MBlu MRav NOra SCoo SDea SLim SPer SPoG WHar WJas WWct
	× ***hartwigii***	CLnd
	'Hillieri'	see *M.* × *scheideckeri* 'Hillieri'
	'Honeycrisp'^{PBR}	CFGn NOra WHar
	hupehensis Υ^{H6}	CAby CDul CEnd CLnd CMCN CSBt CTho CTri EBee EPfP ESps EWTr IMou MBlu MGos MRav NLar NOra SPer WMou WTSh
	'Hyde Hall Spire'	SCoo
	'Indian Magic'	CLnd EBee ESps EWTr LRHS MAsh NLar NOra WHCr
	'Indian Summer'	CLnd
	JELLY KING ('Mattfru') Υ^{H6}	CLnd EBee ECrN EMOT EPfP EPom LBuc LRHS LSRN MAsh NLar NOra SPer SPoG WHCr WHar WMou
	'John Downie' (C)	Widely available
	'Kaido'	see *M.* × *micromalus*
	kansuensis	CLnd
	'Lady Northcliffe'	CDul CLnd
	'Laura' Υ^{H6}	CDul CLnd EBee EMOT EPfP EPom ERea EWTr LRHS LSRN MAsh NLar NOra NPri SCoo SKee SLim SLon SPer SPoG WHar WJas
	'Lisa'	CLnd
	'Louisa'	CLnd EBee EPfP LRHS NOra SCoo SGol SLim
	× ***magdeburgensis***	CCVT CDul CLnd CSBt
	'Makamik'	LPra
	'Mary Potter'	CLnd
§	× ***micromalus***	CLnd
	× ***moerlandsii***	CLnd
	- 'Liset'	CDul CEnd CLnd ECrN EMOT ESps LPra MRav NEgg NOra SCoo WFar
§	- 'Profusion'	CBcs CDul CTri ECrN ELan EMOT EPfP ESps LCro LOPS LPra MGos MJak MRav MSwo NOra NPri NRHS SCob SEND SGol SPer SPoG SRms SWvt WJas
	'Mokum'	CLnd LMaj
	'Molten Lava'	CLnd MAsh
	'Montreal Beauty'	CLnd WJas
	niedzwetzkyana	CLnd CTho
	NUVAR CARNIVAL	SKee
	NUVAR MARBLE	EBee NOra SKee
	PERPETU	see *M.* 'Evereste'
	'Pink Mushroom'	EMOT
	'Pink Perfection'	CEnd ECrN NLar NOra NPri SPoG WHar
	'Pond Red'	CLnd
	'Prairifire'	CDul CLnd EMOT LRHS MAsh NOra NPri SCoo SLim SLon SPoG
	prattii	CLnd CTho EBee EPfP GLog

	- 'Pourpre Noir'	CLnd
	'Princeton Cardinal' ♀H6	CLnd CMac EPfP MAsh SCoo SLim SPoG WHar WMou
	'Professor Sprenger'	see *M.* × *zumi* 'Professor Sprenger'
	'Profusion'	see *M.* × *moerlandsii* 'Profusion'
	prunifolia	MBlu
	- var. ***rinkii***	CLnd
§	× ***purpurea*** 'Aldenhamensis'	CLnd SDea WHar
	- 'Eleyi'	CLnd EPfP LPra
	- 'Lemoinei'	CDul
	- 'Neville Copeman'	CCVT CDul EMOT EPom EWTr WJas
	- 'Pendula'	see *M.* 'Echtermeyer'
	'R.J. Fulcher'	CLnd CTho
	'Ralph Shay'	CLnd
	'Red Ace'	CDul
	'Red Barron'	CLnd
	'Red Glow'	CDul ECrN WJas
	'Red Jade'	see *M.* × *scheideckeri* 'Red Jade'
	RED OBELISK ('Dvp Obel')	CCVT CLnd LBuc LRHS NOra SCoo SPoG
	'Red Peacock'	CLnd
	'Robert's Crab' new	EBee EWTr
§	× ***robusta***	CLnd EMOT ESps LPra LSRN SLon SRms
	- 'Dolgo'	CLnd CSBt EBee EMOT EPom ERea EWTr LCro MBlu NLar NOra SCoo SKee SPoG WHar WMou
	- 'Red Sentinel' ♀H6	Widely available
	- 'Red Siberian'	SDea SPer
	- 'Yellow Siberian'	CLnd
	'Rosehip'	CLnd EBee EMOT LBuc LCro NLar NOra NPri
	'Royal Beauty'	CDul CLnd EMOT EPfP ESps EUJe LMaj LRHS MAsh MBlu MGos MJak MSwo NOra NPri SCoo SLon SPer WHar
	'Royalty'	Widely available
	'Rudolph'	CCVT CDul CLnd EBar ECrN EMOT ESps GKin LBuc LMaj LPra LSRN MAsh MGos NOra NPri SCoo SEWo SLim SPer SPoG WJas WMou
	'Ruth Ann'	CLnd
	sargentii	CDul CLnd CTho EWTr NOra
	- 'Candy Mint'	EBee EWTr LRHS MAsh
	- 'Tina'	CLnd LPra LRHS MAsh NOra SPoG
	'Satin Cloud'	CLnd
§	× ***scheideckeri*** 'Hillieri'	CDul CLnd LPra MBlu
§	- 'Red Jade'	CDul CLnd CTri ECrN ELan EMOT ESps EWTr LPra MGos MJak MRav MSwo SPer SRms WHar WJas
	Siberian crab	see *M.* × *robusta*
	sieboldii	see *M. toringo*
	sieversii	CDul CLnd
	sikkimensis B&SWJ 2431	WCru
	'Silver Drift'	CLnd
	'Snowcloud'	CDul CLnd ECrN EMOT ESps MAsh SLim
	'Snowdrift'	CLnd
	spontanea new	GKev
	'Street Parade'	CLnd
	'Striped Beauty'	LPra
	× ***sublobata***	CLnd
	'Suffolk Pink' new	ECrN
	SUGAR TYME ('Sutyzam')	CLnd
	'Sun Rival' ♀H6	CCVT CDul CEnd CLnd CMac CSBt EBee EMOT EPfP ESps LRHS MAsh MBlu MRav NOra NPri SCoo SEWo SLim SPoG SRms WHar WJas
	sylvestris	CAco CArg CCVT CDul CFGn CHab CLnd CPer ECrN EPfP LBuc LPra MJak MMuc MRav SEND SEWo SPer SPre WHar WMou WTSh
§	***toringo***	CTho ECrN EPfP LEdu LMaj LPra NOra WSHC
I	- var. ***arborescens***	CLnd CTho
	- 'Browers'	LMaj
	- 'Scarlett' ♀H6	CCVT CDul CLnd EMOT EPfP EWTr IArd LMaj LRHS LSRN NLar NOra SCoo SEWo SLim SPer SPoG WHar WMou
	- 'Wintergold'	EWTr MMuc
	- 'Wooster'	CLnd
	toringoides	see *M. bhutanica*
	transitoria ♀H6	CDul CEnd CLnd CMac CRos CTho EBee ECrN ELan EMOT EPfP ESps EWTr GKin LRHS MAsh MBlu MRav NLar NOra SCoo SLau SPer WMou WPGP
	- 'Thornhayes Tansy'	CDul CTho NOra SLim SPoG
	trilobata	CDul CTho EBee ELan EPfP ESps GKin LMaj MBlu MGos MMuc SCoo SEND
	- 'Guardsman'	CMac EMOT EPfP NPri WMou
	tschonoskii	CDul CLnd CMCN CMac CTri ELan EMOT ESps LMaj LRHS MBlu MGos MJak MMuc SEND SPer SRms SWvt WJas WMou WTSh
	- 'Belmonte' new	MBlu
	'Van Eseltine'	CAgr CDul CMac CSBt ECrN EMOT EPfP MMuc SPer WHar WJas
	'Veitch's Scarlet'	CDul CHab CSBt
	VELVET PILLAR ('Velvetcole')	SPoG
	WEEPING CANDIED APPLE ('Weepcanzam')	CLnd
	'White Angel'	CLnd EWTr
	'White Star'	CCVT CDul CLnd CSBt EBee ECrN EMOT NOra SEWo SLon WHar
	'Winter Gold'	CDul LPra SGol
	'Wisley Crab'	CLnd EMOT ESps SDea SKee SLon SRms WMou
	yunnanensis	EPfP
	- var. ***veitchii***	CTho
	× ***zumi***	GLog
	- var. ***calocarpa***	CLnd
§	- 'Golden Hornet'	Widely available
§	- 'Professor Sprenger'	CLnd EPfP LMaj LPra NOra SCoo

Malva (*Malvaceae*)

	alcea	CAgr
	- var. ***fastigiata***	CMac CRos EPPr LRHS SMad SPer SRms WOut
	- 'Royal Flush' new	NRHS
	bicolor	see *Lavatera maritima*
	moschata	CAgr CBcs CBod CFGn EAJP EBWF EBee ECha ELan ENfk EPfP ESps GAbr GPoy MHer MMuc MNHC NLar NMir NWad SPer SPlb SRms WFar WHar WHer WMoo WOut
§	- f. ***alba*** ♀H5	Widely available
	- 'Appleblossom'	EWTr
	- 'Romney Marsh'	see *Althaea officinalis* 'Romney Marsh'
	- 'Rosea'	CRos EPfP GMcL LRHS NPer NRHS SPoG SWvt WHar
	- 'Snow White'	see *M. moschata* f. *alba*
	pusilla	CCCN
	sylvestris	CBod EBWF SRms WMoo XAbr

- 'Blue Fountain'PBR LRHS SAko SRms
- 'Brave Heart' SPav SWvt WOut
- MARINA ('Dema'PBR) NLar
- var. ***mauritiana*** LCro MSpe NPer WArt WMoo WOut
- - 'Bibor Fehlő' CSpe
- - 'Mystic Merlin' CPla SPav
- - 'Primley Blue' CBod ECtt ELan EPfP GMaP ILea LRHS MRav NPer WSpi
- - 'Zebrina' EPfP MSpe NGBl NPer SAko SWvt WMoo
- 'Perry's Blue' NPer
- 'Windsor Castle' MPie

Malvastrum (*Malvaceae*)

× ***hypomadarum*** see *Anisodontea* × *hypomadara* (Sprague) D.M. Bates

Malvaviscus (*Malvaceae*)

arboreus CHll

mandarin see *Citrus reticulata* Mandarin Group

mandarin, Cleopatra see *Citrus reticulata*

Mandevilla ✿ (*Apocynaceae*)

§ × ***amabilis*** CCCN
- 'Alice du Pont' ♀H1c CBcs CCCN ELan EMdy EShb SPre
- 'Passion Pink' (Parfait Series) (d) IDee
× ***amoena*** see *M.* × *amabilis*
'Audrey'PBR (Vogue Series) CBcs CWGN LSou SPoG
boliviensis ♀H1c CCCN CRHN EMdy
'Ginger' (Vogue Series) CAbb CBcs CWGN LSou SPoG
§ ***laxa*** ♀H1c CBcs CBot CCCN CHGN CHll CRHN CSam CSpe ECre ELan EMdy LRHS SBrt SVen WSHC
(Rio Series) RIO DEEP RED ('Fisrix Dered'PBR) CCCN
- RIO PINK ('Fisrix Pinka'PBR) CCCN
- RIO WHITE ('Fisrix Whit'PBR) EMdy
'Ruby' (Vogue Series) CAbb CWGN
sanderi CCCN EShb SPre
- 'Pink of Hint' EMdy
- 'Rosea' CCCN
splendens ♀H1c CBcs CCCN CHll EMdy
suaveolens see *M. laxa*
Sundaville Series CCCN
- SUNDAVILLE CREAM PINK ('Sunparapibra'PBR) EMdy
- SUNDAVILLE DARK RED ('Sunparabeni'PBR) EBee EMdy
- SUNDAVILLE PRETTY RED ('Sunmanderemi'PBR) (Sundaville Series) EMdy
- SUNDAVILLE PRETTY ROSE ('Sunparaprero'PBR) EMdy
- SUNDAVILLE RED ('Sunmandecrim'PBR) EMdy

Mandragora (*Solanaceae*)

sp. CPla
autumnalis GEdr WSFF
§ ***officinarum*** GCal GEdr GPoy XAbr

Manettia (*Rubiaceae*)

inflata see *M. luteorubra*
§ ***luteorubra*** CCCN

Manfreda see *Agave*

elongata see *Agave gracillima*

× *Mangave* see *Agave*

Mangifera (*Anacardiaceae*)

indica (F) CCCN SPre

Manglietia see *Magnolia*

yunnanensis see *Magnolia insignis*

mango see *Mangifera indica*

Manihot (*Euphorbiaceae*)

carthaginensis SPlb

Mantisalca (*Asteraceae*)

salmantica WCot

Mantisia (*Zingiberaceae*)

saltatoria PAB 4208 LEdu WPGP

Maranta (*Marantaceae*)

leuconeura XBlo
var. ***erythroneura*** ♀H1b
- var. ***kerchoveana*** ♀H1b XBlo

Mariscus see *Cyperus*

marjoram, pot see *Origanum onites*

marjoram, sweet see *Origanum majorana*

marjoram, wild, or oregano see *Origanum vulgare*

marrow see AGM Vegetables Section

Marrubium (*Lamiaceae*)

§ ***bourgaei*** var. ***bourgaei*** 'All Hallows Green' ECha ECtt LRHS NEgg NRHS SRms
candidissimum see *M. incanum*
* ***cylleneum*** 'Velvetissimum' WCot XSen
§ ***incanum*** SEND XSen
supinum SEND
vulgare CBod EBee ENfk GPoy MHer MNHC SRms

Marsdenia (*Apocynaceae*)

formosana CWJ 12354 WCru
oreophila CRHN GCal LRHS SPoG WPGP WSHC
- Mabiluo form **new** GCal

Marshallia (*Asteraceae*)

grandiflora EBee
trinerva ELon

Marsilea (*Marsileaceae*)

mutica EWat LLWG
quadrifolia EWat
- variegated (v) LLWG
* ***schelpiana*** XBlo

Massonia (*Asparagaceae*)

depressa ♀H2 CTal NRog SChF WCot
echinata LSou NRog SChF WCot
pustulata ♀H2 EUJe NRog SChF WCot

Mathiasella (*Apiaceae*)

bupleuroides	CFis LSou WHil
– 'Green Dream'	CAby CAvo CBcs CBod CBre CRav CSpe EBee ECtt ELan EUJe EWld GBin ILea LCro LEdu LOPS LRHS MAvō MBel MHol MNrw NPnk NSti SCob SMad SPoG WCot

Matricaria (*Asteraceae*)

chamomilla	see *M. recutita*
maritima	see *Tripleurospermum maritimum*
parthenium	see *Tanacetum parthenium*
§ ***recutita***	ESps GPoy MNHC XAbr
tchihatchewii	XLum XSen
'White Star'	EPfP

Matteuccia ✿ (*Onocleaceae*)

orientalis ♀H5	CAby CBdn CBod CDTJ CKel CRos CTal CWCL ECha EFer ERod GCal GMaP IBal LEdu LLWG LRHS MMoz MMuc NBid NLar NRHS SEND WMoo WPnP XLum
pensylvanica	MMoz
struthiopteris ♀H4	Widely available
– 'Jumbo'	CBdn CCCN GBin
– 'The King'	WCot

Matthiola (*Brassicaceae*)

fruticulosa 'Alba'	CAby EPfP WPGP
– subsp. ***perennis***	NSti WHal
incana	LRHS MArl SVic WKif
– ***alba***	CRav CWld EBee ECha ELan LRHS LSou NPnk SBod SEND SPad SPav WCot WRHF
– 'Pillow Talk'	CRav
– purple-flowered	CSpe CWld SEND
– VINTAGE MIXED	NPri
scapifera	CPBP
sinuata	CWld
white-flowered perennial	CMea CSpe NPer

Maurandella (*Plantaginaceae*)

§ ***antirrhiniflora***	WArt

Maurandya (*Plantaginaceae*)

§ ***barclayana***	CSpe IDee
erubescens	see *Lophospermum erubescens*
lophantha	see *Lophospermum scandens*
lophospermum	see *Lophospermum scandens*
'Magic Dragon'	see *Lophospermum* 'Magic Dragon'
'Red Dragon'	see *Lophospermum* 'Red Dragon'

Maytenus (*Celastraceae*)

boaria	CMCN IArd LEdu MGos SAko SArc SEND
disticha (Hook.f.) Urb.	LEdu
magellanica	EBee WPGP

Mazus (*Phrymaceae*)

miquelii	EBee
reptans	CBod ECtt GEdr MSKA NLar NPer NQui XLum
– B&SWJ	CExl
– 'Albus'	CBod ECtt LLWG NLar SPlb
– 'Blue'	LLWG

Mecardonia (*Plantaginaceae*)

'Goldflake'	CCCN

Meconopsis ✿ (*Papaveraceae*)

§ ***baileyi*** ♀H4	CBcs CBod CRos CTri EBee ELan EPfP GGGa GKev GKin GMcL IBoy ITim LCro LOPS MBel NChi NEgg NHim NRHS NSum WFar WMoo WSFF
* – var. ***alba***	CBod CRos CTsd EBee ELan GCal GGGa GKev IMou LRHS NHim NRHS NSum WHlf
– 'Hensol Violet'	CBod CPne CTsd EBee ETMg GEdr GGGa GKev GMcL NHim NRHS NSum
– violet-flowered	ITim
Ballyrogan form	GEdr
× ***beamishii***	GKev
betonicifolia misapplied	see *M. baileyi*
'Cally Purple'	GCal
cambrica	see *Papaver cambricum*
– 'Rubra'	see *Papaver cambricum* 'Frances Perry'
chelidoniifolia	CAby CRos LRHS NBid NRHS WCru
× ***cookei***	EBee GKev IRob NHpl NSum
– 'Old Rose'	GEdr GGGa GMaP
'Edrom'	GEdr
Fertile Blue Group	ITim
– 'Blue Ice'	see *M.* (Fertile Blue Group) 'Lingholm'
– 'Cally Lingholm'	GCal
– 'Harry Bush' **new**	GEdr
– 'Lingholm'	Widely available
– 'Louise'	GEdr GMaP
– 'Mop-head' ♀H5	GEdr GKev GMaP
§ George Sherriff Group	EBee GCal IRob MArl
– 'Ascreavie'	GEdr GKev GMaP
– 'Barney's Blue'	GEdr GMaP
– 'Dalemain' ♀H5	GEdr GMaP
– 'Branklyn' ambig.	CExl GEdr
– 'Huntfield'	GEdr GGGa GKev GMaP
– 'Jimmy Bayne'	GEdr GMaP
– 'Susan's Reward' ♀H5	GEdr GMaP
grandis misapplied	see *M.* George Sherriff Group
grandis ambig.	CRos IRob ITim NEgg
– GS 600	see *M.* George Sherriff Group
– 'Alba'	ITim
– 'Burgundy'	GWyn
(Infertile Blue Group) 'Bobby Masterton' ♀H5	GEdr GMaP
– 'Bryan Conway'	GEdr
– 'Crarae'	GEdr GGGa
– 'Crewdson Hybrid'	GCal GEdr GMaP
– 'Dawyck'	see *M.* (Infertile Blue Group) 'Slieve Donard'
– 'Maggie Sharp'	GEdr
– 'Mrs Jebb' ♀H5	GEdr GGGa GMaP
– 'P.C. Abildgaard' ♀H5	GEdr GGGa GKev GMaP
§ – 'Slieve Donard' ♀H5	CRos GCal GEdr GGGa GKev GMaP IRob LRHS NRHS
integrifolia	CCCN CRos
'Inverewe' ♀H5	GEdr
'Jim's Ex' **new**	GKev
'Keillour' ♀H5	GEdr GKev
'Keillour Violet' **new**	GKev
'Marit' ♀H5	GEdr GKev GMaP
'Mervyn Kessell'	GEdr
'Mildred'	GEdr
napaulensis misapplied	EBee GAbr GKev ITim
napaulensis DC.	NHim

- B&SWJ 13952	WCru
nudicaulis	see *Papaver nudicaule*
paniculata	CAby CBod CDor EBee GGGa NHim WHlf
- B&SWJ 13922	WCru
- ginger foliage	CHid
pseudointegrifolia	GGGa
punicea	GKev NHpl
- 'Sichuan Silk'	EWld NHpl
quintuplinervia ♀^{H5}	GEdr GKev NHpl NSla
- Farrer's form	GEdr
- 'Kaye's Compact'	GEdr
× ***sheldonii*** misapplied (fertile)	see *M.* Fertile Blue Group
× ***sheldonii*** misapplied (sterile)	see *M.* Infertile Blue Group
× ***sheldonii*** ambig.	CBcs GAbr GMcL IRob LRHS NLar NPer NRHS
'Stewart Annand'	GEdr GKev GMaP
'Strathspey'	GEdr
superba	GGGa GKev
villosa	see *Cathcartia villosa*
wallichii Hook.	GGGa
'Willie Duncan'	GEdr GMaP

Medeola (*Asparagaceae*)

virginiana	EBee

Medicago (*Papilionaceae*)

arborea	SEND SPlb
lupulina	CHab EBWF
sativa	EBWF WHer WSFF

Medinilla (*Melastomataceae*)

magnifica ♀^{H1a}	CCCN

medlar see *Mespilus germanica*

Meehania (*Lamiaceae*)

cordata	EBee
urticifolia	EPPr GCal GEdr
- B&SWJ 1210	WCru
- 'Japanblau'	IMou

Megaskepasma (*Acanthaceae*)

erythrochlamys	SVen

Melaleuca (*Myrtaceae*)

acuminata	SPlb
alternifolia	CAby CBcs CCCN CTsd EShb GPoy MHer SPlb SVen
armillaris	CCCN CTsd SEND SPlb
cuticularis	SPlb
decussata	SPlb
§ ***diosmatifolia***	CExl
diosmifolia	CPbh
ericifolia	CTri CTsd SEND SPlb
erubescens	see *M. diosmatifolia*
fulgens	SPlb
gibbosa	CExl LSou SEND SVen
hypericifolia	CExl SPlb SVen
linariifolia	CCCN SPlb
nesophila	SPlb
pungens	SPlb
pustulata	SVen
squamea	SEND SPlb
squarrosa	CExl SPlb SVen
thymifolia	SPlb
trichophylla	SPlb
wilsonii	IDee

Melampodium (*Asteraceae*)

§ ***montanum*** 'Sunbini'^{PBR}	CCCN LSou NPri

Melandrium see *Vaccaria*

rubrum	see *Silene dioica*

Melanoselinum (*Apiaceae*)

§ ***decipiens***	CSpe IBoy IMou LEdu LRHS MHer WPGP

Melanoseris (*Asteraceae*)

taliensis BWJ 7891	WCru

Melasphaerula (*Iridaceae*)

graminea	see *M. ramosa*
§ ***ramosa***	GEdr NRog

Melia (*Meliaceae*)

§ ***azedarach***	CBcs CCCN CMCN EShb SBrt SPlb XAbr
- var. ***japonica***	see *M. azedarach*

Melianthus (*Melianthaceae*)

comosus	CBot CDTJ EPri EWes NLar NLos SCoo SPhm SPlb WPGP
dregeanus subsp. ***insignis***	NLos
major ♀^{H3}	Widely available
minor	CHid
pectinatus	NLos
villosus	CBot CHGN EBee EWes NLos SPad SPlb WHil

Melica (*Poaceae*)

altissima 'Alba'	LCro LOPS LRHS
- 'Atropurpurea'	CBod CRos ECha EHoe LRHS MNrw NRHS SEND SPlb WMoo
ciliata	EAJP EHoe ELon EPPr EPfP WPtf XLum
cupani new	EPPr
nutans	CWCL EAJP EHoe EPPr EShb GMaP MAsh NWsh SMHy SPhx WCot
persica	EPPr
transsilvanica 'Red Spire'	SGol WMoo XLum
uniflora	EBWF IMou NWsh
- f. ***albida***	CKno CRos ECha EHoe GCal LRHS MAvo MRav NRHS SMHy SPhx WCot WSHC
- 'Variegata' (v)	CBre ECha EHoe EShb GCal LPla MAvo WCot WMoo

Melicytus (*Violaceae*)

alpinus	WThu
crassifolius	EBee
obovatus	NLar
ramiflorus	CDul

Melilotus (*Papilionaceae*)

albus new	SPhx
altissimus new	EBWF
officinalis	CHab GPoy WHer

Meliosma (*Sabiaceae*)

dilleniifolia subsp. ***cuneifolia***	CBcs CExl EBee IArd SBrt WPGP
- subsp. ***flexuosa***	CBcs
- subsp. ***tenuis***	CBcs CExl
myriantha var. ***discolor*** MF 97132 new	WCru

pinnata var. ***oldhamii*** CExl
simplicifolia CBcs CExl
subsp. ***pungens***
veitchiorum CBcs CExl NLar WPGP

Melissa ✿ (*Lamiaceae*)

officinalis CBod CHab CPla ENfk GMaP GPoy LCro LEdu LOPS MHer MMuc MNHC SEND SPhx SPlb SRms SVic WArt WBor XLum
- 'All Gold' CBre ECha EHoe ENfk NBid SPer SPoG SRms
§ - 'Aurea' (v) CBod CExl ELan ESps GMaP GPoy MHer MMuc MNHC MRav NBid NBro SEND SPer SPoG SRms WMoo XAbr
* - 'Compacta' GPoy LEdu
- 'Lemona' CAgr
- 'Lime Balm' LEdu NPol
- 'Variegata' misapplied see *M. officinalis* 'Aurea'

Melittis (*Lamiaceae*)

melissophyllum CAby CRos GAbr IMou IRob LEdu LRHS LSou MAvo MHol MNrw MPie MPnt MRav NRHS SHar WCAu WCot WRHF
- subsp. ***albida*** CBct CBod ILea LEdu SCob SPhx WCAu WCot WTor
- pink-flowered LEdu WBor WCot
- 'Royal Velvet Distinction'[PBR] CBct CBod CRos EBee ETMg GEdr ILea IRob LLWG LRHS MHol MRav MSCN NHpl NPnk NRHS SCob SHar SPad SPoG WBor WCot WHil WPtf

Melliodendron (*Styracaceae*)

xylocarpum CExl SAko

melon see AGM Vegetables Section

Melothria (*Cucurbitaceae*)

scabra SVic

Menispermum (*Menispermaceae*)

canadense CTri GPoy
dauricum NLar

Mentha ✿ (*Lamiaceae*)

angustifolia Corb. see *M.* × *villosa*
angustifolia Host see *M. arvensis*
aquatica CBen CBod CHab CWat EBWF GPoy MHer MJak MWts NMir NPer NPol SPlb SRms SVic WHer WMAq WMoo WPnP WSFF XAbr XLum
§ ***arvensis*** EBWF MHer
- 'Banana' CBod ENfk LEdu MHer MNHC SRms SVic
- 'Lemon' LEdu
- var. ***piperascens*** CBod LEdu MHer SRms
- 'Thai' ENfk
asiatica MHer
'Berries and Cream' CBod ENfk LEdu MHer SRms
Bowles's mint see *M.* × *villosa* var. *alopecuroides* Bowles's mint
cervina CBen CWat LEdu LLWG MHer MSKA MWts SRms XLum
* - ***alba*** ENfk MHer MSKA MWts WMAq
I 'Chocolate Peppermint' CRav ENfk LEdu LLWG NLar
citrata see *M.* × *piperita* f. *citrata*
cordifolia see *M.* × *villosa*
corsica see *M. requienii*
crispa L. see *M. spicata* var. *crispa*
crispa ambig. × (× ***piperita***) MJak
'Eau de Cologne' see *M.* × *piperita* f. *citrata*
eucalyptus mint MHer
× ***gentilis*** see *M.* × *gracilis*
§ × ***gracilis*** CBod ENfk GAbr NLar NPri SPhm SRms SVic
- 'Aurea' see *M.* × *gracilis* 'Variegata'
§ - 'Variegata' (v) ECha GPoy LEdu MCot MHer MNHC NPri SPlb WHer XLum
* 'Hillary's Sweet Lemon' ENfk MHer SRms
'Julia's Sweet Citrus' MHer
lavender mint CBod GPoy LEdu MHer MNHC SRms
§ ***longifolia*** ENfk LEdu MMuc SEND SPlb SRms
- Buddleia Mint Group CChe ENfk GAbr LEdu MHer MRav NSti XLum
- - variegated (v) CBod LEdu
- 'Lake Van' LEdu
- subsp. ***schimperi*** LEdu SRms
- silver-leaved GAbr LEdu MHer MNHC SEND SRms
* - 'Variegata' (v) GAbr SRms
Nile Valley mint LEdu SRms
× ***piperata*** f. ***citrata*** 'Kumin' LEdu
× ***piperita*** CHby ECha EHoe GJos GPoy LCro LOPS MHer MJak MNHC NPol NPri SPhm SPlb SVic XAbr
- 'Black Mitcham' SPhx XAbr
- black peppermint CAgr CBod CHby ENfk EPfP LEdu LLWG MMuc MNHC NLar SEND SRms
§ - f. ***citrata*** CBod CHby CRav CTri ECha ENfk GAbr GMaP GPoy GQue LEdu LLWG MHer MNHC MRav NLar NPer NPri SPlb SRms SVic
- - 'Basil' CBod CRav GLog LEdu MHer MNHC MRav SRms SVic WGwG
- - 'Bergamot' SRms
- - 'Chocolate' CBod ENfk EPfP GJos LEdu MHer MNHC NPer SPlb SRms SVic XLum
- - 'Grapefruit' CBod LSou MHer MNHC NWad SRms
- - 'Lime' ENfk LEdu MHer SPlb SRms SVic
- - 'Orange' ENfk LEdu MHer MMuc MNHC NPer SRms
- - 'Swiss Ricola' MHer
- 'Crispa' NPol
- 'Strawberry' ENfk
- 'Swiss' CBod ENfk GJos LEdu MNHC NLar SRms WHer
pulegium CBod CHby ENfk GPoy LEdu LLWG MHer MNHC MWts SPlb SRms SVic WHer WSFF XAbr
- 'Upright' CBod ENfk GPoy MHer SRms
§ ***requienii*** CBod ENfk GAbr GCal GPoy LEdu LLWG MHer MNHC NRya NWad SPlb SRms WGwG XEll
rotundifolia misapplied see *M. suaveolens*
rotundifolia (L.) Huds. see *M.* × *villosa*
rubra var. ***raripila*** see *M.* × *smithiana*
§ × ***smithiana*** ENfk GPoy LEdu MHer MNHC MRav SRms
§ ***spicata*** CAgr CBod CTri CTsd ENfk GJos GPoy LCro LOPS MCot MHer MJak MMuc MNHC NPol NPri SEND SPlb SRms WHer XAbr XLum

- Algerian fruity	LEdu
- 'Cretan'	LEdu
* - var. ***crispa***	ECha ENfk LEdu MHer MMuc MNHC NRya SPlb SRms
- - 'Moroccan'	CRav ENfk GAbr GJos GLog GPoy LEdu MHer MNHC NLar NPri SRms SVic XAbr
- 'Crispula'	XLum
- 'Guernsey'	SRms
- 'Kentucky Colonel'	LEdu
- 'Newbourne'	SRms
- 'Nile Valley'	LEdu
- 'Russian'	CAgr LEdu MHer
- 'Spanish'	NLar SRms
- 'Spanish Furry'	MHer
- 'Tashkent'	CHby ENfk LEdu MHer MNHC SRms WGwG WHer
I 'Strawberry Mint'	LEdu MHer SRms
§ ***suaveolens***	CAgr CBod CHby ENfk GJos GMaP GPoy GQue MHer MNHC SPlb SRms SVic WSFF
* - 'Grapefruit'	CAgr LEdu
* - 'Pineapple'	CBod ENfk GLog
- subsp. ***timija***	MHer SRms
- 'Variegata' (v)	CTri ECha EHoe GJos GMaP GPoy GQue LEdu MCot MHer MMuc MNHC MRav NPri SPlb SRms SVic WHer XLum
'Sweet Pear'	MHer SRms
sylvestris L.	see *M. longifolia*
I 'Tangerine Mint'	LEdu
§ × ***villosa***	MMuc SEND
§ - var. ***alopecuroides*** Bowles's mint	CBre GPoy LEdu MHer MNHC NLar NSti SRms WHer
viridis	see *M. spicata*

Menyanthes (*Menyanthaceae*)

trifoliata	CBen CWat EWat GPoy LLWG MSKA MWts NPer WHal WMAq WSFF WWtn XLum

Menziesia see *Rhododendron*

alba	see *Daboecia cantabrica* f. *alba*
ciliicalyx lasiophylla	see *Rhododendron multiflorum* var. *purpureum*

Mercurialis (*Euphorbiaceae*)

perennis	EBWF GPoy WHer WSFF WShi

Merendera (*Colchicaceae*)

attica	NRog
eichleri	see *M. trigyna*
filifolia	NRog
§ ***montana***	EPot GKev NRog
- 'Norman Barratt'	WCot
pyrenaica	see *M. montana*
raddeana	see *M. trigyna*
sobolifera	NRog WCot
§ ***trigyna***	NRog

Merrilliopanax (*Araliaceae*)

alpinus B&SWJ 13939 **new**	WCru

Mertensia (*Boraginaceae*)

ciliata	CCse
franciscana	GCal
lanceolata	EBee
§ ***maritima***	CRos CSpe CWCL EWes GKev GPoy LEdu LRHS NRHS SMad SPlb SRms WHoo
- subsp. ***asiatica***	see *M. maritima*
pterocarpa	see *M. sibirica*
pulmonarioides	see *M. virginica*
§ ***sibirica***	CSpe SPlb
§ ***virginica*** 🏆^{H4}	CWCL EBee ECtt EHrv ELan EPfP EPot IFro IRob LAma LCro LEdu LOPS LRHS MBel MHol MNrw MPie MSCN NLar NPnk NSti SDir SRms WFar
viridis	SPlb

Merwilla (*Asparagaceae*)

§ ***plumbea***	WCot

Merxmuellera (*Poaceae*)

cincta	see *Capeochloa cincta*

Mesembryanthemum (*Aizoaceae*)

brownii	see *Lampranthus brownii*
crystallinum	NPri

Mespilus ✿ (*Rosaceae*)

germanica (F)	CBcs CDul CHab CLnd CMCN CTri ECrN ESps EUJe EWTr IDee LMaj LPra MGil NLar SLon WFar
- 'Bredase Reus' (F)	ELan
- 'Dutch' (F)	SDea
- 'Iranian' (F)	SKee
- 'Large Russian' (F)	CAgr
- 'Monstrous' (F)	SDea
- 'Nottingham' (F) 🏆^{H6}	Widely available
- 'Royal' (F)	CAgr CFGn ERea LRHS MCoo MRai NOra SCoo SKee WHar
- 'Westerveld' (F)	CLnd EPom SKee

Metapanax ✿ (*Araliaceae*)

davidii	CFil WPGP
delavayi	WPGP

Metaplexis (*Apocynaceae*)

japonica	SBrt

Metarungia (*Acanthaceae*)

galpinii	WHil

Metasequoia ✿ (*Cupressaceae*)

glyptostroboides	Widely available
- 'Chubby'^{PBR}	EPfP NLar
- 'Emerald Feathers'	SLim
- 'Fastigiata'	see *M. glyptostroboides* 'National'
- GOLD RUSH ('Golden Oji') 🏆^{H7}	Widely available
- 'Golden Dawn'	NLar
- 'Hamlet's Broom'	SLim
- 'Little Creamy'	NLar
- 'Little Giant'	MBlu
- 'Matthaei Broom'	MBlu SLim
- 'McCracken's White' (v)	NLar SLim
- 'Miss Grace'	NLar SLim
§ - 'National'	MBlu
- 'Schirrmann's Nordlicht'	SLim
- 'Sheridan Spire'	CEnd MBlu
- 'Waasland'	MBlu
- 'White Spot' (v)	MBlu

Metrosideros (*Myrtaceae*)

carminea	CCCN
§ ***excelsa***	CHll ECre
- 'Parnell'	CBcs CCCN
- 'Vibrance'	CCCN

kermadecensis 'Twisty' (v) — CBcs
- 'Variegata' (v) — CBcs
lucida — see *M. umbellata*
robusta — CBcs CCCN SPlb
- ***aureovariegata*** (v) — CCCN EShb
§ 'Springfire' — CCCN
× ***subtomentosa*** 'Mistral' — MPkF
'Thomasii' — see *M.* 'Springfire'
tomentosa — see *M. excelsa*
§ ***umbellata*** — CBcs CCCN CTsd
- 'Gold Nugget' — CBcs CCCN LSou MPkF
- MOONLIGHT ('Lowmoo') — CBcs CCCN LSou SEle SLim

Meum (*Apiaceae*)

athamanticum — CSpe EBee GCal GPoy IMou LEdu LRHS MAvo MRav SPhx WHil WSHC

Michauxia (*Campanulaceae*)

campanuloides — CSpe GJos
tchihatchewii — CDTJ CSpe NGBl

Michelia see *Magnolia*

fulgens — see *Magnolia foveolata*
wilsonii — see *Magnolia ernestii*

Microbiota (*Cupressaceae*)

decussata 🏆H5 — CBcs CMac CRos CSBt ESps GMcL GMil LBee LRHS MGos NRHS
- 'Jakobsen' — CKen
- 'Trompenburg' — CKen

Microcachrys ✿ (*Podocarpaceae*)

tetragona — IDee WThu

Microglossa (*Asteraceae*)

albescens — see *Aster albescens*

Microlepia (*Dennstaedtiaceae*)

strigosa — CBdn CCCN CRos EBee LRHS NRHS WPGP
- 'MacFaddeniae' — CBdn CRos EBee LRHS NRHS WPGP

Micromeria (*Lamiaceae*)

sp. — SRms
corsica — see *Acinos corsicus*
juliana — XLum
rupestris — see *M. thymifolia*
§ ***thymifolia*** — SPlb

Microseris (*Asteraceae*)

ringens hort. — see *Leontodon rigens*

Microsorum (*Polypodiaceae*)

§ ***diversifolium*** — EShb WCot WPGP
membranaceum **new** — CBdn
musifolium — NLos
- 'Crocodyllus'[PBR] **new** — EShb
punctatum GREEN FLAME ('Vp005') — NLos

Microtropis (*Celastraceae*)

petelotii HWJ 719 — WCru

Mikania (*Asteraceae*)

araucana — LSou

Milium (*Poaceae*)

effusum 'Aureum' 🏆H7 — Widely available
- 'Yaffle' (v) — CBod CBre CKno CRos EPPr EShb NRHS WPnP

Millettia (*Papilionaceae*)

japonica 'Hime Fuji' — WPGP
murasaki-natsu-fuji — see *M. reticulata*
pachycarpa — CMen
§ ***reticulata*** — CExl

Mimetes (*Proteaceae*)

chrysanthus — SPlb
cucullatus — CPbh
- 'Crackerjack Red' — CCCN

Mimosa (*Mimosaceae*)

pudica 🏆H1c — CCCN CDTJ SPlb

Mimulus (*Phrymaceae*)

'Andean Nymph' — see *M. naiandinus*
§ ***aurantiacus*** 🏆H2 — CMac CSpe CTri EBak ECtt EShb GCal IDee MGil NPer SPlb SRms
- 'Primrose' — MGil
× ***bartonianus*** — see *M.* × *harrisonii*
cardinalis 🏆H1c — EBee ELan EPfP EWes GKev LLWG MSKA WBor WMoo
- gold-flowered — EBee
- 'Red Dragon' — CBod CFis WHrl
cardinalis × ***lewisii*** — EWes
cupreus 'Whitecroft Scarlet' 🏆H5 — GCrg LLWG
eastwoodiae — GKev
'Eleanor' — ECtt
glutinosus — see *M. aurantiacus*
- ***atrosanguineus*** — see *M. puniceus*
- ***luteus*** — see *M. aurantiacus*
§ ***guttatus*** — LCro LOPS NMir NPer WMoo
§ × ***harrisonii*** — EWes
'Highland Orange' — EPfP GWyn MAsh SPlb SPoG
'Highland Pink' — CRos EPfP GWyn MAsh NHpl NRHS SPlb SPoG
'Highland Red' 🏆H5 — EPfP GMaP GWyn MAsh NHpl SPlb SPoG
'Highland Yellow' — GMaP GWyn NHpl SPlb SPoG
hose-in-hose (d) — NPer
× ***hybridus*** MAGIC RAINBOW mixed **new** — ETMg
langsdorffii — see *M. guttatus*
lewisii 🏆H1c — EBee EWes MNrw SRms
'Lothian Fire' — CWat
luteus — CWat GAbr LLWG NPer WBrk WMAq XLum
- 'Variegatus' ambig. (v) — NPer
* 'Major Bees' — ETMg MJak
'Malibu Orange' — EPfP
MAXIMUS MIXED — NPri
moschatus — EBee LLWG
§ ***naiandinus*** 🏆H4 — EWes GKev SPlb
'Orange Glow' — LLWG MJak
§ 'Orkney Gold' (d) — ECtt
'Popacatapetl' — CSpe
primuloides — EWes SPlb
§ ***puniceus*** — CRos CTri NRHS SRkn
ringens — CBen CWat EBee LLWG MSKA NPer SPlb SRms WMAq WMoo
'Threave Variegated' (v) — EBee
'Vortex Hot Spot' — LSou
yellow hose-in-hose — see *M.* 'Orkney Gold'

Mina see *Ipomoea*

mint, apple see *Mentha suaveolens*

mint, Bowles's see *Mentha* × *villosa* var. *alopecuroides*

mint, curly see *Mentha spicata* var. *crispa*

mint, eau-de-Cologne see *Mentha* × *piperita* f. *citrata*

mint, ginger see *Mentha* × *gracilis*

mint, horse or long-leaved see *Mentha longifolia*

mint (pennyroyal) see *Mentha pulegium*

mint (peppermint) see *Mentha* × *piperita*

mint, round-leaved see *Mentha suaveolens*

mint (spearmint) see *Mentha spicata*

Minuartia (*Caryophyllaceae*)

parnassica	see *M. stellata*
§ ***stellata***	EPot GKev
verna subsp. ***caespitosa***	CTri
- - 'Aurea'	see *Sagina subulata* var. *glabrata* 'Aurea'

Mirabilis (*Nyctaginaceae*)

dichotoma	EShb
jalapa	CExl EPfP GKev LAma LEdu SDeJ SDir SRms WHil XAbr
- 'Buttermilk'	CCCN
longiflora	EShb SBrt
multiflora	EBee
nyctaginea	SPhx

Miscanthus (*Poaceae*)

capensis	SPlb
chejuensis B&SWJ 8803	WCru
'Dronning Ingrid'	CKno EPPr IMou MNrw NDov XLum
'Elfin'	CKno
flavidus	SRms XLum
floridulus misapplied	see *M.* × *giganteus*
floridulus ambig.	MMuc MNrw NLos SCob SPlb XLum
floridulus (Labill.) Warb. ex K. Schum. & Lauterb. HWJ 522	WCru
§ × ***giganteus***	CBod CKno EHoe ELon EPPr EUJe GCal GMcL IBoy MAsh MMoz MNrw MWht NLos NWsh SCob SDys SVic WCot WMoo XLum
- 'Aksel Olsen'	SAko
- 'Gilt Edge' (v)	CKno EPPr NWsh
- 'Gotemba' (v)	ELon EPPr EWes
- 'Jubilar' (v) **new**	MWht
- 'Meidl' **new**	SAko
nepalensis	CAby CBot CElw CExl CKno CMea CRos CSam CWCL EAJP EBee ECha ECre EHoe EPed EUJe EWes GCal LEdu LRHS LSun MAvo MNrw NDov NLos NRHS SPlb SPtp SRms WPGP
- NJM 09.141	WPGP
- 'Shikola'	EMFm WCru
oligostachyus	IMou SDys
§ - 'Afrika'	CMea EBee EPPr GBin IMou MAvo MNrw WPGP
I - 'Nanus Variegatus' (v)	CKno EHoe LEdu SAko WCot
'Purpurascens'	CBod CBot CKno CRos CWCL ECha EHoe EPPr EPed IBoy IRob LRHS LSRN MMoz MNrw NLos NRHS SCob SGol SPer WMoo XLum
'Red Cloud' **new**	CRos NRHS
sacchariflorus misapplied	see *M.* × *giganteus*
sacchariflorus ambig.	CBWd CBcs CKno CRos ECha EHrv ELan EPfP LRHS MBrN NGdn NRHS SPer WMoo
sacchariflorus (Maxim.) Hack.	LEdu WSpi
sinensis	CRos CTri EPed ESps LEdu WFar WHar WMoo XSen
- 'Abundance'	CKno CRos EPfP LRHS NRHS
- 'Adagio'	CBar CBod CKno CRos ECtt EHoe ELon EPPr EShb GBin ILea LRHS MNrw NRHS NWad NWsh SCob SMHy SMad WCot WMoo XLum XSen
- 'Afrika'	see *M. oligostachyus* 'Afrika'
- 'Aldebaran'	IMou MNrw
- 'Andante'	CKno EBee
- 'Arabesque'	EMFm EPPr MMoz XLum
- 'Augustfeder'	EPPr MAvo XLum
- 'Autumn Light'	EPPr XLum
- 'Barney Campbell'	NWsh
- 'Blütenwunder'	EPPr NWsh XLum
- 'Bogenlampe'	GBin
- 'China' ♀^{H6}	CKno CPar CRos EHoe ELon EPPr EShb EWes IPot LEdu LRHS MAsh MAvo MNrw NPnk NRHS NWsh SDys SRms WMoo
- 'Cindy'	CKno
- var. ***condensatus***	LEdu
- - NJM 11.021	WPGP
- - 'Cabaret' (v)	CBod CKno CRos EHoe EPPr EPfP EUJe GMaP GMcL ILea LEdu LRHS LSRN MNrw MSpe NRHS NSti NWsh SPoG WCot WFar WHal WMoo WPGP WSpi XLum
- - 'Central Park'	see *M. sinensis* var. *condensatus* 'Cosmo Revert'
§ - - 'Cosmo Revert'	EPPr LEdu NWsh WPGP
- - 'Cosmopolitan' (v) ♀^{H5}	Widely available
- - 'Emerald Giant'	see *M. sinensis* var. *condensatus* 'Cosmo Revert'
- - 'Laigong'	LEdu
- 'David'	ELon EPPr LEdu MBNS MMoz MSpe XLum
- 'Dixieland' (v)	CKno ELan ELon EPPr EWes IFoB IMou LEdu
- 'Dreadlocks'	EBee EPPr GBin MAvo
- 'Dresdner Rotgold'	SAko
- 'Emmanuel Lepage'	CKno EPPr LPla MAvo XLum
- 'Etincelle'	CKno EPPr EWes ILea
- 'Federriese'	EBee GBin
- 'Ferner Osten' ♀^{H7}	Widely available
- 'Feuergold'	SAko
- 'Flamingo' ♀^{H6}	Widely available
- 'Flammenmeer'	SAko
- 'Gearmella'	EPPr
- 'Gewitterwolke' ♀^{H6}	EWes SMHy XLum
- 'Ghana' ♀^{H6}	CSpe EBee ELon EPPr EUJe GBin IMou IRob LEdu LPla MAvo MNrw SDys SMHy SRms SSut XLum
- 'Giraffe'	CDTJ CKno EWes LEdu XLum

- 'Gnome'	CKno EHoe EPPr EShb EUJe IMou LRHS MAsh NRHS
- 'Gold Bar'PBR (v)	CBod CChe CDul CRos CWGN ECha EHoe ELon EPfP EUJe GMcL LRHS LSRN LSou MAsh MBNS NGdn NLar NRHS NWad SEle SGol SPad SPer WMoo
- 'Gold Breeze'	CRos LRHS NRHS
- 'Gold und Silber' ♀H6	XLum
- 'Goldfeder' (v)	EMFm XLum
- 'Goliath'	CKno EHoe ELan ELon EPPr EUJe GBin GLog LEdu MBNS NLos XLum
- 'Gracillimus'	Widely available
- 'Graziella'	CBod CEnd CKno CRos CSam EHoe EPPr EPed EPfP GBin GWyn LRHS NGdn NRHS SPer SRms WFar WMoo XSen
- 'Grosse Fontäne' ♀H6	CRos EHoe ELan ELon EPPr GBin LEdu LRHS LSRN NRHS NWsh SMHy WCot WMoo XLum
- 'Gutenberg Gold'	XLum
- 'Haiku'	CKno EPPr LEdu XLum
- 'Helga Reich'	EWes
- 'Hercules'	EPPr MAvo XLum
- 'Hermann Müssel'	CBWd CKno CRos EBee EPPr EWes IMou LEdu LRHS NLos NRHS SMHy XLum
§ - 'Hinjo' (v)	CDul ECha EHoe ELon GBin LRHS MMoz MSpe NGdn NRHS NWsh SPoG WCot
- 'J.M. Gardiner' **new**	CBod
I - 'Jubilaris' (v)	EMFm EPPr
- 'Juli'	CRos EPPr LRHS NRHS WSpi
- 'Kaskade' ♀H6	CBod CKno CPar CRos EHoe EPPr EUJe GBin LEdu LRHS MMoz MMuc NDov NLar NRHS SMad WMoo
- 'Kirk Alexander' (v)	EPPr
- 'Kleine Fontäne' ♀H6	Widely available
- 'Kleine Silberspinne' ♀H6	Widely available
- 'Korea'	EBee EPPr
- 'Krater'	CRos EBee EHoe EPPr ILea LRHS MBrN NRHS NWsh SDys XLum
- 'Kupferberg'	XLum
- 'Kupferzwerg'	EBee EPPr
§ - 'Little Kitten'	CKno EPPr EPed EUJe LEdu SMad SRms WMoo XLum
- LITTLE NICKY	see *M. sinensis* 'Hinjo'
- 'Little Zebra'PBR (v)	EBee EPfP EUJe GMaP LSRN MGos MPnt NLar NLos SCob SEle SMad SRms
- 'Malepartus'	Widely available
- 'Memory'	EPPr
- 'Morning Light' (v) ♀H6	Widely available
- 'Nippon'	CRos EHoe EPPr GBin IRob LEdu LRHS MMoz NGdn NRHS NWsh SCob SDys SPer WSpi XLum
- 'Nishidake'	EPPr XLum
- 'November Sunset'	EPPr EWes MMoz XLum
- 'Overdam'	ECtt IFoB NGdn
- 'Poseidon'	EPPr MAvo SDys SMad XLum
- 'Positano'	CKno XLum
- 'Professor Richard Hansen'	CKno EBee EPPr EWes SMHy XLum
- 'Pünktchen' (v)	CRos ECha EHoe ELon EPPr GBin LEdu LRHS MSpe NRHS SCob SMHy SMad SRms WMoo XLum
- 'Purple Fall'	CBot CPar CSpe EWes GBin GMaP IPot LRHS LSou MAvo MNrw NRHS STPC
- 'Red Chief'	CRos EPPr EUJe EWes IMou LPla LRHS MAvo NDov NRHS SCob WMoo WTor
- 'Red Meister'	CKno CRos EPfP LRHS NRHS
- 'Red Tower'	EWes
- 'Red Wine'	GBin MNrw
- 'Roland'	CKno EHoe EPPr SMad XLum
- 'Rosi'	GBin
- 'Roterpfeil'	EPPr
- 'Rotfeder'	EPPr
- 'Rotfuchs'	EBee MAvo XLum
- 'Rotsilber'	CBWd CBod CKno CRos CSpe ECha EHoe EPPr EUJe GMaP IArd LRHS MJak MMuc NRHS NWsh WHoo WMoo XLum
- 'Russia'	MAvo NWsh
- 'Samurai'	EPPr GMaP MAvo MNrw
- 'Sarabande' ♀H6	EHoe EPPr SMHy WMoo WSpi
- 'Septemberrot' ♀H6	CKno EPPr MMuc SCob SEND
- 'Serim'	EPPr
§ - 'Silberfeder' ♀H6	Widely available
- 'Silberpfeil' (v)	NWsh
- 'Silberspinne'	CCse CRos EBee EPPr GBin IBoy ILea LRHS MWat NLos NRHS SCob SMHy SPlb XLum
- 'Silberturm'	EPPr XLum
- SILVER FEATHER	see *M. sinensis* 'Silberfeder'
- 'Silver Sceptre'	MAvo SMHy
- 'Silver Stripe'	EPPr MAvo
- 'Sioux'	CRos ECtt EHoe EPPr EShb EUJe GBin GQue LRHS MBNS NRHS SPer
- 'Sirene'	EHoe EPPr MBNS MMuc MSpe
- 'Spätgrün'	EPPr
- 'Starlight'	CKno
- 'Strictus' (v) ♀H6	Widely available
- 'Super Stripe' (v)	EPPr IMou
- 'Taiwan'	EBee EPPr
- 'Tiger Cub' (v)	CWCL EPPr EWes
- 'Undine' ♀H6	CBWd CKno CMea ECha EHoe ELan EPPr EPfP MBel MBrN MMuc NWsh WMoo XLum
- 'Variegatus' (v)	CBod CRos ECha ECtt EHoe ELan ELon EPPr EPfP ESps EUJe GMaP GMcL LEdu LRHS LSRN MBrN MMuc MRav NGdn NRHS NSti SCob SGol SPer SPoG SRms WCot WMoo XLum
- 'Verneigung'	GBin
- 'Vorläufer'	EPPr GBin
- 'Westacre Wine'	EWes
- 'Wetterfahne'	EPPr LEdu
§ - 'Yaku-jima'	CBod CSam ECha ECtt EPPr MMuc MWht NLos SCob
- 'Yakushima Dwarf'	Widely available
- 'Zebrinus' (v) ♀H6	Widely available
- 'Zwergelefant'	EBee MAvo MMoz SMHy XLum
tinctorius 'Nanus Variegatus' misapplied	see *M. oligostachyus* 'Nanus Variegatus'
transmorrisonensis	CKno CRos EHoe ELan EPPr EUJe LEdu LPla LRHS MAvo MMoz NDov NLos NRHS NWsh WCot WPGP
yakushimensis	see *M. sinensis* 'Little Kitten', *M. sinensis* 'Yaku-jima'

Mitchella (*Rubiaceae*)

repens	CBcs EBee GEdr IMou LEdu MNrw WCru
undulata B&SWJ 10928	WCru
* - f. ***quelpartensis*** B&SWJ 4402	WCru

Mitella (*Saxifragaceae*)

acerina B&SWJ 11029	EWld WCru
breweri	CHid CMac ECha EWld GCal GLog IMou MAvo MMoz MPnt MRav NSti WBor WMoo WOut WPnP
caulescens	ECha NBro
diphylla	MHer
formosana B&SWJ 125	EPPr WCru
furusei var. ***subramosa*** B&SWJ 11097	WCru
× ***inami***	IMou
- B&SWJ 11122	WCru
japonica B&SWJ 4971	WCru
kiusiana B&SWJ 5888	WCru
makinoi	EWld MAvo MMoz
- B&SWJ 4992	CExl WCru
pauciflora B&SWJ 6361	WCru
stylosa B&SWJ 5669	WCru
yoshinagae B&SWJ 4893	CExl CHid EPPr WCru WMoo

Mitraria (*Gesneriaceae*)

coccinea	CBcs CCCN CExl CHll CMac CPbh CTsd ELan ESps GEdr GKev LSou MBlu NLar SLim SLon SPer SPlb
- Clark's form	EUJe LRHS NLar
- 'Lago Puyehue'	CAbb CBcs CCCN CExl CRos EBee EPfP LRHS MAsh MGil SPlb SVen SWvt WSHC WThu
- 'Lake Caburgua'	CAby CCCN CSpe ELon GCal NLar

Modiolastrum (*Malvaceae*)

lateritium	CHll CRHN CRos CSpe CTri ELan EPPr EPri LRHS MAvo SPhx SPoG SRms WAvo WHal WHar WSHC XLum

Moehringia (*Caryophyllaceae*)

muscosa	WCot

Molinia ✿ (*Poaceae*)

altissima	see *M. caerulea* subsp. *arundinacea*
'Autumn Charm'	CKno
caerulea	CKno CRos EBWF EPPr LRHS MAsh MBlu NRHS
§ - subsp. ***arundinacea***	CKno CSpe CWCL ECha EPPr SSut XLum
- - 'Automne Bronze'	EPPr
- - 'Bergfreund'	CKno CSam EBee EHoe EPPr EPed GBin MAvo SMHy
- - 'Black Arrows'	MAvo NDov
- - 'Breeze'	CKno NDov
- - 'Cordoba'	CBod CKno EBee EPPr GBin GQue IPot MAvo NDov SMHy SPhx WMoo XLum
- - 'Fontäne'	CSam EHoe EPPr GQue MAsh MAvo SPhx
- - 'Granada'	EPPr
- - 'JS Mostenveld' (v)	GBin
- - 'JS Witches Broom'	GBin
- - 'JS Yellow Pipe'	GBin
- - 'Karl Foerster'	CBWd CBod CKno CRos CWCL EHoe EPPr EPed EPfP EShb ESps EUJe GBin GMaP GQue IRob LRHS LSun MMoz MNrw NBid NLar NRHS SCob SPer SPhx WCot WMoo XLum XSen
- - 'Les Ponts de Cé'	EPPr
- - 'Liebreiz'	EPPr
- - 'Moorland Mist' **new**	WMoo
- - 'Skyracer'	CBWd CKno CRos EBee EHoe ELan ELon EPPr EUJe GBin GCal GLog GMaP GQue IRob LEdu LRHS MAvo MMoz MNrw NRHS SMHy SPhx WCot WGrn WMoo
- - 'Staefa'	EHoe
- - 'Sunbeam'	EPPr
- - 'Tears of Joy'	EPPr
- - 'Transparent'	Widely available
- - 'Windsaule'	CKno EPPr MAvo NDov SPhx
- - 'Windspiel'	CBWd CBod CKno CRos CSam CWCL EBee ECha EHoe EPPr EPed EShb GBin GMcL GQue LRHS MAvo MNrw MSpe NDov NRHS NWsh SPer SPhx SPoG WCot WMoo WPtf XLum
- - 'Zuneigung'	CKno CRos CSam EPPr LRHS MAvo NRHS SPhx
- subsp. ***caerulea***	EPPr
- - 'Carmarthen' (v)	CRos EHoe EPPr LRHS NRHS
- - 'Claerwen' (v)	ECha EPPr MAvo SPhx WMoo
- - 'Coneyhill Gold' (v)	EPPr
- - 'Dark Defender'	EPPr NDov SPhx
- - 'Dauerstrahl'	CKno EBee EPPr GCal GQue MAsh MNrw NDov
- - 'Edith Dudszus'	CBWd CBod CKno CMea CRos ECha EHoe ELan ELon EPPr EPed GBin GQue LRHS MBel MBrN NDov NGdn NRHS SCob SPer SPhx WGrn WMoo
- - 'Heidebraut'	CBod CRos EBee EHoe EHrv ELon EPPr GBin GMaP GQue IBoy IRob LCro LOPS LRHS MBel MRav NDov NRHS SCob SPhx WMoo XSen
- - 'Heidezwerg'	EBee EPPr GBin
- - 'Igel'	EBee EPPr GBin
- - 'Moorflamme'	CSam EPPr MAvo SPhx
- - 'Moorhexe'	Widely available
- - 'Overdam'	EPPr NDov
- - 'Poul Petersen'	CKno EBee EHoe EPPr GBin MBel NDov SPhx
- - 'Rotschopf'	EBee
- - 'Strahlenquelle'	CBWd CBod CSam ELan EPPr GBin GQue LRHS MSpe NDov NRHS NWsh
- - 'Variegata' (v) 🏆H7	Widely available
- 'Showers of Gold'	SPhx
litoralis	see *M. caerulea* subsp. *arundinacea*

Molopospermum (*Apiaceae*)

peloponnesiacum	CAby CSpe EBee GCal IMou LEdu MMrt NDov SBrt SMHy SPhx WCot WCru WPGP WSHC

Moltkia (*Boraginaceae*)

§ ***doerfleri***	EBee GCal NChi SBrt WSHC
§ × ***intermedia*** 🏆H5	CMea CRos LRHS NRHS SBrt WAbe WThu
petraea	CRos LLHF LRHS NRHS

Moluccella (*Lamiaceae*)

laevis	CSpe LCro LOPS SPhx SVic

Monadenium (*Euphorbiaceae*)

coccineum **new**	LToo
echinulatum **new**	LToo
schubei	LToo
spectabile **new**	LToo

Monanthes (*Crassulaceae*)

	laxiflora	WCot
	pallens	WCot

Monarda ✿ (*Lamiaceae*)

	'Adam'	GCal GQue IRob LSRN MRav NLar WMon WSHC
	'Aquarius'	CBod CRos CWCL CWld EAJP EPPr EPed GAbr GQue IBoy LRHS NLar NRHS WFar WMon WMoo XLum
	'Baby Spice'	WMon
§	'Balance'	EBee ECtt MMrt MRav NBro NGdn WMon WSHC XLum
	BALMY LILAC ('Balbalmal') **new**	MHol
	'Beauty of Cobham' Y^{H4}	Widely available
	'Bergamo'	CBod LCro LPmr MHol
§	'Blaustrumpf'	CBot CElw CRos EAJP ECtt EPfP EWes LRHS NLar NRHS SPer WFar WMon WSHC XLum
	BLUE STOCKING	see *M.* 'Blaustrumpf'
	BOWMAN	see *M.* 'Sagittarius'
	bradburyana	CBWd GJos LPla MMuc SAko SBrt SPhx
	- Schm. 2004-0076 **new**	WMon
	- 'Maramek' **new**	IPot
	- 'Ozark'	SAko
	'Cambridge Scarlet'	Widely available
	'Cambridge Star' **new**	MArl
	'Camilla' **new**	WMon
	'Capricorn'	WMon XLum
	'Cherokee'	WMon
	citriodora	NSti SRms
	'Comanche'	EWes NLar WMon
	'Croftway Pink'	CBWd CBcs CRos CSBt CWCL ECha ECtt ELan EPfP ESps EUJe GMaP IBoy IRob LCro LRHS MAvo MNHC MTis NLar NRHS SPer SWvt WAvo WBor WCAu WFar WMon WSHC XLum
I	'Dark Ponticum'	WMon
	didyma	CBod ENfk EPfP ESps MNHC NBro SRms SVic WFar WHar XAbr
	- 'Alba'	NLar
	- BALMY PURPLE ('Balbalmurp'^{PBR})	CPla MHol SPoG WFar
	- 'Coral Reef'	CRos EWes LRHS NRHS WFar WMon
	- 'Cranberry Lace'^{PBR}	CBot CRos EBee ECtt EPfP ETMg LRHS MSCN NLar NRHS SPoG WCAu
	- 'Pardon my Pink'	CBod CPla NLar NPnk SPad
	- 'Pardon My Purple' **new**	CBod NLar
	- 'Pink Lace'^{PBR}	CBot CRos ECtt EPfP IBoy LRHS LSou LSun MHol MNrw NDov NLar NRHS SCob SPoG WCAu WFar WHil WMon WMoo
	- 'Sugar Lace'^{PBR}	CRos LRHS NLar NRHS
	'Earl Grey'	EBee ECtt GAbr SCoo WFar WMon
	'Elsie's Lavender'	EBee EPfP LRHS NDov NLar NRHS WFar WMon WSHC
	'Elworthy'	CElw WWFP
	'Eugens Kirschrot' **new**	WMon
	'Eugens Purpursamt' **new**	WMon
§	'Feuerschopf'	EBee
	'Fireball'^{PBR}	Widely available
	FIRECROWN	see *M.* 'Feuerschopf'
§	'Fishes'	CExl CMac CRos EBee ECtt EHrv ELan EPPr EWes GQue LEdu LRHS MRav NDov NGdn NLar NRHS SGbt SPoG SWvt WFar WMon WMoo WPtf
	fistulosa	CBod CHby CMac GJos MMuc MNHC SRms WArt WMoo XAbr XLum
	- var. ***menthifolia*** 'Mohikaner'	EBee NDov SAko WMon
	- 'Wahpe Washtemna' **new**	NDov
	'Gardenview Scarlet' Y^{H4}	Widely available
	GEMINI	see *M.* 'Twins'
	'Gewitterwolke'	CSam ECtt MNrw NDov WMon
	'Hartswood Wine'	EWes LEdu WFar WMon
	'Häuptling' **new**	WMon
	'Heidelerche'	EBee
	'Huckleberry' **new**	WMon
	'Jacob Cline'	CMea CRos EAJP ECtt EPPr EWes GBin GWyn IPot LEdu LPla LRHS MBel MNrw NBre NLar NRHS SGbt SHar SMHy SPhx WBor WFar WMon WMoo XLum
	'Kardinal'	GBin LRHS MTis NDov NLar WMon XLum
	'Lambada'	GJos LPmr
	'Lederstrumpf'	EBee
	LIBRA	see *M.* 'Balance'
	'Loddon Crown'	CRos CTsd ECtt LPla LRHS MBNS MHer NLar NRHS SHar WFar WMon WSHC
	'Mahogany'	CRos EBee ECtt ELan EPed ESps GMaP IBoy IPot LRHS MCot MNrw MRav NRHS NSti SCob SPer SPhx SPoG WFar WMon XLum
	'Marshall's Delight' Y^{H4}	CBod CRos CWCL EBee ECtt EPfP EWes GQue IBoy LEdu LRHS MNrw MRav NDov NLar NRHS SWvt WCAu WFar WMon
	'Melissa'	CRos EBee LRHS LSRN NBre NLar NRHS WMon WSHC
	menthifolia	SRms
	'Mohawk'	CBod ECtt EHrv EPPr EPed EPfP ESps GMcL GQue ILea LRHS MPie MRav NDov NGdn NRHS SPoG WAvo WCAu WMon WPtf XLum
	'Mrs Perry'	EWes
	'Neon'	LRHS NDov SPhx WMon
	'On Parade'	CBod CElw CSam CWCL CWld ECtt ELon GPSL LEdu LPla LRHS MMrt MTis NDov NGdn NRHS WAul WMon
	'Othello'	NDov WMon
	'Ou Charm'	EBee EWes NLar WFar WMon
	Panorama Series	SPlb WMoo
	- 'Panorama Red Shades'	EPfP WCFE WFar WMon WMoo
	'Pawnee'	WMon
	PETITE DELIGHT ('Acpetdel')	LSou NLar WMon XLum
	'Petite Wonder'	EBee WFar WMon
	'Pink Supreme'^{PBR}	CBct CBod CRos ECtt ELan EPfP GMcL LRHS LSou MSpe MTis NDov NLar NRHS SCoo WFar WHil WMon WMoo WTor
	'Pink Tourmaline'	NDov WMon
	PISCES	see *M.* 'Fishes'
	'Poyntzfield Pink'	GPoy LEdu LPla
	PRAIRIE NIGHT	see *M.* 'Prärienacht'
§	'Prärienacht'	Widely available
	punctata	GJos MNHC
	- 'Bee Bop' **new**	WHlf
	'Purple Ann'	XLum

	'Purple Lace'^{PBR}	CRos LRHS NDov NRHS WFar WMon
	'Purple Tower'	EWes
	'Raspberry Wine'	CRos EBee ECtt EPPr EWes LEdu LRHS MTis NRHS WFar WMon WMoo WPGP
	'Rebecca' **new**	WMon
	'Remie' **new**	WMon
	'Ruby Glow'	CRos CSam EHrv GMcL GWyn LRHS LSRN MMrt NRHS WMon
§	'Sagittarius'	EBee LRHS MAvo MBNS MSpe NGdn NRHS NSti WFar WMon
	'Saxon Purple'	LPla NDov NLar WMon XLum
§	'Schneewittchen'	CAby CBWd EBee ECha ECtt EHrv ELan EPfP IBoy LCro LRHS MRav MTis NLar SCob SCoo SGbt SPer SPoG SWvt WCAu WFar WHar WMon WMoo XLum
	'Scorpion'	CBWd CRos EBee ECtt EHrv ELan EPfP GBin GMcL GQue IBoy LCro LEdu LOPS LRHS MRav NDov NEgg NGdn NLar NRHS NSti SBod SWvt WCAu WMon XLum
	'Shelley'	ECha WMon
	'Sioux'	EHrv EWes
	'Snow Maiden'	see *M.* 'Schneewittchen'
	'Snow Queen'	EBee ECtt EShb LRHS MBel MPie NDov NRHS
	SNOW WHITE	see *M.* 'Schneewittchen'
	'Squaw' 🏆^{H4}	Widely available
	'Talud' 🏆^{H4}	IPot MNrw NDov WMon
	'Tante Polly' **new**	WMon
§	'Twins'	EAJP GKev LSRN NLar SWvt WFar WMon WMoo WSHC
	'Vintage Wine'	CElw NDov WMon
	'Violacea'	WFar WMon
	'Violet Queen' 🏆^{H4}	CRos CWCL EBee ECtt ELan EPed EWes GQue LEdu LRHS MAvo MBel MCot MSpe NEoE NRHS SCoo SPhm SPhx WCot WFar WMon WPtf
	'Violette'	EBee WMon
	'Westacre Purple'	EBee EPPr EWes

Monardella (*Lamiaceae*)

	macrantha subsp. ***hallii***	CPBP
	odoratissima	MHer SPhx

Monochoria (*Pontederiaceae*)

§	***hastata***	LLWG MSKA

Monstera (*Araceae*)

	deliciosa (F) 🏆^{H1b}	LCro XBlo

Montbretia see *Crocosmia*

Montia (*Portulacaceae*)

	perfoliata	see *Claytonia perfoliata*
	sibirica	see *Claytonia sibirica*

Moraea (*Iridaceae*)

	alticola	CPne GCal SPlb
§	***aristata***	CTal NRog
	atropunctata	NRog
§	***bellendenii***	NRog WCot
	bipartita	NRog WCot
	ciliata	NRog WCot
§	***collina***	GKev NRog
	gigandra	NRog
	glaucopsis	see *M. aristata*
	huttonii	CCCN CFis CPbh CSpe CTsd EPri GAbr GKev MHer NWad SBrt SMad WKif WSHC
	iridioides	see *Dietes iridioides*
	longifolia (Jacq.) Pers.	MHol
	loubseri	NRog
	lugubris	NRog
	lurida	CTal
	macrocarpa	NRog
	mediterranea	GKev
	ochroleuca	GKev NRog
	pavonia var. ***lutea***	see *M. bellendenii*
	polystachya	CGrW NRog
	sisyrinchium	GKev
	- dwarf **new**	GKev
	spathacea	see *M. spathulata*
§	***spathulata***	CExl GCal GKev WCot
	thomsonii	NRog
	tricuspidata	NRog
	tripetala	NRog
	tulbaghensis	NRog
	vegeta	CTal NRog
	villosa	CTal NRog

Morella (*Myricaceae*)

	californica	CAgr
	pensylvanica	CAgr NLar

Moricandia (*Brassicaceae*)

	moricandioides	WCot

Morina (*Caprifoliaceae*)

*	***afghanica***	GAbr
	alba	GKev
	betonicoides	GKev
	bulleyana	see *M. nepatensis* var. *delavayi*
	longifolia	Widely available
§	***nepatensis*** var. ***delavayi***	GKev
	persica	EWes NWad
	polyphylla	GPoy

Morinda (*Rubiaceae*)

	umbellata WWJ 11688	WCru

Morisia (*Brassicaceae*)

	hypogaea	see *M. monanthos*
§	***monanthos***	CTsd GCrg GEdr LRHS SRot
	- 'Fred Hemingway'	ELan EPot LRHS NSla WAbe

Morus ✿ (*Moraceae*)

§	***alba***	CBcs CCVT CDul CHab CLnd CMCN ECrN ELan EMOT EPfP ERea ESps LBuc LMaj LPra MRav SDea SPre SVic WFar WHar WMou WTSh
	- 'Baby Doll'	CBot
	- 'Black Tabor'	CAgr
	- 'Issai'	GKev MGos
	- 'Laciniata'	ELan
	- 'Macrophylla'	CMCN MBlu
	- 'Pakistan' (F)	CAgr ERea
	- 'Paradise'	CAgr
	- 'Pendula'	CDul CEnd CMCN CMac CTri ECrN ELan ESps LPra MBlu NOra NPri SCoo SDea SLim SPoG SWvt
	- 'Platanifolia'	CLnd LPra MBlu
	- 'San Martin'	ERea
	- var. ***tatarica***	CAgr LEdu NLar
	'Capsrum' (F)	CAgr
	'Carmen' (F)	CAgr
	cathayana	WPGP

'Illinois Everbearing' (F)	CAgr ERea
'Italian' (F)	CAgr
'Ivory' (F)	CAgr
kagayamae	see *M. alba*
latifolia 'Spirata'	NLar
nigra (F)	Widely available
§ - 'Chelsea' (F) ♀H6	CDul CEnd CRos CSBt CTho CTri ECrN EPfP EPom ERea LRHS MGos NOra SCoo SEWo SKee SLim SPer SPoG SSFT WHar
- 'Izvor' (F)	CAgr
- 'Jerusalem' (F) ♀H6	MCoo NOra WHar
- 'King James'	see *M. nigra* 'Chelsea'
- 'Large Black' (F)	EPom
- 'Repsime' (F)	CAgr
- 'Sham Dudu' (F)	CAgr
rubra	EBtc
- 'Nana'	NLar
'Wellington' (F)	CCVT CEnd CLnd CTri EMOT LCro LOPS LRHS LSRN NOra SSFT

Mosla (*Lamiaceae*)

dianthera	EWld GCal MAvo

Muehlenbeckia ✿ (*Polygonaceae*)

astonii	LRHS WPGP
axillaris misapplied	see *M. complexa*
§ ***axillaris*** (Hook. f.) Endl.	CBcs CTri EBee EShb GBin SBig XLum
§ ***complexa***	CBcs CFlo CHll CMac CRos CTri EBee EPfP EShb ETod EUJe LRHS MBlu MGil NQui SAdn SArc SBig SCob SEND SLim SLon SNig SPer SPoG SWvt WCFE WPGP WSHC XLum
- 'Nana'	see *M. axillaris* (Hook. f.) Endl.
- small-leaved	EUJe
- 'Spotlight'PBR (v)	EShb
- 'Texture Big Leaf' **new**	WPGP
- var. ***trilobata***	CBcs EShb EUJe SSta XLum
platyclados	see *Homalocladium platycladum*

Muhlenbergia (*Poaceae*)

capillaris	EBee MBNS MMrt SBee SMad WCot
dumosa	CKno WCot WPGP
emersleyi	EBee
japonica 'Cream Delight' (v)	EHoe
lindheimeri	CKno EBee WCot
mexicana	SRms
rigens	CKno XLum

Mukdenia (*Saxifragaceae*)

acanthifolia	GCal LEdu WPGP
rossii	CAby CRos CTal EHrv ELon EWTr GBin GCal IFro LEdu LPla LRHS MBel MNrw NBid NLar NPnk NRHS WOld WPGP WThu XLum
- from Japan	GCal
- from Korea	GCal
- 'Crimson Fans'	see *M. rossii* 'Karasuba'
- dwarf	CTal GCal MNrw
§ - 'Karasuba'	Widely available
- 'Shishiba'	LEdu MMoz NPnk

× *Mukgenia* (*Saxifragaceae*)

§ 'Flame' **new**	CAby CBct EUJe LRHS MPnt NRHS SPad WAvo
NOVA	see × *M.* 'Flame'

mulberry see *Morus*

Murraya (*Rutaceae*)

exotica	see *M. paniculata*
koenigii	see *Bergera koenigii*
§ ***paniculata***	EShb

Musa ✿ (*Musaceae*)

from Yunnan, China	see *M. itinerans* 'Yunnan'
acuminata Cavendish Group (AAA Group) (F) **new**	EUJe
§ - 'Dwarf Cavendish' (AAA Group) (F) ♀H1b	CAbb CBct ELan EUJe NLos NPla XBlo
- 'Siam Ruby' (AA Group) (F)	NLos
- 'Williams' (AAA Group) (F)	XBlo
- 'Zebrina' ♀H1b	CDTJ CRos LRHS NLos XBlo
basjoo ♀H2	CAbb CBcs CHll CSBt ELan EPfP EUJe LCro LEdu LOPS MGos MMuc NLos NPla SArc SChr SEND SMad SPlb SPoG
I - 'Rubra'	CCCN
'Cavendish Super Dwarf'	NLos XBlo
cavendishii	see *M. acuminata* 'Dwarf Cavendish'
§ ***coccinea*** ♀H1b	XBlo
ensete	see *Ensete ventricosum*
hookeri	see *M. sikkimensis*
itinerans	NLos
- var. ***xishuangbannaensis*** 'Mekong Giant'	EUJe
§ - 'Yunnan'	NLos
lasiocarpa ♀H1c	CDTJ CHll EUJe LCro LOPS MGos MPkF NLos NPla SBig SPlb
nana misapplied	see *M. acuminata* 'Dwarf Cavendish'
ornata ♀H1b	CCCN XBlo
× ***paradisiaca*** 'Ney Poovan' (AB Group) (F)	CCCN
§ ***sikkimensis*** ♀H1c	CDTJ EUJe NLos SBig SPlb XBlo
- 'Red Tiger'	CCCN CDTJ LRHS MPkF NLos
uranoscopus misapplied	see *M. coccinea*
velutina ♀H1b	CCCN EUJe NLos SBig

Muscari ✿ (*Asparagaceae*)

adilii	NRog
'Aleyna'	NRog
ambrosiacum	see *M. muscarimi*
anatolicum	NRog WCot
- giant **new**	GKev
armeniacum ♀H5	CArg CRav CRos CTri GKev GWyn LCro LOPS LRHS MJak NRHS NRog SCob SDir SEND SPer SRms WCot WShi
- PAB 6748	LEdu
- 'Album'	SCob
- 'Alida' **new**	GKev
- 'Argaei Album'	GKev NRog
- 'Artist'	GKev NRog SDeJ
- 'Atlantic'	CRos EPfP GKev LRHS NRHS NRog
- 'Blue Pearl'	NRog
- 'Blue Spike' (d)	GKev LAma NEgg NRog SDeJ SDir WGwG
- 'Cantab'	SDeJ XLum
- 'Carola' **new**	GKev
- 'Christmas Pearl' ♀H4	GKev NPnk NRog
- 'Cupido'	GKev
- 'Dark Eyes'	EPfP GKev IBoy SCob SDeJ SDir

- 'Early Giant'	SDeJ
- 'Esther' **new**	GKev
- 'Fantasy Creation'	GKev NRog SDeJ
- 'Gül'	WCot
- 'Helena' **new**	GKev
- 'Icicle'	WHil
- 'Lady Blu'	LRHS
- 'Manon' **new**	GKev
- 'Pauline' **new**	GKev
- 'Peppermint'	CRos ERCP GKev LAma LRHS NRHS SDeJ SDir
- 'Saffier' ♀H5	GKev LAma NRog WCot WHil
- 'Siberian Tiger'	EPot GKev WTor
- 'Touch of Snow'	GKev LAma
- 'Valerie Finnis'	CAby CAvo CBre CMea EPfP EPot ERCP EShb GKev LRHS NLar NPnk SCob SDeJ SDir SMad WBrk WCot
aucheri ♀H5	NRya
* - var. ***bicolor***	WCot
- 'Blue Magic'	CAvo EPot ERCP GKev LAma NRog SDeJ
- 'Ocean Magic'	CAvo GKev LAma NHpl NLar NPnk
- 'White Magic'	CAvo ERCP GKev LAma LRHS NHpl SCob SDeJ WBrk
§ ***azureum*** ♀H5	CAvo CPla CTca ELan ERCP GKev GMaP LAma LRHS NLar NRog SPer SPhx WCot
- 'Album'	GKev LAma NRog SPhx WCot
- 'Bling Bling'	ERCP GKev LAma LRHS WCot
'Baby's Breath'	see *M.* 'Jenny Robinson'
'Big Smile'	CRos LRHS NRHS NRog WCot
'Blue Eyes'	WCot
botryoides	LAma NRog SCob WCot
- 'Album'	CAvo CTca CTri EPfP GKev IRob LAma LCro LOPS NRog SCob SDeJ SRms WCot WShi
bourgaei	GKev WCot
caucasicum	WCot
chalusicum	see *M. pseudomuscari*
coeleste	GKev WCot
commutatum	GKev
- white-flowered **new**	GKev
§ ***comosum***	CBro ERCP GKev MCot NEgg NRog SDir WCot
- 'Monstrosum'	see *M. comosum* 'Plumosum'
§ - 'Plumosum'	ELan EPfP GKev LAma NRog SCob SDeJ WCot
discolor	NRog
'Ivor's Pink'	WCot
§ 'Jenny Robinson' ♀H5	EHrv GKev IFoB LAma LRHS NPnk SDys SMad SPhx WArt WCot
'Joyce Spirit'	ERCP GKev LAma LRHS
latifolium ♀H5	CAby CRos CTca ERCP GKev LAma LCro LOPS LRHS MJak MWat NEgg NLar NRHS NRog SCob SDeJ SDir WBor WCot
macbeathianum	WCot
§ ***macrocarpum***	CBro CTal CTca ECha LAma NRog
- 'Golden Fragrance'PBR	CAby CAvo CBro CExl CHid EPot ERCP GKev IFoB LAma MCot MNrw NPnk NRog SDeJ WHil
'Memory of Gary Fisher'	WCot
mirum	WCot
'Morgenhimmel'	GKev
moschatum	see *M. muscarimi*
'Mount Hood'	ERCP GKev NPnk SCob SDeJ
'Mountain Lady'	GKev
§ ***muscarimi***	CAvo CTca GKev IFoB LAma NRog SDeJ WCot
- var. ***flavum***	see *M. macrocarpum*
§ ***neglectum***	GKev LAma NLar NRog SEND WCot WShi
pallens	GKev NRog
paradoxum	see *Bellevalia paradoxa*
parviflorum	WCot
'Pink Sunrise'	EPot ERCP EWTr GKev LRHS NHpl SCob SDeJ WCot
'Pink Surprise'	LAma
§ ***pseudomuscari*** ♀H5	WCot
pulchellum subsp. ***clepsydroides*** **new**	GKev
- subsp. ***pulchellum*** **new**	GKev
racemosum	see *M. neglectum*
'Rosy Sunrise'	WArt WCot
'Sky Blue'	WCot
§ ***spreitzenhoferi***	NRog
'Superstar'	GKev
§ ***tenuiflorum***	WCot
aff. ***tenuiflorum*** JCA 0.691.251	WCot
'Venus'	GKev LAma NPnk SDir WCot
verticillaris	GKev
'White Beauty'	GKev WCot
'Winter Amethyst'	WCot

Muscarimia (*Asparagaceae*)

ambrosiacum	see *Muscari muscarimi*
macrocarpum	see *Muscari macrocarpum*

Musella see *Musa*

Mussaenda (*Rubiaceae*)

'Tropic Snow'	CCCN

Mutisia (*Asteraceae*)

oligodon	GKev

Myoporum (*Scrophulariaceae*)

acuminatum	see *M. tenuifolium*
laetum	CExl IDee SPlb SVen
§ ***tenuifolium***	SPlb SVen

Myosotidium (*Boraginaceae*)

§ ***hortensia***	CAbb CAby CBcs CBct CExl CRos CSpe CTsd EPot ETod EUJe EWes GBin GCal GKev IBoy LRHS NRHS SChr WBor
- 'True Blue'	CHid
nobile	see *M. hortensia*

Myosotis (*Boraginaceae*)

arvensis	EBWF
australis	WCot
capitata	GEdr
decumbens	GEdr
dissitiflora 'Elegantissima' (v)	CNat
explanata	EWld
glabrescens	EPot
'Malmesbury'	CNat
MY OH MY ('Myomark'PBR)	CBod
palustris	see *M. scorpioides*
pulvinaris	CPBP SPlb
§ ***scorpioides***	CHab CWCL CWat EBWF LLWG MMuc MNrw MSKA MWts NMir SCoo SPlb SRms WBrk WMAq WMoo WPnP WRHF XLum
- 'Alba'	LLWG MSKA MWts NPnk
- 'Ice Pearl'	ECha
- MAYTIME ('Blaqua') (v)	LLWG

- 'Mermaid'	CBen CWat ECha EWat LLWG SRms WPtf
- 'Pinkie'	CWat LLWG
- 'Snowflakes'	CWat EWat
- variegated (v)	MSKA
secunda	EBWF
sylvatica	EBWF LCro LOPS MMuc NMir
- 'Bluesylva' (Sylva Series) 🏆^{H6}	LRHS SPhx WHil
- 'Ultramarine' 🏆^{H6}	WMoo
- 'Victoria Indigo-blue' (Victoria Series)	EPfP
terglovensis **new**	GEdr

Myrica (*Myricaceae*)

gale	CAgr GPoy NLar WGwG WSpi

Myricaria (*Tamaricaceae*)

germanica	NLar

Myriophyllum (*Haloragaceae*)

propinquum	LLWG
spicatum	MSKA MWts WMAq
verticillatum	CWat EWat MSKA SCoo

Myrrhidendron (*Apiaceae*)

glaucescens B&SWJ 14252 **new**	WCru
pennellii B&SWJ 14240 **new**	WCru

Myrrhis (*Apiaceae*)

odorata	CBre CHby CHid CMac CSpe EBWF ECha ENfk GBin GPoy IFro LCro LOPS LRHS MHer MMuc MNHC SCob SPad SPer SPhx SRms SWvt WPGP WSFF WWFP XAbr
- 'Forncett Chevron'	LEdu SPhx

Myrsine (*Primulaceae*)

africana	CFil EShb MHer
australis	SVen
divaricata	SVen
nummularia	WThu

Myrteola (*Myrtaceae*)

§ ***nummularia***	ITim WAbe WThu

Myrtus ✿ (*Myrtaceae*)

apiculata misapplied	see *Luma apiculata*
bullata	see *Lophomyrtus bullata*
chequen	see *Luma chequen*
communis 🏆^{H4}	Widely available
- 'Flore Pleno' (d)	MHer
- 'Jenny Reitenbach'	see *M. communis* subsp. *tarentina*
- 'Microphylla'	see *M. communis* subsp. *tarentina*
- 'Nana'	see *M. communis* subsp. *tarentina*
- 'Pyewood Park'	SRms
§ - subsp. ***tarentina*** 🏆^{H4}	Widely available
- - 'Compacta'	SCoo SLon
- - 'Microphylla Variegata' (v)	CRos EShb LRHS MHer MNHC NRHS SPer SRms WHar
I - - 'Variegata' (v)	CBod EPfP
- 'Tricolor'	see *M. communis* 'Variegata'
§ - 'Variegata' (v)	CBot CMCN CMac CRos CSBt CTri CWld EBee ELan ELon ENfk EPfP EShb EUJe LEdu LRHS MGil MHer MSwo NLar NRHS SGbt SGol SLon SPer SPoG WAvo WCFE WFar WSHC
'Glanleam Gold'	see *Luma apiculata* 'Glanleam Gold'
lechleriana	see *Amomyrtus luma*
luma	see *Luma apiculata*
nummularia	see *Myrteola nummularia*
ugni	see *Ugni molinae*

N

Nabalus (*Asteraceae*)

albus	see *Prenanthes alba*

Nandina (*Berberidaceae*)

BLUSH PINK ('Aka'^{PBR})	CMac CRos EBee LRHS NRHS SCob SPoG
BRIGHTLIGHT ('Selten004') **new**	LCro LOPS
domestica	Widely available
- B&SWJ 4923	WCru
- B&SWJ 11113	WCru
- 'Filamentosa'	EPfP ETMg LRHS NLar SCob SGol
- 'Fire Power'	Widely available
- FLIRT ('Murasaki'^{PBR})	CRos LRHS NRHS SCob SGol
- 'Gulf Stream'	CRos ELan EPfP LBuc LRHS LSRN MGos MPkF NLar NRHS SPad
- 'Harbour Dwarf'	CEnd LRHS WFar
- 'Lemon-Lime'	LCro LRHS NRHS
- var. ***leucocarpa***	CMCN NLar
- 'Nana'	see *N. domestica* 'Pygmaea'
- OBSESSED	see *N. domestica* 'Seika'
- PLUM PASSION ('Monum')	EPfP LCro LRHS MAsh MGos NRHS SCob SPoG
§ - 'Pygmaea'	CMen SGol
- 'Richmond' 🏆^{H5}	CBcs CBot CDul CRos EBee ELan EPfP LRHS MAsh MGos NLar NPri NRHS SCob SPer SPoG SWvt WFar
§ - 'Seika'^{PBR}	CBot CMac EBee ELan EPfP EUJe LCro LRHS MGos MPkF NRHS SCob SMad SPoG
- SIENNA SUNRISE ('Monfar')	LCro LOPS
- 'Sunset'^{PBR}	EBee LSRN NLar SCob
- 'Tuscan Flame'	LRHS
- 'Twilight' (v) **new**	LCro LOPS
- 'Wood's Dwarf'	CBcs MPkF NLar

Nannorrhops (*Arecaceae*)

arabica	see *N. ritchieana*
§ ***ritchieana***	SPlb
- blue-leaved	SPlb

Napaea (*Malvaceae*)

dioica	SPhx WCot

Narcissus ✿ (*Amaryllidaceae*)

'Abba' (4) 🏆^{H6}	CFen CQua
'Abbey Road' (5)	CQua
'Aberfoyle' (2) 🏆^{H6}	CQua
'Abstract' (11a)	CQua
'Accent' (2)	CQua
'Accomplice' (3)	IRhd
'Achduart' (3)	CQua
'Achentoul' (4)	CQua
'Achnasheen' (3)	CQua
'Acropolis' (4)	CQua GKev SDeJ
'Actaea' (9) 🏆^{H6}	CBro CFen CQua CRav GBin GKev LCro LOPS SCob SDeJ SDir

'Acumen' (2)	CQua
'Admiration' (8)	CQua
'Adorable Lass' (6)	CQua
'Ad-Rem' (2)	CFen
'Adversane' (3)	CQua
'Advocat' (3)	CQua
'Aflame' (3)	CFen GKev
'After All' (3)	CFen
'Agnes Mace' (2)	IRhd
'Ahwahnee' (2)	CQua IRhd
'Ainley' (2)	CQua
'Aintree' (3)	CQua
'Aircastle' (3)	CQua
'Airtime' (2)	IRhd
'Akita' (2)	GKev
'Albatross' (3)	CQua WShi
'Albus Plenus Odoratus'	see *N. poeticus* 'Plenus' ambig.
'Alex Jones' (2)	CQua
'All Rounder' (3)	IRhd
'Alpine Winter' (1)	IRhd
'Alto' (2)	IRhd
'Altruist' (3)	CQua ERCP SDeJ
'Altun Ha' (2)	CQua IRhd
'Amabilis' (3)	GCro
'Amazing Grace' (2)	CQua IRhd
'Amber Castle' (2)	CQua
'Ambergate' (2)	CQua GKev LAma SDeJ SDir
'Ambergris Caye' (1)	CQua
'American Dream' (1)	CQua
'American Goldfinch' (7)	CQua
'American Heritage' (1)	CQua
'American Robin' (6)	CQua
'Amstel' (4)	CQua
'Andalusia' (6)	CQua
'Andrew's Choice' (7) ♀H6	CQua
'Angel' (3)	CQua
'Angel Face' (3)	CQua IRhd
'Angel Wings'	see *N.* 'Celtic Wings'
'Angel's Breath' (5) ♀H6	CQua
Angel's tears	see *N. triandrus* subsp. *triandrus* var. *triandrus*
'Angel's Whisper' (5)	CQua
'Angel's Wings' (2)	CQua
'Angels Wood' (2)	IRhd
'Angkor' (4)	CQua
'An-gof' (7)	CQua
'Animal Crackers' (2)	CQua
'Ann Sonia' (4)	IRhd
'Anna Panna' (3)	IRhd
'Annequin' (3)	CQua
'Apollo Gold' (10)	CQua NHpl
'Apotheose' (4)	CFen SDeJ SDir
'Apple Pie' (11a) **new**	GKev
'Apricot' (1)	CBro GCro
'Apricot Whirl' (11a)	CQua GKev
'April Dawn' (2)	IRhd
'April Love' (1)	CQua
'Ara' (6)	CQua GKev
'Aranjuez' (2)	CFen CQua
'Arctic Gem' (3)	CQua
'Arctic Gold' (1) ♀H6	CQua LAma
'Ard Righ' (1)	GCro
'Areley Kings' (2)	CQua
'Argent' (4)	CQua
'Argosy' (1)	CQua
'Arid Plains' (3)	IRhd
'Ariel'[PBR] (8)	GKev
'Ark Royal' (1)	CFen
'Arkle' (1) ♀H6	CQua GKev SDeJ
'Arleston' (2)	CQua IRhd
'Armada' (2)	CFen CQua
'Armidale' (3)	CQua IRhd
'Armoury' (4)	CQua
'Arndilly' (2)	CQua
'Arpege' (2)	CQua
'Arthurian' (1)	IRhd
'Articol' (11a)	CQua
'Arwenack' (11a)	CQua
'Ascot' (4) **new**	SDeJ
'Ashland' (2)	IRhd
'Ashmore' (2)	CQua IRhd
'Ashton Wold' (2)	CQua
§ ***assoanus*** (13)	EPot GKev LLHF WCot WShi
'Astropink' (11a)	CQua
§ ***asturiensis*** (13)	GKev LLHF SEND
- giant	see *N. asturiensis* 'Wavertree'
§ - 'Wavertree' (1)	CQua LLHF
'Auchranie' (2)	IRhd
'Audubon' (2)	CQua GKev SDeJ
'Aunt Betty' (1)	CQua
'Auntie Eileen' (2)	CQua
§ ***aureus*** (13)	CQua GKev
'Autocrat' (2)	GCro
'Autumn Habit' (3)	IRhd
'Avalanche' (8) ♀H4	CFen CQua CRav EPfP GKev LCro LOPS SDeJ
'Avalanche of Gold' (8)	CQua
'Avalon' (2)	CQua ERCP GKev SDeJ
'Baby Boomer' (7)	CRav ERCP GKev LAma LRHS SDir
'Baby Moon' (7)	CAby CFen CQua EPot ERCP GKev LAma SDeJ SDir
'Back Flash' (2)	CQua
'Badanloch' (3)	CQua
'Badbury Rings' (3) ♀H6	CQua IRhd
'Bailey' (2)	IRhd
'Bala' (4)	CQua
'Balalaika' (2)	CQua
'Baldock' (4)	CQua
'Ballydorn' (9)	IRhd
'Ballygarvey' (1)	CQua
'Ballyrobert' (1)	CQua
'Balvenie' (2)	CQua
'Bandesara' (3)	CQua
'Bandit' (2)	CQua IRhd
'Banker' (2)	CQua IRhd
'Banstead Village' (2)	CQua
'Bantam' (2) ♀H6	CBro CQua GKev SDeJ
'Barbara Hunt' (7)	CQua
'Barbary Gold' (2)	CQua
'Barn Dance' (3)	CQua
'Barnesgold' (1)	IRhd
'Barnham' (1)	CQua
'Barnsdale Wood' (2)	CQua
'Barrett Browning' (3)	SDeJ
'Barrii' (3)	CAvo CQua
'Bath's Flame' (3)	CAvo CQua GCro WShi
'Bear's Gold' (4)	CQua
'Beaulieu' (1)	CQua
'Beautiful Dream' (3)	CQua
'Beautiful Eyes' (7) **new**	GKev
'Beauvallon' (4)	SDeJ
'Bebop' (7)	CBro
'Bedruthan' (2)	CQua
'Beersheba' (1)	CQua GKev
'Belcanto' (11a)	CQua GKev SDeJ
'Belisana' (2)	SDeJ
'Bell Rock' (1) ♀H6	CQua
'Bell Song' (7)	CBro CFen CMea CQua GKev LSou SDeJ WShi
'Bella Estrella' (11a)	ERCP GKev

'Bells of Joy' (5)	IRhd
'Belzone' (2)	CQua
'Ben Hee' (2)	CQua IRhd
'Berceuse' (2)	CQua
'Bere Ferrers' (4)	CQua
'Bergerac' (11a)	CQua
'Bernardino' (2)	CQua GCro
'Beryl' (6)	CQua GKev WShi
'Best Friend' (3)	CQua
'Best Seller' (1)	CArg
'Bethal' (3)	CQua
'Bethan-Sîan' (2)	CQua
'Betsy MacDonald' (6)	CQua
'Biffo' (4)	CQua
BIGGAR BOUNTIFUL (2)	GCro
'Bikini Beach' (2)	IRhd
'Bilbo' (6)	CBro CQua
'Billy Graham' (2)	CQua
'Binkie' (2)	CQua SPer
'Birchwood' (3)	CQua
'Birma' (3)	SDeJ
'Birthday Girl' (2)	IRhd
'Bishops Light' (2)	CQua
'Bittern' (12)	CQua GKev SDeJ
'Blackstone' (2)	CQua
'Blair Athol' (2)	CQua
'Blakey' (2)	CQua
'Blarney' (3)	CQua
'Blisland' (9)	CQua
'Blossom' (4)	CQua
'Blossom Lady' (4)	CQua
'Blue Danube' (1)	CQua IRhd
'Blushing Maiden' (4)	CQua
'Bob Spotts' (2)	CQua
'Bobbysoxer' (7)	CBro CQua
'Bobolink' (2)	CQua
'Boconnoc' (2)	CQua
'Bodelva' (2)	CQua
'Bodwannick' (2)	CQua
'Bolton' (7)	GCro
'Bombay' (2)	CFen
'Bon Viveur' (11a)	IRhd
'Bonython' (1)	GCro
'Border Beauty' (2) ♀H6	CQua
'Bosbigal' (11a)	CQua
'Boscastle' (7)	CQua
'Boscoppa' (11a)	CQua
'Boslowick' (11a) ♀H6	CQua
'Bosmeor' (2)	CQua
'Bossa Nova' (3)	CQua
'Bossiney' (11a)	CQua
'Bosvale' (11a)	CQua
'Bosvigo' (11a)	CQua
'Boulder Bay' (2) ♀H6	IRhd
'Bouzouki' (2)	IRhd
'Brackenhurst' (2)	SDeJ
'Brahms' (2)	CFen
'Brandaris' (11a)	CQua
'Bravoure' (1) ♀H6	CQua GBin GKev SDeJ SDir
'Breezand Tristar' (11a) ♀H6	CBro
'Brentswood' (8)	CQua
'Brian's Favorite' (2)	CQua
'Bridal Crown' (4) ♀H6	CFen EPfP GKev LAma LCro LOPS LRHS SDeJ
'Brideshead' (2)	CFen
'Bright Flame' (2)	CQua
'Bright Spangles' (8)	IRhd
'Bright Spot' (8)	CQua
BRIGHTERWELL (2/3)	GCro
'Brightling' (2)	GCro
'Brilliancy' (3)	CQua GCro
'Brindle Pink' (2)	IRhd
'Broadland' (2)	CQua
'Broadway Star' (11b)	LAma SDeJ
'Broadway Village' (2)	CQua
'Brodick' (3)	CQua
'Bronzewing' (1)	IRhd
'Brooke Ager' (2) ♀H6	IRhd
'Broomhill' (2) ♀H6	CQua
'Broughshane' (1)	CQua GKev
broussonetii (13)	CFil GKev
- from Morocco	WPGP
'Brunswick' (2)	CFen GCro SDeJ
'Bryanston' (2) ♀H6	CQua
'Buckshead' (4)	CQua
'Budock Water' (2)	CQua
'Bugle Major' (2)	CQua
bulbocodium (13) ♀H4	CBro CRos GKev LCro LOPS LRHS NRHS SRms
§ - subsp. ***bulbocodium*** (13)	CBro
§ - - var. ***citrinus*** (13)	CRos LRHS NRHS
- - - 'Bayonne' (10)	CPne
- - var. ***conspicuus*** (13)	CBro CQua CTca CWld ERCP GKev LAma MPie SDeJ WCot WShi XLum
* - - var. ***filifolius*** (13)	CBro
- - var. ***nivalis*** (13)	EPot GKev
§ - Golden Bells Group (10)	CAby CHid CQua CRos CTri CWCL EPfP EPot GBin GKev LRHS MPie NPnk NRHS SCob SDeJ
- var. ***mesatlanticus***	see *N. romieuxii* subsp. *romieuxii* var. *mesatlanticus*
- subsp. ***obesus*** (13)	GKev WAbe WCot
- - JW 90-13 new	GKev
§ - - 'Diamond Ring' (10)	CQua CRos EPot GKev LAma LRHS MNrw NRHS SDir
- subsp. ***praecox*** (13)	CRos LRHS NRHS
- - var. ***paucinervis*** (13)	GKev
- subsp. ***tananicus***	see *N. cantabricus* subsp. *tananicus*
- subsp. ***vulgaris***	see *N. bulbocodium* subsp. *bulbocodium*
'Bunclody' (2)	CQua
'Bunting' (7) ♀H6	CQua
'Burning Bush' (3)	IRhd
'Burning Ring' (3)	IRhd
'Burravoe' (1)	CQua
'Burt House' (2)	IRhd
'Busselton' (3)	IRhd
'Bute Park' (4)	CQua
'Butter and Eggs' (4)	GKev
'Butterscotch' (2)	CQua
'Cadgwith' (2)	CQua
'Cairngorm' (2)	SDeJ
'Cairntoul' (3)	CQua
'Calamansack' (2)	CQua
'Calgary' (4)	CQua GKev WCot
'California Rose' (4)	CQua
'Camaraderie' (2)	IRhd
'Camelot' (2) ♀H6	CFen CQua SDeJ
'Cameo Angel' (2)	CQua
'Cameo Baron' (2)	CQua
'Cameo Frills' (2)	CQua
'Cameo Gem' (1)	CQua
'Cameo King' (2)	CQua
'Cameo Marie' (3)	CQua
'Camilla Duchess of Cornwall' (2)	CFen CQua
'Camoro' (10)	EPot
'Campernelli' (7)	CQua
'Campernelli Plenus'	see *N.* 'Double Campernelle'
'Campion' (9)	CQua

	'Canaliculatus' (8)	CAby CArg CFen CQua CRos CTri EPfP ERCP GKev LAma LCro LOPS LRHS NRHS SCob SDeJ SPer
	canaliculatus Gussone	see *N. tazetta* subsp. *lacticolor*
	canariensis (13)	CQua
	'Canary' (7)	CQua
	'Canarybird' (8)	CQua GKev
	'Canasta' (11a)	CQua
	'Candlepower' (1)	CQua
	'Canisp' (2)	CQua
	'Cantabile' (9) 🏆^{H6}	CQua
	cantabricus (13)	CPne CQua
	- subsp. ***cantabricus*** (13)	CFil EPot GKev
	- - var. ***foliosus*** (13) 🏆^{H4}	CFil WAbe
§	- subsp. ***tananicus*** (13)	GKev
	'Cantatrice' (1)	CQua
	'Canterbury' (5)	CQua
	'Canticle' (9)	IRhd
	'Capax Plenus'	see *N.* 'Eystettensis'
	'Cape Cornwall' (2)	CQua
	'Cape Helles' (3)	IRhd
	'Cape Point' (2)	CQua IRhd
	'Capisco' (3)	CQua
	'Capree Elizabeth' (2) **new**	GKev
	'Carbineer' (2)	CQua GCro SDeJ
	'Cardiff' (2)	CFen CQua
	'Cargreen' (9)	CQua
	'Carib Gipsy' (2) 🏆^{H6}	CQua
	'Caribbean Snow' (2)	CQua
	'Carlton' (2) 🏆^{H6}	CArg CFen CQua EPfP GKev LAma LCro LOPS SCob SDeJ SDir
	'Carn Brea' (3)	CQua
	'Carnearny' (3)	CQua
	'Carnkeeran' (2)	CQua
	'Carnkief' (2)	CQua
	'Carnyorth' (11a)	CQua
	'Carole Lombard' (3)	CQua
	'Carolina Dale' (2)	IRhd
	'Carra' (8)	CQua
	'Carwinion' (2)	CQua
	'Casiah' (2)	CQua
	'Cassata' (11a)	GKev LAma SDeJ SDir
	'Cassopolis' (2)	CQua
	'Castanets' (8)	CQua IRhd
	'Casterbridge' (2)	CQua
	'Castle Rings' (4)	CQua
	'Castlerock' (2)	CFen
	'Cataract' (1)	IRhd
	'Catistock' (2)	CQua
	'Causeway Gem' (6)	IRhd
	'Causeway Julie' (3) **new**	IRhd
	'Causeway Ringer' (3)	IRhd
	'Causeway Sunset' (2)	IRhd
	'Causeway Sunshine' (1)	IRhd
	'Causeway Torch' (2)	IRhd
	'Causeway Winner' (2)	IRhd
	'Cavalli King' (4)	CQua
	'Caye Chapel' (3)	CQua
	'Cazique' (6)	CQua
	× ***cazorlanus*** (13)	EPot
	'Cedar Hills' (3)	CQua
	'Cedric Morris' (1)	CQua ECha
	'Celestial Fire' (2)	CQua
	'Celtic Gold' (2)	CQua
§	'Celtic Wings' (5)	SDir
	'Centenary Gold' (2)	CQua
	'Centrefold' (3)	CQua
	'Cha-cha' (6)	CBro CQua
	'Changing Colors' (11a)	GKev SDeJ
	'Chanson' (1) 🏆^{H6}	CQua IRhd
	'Chanterelle' (11a)	GKev LAma SDeJ
	'Charity May' (6)	CQua
	'Charleston' (2)	CQua
	'Charlie Connor' (1)	CQua
	'Chasseur' (2)	IRhd
	'Chaste' (1)	CQua IRhd
	'Chat' (7)	CQua
	'Cheer Leader' (3)	CQua
	'Cheerfulness' (4) 🏆^{H6}	CArg CAvo CFen CQua ESps GKev LAma LCro LOPS NPer NRHS SDeJ
	'Cheesewring' (3)	CQua
	'Chelsea Girl' (2)	CQua
	'Cheltenham' (2)	CQua
	'Chemeketa' (2)	GKev
	'Chérie' (7)	CQua
	'Cherish' (2)	CQua
	'Cherry Glow' (3)	IRhd
	'Cherry Ice' (2)	CQua
	'Cherrygardens' (2)	CQua IRhd
	'Chesapeake Bay' (1)	CQua
	'Chesterton' (9) 🏆^{H6}	CQua
	'Chickadee' (6)	CQua
	'Chicken Hill' (1)	CQua
	'Chickerell' (3)	CQua
	'Chief Inspector' (1)	CQua IRhd
	'Chiffon' (2)	CFen
	'Chiloquin' (1)	CQua
	'China Doll' (2)	CQua
	'China Gold' (10)	CQua
	'Chinchilla' (2)	CQua
	'Chingah' (1)	IRhd
	'Chinita' (8)	CQua
	'Chipper' (5)	CQua
	'Chit Chat' (7) 🏆^{H4}	CQua LLHF SDeJ SPlb
	'Chiva' (7)	GKev LLHF
	'Chobe River' (1)	CQua IRhd
	'Chortle' (3)	IRhd
	'Chromacolor' (2) 🏆^{H6}	GKev
	'Churchfield Bells' (5)	CQua
	'Churston Ferrers' (4)	CQua
	'Chy Noweth' (2)	CQua
	'Cinder Hill' (2)	IRhd
	'Cisticola' (3)	CQua IRhd
	citrinus	see *N. bulbocodium* subsp. *bulbocodium* var. *citrinus*
	'Citron' (3)	CQua
	'Citronita' (3)	CQua
	'Citrus Souffle' (4)	IRhd
	'Clare' (7)	CQua
	'Classic Gold' (10) 🏆^{H6}	CQua
	'Claverley' (2)	CQua
	'Clean Sweep' (3)	IRhd
	'Cloth of Gold' (8)	CQua
	'Cloud Nine' (2)	CBro
	'Clouded Yellow' (2)	CQua
	'Clouds Hill' (4)	CQua
	'Clovelly Ayr' (9)	CQua
	'Codlins and Cream'	see *N.* 'Sulphur Phoenix'
	'Coker's Frome' (9)	CQua
	'Coldbrook' (2)	CQua
	'Colin's Joy' (2)	CQua
	'Coliseum' (2)	IRhd
	'Colleen Bawn' (1)	CQua WShi
	'Colley Gate' (3)	CQua
	'Colliford' (2)	CQua
	'Colorama' (11a)	CQua
	'Colorful' (2)	IRhd
	'Colville' (9)	CQua
	'Comal' (1)	CQua

'Come to Good' (2)	CQua
'Compressus'	see *N.* × *intermedius* 'Compressus'
'Conestoga' (2)	CQua
'Congress' (11a)	CQua
'Conowingo' (11a)	CQua
'Conspicuus' ambig.	LAma
'Conspicuus' ambig. (3)	GCro WShi
'Constantinople' (4) **new**	GKev
'Content' (1)	CQua
'Contralto' (2)	IRhd
'Cool Autumn' (2)	CQua
'Cool Crystal' (3)	CQua
'Cool Evening' (11a)	CQua
'Cool Shades' (2)	CQua
'Coolmaghery' (2)	IRhd
'Coombe Creek' (6)	CQua
'Copper Bowl' (2)	GCro
'Copperfield' (2)	CQua
'Cora Ann' (7)	CBro
'Coral Ribbon' (2)	GKev
'Corbiere' (1)	CQua
'Corbridge' (2)	CQua
'Corby Candle' (2)	CQua
'Corky's Song' (2)	CQua
'Cornish Chuckles' (12) ♀H6	CBro CFen CQua
'Cornish Gold' (1) **new**	LCro LOPS
'Cornish King' (1)	GKev
'Cornish Pride' (2)	CFen
'Cornish Sun' (2)	CQua
'Cornish Vanguard' (2) ♀H6	CFen CQua
'Cornsilk' (11a)	CQua
'Corofin' (3)	CQua
'Corozal' (3)	CQua
'Corroboree' (2)	IRhd
'Cosine' (11a)	IRhd
'Cotinga' (6)	CBro CQua GKev SDeJ
'Countdown' (2)	CQua
'Court Martial' (2)	CFen
'Coverack Glory' (2)	CQua
'Crackington' (4) ♀H6	CQua IRhd
'Cragford' (8)	SDeJ
'Craig Stiel' (2)	CQua
'Creag Dubh' (2)	CQua
'Creed' (6)	CQua
'Crenver' (3)	CQua
'Crevenagh' (2)	IRhd
'Crewenna' (1)	CQua
'Crill' (7)	CQua
'Crimson Chalice' (3)	CQua
'Cristobal' (1)	CQua
'Croesus' (2)	CQua GCro
'Crofty' (6)	CQua
'Croila' (2)	CQua
'Crowndale' (4)	CQua IRhd
'Crugmeer' (11a)	CQua
'Cryptic' (1)	CQua IRhd
'Crystal Star' (2)	CQua
cuatrecasasii var. ***segimonensis*** (13)	GKev
'Cudden Point' (2)	CQua
'Cul Beag' (3)	CQua
'Culmination' (2)	CQua
'Cultured Pearl' (2)	CQua IRhd
'Cum Laude' (11a)	ERCP SDeJ SDir
'Curlew' (7) ♀H6	CQua GKev LCro LOPS SDeJ WShi
'Curly' (2)	GKev SDeJ
'Cuscarne' (8)	CQua
cyclamineus (13) ♀H6	CAvo CBro CExl CFil CRos CWCL GKev LEdu LLHF LRHS NRHS SRms

'Cyclope' (1)	CQua
'Cynosure' (2)	GCro
cypri (13)	CQua
'Cyros' (1)	CQua
'Dailmanach' (2)	CQua IRhd
'Dailmystic' (2)	IRhd
'Dainty Miss' (7)	CQua GKev
'Dallas' (3)	CFen CQua CRav
'Dalmeny' (2)	CQua
'Dambuster' (4)	IRhd
'Damson' (2)	CQua GCro
'Dan du Plessis' (8)	CFen CQua
'Dardanelles' (2)	IRhd
'Dateline' (3)	CQua
'David Alexander' (1)	CQua
'David Mills' (2)	CQua
'Dawn Brooker' (2)	CQua
'Dawn Cloud' (2)	CQua
'Dawn Sky' (2)	CQua
'Daydream' (2)	CQua
'Daymark' (8)	CQua
'Daymer Bay' (1)	CFen
'Dayton Lake' (2)	CQua
'De Lacey' (11a)	CQua
'Dean' (2)	CQua
'Debutante' (2)	CQua
'December Bride' (11a)	CQua
'Decision' (2)	IRhd
'Defence Corps' (1)	IRhd
'Del Rey' (1)	CQua
'Dell Chapel' (3)	CQua
'Delnashaugh' (4)	CQua ERCP GKev LAma SDeJ SDir
'Delos' (3)	CQua
'Delta' (11a)	CQua
'Delta Flight' (6)	IRhd
'Demand' (2)	CQua
'Demeanour' (3)	IRhd
'Demmo' (2)	CQua IRhd
'Dena' (3)	IRhd
'Denali' (1)	CQua IRhd
'Derek Tangye' (2)	CQua
'Derringer' (7)	CAvo MJak
'Descant' (1)	IRhd
'Desdemona' (2) ♀H6	CQua GKev SDeJ
'Desert Bells' (7)	CQua GKev
'Desert Orchid' (2)	CQua
'Dewy Dell' (3)	IRhd
'Diamond Ring'	see *N. bulbocodium* subsp. *obesus* 'Diamond Ring'
'Dick Wilden' (4)	SDeJ
'Dickcissel' (7) ♀H6	CQua ERCP GKev SDir
'Dignitary' (2)	IRhd
'Dimity' (3)	CQua
'Dimple' (9)	CQua
'Dinkie' (3)	CBro
'Discreet' (2)	IRhd
'Disquiet' (1)	CQua IRhd
'Diversity' (11a)	IRhd
'Doctor Hugh' (3) ♀H6	CQua IRhd
'Doctor Jazz' (2)	CQua
'Doctor Who' (4)	CQua
'Dolcoath' (2)	CQua
'Doombar' (1)	CQua
'Dorchester' (4)	CQua IRhd
'Dorneywood' (1)	IRhd
'Dorothy Yorke' (2)	GCro
§ 'Double Campernelle' (4)	CQua GKev SDeJ WShi
double pheasant eye	see *N. poeticus* 'Plenus' ambig.
double Roman	see *N.* 'Romanus'
'Double Smiles' (4)	MJak

	'Double White' (4)	CQua
	'Doublet' (4)	CQua
	'Doubtful' (3)	CQua
	'Dove Song' (2)	IRhd
	'Dove Wings' (6)	CQua
	'Dover Boy' (11a)	CQua
	'Dover Cliffs' (2)	CQua
	'Downfield' (4)	IRhd
	'Downing College' (2)	CQua
	'Downlands' (3)	CQua
	'Dragon Run' (2)	CQua
	'Drama Queen' (11a)	IRhd
	'Dream Catcher' (2)	IRhd
	DREAM TORTE (1)	GCro
	'Dreamlight' (3)	CQua GKev
	dubius (13)	EPot GKev
	'Duchess of Westminster' (2)	GCro
	'Duiker' (6)	IRhd
	'Duke of Windsor' (2)	CFen
	'Dunkeld' (2)	CQua GCro
	'Dunkery' (4)	CQua
	'Dunley Hall' (3)	CQua IRhd
	'Dunskey' (3)	CQua
	'Dunstan's Fire' (1) **new**	IRhd
	'Dupli Kate' (4)	IRhd
	'Dutch Lemon Drops' (5) ♀H6	CMea CQua EPot
	'Dutch Master' (1) ♀H6	CFen CQua ESps GKev LAma LCro LOPS SCob SDeJ SDir
	'Early Bird' (3)	EPot
	'Early Bride' (2)	CFen CQua
	'Early Flame' (2)	CFen
	'Early Splendour' (8)	CQua GKev
	'Earthlight' (3)	CQua
	'Easter Moon' (2)	CQua LCro
	'Eastern Dawn' (2)	CFen CQua SDeJ
	'Eastern Promise' (2)	CQua
	'Eaton Song' (12) ♀H6	CQua
	'Ebony' (1)	CQua
	'Eddy Canzony' (2)	CFen CQua
	'Eden Gold' (2)	CFen
	'Edenderry' (1)	IRhd
	'Edgbaston' (2)	CQua
	'Edge Grove' (2)	CQua
	'Editor' (2)	IRhd
	'Edna Earl' (3)	SDeJ
	'Edward Buxton' (3)	CFen CQua GCro
	'Egard' (11a)	CQua
	'Egmont King' (2)	CQua
	'Eira Hibbert' (3)	CQua
	'Eland' (7)	CQua
	'Elburton' (2)	CQua
	'Elegance' (2)	CQua
	'Elegant Queen' (2)	IRhd
	'Elf' (2)	CQua
	'Elfin Gold' (6)	CQua
	'Elizabeth Ann' (6)	CQua
	'Elka' (1) ♀H6	CAby CAvo CBro CQua CRav ERCP GKev LLHF SDir WShi
	'Ellen' (2)	CArg
	'Elmbridge' (1)	IRhd
	'Elphin' (4)	CQua
	'Elrond' (2)	CQua
	'Elven Lady' (2)	CQua
	'Elvira' (8)	CQua WShi
	'Emcys' (6)	GKev LLHF
	'Emerald City' (3)	IRhd
	'Emerald Pink' (3)	CQua
	'Emily' (2)	CQua
	'Eminent' (3)	CQua
	'Emperor' (1)	CQua GCro
	'Empress' (1)	GCro
	'Empress of Ireland' (1)	CQua IRhd
	'English Caye' (1)	CQua IRhd
	'Ensemble' (4)	CQua
	'Epona' (3)	CQua
	'Erin' (3)	CQua
	'Erlicheer' (4)	CQua GKev SDeJ
	'Estrella' (3)	CQua
	'Estremadura' (2)	CQua
	'Ethos' (1)	IRhd
§	***eugeniae*** (13)	CFil GKev WCot
	'Euryalus' (1)	CQua
	'Eve Robertson' (2)	CQua
	'Evelyn Roberts' (11a)	CQua
	'Evening' (2)	CQua
	'Evesham' (3)	CQua IRhd
	'Exotic Beauty' (4)	CQua
	'Exotic Mystery' (11a) **new**	GKev
	'Extravaganza' (4) **new**	SDeJ SDir
	'Eyeglass' (3)	CQua
	'Eyelet' (3)	CQua
	'Eyrie' (3)	CQua
§	'Eystettensis' (4)	IBlr WFar
	'Fair Prospect' (2)	CQua
	'Fairgreen' (3)	CFen
	'Fairlawns' (3)	CQua
	'Fairmile' (3)	CQua
	'Fairy Chimes' (5)	CQua
	'Fairy Footsteps' (3)	CQua
	'Fairy Island' (3)	CQua
	'Fairy Magic' (2)	IRhd
	'Fairy Tale' (3)	CQua
I	'Faith' (1)	SDeJ
	'Falaise' (4)	CQua
	'Falconet' (8) ♀H6	CQua GKev SDeJ
	'Falmouth Bay' (3)	CQua
	'Falstaff' (2)	CQua
	'Far Country' (2)	CQua
I	'Fashion' (11b)	CQua
	'Fashion Model' (2)	IRhd
	'Fastidious' (2)	CQua
	'February Gold' (6) ♀H6	CArg CAvo CBro CQua CRos CTri EPfP EPot ERCP ESps GCro GKev LAma LCro LOPS LRHS MJak NRHS SDeJ SDir SRms WShi
	'February Silver' (1)	CBro CQua EPot ERCP GKev LAma SDeJ
	'Feeling Lucky' (2)	CQua
	'Felindre' (9)	CRav EPot
	'Feline Queen' (1)	IRhd
	'Feock' (3)	CQua
	'Ferial Wendy' (2)	CFen
	fernandesii (13)	WAbe WCot WThu
	- var. ***cordubensis*** (13)	CBro CFil CQua GKev LLHF
	'Ferndown' (3)	CQua
	'Fertile Crescent' (7)	CQua
	'Ffitch's Ffolly' (2)	CQua
	'Fiery Maiden' (2)	CFen CQua
	'Fiery Ring' (3) **new**	IRhd
	'Filoli' (1)	CQua IRhd
	'Filskit' (2)	CQua
	'Finchcocks' (2)	CQua
	'Fine Gold' (1)	CQua
	'Fine Romance' (2)	CQua
	'Fine Trim' (2)	IRhd
	'Finland' (2)	CFen CQua
	FINTRY BEAUTY (2)	GCro
	'Fiona MacKillop' (2)	CQua

'Firebird' (3) **new**	GKev
'Fire-Blade' (2)	CQua
'Firebrand' (3)	CQua
'Firefighter' (3)	IRhd
'Firehills' (2)	CQua
'Firetail' (3)	CQua GCro GKev WShi
'First Born' (6)	CQua
'First Hope' (6)	CFen
'Flambards Village' (4)	CQua
'Fletching' (1)	CQua IRhd
'Flirt' (6)	CQua
'Flomay' (7)	CQua
'Flower Drift' (4)	GKev
'Flower Record' (2)	LAma
'Flusher' (2)	CQua
'Flycatcher' (7)	CQua
'Flying High' (3)	CQua
'Foff's Way' (1)	CQua
'Folkestone Girl' (11a)	CQua
'Forge Mill' (2)	CQua
'Forged Gold' (2)	IRhd
'Fortissimo' (2)	GKev SDeJ SPer
'Fortune' (2)	CArg CQua LAma SDeJ SDir
'Fossie' (4)	CQua
'Foundling' (6)	CQua
'Fowey' (3)	CFen
'Foxfire' (2)	CQua
'Foxhunter' (2)	CQua GKev
'Fragrant Breeze' (2)	CQua GKev SDeJ
'Fragrant Rose' (2)	CQua ERCP GKev
'Frances Delight' (11a)	CQua
'Frank' (9)	IRhd
'Frank Miles' (2)	CQua
'Freedom Rings' (2)	CQua
'Freedom Stars' (11a) 🏆^{H6}	IRhd
'Fresco' (11a)	IRhd
'Fresh Lime' (1)	CQua
'Frigid' (3)	CQua
'Front Royal' (2)	CQua
'Frosted Pink' (2)	IRhd
'Frostkist' (6)	CBro CQua
'Frosty Snow' (2) **new**	GKev
'Frozen Jade' (1)	CQua
'Fruit Cup' (7)	GKev LCro SDeJ
'Fuco' (1)	CQua
'Full House' (4)	GKev SDeJ
'Fulwell' (4)	CQua
'Furbelow' (4)	CQua
'Gabriella Rose' (4)	CQua
gaditanus (13)	CBro
gaditanus* × *rupicola subsp. ***watieri*** (13)	GKev
'Gambas' (1)	CQua
'Gamebird' (1)	CQua IRhd
'Ganilly' (2)	CFen
'Garden Opera' (7) 🏆^{H6}	CFen
'Garden Treasure' (2)	IRhd
'Gatecrasher' (1)	IRhd
'Gay Kybo' (4) 🏆^{H6}	CQua
'Gay Song' (4)	CQua
'Gay Time' (4)	CFen SDeJ
gayi (13)	CQua WShi
'Geevor' (4)	CQua
'Gellymill' (2)	CQua
'Gemini Girl' (2)	CQua
'Gentle Giant' (2)	SDeJ
'Geometrics' (2)	IRhd
'George Leak' (2)	CFen CQua
'Georgia Moon' (2)	CFen
'Georgie May' (2)	CQua
'Geranium' (8) 🏆^{H6}	CBro CFen CQua CRav ERCP ESps GKev LAma LCro LOPS NRHS SDeJ SDir SPer WShi
'Gettysburg' (2)	CQua
'Gigantic Star' (2)	SDeJ
'Gillan' (11a)	CQua
'Gin and Lime' (1)	CQua
'Gipsy Moon' (2)	CQua
'Gipsy Queen' (1)	CBro CQua EPot LLHF WCot WFar WShi
'Gironde' (11)	CQua
'Glacier' (1)	CQua
'Glapthorne' (2)	CQua
'Glasnevin' (2)	CQua IRhd
'Glasney' (3)	CQua
'Glen Cassley' (3)	CQua IRhd
'Glen Clova' (2)	CQua
'Glendermott' (2)	CQua
'Glendurgan' (2)	CQua
'Glenfarclas' (1)	CQua
'Glenside' (2)	CQua
'Glissando' (2)	CQua
'Gloria Townsin' (4)	CQua
'Gloriosus' (8)	CQua
'Glorious' (8)	CQua
'Glory of Lisse' (9)	WShi
'Glover's Reef' (1)	CQua
'Glowing Phoenix' (4)	CQua
'Glowing Red' (4)	CQua
'Goblet' (1)	SDeJ
'Golant' (2)	CQua
'Gold Bond' (2)	CQua
'Gold Cache' (11a)	CQua
'Gold Charm' (2)	CQua
'Gold Convention' (2) 🏆^{H6}	CQua IRhd
'Gold Ingot' (2) 🏆^{H6}	IRhd
'Gold Medallion' (1)	CQua
'Gold Top' (2)	CQua
'Golden Amber' (2)	CQua
'Golden Anniversary' (2)	CFen CQua
'Golden Aura' (2) 🏆^{H6}	CQua
'Golden Bear' (4)	CQua
'Golden Bells'	see *N. bulbocodium* Golden Bells Group
'Golden Cheer' (2)	CFen CQua
'Golden Cycle' (6)	CQua
'Golden Dawn' (8) 🏆^{H4}	CFen CQua GKev SDeJ SDir
'Golden Ducat' (4)	CArg CFen CQua LAma SDeJ
'Golden Flute' (2)	IRhd
'Golden Gamble' (11a)	IRhd
'Golden Harvest' (1)	CQua ESps LAma NPer
'Golden Incense' (7)	CQua
'Golden Jewel' (2) 🏆^{H6}	CQua
'Golden Joy' (2)	CQua
'Golden Lady' (1)	CQua
'Golden Lion' (1)	CFen
'Golden Marvel' (1)	CQua
'Golden Mary' (3)	GCro
'Golden Orbit' (4)	CQua
'Golden Peak' (1)	IRhd
'Golden Perfection' (7)	CQua
'Golden Phoenix' (4)	CQua WShi
'Golden Rain' (4)	CQua
'Golden Rapture' (1)	CQua
'Golden Sheen' (2)	CQua
'Golden Splash' (11a)	IRhd
'Golden Spur' (1)	CQua GCro LAma
'Golden Torch' (2)	CQua
'Golden Twins' (7)	CQua
'Golden Vale' (1)	CQua

'Goldfinger' (1) ♀H6	CQua IRhd SDeJ
'Goldhanger' (2)	CQua IRhd
'Golitha Falls' (2)	CQua
'Good Fella' (2)	CQua
'Good Intentions' (2)	IRhd
'Good Measure' (2)	CQua
'Good Success' (11a)	CQua
'Goonbell' (2)	CQua
'Goose Green' (3)	GKev
'Gorran' (3)	CQua
'Gossmoor' (4)	CQua
'Grand Monarque'	see *N. tazetta* subsp. *lacticolor* 'Grand Monarque'
'Grand Opening' (4)	IRhd
'Grand Primo' (8)	LCro LOPS
'Grand Primo Citronière' (8)	CQua
'Grand Prospect' (2)	CQua
'Grand Soleil d'Or' (8)	CQua GKev LAma LCro LOPS SDeJ
'Great Expectations' (2)	CQua
'Greatwood' (1)	CQua
'Greek Surprise' (4)	IRhd
'Green Eyed Lady' (3) **new**	GKev XEll
'Green Howard' (3)	CQua
'Green Island' (2)	CFen SDeJ
'Green Lawns' (9)	CQua
'Green Lodge' (9)	IRhd
'Green Pearl' (3)	XEll
'Greenodd' (3)	CQua
'Greenpark' (9)	IRhd
'Grenoble' (2)	CQua
'Gresham' (4)	CQua
'Gribben Head' (4)	CQua
'Guiding Spirit' (4)	CQua
'Gulliver' (3)	CQua GCro
'Gunwalloe' (11a)	CQua
'Guy Wilson' (2)	CQua
'Gwawr' (2)	CQua
'Gwendoline Rae' (3)	CQua
'Gwenllian' (3)	CQua
'Gwennap' (1)	CQua
'Gwinear' (2)	CQua
'Habit' (1)	IRhd
'Hacienda' (1)	CQua
'Half Moon Caye' (2)	CQua
'Halley's Comet' (3)	CQua
'Halloon' (3)	CQua
'Halzephron' (2)	CQua
'Hambledon' (2) ♀H6	CQua
'Hampton Court' (2)	CQua IRhd
'Hannah Jesse' (7)	CQua
'Happy Dreams' (2)	IRhd
'Happy Fellow' (2)	CQua
'Happy Valley' (2)	IRhd
'Harbour View' (2)	IRhd
'Harmony Bells' (5)	CQua
'Harpers Ferry' (1)	CQua
HARTLAND'S IRVING (1)	GCro
'Hartlebury' (3)	CQua
'Harvard' (2)	CQua
* 'Hat' (10)	EPot
'Havelock' (2)	GCro
'Hawera' (5) ♀H6	CArg CAvo CBro CFen CQua CRav CTca CTri EPfP EPot ERCP GKev LAma LCro LOPS LRHS MJak NPnk SDeJ SDir WShi
'Heamoor' (4) ♀H6	CQua
hedraeanthus (13)	EPot
'Helford Dawn' (2)	CQua
'Helford Sunset' (2)	CQua
'Helios' (2)	CQua
hellenicus	see *N. poeticus* var. *hellenicus*
'Hello Gorgeous' (11a)	IRhd
henriquesii	see *N. jonquilla* var. *henriquesii*
'Henry Irving' (1)	CQua GCro
'Hero' (1)	CQua
'Heslington' (3)	CQua
'Hexameter' (9)	CQua
'Hexworthy' (3)	CQua
'Hibernian' (4)	IRhd
'Hicks Mill' (1)	CQua
'High Life' (2)	CFen
'High Society' (2) ♀H6	CQua LCro LOPS SDeJ
'Highfield Beauty' (8) ♀H6	CQua
'Highgrove' (1)	CQua
'Highlite' (2)	CQua
'Hilda's Pink' (2)	CQua
'Hill Head' (9)	IRhd
'Hillstar' (7) ♀H6	CQua GKev SDeJ
'Hindenburg' (1)	CQua
hispanicus (13)	CQua GKev
- var. ***propinquus*** (13) **new**	GKev
'Hocus Pocus' (3)	IRhd
'Holland's Glory' (4)	GCro
'Holly Berry' (2)	CFen
'Hollywood' (2)	CFen
'Holme Fen' (2)	CQua
'Home Fires' (2)	CFen CQua
'Homestead' (2) ♀H6	IRhd
'Honey Pink' (2)	CQua
'Honeybird' (1)	CQua
'Honeybourne' (2)	CQua IRhd
'Honeyorange' (2)	IRhd
'Hoopoe' (8) ♀H6	CQua GKev
'Hope House' (2)	IRhd
'Horace' (9)	CQua GCro
'Horn of Plenty' (5)	CQua GKev
'Hornpipe' (1)	IRhd
'Hors d'Oeuvre' (1)	CBro
'Hospodar' (2)	CQua
'Hot Affair' (2)	IRhd
'Hot Date' (3)	IRhd
'Hot Gossip' (2)	CFen CQua
'Hot Lava' (2)	IRhd
'Hotspur' (2)	CQua
HOWICK BEAUTY (2)	GCro
HOWICK'S HALF NELSON (2)	GCro
'Hugh Town' (8)	CQua SEND
'Hugus' (7)	CQua
'Hullabaloo' (2)	IRhd
'Hummingbird' (6)	EPot
'Hunting Caye' (2)	CQua
'Huntley Down' (1)	CQua
'Hyperbole' (2)	IRhd
'Ice Dancer' (2)	CQua IRhd
'Ice Diamond' (4)	CQua
'Ice Emerald' (3)	IRhd
'Ice Follies' (2) ♀H6	CArg CFen CQua EPfP ESps GKev LAma LCro LOPS SCob SDeJ SDir
'Ice King' (4)	GKev SDeJ
'Ice Wings' (5) ♀H6	CAvo CBro CFen CQua EPot GKev NPnk SDeJ SDir WShi
'Idless' (1)	CQua
'Idol' (7)	CBro CQua EPot GKev
'Immaculate' (2)	CQua
'Impeccable' (2)	IRhd
'Inara' (4)	CQua
'Inbal'PBR (8)	CRav GKev
'Inca' (6)	CQua
'Inchbonnie' (2)	CQua
× ***incomparabilis*** (13)	MMuc SEND

'Independence Day' (4)	CQua
'Indian Maid' (7) 🏆^{H6}	CQua IRhd
'Indian Ruler' (2)	CFen
'Indora' (4)	CQua
'Inglescombe' (4)	GCro WShi
'Innisidgen' (8)	CQua
'Innovator' (4)	CQua
'Innuendo' (2)	IRhd
'Insulinde' (4)	CQua
'Interim' (2)	CFen CQua SDeJ
× ***intermedius*** (13)	CBro CQua GKev WAbe
§ – 'Compressus' (8)	CBro CQua WShi
'Intrigue' (7) 🏆^{H6}	CQua SPer
'Invercassley' (3)	CQua
'Inverpolly' (2)	CQua
'Ipi Tombi' (2)	GKev
'Irene Copeland' (4)	CQua GCro GKev
'Irish Cream' (3)	CQua
'Irish Fire' (2)	CQua
'Irish Light' (2)	CQua
'Irish Linen' (3)	CQua
'Irish Luck' (1)	CArg
'Irish Minstrel' (2) 🏆^{H6}	CFen CQua
'Irish Rum' (2)	CQua
'Irish Trip' (7)	IRhd
'Irish Wedding' (2)	CQua
'Isambard' (4)	CQua
'Island Pride' (8)	CQua
italicus (13)	GKev
'Itsy Bitsy Splitsy' (11a)	IRhd
'Itzim' (6) 🏆^{H6}	CBro CQua GKev SDeJ
'Jabberwocky' (11a)	CQua
'Jack Snipe' (6) 🏆^{H6}	CAby CBro CQua EPot ERCP ESps GKev LAma LCro LRHS SCob SDeJ SDir SEND WCot WShi XEll
'Jack Wood' (11a)	CQua IRhd
'Jacob Maurer' (6)	CQua
'Jamage' (8)	CQua
'Jamaica Inn' (4)	CQua
'Jambo' (2)	CQua
'Jamboree' (2)	CQua
'Jamestown' (3)	NPnk
'Jammin' (3)	IRhd
'Janelle' (3)	CQua
'Janet's Gold' (2)	IRhd
'Jantje' (11a)	CQua
'Jauno' (1)	IRhd
'Javelin' (2)	CQua
'Jeanine' (2)	CQua
'Jeanne Bicknell' (4)	CQua
'Jeannie Tangye' (2)	CQua
'Jenny' (6) 🏆^{H6}	CBro CMea CQua EPot ERCP ESps GKev LAma LCro LOPS SDeJ SDir WShi
'Jenny Out' (7) 🏆^{H6}	CFen
'Jersey Lace' (2)	CQua
'Jersey Roundabout' (4)	CQua
'Jersey Star' (4)	CQua
'Jersey Torch' (4)	CQua
'Jetfire' (6) 🏆^{H6}	CArg CQua CRos EPfP EPot ERCP ESps GKev IFro IRob LAma LCro LOPS LRHS MJak NRHS SCob SDeJ SDir WShi
'Jimmy Noone' (1)	CQua
'Jim's Gold' (2)	CQua
'Jodi' (11b)	IRhd
'Jodi's Sister' (11a)	IRhd
'Johanna' (5)	CBro
'John Daniel' (4)	CQua
'John Evelyn' (2)	GCro

'John Lanyon' (3)	CQua
'John's Delight' (3)	CQua
'Joke Fulmer' (2)	CFen
'Jolly Good' (2)	IRhd
jonquilla (13)	CBro CQua EPot GKev LAma MJak WShi
– EVAN SCENT mixed (7) **new**	CRav
§ – var. ***henriquesii*** (13)	CFil CQua EPot
'Joppa' (7)	CQua
'Joy Bishop'	see *N. romieuxii* 'Joy Bishop'
'Joybell' (6)	CQua
'Juanita' (2)	CFen NPer SDeJ
'Jules Verne' (2)	CQua
'Julia Jane'	see *N. romieuxii* 'Julia Jane'
'Jumblie' (12) 🏆^{H6}	CBro CRos EPot LRHS NRHS SDeJ
'Jumbo Gold' (1)	CTri
juncifolius Req. ex Lag.	see *N. assoanus*
'June Allyson' (2)	CFen
'June Lake' (2)	CQua IRhd
'Kabani' (9)	CQua
'Kaka Point' (2)	IRhd
'Kamms' (1)	CQua
'Kamura' (2)	CQua
'Kantzeewai' (2)	IRhd
'Karamudli' (1)	CQua
'Kate Davies' (2)	CQua
'Katherine Jenkins' (7) 🏆^{H6}	CQua
'Kathy A' (5)	IRhd
'Kathy's Clown' (6)	CQua
'Katie Heath' (5)	ERCP GKev SDeJ SDir
'Katrina Rea' (6)	CQua
'Kaydee' (6) 🏆^{H6}	CQua GKev SDeJ
'Kea' (6)	CQua
'Keats' (4)	CAvo CQua
'Kebaya' (2)	CQua
'Kedron' (7)	ERCP GKev
'Kelly Bray' (1)	CQua
'Ken Sunshine Johnson' (2)	CQua
'Kerensa' (1) **new**	SDir
'Kernow' (2)	CQua
'Kidling' (7)	CQua GKev
'Killara' (8)	CQua
'Killearnan' (9)	CQua
'Killigrew' (2)	CQua
'Killivose' (3)	CQua
'Kilworth' (2)	CQua
'Kimmeridge' (3)	CQua
'King Alfred' (1)	CArg CQua LCro LOPS SDeJ SPer
'Kingham' (1)	CQua
'Kinglet' (7)	CQua
'King's Grove' (1)	CQua
'Kings Pipe' (2)	CQua
'Kingscourt' (1)	CQua
'Kingsleigh' (1)	IRhd
'Kingsmill Lake' (2)	CQua
'Kiss Me' (1)	GKev
'Kissproof' (2)	GKev SDeJ
'Kit Hill' (7)	CQua
'Kitten' (6)	CQua
'Kiwi Magic' (4)	CQua IRhd
'Kiwi Sunset' (4)	CQua IRhd
'Knight of Saint John' (2)	CFen
'Knightsbridge' (1)	CQua
'Knocklayde' (3)	CQua
'Knowing Look' (3)	IRhd
'Kokopelli' (7) 🏆^{H6}	CBro CQua EPfP GKev SDeJ
'Korora Bay' (1)	IRhd
'La Belle' (7)	LLHF SDeJ
'Ladies' Choice' (7)	IRhd

'Lady Ann' (2)	IRhd
'Lady Be Good' (2)	CQua
'Lady Diana' (2)	CQua IRhd
'Lady Eve' (11a)	IRhd
'Lady Godiva' (3)	GCro
'Lady Hilaria' (2)	CQua
'Lady Margaret Boscawen' (2)	CQua GCro
'Lady Marina Cowdray' (1)	CFen
'Lady Moore' (3)	GCro
'Lady Sainsbury' (2)	CFen
'Lady Serena' (9)	CQua GKev
'Lake Alabaster' (2)	CQua
'Lake District' (2)	IRhd
'Lalique' (3)	CQua
'Lamanva' (2)	CQua
'Lamlash' (2)	IRhd
'Lancaster' (3)	CFen CQua GKev
'Landewednack Lady' (4)	CQua
'Langarth' (11a)	CQua
'Lapwing' (5)	IRhd
'Larkhill' (2)	CQua
'Larkwhistle' (6)	GKev SDeJ
'Las Vegas' (1)	GKev SDeJ
'Latchley Meadows' (2)	CQua
'Laura Webb' (4)	CQua
'Laurelbank' (2)	IRhd
'Lauren' (3)	IRhd
'Laurens Koster' (8)	CQua
'Lava Flow' (3)	IRhd
'Lavender Lass' (6)	CQua
'Lavender Mist' (2)	CQua
'Leading Light' (2)	CQua
'Lee Moor' (1)	CQua
'Leedsii' (3)	CQua
'Lemon Beauty' (11b)	CQua GKev SDeJ SDir
'Lemon Brook' (2)	CQua
'Lemon Cocktail' (1)	IRhd
'Lemon Cycla' (6)	CQua
'Lemon Drizzle' (2)	CQua
'Lemon Drops' (5)	CQua CTca EPot ERCP GKev SDeJ SPhx
'Lemon Haze' (2)	CQua
'Lemon Shake' (1)	GKev
'Lemon Silk' (6)	CBro CQua GKev SDir
'Lemonade' (3)	CQua
'Lennymore' (2)	CQua IRhd
'Lewis George' (1)	CQua
'Lezant' (3)	CQua
'Liberty Bells' (5)	CQua LAma
'Liebeslied' (3)	CQua
'Lieke'	EPfP EPot ERCP GKev LCro LOPS SDeJ
'Life' (7)	CQua
'Lifeline' (1)	IRhd
'Lighthouse' (3)	CQua
'Lighthouse Reef' (1)	CQua IRhd
'Lilac Charm' (6)	CQua IRhd
'Lilac Hue' (6)	CBro
'Lilac Mist' (2)	CQua IRhd
'Lilliput' ambig.	CQua
'Lima's Green Goddess' (8)	IRhd
'Lima's Shooting Stars' (12)	IRhd
'Limbo' (2)	CQua
'Limequilla' (7)	CQua IRhd
'Lincolnshire Lady' (3)	CQua
'Lindsay Joy' (2)	CQua
'Little Alice' (4)	IRhd
'Little Beauty' (1)	CBro CQua LAma
'Little Dancer' (1)	CBro CQua
'Little Dianne' (8)	IRhd
'Little Dorr' (4)	IRhd
'Little Flik' (12)	CQua
'Little Jewel' (3)	CQua
'Little Meg' (7)	CQua
'Little Oliver' (7)	EPfP
'Little Rusky' (7)	CBro CQua
'Little Sentry' (7)	CBro CQua
'Little Soldier' (10)	CQua
'Little Spell' (1)	GKev
'Little Tyke' (2)	CQua
'Little Witch' (6)	CBro CQua GKev LAma SCob SDeJ WShi
'Littlefield' (7)	CQua
'Livelands' (1)	CQua
'Liverpool Festival' (2)	CQua
'Living Colour' (3)	CQua
'Lizard Beacon' (2)	CQua
'Lobularis'	see *N. lobularis* (Haw.) Schult. & Schult. f.
lobularis misapplied	see *N. nanus*
§ ***lobularis*** (Haw.) Schult. & Schult. f.	CAby CAvo CBro CQua CRos CTca CTri CWld EPot ERCP GKev LCro LOPS LRHS NRHS SCob SDeJ
'Loch Alsh' (3)	CQua IRhd
'Loch Assynt' (3)	CQua
'Loch Brora' (2)	CQua
'Loch Coire' (3)	CQua
'Loch Fada' (2)	CQua
'Loch Fyne' (2)	GCro
'Loch Hope' (2)	CQua
'Loch Leven' (2)	CQua
'Loch Loyal' (2)	CQua
'Loch Lundie' (2)	CQua
'Loch Maberry' (2)	CQua
'Loch Naver' (2)	CQua
'Loch Owskeich' (2)	CFen CQua
'Logan Rock' (7)	CQua
'Longitude' (1)	IRhd
'Lord Grey' (1)	GCro
'Lordship' (1)	CQua
'Lorikeet' (1)	CQua GKev
'Lostwithiel' (2)	CQua
'Lothario' (2)	EPfP LAma
'Lough Gowna' (1)	IRhd
'Louise de Coligny' (2)	ERCP
'Loveday' (2)	CFen
'Lowin' (1)	CFen
'Lubaantun' (1)	CQua
'Lucie Nottingham' (4)	CQua
'Lucifer' (2)	CAvo CQua GCro WShi
'Lundy Light' (2)	CQua
'Lutana' (2)	IRhd
'Lyme Bay' (1)	IRhd
'Lynher' (2)	CQua
'Lyrebird' (3)	CQua
'Lyric' (9)	CQua
'Lysander' (2)	CQua
'Ma Belle' (1) **new**	GKev
'Madam Speaker' (4)	CQua
'Madame Plemp' (1)	GCro
'Madison' (4)	CQua GKev
MAGGIE MAYBE (2)	GCro
'Magic Moment' (3)	CQua
'Magician' (2)	CQua
'Magna Carta' (2)	CQua
'Magnificence' (1)	CFen CQua GCro
'Maker's Mark' (1)	CQua
'Malpas' (3)	CQua
'Malvern City' (1)	CFen CQua

'Mamma Mia' (4)	IRhd
'Manaccan' (1)	CQua
'Mangaweka' (6)	CQua
'Manly' (4) ♀H6	CQua ERCP GKev SDeJ
'Manon Lescaut' (2)	GKev
'Mantle' (2)	CQua
'Margaret Herbert' (7)	CQua
'Maria Pia' (11a)	IRhd
'Marie Curie Diamond' (7) ♀H6	CFen CQua
'Marieke' (1)	LAma SDeJ
'Marilyn Anne' (2)	CQua
'Marine Corps' (2) **new**	IRhd
'Marjorie Hine' (2)	CQua
'Marjorie Treveal' (4)	CQua
'Market Merry' (3)	GCro
'Marlborough' (2)	CQua
'Marlborough Freya' (2)	CQua
'Marshfire' (2)	CQua
'Martha Washington' (8)	CQua
'Martinette' (8)	CAvo CFen CQua CRav SDeJ
'Martinsville' (8)	CQua
'Mary Bohannon' (2)	GKev
'Mary Copeland' (4)	CQua
'Mary Kate' (2)	CQua
'Mary Lou' (6)	IRhd
'Mary Moore' (2)	CQua
'Mary Rosina' (4)	CQua
'Mary Veronica' (3)	CQua
'Marzo' (7)	IRhd
'Masked Light' (2)	CFen
'Matador' (8)	CFen CQua IRhd
'Mawla' (1)	CQua
'Max' (11a)	CQua
'Maximus Superbus' (1)	CQua
'Maya Dynasty' (2)	CQua
'Mayor's Choice' (11a)	CQua
'Maywood' (11a)	CQua
'Mazzard' (4)	CQua
'Media Girl' (2)	IRhd
× ***medioluteus*** (13)	CBro CQua GCro WShi
'Medway Gold' (7)	CQua
'Melancholy' (1)	CQua
'Melbury' (2)	CQua
'Meldrum' (1)	CQua
'Melen' (2)	CFen
'Memento' (1)	CQua
'Menabilly' (4)	CQua
'Mên-an-Tol' (2)	CQua
'Menehay' (11a) ♀H6	CQua
'Mer d'Or' (1)	IRhd
'Merlin' (3) ♀H6	CFen CQua GKev LAma SDeJ SDir
'Merry Bells' (5)	CQua
'Merrymeet' (4)	CQua
'Mersing' (3)	CQua
'Merthan' (9)	CQua
'Midas Touch' (1)	CQua
'Midget'	see *N. nanus* 'Midget'
MIDTOWN AEROLITE (2)	GCro
MIDTOWN ALFIE (1)	GCro
MIDTOWN AMBER (2)	GCro
MIDTOWN BRIGADIER (2)	GCro
MIDTOWN LAURIE (1)	GCro
MIDTOWN RUCKLE (1)	GCro
'Mike Pollock' (8)	CFen CQua
'Milan' (9)	CQua
'Millennium Gold' (1)	CQua
'Millennium Sunrise' (2)	CQua
'Millennium Sunset' (2)	CQua
'Milly's Magic' (2)	CQua
'Minard' (4)	CQua
minimus misapplied	see *N. asturiensis*
'Minnow' (8) ♀H4	CArg CAvo CBro CFen CHid CQua CRav CRos EPfP EPot ERCP ESps GKev LAma LCro LOPS LRHS MJak NRHS SCob SDeJ SDir SPer
'Minnowlet' (11a)	CQua
minor (13) ♀H5	CBro CPne CQua ECha EPot GCro GKev WFar WShi
- 'Douglasbank' (1)	ITim LLHF
- 'Little Gem' (1) ♀H6	CBro CQua CTri GKev LAma SDeJ
- var. ***pumilus*** 'Plenus'	see *N.* 'Rip van Winkle'
- Ulster form (13)	IBlr
'Mint Julep' (3) ♀H6	SDeJ
'Mirar' (2)	CQua
MISLEEDING (2)	GCro
'Misquote' (1)	CQua
'Miss Diddles' (7)	CQua
'Miss Klein' (7)	LLHF
'Miss Muffit' (1)	CQua
'Miss Primm' (2)	IRhd
'Mission Bells' (5) ♀H6	CQua
'Mission Impossible' (11a)	CQua
'Mist of Avalon' (4)	CQua
'Misty Glen' (2) ♀H6	CQua EPfP GKev SDeJ SDir
'Mite' (6) ♀H6	CAvo CBro CQua EPot GKev LAma LLHF NHpl
'Mithrel' (11a)	CQua
'Mitylene' (2)	CQua
'Mitzy' (6)	LLHF
'Modern Art' (2)	CQua SDeJ
'Modulation' (2)	SDeJ
'Mondragon' (11a)	CQua GKev
'Mongleath' (2)	CQua
'Monks Wood' (1)	CQua
'Monksilver' (3)	CQua
'Monmouthshire' (2)	CQua
'Montclair' (2)	CQua
'Montego' (3)	CQua
'Monterrico' (4)	CFen
'Montroig' (2)	IRhd
'Moon Dream' (1)	CQua
'Moon Ranger' (3)	CQua
'Moon Shadow' (3)	CQua IRhd
'Moonstruck' (1)	CQua
'Morab' (1)	CQua
'Moralee' (4)	CQua
'Morval' (2)	CQua
moschatus (13) ♀H6	CAvo CBro CQua EPot GKev WShi
'Mother Duck' (6)	LAma SDir
'Motmot'	CQua
'Mount Fuji' (2)	CQua
'Mount Hood' (1) ♀H6	CArg EPfP GKev LAma SDeJ SDir
'Mountain Poet' (9)	CQua
'Mousehole' (3)	CQua
'Mowser' (7)	CQua
'Mr Sweet' (2)	CQua
'Mrs Langtry' (2)	CQua WShi
'Mrs R.O. Backhouse' (2)	CQua WShi
'Muiranna' (1)	IRhd
'Mullion' (3)	CQua
'Mulroy Bay' (1)	CQua
'Murlough' (9)	CQua
'Muscadet' (2)	CFen CQua
'Music Maker' (2) **new**	IRhd
'My Story' (4) ♀H6	SDeJ SDir
'My Sunshine' (2)	CQua
'My Sweetheart' (3)	CQua
'My Word' (2)	CFen
'Mystic' ambig. (3)	CQua

	'Mzungu' (2)	IRhd
	'Namraj' (2)	CQua
	'Nancegollan' (7)	CBro CQua GKev
	'Nangiles' (4)	CQua
	'Nanpee' (7)	CQua
	'Nanpusker' (2)	CFen
	'Nansidwell' (2)	CQua
	'Nanstallon' (1)	CQua
	'Nantucket Red' (3)	IRhd
§	***nanus*** (13)	CQua CWCL
§	- 'Midget' (1)	CBro CQua EPot ERCP GKev LAma NHpl
	'Nare Celebration' (2)	CFen
	'Narrative' (2)	IRhd
	'National Treasure' (2) new	IRhd
	'Navarre' Buckland (2)	CFil
	'Navigator' (2)	IRhd
	'Nelly' ambig.	CQua
	(Nelsonii Group) 'Minor' (2)	GCro
	'Nessa' (7)	CQua
	'Nether Barr' (2)	CQua
	'New Hope' (3)	CQua
	'New Life' (3)	CQua
	'New Penny' (3)	CQua IRhd
	'New World' (2)	CQua
	'New-Baby' (7)	CQua ERCP GKev MMrt SDeJ
	'Newcomer' (3)	CQua
	'Nickelodeon' (8)	CQua
	'Night Music' (4)	CQua
	'Nightcap' (1)	CQua
	'Niphetos' (2)	GCro
	'Nirvana' (7)	CBro
	'Niveth' (5)	CAvo CFen CQua GCro
§	***nobilis*** (13)	CQua EPot GKev
	- var. ***leonensis*** (13)	CFil ITim
	'Nonchalant' (3)	CQua
	'Norma Jean' (2)	CQua
	'North Rim' (2)	CQua
	'Noss Mayo' (6)	CQua
	'Notre Dame' (2) 🏆H6	CQua
	'Nuage' (2)	CFen
	Nylon Group (10)	CBro EPot EPri GKev
	'Nynja' (2)	CQua
	'Oadby' (1)	CQua
	'Obdam' (4)	SDeJ
	'Obsession' (2)	CQua
	obsoletus (13) new	GKev WCot
	obvallaris (13) 🏆H6	CAvo CBro CFen CQua CTca EPot ERCP GCro GKev LCro SDeJ SDir WHer WShi
	'Ocarino' (4)	CFen CQua
	'Odd Job' (12)	CQua
	× ***odorus*** (13)	CQua WShi
	- 'Plenus' (4)	CQua ERCP
	'Oh Wow' (3)	IRhd
	old pheasant's eye	see *N. poeticus* var. *recurvus*
	'Olympic Medal' (1)	IRhd
	'Ombersley' (1)	CQua
	'Omri' (8)	GKev
	'Oops' (2)	IRhd
	'Orange Phoenix' (4)	CQua WShi
	'Orange Progress' (2)	SDeJ
	'Orange Queen' (3)	GKev
	'Orange Supreme' (2)	CQua
	'Orange Tint' (2)	CQua
	'Orange Walk' (3)	CQua
	'Orangery' (11a)	GKev LAma SDeJ
	'Orbital Pink' (3)	IRhd
	'Orchard Place' (3)	CQua
	'Oregon Pioneer' (2)	IRhd

	'Orkney' (2)	CQua
	'Ormeau' (2)	CQua
	'Ornatus' (9)	CQua GCro GKev
	'Oryx' (7) 🏆H6	CQua
	'Osmington' (2)	CQua
	'Ouma' (1)	CQua
	'Ouzel' (6)	CQua
	'Owyhee' (2)	CQua
	'Oxford Gold' (10) 🏆H6	CAvo CQua GKev SDir
	'Oykel' (3)	CQua
	'Oz' (12)	LLHF
	pachybolbus (13)	CQua
	'Pacific Coast' (8) 🏆H6	CQua LCro LLHF LOPS
	'Pacific Mist' (11a)	CQua
	'Pacific Rim' (2)	CQua IRhd
	'Pacific Waves' (3)	CQua
	'Painted Desert' (3)	CQua
	'Palace Pink' (2)	IRhd
	'Pale Sunlight' (2)	CQua
	pallidiflorus (13)	ECha
	'Palmares' (11a)	CQua SDeJ
	'Pamela Hubble' (2)	CQua
	'Pamela Joan' (2)	CQua
	'Pampaluna' (11a)	CQua
	'Panache' (1)	CQua
	panizzianus (13)	CFil CQua
	'Panorama Pink' (3)	IRhd
	'Pantaloon' (4)	IRhd
	'Paper White'	see *N. papyraceus*
	'Paper White Grandiflorus' (8)	CQua EPfP NRHS SDeJ SPer
	'Papillon Blanc' (11b)	ERCP GKev
	'Papua' (4)	CFen CQua
§	***papyraceus*** (13)	CFil CQua GKev SDir
	- subsp. ***polyanthos***	GKev
	- 'Ziva' (8)	CAvo CRav GKev LCro LOPS MJak SDeJ
	'Paramour' (4)	IRhd
	'Parcpat' (7)	CBro CQua
	'Parisienne' (11a)	GKev SDeJ
	'Park Springs' (3)	CQua
	'Parkdene' (2)	CQua
	'Partisan' (2)	IRhd
	'Passionale' (2) 🏆H6	CQua LAma
	'Pastiche' (2)	CQua
	'Pat Brown' (2)	CQua
	'Pat Redman' (3)	CQua
	'Patabundy' (2)	CQua
	'Pathos' (3)	IRhd
	'Patois' (9)	CBro CQua
	'Patrick Hacket' (1) 🏆H6	CFen CQua
	'Pay Day' (1)	CQua
	'Peach Prince' (4)	CQua
	'Pearl Wedding' (3)	CQua
	'Pearlshell' (11a)	CQua
	'Peeping Jenny' (6)	GKev SDeJ
	'Peeping Tom' (6) 🏆H6	CBro CQua ERCP GKev LAma SDeJ SDir SRms
	'Peggy's Gift' (3)	IRhd
	'Pelynt' (3)	CQua
	'Pemboa' (1)	CQua
	'Pencrebar' (4)	CQua EPot GKev LAma SDeJ WShi
	'Pend Oreille' (3)	CQua
	'Pengarth' (2)	CQua
	'Penjerrick' (9)	CQua
	'Penkivel' (2) 🏆H6	CQua
	'Pennance Mill' (2)	CQua
	'Pennine Way' (1)	CQua
	'Penny Perowne' (7)	CQua
	'Pennyfield' (2)	CQua

	'Penpol' (7)	CBro CFen CQua
	'Penril' (6)	CQua
	'Penselwood' (2)	CQua
	'Penstraze' (7)	CQua
	'Pentewan' (2)	CQua GCro
	'Pentille' (1)	CQua
	'Pentire' (11a)	CQua
	'Penvale' (7)	CQua
	'Peppercorn' (6)	CQua
	'Percuil' (6)	CQua
	'Perdredda' (3)	CQua
	perez-chiscanoi (13)	CFil
	'Perimeter' (3)	CQua
	'Peripheral Pink' (2)	CQua
	'Perlax' (11a)	CQua
	'Perpetuation' (7)	CQua
	'Personable' (2)	CQua
	'Petanca' (5)	IRhd
	'Peter Chown' (11a)	CQua
	'Petit Four' (4)	GKev LAma LRHS SDeJ SDir
	'Petrel' (5)	CBro CQua CRav ERCP GKev SDeJ SDir WShi
	'Phantom' (11a)	CQua
	'Phil's Gift' (1)	CQua
	'Phoenician' (2)	CQua IRhd
	'Picatou' (3)	IRhd
	'Picket Post' (3)	IRhd
	'Picoblanco' (2)	CBro CQua
	'Pinafore' (2)	EPfP WFar
	PINEAPPLE PLEMP (1)	GCro
	'Pineapple Prince' (2) ♀^{H6}	CQua
	'Pink Angel' (7)	CQua
	'Pink Champagne' (4)	CQua
	'Pink Charm' (2)	CQua GKev SDeJ
	'Pink China' (2)	CQua
	'Pink Formal' (11a)	CQua
	'Pink Glacier' (11a)	CQua
	'Pink Holly' (11a)	CQua
	'Pink Ice' (2)	CQua
	'Pink Pageant' (4)	CQua
	'Pink Paradise' (4)	CQua
	'Pink Parasol' (1)	SDeJ
	'Pink Pride' (2)	CArg
	'Pink Silk' (1)	CQua GKev SDeJ
	'Pink Smiles' (2)	CFen
	'Pink Surprise' (2)	CQua
	'Pink Tango' (11a)	CQua
	'Pinza' (2) ♀^{H6}	CQua SDeJ
	'Pipe Major' (2)	CQua GKev
	'Pipers Barn' (7)	CQua
	'Piper's Gold' (1)	CQua
	'Pipestone' (2)	CQua
	'Pipit' (7)	CAvo CBro CFen CQua EPfP EPot ERCP GKev LAma LRHS MJak SDeJ WShi
	'Pismo Beach' (2)	CQua
	'Pistachio' (1) ♀^{H6}	GKev
	'Pitchroy' (2)	CQua
	'Pitt's Diamond' (3)	CQua
	'Pixie's Sister' (7) ♀^{H6}	CQua LLHF
	'Pledge' (1)	CQua
	'Plymouth Hoe' (1)	CQua
§	***poeticus*** var. ***hellenicus*** (13)	CBro CQua GCro IRhd
	- old pheasant's eye	see *N. poeticus* var. *recurvus*
	- var. ***physaloides*** (13)	CFil CQua GKev
	- 'Plenus' misapplied	see *N. poeticus* 'Spalding Double White', *N.* 'Tamar Double White'
§	- 'Plenus' ambig. (4)	CAby CBro CQua ERCP GKev SDeJ WShi

§	- var. ***recurvus*** (13) ♀^{H6}	CAby CAvo CBro CFen CQua CRav CTca EPfP ERCP GKev LAma LCro LOPS MJak NPoe SCob SDeJ SDir SEND SPer SPhx WShi
§	- 'Spalding Double White' (4)	CQua
	- white-flowered (13)	SDeJ
	'Poetry in Motion' (9)	IRhd
	'Poet's Way' (9)	CQua IRhd
	'Pol Crocan' (2)	CQua IRhd
	'Pol Dornie' (2)	CQua
	'Pol Voulin' (2)	CQua IRhd
	'Polar Ice' (3)	CFen CQua GKev LAma SDeJ SDir
	'Polbathic' (2)	CQua
	'Polgoon' (2)	CFen
	'Polgooth' (2)	CQua
	'Polindra' (2)	GCro
	'Polly's Pearl' (8)	CQua
	'Polmenor' (2)	CQua
	'Polnesk' (7)	GCro
	'Polonaise' (2)	CQua
	'Polruan' (7)	CQua
	'Poltreen' (4)	CQua
	'Polwheveral' (2)	CQua
	'Polyphant' (2)	CQua
	'Pomona' (3)	GCro
	'Pooka' (3)	CQua IRhd
	POOLEWE PINTUCK (2)	GCro
	'Poppy's Choice' (4)	CQua
	'Pops Legacy' (1)	CQua
	'Porthchapel' (7)	CQua
	'Portloe Bay' (3)	CQua
	'Portrait' (2)	CQua
	'Portrush' (3)	CQua
	'Potential' (1)	CQua
	'Powerstock' (2)	IRhd
	'Praecox' (9)	CBro
	'Prairie Fire' (3)	CQua
	'Pratincole' (3)	IRhd
	'Preamble' (1)	CQua
I	'Precocious' (2) ♀^{H6}	CQua GKev SDeJ SDir
	'Predator' (1)	IRhd
	'Premiere' (2)	CQua
	'Presidential Pink' (2)	CQua
	'Pretty Baby' (3)	CQua
	'Pride of Cornwall' (8)	CQua
	'Primegold' (2)	CFen
	'Primrose Beauty' (4)	CFen CQua
	'Princeps' (1)	CQua GCro
	'Princess Alexandra' (6)	CFen
	'Princess Diana' (6)	CFen
	'Princess Zaide' (3)	GKev
	'Printal' (11a)	SDeJ
	'Priorsford' (2)	IRhd
	'Prism' (2)	CQua
	'Problem Child' (2)	IRhd
	'Probus' (1)	CQua
	'Professor Einstein' (2)	GKev SDeJ
	'Prologue' (1)	CQua
	'Prom Dance' (11a) ♀^{H6}	GKev SDir
	'Prototype' (6)	GKev LAma LRHS
	'Proud Fellow' (1)	IRhd
	'Proverbial Pink' (2)	IRhd
	pseudonarcissus (13)	CArg CHab CQua CRav CWld MMuc NPoe WHer WShi
	- JMH 7821 **new**	GKev
	- subsp. ***eugeniae***	see *N. eugeniae*
	- subsp. ***nobilis***	see *N. nobilis*
	- var. ***porrigens*** (13)	GCro

- subsp. ***pseudonarcissus*** (13) ♀H5 **new**	SDir
- - double-flowered (4)	CQua
'Ptolemy' (1)	CFen
'Pueblo' (7)	CQua CRav GKev LRHS SDeJ
'Pukenui' (4)	CQua
pumilus ambig. (13)	CQua LLHF SDeJ
'Punchline' (7) ♀H6	CQua
'Punter' (2)	CQua IRhd
'Puppet' (5)	CQua EPfP GKev
'Purbeck' (3) ♀H6	CQua
'Quail' (7) ♀H6	CFen CQua CTca ESps GKev LAma LSou SDeJ
'Quasar' (2) ♀H6	CQua
Queen Anne's double daffodil	see *N.* 'Eystettensis'
'Queen Fiona' (1)	IRhd
'Queen Juliana' (1)	CQua
'Queen Mum' (1)	CQua
'Queen of Spain' (5)	CQua GKev
'Queen of the North' (3)	GCro
'Queen's Guard' (1)	IRhd
'Queensland' (2)	CFen
'Quetta' (3)	GCro
'Quick Step' (7)	CQua
'Quiet Hero' (3)	IRhd
'Quiet Magic' (2)	IRhd
'Quiet Waters' (1)	IRhd
'Radiant Gem' (8)	CQua
radiiflorus (13)	EPot GKev
- var. ***poetarum*** (13)	CBro CQua
- var. ***radiiflorus*** (13)	GCro
- var. ***stellaris*** (13)	GCro
'Radjel' (4)	CQua
'Rainbow' (2) ♀H6	CQua
'Raj' (2)	CQua
'Rame Head' (1)	CQua
'Rameses' (2)	CQua
'Raoul Wallenberg' (2)	GKev
'Rapid Stride' (6)	IRhd
'Rapture' (6) ♀H6	CBro CQua ERCP GKev IRhd WShi
'Rashee' (1)	CQua
'Raspberry Ring' (2)	CQua
'Rathowen Gold' (1)	CQua
'Ravenhill' (3)	CQua
'Rebekah' (4)	CQua
'Recital' (2)	CQua
'Red Devon' (2)	CArg CFen GKev LCro LOPS SDeJ
'Red Era' (3)	CQua
'Red Mantle' (2)	CQua
'Red Marvel' (3)	CFen
'Red Reed' (1)	IRhd
'Red Rim' (9) **new**	GCro
'Red Socks' (6)	CQua
'Refrain' (2)	CQua
'Regal Bliss' (2)	CQua
'Regal Glow' (1) **new**	IRhd
'Reggae' (6) ♀H6	CBro CQua GKev LRHS SDeJ
'Rembrandt' (1)	CFen CQua
'Rendezvous Caye' (2)	CQua
'Renovator' (1)	CQua
'Repertoire' (3)	IRhd
'Replete' (4)	CQua CWld GKev SDir
requienii	see *N. assoanus*
'Resistasol' (1)	IRhd
'Resolute' (2)	GCro
'Reverse Image' (11a)	CQua
'Rheban Red' (2)	IRhd
'Richard Lionheart' (2)	GKev
'Ridgecrest' (3)	CQua

rifanus	see *N. romieuxii* subsp. *romieuxii* var. *rifanus*
'Rijnveld's Early Sensation' (1) ♀H6	CAvo CBro CFen CMea CQua ECha ERCP GKev LCro LOPS SDeJ SDir
'Rikki' (7)	CBro CQua
'Rima' (1)	CQua
'Rimmon' (3)	CQua
'Rimski' (2)	IRhd
'Ring Fence' (3)	IRhd
'Ring Flash' (2)	IRhd
'Ringing Bells' (5)	CQua
'Ringleader' (2)	CQua
§ 'Rip van Winkle' (4)	CAby CBro CFen CQua CRav CRos CTca EPfP EPot ERCP ESps GKev LAma LRHS NHpl NRHS SCob SDeJ SPer WShi
'Rippling Waters' (5)	CQua LAma SDir
'Rising Star' (7) ♀H6	IRhd
'Rival' (6)	CQua
'River Queen' (2)	CQua IRhd
'Roberta' (1)	CFen
'Roberta Watrous' (7)	IRhd
'Rockall' (3)	CQua
'Rocoza' (2)	IRhd
'Roger' (6)	CQua
'Rogue' (2)	CBro
'Romance' (2) ♀H6	GKev LAma
§ 'Romanus' (4)	CAvo CQua
romieuxii (13) ♀H4	CBro CRos EPri GKev ITim LRHS NRHS WCot
- JCA 805	CFil EPot
- SF 370	WCot
- subsp. ***albidus*** (13)	GKev
- - SF 110	WCot
- - var. ***zaianicus*** SB&L 82 from Morocco	WCot
§ - 'Joy Bishop' (10)	EPot
§ - 'Julia Jane' (10)	CQua EPot ERCP GKev WCot
* - subsp. ***pallidus*** SB&L 237	WCot
§ - subsp. ***romieuxii*** var. ***mesatlanticus*** (13)	EPot
§ - - var. ***rifanus*** (13) B 8929	WCot
§ - 'Treble Chance' (10)	EPot
'Rongoiti Gem' (4)	CQua
'Rosannor Gold' (11a)	CQua
'Roscarrick' (6)	CQua
'Rose of May' (4)	CQua CRav WShi
'Rose of Tralee' (2)	CQua
'Rose Royale' (2)	CQua
'Rose Villa' (2)	CQua
'Rosemary Pearson' (2)	CQua
'Rosemerryn' (2)	CQua
'Rosemoor Gold' (7) ♀H6	CBro CFen CQua
'Rosemullion' (4)	CQua
'Rosevine' (3)	CQua
'Roulette' (2) **new**	SDeJ
'Round Oak' (1)	CQua
'Roxton' (4)	IRhd
'Royal Armour' (1)	CFen
'Royal Ballet' (2)	CQua
'Royal Connection' (8)	CQua
'Royal Marine' (2)	CQua
'Royal Princess' (3)	CQua GKev
'Royal Regiment' (2)	CQua
'Rubh Mor' (2)	CQua
'Ruby Red' (2)	CQua
'Ruby Wedding' (2)	IRhd
'Rubythroat' (2)	CQua
'Ruddy Duck' (2)	IRhd
'Ruddy Rascal' (2)	IRhd

	'Rugulosus' (7)	CBro CQua
	'Runkerry' (4)	IRhd
	rupicola (13)	CBro CQua LLHF NSla WCot
§	- subsp. ***watieri*** (13)	CBro CQua EPot ERCP LLHF NHpl
	'Rustom Pasha' (2)	CQua GCro
	'Rytha' (2)	CQua
	'Saberwing' (5)	CQua
	'Sabine Hay' (3)	CQua EPot GKev
	'Sabrosa' (7) ♀^{H4}	CBro CQua GKev LLHF
	'Sacajawea' (2)	CFen
	'Sacré Coeur' (2)	IRhd
	'Saffron Strand' (3)	IRhd
	'Sagana' (9)	CQua GKev
	'Sailboat' (7) ♀^{H6}	CAvo CBro CQua GKev LCro LOPS SPer
	'Saint Agnes' (8)	CQua
	'Saint Budock' (1)	CQua
	'Saint Day' (5)	CQua
	'Saint Dilpe' (2)	CQua
	'Saint Keverne' (2) ♀^{H6}	CFen CQua SDeJ
	'Saint Keyne' (8)	CQua
	'Saint Louie Louie' (6)	IRhd
	'Saint Olaf' (3)	GCro
	'Saint Patrick's Day' (2)	CFen CQua GKev LAma SDeJ SDir
	'Saint Peter' (4)	CFen CQua
	'Saint Petroc' (9)	CQua
	'Saint Piran' (7)	CQua
	'Salakee' (2)	CQua
	'Salcey Forest' (1)	CQua
	'Salome' (2) ♀^{H6}	CQua LAma LCro LOPS NPer SCob SDeJ
	'Salute' (2)	CQua
	'Samantha' (4)	CQua
	'Samaria' (3)	GCro
	'Sandra's Diamond' (3)	CQua
	'Sandycove' (2)	CQua
	'Sandymount' (2)	CQua
	'Santa Claus' (4)	CQua
	'Sarah Dear' (2)	CQua
	'Sarah Markillie' (11a)	CQua
	'Sargeant's Caye' (1)	CQua IRhd
	'Satchmo' (1)	CQua
	'Satin Blanc' (7)	IRhd
	'Satsuma' (1)	CQua
	'Saturn' (3)	CQua
	'Savoir Faire' (2)	IRhd
	'Saxby' (11a)	CQua
	'Scarlet Chord' (2)	CQua
	'Scarlet Elegance' (2)	CQua
	'Scarlet Gem' (8)	SDeJ
	'Scarlet Tanager' (2)	IRhd
	'Scarlett O'Hara' (2)	CFen
	'Scilly White' (8)	CFen CQua WShi
	'Scorrier' (2)	CQua
	'Scrumpy' (2)	CQua
	'Sea Dream' (3)	CQua
	'Sea Green' (9)	CQua
	'Sea Legend' (2)	CQua
	'Sea Moon' (2)	IRhd
	'Sea Princess' (3)	GKev SDeJ
	'Seagull' (3)	CQua GCro LAma WShi
	'Sealing Wax' (2)	CFen CQua
	'Season's Greetings' (7)	IRhd
	'Segovia' (3) ♀^{H6}	CAvo CBro CQua CRav EPot ERCP GKev IFro LAma MJak SDeJ
	'Sempre Avanti' (2)	CArg GKev LAma SDeJ
	'Seraglio' (3)	CQua
	'Serena Lodge' (4) ♀^{H6}	CQua
	serotinus (13)	EPot
	'Sextant' (6)	CQua
	'Sheelagh Rowan' (2)	CQua IRhd
	'Sheer Joy' (6)	CQua
	'Shepherd's Hey' (7)	CQua SDeJ
	'Sherborne' (4) ♀^{H6}	CQua
	'Sherpa' (1)	CQua IRhd
	'Sheskin' (2)	IRhd
	'Shining Light' (2)	CQua
	'Shockwave' (2)	CQua
	'Shrimp Boat' (11a)	IRhd
	'Sidley' (3)	CQua IRhd
	'Sidney Torch' (2)	CFen
	'Signet Ring' (3)	IRhd
	'Signorina' (2)	IRhd
	'Silent Valley' (1)	IRhd
	'Silk Cut' (2)	CQua
	'Silver Chimes' (8)	CAvo CBro CFen CQua CRav GKev IBoy LAma LCro LOPS SDeJ
	'Silver Convention' (1)	CQua
	'Silver Crystal' (3)	IRhd
	'Silver Kiwi' (2)	CQua
	'Silver Monarch' (2) **new**	IRhd
	'Silver Moon' (2)	CFen
	'Silver Plate' (11a)	CQua
	'Silver Sabre' (2)	IRhd
	'Silver Smiles' (7)	GKev SPhx
	'Silver Surf' (2)	CQua
	'Silversmith' (2)	CQua
	'Silverthorne' (3)	CQua
	'Silverwood' (3)	CQua
	'Sinopel' (3)	LAma SDeJ
	'Sir Samuel' (2)	CQua
	'Sir Watkin' (2)	CQua GCro
	'Sir Winston Churchill' (4) ♀^{H6}	CQua ESps GKev LAma LCro LOPS SCob SDeJ SPer
	'Sirius' (2)	GCro
	'Sissy' (6)	CQua
	'Skerry' (2)	CQua
	'Skilliwidden' (2) ♀^{H6}	CQua
	'Skookum' (3)	CQua
	'Slieveboy' (1)	CQua
	'Slim Whitman' (2)	GKev
	'Small Fry' (1)	CQua
	'Small Talk' (1) ♀^{H6}	CQua LLHF
	'Smiling Twin' (11a)	GKev SDeJ
	'Smokey Bear' (4)	CQua
	'Smooth Sails' (3)	CQua
	'Snipe' (6)	CAvo CQua GKev WShi
	'Snook' (6)	CQua
	'Snoopie' (6)	CQua
	'Snow Bunting' (7)	CBro
	'Snow Frills' (2)	CQua
	'Snowball' (4)	GKev
	'Snowcrest' (3)	CQua
	'Snowshill' (2)	CQua
	'Snowy Canyon' (4)	IRhd
	'Soft Focus' (2)	IRhd
	'Solar Eclipse' (2)	IRhd
	'Solar Tan' (3)	CQua
	'Soleil d'Or' (8)	CQua SDir
	'Solera' (2)	IRhd
	'Solferique' (2)	CQua
	'Solveig's Song' (12)	EPot WAbe
	'Sonata' (9)	CQua
	'Songket' (2)	CQua
	'Sophia' (2)	CQua
	'Sophie Girl' (2)	GKev
	'Sophie's Choice' (4)	CAvo
	'Soprano' (2)	CQua IRhd
	'Sorcerer' (3)	CQua
	'South Street' (2)	CQua

	'Southease' (2)	CQua
	'Southern Gem' (2)	GCro
	'Spaniards Inn' (4)	CQua
	'Sparkling Tarts' (8)	CQua
	'Sparnon' (11a)	CQua
	'Spartan Gold' (2)	IRhd
	'Special Envoy' (2)	CQua
	'Speenogue' (1)	IRhd
	'Spellbinder' (1)	CQua GKev SDeJ
	'Spencer Tracy' (2)	CFen CQua
	'Spin Doctor' (3)	IRhd
	'Spirit of Rame' (3)	CQua
	'Spoirot' (10) 🏆H6	CAby CQua ERCP GBin GKev LEdu MNrw NPnk SDeJ
	'Sportsman' (2)	CQua
	'Spring Dawn' (2)	LCro LOPS SPer
	'Spring Lustre' (3) **new**	IRhd
	'Spring Morn' (2)	CQua
	'Spring Sunshine' (12)	GKev
	'Spun Honey' (4)	CQua
	'Stadium' (2)	CFen
	'Stainless' (2)	GKev SPhx
	'Standard Value' (1)	CFen
	'Stann Creek' (1)	CQua
	'Stanway' (3)	CQua
	'Star Glow' (2)	CQua
	'Star Quality' (3)	IRhd
	'Starfire' (7)	CQua
	'State Express' (2)	CQua
	'Steenbok' (3)	IRhd
	'Stella' (2)	CQua GCro WShi
	'Stellar Glow' (3)	IRhd
	'Stenalees' (6)	CQua
	'Step Child' (6)	CQua
	'Step Forward' (7)	CQua
	'Steren' (7)	CQua
	'Stilton' (9)	CQua
	'Stinger' (2)	CQua
	'Stint' (5) 🏆H6	CQua GKev SDeJ WCot
	'Stocken' (7)	CBro CQua EPri WAbe
	'Stoke Charity' (2)	CQua
	'Stoke Doyle' (2)	CQua
	'Stonham Gold' (2)	CQua
	'Stormy Weather' (1)	CQua
	'Stratosphere' (7) 🏆H6	CQua SDeJ
	'Strines' (2) 🏆H6	CQua
	'Suave' (3)	CQua GKev
	'Subtle Shades' (2)	IRhd
	'Suda' (2) **new**	GCro
	'Sugar and Spice' (3)	CQua
	'Sugar Cups' (8)	CQua
	'Sugar Loaf' (4)	CQua
	'Sugar Rose' (6)	CQua
	'Sugarbush' (7)	WShi
	'Suisgill' (4)	CQua
	'Sukey' (6)	CQua
§	'Sulphur Phoenix' (4)	CQua GCro WShi
	SULPHUR STAR (2)	GCro
	'Sumo Jewel' (6)	CQua
	'Sun Disc' (7) 🏆H6	CBro CFen CQua CTri GKev LAma LCro LOPS SCob SDeJ WShi
	'Sunday Chimes' (5)	CQua
	'Sundial' (7)	CBro LAma
	'Sunny Girlfriend' (11a)	SDeJ
	'Sunnyside Up' (11a) 🏆H6	SDeJ
	'Sunrise' (3)	CQua
	'Sunrise Kingdom' (2) **new**	GKev
	'Sunstroke' (2)	CQua
	'Suntory' (3)	CQua
	'Surfside' (6) 🏆H6	CQua CWld GKev SDeJ
	'Surprise Packet' (2)	IRhd
	'Surrey' (2)	CQua
	'Suzie Dee' (6)	IRhd
	'Suzie's Sister' (6)	IRhd
	'Suzy' (7) 🏆H6	CBro CFen IBoy SDeJ
	'Swaledale' (2)	CQua
	'Swallow' (6)	CQua SDeJ
	'Swan of Avon' (1)	CQua
	'Swanpool' (3)	CQua
	'Sweet Blanche' (7)	CQua
	'Sweet Lorraine' (2)	CQua
	'Sweet Love' (7)	GKev
	'Sweet Memory' (2)	CQua
	'Sweet Pomponette' (4) **new**	SDeJ
	'Sweet Sue' (3)	CQua
	'Sweetness' (7) 🏆H6	CAvo CBro CFen CQua GCro GKev LAma LCro LOPS WShi
	'Swift Arrow' (6) 🏆H6	CQua
	'Swing Wing' (6)	CQua
	'Swoop' (6)	SDeJ
	'Sydling' (5)	CQua
	'Taffeta' (10)	EPri
	'Tahiti' (4) 🏆H6	CFen CQua GKev LAma LCro LOPS SCob SDeJ
	× ***taitii*** (13)	WShi
	'Talgarth' (2)	CQua
	'Talskiddy' (6)	CQua
§	'Tamar Double White' (4)	CBro CFil CQua
	'Tamar Fire' (4) 🏆H6	CQua
	'Tamar Lad' (2)	CQua
	'Tamar Lass' (3)	CQua
	'Tamar Snow' (2)	CQua
	'Tamara' (2)	CArg CFen CQua
	'Tangent' (2)	CQua
	'Tangerine Tango' (4)	IRhd
	'Tao' (3)	CQua
	'Tasgem' (4)	CQua
	'Taslass' (4)	CQua
	tazetta (13)	CQua
	- subsp. ***aureus***	see *N. aureus*
§	- subsp. ***lacticolor*** (13)	CFil CQua ERCP SDeJ
§	- - 'Grand Monarque' (8)	CBro CQua
	- subsp. ***ochroleucus*** (13)	CQua
*	- var. ***odoratus***	CQua WShi
	- subsp. ***tazetta***	CQua
	'Teal' (1)	CQua
	'Tehidy' (3)	CQua
§	'Telamonius Plenus' (4)	CBro CQua GBin GCro GKev SEND WShi
	'Temba' (1)	IRhd
	'Temple Cloud' (4)	IRhd
	Tequila Sunrise Group (12)	IRhd
	'Terminator' (2)	CQua IRhd
	'Terracotta' (2)	CQua
	'Terwegen' (4)	CFen
	'Tête Rosette' **new**	LCro LOPS
	'Tête-à-tête' (12) 🏆H6	CArg CAvo CBro CFen CQua CRav CRos CTca CWCL EPfP EPot ERCP ESps GAbr GKev GQue LAma LCro LOPS LRHS LSou MJak NHpl NRHS SCob SDeJ SDir SPer
	'Thalia' (5)	CArg CAvo CBro CQua CRav CTca EPfP ERCP ESps GKev IFro LAma LCro LOPS MJak SCob SDeJ SDir SPer SPhx WCot WShi
	'The Alliance' (6) 🏆H6	CBro CQua
	'The Caley' (2)	CQua
	'The First' (1)	GCro
	'The Grange' (1)	CQua

'The Mount' (2)	IRhd
'Thistin' (1)	IRhd
'Thomas Kinkade' (2)	CQua
'Thoughtful' (5)	CBro CQua
'Three Oaks' (1)	CQua
'Tibet' (2)	CFen CQua
'Tickled Pink' (11a)	IRhd
'Tideford' (2)	CQua
'Tidy Tippet' (2)	IRhd
'Tiercel' (1)	CQua
'Tiffany Jade' (3)	CQua
'Tiger Moth' (6)	CQua
'Timolin' (3)	CQua
'Tinhay' (7)	CQua
'Tiritomba' (11a)	CQua
'Tittle-tattle' (7)	CFen CQua
'Toby' (2)	SDeJ
'Toby the First' (6)	GKev
'Top Hit' (11a)	CQua
'Topolino' (1) ♀H6	CAvo CBro CFen CQua CRos EPot ERCP GKev IFro LAma LCro LOPS LRHS NRHS SCob SDir
'Topsy Turvy' (4)	CQua
'Toreador' ambig. (3)	CFen
'Toretta' (3)	IRhd
'Torianne' (2) ♀H6	CQua
TOROSAY ELEGANCE (2)	GCro
'Torridon' (2)	CQua
'Toto' (12) ♀H6	CAvo CBro CQua ERCP GKev LCro LOPS SDeJ SDir
'Tracey' (6)	CQua GKev IRhd
'Transmitter' (4)	CQua
'Treasure Hunt' (2)	IRhd
'Trebah' (2) ♀H6	CQua
'Treble Chance'	see *N. romieuxii* 'Treble Chance'
'Treble Two' (7)	CQua
'Trecara' (3)	CQua
'Tregarrick' (2)	CQua
'Treglisson' (2)	CFen
'Trelawney Gold' (2)	CFen CQua
'Trelissick' (7)	CQua
'Tremelling' (2)	CFen
'Tremough Dale' (11a)	CQua
'Trena' (6) ♀H6	CQua ERCP SDeJ
'Trendy Trail' (3)	IRhd
'Trentagh' (3)	IRhd
'Trenwith' (1)	CQua
'Trepolo' (11b)	SDeJ
'Tresamble' (5)	CBro CQua EPfP GCro GKev LAma LCro LOPS SDeJ
'Tresserve' (1)	GCro
'Trevaunance' (6)	CQua
'Treverva' (6)	CQua
'Treviddo' (2)	CQua
'Trevithian' (7)	CBro CQua CRav GCro GKev LAma SDeJ
'Trewarvas' (2)	CQua
'Trewirgie' (6)	GCro
triandrus var. ***albus***	see *N. triandrus* subsp. *triandrus* var. *triandrus*
§ - subsp. ***triandrus*** var. ***triandrus*** (13)	GBin
'Tricollet' (11a)	GKev SDeJ
'Trident' (3)	CQua
'Trielfin' (5)	IRhd
'Trigonometry' (11a) ♀H6	CQua IRhd
'Tripartite' (11a) ♀H6	CFen CQua GKev IRhd SDeJ
'Triple Crown' (3) ♀H6	CQua IRhd
'Tristram' (2)	CQua
'Tropic Isle' (4)	CQua
'Trousseau' (1)	CFen CQua
'Tru' (3)	CQua
'Truculent' (3)	CQua
'Trumpet Warrior' (1) ♀H6	CQua IRhd
'Tryst' (2)	CQua
'Tudor Minstrel' (2)	CQua
'Tuesday's Child' (5) ♀H6	CQua
'Turncoat' (6)	CQua
'Tutankhamun' (2)	CQua
'Tweety Bird' (6)	SPer
'Twicer' (2)	CQua IRhd
'Twilight Zone' (2)	IRhd
'Twink' (4)	CQua GCro
'Twinkling Yellow' (7) ♀H6	CBro GKev
'Tyrone Gold' (1) ♀H6	CQua
'Tyrree' (1)	IRhd
'Tywara' (1)	CQua
'Ulster Bank' (3)	CQua
'Ulster Bride' (4)	CQua
'Ultimus' (2)	CQua
'Uncle Duncan' (1)	CQua
'Unique' (4) ♀H6	CQua GKev LAma SDeJ
'Unsurpassable' (1)	CFen CQua GCro LAma
'Upalong' (12)	CQua
'Upshot' (3)	CQua
'Urchin' (2)	IRhd
'Utiku' (6)	CQua
'Val d'Incles' (3)	CQua
'Valdrome' (11a)	CQua
'Valediction' (3)	CQua
'Valinor' (2)	CQua
'Van Sion'	see *N.* 'Telamonius Plenus'
'Vanilla Peach' (11a)	GKev LRHS SDeJ SDir
'Vantage' (2)	CQua
'Vaticaan' (1)	SDeJ
'Velocity' (6)	GKev LAma
'Vendell' (3)	IRhd
'Verdant Sparks' (7)	IRhd
'Verdin' (7)	CQua CWld
'Verger' (3)	LAma SDeJ
'Vernal Prince' (3) ♀H6	CQua
'Verona' (3) ♀H6	CQua
'Vers Libre' (9)	CQua
'Version' (2)	IRhd
'Victoria' (1)	CQua
'Video Kid' (2)	IRhd
'Viking' (1) ♀H6	CQua
'Village Green' (3)	IRhd
'Vineland' (6)	CQua
'Violetta' (2)	CQua
'Virginia Waters' (3)	CQua
'Viva Diva' (3)	IRhd
'Volare' (2)	CQua
'Volcanic Rim' (3)	IRhd
'Vulcan' (2)	CQua
'W.P. Milner' (1)	CAby CAvo CBro CQua CRav EPfP EPot ERCP GKev LAma LCro LOPS SDeJ SEND WShi
'Walden Pond' (3)	CQua
'Waldorf Astoria' (4)	CQua
'Walton' (7)	CQua
'Waltz' (11a)	CQua
'Warbler' (6) ♀H6	CQua GKev LAma SDeJ
'Warleggan' (2)	CFen
'Warm Day' (2)	IRhd
'Warm Welcome' (2)	IRhd
'Warmington' (3)	CQua
'Warmwell' (3)	IRhd
'Watamu' (3)	IRhd
'Waterperry' (7)	CBro GKev LAma

'Watership Down' (2)	CQua
'Watersmeet' (4)	CQua
watieri	see *N. rupicola* subsp. *watieri*
'Wave' (4)	CQua GKev SDeJ
'Wavertree'	see *N. asturiensis* 'Wavertree'
'Waxwing' (5)	CQua
'Wee Bee' (1)	CQua
'Welcome' (2)	CFen CQua
'Welsh Rugby Union' (1)	CQua
'Welsh Warrior' (1)	CQua
'Wendron' (1)	CFen
'West Post' (3)	IRhd
'Westward' (4)	CQua
'Whang-hi' (6)	CQua
'Wheal Bush' (4)	CQua
'Wheal Coates' (7) ♀H6	CQua
'Wheal Jane' (2)	CQua
'Wheal Kitty' (7)	CQua
'Wheal Rose' (4)	CQua
'Wheatear' (6) ♀H6	CQua IRhd
'Whetstone' (1)	CQua
'Whipcord' (7) ♀H6	CQua IRhd
'Whisky Galore' (2)	CQua
'Whisky Mac' (2)	CQua
'White Emperor' (1)	GCro
'White Empress' (1)	CQua
'White Giant' (1)	GKev
'White Lady' (3)	CAvo CQua GCro GKev LAma SDir WShi
'White Lion' (4) ♀H6	CFen CQua ESps LAma SDeJ SDir
'White Marvel' (4)	CQua GKev MMrt SDeJ
'White Medal' (4)	GKev SDeJ
'White Nile' (2)	CQua GCro
'White Star' (1)	IRhd
'White Tea' (2)	CQua IRhd
'White Tie' (3)	CQua
'Whitewell' (2)	GCro
'Wicklow Hills' (3)	CQua
'Widgeon' (2)	CQua
'Wild Honey' (2)	CQua
'Wild Rover' (1)	IRhd
'Will Scarlett' (2)	CQua GCro
willkommii (13)	CBro CQua EPot GKev
'Wimbledon County Girl' (2) ♀H6	CQua
'Winholm Jenni' (3)	CQua
'Winifred van Graven' (3)	CFen CQua
'Winter Waltz' (6)	CQua CWld
'Wisley' (6) ♀H6	ERCP
'Witch Doctor' (3)	CQua
WOODCROFT BEAUTY (2)	GCro
WOODCROFT GOLD (2)	GCro
'Woodland Prince' (3)	CQua
'Woodland Star' (3)	CQua GKev
'Woodley Vale' (2)	CQua
'Woolsthorpe' (2)	CQua
'World Class' (5)	CQua
'Wy' East' (1) **new**	IRhd
'Xit' (3)	CAvo CBro CQua
'Xunantunich' (2)	CQua
'Yellow Cheerfulness' (4) ♀H6	CArg CQua EPfP GKev LAma LCro LOPS NRHS SCob SDeJ
'Yellow River' (1) ♀H6	LAma
'Yellow Triumphator' (1)	CFen
'Yellow Xit' (3)	CQua GKev
'York Minster' (1)	CQua
'Young American' (1)	CQua
'Young Blood' (2)	CQua IRhd
'Your Grace' (2)	CQua
'Yummy Mummy' (2)	IRhd
'Yum-Yum' (3)	IRhd
'Zekiah' (1)	CQua
'Zion Canyon' (2)	CQua
'Zoë's Pink' (3)	CQua
'Zwynner' (2)	IRhd

Nardostachys (*Caprifoliaceae*)

grandiflora	see *N. jatamansi* 'Grandiflora'
§ ***jatamansi*** 'Grandiflora'	GPoy

Nardus (*Poaceae*)

stricta	EBWF

Nassauvia (*Asteraceae*)

darwinii	WAbe
digitata **new**	SPlb
gaudichaudii	SPlb WAbe
lagascae	WAbe

Nassella (*Poaceae*)

tenuissima	see *Stipa tenuissima*
trichotoma	CAby CKno EHoe LPla SPer WHal
- 'Palomino'	LRHS NRHS

Nasturtium (*Brassicaceae*)

'Banana Split'	CCCN ELan
officinale	EBWF MSKA MWts SVic WMAq

Natal plum see *Carissa macrocarpa*

nectarine see *Prunus persica* var. *nectarina*

Nectaroscordum (*Alliaceae*)

sp.	SDir
§ ***siculum***	CArg CAvo CBre CBro CSpe CTri EAJP ELan EPfP ERCP GKev LCro LEdu LOPS LRHS MBel MJak NChi NSti SCob SDeJ SPer SPoG WBor
§ - subsp. ***bulgaricum***	CAby CBro CRos CTca CWCL EBee ECha EHrv EPfP EPot IBlr IBoy LRHS MNrw NRHS SPhx WBrk WCot WPnP XEll XLum
- subsp. ***bulgaricum*** × ***tripedale*** **new**	GKev
tripedale	CAvo CBro EPot GKev

Neillia (*Rosaceae*)

affinis	CDul CExl CRos EBee EPfP GCal IDee LLHF LRHS MGil NBid NLar SLon SPad SPoG SWvt
longiracemosa	see *N. thibetica*
sinensis	NLar
§ ***thibetica***	Widely available
thyrsiflora	EBee
- PAB 3267	LEdu
- var. ***tunkinensis*** HWJ 505	WCru

Nelumbo (*Nelumbonaceae*)

'Beautiful Dancer'	LLWG
'Beijing' **new**	LLWG
'Bold Protector' **new**	LLWG
§ 'Boli Furen'	LLWG
'Carolina Queen'	LLWG
'Cranberry Kiss' **new**	LLWG
'Emerald Daybreak' (d)	LLWG
'Fenghung Xiang' **new**	LLWG
'Fenling Long' **new**	LLWG
'First Lady'	LLWG
'High Noon'	LLWG
'Hong Denglong' **new**	LLWG

'Hong Wanlian' **new** LLWG
'Huadeng Chushang' **new** LLWG
'Huohua' **new** LLWG
'Lanhua Zhi Fen' **new** LLWG
lutea LLWG XBlo
'Momo Botan' LLWG
'Mrs Perry D. Slocum' see *N.*'Boli Furen'
nucifera XBlo
- 'Alba Striata' LLWG
- 'Chawan Basu' LLWG
- 'Hindu' LLWG
'Penelope' LLWG
'Perry's Giant Sunburst' LLWG
'Pink 'n'Yellow' EWat
'Pink Pretty Princess Payton' LLWG
'Pizhen Fen' **new** LLWG
'Qinhuai Baiyu' **new** LLWG
'Rosey Clouds' **new** LLWG
'Russian Red' LLWG
'Shanghai' **new** LLWG
'Shen Qing' **new** LLWG
'Shenghuo' **new** LLWG
'Shuijing Bai' **new** LLWG
'The President' LLWG
'Tongshuai' **new** LLWG
'Wa Ba Sabie' LLWG
'Wann Shou Hing' LLWG
'Xiao Xiangsi Hong' **new** LLWG
'Xihu Honglian' **new** LLWG
'Xin Pi Zhen Hong' **new** LLWG
'Xinghua Fen' **new** LLWG
'Yaochi Huanying' **new** LLWG
'Yiliang' **new** LLWG
'Yingbin Furong' **new** LLWG
'Ziye' **new** LLWG

Nematanthus (*Gesneriaceae*)

'Apres' WDib
'Black Magic' WDib
'Christmas Holly' WDib
'Freckles' WDib
§ ***gregarius*** ♀H1c WDib
§ - 'Golden West' (v) WDib
- 'Variegatus' see *N. gregarius* 'Golden West'
'Lemon and Lime' WDib
radicans see *N. gregarius*
'Tropicana' ♀H1c WDib

Nemesia (*Scrophulariaceae*)

§ AMELIE ('Fleurame'PBR) EPfP LBuc SPoG
'Azure Flame' (Penhow Little Dragons Series) **new** CRos NRHS
BERRIE WHITE ('Fleurow'PBR) LSou
BERRIES AND CREAM ('Fleurbac'PBR) ECtt EPfP LBuc LSou SPoG
BLUE LAGOON ('Pengoon'PBR) (Maritana Series) EBee SCoo
'Blueberry Ripple' LSou
BLUEBIRD ('Hubbird'PBR) CHll
caerulea 'Joan Wilder' (clonal) WAvo
CANDY GIRL ('Pencand') (Maritana Series) SCoo
§ ***denticulata*** ♀H3 CRos ELon LRHS MHer NEgg SCoo SPoG
- 'Confetti' see *N. denticulata*
'Easter Bonnet' (French Connection Series) **new** LSou
ELPH DARK BLUE (Elph Series) WCot
'Fleurie Blue' EPfP LBuc SPoG
FRAMBOISE ('Fleurfram'PBR) EPfP LBuc LSou SPoG
fruticans Benth. ELon
HONEY GIRL ('Penhon') (Maritana Series) SCoo
ICE PINK ('Fleuripi') EPfP
'Innocence' ♀H3 SCoo
(Karoo Series) KAROO BLUE ('Innkablue'PBR) SCoo
- KAROO SOFT BLUE ('Innkarsofb'PBR) MCot
- KAROO VIOLET ICE ('Innemkavic'PBR) NPri
MARITANA SKY LAGOON ('Pensky') (Maritana Series) SCoo
'Mirabelle' EPfP LBuc SPoG
MYRTILLE ('Fleurmyr'PBR) EPfP LBuc LSou SPoG
(Nesia Series) NESIA BURGUNDY **new** NPri
- NESIA SNOW ANGEL **new** NPri
- NESIA SUNSHINE **new** NPri
OPAL INNOCENCE see *N.* AMELIE
PINK LAGOON ('Penpink') (Maritana Series) EBee
PROVENÇAL DUSKY BLUE ('Fleurpdblu'PBR) EPfP
PROVENÇAL DUSKY PINK ('Fleurpdpnk'PBR) EPfP
RASPBERRIES AND CREAM ('Fleurrac') EPfP LBuc SPoG
'Sugar Almond' CMac
'Sundrops' NPri
(Sunsatia Series) SUNSATIA CHERRY ON ICE CPla NPri SPoG
- SUNSATIA BLACKBERRY ('Inuppink'PBR) SCoo
- SUNSATIA CRANBERRY ('Intraired'PBR) SCoo
- SUNSATIA LEMON ('Intraigold'PBR) SCoo
- SUNSATIA PEACH ('Inupcream') SCoo
SUNSATIA PLUS PAPAYA ('Innemnewpa') (Sunsatia Plus Series) NPri
'Sweet Lady' LSou NPri
sylvatica CSpe
'Vanilla Lady' ECtt LSou NPri
'Wisley Vanilla' CRos EPfP LBuc LRHS NRHS SPoG

Nemophila (*Boraginaceae*)

menziesii 'Penny Black' CSpe SPer

Neodypsis (*Arecaceae*)

decaryi see *Dypsis decaryi*

Neolepisorus (*Polypodiaceae*)

lancifolius CExl

Neolitsea (*Lauraceae*)

glauca see *N. sericea*
polycarpa B&SWJ 11705 WCru
- KWJ 12309 WCru
§ ***sericea*** CBcs CCCN EBee WPGP
- B&SWJ 12738 **new** WCru
- CWJ 12800 WCru

	– yellow-fruited CWJ 12830 new	WCru

Neomarica (*Iridaceae*)

	caerulea	WCot

Neopanax ✿ (*Araliaceae*)

§	***arboreus***	CDTJ CTsd EBee LEdu SBig
§	***laetus*** ♀H3	SArc SBig WPGP

Neoregelia ✿ (*Bromeliaceae*)

	'Atlantis' new	NCft
	carolinae (Meyendorffii Group) 'Meyendorffii'	XBlo
	'Chiquita Linda'	NLos
	'Dr Oeser'	NLos
	'Fireball'	NCft NLos
	'Hannibal Lector' × ***punctatissima*** var. ***rubra***	NLos
	'Hojo Rojo'	XBlo
	lilliputiana	NCft
	'Marconfos'	XBlo
	'Narciss' new	NCft
	pauciflora	NCft
I	***paulinae*** 'Paulinae' new	NCft
	'Red on Green'	NLos
	'Scarlet Charlotte'	NLos
I	***schultesiana*** new	NCft
I	– 'Variegata' (v) new	NCft
	'Spicy'	NLos
	'Zuleica'	NLos

Neoshirakia (*Euphorbiaceae*)

	japonica	MBlu WPGP
	– B&SWJ 8744	WCru

Nepenthes ✿ (*Nepenthaceae*)

	sp.	SRms
	alata	NLos
	alata × ***ventricosa*** ♀H1b	SHmp
	albomarginata	NLos
	aristolochioides × ***spectabilis***	NLos
	'Black Beauty'	NLos
	'Bloody Mary'PBR	SHmp
	bongso	NLos SHmp
	bongso × ***inermis***	NLos
	boschiana × ***densiflora***	NLos
	burbidgeae	NLos
	burbidgeae × ***robcantleyi***	SHmp
	× ***burkei***	NLos
	× ***burkei*** × ***hamata***	SHmp
	× ***burkei*** × ***singalana***	SHmp
	chaniana × (***clipeata*** × ***eymae***)	NLos
	chaniana × ***veitchii***	NLos
	clipeata × ***eymae***	NLos
	copelandii	NLos
	(***copelandii*** × ***truncata***) × ***spathulata***	SHmp
	densiflora	NLos SHmp
	densiflora × ***spectabilis***	NLos
	diatas	NLos SHmp
	dubia × ***singalana***	SHmp
	dubia × ***spathulata***	SHmp
	eymae	NLos
	fusca	NLos SHmp
	fusca × ***maxima***	SHmp
	glabrata	NLos
	glabrata × ***spathulata***	SHmp
	gracillima	NLos
	× ***hookeriana*** ♀H1a	NLos SHmp
	inermis	NLos
	inermis × ***singalana***	NLos
	inermis × ***ventricosa***	NLos
	jacquelineae × ***spectabilis***	SHmp
	'Lady Pauline' ♀H1b	NLos
	'Linda'PBR	SHmp
	'Louisa'	SHmp
	lowii	NLos
	macfarlanei	SHmp
	maxima	NLos
	maxima × (× ***mixta***)	SHmp
	maxima × ***talangensis***	SHmp
	mikei	NLos
	mira × ***spathulata***	NLos SHmp
	mira × ***spectabilis***	NLos
	muluensis × ***lowii***	NLos
	ovata	NLos SHmp
	ovata × ***ventricosa***	SHmp
	petiolata × ***veitchii***	SHmp
	pilosa	NLos
	pilosa × ***veitchii***	NLos
	platychila × ***spathulata***	SHmp
	platychila × ***veitchii***	NLos
	rajah	NLos
	ramispina	NLos SHmp
	'Rebecca Soper' ♀H1b	SHmp
	robcantleyi	SHmp
	robcantleyi × ***spathulata***	SHmp
	robcantleyi × ***talangensis***	SHmp
	sanguinea	NLos SHmp SPlb
	sibuyanensis	SHmp
	sibuyanensis × ***spectabilis***	NLos
	sibuyanensis × ***ventricosa***	NLos
	singalana	NLos SHmp
	spectabilis	NLos SHmp
	spectabilis × ***talangensis***	NLos
	talangensis	NLos SHmp
	talangensis × ***veitchii***	SHmp
	tobaica	NLos
	truncata	NLos
	– highland form	SHmp
	– 'King of Spades' × ***truncata*** 'Queen of Hearts'	SHmp
	veitchii	NLos
	ventricosa	SHmp

Nepeta ✿ (*Lamiaceae*)

	from China	EWes
	'Blue Beauty'	see *N. sibirica* 'Souvenir d'André Chaudron'
	'Blue Dragon'	CBod CMea ECtt EPed GBin GPSL GQue GWyn LRHS LSou MAvo MPie MSpe MTis NLar NRHS SBee SPad SPoG SRms WCot WHoo
*	***buddlejifolium***	NLar
*	– 'Gold Splash'	NLar
	camphorata	WSpi
	cataria	CBod CTsd EBWF ENfk GJos GPoy MHer MNHC NBro SRms SVic WMoo WSpi XAbr
§	– 'Citriodora'	CBod ENfk MHer SPhx SRms

	'Chettle Blue'	CDor MAvo
	citriodora Dum.	see *N. cataria* 'Citriodora'
	clarkei	GMaP MRav MTis WArt WMoo WSpi
	curviflora	SPhx
	'Dropmore'	EBee GWyn MTis NLar
	'Early Bird'	IPot
§	× ***faassenii*** ♀H7	Widely available
	- 'Alba'	EBee ECtt ELan EPfP LRHS NLar SRms
	- 'Blue Wonder'	CRos EBee ELan EPfP LRHS MHol MTis NLar NRHS WFar WSpi
	- 'Gletschereis'	EBee
	- 'Kit Cat'	CRos CSpe ECtt EPfP GBin GWyn IBoy IRob LRHS LSRN MAsh MHol MTis NRHS SPhm WCAu WCFE
	- 'Limelight'	EBee IBoy MTis
	- 'Purssian Blue' **new**	CBod MHol MTis NCou
	- 'Senior'	XLum
	glechoma 'Variegata'	see *Glechoma hederacea* 'Variegata'
	govaniana	CAby CBWd CBod CDor CRos CSam EBee ECha ELan EPfP GCal GMaP LEdu LRHS MCot MHol MRav MSpe NBid NDov NRHS NSti SBrt SPer SPhx SRms SSut WBor WPGP XLum
	grandiflora	CDor MRav NBre
	- 'Blue Danube'	EBee GBin GWyn MTis XLum
	- 'Blue Elf'	NDov
	- 'Bramdean' ♀H6	CBod CDor CMea CRos EBee ECtt EPfP EWes GBin GWyn LRHS MCot MRav MTis NRHS SPhx SRms WCAu WCot XLum
	- 'Dawn to Dusk'	Widely available
	- 'Pool Bank'	CElw EBee ECtt EWes IRob MAvo MTis XLum
	- 'Summer Magic'	CBWd CRos EBee ECha EPfP GBin LRHS NRHS SCob SHar SPoG SRkn WFar WTor
	- 'Wild Cat'	EPfP MTis SPhx WCAu
	- 'Zinser's Giant'	EBee SAko
	hederacea 'Variegata'	see *Glechoma hederacea* 'Variegata'
	'Hill Grounds'	MAvo WCot
	italica	SHar SPhx
	'Joanna Reed'	GBin
	JUNIOR WALKER ('Novanepjun')	CKno CRos EWTr LCro LOPS LRHS MAsh MBel NDov NRHS SCob
	kubanica	CBWd CRos CSpe EBee IMou LRHS MRav NRHS SBee SMHy SPhx WCAu WCot WSHC
	'Lamendi'	NDov
	latifolia 'Super Cat'	EBee ELan EPfP
§	'Leeds Castle'	CBod EBee ECtt EPed LRHS MTis NGdn NRHS NSti SHar SPer WCAu WHal WOut WTor
	'Limelight'	NLar
	longipes hort.	see *N.* 'Leeds Castle'
	macrantha	see *N. sibirica*
	manchuriensis 'Manchu Blue'	EBee
	mussinii misapplied	see *N.* × *faassenii*
	mussinii Spreng.	see *N. racemosa*
	nervosa	CDor CSpe ECha ELan EPfP NBro NLar NSti SBrt SHar SPer WHar XSen
	- 'Blue Carpet'	CRos CSpe LRHS NEgg NRHS
	- 'Blue Moon'	CBod CRos EBee EPfP EWes GJos IBoy LRHS LSou MBNS MHol MMrt MSCN NQui NRHS SRms WSpi
	- 'Forncett Select'	CSam MRav NBre
	- 'Pink Cat'	CBod CDor CMea CRos EPfP LRHS MSCN NLar NRHS WArt WFar
	- 'Schneehäschen'	SAko WSpi
§	***nuda***	ECha EWes LPla MAvo MRav SHar SMHy
	- 'Accent'	EBee
	- subsp. ***albiflora***	ECha
*	- 'Grandiflora'	NBre WMoo
	- 'Purple Cat'	EBee EPfP LLHF NDov
	- 'Romany Dusk'	LEdu LPla
	- 'Snow Cat'	SPhx
	pannonica	see *N. nuda*
	parnassica	EPPr EWTr GLog GQue MAvo MBel MCot MHol MMuc MTis WArt WHrl WMoo
	phyllochlamys	CBot CPBP
	'Pink Candy'	SPhx SRms
	'Poseidon' **new**	MAvo
§	***prattii***	CBod MWat NLar SEND
	'Purple Haze'PBR	ECtt MHol NLar
§	***racemosa*** ♀H7	CHby CMac CRos EPfP GJos GWyn LRHS MCot MNHC SCob WMoo
	- RCB AM 3	CDor WCot
	- ***alba***	CBod CDor XLum
	- 'Amelia'	CBWd EBee EPfP MHer WAvo WCAu WTor
	- 'Grog'	CBod CWld EWTr GBin GWyn LRHS MAvo MTis NLar SPoG
	- 'Little Titch'	CBod EBee ECha ECtt EPfP GWyn LRHS LSRN MAsh MCot NGdn NLar SCob
	- 'Senior'	MHol
	- 'Snowflake'	CBcs CMea CRos ECtt ELan ELon EPfP EShb GMaP GPSL GQue GWyn LRHS MTis NRHS SCob SPer SPoG SWvt WAvo WCAu WSpi WTor
	- 'Superba'	NBre
	- 'Toria'	IMou MTis NDov
	- 'Walker's Low' ♀H7	Widely available
*	'Rae Crug'	ECtt EWes
	reichenbachiana	see *N. racemosa*
§	***sibirica***	CRos ECha ELan EPfP IRob LRHS MMuc NBid NBro NLar NRHS SRkn WCot XLum
§	- 'Souvenir d'André Chaudron' ♀H6	CAby CBod CDor CRos CSam CWCL EBee EHrv ELan EPed EPfP GCal GMaP GWyn IPot LRHS LSou MCot MRav MTis MWat NLar NRHS SCob SPer SPoG WSpi
	'Six Hills Giant'	Widely available
	'Six Hills Gold'	CAby CDor EBee LBuc SCob WSpi WTor
	spicata	LRHS
	stewartiana	LLHF MRav WMoo
	subsessilis	CAby CBod CRos ECtt EHrv ELan EPfP GLog GMaP IBoy LRHS MBel MCot MRav MSpe NBid NGdn NLar NRHS NSti NWad SCob SPhm SPhx SPoG SRms WCAu WCru
	- 'Blue Dreams'	ELon GQue GWyn MHol MNHC NLar SCob SHar SPhx SRkn WArt WHar WSpi XLum
	- 'Candy Cat'	ELan IBoy MTis NBre NLar
	- 'Cool Cat'	EBee ELan EPfP LSRN NBre NLar
	- 'Laufen'	IPot
	- NIMBUS ('Yanim')	MHol MPnt
	- 'Pink Dreams'	CBod EAJP EBee ELan EPfP GJos GWyn LRHS MHer SCob XLum
	- pink-flowered	ECha EPPr SPhx

- 'Sweet Dreams'	EPfP EShb GJos IRob LRHS MRav MTis NLar NRHS NSti XLum
- 'Washfield'	MTis NLar SAko
transcaucasica	SPhx
- 'Blue Infinity'	CNor WMoo
tuberosa	CDor EBee ECha EPPr WCot WMoo XSen
'Veluws Blauwtje'	NLar WSpi
'Veluwse Wakel'	IMou
'Weinheim Big Blue' new	MAvo
wilsonii	GBin
yunnanensis	EBee EPPr IPot MPie SPhx WOut WPGP

Nephrolepis (*Lomariopsidaceae*)

cordifolia	CBdn NLos
duffii	EShb
exaltata 'Smithii'	EShb
- 'Verona'	WCot
falcata	NLos
- f. ***furcans***	NLos

Nerine ✿ (*Amaryllidaceae*)

'Afterglow'	LAma LRHS WCot
'Alexandra'	WCot
alta	see *N. undulata* Alta Group
angustifolia	WAbe
'Audrey Clarke'	CPne
'Aurora'	WCot
'Baghdad'	SChr WCot
'Belladonna'	CWCL WCot
'Bennett-Poë'	WCot
'Berlioz'	WCot
'Blanchefleur'	CTal WCot
bowdenii ♀H5	Widely available
- 'Alba' misapplied	see *N. bowdenii* 'Pallida'
- 'Alba' ambig.	CPrp CTca EBee ELan EPot ERCP SCoo SMHy
- 'Alba'	CAby CBro CRos CWCL ECha EPri ETMg GKev IBal IRob LAma LRHS MNrw NRHS SCob SDeJ SDir WCot WFar
- 'Albivetta'	EBee ELon EPri GKev IBal LAma MNrw SDir
- 'Blanca Perla'	EBee EPri EShb GKev LAma WHil
- 'Castlewellan'	IBlr
- 'Codora'	see *N.* 'Codora'
- 'Elegance Red'	CBro ELan
- 'Ella K'	CBod EPfP EPot EPri GKev IBal LAma LCro LOPS MNrw SPer WHil
- 'Eric Smith'	WCot
- 'Gletsjer'	WCot
- Irish clone	WCot
- 'Isabel'	CAby CBro ECha ELan EPot EPri ERCP ETMg EWes GKev IBal LAma SDeJ SDir WBor WCot WHil WHoo
- 'Kathleen Pollock'	WCot
- 'Linda Vista'	WCot
- 'Manina'	CCse
- 'Marjorie'	EMal
- 'Mark Fenwick'	CBro WCot
- 'Marney Rogerson'	CBro CPne SMHy WCot
§ - 'Mollie Cowie' (v)	CCse GCal IBlr WCot WCru
- 'Mount Stewart'	CPne IBlr WCot
- 'Nikita'	CPne CRos EPri ERCP GKev IBal LAma LRHS MNrw NRHS SCob SDeJ WCot
- 'Ostara'	CBod CRav ELan EPot EPri GKev IBal LAma LCro LOPS LRHS MNrw SDir WCot WFar
§ - 'Pallida'	LRHS
- 'Patricia'	EPot EPri GKev IBal LAma MNrw SDir
- 'Pink Frostwork'	EPri
- 'Pink Surprise'	CAvo EPri WCot
- 'Pink Waveline' new	SMHy
§ - 'Quinton Wells'	CTca WCot
- 'Richard Blakeway-Phillips'	WCot
- 'Robert Smith'	WCot
- 'Rowie'	EPri LRHS
- 'Sheila Owen'	WCot
- 'Stam 63'	EPot ERCP IBal LAma
- 'Stefanie'	CAby ELan EPri EShb ETMg EWTr GKev IBal LAma SDeJ
- Ted Allen No 2	WCot
- 'Variegata'	see *N. bowdenii* 'Mollie Cowie'
- 'Vesta K'	EBee EPot EPri GKev IBal LAma LRHS SDir
- 'Wellsii'	see *N. bowdenii* 'Quinton Wells'
bowdenii* × *sarniensis new	SDir
bowdenii* × *undulata new	SDir
'Canasta'	WCot
'Caryatid'	WCot WFar
'Catherine'	CPne WCot
'Catkin'	CPne WCot
'Clent Charm'	WCot
§ 'Codora'	CCCN EPfP SPer WCot WFar
'Corlette'	WCot
corusca 'Major'	see *N. sarniensis* var. *corusca*
'Countess of Mulgrave' new	WCot
'Cranfield'	WCot
crispa	see *N. undulata* Crispa Group
'Cynthia Chance'	WCot
'Diana Oliver'	CPne WCot
'Doris Vos'	WCot
'Elegance'	LRHS
'Elegance Gem' new	WCot
'Elspeth'	WCot
'Exbury Red'	WCot
'Falaise' new	WCot
filamentosa misapplied	see *N. filifolia* Baker
filamentosa ambig.	CBro
filamentosa W.F. Barker	CTal
§ ***filifolia*** Baker	WAbe
'Firelight'	CPne WCot
flexuosa	see *N. undulata* Flexuosa Group
gaberonensis	WAbe
'Giraffe' new	WCot
'Glacier'	EBee LRHS MNrw
gracilis	WCot
'Hamlet'	CPne
'Harlequin'	WCot
'Helena'	WCot
'Hera'	CBro ELon
'Hertha Berg'	WCot
* ***hirsuta***	WCot
humilis ♀H2	CBro
- from Bredarsdorp, South Africa new	WCot
- from Franschhoek, South Africa	CTal
- Breachiae Group	CTal
- Peersii Group from Toorwaterpoort, South Africa	CTal
'Iman'	WCot
'Isobel'	LEdu LRHS XEll
'Janet'	WCot
'Jenny Wren'	WCot

'King Leopold'	WCot WFar
'King of the Belgians'	LAma LRHS
'Kinn McIntosh'	EPri WCot
krigei	WCot XEll
'Kyle'	WCot
'Lady Cynthia Colville'	WCot
'Lady Downe'	WCot
'Lady Eleanor Keane'	WCot
'Lady Havelock-Allen'	WCot
'Lady Llewellyn'	WCot
'Lady St Aldwyn'	WCot
'Lambourne'	WCot
laticoma	WCot
'Lawlord'	WCot
'Leila Hughes'	WCot
'Long Island Beauty' **new**	WCot
'Lucinda'	WCot
'Lyndhurst Salmon'	WCot
'Malvern'	WCot
'Maria'	WCot
'Mars'	CTal
masoniorum ♀H2	CTal SBch WAbe
'Meadowbankii'	WCot
'Miss E. Cator'	CPne CTal WCot
'Miss Florence Brown'	WCot
'Miss Frances Clarke'	WCot
'Mr John'	CBro CPne EBee EPri ERCP GKev LAma LRHS SDir WCot XEll
'Mrs Cooper'	WCot
'Mrs Dent Brocklehurst'	WCot
'Natasha'	WCot
'Nena'	WCot
'November Cheer'	LAma
'Oberon'	WCot
'Ophelia'	WCot
'Owslebury' **new**	WCot
'Pamela' **new**	LRHS
'Pink Triumph'	CBcs CTsd EBee ELan EPot ERCP EShb GKev IBal IRob LAma LRHS NRHS SDeJ SPer WCot WHoo
'Plymouth'	CTal SChr
pudica	CTal
- pink-flowered	WCot
'Quivotina'	WCot
'Red Pimpernel'	LAma
'Regina'	WCot
'Rembrandt'	WCot
'Rose Princess'	WCot
'Rotherside'	CTal
'Rushmere Star'	CTal SChr WCot
'Ruth'	WCot WFar
sarniensis	CBro CPne ECha EPot EPri LRHS SDeJ WCot
* - 'Borde Hill White'	WCot
§ - var. ***corusca***	LAma
- - 'Major'	MPie SChr WCot
- var. ***curvifolia***	CBro
- - f. ***fothergillii***	WCot
- 'Hanley Castle' **new**	WCot
- 'Mother of Pearl' **new**	WCot
- 'Mottistone'	WCot
- 'Pink Petticoat'	CTal
- 'Salmon Star'	LRHS
- 'Shell Pink'	CTal
'Sidney Smee'	CTal
'Snowflake'	WCot
'Stephanie'	CCCN CPne CTca ELon EShb LAma LEdu MNrw WCot WHoo
'Susan Norris'	WCot
'Tweedledee'	WCot
undulata	CAby CCCN CPne CTal CTca ECha EHrv EPri GCal GKev IBal LAma MPie SDeJ SPer
§ - Alta Group	WCot
§ - Crispa Group	CBod EPfP WFar
§ - Flexuosa Group	MRav
- - 'Alba' ♀H3	CBro CPne CRos CTca ECha EPri EWTr MRav WAbe WCot
× ***versicolor*** 'Mansellii'	CBro
'Vicky'	WCot
'Virgo'	LAma
'Winter Sun'	LRHS SRms
'Wolsey'	CPne
'Zeal Giant' ♀H3	CAvo CBro CPne EPri GCal WCot
'Zeal Grilse'	CPne WCot
'Zeal Purple Stripe'	WCot
'Zennor'	WCot

Nerium (*Apocynaceae*)

§ ***odoratum*** 'Miss Agnes Campbell'	SEND
oleander misapplied	see *N. oleander* 'Soeur Agnès'
oleander L.	CAbb CBcs CHll CTri EBak ELan EShb ESps SEND SPer SPlb SPoG
- 'Agnes Campbell'	see *N. odoratum* 'Miss Agnes Campbell'
- 'Album'	CTri LRHS SEND
- 'Album Maximum'	CCCN
- 'Album Plenum' (d)	XSen
- 'Alsace'	SEND
* - 'Atlas'	XSen
* - 'Barcelona'	SEND
- 'Cavalaire' (d)	XSen
* - 'Claudia'	SEND
- 'Commandant Barthélemy' (d)	XSen
- double apricot (d) **new**	SEND
- 'Flavescens Plenum' (d)	EShb XSen
- 'Hardy Red'	XSen
- 'Isle of Capri'	CCCN
- 'Italia'	XSen
- 'Jannoch'	XSen
- 'Louis Pouget' (d)	XSen
- 'Madame Allen' (d)	EShb
- 'Magaly'	SEND
- 'Margaritha'	SEND XSen
* - 'Maurin des Maures'	CCCN
- 'Minouche'	SEND
- pink-flowered	LRHS
- 'Professeur Granel' (d)	EShb
- 'Provence' (d)	XSen
- 'Red Beauty'	XSen
- 'Roseum Plenum' (d)	SEND
§ - 'Soeur Agnès'	CAco
- 'Soleil Levant'	XSen
- 'Splendens Giganteum' (d)	EShb
- 'Tito Poggi'	XSen
- 'Variegatum' (v) ♀H2	CHll ELan EShb
- 'Villa Romaine'	XSen

Neviusia (*Rosaceae*)

alabamensis	CJun NLar

Nicandra (*Solanaceae*)

physalodes	CHby ELan ENfk SEle WSFF XAbr
- 'Splash of Cream' (v)	CCCN MNHC
- 'Violacea'	CSpe GLog SRms SWvt

Nicotiana ✿ (*Solanaceae*)

alata	CBod CSpe EPfP GDun LCro WSFF

- 'Grandiflora'	LCro
alata* × *mutabilis	GDun
excelsior new	GDun WCot
glauca	CCCN CDTJ CHll GDun SPlb
glutinosa	GDun
'Hopleys'	CSpe
knightiana	CDTJ CSpe GDun
langsdorffii ♀H2	CSpe GDun SPav SPhx
- 'Hot Chocolate'	CSpe
'Lime Green' ♀H2	CRav CSpe ELan LCro LOPS
maritima new	GDun
mutabilis	CBre CSpe GDun LCro LOPS SDys SPhx
'Perfume Deep Purple' (Perfume Series)	CSpe
quadrivalvis	GDun
rustica	GDun
× ***sanderae*** Cuba Series	NPri
- - 'Cuba Deep Lime'	NPri
- EAU DE COLOGNE MIXED new	ETMg
solanifolia	GDun SPlb
suaveolens	GDun LCro SPhx
sylvestris ♀H2	CBod CDTJ CRav CSpe ELan EPfP GDun LCro LOPS MMuc NPri SDys SEND SPav SPhx SPoG SWvt WHil
tabacum	GDun XAbr
'Tinkerbell'	CSpe
WHISPER MIXED new	CRav

Nidularium (*Bromeliaceae*)

correia-araujoi	NLos
innocentii	XBlo

Nierembergia (*Solanaceae*)

frutescens	see *N. scoparia*
§ ***repens***	NLar WCot XLum
rivularis	see *N. repens*
§ ***scoparia***	CSpe

Nigella (*Ranunculaceae*)

damascena	CPla
- 'Albion Green Pod' new	LCro
- 'Miss Jekyll' ♀H7	LCro LOPS LRHS MNHC SPhx
- 'Miss Jekyll Alba' ♀H7	CSpe
- 'Oxford Blue'	LCro LOPS
- Persian Jewels Group	SVic
hispanica L.	CRav SPhx
papillosa 'African Bride'	CRav CSpe MNHC SPhx
- 'Delft Blue' new	LCro
- 'Midnight'	CSpe
sativa	XAbr

Niphidium (*Polypodiaceae*)

crassifolium	EShb WCot

Nipponanthemum (*Asteraceae*)

§ ***nipponicum***	CBod EBee ELon GBin GCal GWyn LRHS MMuc NLar NSti SAko SPoG SRms WHil XLum
- 'Hama-giku'	NWad

Noccaea see *Thlaspi*

Nolina (*Asparagaceae*)

bigelovii	WCot XSen
* ***brevifolia***	CFil
durangensis	CFil EUJe
hibernica	CFil XSen
lindheimeriana	WCot
microcarpa	XSen
nelsonii	CCht CFil NLos SArc SPlb
parviflora	XSen
texana	WCot XSen

Nomocharis (*Liliaceae*)

aperta	CExl EHrv GCal GGGa GKev LAma LRHS SDir WCru
- ACE 2271	EHrv
- CLD 229	EHrv
× ***finlayorum***	LLHF
mairei	see *N. pardanthina*
meleagrina	GEdr LRHS NHpl SDir
nana	see *Lilium nanum*
oxypetala	see *Lilium oxypetalum*
§ ***pardanthina***	EBee
- f. ***punctulata***	GGGa
saluenensis	GGGa

Nonea (*Boraginaceae*)

lutea	EPPr LSou NSti WHal

Nothochelone see *Penstemon*

Nothofagus ✿ (*Nothofagaceae*)

sp.	LPra
antarctica	CBcs CDul CMCN CTho EBee ELan EPfP EWTr GKin LMaj LPra MAsh MBlu MGos NOra SAko SWvt
betuloides	GBin IArd SAko SPlb
cunninghamii	CBcs CBrP IArd IDee SAko SPlb
dombeyi ♀H5	CBcs CFil CMCN EPfP GBin IArd IDee MBlu SAko SArc SWvt WPGP WSpi
fusca	SAko WPGP
menziesii	WPGP
moorei	WPGP
obliqua	CMCN GAbr SPlb WMou

Notholaena see *Cheilanthes*

Notholirion (*Liliaceae*)

bulbuliferum	EBee GBin GKev
campanulatum	EBee
macrophyllum	EBee GBin
thomsonianum	CTal GKev

Nothoscordum (*Alliaceae*)

bivalve	IMou
dialystemon	EPot LLHF NHpl NPnk WAbe
montevidense	WCot
neriniflorum	see *Allium neriniflorum*
ostenii	WCot

Nuphar (*Nymphaeaceae*)

japonica	LLWG
lutea	CBen CHab LCro LLWG LOPS MSKA
- subsp. ***advena***	LLWG
pumila	LLWG

Nuytsia (*Loranthaceae*)

floribunda	SPlb

Nylandtia (*Polygalaceae*)

spinosa	SPlb

Nymphaea ✿ (*Nymphaeaceae*)

alba (H)	CBen CHab CWat LCro LOPS MSKA MWts SVic WMAq

	'Alba Plenissima' (H)	EWat
	'Albatros' misapplied	see *N.* 'Hermine'
§	'Albatros' Latour-Marliac (H)	CBen CWat LLWG MSKA NPer XBlo
	'Albatross'	see *N.* 'Albatros' Latour-Marliac, *N.* 'Hermine'
	'Albert Greenberg' (T/D)	LLWG
*	'Albida'	LLWG WMAq XBlo
	'Almost Black' (H)	CBen EWat LCro LLWG LOPS MSKA
	'Amabilis' (H)	CBen EWat WMAq
	'Andreana' (H)	EWat LLWG MSKA
	'Anna Epple' (H)	LLWG
	'Arc-en-ciel' (H)	CBen EWat LLWG WMAq
	'Atropurpurea' (H)	CBen EWat LLWG MSKA NPer WMAq
	'Attraction' (H)	CBen EWat LLWG MSKA MWts NPer SVic WMAq XBlo XLum
	'August Koch' (T/D) **new**	LLWG
	'Augustus McCray' (H)	LLWG
	'Aurora' (H)	CWat LCro LLWG LOPS MWts SVic WMAq
	'Avalanche' (T/D) **new**	LLWG
	'Barbara Davies' (H)	EWat LLWG MSKA
	'Barbara Dobbins' (H)	CBen EWat LCro LLWG LOPS MSKA
	'Bateau' (H)	CBen LLWG
	'Berit Strawn' (H)	EWat
	'Bernice Ikins' (H)	LLWG
	'Betsy Sakata' (H)	EWat LLWG
	'Betty Lou' (T) **new**	LLWG
	'Black Cherry' (H) **new**	LLWG
	'Black Princess' (H)	EWat LLWG
	'Blue Beauty' (T/D)	LLWG
	'Brakeleyi Rosea' (H)	MSKA WMAq
	'Burgundy Princess' (H)	CBen CWat EWat LLWG MSKA NPer
	candida (H)	CBen MSKA MWts NPer WMAq
	'Candidissima' (H)	CBen MWts
§	***capensis*** (T/D)	LLWG XBlo
	'Carolina Sunset' (H)	EWat LLWG
	'Caroliniana Nivea' (H)	CBen
	'Caroliniana Perfecta' (H)	CBen MSKA
	'Celebration' (H)	EWat LLWG
	'Charlene Strawn' (H)	EWat LLWG WMAq
	'Charles de Meurville' (H)	LCro LLWG LOPS MSKA NPer SVic WMAq
	'Château le Rouge' (H)	LLWG
	'Chubby' (H)	LLWG
	'Clyde Ikins' (H)	EWat LLWG MSKA XBlo
	'Colonel A.J. Welch' (H)	CBen MSKA NPer WMAq
	'Colorado' (H)	CBen EWat LLWG MSKA NPer
	colorata	see *N. capensis*
	'Colossea' (H)	CBen CWat MSKA NPer
	'Comanche' (H)	CBen EWat LLWG MSKA NPer WMAq
	'Conqueror' (H)	CBen LLWG MSKA NPer SVic
	'Cynthia Ann' (H) **new**	LLWG
	'Dallas' (H)	LLWG
§	'Darwin' (H)	CBen CWat LLWG MSKA MWts NPer SLon WMAq
	'David' (H)	CBen EWat LLWG
	'Debbie June' (H)	LLWG
	'Denver' (H)	EWat LLWG MSKA
	'Ellisiana' (H)	LLWG MSKA NPer
	'Escarboucle' (H) ♀H7	CBen CWat EWat LLWG MSKA NPer SVic WMAq XBlo
§	'Fabiola' (H)	LLWG MSKA NPer WMAq
	'Fantasy'	LLWG
	'Fiesta' (H)	CBen MSKA
	'Fire Crest' (H)	CBen LLWG NPer SVic WMAq

	'Florida Sunset' (H)	EWat
	'Fritz Junge' (H)	CBen
	'Froebelii' (H)	CBen CWat EWat MSKA NPer WMAq
	'Fuchsia Pom-pom' (H) **new**	LLWG
	'Fulva' (H)	LLWG
	'Galatée' (H)	CBen MSKA
	'Geisha Girl' (H)	MSKA
	'Georgia Peach' (H)	EWat LLWG MSKA
	'Gladstoniana' (H) ♀H7	CBen MSKA NPer WMAq
	'Gloire du Temple-sur-Lot' (H)	CBen EWat LLWG NPer WMAq
	'Gloriosa' (H)	CBen LLWG NPer
	'Gold Medal' (H)	CBen EWat LLWG MSKA
	'Gonnère' (H) ♀H7	CBen CWat EWat LLWG MSKA MWts NPer SLon WMAq
	'Graziella' (H)	MSKA WMAq
	'Gypsy' (H)	EWat LLWG
	'Hal Miller' (H)	LLWG
	'Hassell' (H)	LLWG
	'Hazorea Dagan White' (H)	EWat LLWG
	'Helen Fowler' (H)	WMAq
	'Helen Hariot' (H)	LLWG
	× ***helvola***	see *N.* 'Pygmaea Helvola'
§	'Hermine' (H)	CBen MSKA NPer WMAq
	'Hidden Violet' (H)	LLWG
§	'Highlight' (H)	EWat LLWG
	'Hilite'	see *N.* 'Highlight'
	'Hollandia' misapplied	see *N.* 'Darwin'
	'Indiana' (H)	CBen LLWG MSKA NPer WMAq
	'Inner Light' (H)	EWat LLWG MSKA
	'Irene Heritage' (H)	CBen
	'J.C.N. Forestier' (H)	CBen
	'James Brydon' (H) ♀H7	CBen CWat EWat LLWG MSKA MWts NPer SLon SVic WMAq
	'Jean de Lamarsalle' (H)	LLWG MSKA
	'Jerusalem Dawn' (H)	LLWG MSKA
§	'Joanne Pring' (H)	CBen
	'Joey Tomocik' (H)	CBen CWat EWat LLWG MSKA WMAq
	'King of Siam' (T/D)	LLWG
	'Lactea' (H)	CBen LLWG
	'Laura Strawn' (H)	EWat
	'Laydekeri Fulgens' (H)	CBen EWat LLWG MSKA MWts WMAq
	'Laydekeri Lilacea' (H)	CBen LLWG WMAq
	'Laydekeri Purpurata' (H)	EWat
	'Laydekeri Rosea' misapplied	see *N.* 'Laydekeri Rosea Prolifera'
§	'Laydekeri Rosea Prolifera' (H)	CBen EWat
	'Lemon Meringue' (H) **new**	LLWG
	'Lemon Mist' (H)	LLWG
	'Lily Pons' (H)	CBen EWat LLWG
	'Liou' (H)	CBen LLWG MSKA
	'Little Sue' (H)	EWat LLWG MSKA
	'Livingstone' (H)	LLWG
	'Lucida' (H)	CBen LLWG MSKA WMAq
	'Madame Wilfon Gonnère' (H)	CBen CWat EWat LLWG MSKA MWts NPer SVic WMAq
	'Marliacea Albida' (H)	CBen CWat EWat LCro LLWG LOPS MSKA MWts NPer WMAq XBlo XLum
	'Marliacea Carnea' (H)	CBen LCro LOPS MSKA MWts NPer WMAq
§	'Marliacea Chromatella' (H) ♀H7	CBen CWat EWat MSKA MWts SVic WMAq XBlo XLum
	'Marliacea Rosea' (H)	CBen MSKA WMAq XBlo XLum
	'Martha' (H)	EWat
	'Mary' (H)	EWat LLWG

	'Masaniello' (H)	CBen MSKA WMAq
	'Maurice Laydeker' (H)	CBen LLWG
	'Maxima'	see *N.* 'Odorata Maxima'
	'Mayla' (H)	CBen EWat LLWG MSKA NPer
§	'Météor' (H)	CBen EWat MSKA WMAq
	mexicana	LLWG
	'Millennium Pink' (H)	MSKA
	'Moon Dance' (H) **new**	LLWG
	'Moorei' (H)	CBen MSKA WMAq
	'Mrs Richmond' misapplied	see *N.* 'Fabiola'
	'Mrs Richmond' Latour-Marliac (H)	CBen XBlo
	'Munkala Ubon' (H)	LLWG
	'Murillo' (H)	EWat
	'Neptune' (H)	LLWG
	'Newchapel Beauty'	WMAq
	'Newton' (H)	CBen CWat EWat LLWG MSKA WMAq
	'Nigel' (H)	EWat LLWG MSKA
	'Norma Gedye' (H)	CBen CWat MSKA WMAq
§	***odorata*** (H)	CBen LLWG MSKA WMAq
§	- var. ***minor*** (H)	CBen EWat MSKA WMAq
	- 'Pumila'	see *N. odorata* var. *minor*
	- subsp. ***tuberosa*** (H)	CBen
	'Odorata Alba'	see *N. odorata*
	'Odorata Juliana' (H)	EWat
§	'Odorata Maxima' (H)	WMAq
	'Odorata Sulphurea' (H)	LLWG
§	'Odorata Sulphurea Grandiflora' (H)	LLWG XBlo
§	'Odorata Turicensis' (H)	MSKA
	'Odorata William B. Shaw'	see *N.* 'W.B. Shaw'
	'Panama Pacific' (T/D)	LLWG XBlo
	'Patio Joe' (H)	EWat LLWG MSKA
	'Paul Hariot' (H)	EWat LLWG MSKA NPer WMAq
	'Peace Lily' (H)	EWat LLWG MSKA
	'Peach Glow' (H)	EWat LLWG MSKA
	'Peaches and Cream' (H)	EWat LLWG MSKA
	'Perry's Baby Red' (H)	CBen CWat EWat LLWG MSKA MWts NPer WMAq
	'Perry's Double White' (H)	EWat LLWG NPer
	'Perry's Double Yellow' (H)	LLWG MSKA
	'Perry's Dwarf Red' (H)	LLWG MSKA
	'Perry's Fire Opal' (H)	EWat LLWG NPer
	'Perry's Orange Sunset' (H)	LLWG MSKA
	'Perry's Pink' (H)	WMAq
	'Perry's Red Bicolor' (H)	LLWG
	'Perry's Red Glow' (H)	LLWG MSKA
	'Perry's Red Star' (H)	EWat MSKA
	'Perry's White Star' (H)	LLWG
	'Perry's Yellow Sensation'	see *N.* 'Yellow Sensation'
	'Peter Slocum' (H)	CBen EWat
	'Phoebus' (H)	CBen
	'Picciola' (H)	LLWG
	'Pink Beauty' (H)	LLWG
	'Pink Domino' (H)	MSKA
	'Pink Grapefruit' (H)	LLWG XBlo
	'Pink Opal' (H)	EWat LLWG
	'Pink Peony' (H)	EWat MSKA
	'Pink Pom-pom' (H) **new**	LLWG
	'Pink Pumpkin' (H)	EWat LLWG MSKA
	'Pink Sensation' (H)	CBen EWat LLWG MSKA NPer SLon WMAq
	'Pink Sparkle' (H)	EWat LLWG
	'Pink Starlet' (H)	EWat
	'Pink Sunrise' (H)	EWat LLWG MSKA
	'Pinwaree' (H)	LLWG
	'Pöstlingberg' (H)	LLWG MSKA
	'Princess Elizabeth' (H)	LLWG SVic
	'Purple Fantasy' (H) **new**	LLWG
	'Pygmaea Alba'	see *N. tetragona*
§	'Pygmaea Helvola' (H) ♀H7	CBen CWat EWat LCro LLWG LOPS MSKA MWts NPer SLon SVic WMAq
	'Pygmaea Rubis' (H)	WMAq
	'Pygmaea Rubra' (H)	CBen CWat EWat LCro LLWG LOPS MSKA MWts NPer SVic WMAq
	'Queen of Siam' (T/D)	LLWG
	'Queen of the Whites' (H) **new**	LLWG
	'Radiant Red' (H)	LLWG
	'Ray Davies' (H)	CBen LLWG
	'Razzberry' (H) **new**	LLWG
	'Red Cup' (T/N)	LLWG
	'Red Paradise' (H)	LLWG MSKA
	'Red Spider' (H)	CWat EWat LLWG MSKA NPer SVic
	'Reflected Flame' (H)	EWat LLWG
	'Rembrandt' misapplied	see *N.* 'Météor'
	'René Gérard' (H)	CBen LLWG MSKA MWts NPer WMAq
	'Rosanna Supreme' (H)	LLWG
	'Rose Arey' (H)	CBen EWat LCro LOPS MSKA NPer WMAq
	'Rose Magnolia' (H)	CWat
	'Rosennymphe' (H)	CBen MSKA NPer WMAq
	'Rosy Morn' (H)	CBen LLWG MSKA
	'Seignouretti' (H)	LLWG
	'Shady Lady' (H)	LLWG MSKA
	'Siam Purple 1' (H)	LLWG
	'Siam Purple 2' (H)	LLWG
	'Sioux' (H)	CBen LLWG MSKA NPer SVic WMAq XBlo
	'Sirius' (H)	CBen LLWG MSKA
	'Snow Princess' (H)	EWat
	'Snowflake' (H) **new**	LLWG
	'Solfatare' (H)	EWat LLWG
	'Splendida' (H)	WMAq
	'Star of Siam' (T/D) **new**	LLWG
	'Starbright' (H)	EWat LLWG
	'Starburst' (H)	LLWG MSKA
	'Steven Strawn' (H)	LLWG
	'Sultan' (H)	MSKA
	'Sunny Pink' (H)	CBen EWat LLWG MSKA
	'Sunrise'	see *N.* 'Odorata Sulphurea Grandiflora'
	'Superba' (H)	CBen
	'Tan-khwan' (H)	LLWG
	'Tanzanite' (T/D) **new**	LLWG
§	***tetragona*** (H)	CWat EWat LCro LLWG LOPS NPer WMAq
	- 'Alba'	see *N. tetragona*
	- 'Johann Pring'	see *N.* 'Joanne Pring'
	'Texas Dawn' (H)	CBen CWat EWat LLWG MSKA SLon WMAq XBlo
	'Thomas O'Brian' (H)	LLWG
	'Tropic Punch' (T/D) **new**	LLWG
	'Tuberosa Flavescens'	see *N.* 'Marliacea Chromatella'
	'Tuberosa Richardsonii' (H)	CBen MSKA NPer
	'Turicensis'	see *N.* 'Odorata Turicensis'
	'Ultra Violet' (T/D) **new**	LLWG
	'Venusta' (H)	EWat
	'Vésuve' (H)	LLWG MSKA
	'Virginalis' (H)	CBen LLWG MSKA NPer WMAq
	'Virginia' (H)	LLWG
§	'W.B. Shaw' (H)	CBen MSKA NPer WMAq
	'Walter Pagels' (H)	EWat LLWG MWts WMAq
	'Wanvisa' (H)	LCro LLWG LOPS
	'Weymouth Red' (H)	CBen
	'White Star' (H) **new**	LLWG
	'White Sultan' (H)	CWat LLWG MSKA
	'William Doogue' (H)	MSKA

	'William Falconer' (H)	CBen LLWG MSKA NPer
	'Wood's Blue Goddess' (T/D) **new**	LLWG
	'Wow' (H)	MSKA
	'Yellow Princess' (H)	EWat
	'Yellow Queen' (H)	LLWG MSKA
§	'Yellow Sensation' (H)	CBen
	'Yul Ling' (H)	EWat LLWG
	'Zeus'	MSKA
	'Ziyu' (H)	EWat

Nymphoides (*Menyanthaceae*)

	indica	XBlo
	peltata	CBen CBod CHab CWat EWat LCro LLWG LOPS MSKA NPer SVic WMAq WPnP XLum

Nyssa ✿ (*Nyssaceae*)

	sp.	LPra
	aquatica	CBcs IDee MBlu
	leptophylla	NLar SBir WPGP
	shweliensis FMWJ 13122	WCru
	sinensis	CBcs CMCN CRos CTho ELan EPfP IDee LRHS MAsh MBlu MPkF NLar SBir SPer
	- 'Inferno'	CTho EBee SPoG
	- 'Jim Russell' ♀H5	EBee SBir WPGP
	- Nymans form	CRos SBir
	sylvatica	Widely available
	- 'Autumn Cascades'	CJun CRos ELan EPfP LRHS MAsh MBlu SBir SSta
	- var. ***biflora***	SSta
	- Bulk's form	SSta
	- 'Haymen's Red'	see *N. sylvatica* RED RAGE
	- 'Isabel Grace'	CRos EPfP LRHS MAsh SBir
	- 'Jermyns Flame'	CRos EPfP LRHS MAsh NLar SBir
	- JOLLY ('Yiping') (v)	MPkF
	- 'Lakeside Weeper'	EBee LRHS SBir
	- 'Miss Scarlet' (f)	NLar SBir SSta
	- 'Pendula'	SBir
§	- RED RAGE ('Haymanred')	EPfP LRHS MAsh MPkF SBir
	- 'Red Red Wine'	NLar SBir
	- 'Sheffield Park'	CRos LRHS MAsh SBir SLim SPer
	- 'Valley Scorcher'	NLar
	- 'Wildfire'	LRHS MPkF SBir SGol
	- 'Windsor'	CRos EPfP LRHS MAsh NLar SBir
	- 'Wisley Bonfire' (m) ♀H6	CJun CRos ELan EPfP LRHS MAsh NLar NRHS SBir SMad SPoG SSta WPGP

O

Oakesiella see *Uvularia*

Ochagavia (*Bromeliaceae*)

	carnea	WCot
	- RCB RA S-2	LSou
	elegans	CFil WCot
§	***litoralis***	SArc SMad
*	***rosea***	SPlb

Ochna (*Ochnaceae*)

	serrulata	CCCN

Ocimum (*Lamiaceae*)

	'African Blue'	CBod CSpe ENfk GPoy LSou MHer SPhx SPoG SRms
§	× ***africanum***	ENfk MNHC
	- 'Lime'	ENfk MNHC
§	- 'Perpetuo'PBR (v)	ENfk
	- PESTO PERPETUO	see *O.* × *africanum*
	- 'Siam Queen'	MHer SRms
	basilicum	GPoy NPri SRms XAbr
	- 'Anise'	see *O. basilicum* 'Horapha'
	- 'Ararat'	SRms
	- 'Aristotle' **new**	SRms
I	- 'British Basil' **new**	SRms
	- ***camphorata***	see *O. kilimandscharicum*
	- 'Christmas' **new**	SRms
	- 'Cinnamon'	ENfk MNHC SRms XAbr
	- 'Crimson King'PBR **new**	MHer SRms
	- 'Dark Opal'	ENfk SRms
	- 'Genovese'	CRav MHer MNHC
	- 'Glycyrrhiza'	see *O. basilicum* 'Horapha'
	- 'Green Globe'	SRms
	- 'Green Ruffles'	EPfP SRms
	- 'Holy'	see *O. tenuiflorum*
§	- 'Horapha'	ENfk MNHC
*	- 'Horapha Nanum'	ENfk SRms
	- 'Lemonade' ♀H1c **new**	SRms
	- 'Magic Mountain'	SPoG
	- 'Magic White'	SPoG
	- 'Mrs Burns' Lemon' ♀H1c	EKin MCtn SRms
	- 'Napoletano'	ENfk SRms
	- 'Pluto' ♀H1c **new**	EUnw
	- 'Puck' **new**	SRms
	- var. ***purpurascens*** 'Purple Ruffles'	ENfk EPfP LCro SRms
	- - 'Red Rubin'	SRms
	- var. ***purpurascens*** × ***kilimandscharicum***	CRav CSpe GPoy
	- 'Sweet Genovese'	SVic
	- 'Thai'	see *O. basilicum* 'Horapha'
	× ***citriodorum***	see *O.* × *africanum*
§	***kilimandscharicum***	GPoy
	minimum	ENfk MHer MNHC SRms
	sanctum	see *O. tenuiflorum*
	'Spice'	ENfk
§	***tenuiflorum***	GPoy MNHC SPre XAbr

Odontonema (*Acanthaceae*)

	schomburgkianum	CCCN
	tubaeforme	CCCN

Oemleria (*Rosaceae*)

	cerasiformis	CBcs CHGN CJun CTri EBtc EPfP LEdu LRHS MGil MMuc WCot WGwG WSHC

Oenanthe (*Apiaceae*)

	fistulosa	LLWG MSKA
	javanica	LEdu
	- 'Flamingo' (v)	CBod CWat EBee ELan EWat GCal LEdu LLWG MSKA MWts NBro WMAq XLum
	lachenalii	EBWF LLWG
	pimpinelloides	CHab LLWG

Oenothera ✿ (*Onagraceae*)

	sp.	ESps MHol
§	***acaulis***	CSpe GKev MNrw WCot
§	- 'Aurea'	XLum
	- 'Lutea'	see *O. acaulis* 'Aurea'
	'Apricot Delight'	CPla NPnk SGbt SPad WHar WMoo
	berlandieri	see *Calylophus berlandieri*

§ ***biennis***	CFis EBWF ELan ENfk GAbr GPoy LOPS MHer MNHC NBro SPhx SRms WBrk WHer WSFF
'Blood Orange'	GEdr
childsii	see *O. speciosa*
cinaeus	see *O. fruticosa* subsp. *glauca*
'Colin Porter'	WMoo
'Crown Imperial'	CChe CMac LSou MArl SHar SLon
CROWN OF GOLD ('Lishal')	LRHS
§ ***elata*** subsp. ***hookeri***	EWes NBre
'Finlay's Fancy'	WCru
§ ***fruticosa***	NLar SPlb
- 'African Sun'PBR	CRos ECtt ETMg LRHS MMrt NRHS SRot
- 'Camel' (v)	MNrw NEoE XLum
- FIREWORKS	see *O. fruticosa* 'Fyrverkeri'
§ - 'Fyrverkeri'	CBcs CMea CRos ECtt GMaP GMcL GWyn LEdu LRHS MRav NRHS SCob SMad SPer SWvt XLum
§ - subsp. ***glauca***	CElw CFis EPfP ILea MHer SRms
- - 'Erica Robin' (v)	CChe CDor CRos ECtt EHoe GBin LPla LRHS LSou MNrw MRav NEgg NGdn NRHS SMad SRot SWvt WCot WHoo
- - 'Longest Day'	MBrN
- - SOLSTICE	see *O. fruticosa* subsp. *glauca* 'Sonnenwende'
§ - - 'Sonnenwende'	CBre CElw CRos ILea IMou LRHS MMrt NEoE NLar NRHS WMoo XLum
- HIGHLIGHT	see *O. fruticosa* 'Hoheslicht'
§ - 'Hoheslicht'	EBee
- 'Lady Brookeborough'	MRav
- 'Michelle Ploeger'	NBre XSen
- 'Silberblatt' (v)	EBee
- 'Yellow River'	CElw EBee
- 'Youngii'	EPfP MMuc SEND
'Give-me-Sunshine'	SLon WMoo
glabra Miller	see *O. biennis*
hookeri	see *O. elata* subsp. *hookeri*
kunthiana	ECha WMoo
- 'Glowing Magenta'	SPoG
LEMON DROP ('Innoeno131'PBR)	CRos LRHS NRHS
'Lemon Sunset'	EHoe LSou WHar WMoo
linearis	see *O. fruticosa*
§ ***macrocarpa*** ♀H5	CBod CHab EBee ECha ELan EPfP EShb GMcL LPmr LRHS MBel MHer MMuc MNHC SEND SPer SPhx SPlb SPoG SRms SRot SVic SWvt WCAu WGwG WHar WHoo WMoo XLum XSen
- subsp. ***fremontii*** 'Silver Wings'	SPhx
- subsp. ***incana***	CSpe SPhx
- - 'Silver Blade'	LLHF
missouriensis	see *O. macrocarpa*
oakesiana	SPhx
odorata misapplied	see *O. stricta*
odorata Hook. & Arn.	see *O. biennis*
odorata Jacquin	XLum
- cream-flowered	CSpe
organensis	EBee MNrw
pallida	CFis GJos
- 'Innocence'	LCro
§ ***perennis***	MPie SRms WThu XLum
pilosella	IMou
pumila	see *O. perennis*
rosea	XLum
§ ***speciosa***	GCal MMuc SEND SRms XLum
* - 'Alba'	EBee EWes XSen
- var. ***childsii***	see *O. speciosa*
- 'Pink Petticoats'	ECha LSun NPer
- 'Rosea'	SPlb
- 'Siskiyou'	CBcs CRos ECtt ELan EPfP ILea LEdu LRHS MHol MNrw NRHS SCob SCoo SPer SPhm SPoG WGwG WHil XLum
- TWILIGHT ('Turner01'PBR) (v)	CAbb ECtt ILea LRHS LSou NEoE SCob SHar
§ ***stricta***	CMea EBWF GCal MNrw WGwG
- 'Sulphurea'	CDor CMea EAJP ELan GCal IFro LCro LRHS NPer SPhx
'Summer Sun'	GMcL LRHS NRHS WCAu
'Sunny Delight'	CBod ECtt LBuc MHol
taraxacifolia	see *O. acaulis*
tetragona	see *O. fruticosa* subsp. *glauca*
- var. ***fraseri***	see *O. fruticosa* subsp. *glauca*
versicolor 'Sunset Boulevard'	CRos CSpe CTsd EAJP ESps GCal LPmr LRHS NRHS SPer WMoo XLum

Olea (*Oleaceae*)

sp.	ETod LPra
europaea (F)	Widely available
- 'Arbequina' (F)	ETod SBig
§ - 'Cipressino' (F)	ETod SBig
- 'El Greco' (F)	CBcs
- 'Fastigiata'	EBee LRHS NPri
- 'Frantoio' (F)	ETod SBig
- 'Hojiblanca' (F)	SBig
- 'Leccino' (F)	ETod LMaj SBig
- 'Manzanillo' (F)	ETod
- 'Maurino' (F)	SBig
- 'Peace' (F)	CDoy
- 'Pendolino' (F)	SBig
- 'Picual' (F)	ETod SBig
- 'Pyramidalis'	see *O. europaea* 'Cipressino'

Olearia ✿ (*Asteraceae*)

arborescens 'Moondance' (v)	LRHS SCob
argophylla	CExl
avicenniifolia	CMac
canescens	CPne
× ***capillaris***	CBcs
§ ***cheesemanii***	CExl GMcL NLar NWad SVen
- compact	LRHS
erubescens	LRHS
erubescens × ***ilicifolia***	SVen
gunniana	see *O. phlogopappa*
× ***haastii***	Widely available
§ 'Henry Travers'	CCCN CExl EPfP GCal SVen
ilicifolia	CRos EPfP LRHS
insignis	see *Pachystegia insignis*
lacunosa	WHor WPGP
lepidophylla	NLar
macrodonta ♀H4	Widely available
- 'Major'	CCCN NLar SCob
- 'Minor'	CCCN CMac EBee ELan EPfP GCal SPlb SRms WPGP WSpi
§ × ***matthewsii***	SPer
× ***mollis*** misapplied	see *O.* × *matthewsii*
× ***mollis*** (Kirk) Cockayne	CMac CRos EBee LRHS WKif
- 'Zennorensis' ♀H3	CBcs CCCN
nummularifolia	CBcs CCCN CTri CTsd ELan EPfP GBin GKin LRHS NLar SBod SPer SVen SWvt
odorata	CPne

× ***oleifolia*** 'Waikariensis'	CExl CRos GKin LRHS SEND SLon WCFE
paniculata	CCCN CRos CTri CTsd EPfP LRHS MMuc SEND SRms SVen
§ ***phlogopappa***	CTri SVen WSHC
- 'Comber's Blue'	CBcs CCCN CRos ELan EPfP GKin LRHS MMuc SAko SCob SPer WGrn
§ - 'Comber's Pink'	CBcs CBod CCCN CExl CRos ELan EPfP GKin LRHS MAsh MMuc NPer SAko SCob SEle SPer SPoG WGrn WKif WSHC
- 'Rosea'	see *O. phlogopappa* 'Comber's Pink'
ramulosa	CCCN CExl
- 'Blue Stars'	CMac LRHS SRms
rani misapplied	see *O. cheesemanii*
× ***scilloniensis*** misapplied	see *O. stellulata* DC.
× ***scilloniensis*** ambig.	CBcs CRos EWld GMcL LRHS MAsh MGil SCob SPoG WKif
× ***scilloniensis*** Dorrien-Smith 🏆^{H3}	CCCN MMuc
- 'Master Michael' 🏆^{H3}	CCCN CCht CRos CTri ELon EWld LRHS NLar SPer SPoG WCFE WGrn WSHC
semidentata misapplied	see *O.* 'Henry Travers'
solandri	CBod CCCN CMac EHoe EPPr IDee LRHS NLar SEND
- 'Aurea'	CBcs
'Stardust'	LRHS SPlb SVen
stellulata misapplied	see *O. phlogopappa*
§ ***stellulata*** DC.	CCht CExl CMac CSBt EPfP MAsh SLim SPer
- 'Michael's Pride'	CExl
traversii	CBcs CBod CCCN CRos CSBt CTsd EPfP LRHS SEND SLim WHer
- 'Compacta' **new**	CCCN
- 'Tweedledee' (v)	SEND
- 'Tweedledum' (v)	CBod CCCN EHoe
- 'Variegata' (v)	CBcs
virgata	CCCN NLar
- var. ***laxiflora***	WHer
- var. ***lineata***	MMuc NLar SEND WHer WSHC
- - 'Dartonii'	CBcs CRos LRHS NLar SPlb SSta SVen

Oligoneuron see *Solidago*

Oligostachyum (*Poaceae*)

lubricum	see *Semiarundinaria lubrica*

olive see *Olea europaea*

Olsynium (*Iridaceae*)

biflorum	GEdr
§ ***douglasii*** 🏆^{H5}	CBro ELon EPot GEdr LLHF NHpl NRHS NRya NSla SBrt
- 'Album'	EBee ELon EPot EWes LLHF MNrw NRya NSla SBrt WWFP
- var. ***inflatum***	EWes
§ ***junceum***	CSpe SPlb WKif
trinerve B&SWJ 10459	WCru

Omphalodes ✿ (*Boraginaceae*)

'Blue Eyes'	EBee ELon GEdr MHol WCot
cappadocica 🏆^{H5}	CMac EPfP EPot EWld GBin IFoB NBro NPer NWad SRms WBrk
- 'Alba'	SPoG
- 'Cherry Ingram' 🏆^{H5}	Widely available
- 'Lilac Mist'	EBee NPnk SRms SWvt
- 'Starry Eyes'	Widely available
§ ***linifolia*** 🏆^{H3}	CSpe GWyn MCot SPhx
- ***alba***	see *O. linifolia*
luciliae	GKev
nitida	CSpe EWes EWld GWyn IMou LLHF MMuc MNrw NQui
verna	CBod CRos CTri EBee ECha ELan EPPr EPfP EWTr GAbr GEdr GJos GMaP GWyn LRHS MCot MNrw NChi NLar NRHS SCob SPer SPlb SPoG WBor WCAu WFar
- 'Alba'	CBod CBre CMac EBee ECha ELan EPPr EPfP GAbr GEdr GMaP MBel MCot MNrw NBid NChi NGdn NLar SBod SCob SPer SRms SWvt WBor WBrk WPnP
- 'Elfenauge'	EBee GMaP IMou NLar WCot
I - 'Grandiflora'	WCot

Omphalogramma (*Primulaceae*)

delavayi	EPot GEdr

Oncostema see *Scilla*

onion see *Allium cepa*; also AGM Vegetables Section

Onixotis (*Colchicaceae*)

stricta	see *Wurmbea stricta*

Onobrychis (*Papilionaceae*)

viciifolia	CWld EBWF SPhx

Onoclea ✿ (*Onocleaceae*)

sensibilis 🏆^{H6}	Widely available
- copper-leaved	CJun EBee EPfP EWes MMoz WPGP
- 'Rotstiel'	EBee

Ononis (*Papilionaceae*)

cristata	WAbe
natrix **new**	SPhx
spinosa	CDor EBWF IMou MHer WSpi

Onopordum (*Asteraceae*)

acanthium	CDor CRos ECha ELan ENfk GAbr GMaP GPoy LRHS LSun MWat NBid NGBl NRHS SHar SPhx WSpi
algeriense	EBee
arabicum	see *O. nervosum*
boissierianum **new**	EBee
bracteatum	EBee
cyprium **new**	SPhx
illyricum	SPhx
messeniacum **new**	WHil
§ ***nervosum*** 🏆^{H7}	CSpe SEND

Onosma (*Boraginaceae*)

alborosea	ECha ECre ELan GCal IMou SEND WKif
nana	CPBP CTal EPot WAbe WOld

Onosmodium (*Boraginaceae*)

molle **new**	SBrt

Onychium ✿ (*Pteridaceae*)

contiguum	WCot
japonicum	CBdn CExl CRos EBee EFer LEdu LRHS MRav NLos NRHS SPlb WAbe WCot

Ophiopogon ✿ (*Asparagaceae*)

BWJ 8244 from Vietnam	WCru
from India	GCal

	'Black Dragon'	see *O. planiscapus* 'Nigrescens'
	bodinieri	EShb EWes LEdu
	- B&L 12505	EBee EPPr MMoz
	caulescens B&SWJ 8230	WCru
	- B&SWJ 11813	WCru
	aff. ***caulescens*** B&SWJ 11287	WCru
	- HWJ 590	WCru
	chingii	EPPr EWes GCal IMou LEdu WCot
*	- 'Crispum'	EBee
	clarkei	MMoz
	clavatus KWJ 12267	WCru
	formosanus B&SWJ 3659	WCru
	'Gin-ryu'	see *Liriope spicata* 'Gin-ryu'
	graminifolius	see *Liriope muscari*
	'Hosoba Kokuryu'	CAbb EShb LLHF LRHS NEoE WOut
	intermedius	CSpe EPPr EShb WCot
	- GWJ 9387	WCru
§	- 'Argenteomarginatus' (v)	EWes
	- 'Variegatus'	see *O. intermedius* 'Argenteomarginatus'
§	***jaburan***	CMac EBee LEdu NPnk WMoo WPtf
	- 'Variegatus'	see *O. jaburan* 'Vittatus'
§	- 'Vittatus' (v)	ELan EWes LEdu WCot
	japonicus	CMac CTsd EBee EPPr EShb LEdu LRHS SCob SGol XLum XSen
	- B&SWJ 1871	WCru
	- 'Albus'	EPri
	- 'Compactus'	WPGP
	- 'Gyoku-Ryu'	EBee GCal
	- 'Kigimafukiduma'	CExl CMac MRav NGdn SGol SPad
	- 'Kyoto'	EPPr
	- 'Lengteng Giant'	LEdu
	- 'Minor'	CKno ELon EPPr LRHS NLar SCob WPGP XLum
	- 'Nanus Variegatus' (v)	CFil EBee
	- 'Nippon'	EHoe EPPr NGdn
	- 'Silver Dragon' (v)	EPPr WCFE
*	- 'Variegatus' (v)	CDTJ CMac LEdu SRms
	aff. ***latifolius*** KWJ 12031	WCru
	malcolmsonii B&SWJ 7271 new	WCru
	parviflorus GWJ 9387	WCru
	- HWJK 2093	WCru
	planiscapus	CExl CKno CSpe ECha EPPr NBro NWsh SPtp WMoo
*	- 'Albovariegatus' (v)	WFar
	- 'Black Beard'	CKno EUJe GWyn LRHS MAsh NRHS SHar WFar
	- 'Black Needle'	EBee
	- 'Black Smaragd'	EBee
	- 'Green Dragon'	CRos LRHS NRHS
	- f. ***leucanthus***	EPPr WCot
	- 'Little Tabby' (v)	CFil CMil EBee MMoz WCot WGrn WHal WOut WSHC
§	- 'Nigrescens' 🏆H5	Widely available
	scaber B&SWJ 1842	WCru
	- B&SWJ 3655	WCru
	'Spring Gold'	EShb

Oplopanax (*Araliaceae*)

horridus B&SWJ 9551	WCru
japonicus	WCru

Opopanax (*Apiaceae*)

chironium	SPhx
- PAB 845	LEdu WPGP
- PAB 872 new	WPGP

Opuntia (*Cactaceae*)

	angustata	see *O. phaeacantha*
	arenaria SB 964 from El Paso County, Texas	CCac
	atrispina DJF 1020	CCac
	aurea	CCac
	- red-flowered, from St George, Utah	CCac
	aureispina SB 1002	CCac
	basilaris	CCac
	- SB 1819 from Yucca Valley, California	CCac
	- SB 1976 from Silver Peak, Nevada	CCac
	- from Tonopah, Nevada	CCac
	- 'Berlin'	CCac
	- var. ***cordata*** new	SPlb
	bentonii from Galveston, Texas	CCac
	'Budapest'	CCac
	camanchica	see *O. phaeacantha*
	chisosensis SB 992 from Brewster County, Texas	CCac
	chlorotica	CCac
	- 'Kurt'	CCac
	'Claude Arno'	CCac
	× ***columbiana*** from Wishram, Washington State	CCac
	- 'Smithwick'	CCac
	compressa	see *O. humifusa*
	cylindrarticulata	see *Cumulopuntia boliviana* subsp. *dactylifera*
	cymochila	see *O. tortispina*
	echinocarpa	see *Cylindropuntia echinocarpa*
	elata	SChr
§	***engelmannii***	CCac SChr
	- from Beeville, Texas	CCac
	- from Carrizozo, New Mexico	CCac
	- var. ***engelmannii*** DJF 1400	CCac
	- - 'Natural Bridge'	CCac
*	- f. ***inerme***	CCac
*	- var. ***sandia*** HK 1809	CCac
	erinacea var. ***utahensis***	see *O. polyacantha* var. *erinacea*
§	***ficus-indica***	CCac SPlb
	fragilis	CCac SPlb XSen
	- from Black Canyon, Gunnison, Colorado	CCac
	glomerata	see *Maihueniopsis glomerata*
§	***humifusa***	CCac CDTJ SChr XLum XSen
	- from Monmouth County, New Jersey	CCac
	- 'Louisiana'	CCac
	joconostle	see *O. ficus-indica*
	lindheimeri	see *O. engelmannii*
	linguiformis	see *O. engelmannii*
	mackensenii	see *O. macrorhiza*
	macrocentra	CBlu CCac
	- SB 103 from Rincon, New Mexico	CCac
	- SB 911 from Orogrande, New Mexico	CCac
	- SB 994 from Eddy County, New Mexico	CCac
§	***macrorhiza***	CBlu CCac
	- DJF 720 from Kenton, Oklahoma	CCac

- DJF 1299 from Reagan County, Texas CCac
- DJF 86512 from Huerfano County, Colorado CCac
- 'Apricot' CCac
- 'Viola' CCac

megapotamica BKN 124 from La Cumbrecita, Argentina CCac

monacantha SEND

orbiculata from Seymour, Texas CCac

§ ***phaeacantha*** CCac SChr
- DJF 162 CCac
- DJF 913 CCac
- DJF 970.18 from Fremont County, Colorado CCac
- DJF 1139 from Albuquerque, New Mexico CCac
- NNS 99-264 **new** WCot
- SB 1070 from Larimer County CCac
- from White Canyon, Wayne County, Utah CCac
- * - var. ***albispina*** MUG 177 from Mohave County, Arizona CCac
- 'Judge' CCac
- var. ***major*** DJF 1138 CCac
- - DJF 1139 from Albuquerque, New Mexico CCac
- - NNS 95-285 WCot
- - SB 1092 from Santa Fe, New Mexico CCac
- - SB 1763 from Manzano Mountains, New Mexico CCac
- 'Minor' CCac
- 'Pueblitos' CCac
- 'Salmonea' CCac
- 'Sunrise' CCac

phaeacantha* × *pottsii CCac

pisciformis CCac

pollardii see *O. humifusa*

polyacantha CCac SChr SPlb
- SB 912 CCac
- SB 928 from Wyoming CCac
- SB 1765 from Manzano Mountains, New Mexico CCac
- SB 1911 from Lybrook, New Mexico CCac
- from Alberta, Canada CCac
- from Bicknell, Utah CCac
- from Blind Valley, Millard County, Utah CCac
- from Chaffee County, Colorado CCac
- * - from Januskowetz, Canada CCac
- from North Dakota CCac
- from Trout Creek Pass, Colorado CCac
- from Wyoming CCac
- 'Carmin' XSen
- 'Crystal Tide' CCac
- * - ***eranthemum*** CCac
- § - var. ***erinacea*** CCac SChr WCot
- - from St George, Utah CCac
- - from Torrey, Utah CCac
- - from Yucca Valley, California CCac
- § - var. ***hystricina*** CCac
- - DJF 1001 CCac
- - DJF 1338 CCac
- - DJF 1339 from Belen, New Mexico CCac
- - SB 478 CCac
- - SB 485 from Marble Canyon, Arizona CCac
- - 'Cactusmannia' CCac
- - 'Hagen Miniature' CCac
- - 'Halblech' CCac
- - 'Hamm' CCac
- - 'Heather' CCac
- - 'Heidelberg' CCac
- - 'Thornless Judge' CCac
- 'Linz' CCac
- * - 'Nigra' CCac
- 'Oettingen' CCac
- var. ***polyacantha*** CCac
- - from Laguna Pueblo, New Mexico CCac
- 'Rom' CCac
- 'Wibke' CCac

pottsii DJF 1441 from Albuquerque, New Mexico CCac
- DJF 1447 from Albuquerque, New Mexico CCac
- DJF 1394 from Hildago County, New Mexico CCac
- from Albuquerque, New Mexico CCac
- 'Bochum' CCac
- * - var. ***montana*** DJF 667 CCac

rhodantha see *O. polyacantha* var. *hystricina*

salmiana SEND

* ***sandiana*** CCac
- DJF 475A CCac

sanguinocula DJF 801 CCac

santarita CCac

spinosior see *Cylindropuntia spinosior*

stenopetala HK 1985 CCac

stricta CCac

'Super Rutila 2' CCac

tardospina see *O. engelmannii*

§ ***tortispina*** DJF 1139.38 CCac
- from Gaza County, Colorado CCac

orange, sour or Seville see *Citrus* × *aurantium* Sour Orange Group

orange, sweet see *Citrus* × *aurantium* Sweet Orange Group

Orbea (*Apocynaceae*)

speciosa LToo

Orbexilum (*Papilionaceae*)

pedunculatum var. ***psoralioides*** SBrt SPhx

Orchis (*Orchidaceae*)

elata see *Dactylorhiza elata*

foliosa see *Dactylorhiza foliosa*

fuchsii see *Dactylorhiza fuchsii*

maculata see *Dactylorhiza maculata*

	maderensis	see *Dactylorhiza foliosa*
	majalis	see *Dactylorhiza majalis*
§	***mascula***	WHer

oregano see *Origanum vulgare*

Oreocharis (*Gesneriaceae*)

	aurea B&SWJ 11718	WCru

Oreomyrrhis (*Apiaceae*)

	argentea	CSpe

Oreopanax ✿ (*Araliaceae*)

	capitatus	CFil
	dactylifolius	WCot
	floribundus	see *O. incisus*
§	***incisus*** B&SWJ 10669	WCru
	xalapensis	CFil
	- B&SWJ 10444	WCru

Oreopteris ✿ (*Thelypteridaceae*)

§	***limbosperma***	CBdn EFer

Oreostemma (*Compositae*)

	alpigenum var. ***alpigenum***	LLHF
	- var. ***haydenii***	LLHF

Origanum ✿ (*Lamiaceae*)

	from Kalamata, Greece	SEND
	acutidens	XSen
	amanum ♀H3	CPBP EWes NRHS NSla SBch WAbe
	- var. ***album***	SBch WAbe
	'Amethyst Falls'	CWCL WTor XSen
	'Barbara Tingey'	CTal EPot EWes ITim MNrw SRms WCFE
	'Bristol Cross'	CTal EBee ECtt EPPr LEdu MHer WTor XSen
	'Buckland'	ECtt ELon EPot WAbe WSHC
	caespitosum	see *O. vulgare* 'Nanum'
§	***calcaratum***	LLHF
	creticum	see *O. vulgare* subsp. *hirtum*
	dictamnus	EPot GPoy LLHF MHer WAbe WOld XEll XSen
	'Dingle Fairy'	ECtt EPot EWTr EWes GJos MCot MHer SBch SRot SWvt WMoo WSpi XSen
	ehrenbergii	XSen
	'Emma Stanley'	CPBP WAbe
	'Frank Tingey'	LLHF
	'French'	SRms
	'Gold Splash'	EPfP WMoo
	'Golden Narrow'	CRos LRHS NRHS
	heracleoticum L.	see *O. vulgare* subsp. *hirtum*
	heracleoticum ambig.	XAbr
	'Hot and Spicy'	CBod ENfk SRms XSen
§	× ***hybridinum***	WAbe
	'Kent Beauty' ♀H4	CMea CSpe CWCL EBee ECtt ELan EPfP EShb EWTr IMou IPot LRHS LSou MBel MHer NRHS SPhm SPhx SWvt WAbe WFar WHoo WKif WSHC WSpi WTor XSen
	laevigatum ♀H7	ELan MHer NBro NPer WCot WKif WMoo WSHC XSen
I	- 'Aromaticum'	IMou
	- 'Herrenhausen' ♀H7	Widely available
	- 'Hopleys'	CBod CDor CMea CRos CTri EAJP EBee ECha EHrv ELan EPfP IRob LEdu LRHS MCot MHer MHol MMuc MRav MWat NLar NRHS SEND SPer SPhx SRms WHoo WSHC XSen
	- 'Purple Charm'	EDAr SRms
	majorana	CHab ENfk MHer MJak MNHC SRms SVic
I	- 'Aureum'	GKev
	- PAGODA BELLS ('Lizbell'PBR)	CBod XSen
	'Marchants Seedling'	SPhx
	minutiflorum	LLHF
	'Norton Gold'	CBre ECha ECtt MHer NPer
	'Nymphenburg'	XSen
	onites	CBod CHby ENfk MHer MNHC SPlb SRms
	- 'Limelight' new	NWad
	'Pilgrim'	XSen
	pulchellum	see *O.* × *hybridinum*
	'Rosenkuppel' ♀H7	CAby CBod CDor CMea EBee ECha ECtt ELan EPPr GQue LCro LOPS MHer NDov NLar SBch SPer SPhx SPlb SWvt WCAu WMoo XSen
	'Rotkugel'	ELon WCFE XSen
	rotundifolium ♀H4	CMea ELan ELon IMou LEdu MHer SBch WThu
	- hybrid	CMea
	scabrum	EPot
	subsp. ***pulchrum*** - - 'Newleaze'	SBch
	tournefortii	see *O. calcaratum*
	vulgare	CHab CMea CTsd CWld EBWF ESps GJos GMaP GPoy LOPS MHer MMuc MNHC NBro NMir NPol NPri SEND SPlb SRms SVic WArt WHer WSFF XAbr XLum
	- 'Acorn Bank'	CBod ECtt ENfk EWes LEdu MHer MNHC NLar SPoG SRms WHer
	- var. ***album***	WArt
	- 'Aureum' ♀H6	Widely available
	- 'Aureum Crispum'	CBod ECha ENfk GBin GQue GWyn NBid SRms
	- 'Compactum'	CBod CMea EBee ECha ECtt ENfk GCal GPoy LEdu MHer MNHC NPol NRHS NSla SPlb SRms WAbe XLum XSen
	- 'Corinne Tremaine' (v)	WHer
	- 'Country Cream' (v)	CElw EBee ECtt EHoe ENfk EPfP ESps EWes MHer MNHC NGdn NPri SPer SPoG SRms SRot WCFE
§	- 'Gold Tip' (v)	CBod CMea ENfk GJos MCot MHer MHol MNHC SPlb SRms WHer
	- 'Golden Shine'	EHoe EWes
§	- subsp. ***hirtum***	CHby GPoy SPlb XSen
	- - 'Greek'	CBod ENfk MHer MNHC SRms
§	- 'Nanum'	SRms XSen
	- 'Nyamba'	GPoy
	- 'Pink Mist'	MNrw WHoo
	- 'Polyphant' (v)	LSou SRms XSen
	- 'Thumble's Variety'	CBod CMea CRos EBee ECha ECtt EHoe EPfP GCal IRob LRHS MAsh MHer MRav NRHS SWvt WCFE WMoo XLum XSen
	- 'Tomintoul'	GPoy
	- 'Variegatum'	see *O. vulgare* 'Gold Tip'
	- 'White Charm'	CBod EBee NWad

Orixa (*Rutaceae*)

	japonica	CExl NLar WPGP
	- 'Variegata' (v)	NLar

Orlaya (*Apiaceae*)

grandiflora 🏆H7	CAvo CBre CRav CSam CSpe LCro LEdu LOPS LRHS MAvo MCot NPnk SBch SPav SPhx WCot WHal WTor

Ornithogalum (*Asparagaceae*)

arabicum	CBro CCCN GKev IMou LAma SDeJ SRms
arcuatum	WCot
atticum	GKev
baeticum **new**	GKev
balansae	see *O. oligophyllum*
caudatum	see *O. longibracteatum*
cuspidatum	GKev
dubium 🏆H2	CAby CTal ELan
- hybrids	GKev
fimbriatum	GKev
- 'Ai-Petri'	CTal
- 'Oreanda'	CTal
lanceolatum	CTal GKev WCot
§ ***longibracteatum***	SChr WHer
magnum	CAvo CBro CMea CRav CWCL EBee ERCP GBin GKev MCot MNrw SDeJ WCot XEll
- 'Saguramo'	GKev
montanum	GKev
'Mount Everest'	GKev
'Mount Fuji'	GKev
'Namib Gold'	EUJe GKev SDeJ
nanum	see *O. sigmoideum*
narbonense	GKev WCot
nutans 🏆H4	CAby CAvo CHid CMea CWCL EBee EPot GKev LAma LRHS MAvo MMuc MNrw NRHS SDeJ SEND WFar WShi
§ ***oligophyllum***	EPot GKev MNrw
ponticum	WCot
- 'Sochi'	EBee GKev
pyramidale	EBee GKev
- short	SMHy
pyrenaicum	CAvo CSpe ECha WCot WShi XEll
reverchonii	EBee ERCP GKev WShi
saundersiae	EUJe GKev
sibthorpii	see *O. sigmoideum*
§ ***sigmoideum***	GKev
sintenisii	CTal GKev
thyrsoides 🏆H2	CCCN GKev LAma LCro LOPS LRHS SDeJ
umbellatum	CAvo CHab CRos CTri EBee GKev GPoy LAma LRHS MCot MMuc MNrw NRHS SDeJ SEND SRms WShi

Orontium (*Araceae*)

aquaticum	CWat EWat LLWG MSKA MWts NPer SEND WMAq

Orostachys (*Crassulaceae*)

furusei	WHal
iwarenge	CBod CPla CRos GKev SPlb
§ ***spinosa***	CRos EDAr EWes LRHS NRHS SPlb WAbe WCot

Orthophytum (*Bromeliaceae*)

gurkenii	WCot

Orthrosanthus (*Iridaceae*)

chimboracensis JCA 13743	CPou
laxus	CAbb CBod CWCL EAJP ECre LLHF WMoo
multiflorus	CPbh EBee EPri
polystachyus	CAby CTsd LPla MPie WSHC

Orychophragmus (*Brassicaceae*)

violaceus	CCCN

Oryzopsis (*Poaceae*)

hymenoides 'Rimrock'	SPhx
lessoniana	see *Anemanthele lessoniana*
miliacea	CSpe EHoe EPPr MAvo MMoz NSti NWsh SBee SEND SMHy WCot WPGP WSHC WWtn
paradoxa	EPPr

Osbeckia (*Melastomataceae*)

stellata NJM 13.058 **new**	WPGP

Oscularia (*Aizoaceae*)

§ ***deltoides*** 🏆H2	CCCN EShb MSCN SAll SVen

Osmanthus (*Oleaceae*)

armatus	CBcs CJun CMac EPfP IDee LRHS NLar SEND SGol
× ***burkwoodii*** 🏆H5	Widely available
§ ***decorus***	CBcs CHll CMac CTri EBee ELan EPfP MGos MRav NLar SBrt SGol SPer
- 'Angustifolius'	NLar
delavayi 🏆H5	Widely available
- 'Frank Knight'	LRHS MAsh
- 'George Gardner'	CMac SRms
- 'Latifolius'	CExl CJun CRos LRHS MAsh SLon SPoG SWvt
- 'Pearly Gates'	CRos LRHS
forrestii	see *O. yunnanensis*
× ***fortunei***	CBcs CBot CCVT CExl CRos EBee ECrN EPfP LLHF LMaj LRHS
fragrans	CBcs SLon SWvt WPGP
- f. ***aurantiacus***	GBin SCob
§ ***heterophyllus***	CBcs CDul CMac EBee ECrN ELan EPfP ESps EWTr GMcL LMaj MGos MRav NLar SCob SGol SPer SRms SSta SWeb
§ - all gold	EBee ELan EMil EPfP LRHS SPer SPoG
- 'Argenteomarginatus'	see *O. heterophyllus* 'Variegatus'
§ - 'Aureomarginatus' (v)	CBcs CTsd EHoe ELon MGil SCob SLon SRms WCFE
- 'Aureus' misapplied	see *O. heterophyllus* all gold
- 'Aureus' Rehder	see *O. heterophyllus* 'Aureomarginatus'
§ - 'Goshiki' (v) 🏆H5	Widely available
- 'Gulftide'	CDul CRos EPfP LRHS MAsh MGos MJak NLar NRHS SPoG
- 'Kembu' (v)	NLar
- 'Myrtifolius'	CMac NLar
- 'Ōgon'	EPfP NLar
- 'Purple Shaft' 🏆H5	CRos ELan EPfP LRHS MAsh NRHS
- 'Purpureus'	CBcs CDul CMac CTsd EBee ELon MGos MRav MSwo NLar SCob SCoo SEND SGol SLon SPer
- 'Rotundifolius'	CMac NLar
- 'Sasaba'	IArd
- TRICOLOR	see *O. heterophyllus* 'Goshiki'
§ - 'Variegatus' (v) 🏆H5	CBcs CDul CMac CRos CSBt ECrN EHoe ELan ELon EPfP ESps GMcL LRHS LSRN LSou MAsh MGos MRav MSwo NEgg NLar

SEND SGbt SGol SLim SPer SPoG SRms SVen WSHC

ilicifolius see *O. heterophyllus*

serrulatus CBot EPfP LRHS NLar

suavis NLar

§ ***yunnanensis*** ♀H5 CBcs CBot CMCN EBee EPfP MBlu MRav NLar SArc WPGP WSHC

× *Osmarea* see *Osmanthus*

Osmaronia see *Oemleria*

Osmorhiza (*Apiaceae*)

aristata B&SWJ 1607 WCru

Osmunda ✿ (*Osmundaceae*)

sp. CCCN

asiatica EBee WCru

cinnamomea ♀H7 CAby CBod CCCN CKel CRos CWCL EBee EUJe EWes LEdu LRHS MMoz MMuc NBro NLar NRHS

claytoniana CBdn CRos EBee EFer IBal LRHS NBro NLar NRHS WCot XLum

japonica EBee NBro

regalis ♀H6 Widely available

- 'Cristata' ♀H6 CRos GCal LRHS MMoz NBid NRHS SWvt WFib

- 'Purpurascens' Widely available

- var. ***spectabilis*** CCCN CRos GBin LRHS NRHS

- 'Undulata' WFib

Osteospermum (*Asteraceae*)

3D Series **new** SPoG

'African Queen' see *O.* 'Nairobi Purple'

'Akila White Purple Eye' (Akila Series) **new** CRav

BANANA SYMPHONY ('Sekiin47') (Symphony Series) CCCN MBNS

barberae misapplied see *O. jucundum*

barberae (Harv.) Norl. 'Compactum' WFar

BLUE EYED BEAUTY ('Balostlueye') **new** ETMg

'Blue Streak' CCCN CMac

'Buttermilk' ♀H3 CCCN ELan

'Cannington John' CCCN

'Cannington Joyce' CCCN

'Cannington Roy' CBcs CCCN CEnd CMac CRos CSma EBee ECtt ELan ELon EPfP LRHS WFar

caulescens misapplied see *O.* 'White Pim'

ecklonis CBcs CCCN CDTJ CHll CTri NBro NGdn

- var. ***prostratum*** see *O.* 'White Pim'

Flower Power Double Series (d) LBuc

- FLOWERPOWER DOUBLE PINK ('Kleoe10180'[PBR]) (d) EPfP

- FLOWERPOWER DOUBLE WHITE ('Kleoe10179'[PBR]) (d) NPri

'Giles Gilbey' (v) CCCN

'Gweek Variegated' (v) CCCN

'Helen Dimond' LRHS NRHS

'Hopleys' ♀H3 SEND

'Iced Gem' LBuc LRHS NRHS

'In the Pink' LCro LOPS SPoG

'Irish' ECtt EPot

§ ***jucundum*** ♀H3 CCht CMea CTri ECha LRHS LSRN NPer NRHS SPlb SPoG SRms WThu

- 'Blackthorn Seedling' ♀H3 CCCN CMea CWGN ECha

- var. ***compactum*** CBod CMac CPrp CRos CTsd ELan ELon EPfP ETMg GLog GMaP LRHS LSRN MHol NPer NPri SPer SWvt WBrk WHil WWFP

- 'Elliott's Form' WHoo

- 'Langtrees' ♀H3 IRob

- 'Nanum' EDAr

'Keia' (Springstar Series) CCCN

§ 'Lady Leitrim' ♀H3 CBar CBod CCCN CPrp CSma CWGN ECha ECtt ELan ELon EPfP GLog LPmr LRHS LSRN MCot MHol MSpe NPer NPri NRHS SEND SPer SPoG SWvt

'Lisa Traxler' SVen

MILK SYMPHONY ('Seiremi') (Symphony Series) CCCN

§ 'Nairobi Purple' CBcs CBod CCCN CCht CPla CPrp EBee ECtt ELan ETMg MHol NPri SSut SWvt WBor WBrk WFar WHil WHoo

NASINGA CREAM ('Aknam'[PBR]) (Cape Daisy Series) CCCN

ORANGE SYMPHONY ('Seimora'[PBR]) (Symphony Series) CBcs CCCN MBNS

'Pale Face' see *O.* 'Lady Leitrim'

'Peggyi' see *O.* 'Nairobi Purple'

'Pink Gem' EDAr WFar

'Pink Whirls' ♀H3 CCCN

'Port Wine' see *O.* 'Nairobi Purple'

'Serenity Bronze' **new** CRav WBor

'Silver Sparkler' (v) ♀H3 CCCN CDTJ MHer SVen

'Snow Pixie' CBod CWGN EBee ECtt ELan ELon ETMg LCro LOPS SPoG SWvt

SONJA see *O.* (Sunny Series) 'Sunny Sonja'

'Sparkler' CCCN

'Stardust'[PBR] CRos ECtt LBuc LRHS NPer NRHS SCoo SPoG

(Sunny Series) 'Sunny Bronze' CSpe

- 'Sunny Carlos'[PBR] **new** SPoG

- 'Sunny Cherry' **new** SPoG

- 'Sunny Mary'[PBR] SPoG

§ - 'Sunny Sonja'[PBR] SPoG

- 'Sunny Victoria'[PBR] SPoG

- 'Sunny Xena'[PBR] SPoG

I 'Superbum' EBee MHol WFar

'Tauranga' see *O.* 'Whirlygig'

'Tresco Peggy' see *O.* 'Nairobi Purple'

'Tresco Pink' CCCN

'Tresco Purple' see *O.* 'Nairobi Purple'

'Weetwood' ♀H3 CCCN CEnd CPrp CRos ECtt ELan EPot GLog LRHS MHer NRHS SPoG SWvt WFar WTor

'Westwood White' **new** EDAr

§ 'Whirlygig' ♀H3 CCCN

§ 'White Pim' ♀H3 CDTJ CHll NPer SEND

'Wine Purple' see *O.* 'Nairobi Purple'

'Wisley Pink' NEgg

'Zaurak' (Springstar Series) CCCN

'Zulu' (Cape Daisy Series) CCCN

Ostrowskia (*Campanulaceae*)

magnifica EPot GKev

Ostrya (*Betulaceae*)

sp. LPra

carpinifolia	CBcs CCVT CDul CLnd CMCN EBee ELan EMOT EPfP LMaj LPra MBlu MMuc NLar NOra SEND SGol SWvt WTSh
japonica	CDul CMCN

Otatea (*Poaceae*)

aztecorum	ERod

Otholobium (*Papilionaceae*)

glandulosum new	EBee

Othonna (*Asteraceae*)

cheirifolia	see *Hertia cheirifolia*
coronopifolia	SVen

Othonnopsis see *Hertia*

Ourisia (*Plantaginaceae*)

× ***bitternensis*** 'Cliftonville Canary'	WAbe
- 'Cliftonville Crimson'	WAbe
- 'Cliftonville Damask'	WAbe
- 'Cliftonville Ling'	WAbe
- 'Cliftonville Old Rose'	WAbe
- 'Cliftonville Pink'	WAbe
- 'Cliftonville Roset'	WAbe
caespitosa	GAbr
- var. ***gracilis***	MHol
coccinea	CTal EWes EWld GAbr GBin GKev NHpl WHal
'Loch Ewe'	CExl CTal EWld GAbr GKev
macrophylla	CTal NWad
microphylla	WAbe
- f. ***alba***	WAbe
- 'Hollowcliffe'	WAbe
polyantha 'Cliftonville Scarlet'	WAbe
'Snowflake' ♀H5	GAbr IMou NHpl

Oxalis (*Oxalidaceae*)

	from Mount Stewart	WMoo
	acetosella	EBWF GPoy MHer MMuc NMir NQui WHer WShi
	- var. ***rosea***	IFro IMou
	- var. ***subpurpurascens***	WCot
	adenodes	NRog
	adenophylla ♀H4	CExl CRos ELan ELon EPfP EPot GBin GKev GMaP LAma LRHS MJak MPie NEgg NHpl NLar NRHS SDeJ SPoG SRms
	adenophylla × ***enneaphylla***	see *O.* 'Matthew Forrest'
	'Anne Christie'	CPBP NSla
	arenaria F&W 10584	WCot
§	***articulata***	ELan MAvo NPer SEND WSHC XLum
	- 'Alba'	ELan WCot XLum
	- f. ***crassipes*** 'Alba'	WCot
	- 'Festival'	GKev
§	- subsp. ***rubra***	GKev SDeJ
	bowiei	EPot WCot
	- 'Amarantha'	GKev
	brasiliensis	GKev
	compressa	NRog
	convexula	NRog
	'Dark Eye'	EPot
	dentata 'Pot of Gold'	GKev
	deppei	see *O. tetraphylla*
§	***depressa***	EPot EWes GKev LLHF SDeJ
	'Double Trouble' (d)	GKev
	ecklonia*na** var. ***sonderi	NRog
	enneaphylla ♀H4	CElw CRos ELon GBin GEdr GMaP LLHF LRHS NRHS NRya
	- F&W 2715	CPBP
	- 'Alba'	CElw CPBP NRya NSla
	- subsp. ***ibari***	EPPr GEdr NRHS NRya NSla
	- 'Minutifolia'	NRya
*	- 'Minutifolia Rosea'	CPBP
	- 'Rosea'	CElw EPot GKev ITim LLHF NLar NRya NSla
	- 'Sheffield Swan'	CPBP GEdr LLHF NRHS NSla WAbe
	- 'Ute'	GEdr NRya
	'Fanny'	GKev
	flava	NRog
	- white-flowered	GKev
	floribunda misapplied	see *O. articulata*
	fourcadei	NRog
	foveolata	NRog
	gracilis	GKev
	griffithii 'Pink Charm'	GEdr
	- 'Snowflake'	GEdr MMoz
	'Gwen McBride'	CPBP GEdr WAbe
	hedysaroides misapplied	see *O. spiralis* subsp. *vulcanicola*
	hedysaroides Kunth	CCCN
	'Hemswell Knight'	CPBP
	hirta	EPot GKev SBch
	- 'Gothenburg'	EPri GKev ITim NRog
	imbricata	LLHF NRog
	inops	see *O. depressa*
	'Ione Hecker' ♀H4	EPot GCrg GEdr GKev ITim NHpl NLar NRya WOld
*	***karroica***	NHpl WCot
§	***laciniata***	CPBP EPot
	- hybrid	GEdr
	- 'Julia Johnston' new	CPBP
	lactea double-flowered	see *O. magellanica* 'Nelson'
	lasiandra	CCCN GKev
§	***latifolia***	LLHF
	magellanica	GAbr IMou SPlb WMoo
	- 'Flore Pleno'	see *O. magellanica* 'Nelson'
§	- 'Nelson' (d)	EWTr GBin NPer WMoo WPtf
	magnifica	GKev
	massoniana ♀H2	WAbe WCot
§	'Matthew Forrest'	CPBP WCot
§	***megalorrhiza***	NWad SChr
	melanosticta	EPot GEdr GKev LLHF NRog SDeJ WCot
§	- 'Ken Aslet' ♀H2	GKev ITim NHpl SDeJ
	obtusa	EPot GKev MPie
	- apricot-flowered	SDeJ
	oregana	CHid CMac ELon EWld GCal MMoz SPhx WCot WCru
	- 'Bob Haszeldine'	GEdr
	- 'Klamath Ruby'	WSHC
	- f. ***smalliana***	GEdr IMou WCot WCru
	perdicaria	CRos EPot EWes GKev LRHS NRHS NRog WAbe
	- 'Citrino'	WAbe
	polyphylla var. ***heptaphylla***	GEdr
	purpurea 'Ken Aslet'	see *O. melanosticta* 'Ken Aslet'
	regnellii	see *O. triangularis* subsp. *papilionacea*
	'Ridgeway Jewel'	CPBP
	'Ridgeway Sapphire'	CPBP
	rosea misapplied	see *O. articulata* subsp. *rubra*
	semiloba	GCal
	Slack Top hybrids	NSla
	'Slack's 53'	NSla

'Snipe'	NSla
§ ***spiralis***	CCCN GCal LSou
subsp. ***vulcanicola***	
- - 'Burgundy'	NPri
- - 'Sunset Velvet'	CSpe WCot
squamata	LLHF
squamoso-radicosa	see *O. laciniata*
succulenta Barnéoud	see *O. megalorrhiza*
succulenta ambig.	CHll GCal
'Sunny'	ETMg GKev
'Sweet Sue'	CPBP
§ ***tetraphylla***	CExl GKev NPer
- 'Iron Cross'	CHid GKev LAma MPie NLar SDeJ SPlb
'Tina'	CPBP
triangularis	CCCN CExl CPla NPer
- 'Birgit'	GKev SDeJ
- BURGUNDY WINE ('JR Oxburwi') (Xalis Series)	CWGN NPer
- 'Marmer' (v)	GKev
- 'Mijke'	GKev
§ - subsp. ***papilionacea*** ♀H2	GKev LAma
- - 'Atropurpurea'	CSpe SDeJ
- subsp. ***triangularis***	CHid EUJe GKev WWFP
tuberosa	EPfP GPoy LEdu SPoG WHer
- 'Amarillo'	LEdu
- 'Baumi Golden'	LEdu
- 'Polar Bere'	LEdu
- scarlet-flowered, white-eye	LEdu
'Ute'	CPBP NRHS NSla
valdiviensis	CPla NWad
versicolor ♀H2	EPot GEdr GKev ITim NRog SDeJ WHil XEll
- 'Golden Cape'	GKev
vespertilionis Zucc.	see *O. latifolia*
virginea	NRog
I 'Waverley Hybrid'	GCrg GKev LLHF
zeekoevleyensis	NRog

Oxycoccus see *Vaccinium*

Oxydendrum ✿ (*Ericaceae*)

arboreum	CBcs CBct CEnd CMCN CRos EBee EPfP IArd LRHS MAsh MBlu MMuc NLar SPer SPoG SSta WHar WHor

Oxypetalum (*Apocynaceae*)

caeruleum	see *Tweedia coerulea*

Oxyria (*Polygonaceae*)

digyna	CAgr

Oxytropis (*Papilionaceae*)

campestris	EBee
- var. ***gracilis***	GKev
podocarpa	SPlb
purpurea	SPlb
sajanensis	CPBP

Ozothamnus (*Asteraceae*)

§ ***coralloides***	ITim WAbe WThu
§ 'County Park Silver'	EWes GCrg GEdr GKev
§ ***hookeri***	CBcs CBct EBee MBrN SVen WCFE WPGP
§ ***ledifolius***	CBcs CBod CCht ELan EPfP GMcL LRHS SBrt SPer WSHC
§ ***rosmarinifolius***	CBcs CRos CTsd ELan EPfP EWld GMcL LRHS MAsh MSwo SPer SVen
- 'Silver Jubilee'	CBcs CCht CRos CSBt ECrN ECre ELan EPfP GCal GMcL LRHS MAsh MMuc MRav MSwo SLon SPer SPlb SRkn
§ ***selago***	ELan EPot
- 'Major'	SPlb
§ - var. ***tumidus***	ITim WThu
'Threave Seedling'	CCht CRos EBee ELan LRHS MAsh SPer

P

Pachycymbium (*Apocynaceae*)

dummeri new	LToo

Pachyphragma (*Brassicaceae*)

§ ***macrophyllum***	ECha EHrv ELon EWTr EWld GCal IBlr IMou LEdu MMuc MRav NLar NSti WCot WCru WPGP WPnP WSHC

Pachyphytum (*Crassulaceae*)

oviferum ♀H2	WCot

Pachypodium (*Apocynaceae*)

bispinosum	LToo
brevicaule	LToo
geayi ♀H1a	LToo
lamerei ♀H1a	EUJe SPlb
lealii subsp. ***saundersii***	LToo
namaquanum	LToo
succulentum	LToo

Pachysandra (*Buxaceae*)

axillaris	EBee GCal WCot
- BWJ 8032	WCru
- 'Crûg's Cover'	EWld SMad WCru
procumbens	EHrv GKev IMou MNrw NLar WCot
- 'Angola' (v)	WCot
stylosa	MRav
terminalis	Widely available
- 'Green Carpet'	CBcs CChe CExl CRos CSBt EBee ELan EPfP ESps ETMg EUJe GMaP GMcL LRHS LSRN MAsh MGos MSwo NEgg NLar NRHS SCob SGol SLim SPer SPoG SWvt WHar XLum
- 'Green Sheen' ♀H5	CRos ECha ELan EPfP EWTr LRHS NRHS
- 'Silver Edge' (v)	EBee WHar
- 'Variegata' (v) ♀H5	Widely available

Pachystachys (*Acanthaceae*)

lutea ♀H1b	CCCN

Pachystegia (*Asteraceae*)

§ ***insignis***	CPne LRHS SBrt SLim

Paederota (*Plantaginaceae*)

§ ***bonarota***	WAbe
lutea	GEdr GKev WCot

Paeonia ✿ (*Paeoniaceae*)

sp.	NRHS
'Ace of Hearts'	GBin
'Age of Gold' (S)	XGra
albiflora	see *P. lactiflora*
'Al's Choice' new	CBot XGra

	'America'	CKel GBin
	anomala	CBot GKev MPhe NLar
	arietina	see *P. mascula* subsp. *arietina*
	'Armani'	EBee EPfP LRHS
	'Asahiminato' **new**	CKel
	'Athena'	CRos GBin LRHS NRHS WCAu
	'Aurelia'	GKev
	'Auten's Red'	WCAu
	'Avant Garde'	GBin
	'Bai Xue Ta' (S)	NTPC
	banatica	see *P. officinalis* subsp. *banatica*
§	'Bartzella' (d) ♀H5	CBod CBot CKel CRos ELan ELon GBin ILea LCro LMea LPla LPmr LRHS NLar NRHS SPoG WCAu WCot WHil XGra
	beresowskii	GKev
	'Berry Garcia' **new**	NRHS
	'Black Pirate' (S) ♀H5	CKel
	'Blaze'	CKel CRos EWTr GMaP ILea LMea LRHS NRHS WCAu WCot
	'Border Charm'	CKel ILea SDir XGra
	'Boreas' (S)	XGra
	'Bridal Icing'	CKel GBin WCAu
	'Bride's Dream'	GBin
	'Brightness'	XGra
	broteroi	CBot WThu
	'Buckeye Belle' (d)	CKel EBee ELan EPfP EWTr GBin GMaP GMcL IBoy ILea LCro LMea LOPS LRHS LSRN MBel NLar SCob SPer SPoG WCAu WCot XGra
	'Burma Joy'	WCAu XGra
	'Burma Midnight'	GBin WKif
	'Callie's Memory'	CBot CKel ELon GBin ILea NRHS WCAu
	cambessedesii ♀H3	CBot CBro CRos CTal EPot GBin GEdr GKev LRHS NRHS NSla WAbe WKif
	- dwarf	GKev
	cambessedesii* × *mlokosewitschii	CRos LRHS NRHS
	'Cameo Lullaby'	GBin
	'Canary Brilliant'PBR	CKel GBin ILea LMea XGra
	'Candy Cane' **new**	CBot
	'Carina'	CKel
	'Carol'	ILea WCAu
	caucasica	see *P. mascula* subsp. *mascula*
	× ***chamaeleon***	GKev LPla WCAu
	'Cherry Ruffles'	WCAu
	'Chocolate Soldier'	WCAu
	'Claire de Lune'	CKel GBin GMaP ILea IRob LRHS WCAu WCot WKif WTor
	'Claudia'	GBin
	clusii	CBot
	'Color Magnet'	GBin WCAu XGra
	'Command Performance'	GBin WCAu
	'Convoy' (d)	GBin WCAu
	'Copper Kettle'	CBot CKel ILea
	'Cora Louise'	CBot CKel ELan ELon ILea LMea LPmr LRHS WCAu XGra
	'Coral Charm' ♀H7	CKel EPfP GBin GMaP IBoy ILea LCro LMea LRHS LSRN MMrt NLar NPnk SCob SDeJ WCAu WCot XGra XSen
	'Coral Fay'	GBin
	'Coral 'n' Gold'	NPnk
	'Coral Sunset'	CKel CWCL ETMg EWTr GBin IBoy ILea LCro LMea MAvo NLar SCob SDeJ SPer WCAu WCot XGra
	'Coral Supreme'	GBin
	corallina	see *P. mascula* subsp. *mascula*
	coriacea	GBin
	'Court Jester'	CKel ELan ILea
	'Cutie'	GBin WCAu
	'Cytherea'	GBin LRHS WCAu
	'Dancing Butterflies'	see *P. lactiflora* 'Zi Yu Nu'
	'Dao Jin' (S)	LMea
	'Daredevil' (S)	GBin
	daurica misapplied	see *P. mascula* subsp. *triternata*
	- subsp. ***coriifolia***	CBot
	- - RCB UA 12	WCot
	'Dawn Glow'	GBin
	decomposita	MPhe
	decora	see *P. peregrina*
	delavayi (S)	CKel CRos CTho CTsd ELan EPfP GCal GKev GMaP LCro LRHS MAsh MGos NEgg SPer SPoG SRms WCot
	- BWJ 7775	WCru
	- from China (S)	MPhe
	- var. ***angustiloba*** f. ***alba*** (S)	CBot CExl
§	- - f. ***angustiloba*** (S)	CBot GBin GKev MMuc SCob SEND
§	- - f. ***trollioides*** (S)	CExl
	- var. ***atropurpurea***	see *P. delavayi* var. *delavayi* f. *delavayi*
	- 'Cally Amber' **new**	GCal
	- copper-flowered	CBot
§	- var. ***delavayi*** f. ***delavayi*** (S)	CPla
§	- - f. ***lutea*** (S)	CBot CCVT CDul CJun CKel CRos CTho EPfP EUJe GBin GKev GLog IBoy IFro LEdu LRHS MAsh MGos NEgg SCob SLon SMad SPoG SRms WHar WHoo
	- - f. ***lutea*** × 'Right Royal'	XGra
	- - f. ***lutea*** × 'Tria'	XGra
	- var. ***lutea***	see *P. delavayi* var. *delavayi* f. *lutea*
	- 'Mrs Colville' (S)	GCal
	- Potaninii Group	see *P. delavayi* var. *angustiloba* f. *angustiloba*
	- 'Tapestry' (S)	CSpe
	- Trollioides Group	see *P. delavayi* var. *angustiloba* f. *trollioides*
	- var. ***delavayi*** f. ***delavayi*** × ***delavayi*** var. ***delavayi*** f. ***lutea***	EUJe IBoy
	delavayi* × *suffruticosa	LSRN
	'Diana Parks'	GBin ILea NLar XGra
	'Don Richardson'	WCAu
	DRIZZLING RAIN CLOUD	see *P. suffruticosa* 'Shiguregumo'
	'Early Bird'	GBin
	'Early Glow'	WCAu XGra
	'Early Scout'	CRos ELon GBin LRHS NRHS SCob WCAu XGra
	'Early Windflower'	CKel ILea WCAu
	'Eden's Perfume'	CBod CKel ELon EPfP ETMg NLar SPer
	'Eliza Lundy' (d)	GBin WCAu XGra
	'Ellen Cowley'	WCAu XGra
	emodi	CBot CKel GBin GKev ILea LRHS WCAu WCot
	'Estrellia' **new**	CBot
	'Etched Salmon'	CKel GBin
	'Eventide'	WCAu
	'Fairy Princess'	GBin WCAu XGra
	'Firelight'	WCAu
	'First Arrival'	CKel GBin ILea WCAu XGra
	'First Dutch Yellow'	see *P.* 'Garden Treasure'
	'Flame'	CRos EBee EPfP GMaP ILea IRob LRHS MNrw NRHS NSti SDeJ WCot XGra

	'Fragrant Pink Imp'	GBin
	'Fuchsia Cuddles'	XGra
§	Gansu Group (S)	CBot CKel MPhe NTPC
	- 'Bai Bi Lan Xia' (S)	MPhe
	- 'Bai Zhang Bing' (S)	NTPC
	- 'Bing Shan Xue Lian' (S)	MPhe
	- 'Bing Xin Zi' (S)	NTPC
	- 'Danfeng Lingkong' (S)	NTPC
	- 'Dan Feng Zhan Chi' (S)	NTPC
	- 'Dian Jin Bai Yan Wei' (S)	MPhe
	- 'Er Long Nao Hai' (S)	MPhe
	- 'Fen Die' (S)	NTPC
	- 'Fen Guan Yu Zhu' (S)	NTPC
	- 'Fen He' (S)	MPhe NTPC
	- 'Fen Jin Yu' (S)	NTPC
	- 'Fen Lou Dan Xia' (S)	MPhe
	- 'Feng Xian' (S)	MPhe
	- 'Gan Lan Yu' (S)	NTPC
	- 'Guan Yu Zhu' (S)	NTPC
	- 'Gu Cheng Xiang Hui' (S)	MPhe
	- 'Guang Hui Li Cheng' (S)	IRob
	- 'Han Hai Bing Xin' (S)	MPhe
	- 'He Hua Deng' (S)	MPhe
	- 'Hei Fa Nü Lang' (S)	MPhe
	- 'Hei Feng Die' (S)	MPhe NTPC
	- 'Hei Tian E' (S)	MPhe
	- 'Hei Xuan Feng' (S)	MPhe NTPC
	- 'Hei Yuan Shuai' (S)	MPhe
	- 'Hong Lian' (S)	MPhe
	- 'Huang He' (S)	MPhe
	- 'Hui He' (S)	MPhe
	- 'Jiao Rong' (S)	MPhe
	- 'Ju Hua Fen' (S)	MPhe
	- 'Lan He' (S)	MPhe
	- 'Lan He Qi Ming' (S)	NTPC
	- 'Lan Tian Meng' (S)	MPhe
	- 'Lan Yu San Cai' (S)	MPhe NTPC
	- 'Lian Chun' (S)	MPhe
	- 'Long Yuan Hong' (S)	MPhe
	- 'Mo Guan Yu Zhu' (S)	MPhe
	- 'Mo Hai Yin Bo' (S)	MPhe
	- 'Pan Pan' (S)	MPhe
	- 'Ren Mian Tao Hua' (S)	NTPC
	- 'Ri Yue Tong Hui' (S)	MPhe
	- 'San Hua Nu' (S)	MPhe
	- 'Shu Sheng Peng Mo' (S)	IRob MPhe
	- 'Tao Hua Nu' (S)	MPhe
	- 'Tie Mian Wu Si' (S)	MPhe
	- 'Tong Xin Tong De' (S)	MPhe
	- 'Xiao Xue' (S)	MPhe
	- 'Xiong Mao' (S)	MPhe
	- 'Xue Hai Bing Xin' (S)	MPhe NTPC
	- 'Xue Hai Dan Xin' (S)	NTPC
	- 'Xue Lian' (S)	NTPC
	- 'Xue Shan Fei Cai' (S)	NTPC
	- 'Xue Yuan Yu Hui' (S)	NTPC
	- 'Yan Wei Bai' (S)	MPhe
	- 'Ye Guang Bei' (S)	MPhe
	- 'Yi Du Chun Qiu' (S)	NTPC
	- 'Yin Yang Shan' (S)	MPhe
	- 'Yu Ban Xiu Qiu' (S)	MPhe
	- 'Yu Lou Cang Jiao' (S)	MPhe
	- 'Yu Lu Lian Dan' (S)	MPhe
	- 'Yuan Yang Pu' (S)	MPhe
	- 'Zi Ban Bai' (S)	NTPC
	- 'Zi Die Ying Feng' (S)	MPhe NTPC
	- 'Zi Hai Yin Bo' (S)	MPhe
	- 'Zi Yan' (S)	NTPC
	- 'Zong Ban Bai' (S)	MPhe NTPC
	Gansu Mudan Group	see *P.* Gansu Group

	'Garden Peace'	WCAu
§	'Garden Treasure'	CKel CRos ETMg LPmr LRHS NRHS SDeJ SPoG WCAu XGra
	'Going Bananas'	CKel XGra
	'Golden Bowl'	CKel GBin
	'Golden Dream'	see *P.* 'Bartzella'
	'Golden Isles'	CKel
	'Golden Thunder'	CKel
	'Happy'	GBin
	'Hei Hua Kui'	see *P. suffruticosa* 'Hei Hua Kui'
	'Henry Bockstoce' (d)	CBod ELon GBin GMaP ILea NLar WCAu XGra
	'Hephestos' (S)	XGra
	'Hillary'	CKel ELan GBin ILea LMea LPmr WCAu
	'Ho-gioku'	CKel GBin
	'Hong Bao Shi' (S)	NTPC
	'Honor'	WCAu
	'Hua Er Qiao' (S)	LMea
	humilis	see *P. officinalis* subsp. *microcarpa*
	'Huo Lian Jin Dan' (S)	NTPC
	'Icarus' (S)	XGra
	'Illini Warrior'	CKel
	'Impossible Dream' **new**	CBot
	'Isani Gidui'	see *P. lactiflora* 'Isami-jishi'
	japonica misapplied	see *P. lactiflora*
	japonica ambig.	CBot
	japonica (Makino) Miyabe & Takeda	CAby
	'Jay Cee'	GBin WCAu
	'Jin Ge' (S)	NTPC
	jishanensis	MPhe
	'Joanna Marlene' **new**	WCAu
	'John Harvard' **new**	WCAu
	'Joseph Rock'	see *P. rockii*
	'Joyce Ellen'	NLar
	'Julia Rose'	CBod CBot CKel CRos GBin ILea LMea LPmr LRHS NLar NRHS SPoG WCAu WHil XGra
	'Kasagayama' **new**	CKel
	kesrouanensis	GKev
	'Kiev Perfect' **new**	CRos NRHS
	'Kinkaku'	see *P.* × *lemoinei* 'Souvenir de Maxime Cornu'
	'Kinko'	see *P.* × *lemoinei* 'Alice Harding'
	'Kinshi'	see *P.* × *lemoinei* 'Chromatella'
	'Koikagura'	CKel
	'Kokamon'	CKel
	'La Donna' (d)	GBin
§	***lactiflora***	CBot ESps GCal
	- from East Russia	GCal
	- 'Abalone Pearl'	GBin XGra
	- 'Adolphe Rousseau'	CKel IBoy ILea LCro LOPS LRHS WCAu
	- 'Agida'	ECtt GBin LRHS MRav NRHS WGwG
I	- 'Alba'	MBel
	- 'Albert Crousse'	CBcs CKel GBin MRav
	- 'Albâtre'	CKel
	- 'Alertie'	GBin
	- 'Alice Harding'	CKel GBin WCAu
	- 'Allan Rogers'	GBin WCAu
	- 'Amabilis'	ILea
	- 'Amalia Olson'	WCAu
	- 'Amibilis'	ELon WCAu
	- 'Angel Cheeks'	CKel GBin LCro LOPS NLar WCAu
	- 'Ann Cousins'	CKel GMcL WCAu
	- 'Antwerpen'	LRHS NRHS
	- 'Argentine'	CKel
	- 'Armistice'	WCAu

- 'Asa Gray'	CKel
- 'Auguste Dessert'	CKel WCAu WCFE
§ - 'Augustin d'Hour'	CKel IBoy ILea SHar WGwG
- 'Aureole'	MRav
- 'Avalanche'	CKel CRos EPfP GBin ILea IRob LPmr LRHS NLar NRHS WTor
- 'Avalon'	WCAu
- 'Bai Yu Pan'	CBot
- 'Ballerina'	MRav
- 'Balliol'	EBee EPfP
- 'Barbara'	CKel GBin WCAu
- 'Baroness Schröder'	CKel GBin WCAu XGra
- 'Barrington Belle'	CKel CRos EBee EPfP LPmr LRHS MBel NRHS WCAu WFar WHoo
- 'Belle Center'	WCAu
- 'Bess Bockstoce'	WCAu
- 'Bessie'	GBin
- 'Best Man'	EBee WCAu
- 'Better Times'	WCAu
- 'Bev'	GBin
- 'Big Ben'	CBod CKel GBin ILea LRHS NLar
- 'Bing Qing'	CBot
- 'Black Beauty'	CRos EBee GBin IPot LMea LRHS NRHS SCob SDeJ SMad WHil
- 'Blush Queen'	CKel GBin WCAu
- 'Border Gem'	CSam LRHS MRav NRHS WCAu
- 'Bouchela'	LPmr NSti
- 'Boule de Neige'	GBin LPmr
- 'Bouquet Perfect'	CRos GBin LMea NRHS WCAu
- 'Bowl of Beauty' ♀^{H7}	Widely available
- 'Bowl of Cream'	CKel GBin LRHS SWvt WCAu XGra
- 'Break o' Day'	WCAu
- 'Bridal Gown'	GBin WCAu
- 'Bridal Veil'	CKel
- 'Bunker Hill'	CKel CRos ECtt ELon GBin IBoy ILea LRHS MPie NRHS SPer SWvt WCAu WGwG
- 'Butter Bowl'	GBin WCAu
- 'Candidissima'	GBin
- 'Candy Stripe'	CKel GBin
- 'Catharina Fontijn'	CKel GBin ILea LPmr WCAu WHar
- 'Celebrity'	CBod CKel CWCL LMea SCob SDir WHil
- 'Charles Burgess'	CKel ELon GBin ILea LPmr SCob WCAu
- 'Charlie's White'	CKel GBin ILea LRHS MAvo NLar SDeJ WCAu XGra
- 'Charm'	WCAu
- 'Cheddar Charm'	GBin
- 'Cheddar Cheese'	CKel
- 'Cheddar Gold'	WCAu
- 'Cheddar Supreme'	GBin
- 'Cherry Hill'	GBin
- 'Chiffon Clouds'	WCAu
- 'Chiffon Parfait'	GBin XGra
- 'Circus Circus'	XGra
- 'Claire Dubois'	CKel
- 'Class Act'	GBin
- 'Cora Stubbs'	CKel GBin SPer WCAu
- 'Corinne Wersan'	GBin
- 'Cornelia Shaylor'	CKel WCAu
- 'Couronne d'Or'	GBin ILea
- 'Cream Puff'	WCAu
- 'Crimson Glory'	CKel
- 'Cringley White'	SRms
- 'Crinkles Linens'	GBin
- 'Da Ban Fen'	CBot
- 'Daisy Coronet'	XGra
- 'Dawn Pink'	EBee EPfP WCAu
- 'Daystar'	MRav
- 'Dayton'	WCAu
- 'Dinner Plate'	CKel GBin SHar SPer WCAu
- 'Do Tell'	CKel EBee ELon EPfP GBin ILea NLar SPer WCAu
- 'Docteur H. Barnsby'	CKel
- 'Doctor Alexander Fleming'	CBod CKel CRos EBee GBin ILea LPmr LRHS MBNS MHol MNrw NRHS SDeJ SWvt WCAu WFar WHar
- 'Doreen'	CKel EBee GBin LMea WCAu
- 'Doris Cooper'	WCAu
- 'Dresden'	WCAu
- 'Drumline'	SDeJ
- 'Duchesse de Nemours' ♀^{H7}	Widely available
- 'Duchesse d'Orléans'	GBin
- 'Edulis Superba'	ELan EUJe GBin ILea LEdu LRHS MBNS MRav NPer NRHS SPer WCAu WHoo
- 'Elaine'	MRav
- 'Elizabeth Queen of the Belgians'	XGra
- 'Elsa Sass'	CKel GBin ILea WCAu
- 'Embraceable Pink'	GBin
- 'Emma Klehm'	CKel GBin ILea LSRN WCAu
- 'Emperor's Buttons'	XGra
- 'Evelyn Tibbets'	GBin
- 'Fairy's Petticoat'	CKel GBin WCAu
- 'Fancy Nancy'	GBin
- 'Félix Crousse' ♀^{H7}	CBcs CGar CKel CTri ELan ELon GBin GMaP IBoy ILea IRob LRHS LSRN MBNS MRav NLar NPri SDeJ SPer WCAu WFar WHar XSen
- 'Felix Supreme'	GBin XGra
- 'Festiva Maxima' ♀^{H7}	CKel CRos CSBt CTri CWld EBee ELan EPfP GBin IBoy ILea LCro LMea LOPS LPmr LRHS LSun NEgg NLar NPri NRHS SPer SPoG SRkn SRms SWvt WCAu WFar WKif
- 'Festiva Supreme'	CKel GBin
- 'Fiesta Posey'	WCAu
- 'Fiona'	WCAu
- 'Firebelle'	WCAu
- 'Florence Ellis'	WCAu
- 'Florence Nicholls'	CKel ELan GBin ILea WCAu XGra
- 'Foxtrot'	GBin XGra
- 'François Ortegat'	LMea
- 'Fuchsia Dragonfly'	GBin
- 'Garden Lace'	SDeJ WCAu
- 'Gardenia'	CKel CRos ELan EWTr GBin IBoy LMea LRHS NLar NRHS SDeJ WCAu WCot WKif XGra
- 'Gay Paree'	CKel CWCL GBin IBoy ILea LMea LPmr MRav NLar SCob SHar WCAu WKif WTor
- 'Gayborder June'	GMcL
- 'Général Joffre'	MRav
- 'Général MacMahon'	see *P. lactiflora* 'Augustin d'Hour'
- 'Germaine Bigot'	CKel MRav WCAu
- 'Gertrude Allen'	GBin
- 'Gilbert Barthelot'	WCAu
- 'Gladys McArthur'	GBin
- 'Gleam of Light'	CKel
- 'Globe of Light'	CKel
- 'Glory Hallelujah'	WCAu
- 'Go-Daigo'	GBin
- 'Golden Fleece'	WCAu
- 'Goldilocks'	GBin WCAu
- 'Great Sport'	MRav
- 'Green Halo'	CKel GBin WCAu WCot
- 'Green Lotus'	XGra

	- 'Guidon'	WCAu
	- 'Hakodate'	CKel
	- 'Hansina Brand'	GBin
	- 'Hari-ai-nin'	ILea
	- 'Helen Hayes'	WCAu
	- 'Henri Potin'	CKel
	- 'Hermione'	GBin XGra
	- 'Hit Parade'	WCAu
	- 'Honey Gold'	CKel GBin LMea SPoG WCAu XGra
	- 'Hot Chocolate'	CKel GBin WCAu XGra
	- 'Immaculée'	CKel CWCL GBin IBoy ILea IRob LCro LOPS LRHS MMrt MRav SCob SPer SPoG WKif XGra
	- 'Inspecteur Lavergne'	CKel CRos EBee ECtt EPfP GBin IBoy ILea LMea LRHS NGdn NRHS SGol SPer WCAu WCot WHar XGra
	- 'Instituteur Doriat'	CKel LRHS WCAu
§	- 'Isami-jishi'	CKel
	- 'Jacorma'	ILea LRHS NLar
	- 'Jadwigha'	ILea
	- 'James Kelway'	CKel
	- 'Jan van Leeuwen'	CKel ELon EPfP EWTr GBin GMaP LCro LOPS LRHS SPer WCAu WCot WKif WTor XGra
	- 'Jappensha-ikhu'	GBin
	- 'Jean Ericksen'	WCAu
	- 'Jeanne d'Arc'	CKel
	- 'Joker'	GBin WCAu
	- 'Judith Eileen'	WCAu
	- 'June Rose'	GBin
	- 'Kansas'	CKel CRos CWCL EBee ELan EPfP GBin GMcL IBoy ILea IRob LPmr LRHS MHol NGdn NLar NRHS SPoG WCAu WCot WFar
	- 'Karen Gray'	WCAu
	- 'Karl Rosenfield'	Widely available
	- 'Katherine Havemeyer'	XGra
	- 'Kelway's Glorious'	CKel EPfP EWTr GBin ILea LRHS MBNS MRav NLar NRHS WCAu WGwG WKif
	- 'Kelway's Majestic'	MRav
§	- 'Koningin Wilhelmina'	EPfP MNrw
	- 'Krekler's Red'	WCAu
	- 'Krinkled White'	CBod CKel CRos ELon EPfP GBin GKev GMaP ILea LMea LRHS MRav NLar NRHS NSti SDeJ SPoG WCAu WHar WKif XGra
	- 'La Belle Hélène'	CKel
	- 'Lady Alexandra Duff' ♀H7	CKel ELon EWTr GBin ILea LPmr LRHS MRav NGdn SWvt WCAu WKif XGra
	- 'Lady Anna' **new**	ILea
	- 'Lady Orchid'	EPfP WCAu
	- 'Lancaster Imp'	GBin WCAu
	- 'Largo'	WCAu
	- 'Laura Dessert' ♀H7	CKel GBin IBoy ILea IRob LCro LRHS WCAu WKif
	- 'Laura Shaylor'	WCAu
	- 'Lavender Lotus'	XGra
	- 'Le Cygne'	CKel
	- 'L'Éclatante'	LRHS
	- 'Lemon Queen'	GKev
§	- 'L'Étincelante'	GBin
	- 'Liebchen'	WCAu
	- 'Lilac Times'	CKel WCAu
	- 'Little Medicineman'	XGra
	- 'Little Pink Lullaby'	GBin
	- 'Lois Kelsey'	WCAu
	- 'Longfellow'	CKel
	- 'Lord Kitchener'	CKel CSam EPfP GBin LRHS MWat NRHS WCAu WGwG
	- 'Louis van Houtte'	ILea NEgg
	- 'Love's Touch'	GBin
	- 'Lowell Thomas'	GBin WCAu
	- 'Lucky'	XGra
	- 'Ma Petite Cherie'	GBin WCAu
	- 'Madame Calot'	CKel CRos LMea LRHS NRHS WCAu
	- 'Madame Claude Tain'	WCot
	- 'Madame Emile Debatène'	CKel EBee MBNS MHol WCAu WFar WHar
	- 'Madame Gaudichau'	EBee MAvo WCot
	- 'Madelon'	CKel
	- 'Maestro'	GBin XGra
	- 'Magenta Glow'	XGra
	- 'Magenta Moon'	WCAu
	- 'Magic Melody'	CKel
	- 'Mammoth Rose'	GBin
	- 'Margaret Truman'	WCAu
	- 'Marie Lemoine'	CKel GBin ILea LMea LRHS WCAu WCot XGra
	- 'Martha Reed'	WCAu
	- 'Matilda Lewis'	GBin
	- 'Midnight Sun'	WCAu
	- 'Minnie Shaylor'	WCAu
	- 'Mischief'	MRav WCAu
	- 'Miss America' ♀H7	CKel EPfP GBin LMea WCAu WKif XGra
	- 'Miss Eckhart'	CKel
	- 'Mister Ed'	GBin WCAu
	- 'Mistral'	CKel
	- 'Monsieur Jules Elie' ♀H7	CBod CKel CRav EBee ELan EPfP GBin IBoy ILea IRob LCro LMea LRHS NGdn NLar SHar SPer WCAu WHar
	- 'Monsieur Martin Cahuzac'	CKel ILea LRHS
	- 'Moon of Nippon'	CRos GMcL ILea LRHS NRHS WCAu
	- 'Moon River'	CKel EPfP GBin NLar WCAu
	- 'Moonstone'	CKel SCob
	- 'Morning Kiss'	LPmr
	- 'Mother's Choice'	CKel GBin LSRN NGdn NLar SHar WCAu WCot
	- 'Mr G.F. Hemerik'	CKel GBin IBoy WCAu WCot XGra
	- 'Mrs Edward Harding'	CKel
	- 'Mrs Franklin D. Roosevelt'	XGra
	- 'Mrs Livingston Farrand'	GBin
	- 'My Pal Rudy'	GBin WCAu
	- 'Myrtle Gentry'	CKel GBin WCAu
	- 'Nancy Nicholls'	WCAu
	- 'Nancy Nora'	ILea SPer
	- 'Nellie Shaylor'	CKel GBin ILea WCAu
	- 'Neomy Demay'	CKel
	- 'Neon'	GBin IBoy LRHS
	- 'Nice Gal'	GBin WCAu
	- 'Nick Shaylor'	GBin WCAu
	- 'Nippon Beauty'	CKel GBin GMcL ILea LRHS NLar SCob SDeJ WCAu WCot WFar WTor
	- 'Noémie Demay'	LRHS
	- 'Norma Volz'	WCAu XGra
	- 'Nymphe'	CKel EBee MRav NLar SDeJ WCAu
	- 'Paul M. Wild'	CKel ELan IBoy ILea NLar WCAu
I	- 'Peaches and Cream'	LMea
*	- 'Pecher'	CBod EPfP LRHS NLar NPer SDeJ WHar
	- 'Peter Brand'	CKel ECtt ELan GBin ILea LPmr LSRN NLar SCob
	- 'Petite Elegance'	CKel GBin WCAu
	- 'Petite Porcelain'	GBin WCAu XGra

- 'Philippe Rivoire'	CKel GBin ILea WCAu
- 'Philomèle'	CKel WCAu
- 'Picotee'	WCAu
- 'Pietertje Vriend Wagenaar'	GBin
- 'Pillow Cases'	WCAu
- 'Pillow Talk'	CKel CRos EBee ELan GBin ILea LRHS NLar NRHS SPoG WCAu
- 'Pink Cameo'	WCAu WCot WFar
- 'Pink Delight'	GBin
- 'Pink Giant'	EUJe GBin WCAu
- 'Pink Jitterburg'	XGra
- 'Pink Parfait'	CKel ILea LPmr NLar SPer WCAu
- 'Pink Princess'	GBin WCAu
- 'Pink Spinners'	XGra
- 'Plink Platters'	GBin
- 'Port Royale'	GBin
- 'President Franklin D. Roosevelt'	ECtt LRHS MPie NRHS
- 'President Lincoln'	WCAu
- 'Président Poincaré'	MRav
- 'President Taft'	see *P. lactiflora* 'Reine Hortense'
- 'Primevère'	CKel ECtt EWTr GMcL ILea IRob LPmr LRHS NLar SCob SPer WFar
- 'Princess Bride'	GBin
- 'Princess Margaret'	WCAu
- 'Purple Spider'	EBee LPmr MHol
- 'Queen of Sheba'	WCAu
- 'Queen Wilhelmina'	see *P. lactiflora* 'Koningin Wilhelmina'
- 'Raoul Dessert'	WCAu
- 'Raspberry Sundae'	CKel CRos ELan ELon EWTr GBin ILea LMea LRHS MRav NLar NRHS SDir SPer SPoG WCAu WCot
- 'Ray Payton'	GBin
- 'Red Emperor'	WCAu
- 'Red Queen'	CKel GBin
- RED SARAH BERNHARDT	EPfP EUJe GBin ILea SDeJ SPer
- 'Red Satin'	WCAu
§ - 'Reine Hortense'	CKel ECtt LRHS MRav
- 'Renato'	LSun WHar XGra
- 'Riches and Fame'	LRHS
- 'Roland'	WCAu
- 'Ruth Cobb'	WCAu
- 'Salmon Dream'	CKel GBin WCAu
- 'Santa Fe'	CKel EPfP ILea NLar WCAu
- 'Sarah Bernhardt' 🏆H7	Widely available
- 'Sea Shell'	GBin GMaP ILea MAvo WCAu XGra
- 'Sebastiaan Maas'	EBee ILea
- 'Serene Pastel'	GBin WCAu
- 'Shawnee Chief'	GBin
- 'Shirley Temple'	CBod CKel CRos EBee ELan EPfP GBin IBoy ILea IRob LCro LOPS LPmr LRHS MBNS MGos MHol MJak MRav NGdn NPri NRHS SDeJ SPoG WCAu WCot WFar WHar
- 'Silver Flare'	see *P. lactiflora* 'L'Étincelante'
- 'Silver Rose'	GBin
- 'Sir Ernest Shackleton'	MRav
- 'Soft Salmon Joy'	GBin WCAu XGra
- 'Solange'	CKel ILea LRHS NLar WCAu
- 'Sorbet'	CKel EBee ELon EPfP ILea IPot IRob LMea LPmr LRHS MHol NLar NPer SDeJ SMad WCAu WFar
- 'Springfield'	XGra
- 'Summer Carnival'	XGra
- 'Super Gal'	WCAu
- 'Surugu'	WCAu
- 'Suzanne Krekler'	WCAu
- 'Sweet Sixteen'	WCAu

- 'Sword Dance'	CKel CRos ELon EPfP GBin GMcL IBoy ILea LMea LRHS NRHS SDeJ WCAu WSpi XGra
- 'Taff'	EBee
- 'Tamate-boko'	WCAu
- 'The Fawn'	CKel GBin ILea WCAu
- 'The Mighty Mo'	GBin WCAu
- 'The Nymph'	LRHS
- 'Theatrical'	WCAu
- 'Thérèse'	WCAu
- 'Tom Eckhardt'	CKel GBin SPer WCAu
- 'Top Brass'	CKel ECtt ILea LMea MRav NLar SDeJ WCAu
- 'Top Hat'	LMea
- 'Topeka Garnet'	WCAu XGra
- 'Twitterpated'	ELon
- 'Unique'	CKel ELan
- 'Ursa Minor'	WCAu
- 'Victoire de la Marne'	CKel IBoy ILea
- 'Victoria Blush'	WCAu
- 'Violet Dawson'	GBin
- 'Vivid Rose'	GBin WCAu
- 'Vogue'	CKel CWld EBee EPfP LRHS MRav NRHS SWvt WCAu
- 'W.F. Turner'	CKel
- 'Walter Faxon'	GBin
- 'Waltz'	GBin
- 'Westerner'	GBin WCAu
- 'White Cap'	CKel GBin ILea NLar WCAu
- 'White Imp'	WCAu
- 'White Sands'	GBin
- WHITE SARAH BERNHARDT	SPer
- 'White Wings'	CBcs CKel CTri ECtt ELan EPfP EWTr GBin GMaP ILea IRob LPmr LRHS MBel NLar NRHS NSti SMad SPer SWvt WCot
- 'Whitleyi Major' 🏆H7	WCot
- 'Wilbur Wright'	CKel GBin WCAu
- 'Wine Red'	GBin
- 'Władysława'	CKel GBin IRob LRHS SHar SPer WCot
- 'Zi Hong Kui'	CBot
§ - 'Zi Yu Nu'	CRos LRHS LSRN NRHS
- 'Zuzu'	GBin WCAu
'Lafayette Escadrille' (S)	XGra
× ***lagodechiana***	GKev LEdu
'Lan Yue Liang'	LMea
'Late Windflower'	CKel GBin LPla WCAu
'Le Printemps'	CKel GBin LMea
'Leda' (S)	GBin XGra
'Legion of Honour'	GBin
× ***lemoinei*** (S)	WHal
§ - 'Alice Harding' (S)	CKel NTPC
§ - 'Chromatella' (S)	CKel
- 'High Noon' (S) 🏆H5	CKel LRHS MPhe
§ - 'Souvenir de Maximė Cornu' (S)	CKel LRHS
'Lemon Chiffon'	GBin WCAu
'Lemon Dream' PBR	CKel ELan WCAu XGra
lithophila	see *P. tenuifolia* subsp. *lithophila*
lobata 'Fire King'	see *P. peregrina*
'Lollipop' (d)	CBot CKel ELan ILea LPmr
'London'	CRos LRHS NRHS
'Lorelei' (d)	GBin
'Love Affair' **new**	WCAu
'Lovebirds'	WCAu
'Lovely Rose'	WCAu
ludlowii (S)	Widely available
lutea	see *P. delavayi* var. *delavayi* f. *lutea*
'Mackinac Grand'	GBin WCAu

macrophylla	CBot MPhe
'Madrid'	CRos LMea LRHS NRHS
'Magenta Gem'	GBin XGra
'Magical Mystery Tour'	CBot
'Mai Fleuri'	WCAu
mairei	CBot CExl GGGa MPhe
'Many Happy Returns'	CKel GBin ILea
'Martha Bulloch' **new**	CKel
mascula	CBot CBro GEdr GKev GLog IMou LLHF WCot
§ - subsp. ***arietina***	CBot CSpe
- - W&B BG A-4 **new**	WCot
- subsp. ***bodurii***	CBot
- 'Immaculata'	MHol
§ - subsp. ***mascula***	CBot GKev
§ - subsp. ***russoi***	CBot CTal GKev LPla WCot WThu
§ - subsp. ***triternata***	CBot EPot GKev WCot
'May Apple'	WCAu XGra
'Merry Mayshine'	GBin XGra
'Mikokunohata' **new**	CKel
'Mikuhino-akebono'	CKel SDeJ
mlokosewitschii ♀H7	CBot CBro CExl CFil CJun CMea CRos CTal EBee ECha ELan GBin GEdr GKev ILea LRHS MNrw NEgg NRHS SLon SWvt WAbe WCot WHoo WKif WSpi
- hybrids	EBee GKev
'Mock Orange Yellow' **new**	CBot
mollis	see *P. officinalis* subsp. *villosa*
'Montezuma'	GBin XGra
'Moonrise'	CKel GBin WCAu
'Morning Lilac'	CBot CKel GBin WCAu
'Murad of Hershey Bar' (S)	GBin XGra
'Muramatsu No Yuki' **new**	CKel
'My Love'	GBin WCAu XGra
'Nike' (d)	XGra
'Nobi' **new**	CBot
'Normie' (d)	WCAu
'Norwegian Blush'	CBot CKel WCAu XGra
'Nosegay'	GBin WCAu
'Nova'	CKel GBin
obovata	CBot GKev LLHF MPhe
- var. ***alba*** ♀H5	CExl GEdr GKev LLHF
- var. ***willmottiae***	CExl MPhe
officinalis	CBot GKev MCot WCot
- from NW Croatia	LEdu
- WM 9821 from Slovenia	MPhe
- 'Alba Plena' (d)	CKel CPou CRos EBee GMaP ILea LMea LPmr LRHS MBel MRav NEgg NLar NRHS SPer SWvt WCAu WFar WHil WTor
- 'Anemoniflora Rosea' ♀H7	CRos EBee EPfP LRHS NRHS SPer SWvt WCAu
§ - subsp. ***banatica***	CBot GKev MPhe
- subsp. ***humilis***	see *P. officinalis* subsp. *microcarpa*
- 'James Crawford Weguelin'	WCot
§ - subsp. ***microcarpa***	GKev
- 'Mutabilis Plena' (d)	IBlr
- 'Rosea Plena' (d) ♀H7	CRos EBee ECtt ELan EPfP GMaP LRHS NEgg SCob SPer SWvt WCAu WCot WFar XGra
- 'Rubra Plena' (d) ♀H7	CKel CPou CRos CTri EBee ECtt ELan EPfP GBin GMaP ILea LPmr LRHS LSun MBel MHol MRav NEgg NGdn NLar SCob SPer SRms SWvt WBor WCAu WCot XGra
§ - subsp. ***villosa***	CBot LRHS SEND
'Old Faithful'	GBin XGra
'Old Rose Dandy'	CKel ELan GBin ILea
'Orange Glory' **new**	CKel
'Oriental Gold'	CKel
'Oslo' **new**	LMea
ostii (S)	CExl CKel MPhe
§ - 'Feng Dan Bai' (S)	CKel MPhe
'Oukan' (S) **new**	CKel
'Pageant'	XGra
'Paladin'	GBin
papaveracea	see *P. suffruticosa*
paradoxa	see *P. officinalis* subsp. *microcarpa*
'Paris'	CRos LRHS NRHS
'Pastel Splendor'	CKel ELan GBin ILea WCAu
'Pastelegance' (d)	GBin
'Paula Fay'	CKel EBee EPfP EWTr GBin GMaP ILea IMou IRob MRav NLar SDeJ WCAu WCot XGra
PEONY WITH THE PURPLE ROOTS	see *P. suffruticosa* 'Shou An Hong'
§ ***peregrina***	CBot CBro CKel GEdr GKev LEdu MPhe SBrt
- 'Fire King'	CKel ILea
§ - 'Otto Froebel' ♀H7	CKel GBin GEdr NLar WCAu WCot
- 'Rosabella'	CRos LMea LRHS NRHS
- 'Sunshine'	see *P. peregrina* 'Otto Froebel'
'Picotee'	GBin WCAu
'Pink Doodle Dandy' **new**	CBot
'Pink Hawaiian Coral'	CKel EBee GBin ILea LMea LPmr NLar WCot WTor XGra
'Pink Pom Pom' **new**	WCAu
'Pink Tea Cup'	XGra
potaninii	see *P. delavayi* var. *angustiloba* f. *angustiloba*
'Prairie Charm'	CKel ILea XGra
'Prairie Moon'	CKel GBin NLar WCAu
qiui	MPhe
'Raggedy Ann' **new**	CBot
'Raspberry Charm'	XGra
'Red Charm'	CBod CKel CWCL EBee EPfP GBin IBoy ILea IRob LPmr LRHS SPer WCAu WFar WKif WSpi WTor
'Red Glory'	WCAu
'Red Grace' (d)	GBin WCAu XGra
'Red Magic'	EBee EPfP WFar WSpi
'Red Red Rose'	GBin WCAu XGra
'Renown' (S)	CKel
'Requiem'	WCAu
'Ri Yue Jin' (S)	LMea
§ ***rockii*** (S)	CKel CSpe EPfP GBin MPhe WSpi
- from Tianshui, Gansu	MPhe
- from Wenshian, Gansu	MPhe
- hybrid	see *P.* Gansu Group
- subsp. ***linyanshanii*** (S)	CBot MPhe
- subsp. ***taibaishanica*** (S) **new**	GKev
'Roman Gold'	CKel
romanica	see *P. peregrina*
'Rome'	CRos LRHS NRHS
'Rooster Reveille' (d)	XGra
'Rose Flame' (S)	WCAu
'Rosedale'	WCAu XGra
'Roselette'	GBin LRHS WCAu
'Rubyette'	XGra
ruprechtiana	CBot
russoi	see *P. mascula* subsp. *russoi*
'Salmon Beauty' (d)	WCAu
'Salmon Chiffon'	GBin
'Sango-kai' **new**	CKel
'Scarlet Heaven'	CBot CKel ELan GBin ILea XGra
'Scarlet O'Hara'	CBod GBin SPer WCAu WCot
'Scrumdidleumptious' (d)	XGra
'Sequestered Sunshine'	CBot CKel WCAu XGra

	'Serenade'	WCAu
	'Shikounishiki' **new**	CKel
	'Shimano-fuji'	CKel LRHS
	'Shining Light'	SCob
	'Show Girl'	GBin WCAu XGra
	'Showanohokori'	CKel
	'Silver Dawn'	GBin
	'Simply Red'	CBot CKel
	sinensis	see *P. lactiflora*
	'Singing in the Rain'	CBot CKel ILea
	'Smith Family Yellow'	CBot
	× ***smouthii***	CBot GEdr
	'Sonoma Kaleidoscope'	CKel ILea
	'Sonoma Sun' **new**	CKel
	'Soshi'	GBin LRHS NLar SHar
	'Spring Carnival' (S)	GBin
	'Stardust'	WCAu
	'Starlight'	CKel GBin LCro LOPS LRHS WCAu WCot WTor
	sterniana	CExl
§	***suffruticosa*** (S)	GKev MGil MGos
	- 'Akashigata' (S)	CKel
	- 'Alice Palmer' (S)	CKel
	- 'Bai Yuan Hong Xia' (S)	LMea
	- BIRD OF RIMPO	see *P. suffruticosa* 'Rimpo'
	- BLACK DRAGON BROCADE	see *P. suffruticosa* 'Kokuryū-nishiki'
	- BLACK FLOWER CHIEF	see *P. suffruticosa* 'Hei Hua Kui'
	- BROCADE OF THE NANIWA	see *P. suffruticosa* 'Naniwa-nishiki'
	- 'Cang Zhi Hong' (S)	CBot SPer
	- 'Cardinal Vaughan' (S)	CKel
	- CHARMING AGE	see *P. suffruticosa* 'Howki'
	- 'Chu Wu' (S)	LMea NTPC
	- 'Dou Lu' (S)	NTPC
	- DOUBLE CHERRY	see *P. suffruticosa* 'Yae-zakura'
	- 'Duchess of Kent' (S)	CKel
	- 'Duchess of Marlborough' (S)	CKel
	- ETERNAL CAMELLIAS	see *P. suffruticosa* 'Yachiyo-tsubaki'
	- 'Feng Dan Bai' (S)	SPer
	- FLIGHT OF CRANES	see *P. suffruticosa* 'Renkaku'
	- FLORAL RIVALRY	see *P. suffruticosa* 'Hana-kisoi'
	- FRAGRANT JADE	see *P.* 'Xiang Yu'
	- 'Gekkyu-den' (S)	LRHS
*	- 'Glory of Huish' (S)	CKel
	- 'Godaishu' (S)	CKel LRHS NTPC
	- 'Guardian of the Monastery' (S)	XGra
	- 'Hai Huang' (S)	IRob NTPC
§	- 'Hakuo-jisi' (S/d)	CKel LRHS
	- 'Hakushin' (S) **new**	LRHS
§	- 'Hana-daijin' (S)	LRHS
§	- 'Hana-kisoi' (S)	CKel LRHS
§	- 'Hei Hua Kui' (S)	NTPC
§	- 'Howki' (S)	LRHS NTPC
	- 'Iso-no-nami' (S)	LRHS
	- JEWEL IN THE LOTUS	see *P. suffruticosa* 'Tama-fuyo'
	- JEWELLED SCREEN	see *P. suffruticosa* 'Tama-sudare'
	- 'Jin Jiang Hong' (S) **new**	NTPC
	- 'Jitsugetsu-nishiki' (S)	CKel
	- 'Joseph Rock'	see *P. rockii*
	- KAMADA BROCADE	see *P. suffruticosa* 'Kamada-nishiki'
§	- 'Kamada-fuji' (S)	CKel LRHS
§	- 'Kamada-nishiki' (S)	CKel
§	- 'Kaow' (S)	CKel
	- KING OF FLOWERS	see *P. suffruticosa* 'Kaow'
	- KING OF WHITE LIONS	see *P. suffruticosa* 'Hakuo-jisi'
	- 'Kinkaku'	see *P.* × *lemoinei* 'Souvenir de Maxime Cornu'
	- 'Kinshi'	see *P.* × *lemoinei* 'Alice Harding'
	- 'Kokucho' (S)	CKel
§	- 'Kokuryū-nishiki' (S)	CKel SPer
	- 'Koshino-yuki' (S)	CKel LRHS
	- 'Lan Bao Shi' (S)	NTPC
	- MAGNIFICENT FLOWER	see *P. suffruticosa* 'Hana-daijin'
	- 'Montrose' (S)	CKel
*	- 'Mrs Shirley Fry' (S)	CKel
	- 'Mrs William Kelway' (S)	CKel
§	- 'Naniwa-nishiki' (S)	CKel
	- 'Nigata Akashigata' (S)	CKel
	- PRIDE OF TAISHO	see *P. suffruticosa* 'Taisho-no-hokori'
	- 'Reine Elisabeth' (S)	CKel
§	- 'Renkaku' (S)	CKel LRHS NTPC
§	- 'Rimpo' (S)	CKel WSpi XGra
	- 'Rou Fu Rong' (S)	LMea WSpi
	- 'Seidai' (S)	LRHS
§	- 'Shiguregumo' (S)	CKel
	- 'Shimadaigin' (S)	CKel LRHS
	- 'Shimane-chōjuraku' (S)	CKel LRHS
	- 'Shimane-hakugan' (S)	CKel
	- 'Shimane-seidai' (S)	CKel
	- 'Shimanishiki' (S)	CKel
	- 'Shin Shima Kagayaki' (S)	CKel LRHS
	- 'Shin-fusōtsukasa' (S)	LRHS
	- 'Shintoyen' (S)	CKel
§	- 'Shou An Hong' (S)	NTPC
	- SNOWY PAGODA	see *P. suffruticosa* 'Xue Ta'
	- 'Sumi-no-ichi' (S)	CKel
	- 'Superb' (S)	CKel
§	- 'Taisho-no-hokori' (S)	CKel
§	- 'Taiyo' (S)	CKel LRHS NTPC
§	- 'Tama-fuyo' (S)	CKel
§	- 'Tama-sudare' (S)	CKel
	- THE SUN	see *P. suffruticosa* 'Taiyo'
	- 'Toichi Ruby' (S)	XGra
	- WISTERIA AT KAMADA	see *P. suffruticosa* 'Kamada-fuji'
	- 'Wu Long Peng Sheng' (S)	CKel WSpi
§	- 'Xue Ta' (S)	CKel
	- 'Xue Ying Tao Hua' (S)	LMea
§	- 'Yachiyo-tsubaki' (S)	CKel LRHS NTPC
§	- 'Yae-zakura' (S)	LRHS
	- yellow-flowered (S)	GMcL
	- 'Yin Hong Qiao Dui' (S)	CKel LMea NTPC SPer
	- 'Yoshinogawa' (S)	LRHS
	- 'Zhao Fen' (S)	NPer
	suffruticosa × 'Ezra Pound' (S)	XGra
	suffruticosa × ***suffruticosa*** 'Hinode-sekai' (S)	XGra
	'Sunny Girl'	WCAu
	'Sunshine'	see *P. peregrina* 'Otto Froebel'
	'Syukiden' **new**	CKel
	'Taiheko'	CKel
	'Tango'	WCAu
	'Ten' i'	CKel
	tenuifolia	CAby CBot CBro CJun EBee GBin GCal GEdr GKev ILea LLHF MAvo MBel SMad WCAu WCot WSpi
	- RCB UA 11	WCot
	- subsp. ***biebersteiniana***	GKev
*	- subsp. ***carthalinica***	CBot
§	- subsp. ***lithophila***	CBot GKev MPhe
	- 'Plena' (d)	GBin
	- 'Rosea'	GBin
	tenuifolia × ***veitchii*** var. ***woodwardii*** **new**	CJun
	'Terpsichore' (S)	XGra
	'Terrific Gal' **new**	GBin

veitchii CBot CKel EPot GCal GKev GMaP NBid NLar WCot WPGP WSpi
- from China MPhe
- pale-flowered GCal
- var. ***woodwardii*** CExl CJun GAbr GKev LLHF LPla NWad WCAu WCot WHoo WThu
'Vesuvian' CKel
'Viking Full Moon' CKel
'Vision of Sugar Plums' **new** CBot
'Walter Mains' WCAu
'Watermelon Wine' **new** CKel WCAu
'White Emperor' CKel
WHITE PHOENIX see *P. ostii* 'Feng Dan Bai'
'White Towers' EBee EPfP WFar
'Whopper' GBin XGra
'Wine Angel' GBin
wittmanniana CBot GBin GCal GEdr
- PAB 3673 LEdu
- 'Rosea' **new** WCAu
§ 'Xiang Yu' (S) LMea
'Xin Ri Yue' (S) LMea
'Yankee Doodle Dandy' (d) CBot XGra
§ 'Yao Huang' (S) SPer
YAO'S YELLOW see *P.* 'Yao Huang'
'Yellow Crown' CKel MHol SDir
'Yellow Doodle Dandy' **new** CBot
'Yellow Emperor' CKel
'Yellow Gem' CKel GBin
'Yellow Waterlily' CBot CKel LRHS NRHS
'Yokohama' GBin
I 'Zephyrus' (S) XGra

Paesia (*Dennstaedtiaceae*)

scaberula CFil WCot

pak choi see AGM Vegetables Section

Pallenis (*Asteraceae*)

§ ***maritima*** CCCN

Panax (*Araliaceae*)

ginseng GPoy
japonicus WCru
- BWJ 7932 WCru

Pancratium (*Amaryllidaceae*)

illyricum XEll
maritimum GKev NRog SDeJ WCot

Pandorea (*Bignoniaceae*)

jasminoides ♀H1c CCCN CHll CRHN CTri EBak EShb
- 'Alba' CRHN SPer
§ - 'Charisma' (v) CBcs CCCN CHll EPfP EShb SEND SPer WAvo
- 'Lady Di' CCCN
- 'Rosea' CCCN WAvo
- 'Rosea Superba' ♀H1c CBcs CRHN SEND SPer
- 'Variegata' see *P. jasminoides* 'Charisma'
lindleyana see *Clytostoma calystegioides*
pandorana CHll CRHN MGil SLim WAvo
- 'Golden Showers' CBcs CCCN CRHN MRav

Panicum (*Poaceae*)

amarum **new** EPPr
- 'Dewey Blue' EPPr SMHy
bulbosum EHoe EPPr
clandestinum CRos EHoe EPPr EShb EWes IMou LRHS MMoz MMuc NRHS
§ 'Fibre Optics' CSpe
'Frosted Explosion' **new** CRav LRHS
miliaceum LRHS NRHS
- 'Violaceum' SPhx
oligosanthes SPhx
var. ***scribnerianum***
virgatum CKno EPPr MAsh XLum
- 'Blue Tower' CKno CRos ELon EPPr LRHS NRHS XLum
- 'Cardinal' EBee EPPr MNrw WHoo
- 'Cheyenne Sky' **new** EBee
- 'Cloud Nine' CKno EPPr EPed LRHS MAvo WHal WRHF
- 'Dallas Blues' CBWd CBod CKno CSpe EAJP EBee ECha EHoe ELon EPPr EPed EShb EUJe EWes LRHS MAvo NRHS NSti SCob SMHy SPer SPoG WMoo XLum
- 'Emerald Chief' LRHS
- 'Farbende Auslese' EPPr MAvo
- 'Hänse Herms' CBod CKno CRos EHoe ELon EPPr EPed LRHS NLar NRHS WFar
- 'Heavy Metal' Widely available
- 'Heiliger Hain' CRos EPPr LRHS MAvo NRHS WCot
I - 'Kupferhirse' EPPr GQue MAvo
- 'Külsen Moor' **new** WCot
- 'Nican' EPPr
- 'Northwind' CBWd CKno CRos EBee EHoe ELon EPPr EPfP GBin LRHS MAvo NRHS SCob SMHy SMad SRms WFar
- 'Prairie Fire' ECtt
- 'Prairie Sky' CBod CKno CRos EBee EHoe ELon EPPr EUJe GMaP LEdu LRHS MAsh MAvo MMuc NBro NLar NRHS NWsh SCob SGbt SMHy SMad SRms WMoo
- 'Purple Haze' CKno CRos EHoe LRHS MAvo NRHS
- 'Red Cloud' CKno MAvo SMHy
- 'Rehbraun' CBod CRos EBee EHoe EPPr EPfP LCro LOPS LRHS LSRN MJak MMrt NRHS SRms XLum
- 'Rotstrahlbusch' CKno EBee EHoe EPPr GMaP LSun MAvo SPer SRms WCot WMoo XLum XSen
- 'Rubrum' EHoe ELan EPPr ESps MAvo SRms WAvo WMoo
- 'Shenandoah' Widely available
- 'Squaw' CBod CKno CMac CRos EAJP ECtt EHoe EPPr EPfP EShb EUJe GMcL LRHS MAvo MJak MMuc MSCN NDov NRHS NWsh SMad SPer SRms WCot WFar WMoo XSen
- 'Straight Cloud' EPPr
- 'Strictum' EHoe EPPr EWes GQue SBee SCob SMHy SPer SPhx WMoo
I - 'Strictum Compactum' CBod
- 'Warrior' CBWd CBod CKno CRos CTri ECtt EHoe EHrv ELan ELon EPPr EPau EPfP EWTr LRHS MAsh MAvo NRHS SCob SPer WFar
- 'Wood's Variegated' (v) WCot

Papaver ✿ (*Papaveraceae*)

alboroseum CRos LLHF LRHS NRHS
alpinum CRos CSpe ESps LRHS MAsh NGdn NRHS
anomalum SPhx
atlanticum NBro NGdn SPhx SPlb
- 'Flore Pleno' (d) CSpe GAbr IFro NBro NGdn
burseri SRot

§	***cambricum***	CCCN CExl CMac CRav CTri EBee EHrv ELan LEdu MMuc SPer WBrk WCot WFar WHer
	- 'Anne Greenaway' (d)	WCot
	- var. ***aurantiacum***	WCot
	- double-flowered (d)	WCot
	- - orange (d)	WCot
§	- 'Frances Perry'	GCal GKev WCot
	- 'Muriel Brown' (d)	WCot
	carmeli new	SPhx
	commutatum ♀H5	CSpe LCro LOPS SPhx
	- 'Ladybird' ♀H5	CBot GAbr SPoG SVic
	dubium	CSpe LRHS SPhx
	- subsp. ***lecoqii***	SPhx
	- - 'Albiflorum'	LRHS SPhx
§	'Fire Ball' (d)	NBro
	glaucum	LRHS SPhx
	'Heartbeat' (Super Poppy Series)	CSpe EBee EPfP IPot LRHS MHol NCou SPoG WCot WFar
	heldreichii	see *P. pilosum* subsp. *spicatum*
	lateritium	CHid CPou SRms
	- 'Nanum Flore Pleno'	see *P.* 'Fire Ball'
	'Lauffeuer'	CSam
	'Matador'PBR ♀H7	CRos EBee LRHS NLar NNor NRHS WCot
	'Medallion' (Super Poppy Series)	EPri LRHS
§	***miyabeanum***	CRos CSpe ELan LRHS NRHS SRot
	- ***tatewakii***	see *P. miyabeanum*
	'Moondance'	CRos LRHS NRHS
	nanum 'Flore Pleno'	see *P.* 'Fire Ball'
§	***nudicaule***	LCro LOPS SVic WCot
	- Champagne Bubbles Group	CBod CSBt NNor
	- var. ***croceum*** 'Flamenco'	NNor
	- Garden Gnome Group	see *P. nudicaule* Gartenzwerg Group
§	- Gartenzwerg Group ♀H7	CRos CSpe EPfP LPmr LRHS NRHS SPoG SRot SWvt WHar
	- 'Kelmscott Giant'	SVic
	- orange-flowered	LRHS
	- 'Pacino'	CRos CSBt EAJP LRHS NRHS
	- 'Party Fun' (mixed)	CSpe EAJP
	- 'Solar Fire Orange' ♀H7	EUJe
	- Wonderland Series	NNor
	orientale	CBcs CTsd EPfP ESps SRms SVic WHar
	- 'Aglaja' ♀H7	CBcs CDor CElw CKno ECtt LRHS MPie NEgg NGdn SPad WCot WSpi
	- 'Allegro'	CBod CMac CRos CSBt EBee EPfP GMaP IBoy IRob LRHS MBNS MRav NGdn NRHS SCob SPlb SPoG SVic SWvt WFar
	- 'Baby Kiss'PBR	ECtt WFar
	- 'Beauty Queen'	CDor ECha MRav NGdn
	- 'Black and White' ♀H7	MRav NEgg
	- 'Bolero'	CElw CRos ECtt EPri NLar
	- 'Bonfire'	SCob
	- 'Brilliant'	CBod CRos EPfP ESps EUJe IBoy LRHS NGdn NRHS WFar WMoo
	- 'Brooklyn' (New York Series)	ECtt LRHS LSRN
	- 'Burning Heart'	CRos CWGN ECtt EPri IBoy LRHS WCAu
	- 'Carmen'PBR	ECtt
*	- 'Carneum'	CRos LRHS NRHS SPoG SRms
	- 'Cedar Hill'	EPri MRav
	- 'Cedric Morris' ♀H7	ECha
	- 'Central Park' (New York Series)	CRos ILea LRHS NRHS SPoG WFar WHar
I	- 'Charming' pink-flowered	CMac ECtt SPhx
	- 'Charming' red-flowered	LRHS NRHS
	- 'Clochard'	CElw ECtt WCot
	- 'Coral Reef'	EPfP WHar WMoo
	- 'Curlilocks'	CRos GMcL IBoy LRHS MRav NRHS SRms SWvt WFar
	- 'Double Pleasure'	ECtt
	- double red shades (d)	NGdn
	- 'Doubloon' (d)	WFar
	- 'Dwarf Allegro Vivace'	CRos LRHS NRHS
	- 'Eyecatcher'	EBee
	- 'Fancy Feathers'PBR	ECtt WHil
	- 'Fiesta'	ELon
	- 'Flamenco'	EBee IBoy WFar
	- 'Flamingo'	IBoy
*	- 'Flore Pleno' (d)	NGdn
	- 'Forncett Summer'	ECtt MHol SPer WCot
	- 'Frosty' (v)	SHar
	- 'Fruit Punch'	MNHC WHar
	- 'Garden Glory'	ECtt LSRN
	- 'Glowing Embers'	ECtt
	- Goliath Group	ELan MRav NBro SCob SRms WFar
	- - 'Beauty of Livermere'	CBod CDor CRos CSam CTri CWCL ECha ELan EPfP ESps GMaP IBoy IRob LCro LOPS LRHS NGdn NNor NRHS SGbt SPer SPoG SRms WArt WCAu WFar WHar WMoo
§	- - 'Beauty of Livermere' clonal	ECtt WCot
	- 'Graue Witwe'	EBee
	- 'Guardsman'	see *P. orientale* (Goliath Group) 'Beauty of Livermere' clonal
	- 'Harlem' (New York Series)	CBcs CBod CElw CRos ELon EPfP LRHS MSCN NRHS SPer STPC
	- 'Harvest Moon' (d)	CBod CRos ECtt LRHS NPer NRHS WHal
	- 'Indian Chief'	EPri LRHS NPer NRHS WFar
	- 'Inferno'PBR	ECtt
	- 'John III' ♀H7	SPhx
	- 'John Metcalf'	ECtt MRav
	- 'Juliane'	ECha
	- 'Karine' ♀H7	CRos ECha EPPr IBoy LRHS NRHS WTor
	- 'King Kong'	ECtt NCou SPer WCot WFar
	- 'Kleine Tänzerin'	GMcL SEND WFar
	- 'Ladybird'	CRos EPfP LPmr LRHS NRHS
	- 'Laffeuer'	SPhx
	- 'Lauren's Lilac'	LSRN
	- 'Little Patty Plum'PBR	EPfP
	- 'Louvre' (Parisienne Series)	WFar
	- 'Maiden's Blush'	ECtt
	- 'Mandarin'PBR	MHol WCot
	- 'Manhattan' (New York Series)	CElw CSam CSpe ECtt EPfP EWes ILea IRob LRHS MNrw NPnk NSti SGbt WFar WHar WHoo
	- 'Marcus Perry'	CRos LRHS NRHS
	- 'Marlene'	IBoy IPot LRHS
	- 'May Queen' (d)	ECtt EWes IBlr MRav WCot WFar
	- 'Miss Piggy'PBR	EBee ECtt SGbt WCot WFar
	- 'Mrs Marrow's Plum'	see *P. orientale* 'Patty's Plum'
	- 'Mrs Perry'	CRos ECtt ELan GMcL IFro LRHS MNHC NPer NRHS SGbt SRms WBrk WFar
	- 'Nanum Flore Pleno'	see *P.* 'Fire Ball'
	- 'Orange Glow'	WMoo
	- 'Pagode'	EWTr
	- 'Papillon'PBR	CBcs LRHS NRHS WCot WHar
	- 'Paradiso'PBR	EPfP
§	- 'Patty's Plum'	Widely available

- 'Perry's White' CBcs CRos EBee ECtt EPfP GMcL IBoy LRHS MRav NChi NRHS SRkn SWvt WCAu WSpi
- 'Petticoat' ECtt
- 'Picotée' CBcs CRos ECtt ELan ESps GMcL IRob LRHS MRav NEgg NRHS SRot SWvt WFar WMoo
- 'Pink Ruffles'^{PBR} CRos ECtt LRHS NRHS SGbt WFar
- 'Pinnacle' WFar
- 'Pizzicato' CRos ELan EPfP IBoy LRHS NNor NPer NRHS WFar WHar WMoo
- 'Place Pigalle' (Parisienne Series) ECtt EPfP
- 'Plum Pudding' ELan
- 'Prince of Orange' SWvt
- PRINCESS VICTORIA LOUISE see *P. orientale* 'Prinzessin Victoria Louise'
- 'Prinz Eugen' WFar

§ - 'Prinzessin Victoria Louise' CDor CRos ELan EPfP GMaP IBoy LRHS NGdn NNor NRHS SPoG SRms WBrk WHar

- 'Queen Alexandra' IBoy WArt
- 'Raspberry Brûlée' **new** ELan
- 'Raspberry Queen' CDor CMac CRos ECtt EPfP IBoy LRHS MBel MRav NChi NRHS WHal WHar
- 'Rembrandt' MJak WCot
- 'Roter Zwerg' ECha
- 'Royal Chocolate Distinction' CSpe ECtt ELan EPPr EPfP LRHS LSRN NSti WFar
- 'Royal Wedding' Widely available
- 'Ruffled Patty'^{PBR} ECtt EPfP SGbt SPad WCot
- 'Salmon Glow' (d) WFar
- 'Scarlet King' CMac
- scarlet-flowered SEND
- 'Scarlett O'Hara'^{PBR} (d) ECtt EPfP WFar
- 'Snow Goose' CDor CSam CSpe CWGN EBee ECtt EPfP GAbr ILea IPot IRob LRHS LSun MBel MSCN NCou NLar WCot WHoo WKif
- 'Springtime' MRav
- 'Tiffany' CMac ECtt LSRN NEgg
- 'Turkish Delight' CRos ILea LRHS MRav NRHS SWvt
- 'Türkenlouis' CBod CRos ECtt GMcL IBoy LRHS MRav NRHS SPoG WBrk WFar
- 'Walking Fire' MNrw
- 'Watermelon' GMcL
- 'White Ruffles'^{PBR} CBod SGbt

pavoninum **new** SPhx

§ ***pilosum*** subsp. ***spicatum*** CSpe ECha SPhx WCot WMoo

pseudocanescens SPhx

rhoeas CHab EBWF GPoy LCro LOPS MNHC NNor SPhx SVic

- Angels' Choir Group (d) NNor
- 'Bridal Silk' **new** LCro
- 'Bridal White' SPhx
- 'Flanders' CRos LRHS NRHS
- Mother of Pearl Group CSpe LCro LOPS LRHS SPhx
- Shirley Group NNor

rupifragum CPla ECha MMuc SBee SPhx WCot

- 'Double Tangerine Gem' see *P. rupifragum* 'Flore Pleno'

§ - 'Flore Pleno' (d) CDor CRav CSpe EPPr GBin NChi SVic WBrk WMoo

- 'Tangerine Dream' GPSL

'Shasta' (Super Poppy Series) LRHS WFar

'Snow White' (Super Poppy Series) EBee

somniferum ENfk GPoy SVic

- var. ***album*** XAbr
- 'Blackcurrant Fizz' (d) LCro LOPS SPhx
- 'Boudoir Babe' (d) CSpe
- 'Double Shiraz' (d) LRHS SPhx
- (Laciniatum Group) 'Crimson Feathers' NNor
- - 'Danebrog' NNor
- 'Lauren's Grape' CSpe LCro SPhx WArt
- 'Lilac Pompom' (d) **new** LCro LOPS
- (Paeoniiflorum Group) 'Black Beauty' (d) CSpe LRHS SDeJ SPhx SVic
- - 'Black Paeony' (d) CBot LCro LOPS LRHS SPhx
- - 'Schwarzer Drachen' (d) LRHS SPhx
- 'Persian White' SPhx
- 'Ragged Red' (d) CSpe
- subsp. ***setigerum*** NNor
- single white-flowered CSpe
- 'White Cloud' (d) CSpe

thianschanicum SPhx

triniifolium CSpe GCal MMuc SPhx WCot

'Water Melon' EPri

papaya (pawpaw) see *Carica papaya*

Parabenzoin see *Lindera*

Parachampionella see *Strobilanthes*

Paradisea (*Asparagaceae*)

liliastrum misapplied see *P. lusitanica*

liliastrum (L.) Bertol. 🏆^{H5} CHid EBee EPri GCal LRHS NBid NChi WHil WPtf

- 'Major' GKev ITim

§ ***lusitanica*** CAvo CNor CSam CSpe CTca EBee ECtt EPot EPri GBin GCal GKev IBlr IBoy LEdu MCot MHol WCot WPGP XEll

Parahebe (*Plantaginaceae*)

'Angela' MSCN

× ***bidwillii*** GCrg GJos MHer SRms SRot

- 'Kea' ECtt SRot

§ ***catarractae*** CExl ELan EPfP ITim MSCN SRms WKif

- 'Avalanche'^{PBR} GBin GMaP LRHS MAsh SCob SPhm WNPC
- blue-flowered SPer

§ - 'Delight' 🏆^{H4} CExl CRos EWes GMaP LRHS MHer NPer NRHS SRot

- subsp. ***diffusa*** NPer SRot
- 'Miss Willmott' ECtt SPer SPlb
- 'Porlock' CBod GKev GWyn SRms SRot WHoo WTor
- 'Porlock Purple' see *P. catarractae* 'Delight'
- 'Rosea' MAsh SRms
- white-flowered CBot CSpe SRms
- 'Whittallii' GBin

§ ***formosa*** SPlb SVen

'Greencourt' see *P. catarractae* 'Delight'

'Jean' GBin

'Kenty Pink' MMuc

linifolia 'Blue Skies' ECtt EPot GBin GCrg

§ ***lyallii*** CTri EBee ELan EPfP GMaP MCot MHer MMuc MRav MSwo NQui SPlb SRms WKif

- 'Julie-Anne' 🏆^{H4} GCal LRHS
- 'Snowcap' LRHS MRav SPlb SRms
- 'Summer Snow' ELan

'Mervyn' CNor CTri

§ ***perfoliata*** CBot CDor CExl CMea CRos EBee ECha ECre ELan GAbr GCal GMaP

	LEdu MAsh MCot MNrw MRav SBrt SEND SPer SRms WWFP XLum
'Snow Clouds'	CMea CRos EBee ECtt EPfP GKev LRHS MMuc NEoE NHpl NRHS SBch SMHy SRot WFar WHoo WTor WWFP

Parajubaea (*Arecaceae*)

torallyi	LRHS

Parakmeria see *Magnolia*

Paramongaia (*Amaryllidaceae*)

weberbaueri	CPne

Paranomus (*Proteaceae*)

reflexus	SPlb

Paraquilegia (*Ranunculaceae*)

adoxoides	see *Semiaquilegia adoxoides*
§ ***anemonoides***	CExl GKev WAbe
grandiflora	see *P. anemonoides*

Parasenecio (*Asteraceae*)

delphiniifolius B&SWJ 5789	WCru
- B&SWJ 10885	WCru
- B&SWJ 11189	WCru WSHC
- B&SWJ 11415	WCru
farfarifolius	WCru
- var. ***acerinus*** B&SWJ 11549	WCru
- - B&SWJ 11554	WCru
- var. ***bulbifer***	WCru
hastatus var. ***farfarifolius***	see *P. maximowiczianus*
kiusianus B&SWJ 11460	WCru
§ ***maximowiczianus*** B&SWJ 11468	WCru
mortonii GWJ 9419	WCru
- HWJK 2214	WCru
tebakoensis B&SWJ 11167	WCru
- B&SWJ 11536	WCru

Paraserianthes (*Mimosaceae*)

distachya	see *P. lophantha*
§ ***lophantha*** ♀H2	CExl EBak SPlb

Parasyringa see *Ligustrum*

Parathelypteris (*Thelypteridaceae*)

§ ***novae-boracensis***	NLos

× *Pardancanda* (*Iridaceae*)

norrisii	see *Iris* × *norrisii*

Pardanthopsis (*Iridaceae*)

dichotoma	see *Iris dichotoma*

Parietaria (*Urticaceae*)

judaica	GPoy WHer WSFF

Paris ✿ (*Melanthiaceae*)

chinensis	WCru
- B&SWJ 265 from Taiwan	WCru
delavayi	WCru
fargesii	LAma SDir WCru
- var. ***brevipetalata***	WCru
- var. ***petiolata***	WCru
forrestii	WCru
incompleta	GCal LEdu MAvo WCru
japonica	GEdr LAma SDir WCru
lancifolia B&SWJ 3044 from Taiwan	WCru
mairei	WCru
polyphylla	CBro GEdr GKev LAma LRHS MNrw NBid NHpl NLar SDir WCru WPnP
- B&SWJ 2125	WCru
- HWJCM 475	WCru
- var. ***polyphylla***	SDir
- var. ***stenophylla***	EBee GKev LAma WCru
- var. ***yunnanensis***	GEdr
* - - ***alba***	GCal
quadrifolia	CSpe EBee EPfP GCal GEdr GKev GPoy LEdu MAvo MNrw NLar SPhx WCru WFar WHer WPnP WShi
- SDR 2828	GKev
tetraphylla	WCru
thibetica	EBee GKev LRHS MMoz NBid SDir WCru
- var. ***apetala***	WCru
- var. ***thibetica***	GEdr
verticillata	LAma WCru
- 'Ryokutei' (d)	WCru

Parnassia (*Celastraceae*)

SDR 5128	EBee
cabulica	GKev
foliosa	GEdr WCot
gansuensis SDR 5128	GKev
nubicola	GKev
palustris	WHer

Parochetus (*Papilionaceae*)

communis ambig.	CExl MSCN NPer SBrt
- subsp. ***africanus*** ♀H2	CHid
* - 'Blue Gem'	CCCN

Parolinia (*Brassicaceae*)

ornata new	WCot

Paronychia (*Caryophyllaceae*)

§ ***capitata***	CTri SRms WHoo
kapela	SPlb XSen
§ - subsp. ***serpyllifolia***	XLum
- - 'Binsted Gold' (v)	XLum
nivea	see *P. capitata*
serpyllifolia	see *P. kapela* subsp. *serpyllifolia*

Parrotia ✿ (*Hamamelidaceae*)

persica	Widely available
- PAB 13.046	LEdu
- 'Bella'	CJun EMOT MBlu WMou
- 'Biltmore'	CJun NLar SSta
- 'Burgundy'	CJun EPfP NLar
- fastigiate	CJun
- 'Felicie'	CJun EPfP IArd NLar
- 'Het Plantsoen'	NLar
- 'Horizontalis' new	CJun
- 'Jodrell Bank'	CJun MBlu NLar SBir
- 'Pendula'	CJun CMCN EPfP MBlu SSta
- 'Persian Carpet'	NLar
- 'Summer Bronze'	CJun CRos LRHS LSRN MAsh SBir
- 'Vanessa' ♀H6	CBcs CCVT CJun CMCN CMac CRos CTho EPfP ESps EWes GKin IArd IRob LMaj LRHS MAsh MBlu NLar SBir SGol SSta WMou
subaequalis	CBcs CDul CJun EBee NLar WPGP

Parrotiopsis (*Hamamelidaceae*)

jacquemontiana	CBcs CJun GBin MBlu NLar

parsley see *Petroselinum crispum*

parsnip see AGM Vegetables Section

Parthenium (*Asteraceae*)

integrifolium	GPoy IMou LRHS NRHS SPhx WCot

Parthenocissus (*Vitaceae*)

§ ***henryana*** ♀H5	Widely available
- 'Malene' **new**	EShb
himalayana	CBcs
- 'Purpurea'	see *P. himalayana* var. *rubrifolia*
§ - var. ***rubrifolia***	CBcs CMac CRos CWCL ELan EUJe GBin LRHS MAsh MRav SLim SLon SPtp WCru
inserta misapplied	see *P. quinquefolia*
inserta ambig.	CMac CTsd NLar
laetevirens	NLar
§ ***quinquefolia***	Widely available
- var. ***engelmannii***	CBcs EBee EMOT EShb LBuc SCob SEND WCFE
- 'Guy's Garnet'	WCru
- RED WALL ('Troki')	CRos ETho LRHS NRHS
- STAR SHOWERS ('Monham') (v)	EBee EPfP NLar
- 'Yellow Wall'PBR	CRos ETho LRHS NRHS
semicordata B&SWJ 6551	WCru
striata	see *Cissus striata*
thomsonii	see *Cayratia thomsonii*
§ ***tricuspidata***	CCVT CDul EPfP IBoy MAsh MGos SArc SCob SGol SPer
- 'Beverley Brook'	CRHN ELon IRob LSRN NLar SNig SRms
- 'Crûg Compact'	WCru
- 'Fenway Park'	CFlo CKel EBee ELan LRHS MRav NLar
- 'Green Spring'	CBcs ELan IArd MGos NLar
- 'Lowii'	CMac CRos EPfP LRHS MBlu MRav NLar NRHS SLon SNig SPoG
- 'Purpurea'	CKel
- 'Robusta'	EBee EMOT GMcL SPer
§ - 'Veitchii' ♀H5	Widely available

Pasithea (*Hemerocallidaceae*)

caerulea	EBee EPri MHol SMHy WCot WPGP

Paspalum (*Poaceae*)

glaucifolium	MNrw
quadrifarium RCB RA S-5	WCot

Passiflora ✿ (*Passifloraceae*)

sp.	ESps
actinia	CCCN CRHN SPlb
'Adularia'	CCCN
alata (F) ♀H1a	CCCN ETMg
× ***alatocaerulea***	see *P.* × *belotii*
× ***allardii***	CCCN
ambigua	CCCN
§ 'Amethyst' ♀H3	CBcs CCCN CFlo CKel CRHN CSBt LSRN NLos SPoG
amethystina misapplied	see *P.* 'Amethyst'
§ ***amethystina*** Mikan	CRos ECre LRHS
'Anastasia'	CCCN
'Andy'	CCCN
'Anemona'	CCCN
'Angelo Blu'	CCCN
'Annika'	CCCN
antioquiensis misapplied	see *P.* × *exoniensis*
antioquiensis ambig.	CBcs CCCN CTsd
antioquiensis H. Karst. ♀H2	CHll CRHN
'Ariane'	CCCN
× ***atropurpurea***	CCCN
§ ***aurantia***	CCCN
banksii	see *P. aurantia*
§ × ***belotii***	CCCN
- 'Impératrice Eugénie'	see *P.* × *belotii*
- 'Perfume Passion'PBR	CCCN
'Betty Myles Young'	CCCN CKel CRHN CRos ECre LRHS NRHS
'Blue Bird'	CCCN
'Blue Bouquet'	CCCN
'Blue Crown'	CCCN
'Blue Moon'	CCCN
'Blue Stripper'	CCCN
'Blue Velvet'	CCCN
'Byron Beauty'	CCCN
'Byte'	CCCN
§ ***caerulea*** ♀H4	Widely available
- 'Chinensis'	CCCN
- 'Clear Sky'PBR	CCCN CFlo CKel CRos ELan EPfP EUJe EWTr LRHS NLar NRHS SNig
- 'Constance Eliott' ♀H4	CAgr CBcs CCCN CFlo CKel CMac CRHN CRos CSBt EBee ELan EPfP ESps LCro LRHS MAsh MGos MHer NLar NLos NRHS SCob SGol SNig SPer SWvt
- 'Pierre Pomié'	CCCN
I - 'Rubra'	CSBt
- 'White Lightning'	CCCN CFlo CKel CRos ELan EMOT EUJe LRHS NPri NRHS SLim SPoG SWvt
× ***caeruleoracemosa***	see *P.* × *violacea*
× ***caponii***	CCCN
- 'John Innes'	CCCN
'Celine'	CCCN
chinensis	see *P. caerulea*
citrifolia	CCCN
citrina	CCCN
* ***classica*** × ***coccinea***	CCCN
× ***colvillii***	CCCN CHll
'Coordination'	CCCN
§ ***coriacea***	CCCN
'Crimson Tears'	CCCN
§ 'Damsel's Delight'	CCCN CFlo CKel CRos ECre LRHS NRHS
'Daylight'	CCCN
'Debby'	CCCN
× ***decaisneana*** (F)	CCCN
'Divertido'	CCCN
EDEN ('Hil Pas Eden') ♀H3	CCCN CFlo CKel SCoo SRkn
edulis (F)	CBcs CCCN NLos SPre SVic
- 'Byte' (F)	CCCN
§ - f. ***edulis*** (F)	CCCN
- f. ***flavicarpa*** (F)	CBlu CCCN
- 'Frederick' (F) **new**	ETMg
- 'Norfolk' (F)	CCCN
- 'Parati' (F)	CCCN
'Elizabeth' (F)	CCCN
'Empress Eugenie'	see *P.* × *belotii*
'Evatoria'	CCCN
§ × ***exoniensis*** ♀H2	CCCN CHll CRHN CSBt ECre
'Fairylights'	CCCN
'Fantasma'	CCCN
'Fata Confetto'	CCCN
'Fledermouse'	CCCN
'Flying V'	CCCN
'Grand Duchess'	CCCN
gritensis	CCCN

'Guglielmo Betto'	CCCN
'Heidi'	CCCN
'Hetty Nicolaas'	CCCN
'Hildegard'	CCCN
'Hill House'	CHll
incarnata (F)	CCCN GPoy SPlb
'Incense' (F) ♀H2	CCCN SPlb
'Inspiration'	CCCN
'Jara'	CCCN
'Jelly Joker'	CCCN
'Justine Lyons'	CCCN CKel CRos LRHS NRHS
karwinskii	CCCN
× ***kewensis***	CCCN
'Lady Margaret'	CCCN
'Lambiekins'	CCCN CFlo CKel CRos LRHS NRHS
§ ***ligularis*** (F)	CCCN
'Lilac Lady'	see *P.* × *violacea* 'Tresederi'
'Livie'	CCCN
lowei	see *P. ligularis*
lutea	CCCN
'Luzmarina'	CCCN
'Manapany'	CCCN
manicata (F)	CCCN
- B&SWJ 14284 **new**	WCru
'Maria'	CCCN
'Marijke'	CCCN
'Mary Jane'	CCCN
I ***matthewsii*** 'Alba'	CRHN
'Mavis Mastics'	see *P.* × *violacea* 'Tresederi'
mayana	see *P. caerulea*
membranacea (F)	CCCN
'Michael'	CCCN
'Minai'	CCCN
'Mini Lamb'	CCCN
mixta (F)	CCCN
- clone 2	CCCN
- red-flowered	CCCN
mollissima misapplied	see *P. tarminiana*
mollissima ambig. (F)	CBcs CBlu CCCN SPlb
mollissima (Kunth) L.H. Bailey (F) ♀H2	CRHN
'Monika Fischer'	CCCN
mucronata	CCCN
murucuja	CCCN
'New Incense'	CCCN
'Nightshift'	CCCN
obtusifolia	see *P. coriacea*
onychina	see *P. amethystina* Mikan
'Panda'	CCCN
'Party Animal'	CCCN CFlo CKel CRos ECre LRHS NRHS
'Pink Festival'	CCCN
'Pink Nightmare'	CCCN
'Pink Passion'PBR	CCCN ELan
'Pinky'	CCCN
× ***piresiae***	CCCN
'Poppet'	CCCN CKel CRos LRHS NRHS
'Precioso'	CCCN
'Pura Vida'	CCCN
'Purple Companion'	CCCN
'Purple Haze'	CCCN CKel CRos CTsd ELan LCro LRHS NLar NLos NRHS WFar
'Purple Passion'	see *P. edulis* f. *edulis*
'Purple Pendulum'	CCCN
'Purple Rain'	CCCN
quadrangularis (F) ♀H1a	CBlu CCCN CHll
quinquangularis	CCCN
racemosa ♀H1b	CCCN
- 'Buzios'	CCCN
- pink-flowered **new**	CCCN
'Red Inca'	CCCN
reitzii	CCCN
riparia	CCCN
rubra	CCCN SLim
sexocellata	see *P. coriacea*
'Silly Cow'	see *P.* 'Damsel's Delight'
'Silvie'	CCCN
'Simply Red'	CCCN
'Smythiana'	CBot
'Snow Queen' **new**	LCro LOPS
'Star of Bristol' ♀H2	CKel
'Star of Kingston'	CCCN
'Star of Surbiton'	CCCN CRos LRHS NRHS
'Sunburst'	CCCN
'Surprise'	CCCN
§ ***tarminiana*** (F)	CCCN CRHN CSBt
- white-flowered	CCCN
'Temptation'	CCCN
tetrandra	CExl
× ***tresederi***	see *P.* × *violacea* 'Tresederi'
trifasciata	CCCN
tucumanensis tetraploid	CCCN
tulae	CCCN
venusta	CCCN
§ × ***violacea*** ♀H2	CCCN CRHN EBee
- 'Eynsford Gem'	CCCN
- 'Lilac Lady'	see *P.* × *violacea* 'Tresederi'
- 'Sabin'	CCCN
§ - 'Tresederi'	CCCN
- 'Twin Star'	CCCN
- 'Victoria'	CCCN CSBt ETMg NLar
vitifolia (F)	CCCN
- 'Innocentiae'	CCCN
'White Queen'	CCCN
'White Surprise'	CCCN
'White Wedding'	CCCN CKel EWTr
'Wilgen Heintje'	CCCN
'Wilgen K Verhoeff'	CCCN
'Wilgen Marieke'	CCCN
'Winterland'	CCCN

passion fruit see *Passiflora*

passion fruit, banana see *Passiflora mollissima* (Kunth) L.H. Bailey

Pastinaca (*Apiaceae*)

sativa	CHab EBWF SVic WCot

Patersonia (*Iridaceae*)

occidentalis	LRHS SPlb

Patrinia ✿ (*Caprifoliaceae*)

gibbosa	CSam CSpe CTal ECtt GEdr MMrt MMuc NLar NPnk SPhx WFar WMoo WPnP
- B&SWJ 874	WCru
cf. ***monandra*** **new**	EBee
aff. ***punctiflora***	NDov
rupestris B&SWJ 12654	WCru
scabiosifolia	CBWd CElw CHll CKno CSpe ECha ECtt EWld GJos IRob MAvo NLar NPnk SPhx WFar WHoo WMoo
- B&SWJ 8740	WCru
- 'Nagoya'	MNrw
triloba	CSpe CTal GCal GEdr IRob LRHS LSou MMrt NPnk NRHS WFar WMoo
* - 'Minor'	ECtt
- var. ***palmata***	EBee GKev NPnk WMoo
villosa	CExl EBee GJos IMou NPnk SPhx

Paulownia (*Paulowniaceae*)

catalpifolia	EBee NLar SAko
elongata	NLar
fargesii misapplied	see *P. tomentosa* 'Lilacina'
fortunei	MBlu SAko SPlb
- FAST BLUE ('Minfast') ♀H5	CExl CHGN LSRN SGol
kawakamii	CBct CMCN EBee EPfP SChF WPGP
- RWJ 9909	WCru
'Purple Spendour'	SAko
tomentosa ♀H5	Widely available
- W 769	WPGP
- 'Coreana'	WCru
§ - 'Lilacina'	NChi

Pauridia (*Hypoxidaceae*)

capensis	NRog

Pavonia (*Malvaceae*)

multiflora ambig.	CCCN
strictiflora	CCCN
* ***volubilis***	CCCN

pawpaw (false banana) see *Asimina triloba*

pawpaw (papaya) see *Carica papaya*

pea see AGM Vegetables Section

peach see *Prunus persica*

pear see *Pyrus communis*

pear, Asian see *Pyrus pyrifolia*

pecan see *Carya illinoinensis*

Pedicularis (*Orobanchaceae*)

bicornata new	CPla

Peganum (*Nitrariaceae*)

harmala	SBrt XAbr

Pelargonium ✿ (*Geraniaceae*)

'A.M. Mayne' (Z/d)	WFib
'Aaron West' (St) new	WFib
'Abba' (Z/d)	WFib
'Abbie Hillier' (R)	WFib
'Abel Carrière' (I/d)	WFib
abrotanifolium (Sc)	ENfk MHer SVen WFib WGwG
acetosum	GCal MHer WFib
'Ada Green' (R)	WFib
'Ada Sutterby' (Dw/d)	WFib
'Adam's Quilt' (Z/C)	SAll
'Ade's Elf' (Z/St)	WFib
'Ainsdale Beauty' (Z)	WFib
alchemilloides	WFib
'Alcyone' (Dw/d)	SAll
'Alde' (Min)	SAll
'Aldwyck' (R) ♀H1c	CRav WFib
'Alex Kitson' (Z)	WFib
'Algenon' (Min/d)	WFib
I 'Alice' (Min)	WFib
'Alison March' (Dw/Z/v/d)	WFib
'Allesley Shadow' (Dw/d)	ECtt WFib
alpinum	MHer
'Alta Bell' (R)	ELan
'Always' (Z/d)	SAll
'Amari' (R)	WFib
'Ambrose' (Min/d)	SAll WFib
AMELIT ('Pacameli'[PBR]) (I/d)	MCot SSea
'American Prince of Orange' (Sc)	SPet
AMETA ('Pacmeta'[PBR]) (Z)	SSea
'Amethyst' (R)	SAll SCoo WFib
I 'Amy' (Dw)	WFib
'Angel Eyes Blueberry' (A)	LSou
(Angeleyes Series) ANGELEYES BICOLOR ('Pacbicolor'[PBR]) (A)	MCot
- ANGELEYES ORANGE ('Paccrio'[PBR]) (A)	SPhm WCot
- ANGELEYES RANDY (A)	SSea
'Angelique' (Dw/d)	SAll WFib
'Ann Hoystead' (R) ♀H1c	WFib
'Annabelle Stephenson' (Dw/d) new	WFib
'Annsbrook Beauty' (A/C)	SPet WFib
'Annsbrook Jupitor' (Z/St)	WFib
(Antik Series) ANTIK ORANGE ('Tikorg'[PBR]) (Z) ♀H1c	SPoG
- ANTIK PINK ('Tikpink'[PBR]) (Z)	SPoG
- ANTIK SCARLET ('Tikscarl'[PBR]) (Z)	SPoG
- ANTIK VIOLET ('Tikvio'[PBR]) (Z)	SPoG
'Antoine Crozy' (Z × I/d)	WFib
'Apache' (Z/d)	WFib
appendiculatum	MHer
'Apple Betty' (Sc)	NWsh WFib
'Apple Blossom Rosebud' (Z/d) ♀H1c	ECtt EShb ETMg MHer SAll WFib
'Apricot' (Dw/v)	SAll
'Apricot Fool' (U/Sc)	WFib
'Apricot Glace' (U/Sc)	WFib
'April Hamilton' (I)	CRav LCro WFib
'April Showers' (A)	WFib
'Arctic Frost' (I)	WFib
§ 'Arctic Star' (St) ♀H1c	CSpe WBrk WFib
'Ardens' ♀H1c	CNor CPbh CSpe EBee EUJe LCro MCot MHer SAll SBod SCob SWvt WCot WFib WWFP
'Ardwick Cinnamon' (Sc)	ENfk MHer NWsh SAll SPet SRms WFib
'Arnside Fringed Aztec' (R)	MHer WFib
'Ashby' (Dec/Sc) ♀H1c	CRav ECtt ENfk MHer SAll SPet WFib
'Ashfield Blaze' (Z/d)	SAll
'Ashfield Jubilee' (Z/C)	SAll WFib
'Ashfield Serenade' (Z) ♀H1c	WFib
'Askham Fringed Aztec' (R) ♀H1c	WFib
asperum Ehr. ex Willd.	see *P.* 'Graveolens'
'Athabasca' (Min)	SAll
§ 'Atomic Snowflake' (Sc/v)	ECtt ENfk MNHC NWsh SAll SPet SRms WFib
'Atrium' (U)	MHer NWsh WFib
'Attar of Roses' (Sc) ♀H1c	CCht CRav ECtt ENfk LCro MCot MHer MNHC NCou NPri NWsh SAll SBch SPet SPhm SPoG SRms WBrk WFib WGwG
'Aurora' (Z/d)	ECtt SAll
australe	MCot MHer NWsh SBch SVen WFib
'Australian Mystery' (R/Dec) ♀H1c	CRav CSpe ECtt WFib
'Aztec' (R) ♀H1c	SAll WFib
'Baby Bird's Egg' (Min)	WFib

	'Baby Brocade' (Min/d)	SAll
	'Baby Harry' (Dw/v)	WFib
	'Balcon Lilas'	see *P.* 'Roi des Balcons Lilas'
	'Balcony Red' (I)	ECtt
	'Ballerina' (R)	see *P.* 'Carisbrooke'
I	'Ballerina' (Min)	WFib
	'Banstead Village' (Z)	SAll
	'Barbara Eldridge' (Z)	WFib
§	'Barbe Bleu' (I/d) ℽH1c	LCro WFib
	barklyi	WFib
	'Baronne A. de Rothschild' (Z/d)	WFib
	'Bath Beauty' (Dw)	CSpe
	'Beacon Hill' (Min)	SAll
	'Beatrice Cottington' (I/d)	WFib
	'Beauty of Calderdale' (Z/C)	WFib
	'Beauty of Eastbourne' misapplied	see *P.* 'Lachskönigin'
	'Belinda Adams' (Min/d) ℽH1c	SAll
	BELLADONNA ('Fisopa') (I/d)	SCoo
	'Bembridge' (Z/St/d)	WFib
	'Ben Matt' (R)	WFib
§	'Bergpalais'PBR	SSea
	'Berkswell Carnival' (A)	ELan
	'Berkswell Jester' (A)	SAll
	'Berkswell Lace' (A)	MHer
	'Beromünster' (Dec)	ECtt MHer WFib
	'Bert Pearce' (R)	WFib
	'Beryl Gibbons' (Z/d)	SAll WFib
	'Beryl Reid' (R)	WFib
	'Best Red' (Z) **new**	ETMg
	'Betty' (Z/d)	SAll
	betulinum	CPbh WFib
	'Betwixt' (Z/v)	WFib
	'Big Apple' (Sc)	SRms
	'Bird Dancer' (Dw/St) ℽH1c	CSpe MHer SAll WBrk
	(Birdbush Series) 'Birdbush Bobby' (Sc)	SRms
	- 'Birdbush Bold and Beautiful' (Sc)	SRms
	- 'Birdbush Eleanor' (Z)	WFib
	- 'Birdbush Nutty' (Sc)	SRms
	'Birthday Girl' (R)	ECtt WFib
	'Bitter Lemon' (Sc)	ECtt WFib
	'Black Butterfly'	see *P.* 'Brown's Butterfly'
	'Black Country Bugle' (Z/d)	WFib
	'Black Knight' (R)	ECtt MHer
	'Black Knight' (A)	SPet
	'Black Pearl' (Z/d)	SAll
	'Black Prince' (R/Dec)	WFib
	'Black Velvet' (R)	ETMg MCot
	'Black Vesuvius'	see *P.* 'Red Black Vesuvius'
	BLANCHE ROCHE ('Guitoblanc') (I/d)	MCot MHer SAll SCoo SSea
§	'Blandfordianum' (Sc)	MHer NWsh
I	'Blandfordianum Album' (Sc)	WFib
	'Blandfordianum Roseum' (Sc)	MHer WFib
	'Blazonry' (Z/v)	WFib
	(Blizzard Series) BLIZZARD BLUE ('Fisrain'PBR) (I)	SCoo
	- BLIZZARD RED ('Fizzard') (I)	SCoo
	- BLIZZARD WHITE ('Fisbliz'PBR) (I)	SCoo
	'Blue Beard'	see *P.* 'Barbe Bleu'
	'Bob Newing' (Min/St)	WFib
	'Bobberstone' (Z/St)	WFib
	'Bold Ann' (Dw/Z/d)	WFib
	'Bold Appleblossom' (Z)	WFib
	'Bold Bridesmaid' (Dw/d)	WFib
	'Bold Carousel' (Z/d)	WFib
	'Bold Cherie' (Dw/d)	WFib
	'Bold Cherub' (Z/d)	WFib
	'Bold Cyclamen' (Dw/d)	WFib
	'Bold Debonair' (Dw/d)	WFib
	'Bold Dove' (Dw)	WFib
	'Bold Flame' (Z/d)	WFib
	'Bold Gem' (Z/d)	WFib
	'Bold Limelight' (Z/d)	WFib
	'Bold Minstrel' (Z/d)	WFib
	'Bold Moonlight' (Dw)	WFib
	'Bold Pixie' (Dw/d)	WFib
	'Bold Princess' (Z/d)	WFib
	'Bold Special' (Z)	WFib
	'Bold Spirit' (Z)	WFib
	'Bold Sunset' (Z/d) ℽH1c	WFib
	'Bolero' (U) ℽH1c	SAll WFib
	'Bon Bon' (Min/St)	WFib
	'Bontrosai'PBR (Sc)	MCot
	'Bornholm' (d)	SAll
	'Bosham' (R)	WFib
	'Both's Snowflake' (Sc/v)	WFib
	bowkeri	WFib
	'Brackenwood' (Dw/d) ℽH1c	SAll
	'Bramford' (Dw)	SAll
	BRAVO ('Fisbravo') (Z/d)	WFib
	'Brenda' (Min/d)	WFib
	'Brenda Hyatt' (Dw/d)	SAll WFib
	'Brian West' (Min/St/C)	WFib
	'Brian West Butterfly' (Z/St) ℽH1c	WFib
	'Bright Eyes' ambig. (Dw)	WFib
	'Brightstone' (Z/d)	ECtt WFib
	'Brilliant' (Dec)	ENfk SPet WFib
	'Brilliantine' (Sc)	ENfk MHer SRms WFib
	'Britannia' (R)	WFib
	'Brixworth Charmer' (Z/v)	SAll
	'Brixworth Pearl' (Z)	WFib
	'Broadway' (Min)	SAll
	'Brook's Purple'	see *P.* 'Royal Purple'
	'Brookside Flamenco' (Dw/d)	SAll WFib
	'Brookside Primrose' (Min/C/d)	WFib
	'Brookside Serenade' (Dw)	WFib
§	'Brown's Butterfly' (R)	ECtt WFib
	'Brunswick' (Sc)	MHer WFib
	'Bushfire' (R) ℽH1c	WFib
	BUTTERFLY ('Fisam'PBR) (I)	SCoo
	caespitosum	MHer
	caffrum	WFib
	- 'Diana' **new**	MHer
	'Cal'	see *P.* 'Salmon Irene'
	'California Brilliant' (U)	MHer
	'Calignon' (Z/St)	WFib
	'Caligula' (Min/d)	SAll
	'Cameo' (Dw/d)	SAll WFib
	'Camisole' (Dw/d)	SAll
	'Camphor Rose' (Sc) ℽH1c	SRms
	'Can-can' (I/d)	WFib
	canescens	see *P.* 'Blandfordianum'
	'Cape Town' (Dw/Z/v)	WFib
	capitatum	ENfk WFib
	'Capri' (Sc)	CRav WFib
	'Captain Starlight' (A) ℽH1c	MHer SPet WFib

	'Carefree' (U) ♀H1c	ECtt WFib
§	'Carisbrooke' (R) ♀H1c	WFib
	'Carmel' (Z)	WFib
	carnosum	MHer
	'Carol Gibbons' (Z/d) ♀H1c	SAll
	'Carole Munroe' (Z/d)	WFib
	'Caroline' (Dec)	WFib
	'Caroline Schmidt' (Z/d/v)	ECtt MCot SAll WBrk WFib
	'Carolyn Hardy' (Z/d)	WFib
	CASCADE LILAC	see *P.* 'Roi des Balcons Lilas'
	caucalifolium	MHer
	subsp. ***caucalifolium***	
	- subsp. ***convolvulifolium***	WFib
	'Cedric Morris Corvette' (Z) **new**	WFib
	'Celebration' (Z/d)	WFib
	'Celestial Rose' (Z/d) **new**	WFib
	'Cézanne' (R)	MCot SAll
	'Charity' (Sc) ♀H1c	ENfk MCot MHer MNHC NWsh SAll SPet SRms WFib
	'Charlotte Bronte' (Dw/v)	WFib
	'Charmay Cocky' (Z/d)	WFib
	'Charmay Hampshire' (Z/d) **new**	WFib
	'Charmay Snowflake' (Sc/v)	SRms
	'Charmay Snowflurry' (Sc/v)	WFib
	'Chavarri Hermanos' (Z/d)	WFib
	'Chelsea Gem' (Z/d/v) ♀H1c	WFib
	'Chelsea Morning' (Z/d)	WFib
	'Cherry' (Min)	WFib
	'Cherry Baby' (Dec) ♀H1c	ECtt WFib
	'Cherry Orchard' (R)	WFib
	'Chew Magna' (R)	WFib
	'Chieko' (Min/d)	WFib
	'Chinese Cactus' (Z/St) **new**	WFib
	'Chinz' (R)	ECtt
§	'Chocolate Peppermint' (Sc)	ECtt ELan ENfk MCot MHer NWsh SPet SRms WFib
	'Chocolate Tomentosum'	see *P.* 'Chocolate Peppermint'
	'Chocolate Twist' (St/C)	SAll
	'Choun Cho' (I)	LCro WFib
	'Chrissie' (R)	WFib
	'Christopher Ley' (Z)	SAll
	'Cindy' (Dw/d)	WFib
	'Citriodorum' (Sc) ♀H1c	ELan MCot MHer WFib
	'Citronella' (Sc)	CPla SPhm SRms WFib
	'Claret Rock Unique' (U)	WFib
	'Clatterbridge' (Dw/d) ♀H1c	SAll
	'Clorinda' (U/Sc)	ENfk MCot MHer MNHC NWad SAll SPet SRms WFib
	'Clown' (R)	WFib
	'Coddenham' (Dw/d)	WFib
	'Cola Bottles'	CPla NPer SPet SPoG WFib
§	'Colonel Baden-Powell' (I/d)	WFib
	COLORADO NOVA ('Genu'PBR) (Z) **new**	SSea
	COLUMBIA (St)	WFib
	'Colwell' (Min/d)	WFib
	'Concolor Lace'	see *P.* 'Shottesham Pet'
	'Contrast' (Z/C/v)	SAll SCoo SPoG WFib
	'Cook's Peachblossom' (Z/d)	SAll WFib
	'Copthorne' (U/Sc) ♀H1c	MCot MHer NWsh SPet SRms WFib
	cordifolium	GCal WFib
	- var. ***rubrocinctum***	MHer NWsh
	coriandrifolium	see *P. myrrhifolium* var. *coriandrifolium*
	'Cornell' (I/d)	WFib
	cortusifolium	MHer
	'Cotta Lilac Queen' (I/d)	ECtt SAll
	'Cottenham Bliss' (A)	WFib
	'Cottenham Cynthia Haird' (A)	WFib
	'Cottenham Delight' (A)	WFib
	'Cottenham Glamour' (A) ♀H1c	MHer
	'Cottenham Harmony' (A)	WFib
	'Cottenham Jubilee' (A)	MHer
	'Cottenham Surprise' (A) ♀H1c	SPet
	'Cottenham Wonder' (A) ♀H1c	CRav SPet WFib
	'Cottontail' (Min)	SAll
	cotyledonis	WFib
	'Countess of Scarborough'	see *P.* 'Lady Scarborough'
	'Cover Girl' (Z/d)	WFib
	'Covina' (R)	WFib
	'Cramdon Red' (Dw)	WFib
	'Crampel's Master' (Z)	SAll WFib
	'Creamery' (d)	WFib
	'Creamy Nutmeg' (Sc/v)	ENfk EShb MHer NWad SEND SRms
	'Credo' (Z) **new**	WFib
	'Creeting St Peter' (Min)	SAll
	'Crimson Unique' (U) ♀H1c	CSpe ELan ENfk MCot MHer WFib
§	***crispum*** (Sc)	GPoy
	- 'Cy's Sunburst' (v)	CRav ECtt MHer NWsh WCot WFib
§	- 'Golden Well Sweep' (Sc/v)	WFib
	- 'Major' (Sc)	WFib
	- 'Peach Cream' (Sc/v)	ENfk WFib
	- 'Prince Rupert' (Sc)	NWsh
	- 'Variegatum' (Sc/v) ♀H1c	ECtt ENfk GBin GPoy MHer NWsh SAll SBch SPet SRms WCot WFib
	crithmifolium	MHer
	'Crock O Day' (I/d)	ECtt SAll
	'Crocodile' (I/C/d) ♀H1c	ECtt ELan MHer MNHC NWad WFib
	'Crowfoot Rose' (Sc)	WFib
	'Crystal Palace Gem' (Z/v)	ECtt SAll WFib
	cucullatum	WFib
	- 'Flore Pleno' (d)	MHer WFib
	'Cupid' (Min/Dw/d)	WFib
§	'Czar' (Z/C)	SCoo
	'Dainty Maid' (Sc)	ECtt ENfk
	'Dale Queen' (Z)	WFib
	'Dame Anna Neagle' (Dw/d)	SAll
	'Dark Red Irene' (Z/d)	SAll WFib
	'Dark Secret' (R)	CRav CSpe WFib
	'Dark Venus' (R)	WFib
	'David John' (Dw/d)	SAll
	'Davina' (Min/d)	WFib
	'Deacon Arlon' (Dw/d)	ECtt SAll
	'Deacon Avalon' (Dw/d)	WFib
	'Deacon Barbecue' (Z/d)	SAll WFib
	'Deacon Birthday' (Z/d)	SAll
	'Deacon Bonanza' (Z/d)	SAll WFib
	'Deacon Clarion' (Z/d)	SAll WFib
	'Deacon Constancy' (Z/d)	SAll
	'Deacon Coral Reef' (Z/d)	SAll WFib
	'Deacon Fireball' (Z/d)	SAll WFib
	'Deacon Gala' (Z/d)	SAll WFib
	'Deacon Golden Bonanza' (Z/C/d)	WFib
	'Deacon Golden Lilac Mist' (Z/C/d)	WFib
	'Deacon Jubilant' (Z/d)	SAll
	'Deacon Lilac Mist' (Z/d)	WFib
	'Deacon Mandarin' (Z/d)	WFib
	'Deacon Minuet' (Z/d)	ECtt SAll WFib
	'Deacon Peacock' (Z/C/d)	WFib

	'Deacon Picotee' (Z/d)	SAll WFib
	'Deacon Regalia' (Z/d)	SAll
	'Deacon Romance' (Z/d)	SAll
§	'Deacon Summertime' (Z/d)	SAll WFib
	'Deacon Sunburst' (Z/d)	SAll
	'Deacon Trousseau' (Z/d)	SAll
	'Deborah Miliken' (Z/d) ♀H1c	WFib
	'Decora Impérial' (I)	SAll
	'Decora Lavender'	see *P.* 'Decora Lilas'
§	'Decora Lilas' (I)	ECtt
	'Decora Mauve'	see *P.* 'Decora Lilas'
	'Decora Pink'	see *P.* 'Decora Rouge'
	'Decora Red'	see *P.* 'Decora Rouge'
§	'Decora Rose' (I)	ECtt
§	'Decora Rouge' (I)	ECtt
	'Deerwood Angel Wings' (A) **new**	WFib
	'Deerwood Darling' (Min/v/d)	WFib
	'Deerwood Lavender Lad' (Sc)	ENfk MHer WFib
	'Deerwood Lavender Lass' (Sc)	MCot MHer SRms
	'Deerwood Pink Puff' (St/d)	WFib
	'Delightful' (R)	WFib
	'Delli' (R) ♀H1c	MHer NPer WFib
	'Denebola' (Min/d)	SAll
	denticulatum	MHer
§	- 'Filicifolium' (Sc)	ELan ENfk EPri MCot MHer NWsh SAll WFib
	'Diana Louise' (Z/d) **new**	WFib
	'Diana Palmer' (Z/d)	SAll WFib
	'Diane' (Min/d)	SAll
	'Dibbinsdale' (Z) ♀H1c	SAll
	dichondrifolium (Sc)	SAll WFib
	'Dick Key' (Z/d) **new**	WFib
	'Didi' (Min)	SAll
	'Display' ambig. (Dw/v)	WFib
	'Distinction' (Z)	SAll SPoG WFib
	'Dodd's Super Double' (Z/d)	WFib
	'Dolly' (R) **new**	WFib
	'Dolly Varden' (Z/v) ♀H1c	ECtt SAll WFib
	'Don's Helen Bainbridge' (Z/C)	WFib
	'Don's Richard A. Costain' (Z/C)	WFib
	'Don's Silver Wedding' (d)	SAll
	'Don's Stokesley Gem' (Z/C)	WFib
	'Don's Swanland Girl' (Min)	SAll
	'Doris Hancock' (R)	WFib
	'Doris Shaw' (R)	WFib
	'Dorothy Baker' (R)	WFib
	'Double New Life' (Z/d)	WFib
	'Double Pink' (R/d)	WFib
	'Dovedale' (Dw/C)	WFib
	'Downlands' (Z/d)	WFib
	'Dragon's Breath' (Z/St)	SAll
	'Dresden White' (Dw)	WFib
	'Dubonnet' (R)	WFib
	'Duchess of Devonshire' (U)	WFib
	'Duke of Buckingham' (Z/d)	SAll WFib
	'Duke of Devonshire' (Z/d)	SAll
	'Duke of Edinburgh'	see *P.* 'Hederinum Variegatum'
	'Dunkery Beacon' (R)	WFib
§	'Dwarf Miriam Baisey' (Min)	SAll
	'Dwarf Miriam Read'	see *P.* 'Dwarf Miriam Baisey'
	'E. Dabner' (Z/d)	WFib
	'East Sussex' (Dw/C)	SAll
§	'Eastbourne Beauty' (I/d)	WFib
	echinatum	MHer
	- 'Album'	WFib
	'Eclipse' (Dw/d)	ECtt
	'Eden Gem' (Min/d)	SAll WFib
	'Edith Stern' (Dw/d)	SAll
	'Edmond Lachenal' (Z/d)	WFib
	'Edward Hockey' (Z)	WFib
	'Eileen Postle' (R) ♀H1c	WFib
	'Elaine Ward' (R)	WFib
	ELBE SILVER ('Pensil') (I) ♀H1c	SCoo
	'Electra' (Z/d)	SAll
	'Elizabeth Read' (Dw)	SAll
	'Elizabeth Taylor' (Z) **new**	WFib
	'Ella Jane' (Z/d)	WFib
	'Ellen Gray' (v)	SAll
	'Elmsett' (Dw/C/d)	ECtt SAll WFib
	'Els' (Dw/St)	WBrk
	'Els' (1870)	SAll
	'Elsi' (I × Z/d/v)	SAll WFib
	'Elsie Gillam' (St)	WFib
	'Embassy' (Min)	WFib
	EMILIA ('Pactina' PBR) (Z)	SSea
	'Emma Hössle'	see *P.* 'Frau Emma Hössle'
	'Emma Jane Read' (Dw/d)	WFib
	'Emma Louise' (Z)	WFib
	'Emperor Nicholas' (Z/d)	WFib
	'Encore' (Z/d/v)	SAll
	endlicherianum	MHer SPhx WAbe WCot XEll
	'Endsleigh' (Sc)	WFib
	'Erwarton' (Min/d)	SAll
	'Escapade' (Min/d)	SAll
	'Eskay Gold' (A)	WFib
	'Eskay Jewel' (A)	WFib
	'Eskay Ruby' (A)	MHer
	'Eskay Sugar Candy' (A)	WFib
	'Eskay Verglo' (A)	WFib
	EVENING GLOW	see *P.* 'Bergpalais'
	'Evka' PBR (I/v)	ECtt SCoo
	exstipulatum	MHer SVen
	'Fair Ellen' (Sc)	MHer WFib
	'Fairlee' (Dw/I)	WFib
	'Fairy Lights' (Dw/St)	SAll
	'Fairy Orchid' (A)	WFib
	'Fallen Angel' (Z/St)	ECtt SAll
	'Fandango' (Z/St)	SAll WFib
	'Fanny Eden' (R)	WFib
	'Fantasia' white-flowered (Dw/d) ♀H1c	WFib
	'Fareham' (R) ♀H1c	WFib
	'Faye Brawner' (Z/St)	SAll
	'Fern Mint' (Sc)	SRms
	'Feuerriese' (Z)	SAll
	'Fiat Queen' (Z/d)	WFib
	'Fieldings Unique' (U)	SPet
	'Fiery Sunrise' (R)	WFib
	'Fifth Avenue' (R)	WFib
	'Filicifolium'	see *P. denticulatum* 'Filicifolium'
	'Fir Trees Catkins' (A)	MHer
	'Fir Trees Fiesta' (R) ♀H1c	ECtt
	'Fir Trees Hayley' (R) **new**	WFib
	'Fir Trees Pearl Anniversary' (Z/C)	WFib
	'Fir Trees Silver Wedding' (Z/C/d)	WFib
	'Firebrand' (Z/d)	SAll
	'First Blush' (R)	WFib

FIRST YELLOW ('Pacyell'^{PBR}) (Z/d)	WFib
'Fleur d'Amour' (R)	WFib
'Fleurisse' (Z)	WFib
(Flower Fairy Series)	ETMg SSea
FLOWER FAIRY BERRY ('Sweberry'^{PBR}) (Z)	
- FLOWER FAIRY VELVET ('Swevel'^{PBR}) (Z)	SSea
- FLOWER FAIRY WHITE SPLASH ('Swewhi'^{PBR}) (Z)	SSea
fragrans	ECtt ENfk SAll SPet SRms
Fragrans Group (Sc)	GPoy MCot MHer NWsh WFib WGwG
§ - 'Fragrans Variegatum' (Sc/v) ♀H1c	NWsh SPet SPoG WFib
- 'Snowy Nutmeg'	see *P.* (Fragrans Group) 'Fragrans Variegatum'
'Fraiche Beauté' (Z/d)	WFib
'Francis Gibbon' (Z/d)	WFib
'Francis Parrett' (Min/d) ♀H1c	WFib
'Frank Headley' (Z/v) ♀H1c	ECtt EShb MCot NPer SAll SCoo SPoG WFib WOld
§ 'Frau Emma Hössle' (Dw/d)	SAll WFib
'Freak of Nature' (Z/v)	MHer SAll WFib
'Frensham' (Sc)	ENfk MHer NWsh WFib
'Freshwater' (St/C)	WFib
'Friary Wood' (Z/C/d)	WFib
'Friesdorf' (Dw/Fr)	MCot MHer WBrk WFib
'Fringed Apple' (Sc)	WFib
'Fringed Aztec' (R) ♀H1c	MHer WFib
'Frosty' misapplied	see *P.* 'Variegated Kleine Liebling'
'Frosty Petit Pierre'	see *P.* 'Variegated Kleine Liebling'
'Fruity' (Sc)	SRms
frutetorum	MHer
fruticosum	WFib
fulgidum	MCot MHer SAll WFib
'Gabriel' (A)	WFib
'Galilee' (I/d)	SAll
GALLERIA SUNRISE ('Sunrise') (R)	SAll
'Galway Star' (Sc/v) ♀H1c	MHer WFib
'Ganther' (Dec)	WFib
'Gareth Mark Pratt' (Z/C)	WFib
'Garland' (Dw/d)	SAll
'Garland' (R)	WFib
'Garnet Rosebud' (Min/d)	SAll WFib
'Garnet Wings' (R)	WFib
'Gartendirektor Herman' (Dec) ♀H1c	ELan WFib
'Gaudy' (Z)	WFib
'Gemini' (Z/St/d) ♀H1c	WFib
'Gemma' (R)	SAll
'Gemstone' (Sc) ♀H1c	ENfk MHer SPet WFib
'Genie' (Z/d)	SAll WFib
'Gentle Georgia' (R)	WFib
'Georgia' (R)	WFib
'Georgia Peach' (R)	WFib
'Georgina Blythe' (R) ♀H1c	WFib
Gerainbow Series (I) **new**	ETMg
'Gerald Wells' (Min)	SAll
'Giant Butterfly' (R)	WFib
gibbosum	CSpe MHer WFib
'Gillian Shaw' (R) **new**	WFib
'Glacis'^{PBR} (Quality Series) (Z/d)	SSea
'Gladys Evelyn' (Z/d)	WFib
'Gladys Weller' (Z/d) ♀H1c	WFib
glaucum	see *P. lanceolatum*
'Gleam' (Z/d)	SAll
§ ***glutinosum***	WFib
'Goblin' (Min/d)	SAll
'Goesta' (Z/d)	SSea
GOLDEN ANGEL	see *P.* 'Sarah Don'
'Golden Brilliantissimum' (Z/v)	WFib
'Golden Chalice' (Min/v)	WFib
'Golden Clorinda' (U/Sc/C)	NWsh SEND SPet WFib
'Golden Ears' (Dw/St/C) ♀H1c	NPer WFib
'Golden Edinburgh' (I/v)	WFib
'Golden Harry Hieover' (Z/C)	SAll
'Golden Lilac Gem' (I/d)	WFib
'Golden Princess' (Min/C)	WFib
'Golden Square' (Dw/St)	WFib
'Golden Staphs' (Z/St/C)	MHer SAll
'Golden Stardust' (Z/St)	SAll
'Golden Tears' (Min/I/C/d)	ECtt
'Golden Well Sweep'	see *P. crispum* 'Golden Well Sweep'
'Good Vibrations' (Min/Z/St/d)	SAll
'Gooseberry Leaf'	see *P. grossularioides*
'Gosport' (Z/v) **new**	WFib
'Grace Thomas' (Sc) ♀H1c	MHer WFib
'Grace Wells' (Min)	WFib
'Grand Slam' (R) ♀H1c	WFib
grandiflorum	MCot MHer WFib
graveolens L'Hér.	see *P.* 'Graveolens'
graveolens ambig.	SEND
graveolens sensu J.J.A. van der Walt	SBch WFib
§ 'Graveolens' (Sc)	ENfk GPoy MHer SAll SVen WBrk WFib
'Great Blakenham' (Min)	SAll
'Great Bricett' (Dw/d)	SAll
'Green Eyes' (I/d)	MHer
'Greetings' (Min/v)	SAll WFib
§ 'Grenadier' (Z)	SAll
'Grey Lady Plymouth' (Sc/v)	CPbh LCro MCot MHer NWsh WFib
'Grey Sprite' (Min/v)	WFib
§ ***grossularioides***	MHer
§ 'Hannaford Star' (Z/St)	WFib
'Hansen's Pinkie' (Dec)	WFib
'Hansen's Wild Spice' (Sc)	NWsh WFib
'Happy Appleblossom' (Z/v/d)	SAll
'Happy Thought' (Z/v) ♀H1c	ECtt MCot SAll SCoo WFib
'Harbour Lights' (R)	WFib
'Harewood Slam' (R)	WFib
'Harlequin Pretty Girl' (I × Z/d)	SAll WFib
'Harlequin Rosie O'Day' (I)	ECtt WFib
'Harvard' (I/d)	WFib
'Hazel' (R)	WFib
'Hazel Cherry' (R)	WFib
'Hazel Dean' (R)	ECtt
'Hazel Glory' (R)	WFib
'Hazel Gypsy' (R)	WFib
'Hazel Peach' (R)	WFib
'Hazel Star' (R)	WFib
'Hazel's Finale' (Dec) **new**	WFib
§ 'Hederinum Variegatum' (I/v)	ECtt WFib
'Helen Bainbridge' (Z/C)	SAll
'Helen Christine' (Z/St)	MHer WFib

	'Hemley' (Sc)	SAll
	'Henry Weller' (A) ♀H1c	WFib
	'Hermanus Show' (Sc)	WFib
	'Hermione' (Z/d)	WFib
	'Highfields Always' (Z/d)	SAll
	'Highfields Appleblossom' (Z)	SAll
	'Highfields Attracta' (Z/d)	WFib
	'Highfields Ballerina' (Z/d)	SAll
	'Highfields Candy Floss' (Z/d)	ECtt SAll WFib
	'Highfields Charisma' (Z/d)	SAll
	'Highfields Choice' (Z) ♀H1c	WFib
	'Highfields Dazzler' (Z)	SAll
	'Highfields Delight' (Z)	WFib
	'Highfields Fancy' (Z/d)	SAll
	'Highfields Festival' (Z/d) ♀H1c	ECtt WFib
	'Highfields Flair' (Z/d)	SAll WFib
	'Highfields Melody' (Z/d)	WFib
	'Highfields Orange' (Z)	SAll
	'Highfields Pink' (Z)	SAll WFib
	'Highfields Pride' (Z)	WFib
	'Highfields Prima Donna' (Z/d)	SAll
	'Highfields Salmon' (Z/d)	SAll
	'Highfields Serenade' (Z)	SAll
	'Highfields Snowdrift' (Z)	WFib
	'Highfields Sugar Candy' (Z/d)	SAll
	'Highfields Supreme' (Z)	SAll
	'Highfields Symphony' (Z)	SAll WFib
	'Highfields Vogue' (Z)	SAll WFib
	'Hilda's Memory' (Dw/Z/d)	WFib
	'Hills of Snow' (Z/v)	MHer SAll WFib
	'Hindoo' (R × U) ♀H1c	WFib
	hispidum	MHer
	'Hit Parade' (I/d) **new**	WFib
	'Hitcham' (Min/d)	WFib
	'Holbrook' (Dw/C/d)	WFib
	'Honeywood Lindy' (R)	WFib
	'Honeywood Suzanne' (Min/Fr)	SAll
	HORIZON ALL STARS MIXED (Z) **new**	ETMg
	HOT SPOT RIA ('Ria'PBR) (Z)	SAll
	'House and Garden' (R)	ECtt
	'Hula' (R × U)	WFib
	hystrix **new**	LToo
	'Ian Read' (Min/d)	SAll
	'Ice Cap' (Min)	SAll
	'Icing Sugar' (I/d)	WFib
	ignescens	WFib
	'Immaculatum' (Z)	WFib
	'Imperial Butterfly' (A/Sc) ♀H1c	ENfk SPet SRms WFib
	ionidiflorum	CSpe EShb MCot MHer MNHC SRms
	'Irene' (Z/d)	WFib
	'Irene Cal' (Z/d)	WFib
	'Irene Toyon' (Z)	WFib
	'Islington Peppermint' (Sc)	SPet SRms WFib
	'Ivalo' (Z/d)	WFib
	'Ivory Snow' (Z/d/v)	WFib
	'Jacey' (Z/d)	SAll
	'Jack of Hearts' (I × Z/d)	WFib
	'Jack Phillips' (Z/d)	WFib
§	'Jackie' (I/d)	SAll WFib
	'Jackie Gall'	see *P.* 'Jackie'
	'Jackie Totlis' (Z/St)	WFib
	JACKPOT MIXED (Z) **new**	ETMg
	'Jackpot Wild Rose' (Z/d)	WFib
	'Jacqui Caws' (Dw)	SAll
	'Jane Innes' (I/d)	WFib
	'Janet Hofman' (Z/d)	WFib
	'Janet James' (Dw/Z/d)	SAll
	'Janet Kerrigan' (Min/d)	WFib
	'Jayne' (Min/d)	SAll
	'Jayne Eyre' (Min/d)	WFib
	'Jean Bart' (I)	SAll
§	'Jeanne d'Arc' (I/d)	WFib
	'Jer'Rey' (A)	WFib
	'Jessica' (Z/d)	SAll
	'Jip's Bishops Wood' (Dw/d)	WFib
	'Jip's Desert Poppy' (Z/Min)	WFib
	'Jip's Eleanor Renton' (Dw/d)	WFib
	'Jip's Freda Burgess' (Z/C/d)	SAll
	'Jip's Little Lady' (Dw)	WFib
	'Jip's Megan' (Z/C/D)	ECtt
	'Jip's Pippin' (Dw)	WFib
	'Jip's Proud Sentinel' (Dw/d)	WFib
	'Jip's Sky Gipsy' (Dw)	WFib
	'Jip's Twilight' (Dw)	WFib
	'Joan Fontaine' (Z)	WFib
	'Joan Morf' (R) ♀H1c	WFib
	'Joan of Arc'	see *P.* 'Jeanne d'Arc'
	'John Squires' (Z/C/d)	SAll
	'John's Angela'	SAll
	'Joy' (R) ♀H1c	CSpe ECtt WFib
	'Joy Lucille' (Sc)	NWsh
	'Judith Thorp' (R)	SAll
	'Julie Smith' (R)	WFib
	'Juniper' (Sc)	WFib
	'Just Beth' (Z/C/d)	WFib
	'Just Jip' (Dw/Z)	WFib
	'Just Joss' (Dw/d)	WFib
	'Just William' (Min/C/d)	WFib
	'Kamahl' (R)	WFib
	'Karen' (Dw/C)	LSou
	'Karl Hagele' (Z/d)	WFib
	'Karmin Ball'	WFib
	'Karrooense'	see *P. quercifolium*
	'Katie Hillier' (R)	WFib
	'Kaufman's Bonfire' (R)	WFib
	'Keepsake' (Min/d)	SAll WFib
	'Kenny's Double' (Z/d)	ECtt WFib
	'Kerensa' (Min/d)	WFib
	'Kesgrave' (Min/d)	WFib
	'Kewense' (Z)	EShb WFib
	'Key's Unique' (U)	WFib
	'Kimono' (R) ♀H1c	ECtt
	'King Edmund' (R) ♀H1c	CRav WFib
	'King of Denmark' (Z/d)	SAll WFib
	'King Solomon' (R)	WFib
	'King's Ransom' (R)	WFib
§	'Kleine Liebling' (Min)	WFib
	'Kyra' (Min/d)	SAll
	'La France' (I/d) ♀H1c	ECtt LCro SAll WFib
	'La Jolla' (Z/d)	WFib
	'La Paloma' (R)	WFib
§	'Lachskönigin' (I/d)	WFib
	'Lady Alice of Valencia'	see *P.* 'Grenadier'
	'Lady Ilchester' (Z/d)	WFib

'Lady Love Song' (R)	WFib
'Lady Mary' (Sc)	MHer SRms WFib
'Lady Mavis Pilkington' (Z/d)	WFib
'Lady Plymouth' (Sc/v) ♀H1c	CPbh CSpe ECtt ELan ENfk EPfP GLog MCot MHer NWad NWsh SAll SEND SPet SPhm SRms WFib WGwG
§ 'Lady Scarborough' (Sc)	ENfk MHer SRms WFib
laevigatum	MHer
'Lancastrian' (Z/d)	ECtt WFib
§ ***lanceolatum***	MHer
'Lara Ballerina' (Sc/d) ♀H1c	SPet SRms
'Lara Candy Dancer' (Sc) ♀H1c	MAsh NWsh SPet WFib
'Lara Jester' (Sc)	ECtt ENfk NWsh WFib
'Lara Starshine' (Sc) ♀H1c	CRav ENfk MHer SPet SRms WFib
'Lara Waltz' (R/d)	WFib
'Laurel Hayward' (R)	WFib
'Lauren Alexandra' (Z/d)	WFib
'Lavender Grand Slam' (R) ♀H1c	SAll
'Lavender Lindy' (Sc)	NWsh WCot WFib
'Lavender Sensation' (R)	WFib
'Lawrenceanum'	LCro WFib
laxum	WFib
'L'Élégante' (I/v) ♀H1c	MCot MHer SAll WFib
'Lemon Air' (Sc)	WFib
'Lemon Crisp'	see *P. crispum*
'Lemon Fancy' (Sc) ♀H1c	MHer NWad NWsh SAll SPet WFib
'Lemon Kiss' (Sc)	CSpe NWsh WFib
'Lemon Meringue' (Sc)	WFib
'Letitia' (A)	ENfk
LILA COMPAKT-CASCADE	see *P.* 'Decora Lilas'
LILAC ('Paclilac'PBR) (I) **new**	SSea
LILAC CASCADE	see *P.* 'Roi des Balcons Lilas'
'Lilac Gem' (Min/I/d)	ENfk
'Lilian Pottinger' (Sc) ♀H1c	ENfk MHer NWsh WFib
'Lilian Woodberry' (Z)	WFib
'Limoneum' (Sc)	ENfk MHer WFib
'Lincolnshire Lady' (R)	ECtt
'Lipstick' (St)	WFib
'Lisa' (Min/C)	WFib
'Lisa Jo' (St/v/Dw/d)	WFib
'Little Alice' (Dw/d) ♀H1c	SAll WFib
'Little Gem' (Sc)	ENfk MHer WFib
'Little Jip' (Z/d/v) ♀H1c	SAll WFib
'Little Spikey' (St/Min/d)	WFib
'Lizzie Hillier' (R)	WFib
'Lollipop' (Z/d)	WFib
'Lord Baden-Powell'	see *P.* 'Colonel Baden-Powell'
'Lord Bute' (R) ♀H1c	CRav CSpe ECtt LCro MCot MHer NPer SPet SPhm SVen WFib WGwG
'Lord de Ramsey'	see *P.* 'Tip Top Duet'
'Lord Roberts' (Z)	WFib
'Lottie Lungburgh' (Z/St) **new**	WFib
'Lotusland' (Dw/St/C) ♀H1c	ECtt SPoG WFib
I 'Louise' (R) ♀H1c	ECtt WFib
'Love Song' (R/v)	WFib
'Lucy Gunnett' (Z/d/v) ♀H1c	ECtt WFib
'Lyewood Bonanza' (R)	WFib
'Lyric' (Min/d)	WFib
'Mabel Grey' (Sc) ♀H1c	CSpe ECtt ENfk MHer MNHC NPer NWsh SAll SPet WFib
§ 'Madame Auguste Nonin' (U/Sc)	CRav ENfk MHer NWsh SAll SPet WFib
'Madame Crousse' (I/d) ♀H1c	WFib
'Madame Layal' (A) ♀H1c	MHer WFib
'Madame Margot'	see *P.* 'Hederinum Variegatum'
'Madame Recamier' (Z/d)	ECtt
'Madame Salleron' (Min/v)	SAll
'Maestro Salmon' (I) **new**	ETMg
'Magda' (Z/d)	SAll
magenteum	MHer
'Magnum' (R)	WFib
'Majestic' (Z/d) **new**	WFib
'Mandarin' (R)	ECtt SAll
'Mangles' Variegated' (Z/v)	WFib
'Maple Leaf' (Sc)	NWsh
'Maréchal MacMahon' (Z/C)	ENfk
'Margaret Soley' (R) ♀H1c	WFib
'Margaret Thorp'	SAll
'Margaret Waite' (R)	WFib
'Margery Stimpson' (Min/d)	WFib
'Marie Rudlin' (R)	SAll
'Marie Thomas' (Sc)	SBch
MARIMBA ('Fisrimba'PBR)	SCoo
'Marion Saunders' (Dec)	CRav WFib
'Mariquita' (R)	WFib
'Mark' (Dw/d)	WFib
'Marmalade' (Min/d)	SAll
'Marquis of Bute' (R/v)	MHer SPet
'Martha Parmer' (Min)	SAll
'Martin Parrett' (Min/d)	WFib
'Mary Harrison' (Z/d)	WFib
'Maureen' (Min)	SAll
I 'Maureen' Hoddinott (Z/d)	MHer
'Mauve Beauty' (I/d)	WFib
'Maxime Kovalevski' (Z)	WFib
'Maxine Colley' (Z/d/v)	SAll
'May Day' (R)	WFib
'May Magic' (R)	WFib
'Meadowside Dark and Dainty' (St)	WFib
'Meadowside Fancy' (Z/d/C)	SAll
'Meadowside Mahogany' (Z/C)	SAll
'Meadowside Midnight' (St/C)	WFib
'Medley' (Min/d)	WFib
MELOCHERRY ('Pacmel'PBR) (Tempo Series) (Z/d)	SSea
MELOSILVER ('Penber') (Tempo Series) (Z/d/v)	SAll
'Memento' (Min/d)	SAll WFib
'Mendip' (R)	WFib
'Mendip Candy Floss' (R)	WFib
'Mendip Royale' (R)	WFib
'Meon Maid' (R)	WFib
'Mere Casino' (Z)	WFib
'Mexican Beauty' (I)	WFib
'Mexicana'	see *P.* 'Rouletta'
'Mexicanerin'	see *P.* 'Rouletta'
'Michael' (A) ♀H1c	MHer SPet
'Michelle West' (Min)	WFib
'Mike West' (St) **new**	WFib
MILLENNIUM DAWN (Dw)	SAll
'Millfield Gem' (I/d)	WFib
'Millfield Rose' (I/d)	SAll
'Mini-Czech' (Min/St)	ECtt SAll WBrk
'Minnie' (Z/d/St)	WBrk WFib
'Minstrel Boy' (R)	WFib
'Minx' (Min/d)	WFib
'Miriam Basey'	see *P.* 'Dwarf Miriam Baisey'
'Miss Burdett Coutts' (Z/v)	MHer WFib
'Miss Muffett' (Min/d)	WFib
§ 'Miss Stapleton'	LCro MHer WFib

'Misterioso' (R)	WFib
'Misty Morning' (R)	WFib
'Mixed Blessings' (Min/C)	SAll
'Modesty' (Z/d)	WFib
'Mohawk' (R)	WFib
'Mole'	see *P.* 'The Mole'
'Molly' (A)	ENfk
'Monique McEwan' (Z/St) new	WFib
'Monsieur Ninon' misapplied	see *P.* 'Madame Auguste Nonin'
§ 'Monsieur Ninon' (U)	WFib
'Mont Blanc' (Z/v)	SAll WFib
'Montague Garabaldi Smith' (R)	WFib
'Monty's Magic' (R) new	ECtt
'Moon Maiden' (A)	WFib
MOONLIGHT VIOLINO (Moonlight Series) (Z)	SSea
'Moor' (Min/d)	SAll
'More's Victory' (U/Sc)	WFib
MORNING SUN ('Pacmorsu'^{PBR}) (Green Leaf Series) (Z)	SAll
'Morval' (Dw/C/d) 🏆^{H1c}	SAll WFib
'Morwenna' (R)	MHer WCot WFib
'Mosaic Gay Baby' (I/v/d)	WFib
'Mosquitaway Eva' (A) new	ETMg
'Mosquitaway Lizzy' (A) new	ETMg
'Mr Henry Cox' (Z/v) 🏆^{H1c}	MHer SAll WFib
'Mr Wren' (Z)	ECtt ELan SAll WFib
'Mrs Cannell' (Z)	WFib
'Mrs Farren' (Z/v)	MCot
'Mrs G.H. Smith' (A) 🏆^{H1c}	ECtt SPet WFib
'Mrs J.C. Mappin' (Z/v) 🏆^{H1c}	ECtt
'Mrs Kingsbury' (U)	WFib
'Mrs Martin' (I/d)	WFib
'Mrs McKenzie' (Z/St)	WFib
'Mrs Morf' (R)	ECtt
'Mrs Parker' (Z/d/v)	ECtt SAll WFib
'Mrs Pollock' (Z/v)	ECtt ELan MCot NEgg SAll SCoo WBrk WFib
'Mrs Quilter' (Z/C) 🏆^{H1c}	ECtt SAll WBrk WFib
'Mrs Salter Bevis' (Z/Ca/d)	SAll
'Mrs W.A.R. Clifton' (I/d)	WFib
multibracteatum	WFib
multiradiatum	WFib
mutans	WFib
§ 'Mutzel' (I/v)	SAll
'My Chance' (Dec)	WFib
§ ***myrrhifolium*** var. ***coriandrifolium***	MHer WFib
'Mystery' (U) 🏆^{H1c}	CRav ECtt LCro WFib
'Narina' (I)	SCoo
'Needham Market' (A)	ENfk SPet
'Neil Jameson' (Z/v)	SAll
'Nellie Nuttall' (Z)	WFib
NEONA ('Pacneon'^{PBR}) (Z)	SSea
'Nervous Mabel' (Sc) 🏆^{H1c}	MHer WFib
'Nettlestead' (Dw)	SAll
'Newbridge' (St/Min/d)	SAll
'Newchurch' (Z/St)	WFib
'Nicor Star' (Min)	WFib
'Noel' (Z/Ca/d)	ECtt SAll
'Noele Gordon' (Z/d)	SAll WFib
'Occold Embers' (Dw/C)	SAll
'Occold Shield' (Dw/C/d) 🏆^{H1c}	ECtt MHer NEgg SAll WBrk WFib
'Occold Tangerine' (Z)	WFib
'Occold Volcano' (Dw/C/d)	WFib
'Octavia Hill' (Z)	ETMg

odoratissimum (Sc) 🏆^{H1c}	ENfk GPoy MHer SAll SPet SRms WFib
'Odyssey' (Min)	WFib
'Old Spice' (Sc/v)	ENfk WFib
'Oldbury Duet' (A/v) 🏆^{H1c}	MHer SPet
'Olivia' (R)	WFib
'Opera House' (R)	WFib
'Orange Fizz' (Sc) 🏆^{H1c}	CRav MHer NWsh SPet SRms WFib
'Orange Imp' (Dw/d)	SAll
'Orange Parfait' (R)	WFib
'Orange Splash' (Z)	SAll
'Orangeade' (Dw/d)	SAll WFib
'Orangesonne' (Z/d)	SAll
'Orchid Clorinda' (Sc)	WFib
'Orchid Paloma' (Dw/d)	ECtt WFib
'Orion' (Min/d)	WFib
'Orsett' (Sc) 🏆^{H1c}	GLog SAll
otaviense	WFib
'Our Flynn' (Z/St)	WFib
'Our Gynette' (Dec)	SAll
'Our Henry' (Dw/d)	WFib
PAC cultivars	see under selling name
'Pagoda' (Z/St/d)	MHer SAll WFib
'Paisley Red' (Z/d)	WFib
'Pamela Vaughan' (Z/St)	WFib
'Pampered Lady' (A)	SPet
panduriforme	WFib
papilionaceum	ELan MCot MHer WFib
'Parisienne' (R)	WFib
'Party Dress' (Z/d)	WFib
'Pat Hannam' (St)	WFib
'Paton's Unique' (U/Sc) 🏆^{H1c}	ECtt ELan ENfk MCot MHer SAll SPet SPhm SVen WCot WFib
'Patricia Andrea' (Z/T) 🏆^{H1c}	NPer SAll WFib
patulum	WFib
'Paul Crampel' (Z)	MCot MHer WFib
'Paul West' (Min/d)	NWad SAll SBch
'Pauline Harris' (R)	WFib
'Peace' (Min/C)	WFib
'Peach Princess' (R)	ECtt
'Pegasus' (Min)	SAll
'Peggy Franklin' (Min)	SAll
'Peggy Sue' (R)	SAll
PELFI cultivars	see under selling name
peltatum	WFib
'Penny' (Z/d)	WFib
'Penny Lane' (Z)	WFib
'Pensby' (Dw)	WFib
'Peppermint Lace' (Sc)	NWsh
'Peppermint Scented Rose' (Sc)	MSCN
'Perfect' (Z)	WFib
'Pershore Princess'	WBrk
'Petals' (Z/v)	SPoG
'Peter Beard' (Dw/d)	SAll
'Peter Godwin' (R)	WFib
'Peter's Choice' (R)	WFib
'Petit Pierre'	see *P.* 'Kleine Liebling'
'Phyllis Richardson' (R/d)	SAll WFib
'Phyllis Variegated' (U/v)	ECtt ENfk MHer SAll SPet WCot WFib
'Pink Aurore' (U)	CRav WFib
'Pink Bonanza' (R)	WFib
'Pink Capitatum'	see *P.* 'Pink Capricorn'
§ 'Pink Capricorn' (Sc)	CRav ECtt ENfk LCro NWsh SAll SRms WFib
'Pink Champagne' (Sc)	MHer
'Pink Dolly Varden' (Z/v)	ECtt WFib
'Pink Fondant' (Min/d)	WFib
'Pink Gay Baby'	see *P.* 'Sugar Baby'

'Pink Happy Thought' (Z/v)	ECtt SAll WFib
'Pink Needles' (Min/St)	MHer WFib
'Pink Pandora' (T)	WFib
'Pink Pet' (U)	ECtt
'Pink Rambler' (Z/d)	WFib
'Pink Rosebud' (Z/d)	WFib
'Playboy Blush' (Dw)	SAll
'Playmate' (Min/St)	WFib
'Plum Rambler' (Z/d)	ECtt EShb WBrk WFib
'Polka' (U) ♀H1c	SPet WFib
POLKA (Z/d)	SAll
'Pompeii' (R)	WFib
'Poquita' (Sc)	SRms
'Porchfield' (Min/St)	WBrk
praemorsum	WFib
'Preseli Lottie' (Z/d)	WFib
'Preston Park' (Z/C)	WFib
'Pretty Polly' (Sc)	WFib
'Prim' (Dw/St/d)	WFib
'Prince of Orange' (Sc) ♀H1c	CRav ECtt ENfk GPoy MCot MHer NWsh SPet SPhm SRms WFib
'Princeanum' (Sc) ♀H1c	WFib
'Princess Abigail' (Dw/d)	ECtt WFib
'Princess Alexandra' (Z/d/v)	SAll
'Princess Josephine' (R)	WFib
'Princess of Balcon'	see *P.* 'Roi des Balcons Lilas'
'Princess of Wales' (R)	WFib
'Princess Virginia' (R/v)	WFib
'Priory Salmon' (St/d)	EShb
'Priory Star' (St/Min/d)	WFib
pseudoglutinosum	WFib
'Pulsar Salmon Splash' (Pulsar Series) (Z)	LRHS NRHS
'Pungent Peppermint' (Sc)	SRms
'Purple Rogue' (R)	WFib
'Purple Unique' (U/Sc)	ECtt ENfk MCot MHer SPet SVen WFib
'Pygmalion' (Z/d/v)	WFib
'Quantock' (R)	WFib
'Quantock Angelique' (A)	SPet
'Quantock Butterfly' (A)	SPet
'Quantock Candy' (A) ♀H1c	ELan SPet
'Quantock Clare' (A)	SPet
'Quantock Kirsty' (A) ♀H1c	SPet
'Quantock Marjorie' (A) ♀H1c	SPet
'Quantock Perfection' (A) ♀H1c	SPet WFib
'Quantock Sally' (A/d)	SPet
'Quantock Ultimate' (A) ♀H1c	ECtt SPet
'Queen Esther' (Z/d/St)	SAll
'Queen of Denmark' (Z/d)	SAll WFib
'Queen of Hearts' (I × Z/d)	WFib
quercifolium (Sc)	ECtt ELan GPoy WFib
quinquelobatum	WFib
radens (Sc)	ENfk WFib
'Radula' (Sc) ♀H1c	ELan MHer SAll SPet SRms WFib
'Radula Roseum' (Sc)	WFib
'Ragamuffin' (Dw/d)	SAll
'Rager's Star' (Dw)	SAll
(Rainbow Series) RAINBOW NEON ('Genraineon') (I)	SSea
- RAINBOW WHITE ('Genrawhite') (I)	SSea
'Raspberry Sundae' (R)	SAll
'Ray Bidwell' (Min)	WFib
'Red Admiral' (Min/d/v)	SAll
§ 'Red Black Vesuvius' (Min/C)	MHer WFib
'Red Cascade' (I) ♀H1c	SAll WFib
'Red Gables'	WAvo
'Red Ice' (Min/d)	SAll
'Red Pandora' (Z/T) ♀H1c	SAll WFib
'Red Pimpernel' (Z/T)	WFib
'Red Pimpernella'	SAll
'Red Rambler' (Z/d)	SAll WBrk WFib
'Red Robin' (R)	ENfk WCot
'Red Silver Cascade'	see *P.* 'Mutzel'
'Red Spider' (Dw/Ca)	WFib
'Red Startel' (Z/St/d)	WFib
'Red Susan Pearce' (R)	WFib
'Red Witch' (Dw/St/d)	MHer SAll WBrk WFib
§ RED-MINI-CASCADE ('Rotemica') (I)	SAll
'Redondo' (Dw/d)	SAll
'Reflections' (Z/d)	WFib
'Reg 'Q'' (Z/C)	ECtt
'Regina' (Z/d)	ECtt SAll WFib
'Rembrandt' (R)	SAll WFib
'Renate Parsley' ♀H1c	LCro MHer WFib
reniforme	GPoy MHer WFib
'Reunion Rose' (Sc)	WFib
'Richard Collins' (St)	SAll
'Richard Gibbs' (Sc)	ENfk MHer
'Richard Key' (Z/d/C)	WFib
'Rietje van der Lee' (A)	ENfk WFib
'Rigel' (Min/d)	SAll
'Rimfire' (R) ♀H1c	LCro MHer NWad WFib
'Rio Grande' (I/d)	MHer SAll WFib
'Rober's Lemon Rose' (Sc)	ENfk MHer SEND SPet SRms WBrk WFib
'Rober's Salmon Coral' (Dw/d)	SAll
'Robert Fish' (Z/C)	ECtt SCoo
'Robert McElwain' (Z/d)	WFib
'Robin' (Sc)	SAll
'Robin' (R)	ECtt
'Robin's Unique' (U)	WFib
'Robyn Hannah' (St/d) ♀H1c	MHer
'Rogue' (R)	WFib
§ 'Roi des Balcons Lilas' (I)	SAll SSea
'Roller's Echo' (A)	WFib
'Roller's Pioneer' (I/v)	ENfk SAll
'Roller's Satinique' (U)	MHer
'Rollison's Unique' (U)	MHer WFib
'Rosa della Sera' (St)	SAll
'Rose Bengal' (A)	ENfk
'Rose Eye' (Dw)	WFib
'Rose of Amsterdam' (Min/d)	WFib
'Rose Silver Cascade' (I)	ECtt MCot MHer SAll
'Rosebud Supreme' (Z/d)	WFib
'Rosina Read' (Dw/d)	SAll
'Rosita' (Dw/d)	SAll
ROSITA ('Pacsita'[PBR]) (Z) **new**	SSea
'Rosmaroy' (R)	WFib
'Rosy Dawn' (Min/d)	WFib
'Rote Mini-cascade'	see *P.* RED-MINI-CASCADE
§ 'Rouletta' (I/d)	WFib
'Royal Ascot' (R)	SPet
(Royal Series) ROYAL CANDY CANE ('Klep01028') (I)	SSea
- ROYAL LAVENDER ('Klepp07196'[PBR]) (I)	SSea
- ROYAL RED ('Kleroder'[PBR]) (I)	SSea
'Royal Norfolk' (Min/d) ♀H1c	SAll

'Royal Oak' (Sc) ♀^{H1c}	CPbh ECtt ENfk MCot MHer MNHC NWad NWsh SAll SPet SPoG SRms SVen WFib
§ 'Royal Purple' (Z/d)	WFib
'Royal Sovereign' (R)	WFib
'Ruben' (d)	LSou
'Ruby' (Min/d)	WFib
'Rushmere' (Dw/d)	WFib
'Rushmoor Golden Rosebud' (Z)	ECtt WFib
'Rushmoor Mrs Eve Scott' (Z/d)	ECtt WFib
SAILING ('Klesail') (Z/d)	SSea
'Saint Elmo's Fire' (St/Min/d)	MHer WFib
SAINT MALO ('Guisaint') (I)	ECtt
'Salmon Beauty' (Dw/d)	WFib
§ 'Salmon Irene' (Z/d)	WFib
SALMON PRINCESS ('Pacsalpri'^{PBR}) (Z/d)	ETMg
'Salmon Queen'	see *P.* 'Lachskönigin'
SALMON QUEEN ('Pacsalque'^{PBR}) (Z)	SSea
'Salmon Slam' (R)	SAll
salmoneum	WFib
'Samantha' (R)	WFib
'Samantha Stamp' (Dw/C/d)	WFib
SAMELIA ('Pensam'^{PBR}) (Dark Line Series) (Z/d)	SSea
'Sammi Brougham' (Dw/Z)	WFib
'Sancho Panza' (Dec)	CSpe WFib
'Sandra Lorraine' (I/d)	WFib
SANGRIA NOVA ('Gendana'^{PBR}) (Z)	SSea
'Sanguineum'	CSpe NHim
'Santa Maria' (Z/d)	SAll
§ 'Sarah Don' (A/v)	ECtt WFib
'Sarah Jane' (Sc)	WFib
'Sassa'^{PBR} (Quality Series) (Z/d)	ETMg SSea
'Satsuki' (R) ♀^{H1c}	ECtt
'Saxifragoides'	WFib
'Scarlet Gem' (Z/St)	WBrk WFib
'Scarlet Pet' (U) ♀^{H1c}	ECtt ENfk NWsh SPet
'Scarlet Rambler' (Z/d)	ECtt EShb WFib
'Scarlet Unique' (U)	MCot MNHC WFib
schizopetalum	MHer WFib
'Schottii' ♀^{H1c}	CPbh LCro MHer WFib
'Scottow Star' (Z/C)	WFib
'Seaview Silver' (Min/St)	WFib
'Seaview Sparkler' (Z/St)	WFib
'Secret Love' (Sc)	SRms
'Seeley's Pansy' (A)	MHer
'Sefton' (R) ♀^{H1c}	WFib
'Shannon'	WFib
'Shaun Jacobs' (Min/d)	SAll
'Shimmer' (Z/d)	SAll
§ 'Shottesham Pet' (Sc)	ECtt ENfk MHer NWad SPet SRms
sidoides ♀^{H1c}	CPbh CRav CSpe EAJP ECtt GPoy IPot LCro MCot MHer SAll SBch SChr SPhm SPhx SPlb SVen WAvo WFib WHer WKif
- black-flowered	SBrt
- 'Sloe Gin Fizz'	CSpe
'Sil Falko'^{PBR} (I)	LSou
'Sil Linus'^{PBR} (Z)	LSou
'Sil Malaika'^{PBR} (I)	LSou
'Sil Tomke'^{PBR} (I)	LSou
'Silver Blazon' (Z/Dw/C/v)	WFib

'Silver Delight' (v/d)	WFib
'Silver Kewense' (Dw/v)	WFib
'Silver Snow' (Min/St/d)	WFib
'Silver Wings' (Z/v)	SAll
'Simplicity' (Z)	SAll
'Skelly's Pride' (Z)	WFib
'Skies of Italy' (Z/C/d)	WFib
'Snow Flurry' (Sc)	WFib
'Snowbaby' (Min/d)	WFib
'Snowdrift' (I/d)	SAll WFib
'Snowflake' (Min)	see *P.* 'Atomic Snowflake'
'Snowstorm' (Z)	WFib
'Sofie'	see *P.* 'Decora Rose'
'Solferino' (A)	ENfk
SOLO ('Guillio') (Z/I)	SAll
'Something Else' (Z/St/d)	SAll
'Something Special' (Z/d) ♀^{H1c}	SAll WFib
SOPHIE CASADE	see *P.* 'Decora Rose'
'Sophie Dumaresque' (Z/v) ♀^{H1c}	WFib
'Sophie Emma' (Z)	WFib
'Sophie Marion' (Dw/Z)	WFib
'South American Bronze' (R) ♀^{H1c}	WFib
'South American Delight' (R)	SAll
'Southern Peach' (Min/d)	SAll
'Southern Rosina' (Dw)	WFib
'Spanish Angel' (A) ♀^{H1c}	MHer SPet WFib
SPANISH WINE BURGUNDY ('Pacswibu') (Z) **new**	SSea
'Sparkler' (Z)	SAll
'Spellbound' (R)	WFib
'Spital Dam' (Dw/d)	SAll WFib
'Spitfire' (Z/Ca/d/v)	ECtt SAll WFib
§ 'Splendide' ♀^{H1c}	CPbh CSpe MHer SWvt WFib
'Spot-on-bonanza' (R) ♀^{H1c}	ECtt WFib
'Springfield Black' (R)	MCot SAll
'Springtime' (Z/d)	WFib
'Stadt Bern' (Z/C)	SAll
× ***stapletoniae***	see *P.* 'Miss Stapleton'
'Star Flecks' (St) ♀^{H1c}	SAll
'Startel Salmon' (Z/St)	MHer
'Stella Vernante' (Z/St/Dw)	SAll
'Stellar Arctic Star'	see *P.* 'Arctic Star'
'Stellar Hannaford Star'	see *P.* 'Hannaford Star'
'Stewart Meehan' (R)	WFib
'Stolen Kisses' (Min/D)	SAll
'Strawberry Fayre' (Dw/St)	WFib
'Stringer's Souvenir' (Dw/d/v)	SAll
§ 'Sugar Baby' (DwI)	MHer SAll WFib
'Summer Cloud' (Z/d)	WFib
'Summertime' (Z/d)	see *P.* 'Deacon Summertime'
'Sun Rocket' (Dw/d)	WFib
'Sundridge Moonlight' (Z/C)	WFib
'Sundridge Surprise' (Z)	WFib
SUNFLAIR ROSE ('Genrose') (Sunflair Series) (I/d)	SAll
'Sunraysia' (Z/St)	WFib
'Sunset Snow' (R)	SAll WFib
'Sunspot Petit Pierre' (Min/v)	WFib
'Sunstar' (Min/d)	WFib
'Supernova' (Z/St/d)	WFib
'Surcouf' (I)	CRav WFib
'Susan Hillier' (R)	WFib
'Susan Payne' (Dw/d)	MHer SAll

'Susan Pearce' (R)	SAll
'Susie' (Z/C)	WFib
'Susie 'Q'' (Z/C)	SAll
'Sussex Gem' (Min/d)	SAll WFib
'Swainham Mellow Yellow' (Z)	SAll
'Swanland Lace' (I/d/v)	WFib
'Swedish Angel' (A)	WFib
'Sweet Mimosa' (Sc) ♀H1c	CPbh CRav ECtt ELan ENfk MCot MHer NWsh SAll SBch SPet SRms WFib WGwG
'Sweet Sixteen' (R)	WFib
'Sweet Sue' (Min)	SAll
'Swiss Star' (Z/St)	SAll
'Sybil Holmes' (I/d)	ECtt WFib
'Tammy' (Dw/d)	SAll WFib
'Tangerine' (Min/Ca/d)	SAll
'Tara Caws' (Z)	WFib
tetragonum	MHer WFib
'The Boar' (Fr) ♀H1c	EShb MCot WFib
'The Culm' (A)	MHer WFib
'The Czar'	see *P.* 'Czar'
'The Joker' (I/d)	WFib
'The Marchioness of Bute' (R)	MHer SAll SPet WFib
§ 'The Mole' (A)	WFib
'The Tamar' (A)	MHer
'The Yar' (Z/St)	WFib
'Thomas Earle' (Z)	WFib
'Tinker West' (Z/St/Dw)	WFib
§ 'Tip Top Duet' (A) ♀H1c	MHer WFib
'Tirley Garth' (A)	WFib
tomentosum (Sc) ♀H1c	CPbh CSpe ENfk GLog GPoy LCro MCot MHer NWad NWsh SAll SPet SPhm WFib
- 'Chocolate'	see *P.* 'Chocolate Peppermint'
TOMMY ('Pactommy') (I)	SSea
tongaense	WFib
'Topscore' (Z/d)	WFib
'Tornado' (R) ♀H1c	LCro WFib
'Torrento' (Sc)	MHer NWsh SPet SRms WFib
'Tortoiseshell' (R)	WFib
'Toscana Okka' (Toscana Series) (I)	LSou
'Tracy' (Min/d)	SAll
transvaalense	CPbh
tricolor misapplied	see *P.* 'Splendide'
tricolor Curt.	CPbh
tricuspidatum	WCot WFib
trifidum	WFib
'Triomphe de Nancy' (Z/d)	WFib
triste	MHer WFib
'Trudie' (Dw/Fr)	MHer SAll WFib
'Turkish Coffee' (R)	WFib
'Turkish Delight' (Dw/C)	WFib
'Turtle's Surprise' (Z/d/v)	WBrk
'Turtle's White' (R)	SAll
'Two Dees' (Dw/d)	SAll WFib
'Uncle Ernie' (Z/C)	SAll
'Unique Aurore' (U)	MHer
'Unique Mons Ninon'	see *P.* 'Monsieur Ninon'
'Urchin' (Min/St)	WFib
'Ursula Key' (Z/c)	WFib
'Ursula's Choice' (A)	WFib
'Val Merrick' (Dw/St)	WFib
'Valentine' (Z/C)	WFib
'Vancouver Centennial' (Dw/St/C) ♀H1c	ECtt MCot MHer NEgg SAll SCoo SPoG SSea WFib
'Vandersea' (Sc)	MCot
'Variegated Clorinda' (Sc/v)	WFib

'Variegated Fragrans'	see *P.* (Fragrans Group) 'Fragrans Variegatum'
§ 'Variegated Kleine Liebling' (Min/v)	WFib
'Variegated Petit Pierre' (Min/v)	MHer WFib
'Vectis Glitter' (Z/St) ♀H1c	SAll WBrk WFib
'Vectis Imp' (Min/Z)	SAll
'Vectis Pink' (Dw/St)	WFib
'Vectis Purple' (Z/d)	WFib
'Vectis Spider' (Dw/St)	SAll
'Vectis Starbright' (Dw/St)	SAll WFib
'Vectis Volcano' (Z/St)	WFib
'Venus' (Min/d)	SAll
'Vicki Town' (R)	WFib
'Vicky Claire' (R)	WFib
VICKY ('Pacvicky'[PBR]) (I)	SSea
'Village Hill Oak' (Sc)	SAll
'Vina' (Dw/C/d)	WFib
violareum misapplied	see *P.* 'Splendide'
'Viscossisimum' (Sc)	MHer
viscosum	see *P. glutinosum*
'Vivat Regina' (Z/d)	WFib
'Voodoo' (U) ♀H1c	CPbh CSpe ECtt MCot MHer SPet SPhm WCot WFib
'Wallis Friesdorf' (Dw/C/d)	WFib
'Wantirna' (Z/v) ♀H1c	ECtt SAll
'Warrenorth Coral' (Z/C/d)	WFib
'Waveney' (Min)	SAll
'Wedding Royale' (Dw/d)	SAll WFib
'Welling' (Sc)	ENfk MHer SPet WFib
'Wendy Jane' (Dw/d)	WFib
'Wendy Read' (Dw/d)	SAll WFib
'Westdale Appleblossom' (Z/C/d)	ECtt SAll WFib
'Westside' (Z/d)	MHer WFib
'Westwood' (Z/St)	WFib
'Whisper' (R)	WFib
'White Bird's Egg' (Z)	WFib
'White Boar' (Fr)	CSpe ECtt EShb WFib
'White Bonanza' (R)	WFib
'White Butterfly' (Z/C)	SAll
'White Chiffon' (R)	SAll
'White Eggshell' (Min)	WFib
'White Feather' (Z/St)	MHer
'White Strigofolium' (R) **new**	CRav
'White Unique' (U)	SPet WFib
'Wild Spice' (Sc)	SAll
'Wilhelm Kolle' (Z)	WFib
'Wilhelm Langath' (Z/v)	ECtt EShb SCoo WBrk
'Willa' (Dec)	WFib
'Winford Festival'	SAll
'Winnie Read' (Dw/d)	SAll
'Wirral Moonlight' (Z/C/d)	WFib
'Wolverton' (Z)	WFib
'Yale' (I/d) ♀H1c	WFib
'Yan le Grounch' (Z/C)	WFib
'Yhu' (R)	WFib
'York Florist' (Z/d/v)	ECtt SAll
'Yvonne' (Z)	WFib
'Zena' (Dw)	SAll
'Zinc' (Z/d)	WFib
zonale	WFib
'Zulu King' (R)	WFib
'Zulu Warrior' (R)	WFib

Peliosanthes (*Asparagaceae*)

arisanensis B&SWJ 3639	WCru
caesia B&SWJ 5183	WCru

teta subsp. ***humilis*** RWJ 10044 — WCru

Pellaea (*Pteridaceae*)

atropurpurea — NLos
falcata — EShb NLos
ovata — SPlb WCot
rotundifolia ♀H1b — CAby CRos EShb EUJe LLWG LRHS NLos NRHS WBor WCot
viridis — CBdn

Peltandra (*Araceae*)

undulata — see *P. virginica* (L.) Schott
§ ***virginica*** (L.) Schott — EWat LLWG NPer
- 'Snow Splash' (v) — EWat

Peltaria (*Brassicaceae*)

alliacea — CSpe LEdu WCot

Peltiphyllum see *Darmera*

Peltoboykinia (*Saxifragaceae*)

§ ***tellimoides*** — CElw GCal GKev MPnt WFar WMoo WPnP
watanabei — CElw CSpe CWld EBee GEdr GPSL IMou LEdu MMoz MMrt NLar SPad WCru WMoo WPnP

Pennellianthus see *Penstemon*

Pennisetum ✿ (*Poaceae*)

× ***advena*** 'Fireworks'PBR (v) — CMea CRos EBee EPfP LRHS MAsh NRHS SCob SWvt
§ - 'Rubrum' ♀H2 — CBcs CExl CKno CMea CRos CWCL EMOT EShb LCro LOPS LRHS MAsh NRHS NWsh SCoo SMad SPhm SRot SWvt XSen
§ ***alopecuroides*** — CAco CBcs CBod CRos ECha EHoe EPed EPfP ETMg GMcL LRHS LSou NGdn NRHS SCob SLim SPer SPlb SWvt WHar XLum XSen
- B&SWJ 11434 — WCru
- AUTUMN WIZARD — see *P. alopecuroides* 'Herbstzauber'
- 'Black Beauty' — CSpe MAvo SMHy SSut WHoo
- 'Cassian's Choice' — CKno EHoe EWes GWyn IBoy ILea SHar
- 'Caudatum' — CKno
- 'Dark Desire' — CKno CRos LEdu LRHS NRHS
- 'Foxtrot' — EPPr
- 'Gelbstiel' — CKno CRos ELon LRHS NRHS
- 'Goldstrich' — XSen
- 'Hameln' — Widely available
- 'Hameln Gold' new — WTor
§ - 'Herbstzauber' — CBod CKno EHoe ELon NLar XLum XSen
- 'Little Bunny' — CBod CKno CMea CRos EBee EHoe ELan ELon EPfP EShb ESps EUJe EWTr GCal GMcL LRHS LSRN NDov NGdn NRHS SCob SWvt XSen
- 'Little Honey' (v) — CKno ELon NLar XLum XSen
- 'Magic' — CBod EBee ELon
- 'Moudry' — CBod CExl CKno EBee EHoe ELon EPed EPfP EShb EUJe LRHS MAvo NLar NSti WHar XLum
- 'Piglet'PBR — EBee
- 'Red Head' — CBWd CBod CKno CMea CRos EBee ELon EPfP EUJe EWes LRHS LSou LSun MAvo NRHS NSti SPoG WCot XSen
- f. ***viridescens*** — CRos ELan ELon EPPr EShb EUJe LEdu LRHS NDov NRHS SCob SMad SPtp WPtf XLum XSen
- 'Weserbergland' — CKno EBee EHoe ELon
- 'Woodside' — CKno EHoe EPed ESps SMad XLum
caffrum — WCot
clandestinum — EShb
compressum — see *P. alopecuroides*
'Fairy Tails' — CBWd CKno CRos EPPr EPfP EUJe LPla LRHS MAsh NDov NRHS SMHy SPoG WCot
flaccidum — EPPr
glaucum 'Purple Majesty' — CSpe SWvt
incomptum — EHoe XLum
- purple-flowered — MMoz
longistylum misapplied — see *P. villosum*
macrourum — CBWd CBod CKno CRos CSam CSpe EAJP ECha EHoe ELon EUJe LEdu LRHS MAvo MNrw MSpe NDov NRHS NWsh SEND SMHy SMad SPtp WArt WPGP
- 'Short Stuff' — CKno
massaicum 'Red Bunny Tails' — CChe LRHS SRms
- 'Red Buttons' — see *P. thunbergii* 'Red Buttons'
orientale ♀H5 — CKno CRos CSpe EAJP ECha EHoe EPfP ESps LRHS LSun MRav NRHS NWsh SEND SPer SPtp SRkn SWvt WKif XLum
- 'Flamingo' new — CRos NRHS
- 'Karley Rose'PBR — CKno CPar CRos CSpe EHoe EPed EWes IBoy IPot LRHS MAvo NDov NRHS SCob SMad SWvt
I - 'Robustum' — EBee EPPr MAvo WPGP
- 'Shogun' — CKno CRos CSam EPfP LRHS NRHS SMHy
- 'Tall Tails' — CRos EHoe EPPr EWes LRHS NDov NRHS XLum
'Paul's Giant' — CKno EBee ELon EUJe XLum
purpureum — SRms
rueppellii — see *P. setaceum*
§ ***setaceum*** ♀H6 — EAJP EPfP LCro LOPS SWvt WCot
- 'Rubrum' — see *P.* × *advena* 'Rubrum'
- 'Sky Rocket'PBR (v) — CRos LRHS NRHS
- 'Summer Samba' — CRos LRHS NRHS
thunbergii — CAby CBod CRos LRHS NRHS
§ - 'Red Buttons' — CBWd CElw CKno CRos EHoe ELon EPfP EShb LCro LEdu LOPS LRHS MAsh MAvo MGos NRHS SMHy SPoG SSut WAvo WHoo
VERTIGO ('Tift-8'PBR) — CBod
§ ***villosum*** ♀H3 — CAby CBod CExl CKno CMac CRos CSpe EAJP ECha EHoe ELan EPPr EPfP EShb EUJe LEdu LOPS LRHS LSRN NRHS NWsh SEND SPer SPhx SRms XLum XSen
- 'Cream Falls' — CBod

pennyroyal see *Mentha pulegium*

Penstemon ✿ (*Plantaginaceae*)

'Abbotsmerry' — ECtt EPfP LLHF MBNS MCot NLar SLon
§ 'Alice Hindley' ♀H4 — CBar CBcs CRos CSpe CTri EAJP ELan EPfP LRHS LSRN MCot MRav MWat NRHS SBod SCob SLon SPhm SRms SWvt WAvo WCFE WCot WHoo WKif XLum
alpinus — GWyn
'Amy Gray' — WAvo

§ 'Andenken an Friedrich Hahn' ♀^{H5}	Widely available
'Apple Blossom' misapplied	see *P.* 'Thorn'
'Apple Blossom' ♀^{H3}	Widely available
'Arabesque Appleblossom'	CRos LRHS NRHS
'Arabesque Pink'	CRos LRHS NRHS
'Arabesque Red'	CRos LRHS NRHS
'Arabesque Violet'	CRos LRHS NRHS
aridus	GEdr
arizonicus	see *P. whippleanus*
'Ashton'	WAvo
attenuatus subsp. ***militaris***	SPlb
'Audrey Cooper'	CMac MBNS
'Avon Belle' **new**	WHrl
'Axe Valley Penny Mitchell'	ECtt
azureus	GKev
'Barbara Barker'	see *P.* 'Beech Park'
§ ***barbatus***	CFis SPer SRms SSut
- 'Coccineus'	CAby CSpe EAJP GBin MBNS XLum
- 'Iron Maiden'	LRHS
- 'Jingle Bells'	IFro
- orange-flowered	SPlb
- 'Peter Catt'	CMea
- Pinacolada Series	LRHS NRHS
- - 'Pinacolada Blue'	CRos LRHS NRHS
- - 'Pinacolada Dark Rose'	CRos LRHS NRHS
- - 'Pinacolada Rosy Red'	CRos LRHS NRHS
- - 'Pinacolada White'	CRos LRHS NRHS SRms
- var. ***praecox***	MBNS SRot
- - f. ***nanus*** 'Rondo'	CRos EAJP LRHS NRHS
'Beckford'	LLHF MBNS
§ 'Beech Park' ♀^{H3}	ELan EPfP EWes LRHS
'Bisham Seedling'	see *P.* 'White Bedder'
'Blackbird'	Widely available
'Blue Riding Hood'^{PBR} (Riding Hood Series)	CRos LCro LOPS LRHS NRHS SPoG
'Blue Spring' misapplied	see *P. heterophyllus* 'Blue Spring'
'Blueberry Fudge' (Ice Cream Series)	ETMg LSou
'Blueberry Taffy'^{PBR}	ECtt
'Bodnant'	LLHF MBNS WAvo WHoo WHrl
bradburii	see *P. grandiflorus*
'Bredon'	MBNS WAvo
'Bubblegum' (Ice Cream Series)	CAby
'Burford Purple'	see *P.* 'Burgundy'
'Burford Seedling'	see *P.* 'Burgundy'
'Burford White'	see *P.* 'White Bedder'
§ 'Burgundy'	CBod CMac ECtt ESps GMaP LRHS NPer NRHS SPer SRms WAvo XLum
californicus	SBrt
§ ***campanulatus***	CRos EPot EWes LRHS NRHS SRms
- PC&H 148	SDys
- ***pulchellus***	see *P. campanulatus*
- 'Roseus' misapplied	see *P. kunthii*
'Candy Pink'	see *P.* 'Old Candy Pink'
cardwellii	EWes
'Castle Forbes'	GMaP MBNS SRms
'Cathedral Rose'	ELan EPfP LRHS
'Catherine de la Mare'	see *P. heterophyllus* 'Catherine de la Mare'
'Centra'	MBNS
'Charles Rudd'	ECtt ELan ELon EPfP LSRN MBNS NLar SRms SWvt WHrl
§ 'Cherry' ♀^{H3}	ECtt ESps MBNS SHar
'Cherry Ripe' misapplied	see *P.* 'Cherry'
§ 'Chester Scarlet' ♀^{H3}	ECtt MBNS WCFE WKif
'Choirboy'	EWes
clutei	LLHF
cobaea	CSpe
'Comberton'	MBNS WAvo
confertus	CTri EBee EPot MMuc
- RCB/MO A-7	WCot
'Connie's Pink' ♀^{H4}	MBNS SRms WAvo
'Coral Sea'	WFar
'Cottage Garden Red'	see *P.* 'Windsor Red'
§ 'Countess of Dalkeith'	ECtt ELan GBin MCot MRav SHar SRms SWvt WAvo WCFE
crandallii	EPot
cristatus	see *P. eriantherus*
* ***cyananthus*** var. ***utahensis***	WCot
'Dark Towers'^{PBR}	CAbb CBod CRos CSpe ECtt EPfP EUJe IPot LRHS LSou MBNS MHol MNrw MSCN NHpl NRHS SLon SPad SPoG WCot WHlf WKif
davidsonii	EWes GCrg GEdr NSla WOld
- var. ***davidsonii***	WAbe
- var. ***menziesii*** 'Microphyllus'	GCrg GEdr LLHF NWad WAbe
- var. ***praeteritus***	GEdr
- 'Silverwells'	GEdr
'Dazzler'	SWvt
'Delfts Blue Riding Hood'^{PBR} (Riding Hood Series)	CRos CSpe LCro LOPS LRHS NRHS
'Devonshire Cream'	MBNS
diffusus	see *P. serrulatus*
digitalis	MBNS SRms
§ - 'Husker Red'	Widely available
- 'Isa'	WCot
- 'Mystica'	CRos EBee LRHS NRHS
- 'Purpureus'	see *P. digitalis* 'Husker Red'
- 'Ruby Tuesday'	EWes
- white-flowered	EBee
§ 'Drinkstone Red'	EHrv MBNS SDys
'Drinkwater Red'	see *P.* 'Drinkstone Red'
(Elgar Series) 'Elgar Crown of India'	WCot
- 'Elgar Firefly'	WCot
- 'Elgar Light of Life'	WCot
- 'Elgar Nimrod'	WCot
'Ellenbank Amethyst'	SDys
'Ellenbank Cardinal'	WKif
'Ellwood Red Phoenix'	MBNS
'Elmley'	MBNS WAvo
§ ***eriantherus***	LLHF SPlb
ETNA ('Yatna') (Volcano Series)	CRos ECtt EPfP EUJe GMcL LRHS MBNS NRHS SAll SRms
euglaucus	EBee GKev LLHF
- NNS 07-397	GKev
§ 'Evelyn' ♀^{H4}	CTri ECha ELan EPfP ESps IBoy IRob LRHS LSRN MBNS MCot MHer MRav SPer SPoG SRGP SRms SWvt WAvo WKif XLum
'Fanny's Blush'	SWvt
'Firebird'	see *P.* 'Schoenholzeri'
'Flame'	MBNS WAvo
'Flamingo'	CRos EAJP ECtt ELon EPfP EWes GBin LRHS MBNS NLar NRHS SGbt SHar SRms SWvt
§ ***fruticosus***	MAsh
var. ***scouleri*** ♀^{H5}	
- - 'Albus' ♀^{H5}	CSpe WAbe
- - 'Amethyst'	WAbe
FUJIYAMA ('Yayama'^{PBR})	CBod CChe CPla CRos ECtt EPfP LRHS NRHS SAll SLon SPad SRms SWvt
'Garden Red'	see *P.* 'Windsor Red'

	'Garnet'	see *P.* 'Andenken an Friedrich Hahn'
	gentianoides B&SWJ 10271	WCru
	'Geoff Hamilton'	CRos ECtt MBNS NLar SLon SPoG WAvo
	'George Elrick'	LLHF WHoo
§	'George Home' ♀H3	EWes GBin MBNS SRms
	'George Moon'	SPad
	'Gilchrist'	ECtt
	glaber	EWld SPlb WKif
	- 'Roundway Snowflake'	SHar SRms
	'Gloire des Quatre Rues'	XLum
§	***grandiflorus***	EPfP
	- 'War Axe'	WHil
	hallii	CPBP EPot EWes
	hartwegii 'Albus'	SHar SRms
	- 'Picotee Red'	CRos LRHS NRHS
§	***heterophyllus***	LRHS MNrw MSCN NGBl SRkn SRms
	- 'Blue Gem'	CElw CTri
§	- 'Blue Spring'	CRos CSpe EPfP LRHS MRav NRHS
§	- 'Catherine de la Mare' ♀H4	CRos EBee ELan GBin LRHS LSRN MWat NRHS SBod SCob SHar SPer SWvt WKif WSpi XLum
	- 'Electric Blue'	CBod CRos LRHS MHol NRHS SLon SPhm
	- 'Heavenly Blue'	Widely available
	- 'Jeanette'	CMea WTor
	- 'True Blue'	see *P. heterophyllus*
	- 'Züriblau'	EBee SPlb WHil
§	'Hewell Pink Bedder' ♀H4	CBod CRos EPfP GBin GPSL LRHS MBNS MRav NCou NRHS SPtp SRms SWvt
	'Hewitt's Pink'	SLon
	hidalgensis	WCot
	'Hidcote Pink' ♀H3	Widely available
	'Hidcote Purple'	SHar WHoo XLum
	'Hidcote White'	MHer SWvt
	'Hillview Pink'	SLon XLum
§	***hirsutus***	EBee XLum
	- 'Blue Foam'	GWyn
	- var. ***pygmaeus***	CMea EDAr NHpl NRya SPlb SRms WHoo
*	- - f. ***albus***	WHoo
	- - 'Purpureus'	WAbe
	'Hopleys Variegated' (v)	SWvt
	'Hot Pink Riding Hood'PBR (Riding Hood Series)	CRos LCro LOPS LRHS NRHS SPoG
	'James Bowden'	MBNS
	JEAN GRACE ('Penbow')	ECtt LCro LOPS
	'John Booth'	MBNS
	'John Nash' misapplied	see *P.* 'Alice Hindley'
	'John Nash'	SRms
	'Juicy Grape' (Ice Cream Series)	CPla ETMg SAll WCot
	'June'	see *P.* 'Pennington Gem'
	'Jupiter'	XLum
	KILIMANJARO ('Yajaro') (Volcano Series)	CRos EPfP LRHS SLon SRms WFar
	'King George V'	Widely available
	'Knight's Purple'	ECtt
§	***kunthii***	MAsh
§	***laetus*** subsp. ***roezlii***	EPot GCrg
	'Lavender Riding Hood' (Riding Hood Series)	CRos LRHS NRHS
§	'Le Phare'	XLum
	'Lilac and Burgundy'	MBNS SRms SWvt
	'Lilac Frost'	LLHF SRGP WMoo
	linarioides	SBrt
	- 'Marilyn Ross'	ECtt
	'Lord Home'	see *P.* 'George Home'
	lyallii	ELan GWyn MPie SRms WCot
	'Lynette'	MBNS SBch
	'Macpenny's Pink'	CMac MBNS WAvo XLum
	'Madame Golding'	MBNS XLum
	'Marble Riding Hood'PBR (Riding Hood Series)	CRos LRHS NRHS
	'Margery Fish' ♀H3	CFis ECtt EWes
	'Maurice Gibbs' ♀H3	CBcs ECtt EPfP ESps EWes LSRN MBNS MBel SBod SRms
	'Melting Candy' (Ice Cream Series)	WCot
	mensarum	CFis LRHS
	Mexicali hybrids (Carillo Series) 'Carillo Purple'	CRos LRHS NRHS
	- - 'Carillo Red'	CRos LRHS NRHS
	× ***mexicanus*** 'Sunburst Amethyst'	ECtt SRms XLum
	- 'Sunburst Ruby'	SLon
	'Midnight'	ECtt ELan EWTr GBin MBNS MRav MSwo SEND SHar SWvt WCFE XLum
	'Modesty'	MBNS SRms
	'Mother of Pearl'	CBcs CRos CTri ELan EPfP EShb ESps GBin GMaP LRHS LSRN MBNS MCot MSwo MWat SHar SRms SWvt
	'Mrs Miller'	MBNS
	'Mrs Morse'	see *P.* 'Chester Scarlet'
	'Mrs Oliver'	EWes
	multiflorus	EBee
§	'Myddelton Gem'	MWat SRms
	'Myddelton Red'	see *P.* 'Myddelton Gem'
	newberryi f. ***humilior***	EPot
§	- subsp. ***sonomensis***	GCrg SRms WAbe
	'Newbury Gem'	MBNS SHar SWvt
	'Oaklea Red'	GBin
§	'Old Candy Pink'	SWvt
	'Osprey' ♀H3	CMac CMea CRos EAJP ECtt ELan EPfP ESps GBin IRob LRHS MBNS SRms SWvt
	ovatus	CMac ELan SPhx SRms WKif
	'Overbury'	ECtt SRms WAvo
	'Papal Purple'	MAsh MBNS MHer SHar SRms XLum
	'Patio Bells Pink'	CRos
	PATIO BELLS RED ('Yapbred')	CRos
	'Patio Wine'	WAvo
	'Peace'	GBin MBNS
§	'Pennington Gem' ♀H3	CTri ELan MHer SRms SWvt
	(Pensham Series) 'Pensham Amelia Jane'	CAby CRos CWGN ECtt ELon EPau EPfP GMcL GWyn LRHS LSRN LSou MBNS MTis NLar NRHS SAll SLon SPer SRms SWvt WCot
	- 'Pensham Arctic Fox'	CSpe ECtt LRHS SLon
	- 'Pensham Arctic Sunset'	WHrl
	- 'Pensham Avonbelle'	MBNS SRms
	- 'Pensham Bilberry Ice'	MBNS SWvt
	- 'Pensham Blackberry Ice'	ECtt LSou MBNS SLon SRms
	- 'Pensham Blueberry Ice'	ECtt LSou MBNS SAll SWvt
	- 'Pensham Capricorn Moon'	ECtt
	- 'Pensham Charlotte Louise'	CRos ECtt ELon LRHS NRHS SRms
	- 'Pensham Czar'	Widely available
	- 'Pensham Dorothy Wilson'	CRos LRHS NRHS
	- 'Pensham Eleanor Young'	CRos ECtt EPfP LRHS MBNS SLon SPoG SPtp SWvt
	- 'Pensham Freshwater Pearl'	SRms WHoo

- 'Pensham Great Expectations'	ECtt
- 'Pensham Jessica Mai'	CRos ECtt LRHS LSou NRHS SPer SRms SWvt
- 'Pensham Just Jayne'	CRos ECtt ELon EPfP LRHS LSRN MBNS NRHS SAll SLon SPer SRms SWvt WHoo WSpi XLum
- 'Pensham Kay Burton'	EPfP
- 'Pensham Laura'	CAby CDor CRos CSam CWGN ECtt EPfP LCro LOPS LRHS LSRN LSun MAsh MAvo MBNS NPri NRHS SAll SLon SPad SPer SRms SWvt WBor WHoo
- 'Pensham Loganberry Ice'	LSou MBNS SLon
- 'Pensham Miss Wilson'	SRms
- 'Pensham Plum Jerkum'	CAby CDor CRos CWGN ECrN ECtt ELon EPfP GMcL LCro LOPS LRHS LSou MAvo MBNS MCot MHer MPie NLar NRHS SAll SCob SLon SPad SPer SRms SWvt WHil WHoo
- 'Pensham Raspberry Ice'	CRos MBNS SLon
- 'Pensham Son of Raven'	WAvo
- 'Pensham Tayberry Ice'	CRos ECtt MBNS SLon SRms
- 'Pensham Ted's Purple'	WCFE
- 'Pensham Victoria Plum'	CElw EShb SHar WHoo
- 'Pensham Wedding Bells'	ETMg SRms
- 'Pensham Wedding Day'	CBod CMea CRos CSpe ECrN EPfP GMcL LRHS LSRN MBNS MCot NLar NRHS SAll SCob SLon SPer SPoG SPtp WHoo
- 'Pensham Westminster Belle'	ECtt LBuc MTis WHil
'Pershore Anniversary'	WAvo
'Pershore Carnival'	SRms WAvo WHrl
'Pershore Fanfare'	WAvo WHrl
'Pershore Festival'	WAvo
'Pershore Pink Necklace'	SRms SWvt WAvo
'Phare'	see *P.* 'Le Phare'
(Phoenix Series) PHOENIX APPLEBLOSSOM 09 ('Peni Ablos09')	CRos LRHS NRHS
- PHOENIX LAVENDER ('Peni Laver')	CRos LRHS NRHS
- PHOENIX MAGENTA 09 ('Peni Mag09')	CRos LRHS NRHS
- PHOENIX PINK ('Pheni Pinka')	CRos LRHS NRHS
- PHOENIX RED ('Pheni Reeda' PBR)	CRos LRHS NRHS
- PHOENIX ROSE ('Penharros' PBR)	CRos LRHS NRHS
- PHOENIX VIOLET 09 ('Peni Vio09' PBR)	CRos EPfP LRHS NRHS
'Phyllis'	see *P.* 'Evelyn'
pinifolius ♀H4	CBod CMea CRos CTri ELon EPot EUJe GCrg GKev ITim LRHS MMuc NRHS SRms WAbe WHoo WThu
- 'Mersea Yellow'	CMea CRos ELan EPfP EPot GCrg GKev LRHS MHer MMuc NLar NRHS SLon SPlb SRms WAbe XLum
- 'Wisley Flame' ♀H4	EPfP EPot EWes GCrg MBNS MHer NHpl SCob
'Pink Bedder'	see *P.* 'Hewell Pink Bedder', 'Sutton's Pink Bedder'
'Pink Endurance'	MBNS WHal
'Port Wine' ♀H3	CMea CTri ELon EPfP GMaP LRHS MWat SPer SPoG SWvt WAvo WKif
'Powis Castle'	ECtt
'Prairie Twilight' PBR	MHol
'Pretty Petticoat'	CRos LRHS NRHS
procerus	GKev
- var. ***brachyanthus***	GKev
§ - var. ***formosus***	WAbe
- 'Hawkeye'	CPBP
§ - 'Roy Davidson' ♀H5	CMea EPot WAbe
- var. ***tolmiei***	EPot GCal GEdr GKev MPie WAbe
pubescens	see *P. hirsutus*
pulchellus Greene	see *P. procerus* var. *formosus*
pulchellus Lindl.	see *P. campanulatus*
'Purple and White'	see *P.* 'Countess of Dalkeith'
'Purple Bedder'	CMac CRos ELan EPfP GBin LRHS LSRN MWat NRHS SPoG SPtp SRkn SRms SWvt XLum
'Purple Passion'	CElw CRos EBee ELan ELon EPfP EWes IRob LRHS NRHS SCob
'Purple Riding Hood' PBR (Riding Hood Series)	CRos LCro LOPS LRHS NRHS SPoG
'Purple Sea'	MHol WFar
'Purpureus Albus'	see *P.* 'Countess of Dalkeith'
'Raven' ♀H3	CBar CMac CRos EAJP EBee ECtt EHoe EPau EShb GMaP IBoy LCro LEdu LOPS LRHS MCot MRav NRHS SAll SCob SEND SPer SRms SWvt WCAu WHal WHar WHil WWFP
'Razzle Dazzle'	SPlb SRms WCot
'Red Knight'	MBNS
'Red Riding Hood' PBR (Riding Hood Series)	CRos EPfP LCro LOPS LRHS NRHS
'Red Rocks'	EWTr GBin WCot
'Red Sea'	MHol WFar
'Rich Purple'	MBNS SPlb XLum
'Rich Ruby' ♀H3	CAby CFis CRos EHrv ELan EPfP EWes LRHS NRHS SBee SHar SPlb SPtp SWvt WCAu XLum
roezlii Regel	see *P. laetus* subsp. *roezlii*
roezlii ambig.	MAsh
'Roger Skipper' new	ECtt
'Ron Sidwell'	WAvo
'Rosy Blush'	MBNS SPlb
'Roy Davidson'	see *P. procerus* 'Roy Davidson'
'Royal White'	see *P.* 'White Bedder'
'Rubicundus' ♀H4	CBod CRos ELan EPfP LRHS LSRN MBNS NRHS SLon SWvt WBor
'Ruby' misapplied	see *P.* 'Schoenholzeri'
'Ruby Candle'	CRos ECtt LRHS NRHS
rupicola ♀H5	NSla
- 'Conwy Lilac'	WAbe
- 'Conwy Rose'	EPot GCrg WAbe WThu
'Russian River'	ECtt EPfP ESps LRHS SPlb SWvt XLum
rydbergii	SBrt SPlb
'Samsong'	WCFE
§ 'Schoenholzeri' ♀H4	Widely available
scouleri	see *P. fruticosus* var. *scouleri*
§ ***serrulatus***	EWes GKev XLum
- 'Albus'	WArt
'Sherbourne Blue'	WAvo WCot
'Sissinghurst Pink'	see *P.* 'Evelyn'
'Six Hills'	EPot SDys WAbe WOld
'Skyline'	EPfP
smallii	CAby CFis CRos EPPr EPfP EWes GBin LRHS LSRN MHer NRHS SPhx
'Snow Storm'	see *P.* 'White Bedder'
'Snowflake'	see *P.* 'White Bedder'
sonomensis	see *P. newberryi* subsp. *sonomensis*
'Sour Grapes' misapplied	see *P.* 'Stapleford Gem'
'Sour Grapes' ambig.	CAby CBcs CDor CRav CTri EAJP EHoe IBoy MJak NGdn SAll SCob WCAu

§ 'Sour Grapes' M. Fish YH4	CMac CRos EBee ECha ELan EPau EPfP EShb ESps GBin GMaP IBoy LCro LOPS LRHS LSRN MSwo NLar NRHS SEND SHar SPer SPtp SRms WHar WKif
'Southgate Gem'	GMcL GWyn LCro MBNS MHCG MWat SRms SWvt WAvo
'Souvenir d'Adrian Regnier'	MBNS MHCG
'Souvenir d'André Torres' misapplied	see *P.* 'Chester Scarlet'
§ 'Stapleford Gem' YH3	CFis CMac EWTr LRHS MRav SHar SRms SWvt WHar WHoo
'Storm'	WHrl
'Strawberries and Cream' (Ice Cream Series)	EPfP ETMg MTis NLar SAll SCob SRkn WBor WCot WHil
'Strawberry Fancy' **new**	SRms
'Strawberry Fizz'	SRms
strictus	EBee GKev MBNS MMuc SBrt SPhx
STROMBOLI ('Yaboli')	CTri
§ 'Sutton's Pink Bedder'	MBNS
'Sweet Cherry' (Ice Cream Series)	CPla ECtt LSou WCot
tall, pink-flowered	see *P.* 'Welsh Dawn'
teucrioides	CPBP
'The Juggler'	ECtt MBNS SWvt
§ 'Thorn'	ECtt ESps LRHS MWat SRms SWvt WAvo WHrl
'Threave Pink'	ECtt MRav SHar SWvt WAvo
'Thundercloud'	ECtt WAvo
'Tiger Bell Coral' **new**	NChi
'Torquay Gem'	MBNS
'True Sour Grapes'	see *P.* 'Sour Grapes' M. Fish
'Tubular Bells Red'	MHol
uintahensis	CPBP
'Vanilla Plum' (Ice Cream Series)	LSou MAvo
venustus purple-flowered	SBrt
VESUVIUS ('Yasius') (Volcano Series)	CRos EPfP LRHS NRHS SLon SRms WFar
virens	EPot
virgatus 'Blue Buckle'	CRos LRHS NRHS SPlb WFar
'Watermelon Taffy'PBR (Taffy Series)	ECtt
§ 'Welsh Dawn'	MBNS
§ ***whippleanus***	LRHS MMuc SPlb
- black-flowered	SBrt
§ 'White Bedder' YH3	Widely available
'Whitethroat' Sidwell	MBNS
I 'Whitethroat' purple-flowered	WCot
'Willy's Purple'	ECtt
§ 'Windsor Red'	CTri ECtt EPfP IRob LRHS MBNS SCob SLon SRms SWvt WAvo WCot
'Woodpecker'	ECtt IPot MBNS SRms WAvo WHoo WHrl

Pentaglottis (*Boraginaceae*)

§ ***sempervirens***	EPfP SRms WSFF

Pentapanax see *Aralia*

Pentapterygium see *Agapetes*

Pentas (*Rubiaceae*)

lanceolata	CCCN EShb

Penthorum (*Saxifragaceae*)

sedoides	LLWG

Peperomia (*Piperaceae*)

ferreyrae **new**	EShb

pepino see *Solanum muricatum*

peppermint see *Mentha* × *piperita*

Pericallis (*Asteraceae*)

× ***hybrida*** Senetti Series	NPer NPri SPoG
- - SENETTI BLUE BICOLOR ('Sunseneribuba'PBR)	MGos SPoG
- - SENETTI BLUE ('Sunsenebu'PBR)	SPoG
- - SENETTI MAGENTA BICOLOR ('Sunsenereba'PBR)	MGos SPoG
- - SENETTI MAGENTA ('Sunsenere'PBR)	SPoG
§ ***lanata*** (L'Hér.) B. Nord.	CHll EShb
- Kew form	CSpe

Perilla (*Lamiaceae*)

§ ***frutescens*** var. ***crispa*** YH3	CSpe
- var. ***japonica***	GPoy
- var. ***nankinensis***	see *P. frutescens* var. *crispa*

Periploca (*Apocynaceae*)

graeca	CBcs EBee EWTr MGil
sepium	CExl

Pernettya see *Gaultheria*

Perovskia (*Lamiaceae*)

abrotanoides	XLum
atriplicifolia	CBot CDul CMea ELan LSun MGil MHer MNHC NSti WKif
- 'Blue Shadow'	CRos LRHS NLar NRHS
'Blue Haze'	GCal
'Blue Spire' YH5	Widely available
'Filigran'	CRos CWld ELan EPed EPfP GBin LRHS LSou NLar NRHS SBod SPad SPoG WGrn WGwG WSpi XSen
'Hybrida'	GCal LRHS
LACEY BLUE ('Lisslitt'PBR)	CRos ECrN EPfP IPot LCro LOPS LPla LRHS MAsh NLar NRHS SCob SWvt
'Little Spire'PBR	Widely available
'Longin'	LRHS XLum
SILVERY BLUE ('Lissvery'PBR)	CRos LCro LOPS LRHS NLar NRHS

Persea (*Lauraceae*)

americana	CCCN
indica	CCCN
- B&SWJ 12535	WCru
japonica B&SWJ 12789	WCru
thunbergii	CBcs CFil
- B&SWJ 12747	WCru

Persicaria (*Polygonaceae*)

sp.	CHab ESps
B&SWJ 11268 from Sumatra	WCru
§ ***affinis***	CBcs CSBt GAbr LSun MSCN NBro SCob WArt WFar WMoo
- 'Darjeeling Red' YH5	Widely available
- 'Dimity'	see *P. affinis* 'Superba'
- 'Donald Lowndes' YH5	Widely available
- 'Kabouter'	GBin GWyn NLar SCob WBor
§ - 'Superba' YH5	Widely available
alata	see *P. nepalensis*

	alpina	CBct CBot CSpe EBee ECha ECtt EHoe EPPr GBin GMaP GMcL GQue IPot LEdu LRHS MAvo MHol MRav NDov NLos NRHS SMad SPoG WCAu WCot WHil WMoo WPnP WSpi WWtn
	amphibia	LLWG MSKA XLum
§	***amplexicaulis***	CBre CKno ELan EWTr EWes GMaP ILea MBel MCot NChi WBor WBrk WFar WMoo WRHF WWtn XLum
	- 'Alba'	Widely available
	- 'Amethyst' **new**	LPla
	- 'Ample Pink' **new**	MAvo
	- 'Anouk'	EBee
	- 'Atrosanguinea'	CBod CKno CMac CRos CTri ECha ELan ELon GLog LRHS MMuc MRav MSpe NLar NRHS SEND SPer SRms SWvt WFar WOld XLum
	- 'Betty Brandt'	GBin GWyn
	- 'Black Adder' **new**	ELon
	- 'Blackfield' PBR	Widely available
	- 'Blush Clent'	WHoo
	- 'Clent Charm'	MHCG NChi WOut
	- 'Cottesbrooke Gold'	ECtt MAvo
	- 'Dikke Floskes'	CAby CBct CBod CKno EBee ECtt ELon EPPr GBin IRob MAvo MHol MSpe NCou SPoG WBrk WCot WHoo
	- 'Early Pink Lady'	ELon WMoo
	- 'Eastfield' (v)	WCot
	- 'Fascination'	ELon MAvo WCot
	- 'Fat Domino' PBR	CBWd CBct CBod CKno CRos EBee ECtt EHoe GBin GQue ILea IPot LPla LRHS MAvo MBel MCot MHol MNrw NCou NDov NLar NRHS SAko SCob SPoG WCAu WCot
	- 'Fat White'	ELon
	- 'Firedance'	CKno ECtt EHoe ELon EPPr GBin GQue IPot MSpe NDov SMHy SPhx WCot WFar
	- 'Firetail'	Widely available
	- 'Golden Arrow' (v)	CAby CBct CRos ECtt ELon EUJe GBin IRob LRHS MBel NEoE NRHS SCob SHar SRms WFar WHil WMoo
	- 'High Society'	CKno GBin SPoG WCAu WMoo
	- 'Inverleith'	CBct CBod CBre CKno CRos EBee ECha ECtt ELon GBin GMaP GMcL GQue LRHS MAvo MBel MHer MMuc MSpe NRHS SCob WCAu WHar WMoo WOut WPnP WWFP
I	- 'Jo and Guido's Form'	ELon NLar WCAu WFar
	- 'JS Caliente' PBR	CBod CKno ECtt ELon GBin GQue IRob LRHS LSun MNrw SCob SRms WArt WCot WPnP WSpi
	- 'JS Delgado'	CKno EBee ELon GBin MNrw SRms
	- 'Lisan'	EBee ELon GBin MNrw
	- ORANGE FIELD ('Orangofield' PBR)	CBct CBod CKno CMea CRos EBee ECtt ELon EPPr EPfP GBin GMaP GQue LRHS MHol MJak MNrw MSCN NDov NLar NPnk NRHS SAko SCob WBor WCAu WHoo WMoo
	- var. ***pendula***	EBee ELon GBin IMou IRob SMHy WFar WMoo
	- - HWJK 2255	WCru
	- 'Pink Elephant'	see *P.* 'Pink Elephant'
	- 'Pink Knot'	CRos LRHS NRHS
	- 'Pink Lady'	MPie
	- 'Rosea'	Widely available
	- 'Rowden Gem'	EBee ELon GBin IPot WMoo WOut
	- 'Rubie's Pink'	ECha
	- 'Sangre'	GBin
	- 'September Spires'	NDov
	- 'Seven Oaks Village'	EBee GBin SCob
	- 'Summer Dance'	CKno EBee ECtt ELon EPPr GQue SMHy
	- TAURUS ('Blotau')	CElw CKno CRos CSam ECha ECtt ELon EPPr IPot IRob LRHS MCot NLar NPnk NRHS NSti SCob SMHy SRkn SRms WCAu WFar WHoo
	- 'White Eastfield'	CKno
§	***bistorta***	EBWF GBin GPoy MHer MMuc NLar SEND SRms WArt WFar WOut
	- subsp. ***carnea***	CBod CRos EBee ECha EHoe ELon EPPr GBin IRob LRHS MBNS MMuc NBro NDov NPnk NRHS WCot WMoo WWtn
	- 'Hohe Tatra'	CBWd CRos EBee ECtt EPPr GMaP IPot LRHS LSun MBel MHol NCou NDov NRHS SPoG WCot WFar
	- 'JS Calor' PBR	EBee GQue
	- 'Superba' ♀H7	Widely available
	campanulata	CBod CElw ECha ECtt EHoe GAbr GMaP IFro MAvo MMuc MRav NEgg NSti SPer WFar WMoo WOut WWFP WWtn
	- Alba Group	CElw MPie WMoo
	- 'Madame Jigard'	GBin
	- 'Rosenrot'	CBre ILea SAko WOld
	- 'Southcombe White'	GBin
§	***capitata***	LLWG XLum
	- 'Pink Bubbles'	CPla EHoe ELon SWvt
	chinensis B&SWJ 11268	WCru
	dshawachischwilii	LPla SMHy
	emodi	GKev
	× ***fennica*** 'Johanniswolke'	EBee GBin IPot
	'Indian Summer'	GCal LPla WCot
*	***kahil***	GBin WCot
*	***macrophylla***	EBee
	microcephala	EWes MHer WHil
	- 'Dragon's Eye' PBR	EBee WNPC
	- 'Red Dragon' PBR	Widely available
	milletii	CAby CRos LRHS NDov NRHS WCru
§	***mollis***	WPGP
	neofiliformis	EShb
§	***nepalensis***	CExl EPPr EShb IMou
	'October Pink'	CSam SMHy
§	***odorata***	ENfk GPoy MHer MNHC SPre SRms WHer WTre XAbr
	orientalis	CSpe SPav SPhx
§	'Pink Elephant'	CBot CKno CSam ELon EPPr GBin ILea MNrw NDov NLar SCob SRms WFar WHoo WSpi
	polystachya	see *P. wallichii*
	'Red Baron'	ECtt EPPr
§	***runcinata***	EBee MMuc WMoo WWtn
	- 'Purple Fantasy'	CBod CBot ECtt EUJe LPla MAvo MBel MHol MNrw MSpe NSti SCob SMad WFar WHil WMoo WNPC
	scoparia	see *Polygonum scoparium*
	'Silver Dragon' PBR	CBct LLWG LPla LSou LSun MAvo MBel NSti SPoG WCot
	sphaerostachya Meisn.	see *P. macrophylla*
	tenuicaulis	CBre EHrv GBin SBch SBrt WCru WMoo WWtn
§	***tinctoria***	WSFF
§	***vacciniifolia*** ♀H5	Widely available
§	***virginiana***	EPPr GCal LEdu LSun WMoo WWtn
	- 'Alba'	EPPr

- var. ***filiformis***	CAby CBod CBot CSam CSpe ELan LEdu MBel MMoz MPie NChi SBrt SPoG SRkn SWvt WAul WCot
- - 'Ballet'	WCot
- - 'Batwings'	CRos LRHS NRHS SPtp
- - 'Compton's Red'	CBod CSam ECha ECtt EShb EUJe MAvo MMoz NLos SBrt WAul WCot
- - 'Guizhou Bronze' **new**	LEdu
- - 'Lance Corporal'	CMac EHoe EPPr EShb EUJe GBin MAvo MMoz NLar
- - 'Moorland Moss'	WMoo
- Variegated Group (v)	ECha EShb MBNS WCot WMoo
- - 'Painter's Palette' (v)	CBod CMac CRos ECha ECtt EHoe ELan EPPr EShb EUJe GMcL GWyn LLWG LRHS MHol MRav NBid NRHS NSti SPer SRms SWvt WAul WCot WCru WMoo XLum
§ ***wallichii***	CSpe MMuc NLar SEND WCot WMoo WWtn XLum
§ ***weyrichii***	EPPr GCal NBro NLar WFar WMoo WWtn XLum

persimmon see *Diospyros virginiana*

persimmon, Japanese see *Diospyros kaki*

Petalostemon see *Dalea*

Petamenes see *Gladiolus*

Petasites (*Asteraceae*)

albus	GPoy MHer NLar NSti
fragrans	LLWG SRms WHer XLum
§ ***frigidus*** var. ***palmatus***	NLar
- - JLS 86317CLOR	SMad
- - 'Golden Palms'	CHid EUJe WBor WCot
hybridus	MSKA
- 'Variegatus' (v)	XLum
japonicus	CAgr CBcs CFGn GPoy
- var. ***giganteus***	CHid ECha EPfP EUJe LEdu MBel WCru
§ - - 'Nishiki-buki' (v)	CMac EBee ECha EUJe EWld GQue LEdu MHer MSKA NSti SMad WBor WFar XLum
- - 'Variegatus'	see *P. japonicus* var. *giganteus* 'Nishiki-buki'
- f. ***purpureus***	EPPr MMoz
palmatus	see *P. frigidus* var. *palmatus*
paradoxus	EWld LEdu MBel WCot WFar WPGP

× *Petchoa* (*Solanaceae*)

'Peach Sundae' **new**	ETMg

Petopentia (*Apocynaceae*)

natalensis **new**	LToo

Petrea (*Verbenaceae*)

volubilis	CCCN

Petrocallis (*Brassicaceae*)

lagascae	see *P. pyrenaica*
§ ***pyrenaica***	CPla GEdr WAbe
- white-flowered	WAbe

Petrocoptis (*Caryophyllaceae*)

pyrenaica	SRms WHoo

Petrocosmea ✿ (*Gesneriaceae*)

barbata	WDib
begoniifolia	WAbe WDib
coerulea	WDib
§ ***cryptica***	CTal WAbe WDib
- 'Yumebutai'	WDib
flaccida	WDib
'Fluffer Nutter'	WDib
forrestii	CTal WAbe WDib
grandiflora	WAbe WDib
- 'Crème de Crûg'	WCru
'Ht-2'	WDib
iodioides	WDib
kerrii	WCot WDib
'Keystone's Angora'	WDib
'Keystone's Bantam'	WDib
'Keystone's Barnswallow'	WDib
'Keystone's Belmont'	WDib
'Keystone's Blue Jay'	WDib
'Keystone's Magic'	WDib
martini	CTal
mengliangensis	WDib
minor	WDib
parryorum	WDib
'Paul Kroll'	WDib
'Rosemary Platz'	WDib
rosettifolia misapplied	see *P. cryptica*
sericea	WAbe WDib

Petromarula (*Campanulaceae*)

pinnata	EBee

Petrophytum (*Rosaceae*)

caespitosum	CMea EPot WAbe
cinerascens	GEdr
§ ***hendersonii***	WAbe

Petrorhagia (*Caryophyllaceae*)

'Pink Starlets'	EPfP
saxifraga ♀H4	CSpe EPPr EWTr GLog NLar NSla SRms WMoo XLum

Petroselinum (*Apiaceae*)

§ ***crispum***	ENfk GPoy MNHC NPol NPri SPoG SRms XAbr
- 'Bravour' ♀H4	MHer MShS NRHS
- 'Champion Moss Curled'	SVic
- var. ***crispum***	SPhm
- French	ENfk MHer MNHC NPri SPoG SRms
- 'Gigante Di Napoli' **new**	CRav
- 'Italian'	see *P. crispum* var. *neapolitanum* plain-leaved
- 'Moss Curled' ♀H4	CHby CRos EKin EMsh MCtn MShS NRHS NRob SRms
§ - var. ***neapolitanum***	ENfk SPoG SRms SVic
§ - var. ***tuberosum***	MNHC SRms SVic
hortense	see *P. crispum*
tuberosum	see *P. crispum* var. *tuberosum*

Petteria (*Papilionaceae*)

ramentacea	EBtc

Petunia (*Solanaceae*)

'Art Deco' (d) **new**	ETMg
BLACK NIGHT ('Pe11037') (d) **new**	ETMg
BLACK VELVET IMPROVED	NPri
(Cascadias Series) CASCADIAS INDIAN SUMMER ('Dcas303') **new**	LSou
- CASCADIAS RIM MAGENTA ('Dcas298'[PBR])	ETMg LSou NPri

- CASCADIAS RIM VIOLET NPri
'Corona Amethyst' (Corona Series) NPri
(Crazytunia Series) CRAZYTUNIA CLOUD 9 new ETMg
- CRAZYTUNIA GREEN WITH ENVY new ETMg
- CRAZYTUNIA MANDEVILLE ('Wespecramand') new ETMg
- CRAZYTUNIA PULSE ('Wespecrapul') new ETMg
- CRAZYTUNIA STARLIGHT BLUE new ETMg
(Easy Wave Series) EASY WAVE BLUE ('Pas320593') NPri
- EASY WAVE BUBBLEGUM see *P.* EASY WAVE PINK PASSION
- EASY WAVE BURGUNDY STAR ('Pas760702') NPri
- EASY WAVE BURGUNDY VELOUR ('Pas933562') new NPri
- EASY WAVE NEON ROSE ('Pas760700') NPri
§ - EASY WAVE PINK PASSION ('Pas882697') new ETMg NPri
- EASY WAVE PLUM VEIN ('Pas739163') NPri
- EASY WAVE RED VELOUR ('Pas933560') new NPri
- EASY WAVE SILVER ('Pas1016992') new NPri
- EASY WAVE WHITE ('Pas760712') NPri
exserta CSpe EBee
'Fanfare Hot Rose' (Fanfare Series) NPri
Frenzy Series ETMg
'Happy Magic Cremissimo' (Happy Magic Series) new ETMg
LITTLETUNIA PINK ('Danlittun1'PBR) (Littletunia Series) NPri
NIGHT SKY ('Kleph15313') new ETMg NPri
'Orange Punch' new ETMg
ORCHID PICOTEE MIXED new ETMg
ORCHID-FLOWERED MIXED (d) new ETMg
patagonica SPlb WAbe
'Purple Rocket' (d) new ETMg
'Purple Wave' (Fortunia Series) new ETMg
SHOCK WAVE YELLOW ('Pas1003475') (Shock Wave Series) new NPri
STARS AND STRIPES MIXED new ETMg
(Supertunia Series) SUPERTUNIA BORDEAUX ('Lanbor'PBR) CPla
- SUPERTUNIA PRETTY MUCH PICASSO ('Bhtun31501'PBR) NPri
- SUPERTUNIA ROYAL VELVET ('Kakegawa S28'PBR) CRav
Surfinia Series ETMg
- SURFINA HEAVENLY BLUE ('Sunsurf Skytatsu') new LSou
- SURFINIA BLUE PICOTEE LSou
- SURFINIA BLUE ('Sunblu') ETMg LSou NPri
- SURFINIA BLUE VEIN ('Sunsolos'PBR) CRav ESps
- SURFINIA BURGUNDY ('Keiburtel'PBR) CRav
- SURFINIA HOT PINK 06 ('Sunrovein'PBR) ETMg
- SURFINIA HOT PINK ('Marrose') LSou
- SURFINIA LIME ('Keiyeul'PBR) ESps
- SURFINIA PURPLE ('Shihi Brilliant') ♀H2 ETMg LSou NPri
- SURFINIA RED ('Keirekul'PBR) ETMg
- SURFINIA SKY BLUE ('Keilavbu'PBR) ♀H2 NPri
- SURFINIA SWEET PINK ('Sunsurfmomo'PBR) LSou NPri
- SURFINIA VANILLA ('Sunvanilla'PBR) LSou
* - SURFINIA VELVET CRav
- SURFINIA WHITE ('Kesupite') ESps ETMg
- SURFINIA YELLOW DREAM NPri
Surfinia Sumo Series new ETMg
TIDAL WAVE IMPROVED MIXED new ETMg
'Titan Blue Velvet' (Titan Series) new ETMg
(Tumbelina Series) TUMBELINA ANNA (d) new ETMg
- TUMBELINA BELINDA (d) ETMg
- TUMBELINA CANDYFLOSS ('Kercan'PBR) (d) LSou NPri
- TUMBELINA CHERRY RIPPLE ('Kerripcherry'PBR) (d) CPla ETMg
- TUMBELINA CLARA ('Kerclara'PBR) (d) ETMg
- TUMBELINA DAMSON RIPPLE new ETMg
- TUMBELINA INGA (d) LSou
- TUMBELINA JOANNA LSou
- TUMBELINA MELISSA ('Kermelis'PBR) (d) LSou
- TUMBELINA PRISCILLA ('Kerpril'PBR) (d) ETMg LSou NPri
- TUMBELINA SUSANNA ETMg

Peucedanum (*Apiaceae*)

* ***aromaticum*** IMou
litorale see *Kitagawia litoralis*
longifolium WCot
officinale CRos GBin LRHS NRHS SPhx SPlb SPtp
ostruthium GPoy LEdu
- 'Daphnis' (v) CSpe EBee LEdu MAvo MMoz MNrw NChi NEoE NLar WAvo WCFE WCot WHrl WSHC XLum
palustre EBWF
rablense LEdu NDov
verticillare CRos CSam CSpe EBee GBin GWyn IMou LEdu LPla LRHS MBel NRHS SBrt SPhx WCot WSHC

Peumus (*Monimiaceae*)

boldus IDee

Phacelia (*Boraginaceae*)

bolanderi	EBee EWes GEdr
tanacetifolia	LCro WSFF

Phaedranassa (*Amaryllidaceae*)

dubia	NRog
glauciflora	NRog
tunguraguae	NRog
viridiflora	NRog WCot

Phaedranthus see *Distictis*

Phaenocoma (*Asteraceae*)

prolifera	SPlb

Phaenosperma (*Poaceae*)

globosa	CSam CSpe ECha EHoe EPPr EShb GCal GQue MMuc NLos NWsh WCot WPGP WWtn XLum

Phaiophleps see *Olsynium*

nigricans	see *Sisyrinchium striatum*

Phalaris (*Poaceae*)

arundinacea	EBWF MBNS MSKA SCob SPlb SVic
- 'Elegantissima'	see *P. arundinacea* var. *picta* 'Picta'
- var. ***picta***	CDul CTri ESps MJak MSKA NPer WFar XLum
- - 'Arctic Sun' (v)	CKno EBee ELon EPPr ESps GBin LLWG LRHS MAsh MMuc NEoE SEND SPoG
- - 'Aureovariegata' (v)	MRav NPer WMoo XLum
- - 'Feesey' (v) 🏆H7	Widely available
- - 'Luteopicta' (v)	EPPr MMuc XLum
§ - - 'Picta' (v)	CBod CRos ELan EPfP GBin LRHS MMuc NRHS SEND SPer WMoo
- - 'Streamlined' (v)	EPPr NWsh
- - 'Tricolor' (v)	EHoe

Phanerophlebia ✿ (*Dryopteridaceae*)

falcata	see *Cyrtomium falcatum*
fortunei	see *Cyrtomium fortunei*

Pharbitis see *Ipomoea*

Pharnaceum (*Molluginaceae*)

aurantium new	SBrt

Phaseolus (*Papilionaceae*)

caracalla	see *Cochliasanthus caracalla*

Phedimus see *Sedum*

Phegopteris (*Thelypteridaceae*)

§ ***connectilis***	CBdn EFer
decursive-pinnata	CBdn EBee LRHS MMuc NRHS SEND WFib WPnP
hexagonoptera	CBdn NLos

Phellodendron (*Rutaceae*)

amurense	CBcs CCCN CDul CMCN EPfP GBin LMaj MBlu WBor
- B&SWJ 11000	WCru
japonicum B&SWJ 11175	WCru

Phemeranthus (*Portulacaceae*)

sediformis	GKev
- 'Zoe' new	GKev

Phenakospermum (*Strelitziaceae*)

guianense	XBlo

Pherosphaera ✿ (*Podocarpaceae*)

fitzgeraldii	CKen WThu

Philadelphus ✿ (*Hydrangeaceae*)

sp.	ESps
SDR 2823	CExl
SDR 4862	GKev
SDR 4946	CExl GKev
affinis	CFil
'Atlas' (v)	NLar
'Avalanche'	CExl MMuc NLar SPer SRms
'Beauclerk' 🏆H6	CBod CCCN CDul CTri EBee ECrN EPfP EWTr LRHS MGos MMuc MRav NLar SCob SLim SMad SPer SRms SWvt WHar WSpi
'Belle Étoile' 🏆H6	Widely available
'Bialy Karzel'	NLar
'Bialy Sopel'	CCCN WAvo
'Bicolore'	NLar WAvo WHar WSpi
'Bouquet Blanc'	MRav NLar SGol SRms WCFE
brachybotrys	MRav
'Buckley's Quill' (d)	CAby CWld EBee EPfP EWes LRHS MRav SGol SMad SWvt WGrn
'Burfordensis'	CBot MMuc MRav SEND WSpi
calcicola	CFil
caucasicus	CFil
coronarius	CBcs CDul EPfP ESps LBuc MRav SPer WSpi
- 'Aureus' 🏆H6	Widely available
- 'Bowles's Variety'	see *P. coronarius* 'Variegatus'
§ - 'Variegatus' (v) 🏆H6	CBot CRos ELan ELon EPfP ESps EWTr GBin GMcL LRHS MGil MGos MMuc MRav MSwo NLar SLim SPer SPoG SRms WAvo WCFE WCot WFar WKif WSHC WSpi
coulteri	CFil SBrt WPGP
'Coupe d'Argent'	MRav
'Dainty Lady' PBR	GBin LRHS SLon
'Dame Blanche' (d)	ECrN EPfP LSou MRav NLar
delavayi	CFil EPfP EWTr GBin IDee LEdu LLHF NLar SPer WPGP WSpi
- var. ***calvescens***	LRHS MRav
- aff. var. ***calvescens*** BWJ 8005	WCru
- f. ***melanocalyx***	EPfP MRav SChF WPGP
- - B&L 12168	CFil EBee WPGP
- - 'Nyman's Variety' 🏆H6	CBot CExl CFil CTho WKif WPGP
aff. ***delavayi***	SBrt
'Enchantement' (d)	MRav
'Erectus'	CSBt EBee ELon EPfP EWTr LRHS MRav NLar SPer SPoG WAvo WSpi
'Étoile Rose'	WAvo WMoo
'Falconeri'	MRav
'Frosty Morn' (d)	CBcs EPfP LEdu MBlu MMuc MRav NLar SEND SPer SPoG
incanus B&SWJ 8616	WCru
§ 'Innocence' (v) 🏆H6	CAgr CBot CExl CMac CRos CTsd EHoe ELan EPfP LRHS MAsh MGos MMuc MRav MSwo NEoE NRHS SEND SGol SPad SPer SPoG SRms WFar WSHC
'Innocence Variegatus'	see *P.* 'Innocence'
§ ***insignis***	MRav
karwinskianus	CFil
- F&M 152	WPGP

'Lemoinei'	CBcs CBod CDul CTri ESps GMcL MGos SCob SGol WGrn WHar WSpi
'Lemon Hill'	NLar
lewisii	CExl
- L 1896	CExl
- 'Snow Velvet'	CAby EPfP LLHF LRHS MMrt
- 'Waterton'	WAvo WSpi
'Limestone'	MRav
maculatus	CFil
- 'Mexican Jewel'	CBcs CExl CFil CRos EBee ELon GBin NLar SBod SChF SMad SPad WGob WKif WPGP WSHC
- 'Scented Storm'	WPGP
- 'Sweet Clare' $\mathbb{Y}^{H5}$	CRos EPfP LCro LOPS LRHS NRHS SPoG WSpi
maculatus* × *mexicanus	CFil
madrensis	MRav
- F&M 326	CFil WPGP
'Manteau d'Hermine' (d) $\mathbb{Y}^{H6}$	Widely available
'Marjorie'	NLar
mexicanus	CFil GCal
- B&SWJ 10253	WCru
- 'Rose Syringa'	CExl CFil SBrt WPGP
mexicanus* × *palmeri	EBee WPGP
microphyllus	CAby CBot CDul CMCN CTho CTri EBee ELan ELon EPfP ESps EWTr GBin IRob LRHS MAsh MGos MRav NLar SLon SPer SPoG WFar WKif WSHC
- var. ***occidentalis***	NLar
'Miniature Snowflake' (d)	MAsh
'Minnesota Snowflake' (d)	CBcs CRos CSpe ELon EPfP EWes LRHS LSRN MMuc MRav NLar NRHS SEND SGol WFar
'Mont Blanc'	CBcs GKin MRav NLar
'Mrs E.L. Robinson' (d)	CMac CRos ELon EPfP GLog LLHF LRHS MGos NEgg NRHS WAvo WCFE
myrtoides B&SWJ 10436	WCru
'Natchez' (d)	CMac ELon LEdu LLHF NLar SCob SMad
'Oeil de Pourpre'	MRav
palmeri	CFil EBee WPGP
'Patricia'	WAvo
pekinensis	CExl NLar
'Perryhill'	MRav
'Polar Star'	ELon NLar WKif
purpurascens	CBot CExl CJun EBee EPfP EWes GLog LLHF MGos MRav NLar SChF WPGP
- BWJ 7540	WCru
'Purpureomaculatus'	ELon LLHF MAsh MRav NLar WPGP
sargentianus	CFil
satsumi	NLar
- B&SWJ 10811	WCru
- B&SWJ 11004	WCru
schrenkii	CFil NLar
- B&SWJ 8465	WCru
sericanthus	NLar
§ 'Silberregen' $\mathbb{Y}^{H6}$	CDul CMac CRos EBee ELon EPfP EWTr GBin LRHS MAsh MGos MMuc MRav NEoE NGdn NLar SEND SGol SMad SPoG SRms SWvt WGrn
SILVER SHOWERS	see *P.* 'Silberregen'
'Snowbelle' (d)	CCCN CRos EPfP ESps IRob LRHS MAsh NGdn NLar NPri NRHS SPoG SRms SWvt
'Snowflake'	WMoo
'Snowgoose'	LRHS
'Souvenir de Billiard'	see *P. insignis*
'Starbright'[PBR]	CAby CBcs CCCN EPfP LRHS MAsh MMrt NRHS SCob SPoG
subcanus	CExl
- L 524	CExl CFil
'Sybille' $\mathbb{Y}^{H6}$	CBot CDul CMac CTho ECrN EPfP LRHS MAsh MRav MSwo SRms WKif WSpi
tomentosus	CExl
- B&SWJ 2707	WCru
- GWJ 9215	WCru
'Velléda'	WAvo
'Virginal' (d)	Widely available
× ***virginalis***	IRob
'Voie Lactée'	LLHF MRav NLar WSpi
WHITE ROCK ('Pekphil') $\mathbb{Y}^{H6}$	CBot CMac CRos EBee EPfP LLHF LRHS LSRN MRav NLar SPer
'Yellow Cab'	LRHS
'Yellow Hill'	CMac EPfP LRHS

Philesia (*Philesiaceae*)

buxifolia	see *P. magellanica*
§ ***magellanica***	CExl CFil CRHN GGGa ITim MGil SBrt WCru WSHC
- 'Rosea'	CRHN EPfP

Phillyrea (*Oleaceae*)

angustifolia	CBcs CBod CDul CFil CHll CMCN CRos CTho EBee ELan ELon EPfP EShb EUJe LRHS MGos MRav NLar SBig SEND SPer WPGP WSHC XSen
- f. ***rosmarinifolia***	CCCN CExl ELan
- - 'French Fries'	EBee EPfP WPGP
decora	see *Osmanthus decorus*
§ ***latifolia***	CBcs CDul CFil CRos CTho CTsd EBee ELan EPfP EUJe LRHS NLar SArc SEND WPGP XSen
media	see *P. latifolia*

Philodendron (*Araceae*)

'Angra dos Reis'	see *P. cordatum*
§ ***angustisectum*** $\mathbb{Y}^{H1b}$	XBlo
'Atom'	NLos
bipennifolium new	SPlb
bipinnatifidum $\mathbb{Y}^{H1c}$	NLos XBlo
corcovadense	XBlo
§ ***cordatum***	XBlo
elegans	see *P. angustisectum*
erubescens 'Imperial Red'	NLos
- 'Red Emerald'	XBlo
'Imperial Green'	NLos
* ***radiatum*** var. ***pseudoradiatum*** 'Simmonds'	XBlo
* ***rubrum***	XBlo
scandens $\mathbb{Y}^{H1a}$	EUJe LOPS
- 'Green Emerald'	XBlo
- 'Mica'	XBlo
tripartitum	XBlo
xanadu	LOPS NLos XBlo

Philotheca (*Rutaceae*)

§ ***myoporoides***	LRHS MPkF

Phlebodium (*Polypodiaceae*)

§ ***aureum*** $\mathbb{Y}^{H1b}$	CSpe SPlb WCot
- var. ***areolatum***	EShb
- 'Blue Star'	NLos
- 'Glaucum'	CSpe WCot

- 'Mandaianum'	NLos
pseudoaureum	WCot

Phleum (*Poaceae*)

bertolonii	EBWF
phleoides	CRos LRHS NRHS
pratense	EHoe NMir WSFF

Phlomis ✿ (*Lamiaceae*)

NJM 10.020	WPGP
PAB 13.132	LEdu
alpina	SPlb
* ***anatolica***	CRos LRHS
- 'Lloyd's Variety'	see *P. grandiflora* 'Lloyd's Silver'
anisodonta white-flowered	XSen
armeniaca	XSen
atropurpurea	GKev
- BWJ 7922	WCru
bourgaei	XSen
- NJM 12.008 **new**	WPGP
bovei subsp. ***maroccana***	SEND WHal XLum
breviflora HWJCM 250	WCot WCru
capitata	XSen
cashmeriana	CBod CFis CRos CSpe EBee ECha EHoe EWTr GCal GJos ILea LRHS LSou MCot MHol NQui NRHS SMad SPhx WArt WAvo WCFE WHil WSpi
chrysophylla ♀H4	CRos ECha ELan EPfP LRHS MAsh MRav NLar WCFE WSpi XSen
cretica	SVen
× ***cytherea***	XSen
'Edward Bowles'	CBot CDul CRos EBee ECha EPfP GBin LRHS LSRN MRav NLar SEND SWvt WAvo WSpi XSen
* 'Elliot's Variety'	CExl
fruticosa ♀H4	Widely available
- white-flowered	CBcs
aff. ***fruticosa*** **new**	WSpi
grandiflora	EBee EPfP MMuc SEND XSen
- NJM 10.014	WPGP
§ - 'Lloyd's Silver' ♀H5	CRos CSam ELan GBin LRHS MAsh NLar SHar SPer
herba-venti	XSen
italica	CBcs CBod CBot CRos CSam CSpe CTri EBee ECha ELan EPfP GBin GMaP LRHS LSRN MAsh MMuc MNrw MRav SCob SEND SPer SPoG SRkn SRms SWvt WCFE WCot WFar XSen
- 'Pink Glory'	CMac
lanata	CRos ELan EPfP LRHS SBrt SCob WCFE XSen
'Le Sud'	WCot XSen
leucophracta	SVen
longifolia	CBod CRos EBee EPfP LRHS MNrw SBrt SEND SPer WGrn WPGP XSen
- var. ***bailanica*** ♀H4	CBot CRos CSam EPfP LRHS NRHS XLum
- var. ***longifolia***	WSpi
lychnitis	XSen
lycia	CRos LRHS NRHS XSen
- NJM 10.016	WPGP
macrophylla	SPhx
× ***margaritae***	XSen
monocephala	XSen
purpurea	CBod CExl CRos ELan EPfP LRHS MAsh MMuc NRHS SEND WCot XSen
I - 'Alba'	CBod CBot EPfP EWTr GBin GCal GMaP LRHS MMrt XSen
- subsp. ***caballeroi***	XSen
§ ***russeliana*** ♀H7	Widely available
- PAB 7444	LEdu
- 'Dappled Shade' (v)	WCot
- 'Mosaic' (v)	MAvo
samia Boiss.	see *P. russeliana*
samia L.	CKno CMac CRos LRHS MMrt MMuc NGdn NLar NRHS SAko SBrt SEND WPtf XSen
- JMT **new**	EPPr
- 'Green Glory'	WCot
taurica	EPfP SEND SPhx
× ***termessi***	XSen
'Toob' **new**	WPGP
tuberosa	CAby CBWd CBcs CBod CPou EHoe EPfP ILea LEdu LRHS LSRN MMuc MPnt NGdn NRHS SPhx WArt WCAu WCFE WPtf XLum XSen
- 'Amazone' ♀H5	CKno ECha EHrv EPfP GBin GMaP LCro LOPS LPla MBel MNrw MRav MSCN MTis NBid NDov NGBl NPnk NSti SCob SMad SPer SRms WCot WFar WHil WSHC WSpi
- 'Bronze Flamingo'	CBWd CMac EPfP GBin GJos LRHS MBel MNrw MPnt MRav NLar SBee SPoG WSpi
viscosa misapplied	see *P. russeliana*

Phlox ✿ (*Polemoniaceae*)

'21st Century Blue' **new**	CRav
'21st Century White' **new**	CRav
ADESSA WHITE (Adessa Series)	EBee
adsurgens 'Wagon Wheel'	CRos ECtt EPot EWes GCrg LRHS NHpl NRHS SPlb SRms SRot
amplifolia	LRHS MSpe NRHS WCot XLum
- 'Winnetou'	IPot
× ***arendsii*** 'Andrew'	WCot
- 'Autumn's Pink Explosion'	WCot
- 'Babyface'	ELon NGdn
- 'Casablanca'	NDov
- 'Dylan'	WCot
- 'Eyecatcher'	NBro
- 'Gary'	WCot
- 'Hesperis'	CBWd EBee ECha ELon GBin GWyn LRHS MAvo MNrw MSpe MTis NDov NLar SPhx WCAu WHil
- 'Luc's Lilac' ♀H7	CBWd ECtt EPPr LLHF MCot MSpe NBro NDov NEgg NGdn NSti SGbt SPhm SPhx WAul WCot
- 'Miss Jessica' (Spring Pearl Series)	MSpe
§ - 'Miss Jill' (Spring Pearl Series)	EBee ELan EPfP IPot LCro LOPS WCot
§ - 'Miss Karen' (Spring Pearl Series)	EBee ELan NBro
§ - 'Miss Margie' (Spring Pearl Series)	MSpe
§ - 'Miss Mary' (Spring Pearl Series) ♀H7	CRos ECtt ELan ELon EPfP IBoy ILea LRHS MSpe NRHS SRkn WRHF
§ - 'Miss Wilma' (Spring Pearl Series)	EBee ELan EPfP
- 'Paul'	MNrw WCot
- 'Ping Pong'	SGbt
- 'Pink Attraction'	NBro NRHS
- 'Purple Star'	EPfP
- 'Utopia' ♀H7	EBee ELon IMou MAvo NDov SPhx WCot
austromontana	CTal EPot NWad

	bifida 'Alba'	LLHF
	- 'Ralph Haywood'	CPBP ECtt EPot
	- 'Thefi'	ECtt
	borealis	see *P. sibirica* subsp. *borealis*
	caespitosa	CMea EWes
	- subsp. ***pulvinata***	see *P. pulvinata*
	- 'Zigeunerblut'	CMea CPBP ECtt EPot GCrg ITim NWad WAbe WHal WHoo
	canadensis	see *P. divaricata*
	carolina 'Bill Baker'	see *P. glaberrima* 'Bill Baker'
	- 'Magnificence'	EBee EWes GWyn SBod SMad SPlb WCot
	- 'Miss Lingard' ♀H5	CBod CDor CRos CSam EAJP ECtt LRHS LSou MCot MMuc MRav MTis NGdn NLar NRHS NSti SBee WCot
	'Charles Ricardo'	CSam
	'Chattahoochee'	see *P. divaricata* subsp. *laphamii* 'Chattahoochee'
	colubrina	GKev
	'Daniel's Cushion'	see *P. subulata* 'McDaniel's Cushion'
	diffusa	EPot
§	***divaricata*** ♀H4	EWTr IBoy SPlb
	- 'Blue Dreams'	ECtt ESps MNrw WFar
	- 'Blue Perfume'	EBee ECtt GWyn LCro NBro
	- 'Charles'	XLum
	- 'Clouds of Perfume'	Widely available
	- 'Dirigo Ice'	CRos LRHS NRHS SAko WSHC
	- 'Fuller's White'	CWCL
	- subsp. ***laphamii***	CWCL EBee EWes
§	- - 'Chattahoochee' ♀H4	CBcs CBod CPla CRos CWCL EAJP ECtt EHrv ELan ELon EPfP EWes GBin GWyn IBoy ILea LCro LOPS LRHS MCot MNrw NHpl NLar NRHS SPoG SRot SWvt WCAu WCFE WSpi
	- 'May Breeze'	CRos CWCL EAJP ECtt EHrv GMaP LRHS MNrw MSCN NPnk NRHS WSHC
	- 'Plum Perfect'	ECtt
	- 'White Perfume'	CRos CWCL EBee EWes IBoy ILea LRHS NBro NLar NRHS WFar XLum
	douglasii	SRms
	- 'Apollo'	CPBP CTri ECtt EPot
	- 'Boothman's Variety' ♀H5	ECtt ELan GCrg ITim SRms
	- 'Crackerjack' ♀H5	CBod CMea CRos CTri ECtt EDAr ELan ELon EPot EUJe GAbr GCrg GMaP ITim LRHS MAsh MHol NEgg NHpl NRHS NSla SPoG
	- 'Eva'	CRos ECtt EDAr ELon GCrg GMaP IRob ITim LRHS LSRN MAsh MHol NHpl NLar NRHS NSla NWad
	- 'Georg Arends'	ECtt GJos
	- 'Ice Mountain'	CBod CMea ECtt ELan EPot NEgg NWad SPoG SRot
	- 'Iceberg' ♀H5	GJos
	- 'J.A. Hibberson'	EPot GCrg NWad
	- 'Lilac Cloud'	ECtt GJos
	- LILAC QUEEN	see *P. douglasii* 'Lilakönigin'
§	- 'Lilakönigin'	CTri
	- 'Napoleon'	ECtt EPot ITim NWad
	- 'Ochsenblut'	CRos CSma ECtt GCrg LLHF LRHS NLar NRHS NWad
	- 'Red Admiral' ♀H5	ECtt ELan EPfP ETMg EWes GJos GMaP MHol NWad WCFE
	- 'Rose Cushion'	EWes GCrg
	- 'Rose Queen'	ESps
	- 'Rosea'	ELan MMuc NHpl
	- 'Sprite'	SRms
	- 'Tycoon'	see *P. subulata* 'Tamaongalei'
	- 'Waterloo'	CRos ECtt EPot LRHS NRHS
I	- 'White Admiral'	CRos CTri ECtt ELan ETMg GBin LRHS LSRN MHol NRHS
	drummondii 'Grammy Pink and White'	NPri
	- POPSTARS MIXED **new**	ETMg
	'Flare'	see *P. paniculata* 'Neon Flare'
§	***glaberrima*** 'Bill Baker' ♀H5	CSam ECha ECtt EPPr EPfP GMaP MNrw NGdn NSti WCAu WKif WPtf XLum
	- 'Morris Berd'	EBee MAvo WFar WSHC
	'Goliath' **new**	WHlf
	hendersonii	WAbe
	'Jeff's Pink'	ECtt
	'Kelly's Eye' ♀H5	CRos ECtt EPot GCrg LRHS NRHS SPoG
	kelseyi 'Lemhi Purple'	CPBP EPot WAbe
	- 'Rosette'	NWad
	LIGHT PINK FLAME ('Bareleven'PBR)	CBod ECtt EPfP SPoG
	LILAC FLAME ('Barten'PBR)	EPfP LRHS WHil
	longifolia subsp. ***brevifolia***	WAbe
	maculata	ESps
	- 'Alba'	SAko WAul
	- 'Alpha' ♀H6	CBot CMea CRos CSam CWCL EBee ECha ECtt EPfP GMaP ILea LEdu LRHS LSou NLar NRHS SGbt SPer SWvt WCAu WFar WSHC XLum
	- AVALANCHE	see *P. maculata* 'Schneelawine'
	- 'Delta'	CRos EAJP EBee EPPr LRHS NLar SAko SGbt SPer SRkn SWvt
	- 'Natascha' ♀H7	CMac CMea CRos CSam EBee ECtt EPfP EWTr EWes GMaP GMcL IRob LRHS LSRN LSou MCot NGdn NLar NPnk NRHS NWad SAko SGbt SMad SPer SRkn SWvt WCAu WFar WHil
	- 'Omega' ♀H6	CBod CExl CMac CMea EBee ECtt EWTr GMcL ILea IRob LEdu LSou MCot MMuc MNrw MPie NGdn NLar NPnk SGbt SPer SWvt WCAu WFar WSpi
	- 'Reine du Jour'	CSam IRob NDov SPhx
	- 'Rosalinde'	CRos ECtt GBin LRHS LSou MCot NLar NPnk NRHS SAko SWvt WSHC
§	- 'Schneelawine'	CRos LRHS NRHS SPlb WSpi
	'Millstream'	see *P.* × *procumbens* 'Millstream'
	'Millstream Blue'	EPfP
	'Minnie Pearl'	EWes LPla MPie NDov WCot
	nivalis 'Nivea'	WAbe
	paniculata	ESps NBid NDov WCot
	- 'Aida'	EBee
	- var. ***alba***	WCAu WCot
	- 'Alba Grandiflora' ♀H7	GMaP MNrw NChi WCot WHoo
	- 'Amethyst' misapplied	see *P. paniculata* 'Lilac Time'
	- 'Amethyst' Foerster	CRos ELon GBin GQue GWyn LRHS MRav MSpe MTis NLar WCAu WMoo
	- 'André'	LRHS NRHS
	- 'Anne'	CSam MSpe
	- 'Argus'	ECtt MSpe
	- 'Auslese D. Bach'	CSam
	- 'Autumn Joy' **new**	MSCN
	- 'Balmoral'	CMac EBee ECtt MSpe NCou NEgg NSti SWvt
	- 'Becky Towe'PBR (v) ♀H7	ECtt ELon LLHF MHer MHol MNrw NEgg SPoG WCot
	- 'Blauer Morgen'	XLum

	- 'Blue Boy'	CRos EBee ECtt ELan ELon EPfP GMaP GWyn LRHS MSpe NBro NEgg NRHS SWvt WFar
	- 'Blue Evening'	EBee LCro LOPS MCot MSpe
	- 'Blue Ice'	NBro
	- 'Blue Paradise'	Widely available
	- 'Blushing Bride'	SRms
	- 'Bonny Maid'	MAvo
	- 'Border Gem'	CAby CBWd CBcs CBod CMac ECtt ELon EShb LRHS MCot MRav MSpe MTis MWat SWvt WBrk WCot WHrl
	- 'Bosvigo Pink'	MAvo SHar
	- 'Brigadier'	CBod CTri EBee ECtt ELan LRHS MAvo MCot MSpe NEgg NGdn SPer SRms
	- 'Bright Eyes'	Widely available
	- 'Candy Floss'	ELon
	- 'Cardinal'	MTis NDov
	- 'Caroline van den Berg'	SRms
	- 'Charlotte'	MSpe
	- 'Cheriton' **new**	CRos NRHS
	- 'Cherry Red'	WMoo
	- 'Chintz'	CRos LRHS MRav NRHS SRms
	- 'Cinderella'	ECtt IRob
	- 'Cleopatra'	MSCN SPad WHar WHlf
	- COMPACT LILAC	see *P. paniculata* (Sweet Summer Series) SWEET SUMMER FAVOURITE
	- COMPACT ROSE WHITE	see *P. paniculata* (Sweet Summer Series) SWEET SUMMER CANDY
§	- 'Cool of the Evening'	WKif
	- 'Cool Water'	EBee
	- CORAL FLAME ('Barsixtytwo'PBR) (Flame Series)	CBod CBot CMac ELon EUJe LSou NLar SCob SRkn WHil
	- 'Coral Queen'	SRms
	- 'Cosmopolitan'PBR	MNrw NLar WHar
	- COUNT ZEPPELIN	see *P. paniculata* 'Graf Zeppelin'
	- 'Danielle' 🏆H7	LRHS NRHS SHar WHil
	- 'Darwin's Choice'	see *P. paniculata* 'Norah Leigh'
	- 'David' 🏆H7	Widely available
	- 'David's Lavender' 🏆H7	CRos ELon IPot LRHS NRHS WSpi
	- 'Delilah'PBR	CWGN ECtt NHpl
	- 'Discovery'	EHrv EShb EWes LRHS MCot MRav MSpe NEgg NRHS SHar
	- 'Dodo Hanbury-Forbes'	MNrw
	- 'Doghouse Pink'	IRob
	- 'Dresden China'	SHar
	- 'Duchess of York'	MAvo MNrw MSpe
§	- 'Düsterlohe'	CRos CSam EBee ECtt ELon GBin GQue GWyn ILea IPot LPla LRHS MHer MRav MSpe MTis NDov NLar NRHS SPer SRkn SRms WCot WHar WHil WSpi XLum
	- 'Early Light Pink'	IPot
	- 'Early Pink Dark Eye' **new**	LOPS
	- 'Eclaireur' misapplied	see *P. paniculata* 'Düsterlohe'
	- 'Eclaireur' Lemoine	MAvo
	- 'Eden's Flash'	CElw ECtt MPie MSpe
	- 'Eden's Glory'	MAvo
	- 'Eden's Smile'	ECtt MSpe
	- 'Edentuin' **new**	IPot
	- 'Elisabeth' (v)	EPfP LSRN NWad WHil
	- 'Elizabeth Arden'	ECtt ELon MSpe MTis
	- 'Elizabeth Campbell'	CRos GCal LRHS NRHS
	- 'Ending Blue'	MAvo
	- 'Etoile de Paris'	see *P. paniculata* 'Toits de Paris' Symons-Jeune
	- 'Europa'	EBee ECtt ELan IPot MCot MSpe NGdn NLar SPer
	- 'Eva Cullum' 🏆H7	CBod CRos CSam EBee ECtt EHrv ELan ELon EPfP ESps GMaP GWyn LCro LOPS LRHS MArl MCot MSpe NHpl NRHS SAko SPer WCot
	- 'Eva Foerster' 🏆H7	CRos EBee GWyn LRHS NRHS XLum
	- 'Eventide'	CMac CRos CSam ECtt EPfP GQue LRHS MArl MAvo MCot MNrw MRav MSpe MWat NRHS SPer WFar WHrl
	- 'Ferris Wheel'	EBee ECtt WHlf
	- 'Flamingo' 🏆H7	CRos EBee ECtt IRob LRHS MSpe SWvt XLum
	- 'Fondant Fancy'PBR	NLar
	- 'Franz Schubert' 🏆H7	CDor CRos CSam ECtt ELan EPfP ESps GBin GWyn ILea LCro LRHS MAvo MCot MSpe MWat NChi NGdn NLar NRHS NSti SPer SWvt WCot WFar WHoo WMoo
§	- 'Frau Alfred von Mauthner'	GKev
	- 'Fujiyama'	see *P. paniculata* 'Mount Fuji'
	- 'Glebe' **new**	CSam
	- 'Glow'	MSpe
	- 'Goldmine'PBR (v)	CAby CRos EBee IRob LRHS MHol MNrw NHpl NRHS SRms WCot
§	- 'Graf Zeppelin'	ECtt MSpe MTis SRms XLum
	- 'Grenadine Dream'PBR 🏆H7	CRos CWGN EBee LRHS MNrw NHpl NRHS WCot
	- 'Grey Lady' 🏆H7	CRos LRHS MNrw NRHS
	- 'Harlequin' (v)	CMac CWGN ECha ECtt ELon MHol NBro NEgg WCot
	- 'Herbstwalzer'	IPot WCot
	- 'Ice Cream'	ELon
	- 'Irene Mast'	CSam
	- 'Iris'	MNrw SRms WCot
	- 'Jade'	CAby CRos EBee ECtt EWTr GBin GQue LRHS MCot MHol MNrw MSpe NLar NPnk NRHS NSti WCot WHil
	- 'Jeana' **new**	MBel MNrw
	- 'Jeff's Blue'	EBee MHol WCot
	- 'Judy'	GBin LSRN MAvo
§	- 'Juliglut'	WCot
	- JULY GLOW	see *P. paniculata* 'Juliglut'
	- 'Junior Bouquet'	MHol NLar
	- 'Junior Dream'	NLar
	- 'Katherine'	CRos ELon IPot LRHS MSpe NLar NRHS WHar
	- 'Katja'PBR	CNor IPot
	- 'Kirchenfürst'	CElw CRos LCro LOPS LRHS MSpe MTis NLar NRHS SAko
	- 'Kirmesländler'	ECtt EWTr IPot MSpe MTis NLar SAko
	- 'Lady Clare'	SRms
	- 'Larissa' **new**	LSou
	- 'Laura'	see *P. paniculata* 'Uspekh'
§	- 'Lavendelwolke'	GCal LRHS MSpe NLar WCot
	- LAVENDER CLOUD	see *P. paniculata* 'Lavendelwolke'
	- 'Le Mahdi' 🏆H7	NLar SRms WBor
	- 'Lichtblick'	MSpe
	- 'Lichtspel'	EBee LPla NDov SPhx
§	- 'Lilac Time'	CElw CRos EBee ECtt EPfP EWTr GMaP LRHS MMuc MTis NLar NRHS SPer SWvt WSpi
	- 'Little Boy'	CElw ELon MNrw NLar SGbt WHil
	- 'Little Laura'	CBod ECtt EWTr LSRN MNrw MSpe NLar SPoG WCot WHoo
	- 'Little Princess'	ELon NLar

- 'Little Sara' NDov
- 'Lizzy'PBR NLar
- 'Logan Black' GCal MSpe SHar WSHC
- MAGICAL DREAM see *P. paniculata* (Sweet Summer Series) SWEET SUMMER DREAM
- MAGICAL FAVORITE see *P. paniculata* (Sweet Summer Series) SWEET SUMMER FAVOURITE
- MAGICAL SURPRISE see *P. paniculata* (Sweet Summer Series) SWEET SUMMER SURPRISE
- 'Manoir d'Hézèques' WCot
- 'Mardi Gras' EBee
- 'Marlborough' IRob
- 'Mary Christine' (v) LRHS NBid NRHS
- 'Maude Stella Dagley' ELon MSpe WCot
- 'Mia Ruys' MArl
- 'Mike's Favourite' EBee
- 'Milly van Hoboken' WKif
- 'Miss Holland' ELon NGdn SGbt XLum
- 'Miss Jill' see *P.* × *arendsii* 'Miss Jill'
- 'Miss Karen' see *P.* × *arendsii* 'Miss Karen'
- 'Miss Kelly' EHrv ELon EShb MSpe NLar
- 'Miss Margie' see *P.* × *arendsii* 'Miss Margie'
- 'Miss Mary' see *P.* × *arendsii* 'Miss Mary'
- 'Miss Pepper' ♀H7 CRos CWCL ECtt ELon LRHS MMuc MSpe NGdn NLar NRHS WBor
- 'Miss Universe' ELon
- 'Miss Wilma' see *P.* × *arendsii* 'Miss Wilma'
- 'Monica Lynden-Bell' ♀H7 CAby CBWd CDor CWGN ELon GBin GMaP GWyn IRob LRHS MHol MNrw MPie MRav MSCN MSpe NBid NChi NDov NLar NSti SBod SGbt WAul WCot WKif WPtf
- 'Monte Cristallo' GBin GWyn MSpe
- 'Mother of Pearl' ♀H7 ESps GQue GWyn IPot LRHS MSpe MWat NEgg WSpi

§ - 'Mount Fuji' Widely available
- 'Mount Fujiyama' see *P. paniculata* 'Mount Fuji'
- 'Mrs A.E. Jeans' SRms
- 'Mystique Black' WPtf
- 'Nadia'PBR LRHS NRHS
- 'Natural Feelings'PBR (Feelings Series) NLar

§ - 'Neon Flare' (Neon Series) CWGN ECtt
- 'Newbird' CRos EBee ECtt EPfP IBoy LRHS MSpe NRHS SRms
- 'Nicky' see *P. paniculata* 'Düsterlohe'
- 'Nirvana' CSam

§ - 'Norah Leigh' (v) ♀H7 CElw CMac CRos CWGN ECha ECtt EHoe EHrv ELan ELon EWes GCal GMcL GWyn IFoB LRHS MHer MHol MWat NPer NRHS NSti NWad SPer SPoG SRms SWvt WCFE WCot WPtf
- 'Orange Perfection' see *P. paniculata* 'Prince of Orange'
- 'Othello' CBod CSam ECtt ELon MSpe NGdn NSti WHoo
- 'Otley Choice' CRos CSam EBee ECtt GBin GWyn LRHS MRav NCou NLar NRHS NSti WHrl
- 'Otley Purple' MHer MSpe NCou
- 'P.D. Williams' WCot
- 'Pallas Athene' IPot
- 'Pastorale' WCot
- (Peacock Series) PEACOCK CHERRY RED ♀H7 CRos GMcL LRHS NRHS WCFE WTor
- - PEACOCK LILAC ♀H7 CRos EPfP GMcL LRHS NRHS
- - PEACOCK NEON PURPLE ♀H7 CRos LRHS NRHS WMoo
- - PEACOCK PURPLE BICOLOR CRos GMcL LRHS NRHS
- - PEACOCK WHITE ♀H7 CRos GMcL LRHS NRHS WTor
- 'Peppermint Twist' CRos CWGN EBee ELon GWyn LRHS LSou MHol MNrw MSCN NEgg NLar NRHS SWvt WFar WHil
- 'Picasso' ECtt IPot MSpe
- 'Pina Colada'PBR CWGN EBee ECtt ELon NPri WFar WHil
- PINK EYE FLAME ('Barthirtyfive'PBR) ♀H7 EPfP LRHS LSou NRHS SCob SPoG SRkn SRms
- 'Pink Lady'PBR ELon WFar
- 'Pink Posie' (v) WCot
- PINK RED EYE FLAME ('Barthirtyfour') CRos EPfP LSou SPoG
- 'Pinky Hill' WCot WHar
- 'Polarstern' **new** CSam
- 'Popeye' IPot LPla WCot
- 'Prime Minister' ELon

§ - 'Prince of Orange' ♀H7 CBcs CBod CRos CSBt CSam EBee ECtt ELon EPfP EUJe GMcL IBoy LPla LRHS MAvo MCot MJak MRav MSpe MWat NEgg NLar NRHS SGbt SPer SWvt WBor WCot WMoo XLum
- 'Prospero' ♀H7 CSpe GWyn MRav NBid
- PURPLE EYE FLAME ('Barthirtythree'PBR) ♀H7 CRos LLHF LRHS LSou NRHS SRkn SWvt WFar WHil
- 'Purple Kiss'PBR CWGN ECtt MHol NHpl NPri WFar
- 'Purple Paradise' LRHS NRHS
- 'Rainbow' ELon NLar
- 'Rainbow Dancer' **new** LSou
- 'Raving Beauty' **new** NRHS
- 'Rectory Pink' MSpe
- 'Red Caribbean' ECtt NLar NPri
- 'Red Feelings' (Feelings Series) CBod LRHS NRHS
- 'Red Flame' CRos CWGN ECtt EPfP LRHS LSou MHol MNrw NRHS SAko SRkn WFar
- 'Red Riding Hood' see *P.* × *arendsii* 'Miss Mary'

I - 'Reddish Hesperis' MAvo
- 'Rembrandt' CExl ELon EPfP GBin IRob LCro LOPS XLum
- 'Rijnstroom' CBcs ECha ECtt ELon GMcL MArl NLar SCob WBrk WHil
- 'Robert Poore' ECtt ELon
- 'Roberta' LCro LOPS
- 'Rosa Goliath' CSam
- 'Rosa Pastell' ♀H7 CAby CDor CEnd CSpe ECtt EHrv ELon GBin GQue IPot IRob LRHS MAvo MHol MPie MTis NBid NDov NLar SPer SPoG WAul WCot
- 'Rowie' NBid
- 'Sandringham' CRos EHrv IRob LRHS MArl MRav MSpe NCou NRHS SPer SWvt

§ - 'Schneerausch' LPla SPhx
- 'Septemberglut' CRos EBee EPfP LRHS NRHS
- 'Shockwave' (v) WCot
- 'Skylight' NBro
- SNOWDRIFT see *P. paniculata* 'Schneerausch'
- 'Spätsommer' **new** IPot
- 'Speed Limit 45' WCot
- 'Spitfire' see *P. paniculata* 'Frau Alfred von Mauthner'
- 'Starfire' ♀H7 Widely available

I	- 'Stars and Stripes'	LRHS NRHS
	- 'Steeple Bumpstead'	WCot
I	- 'Stellata'	CRos EBee LRHS
	- 'Sterling Brocade' (v) **new**	WCot
	- 'Sternhimmel'	LPla MSpe MTis
	- 'Strawberry Daiquiri'PBR	WFar
§	- (Sweet Summer Series) SWEET SUMMER CANDY ('Ditosdre'PBR)	CRos LRHS NRHS WTor
§	- - SWEET SUMMER DREAM ('Ditomdre'PBR)	MAvo
	- - SWEET SUMMER FANTASY ('Ditopur'PBR)	CRos LRHS NRHS WTor
§	- - SWEET SUMMER FAVOURITE ('Ditomfav'PBR) ♀H7	WCAu
	- - SWEET SUMMER PURPLE WHITE	see *P. paniculata* (Sweet Summer Series) SWEET SUMMER TEMPTATION
	- - SWEET SUMMER QUEEN ('Ditoran'PBR)	CRos NRHS
§	- - SWEET SUMMER SURPRISE ('Ditomsur'PBR)	ECtt WCAu
§	- - SWEET SUMMER TEMPTATION ('Ditostem'PBR)	CRos LRHS NRHS
	- - SWEET SUMMER WINE ('Ditowine'PBR)	ECtt IPot MAvo
	- 'Swizzle'	CWGN ECtt NPri WFar
	- 'Tatjana'PBR	EBee IPot
	- 'Tenor'	CMac CRos CTri CWCL ECtt ELon EPfP GBin IBoy LEdu LRHS MCot MJak NLar NRHS SCob SRms SWvt WCAu WMoo WSHC
	- 'Tequila Sunrise'PBR	EBee ECtt MNrw
	- 'The King' ♀H7	EBee ECtt MAvo MSpe NBro NLar WSHC WSpi
	- 'Tiara'PBR (d)	EBee ECtt LRHS MPie NGdn SWvt WCot
	- 'Toits de Paris' misapplied	see *P. paniculata* 'Cool of the Evening'
§	- 'Toits de Paris' Symons-Jeune	WCot WSHC
	- 'Twister'	EBee MNrw MSCN WFar
§	- 'Uspekh' ♀H7	Widely available
	- 'Valentina'PBR	EBee
	- 'Van Gogh'	CCse
	- 'Veg Plot Pink' **new**	SMHy
	- 'Veg Plot White' **new**	SMHy
	- 'Velvet Flame' ♀H7	EPfP LSou
	- 'Vintage Wine'	MNrw
	- 'Visions' ♀H7	CRos LRHS NRHS WHil
	- 'Volcano Betty'	MNrw
	- 'Watermelon Punch'	ECtt NLar NPri WFar
	- 'Wendy House'	ECtt MAvo MNrw
	- 'Wenn Schon Denn Schon'	EBee
	- 'White Admiral' ♀H7	CBcs CElw CRos EBee ECtt ELan ELon EPfP GKev GMaP IBoy LRHS MHer MNrw MSpe MWat NEgg NRHS SCob SPer SPhx SRms SWvt WCAu WSHC XLum
	- WHITE FLAME ('Bartwentynine'PBR) ♀H7	CDor CWGN ECtt EPfP IPot LBuc LRHS LSou NLar NRHS SCob SWvt WCot
	- 'Wilhelm Kesselring'	CRos EBee ECtt ELon LRHS MTis NChi NRHS WBor
	- 'Willow Lodge'	SHar
	- 'Windsor'	EBee ECtt EPfP EWTr MSpe NCou NEgg SRms SWvt

	- (Younique Series) YOUNIQUE BICOLOR ('Versbicolor') **new**	WFar
	- - YOUNIQUE OLD CERISE **new**	WFar
	- - YOUNIQUE OLD BLUE ('Versoldblue') **new**	WFar
	- - YOUNIQUE OLD PINK ('Versoldpink') **new**	WFar
	- - YOUNIQUE OLD PURPLE **new**	WFar
	- - YOUNIQUE WHITE	LEdu MNrw WFar
	PAPARAZZI ANGELINA (Paparazzi Series)	CRos LRHS NRHS
	- PAPARAZZI BRITNEY ('Ppphl0604')	CRos LRHS NRHS
	- PAPARAZZI GAGA ('Ppphl07301')	CRos LRHS NRHS
	'Peppermint Candy'	WFar
	'Petticoat'	CMea CPBP CSma ECtt
	PINK FLAME ('Bartwelve'PBR)	CMea CRos EPfP LLHF LRHS LSou NLar NRHS SCob SRkn SRms WHil
	'Pride of Rochester'	CRos ECtt LRHS NRHS
§	× ***procumbens*** 'Millstream' ♀H5	ECtt
	- 'Variegata' (v)	ECha ECtt SRot
§	***pulvinata***	SPlb WAbe
	PURPLE FLAME ('Barfourteen'PBR)	CBod CRos EPfP GWyn LRHS LSou NRHS SCob SRkn SRms WFar WHil
	× ***rugelii***	EWld
	'Sherbet Cocktail'PBR	CWGN EBee WHlf WPtf
§	***sibirica*** subsp. ***borealis***	WAbe
	'Sileniflora'	EPot WAbe
	stolonifera	MNrw
I	- 'Alba'	EBee EPfP WFar
	- 'Ariane'	ECha ECtt MCot MNrw
	- 'Blue Ridge' ♀H5	CExl CRos EBee ECha ECtt EPfP EWld LRHS LSRN MHol MRav SRms WFar WHar
	- 'Fran's Purple'	ECtt EWld MNrw NBro WAvo
	- 'Home Fires'	CRos EBee ECtt EPfP LEdu LRHS MNrw NBro SPlb
	- 'Janusz'	NWad
	- 'Montrose Tricolor' (v)	NBro
	- 'Pink Ridge'	XLum
	- 'Purpurea'	EBee EPfP LEdu
	subulata	ESps
	- 'Alexander's Surprise'	CMea CRos ECtt EPfP EPot LRHS MAsh NRHS
	- 'Amazing Grace'	CRos CTri CWCL ECtt EPfP EWes GJos IPot IRob LRHS NRHS NSla NWad SPoG WHoo
	- 'Apple Blossom'	SPoG SRms
	- 'Atropurpurea'	EPfP SPoG XLum
	- 'Bavaria'	CMea CPBP CRos ECtt EPfP ETMg GJos IPot LLHF LRHS MBel NRHS
	- BEAUTY OF RONSDORF	see *P. subulata* 'Ronsdorfer Schöne'
	- 'Blue Eyes'	see *P. subulata* 'Oakington Blue Eyes'
	- 'Bonita'	CRos ECtt EPot GCrg GJos LRHS MAsh NRHS WHoo
	- 'Bressingham Blue Eyes'	see *P. subulata* 'Oakington Blue Eyes'
	- 'Candy Stripe'	see *P. subulata* 'Tamaongalei'
	- 'Cavaldes White'	ECtt
	- 'Coral Eye'	ECtt
	- 'Daisy Hill'	XLum
	- 'Drumm'	see *P. subulata* 'Tamaongalei'
	- EARLY SPRING PURPLE ('Barseventyfour'PBR)	CRos LRHS NRHS

- 'Emerald Cushion'	CTri ECtt ELon EPfP LRHS MHol NHpl NLar NSla SGbt WCFE WTor XLum
- 'Emerald Cushion Blue'	CExl CTri ECtt EPfP LRHS MAsh MHCG MHol NRHS SPlb SPoG
- 'Fort Hill'	ECtt
- 'G.F.Wilson'	see *P. subulata* 'Lilacina'
- 'Holly'	EPot ITim NWad
- 'Kimono'	see *P. subulata* 'Tamaongalei'
§ - 'Lilacina'	CMea ECha MAsh
§ - 'Maischnee'	CTri ECtt MAsh SPlb
- 'Marjorie'	ECtt GJos IRob MHer SPoG
- MAY SNOW	see *P. subulata* 'Maischnee'
§ - 'McDaniel's Cushion' 𝕐H5	CBod CExl CRos CTri ECha ECtt EDAr ELan ELon EPfP EPot ESps EUJe GJos GMaP LRHS MAsh MMuc NLar NRHS SPlb SPoG WCFE WHoo
- 'Mikado'	see *P. subulata* 'Tamaongalei'
- 'Millstream Daphne'	ECtt LLHF
I - 'Moerheimii' **new**	IPot
- 'Nettleton Variation' (v)	CRos ECtt ELon EPot EWes LRHS MMuc NRHS SPoG SRms WHoo
§ - 'Oakington Blue Eyes'	CTri GWyn SRms
- 'Purple Beauty'	CMea CRos ECtt GJos GMaP IRob LLHF LRHS NRHS NWad SPoG WCFE WHoo WSHC XLum
- 'Red Wings' 𝕐H5	ECtt EPfP ESps SRms
§ - 'Ronsdorfer Schöne'	ECtt EPfP LLHF
- 'Samson'	GJos LSRN WOld
- 'Scarlet Flame'	CMea ECtt ELon EPfP EPot GJos MAsh MHol NHpl WHoo
- 'Snow Queen'	see *P. subulata* 'Maischnee'
- 'Snowflake'	GCrg
§ - 'Tamaongalei'	CBod CMea CPla CRos CTri ECtt ELon EWes GKev LRHS MHol MMuc NRHS NWad WCFE XLum
- 'Temiskaming'	CRos CTri ECtt EWes IRob LRHS MBel NRHS SRms WSHC
- 'White Delight'	CMea ECtt ELon EPfP ESps GJos SPoG
- 'Winifred'	NEgg
'Tiny Bugles'	CPBP
VIOLET FLAME ('Barsixtyone'PBR)	CBod CDor CMea EPfP EUJe GAbr IRob LPla LRHS LSun MAvo MHol NLar SCob SPer SPoG WBor WCot
WHITE EYE FLAME ('Barsixty'PBR)	CBod CBot CDor CMea CRos CWGN EPau EPfP IPot LRHS NLar NRHS SCob
'White Kimono'	CRos LRHS NRHS
'Zwergenteppich'	CRos EPfP LRHS NRHS

Phoenix (*Arecaceae*)

canariensis 𝕐H1c	CBcs CExl EPfP ESps EUJe SArc SEND SPlb SPoG SWeb
dactylifera (F)	SBig
loureiroi	LRHS
reclinata	XBlo
roebelenii 𝕐H1b	CDTJ EUJe LCro NLos SBig
- 'Multistem'	XBlo
theophrasti	CPHo LRHS

Phormium ✿ (*Hemerocallidaceae*)

§ 'Alison Blackman'PBR	CBcs CBod EBee EMOT EPfP ESps EUJe LRHS LSRN MAsh MGos MJak NLar NRHS SCob SCoo SEND SPoG SWvt
'Amazing Red'	SCob
'Apricot Queen' (v)	CAbb CBcs CCCN CSBt EMOT EPfP ESps GMcL IBoy LCro LOPS LRHS LSRN MGos NLar NRHS SCob SEND SPer SPoG
BACK IN BLACK ('Seilack'PBR)	CPla EUJe LRHS NRHS SCob WFar
'Black Adder'PBR	CBcs CBot EBee EPfP EUJe IBoy ILea LBuc LRHS LSRN MAsh MJak NRHS SCob SEND SPer SPoG
'Black Rage'	CBcs EPfP EUJe LRHS NLos NRHS
BLACK VELVET ('Seivel'PBR)	CSpe EUJe IBoy LRHS MSwo
'Bronze Baby'	CBcs CCCN CMea CSBt EHoe ELan EMOT EPfP ESps EUJe LCro LOPS LRHS LSRN MGos MSwo NLar NRHS SCob SLim SPer SPoG SWvt
'Chocomint'PBR	CBod EUJe LRHS NLar NRHS
colensoi	see *P. cookianum*
§ ***cookianum***	SArc SCob
- 'Alpinum Purpureum'	see *P. tenax* 'Nanum Purpureum'
- subsp. ***hookeri*** 'Cream Delight' (v) 𝕐H4	CAbb CBcs CCCN CEnd CSBt EBee EMOT EPfP ESps EUJe GMcL IBoy LRHS LSRN MAsh MGos MSwo NRHS SCob SCoo SGol SPer SWvt WGrn
- - 'Tricolor' (v) 𝕐H4	CBcs CChe CDTJ CDul CSBt ELan ELon EMOT EPfP ESps EUJe GMcL LCro LOPS LRHS MGos MMuc NPla NRHS SAko SArc SCob SEND SGol SLim SPer SPoG SRms SWvt WGrn
'Crimson Devil'	CBcs LRHS NRHS SAko
DARK AVOCADO ('Westado'PBR)	MAsh
'Dark Delight'	CBcs
'Dazzler' (v)	ESps
'Duet' (v) 𝕐H3	CBcs CCCN EPfP ESps SEND SWvt WHar
'Dusky Chief'	CSBt EBee EPfP
'Evening Glow' (v)	CBcs CCCN ELon EMOT EPfP ESps EUJe GMcL LCro LOPS LRHS LSRN MGos NLar NRHS SCob SPoG SRms SWvt WGrn
'Firebird'	ELon EUJe LRHS LSRN SWvt
'Flamingo' (v)	CBcs CCCN CDTJ ELon EMOT EPfP EUJe GMcL LRHS LSou MGos MHol NLar NRHS SCob SLim SPer SPoG
'Gold Ray' (v)	CBcs EPfP EUJe GMcL LRHS MJak NLos NRHS SCob SCoo SWvt WHil
'Gold Sword' (v)	CCCN CSBt EPfP ESps GMcL LRHS MJak NEgg NRHS SCob
'Golden Alison'	see *P.* 'Alison Blackman'
'Green Sword'	CBcs CCCN
'Jack Spratt' (v)	EHoe SWvt WHar
'Jessie'	NLos
'Jester' (v)	Widely available
'Limelight'	SEND SWvt
§ 'Maori Chief' (v)	CSBt EMOT EPfP ESps LRHS SWvt WFar
'Maori Eclipse' (v)	GMcL
§ 'Maori Maiden' (v)	CCCN CDul CTri EBee ELon EPfP GMcL LRHS MSwo NRHS SRms SWvt
§ 'Maori Queen' (v)	CBcs CBod CCCN CDTJ EBee ELon EPfP ESps EUJe ILea LCro LOPS LRHS MGos MSwo NRHS SCob SCoo SEND SPer SWvt
§ 'Maori Sunrise' (v)	CBcs CCCN CPla ELon GMcL IArd LCro LOPS LRHS LSRN MGos NRHS SCob SCoo SLim SPer SRms SWvt
'Margaret Jones'PBR	CCCN LSRN
'Moonraker'PBR	CBcs MHol
'Pink Jester' (v)	GMcL

	'Pink Panther' (v)	CAbb CBcs CCCN CDul ELon EMOT EPfP ESps LRHS LSRN MGos NLar NRHS SCob SPoG SRms
	'Pink Stripe' (v)	CBcs CBod CSBt EPfP GMcL LCro LOPS LRHS MAsh MGos MJak NRHS SCob SPoG SWvt
	'Platt's Black'	CCCN EMOT EPfP ESps GMcL IBoy LCro LOPS LRHS LSRN MGos MSwo NLar NRHS SCob SLim SPer SPoG SWvt WFar WGrn
	'Rainbow Chief'	see *P.* 'Maori Chief'
	'Rainbow Glossy' (v)	NLos
	'Rainbow Maiden'	see *P.* 'Maori Maiden'
	'Rainbow Queen'	see *P.* 'Maori Queen'
	'Rainbow Sunrise'	see *P.* 'Maori Sunrise'
	'Red Sensation'	LSRN
	'Sundowner' (v) 🏆H3	CBcs CCCN CDul CSBt EBee ELan EMOT EPfP ESps GMcL LCro LOPS LRHS MAsh MGos MJak NEgg NRHS SCob SCoo SEND SLim SPer SPoG SWvt WGrn
	'Sunset' (v)	CBcs CCCN CSBt SWvt
	'Surfer' (v)	WGrn
	'Surfer Bronze'	CCCN
	'Surfer Green'	CCCN NLos
	'Sussex Velvet'	SCoo SLim
	tenax	CAco CAgr CBcs CDul CFGn CTsd ECrN ELan ELon EPfP ESps EUJe GMcL LCro LOPS LRHS MGos MSwo NGdn NPri NRHS SArc SCob SEND SGol SPer SPlb SPoG SWvt
	- 'All Black'	LRHS MGos SCoo
	- 'Bronze'	CTsd SWvt
	- 'Chocolate Dream'	IBoy
	- 'Co-ordination' (v)	CBcs CCCN EMOT
	- dwarf	CSpe
	- 'Joker' (v)	CBcs CBod CMea ELon NLar NLos
*	- ***lineatum***	SEND
§	- 'Nanum Purpureum'	SArc
	- Purpureum Group 🏆H4	CBar CDul EBee ELan ELon EPfP ESps EUJe GMcL IBoy LRHS MGil MJak MMuc MSwo NLar NRHS SCob SEND SGol SLim SLon SPer SPlb WFar XLum
	- 'Thumbelina'	CCCN
	- 'Tiny Tiger' (v)	EPfP
	- 'Variegatum' (v) 🏆H5	CDTJ CDul CPla EBee EPfP GMcL MGos MJak MMuc SArc SCob SEND SPer SRms
	- 'Veneer'[PBR] (v)	NLos
	- 'Yellow Queen' (v)	WFar
	variegated (v)	SCob
	'Yellow Wave' (v) 🏆H4	CAbb CBcs CBod CChe CDul CEnd EBee ELan ELon EPfP ESps EUJe GMcL LRHS LSRN MAsh MGos MJak MSwo NEgg NPla NRHS SCob SEND SLim SPer SPoG SWvt

Photinia ✿ (*Rosaceae*)

	arbutifolia	see *Heteromeles salicifolia*
	arguta var. ***arguta*** KR 10738 **new**	WPGP
	beauverdiana var. ***notabilis***	CJun EPfP NLar
	CORALLINA ('Bourfrits'[PBR])	LPra
	davidiana	CMac CTri ELan EPfP GMcL IDee MGil MRav NLar SCob SRms SVen
	- PAB 8097	LEdu
	- 'Palette' (v)	CBcs CDul CMac EBee EHoe ELan ELon EPfP ESps GMcL LRHS MAsh MGos MMuc MSwo NEgg NLar SCob SGol SPer SPoG SRms SWvt WFar WMoo
	- var. ***undulata*** 'Fructu Luteo'	MMuc MRav
	- - 'Prostrata'	CMac CTri MRav NLar WCFE
	× ***fraseri***	LPra WTSh
I	- 'Atropurpurea Nana'	EPfP MGos
	- 'Birmingham'	CMac EWes SRms
	- 'Canivily' 🏆H5	CEnd CRos ESps LRHS MGos NLar NRHS SGol
	- CRACKLIN' RED ('Parred'[PBR])	WMoo
	- 'Little Red Robin'	Widely available
	- 'Louise' (v)	CSBt GMcL LBuc LRHS MGos MJak NRHS WFar
	- MAGICAL VOLCANO ('Kolmavoca'[PBR])	LRHS MAsh SGol SPoG
	- PINK MARBLE ('Cassini') (v) 🏆H5	Widely available
	- 'Red Robin' 🏆H5	Widely available
	- 'Robusta'	CMac EPfP LRHS NRHS SRms SWvt
I	- 'Robusta Compacta'	LSRN
	- 'Scarlet Blaze'	LRHS
	glabra	SArc
§	- 'Parfait' (v)	CMac EBee LRHS MAsh SLon
	- 'Pink Lady'	see *P. glabra* 'Parfait'
	- 'Rubens'	EPfP LRHS MAsh MRav
	- 'Variegata'	see *P. glabra* 'Parfait'
	integrifolia HWJ 946	WCru
	lasiogyna	CMCN
	lucida	WCru
	microphylla B&SWJ 11837	WCru
	- HWJ 564	WCru
	niitakayamensis CWJ 12435	WCru
	'Redstart'	CMac ELan EPfP LRHS MMuc NLar SLon SPer SWvt WFar WMoo
§	***serratifolia***	CBcs CBot CMCN EPfP NLar SArc SBrt SEND SPer WFar WPGP
	- CRUNCHY ('Rev100') **new**	LBuc
	- CURLY FANTASY ('Kolcurl'[PBR])	LRHS MRav NLar
	- 'Jenny'	NLar WFar
	- PINK CRISPY ('Oploo5') **new**	SPoG
	serrulata	see *P. serratifolia*
	SUPER HEDGE ('Branpara'[PBR])	GBin LRHS MSwo WFar
	'Super Red'	CAby CSBt NLar
	villosa	CTho EPfP
	- B&SWJ 8665	WCru
	- var. ***coreana*** B&SWJ 8789	WCru
	- var. ***laevis***	CExl EBee EPfP WPGP
	- - B&SWJ 8877	WCru
	- f. ***maximowicziana***	CJun LRHS NLar
*	- var. ***zollingeri*** B&SWJ 8903	WCru

Phragmites (*Poaceae*)

	sp.	CHab
	from Sichuan, China	EPPr
§	***australis***	CBen CHab CWat EBWF MSKA NMir SVic WMAq WPnP XLum
	- subsp. ***australis*** var. ***striatopictus***	EPPr
	- - 'Variegatus' (v)	CBen CKno CWat EPPr EShb LLWG MMuc MPie SEND SMad WWtn XLum

- subsp. ***humilis***	CHab
- subsp. ***pseudodonax***	EPPr
communis	see *P. australis*
karka 'Candy Stripe' (v)	MSKA

Phuopsis (*Rubiaceae*)

§ ***stylosa***	CBod CTri EBee ECha ELan ELon EPPr EPfP GAbr GMaP IFoB LSou MHer MHol MMuc MSpe NBid NBro NChi NSti SEND SRms SWvt WHlf WMoo XLum
- 'Purpurea'	EBee MNrw MRav NChi

Phycella (*Amaryllidaceae*)

cyrtanthoides	WCot

Phygelius (*Scrophulariaceae*)

aequalis	MRav WMoo
- ***albus***	see *P. aequalis* 'Yellow Trumpet'
- 'Aureus'	see *P. aequalis* 'Yellow Trumpet'
- 'Cream Trumpet'	see *P. aequalis* 'Yellow Trumpet'
- 'Indian Chief'	see *P.* × *rectus* 'African Queen'
- 'Sani Pass'	ELon MHer SCob SPer SPlb WSpi
- 'Trewidden Pink' 🏆H5	ELan ELon GBin MHer MSCN SWvt WMoo XLum
§ - 'Yellow Trumpet' 🏆H5	CSBt CTca ELan ELon EPfP ESps GKev GMaP GMcL IBoy LSRN MAsh MGil MMuc SEND SGbt SLim SWvt WAvo WMoo
(Candy Drops Series) CANDY DROPS CREAM ('Kerphycrem'PBR)	NGBl SCob
- CANDY DROPS DEEP ROSE ('Kerphyros'PBR)	NGBl
- CANDY DROPS RED ('Kerphyrouge'PBR)	GMcL
- CANDY DROPS SALMON ORANGE ('Kerphysalm'PBR)	SRms
capensis	CHll CTri GMcL MHer SRms WOut WRHF
'Golden Gate'	see *P. aequalis* 'Yellow Trumpet'
Logan form	GBin
NEW SENSATION ('Blaphy'PBR)	EPfP GMcL MRav SCob SRms SWvt
'Passionate'PBR	NLar
§ × ***rectus*** 'African Queen' 🏆H5	CTri ELan EPfP ESps MGil MRav MSwo NGdn SEND SPlb SWvt WAvo WKif XLum
- 'Bridgetown Beauty'	GCal
- 'Devil's Tears' 🏆H5	CBcs ESps MMuc NEgg SCob SEND SLim SWvt WHar WMoo
- 'Ivory Twist'	ELon
- 'Jodie Southon'	ELon LSou SDys WCot
- 'Moonraker'	CAby CBcs CBod CHll CTri ELan ELon EPfP GBin GWyn MAsh MHer MRav NGdn NLar SCob SEND SPer SPlb SRms WKif XLum
- 'Salmon Leap' 🏆H5	CBcs CBod CTri ELan EPfP LRHS LSRN MBNS MGos MRav NEgg SCob SLim SPlb SRms SWvt
- Somerford Funfair Series	IBoy
- - SOMERFORD FUNFAIR APRICOT ('Yapapr')	SWvt
- - SOMERFORD FUNFAIR CORAL ('Yapcor'PBR)	CRos EPfP LRHS MAsh NCou NLar NRHS SBod SCob SLim SRkn SWvt
- - SOMERFORD FUNFAIR CREAM ('Yapcre'PBR)	EPfP LRHS NLar NRHS SLim SPoG SWvt
- - SOMERFORD FUNFAIR ORANGE ('Yapor'PBR)	CPla CRos EPfP LRHS MAsh NLar NRHS SLim SRms SWvt
- - SOMERFORD FUNFAIR WINE ('Yapwin')	CAby CBot CChe CDul CRos ELan EPfP LRHS MAsh MBNS NRHS SCob SLim SPoG SWvt
- - SOMERFORD FUNFAIR YELLOW ('Yapyel'PBR)	CChe CRos EPfP LRHS MAsh NRHS SLim SWvt
§ - 'Winchester Fanfare'	CSBt GBin GMcL GWyn MGos MRav SCob SEND SLim SWvt WSpi
- 'Winton Fanfare'	see *P.* × *rectus* 'Winchester Fanfare'
'Rory'PBR	SRms
SNOW QUEEN ('Crosnoque'PBR) (Croftway Series)	SCob

Phyla (*Verbenaceae*)

lanceolata	LLWG
§ ***nodiflora***	ECha MHer SRms XSen
- 'Alba'	MMuc SEND
§ - var. ***canescens***	CMea XLum
- var. ***rosea***	SRot

Phylica (*Rhamnaceae*)

pubescens	CPbh

Phyllanthus (*Phyllanthaceae*)

angustifolius	EPed

× *Phylliopsis* (*Ericaceae*)

'Coppelia' 🏆H5	EPot ITim
hillieri 'Askival'	EPot WThu
- 'Pinocchio'	GEdr WThu
- 'Sugar Plum'	CCCN GEdr SWvt WThu
'Hobgoblin'	ITim
'Mermaid'	EPot ITim WThu
'Sprite'	EPot ITim
'Swanhilde'	WThu

Phyllitis see *Asplenium*

scolopendrium	see *Asplenium scolopendrium*

Phyllocladus ✿ (*Podocarpaceae*)

trichomanoides var. ***alpinus***	CBcs NWad WThu

Phyllodoce (*Ericaceae*)

aleutica	WThu
§ - subsp. ***glanduliflora***	EPot
§ - - 'Flora Slack'	WThu
- - white-flowered	see *P. aleutica* subsp. *glanduliflora* 'Flora Slack'
caerulea japonica	see *P. nipponica*
- 'Murray Lyon'	WThu
empetriformis	WThu
glanduliflora	see *P. aleutica* subsp. *glanduliflora*
§ ***nipponica***	WThu
'Peach'	NLar WThu

Phyllostachys ✿ (*Poaceae*)

sp.	LPra
angusta	ERod MWht SBig
arcana 'Luteosulcata'	CFil ERod MMoz MMuc MWht
§ ***atrovaginata***	ERod SGol
aurea 🏆H5	Widely available
- 'Albovariegata' (v)	CRos EPfP ERod LRHS MWht NRHS SPoG
- 'Flavescens Inversa'	ERod MWht
- 'Holochrysa'	CDTJ CFil CJun ERod MMuc MWht NLar
- 'Koi'	CDTJ ERod MMoz MWht SBig SGol

aureocaulis see *P. aureosulcata* f. *aureocaulis*, *P. vivax* f. *aureocaulis*
aureosulcata ERod MMoz WMoo
- f. ***alata*** see *P. aureosulcata* f. *pekinensis*
§ - f. ***aureocaulis*** Widely available
- 'Harbin' ERod
- 'Harbin Inversa' ERod
- 'Lama Tempel' CDTJ CFil CJun
§ - f. ***pekinensis*** SBig
- f. ***spectabilis*** ♀H5 Widely available
bambusoides CDTJ ERod SBig
- 'Allgold' see *P. bambusoides* 'Holochrysa'
- 'Castillonii' ♀H5 CBcs CBdn ENBC ERod EUJe EWes LEdu MMoz MMuc MWht SBig SEND
- 'Castillonii Inversa' ENBC ERod LEdu MMoz MWht
- 'Castillonii Variegata' (v) ERod
§ - 'Holochrysa' ♀H5 CBdn CDTJ ERod MMuc MWht SEND WPGP
- 'Kawadana' (v) ERod
- f. ***lacrima-deae*** CDTJ
- 'Marliacea' CBdn ERod SBig
- 'Sulphurea' see *P. bambusoides* 'Holochrysa'
- 'Tanakae' CDTJ MMoz SBig
- 'Violascens' SBig
bissetii ♀H5 Widely available
congesta misapplied see *P. atrovaginata*
decora ERod MMuc MWht
dulcis CBdn CFGn EPfP ERod MWht SBig
§ ***edulis*** CAgr CBlu ELon ERod SBig SPlb
§ - 'Heterocycla' XBlo
- f. ***pubescens*** see *P. edulis*
flexuosa CBcs CBdn MWht SGol
glauca EPfP ERod LCro LOPS MMoz MWht SBig
- f. ***yunzhu*** ERod MWht
heteroclada CBlu
- 'Solid Stem' misapplied see *P. purpurata* 'Straight Stem'
heterocycla see *P. edulis* 'Heterocycla'
- var. ***pubescens*** see *P. edulis*
humilis CBdn ENBC ERod EUJe MMoz MMuc MWht SBig SEND
iridescens ♀H5 ERod ETod MWht SBig
lithophila ERod
makinoi ERod
mannii ERod MWht
nidularia ERod MMoz SBig
nigra ♀H5 Widely available
- 'Boryana' CBdn CCVT CEnd EPfP ERod EUJe MGos MMoz MMuc MWht SBig SEND SWvt WMoo
- 'Hale' MWht
- f. ***henonis*** ♀H5 CBdn ENBC ERod MMoz MMuc MWht NLar SBig SEND SGol WPGP
- 'Megurochiku' ERod MWht
- f. ***nigra*** CFil
- f. ***punctata*** ENBC ERod MAvo MMuc SEND WMoo
- 'Tosaensis' ERod
nuda CBdn ERod MMoz MWht
- f. ***localis*** ERod MWht
parvifolia CBdn ERod MWht
platyglossa ERod
praecox CBdn
- f. ***viridisulcata*** ERod
prominens ERod
propinqua ERod MWht
§ ***purpurata*** 'Straight Stem' MWht
rubromarginata ERod MMuc MWht
'Shanghai 3' ERod
stimulosa ERod MWht
sulphurea 'Houzeau' ERod MMuc SEND
§ - f. ***sulphurea*** ERod
- 'Sulphurea' see *P. sulphurea* f. *sulphurea*
§ - f. ***viridis*** ERod SBig
violascens CAgr ERod EUJe MMoz MWht SBig
viridiglaucescens CAgr CDTJ ERod ETod MBrN MMoz MMuc MWht SBig SEND WCot
viridis see *P. sulphurea* f. *viridis*
vivax CBdn ENBC EPfP ERod EUJe MMoz MWht NLar SBig
§ - f. ***aureocaulis*** ♀H5 CAbb CAgr CBcs CBdn CCVT CDul CEnd ENBC EPfP ERod ETod EUJe IBoy LEdu LRHS LSRN MGos MMoz MMuc MWht NLar SBig SCob SEND SGol WPGP
- - 'Huangwenzhu' CDTJ ENBC ERod EUJe MMoz MWht
- 'Katrin' LEdu
* - 'Sulphurea' XBlo

× *Phyllothamnus* (*Ericaceae*)

erectus WThu

Phymatosorus (*Polypodiaceae*)

diversifolius see *Microsorum diversifolium*

Phymosia (*Malvaceae*)

§ ***umbellata*** EBee WPGP

Phyodina see *Callisia*

Physalis (*Solanaceae*)

alkekengi ♀H7 CTri EPfP ESps NLar NPnk SWvt
- var. ***franchetii*** CBcs CMac CRos CSBt CTri EBee ECha ELan EPfP ILea LCro LRHS MBel MHer MNrw NBro NEgg SPer SPoG SRms WFar WOld
- - dwarf CRos LRHS NLar NRHS
- - 'Gigantea' CBod CRos CWld LRHS LSun NLar NRHS SPlb WFar
- - 'Gnome' see *P. alkekengi* var. *franchetii* 'Zwerg'
- - 'Variegata' (v) EWes LEdu SEND WPGP
§ - - 'Zwerg' CDor CRos EBee ELon GMcL LPmr LRHS NRHS
- 'Halloween King' CRos EBee LRHS NLar NRHS
- 'Halloween Queen' LRHS NLar NRHS
campanula B&SWJ 10409 WCru
edulis see *P. peruviana*
§ ***peruviana*** (F) CCCN SPlb SVic XAbr

Physaria (*Brassicaceae*)

alpina SPlb
saximontana GKev

Physocarpus (*Rosaceae*)

capitatus 'Tilden Park' SGol
LITTLE DEVIL see *P. opulifolius* 'Donna May'
'Midnight' GBin LRHS MAsh MMrt NEoE WHar WMoo
opulifolius AMBER JUBILEE ('Jefam'PBR) ELan EPfP LCro LOPS NEoE
- 'Angel Gold' CRos ELan LRHS MAsh NPri NRHS SPoG
- 'Anny's Gold'PBR **new** EBee SRms
- 'Burning Embers' SRms
- 'Chameleon' EMil GBin LBuc MAsh NEoE SPoG WMoo
- COPPERTINA see *P. opulifolius* DIABLE D'OR

	- 'Dart's Gold' 🏆^{H7}	Widely available
§	- DIABLE D'OR ('Mindia'^{PBR})	CBar CRos EPfP IBoy IRob LCro LOPS LRHS LSRN MAsh MBlu MGos MPkF NEgg NLar NOra NPla NRHS SGbt SGol WCot WMoo
	- 'Diabolo'^{PBR} 🏆^{H7}	Widely available
§	- 'Donna May'^{PBR}	ELan EPfP EShb NEoE SCob SPoG
	- 'Firebrand' **new**	NEoE
§	- LADY IN RED ('Tuilad'^{PBR}) 🏆^{H7}	Widely available
	- LITTLE ANGEL ('Hoogi016')	LCro LOPS
§	- 'Luteus'	MRav WMoo
	- MIDNIGHT ('Jonight') **new**	CBcs
	- 'Nugget'	CRos LRHS NRHS
	- 'Red Baron'	GMcL
	- RUBY SPICE	see *P. opulifolius* LADY IN RED
	- SUMMER MOON ('Tuimon')	CBcs NEoE WMoo
	- SUMMER WINE ('Seward'^{PBR})	EPfP EWes LRHS MAsh NLar WSpi
	- TINY WINE ('Smpotw') **new**	SPoG
	ribesifolius 'Aureus'	see *P. opulifolius* 'Luteus'

Physochlaina (*Solanaceae*)

	orientalis	GEdr

Physoplexis (*Campanulaceae*)

§	***comosa*** 🏆^{H5}	EPot WAbe

Physostegia (*Lamiaceae*)

	angustifolia	NBre
I	'Aquatica'	LLWG
§	***virginiana***	CBod CSBt CTri GMaP ILea MBel SRms WCFE WOld
	- 'Alba'	CAby CMac CSBt CTri EAJP EBee EHrv ELon GAbr GJos GMaP LEdu LSun SPlb WArt WOut XLum
§	- 'Crown of Snow'	EBee EPfP GMcL GWyn MHer MRav SWvt WHar WMoo
	- 'Crystal Peek White'	LRHS WFar
	- 'Miss Manners'	ECtt LRHS MPie NBre NGdn NLar NRHS
	- 'Olympic Gold' (v)	NWad
	- 'Pink Manners'	NLar STPC
	- 'Rose Crown'	SPer
	- 'Rose Queen'	CTri EAJP NBre WFar
	- 'Rosea'	EPfP GJos GPSL GWyn IFoB LSun MMuc NChi NCou NGdn SHar SPoG SWvt WHar WHrl
	- SCHNEEKRONE	see *P. virginiana* 'Crown of Snow'
	- 'Snow Queen'	see *P. virginiana* 'Summer Snow'
§	- var. ***speciosa*** 'Bouquet Rose'	CBod CMac CRos EBee ECha EHrv EPfP LEdu LRHS MRav NLar NRHS SGbt SPer SRms SWvt WCAu WHar WMoo WRHF XLum
	- - ROSE BOUQUET	see *P. virginiana* var. *speciosa* 'Bouquet Rose'
	- - 'Variegata' (v)	CMac EBee ECtt EHoe EHrv ELan ELon EPfP GLog MRav NGdn SPer SPoG SRms WCAu WCot WFar XLum
§	- 'Summer Snow' 🏆^{H7}	CBcs CRos ECha ELan EPfP LRHS NGBl NLar NRHS SPer SRms WCAu WCot
	- 'Summer Spire'	EHrv
	- 'Vivid' 🏆^{H7}	CAby CBod CMac CRos ECha ELan ELon EPfP LRHS MHer MNrw MPie MRav NDov NEgg NGBl NLar NRHS SPer SPlb SRms WGwG WHil WWtn XLum

Phyteuma (*Campanulaceae*)

	balbisii	see *P. cordatum*
	betonicifolium	CPla EPPr WHoo
	charmelii	GEdr WHoo
	comosum	see *Physoplexis comosa*
	confusum **new**	GJos
§	***cordatum***	GJos
	halleri	see *P. ovatum*
	hemisphaericum	GEdr NSla
	humile	WThu
	nigrum	GEdr NBid WBor WCot
	orbiculare	EBWF GEdr GJos
§	***ovatum***	SPlb
	scheuchzeri	EBee EPfP EWld GEdr GJos GWyn MMrt SMad SPad SRms WCot WRHF XLum
	sieberi	GJos
	spicatum	GEdr GJos NBro
	- subsp. ***coeruleum***	GJos

Phytolacca (*Phytolaccaceae*)

	acinosa	EWld SBrt WHil
	- HWJ 647	WCru
§	***americana***	CAby EBee ELan EPfP EUJe GPoy MBNS MHer MPie NChi NLos SPlb SRms
	- B&SWJ 8817A	WCru
	- 'Silberstein' (v)	CPla EBee MHol NLos WHer
	bogotensis	WCru
	- B&SWJ 14221 **new**	WCru
	clavigera	see *P. polyandra*
	decandra	see *P. americana*
	dioica	CExl SPlb
	esculenta	LEdu SEND
	icosandra B&SWJ 8988	WCru
	- Purpurascens Group B&SWJ 11251	WCru
	japonica B&SWJ 3005	NBid WCru
	- B&SWJ 3522	WCru
	octandra B&SWJ 9514	WCru
§	***polyandra***	GAbr NBid NBro SRms
	rivinoides B&SWJ 10264	WCru
	rugosa B&SWJ 10263	WCru

Picea ✿ (*Pinaceae*)

	sp.	LPra
§	***abies***	CCVT CDul CLnd CMac CPer CSBt CTho CTri EPfP ESps GMcL GQue IBoy LBuc LPra MJak MMuc NEgg SCoo SEND SPoG WHar WMou WTSh
	- 'Acrocona' 🏆^{H7}	GMil LRHS NLar
	- 'Archer'	CKen
	- 'Bago' **new**	CKen
	- 'Barus'	NLar
	- 'Brunn'	NLar
	- 'Capitata'	CKen
	- 'Clanbrassiliana' 🏆^{H7}	CKen ELan GMil LRHS NWad
	- Columnaris Group	LRHS NEgg
I	- 'Congesta'	CKen
	- 'Crippsii'	CKen
I	- 'Cruenta'	CKen
	- 'Cupressina'	CKen
	- 'Diffusa'	CKen
	- 'Dumpy'	CKen
	- 'Excelsa'	see *P. abies*
	- 'Fahndrich'	CKen CMen

	- 'Four Winds'	CKen
	- 'Frohburg'	CKen LRHS NEgg
	- 'Gold Drift'	NLar
	- 'Gold Finch' **new**	NLar
	- 'Gregoryana'	CKen
	- 'Heartland Gem'	CKen
	- 'Horace Wilson'	CKen CMen
	- 'Humilis'	CKen
	- 'Hystrix'	CMen NLar NWad
	- 'Inversa' ♀H7	CKen MBlu SLim
	- 'J.W. Daisy's White'	see *P. glauca* var. *albertiana* 'J.W. Daisy's White'
	- 'Jana'	CKen NLar
	- 'Jermyns Broom No. 1'	CKen
	- 'Kral'	CKen
	- 'Krenek' **new**	NLar
	- 'Little Gem' ♀H7	CKen CMen ELan ESps EUJe GEdr GMil LRHS MAsh MGos NLar NWad SCoo SLim
	- 'Marcel'	CKen
	- 'Maxwellii'	GMil
	- 'Mini Kalous'	CKen
	- 'Nana Compacta'	CKen CMen
	- 'Nidiformis' ♀H7	CKen CMac CMen CSBt CTri ESps EUJe GMcL GMil IBoy LRHS MGil MGos SGol SRms
	- 'Norrköping'	CKen
	- 'Ohlendorffii'	CKen GMcL
	- 'Pachyphylla'	CKen
	- 'Pseudomaxwellii'	LRHS
	- 'Pumila'	WCFE
	- 'Pusch'	CKen CMen NLar SLim
	- 'Pygmaea'	CKen NWad
	- 'Reflexa'	GMil NEgg
	- 'Remontii'	GMil
	- 'Repens'	GMil
	- 'Rydal' ♀H7	CBcs CDul CKen GMil LRHS MAsh NEgg NLar
	- 'Saint Mary's Broom'	NEgg
	- 'Spring Fire'	CKen
	- 'Tompa'	NLar
	- 'Tutsberg' **new**	NLar
	- 'Typner'	CKen NLar
	- 'Vermont Gold'	CKen LRHS NLar
	- 'Wagner' **new**	NLar
	- WILL'S DWARF	see *P. abies* 'Wills Zwerg'
§	- 'Wills Zwerg'	ELan LRHS
§	***alcoquiana*** var. ***alcoquiana***	SLim
	- var. ***reflexa***	MPkF
	asperata 'Mongolei'	NLar
	bicolor	see *P. alcoquiana* var. *alcoquiana*
I	- 'Prostrata'	NEgg
	breweriana ♀H6	CAco CDul CMac CTho EPfP GKin GMil IDee LEdu LRHS MBlu MGos MJak NEgg NRHS SLim SSta WCFE WTSh
	- 'Kohout's Dwarf'	CKen NLar
	engelmannii	CAco CDul
	- 'Bush's Lace'	NLar
	- 'Compact'	SLim
	- subsp. ***engelmannii***	CKen
	- 'Jasper'	CKen NLar
	farreri **new**	CAco
	glauca	SWvt
	- var. ***albertiana*** ALBERTA BLUE ('Haal'PBR)	CKen GMil LRHS NRHS
	- - 'Alberta Globe' ♀H7	CAco ESps EUJe GKin GMcL GMil LRHS MAsh MGos NEgg NRHS NWad SCoo SPoG
	- - 'Conica' ♀H7	CBcs CMac CMea CSBt EPfP ESps EUJe GMcL GMil IBoy LCro LOPS LRHS MAsh MGil MGos MMuc NEgg NLar NRHS NWad SEND SGol SPer SPoG SRms SWvt WCFE
	- - 'Gnome'	CKen
§	- - 'J.W. Daisy's White' ♀H7	CBcs CKen ELan EPfP ESps EUJe GKin GMil LRHS MAsh MGos MJak NLar NRHS SCoo SLim SPoG
	- - 'Laurin' ♀H7	CKen GMil NWad
	- - 'Lilliput'	CKen GMil NLar NWad SPoG
	- - 'Piccolo'	CKen NEgg NLar NWad
	- - 'Sander's Blue'	CAco CKen EPfP GKin GMil LCro LOPS LRHS NRHS SPoG
	- - 'Tiny'	CKen GMil NWad
	- 'Arneson's Blue Variegated' (v)	CKen GMil MAsh SLim
	- 'Baby' **new**	CKen
	- 'Biesenthaler Frühling'	CKen GMil
	- 'Blue Planet'	CKen
	- 'Blue Teardrop' **new**	NLar
	- 'Coerulea'	NEgg
	- 'Cy's Wonder'	CKen
	- 'December'PBR **new**	LCro LOPS
	- 'Dendroforma Gold'	CKen
	- 'Echiniformis' ♀H7	CKen ESps GMcL GMil LRHS MGil NLar
	- 'Goldilocks'	CAco CKen NLar
I	- 'Julian Potts Monstrosa'	NLar
§	- 'Nana'	CKen
	- 'Pendula'	CKen SLim
	- 'Pixie'	CKen
	- 'Pixie Dust'	CKen
	- 'Rainbow's End' (v)	CKen NLar
	- 'Sleeping Giant'	NLar
	- 'Spring Surprise'	CKen
	- 'Zuckerhut'	GMil LRHS
	glehnii 'Sasanosei'	CKen
	- 'Shimezusei'	CKen
	jezoensis	CKen CMen
	- 'Aurea'	SLim
	- subsp. ***hondoensis***	CMen
	- 'Marianbad'	CKen
	- 'Mariánské Làzně'	NLar
	- 'Yatsabusa'	CKen CMen
	koraiensis	CDul
	kosteri 'Glauca'	see *P. pungens* (Glauca Group) 'Koster'
	koyamae 'Bedgebury Cascade'	SLim
	likiangensis	CAco CDul CMCN EBtc EPfP
	- var. ***balfouriana***	see *P. likiangensis* var. *rubescens*
§	- var. ***rubescens***	LRHS SLim WHor
	mariana	EPfP
	- 'Austria Broom'	CKen
	- 'Bill Archer'	NWad
	- 'Blue Teardrop'	CKen
	- 'Fastigiata'	CKen
	- 'Nana' ♀H7	CKen CMac CMen EPfP GEdr GMcL GMil MGos MMuc NWad SBod SCoo SLim SPoG
I	- 'Pygmaea'	CKen NWad
	- 'Smoke Jumper' **new**	NLar
	× ***mariorika*** 'Machala'	GMil
	meyeri	CTho EPfP
	morrisonicola	CKen EUJe
	obovata var. ***coerulea***	EPfP
	omorika ♀H7	CBcs CCVT CDul CJun CMCN CMac CPer CTho EPfP ESps LPra MMuc SEND SEWo WCFE WHar

I	- 'Aurea'	ESps
	- 'Berliner's Weeper' witches' broom	NLar
	- 'Bruns'	NLar
	- 'Cinderella' **new**	NLar
	- 'de Ruyter'	NEgg
	- 'Frohnleiten'	CKen
	- 'Frondenberg'	CKen
	- 'Halone'	CKen
	- 'Karel'	CKen LRHS
	- 'Minimax'	CKen
	- 'Nana' ♀H7	GMil LRHS NEgg NRHS SLim WCFE
	- 'Pendula' ♀H7	CAco MBlu SSta
	- 'Pendula Bruns'	MBlu NLar SLim SMad
	- 'Peve Tijn'	LRHS NLar
	- 'Pimoko'	CKen NEgg NLar SLim
	- 'Pygmy'	CKen
	- 'Schneverdingen'	CKen
	- 'Tijn'	CKen SLim
	- 'Treblitsch'	CKen NLar SLim
	orientalis ♀H7	CDul IDee WThu
	- 'Aurea' (v) ♀H7	ELan MJak SMad
	- 'Aureospicata'	CTho GMil IRob MAsh MBlu MJak NEgg
	- 'Bergman's Gem'	CKen
	- 'Golden Start'	GMil NEgg SLim
	- 'Gowdy Gold' **new**	NLar
	- 'Gracilis' **new**	GMil
	- 'Juwel'	CKen NLar
	- 'Kenwith'	CKen
	- 'Mount Vernon'	CKen
	- Nana Group	GKin
	- 'Peve Tiny Gold' **new**	CKen
	- 'Professor Langner'	CKen NLar
	- 'Shadow's Broom'	CKen CMen NEgg
§	- 'Silver Seedling' **new**	NLar
	- 'Skylands' ♀H7	CKen ELan GMil MAsh NEgg SLim
	- 'Spring Grove' **new**	NLar
	- 'Sulphur Flush'	see *P. orientalis* 'Silver Seedling'
	- 'Tom Thumb'	CKen NLar
	- 'Wittboldt'	CKen
	pungens	CCVT ESps LMaj
	- 'Anton' **new**	NLar
	- 'Blaukissen'	CKen
	- 'Blue Ball' **new**	NLar
	- 'Blue Diamond'	LRHS MJak SPoG
	- 'Blue Pearl'	CKen
	- 'Donna's Rainbow'	NLar
	- 'Edith' ♀H7	CAco CDul CKen ESps GMcL GMil NEgg NLar NOra SCoo SEWo SLim
	- 'Erich Frahm'	CAco CCVT GMcL IRob MAsh NOra SCoo SPoG
	- 'Fat Albert' ♀H7	CAco CCVT LMaj LRHS NEgg SLim SPoG
	- 'Frieda'	SLim
	- 'Glauca Globosa'	see *P. pungens* (Glauca Group) 'Globosa'
	- Glauca Group	CAco CCVT CDul CMac CPer LPra MMuc SCoo SPoG WHar WMou WTSh
	- - 'Glauca Pendula'	CAco
	- - 'Glauca Procumbens'	CKen
§	- - 'Glauca Prostrata'	SLim
I	- - 'Globosa' ♀H7	CAco CBcs CCVT CKen CSBt EPfP ESps GMcL LRHS MAsh NEgg NRHS SCoo SLim SPoG
	- - 'Hoopsii' ♀H7	CAco CDul EPfP ESps GKin GMcL LRHS MAsh MGos MJak NEgg NRHS SCoo SPoG SWvt
	- - 'Iseli Fastigiate'	CCVT GKin GMcL GMil NEgg SCoo SLim SPoG
§	- - 'Koster'	EPfP ESps MAsh SPoG
	- - 'Moerheimii'	CDul
	- - 'Oldenburg'	NEgg SLim
	- 'Globe'	CKen CMen
	- 'Gloria'	CKen SLim
	- 'Katy' **new**	GMil
	- 'Koster Fastigiata'	GMcL
	- 'Lucky Strike'	CKen NLar
	- 'Maigold' (v)	CKen NLar SLim
	- 'Montgomery'	CKen
	- 'Mrs Cesarini'	CKen NLar SLim
	- 'Nimetz'	CKen
	- 'Prostrata'	see *P. pungens* (Glauca Group) 'Glauca Prostrata'
	- 'Saint Mary's Broom'	CKen
	- 'Snowkiss'	NEgg
	- 'The Blues'	CKen NLar
	- 'Thuem'	NEgg
	- 'Waldbrunn'	CKen NLar
	- 'Yvette'	NLar
	purpurea	EPfP LRHS
	schrenkiana	CMCN
	sitchensis	CAco CPer LPra MMuc WTSh
	- 'Nana'	NLar
	- 'Papoose'	CAco GMcL SLim
	- 'Pévé Wiesje'	NLar
	- 'Silberzwerg'	CKen SLim
	- 'Strypemonde'	CKen NEgg
	- 'Tenas'	CKen SLim SPoG
	smithiana	CAco CTho EPfP
	- 'Sunray'	LRHS SLim
	wilsonii	CKen

Picrasma (*Simaroubaceae*)

	ailanthoides	see *P. quassioides*
§	***quassioides***	CMCN EBee EPfP WPGP

Picris (*Asteraceae*)

echioides	see *Helminthotheca echioides*

Picrorhiza (*Plantaginaceae*)

kurrooa	GPoy LEdu

Pieris (*Ericaceae*)

'Balls of Fire'	CMac
'Bert Chandler'	CMac GKin SAko WSpi
'Brouwer's Beauty'	SPoG
'Firecrest' ♀H5	NLar
'Flaming Silver' (v) ♀H5	Widely available
'Forest Flame' ♀H5	Widely available
formosa B&SWJ 2257	WCru
- var. ***forrestii*** 'Charles Michael'	CExl
- - 'Jermyns'	CMac MRav
- - 'Wakehurst' ♀H5	CDul CExl CMac CRos CTri EPfP GKin LMil LRHS MAsh MGos MRav SAko SCob SPer WHor WSpi
HAVILA ('Mouwsvila') (v)	CMac MAsh NWad
japonica	CMac ESps
- 'Bisbee Dwarf'	WThu
- 'Bonfire' ♀H5	CCCN CRos ELan GMcL LRHS LSou MGos NRHS SCob SLim SPoG
- 'Carnaval' (v) ♀H5	CCCN CMac CRos CSBt ELan ELon EMOT EShb ESps GMcL IBoy LBuc LRHS LSRN LSou MAsh MGos NLar NPri NRHS SCob SCoo SLim SPer SPoG SWvt WFar

§	– 'Christmas Cheer'	CMac CRos EPfP LRHS LSRN NRHS WMoo
	– 'Cupido'	MAsh NLar SLim WFar
	– 'Debutante' ΨH5	CBcs CRos ELan ESps GKin GMcL LRHS MAsh MGos NLar NRHS SCob SCoo SWvt WFar
	– 'Don'	see *P. japonica* 'Pygmaea'
	– 'Dorothy Wyckoff'	LSRN SSta
	– 'Erik'	IArd NLar SAko
	– 'Flaming Star'	SWvt
	– 'Flamingo'	CMac
I	– 'Katsura' PBR	CBcs CMac CRos ELan EPfP ESps GKin IBoy LBuc LMil LRHS LSRN LSou MAsh MBlu MGos MJak NEgg NLar NRHS SCob SCoo SLim SPer SPoG SWvt WFar
	– 'Little Heath' (v)	Widely available
	– 'Little Heath Green'	CMac ELon ESps GKin IBoy MAsh MGos MMuc NEgg SCob SPer SPoG SWvt WFar WMoo
	– 'Minor'	GKev NWad WFar WThu
	– 'Mountain Fire' ΨH5	Widely available
	– 'Passion' PBR	CBcs CEnd CRos EBee EPfP ETMg GMcL LCro LOPS LRHS LSRN MAsh MPkF NLar NRHS SAko SCob SPer
	– 'Pink Delight' ΨH5	CRos EMOT ESps LMil LRHS LSRN MRav SRms
	– 'Prelude' ΨH5	CRos CSBt LMil LRHS MAsh WAbe
	– 'Purity' ΨH5	CBcs CMac EMOT MAsh MGos NEgg NLar SArc SLim SPer SWvt WFar WHar
§	– 'Pygmaea'	NWad WThu
	– 'Ralto' PBR	CRos LRHS MAsh MRav NLar NRHS SPoG
	– RALTO ROSE ('Opstal10')	MPkF
	– RED MILL ('Zebris')	CEnd LSou SLim SPer
	– 'Sarabande' ΨH5	CRos LRHS MAsh SCob
	– 'Scarlett O'Hara'	CSBt NLar
	– Taiwanensis Group	GKin NLar SRms WFar
	– 'Temple Bells'	CSBt
	– 'Valley Rose'	CSBt ELan GKin MAsh NLar
	– 'Valley Valentine' ΨH5	CBcs CMac CRos CSBt EPfP ESps GMcL LCro LMil LOPS LRHS LSRN MAsh MGos MJak MPkF NHpl NRHS SAko SCob SCoo SLim SPer SPoG SWvt
	– 'Variegata' misapplied	see *P. japonica* 'White Rim'
	– 'Variegata' ambig.	GMcL LMil SCob SPer
	– 'Variegata' (Carrière) Bean (v)	CRos LRHS NRHS
	– 'Wada's Pink'	see *P. japonica* 'Christmas Cheer'
	– 'White Cascade'	NLar
	– 'White Pearl'	CMac EPfP
§	– 'White Rim' (v)	CDul CMac MAsh SPlb
	– 'William Buchanan'	NWad WThu
	– var. ***yakushimensis***	NLar
	nana	WThu
	'Tilford'	CMac

Pilea (*Urticaceae*)

libanensis	EShb

Pileostegia (*Hydrangeaceae*)

viburnoides	CBcs CBot CCCN CMac CRHN CRos EBee ELan EPfP EUJe GCal LRHS MGil MGos MMuc MRav NLar NRHS SArc SEND SLon SPer SPoG SSta WCot WPGP WSHC WSpi
– B&SWJ 3565	WCru
– B&SWJ 3570 from Taiwan	WCru
– B&SWJ 7132	WCru
– variegated (v) **new**	LRHS

Pilgerodendron (*Cupressaceae*)

uviferum	IDee

Pilosella (*Asteraceae*)

§	***aurantiaca***	EBWF ELan IRos LEdu LRHS MHer MNHC NBid SPhx SRms WCot WHer WMoo WOut WSFF
§	– subsp. ***carpathicola***	MMuc SEND
§	***officinarum***	EBWF NRya XSen

Pilularia (*Marsileaceae*)

globulifera	MSKA

Pimelea (*Thymelaeaceae*)

	coarctata	see *P. prostrata*
	drupacea	IDee SAko
	ferruginea	SVen
	oreophila	WThu
§	***prostrata***	CTri EPot
	tomentosa	LRHS

Pimpinella (*Apiaceae*)

anisum	SVic XAbr
major	EBWF LEdu
– 'Rosea'	Widely available
saxifraga	CHab WSFF
siifolia	WHil
tripartita	MAvo SPhx
– PAB 6112	LEdu WPGP
– PAB 7261 **new**	WPGP

pineapple see *Ananas comosus*

pineapple guava see *Acca sellowiana*

Pinellia (*Araceae*)

	cordata	CAby GKev LEdu SMad WCru XLum
	pedatisecta	GKev MRav
	pinnatisecta	see *P. tripartita*
	ternata	EBee EWld GEdr NLar
	– B&SWJ 3532	WCru
§	***tripartita***	CExl GKev WCot
	– B&SWJ 1102	WCru
	– 'Purple Face'	WCru

Pinguicula (*Lentibulariaceae*)

ehlersiae	SPlb
grandiflora ΨH4	EECP EWld GKev NLos NRya
'Tina'	NLos
vulgaris	WHer
'Weser' ΨH1c	NLos

pinkcurrant see *Ribes rubrum* (P)

Pinus ✿ (*Pinaceae*)

	sp.	LPra
	albicaulis 'Flinck'	CKen
	– 'Nana'	see *P. albicaulis* 'Noble's Dwarf'
	– 'No 3'	CKen
§	– 'Noble's Dwarf'	CKen
	aristata ambig.	CAco LRHS
	aristata Engelm.	CAco CDul CMCN CMen WHor
	– 'Bashful'	CKen
	– 'Cecilia'	CKen
	– 'Kohout's Mini'	CKen
	– 'Rich Broom'	NLar

	- 'Sherwood Compact'	CKen MAsh NLar SLim
	armandii	CAco CDul CMCN EPfP LRHS
	austriaca	see *P. nigra* subsp. *nigra*
	ayacahuite	CKen CPne
	- var. ***veitchii***	CTho WPGP
	balfouriana dwarf	CKen
	banksiana	CAco CDul
	- 'Chippewa'	CKen
I	- 'Compacta'	CKen
	- 'Manomet'	CAco
	- 'Neponset'	CKen
	- 'Schneverdingen'	CKen NEgg NLar
	- 'Shoodic' **new**	NLar
	bhutanica	WPGP
	- KR 10358 **new**	WPGP
	brutia var. ***eldarica***	CAco
	- - multi-stemmed **new**	CAco
	- var. ***pityusa*** **new**	CAco
	bungeana	CAco CDul CMCN EPfP MBlu
	- 'Diamant'	CKen
	- 'June's Broom'	CKen
	- 'Temple Gem' **new**	NLar
	canariensis	CAco
	cembra	CAco CAgr CDul EPfP MCoo MJak
	- 'Barnhourie'	CKen
	- 'Blue Mound'	CKen
	- 'Compacta Glauca'	NLar
	- 'Inverleith'	CKen
	- 'Jermyns'	CKen
	- 'King's Dwarf'	CKen
	- 'Nana'	see *P. pumila* 'Nana'
	- 'Ortler'	CKen
	- 'Stoderzinken 8'	NLar
	- 'Stricta'	CKen GMil
	- witches' broom	CKen
	cembroides NJM 09.022A	WPGP
	- 'Fancy Nancy'	CKen
	contorta	CBcs CDul CPer IBoy LPra SPlb
	- 'Asher'	CKen
	- 'Chief Joseph' ♀H7	CAco CKen MAsh NLar
	- 'Frisian Gold'	NLar
	- var. ***latifolia***	CAco CDul
	- 'Spaan's Dwarf'	CKen
	- 'Taylor's Sunburst'	CKen NLar
	coulteri	CAco EPfP
	densiflora	CAco EBtc EUJe
	- 'Alice Verkade' ♀H7	CAco CMen GMil LRHS NEgg NLar NRHS
	- 'Golden Ghost'	NLar
	- 'Haybud'	CAco
	- 'Jim Cross'	CKen
	- 'Kim' **new**	NLar
	- 'Low Glow'	CAco CKen GMil LRHS NEgg NLar NRHS SBod SLim SPoG
	- 'Oculus-draconis' (v)	GMil SLim
	- 'Pendula'	CKen MBlu NEgg SLim
	- 'Pumila' **new**	LRHS
I	- 'Pygmaea'	WHor
	- 'Pygmy'	EUJe
	- 'Rata' **new**	NLar
	- 'Umbraculifera'	CAco CMen GKin GMil SSta
	× ***densithunbergii*** 'Jane Kluis' ♀H7	CMen GMil NLar SLim SPoG
§	***devoniana***	CAco
	edulis	CAco CMCN EGFP
	- 'Juno'	CKen
	elliottii	CAco
	- var. ***densa***	CKen
	engelmannii	CAco
	fenzeliana	CAco CKen
	flexilis	CDul EGFP
	- 'Cow Creek'	NLar
	- 'Damfino' **new**	CAco
	- 'Firmament'	NOra SLim
	- var. ***flexilis*** **new**	CAco
	- 'Glenmore Dwarf'	CKen
	- 'Lil Wolf'	NLar
	- 'Nana'	CKen
	- 'Ririe'	CKen MAsh
	- 'Tara Mae'	NLar
	- 'Tarryall'	CKen
	- WB No 1	CKen
	- WB No 2	CKen
	gerardiana	CAco
	greggii	CDul EBtc
	griffithii McClell.	see *P. wallichiana*
	halepensis	CAco SEND
§	***hartwegii***	CAco
§	***heldreichii***	CAco CDul EPfP GKin NOra SLim
	- 'Aureospicata'	NLar
	- 'Compact Gem' ♀H7	CKen EUJe GMcL GMil LRHS NEgg SLim
	- 'Dolce Dorme'	CKen
	- 'Emerald Arrow' **new**	NLar
	- 'Green Giant' **new**	GMil
	- 'Green Pyramid'	NLar
	- 'Groen'	CKen
	- var. ***leucodermis***	see *P. heldreichii*
	- - 'Irish Bell'	CKen NLar
	- 'Malink'	CKen EUJe
	- 'Pygmy'	CKen
	- 'Satellit' ♀H7	CKen GMcL GMil MAsh NEgg NLar SLim
	- 'Schmidtii'	see *P. heldreichii* 'Smidtii'
§	- 'Smidtii' ♀H7	CKen CMen EUJe LRHS NEgg NLar NPoe SLim SPoG
	- 'Zwerg Schneverdingen'	CKen SLim
	× ***holfordiana***	WPGP
	jeffreyi	CAco CTho
	- 'Joppi'	CAco CDul CKen NLar SLim
	- 'Misty Lemon' **new**	NLar
	koraiensis	CAco GKin LEdu
	- 'Bergman'	CKen
	- 'Blue Ball'	CKen NLar
	- 'China Boy' **new**	NLar
	- 'Compacta Glauca' **new**	CAco
	- 'Dragon Eye'	CKen SLim
	- 'Jack Corbit'	CKen
	- 'Shibamichi' (v)	CKen
	- 'Silvergrey'	CKen
	- 'Spring Grove'	CKen NLar
	- 'Tong Hua' **new**	NLar
	- 'Winton'	CKen NLar
	lambertiana	CAco
	latteri **new**	CAco
	leucodermis	see *P. heldreichii*
	magnifica	see *P. devoniana*
	'Marie Bregéon'PBR	LRHS
	massoniana	CAco
	maximartinezii **new**	CAco
	monophylla	CAco EBtc
	- 'Wrinkle'	NLar
	montezumae misapplied	see *P. hartwegii*
	montezumae ambig.	CAco
	montezumae Lamb.	CAco SArc
	- 'Sheffield Park'	CAco SLim
	monticola	CAco
	- 'Crawford' **new**	NLar
	- 'Ondulata'	NLar
	- 'Pendula'	CKen

	- 'Pygmy'	see *P. monticola* 'Raraflora'
§	- 'Raraflora'	CKen
	- 'Strobicola'	CAco CDul EPfP
	- 'Windsor Dwarf'	CKen
	mugo	CBcs CDul EPfP ESps LPra MGos MJak SCob
	- 'Allgäu'	CKen
	- 'Alpen Hexe'	NLar
	- 'Benjamin'	CKen LRHS NLar
	- 'Bisley Green'	NLar
	- 'Bonita'	LRHS
	- 'Brownie'	CKen
	- 'Carsten' ♀H7	CAco CKen ELan EPfP GMcL GMil LRHS MAsh NEgg NLar NRHS SCoo SLim SPoG
	- 'Columbo'	GMil
	- 'Corley's Mat'	CKen GMil NLar
	- 'Devon Gem'	NEgg
	- 'Dezember Gold'	SLim
	- 'Flanders Belle'	SLim
	- 'Gnom'	CAco CDul ELan ESps GKin GMil LRHS MGos NEgg NRHS SCoo
	- 'Gold Star'	CMen
	- 'Golden Glow'	CAco NLar SLim SPoG
	- 'Heinis Triumph'	GMil
	- 'Hesse'	GMcL SCoo
	- 'Hoersholm'	CKen
	- 'Hulk'	CKen
	- 'Humpy' ♀H7	CAco CKen CMen ESps GMil MAsh NEgg SCoo SLim
	- 'Ironsides'	CKen NLar
	- 'Jacobsen'	CKen GMil NLar
	- 'Janovsky'	CKen
	- 'Kamila'	NLar
	- 'Kissen' ♀H7	CKen EPfP SLim
	- KLOSTERGRUN	see *P. mugo* 'Klosterkötter'
§	- 'Klosterkötter'	LRHS
	- 'Kobold'	NEgg
	- 'Krauskopf'	CKen GMil
	- 'Laarheide'	SPoG
	- 'Laurin'	CKen
	- 'Lemon' **new**	NLar
	- 'March'	CKen GMil
	- 'Mini Mops'	CKen SLim
	- 'Minikin'	CKen GMil
	- 'Mops' ♀H7	CAco CDul CMen EPfP ESps GMcL LRHS MAsh MBlu MGos NEgg NRHS SCob SCoo SLim SPoG SSta
	- 'Mops Midget'	CMen MAsh NEgg
	- var. ***mughus***	see *P. mugo* subsp. *mugo*
§	- subsp. ***mugo***	CAco CSBt GMcL GMil SCob SGol
	- - 'Milky Way'	CKen
	- 'Mumpitz'	CKen GMil LRHS
	- 'Nerost' **new**	NLar
	- 'Northern Lights'	CKen
	- 'Ophir' ♀H7	CAco CBcs CDul CKen CMen ELan EPfP GMil LRHS MAsh MGos NEgg NRHS SCob SCoo SLim SPoG SSta
	- 'Orange Sun'	GMil
	- 'Pal Maleter' (v)	GMil SCoo SLim SPoG
	- 'Paul's Dwarf'	CKen
	- 'Picobello'	LRHS MAsh NLar NRHS SLim
	- 'Piggelmee'	CKen
	- 'Pincushion'	LRHS NLar
	- Pumilio Group	CAco EPfP ESps GMil GQue LRHS MGos MMuc NLar SEND WMoo
	- - 'Emerald Dwarf' **new**	NLar
	- 'Rock Garden' **new**	NLar
	- var. ***rostrata***	see *P. mugo* subsp. *uncinata*
	- subsp. ***rotundata*** 'Ježek'	CKen MAsh NLar
	- 'Rushmore'	CKen
	- 'Ruze'	LRHS
	- 'Sandy' **new**	NLar
	- 'Sherwood Compact'	NLar SLim
	- 'Spaan'	CKen
	- 'Sunshine' (v)	CKen NLar
	- 'Suzi'	CKen
	- 'Suzy Hexe'	NWad
	- 'Trompenburg'	GMil NEgg
	- 'Tuffet'	CAco CKen LRHS SLim
	- 'Uelzen'	CKen LRHS NLar
§	- subsp. ***uncinata***	CAco
	- - 'Etschtal'	CKen
	- - 'Grüne Welle'	CKen GMil NLar
	- - 'Heideperle'	NLar
	- - 'Kostelnicek'	CKen NLar
	- - 'Leuco-like'	CKen
	- - 'Offenpass'	CKen
	- - 'Paradekissen'	CKen NLar
	- - 'Süsse Perle'	CKen
	- 'Varella'	LRHS NLar SCoo SLim
	- 'White Tip'	CKen
	- 'Winter Gold'	CAco ELan EPfP EUJe LRHS MGos MJak NRHS SSta
	- 'Winter Sun'	LRHS MAsh
	- 'Winzig'	CKen
	- 'Zundert'	CKen GMil SPoG
	- 'Zwergkugel'	CKen
	muricata	CAco CDul CPer EBtc
	nigra	CAco CBcs CDul CLnd CMac CTri EMOT EPfP ESps EUJe LPra MAsh MGos SGol
	- var. ***austriaca***	see *P. nigra* subsp. *nigra*
	- 'Bambino'	CKen
	- 'Black Prince' ♀H7	CKen EUJe GMil NEgg NOra
	- 'Bobo'	CKen
	- 'Brepo' **new**	GMil
	- var. ***calabrica***	see *P. nigra* subsp. *laricio*
	- 'Cebennensis Nana'	CKen
	- var. ***corsicana***	see *P. nigra* subsp. *laricio*
	- subsp. ***dalmatica*** **new**	CAco
	- 'Frank'	CKen NLar
	- 'Globosa'	ESps
	- 'Green Tower'	GMil LRHS NLar
	- 'Helga' **new**	NLar
	- 'Hornibrookiana'	CKen GMil
	- 'Karaca Ball' **new**	CAco
	- 'Komet'	GMil NLar SAko
§	- subsp. ***laricio***	CAco CCVT CDul CMac ECrN MMuc SEND
	- - 'Aurea'	MBlu
	- - 'Bobby McGregor'	CKen
	- - 'Globosa Viridis'	NEgg
	- - 'Goldfinger'	NLar
	- - 'Pygmaea'	CKen GMil NEgg
	- - 'Wurstle'	CKen
	- 'Lucia'	NLar
	- subsp. ***maritima***	see *P. nigra* subsp. *laricio*
	- 'Moran'	NLar
	- 'Moseri'	CAco CKen NEgg NLar
	- 'Nana'	GMil LRHS
§	- subsp. ***nigra***	CAco CCVT CLnd CPer CTho GMcL GMil LMaj MMuc SCob SEND SEWo SGol
	- - 'Birte'	CKen
	- - 'Bright Eyes'	GMil NEgg
	- - 'Helga'	NLar
	- - 'Schovenhorst'	CKen
	- - 'Skyborn'	CKen
	- - 'Strypemonde'	CKen NEgg

	- - 'Yaffle Hill'	CKen
	- 'Obelisk'	CKen NLar
	- 'Ola' new	CKen
	- 'Oregon Green'	CKen NLar
	- 'Pierrick Bregéon'PBR	LRHS
	- 'Richard'	CKen NLar SLim
	oocarpa	EBtc
	parviflora	CAco CDul NEgg SPlb
	- 'Aaba-jo'	CKen
	- 'Adcock's Dwarf' ♀H7	CAco CKen GMil NEgg SLim
	- 'Al Fordham'	CKen
	- 'Aoi'	CKen CMen NLar
	- 'Ara-kawa'	CKen CMen
	- 'Atco-goyo'	CKen
	- Azuma-goyo Group	CKen CMen LRHS
I	- 'Baasch's Form'	CKen
	- 'Bergman'	CAco MAsh
	- 'Blue Angel'	LRHS MBlu
	- 'Blue Giant'	GMil IArd MBlu
	- 'Bonnie Bergman' ♀H7	CDul CKen EPfP LRHS
	- 'Catherine Elizabeth'	CKen NLar
	- 'Dai-ho'	CKen
	- 'Daisetsusan'	CKen
	- 'Dougal'	CKen
	- 'Floppy Joe'	NLar
	- 'Fukai' (v)	CKen
	- 'Fukiju'	CKen
	- Fukushima-goyo Group	CKen CMen
	- 'Fuku-zu-mi'	CKen
	- 'Fu-shiro'	CKen
	- 'Gemstar'	CKen
	- 'Gin-sho-chuba'	CKen
	- Glauca Group	CAco LRHS MAsh MBlu NEgg SGol
	- - 'Glauca' ♀H7	CAco GMcL GMil
I	- 'Glauca Nana'	CKen
	- 'Goykuri'	CKen
	- 'Gyok-kasen'	CKen
	- 'Gyo-ko-haku'	CKen
	- 'Gyokusen Sämling'	CKen
	- 'Gyo-ku-sui'	CKen CMen
	- 'Hagaromo Seedling'	CKen CMen
	- 'Hakko'	CKen
	- 'Hatchichi'	CKen GMil
	- 'Ha-tzumari'	NLar
	- 'Hobbit'	NWad
	- 'Ibo-can'	CKen CMen
	- 'Ichi-no-se'	CKen
	- 'Iri-fune'	CKen
	- Ishizuchi-goyo Group	CKen NLar
	- 'Jade Tiers'	LRHS
	- 'Jim's Mini Curls'	CKen
	- 'Ka-ho'	CKen
	- 'Kanrico'	CKen
	- 'Kanzan'	CKen
	- 'Kin-po'	CKen NLar
	- 'Kiyomatsu'	CKen LRHS
	- 'Kobe'	CKen
	- 'Kokonoe'	CKen CMen
	- 'Kokuho'	CKen
	- 'Kusu-dama'	CKen
	- 'Little Hedgehog'	CKen
	- 'Lorraine'	CKen
	- 'Masami'	CKen
	- 'Meiko'	CKen CMen
	- 'Michinoku'	CKen
	- 'Momo-yama'	CKen NLar
	- 'Myo-jo'	CKen
	- Nasu-goyo Group	CKen
	- 'Negishi' ♀H7	CKen CMen LRHS MAsh NEgg NRHS SLim
	- 'Nellie D.'	NLar
	- 'Ōgon-goyo'	CKen
	- 'Ōgon-janome'	CAco CKen MAsh NEgg SLim
	- 'Ossorio Dwarf'	CKen
I	- var. ***pentaphylla*** 'Glauca' new	NLar
	- 'Perido' new	NLar
	- 'Regenhold'	CKen
	- 'Richard Lee'	CKen MAsh NLar
	- 'Ryo-ku-ho'	CKen
	- 'Ryu-ju'	CKen GMil NLar
	- 'Sa-dai-jin'	CKen
	- 'San-bo'	CKen
§	- 'Saphir'	CKen
	- 'Schoon's Bonsai'	LRHS
	- 'Setsugekka'	CKen
	- 'Shika-shima'	CKen
	- Shikoku-goyo Group	LRHS
	- 'Shimada'	CKen
	- 'Shin Sen'	LRHS
	- 'Shin Sho'	LRHS
	- Shiobara-goyo Group	CKen
	- 'Shizukagoten'	CKen SLim
	- 'Shu-re'	CKen NLar
	- 'Sieryoden'	CKen
	- 'Smout'	CKen
	- 'Tani-mano-uki'	CKen
	- 'Tempelhof'	CAco
	- 'Tenysu-kazu'	CKen LRHS MAsh NLar
	- 'Tokyo Dwarf'	CKen
	- 'Walker's Dwarf'	CKen
	- 'Watnong'	CKen
	- 'Zelkova'	CMen
	- 'Zui-sho'	CKen
	patula ♀H4	CAco CBcs CCCN CDul CHll CMCN EPfP EUJe IDee SArc SBig SCoo SLim SMad SPlb SPoG WPGP
	- var. ***patula*** new	EUJe
	peuce	CAco CDul EPfP GMcL MGil
	- 'Arnold Dwarf'	CKen NLar
	- 'Cesarini'	CKen NLar
	- 'Daniel'	CKen
	- 'Harlekin' new	NLar
	- 'Thessaloniki Broom'	CKen
	'Pichounet' new	NLar
	pinaster	CAco CBcs CLnd CPer EPfP ESps MMuc SEND
	pinea ♀H5	CAco CAgr CCVT CDul CLnd CTho EPfP ETod EUJe IDee LMaj LPra MGos MMuc SAko SArc SCoo SEND SEWo SGol SPlb WPGP
	- 'Queensway'	CKen
	ponderosa	CAco CDul CMCN EGFP EPfP LRHS
	- SDL2 new	NLar
	pumila	CAco ESps
	- 'Buchanan'	CKen
I	- 'Compacta' new	GMil
	- 'Dwarf Blue'	LRHS
	- 'Glauca' ♀H7	CKen GMil
	- 'Globe'	SLim
	- 'Jeddeloh'	CKen
§	- 'Nana'	GMil
	- 'Pinocchio'	CKen
	- 'Säntis'	CKen
	- 'Saphir'	see *P. parviflora* 'Saphir'
	pungens	CDul
	radiata	CAco CBcs CBod CCVT CDul CLnd CMCN CMac CPer CTho CTri ECrN ELan EPfP ESps EUJe GMil MMuc SArc SCoo

	- Aurea Group	ELan NEgg SCoo SLim SPoG
	- - 'Aurea' ♈H5	CAco GMil LRHS NOra
	- 'Bodnant'	CKen
	- 'Isca'	CKen
	- 'Marshwood' (v)	CKen
	- 'Nana'	NLar
	resinosa 'Don Smith'	CKen
	- 'Joel's Broom'	CKen
	- 'Nana'	CAco
	- 'Quinobequin'	CKen
	roxburghii	CAco
	sabineana	CAco
	× ***schwerinii***	CKen
	- 'Wiethorst' ♈H7	CAco CKen LRHS NLar NRHS WHar
	sibirica 'Blue Smoke'	CKen
	- 'Mariko'	CKen
	strobiformis	CAco EGFP
	- 'Coronado'	CKen
	- 'Loma Linda'	CKen SLim
	strobus	CAco CBcs CCVT CDul CMen EPfP ESps GMil LMaj LPra LRHS MGos MMuc SEND
§	- 'Alba'	SLim
	- 'Amelia's Dwarf'	CKen
	- 'Angel Falls'	CKen NLar
	- 'Anna Fiele'	CKen NEgg
	- 'Bennett Fastigiate'	NLar
	- 'Bergman's Mini'	CKen
	- 'Bergman's Pendula Broom'	CKen
I	- 'Bergman's Sport of Prostrata'	CKen
	- 'Beth'	CKen
	- 'Bloomer's Dark Globe'	CKen
	- 'Blue Covers'	NLar
	- 'Blue Shag' ♈H7	CAco LRHS NLar NRHS NWad SCoo SLim
	- 'Brevifolia'	CKen SArc
	- 'Cesarini'	CKen
	- 'Contorta'	CAco
	- 'Densa'	CKen
	- 'Diablo' **new**	NLar
	- 'Ed's Broom'	CKen
	- 'Elf'	NLar
	- 'Elkins Dwarf'	CKen GMil LRHS NEgg
	- 'Fastigiata'	CDul CKen
	- 'Golden Candles'	NLar
	- 'Golden Showers'	NLar
	- 'Green Curls'	CKen
	- 'Green Twist'	CKen NLar
	- 'Greg'	CKen NLar
	- 'Ground Hugger' **new**	NLar
	- 'Hershey'	CKen
	- 'Hillside Gem'	CKen
	- 'Horsford'	CKen
	- 'Horsford Sister'	CKen
	- 'Jamaican Curls'	CKen
	- 'Joe's Best Blue' **new**	NLar
	- 'Julian Pott'	CKen
	- 'Julian's Dwarf'	CKen
	- 'Krügers Lilliput'	LRHS NLar NWad
	- 'Louie'	CKen NLar SMad
	- 'Mary Butler'	CKen NLar
	- 'Merrimack'	CKen
	- 'Minima' ♈H7	CKen GMil LRHS MBlu NEgg NRHS SLim SPoG
	- 'Minuta'	CKen GMil LRHS
§	- Nana Group	NEgg SEWo
	- 'Nana'	see *P. strobus* Nana Group
	- 'Nana Compacta'	LRHS NEgg

	- 'Niagara Falls'	CKen NLar
	- 'Nivea'	see *P. strobus* 'Alba'
	- 'Northway Broom'	CKen
	- 'Paul Waxman'	NLar
	- 'Pendula'	CKen LRHS MBlu
I	- 'Pendula Broom'	CKen
	- 'Pygmaea'	LRHS
	- 'Radiata'	CTri ESps GMcL
I	- 'Radiata Aurea'	NEgg
	- 'Reinshaus'	CKen LRHS NRHS
	- 'Sayville'	CKen
	- 'Sea Urchin'	CAco CKen LRHS MAsh NLar NRHS SLim
	- 'Secrest'	LRHS NRHS
	- 'Smokey Hollow' **new**	NLar
	- 'Squiggles'	NLar
	- 'Stowe Pillar'	NLar SLim
	- 'Tiny Kurls'	CAco CKen LRHS MAsh NLar NRHS
	- 'Torulosa'	MBlu
	- 'Uncatena'	CKen
	- 'Verkade's Broom'	CKen NEgg
	- 'White Mountain'	EUJe MBlu
	sylvestris	Widely available
	- 'Abergeldie'	CKen
	- 'Albyns'	GMil NLar
	- 'Alderly Edge'	CMen
	- 'Andorra'	CKen
	- 'Anny's Wintersun' **new**	NLar
	- 'Argentea Compacta'	LRHS
	- Aurea Group	CDul CKen CMen ELan MBlu MJak NEgg SLim SSta
	- - 'Aurea' ♈H7 **new**	GMil
	- 'Avondene'	CKen
	- 'Bergfield'	CMen
	- 'Beuvronensis' ♈H7	CAco CMen GMil NEgg SLim
	- 'Buchanan's Gold'	CKen
	- 'Burghfield'	CMen
	- 'Candlelight' **new**	NLar
	- 'Chantry Blue'	GMcL GMil LRHS MAsh MGos NEgg NOra SCoo SLim SPoG
	- 'Clumber Blue'	CKen
	- 'Denny Boy' **new**	NLar
	- 'Dereham'	CKen NLar
	- 'Doone Valley'	CKen NEgg
	- 'Edwin Hillier'	NEgg NOra WPGP
	- Fastigiata Group	CAco CDul CEnd CKen CLnd CMen GMil LRHS NRHS SCoo SLim WCFE
	- 'Frensham' ♈H7	CKen MAsh
	- 'Globosa'	CAco
	- 'Gold Coin' ♈H7	CAco CDul CKen EPfP GMil NEgg SPoG
	- 'Gold Medal'	CKen
	- 'Grand Rapids'	CKen
	- 'Green Penguin'	NLar
	- 'Gwydyr Castle'	CKen
	- 'Hillside Creeper'	CKen
	- 'Humble Pie'	CKen
	- 'Jeremy'	CKen NEgg
	- 'John Boy'	CMen
	- 'Kenwith'	CKen
	- 'Lodge Hill'	CMen MAsh NEgg SLim
	- 'Longmoor'	CKen
	- 'Martham'	CKen CMen
	- 'Mitsch Weeping'	CKen
	- Nana Group	CAco GMil
	- 'Nana' misapplied	see *P. sylvestris* 'Watereri'
	- 'Nana Compacta'	CMen SWeb
§	- 'Nisbet's Gem'	CKen CMen
	- 'Padworth'	CMen
	- 'Piskowitz'	CKen

	- 'Pixie'	CKen
I	- 'Prostrata'	GMil NEgg SLim
	- 'Repens'	CAco CKen
	- 'Saint George'	CKen
	- 'Sandringham'	NLar
	- 'Saxatilis'	CKen CMen
	- 'Scott's Dwarf'	see *P. sylvestris* 'Nisbet's Gem'
	- 'Sentinel'	CKen
	- 'Skjak I'	CKen
	- 'Skjak II'	CKen
	- 'Spaan's Slow Column'	CKen SLim
	- 'Tage'	CKen
	- 'Tanya'	CKen
	- 'Tilhead'	CKen
	- 'Treasure'	CKen
	- 'Trefrew Quarry'	CKen
	- 'Troll Guld'	CKen NLar
	- 'Umbraculifera'	NEgg
§	- 'Watereri'	GMcL LMaj LRHS MJak NRHS SCob SCoo
	- 'Westonbirt'	CKen CMen
	- 'Wintergold'	NEgg
	- 'Wittichenau'	CKen
	- 'Xavery' new	NLar
	tabuliformis	CAco
	taeda	CAco EPfP
	taiwanensis	CAco CDul EPfP
	teocote new	CAco
	thunbergii	CAco CDul CLnd CMCN CMen ELan IDee MMuc
	- 'Akame'	CKen CMen
	- 'Akame Yatsabusa'	CMen
	- 'Aocha-matsu' (v)	CKen CMen
	- 'Arakawa-sho'	CKen CMen
	- 'Banshosho'	CAco CKen CMen
	- 'Beni-kujaku'	CKen CMen
	- 'Compacta'	CKen CMen
	- var. ***corticosa*** 'Fuji'	CMen
	- - 'Iihara'	CMen
	- 'Dainagon'	CKen CMen
	- 'Eechee-nee'	CKen
	- 'Hayabusa'	CMen
	- 'Iwai'	CMen
	- 'Janome' (v)	CMen
	- 'Katsuga'	CMen
	- 'Kotobuki'	CKen CMen NLar
	- 'Koyosho'	CMen
	- 'Kujaku'	CKen CMen
	- 'Kyokko'	CKen CMen
	- 'Kyushu'	CKen CMen
	- 'Mikawa'	CMen MBlu
	- 'Miyajuna'	CKen CMen
	- 'Nishiki-ne'	CKen CMen
	- 'Nishiki-tsusaka'	CMen
	- 'Ogi-matsu'	CKen
	- 'Ogon'	CAco CMen LRHS NLar
	- 'Porky'	CKen CMen
§	- 'Sayonara' 🏆H7	CMen GMil MAsh NEgg
	- 'Senryu'	CKen CMen
	- 'Shinsho'	CKen CMen
	- 'Shio-guro'	CKen CMen GMil
	- 'Suchiro'	NEgg
	- 'Suchiro Yatabusa'	CKen CMen
	- 'Sunsho'	CKen CMen
	- 'Taihei'	CKen CMen
I	- 'Thunderhead' 🏆H7	CKen CMen GMil SLim
	- witches' broom	CKen
	- 'Yatsubusa'	see *P. thunbergii* 'Sayonara'
	- 'Ye-i-kan'	CKen
	- 'Yoshimura'	CMen
	- 'Yumaki'	CAco CKen CMen
	torreyana	CAco
	uncinata	see *P. mugo* subsp. *uncinata*
	virginiana 'Driscoll' new	NLar
	- 'Wate's Golden'	CKen
§	***wallichiana*** 🏆H6	CAco CCVT CDul CKen CLnd CMCN CTho EPfP ESps EUJe GMcL IDee LMaj LPra LRHS MBlu MGil MGos MJak MMuc NEgg NLar NOra NRHS SBir SEND SEWo SGol SLim WPGP
	- 'Densa Hill'	LMaj LRHS NLar
	- 'Frosty'	CKen
	- 'Nana' 🏆H6	CKen LRHS NLar SCoo SLim
	- 'Umbraculifera'	MAsh
	- var. ***wallichiana***	EUJe
	- 'Winter Light'	NLar
	- 'Zebrina' (v)	CAco MBlu NLar
	yunnanensis	CAco LRHS

Piper (*Piperaceae*)

auritum	GPoy LEdu
betle	GPoy
heydei B&SWJ 10445	WCru
methysticum	GPoy

Piptanthus (*Papilionaceae*)

	forrestii	see *P. nepalensis*
	laburnifolius	see *P. nepalensis*
§	***nepalensis***	CBcs CDul CRos CSBt CSpe EBee ELan EPfP EWld LRHS MGil MGos MPie MSCN NBid NLar SBrt SPer SRms WAvo
	aff. ***nepalensis***	SWvt

Pistacia (*Anacardiaceae*)

atlantica	XSen
chinensis	CBcs EBee EBtc EPfP WPGP
lentiscus	CBcs EUJe LRHS SEND SVen XSen
terebinthus	XSen
- NJM 11.004	WPGP
vera	CBcs CTsd

Pistia (*Araceae*)

stratiotes	LCro LLWG LOPS MSKA NPer SCoo

Pitavia (*Rutaceae*)

punctata	IArd

Pitcairnia (*Bromeliaceae*)

bergii	CHll
heterophylla	CFil WCot
pungens new	WCot
recurvata	WCot
ringens	WCot

Pittosporum ✿ (*Pittosporaceae*)

adaphniphylloides	CBcs
anomalum	CCCN CTsd ELon SEle
'Arundel Green' (f) 🏆H4	CRos ELon EPfP ESps ETod LRHS LSRN MAsh NRHS SCob SLim SPer SWvt
buchananii	SVen
'Collaig Silver'	CRos EPfP LRHS MAsh NRHS SLim
coriaceum	CBrP
crassifolium	CBcs CCCN CTsd
- 'Variegatum' (v)	CBcs CCCN MGil WAvo
'Crinkles' (f)	SVen
daphniphylloides	EBee ELan WPGP
- B&SWJ 6789	WCru

- CWJ 12404	WCru
- RWJ 9913	WCru
eugenioides	CMCN CSam SEND
- 'Platinum' (v)	CCCN
- 'Variegatum' (v) ♀H4	CBcs CCCN CDul CMac CRos ELan EPfP ESps EUJe IArd LRHS MGos NLar NRHS SAko SCob SEND SLim SVen WAvo
'Garnettii' (v) ♀H4	Widely available
glabratum	WPGP
- var. ***neriifolium*** B&SWJ 11685	WCru
heterophyllum	ECrN ELan EPfP EWes LRHS MMrt SEND
- variegated (v)	CCCN EBee EBtc EPfP LRHS WSHC
'Holbrook' (v)	CSam
illicioides var. ***angustifolium***	WPGP
- - B&SWJ 6771	WCru
- - RWJ 9846	WCru
- var. ***illicioides*** B&SWJ 6712	WCru
- - PAB 9004	LEdu WPGP
× ***intermedium***	SWvt
- 'Craxten' (f)	CCCN
'Nanum Variegatum'	see *P. tobira* 'Variegatum'
napaulense new	WCru
oblongilimbum DJHV 06137	WCru
'Oliver Twist'	CRos EPfP ETod LRHS LSRN MAsh NRHS SCob SCoo
omeiense	EWes
- VdL 80626	EBee WPGP
patulum new	WPGP
phillyreoides	CTsd
ralphii	CCCN CMCN CTsd
- 'Variegatum' (v)	CCCN LRHS WPGP
'Saundersii' (v)	SCoo
'Tadina Gold'	ETod
tenuifolium	Widely available
- 'Abbotsbury Gold' (f/v)	CAbb CBcs CBod CCCN CMac CRos CTri EHoe ELan EPfP ESps ETod EUJe EWes GMcL IBoy LRHS MAsh MGos MSwo SCob SEND SGbt SGol SLim SPer SWvt WAvo
- 'Atropurpureum'	CBcs ELan ETod
- 'Brockhill Compact'	CCCN LRHS SAko
- 'Cornish Mist'	CTsd
- 'County Park'	CCCN EUJe SRms
- 'County Park Dwarf'	MAsh
- 'Elizabeth' (m/v)	CBcs CMac CRos EHoe EPfP ETod EUJe GMcL IArd IBoy LRHS LSRN LSou MAsh MGos MRav MSwo NRHS SCob SCoo SEND SGol SLim SPoG SRms
- EMERALD DOME ('Minpitto'PBR)	SArc
- 'French Lace'	CBcs CCCN ELan GMcL WFar
- 'Gold Star'	CBcs CRos EHoe ELan EPfP ESps LRHS MAsh MGos NRHS SBod SCob SCoo SEle SLim SPer SPoG SRms SWvt WFar
- 'Golden King'	CCCN CMac CRos CSBt EPfP ESps LRHS MAsh MGos NRHS SLim SRms
- 'Golf Ball'PBR	CBcs CRos EPfP EUJe GBin LCro LOPS LRHS LSRN MGos NRHS SCob SGbt
- 'Green Thumb'	CMac
- 'Irene Paterson' (m/v) ♀H4	Widely available
- 'James Stirling'	CCCN SEND
- 'John Flanagan'	see *P. tenuifolium* 'Margaret Turnbull'
- 'Limelight' (v)	CBcs CCCN CRos CSBt EBee EPfP EUJe LRHS LSRN SLim SPoG
- 'Loxhill Gold'	CCCN CRos IArd LRHS NRHS SGol
§ - 'Margaret Turnbull' (v)	CRos EPfP EWes GKin LRHS MGos NRHS SGol
- 'Marjory Channon' (v)	CRos EPfP LRHS NRHS
- 'Moonlight' (v)	CBcs LRHS MRav SCob
- 'Mountain Green'	CMac
- 'Nutty's Leprechaun'	CCCN
- 'Pompom'	CCCN LRHS
- 'Purpureum' (m)	CBar CCCN CMac CRos CSBt CTri EPfP EUJe GBin LRHS LSRN MAsh MGil MMuc NEgg NRHS SAko SCob SEND SLim SPer SPoG SRms WAvo WFar WSHC
- 'Silver Magic' (v)	CBcs CRos EPfP ESps GMcL LRHS NRHS SCob SEle SRkn
- 'Silver Queen' (f/v) ♀H4	Widely available
- 'Silver Sheen' (m)	CBcs CMac CRos LRHS NRHS
- 'Stevens Island'	CBcs
- 'Stirling Gold' (f/v)	EWes
- 'Tandara Gold' (v)	CBcs CCCN CMac CRos CSBt ELan ELon EPfP ESps ETod EUJe GMcL LRHS MAsh MGos NRHS SCob SCoo SEND SLim SPoG SRms WAvo
- 'Tiki' (m)	CCCN
- 'Tom Thumb' ♀H4	Widely available
- 'Tresederi' (f/m)	CCCN CTsd
- 'Variegatum' (m/v)	CBcs CPer CRos CSBt EBee ELon ETod GMcL LCro LOPS LRHS LSRN MGos MSwo NRHS SArc SCob SEND SGbt SLim SPer SWvt WFar
- 'Victoria' (v)	CBcs CCCN CRos LRHS LSRN
- 'Warnham Gold' (m) ♀H3	CBcs CCCN CMac CRos EBee ELan EPfP ESps GKin LRHS MAsh MGos NRHS SLim SPer SPoG SRms SVen
- 'Wendle Channon' (m/v)	CBcs CCCN CMac CRos CSBt EHoe EPfP ETod GMcL LRHS MAsh SGol SLim WSHC
- 'Wrinkled Blue'	CBcs CRos EPfP ETod LRHS MAsh MRav MSwo NRHS SPoG
tobira ♀H3	Widely available
- B&SWJ 12758	WCru
* - 'Nanum'	CAco CBcs CCCN CMac CRos ELan EPfP ETod EUJe LCro LOPS LRHS MGos SCob SLim SPer SPoG
§ - 'Variegatum' (v) ♀H4	CBcs CCCN CDul CMac CRos ELan EPfP EUJe LRHS LSRN MGos NLar SArc SCob SEND SLim SLon SPer SPoG WSHC
'Trim's Hedger'	CBod
truncatum	CCCN CExl EPfP
undulatum	WAvo
viridiflorum	EShb

Plagianthus (*Malvaceae*)

betulinus	see *P. regius*
lyallii	see *Hoheria lyallii*
§ ***regius***	CBcs

Plagiorhegma see *Jeffersonia*

Plantago (*Plantaginaceae*)

coronopus	CAgr EBWF
holosteum	GKev

	lanceolata	CAgr CHab EBWF WSFF
	major	GPoy WSFF
	- 'Atropurpurea'	see *P. major* 'Rubrifolia'
	- 'Bowles's Variety'	see *P. major* 'Rosularis'
	- 'Brenda'	CNat
	- 'Frills'	NPoe
	- 'Rosenstolz'	NChi
§	- 'Rosularis'	CBre CFis CSpe EBee LEdu NBro NPoe SPav SRms WHer
§	- 'Rubrifolia'	CBod CHid CPla CSpe EShb LLWG MMuc NBid NBro NPoe SHar SRms WMoo WSFF XLum
	- 'Tony Lewis'	CNat
	maritima	EBWF
	media	CHab EBWF MHer
	nivalis	GEdr
	rosea	see *P. major* 'Rosularis'
	triandra 'Wanaka'	IMou

Platanus ✿ (*Platanaceae*)

	sp.	LPra
	× ***acerifolia***	see *P.* × *hispanica*
§	× ***hispanica*** ♀H6	CBcs CCVT CDul CLnd CMCN ECrN ELan EMOT EPfP ESps LMaj LPra MGos MMuc SArc SCob SEND SEWo SGol SPer WMou WTSh
	- 'Bloodgood'	CTho
	- 'Pyramidalis'	ECrN LMaj
	orientalis	CCVT CDul CLnd CMCN CTho EPfP ESps SCob WPGP
	- PAB 346	LEdu
	- 'Cuneata'	ECrN
§	- f. ***digitata*** ♀H6	CCVT CDul CLnd CMCN CTho EBee EMOT EPfP ERod WMou
	- var. ***insularis***	WPGP
	- 'Laciniata'	see *P. orientalis* f. *digitata*
	- 'Minaret'	CDul EMOT WMou
	- 'Mirkovec'	EPfP IArd

Platycarya (*Juglandaceae*)

	strobilacea	LEdu

Platycerium (*Polypodiaceae*)

	alcicorne misapplied	see *P. bifurcatum*
§	***bifurcatum*** ♀H1b	CCCN EUJe NLos XBlo
	- 'Netherlands'	NLos
	'Dawboy'	NLos
	ellisii	NLos
	grande hort.	see *P. superbum*
	hillii	NLos
	'Lemoinei'	NLos
	'Mount Kitshakood'	NLos
	ridleyi	NLos
§	***superbum*** ♀H1b	CCCN NLos
	willinckii	NLos

Platycladus (*Cupressaceae*)

§	***orientalis*** 'Aurea Nana' ♀H6	CDul CKen CMac CSBt ELan EMOT EPfP ETMg GMcL LBee LPra LRHS MAsh MGos MJak NRHS NWad SGol SLim SPoG WCFE
	- 'Autumn Glow'	CKen
	- 'Beverleyensis'	NLar
	- 'Conspicua'	CKen CSBt EMOT
	- 'Elegantissima'	LRHS
	- 'Flame'	LRHS
	- 'Franky Boy' ♀H6	NLar SPoG
	- 'Golden Pygmy'	CKen
	- 'Kenwith'	CKen
	- 'Meldensis'	CTri
	- 'Miller's Gold'	see *P. orientalis* 'Aurea Nana'
	- 'Minima Glauca'	CKen
I	- 'Pyramidalis Aurea'	ESps LBee
	- 'Rosedalis'	CKen CSBt EMOT EPfP ESps LBee MAsh SLim
	- 'Sanderi'	WCFE
	- 'Shirley Chilcott'	MAsh
	- 'Southport'	LBee LRHS
	- 'Summer Cream'	CKen

Platycodon (*Campanulaceae*)

	grandiflorus ♀H5	CBod CTri CTsd ECha EPfP GKev LRHS MHer SRms WHar WHoo XAbr
	- 'Albus'	CBod EPfP GKev SPer SWvt WHar
	- Apoyama Group ♀H5	WHoo WThu
	- - 'Fairy Snow'	GKev WHoo
	- (Astra Series) 'Astra Blue'	EPfP LRHS NRHS SPoG SRot
	- - 'Astra Double Blue' (d)	CRos
	- - 'Astra Double Lavender' (d)	CRos LRHS NRHS
	- - 'Astra Pink'	CRos LRHS NRHS SPoG
	- - 'Astra White'	SPoG
	- 'Blue Pearl'	WHoo
	- 'Fuji Blue'	ELon WHoo XLum
	- 'Fuji Pink'	MRav SWvt WHoo XLum
	- 'Fuji White'	ELon WHoo
	- 'Hakone'	MRav WHoo
	- 'Hakone Blue'	EPfP NBre
	- 'Hakone Double Blue' (d)	SRms
	- 'Hakone White'	EPfP MRav WRHF
	- 'Mariesii' ♀H5	CAby CSBt ELon EPfP IBoy MNHC MRav NEgg SPer SPlb SRms SWvt WAul WHoo WSHC
	- MOTHER OF PEARL	see *P. grandiflorus* 'Perlmutterschale'
§	- 'Perlmutterschale'	EBee MRav
	- pink-flowered	GKev
	- ***pumilus***	GKev
	- 'Sentimental Blue'	XLum
	- 'Shell Pink'	see *P. grandiflorus* 'Perlmutterschale'
	- 'Willy'	XLum
	- 'Zwerg'	NBre

Platycrater (*Hydrangeaceae*)

	arguta	EBee WCru WPGP
	- B&SWJ 6266	WCru

Plectranthus (*Lamiaceae*)

	sp.	CPla
	ambiguus	EGeo
	- 'Nico'	EGeo
	amboinicus	EGeo MNHC SAll
	- 'Variegatus' (v)	EGeo
	- 'Well Sweep Wedgewood' (v)	EGeo
	argentatus ♀H1c	CSpe CTsd EGeo EUJe EWld GCal IDee MCot MPie SEND SRkn WKif
	- 'Hill House' (v)	CHll EShb MPie
	- 'Silver Shield'	EShb MPie
	australis misapplied	see *P. verticillatus*
	barbatus	EGeo
	behrii	see *P. fruticosus*
	BLUE ANGEL ('Edelblau') (Cape Angels Series)	EGeo
	caninus	SPoG
	ciliatus	CPbh EGeo EShb SRkn
	- 'Easy Gold' (v) ♀H1c	EGeo

	- 'Sasha' (v)	CCCN CHII ECtt EShb EUJe
	coleoides 'Marginatus'	see *P. forsteri* 'Marginatus'
	- 'Variegatus'	see *P. madagascariensis* 'Variegated Mintleaf'
	ernstii	EGeo EWld
§	***forsteri*** 'Marginatus'	EGeo
§	***fruticosus***	CPbh
	- 'Behr's Pride'	EGeo
	- blue-flowered	EGeo
	- 'James' ♀H1c	EGeo
	hadiensis var. ***tomentosus***	EGeo
	- - 'Carnegie'	EGeo
	- - green-leaved	EGeo
	- - 'Penge' (v)	EGeo
	madagascariensis	EGeo
	- 'Lothlorien' (v)	EGeo
§	- 'Variegated Mintleaf' (v) ♀H1c	MNHC SRms
	'Marble Ruffles'	EGeo
	menthol-scented, large-leaved	EGeo
	MONA LAVENDER ('Plepalila'PBR) ♀H1c	EGeo
	mutabilis	EGeo
	neochilus	CSpe
§	***oertendahlii*** ♀H1c	CPbh EBak EGeo EUJe
	ornatus	EGeo NPla
	prostratus	EGeo
	purpuratus ♀H1c	EGeo
	rotundifolius	LEdu
	saccatus subsp. ***longitubus***	EGeo
	sinensis	CRos LRHS NRHS
	spicatus	EGeo
	Swedish ivy	see *P. oertendahlii*, *P. verticillatus*
	venteri	EGeo
§	***verticillatus***	EGeo EWld
	- 'Barberton'	EGeo
	Vick's plant	EGeo
	zuluensis	CPbh EGeo EUJe EWld GCal SRkn WBor

Pleioblastus (*Poaceae*)

	akebono	see *P. argenteostriatus* 'Akebono'
§	***argenteostriatus*** 'Akebono'	ERod
§	- f. ***pumilus***	EHoe ERod ETMg GMaP MMuc MWht NLar NWad SPlb
	auricomus	see *P. viridistriatus*
	- 'Vagans'	see *Sasaella ramosa*
	chino f. ***elegantissimus***	CBdn EPfP ERod EShb MMoz MMuc SBig SEND WMoo
	- var. ***hisauchii***	ERod MWht
	fortunei	see *P. variegatus* 'Fortunei'
	'Gauntlettii'	see *P. argenteostriatus* f. *pumilus*
	glaber 'Albostriatus'	see *Sasaella masamuneana* 'Albostriata'
§	***hindsii***	ERod MMoz
§	***humilis***	ENBC
	- var. ***pumilus***	see *P. argenteostriatus* f. *pumilus*
	kongosanensis 'Aureostriatus' (v)	MWht
	linearis	ERod MMoz MWht SBig WMoo
§	***pygmaeus***	CDul CTri EHoe ELan ENBC GMaP GMcL MBrN SCob SGol SRms WMoo
§	- 'Distichus'	MJak WMoo
§	- 'Mirrezuzume'	CExl
*	- var. ***pygmaeus*** 'Mini'	MMuc WCot
§	***simonii***	CAgr CRos LRHS MMuc MWht NRHS SEND SPoG XBlo
	- 'Variegatus' (v)	CBcs CRos LRHS NRHS SPer SPoG
§	***variegatus*** (v) ♀H4	CBcs CBdn CDul CRos EHoe ELan ELon ENBC EPfP EUJe GMaP LEdu LRHS MBrN MJak MWht NRHS SCob SLim SPlb SWvt WMoo XBlo
§	- 'Fortunei' (v)	CTsd GMcL MMuc SEND SGol
	- 'Tsuboii' (v)	CAbb CDTJ ERod GMcL MBrN MJak SGol WMoo
§	***viridistriatus*** ♀H5	CBcs CDul CExl CRos ECha EHoe ELon EPfP ERod GMaP GMcL LEdu LRHS MJak MMoz MMuc MRav MWht NRHS NWsh SCob SEND SGol SPer SRms WFar WMoo XBlo
	- f. ***variegatus*** (v)	CTsd SWvt WMoo

Pleione (*Orchidaceae*)

	sp.	NDav SDir
	Alishan gx 'Merlin'	LYaf
	- 'Mother's Day'	GEdr LYaf
	- 'Mount Fuji'	LYaf
	Anstice Harris gx	LYaf
	Asama gx 'Red Grouse'	GEdr LYaf
	Askia gx	GEdr
	aurita	GEdr GKev SDir
	× ***barbarae***	GKev IFoB LAma LYaf
	Barcena gx	LYaf
	Berapi gx 'Purple Sandpiper'	LEdu LYaf WPGP
	Bonobo gx new	LYaf
	Brigadoon gx 'Stonechat'	LEdu WPGP
	Britannia gx 'Doreen'	LEdu LYaf WPGP
§	***bulbocodioides***	CExl CFil GEdr GKev LYaf
	- 'New Forest'	GEdr
§	- 'Yunnan'	GEdr GKev IFoB
	Burnsall gx	GEdr
	Captain Hook gx	LYaf
	Caroli gx 'Cape Robin'	LYaf
	chunii	GEdr GKev LAma
	Confirmation gx	LYaf
	Eastfield gx 'Purple Emperor'	LYaf
	Eiger gx	LYaf
	El Pico gx 'Pheasant'	LYaf
	Erebus gx 'Redpoll'	GEdr
	formosana ♀H3	CFil EPot GKev LAma LCro LEdu LOPS LRHS MHer NHpl NRHS SDeJ SDir WFar WPGP
	- Alba Group	GKev WFar
	- - 'Claire'	IFoB LEdu LYaf WPGP
	- - 'Snow Bunting'	LEdu LYaf WPGP
	- 'Blush of Dawn'	NHpl
	- 'Cairngorm'	IFoB
	- 'Greenhill'	LYaf
	- Hyb 8001	IFoB
	- 'Iris'	IFoB
	- 'Pitlochry'	LYaf
	- (Pricei Group) 'Oriental Grace'	IFoB LYaf
	- - 'Oriental Splendour'	LYaf
	- 'Snow White'	CExl CFil LEdu LYaf WPGP
	forrestii	EPot LAma NHpl
	Fuego gx	IFoB
	Gerry Mundey gx	GEdr
	- 'Tinney's Firs'	LYaf
	Glacier Peak gx	LYaf
§	***grandiflora***	GKev LAma LYaf
	Harlequin gx 'Norman'	LYaf
	Hekla gx	IFoB

- 'Locking Stumps'	GEdr
- 'Partridge'	GEdr
- 'Partridge' × **Zeus Weinstein gx**	GEdr
humilis	GKev LYaf SDir
- orange-red-flowered	GKev
- purple-flowered	GKev
Irazu gx	IFoB
- 'Cheryl'	GEdr
Jake Butterfield gx	LYaf
Jorullo gx 'Long-tailed Tit'	GEdr LYaf
Katmai gx 'Crossbill'	LYaf
Keith Rattray gx 'Kelty'	LYaf
Kelut gx new	LYaf
Kenya gx 'Bald Eagle'	LYaf
Krakatoa gx	LYaf
- 'Wheatear'	LYaf
Lascar gx 'Dipper'	LYaf
- 'Purple Finch'	LYaf
Lhasa gx 'Blushes'	LYaf
limprichtii ♀H3	GKev IFoB LEdu LYaf
Lyn Butterfield gx	LYaf
maculata	LYaf
Mageik gx 'Black Kite'	LYaf
Mandalay gx 'Purple Rain'	LYaf
- 'Strawberry Fields'	LYaf
Marco Polo gx	GKev
Marion Johnson gx 'Bubs'	LYaf
- 'Oxpecker' new	LYaf
- 'Whinchat'	LYaf
Matupi gx	CJun
Mauna Loa gx	LYaf
- 'Glossy Starling'	LYaf
Mawenzi gx	LYaf
Michael Butterfield gx	LYaf
Novarupta gx 'Raven'	LYaf
Orinoco gx 'Gemini'	GEdr
Orizaba gx	GEdr
- 'Fish Eagle'	LYaf
Pelee gx 'Cape Weaver'	LYaf
pinkepankii	see *P. grandiflora*
Piton gx	EPot LYaf
§ ***pleionoides***	GKev LYaf
pogonioides misapplied	see *P. pleionoides*
pogonioides (Rolfe) Rolfe	see *P. bulbocodioides*
praecox	GKev
Quizapu gx 'Peregrine'	LYaf
Rakata gx	IFoB
- 'Locking Stumps'	EPot GEdr
- 'Redwing'	LYaf
- 'Shot Silk'	GEdr LYaf
- 'Skylark'	LEdu WPGP
Red Colobus gx	LYaf
'Rossini'	GKev
Salek gx 'Eagle Owl'	LYaf
Santa Maria gx 'Nightjar'	LYaf
Santorini gx	LYaf
- 'Yellow Wagtail'	LYaf
saxicola	GKev LYaf
scopulorum	LYaf
Semeru gx	LYaf
Shantung gx	NHpl SDir
- 'Double Cream'	LYaf
- 'Ducat'	LYaf
- 'Gerry Mundey'	LYaf
- 'Muriel Harberd' ♀H3	GEdr
- 'Silver Anniversary'	LYaf
Shasta gx	LYaf
Sinope gx	LYaf
Sirena gx	LYaf
Sorea gx	GEdr GKev
Soufrière gx	GEdr
speciosa Ames & Schltr.	see *P. pleionoides*
Steve James gx 'Plum Perfection'	LYaf
Stromboli gx 'Fireball'	CExl CFil EPot LEdu WPGP
Taal gx 'Red-tailed Hawk'	LYaf
× ***taliensis***	LYaf
Tibesti gx	LYaf
Toff gx	LYaf
Tolima gx 'Moorhen'	LEdu LYaf WPGP
Tongariro gx	CPBP EPot GEdr GKev LCro LEdu LOPS WPGP
Ueli Wackernagel gx 'Pearl'	GKev LYaf
'Verdi'	GKev
Versailles gx 'Bucklebury'	GEdr LEdu WPGP
- 'Muriel Turner'	GEdr
Vesuvius gx 'Leopard'	LYaf
- 'Phoenix'	EPot LYaf
- 'Tawny Owl'	GEdr
'Vivaldi'	GKev
Volcanello gx 'Honey Buzzard'	GEdr LYaf
- 'Song Thrush'	LYaf
Whakari gx	LYaf
- 'Dusky Sunbird' new	LYaf
- 'Mountain Pipit'	LYaf
Wharfedale gx 'Pine Warbler'	LYaf
yunnanensis misapplied	see *P. bulbocodioides* 'Yunnan'
yunnanensis ambig.	GEdr GKev LAma
Zeus Weinstein gx	IFoB LYaf

Pleomele see *Dracaena*

Pleurospermum (*Apiaceae*)

sp.	CSpe
SDR 7941	GKev
SDR 7985	EBee GKev
benthamii B&SWJ 2988	WCru
camtschaticum B&SWJ 12627	WCru
yunnanense BWJ 7952A	WCru

plum see *Prunus domestica*

Plumbago (*Plumbaginaceae*)

§ ***auriculata*** ♀H2	CBcs CCCN CSBt CTri CWCL EBak ELan EPfP EPri EShb EUJe MGil MRav SEND SPer SPoG SRms WAvo WFib
- f. ***alba*** ♀H2	CBcs CCCN CRHN EPfP EShb IDee SEND
- 'Crystal Waters'	CCCN CSam EShb
- dark blue-flowered	CRHN CSpe
- (Escapade Series) 'Escapade Blue'	CWGN EShb SPre
- - 'Escapade White'	EShb
capensis	see *P. auriculata*
larpentiae	see *Ceratostigma plumbaginoides*

Plumeria (*Apocynaceae*)

sp.	WSFF
rubra ♀H1b	CCCN XBlo
- 'Golden Glow'	XBlo
- 'Velvet Red'	XBlo

Pneumatopteris (*Thelypteridaceae*)

pennigera	EBee NLos

Poa (*Poaceae*)

alpina	XLum
chaixii	EHoe EPPr
cita	IMou
glauca	EShb
labillardierei	CKno CRos CWCL EBee ECha EHoe ELon EPPr IMou LRHS MBel MMuc NRHS SEND XLum
pratensis	CHab EBWF
trivialis	EBWF

Podalyria (*Papilionaceae*)

calyptrata	SPlb
sericea	SPlb

Podanthus (*Asteraceae*)

ovatifolius	SVen

Podocarpus ✿ (*Podocarpaceae*)

acutifolius	CBcs
alpinus R. Br. ex Hook. f.	CDul
andinus	see *Prumnopitys andina*
'Autumn Shades' (m)	NLar
'Blaze' (f)	CBcs GMil LEdu
chilinus	see *P. salignus*
'Chocolate Box' (f)	ELan MAsh NLar SLim
'County Park Fire' PBR (f) 🏆H6	CBcs CDul CRos EMOT EPfP GEdr GMil LRHS MAsh MGos NLar NRHS SCoo SLim SRms SWvt
cunninghamii 'Roro' (m)	CBcs
dacrydioides	see *Dacrycarpus dacrydioides*
'Flame'	EMOT GEdr GMil MAsh NLar SLim
'Guardsman'	LRHS
henkelii	CBcs
'Jill' (f)	CBcs
lawrencei	CBcs
- 'Blue Gem' (f)	CJun EPfP ESps GMil LRHS MAsh MMuc SCoo SLim WThu
- 'Purple King'	NLar
- 'Red Tip'	CRos GMil LRHS NLar NRHS
macrophyllus	CTsd ESps SArc WPGP
- 'Aureus'	CBcs
'Maori Prince' (m)	NLar
matudae	CFil
nivalis	CBcs CDul CMac SRms WThu
- 'Bronze'	GCal
- 'Green Queen' (f)	CBcs
- 'Jack's Pass' (m)	EMOT LRHS
- 'Kilworth Cream' (v) 🏆H6	CBcs EMOT GMil LRHS SAko SLim SWvt
- 'Livingstone' (f)	CBcs
- 'Otari' (m)	MAsh NLar
nubigenus	CMCN
'Red Embers' (f)	CRos EMOT NRHS SCoo SLim
§ ***salignus*** 🏆H5	CBcs CDul CExl EPfP EUJe IDee SArc SLim WPGP WSHC WThu
'Spring Sunshine' (f)	CBcs
totara	CBrP LEdu WPGP
- 'Aureus'	CBcs LRHS
- 'Pendulus'	LRHS
'Young Rusty' (f)	CBcs LRHS MAsh SLim

Podophyllum (*Berberidaceae*)

aurantiocaule	CBct CExl EBee GGGa
- subsp. ***aurantiocaule***	GEdr
§ ***delavayi***	CBct CDTJ CExl GEdr SDir WSHC
difforme	CBct GEdr LEdu SDir
emodi	see *Sinopodophyllum hexandrum* var. *emodi*
- var. ***chinense***	see *Sinopodophyllum hexandrum* var. *chinense*
hexandrum	see *Sinopodophyllum hexandrum*
- var. ***chinense***	see *Sinopodophyllum hexandrum* var. *chinense*
'Kaleidoscope' (v)	CBct EBee ECtt ELan EUJe MBNS MHol NHpl NLar SPoG WCot
peltatum	CAby CBct CBro CHid CTal CWCL EBee EHrv EPfP EWld GBin GEdr GKev GMcL GPoy ILea LAma LEdu NLar NSti SMad SPhx WBor WCru WPGP WPnP
pleianthum	CAby CBct GCal GEdr WCru WPGP
- from Taiwan B&SWJ 282	WCru
- var. ***album*** new	GEdr
- short	WCru
veitchii	see *P. delavayi*
versipelle	LEdu WCru
- 'Spotty Dotty' PBR (v)	Widely available

Podranea (*Bignoniaceae*)

§ ***ricasoliana*** 🏆H1c	CBcs EShb SPoG WBor

Pogonatherum (*Poaceae*)

* ***distichum***	XBlo

Pogonia (*Orchidaceae*)

sp.	NDav

Pogostemon (*Lamiaceae*)

from An Veleniki Herb Farm, Pennsylvania	XAbr
§ ***cablin***	EOHP GPoy
patchouly	see *P. cablin*

Polanisia (*Capparaceae*)

dodecandra	SPhx

Polemonium ✿ (*Polemoniaceae*)

ambervicsii	see *P. pauciflorum* subsp. *hinckleyi*
'Apricot Beauty'	see *P. carneum* 'Apricot Delight'
archibaldiae 🏆H5	SRms WArt WSHC
'Blue Pearl'	CRos EBee ELan EPfP EWld GJos GMcL LRHS MHol MSCN NBro NGdn NLar NRHS SPer WFar WGwG WSpi
§ ***boreale***	GBin NPol SWvt WMoo
- 'Heavenly Habit'	CRos EAJP GJos LRHS NGdn NRHS
brandegeei misapplied	see *P. pauciflorum*
§ ***brandegeei*** Greene	GJos GKev
- subsp. ***mellitum***	see *P. brandegeei* Greene
§ ***caeruleum***	Widely available
- subsp. ***amygdalinum***	see *P. occidentale*
- - 'Album'	see *P. caeruleum* subsp. *caeruleum* f. *album*, *P. occidentale* white-flowered
- 'Azuro'	CRos LRHS NRHS
- 'Bambino Blue'	CBod CRos SWvt WHar
- BRISE D'ANJOU ('Blanjou' PBR) (v)	CMac CRos ECtt ELan EPfP EShb EWes GMcL IBoy IRob LRHS MAsh NGdn NPol NRHS SCob SMad SPer SWvt WWtn
- subsp. ***caeruleum***	GKev
§ - - f. ***album***	CBre CRos CWCL EBee ECha EHrv ELan EPfP EWTr GBin GKev GMcL LRHS MBNS MBel MHer MRav NBro NGBl SGbt SPer SPoG SRms WCAu WMoo WSpi
- - - 'White Pearl'	GWyn
- 'Days of Thunder' new	EBee

I	- f. ***dissectum***	NPol
	- 'Filigree Clouds'	NLar
	- 'Filigree Skies'	MWat NGdn NLar
§	- subsp. ***himalayanum***	CSpe WMoo
	- - CC 7325	EWld
	- 'Humile'	see *P.* 'Northern Lights'
	- 'Idylle'	IRob
	- 'Larch Cottage' (v)	NPol
	- 'Sky Blue'	MBel WRHF WWtn
	- 'Snow and Sapphires' (v)	CWGN ECtt MPnt NPer NPol SWvt
	- 'Southern Skies'	NPol
	- subsp. ***vulgare***	NPol
	- white-flowered	GJos IBoy MMuc
	carneum	CRos CTri EBee ECha LRHS NPol NRHS WMoo
§	- 'Apricot Delight'	GJos GMaP IRob MNHC MNrw NGdn NPol SGbt SRms WSpi WWtn
	cashmerianum	see *P. caeruleum* subsp. *himalayanum*
	chartaceum	LLHF
	'Churchills'	CBre NPol WSHC
	confertum	LLHF
	'Dawn Flight'	NPol
	'Eastbury Purple'	CElw NPol
	'Elworthy Amethyst'	CElw EBee NPol
	eximium	LLHF
	flavum	see *P. foliosissimum* var. *flavum*
	foliosissimum misapplied	see *P. archibaldiae*
	foliosissimum A. Gray	NPol
	- var. ***albiflorum***	see *P. foliosissimum* var. *alpinum*
§	- var. ***alpinum***	NPol
	- 'Cottage Cream'	LEdu NPol WCot WFar
§	- var. ***flavum***	NPol
	- var. ***foliosissimum***	NPol WSpi
	- 'Scottish Garden'	NPol
	- 'White Spirit'	NPol
	'Glebe Cottage Lilac'	CDor EBee NPol
	'Glebe Cottage Violet'	NPol
	'Hannah Billcliffe'	CElw ECtt EWes MBrN NChi NPol WFar
	'Heaven Scent'PBR	CBod EBee ECtt ESps IRob LRHS NDov NLar WCAu WGrn
	'Heavenly Blue'	IBoy
§	'Hopleys'	EBee GCal MNrw NChi
	× ***jacobaea***	EPPr EWes WCot
	'Katie Daley'	see *P.* 'Hopleys'
	'Lambrook Mauve'	Widely available
	'Mary Mottram'	NPol
	mellitum	see *P. brandegeei* Greene
	'North Tyne'	NChi NPol NWad
§	'Northern Lights'	Widely available
	'Norwell Mauve'	MNrw NPol
§	***occidentale***	NPol
§	- white-flowered **new**	NRHS
§	***pauciflorum***	ECtt ELan EWld IFro SBee WMoo
§	- subsp. ***hinckleyi***	GKev NPol NQui
§	- subsp. ***pauciflorum***	NPol
	- silver-leaved	see *P. pauciflorum* subsp. *pauciflorum*
	- 'Sulphur Trumpets'	SWvt WRHF
	- subsp. ***typicum***	see *P. pauciflorum* subsp. *pauciflorum*
	'Pink Beauty'	EBee ECtt ELan EPfP NGdn NPol WWtn
	pulchellum Salisb.	see *P. reptans*
	pulchellum Turcz.	see *P. caeruleum*
	pulcherrimum misapplied	see *P. boreale*
	- 'Tricolor'	see *P. boreale*
	pulcherrimum Hook.	NBro
	- subsp. ***pulcherrimum***	LLHF
§	***reptans***	CFis GPoy MHer NBro NPol SRms WMoo
	- 'Album'	see *P. reptans* 'Virginia White'
	- 'Blue Ice'	NPol
	- 'Firmament'	MAvo
	- 'Jacob's Gold' (v) **new**	ELan
*	- 'Sky Blue'	NBro
	- 'Stairway to Heaven'PBR (v)	Widely available
	- 'Touch of Class'PBR (v)	CWGN EWTr MAsh MHol NLar SPoG
§	- 'Virginia White'	CBre CElw EWes MAvo NChi NPol
	- 'White Pearl'	MHol
	'Ribby'	NPol
	× ***richardsonii*** misapplied	see *P.* 'Northern Lights'
	× ***richardsonii*** Graham	see *P. boreale*
	'Sapphire'	CBre CRos LRHS NRHS
	'Sonia's Bluebell'	CWCL ECtt EPPr EWTr EWes EWld MNrw MPie NDov NLar NPol NSti SBch
	'Sunnyside Storm'	NPol
	'Theddingworth'	NPol
	viscosum	GKev LLHF NPol SPlb
	- f. ***leucanthum***	NPol
	yezoense	NBre NPol
	- var. ***hidakanum***	NPol
	- - BRESSINGHAM PURPLE ('Polbress')	CAby CBod CRos CWCL EBee EHrv ELan ELon EPfP EWes GKev GMaP LRHS MAsh MBNS MBel NLar NPol NPri NRHS NSti NWad SGbt SPad SPer SPhm SPoG SRms WCAu
	- - 'Halfway to Paradise'	SCob
	- - 'Purple Rain'	Widely available

Polianthes (*Asparagaceae*)

	elongata	WCot
	rosei	see *Agave gracillima*
	tuberosa	CBcs CCCN ETMg GKev LCro LOPS SPer XLum
	- 'Cinderella'	GKev
	- 'Golden Harvest'	GKev
	- 'Pink Sapphire'	GKev
	- 'Sensation'	GKev SDeJ
	- 'Super Gold'	SDeJ
	- 'The Pearl' (d)	GKev LAma SDeJ WCot XLum
	- 'Yellow Baby'	GKev

Poliomintha (*Lamiaceae*)

	bustamanta	SPhx

Poliothyrsis (*Salicaceae*)

	sinensis	CBcs EBtc EPfP IArd

Pollia (*Commelinaceae*)

	japonica	EWes WCot

Polygala (*Polygalaceae*)

	'Africana'PBR	CPbh
	africana 'Nana'	LRHS
	calcarea Bulley's form	EPot
	- 'Lillet' 🏆H5	CRos EPot GEdr LLHF LRHS NRHS WAbe
	chamaebuxus 🏆H5	LLHF MAsh MGos NLar NSla SRms WThu
I	- ***alba***	LBee NLar WAbe
§	- var. ***grandiflora*** 🏆H5	CBcs EPfP EPot GAbr GEdr GKev GMcL LBee MAsh MGil MGos NHpl NSla SPlb SPoG SRot WAbe
	- 'Purpurea'	see *P. chamaebuxus* var. *grandiflora*

	- 'Rhodoptera'	see *P. chamaebuxus* var. *grandiflora*
§	× ***dalmaisiana*** ♀H2	CAbb CCCN CSpe CTsd CWGN ECre ELan GBin LRHS SEND WAbe WCFE
	'Dolomite'	GEdr
	myrtifolia ♀H2	CCCN CPbh GBin IDee LRHS MGos SAdn SPlb
	- BIBI PINK ('Polylap')	SAdn
	- 'Grandiflora'	see *P.* × *dalmaisiana*
	'Purple Passion'	CCCN LRHS
	virgata	CCCN ELan

Polygonatum ✿ (*Asparagaceae*)

	sp.	ESps SDir
	Og 94047	LEdu
	SBQE 310	LEdu
	acuminatifolium 'Ogon'	EBee
	altelobatum B&SWJ 286	WCru
	- B&SWJ 1886	WCru
	annamense B&SWJ 9752	WCru
	arisanense B&SWJ 271	WCru
	- B&SWJ 3839	WCru
§	***biflorum***	CBod CHid CPou CRos CWCL EBee ECtt ELan EPfP ETMg EWTr GBin GKev GMaP ILea LRHS MAvo MSCN NLar NRHS NWad SPoG SWvt WCru WFar WPnP XLum
	- dwarf	CRos LRHS NRHS
	canaliculatum	see *P. biflorum*
	cathcartii B&SWJ 2429	WCru
	- yellow-flowered B&SWJ 2412	WCru
	cirrhifolium	CCse EBee EPot GAbr GEdr LEdu LRHS MAvo MMoz MNrw NHpl NWad WCru WPGP
	- ARGS 320	EPPr
	- from China	WCru
	- red-flowered	NLar
	commutatum	see *P. biflorum*
	'Corsley'	CPou
	costatum B&SWJ 6599	WCru
	cryptanthum	EBee WCru
	curvistylum	CAby CAvo CBct CTal EHrv EPPr GEdr IFoB ILea IMou IRob LEdu MAvo NLar NRya WCru WSHC
	cyrtonema misapplied	see *Disporopsis pernyi*
	cyrtonema Hua	WCru
	- B&SWJ 271	LEdu MAvo
*	***desoulavyi*** var. ***yezoense*** B&SWJ 764	WCru
	falcatum misapplied	see *P. humile*
	falcatum A. Gray	CBot EBee NHpl NRya
	- B&SWJ 1077	EHrv WCru
	- B&SWJ 5054	WCru
	- 'Shikoku Silver'	LEdu WCru
	- 'Tiger Stripes' (v) **new**	GKev
	- 'Variegatum'	see *P. odoratum* var. *pluriflorum* 'Variegatum'
	'Falcon'	see *P. humile*
	filipes	EBee EHrv EPPr WCru
	fuscum	WCru
	geminiflorum	CBct LEdu WCru WFar
	- McB 2448	GEdr
	giganteum	see *P. biflorum*
	'Golden Gift'	CBct LPla
§	***graminifolium***	CAby CBct CPBP CTal EPPr WCru WThu
§	***hirtum***	CAby CBct CRos EPPr IFoB LEdu LRHS MMoz NRHS WCru
	- 'Robustum'	WCru
	hookeri	CAby CBct CExl CPBP CRos CSpe CTal EHrv EPPr EPot EWld GBin GEdr GKev GMaP GQue ITim LEdu LRHS NBid NHpl NLar NRHS NRya NSla NWad SPhx WAbe WCru WFar
§	***humile***	CBct CBot CTal CWCL EAJP EBee EHrv ELan EPPr EPfP EPot EWTr GCal GEdr GKev ITim LEdu MAvo MHer NGdn NLar NPnk SCob SWvt WBor WCru WHil WPGP WTor XLum
I	- 'Variegatum' (v)	CMac
§	× ***hybridum*** ♀H7	Widely available
	- 'Bere'	LEdu WPGP
	- 'Betberg'	CAvo CBct ECha EHrv ELon EPPr IFoB IMou LEdu MAvo WCot WFar
	- 'Flore Pleno' (d)	WHer
	- 'Nanum'	CBct CHid MRav WCot
	- 'Purple Katie'	MAvo
§	- 'Striatum' (v)	Widely available
	- 'Variegatum'	see *P.* × *hybridum* 'Striatum'
	- 'Wakehurst'	EHrv LEdu
	- 'Weihenstephan'	GCal IPot LEdu
	- 'Welsh Gold' (v)	CAvo EBee
	inflatum	GEdr WCru
	- B&SWJ 922	WCru
	involucratum	WCru
	- B&SWJ 4285	WCru
	japonicum	see *P. odoratum*
	kingianum yellow-flowered B&SWJ 6545	WCru
	- - B&SWJ 6562	WCru
	'Langthorn's Variegated' (v)	ELan
	lasianthum	SMHy WCru
	- B&SWJ 671	WCru
	latifolium	see *P. hirtum*
	maximowiczii	EPPr WCru WPGP
	mengtzense f. ***mengtzense*** HWJ 588	WCru
	- - HWJ 861	LEdu WCru
	- f. ***tonkinense*** B&SWJ 8246	LEdu WCru
	- - HWJ 551	WCru
	- - HWJ 567	WCru
	- - HWJ 573	CBct WCru
	'Multifide'	EBee
	multiflorum misapplied	see *P.* × *hybridum*
	multiflorum L.	CAby CAgr CBcs CElw CHab CMac CSBt CWCL ECha GAbr GBin GCal GKev LSun MHol MNHC MRav NGdn NLar SPlb SRms SWvt WCAu WCru WFar WHer WMoo XLum
	- CC 4572	WCot
	- 'Flore Pleno' (d)	WFar
	- ***giganteum*** hort.	see *P. biflorum*
	- 'Ramosissima'	LEdu SMHy WCru
	- var. ***ramosum***	LEdu
*	***nanum*** 'Variegatum' (v)	CBcs
	nodosum	WCru
§	***odoratum***	CAvo CBct CBro CTal CTsd EHrv EPfP GMaP LEdu NBid NLar NPnk NRya SCob WCru WHil
	- RBG 93-101	EBee
	- 'Byakko' (v)	GEdr
	- 'Dusky Bere' **new**	WPGP
§	- dwarf	CTal LEdu
	- 'Fireworks' (v) **new**	GKev
	- 'Flatmate'	LEdu WCru

	- 'Flore Pleno' (d)	CAby CAvo EHrv IRob LEdu MHer MMoz WCot WHoo
	- 'Georgia' new	WPGP
	- 'Grace Barker'	see *P.* × *hybridum* 'Striatum'
	- 'Koryu'	GEdr
	- 'Leigong Stripe'	LEdu
§	- var. ***pluriflorum*** 'Variegatum' (v)	Widely available
	- 'Red Stem'	CMea CTal EHrv LEdu MAvo SMHy WCru
	- 'Silver Wings' (v)	CBct ECha EHrv IPot LEdu NLar WFar
	- var. ***thunbergii***	WCru
	- - 'Variegatum' (v)	CWld IRob
	- 'Ussuriland'	EBee EPPr GCal LEdu MAvo
	- 'Ussuriland Roundleaf'	EBee GCal LEdu MAvo
	officinale	see *P. odoratum*
	oppositifolium B&SWJ 2537	WCru
§	***orientale***	CBct GKev
	pluriflorum	see *P. graminifolium*
	polyanthemum	see *P. orientale*
	prattii	CTal EBee GKev ILea WCru
	- CLD 325	LEdu
	pubescens	CBct EHrv LEdu WCru WThu
	pumilum	see *P. odoratum* dwarf
	punctatum ambig.	CBct GEdr LEdu NBid WPGP
	punctatum Royle ex Kunth B&SWJ 2395	CBct WCru
	racemosum	CBct IMou
	roseum	EPPr GKev LLHF MAvo MMoz WCru
	sewerzowii	EPPr
	sibiricum	CBct GEdr WCru WFar
	- DJHC 600	EBee LEdu MAvo WPGP
	singalilense	WCru
	stenanthum B&SWJ 5727	LEdu WCru
	- B&SWJ 11425	WCru
	stenophyllum	IMou WCru
	stewartianum	EBee EPPr ILea NRya
	tessellatum PAB 8336	LEdu
	verticillatum	CBct CBro CRos CTal EBee ECha EPPr EPfP GEdr IFoB LEdu LRHS MNrw MRav NRHS SMad WCru WFar WPGP WWtn
	- B&SWJ 2147	WCru
	- CLD 1308	EPPr
	- PAB 2455	LEdu
	- 'Giant One'	IMou XEll
	- 'Himalayan Giant'	CHid EPPr MAvo WPnP
	- 'Krynica'	LEdu WPGP
*	- 'Roseum'	CAvo
	- 'Rubrum'	CAby CBct CRos EBee EHrv EPPr GEdr ILea LEdu LRHS MAvo NBid NChi NLar NPnk NRHS WCot WCru WHoo
	- 'Serbian Dwarf'	CBct CHid CTal GEdr LEdu WPGP
	aff. ***verticillatum***	CSpe IFoB
	yunnanense	CBct LEdu WPGP
	zanlanscianense	CBct EBee EHrv LEdu WCru

Polygonum (*Polygonaceae*)

	affine	see *Persicaria affinis*
	amplexicaule	see *Persicaria amplexicaulis*
	aubertii	see *Fallopia baldschuanica*
	baldschuanicum	see *Fallopia baldschuanica*
	bistorta	see *Persicaria bistorta*
	capitatum	see *Persicaria capitata*
	compactum	see *Fallopia japonica* var. *compacta*
	equisetiforme misapplied	see *P. scoparium*
	filiforme	see *Persicaria virginiana*
	forrestii	EBee GKev
	molle	see *Persicaria mollis*
	multiflorum	see *Fallopia multiflora*
	odoratum	see *Persicaria odorata*
	polystachyum	see *Persicaria wallichii*
	runciforme	see *Persicaria runcinata*
§	***scoparium***	EHoe EPPr EWes SDys SVen WFar WOld XLum
	sericeum new	MAvo
	tinctorium	see *Persicaria tinctoria*
	vacciniifolium	see *Persicaria vacciniifolia*
	weyrichii	see *Persicaria weyrichii*

Polylepis (*Rosaceae*)

	australis	IDee LEdu SAko
	- tall	WPGP

Polymnia (*Asteraceae*)

	sonchifolia 'Red China' new	WPGP

Polypodiodes (*Polypodiaceae*)

	formosana new	WCot

Polypodium ✿ (*Polypodiaceae*)

	aureum	see *Phlebodium aureum*
	australe	see *P. cambricum*
§	***cambricum***	EFer WCot WFib
	- GG 20131	SMHy
	- 'Barrowii'	WAbe WFib WGwG
	- 'Bob's Choice'	WCot
I	- 'Cambricum' ♀H7	GCal WAbe
	- 'Conwy'	WFib
	- 'Cristatum'	WFib
	- (Cristatum Group) 'Grandiceps Fox' ♀H7	MRav WFib
	- 'Hornet'	WFib
	- 'Macrostachyon'	GBin NBid WFib
	- 'Oakleyae'	EWld MMoz SMHy WCot
	- 'Prestonii'	WCot WFib
	- Pulcherrimum Group	GAbr SDys WAbe
	- - 'Pulcherrimum Addison'	EBee GBin LEdu WCot WFib WPGP
	- - 'Pulchritudine'	LLWG WCot
	- 'Richard Kayse' ♀H7	EShb EWes MMoz SMHy WAbe WCot WFib WPGP
	- Semilacerum Group	EFer
	- - 'Carew Lane'	WFib
	- - 'Falcatum O'Kelly'	WCot
	- - 'Robustum'	WFib
	- 'Whilharris' ♀H7	SMHy WAbe
I	× ***coughlinii*** bifid	WFib
	formosanum	SPlb
	glycyrrhiza	GPoy SMHy WFib
	- bifid	see *P.* × *coughlinii* bifid
	- 'Lawrence Crocker'	WCot
	- 'Longicaudatum' ♀H7	EFer EShb WCot WFib
	- 'Malahatense' (sterile)	EBee WCot WPGP
	guttatum new	SPlb
	interjectum	EFer EShb MMoz MRav WCot
	- 'Glomeratum Mullins'	WFib
	macaronesicum	WCot
	× ***mantoniae***	WFib
	- 'Bifidograndiceps'	NBid WFib
	- 'Cornubiense' ♀H7	EShb EWld MMoz NBid SMHy
	pseudoaureum 'Virginia Blue' new	CRos NRHS
	scouleri	CBdn CFil CRos EBee EFer EShb LRHS MRav NBro NRHS WCot WPGP

	vulgare	Widely available
	- 'Bifidocristatum'	CAby CBdn CWCL ELon EPed EPfP GBin GCal GEdr LLWG MGos MRav NHim NLar SEND WCot WMoo
	- 'Bifidomulticeps'	WCot
*	- 'Congestum Cristatum'	SRms
	- 'Cornubiense Grandiceps'	GCal SRms
*	- 'Cornubiense Multifidum'	WCot
	- 'Elegantissimum'	NBid WFib
	- 'Parsley'	WCot
	- 'Trichomanoides Backhouse'	GCal WAbe WFib
	'Whitley Giant'	CAby CBod EBee ECtt EUJe GBin GEdr GQue ITim LEdu LLWG LPla LSun MMuc MPie NBid NCou SEND SMad WArt WCot

Polypompholyx see *Utricularia*

Polyspora (*Theaceae*)

§	***axillaris***	CBcs CCCN CHll EBee
	- CWJ 12363	WCru
	longicarpa DJHV 06041	WCru
	- WWJ 11604	WCru
	speciosa B&SWJ 11708 from Vietnam	WCru
	- B&SWJ 11750	WCru WSHC
	- WWJ 11934	WCru

Polystichum ✿ (*Dryopteridaceae*)

	acrostichoides	CDTJ EBee ERod GBin LEdu NBro NLar WCot WPGP XLum
	aculeatum ♀H7	CBod CKel CRos ECha EFer ELan ERod EShb GBin GMaP GMcL LCro LEdu LRHS MGos MMuc NBid NEgg NLar NRHS SCob SPoG SRms SWvt WFib WMoo XLum
I	- Densum Group	EFer GMcL
	- 'Portia'	WFib
	bissectum	CExl
	braunii	CBcs CBdn CDor CMac CRos CWCL EPfP GMaP LRHS MMoz NBid NBro NLar NRHS SPoG WFib WPnP XLum
	dracomontanum	CBdn
	× ***dycei*** ♀H6	CBdn CRos EBee LRHS NLos NRHS
	falcatum	see *Cyrtomium falcatum*
	falcinellum	EBee
	fortunei	see *Cyrtomium fortunei*
	interjectum	MRav
	makinoi	CBdn CCCN CRos GBin LLWG LRHS NBid NBro NEgg SPlb WCot WFib WMoo
	mayebarae	CBdn EBee
	monticola new	CBdn
	munitum ♀H7	Widely available
	neolobatum	CBdn EBee LLHF WFib
	- BWJ 8182	WCru
	nepalense	NLos
	polyblepharum ♀H7	Widely available
	- 'Jade'	CMac EBee LRHS
	proliferum misapplied	see *P. setiferum* Acutilobum Group
	proliferum ambig.	GMcL
	proliferum (R. Br.) C. Presl	LBuc SBig WFib WPGP
*	- ***plumosum***	SWvt
	rigens	CBdn CBod CRos CWCL EFer EMOT EPau LRHS LSou NBro NLar NRHS SRms SRot WFib
	setiferum ♀H7	Widely available
§	- Acutilobum Group	CBod CRos ECha EHrv EMOT EUJe GMaP IBoy LLWG LRHS NLos NRHS SCob SPad SPer SRms WMoo WPGP XLum
	- Congestum Group	CBdn CDor CKel EHrv ELon EMOT EUJe GBin MMoz NBro NEgg NLar SPer SRms WFib
	- - 'Congestum'	CRos CWCL ELan EMOT EPPr EPfP EPot ERod GEdr LRHS MRav NEgg NGdn NRHS SPad SPoG SPtp WMoo XLum
	- 'Cristatopinnulum'	CFil WPGP
	- Cristatum Group	EHrv SRms
	- (Decompositum Group) 'Proliferum'	CWCL EBee
	- Divisilobum Group ♀H7	CBdn EFer ELan MCot MGos MMoz SRms WAbe WFar WFib WHoo WPGP
	- - 'Caernarfon'	CFil
	- - 'Dahlem'	CFil CKel CRos EBee ECha ECtt EFer ELan ELon EMOT EPfP EUJe GMaP LRHS LSRN MMoz NBid NEgg NRHS SPer WFib WMoo WPtf XLum
	- - 'Divisilobum Densum' ♀H7	EHrv EPfP MRav
	- - 'Divisilobum Grandiceps'	CFil
	- - 'Divisilobum Iveryanum' ♀H7	CFil EFer SRms WFib
	- - 'Divisilobum Laxum'	CFil EBee
§	- - 'Divisilobum Wollaston'	CBdn CDTJ CFil CKel CRos CTal CWCL ECtt ELon LRHS MGos MMoz MRav NBid NHim NLar NRHS WCot WMoo
	- - 'Herrenhausen'	Widely available
	- - 'Madame Patti'	CFil EBee MMoz
	- - 'Mrs Goffey'	CFil
	- - 'Proliferum'	EUJe
	- Foliosum Group	EFer
	- 'Gabeljurgel'	CFil
	- 'Gracile'	MRav
	- 'Grandiceps'	EFer
	- 'Grandiceps Jentsch'	CFil
	- 'Hamlet'	WFib
	- 'Helena'	WFib
	- 'Hirondelle'	SRms
	- Lineare Group	WFib
	- Multilobum Group	SRms WFib
	- 'Nantes'	CFil
	- 'Othello'	CFil WFib
	- Perserratum Group	NBid WFib
	- 'Plumo-Densum'	see *P. setiferum* Plumosomultilobum Group
	- 'Plumosodensum'	see *P. setiferum* Plumosomultilobum Group
	- Plumosodivisilobum Group	EBee ECha NBid NBro SMHy WAbe WFib WRHF
	- - 'Baldwinii'	WFib
	- - 'Bland'	WFib
§	- Plumosomultilobum Group	CDor CFil CKel CWCL EAJP EBee EPfP EUJe GEdr LCro LPla MCot MGos MMoz NLar SMad WCot WFib WHoo WMoo
I	- - 'Plumosomultilobum Densum'	CAby CBdn CBod CRos ECtt EPed EUJe LLWG LRHS LSun MBel NHim NRHS SCob WCot WFar
	- Plumosum Group	CMac CSpe CTal EFer ELon EPfP LLWG MJak SArc SRot

- - dwarf	CSBt
* - ***plumosum grande*** 'Moly'	SRms
- Proliferum Group	see *P. setiferum* Acutilobum Group
- 'Proliferum Wollaston'	see *P. setiferum* (Divisilobum Group) 'Divisilobum Wollaston'
- 'Pulcherrimum Bevis' 🏆H6	CAby CBdn CFil CSpe EBee ELon ITim MAvo MCot MMuc MPie SArc SEND SWvt WFib WPGP
- 'Seestern'	CFil
- 'Smith's Cruciate'	CFil MRav WFib
- 'Wakeleyanum'	EFer SRms
squarrosum	CBdn
tsussimense 🏆H6	Widely available
- 'K Rex' **new**	CRos NRHS
vestitum	MMoz
xiphophyllum	CBdn WPGP

Polyxena (*Asparagaceae*)

corymbosa	see *Lachenalia corymbosa*
longituba	see *Lachenalia longituba*
pygmaea	see *Lachenalia pygmaea*

Pomaderris (*Rhamnaceae*)

apetala	CExl
elliptica	CExl

pomegranate see *Punica granatum*

Poncirus see *Citrus*

Ponerorchis (*Orchidaceae*)

graminifolia	LAma

Pontederia (*Pontederiaceae*)

cordata 🏆H5	CBen CWat EPfP EWat LCro LOPS MSKA MWts NPer SPlb WMAq WPnP WWtn XLum
- f. ***albiflora***	CWat EPfP EWat LLWG MWts XLum
- 'Blue Spires'	MSKA
§ - var. ***lancifolia***	CBen EWat LLWG MNrw MSKA MWts NPer WWtn
- pink-flowered	LLWG
- 'Sunsplash' (v) **new**	LLWG
dilatata	see *Monochoria hastata*
lanceolata	see *P. cordata* var. *lancifolia*

Populus ✿ (*Salicaceae*)

× ***acuminata***	WMou
alba	CBcs CCVT CDul CLnd CMac CPer CTho CTri ECrN EMOT EPfP ESps LBuc LPra MMuc SCob SEWo SGol SPer WMou WTSh
- 'Bolleana'	see *P. alba* 'Pyramidalis'
§ - 'Pyramidalis'	WMou
§ - 'Raket'	CCVT CLnd CTho ECrN ELan SPer
- 'Richardii'	EBtc EGFP WCot WMou
- ROCKET	see *P. alba* 'Raket'
§ 'Balsam Spire' (f)	CDul CPer CTho WMou
§ ***balsamifera***	CCVT CLnd CSBt CTri ECrN GAbr LPra SPer WCot
- 'Vita Sackville West'	MBlu
× ***canadensis***	EWld
§ - 'Aurea' 🏆H6	CDul CTho ECrN SPer WMou
- 'Aurea' × (× ***jackii*** 'Aurora')	ELan
- 'Columbia'	WMou
- 'Eugenei' (m)	WMou
- 'Robusta' (m)	CCVT CDul CLnd CTri WMou
- 'Serotina' (m)	WMou
× ***canescens***	CLnd LPra
deltoides 'Fuego'	SGol
- 'Purple Tower'PBR	CBcs CEnd CLnd EBee ELan EPfP MBlu MMuc NOra SLim WHar
× ***generosa*** 'Beaupré'	WMou
glauca	WPGP
- KR 3993	WPGP
- MF 20088 **new**	WPGP
× ***jackii*** 'Aurora' (f/v)	CBcs CCVT CDul CMac CSBt CTsd GMcL MGos MMuc NPri SPer WFar WHar WMou
lasiocarpa	CBcs CExl CLnd CMCN CTho EPfP IArd IDee MBlu SGol SMad WMou WPGP
- (m/f)	WPGP
maximowiczii	WMou
nigra	CHab CPer CTho CTri CTsd ESps LPra SCob WSFF
- (f)	ECrN MMuc
- (m)	MMuc
- subsp. ***betulifolia***	CCVT CDul CHab CLnd WMou
- - (f)	EBtc WMou
- - (m)	EBtc WMou
§ - 'Italica' (m) 🏆H6	CCVT CDul CLnd CMac CPer CSBt CTho CTri ECrN ELan EMOT ESps LBuc LPra MGos MMuc SEWo SPer WMou
- 'Pyramidalis'	see *P. nigra* 'Italica'
purdomii	WPGP
'Serotina Aurea'	see *P.* × *canadensis* 'Aurea'
simonii 'Fastigiata'	WMou
szechuanica	WMou
§ - var. ***tibetica***	WMou
tacamahaca	see *P. balsamifera*
'Tacatricho 32'	see *P.* 'Balsam Spire'
tomentosa	WMou
tremula	CCVT CDul CFGn CHab CLnd CMac CPer CTho CTri ECrN ELan ESps GAbr LBuc LMaj LPra MMuc SCob SEWo SPer WHar WMou WSFF WTSh
§ - 'Erecta' 🏆H7	CDul CEnd CTho EMOT MBlu MMuc SBig
- 'Fastigiata'	see *P. tremula* 'Erecta'
- 'Pendula' (m)	CEnd CTho ECrN
tremuloides **new**	CMCN
trichocarpa	CDul SPer
- 'Fritzi Pauley' (f)	CDul CTho WMou
violascens	see *P. szechuanica* var. *tibetica*
× ***wilsocarpa*** 'Beloni'	WPGP
wilsonii	WPGP
yunnanensis	WMou

Portulaca (*Portulacaceae*)

grandiflora	SVic
- HAPPY TRAILS TROPICAL MIXED **new**	ETMg
oleracea	ENfk SVic WTre XAbr
- var. ***aurea***	MNHC

Potamogeton (*Potamogetonaceae*)

crispus	CWat LLWG MSKA WMAq WSFF
malainus	LLWG
natans	LLWG MSKA WSFF XLum
perfoliatus **new**	LLWG
schweinfurthii	XBlo

potato see AGM Vegetables Section

Potentilla ✿ (*Rosaceae*)

	alba	CTri ECha ELan ESps GCal MRav NChi NWad SPer WSHC
	alchemilloides	CMac
	ambigua	see *P. cuneata*
	ancistrifolia var. ***dickinsii***	GEdr
	andicola	EBee
	anserina	CAgr EBWF MHer NMir WHer XLum
	anserinoides	WMoo
	arbuscula misapplied	see *P. fruticosa* 'Elizabeth'
	- 'Beesii'	see *P. fruticosa* 'Beesii'
	'Arc-en-ciel'	Widely available
	argentea	EBWF SPlb WFar XLum
	arguta	EBee
	argyrophylla	see *P. atrosanguinea* var. *argyrophylla*
	atrosanguinea	Widely available
§	- var. ***argyrophylla***	CDor CSam CWCL EBee ECha ELan EPfP GCal GKev GPSL ITim MMuc MRav NBro NChi NLar SMad SRms WMoo XLum
	- - 'Golden Starlit'	CBod EDAr IBoy SVic
§	- - 'Scarlet Starlit'	CAby CBod CDor EDAr EPfP IBoy LRHS LSun NCou NEoE NRHS SVic
	- 'Fireball' (d)	EPfP GJos
	- var. ***leucochroa***	see *P. atrosanguinea* var. *argyrophylla*
*	- 'Sundermannii'	GJos LLHF NWad SBrt
	aurea	CPla ECtt EPfP GBin
	- 'Aurantiaca'	NLar
§	- 'Goldklumpen'	ECtt MRav NEoE
	- 'Plena' (d)	NRya
	'Blazeaway'	CRos ECtt GCal LRHS MArl MAvo MBNS NEoE NGdn NRHS SRms WCot
	calabra	ECha EWes
	caulescens	SBrt
§	***cinerea***	CTri LLHF
§	***crantzii***	CMea SRms
	- 'Nana'	see *P. crantzii* 'Pygmaea'
§	- 'Pygmaea'	ECtt
§	***cuneata*** ♀H5	GKev IRob
	davurica 'Abbotswood'	see *P. fruticosa* 'Abbotswood'
	dombeyi	IMou
	'Emilie' (d)	CSpe CWCL ECtt GCal GMcL GWyn IPot IRob MBNS MBel MCot MNrw NEoE NLar SWvt WBor WCot
§	***erecta***	EBWF GPoy MNHC
	eriocarpa	CPBP EPot GCrg NRHS NSla WAbe
	'Esta Ann'	CAby CMac ECtt LRHS MArl MBNS NLar NRHS SRGP
	'Etna'	CRos CWCL ECtt ELan ELon GCal LRHS MNrw NLar NRHS WCAu WHrl WMoo WPtf
	'Everest'	see *P. fruticosa* 'Mount Everest'
	'Fireflame'	NLar WMoo
	fissa	MNrw NLar SPhx
	'Flambeau' (d)	CWCL ECtt ELon EShb GKin ILea IPot LRHS MArl MAvo MRav MSpe NChi NGdn NLar NRHS NSti WCAu WMoo XEll
	'Flamboyant' (d) **new**	EBee IPot
	'Flamenco'	CRos CSam CTri ECtt ELon IPot IRob LRHS MArl MAvo MBNS MNrw MRav NRHS SMHy WFar WMoo
	fragariiformis	see *P. megalantha*
	fruticosa	EBWF ESps LBuc
§	- 'Abbotswood' ♀H7	Widely available
	- 'Annette'	NEoE NLar
	- var. ***arbuscula*** hort.	see *P. fruticosa* 'Elizabeth'
	- 'Argentea Nana'	see *P. fruticosa* 'Beesii'
	- 'Baby Bethan'PBR (d)	LLHF
§	- 'Beesii'	CRos EPfP LRHS MAsh NRHS
	- 'Bewerley Surprise'	WFar
	- 'Bo-Peep'	CEnd CRos EBee LRHS LSRN NRHS
	- 'Chelsea Star' ♀H7	CMac CRos LRHS LSRN MAsh NRHS SPoG
	- 'Clotted Cream'	SGbt
	- var. ***dahurica*** 'Hersii'	see *P. fruticosa* 'Snowflake'
	- DANNY BOY ('Lissdan'PBR)	CRos EMil LCro LOPS LRHS MAsh NEoE NRHS SLon SPoG
	- 'Daphne'	NWad
	- 'Dart's Golddigger'	CTri
	- 'Daydawn'	CBcs CBod CMac CRos CTri ELan EPfP ESps GMcL LRHS MAsh MMuc MRav MSwo NEgg NLar NRHS NWad SGol SLim SPer SRms SWvt WMoo
	- 'Farreri'	see *P. fruticosa* 'Gold Drop'
	- GLAMOUR GIRL ('Km01'PBR) **new**	SPoG
	- 'Glenroy Pinkie'	MRav
§	- 'Gold Drop'	CMac
	- 'Golden Dwarf'	WMoo
	- 'Goldfinger'	CAco CAgr CBod CChe CRos CSBt EMOT EPfP ESps GMcL IBoy LRHS MAsh MGos MJak MMuc MRav MSwo NEgg NRHS SCob SCoo SLim SPer SPlb SPoG WMoo XSen
	- GOLDKUGEL	see *P. fruticosa* 'Gold Drop'
	- 'Goldstar'	CRos ESps IArd LRHS MMuc NPri NRHS SCob SEND SLim SLon SRms WFar
	- 'Goldteppich'	LBuc
	- 'Grace Darling'	ELan EPfP EWes NEgg SRGP SWvt WMoo WRHF
	- 'Groneland' ♀H7	CRos ELan EPfP LRHS MAsh NRHS SCoo SPoG
	- 'Hopleys Orange' ♀H7	CRos CSBt ELon EPfP ESps EWes LRHS NPri NRHS SCob SGbt SGol SRms WFar WHlf WMoo
	- 'Hurstbourne'	NEoE
	- 'Jackman's Variety' ♀H7	EPfP IBoy LRHS MAsh SCob SRms
	- 'Katherine Dykes'	CDul CRos CTri EBee EPfP ESps GKin GMcL LRHS LSRN MAsh NEgg NRHS SCob SCoo SGbt SLim SPer SRms WAvo WFar WMoo
	- 'King Cup' ♀H7	CRos EPfP LRHS MAsh
§	- 'Klondike'	CBcs CSBt
	- 'Kobold'	CRos GMcL LRHS NLar
	- 'Lemon and Lime'	see *P. fruticosa* 'Limelight'
§	- 'Limelight' ♀H7	CRos CSBt EBee EPfP GKin LRHS MAsh MRav MSwo NEoE NRHS NWad SRms WAvo
	- 'Lovely Pink'	see *P. fruticosa* 'Pink Beauty'
§	- 'Maanelys'	CSBt SPer WMoo
	- 'Macpenny's Cream'	CMac SRms
§	- 'Manchu'	CMac MRav SCob SPer SRms WCFE
	- MANGO TANGO ('Uman'PBR)	CRos CSBt EMOT EPfP ETMg LRHS LSRN MAsh NEoE NLar NRHS SGol SPoG WFar
§	- MARIAN RED ROBIN ('Marrob'PBR) ♀H7	ELan EPfP GKin GMcL IBoy LCro LOPS LRHS MAsh MRav MSwo NPri NRHS SCoo SLim SLon SPoG SRms SWvt

- 'McKay's White'	NLar
- 'Medicine Wheel Mountain' 𝕐H7	CRos EBee ELan EWes IArd LRHS MAsh MRav MTin NLar NRHS NWad SCob SCoo SGol SLim SPer SPoG
- MOONLIGHT	see *P. fruticosa* 'Maanelys'
§ - 'Mount Everest'	CTri GMcL MMuc SLon
- 'Nana Argentea'	see *P. fruticosa* 'Beesii'
- 'New Dawn'	CBcs EMOT GKin MAsh
- 'Orangeade'	CRos EPfP LRHS MAsh NLar SCoo SPoG
* - 'Peachy Proud'	NEoE
§ - 'Pink Beauty'^{PBR} 𝕐H7	Widely available
- PINK PARADISE ('Kupinpa'^{PBR})	ETMg
- 'Pink Pearl'	WMoo
- 'Pink Queen'	NLar WHlf
- 'Pink Whisper'	NEoE SRms
- 'Pretty Polly'	ELan ESps LRHS MSwo NLar NWad WFar WMoo
- 'Primrose Beauty' 𝕐H7	Widely available
§ - PRINCESS ('Blink')	CBcs EBee ELan EPfP ESps GMcL LRHS MAsh MJak MRav NRHS SCob SCoo SGol SLim SRms WFar WMoo
- var. ***pumila***	GKev WAbe
- 'Red Ace'	Widely available
- 'Red Lady'^{PBR}	CRos ELan EMOT EPfP LRHS MAsh NEoE NRHS SCob SPoG WMoo
- RED ROBIN	see *P. fruticosa* MARIAN RED ROBIN
- 'Red Surprise'	WFar
- Rhodocalyx Group	GCal
- 'Royal Flush'	NWad
- 'Snowbird'	NEoE SLim WFar
§ - 'Snowflake'	CBcs
- 'Sommerflor' 𝕐H7	CAco EPfP LRHS MAsh NRHS
- 'Sophie's Blush'	MRav
§ - (Sulphurascens Group) 'Elizabeth'	CBcs CDul CMac CRos ELan EPfP ESps LRHS LSRN MGos MJak MSwo SCob SGol SLim SPer SRms SWvt WCFE WFar WHar WHlf WMoo
- - 'Longacre Variety'	CMac CTri IArd MSwo NLar
- 'Sunset'	CBcs CMac GKin LSRN MJak SCob SCoo SLim SRms WFar WMoo
- 'Tangerine'	CBcs CDul CMac CRos CTri ECrN ELan ELon EPfP ESps GMcL LRHS MAsh MGos MMuc MRav MSwo NRHS SCob SLim SPer SPlb SRms SWvt WFar WHar WMoo
- 'Tilford Cream'	CRos CSBt CTri EBee ECrN ELan EPfP ESps GKin IBoy LRHS LSRN MJak MRav MSwo NEgg NRHS SCob SGbt SGol SLim SPer SRms WCFE WFar WMoo
- 'Tom Conway'	CMac SRms
- var. ***veitchii***	CSBt
- 'Vilmoriniana'	CMac CTri ELan EPfP ESps GCal LRHS MAsh MRav NLar SPer SPoG SWvt WKif WSpi
- 'Whirligig'	CMac
- 'White Lady'^{PBR}	NEoE
- 'William Purdom'	WAvo WHar
- 'Yellow Bird' 𝕐H7	CRos LRHS MAsh
'Gibson's Scarlet' 𝕐H7	Widely available
§ ***glandulosa*** subsp. ***nevadensis***	MAsh
'Gloire de Nancy' (d)	EBee MAvo MRav NChi NLar
'Gold Clogs'	see *P. aurea* 'Goldklumpen'
'Herzblut'	NLar
hippiana	EBee

× ***hopwoodiana***	CMea CSpe CWCL EBee ECha ECtt ELan EPPr GCal GMaP ILea IRob MBel MNrw MRav NChi NDov NLar SCob SPer WCAu WFar WMoo WPtf
× ***hybrida*** 'Jean Jabber'	EBee GLog MRav NEoE NLar WFar
'Jack Elliot'	NEoE
kurdica	GJos XLum
'Lemon Me'	IRob
'Light My Fire'	EBee ECtt LLHF MBNS MNrw
'Mandshurica'	see *P. fruticosa* 'Manchu'
§ ***megalantha***	CBcs CBro CRos EAJP ECtt EDAr ELan EPfP EPri GCal GQue LEdu LRHS MBNS MNrw MRav NBro NRHS SGbt SPer SRms SRot WMoo XLum
- 'Gold Sovereign'	EBee EPfP LRHS NEoE
'Melton Fire'	EPfP GJos GKin GPSL MNrw WHrl WMoo WPnP
micrantha 'Purple Haze'	LEdu
- 'Purple Heart'	WPGP
'Monarch's Velvet'	see *P. thurberi* 'Monarch's Velvet'
'Monsieur Rouillard' (d)	CElw CMac CSam CSpe ECtt IPot LRHS MArl MCot MNrw MPie MRav NGdn NLar NRHS WHoo
'Mont d'Or'	EBee MRav NLar
nepalensis	CRos EHoe LRHS NBro NChi NRHS XLum
- 'Helen Jane'	CDor CPla GBin GJos GQue IBoy LEdu MHer NLar NWad SMad SPad WArt WFar WHrl WKif WMoo WPtf WWFP
§ - 'Miss Willmott'	Widely available
- 'Ron McBeath'	CDor CKno CWCL ECtt ELan EPfP GAbr GBin GJos ILea ITim MAvo MRav MSCN NLar NSti SGol SPer SRGP SRkn SWvt WGwG WHoo WMoo WPtf
- 'Roxana'	ELan GJos MRav NBro SRGP WMoo
- 'Shogran'	GJos LRHS NChi NLar NRHS WPtf
§ ***neumanniana***	CPBP MAsh NPoe
- 'Goldrausch'	IMou MRav XLum
§ - 'Nana'	ECtt EPot GCrg NRya NWad SPlb SRms WHoo WMoo XLum
nevadensis	see *P. glandulosa* subsp. *nevadensis*
nitida	EPot GKev MAsh WAbe
- 'Rubra'	CMea EDAr GCrg GEdr WAbe
palustris	CWat EBWF EBee EWat LLWG MWts NLar WMoo XLum
parvifolia 'Klondike'	see *P. fruticosa* 'Klondike'
pedata	NChi XLum
peduncularis CC 5717	GKev
'Pink Panther'	see *P. fruticosa* PRINCESS
aff. ***polyphylla*** CHP&W 314	GKev
porphyrantha	CPla GEdr LLHF SBrt
pulvinaris	EPot
recta	EBWF GJos SRms XLum
- 'Alba'	GMaP NEgg
- 'Citrina'	see *P. recta* var. ***sulphurea***
- 'Macrantha'	see *P. recta* 'Warrenii'
§ - var. ***sulphurea***	CAby CMea EAJP GAbr GJos GWyn MCot MNrw NLar NSti NWad SPhx SRkn WBrk WCAu WHal WHoo WHrl WMoo XLum
§ - 'Warrenii'	CSBt EPfP GJos GMaP IRob LRHS MRav NEgg NRHS SHar SPer SRms WHal WHar WHrl WMoo XLum
reptans	EBWF
'Roxanne' (d)	LRHS MHer

	rupestris	CMea EBWF ECha EPPr GCal IRob LSun MHer NSti WCAu WFar WHal WMoo
	× ***russelliana***	LRHS NRHS
	'Scarlet Starlet'	see *P. atrosanguinea* var. *argyrophylla* 'Scarlet Starlit'
	speciosa	EWes WMoo
	sterilis	CHid WHer WSFF
*	***sundermanii***	WHrl
	tabernaemontani	see *P. neumanniana*
	thurberi	CMea LRHS MCot NLar NRHS SPhx WHrl WMoo XLum
§	– 'Monarch's Velvet'	Widely available
	tommasiniana	see *P. cinerea*
	× ***tonguei*** 🏆H5	Widely available
	tormentilla	see *P. erecta*
	tridentata	see *Sibbaldiopsis tridentata*
	'Twinkling Star'	EBee IRob MSCN NEoE WPtf
	verna misapplied	see *P. neumanniana*
	– 'Pygmaea'	see *P. neumanniana* 'Nana'
	'Versicolor Plena' (d)	NLar
	villosa	see *P. crantzii*
	'Vogue' new	MBNS
	'Volcan'	CAby CWCL ECtt EWes MAvo NChi WHal
	'White Queen'	GLog MRav SHar SRms
	'William Rollisson' 🏆H6	Widely available
	willmottiae	see *P. nepalensis* 'Miss Willmott'
	'Yellow Queen'	CMac CTri GKin GMaP IRob LRHS MNrw MRav NLar NRHS SBod SPer SRms WCAu

Poterium see *Sanguisorba*

	sanguisorba	see *Sanguisorba minor*

Pratia (*Campanulaceae*)

§	***angulata*** 'Treadwellii'	ECha ECtt EWTr GEdr SPlb SRms WFar WHal
	montana	see *Lobelia montana*
§	***pedunculata***	CTri ECha ECtt EDAr ELan EPfP EWTr LLWG LSun NHpl SPlb SRms SRot WMoo WPtf
I	– 'Alba'	CBod EWes NHpl SRms WFar
	– 'County Park'	CExl CMea CSpe CTri ECha ECtt EDAr ELan ELon EWTr GAbr GWyn LLWG LRHS NHpl SPlb SPoG SRms SRot WBor WMoo XLum
	– 'White Stars'	LLWG

Prenanthes (*Asteraceae*)

§	***alba***	SBrt

Preslia see *Mentha*

Primula ✿ (*Primulaceae*)

	KRW 56/380	EPot
	(Cy)	GKev
	(Si)	MAsh
	from Kath Dryden new	GKev
	acaulis	see *P. vulgaris*
	'Adrian Jones' (Au)	EPot ITim NWad
	agleniana var. ***alba***	GKev
	'Alan Robb' (Pr/Prim/d)	ECtt NGdn
	'Alexina' (*allionii* hybrid) (Au)	MFie
§	***allionii*** (Au)	NSum WAbe
	– HNG 12	ITim
	– 'Agnes' (Au)	ITim MFie
	– 'Aire Waves'	see *P.* × *loiseleurii* 'Aire Waves'
	– var. ***alba*** (Au)	MFie
	– 'Allen Charm' (Au)	ITim
	– 'Allen Moonbeam' (Au)	GAbr GAgs ITim MFie
	– 'Allen Queen' (Au)	MFie
	– 'Anna Griffith' (Au)	CPBP CTal MFie WAbe
	– 'Anne' (Au)	EPot MFie
	– 'Apple Blossom' (Au)	GKev NHpl
	– 'Archer' (Au)	ITim NWad
	– 'Aries Violet' (Au)	ITim
	– 'Austen' (Au)	MFie
	– 'Avalanche' (Au)	MFie
	– 'Bill Martin' (Au)	ITim
	– 'Blood Flake' (Au)	ITim
	– 'Blush' (Au) new	CPBP
	– 'Broadwell No 4' (Au)	CPBP
	– 'Cherry' (Au)	WAbe
	– 'Chivalry' (Au)	CPBP WAbe
	– 'Circe's Flute' (Au)	MFie
	– 'Cissie' (Au)	CPBP ITim MFie
	– 'Claude Flight' (Au)	MFie
	– 'Confection' (Au)	MFie
	– 'Crowsley Variety' (Au)	ITim
	– 'Crusader' (Au)	CTal WAbe
	– 'Crystal' (Au)	CPBP MFie
	– 'Daniel Burrow' (Au)	CPBP
	– 'Elizabeth Baker' (Au)	ITim MFie
	– 'Elizabeth Burrow' (Au)	ITim WAbe
	– 'Elizabeth Earle' (Au)	EPot ITim
	– 'Eureka' (Au)	CPBP EPot LLHF WAbe
	– 'Eveline Burrow' (Au)	CPBP WAbe
	– 'Fanfare' (Au)	MAsh
I	– 'Forma' (Au)	XBar
	– 'Frank Barker' (Au)	NWad
	– 'Gabriele' (Au)	MFie
	– 'Gilderdale Glow' (Au)	CPBP MFie
	– 'Giuseppi's Form'	see *P. allionii* 'Mrs Dyas'
	– 'Grandiflora' (Au)	GKev ITim
	– 'Hartside 6' (Au)	ITim
	– 'Hazey' (Au)	ITim
	– 'Hemswell' (Au)	NHpl
	– 'Henry Burrow' (Au) new	WAbe
	– 'Herald' (Au)	ITim
	– 'Hocker Edge' (Au)	ITim MFie NWad
	– 'Horwood' (Au)	ITim
	– 'Huntsman' (Au)	MFie
	– Ingwersen's form (Au)	MFie NWad
	– 'Isobel' (Au)	LLHF
	– 'James' (Au)	WAbe
	– 'Joe Elliott' (Au)	ITim
	– 'Judy Burrow' (Au)	CPBP
	– 'Julia' (Au)	EPot
	– 'Kate Evans' (Au)	CPBP
§	– 'Ken's Seedling' (Au)	MFie
	– KRW	see *P. allionii* 'Ken's Seedling'
	– 'Lepus' (Au)	WAbe
	– Lismore 81/19/2 (Au)	MFie
	– Lismore 81/19/3 (Au)	EPot MFie
	– Lismore 87/3/2 (Au)	MFie
	– 'Little O' (Au)	NWad
	– 'Malcolm' (Au)	ITim
	– 'Marion' (Au)	XBar
	– 'Marjorie Wooster' (Au)	CPBP EPot MFie XBar
	– 'Martin' (Au)	ITim
	– 'Mary Anne' (Au)	WAbe
	– 'Mary Berry' (Au)	CPBP EPot MFie NWad
§	– 'Mrs Dyas' (Au)	MFie NWad
	– 'Neon' (Au)	CPBP
	– 'Nettleton 855' (Au)	EPot
	– 'New Dawn' (Au)	ITim MFie
	– 'Pale Venus' (Au)	MFie
	– 'Peace' (Au)	MFie
	– 'Peggy Wilson' (Au)	EPot EWld NWad WThu

- 'Pennine Pink' (Au)	CPBP
- 'Phoebe's Moon' (Au)	ITim
- 'Pinkie' (Au)	CPBP WAbe
- 'Pixie' (Au) **new**	MFie
- RAH form (Au)	MFie
- 'Raymond Wooster' (Au)	GKev NWad
- 'Scimitar' (Au)	MFie
- 'Snowflake' (Au)	CPBP GKev MFie
- 'Stanton House' (Au)	MFie
- 'Stephen' (Au)	MFie
- 'Steven Burrow'	CPBP
- 'Tranquillity' (Au)	CPBP CTal ITim NWad
- 'Travellers' (Au)	EPot
- 'Viscountess Byng' (Au)	CPBP
- 'William Earle' (Au)	CPBP CTal ITim XBar
allionii × ***auricula*** misapplied 'Blairside Yellow' (Au)	CPBP NSum
allionii × ***auricula*** misapplied 'Old Red Dusty Miller' (Au)	NWad XBar
allionii × ***hirsuta*** (Au)	NWad
allionii × 'Lismore Jewel' (Au)	CPBP
allionii × 'Lismore Treasure' (Au)	ITim NHpl
allionii × ***pedemontana***	see *P.* × *sendtneri*
allionii × ***pubescens*** (Au)	NHpl
allionii × ***pubescens*** 'Harlow Car' (Au)	IRob ITim WFar
allionii × 'Snow Ruffles' (Au)	ITim
allionii × 'White Linda Pope' (Au)	MFie NHpl NWad
alpicola (Si) $\mathbb{Y}^{H7}$	CAby CTsd CWCL EPot GAbr GKev MFie MMuc NBid NChi NGdn NHim NSum NWad XBar
- var. ***alba*** (Si)	CSta CTsd GAbr GKev NBid WHil
§ - var. ***alpicola*** (Si)	EBee GKev
- hybrids (Si)	NHpl WMoo
- 'Kevock Sky' (Si)	CWCL GKev
- 'La Luna' (Si)	CSta
- var. ***luna***	see *P. alpicola* var. *alpicola*
- mixed (Si)	GKev MFie
- var. ***violacea*** (Si)	CSta EWld GAbr GKev MNrw NBid NWad WArt WHil
- - wine-red-flowered (Si)	GKev MFie
'Altaica'	see *P. elatior* subsp. *meyeri*
altaica grandiflora	see *P. elatior* subsp. *meyeri*
amethystina subsp. ***brevifolia*** (Am)	GKev
amoena	see *P. elatior* subsp. *meyeri*
'Amy Smith' (Pr/Prim)	GAbr
angustifolia (Pa)	GKev WAbe
anisodora	see *P. wilsonii* var. *anisodora*
× ***anisodoxa*** 'Kevock Sunrise' (Pf) **new**	EBee
- 'Kevock Surprise' (Pf)	GKev
'Annemijne'	GEdr WCot
apoclita (Mu)	LLHF XBar
× ***arctotis***	see *P.* × *pubescens*
'Arduaine' (Pe)	LLHF
aurantiaca (Pf)	CPla EBee GKev MFie NHpl XBar
- SDR 7874	GKev
aureata (Pe)	WAbe
auricula ambig. (Au)	EWld NSla
auricula L. (Au) $\mathbb{Y}^{H5}$	EDAr GKev LRHS MFie NRHS SPer SPlb SPoG WRHF
- SDR 5705	GKev
- SDR 6960	GKev
- subsp. ***bauhinii*** (Au)	GKev
auricula misapplied (Au)	ECha LRHS NRHS
- A74 (Au)	MMuc SEND
- K85 (Au/S)	SPop
I - '1-2-3' (Au)	EBee
- '2nd Vic' (Au/S)	SPop
- 'A.C. Hadfield' (Au)	MFie
- 'Abdor' (Au/St)	NDro SPop
- 'Abrigde' (Au/d)	WAln
- 'Abundance' (Au/A)	NDro SPop
- 'Achates' (Au/A)	WAln
- 'Admiral' (Au/A)	WAln
- 'Adrian' (Au/A)	GAgs MFie NDro SPop WHil XBar
- 'Adrienne' (Au/A)	SPop
- 'Adrienne Ruan' (Au/A)	NDro WAln
- 'After Glow' (Au/St)	NDro SPop
- 'Aga Khan' (Au/A)	NDro WAln
- 'Agamemnon' (Au/A)	GAgs LLHF MFie NDro SPop
- 'Airy Fairy' (Au/S)	NDro SPop
- 'Alamo' (Au/A)	MFie NDro SPop
- 'Alan Ravenscroft' (Au/A)	MFie SPop WHil
- 'Albert Bailey' (Au/d)	GAbr GAgs ITim MFie NDro SPop WFar WHil
- 'Alchemist' (Au/S)	SPop
- 'Aldgate' (Au/S) **new**	NDro
- 'Alexandra Georgina' (Au/A)	MFie SPop WAln
- 'Alf' (Au/A)	GAgs MFie NDro NSum SPop WHil
- 'Alfred Charles' (Au/A)	SPop WAln
- 'Alfred Niblett' (Au/S)	GAgs
- 'Alice' (Au/d)	NDro
- 'Alice Haysom' (Au/S)	ELan GAbr GAgs ITim MAsh NDro SPop WHil XBar
- 'Alicia' (Au/A)	GAbr GAgs MFie NDro NSum SPop XBar
- 'Alien' (Au/S)	SPop
- 'Alison' (Au/S)	GAgs NDro
- 'Alison Jane' (Au/A)	GAgs MFie NDro SPop WHil XBar
- 'Alison Rose' (Au/B)	NDro
- 'Alison Telford' (Au/A)	GAgs WHil
- 'All Gold' (Au/d) **new**	SPop
- 'Allard' (Au/A)	WAln
- 'Allegro' (Au/A)	WAln
- 'Alloway' (Au/d)	WAln
- 'Almand' (Au/d)	WAln
- 'Almondbury' (Au/S)	NDro SPop
- alpine mixed (Au/A)	EPfP SRms
- 'Amanda' (Au/d)	SPop
- 'Amazon' (Au/St)	SPop
- 'Amber Light' (Au/S)	SPop WAln
- 'Amethyst' (Au/S)	GAgs
- 'Amicable' (Au/A)	GAgs MFie NDro NSum SPop WHil
- 'Amore' (Au/St)	GAgs NDro SPop WAln
- 'Amy Nuttall' (Au/A) **new**	SPop
- 'Ancient Order' (Au/A)	WAln
- 'Ancient Society' (Au/A)	GAgs MFie NSum NWad SPop WHil
- 'Andrea Julie' (Au/A)	GAgs NDro SPop WHil
- 'Andrew Hunter' (Au/A)	GAgs MFie NDro NSum SPop
- 'Andy Cole' (Au/A)	NDro SPop WAln
- 'Angel Eyes' (Au/St)	NDro SPop WHil
- 'Angel Islington' (Au/S)	NDro
- 'Angela Gould' (Au)	MFie NDro SPop WHil
- 'Angela Grace' (Au/d)	XBar
- 'Angela Short' (Au/St)	SPop
- 'Angostura' (Au/d)	GAgs SPop WHil
- 'Ann Brookes' (Au/d)	WAln
- 'Ann Taylor' (Au/A)	GAgs WAln
- 'Anna' (Au/B) **new**	NDro
- 'Anne Hyatt' (Au/d)	GAbr NDro SPop

– 'Anne Swithinbank' (Au/d) WAln
– 'Annette' (Au/B) NDro
– 'Annie Tustin' (Au/S) SPop
– 'Ansells' (Au/S) SPop WAln
– 'Antoc' (Au/S) SPop
– 'Anwar Sadat' (Au/A) GAgs MFie NDro NSum WHil
– 'Apple Blossom' (Au/B) NDro WHil
– 'Applecross' (Au/A) GAgs NDro NHpl NSum SPop WHil
– 'Apricot Truffle' (Au/d) SPop
– 'April Moon' (Au/S) GAgs MFie NDro SPop WHil
– 'Aquarius' (Au/d) SPop
– 'Arab Prince' (Au/A) WAln
– 'Arab Queen' (Au/A) WAln
– 'Arabian Night' (Au/A) WAln
– 'Arapaho' (Au/A) SPop WAln
– 'Arctic Fox' (Au) MFie WAln WHil
– 'Argentine' (Au/S) SPop XBar
– 'Argus' (Au/A) GAgs LSun MFie NSum NWad SPop WHil XBar
– 'Arlene' (Au/A) WAln
– 'Art Deco' (Au/B) WAln
– 'Arthur Delbridge' (Au/A) MFie NDro SPop WHil
– 'Arundell' (Au/S/St) EBee GAgs ITim MFie NDro NSum SPop WFar WHil XBar
– 'Arwen' (Au/A) MFie SPop
– 'Ascot Gavotte' (Au/S) NDro
– 'Ashcliffe Gem' (Au/A) GAgs NDro WAln
– 'Astolat' (Au/S) EBee GAgs NDro NHpl SPop WHil XBar
– 'Athene' (Au/S) ITim NDro SPop
– 'Atlantic' (Au/S) NDro NEgg SPop
– 'Aubergine' (Au/B) NDro SPop
I – 'Aubergine' (Au/d) SPop
– 'Audacity' (Au/d) MFie NDro WAln
– 'Audrey' (Au/S) NDro SPop
– 'Aurora' (Au/A) EDAr NSum WAln
– 'Austin' (Au/A) NDro SPop WAln
– 'Autumn Fire' (Au/A) GAgs SPop
– 'Autumn Glow' (Au/d) SPop
– 'Autumn Gold' (Au/B) **new** NDro
– 'Avon Angel' (Au/d) SPop
– 'Avon Bunny' (Au/d) SPop
– 'Avon Buster' (Au/d) SPop
– 'Avon Carrier' (Au/d) SPop
– 'Avon Citronella' (Au) SPop
– 'Avon Eclipse' (Au/d) SPop
– 'Avon Elegance' (Au/d) SPop
– 'Avon Khaki' (Au/d) SPop
– 'Avon Tan' (Au/d) GAbr GAgs
– 'Avon Toro' (Au/d) SPop
– 'Avon Twist' (Au/d) SPop
– 'Avonwick' (Au/B) **new** NDro
– 'Avril' (Au/A) NDro SPop WAln WHil
– 'Avril Hunter' (Au/A) GAgs ITim MFie MHer NDro NSum WHil XBar
– 'Awesome' (Au/St) SPop
– 'Aztec' (Au/d) WAln
– 'Baby Blue' (Au) NDro WHil
– 'Bacchante' (Au/d) SPop WAln
– 'Bacchus' (Au/A) GAgs MFie NDro SPop WHil
– 'Baggage' (Au) GAgs MAsh NDro SPop WHil
– 'Bailey Boy' (Au/B) NDro
– 'Baker's Boy' (Au/d) SPop
– 'Balbithan' (Au/B) NDro
– 'Ballynahinch' (Au) ITim
– 'Baltic Amber' (Au) GAgs MFie NDro SPop WAln WHil
– 'Bank Error' (Au/S) NDro SPop WAln
– 'Barbara Mason' (Au) NDro WAln
– 'Barbarella' (Au/S) MFie NDro SPop
– 'Barber's Pole' (Au/St) **new** NDro
– Barnhaven Border hybrids (Au/B) XBar
– Barnhaven doubles (Au/d) GAbr NSum XBar
– 'Barr Beacon' (Au/A) ITim NDro
– 'Bartl' (Au/A) **new** EWTr
– 'Basilio' (Au/S) NDro
– 'Basuto' (Au/A) GAgs ITim MFie NDro SPop WHil
– 'Beatrice' (Au/A) CTri GAgs MFie NDro NHpl SPop WHil XBar
– 'Beauty of Bath' (Au/S) WAln
– 'Beckminster' (Au/A) WAln
– 'Bedford Lad' (Au/A) NDro
– 'Beechen Green' (Au/S) ITim MAsh SPop
– 'Beeches Variegated' (Au/A/v) **new** WFar
– 'Belgravia Gold' (Au/B) NDro
– 'Bella' (Au/d) WAln
– 'Bellamy Pride' (Au/B) MAsh NDro SPop
– 'Belle Zana' (Au/S) GAgs MFie NDro SPop
– 'Bellini' (Au/d) XBar
– 'Ben Lawers' (Au/S) SPop
– 'Ben Wyves' (Au/S) NDro SPop
– 'Bendigo' (Au/S) NDro SPop WAln
– 'Bengal Rose' (Au/S) SPop
– 'Benny Green' (Au/S) MFie NDro SPop
– 'Beppi' (Au) NDro WHil
– 'Bessie' (Au/d) XBar
– 'Best Wishes' (Au/F) NDro
– 'Bethan McSparron' (Au/B) NDro
– 'Betty Stewart' (Au/A) WAln
– 'Betty Wilson' (Au/St) **new** NDro
– 'Bewitched' (Au/A) MFie NDro WAln
– 'Bilbao' (Au/A) WAln
– 'Bilbo Baggins' (Au/A) MAsh NDro SPop WAln
– 'Bill Bailey' (Au/d) GAgs NDro
– 'Bilton' (Au/S) SPop
– 'Bingley Folk' (Au/B) NDro SPop
– 'Bingley Snowflake' (Au/B) **new** NDro
– 'Bisto' (Au/S) SPop WAln
– 'Bitterne Beauty' (Au/d) SPop
– 'Bitterne Bounty' (Au/d) SPop
– 'Bitterne Buttercup' (Au/d) SPop
– 'Bitterne Delight' (Au/d) SPop
– 'Bitterne Nighthawk' (Au/d) **new** SPop
– 'Bitterne Primrose' (Au/d) SPop
– 'Bizarre' (Au) GAgs NDro
– 'Black Adder' (Au/S) SPop
– 'Black Diamond' (Au/d) MFie SPop WHil
– 'Black Jack'PBR (Au/d) CWCL EBee ECtt GBin MHol NHpl NLar WTor
– 'Black Knight' (Au/d) SPop
– 'Blackberry Crush' (Au) **new** NDro
– 'Blackfield' (Au/S) SPop
– 'Blackhill' (Au/S) ITim MFie NHpl SPop
– 'Blackpool Rock' (Au/St) CWCL MFie NDro SPop XBar
– 'Blairside Yellow' (Au/B) LLHF NDro NSla
– 'Blakeney' (Au/d) MFie NDro
– 'Blossom' (Au/A) MFie SPop
– 'Blossom Dearie' (Au/St) SPop
– 'Blue Angel' (Au/S) **new** SPop
– 'Blue Bella' (Au/B) **new** NDro
– 'Blue Belle' (Au/B) **new** NDro
– 'Blue Bonnet' (Au/A/d) GAgs MFie NDro WAln
– 'Blue Boy' (Au/S) NDro WHil

- 'Blue Chip' (Au/S) MFie NDro SPop WHil
- 'Blue Cliff' (Au/S) SPop WAln
- 'Blue Fire' (Au/S) MFie SPop
- 'Blue Frills' (Au) NDro WAln
- 'Blue Heaven' (Au/A) NDro SPop
- 'Blue Jean' (Au/S) GAgs SPop
- 'Blue Lace' (Au) WAln
- 'Blue Merle' (Au/B) NDro
- 'Blue Mist' (Au/B) NDro
- 'Blue Night' (Au/B) GAgs ITim NDro
- 'Blue Nile' (Au/S) SPop
- 'Blue Ridge' (Au/A) NDro SPop WAln
- 'Blue Skies' (Au/St) NDro SPop
- 'Blue Veil' (Au/S) SPop
- 'Blue Velvet' (Au/B) GAbr LLHF MFie NDro NHpl SBch SPop WHil
- 'Blue Wave' (Au/d) MFie SPop
- 'Blue Waves' (Au/B) NDro SPop
- 'Blue Yodeler' (Au/A) MFie NDro NSum SPop WFar WHil
- 'Blue Yonder' (Au/S) ITim WAln
- 'Blush Baby' (Au/St) EWTr GAbr GAgs NDro NSum NWad SPop WHil XBar
- 'Blyth Spirit' (Au/A) MFie NDro SPop WAln
- 'Bob Dingley' (Au/A) SPop
- 'Bob Lancashire' (Au/S) ITim NDro SPop WHil XBar
- 'Bokay' (Au/d) WAln
- 'Bold Tartan' (Au/St) NDro SPop
- 'Bolero' (Au/A) SPop WAln
- 'Bonafide' (Au/d) SPop WAln
- 'Bonanza' (Au/S) SPop WAln
- 'Bookham Firefly' (Au/A) GAbr GAgs NDro SPop WHil
- 'Border Bandit' (Au/B) GAbr MFie NDro SPop WAln
- 'Border Beauty' (Au/St) NDro
- 'Border Blue' (Au/B) NDro
- 'Border Patrol' (Au/B) ITim NDro WAln
- 'Border Tawny' (Au/B) NDro
- 'Boromir' (Au/A) MFie NDro SPop WAln
- 'Bournebrook' (Au/A) WAln
- 'Bowen's Blue' (Au/B) NDro SPop
- 'Bradford City' (Au/A) CFis CWCL GAgs NDro SPop WFar WHil XBar
- 'Bradmore Bluebell' (Au) GAbr NDro
- 'Bramley Rose' (Au/B) SPop
- 'Bramshill' (Au/S) NDro
- 'Bran' (Au/B) NDro
- 'Brandaris' (Au/A) WAln
- 'Branston' (Au/d) XBar
- 'Brasso' (Au) MAsh MFie NDro SPop WAln
- 'Brazen Hussy' (Au/d) MFie WAln
- 'Brazil' (Au/S) CTal EBee GAbr GAgs NDro SPop WHil
- 'Brazos River' (Au/A) GAgs MFie NDro SPop WHil
- 'Breckland Joy' (Au/A) NDro WAln
- 'Brenda's Choice' (Au/A) GAgs MFie NDro NSum SPop
- 'Brenda's Dilemma' (Au/S) **new** NDro
- 'Brentford Bees' (Au/St) NDro
- 'Brickmaker' (Au/d) SPop
- 'Bright Eyes' (Au/A) MFie
- 'Bright Ginger' (Au/S) NDro SPop WAln
- 'Brimstone and Treacle' (Au/d) SPop WAln
- 'Brixton' (Au/S) **new** NDro
- 'Broad Gold' (Au/A) MFie SPop
- 'Broadwell Gold' (Au/B) NDro NSum SPop
- 'Brocade' (Au/St) NDro
- 'Brompton' (Au/S) SPop
- 'Brookfield' (Au/S) GAbr MFie NDro NHpl SPop WHil
- 'Broughton' (Au/S) NDro SPop
- 'Brown Ben' (Au) MFie SPop WFar WHil
- 'Brown Bess' (Au/A) GAbr GAgs ITim MFie WHil
- 'Brown Sugar' (Au/d) SPop
- 'Brown Tan Double' (Au/d) GAgs
- 'Brownie' (Au/B) GAbr GAgs NDro NSum SPop WHil XBar
- 'Brownie Guider' (Au/B) NDro
- 'Brownie Point' (Au/B) NDro
- 'Brunhilde' (Au/B) **new** NDro
- 'Bucks Green' (Au/S) GAbr NDro SPop
- 'Buffy' (Au/St) **new** NDro
- 'Bunty' (Au/A) MFie
- 'Buoyance' (Au/A) WAln
- 'Burnished Gold' (Au/d) WAln
- 'Bush Baby' (Au/B) NDro
- 'Buttercup' (Au/d) SPop
- 'Buttermere' (Au/d) WAln
- 'Butterscotch' (Au/d) **new** SPop
- 'Butterwick' (Au/A) GAbr GAgs MFie NDro NEgg SPop XBar
- 'C.F. Hill' (Au/A) NDro SPop
- 'C.G. Haysom' (Au/S) NDro SPop WHil
- 'C.W. Needham' (Au/A) GAgs ITim NDro SPop XBar
- 'Cadiz Bay' (Au/d) WAln
- 'Café au Lait' (Au/A) XBar
- 'Callisto' (Au/d) SPop
- 'Calypso' (Au/d) NDro SPop WAln
- 'Cambodunum' (Au/A) MFie NDro NSum SPop WFar WHil
- 'Camelot' (Au/d) MFie NDro SPop WFar WHil
- 'Cameo' (Au/A) GAbr GAgs NHpl
- 'Cameo Beauty' (Au/d) NDro SPop
- 'Camilla' (Au/A) WAln
- 'Candida' (Au/d) SPop
- 'Candy Stripe' (Au/St) GAgs NDro SPop
- 'Cannelle' (Au/d) **new** XBar
- 'Cappela' (Au/d) SPop WAln
- 'Caramel' (Au/A) GAgs WAln
- 'Cardinal Red' (Au/d) NDro SPop
- 'Cardington' (Au/A) WAln
- 'Carioca' (Au/A) WAln
- 'Carl Andrew' (Au/S) WAln
- 'Carmel' (Au/d) GAbr MAsh SPop WAln
- 'Carnaval' (Au/B) XBar
- 'Carne' (Au/D) NDro
- 'Carnival' (Au/A) WAln
- 'Carole' (Au/A) MFie SPop WHil
- 'Carousel' (Au/B) NDro
- 'Carreras' (Au) MFie NDro
- 'Carsa Wakes' (Au/d) NDro SPop WAln
- 'Carzon' (Au/A) NDro
- 'Caslon' (Au/A) **new** SPop
- 'Catherine Wheel' (Au/St) SPop
- 'Cathy McKay' (Au/B) NDro
- 'Catta Ha' (Au/d) NDro
- 'Celtic One' (Au/St) NDro SPop
- 'Ceri Nicolle' (Au/B) NDro
- 'Chaffinch' (Au/S) GAbr GAgs NDro SPop
- 'Chamois' (Au/B) GAbr MFie NDro WHil
- 'Chanel' (Au/S) SPop WAln
- 'Chantilly Cream' (Au/d) WAln
- 'Charles Bronson' (Au/d) GAgs MFie NDro SPop WAln
- 'Charles Rennie' (Au/B) ITim MFie NDro SPop
- 'Charlie's Aunt' (Au/A) NDro WAln
- 'Charlotte' (Au/B) **new** NDro
- 'Charlotte Brookes' (Au/d) SPop WAln
- 'Checkmate' (Au/d) MFie SPop WAln
- 'Cheeky' (Au/d) SPop
- 'Chelsea Bridge' (Au/A) GAgs NDro SPop WHil
- 'Chelsea Girl' (Au/d) NDro

– 'Cheops' (Au/A) GAgs MFie NDro NEgg NSum SPop XBar
– 'Cherille' (Au/S) **new** NDro
– 'Cherry' (Au/S) GAbr GAgs SPop
– 'Cherry Picker' (Au/A) GAgs MFie NDro SPop
– 'Chestnut' (Au/B) **new** NDro
– 'Cheyenne' (Au/S) GAbr GAgs MFie NDro SPop
– 'Chiffon' (Au/S) GAbr GAgs NDro NSum SPop
– 'Chiquita' (Au/d) NDro SPop
– 'Chirichua' (Au/S) WAln
– 'Chloë' (Au/S) MFie NDro NHpl SPop
– 'Chloris' (Au/S) MFie SPop
– 'Choir Boy' (Au/A) WAln
– 'Chorister' (Au/S) GAbr GAgs ITim MFie NDro NSum SPop WHil
– 'Chyne' (Au) NDro
– 'Cicero' (Au/A) MFie SPop WAln
– 'Cinders' (Au/St) SPop
– 'Cindy' (Au/A) NDro
– 'Cinnamon' (Au/d) GAgs ITim MFie NDro SPop WFar WHil
– 'Cinnamon' (Au/S) GAbr
– 'Ciribiribin' (Au/A) WAln
– 'Citron-Ella' (Au/d) MFie SPop
– 'Clara' (Au/d) SPop WFar
– 'Clare' (Au/S) MFie NDro SPop
– 'Classy Stripe' (Au/St) ITim
– 'Clatter-Ha' (Au/d) NSum SPop WHil
– 'Claud Wilson' (Au/St) NDro SPop
– 'Claudia Taylor' (Au) SPop
– 'Cleft Stick' (Au) NDro
– 'Clipper' (Au/S) SPop
– 'Cloth of Gold' (Au/A) NDro SPop
– 'Clotted Cream' (Au/B) NDro
– 'Clouded Yellow' (Au/S) GAbr SPop WHil
– 'Cloudy Bay' (Au) NDro WCot
– 'Cloverdale' (Au/d) WAln
– 'Clown Prince' (Au/St) **new** NDro
– 'Clunie' (Au/S) NDro SPop
– 'Clunie II' (Au/S) GAgs
– 'Cobden Meadows' (Au/A) SPop WAln
– 'Cockle' (Au/S) SPop
– 'Cocoa' (Au/d) XBar
– 'Coffee' (Au/S) MFie NDro SPop WHil XBar
– 'Coffee and Cream' (Au/d) **new** SPop
– 'Colbury' (Au/S) NDro SPop XBar
– 'Coleman' (Au/d) **new** SPop
– 'Colonel Champney' (Au/S) NDro SPop
– 'Comet' (Au/S) NDro NSum
– 'Connaught Court' (Au/A) LLHF NDro
– 'Conquistador' (Au/A) NDro WAln
– 'Conservative' (Au/S) NDro
– 'Consett' (Au/S) GAgs SPop WHil
– 'Cooks Hill' (Au/d) WAln
– 'Cooper's Gold' (Au/B) NDro
– 'Coppi' (Au/A) NDro SPop
– 'Coral' (Au/S) GAgs ITim SPop
– 'Coral Sea' (Au/S) SPop
– 'Corn Dolly' (Au/S) SPop
– 'Cornish Cream' (Au/B) NDro
– 'Cornmeal' (Au/S) GAgs MFie NDro SPop WHil
– 'Corntime' (Au/S) SPop WAln
– 'Corporal Jones' (Au/S) SPop
– 'Corrie Files' (Au/d) MFie SPop WAln
– 'Cortez Silver' (Au/S) SPop
– 'Cortina' (Au/S) GAgs ITim MFie NDro SPop WHil
– 'Countdown' (Au/St) **new** SPop
– 'County Park Red' (Au/B) NDro
– 'Coventry Street' (Au/S) MAsh MFie NDro NSum SPop
– 'Crackling Rosie' (A/d) WAln
– 'Craig Dhu' (Au/B) SPop
– 'Craig Nordie' (Au/B) NDro
– 'Craig Vaughan' (Au/A) MFie NDro NSum SPop XBar
– 'Cranborne' (Au/A) SPop WAln
– 'Crecy' (Au/A) SPop WAln WHil
– 'Cressida' (Au/d) SPop
– 'Crimple' (Au/S) NDro SPop WHil
– 'Crimson Black' (Au/B) SPop
– 'Crimson Glow' (Au/d) GAgs ITim LCro LOPS MAsh MFie NDro NSum SPop WHil
– 'Crimson Maid' (Au/d) SPop
– 'Crinoline' (Au/S) NDro SPop
– 'Cuckoo Fair' (Au/S) ECtt GAgs NDro SPop WFar
– 'Cuddles' (Au/A) MFie NDro SPop WAln
– 'Curry Blend' (Au/B) NDro SPop WHil
– 'Cutie Pie' (Au/St) NDro SPop
– 'Cuttlefish' (Au/St) SPop
– 'Cyrn Las' (Au/St) SPop
– 'D.S.J.' (Au/S) NDro
– 'Daftie Green' (Au/S) GAgs NDro
– 'Dakota' (Au/S) SPop
– 'Dales Red' (Au/B) GAgs MAsh MFie NDro NHpl NSum SPop WHil
– 'Damerham' (Au/A) SPop
– 'Dan Tiger' (Au/St) GAgs MFie SPop WHil
– 'Daniel' (Au/A) NDro SPop WAln
– 'Daniel T. Taylor' (Au/A) NDro WAln
– 'Daphnis' (Au/S) SPop
– 'Darent Tiger' (Au/St) NDro SPop XBar
– 'Dark Eyes' (Au/d) GAgs MFie NDro NSum SPop WHil
– 'Dark Lady' (Au/A) WAln
– 'D'Artagnan' (Au/B) **new** NDro
– 'Darth Vader' (Au/d) XBar
– 'David Beckham' (Au/d) NDro SPop WAln
– 'David McSparron' (Au/B) **new** NDro
– 'Day by Day' (Au/St) NDro SPop
– 'Deal' (Au/S) **new** NDro
– 'Deckchair' (Au/St) MFie NDro SPop
– 'Dedham' (Au/d) WAln
– 'Del Boy' (Au/A) SPop WAln
– 'Delicious' (Au/St) SPop
– 'Delilah' (Au/d) ITim MAsh MFie NDro NSum SPop WFar WHil
– 'Denise' (Au/S) WAln
– 'Denna Snuffer' (Au/d) GAbr MFie NDro SPop
– 'Derrill' (Au/B) NDro SPop
– 'Deuce of Hearts' (Au/St) **new** NDro
– 'Devon Cream' (Au/d) GAgs MFie NDro SPop
– 'Diamond' (Au/d) SPop WAln
– 'Diamond Dust' (Au/B) NDro
– 'Dick Rogers' (Au/B) NDro
– 'Dido' (Au/B) XBar
– 'Digby' (Au/d) NDro WAln
– 'Digit' (Au/d) NDro WAln
– 'Dilemma' (Au/A) SPop
– 'Dill' (Au/A) MFie NDro NSum SPop WHil
– 'Dilly Dilly' (Au/A) MFie NDro SPop
– 'Divint Dunch' (Au/A) LLHF MFie NDro SPop WHil
– 'Doctor Duthie' (Au/S) NDro SPop
– 'Doctor Lennon's White' (Au/B) GAbr MFie MHer NDro SPop WHil
– 'Doctor Woolhead' (Au/S) SPop
– 'Dolly' (Au/B) NDro
– 'Dolly Viney' (Au/d) WAln
– 'Don Carlos' (Au/d) XBar
– 'Donhead' (Au/A) GAgs ITim MFie NDro SPop WHil

- 'Donn' (Au/d) SPop WAln
- 'Donna Clancy' (Au/S) NDro XBar
- 'Dorado' (Au/d) SPop WAln
- 'Doreen Stephens' (Au/A) GAgs NDro
- 'Doris Jean' (Au/A) MFie NDro
- 'Dorothy' (Au/S) WAln
- 'Doublet' (Au/d) GAgs MFie NDro NSum SPop WHil
- 'Doubloon' (Au/d) XBar
- 'Doublure' (Au/d) GAbr NDro SPop WHil
- 'Douglas Bader' (Au/A) GAgs ITim MFie NDro NSum SPop WHil
- 'Douglas Black' (Au/S) GAbr GAgs NDro SPop WHil
- 'Douglas Green' (Au/S) NDro SPop
- 'Douglas White' (Au/S) SPop
- 'Dovedale' (Au/S) NDro SPop
- 'Dowager' (Au/A) MFie
- DOWNTOWN DOUBLES (Au/d) SPop
- 'Doyen' (Au/d) ITim MFie NDro NHpl SPop WAln WHil
- 'Dragon's Hoard' (Au/A) WAln
- 'Drax' (Au/A) SPop WAln
- 'Dream' (Au/St) SPop
- 'Dreamweaver' (Au/S) SPop
- 'Dubarii' (Au/A) MFie NDro SPop WAln
- 'Duchess of Malfi' (Au/S) SPop
- 'Duchess of York' (Au) IRob LLHF
- 'Duke of Edinburgh' (Au/B) NDro
- 'Dusky Girl' (Au/A) NDro WAln
- 'Dusky Maiden' (Au/A) GAbr GAgs MFie NDro NPnk NSum SPop WHil
- 'Dusky Yellow' (Au/B) NDro
- 'Dusty Miller' (Au/B) EBee
- 'Eastern Promise' (Au/A) GAgs MFie NDro NSum SPop WHil
- 'Eaton Dawn' (Au/S) MFie SPop
- 'Ed Spivey' (Au/A) NDro
- 'Eddy Gordon' (Au/A) WAln
- 'Eden Alexander' (Au/B) MFie NDro
- 'Eden Amethyst' (Au/B) NDro SPop
- 'Eden Aramis' (Au/B) **new** NDro
- 'Eden Blue Star' (Au/B) GAbr GAgs NDro NSum SPop WFar
- 'Eden Bonanza' (Au/B) SPop
- 'Eden Bramley' (Au/B) NDro
- 'Eden Brownie' (Au/B) **new** SPop
- 'Eden Carmine' (Au/B) MFie MHer NDro SPop
- 'Eden Cynthia' (Au/B) MFie SPop
- 'Eden Dark Eyes' (Au/B) NDro SPop
- 'Eden David' (Au/B) MFie NDro SPop WHil
- 'Eden Ensign' (Au/B) SPop
- 'Eden Fanfare' (Au/B) NDro WFar
- 'Eden Glow' (Au/B) **new** NDro
- 'Eden Goldfinch' (Au/B) GAbr MAsh NDro SPop
- 'Eden Grace' (Au/B) SPop
- 'Eden Greenfinch' (Au/B) MFie NDro SPop
- 'Eden Lilactime' (Au/B) NDro SPop WFar
- 'Eden Midas' (Au/B) **new** SPop
- 'Eden Moonlight' (Au/B) MFie SPop WHil
- 'Eden Porthos' (Au/B) **new** NDro
- 'Eden Rhiann' (Au/B) NDro SPop
- 'Eden Sunrise' (Au/B) NDro
- 'Eden Surprise' (Au/B) **new** NDro
- 'Edinburgh' (Au/A) WAln
- 'Edith Major' (Au/d) MFie NDro SPop WHil
- 'Edward Sweeney' (Au/S) WAln
- 'Eggborough' (Au/A) SPop
- 'Eglinton' (Au) NDro NSum SPop
- 'Eileen K' (Au/S) NDro
- 'El Zoco' (Au/S) SPop
- 'Elara' (Au/d) SPop
- 'Elegance' (Au/S) SPop
- 'Elf Star' (Au/A) NSum SPop WAln
- 'Eli Jenkins' (Au) WAln
- 'Elizabeth Ann' (Au/A) GAbr NDro SPop
- 'Ellen Thompson' (Au/A) GAbr MFie NDro SPop WHil XBar
- 'Ellie May' (Au/S) XBar
- 'Elsie May' (Au/A) ITim MFie NDro SPop WHil
- 'Elsinore' (Au/S) SPop
- 'Emberglow' (Au/d) SPop WAln
- 'Embley' (Au/S) NDro NHpl SPop
- 'Emery Down' (Au/S) NDro SPop
- 'Emmett Smith' (Au/A) NDro SPop WAln
- 'Ems Blue' (Au/B) WAln
- 'Ems Choice' (Au/B) WAln
- 'Ems Funny Face' (Au/B) NDro
- 'Enigma' (Au/S) SPop WAln
- 'Enlightened' (Au/A) MFie NDro
- 'Envy' (Au/S) WAln
- 'Erica' (Au/A) MFie NDro NSum SPop WHil XBar
- 'Erjon' (Au/S) MFie NDro SPop
- 'Error' (Au/S) NDro
- 'Eschman Starflower' (Au/S) WHil
- 'Esso' (Au/S) WAln
- 'Ethel' (Au) NDro
- 'Ethel Wild' (Au/d) SPop
- 'Ethel Wilkes' (Au/d) WAln
- 'Etna' (Au/S) NDro
- 'Europa' (Au/d) SPop
- 'Euston Road' (Au/S) **new** NDro
- 'Eve Guest' (Au/A) NDro SPop WAln
- 'Eventide' (Au/S) GAgs SPop
- 'Everest Blue' (Au/S) GAbr GAgs ITim NDro SPop XBar
- 'Everest Flush' (Au/S) WAln
- 'Excalibur' (Au/d) GAgs NDro NSum SPop
- 'Exhibition Blau' (Exhibition Series) (Au/B) IBoy WHil
- 'Eye Candy' (Au/St) SPop
- 'Eyeopener' (Au/A) MFie NDro NSum SPop WHil
- 'Fabuloso' (Au/St) GAgs NDro SPop
- 'Fairy' (Au/A) WAln
- 'Fairy Light' (Au/S) NDro SPop
- 'Falcon' (Au/S) SPop
- 'Falstaff' (Au/d) WAln
- 'Fanciful' (Au/S) MFie NDro SPop WHil XBar
- 'Fancy Free' (Au) SPop
- 'Fancy Pants' (Au/S) NDro SPop
- 'Fandancer' (Au/A) WAln
- 'Fandango' (Au/St) NDro
- 'Fanfare' (Au/S) MFie NDro SPop WHil
- 'Fanny Meerbeck' (Au/S) GAbr MFie NDro SPop WHil
- 'Fantasia' (Au/d) SPop
- 'Faro' (Au/S) NDro SPop
- 'Favourite' (Au/S) GAbr GAgs ITim MAsh MFie NDro SPop WHil XBar
- 'Fearless' (Au/S) WAln
- 'Femme Fatale' (Au/St) **new** NDro
- 'Fen Tiger' (Au/St) SPop
- 'Fenby' (Au/S) SPop
- 'Fennay' (Au/S) NSum
- 'Ferrybridge' (Au/A) NDro WAln
- 'Fiddler's Green' (Au/d) GAbr NDro SPop WCot XBar
- 'Figaro' (Au/S) GAbr MFie NDro SPop
- 'Figurine' (Au/d) WAln
- 'Finchfield' (Au/A) GAbr MFie NDro WAln
- 'Fine Art' (Au/S) **new** NDro
- 'Finlay Thomas' (Au/S) SPop

– 'Finley' (Au/B)	NDro
– 'Firecracker' (Au)	ETMg SPop WAln
– 'Firenze' (Au/A)	MFie SPop
– 'Firsby' (Au/d)	MFie NDro SPop WHil
– 'First Green' (Au/St)	SPop
– 'First Lady' (Au/A)	SPop WAln WFar
– 'First Light' (Au/B)	NDro SPop
– 'Fishtoft' (Au/d)	MFie SPop
– 'Fitzroy' (Au/d)	SPop
– 'Fleecy' (Au/S)	SPop
– 'Fleet Street' (Au/S)	GAgs MFie NDro SPop WFar WHil
– 'Fleminghouse' (Au/S)	GAbr NDro SPop
– 'Flirty' (Au/St) **new**	NDro
– 'Florence Baker' (Au/S) **new**	NDro
– 'Florence Brown' (Au/S)	SPop
– 'Fluffy Duckling' (Au/S)	NDro SPop
– 'For You' (Au/St)	NDro SPop
– 'Foreign Affairs' (Au/S)	SPop
– 'Forest Beech' (Au/d)	SPop
– 'Forest Bordeaux' (Au/d)	SPop
– 'Forest Bracken' (Au/d)	SPop
– 'Forest Burgundy' (Au/d)	GAgs SPop
– 'Forest Burnt Gold' (Au/d)	SPop
– 'Forest Cappuccino' (Au/d)	GAgs SPop
– 'Forest Coffee' (Au/D)	NDro
– 'Forest Duet' (Au/d)	NDro SPop WFar
– 'Forest Fire' (Au/d)	GAbr MFie NSum SPop
– 'Forest Glade' (Au/d)	SPop
– 'Forest Glow' (Au/d) **new**	SPop
– 'Forest Gorse' (Au/d)	SPop
– 'Forest Heath' (Au/d)	SPop
– 'Forest Lemon' (Au/d)	MFie SPop
– 'Forest Lime' (Au/d)	SPop
– 'Forest Pecan' (Au/d)	SPop
– 'Forest Pines' (Au/S)	SPop
– 'Forest Rose' (Au/d) **new**	SPop
– 'Forest Shade' (Au/d)	SPop WHil
– 'Forest Sunburst' (Au/d)	SPop
– 'Forest Sunfire' (Au/d) **new**	SPop
– 'Forest Sunlight' (Au/d)	SPop
– 'Forest Sunshine' (Au/d)	SPop
– 'Forest Twilight' (Au/d)	MFie SPop WHil
– 'Foundling' (Au)	ITim
– 'Foxfire' (Au/A)	WAln
– 'Fradley' (Au/A)	MFie NDro WAln WFar WHil
– 'Frances' (Au/d) **new**	SPop
– 'Françoise' (Au/d)	XBar
– 'Frank Bailey' (Au/d)	MFie SPop WAln
– 'Frank Crosland' (Au/A)	MFie NDro NSum SPop WHil
– 'Frank Faulkner' (Au/A)	WAln
– 'Frank Jenning' (Au/A)	NDro WAln
– 'Fred Booley' (Au/d)	GAbr LLHF MFie NDro NSum SPop WFar WHil XBar
– 'Fred Livesley' (Au/A)	WAln
– 'Freestyle' (Au/B)	WAln
– 'Fresco' (Au/A)	SPop WAln
– 'Freya' (Au/S)	NDro SPop
– 'Friends of Ashwood' (Au/S) **new**	NDro
– 'Friskney' (Au/d)	SPop WAln
– 'Frittenden Yellow' (Au/B)	GAbr SPop
– 'Frosty' (Au/S)	NDro SPop
– 'Fuller's Red' (Au/S)	ITim NDro SPop WHil
– 'Funny Valentine' (Au/d)	MFie NDro NSum SPop WHil
– 'G.L. Taylor' (Au/A)	NDro
– 'Gaia' (Au/d)	SPop WHil
– 'Gail Atkinson' (Au/A)	SPop WAln

– 'Galatea' (Au/S)	SPop
– 'Galator' (Au/A)	WAln
– 'Galen' (Au/A)	GAbr SPop
– 'Ganymede' (Au/d)	SPop WAln
– 'Gary Pallister' (Au/A)	SPop WAln
– 'Gas Lane' (Au/A)	SPop
– 'Gay Crusader' (Au/A)	GAbr MFie NDro NSum SPop WFar WHil
– 'Gazza' (Au/A)	WAln
– 'Gee Cross' (Au/A)	MFie NDro NSum SPop
– 'Geldersome Green' (Au/S)	NDro SPop
– 'Geldersome Green No. 2' (Au/S)	ITim
– 'Gemini' (Au/S)	NDro SPop
– 'Generosity' (Au/A)	GAgs NDro NSum WHil
– 'Geoffrey Bick' (Au/A)	SPop
– 'Geordie' (Au/A)	SPop WAln
– 'George Edge' (Au/B)	NDro
– 'George Harrison' (Au/B)	NDro SPop
– 'George Jennings' (Au/A)	MFie SPop
– 'George Swinford's Leathercoat' (Au/B)	GAbr NDro
– 'Geronimo' (Au/S)	GAbr MAsh MFie NDro SPop
– 'Gild Green' (Au/S) **new**	NDro
– 'Gimli' (Au/A)	WAln
– 'Ginger Spice' (Au/B) **new**	NDro
– 'Girl Guide' (Au/S)	SPop WHil
– 'Gizabroon' (Au/S)	CFis GAbr GAgs MFie NDro NEgg NLar SPop WHil XBar
– 'Glazebrook' (Au/S)	SPop
– 'Gleam' (Au/S)	CTal CWCL EBee EDAr GAgs LLHF MFie NDro NSum SPop WHil XBar
– 'Glencoe' (Au/S)	GAgs NDro SPop
– 'Gleneagles' (Au/S)	NDro
– 'Glenelg' (Au/S)	GAbr ITim MFie NDro NSum SPop WHil XBar
– 'Glenluce' (Au/S)	GAgs NDro SPop
– 'Gloire de Dijon' (Au/S)	XBar
– 'Gnome' (Au/B)	GAbr GAgs NDro
– 'Goeblii' (Au/B)	MFie NDro SPop WHil
– 'Gold Seal' (Au/d)	SPop
– 'Gold Seam' (Au/A)	MFie WAln WHil
– 'Gold Star' (Au/St) **new**	NDro
– 'Golden Boy' (Au/A)	MFie NDro NSum SPop WAln
– 'Golden Chartreuse' (Au/d)	GAbr NDro SPop
– 'Golden Fleece' (Au/S)	GAbr MAsh MFie NDro SPop
– 'Golden Girl' (Au/A)	SPop WAln
– 'Golden Glory' (Au/A)	GAgs NDro WAln
– 'Golden Harvest' (Au/A)	SPop
– 'Golden Hill' (Au/S)	ITim SPop
– 'Golden Hind' (Au/d)	GAbr GAgs MFie NDro NSum SPop WHil
– 'Golden Splendour' (Au/d)	GAgs ITim MFie NDro NSum SPop WFar WHil
– 'Golden Wedding' (Au/A)	GAgs MFie NDro SPop WAln WHil
– 'Goldie' (Au/S)	GAgs NDro
– 'Goldwin' (Au/A)	NDro NSum
– 'Gollum' (Au/A)	MFie NDro SPop WAln WFar
– 'Good Report' (Au/A)	MAsh MFie NDro NSum SPop WFar WHil
– 'Goody Goody' (Au/St)	NDro SPop
– 'Googie' (Au/d)	SPop
– 'Gordon Files' (Au/S)	WAln
– 'Gorey' (Au/A)	MFie NDro SPop WHil
– 'Gorgeous George' (Au/St)	SPop
– 'Grabley' (Au/S)	NDro SPop
– 'Grace Ellen' (Au/S)	SPop
– 'Grand Slam' (Au/D)	MFie

- 'Grandad's Favourite' (Au/B)	NDro SPop
- 'Grasmere' (Au/D)	NDro SPop
- 'Green Café' (Au/S)	SPop
- 'Green Finger' (Au/S)	SPop
- 'Green Heart' (Au/S)	SPop
- 'Green Isle' (Au/S)	GAbr MFie NDro SPop XBar
- 'Green Jacket' (Au/S)	NDro SPop
- 'Green Lane' (Au/S)	XBar
- 'Green Meadows' (Au/S)	GAgs SPop
- 'Green Mustard' (Au/S)	NDro SPop
- 'Green Parrot' (Au/S)	GAbr NDro WHil
- 'Green Shank' (Au/S)	NDro SPop WHil XBar
- 'Greenfield's Fancy' (Au)	EBee
- 'Greenheart' (Au/S)	SPop
- 'Greenpeace' (Au/S)	GAbr GAgs NDro SPop WAln XBar
- 'Grenache' (Au/B) **new**	XBar
- 'Greswolde' (Au/d)	MFie SPop
- 'Greta' (Au/S)	GAbr GAgs NDro SPop WHil
- 'Gretna Green' (Au/S)	SPop
- 'Grey Bonnet' (Au/S)	SPop
- 'Grey Cloud' (Au/B)	NDro WHil
- 'Grey Day' (Au/S) **new**	NDro
- 'Grey Friar' (Au/S)	SPop
- 'Grey Hawk' (Au/S)	NDro SPop
- 'Grey Ladywood' (Au/d)	SPop
- 'Grey Lag' (Au/S)	NSum SPop WHil XBar
- 'Grey Monarch' (Au/S)	GAbr MFie SPop WHil
- 'Grey Owl' (Au/S)	NDro SPop
- 'Grey Shrike' (Au/S)	NDro SPop
- 'Grizedale' (Au/S)	SPop
- 'Groupie' (Au/St)	SPop
- 'Grüner Veltliner' (Au/S)	SPop
- 'Guinea' (Au/S)	CTal GAbr ITim NDro SPop
- 'Gwai Loh' (Au)	NDro
- 'Gwen' (Au/A)	MFie NDro SPop WAln XBar
- 'Gwen Baker' (Au/d)	GAbr MFie NDro SPop WAln
- 'Gwenda' (Au/A)	NDro SPop WAln WHil
- 'Gypsy Boy' (Au/A)	WAln
- 'Gypsy Rose Lee' (Au/A)	MFie
- 'H Old Gold' (Au/S)	NDro
- 'Habanera' (Au/A)	MFie NDro NSum SPop WFar
- 'Haffner' (Au/S)	NDro SPop
- 'Hallmark' (Au/A)	MFie NDro WAln
- 'Handsome Lass' (Au/St)	GAgs MFie NDro SPop WAln
- 'Hannah' (Au/A)	WAln
- 'Harlequin' (Au/B)	NDro
- 'Harmony' (Au/B)	MFie NDro NSum SPop XBar
- 'Harry Armitage' (Au/B) **new**	NDro
- 'Harry Hotspur' (Au/A)	GAgs MFie NDro NSum SPop WFar WHil
- 'Harry 'O'' (Au/S)	NDro SPop
- 'Harthorpeburn' (Au/B)	NDro
- 'Harvest Glow' (Au/S)	NDro SPop WFar WHil
- 'Harvest Gold' (Au/S)	NDro
- 'Havana' (Au/d)	SPop WAln
- 'Hawkwood' (Au/S)	GAbr GAgs MFie NDro NEgg WHil XBar
- 'Hazel' (Au/B)	MFie NDro
- 'Hazel' (Au/A)	MFie NDro SPop WHil
- 'Headdress' (Au/S)	GAbr GAgs SPop
- 'Heady' (Au/A)	GAgs MFie NDro SPop WHil XBar
- 'Heart of Gold' (Au/A)	MFie NDro SPop WAln
- 'Hearts of Oak' (Au/A)	WAln
- 'Heaven Scent' (Au)	NDro WHil
- 'Hebers' (Au)	NDro SPop WAln
- 'Helen' (Au/S)	GAbr MFie NDro SPop WHil
- 'Helen Barter' (Au/S)	NDro NSum SPop WHil
- 'Helen Ruane' (Au/d)	EBee GAgs SPop WFar
- 'Helena' (Au/S)	MFie NDro SPop WAln WHil XBar
- 'Helena Brown' (Au/S)	SPop
- 'Helena Dean' (Au/d)	SPop WAln
- 'Helluinn' (Au/d)	SPop
- 'Henry's Bane' (Au/St)	SPop
- 'Her Nibs' (Au/St)	MAsh NDro SPop
- 'Hermia' (Au/A)	MFie SPop
- 'Hetty Woolf' (Au/S)	GAbr NDro SPop
- 'Hew Dalrymple' (Au/S)	NDro SPop
- 'Highland Park' (Au/A)	GAgs NDro SPop WHil
- 'Hillhook' (Au/A)	NSum WAln
- 'Hillview Hermes' (Au/S)	WHil
- Hillview selection (Au)	WHil
- 'Hinton Admiral' (Au/S)	GAbr GAgs NDro SPop WHil XBar
- 'Hinton Fields' (Au/S)	EBee EShb EWTr GAbr GAgs MFie NDro NEgg SPop WFar WHil
- 'Hobby Horse' (Au)	GAgs ITim
- 'Holyrood' (Au/S)	GAbr ITim NDro NHpl SPop XBar
- 'Honey' (Au/d)	GAbr NDro NEgg NSum SPop
- 'Honeydawn' (Au/B)	NDro
- 'Hopleys Coffee' (Au/d)	GAbr NDro SPop WAln
- 'Hopton Gem' (Au/B)	NDro
- 'Hot Chocolate' (Au/d)	SPop
- 'Howard Telford' (Au/A)	MFie SPop
- 'Hughie' (Au/A)	WAln
- 'Humphrey' (Au/S)	WAln
- 'Hurstwood Midnight' (Au)	MFie XBar
- 'Iago' (Au/S)	SPop
- 'Ian Greville' (Au/A)	MFie NDro SPop
- 'Ibis' (Au/A)	NDro WAln
- 'Ice Cap' (Au/d)	SPop
- 'Ice Maiden' (Au/A)	GAbr MFie NDro NSum SPop WHil
- 'Icon' (Au/St)	SPop
- 'Idmiston' (Au/S)	GAbr GAgs NDro SPop WHil XBar
- 'Ilona' (Au/d)	SPop
- 'Imari Stripe' (Au/St)	WHil
- 'Immaculate' (Au/A)	GAgs MFie NDro NSum SPop WHil
- 'Impassioned' (Au/A)	MFie SPop XBar
- 'Impeccable' (Au/A)	MFie
- 'Imperturbable' (Au/A)	MFie NDro SPop
- 'Indian Love Call' (Au/A)	GAbr GAgs ITim MFie NDro SPop WHil
I - 'Innominata' (Au/S) **new**	NDro
- 'Innsworth' (Au/A)	SPop WAln
- 'Iris Scott' (Au/A)	ITim NDro
- 'Isabel' (Au/S)	WAln
- 'Isabella' (Au/A)	NDro WAln
- 'Jac' (Au/S)	SPop
- 'Jack Dean' (Au/A)	GAgs MFie SPop WFar WHil XBar
- 'Jack Horner' (Au)	NDro
- 'Jack Redfern' (Au/A)	NDro
- 'Jaffa' (Au/A)	NDro NSum WAln
- 'James Arnot' (Au/S)	GAbr NDro SPop XBar
- 'James Wattam' (Au/S)	NDro
- 'Jane' (Au/S)	WAln
- 'Jane Myers' (Au/d)	WAln WHil
- 'Janet' (Au)	IRob
- 'Janet Watts' (Au)	GAgs NDro
- 'Janie Hill' (Au/A)	GAbr MFie SPop XBar
- 'Jb' (Au) **new**	GAbr
- 'Je t'Adore' (Au/St) **new**	NDro
- 'Jealous Lover' (Au/St)	SPop
- 'Jean Fielder' (Au/A)	NDro SPop WAln
- 'Jean Jacques' (Au/A)	NDro SPop WAln
- 'Jean Jacques' (Au/d)	XBar
- 'Jean Walker' (Au/B)	SPop
- 'Jeanne' (Au/A)	MFie
- 'Jeannie Jingles' (Au/St)	SPop

- 'Jeannie Jingles II' (Au/St) **new** NDro
- 'Jeannie Telford' (Au/A) MFie NDro SPop
- 'Jeff Scruton' (Au/A) SPop WAln
- 'Jenny' (Au/A) MFie NDro NRya SPop WFar
- 'Jersey Bounce' (Au/A) GAbr ITim NDro SPop
- 'Jesmond' (Au/S) SPop
- 'Jilting Jessie' (Au/St) GAgs NDro SPop
- 'Joan Butler' (Au) SPop
- 'Joan Curtis' (Au/d) SPop
- 'Joan Elliott' (Au/A) GAbr
- 'Joanne' (Au/d) **new** NDro
- 'Joanne' (Au/A) GAgs MFie NDro SPop
- 'Joe Perks' (Au/A) GAgs ITim MFie NDro WHil XBar
- 'Joel' (Au/S) GAgs ITim MFie NDro SPop XBar
- 'Johann Bach' (Au/B) NDro SPop
- 'John Hart' (Au/A) **new** NDro
- 'John Stewart' (Au/A) SPop
- 'John Wayne' (Au/A) GAbr MFie NDro SPop WHil
- 'John Woolf' (Au/S) NDro
- 'Jonathon' (Au/A) NDro WAln
- 'Jorvik' (Au/S) MFie SPop
- 'Joy' (Au/A) LLHF MFie NDro NSum NWad SPop WHil
- 'Joyce' (Au/A) GAbr MFie NDro NSum SPop WFar WHil XBar
- 'Judith Borman' (Au/d) NDro SPop
- 'Julia' (Au/S) NDro SPop
- 'Julia Jane' (Au/B) NDro
- 'Julie Nuttall' (Au/B) GAbr GAgs NDro NSum NWad SPop WHil
- 'June' (Au/A) NDro NSum SPop
- 'Jungfrau' (Au/d) MFie NDro SPop WAln
- 'Jupiter' (Au/S) SPop
- 'Jupp' (Au/d) EBee EWTr GAgs
- 'Jura' (Au/A) WAln
- 'Just Steven' (Au/A) SPop WAln
- 'Justin Case' (Au/B) NDro WAln
- 'K S' (Au/S) NDro
- 'Karen Cordrey' (Au/S) EBee GAbr GAgs ITim NDro NSum SPop WHil
- 'Karen McDonald' (Au/A) NDro SPop
- 'Kate Haywood' (Au/B) NDro WHil
- 'Kelso' (Au/A) SPop
- 'Ken Chilton' (Au/A) GAgs MFie NDro SPop WHil
- 'Kenco' (Au/d) SPop
- 'Kentucky Blues' (Au/d) MFie NDro SPop WAln
- 'Kercup' (Au/A) MFie SPop
- 'Kerry' (Au/A) EBee GAgs SPop WAln
- 'Kersey' (Au/S) NDro SPop
- 'Kevin' (Au/A) SPop WAln
- 'Kevin Keegan' (Au/A) MFie NDro NSum SPop WHil
- 'Key West' (Au/A) NDro SPop WAln
- 'Khachaturian' (Au/A) NDro SPop WAln
- 'Kilby' (Au/A) GAgs NDro NSum SPop
- 'Kim' (Au/A) NDro SPop WHil
- 'Kimberworth Boy' (Au/A) NDro WAln
- 'Kincraig' (Au/S) SPop
- 'King George' (Au/d) MFie WAln
- 'Kingcup' (Au/A) GAbr GAgs MFie NDro SPop
- 'Kingfisher' (Au/A) GAgs MFie NDro SPop WHil
- 'Kingpin' (Au/St) NDro
- 'Kiowa' (Au/S) SPop
- 'Kirklands' (Au/d) ITim MFie NDro SPop WHil
- 'Kitterford Cross' (Au/B) NDro
- 'Knights' (Au/S) SPop
- 'Kohinoor' (Au) MFie WHil
- 'Koho' (Au/d) **new** SPop
- 'Königin der Nacht' (Au/St) MFie NDro SPop WHil
- 'Lady Daresbury' (Au/A) MFie NDro SPop WHil
- 'Lady Day' (Au/d) SPop WAln
- 'Lady Diana' (Au/S) NDro
- 'Lady Emma Monson' (Au/S) NDro SPop
- 'Lady of the Vale' (Au/A) NDro SPop WAln
- 'Lady Zoë' (Au/S) GAgs LLHF MAsh MFie NDro SPop
- 'Laguna' (Au/d) SPop
- 'Lambert's Gold' (Au) GAbr SPop
- 'Lambrook Gold' (Au/B) NDro
- 'Lamplugh' (Au/d) NSum SPop WHil
- 'Lancelot' (Au/d) SPop
- 'Landy' (Au/A) MFie NDro SPop
- 'Langley Park' (Au/A) MFie NDro SPop WHil
- 'Laphroaigh' (Au/S) WAln
- 'Laptop' (Au/St) SPop
- 'Lara' (Au/A) MFie NDro SPop
- 'Laredo' (Au/A) WAln
- 'Larry' (Au/A) GAgs LLHF MFie NDro SPop WFar XBar
- 'Last Chance' (Au/St) NDro
- 'Late Romantic' (Au) CBod CDor ECtt GAbr GBin MHol NHpl NLar WTor
- 'Lavender and Old Lace' (Au/d) SPop
- 'Lavender Hill' (Au/St) **new** NDro
- 'Lavender Lady' (Au/B) NDro NEgg
- 'Lavender Ridge' (Au/B) NDro WAln
- 'Lavenham' (Au/S) SPop WAln
- 'Laverock' (Au/S) NEgg WHil
- 'Laverock Fancy' (Au/S) GAbr GAgs NDro SPop XBar
- 'Lazy River' (Au/A) NDro WAln
- 'Leather Jacket' (Au) GAbr WHil
- 'Leathercoat' (Au) SPop
- 'Lechistan' (Au/S) GAgs MAsh NDro SPop WHil
- 'Lee' (Au/A) MFie NDro WAln
- 'Lee Clark' (Au/A) MFie NDro WAln
- 'Lee Paul' (Au/A) GAgs MFie NDro NSum SPop WHil
- 'Lee Sharpe' (Au/A) MFie NDro NSum SPop WAln
- 'Legolas' (Au/A) SPop WAln
- 'Leicester Square' (Au/S) NDro
- 'Lemmy Getatem' (Au/d) SPop
- 'Lemon Drizzle' (Au/S) WAln
- 'Lemon Drop' (Au/S) GAgs ITim MFie NDro SPop
- 'Lemon Ice' (Au/S) WAln
- 'Lemon Ridge' (Au/B) WAln
- 'Lemon Sherbet' (Au/B) GAbr GAgs NDro SPop WHil
- 'Lemon Zest' (Au/d) WAln
- 'Lemonade' (Au) GAgs
- 'Leona' (Au/d) SPop
- 'Lepton Jubilee' (Au/S) GAbr NDro SPop WAln
- 'Leroy Brown' (Au/A) WAln
- 'Lester' (Au/d) MFie SPop WAln WHil
- 'Leverton' (Au/d) SPop
- 'Lewis Telford' (Au/A) SPop
- 'Lichfield' (Au/A/d) SPop
- 'Light Fantastic' (Au/S) NDro SPop
- 'Light Hearted' (Au/A) MFie NDro SPop XBar
- 'Light Music' (Au/d) WAln
- 'Likely Lad' (Au/St) SPop
- 'Lila' (Au/S) NDro SPop WAln
- 'Lilac Domino' (Au/S) GAbr GAgs MFie NDro NEgg SPop WHil
- 'Lilac Ladywood' (Au/d) MFie SPop WFar
- 'Lilac Mist' (Au/d) XBar
- 'Lillian Hill' (Au/A) MFie WAln
- 'Lillibet' (Au/A) NDro
- 'Lima' (Au/d) SPop WAln
- 'Limaki' (Au/d) SPop

- 'Lime 'n' Lemon' (Au) ITim NDro
- 'Lime Ridge' (Au) WAln
- 'Limelight' (Au/A) SPop
- 'Limelight' (Au/S) NDro SPop
- 'Lincoln Biscuit' (Au/d) SPop
- 'Lincoln Bullion' (Au/d) MAsh NDro SPop XBar
- 'Lincoln Charm' (Au/d) SPop
- 'Lincoln Chestnut' (Au/d) NDro SPop XBar
- 'Lincoln Consort' (Au/d) SPop
- 'Lincoln Cuckoo' (Au/d) NDro
- 'Lincoln Elf' (Au/d) SPop
- 'Lincoln Gem' (Au/d) SPop
- 'Lincoln Glow' (Au/d) SPop
- 'Lincoln Halo' (Au/d) SPop
- 'Lincoln Harmony' (Au/d) **new** SPop
- 'Lincoln Imperial' (Au/d) GAbr NDro SPop
- 'Lincoln Major' (Au/d) SPop
- 'Lincoln Melody' (Au/St/d) XBar
- 'Lincoln Poacher' (Au/d) NDro
- 'Lincoln Pride' (Au/d) SPop
- 'Lincoln Storm' (Au/d) SPop
- 'Lincoln Whisper' (Au/d) NDro
- 'Linda' (Au/A) SPop WAln WHil
- 'Lindley' (Au/S) GAgs NDro SPop
- 'Ling' (Au/A) GAbr MFie NDro SPop
- 'Linnet' (Au/B) NDro
- 'Lintz' (Au/B) MFie NDro SPop WHil
- 'Linze 2' (Au/S) NDro
- 'Lisa' (Au/A) GAgs MFie SPop WFar WHil
- 'Lisa Clara' (Au/S) GAbr GAgs MAsh MFie NDro NHpl SPop WFar
- 'Lisa's Smile' (Au/S) MFie NDro SPop WHil
- 'Little Rosetta' (Au/d) GAbr GAgs NDro NSum WHil
- 'Lizzie Files' (Au/A) SPop WAln
- 'Lockyer's Gem' (Au/B/St) NDro NEgg
- 'Lofty' (Au/St) NDro
- 'Lolita' (Au/St) GAgs NDro SPop WHil XBar
- 'Lord Saye and Sele' (Au/St) CWCL GAbr GAgs MAsh MFie NDro NEgg NSum NWad SPop WHil XBar
- 'Lothlorien' (Au/A) WAln
- 'Louis' (Au/d) XBar
- 'Louisa Woolhead' (Au/d) SPop
- 'Louise Jordan' (Au/A) NDro SPop
- 'Love Nest' (Au/S) SPop
- 'Lovebird' (Au/S) GAbr MFie NHpl SPop XBar
- 'Lucia' (Au/B) XBar
- 'Lucy Locket' (Au/B) EWTr GAbr ITim NDro NEgg NSum SPop WHil
- 'Ludlow' (Au/S) GAbr SPop
- 'Lunar Eclipse' (Au/d) **new** CBod MHol NPnk WTor
- 'Lune Tiger' (Au/St) NDro SPop
- 'Lupy Minstrel' (Au/S) MFie NDro SPop WAln
- 'Lusty Lad' (Au/St) SPop
- 'Lynn' (Au/A) WAln
- 'Lynn Cooper' (Au) SPop
- 'MacWatt's Blue' (Au/B) GAbr NDro SPop WHil
- 'Macy the Cat' (Au) WHil
- 'Madelaine Palmer' (Au/d) SPop
- 'Maggie' (Au/S) GAbr NDro NSum SPop
- 'Magnolia' (Au/B) WHil
- 'Mamba' (Au/S) SPop
- 'Mandarin' (Au/A) GAbr GAgs MFie NDro NSum SPop WHil XBar
- 'Mandy' (Au/S) MFie
- 'Manka' (Au/S) SPop
- 'Marble Arch' (Au/S) **new** NDro
- 'Mardi Gras' (Au/d) WAln
- 'Margaret' (Au/S) GAbr
- 'Margaret Faulkner' (Au/A) GAbr MFie SPop
- 'Margaret Irene' (Au/A) SPop
- 'Margaret Martin' (Au/S) ITim MFie NDro SPop
- 'Margaret Merril' (Au) GAbr
- 'Margery Thompson' (Au/d) SPop
- 'Margot' (Au/S) WAln
- 'Margot Fonteyn' (Au/A) GAbr MFie SPop WHil
- 'Mariandl' (Au/A) EBee EWTr
- 'Marie Crousse' (Au/d) CFis CMea ITim MFie NDro SPop WCot WHil
- 'Marie Pierre' (Au/d) XBar
- 'Marion Howard Spring' (Au/A) MFie
- 'Marion Tiger' (Au/St) NDro SPop
- 'Mark' (Au/A) GAgs MFie NDro SPop
- 'Marmalade' (Au/d) SPop
- 'Marmion' (Au/S) GAbr GAgs ITim MFie NDro SPop WHil XBar
- 'Mars Bars' (Au/St) **new** NDro
- 'Martha Livesley' (Au/A) WAln
- 'Martha's Choice' (Au/A) WAln
- 'Martin Luther King' (Au/S) NDro SPop WHil XBar
- 'Mary' (Au/d) GAbr NDro SPop WAln
- 'Mary Poppins' (Au/S) MFie NDro
- 'Mary Taylor' (Au/S) NDro SPop
- 'Mary Zach' (Au/S) MFie NDro SPop WAln WHil
- 'Marylebone' (Au/S) **new** NDro
- 'Matthew' (Au) **new** GKev
- 'Matthew Yates' (Au/d) GAbr GAgs ITim MFie NDro NHpl SPop WCot WHil
- 'Mattie' (Au/d) GAgs
- 'Maureen Millward' (Au/A) MFie SPop
- 'May' (Au/A) NDro NSum
- 'May Booley' (Au/d) SPop
- 'Mazetta Stripe' (Au/S/St) GAbr GAgs MFie NDro SPop
- 'Meadow Sweet' (Au/S) NDro
- 'Meadowlark' (Au/A) ITim MFie SPop WHil
- 'Meg' (Au/d) SPop
- 'Megan' (Au/d) SPop WAln
- 'Mehta' (Au/A) NDro SPop WAln
- 'Mellifluous' (Au) GAgs MFie WHil
- 'Melody' (Au/S) NDro SPop
- 'Menin' (Au/d) SPop
- 'Mere Peppermint' (Au) SPop
- 'Merlin' (Au/S) MFie NSum
- 'Merlin Stripe' (Au/St) CWCL NDro SPop WHil XBar
- 'Mermaid' (Au/d) GAbr
- 'Merridale' (Au/A) GAbr MFie SPop WHil
- 'Mersey Tiger' (Au/S) GAbr GAgs ITim MFie NDro NSum SPop WHil
- 'Metis' (Au/d) SPop
- 'Mexicano' (Au/A) WAln
- 'Michael' (Au/S) MFie SPop WAln WHil
- 'Michael Wattam' (Au/S) NDro SPop
- 'Mick' (Au/A) MFie WHil
- 'Midland Marvel' (Au/St) NDro SPop
- 'Midnight' (Au/A) WAln
- 'Mikado' (Au/S) NSum SPop WHil XBar
- 'Milkmaid' (Au/A) MFie NSla WMAq
- 'Millicent' (Au/A) MFie NDro NSum SPop WHil
- 'Millicent Betsy' (Au/d) SPop
- 'Millie Redfern' (Au/d) SPop
- 'Minley' (Au/S) GAbr GAgs NDro NEgg SPop
- 'Minotaur' (Au/A) SPop
- 'Minstead' (Au/S) SPop

- 'Minstrel' (Au/S) ITim MFie NDro SPop
- 'Minty' (Au/St) SPop
- 'Mipsie Miranda' (Au/d) SPop
- 'Mirabella Bay' (Au/A) SPop WAln
- 'Miranda' (Au/d) SPop
- 'Mirandinha' (Au/A) NDro SPop
- 'Miriam' (Au/A) GAgs SPop
- 'Mish Mish' (Au/d) GAbr NDro WHil
- 'Miss Bluey' (Au/d) NDro SPop WAln XBar
- 'Miss Jones' (Au/St) NDro SPop
- 'Miss Muffet' (Au/S) WAln
- 'Miss Newman' (Au/A) NSum SPop
- 'Miss Otis' (Au/S) SPop
- 'Miss Pinky' (Au) NDro SPop
- 'Mist' (Au/S) WAln
- 'Misty' (Au/d) **new** SPop
- 'Mojave' (Au/S) GAbr GAgs ITim MFie NDro NEgg NHpl NSum SPop WHil XBar
- 'Mollie Langford' (Au/A) MFie NDro SPop WHil
- 'Mondeo' (Au/A) WAln
- 'Monet' (Au/S) NDro
- 'Moneymoon' (Au/S) GAbr NDro SPop WHil
- 'Monica' (Au/A) MFie
- 'Monk' (Au/S) MFie SPop WHil XBar
- 'Monmouth Star' (Au/St) NDro WHil
- 'Moon Fairy' (Au/S) NDro SPop
- 'Moondance' (Au/d) WAln
- 'Moonglow' (Au/S) GAbr NDro
- 'Moonlight' (Au/S) WAln
- 'Moonrise' (Au/S) MFie NDro SPop
- 'Moonriver' (Au/A) SPop WHil
- 'Moonshine' (Au/d) SPop WAln
- 'Moonshot' (Au/d) NDro SPop
- 'Moonstone' (Au/d) SPop WAln
- 'Morello' (Au/d) XBar
- 'Morning Glory' (Au/B) WAln
- 'Morven' (Au) GAbr
- 'Moscow' (Au/S) SPop
- 'Moselle' (Au/S) MFie NDro SPop
- 'Mossy Vale' (Au/S) SPop
- 'Mr A' (Au/S) GAgs NDro WHil
- 'Mr Bojangles' (Au/d) MFie WAln
- 'Mr Frosty' (Au/d) **new** SPop
- 'Mrs Cairn's Blue' (Au/B) NDro
- 'Mrs Dargan' (Au/d) NDro
- 'Mrs L. Hearn' (Au/A) ITim MFie NDro SPop
- 'Mrs R. Bolton' (Au/A) WHil
- 'Mrs Robinson' (Au/St) SPop
- 'Mrs Wilson' (Au) GAbr
- 'Muriel James' (Au/A) SPop
- 'Murray Lakes' (Au/A) NDro SPop WAln
- 'Mustard Sauce' (Au/B) NDro
- 'My Buddy' (Au/St) SPop
- 'My Delight' (Au/d) SPop
- 'My Fair Lady' (Au/A) MFie NDro SPop
- 'My Friend' (Au/B) GAbr NDro SPop
- 'Myodeboots' (Au/A) SPop
- 'Myrtle Park' (Au/A) WAln
- 'Mystery' (Au) GAbr
- 'Nancy Dalgetty' (Au/B) NDro SPop
- 'Nantenan' (Au/S) GAbr MFie NDro SPop
- 'Neat and Tidy' (Au/S) CTal GAbr GAgs ITim MFie NDro SPop
- 'Nefertiti' (Au/A) NDro SPop WHil
- 'Nessun Dorma' (Au/A) NDro WAln
- 'Neville Telford' (Au/S) GAbr MFie NDro SPop WFar WHil
- 'Newbottle' (Au/S) SPop WHil
- 'Newsboy' (Au/A) WAln
- 'Newton Harcourt' (Au/A) SPop WHil
- 'Nick Drake' (Au/d) SPop
- 'Nickity' (Au/A) GAbr GAgs ITim MFie NDro NSum SPop WHil XBar
- 'Nicola Jane' (Au/A) GAgs SPop WAln
- 'Nigel' (Au/d) GAbr MFie NDro
- 'Night and Day' (Au/St) SPop
- 'Nightwink' (Au/S) WAln
- 'Nil Amber' (Au) GAbr SPop
- 'Nina' (Au/A) NDro SPop WAln
- 'Nita' (Au/d) SPop WAln
- 'No 21' (Au/S) NDro SPop
- 'No Deal' (Au/S) SPop
- 'Nocturne' (Au/S) NDro NSum SPop
- 'Noelle' (Au/S) GAgs NDro
- 'Nona' (Au/d) MFie NDro NSum SPop
- 'Nonchalance' (Au/A) MFie NDro NSum SPop WHil
- 'Norma' (Au/A) MFie NDro SPop
- 'Northern Lights' (Au/S) GAbr NDro
- 'Nureyev' (Au/A) SPop
- 'Nymph' (Au/d) GAbr GAgs MFie NDro SPop WHil
- 'Oakenshield' (Au/A) WAln
- 'Oakie' (Au/S) SPop
- 'Oban' (Au/S) MFie NDro SPop XBar
- 'Odette' (Au) MFie SPop WHil
- 'O'er the Moon' (Au/S) WAln
- 'Oikos' (Au/B) NDro SPop
- 'Ol' Blue Eyes' (Au/St) SPop
- 'Old Black Isle Dusty Miller' (Au/B) NDro WHil
- 'Old Buffer' (Au/St) NDro SPop
- 'Old Clove Red' (Au/B) GAbr MFie NDro NSum WHil
- 'Old Cottage Blue' (Au/B) GAbr NDro
- 'Old Dublin Blue' (Au/B) NDro
- 'Old England' (Au/S) GAbr GAgs MFie NDro SPop
- 'Old Gold' (Au/S) GAbr NDro SPop WFar
- 'Old Gold Dusty Miller' (Au/B) NDro
- 'Old Irish Blue' (Au/B) ITim NDro NEgg
- 'Old Irish Green' (Au/B) GAbr NDro NSum
- 'Old Irish Scented' (Au/B) CTal GAbr MFie NDro SPop WHil
- 'Old Irish Yellow' (Au/B) NDro NEgg NHpl
- 'Old Mustard' (Au/B) GAbr NDro SBch SMHy
- 'Old Pink Dusty Miller' (Au/B) GAbr
- § - 'Old Purple Dusty Miller' (Au/B) GAbr
- 'Old Red' (Au) GAgs
- 'Old Red Dusty Miller' (Au/B) GAbr LLHF NDro NSum SPop WHil
- 'Old Red Elvet' (Au/S) GAbr SPop
- 'Old Smokey' (Au/A) MFie NDro SPop WHil XBar
- 'Old Suffolk Bronze' (Au/B) GAbr GAgs ITim NDro WHil
- 'Old Timer' (Au/S) SPop
- 'Old Yellow Dusty Miller' (Au/B) CTal EWes GAbr NDro NWad WHil
- 'Old-Fashioned' (Au/B) NDro
- 'Oldfield' (Au/d) SPop
- 'Olivia' (Au/d) SPop
- 'Olton' (Au/A) MFie WFar XBar
- 'Optimist' (Au/St) GAgs NDro SPop
- 'Opus One' (Au/A) WAln
- 'Orb' (Au/S) SPop WHil
- 'Ordvic' (Au/S) NDro
- 'Orlando' (Au/S) NDro SPop
- 'Orwell Tiger' (Au/St) GAgs MFie NDro SPop
- 'Osbaston Bullseye' (Au/St) SPop
- 'Osborne Green' (Au/B) GAbr GAgs SPop WHil
- 'Osorno' (Au/d) SPop
- 'Ossett Sapphire' (Au/A) NDro SPop

- 'Otto Dix' (Au/A) SPop WAln
- 'Our Sophie' (Au/B) NDro
- 'Overdale' (Au/A) NDro NSum SPop WAln
- 'Oyster' (Au/B) NDro
- 'Paddlin' Madeleine' (Au/A) NDro WAln
- 'Pageboy' (Au/A) WAln
- 'Paleface' (Au/A) GAgs MFie NDro NSum SPop
- 'Pall Mall' (Au/St) **new** NDro
- 'Panache' (Au/S) WAln
- 'Pang Tiger' (Au/St) NDro SPop
- 'Paphos' (Au/d) SPop
- 'Paradise Yellow' (Au/B) GAbr NDro NEgg SPop
- 'Paragon' (Au/A) WHil
- 'Parakeet' (Au/S) NDro
- 'Paris' (Au/S) SPop
- 'Partney' (Au/d) **new** SPop
- 'Party Animal' (Au/St) NDro SPop XBar
- 'Party Time' (Au/S) SPop
- 'Passchendaele' (Au/d) SPop
- 'Passing Cloud' (Au/d) WAln
- 'Pastures New' (Au) SPop
- 'Pat' (Au/S) SPop
- 'Pat Mooney' (Au/d) NDro
- 'Patience' (Au/S) NDro WHil
- 'Patricia Barras' (Au/S) WAln
- 'Paula' (Au/A) **new** SPop
- 'Pauline' (Au/A) MFie SPop
- 'Pavarotti' (Au/A) ITim NDro NSum SPop
- 'Pegasus' (Au/d) NDro SPop
- 'Peggy' (Au/A) GAbr ITim NSum WHil
- 'People's Choice' (Au/d) SPop
- 'Pequod' (Au/A) NDro NSum SPop
- 'Perirot' (Au) ITim
- 'Perito Moreno' (Au/d) SPop
- 'Persephone' (Au/B) NDro
- 'Phantom' (Au/d) SPop WAln
- 'Pharaoh' (Au/A) GAbr GAgs MFie NDro SPop XBar
- 'Phoenix' (Au/A) WAln
- 'Phyllis Douglas' (Au/A) GAgs MFie NDro NEgg SPop WHil
- 'Piccadilly' (Au/S) MAsh MFie NDro SPop
- 'Piccalilli' (Au/d) XBar
- 'Pierot' (Au/A) GAgs MFie NDro NSum SPop WHil XBar
- 'Piers Telford' (Au/A) CTal EBee GAbr GAgs MFie NDro NEgg NSum SBch SPop WFar WHil XBar
- 'Piglet' (Au/d) GAbr NDro SPop WHil
- 'Pikey' (Au/S) NDro SPop
- 'Pimlico' (Au/S) SPop
- 'Pimroagh' (Au/A) GAbr SPop
- 'Pink Floyd' (Au/A) SPop
- 'Pink Fondant' (Au/d) GAbr NDro
- 'Pink Hint' (Au/B) NDro SPop
- 'Pink Lady' (Au/A) GAbr GAgs MFie NSum SPop WHil
- 'Pink Lilac' (Au/A/S) NDro
- 'Pink Triumph' (Au) NDro WHil
- 'Pinkerton' (Au/d) SPop WAln
- 'Pinkie' (Au/A) WHil
- 'Pinkie Dawn' (Au/B) NDro SPop
- 'Pinstripe' (Au) GAbr GAgs NDro NSum SPop WHil
- 'Pioneer Stripe' (Au/S) GAbr GAgs SPop
- 'Pippin' (Au/A) GAbr GAgs MFie NDro SPop WHil XBar
- 'Pixie' (Au/A) GAgs MFie NDro SPop
- 'Playboy' (Au/A) NDro SPop WAln
- 'Plum Pudding' (Au/d) SPop WAln
- 'Plums and Custard' (Au/B) XBar
- 'Poacher's Lady' (Au/d) NDro
- 'Poacher's Starlight' (Au/d) NDro
- 'Polestar' (Au/A) MFie NDro NSum SPop WHil
- 'Polly' (Au/B) GAgs NDro NSum WHil
- 'Pop's Blue' (Au/S/d) NEgg SPop
- 'Portree' (Au/S) GAbr SPop
- 'Post Master' (Au/S) WAln
- 'Pot o' Gold' (Au/S) EBee GAgs NDro NEgg SPop WHil XBar
- 'Powder and Paint' (Au/A) WAln
- 'Powder Puff' (Au/B) NDro SPop
- 'Prague' (Au/S) GAbr MFie NDro SPop
- 'Pretender' (Au/A) SPop
- 'Pretty Prop' (Au/St) SPop
- 'Pretty Purple' (Au/d) SPop WAln
- 'Pride of Poland' (Au/S) SPop
- 'Prima' (Au/d) NDro
- 'Primary Red' (Au/S) **new** SPop
- 'Prince Bishops' (Au/S) SPop WAln
- 'Prince Charming' (Au/S) GAgs NDro SPop
- 'Prince Igor' (Au/A) SPop
- 'Prince John' (Au/A) MFie NDro SPop WHil
- 'Pristine' (Au/B) WAln
- 'Proctor's Yellow' (Au/B) GAbr NDro WHil
- 'Prometheus' (Au/d) GAbr ITim LLHF MFie NDro NSum SPop WHil
- 'Prosperine' (Au/S) SPop
- 'Psyche' (Au/S) NDro SPop
- 'Ptarmigan' (Au) SPop
- 'Pumpkin' (Au) GAbr NHpl
- 'Puppy Love' (Au/St) SPop
- 'Purbeck' (Au/B) SPop
- 'Purple Dusty Miller' see *P. auricula* 'Old Purple Dusty Miller'
- 'Purple Emperor' (Au/A) MFie SPop
- 'Purple Flake' (Au/d) **new** SPop
- 'Purple Frills' (Au) MFie
- 'Purple Glow' (Au/d) WAln
- 'Purple Haze' (Au) SPop
- 'Purple Heart' (Au/d) **new** SPop
- 'Purple Knight' (Au/S) WAln
- 'Purple Lace' (Au/d) SPop
- 'Purple Lovely' (Au) MFie SPop
- 'Purple Orient' (Au/d) SPop
- 'Purple Patch' (Au/d) SPop
- 'Purple Pip' (Au/d) **new** CBod MHol
- 'Purple Pompom' (Au/d) **new** SPop
- 'Purple Prolific' (Au/B) NDro
- 'Purple Promise' (Au) GAbr ITim NDro SPop
- 'Purple Prose' (Au/St) MFie SPop WHil
- 'Purple Rose' (Au/d) ITim WAln
- 'Purple Royale' (Au/B) NDro
- 'Purple Sage' (Au/S) ITim NDro SPop WHil
- 'Purple Star' (Au/d) SPop
- 'Purple Velvet' (Au/S) NDro SPop
- 'Pye Powder' (Au/S) **new** SPop
- 'Quatro' (Au/d) GAgs SPop
- 'Queen' (Au/d) **new** SPop
- 'Queen Alexandra' (Au/B) GAbr NDro WHil
- 'Queen Bee' (Au/S) GAbr GAgs NDro SPop
- 'Queen's Bower' (Au/S) SPop
- 'Quintessence' (Au/A) MFie NDro SPop WHil
- 'R.L. Bowes' (Au/A) NDro
- 'Rab C. Nesbitt' (Au/A) SPop WAln
- 'Rabley Heath' (Au/A) GAbr GAgs ITim MFie NDro SPop WHil
- 'Rachel' (Au/A) WAln
- 'Rachel de Thame' (Au/S) WAln

- 'Rachel Labouchere' (Au/S) WAln
- 'Radiance' (Au/A) SPop
- 'Rag Doll' (Au/S) NDro
- 'Ragnald the Magnificent' (Au/S) WAln
- 'Rainy Days' (Au/B) NDro
- 'Rajah' (Au/S) GAbr GAgs MAsh MFie NEgg NHpl SPop WHil XBar
- 'Raleigh Stripe' (Au/St) GAbr GAgs SPop
- 'Rameses' (Au/A) MFie NDro SPop
- 'Rebecca Baker' (Au/d) SPop WHil
- 'Red Admiral' (Au) NDro SPop WAln
- 'Red Arrows' (Au) SPop WAln
- 'Red Baron' (Au/S) WAln
- 'Red Beret' (Au/S) SPop
- 'Red Bordeaux' (Au/S) GAgs NDro
- 'Red Carpet' (Au/S) SPop
- 'Red Diamond' (Au/d) WAln
- 'Red Embers' (Au/S) SPop WAln
- 'Red Ensign' (Au/B) NDro
- 'Red Gauntlet' (Au/S) GAbr GAgs MFie NDro SPop
- 'Red King' (Au/S) WAln
- 'Red Mark' (Au/A) MFie SPop WHil XBar
- 'Red Rum' (Au/S) GAbr SPop WAln
- 'Red Sonata' (Au/S) SPop
- 'Red Spin' (Au/S) SPop
- 'Red Wire' (Au/St) NDro NSum SPop
- 'Red Wrekin' (Au/S) **new** NDro
- 'Redcar' (Au/A) GAbr MFie NDro
- 'Reddown Apricot' (Au/B) NDro
- 'Reddown Barley Meal' (Au/B) NDro
- 'Reddown Bat' (Au/d) SPop
- 'Reddown First Swallow' (Au/B) NDro
- 'Reddown Rainman' (Au/B) NDro SPop
- 'Reddown Tickled Pink' (Au/B) NDro
- 'Redstart' (Au/S) EBee GAgs GKev ITim WHil
- 'Regency' (Au/A) NDro
- 'Regency Carousel' (Au/St) SPop
- 'Regency Dandy' (Au/St) SPop
- 'Regency Emperor' (Au/St) NDro SPop WHil
- 'Regency Paperchase' (Au/St) NDro SPop
- 'Regency Peppermint Tea' (Au/St) SPop
- 'Regency Saint Clements' (Au/St) NDro SPop
- 'Remus' (Au/S) ELan GAbr GAgs ITim LLHF MFie NDro NEgg SPop WHil XBar
- 'Renata' (Au/S) SPop
- 'Rene' (Au/A) GAbr SPop WHil XBar
- 'Renishaw Hall' (Au/S) **new** SPop
- 'Renown' (Au/A) NDro WAln
- 'Repton' (Au/S) SPop
- 'Requiem' (Au/d) WAln
- 'Reresby Sitwell' (Au/S) **new** SPop
- 'Resi' (Au) GAgs WHil
- 'Respectable' (Au/A) WAln
- 'Reverie' (Au/d) SPop WAln
- 'Reynardine' (Au/d) SPop WAln
- 'Rhinegold' (Au/d) XBar
- 'Riatty' (Au/d) GAbr GAgs MFie NDro SPop
- 'Richard Shaw' (Au/A) NDro SPop
- 'Ring of Bells' (Au/S) SPop WAln
- 'Ring of Fire' (Au/A) WAln
- 'Rintein' (Au/B) **new** NDro
- 'Risdene' (Au) SPop WAln
- 'Rivendell' (Au/A) WAln
- 'Robbo' (Au/B) GAbr NDro
- 'Robert Green' (Au/S) SPop
- 'Robert Lee' (Au/A) WAln
- 'Roberto' (Au/S) NDro SPop
- 'Robin Hood Stripe' (Au/St) GAgs NDro SPop
- 'Robinette' (Au/d) GAbr SPop
- 'Rock Sand' (Au/S) GAbr GAgs MFie NDro SPop WHil
- 'Rockbourne' (Au/A) SPop
- 'Rodeo' (Au/A) GAbr GAgs SPop
- 'Rolts' (Au/S) GAbr GAgs NDro SPop WHil XBar
- 'Rondy' (Au/S) ITim SPop WHil
- 'Ronnie Johnson' (Au) WAln
- 'Rosalie' (Au) SPop
- 'Rosalie Edwards' (Au/S) MFie NDro SPop
- 'Rose Conjou' (Au/d) GAbr GAgs MFie NDro SPop WHil XBar
- 'Rose Kaye' (Au/A) GAbr SPop
- 'Rose Petal' (Au/d) XBar
- 'Rosebud' (Au/S) GAbr GAgs NDro
- 'Rosemarket Rackler' (Au/B) NDro
- 'Rosemary' (Au/S) GAbr NDro SPop WHil
- 'Rosewood' (Au) SPop WAln
- 'Rosie' (Au/S) NDro
- 'Rostock' (Au/B) NDro
- 'Rothesay Robin' (Au/A) WAln
- 'Rouge Gorge' (Au/B) XBar
- 'Rowena' (Au/A) MFie NDro NSum SPop WHil
- 'Roxborough' (Au/A) GAgs
- 'Roxburgh' (Au/A) MFie NDro SPop
- 'Roy Keane' (Au/A) MFie NSum SPop WAln
- 'Royal Mail' (Au/S) MFie NDro SPop
- 'Royal Marine' (Au/S) MFie SPop WAln
- 'Royal Scot' (Au/S) SPop
- 'Royal Velvet' (Au/S) GAbr GAgs NDro WFar WHil
- 'Ruby Hyde' (Au/B) GAbr NDro SPop
- 'Ruddy Duck' (Au/S) SPop
- 'Rumbled' (Au/St) MAsh
- 'Runwell' (Au/B) NDro
- 'Runwell Red' (Au/B) SPop
- 'Rusty Dusty' (Au) GAbr
- 'Ryecroft' (Au/A) WAln
- 'Sabrina' (Au/A) WAln
- 'Saginaw' (Au/A) WAln
- 'Sailor Boy' (Au/S) NDro SPop WAln
- 'Saint Boswells' (Au/S) GAbr SPop
- 'Saint Elmo' (Au/A) GAbr GAgs MFie SPop
- 'Salad' (Au/S) GAbr GAgs NDro SPop
- 'Sale Green' (Au/S) NDro SPop
- 'Sally' (Au/A) MFie NDro
- 'Sam Brown' (Au/S) WAln
- 'Sam Gamgee' (Au/A) NDro SPop WAln
- 'Sam Hunter' (Au/A) NDro SPop
- 'Samantha' (Au/A) MFie NDro WAln
- 'Samantha' (Au/d) MFie NDro SPop WAln WFar
- 'San Antonio' (Au/A) NDro
- 'San Gabriel' (Au/A) WAln
- 'Sanctuary Wood' (Au/d) SPop
- 'Sandhills' (Au/A) GAgs MAsh MFie SPop WHil
- 'Sandpiper' (Au/d) SPop WAln
- 'Sandra' (Au/A) ELan GAbr GAgs MFie NDro SPop WHil
- 'Sandra's Lass' (Au/A) SPop

- 'Sandwood Bay' (Au/A) GAbr MFie NDro NEgg SPop WHil
- 'Sappho' (Au/S) SPop
- 'Sarah Gisby' (Au/d) MAsh MFie NDro SPop
- 'Sarah Grey' (Au/d) WAln
- 'Sarah Humphries' (Au/d) WAln
- 'Sarah Lodge' (Au/d) GAbr GAgs NDro SPop WHil
- 'Sarah Suzanne' (Au/B) NDro
- 'Saruman' (Au/A) WAln
- 'Sasha Files' (Au/A) WAln
- 'Satchmo' (Au/S) SPop
- 'Satin Doll' (Au/d) MFie SPop
- 'Satsuma' (Au/d) SPop WAln
- 'Scaraben' (Au) GAbr
- 'Schaumburg' (Au/B) NDro
- 'Schicchi' (Au/d) XBar
- 'Scipio' (Au/S) NDro SPop
- 'Scorcher' (Au/S) GAbr LLHF MFie NDro NSum SPop WHil
- 'Scrumpy' (Au/St) **new** NDro
- 'Sea Lavender' (Au/d) WAln
- 'Sea Mist' (Au/d) SPop WAln
- 'Second Victory' (Au) NDro WHil XBar
- 'Seen-a-Ghost' (Au/S) NDro SPop
- 'Serendipity' (Au/B) WAln
- 'Serenity' (Au/S) MFie SPop WHil XBar
- 'Sergeant Wilson' (Au) SPop
- 'Serre' (Au/d) SPop
- 'Shalford' (Au/d) GAbr MFie SPop WCot WHil
- 'Sharmans Cross' (Au/S) MFie SPop
- 'Sharon Louise' (Au/S) SPop
- 'Shaun' (Au/d) ECtt GAbr GAgs GBin MHol NHpl NLar WTor
- 'Sheila' (Au/S) GAbr NDro SPop WHil
- 'Sherbet' (Au/d) SPop
- 'Shere' (Au/S) NDro NSum SPop
- 'Shergold' (Au/A) SPop WHil
- 'Sherwood' (Au/S) GAbr NDro NHpl SPop XBar
- 'Shining Hour' (Au/St) SPop
- 'Shirley' (Au/S) NDro SPop
- 'Shotley' (Au/A) SPop
- 'Show Bandit' (Au/St) NDro SPop
- 'Showtime' (Au/S) GAgs NDro SPop
- 'Sibsey' (Au/d) GAgs NDro NSum SPop WFar
- 'Sidney' (Au/A) WAln
- 'Silas' (Au/B) NDro
- 'Silbermond' (Au/B) NDro
- 'Silmaril' (Au) SPop WAln
- 'Silver Surfer' (Au/St) NDro
- 'Silverway' (Au/S) NDro SPop WHil
- 'Simply Red' (Au) MAsh MFie NDro NSum SPop XBar
- 'Sir John' (Au/A) NDro SPop WHil
- 'Sir John Hall' (Au) MFie
- 'Sir Robert' (Au/d) SPop WAln
- 'Sir Titus Salt' (Au/S) WAln
- 'Sirbol' (Au/A) GAbr GAgs MFie NDro NSum SPop WHil
- 'Sirius' (Au/A) GAbr GAgs MFie MHer NDro NSum NWad SPop WHil XBar
- 'Skerne Tiger' (Au/St) SPop
- 'Skylark' (Au/A) GAbr GAgs ITim NDro SPop WHil XBar
- 'Skyliner' (Au/A) NDro
- 'Slack Top Red' (Au) NSla WHil
- 'Sleeping Beauty' (Au/d) SPop
- 'Slim Whitman' (Au/A) MFie NDro NSum SPop WHil
- 'Slioch' (Au/S) GAbr GAgs NSum SPop WHil XBar
- 'Slip Anchor' (Au/A) WAln
- 'Smart Tar' (Au/S) WAln
- 'Smoothy' (Au/St) NDro SPop
- 'Snips' (Au/St) SPop
- 'Snitched' (Au/St) **new** NDro
- 'Snooty Fox' (Au/A) GAbr SPop
- 'Snooty Fox II' (Au/A) NDro
- 'Snow Maiden' (Au/d) SPop WAln
- 'Snowball' (Au/d) SPop
- 'Snowline' (Au/S) **new** SPop
- 'Snowstorm' (Au/S) NDro SPop
- 'Snowy Owl' (Au/S) GAbr MFie NDro SPop
- 'Snowy Ridge' (Au/B) NDro
- 'Solario' (Au/F) NDro SPop
- 'Solero' (Au/St) SPop
- 'Soliloquy' (Au) NDro
- 'Somersby' (Au/d) SPop
- 'Soncy Face' (Au/A) SPop WHil
- 'Song of India' (Au/A) SPop
- 'Sonia Nicolle' (Au/B) NDro
- 'Sonny Boy' (Au/A) SPop WAln
- 'Sooty' (Au/d) NDro SPop
- 'Sophie' (Au/d) MFie SPop WAln
- 'Sophie' (Au/A) NDro SPop
- 'South Barrow' (Au/d) GAbr GAgs SPop WHil
- 'Southport' (Au) GAbr NDro
- 'Sparky' (Au/A) NDro SPop WAln
- 'Spartan' (Au/A) SPop WAln
- 'Spitfire' (Au/S) MFie
- 'Splash' (Au) **new** WHil
- 'Split Ends' (Au/St) **new** SPop
- 'Spring Meadows' (Au/S) GAbr MAsh MFie NDro NEgg SPop WHil
- 'Springtime' (Au/A) SPop
- 'Stafford Blue' (Au/B) NDro
- 'Standish' (Au/d) GAbr
- 'Stant's Blue' (Au/S) NDro SPop
- 'Star Spangle' (Au/St) NDro
- 'Star Wars' (Au/S) GAbr GAgs MFie SPop WHil
- 'Star Wars II' (Au) MAsh
- 'Starlight' (Au/S) SPop
- 'Starling' (Au/B) GAbr NDro SPop
- 'Starry' (Au/S) NDro
- 'Starsand' (Au/S) NDro
- 'Steiff' (Au/S) **new** NDro
- 'Stella' (Au/S) SPop
- 'Stella Coop' (Au/d) NDro WAln
- 'Stella North' (Au/A) SPop WAln
- 'Stella South' (Au/A) SPop WFar
- 'Stepney Green' (Au/S) **new** NDro
- 'Stetson' (Au/A) WAln
- 'Stirling Castle' (Au/St) **new** NDro
- 'Stoke Poges' (Au/A) NDro
- 'Stoney Cross' (Au/S) SPop WAln
- 'Stonnal' (Au/A) SPop WHil
- 'Stormin' Norman' (Au/A) MFie NDro SPop WHil
- 'Stormy Weather' (Au/St) SPop
- 'Strand' (Au/St) **new** NDro
- 'Strawberry Fields' (Au/S) GAgs NDro SPop
- 'Stripe Tease' (Au/St) SPop
- 'Stripe U Like' (Au/St) **new** NDro
- 'Striped Ace' (Au/St) NDro SPop WHil
- 'Stromboli' (Au/d) GAbr GAgs MFie NDro SPop WCot
- 'Stubb's Tartan' (Au/S) MFie WAln
- 'Subliminal' (Au/A) NDro
- 'Sue' (Au/A) MFie SPop
- 'Sue Ritchie' (Au/d) SPop
- 'Suede Shoes' (Au/S) SPop
- 'Sugar Plum Fairy' (Au/S) GAbr GAgs NDro NSum SPop WHil
- 'Sultan' (Au/A) WAln
- 'Summer Sky' (Au/A) NDro SPop
- 'Summer Wine' (Au/A) MFie NDro SPop

- 'Sumo' (Au/A)	GAbr GAgs MFie NDro SPop WHil
- 'Sunflower' (Au/A/S)	GAbr GAgs ITim MAsh NDro SPop WHil
- 'Sunlight' (Au/A)	WAln
- 'Sunlit Tiger' (Au/S)	GAbr NDro
- 'Sunray' (Au/St)	SPop
- 'Sunrise Beauty' (Au/S)	SPop
- 'Sunspot' (Au/A)	WAln
- 'Sunstar' (Au/S)	NDro NSum
- 'Super Para' (Au/S)	GAbr GAgs MFie NDro SPop WHil
- 'Superb' (Au/S)	MFie SPop
- 'Surething' (Au/A)	WAln
- 'Susan' (Au/A)	GAbr MFie NDro SPop
- 'Susannah' (Au/d)	GAgs GMaP MFie NDro NSum SPop WFar WHil XBar
- 'Sweet Chestnut' (Au/S)	WAln
- 'Sweet Georgia Brown' (Au/A)	NDro SPop WAln
- 'Sweet Pastures' (Au/S)	GAbr GAgs MFie NDro SPop
- 'Swiss Royal Velvet' (Au/B)	NDro
- 'Sword' (Au/d)	GAbr MFie NDro NSum NWad SPop WFar XBar
- 'Symphony' (Au/A)	GAgs ITim MFie NDro SPop WHil XBar
- 'T.A. Hadfield' (Au/A)	GAgs MFie NDro SPop WHil
- 'Tachete' (Au/d)	XBar
- 'Taffeta' (Au/S)	EBee GAbr GAgs LCro LOPS NDro NSti NSum SPop WFar WHil
- 'Tall Purple Dusty Miller' (Au/B)	SPop
- 'Tally-ho' (Au/A)	SPop WAln
- 'Tamar Gold' (Au/d)	SPop WAln
- 'Tamar Mist' (Au)	WAln WHil
- 'Tamino' (Au/S)	NDro SPop
- 'Tango' (Au/d)	NDro WAln
- 'Tarantella' (Au/A)	GAbr NDro NSum SPop
- 'Tawny Owl' (Au/B)	GAbr
- 'Tay Tiger' (Au/St)	GAbr GAgs MFie NDro SPop WHil XBar
- 'Taylor's Grey' (Au/S)	NDro SPop
- 'Teawell Pride' (Au/d)	ITim NHpl SPop WHil
- 'Ted Gibbs' (Au/A)	NDro SPop WHil
- 'Ted Roberts' (Au/A)	ITim MFie NDro SPop WHil
- 'Teem' (Au/S)	GAbr NDro SPop XBar
- 'Telesto' (Au/d)	SPop
- 'Telford's Surprise' (Au/A)	WAln
- 'Temeraire' (Au/A)	MFie SPop WHil
- 'Tenby Grey' (Au/S)	SPop
- 'Tenderly' (Au/St) new	NDro
- 'Terpo' (Au/A)	GAgs MFie WAln WHil
- 'Tess' (Au/A)	XBar
- 'The Argylls' (Au/St)	NDro SPop
- 'The Baron' (Au/S)	GAbr GAgs GKev SPop WHil XBar
- 'The Bishop' (Au/S)	GAgs ITim SPop WAln WHil XBar
- 'The Bride' (Au/S)	NDro SPop
- 'The Cardinal' (Au/d)	WAln
- 'The Czar' (Au/A)	GAbr NDro SPop
- 'The Egyptian' (Au/A)	GAgs MFie NDro SPop WHil
- 'The Few' (Au/St)	SPop
- 'The Hobbit' (Au/A)	WAln
- 'The Lady Galadriel' (Au/A)	NDro
- 'The Maverick' (Au/S)	SPop
- 'The Raven' (Au/S)	GAbr GAgs ITim SPop WHil
- 'The Sneep' (Au/A)	GAbr GAgs ITim MFie NDro SPop
- 'The Snods' (Au/S)	MFie NDro SPop
- 'The Wrekin' (Au/S)	SPop
I - 'Theodora' (Au/S)	XBar
- 'Thetis' (Au/A)	MFie SPop
- 'Thisbe' (Au/A)	NDro

- 'Thou Swell' (Au/St)	SPop
- 'Three Way Stripe' (St)	GAbr GAgs WHil
- 'Thutmoses' (Au/A)	NDro WAln
- 'Tiger Tim' (Au/St)	SPop
- 'Tilley' (Au/d)	SPop
- 'Tim' (Au)	GAbr ITim NDro NSum SPop
- 'Timpany Blues' (Au/B)	ITim
- 'Tim's Fancy' (Au/S)	NDro
- 'Tinker' (Au/S)	NDro WAln
- 'Tinkerbell' (Au/S)	MFie NDro SPop
- 'Tiptoe' (Au/St)	SPop
- 'Titania' (Au)	SPop
- 'Toffee Apple' (Au/d)	NDro
- 'Toffee Crisp' (Au/A)	GAbr GAgs NDro SPop XBar
- 'Toffee Nosed' (Au/St)	NDro SPop
- 'Tom Farmer' (Au)	SPop
- 'Tomboy' (Au/S)	MFie NDro SPop
- 'Tom's Red' (Au/S) new	SPop
- 'Tony Bray' (Au/A)	SPop
- 'Toolyn' (Au/S)	GAgs NDro SPop WAln
- 'Top Cat' (Au/d)	WAln
- 'Top Style' (Au/d)	SPop WAln
- 'Tosca' (Au/S)	CWCL GAbr GAgs MAsh NSum SPop WHil XBar
- 'Trafalgar Square' (Au/S)	GAbr GAgs MFie NDro SPop
- 'Tregor Stripe' (Au/St)	XBar
- 'Trish' (Au)	GAbr
- 'Tromen' (Au/d)	SPop
- 'Trouble' (Au/d)	GAbr MFie NDro WHil
- 'Troy Aykman' (Au/A)	MFie NDro SPop WAln WHil
- 'Trudy' (Au/S)	GAbr GAgs ITim NDro SPop WHil
- 'True Briton' (Au/S)	MFie NDro
- 'Truman' (Au/B)	NDro
- 'Trumpet Blue' (Au/S)	NDro SPop WAln WHil
- 'Trumpton' (Au/S) new	SPop
- 'Tudor Rose' (Au/S)	WAln
- 'Tumbledown' (Au/A)	MFie NDro SPop
- 'Tummel' (Au/A)	GAbr GAgs NDro SPop WHil
- 'Tupelo Honey' (Au/d)	WAln
- 'Turnberry' (Au/S)	SPop
- 'Tut Tut' (Au/A)	SPop
- 'Tweedy' (Au/St)	SPop
- 'Twiggy' (Au/S)	GAbr NDro NSum SPop
- 'Two Steeples' (Au/A)	SPop
- 'Typhoon' (Au/A)	GAgs MFie SPop WHil
- 'Uncle Arthur' (Au/A)	MFie WAln WHil
- 'Unforgettable' (Au/A)	MFie
- 'Upper Crust' (Au/St)	NDro SPop
- 'Upton Belle' (Au/S)	NDro SPop
- 'Ursula' (Au/d)	WAln
- 'Ushba' (Au/d)	SPop
- 'Valerie' (Au/A)	ITim MFie SPop
- 'Valerie Clare' (Au)	SPop WAln WHil
- 'Valiant' (Au/A)	WAln
- 'Vee Too' (Au/A)	GAbr MFie NDro SPop WHil
- 'Vega' (Au/A)	SPop WAln
- 'Velvet Moon' (Au/A)	MFie NSum SPop WAln
- 'Velvet Truffles' (Au/d)	SPop
- 'Venetian' (Au/A)	GAgs ITim MFie NDro SPop WHil
- 'Venus' (Au/A)	WAln
- 'Vera' (Au/A)	NSum SPop WAln
- 'Vera Eden' (Au)	WAln
- 'Vera Hill' (Au/A)	WAln
- 'Verdi' (Au/A)	SPop WAln
- 'Verity' (Au/S)	SPop
- 'Vesuvius' (Au/d)	GAbr NDro SPop
- 'Victoria' (Au/S)	SPop WAln
- 'Victoria de Wemyss' (Au/A)	GAgs MFie NDro XBar
- 'Victoria Jane' (Au/A)	WAln

- 'Victoria Park' (Au/A)	SPop WAln
- 'Vienna' (Au/B) new	NDro
- 'Violet Surprise' (Au/St)	NDro
- 'Virginia Belle' (Au/St)	SPop
- 'Voodoo Mama' (Au/St) new	NDro
- 'Vulcan' (Au/A)	MFie NDro SPop XBar
- 'Walhampton' (Au/S)	NDro SPop
- 'Walton' (Au/A)	GAbr GAgs MFie NDro SPop WHil XBar
- 'Walton Heath' (Au/d)	GAbr GAgs MFie NDro SPop WCot WFar WHil
- 'Waltz Time' (Au/A)	MFie
- 'Wanda's Moonlight' (Au/d)	SPop WAln
- 'Warpaint' (Au/St)	NDro NSum
- 'Warwick' (Au/S)	MFie SPop
- 'Watchett' (Au/S)	SPop
- 'Wayward' (Au/S)	WAln
- 'Wedding Day' (Au/S)	GAgs SPop
- 'Wentworth' (Au/A)	WAln
- 'Werner Müller' (Au/B)	NDro
- 'Wheal' (Au)	SPop
- 'Whistlejacket' (Au/S)	MFie NDro SPop
- 'White Ensign' (Au/S)	GAbr GAgs NDro NWad SPop WHil
- 'White Pyne' (Au/B)	NDro
- 'White Satin' (Au/S)	NDro SPop
- 'White Water' (Au/A)	MFie NDro SPop WHil
- 'White Wings' (Au/S)	ITim MFie NDro NHpl NSum SPop
- 'Whoopee' (Au/A)	NDro WAln
- 'Whorton's Claret' (Au/S)	WAln
- 'Wichita Falls' (Au/A)	NDro WAln
- 'Wide Awake' (Au/A)	GAgs MFie NDro SPop
- 'Wild and Grey' (Au/S)	NDro
- 'Wilf Booth' (Au/A)	GAgs MFie SPop
- 'William Gunn' (Au/d)	MFie NDro SPop WAln
- 'William of Orange' (Au/d) new	SPop
- 'Willow' (Au/d)	SPop
- 'Willow Tree' (Au/S)	WAln
- 'Wincha' (Au/S)	ITim MFie NDro NEgg SPop
- 'Windward Blue' (Au)	NDro SBch
- 'Windways Mystery' (Au/B)	GAbr GAgs NDro NSum
- 'Windy Goldtop' (Au/A)	WAln
- 'Winifred' (Au/B) new	NDro
- 'Winifrid' (Au/A)	GAbr MFie NDro SPop WHil
- 'Witchcraft' (Au)	SPop
- 'Woodlands Lilac' (Au/B)	NDro WHil
- 'Woodmill' (Au/A)	GAgs MFie NDro NSum SPop WHil XBar
- 'Wookey Hole' (Au/A)	MFie NDro SPop
- 'Wor Jackie' (Au/S)	SPop
- 'Wycliffe Harmony' (Au/B)	NDro
- 'Wycliffe Midnight' (Au/B)	GAbr ITim NDro WAln WHil
- 'Wye Hen' (Au/St)	SPop
- 'Wye Lemon' (Au/S)	SPop
- 'X2' (Au)	GAgs WHil
- 'Yacoubi' (Au/A)	SPop
- 'Yellow Ace' (Au)	GAbr
- 'Yellow Hammer' (Au/S)	WAln
- 'Yellow Isle' (Au/S)	WAln
- 'Yellow Muff' (Au/S)	NDro
- 'Yellow Ribbon' (Au)	WAln
- 'Yes Indeed' (Au/St)	SPop
- 'Yitzhak Rabin' (Au/A)	NDro SPop WHil
- 'Yorkshire Grey' (Au/S)	GAbr NDro SPop
- 'Ypres' (Au/d)	SPop
- 'Yummy' (Au/St) new	NDro
- 'Zambia' (Au/d)	GAbr ITim NDro
- 'Zimmer' (Au/St)	SPop
- 'Zircon' (Au/S)	NDro SPop
- 'Zoe' (Au/A)	SPop WAln
- 'Zoe Ann' (Au/S)	WAln
I - 'Zona' (Au/A)	NDro
- 'Zorro' (Au/St)	NDro
auriculata (Or)	GKev SVic
'Barbara Midwinter' (Pr)	EBee GAbr GEdr NWad SHar WArt WCot
Barnhaven Blues Group (Pr/Prim)	MFie NSum XBar
Barnhaven doubles (Pr/Prim/d)	XBar
Barnhaven Gold-laced Group	see *P.* Gold-laced Group Barnhaven
Barnhaven hybrids	NSum
'Beamish Foam' (Pr/Poly)	GAbr
'Beatrice Wooster' (Au)	EPot GAbr LRHS MFie NRHS
'Beeches' Pink' (Pr/Poly)	GEdr NSum NWad
beesiana (Pf) 🏆H6	Widely available
(Belarina Series) BELARINA AMETHYST ICE ('Kerbelpicotee'PBR) (Pr/Prim/d)	CDor LRHS MFie MHol WBor WHil
- BELARINA BUTTER YELLOW ('Kerbelbut'PBR) (Pr/Prim/d)	CDor CExl CWCL ELon EPfP LRHS MFie MHol NLar SPer SRot WHil WTor
- BELARINA BUTTERMILK ('Kerbelmilk'PBR) (Pr/Prim/d)	NLar
- BELARINA COBALT BLUE ('Kerbelcob'PBR) (Pr/Prim/d)	CAby CExl CRav CWCL ELon LRHS MFie NHpl NLar SPer SRot WHil
- BELARINA CREAM ('Kerbelcrem'PBR) (Pr/Prim/d)	CAby CDor CExl CWCL ELon LRHS MFie NHpl SPer SRot WBor WCAu WHil WTor
- BELARINA PINK CHAMPAGNE ('Kerbelchamp'PBR) new	NPnk
- BELARINA PINK ICE ('Kerbelpice'PBR) (Pr/Prim/d)	CDor CWCL ELon LRHS MFie NHpl NLar SPer WBor WHil
- BELARINA ROSETTE NECTARINE ('Kerbelnec'PBR) (Pr/Prim/d)	CAby CDor CExl CWCL ECtt ELon MAvo MFie MHol NLar NPnk SPer WHil
- BELARINA VALENTINE ('Kerbelred'PBR) (Pr/Prim/d)	CAby CDor CWCL LLHF LRHS MAvo MFie MHol NLar NPnk WCAu WHil WTor
bellidifolia (Mu)	GKev NGdn
beluensis	see *P.* × *pubescens* 'Freedom'
§ × ***berninae*** 'Windrush' (Au)	WAbe
'Bewerley White'	see *P.* × *pubescens* 'Bewerley White'
bileckii	see *P.* × *forsteri* 'Bileckii'
'Blindsee' (Au)	CPBP CTal MFie
blinii (Y)	GKev LLHF
- SDR 7949	GKev
'Blue Gem' (Alaska Series) (Pr/Prim) new	NPri
'Blue Ice' (Pr/Prim/d)	XBar
'Blue Julianas' (Pr)	MFie NSum XBar
'Blue Riband' (Pr/Prim)	LLHF NWad
'Blue Ribbon'	WFar
'Blue Sapphire' (Pr/Prim/d)	GBin XBar
Blue Striped Victorians Group (Pr/Poly)	MFie
'Bon Accord Cerise' (Pr/Poly/d)	GAbr

Name	Suppliers
'Bon Accord Purple' (Pr/Poly/d)	WRHF
boothii subsp. ***repens*** (Pe)	GKev MNrw
'Boothman's Ruby'	see *P.* × *pubescens* 'Boothman's Variety'
boreiocalliantha SDR 8341 **new**	GKev
bracteata (Bu)	EPot WAbe
§ - subsp. ***dubernardiana*** (Bu)	WAbe
§ ***bracteosa*** (Pe)	GKev ITim
brevicula (Cy) SDR 4452	GKev
'Brittany Blue' (Pr/Prim/d)	XBar
'Broadwell Chameleon' (Au)	ITim
'Broadwell Milkmaid' (Au) ♀H5	CPBP ITim MFie WAbe
'Broadwell Oliver' (Au)	MFie
'Broadwell Ruby' (Au)	CPBP ITim WAbe
'Broadwell Snowstorm' (Au)	CPBP ITim
'Broadwell Violet'	MFie
'Broxbourne' ♀H5	ITim MFie
'Buckland Wine' (Pr/Prim)	CElw CFis ECtt EPfP GAbr GEdr
× ***bulleesiana*** (Pf)	CAby CBot CDor CSta EPfP GKev GWyn LRHS MCot MFie MWts NChi NEgg NGdn NLar NRHS NSum NWad SAko WFar WHar WMoo WPnP
bulleyana (Pf) ♀H7	Widely available
- hybrids (Pf)	GKev
burmanica (Pf)	GAbr GKev MMuc WHoo WMoo
- SDR 5801	GKev
'Butter's Bronze' (Pr/Prim)	WOut
'Butterscotch' (Pr/Prim)	MFie NSum XBar
'Caerulea Plena' (Pr/Prim)	NBid
calderiana purple-flowered (Pe) **new**	GKev
- subsp. ***strumosa*** (Pe)	GKev
calliantha (Cy)	GKev
'Camaieu' (Pr/Prim/d)	XBar
Candelabra hybrids (Pf)	CBre CPla GAbr ITim LSou MFie NGdn NHpl WOut
Candy Pinks Group (Pr/Prim)	MFie NSum XBar
capitata (Ca)	CMac EMFm EPfP GCrg GKev IBoy LRHS MAvo NHim NHpl SCob SPer WCot
- CC 3843	GKev SRms
- subsp. ***capitata*** (Ca)	EPot IBoy
- subsp. ***mooreana*** (Ca)	CAby CExl CHid CSta CTsd EDAr EPfP GJos GKev NGdn NHpl NSum SPlb SRot WAbe XBar
- 'Noverna Blue' (Ca)	MHol
- 'Noverna Deep Blue' (Ca)	LRHS NRHS SRms
- subsp. ***sphaerocephala*** (Ca) ♀H5	GKev
'Captain Blood' (Pr/Prim/d)	NHpl
Carnation Victorians Group (Pr/Poly)	XBar
carniolica (Au)	GKev WCot
Casquet mixture (Pr/Prim)	MFie
cawdoriana (So)	GKev
cernua (Mu)	LLHF MAvo NSum XBar
Chartreuse Group (Pr/Poly)	MFie XBar
'Cheshire Life' (Pr)	CMea
§ ***chionantha*** (Cy) ♀H6	CSta GEdr GKev MFie NGdn NSum WFar XBar
- subsp. ***chionantha*** (Cy)	GKev MHol
§ - subsp. ***sinoplantaginea*** (Cy)	NLar
§ - subsp. ***sinopurpurea*** (Cy)	CSta EBee EPfP GKev NSum
- - SDR 4418	GKev
chungensis (Pf)	CBod CDor CSta CTsd EBee ELon EPfP GAbr GBin GKev GLog GQue GWyn IBoy MHol MNrw NGdn NLar NSum SWvt WMAq WMoo XBar
§ ***chungensis*** × ***pulverulenta*** (Pf)	CHid SAko WSpi
× ***chunglenta***	see *P. chungensis* × *pulverulenta*
'Cisca'	WCot
'Clarence Elliott' (Au) ♀H5	CPBP EPot GKev MFie MPnt NRya NWad WAbe WThu
'Clarissa White' (Pr/Poly)	XBar
clarkei (Or)	WAbe
clusiana (Au)	WAbe
- 'Murray-Lyon' (Au)	NDro
cockburniana (Pf) ♀H6	CTsd WCot XBar
- SDR 1967	EBee GKev
- hybrids (Pf)	MFie
- 'Kevock Sunshine' (Pf)	EBee GKev
- orange-flowered **new**	GKev
concholoba (Mu)	GKev XBar
'Corporal Baxter' (Pr/Prim/d)	ECtt EPfP LLHF XBar
cortusoides (Co)	EPfP
'Cottage Cream' (Pr)	SVic
Cowichan Amethyst Group (Pr/Poly)	CWCL GAbr MFie XBar
Cowichan Blue Group (Pr/Poly)	MFie NSum XBar
Cowichan Garnet Group (Pr/Poly)	GAbr MFie NSum XBar
Cowichan strain (Pr/Poly)	CElw
Cowichan Venetian Group (Pr/Poly)	MFie NSum XBar
Cowichan Yellow Group (Pr/Poly)	MFie NSum XBar
'Coy' (Au)	ITim
'Craddock White' (Pr/Prim)	CFis GEdr
'Craven Gem' (Pr/Poly)	EBee
Crescendo Series (Pr/Poly)	ETMg
'Crimson Velvet' (Au)	WThu XBar
crispa	see *P. glomerata*
cuneifolia (Cu)	GKev
- subsp. ***heterodonta*** (Cu)	GKev
darialica (Al)	LLHF
'Dark Rosaleen' (Pr/Poly)	CAby CElw CExl CRos CWGN ECtt EHoe EPfP GAbr GEdr LLHF LRHS MBNS MFie MHol MMuc MNrw MPie NDov NHpl NLar NPnk NRHS NWad SAko SPoG WArt WCot WFar XBar
'David Valentine' (Pr)	CFis GAbr GEdr WCot XBar
'Dawn Ansell' (Pr/Prim/d)	CBod CDor ECtt EPfP GAbr GMaP IBoy MBNS MHol MRav NHpl NPnk NSum WCAu WHer WHil XBar
Daybreak Group (Pr/Poly)	CWCL MFie XBar
denticulata (De) ♀H5	Widely available
- var. ***alba*** (De)	CAby CBcs CTri EBee ECha EPfP GAbr GMaP GWyn LRHS LSun MBel MFie MMuc NGdn NHim NLar NPnk NPri NRHS SCob SGbt SPer SPoG WBor WFar WGwG WMoo WWtn
- blue-flowered (De)	CWCL EPfP GBin GWyn LLWG NHim NLar NPri

- 'Bressingham Beauty' (De)	EBee LRHS NRHS
- var. ***cachemiriana*** hort. (De)	EWTr
- 'Glenroy Crimson' (De)	EBee LLHF
- hybrids	SCob WFar XBar
- 'Karryann' (De/v)	WCot
- lavender-flowered (De)	CAby
- lilac-flowered (De)	EPfP LRHS NRHS SCob WTor
- purple-flowered (De)	WMoo
- red-flowered (De)	CAby EPfP MFie SCob WMoo
- 'Rubin' (De)	CWCL CWat EBee EPfP GAbr GMaP LLWG LRHS MBel MBrN MFie NChi NHim NLar NRHS SPer SPoG SRms XLum
- 'Rubinball' (De)	SBee WCot
'Desert Sunset' (Pr/Poly)	XBar
'Don Keefe' PBR	CBcs CBod EBee ECtt GAbr GBin GMcL LLHF MBNS MBel MFie MHol MMuc MNrw MPie NHpl NLar NPnk NWad SCob WCot WFar WMoo
'Dorothy' (Pr/Poly)	MRav
'Double Lilac'	see *P. vulgaris* 'Lilacina Plena'
dubernardiana	see *P. bracteata* subsp. *dubernardiana*
'Duchess of York' (Pr/Poly)	ECtt GEdr LLHF MHCG NLar WCot
'Duckyls Red' (Pr/Prim)	WHal
'Early Bird' (*allionii* hybrid) (Au)	EPot ITim
'Easter Bonnet' (Pr/Prim)	LRHS MMuc SEND
edgeworthii	see *P. nana*
§ ***elatior*** (Pr) ♀H5	CBod CDor CMac EBWF EPfP GAbr GJos GKev GMaP MBel MHer MHol MNHC MNrw NChi NEgg NLar SPer SPoG SWvt WArt WBrk WCot
- SDR 5439	GKev
- hose-in-hose (Pr/d)	NBid
- hybrids (Pr)	EPfP SPlb
- 'Magnifica' (Pr)	GKev
§ - subsp. ***meyeri*** (Pr)	LLHF SBrt
- subsp. ***pseudoelatior*** (Pr)	WAbe
- subsp. ***ruprechtii*** (Pr)	GKev
'Elizabeth Browning'	ECtt GAbr WCot
'Elizabeth Killelay' PBR (Pr/Poly/d)	CBct CBod CDor CExl CPla CWCL CWGN ECtt ELan GBin IBoy MNrw MPie NEgg NGdn NHpl NLar NPnk NSti NSum NWad SPer WBor WCot WFar
'Ellen Page' (Au)	MFie
'Elpiro' **new**	CBod
erratica (De)	GKev
'Ethel Barker' (Au)	NWad
'Eugénie' (Pr/Prim/d)	ECtt MRav WHil
faberi (Am)	GKev
'Fairy Rose' (Au)	NWad
farinosa (Al)	GKev NGdn
- var. ***denudata*** **new**	GKev
fasciculata (Ar)	SPlb
- CLD 345	GEdr WAbe
'Feuerkönig' (Au)	NDro
'Fire Dance' (Pr/Poly)	MFie
'Fire Opal'	LRHS NRHS
Firefly Group (Pr/Poly)	CWCL MFie WCot XBar
firmipes* × *florindae **new**	GKev
§ ***flaccida*** (Mu)	GEdr GKev NHim NHpl NSum WAbe XBar
- Cox 14026	GKev
Flamingo Group (Pr/Poly)	XBar
florindae (Si) ♀H7	Widely available
- 'Dave's Red' (Si)	LEdu
- hybrids (Si)	CMac EHrv EShb MFie WFar WHar WHil WWtn XBar
- Keillour hybrids (Si)	IBoy NGdn NLar SWvt WBor
- orange-flowered (Si)	GPSL LLWG MNrw SRms WMoo WPnP
- peach-flowered (Si)	CSpe
- 'Ray's Ruby' (Si)	CTsd GEdr MNrw NChi WCot WMoo
- red and copper hybrids (Si)	MWts SWvt WHoo
- 'Red Shades' **new**	NWad
- red-flowered (Si)	CSpe GBin GKev GPSL LLWG MMuc NBid NLar NSum WFar
- terracotta-flowered (Si)	NGdn
Footlight Parade Group (Pr/Prim)	XBar
forbesii (Mo)	GKev
- CC 4084	CExl
forrestii (Bu)	GKev WAbe
- SDR 4304	CExl
§ × ***forsteri*** (Au)	NHpl NLar
§ - 'Bileckii' (Au)	GMaP LLHF NSla
- 'Dianne' (Au)	GAbr GCrg GKev LLHF NRya WAbe WThu
'Francisca' (Pr/Poly)	Widely available
'Fred Salter'	ITim NRya
frondosa (Al) ♀H5	MFie MHol MPnt WAbe
'Frou-frou' (Pr/Prim/d) **new**	XBar
Fuchsia Victorians Group (Pr/Poly)	CWCL MFie XBar
'Gareth' (Pr/Poly)	GEdr
'Garnet' (*allionii* hybrid) (Au)	MFie XBar
'Garryarde Crimson'	GEdr IRob LLHF
'Garryarde Guinevere'	see *P.* 'Guinevere'
gemmifera (Ar)	LLHF
'Gigha' (Pr/Prim)	GKev IRob MNrw WFar XBar
'Gilded Ginger'	MFie XBar
'Ginger Spice' (Au)	NDro WHil
§ ***glomerata*** (Ca)	GKev XBar
'Glowing Embers' (Pf)	MFie
glutinosa All.	see *P. allionii*
Gold-laced Group (Pr/Poly)	Widely available
§ - Barnhaven (Pr/Poly)	MFie XBar
- Beeches strain (Pr/Poly)	CWCL MFie XBar
- red-flowered (Pr/Poly)	XEll
'Gold-laced Jack in the Green' Barnhaven	XBar
gracilipes (Pe)	GKev
- 'Major'	see *P. bracteosa*
- 'Minor'	see *P. petiolaris* Wall.
graminifolia	see *P. chionantha*
Grand Canyon Group (Pr/Poly)	CWCL XBar
grandis (Sr)	CPla GKev XBar
'Green Lace' (Pr/Poly)	ECtt NHpl
'Groenekan's Glorie' (Pr/Prim)	CFis EBee ECtt GAbr GEdr NSum
'Guernsey Cream' (Pr/Prim/d) **new**	XBar
§ 'Guinevere' (Pr/Poly) ♀H6	Widely available
'Hall Barn Blue' (Pr/Prim)	CSam CSpe EBee GEdr GMaP MHCG MMuc SEND WCot
§ ***halleri*** (Al)	GKev MFie XBar
- 'Longiflora'	see *P. halleri*
handeliana	GKev
Harbinger Group (Pr/Prim)	CWCL MFie XBar
Harbour Lights mixture (Pr/Poly)	MFie XBar

	Harlow Car hybrids (Pf)	CRos EPfP IRob LRHS NRHS NSla NWad SPer WMoo
	Harvest Yellows Group (Pr/Poly)	CWCL XBar
	helodoxa	see *P. prolifera*
	'Hemswell Blush' (Au)	EPot LLHF MFie NHpl
	'Hemswell Ember' (Au)	CPBP ECtt
	'Heritage Cream' (Pr/Prim)	EPfP
	heucherifolia (Co)	EBee
	- SDR 3224	GKev
	- SDR 7877	GKev
	hidakana (R)	GEdr
	'High Point' (Au)	MFie
	hirsuta (Au)	GKev MMuc SEND
	- 'Lismore Snow' (Au)	NWad
	- red-flowered (Au)	EBee GKev
	- white-flowered (Au)	NRya
	- white-flowered × ***pedemontana*** 'Alba'	EPot
	hirsuta × minima	see *P. × forsteri*
	hoffmanniana	NSum
	hose-in-hose (Pr/Poly/d)	MNrw
	- Barnhaven (Pr/Poly)	MFie XBar
§	Husky Series (Pr/Prim) ♀H5	ETMg
	'Hyacinthia' (Au)	CAby
	ianthina	see *P. prolifera*
	incana (Al)	GKev
	Indian Reds Group (Pr/Poly)	CWCL MFie XBar
	'Ingram's Blue' (Pr/Poly)	CFis EPfP MHol
	'Innisfree Pink' (Pr/Prim) new	NPnk
	Inshriach hybrids (Pf)	CAby IBoy
	integrifolia (Au)	GKev
§	'Inverewe' (Pf)	GKev IRob NHpl XBar
	involucrata	see *P. munroi*
	'Iris Mainwaring' (Pr/Prim)	CFis EBee ECtt GEdr LLHF MCot
	irregularis (Pe)	ITim WAbe
	'Jackie Richards' (Au)	CTal MFie
	Jack-in-the-Green Group (Pr/Poly)	MNrw WBor WMoo
	- Barnhaven (Pr/Poly)	MFie XBar
	- red-flowered (Pr/Poly)	MMuc WHil
	- white-flowered (Pr/Poly)	IFro
	'Jack-the-Lad' (Pr/Prim/d) new	XBar
	'Janet Aldrich' (Au)	CPBP MFie
	japonica (Pf)	CSam ECha LRHS MSCN NBro NGdn WMoo
	- 'Alba' (Pf)	CAby CBod CSta CTri EPfP EShb GMcL LRHS MBel MFie NGdn NHim NRHS NWad WFar
	- 'Apple Blossom' (Pf)	Widely available
*	- 'Carminea' (Pf)	CDor GKev MSCN NBro NGdn NWad WFar WWtn
	- 'Fuji' (Pf)	GAbr GKev NBro
	- hybrids (Pf)	CMac MFie MRav WFar
	- 'Jim Saunders' (Pf)	SLon
	- 'Miller's Crimson' (Pf) ♀H6	Widely available
	- 'Oriental Sunrise' (Pf)	EHrv GKev XBar
	- pale pink-flowered (Pf)	ITim NSum
	- 'Postford White' (Pf) ♀H6	CBcs CBod CDor CRos CWCL EHrv ELan EPfP EWTr GAbr GBin GKev GMaP IBoy ITim LLWG LRHS LSRN NRHS SPer SPoG SPtp SRms SWvt WMoo XBar
	- 'Valley Red' (Pf)	ITim NRHS
	- Violet Oriental Group new	XBar
	- violet-flowered (Pf)	GKev

	jesoana (Co)	GKev LLHF
	- B&SWJ 618	WCru
	- var. ***pubescens*** (Co)	GKev
	'Jewel' (Pr)	GAbr
	'Joan Hughes' (*allionii* hybrid) (Au)	WAbe
	'Joanna'	ECtt MPnt
	'Johanna' (Pu)	GCrg GKev NGdn NPnk NSum
	'John Fielding' (Pr)	CBro CElw EBee IRob NWad
	'Jo-Jo' (Au)	CTal EPot ITim MFie XBar
	juliae (Pr)	EDAr GCrg LRHS NBid NPnk NRHS NSum SPlb WAbe
I	- 'Millicent' (Pr)	WCot
	- white-flowered (Pr)	NSum
	'Ken Dearman' (Pr/Prim/d)	ECtt MRav NHpl XBar
	kewensis (Sp) ♀H2	CPla GKev MFie XBar
	kialensis (Y)	WAbe
	'Kingscote' (Au)	NDro
	'Kinlough Beauty' (Pr/Poly)	CFis ECtt GMaP LLHF NPnk XBar
§	***kisoana*** (Co)	CExl GEdr GKev LLHF WCru
	- var. ***alba*** (Co)	GEdr XBar
	- 'Iyo-beni' (Co)	GEdr XBar
	- 'Noushoku'	GEdr
	- var. ***shikokiana***	see *P. kisoana*
	komarovii (Pr)	LEdu SPlb
	'Kusum Krishna'	CBod EBee GEdr MBNS MHol MPie NHpl NRya NSti NWad WCot WFar WHil
	'Lady Greer' (Pr/Poly) ♀H5	CBod CMac CSam CTal EBee ECtt EPPr EPfP GAbr GEdr GKev GMaP GWyn MCot MHer MTin NChi NGdn NLar NSum XBar
	'Lambrook Mauve' (Pr/Poly)	CElw CFis GAbr
§	***latifolia*** (Au)	GKev
§	***laurentiana*** (Al)	EWes GKev
	'Lea Gardens' (*allionii* hybrid) (Au)	MFie NWad
	'Lee Myers' (*allionii* hybrid) (Au)	WFar XBar
	'Lemon and Lime'	CMea
	leucophylla	see *P. elatior*
	lilacina	GKev
	'Lilian Foster'	WArt WCot
	limbata (Cy)	GKev
	'Lindum Crepes Suzette' (Au)	ITim MFie
	'Lindum Divine' (Au) new	MFie
	'Lindum Finale' (Au)	ITim
	'Lindum First Kiss'	ITim MFie
	'Lindum Frosty Moon'	ITim
	'Lindum Heavenly' (Au) new	MFie
	'Lindum Lavender Mist'	MFie
	'Lindum Limelight'	ITim
	'Lindum Malcolm's Mate'	CPBP
	'Lindum Moonlight'	LLHF MFie
	'Lindum Rhapsody'	LLHF
	'Lindum Serenade' (Au)	MFie
	'Lindum Wedgwood' (Au)	EPot ITim MFie
	'Lingwood Beauty' (Pr/Prim)	CAby CElw CFis CSam GAbr
	'Lipstick'	CHid
	'Lismore' (Au)	NWad
	'Lismore Bay' (Au)	GKev
	'Lismore Peardrop' (Au)	EPot
	'Lismore Pink Ice' (Au)	NWad
	'Lismore Sunshine'	WThu
	'Lismore Treasure' (Au)	MFie
	'Lismore Yellow' (Au)	CPBP

Lissadel hybrids (Pf)	NSti
'Little Egypt' (Pr/Poly)	XBar
littoniana	see *P. vialii*
'Lizzie Green' (Pr/Prim)	NLar
× ***loiseleurii*** 'Aire Mist' (Au) ♀H5	EPot ITim NHpl NRya NSla NSum NWad WAbe WThu XBar
§ - 'Aire Waves' (Au)	CWCL ITim NRya NWad
- 'Pink Aire Mist' (Au)	ITim
longiflora	see *P. halleri*
longipes (Cy)	GKev
lutea (Au) **new**	GKev
luteola (Or)	GKev LLHF NGdn NHpl NSum XBar
'Ma7' (Au)	EPot
macrocalyx	see *P. veris*
macrophylla (Cy)	GAbr GKev
- var. ***moorcroftiana*** (Cy)	GKev
'MacWatt's Claret' (Pr/Poly)	ECtt GAbr SBch
'MacWatt's Cream' (Pr/Poly)	CFis CRos EBee EWTr GEdr LEdu LLHF LRHS NLar NRHS WCot WHil
magellanica (Al)	SPlb WAbe
mairei (Al)	GKev
- SDR 7967	GKev
'Maisie Michael'	GEdr LLHF WAbe
malvacea (Ma) SDR 7836 **new**	GKev
marginata (Au) ♀H5	CPne CTal LRHS MFie MMuc NRHS NSla NSum SBch SEND WAbe
- 'Adrian Evans' (Au)	EPot GEdr SBch
- 'Alba' (Au)	EPot LRHS MFie NBro NRHS NRya NWad XBar
- 'Ardfearn' (Au)	GEdr
- 'Arthur Branch' (Au)	MFie
- 'Baldock's Purple' (Au)	MFie NRya
- 'Barbara Clough' (Au)	GEdr MFie NRya NWad XBar
- 'Beamish' (Au) ♀H5	GEdr NBro NRya NSla NWad
- 'Beatrice Lascaris' (Au)	CTal GEdr ITim LRHS MFie NRHS NRya
- 'Bill Crow' (Au) **new**	NRya
- 'Caerulea' (Au)	ITim MFie NRya NWad
- 'Clear's Variety' (Au)	ITim LLHF MFie
- 'Crookes Variety' (Au) **new**	NRya
- 'Doctor Jenkins' (Au)	ITim NRya NWad
- 'Dolomites' (Au)	NWad
- 'Drake's Form' (Au)	ITim NLar NRya XBar
- dwarf (Au)	GEdr LRHS MFie NRHS NRya
- 'Earl L. Bolton'	see *P. marginata* 'El Bolton'
§ - 'El Bolton' (Au)	NRya NWad
- 'Elizabeth Fry' (Au)	MFie
- 'Grandiflora' (Au)	NWad
- 'Highland Twilight' (Au)	NSla
- 'Holden Variety' (Au)	ITim MFie NRya NWad
- 'Holly Leaf' (Au)	GEdr
- 'Ivy Agee' (Au)	NRya
- 'Janet' (Au)	GEdr LLHF NWad
- 'Johannes Holler' (Au)	ITim NRya
- 'Kesselring's Variety' (Au)	CMea ITim LLHF MFie NWad WAbe
- 'Laciniata' (Au)	LRHS NRHS
- 'Lemon Sorbet' (Au)	ITim
- 'Linda Pope' (Au) ♀H5	GEdr NSum WThu XBar
- maritime form (Au)	XBar
- 'Millard's Variety' (Au)	ITim NWad
- 'Mrs Carter Walmsley' (Au)	NRya NWad
- 'Mylene' (Au)	CPBP NRya
- 'Napoleon' (Au)	GEdr ITim NRya NWad
- pale blue-flowered (Au)	XBar
- 'Peggy Fell' (Au)	NWad
- 'Prichard's Variety' (Au) ♀H5	GEdr GPSL ITim LLHF MFie NRya WAbe
- 'Sheila Denby' (Au)	NRya NWad XBar
- 'The President' (Au)	NWad
- 'Waithman's Variety' (Au)	NRya NWad
- wild-collected (Au)	MFie
'Maria Talbot' (*allionii* hybrid) (Au)	CTal EPot
'Marianne Davey' (Pr/Prim/d)	WKif
Marine Blues Group (Pr/Poly)	CWCL MFie NSum XBar
'Maris Tabard' (Au)	EPot MFie XBar
'Mars' (*allionii* hybrid) (Au)	XBar
'Marven' (Au)	EPot ITim
'Mascara Blue' (Pr)	SVic
Mauve Victorians Group (Pr/Poly)	MFie XBar
maximowiczii (Cy)	EDAr GBin GEdr LLHF NGdn NSum XBar
§ - var. ***maximowiczii*** (Cy)	GKev MFie NHpl
- Red-flowered Group	see *P. maximowiczii* var. *maximowiczii*
maximowiczii × ***tangutica*** (Cy) **new**	GKev
melanantha (Cy)	GKev
- 'Moonshine' (Cy)	EBee GKev
'Melenoc'h' (Pr/Prim/d)	XBar
§ × ***meridiana*** 'Miniera' (Au)	MFie
Midnight Group	CWCL MFie XBar
'Miel' (Pr/Prim/d)	XBar
'Millstream Cream'	NLar
'Miniera'	see *P.* × *meridiana* 'Miniera'
minima (Au)	GKev NBro WAbe
'Miss Doris' (Pr/Prim/d)	XBar
'Miss Indigo' (Pr/Prim/d)	CWCL ECtt EPfP GMaP MBNS MHol MRav NHpl NPnk NSum SPer WCAu WMoo XBar
mistassinica	see *P. laurentiana* var. ***macropoda***
miyabeana (Pf)	GKev
modesta (Al)	XBar
- var. ***faurieae*** (Al)	MFie
- var. ***samanimontana*** (Al)	GKev
'Moerheimii'	GAbr GEdr
monticola	GKev
'Moorland Apricot'	WMoo
moupinensis (Pe)	CExl LLHF
- subsp. ***barkamensis*** (Pe)	GKev
'Mrs Eagland'	GAbr
'Mrs Frank Neave' (Pr/Prim)	GAbr GEdr WFar
'Mrs Marjorie Banks' (Pr)	GKev
'Mrs McGillivray' (Pr/Prim)	GAbr
§ ***munroi*** (Ar)	GKev MFie WAbe XBar
- subsp. ***munroi*** (Ar) CC 5311 **new**	GKev
- white-flowered (Ar)	WAbe
§ - subsp. ***yargongensis*** (Ar)	EBee EWTr GEdr GKev MFie
- - SDR 3096	GKev
- - SDR 6121	GKev
muscarioides (Mu)	GKev
- SDR 6052 **new**	GKev
Muted Victorians Group (Pr/Poly)	MFie NSum XBar
'Myline'	WThu

§	***nana*** (Pe)	GKev
	nepalensis	see *P. tanneri* subsp. *nepalensis*
	New Pinks Group (Pr/Poly)	MFie NSum XBar
	'Nightingale'	ITim MFie
	nivalis Pallas	see *P. chionantha*
	nivalis ambig.	NSum
	nutans Delavay ex Franch.	see *P. flaccida*
	obconica subsp. ***werringtonensis***	GKev
	odontocalyx 'Snow Flurry' **new**	GKev
	'Old Port' (Pr/Poly)	CSam EBee GEdr NSum
	Old Rose Victorians Group (Pr/Poly)	MFie NSum XBar
	orbicularis (Cy)	GEdr GKev LLHF NHpl
	Osiered Amber Group (Pr/Prim)	MFie NSum NWad XBar
	'Page' (Au)	MFie
	palmata (Co)	GEdr
	'Paris '90' (Pr/Poly)	CWCL MFie NSum XBar
	parryi (Pa)	CSta GKev
	- SDR 8184	GKev
	'Patrick'	NPnk
	pedemontana 'Alba' (Au)	MFie WThu XBar
	'Perle von Bottrop' (Pr/Prim)	ECtt GAbr GEdr WCot
	petelotii (Ch)	WAbe
	'Peter Klein' (Or)	ECtt EPot GCrg GKev
§	***petiolaris*** Wall. (Pe)	NSum
	'Petticoat' (Pr/Prim/d)	ECtt IRob NWad WCot XBar
	'Pink Aire' (Au)	MFie NSum XBar
	'Pink Fairy' (Au)	ITim
	'Pink Grapefruit' (Pr/Prim/d)	XBar
	'Pink Ice' (*allionii* hybrid) (Au)	GKev MFie NWad XBar
	'Pink Star' (Pr/Prim/d)	XBar
	poissonii (Pf)	CDor CFis CSta CTri ELan EPfP GKev LRHS NGdn NHim NHpl NRHS NSum WShi WWtn
	polyanthus (Pr/Poly)	MMuc
	polyneura (Co)	CBod GKev MFie MHol NGdn WCot
	'Port Wine' (Pr)	GEdr
	'Powdery Pink'	LRHS NRHS
	prenantha (Pf) SDR 3909	GKev
	Primlet Series (Pr/Prim)	SVic
§	***prolifera*** (Pf) ♀H4	CSta EPfP GKev GMaP LRHS MFie MNrw NGdn NHim NHpl NRHS NWad WMoo XBar
	- purple-flowered B&SWJ 13951	WCru
§	× ***pubescens*** (Au) ♀H5	CDor LRHS MHer NGdn NRHS
	- 'A.E. Matthews' (Au)	NWad
	- 'Balfouriana' (Au)	NWad
§	- 'Bewerley White' (Au)	EBee EPfP NDro
	- 'Blue Wave' (Au)	MFie SPop
§	- 'Boothman's Variety' (Au)	CAby CBod CTri EPfP GKev ITim MFie NSla WHoo
	- 'Carmen'	see *P.* × *pubescens* 'Boothman's Variety'
	- 'Chamois' (Au)	MFie
	- 'Christine' (Au)	CMea MHer NSum WCot
	- 'Cream Viscosa' (Au)	SPlb
	- 'Faldonside' (Au)	GCrg MFie NPnk NSla NSum
§	- 'Freedom' (Au)	CTal CTri GKev MFie NSla XBar
	- 'George Harrison' (Au)	MFie
	- 'Harlow Car' (Au)	CMea IRob MFie MPnt NSum NWad
	- 'Hazel's White' (Au)	ITim NDro
	- 'Henry Hall' (Au)	ITim
	- 'Joan Danger' (Au)	NDro
	- 'Joan Gibbs' (Au)	ITim MFie NHpl XBar
	- 'Kath Dryden' (Au)	ITim
	- 'Lilac Fairy' (Au)	EPot ITim NPnk NWad WThu
	- 'Moonlight' (Au)	NDro
	- 'Mrs J.H. Wilson' (Au)	CTal GCrg NRya XBar
	- 'Pat Barwick' (Au)	ITim MFie NDro NWad
	- 'Rufus' (Au) ♀H5	GAbr GEdr NDro WThu XBar
	- 'Sid Skelton' (Au)	NRya
	- 'Slack Top Violet' (Au)	NSla
	- 'Snowcap' (Au)	ITim XBar
	- 'The General' (Au)	CTri GEdr MFie
§	- 'Wedgwood' (Au)	GAbr MFie NDro NSum XBar
	- 'Winnifred' (Au)	WHil
	pulchella (Pu)	GKev
	- SDR 7903	GKev
	pulverulenta (Pf) ♀H6	Widely available
	- 'Bartley' (Pf)	WWtn
	- Bartley hybrids (Pf) ♀H6	CBot CPla GKev GWyn NHpl NSum NWad WMoo
	- 'Bartley Pink' (Pf)	CPla
	'Purple' (Primlet Series) (Pr/Prim)	LRHS NRHS
	'Quaker's Bonnet'	see *P. vulgaris* 'Lilacina Plena'
	'Rachel Kinnen' (Au)	GAbr MFie WFar XBar
	'Ramona' (Pr/Poly)	MFie XBar
	'Raspberry Ripple' (Pr/Prim/d)	XBar
	'Ravenglass Vermilion'	see *P.* 'Inverewe'
	'Red' (Primlet Series) (Pr/Prim)	LRHS NRHS
	'Red Ruffles' (Pr/Poly/d)	ECtt
	reidii (So)	GEdr XBar
	- var. ***williamsii*** (So)	GEdr GKev WAbe
*	- - ***alba*** (So)	GEdr
	reticulata (Si)	GKev
	'Reverie' (Pr/Poly)	MFie XBar
	'Rheniana' (Au)	NRya
	'Romeo' (Pr/Prim)	LLHF NWad WCot
	'Rose' (Primlet Series) (Pr/Prim)	LRHS NRHS
	rosea (Or) ♀H5	CAby CBod CWCL EBee EPfP GKev GLog GMaP MFie MMuc NBid NRya WPnP
	- CC 5260	GKev
	- 'Gigas' (Or)	WBor WMAq
	- 'Grandiflora' (Or)	CBod CMac EPfP GCrg GKev GMcL GPSL LRHS NLar SPoG SRms XLum
	'Rosemary Cottage'	GAbr WCot
§	***rotundifolia*** (Cf) SDR 7460	GKev
	'Rowallane Rose' (Pf)	GCal
I	'Rowena'	CFis GAbr LLHF WCot
	roxburghii	see *P. rotundifolia*
	'Roydon Ruby'	GEdr
	Rubens Series (Pr/Prim/d)	LRHS NRHS
	'Ruby Tuesday' (Au)	NDro
	rupicola (Y)	GKev
	rusbyi (Pa)	GKev
	- subsp. ***ellisiae*** (Pa)	GKev
	'Sapphire' (Au)	XBar
	'Saracen' (Au)	MFie
§	'Schneekissen' (Pr/Prim)	CAby CBod CSam CWCL LLHF LRHS MHer NBro NChi NRHS SCob WTor
	scotica (Al)	EBWF GAbr GKev GPoy MFie NRHS NSla WAbe
	secundiflora (Pf)	CSta ELan GKev LLWG MFie NSum NWad SPlb WMoo XBar
	- SDR 4401	GKev
§	× ***sendtneri*** (Au)	MFie

serratifolia (Pf)	GKev XBar
- SDR 5165	GKev
sharmae	GKev
sibthorpii	see *P. vulgaris* subsp. *sibthorpii*
sieboldii (Co) ♀H5	EWld GKev MAsh MNrw NHim NHpl NSla SBch SRms
- 'Aiaigasa' (Co)	WFar
- 'Aka Tonbo' (Co)	CSta
- 'Aki-no-yosooi' (Co)	CSta WFar
- 'Andromeda' (Co)	WHil
- 'Aoba-no-fue' (Co)	CAby CSta
- 'Aoyagi-zome' (Co) **new**	XBar
- 'Arimayama' (Co)	CSta
- 'Asahi' (Co)	WFar
- 'Asahigata' (Co)	CSta WHil
- 'Ayanami' (Co)	WFar
- 'Ayasegawa' (Co)	CSta WFar
- 'Beeches Star' (Co)	EBee
- 'Benjamin' (Co)	CSta WHil
- 'Bide-a-Wee Blue' (Co)	NBid
- 'Bide-a-Wee Lace' (Co)	NBid
- 'Bijyonomai' (Co)	WFar
I - 'Blue Lagoon' (Co)	CSta EBee EPfP LLHF LRHS NLar NRHS WFar WHil
- blue-flowered (Co)	CSta CWCL WHil
- 'Blush' (Co)	CSta WHil
- 'Boykavitch' (Co)	WHil
- 'Bureikou' (Co)	CSta WFar
- 'Carefree' (Co)	CSta ECtt LLHF NBro NLar WHil XBar
- 'Carmine Pink' (Co)	WHil
- 'Cherubim' (Co)	CSta EBee LRHS NRHS WHil
- 'Daikoshi' (Co)	CSta
- 'Daiminnishiki' (Co)	CSta
- 'Dancing Ladies' (Co)	ECtt MFie NBro WFar WHil XBar
- 'Dart Rapids' (Co)	CSta WHil WSHC
- 'Duane's Choice' (Co)	CAby CSta
- 'Edasango' (Co)	WFar
- 'Edomurasaki' (Co)	CSta NPnk WFar WHil
- 'Essie' (Co)	CSta
- 'Flamenco' (Co/d) **new**	WFar XBar
- 'Frilly Blue' (Co)	CSta EBee GEdr LRHS MFie NRHS
- 'Fuji-jishi' (Co/d)	WFar XBar
- 'Galactic' (Co)	CSta
- 'Galaxy' (Co)	NBro
- 'Geisha Girl' (Co)	CDor CSpe CSta EBee ECtt GEdr LRHS MRav NLar NRHS WFar WHil
- 'Gin-pukurin' (Co)	CAby WFar WHil
- 'Girl of the Limberlost' (Co)	WFar XBar
- 'Gloaming' (Co)	XBar
- 'Gunma Niizatia' (Co)	CSta
- 'Hakutsuri' (Co)	WFar
- 'Haña-angya' (Co/d) **new**	XBar
- 'Hanaguruma' (Co)	CSta
- 'Hatu-garasu' (Co)	CSta WFar
- 'Hatu-goromo' (Co)	CSta
- 'Hatusugato' (Co)	WFar
- 'Heart's Desire' (Co)	EBee
- 'Higurasi' (Co)	WFar
- 'Hinokoromo' (Co)	WFar
- 'Hutaezuru' (Co)	WFar
- 'Inikina White' (Co)	WFar
- 'Inukima Mincura' (Co)	WFar
- 'Inukina White' (Co)	CSta
- 'Iso-botan' (Co)	CSta GEdr WFar XBar
- 'Izutu' (Co)	CSta
- 'Jessica' (Co)	CSta WHil
- 'Kansenden' (Co)	WFar
- 'Karakoromo' (Co)	CSta WFar
- 'Kashima' (Co)	CAby CSta NPnk WHil
- 'Kihi-no-yume' (Co)	CSta
- 'Kiraboshi' (Co) **new**	XBar
- 'Kokoroiki' (Co)	CSta WFar
- 'Kotobuki' (Co)	CSta GEdr
- 'Kotonoshirabe' (Co)	CSta WFar
- 'Kurama' (Co)	WFar
- 'Lacewing' (Co)	WHil
- f. ***lactiflora*** (Co)	CSta LRHS NBro NRHS SRot
- 'Lilac Blue' (Co)	CSta
- 'Lilac Crinoline' (Co) **new**	XBar
- 'Lilac Sunbonnet' (Co)	EPfP LLHF WFar
- 'Maiougi' (Co)	CSta
- 'Makazebeni' (Co)	WFar
- 'Managuruma' (Co)	WFar
- 'Manakoora' (Co)	CAby ECtt EHrv MFie NBro NSum WFar XBar
- 'Mangetu' (Co)	CSta WFar
- 'Martin Nest Blue' (Co)	CSta NPnk WHil
- 'Martin Nest Pale Pink' (Co)	CSta WHil
- 'Masasino' (Co)	WFar
- 'Matunoyuki' (Co)	CSta WFar WHil
- 'Miho-no-koji' (Co)	CSta WFar
- 'Mikado' (Co)	CSta EBee ECtt GEdr LRHS NRHS WFar WHil
- 'Mikininonomare' (Co)	CSta WFar
- Minuet Group (Co) **new**	XBar
- 'Mitajiman' (Co)	CSta
- 'Miyakowakare' (Co)	WFar
- 'Miyuki' (Co)	WFar
- 'Musashino' (Co)	CSta WHil
- 'Musasi' (Co)	CSta
- 'Nankin Kazakura' (Co)	CSta GEdr XBar
- 'Nirvana' (Co)	XBar
- 'Noboruko' (Co)	CSta WHil
- 'Nuretubame' (Co)	CSta XBar
- 'Okinanotomo' (Co)	WFar
- 'Old Vienna' (Co)	XBar
- 'Oni-gokko' (Co) **new**	WFar XBar
- 'Oshibori' (Co)	CSta GBin GWyn WHil
- 'Our White' (Co)	WFar WHil
- 'Pago-Pago' (Co)	CSta ECtt EHrv IRob MFie NBro WFar WHil XBar
- 'Pale Moon' (Co)	XBar
- 'Pink Laced' (Co)	WFar
- pink-flowered (Co)	NRya
- 'Purple Dusk' (Co)	XBar
- 'Rasyoumon' (Co)	WFar
- 'Rock Candy' (Co)	CSta
- 'Romance' (Co)	XBar
- 'Saiun' (Co)	CSta WHil
- 'Sakuragana' (Co)	CSta WFar
- 'Sangoguko'	GBin GWyn MNrw
- 'Sato-zakura' (Co) **new**	WFar XBar
- 'Sekidaiko' (Co)	CSta
- 'Senshō' (Co)	WFar WHil
- 'Seraphim' (Co)	CSta EBee LRHS MMrt NLar NRHS WFar WHil
- 'Seto-no-ume' (Co)	CSta WHil
- 'Shiokemuri' (Co)	CSta WHil
- 'Shira-washi' (Co)	CSta
- 'Shiro-tombo' (Co)	CSta GEdr XBar
- 'Shirousagi' (Co)	WFar
- 'Shishifunjin' (Co)	CSta WHil
- 'Sinipukurn' (Co)	CSta WFar
- 'Sinnkirou' (Co)	WFar
- 'Sinseto' (Co)	WFar
- 'Siritonbo' (Co)	WFar

- 'Snow Flakes' (Co)	CSta NRHS
- 'Snowbird' (Co)	XBar
- 'Snowdrop' (Co)	CBcs CBod CDor CSta ECtt GBin GWyn IRob LSou MBel MHol MNrw MPie NCou NPnk WCot WFar WMoo
- 'Snowflake' (Co)	CSta EBee EPfP GKev LRHS NLar WFar
- 'Sorcha's Pink' (Co)	CSta WHil
- 'Sōshiarai' (Co)	CSta WFar
- 'Sotodorihime' (Co)	WFar
- 'Spring Blush' (Co)	CSta WHil
- 'Spring Song' (Co)	CSta WHil
- 'Sumida No Hatu' (Co)	WFar
- 'Sumizomegenji' (Co)	CSta WHil XBar
- 'Sweetie' (Co)	CSta WFar
- 'Syosin' (Co)	CSta
- 'Syutyuka' (Co)	CSta
- 'Tagonoura' (Co)	CSta WFar WHil
- 'Tah-ni' (Co)	NBro NSum WHil XBar
- 'Taoyami' (Co)	CSta WHil
- 'Tatutanoyuube' (Co)	CSta
- 'Tokimeki' (Co)	WFar
- 'Toyonoharu' (Co)	WFar
- 'Trade Winds' (Co)	XBar
- 'Tukasamesi' (Co)	CSta
- 'Turunokegoromo' (Co)	CSta WHil
- 'Usujanome' (Co)	CSta
- 'Vilia' (Co)	XBar
- 'Vivid Pink' (Co)	CSta WHil
- 'Winter Dreams' (Co)	CAby CWCL ECtt EHrv MFie NBid NBro NSum WFar WHil
- 'Yukiguruma' (Co)	WFar
- 'Yuuhibeni' (Co)	CSta
sikkimensis (Si) ♀H6	EBee GAbr GKev LRHS MMuc NGdn NSum SPoG
- CC 5730	GKev
- CC 5986	GKev
- SDR 4919	GKev
- SDR 5933	GKev
- SDR 7426	GKev
- peach-flowered	GKev
- pink-flowered **new**	GKev
- var. ***pseudosikkimensis*** (Si)	GKev
- - SDR 4528	GKev
- var. ***pudibunda*** (Si)	GKev
- red-flowered	GKev
aff. ***sikkimensis*** (Si)	NGdn NRHS
Silver-laced Group (Pr/Poly)	EPfP MMuc SEND SPoG SWvt XBar
- black-flowered (Pr/Poly)	GBin WCAu XEll
sinoplantaginea	see *P. chionantha* subsp. *sinoplantaginea*
sinopurpurea	see *P. chionantha* subsp. *sinopurpurea*
'Sir Bedivere' (Pr/Prim)	EBee WCot
'Siska' (Pr/Poly)	GAbr
smithiana	see *P. prolifera*
'Snow Carpet'	see *P.* 'Schneekissen'
'Snow White' (Pr/Poly)	CRav GBin GEdr MRav
SNOWCUSHION	see *P.* 'Schneekissen'
'Snowruffles'	ITim
sonchifolia (Pe)	GKev
sorachiana	see *P. yuparensis*
'Sorbet' (Pr/Poly)	XBar
spectabilis (Au)	GKev
specuicola (Al)	LLHF
Spice Shades Group (Pr/Poly)	CHid MFie XBar

× ***steinii***	see *P.* × *forsteri*
stenocalyx (Pu)	GKev
stenodonta (Pf)	CPla GKev
'Stradbrook Charm' (Au)	CPBP CWCL EPot NRya
'Stradbrook Dainty' (Au)	MFie NWad
'Stradbrook Dream' (Au)	EPot ITim WFar XBar
'Stradbrook Gem' (Au)	EPot
'Stradbrook Lilac Lustre' (Au)	MFie
'Stradbrook Lucy' (Au)	GEdr ITim NWad
stricta (Al)	GKev
Striped Victorians Group (Pr/Poly)	NSum XBar
'Strong Beer' (d)	CBod EBee ECtt EPfP GBin GEdr GWyn MHol MMuc MNrw MPie NHpl NSum NWad SAko WArt WBrk WCot WFar WKif
'Sue Jervis' (Pr/Prim/d)	EWTr MRav NHpl WGwG
suffrutescens (Su)	WAbe
'Sundae' (Pr/Prim/d)	XBar
'Sunrise' (Primlet Series) (Pr/Prim)	LRHS
'Sunshine Susie' (Pr/Prim/d)	GMaP XBar
szechuanica (Cy)	LLHF
takedana (Bu)	GEdr
'Tango' (Pr/Prim)	MFie NDro XBar
tangutica (Cy)	GKev
tanneri (Pe)	GKev
§ - subsp. ***nepalensis*** (Pe)	GKev
Tartan Reds Group (Pr/Prim)	MFie XBar
'Tatyana' (Pr/Prim)	EBee GKev
'Tawny Port' (Pr/Poly)	CElw CFis
'Theodora' (Pr)	CTal EBee GAbr WFar
'Tie Dye' (Pr/Prim)	CBod ELan LLHF MHol MMrt MNrw MPie NHpl NLar NWad SAko WCot WFar WKif WWFP
'Tinney's Moonlight' (Pe)	LLHF
'Tipperary Purple' (Pr/Prim)	ECtt GAbr NPnk
'Tomato Red' (Pr/Prim)	CAby EBee GAbr GEdr LLHF MFie NHpl WCot WFar
'Tony' (Au) ♀H5	MFie XBar
'Top Affair' (Au/d)	WAln
'Tortoiseshell' (Pr/d)	CHid ECtt
Traditional Yellows Group (Pr)	XBar
tschuktschorum (Cy)	GAbr LLHF
* ***urumiensis***	GEdr
'Val Horncastle' (Pr/Prim/d)	ECtt EPfP EShb GMaP NHpl XBar
Valentine Victorians Group (Pr/Poly)	XBar
'Vera Maud' (Pr)	NSum XBar
§ ***veris*** (Pr) ♀H5	Widely available
- PAB 3777	LEdu NRHS WHar
- subsp. ***columnae*** (Pr)	EDAr GKev
I - 'Coronation Cowslips' (Pr)	XBar
- hose-in-hose (Pr/d)	WBrk
- hybrids (Pr)	GMcL
- 'Katy McSparron' (Pr/d)	CExl EBee ECtt GBin MHol MNrw MPie NHpl NLar NSti SAko SPer WArt WCot WFar WMoo XBar
- 'Lady Agatha' (Pr)	CAby XBar
- Lord Alfred Group hose-in-hose (Pr) **new**	XBar
- subsp. ***macrocalyx*** (Pr)	WCot
- orange-flowered (Pr)	WMoo

- red-flowered (Pr)	NBid NGdn SBee SPer WMoo
- 'Sunset Shades' (Pr)	CDor EAJP EPfP GBin IBoy NGdn NLar SBod SWvt XEll
- subsp. ***veris*** (Pr)	NPnk
vernalis	see *P. vulgaris*
verticillata (Sp)	CPne
§ ***vialii*** (So) ♀H5	Widely available
- SDR 7894	GKev
'Victoriana Red and Gold'	CPla
Violet Victorians Group (Pr/Poly)	MFie XBar
viscosa All.	see *P. latifolia*
§ ***vulgaris*** (Pr/Prim) ♀H7	Widely available
- var. ***alba*** (Pr/Prim)	WBrk
- 'Alba Plena' (Pr/Prim/d)	GAbr NSum
- 'Avoca' (Pr/Prim)	NPnk WCot
- 'Avondale' (Kennedy Irish Series) (Pr/Prim)	CBod CDor EBee GBin LLHF MFie MHol MNrw NPnk SCob WCot
- Barnhaven Gold	XBar
- 'Blarney Castle Blush' (Pr/Prim)	NPnk
- 'Blarney Castle Pink' (Pr/Prim)	NPnk
- 'Blarney Castle Red' (Pr/Prim)	NPnk
- 'Carrigdale' (Pr/Prim)	CDor EBee GEdr NPnk WCot
- 'Claddagh' (Pr/Prim)	CBod EBee NPnk NSti WCot XBar
- Cornish pink (Pr/Prim)	GKev
- DRUMCLIFFE ('K74'PBR) (Pr/Prim)	CBod EBee ECtt EHoe EWTr GAbr GBin GEdr GMaP LLHF MBel MFie MHol MNrw MPie NHpl NLar NPnk NSti WArt WCot WFar XBar
- 'Dunbeg' (Kennedy Irish Series) (Pr/Prim)	CAby CDor EPfP GAbr GBin LLHF LSou MFie NLar NPnk SCob WCot
- 'Glengarriff' (Kennedy Irish Series) (Pr/Prim)	GEdr NPnk SCob WCot
- 'Golden Gem' (Pr/Prim/d)	WCot
- green-flowered	see *P. vulgaris* 'Viridis'
- 'Husky'	see *P.* Husky Series
- hybrids (Pr/Prim)	WFar
- INNISFREE ('K72'PBR) (Pr/Prim)	CAby CBod CDor EBee ECtt EPfP GAbr GBin GEdr GMaP GWyn LLHF MBel MFie MMuc MNrw NHpl NLar NPnk NSti NWad SPad WCot WFar XBar
§ - 'Lilacina Plena' (Pr/Prim/d)	CWCL GCal GMaP IFro IRob MRav NHpl NSum WHer XBar
- 'Moneygall' (Kennedy Irish Series) (Pr/Poly/d)	NPnk
- 'Mount Juliet' (Pr/Prim)	NPnk
§ - subsp. ***sibthorpii*** (Pr/Prim) ♀H5	CAby CDor CSam EBee ELon EPfP GKev IRob LRHS MCot MFie MHer MNrw MRav NBro NChi NRHS NWad SPtp SRms
- 'Taigetos' (Pr/Prim)	CBro CExl CHid
- 'Tara' (Pr/Prim)	EBee GEdr NPnk
§ - 'Viridis' (Pr/Prim/d)	MNrw
- subsp. ***vulgaris*** (Pr/Prim) ♀H5	GMcL WMAq
waltonii (Si)	CSta EPfP EWTr GAbr GKev IRob MNrw NLar NSum
- hybrids (Si)	MFie
'Wanda' (Pr/Prim) ♀H7	CBcs CTri ESps GAbr GBin GKev GMcL GWyn IRob LRHS MBel MHer MMuc NBid NPnk SRms WBrk WCFE WCot
Wanda Group (Pr/Prim)	IRob NBro NRHS SVic
- 'Wanda Grace' (Pr/Prim)	NPnk
- 'Wanda Jack-in-the-Green' (Pr/Prim)	WCot
- 'Wanda Tomato Red' (Pr/Prim)	GAbr
wardii	see *P. munroi*
warshenewskiana (Or)	EPot EWes GCrg GJos GKev NRya WGwG
watsonii (Mu)	GKev MFie
- maroon-flowered (Mu)	GKev
'Wedgwood'	see *P. × pubescens* 'Wedgwood'
Westonbury Mill hybrids	WWtn
'Wharfedale Bluebell' (Au)	WThu
'Wharfedale Buttercup' (Au)	ITim NWad WAbe
'Wharfedale Butterfly' (Au)	NWad
'Wharfedale Gem' (*allionii* hybrid) (Au)	EPot MFie NSla NWad XBar
'Wharfedale Ling' (*allionii* hybrid) (Au)	CTal EPot MFie NWad XBar
'Wharfedale Superb' (*allionii* hybrid) (Au)	MFie XBar
'Wharfedale Village' (Au)	MPnt NSla WAbe WThu
'White Linda Pope' (Au)	NSla NWad WThu
'White Wanda' (Pr/Prim)	GAbr XBar
'White Waves' (*allionii* hybrid) (Au)	ITim
'William Genders' (Pr/Poly)	GAbr
wilsonii (Pf)	CSta CTri GAbr LLWG NGdn WWtn XBar
- SDR 7824	CBcs GKev
§ - var. ***anisodora*** (Pf)	EWTr GKev GLog NGdn NHim NWad XBar
- var. ***wilsonii*** (Pf)	GKev NWad
'Windrush'	see *P. × berninae* 'Windrush'
'Wisley Crimson'	see *P.* 'Wisley Red'
§ 'Wisley Red' (Pr/Prim)	CElw
'Woodland Walk' (Pr/Prim)	EPfP SRms
woodwardii (Cy)	GKev
wulfeniana (Au)	GKev
yargongensis	see *P. munroi* subsp. *yargongensis*
'Yellow' (Primlet Series) (Pr/Prim)	LRHS NRHS
§ ***yuparensis*** (Al)	GKev
- white-flowered (Al)	EBee GKev
zambalensis (Ar)	GKev
'Zebra Blue' (Pr/Prim)	EPfP NPri

Primulina (*Gesneriaceae*)

tabacum 'Deco' new	WDib

Prinsepia (*Rosaceae*)

sinensis	MBlu NLar SLon WSHC

Pritchardia (*Arecaceae*)

affinis	XBlo
pacifica	XBlo

Pritzelago see *Hornungia*

Prosartes (*Liliaceae*)

§ ***hookeri***	EBee LLHF MNrw
§ - var. ***oregana***	EBee EPPr IFoB WCru
§ ***lanuginosa***	CRos EPPr LEdu LRHS NRHS WCru WPGP
§ ***maculata***	CAby CTal IFoB LEdu MNrw NLar WCru
§ ***smithii***	EBee EPfP GKev GLog LEdu MNrw NLar WCot WCru WPGP WSHC
- 'Rick' (v)	CTal
§ ***trachycarpa*** SDR 8177 new	GKev

Prostanthera (*Lamiaceae*)

aspalathoides	CCCN CTsd
'Badja Peak'	CCCN CTsd EBee EUJe MAsh MGil SLim
baxteri 'Silver Ghost'	SLim
cryptandroides	CBcs
cuneata Y^{H4}	Widely available
- 'Alpine Gold' (v)	MAsh
- 'Blushing Bride'	CMac EUJe LBuc
- Kew form	WPGP
denticulata	CTsd
* ***digitiformis***	CTsd
incana	CTsd
incisa	CTsd
lasianthos	CBcs CCCN CHII CTsd SLim SPlb SVen
- 'Kallista Pink'	CTsd
- var. ***subcoriacea***	CExl
latifolia	CTsd
melissifolia	CTsd
§ - var. ***parvifolia***	CCCN CTsd
'Mint Delight'	SLim
'Mint Royale'	CCCN EUJe LEdu LRHS SLim
'Mint-Ice'	LRHS SLim
ovalifolia Y^{H3}	CCCN SEle WAvo
I - 'Variegata' (v)	CBcs CCCN CExl CHGN CMac CTsd EUJe LRHS LSou MGil SEle WAvo WGrn
phylicifolia	CBcs CTsd
'Poorinda Ballerina'	CCCN CTsd EBee LRHS MAsh SEle SLim SPer SRkn
'Poorinda Petite'	CCCN CTsd LRHS SEle
rhombea	CTsd
rotundifolia Y^{H3}	CAbb CBod CCCN CTri CTsd EBee MGil MSCN SEle SPer SVen WCFE WGrn WKif
- 'Chelsea Girl'	see *P. rotundifolia* 'Rosea'
§ - 'Rosea' Y^{H3}	CCCN CTsd EPfP LRHS SEND
rugosa	CTsd
sericea	LRHS
sieberi misapplied	see *P. melissifolia* var. *parvifolia*
sieberi Benth.	CPbh CTsd
I - 'Variegata' (v)	CTsd
spinosa	CTsd
'Starlight' (v)	CTsd
walteri	CBcs CCCN CTsd EBee LRHS SPhx

Protea (*Proteaceae*)

aurea	SPlb
- subsp. ***aurea***	CPbh
burchellii	SPlb
'Clark's Red'	LRHS MPkF
coronata	CPbh SPlb
cynaroides	CBcs CBlu CCCN CPbh LRHS SPlb
- 'King Pine' **new**	CCCN
- 'Little Prince'^{PBR}	CBcs CCCN
- 'Madiba' **new**	CCCN
- 'White Crown'^{PBR} **new**	CCCN
effusa	SPlb
eximia	CCCN CPbh SPlb
grandiceps	CCCN CPbh SPlb
'Juliet' **new**	CCCN
lacticolor	CPbh SPlb
laurifolia	SPlb
lepidocarpodendron	CPbh
longifolia	CPbh
'Mini King' **new**	CCCN
nana	SPlb
neriifolia	CCCN CPbh SPlb
- 'Snowcrest'	CPbh
obtusifolia	SPlb
'Pink Crown'	LRHS MPkF
'Pink Ice'	LRHS
repens	CPbh LRHS SPlb
- 'Ruby Blush'	CCCN
scolymocephala	SPlb
'Southern Cross' **new**	CCCN
'Special Pink Ice' **new**	CCCN
subvestita	CPbh SPlb
susannae	CPbh SPlb
'Susara'	CCCN LRHS MPkF
'Sylvia'	CCCN LRHS MPkF
'White Ice'	LRHS

Prumnopitys ✿ (*Podocarpaceae*)

§ ***andina***	CBcs
elegans	see *P. andina*

Prunella (*Lamiaceae*)

§ ***grandiflora***	CHby ECha ELan ESps SRms WOut
- 'Alba'	CBre EBee ECha ELan EPfP GBin GMaP NBid NLar SPer SRms WCAu WOut
- 'Bella Deep Rose'	CWld
- 'Blue Loveliness'	CWld SWvt
- 'Blue Pearl' **new**	NCou
- 'Carminea'	EBee MRav NSti
- 'Freelander'	WHil
- 'Gruss aus Isernhagen'	EBee GBin
- 'Loveliness'	CMac ECha ELan GMaP MRav NBro NGdn SPer SPlb SRGP WCAu WFar
- 'Pagoda'	CSpe NLar
- 'Pink Loveliness'	SRms WFar
- 'Rosea'	WFar
- 'Rubra'	NLar
- violet-flowered	EPfP
- 'White Loveliness'	CMac SRms
hyssopifolia	XSen
'Icing Sugar'	EBee
incisa	see *P. vulgaris*
laciniata white-flowered	EBee
SUMMER DAZE ('Binsumdaz'^{PBR})	EBee ECtt GMcL LSou SPoG STPC
§ ***vulgaris***	CBod CHab CTri CWld EBWF ENfk ESps GPoy MHer MMuc MNHC NMir SRms WHer WMoo WOut XAbr
- f. ***leucantha***	WHer
- 'Rose Pearl'	CBod LSRN MPie NHpl SRms
× ***webbiana***	see *P. grandiflora*

Prunus ✿ (*Rosaceae*)

sp.	LPra
'Accolade' (d) Y^{H6}	Widely available
§ 'Amanogawa' Y^{H6}	Widely available
amygdalus	see *P. dulcis*
Aprium Series (F)	ERea
armeniaca	NPri
- 'Alfred' (F)	CDul ERea SDea SKee SPer WHar
- 'Bergeron' (F)	LRHS NOra
- 'Blenheim' (F)	ERea
- 'Bredase' (F)	ERea SDea
- 'De Nancy'	see *P. armeniaca* 'Gros Pêche'
- 'Early Moorpark' (F)	CAgr EMOT EPfP LEdu NOra SDea SEND SLon WHar
- 'Farmingdale' (F)	SDea
- FLAVORCOT ('Bayoto'^{PBR}) (F)	CAgr EPfP EPom ERea MCoo NOra SPer WHar
- 'Garden Aprigold' (F)	EPom SPoG

- 'Goldcot' (F)	CAgr CDul CFGn CRos CTho ERea LRHS MCoo NOra SDea SKee SPoG WHar
- 'Golden Glow' (F)	CAgr CFGn CTho CTri EMOT EPfP EPom ERea LRHS MAsh MCoo NOra SDea SKee SSFT WHar
- 'Goldrich' (F)	CAgr
§ - 'Gros Pêche' (F)	SVic WHar
- 'Hargrand' (F)	CAgr SVic
- 'Harogem' (F)	CAgr
- 'Hemskirke' (F)	ERea SKee
- 'Hongaarse' (F)	SDea
- 'Isabella' (F)	ERea
- 'Moniqui' (F)	ERea
- 'Moorpark' (F)	CDul CHab CSBt CTri ELan EMOT LBuc MRav NPri SDea SKee
- 'New Large Early' (F)	ERea SDea SEND
- 'Novi Sad' (F)	MRai
- ORANGE SUMMER ('Zaitorde'PBR) (F)	EPom
- 'Paviot' (F)	MRai
- 'Petit Muscat' (F)	EPom ERea SKee
- 'Tomcot' (F)	CAgr CTho CTri EPfP EPom ERea LBuc LRHS LSRN MCoo NOra SKee SPer WHar
- 'Tross Orange' (F)	SDea
- 'Vigama' (F)	MCoo NOra
'Asano'	CLnd
avium	Widely available
- 'Amber Heart' (F)	EMOT NOra SKee
- 'August Heart' (F)	SKee
- 'Bigarreau de Schrecken' (F)	SKee
- 'Bigarreau Gaucher' (F)	NOra SKee WHar
§ - 'Bigarreau Napoléon' (F)	CArg EPom LMaj LSRN NOra SKee SVic
- 'Birchenhayes'	see *P. avium* 'Early Birchenhayes'
- 'Black Eagle' (F)	SKee
- 'Black Elton' (F)	SKee
- 'Black Heart' (F)	ELan
- 'Black Tartarian' (F)	SKee
- 'Bottlers'	see *P. avium* 'Preserving'
- 'Bradbourne Black' (F)	SKee WHar
- 'Bullion' (F)	CEnd CTho
- 'Burcombe' (F)	CEnd CTho
- 'Cariad' (F)	WGwG
- CELESTE ('Sumpaca'PBR) (D)	CAgr CFGn CMac CTri EMOT ERea MCoo NLar NOra SDea SLim SPoG WHar
- 'Cherokee'	see *P. avium* 'Lapins'
- 'Colney' (F)	EPom ERea NOra SKee WHar WJas
- 'Dun' (F)	CHab CTho
§ - 'Early Birchenhayes' (F)	CEnd CTho
- 'Early Rivers' (F)	CDul CLnd CSBt EMOT IArd LSRN NOra SDea SKee SVic WHar
- 'Elton Heart' (F)	SKee
- 'Emperor Francis' (F)	SKee
- 'Fastigiata'	WHar
- 'Fice' (F)	CEnd CTho
- 'Florence' (F)	SKee
- 'Garden Bing' (F)	EPom
- 'Goodnestone Black' (D)	SKee
- 'Grandiflora'	see *P. avium* 'Plena'
- 'Greenstem Black' (F)	CTho
- 'Hannaford' (D/C)	CHab
- 'Hertford' (F)	NOra SKee WHar
- 'Inga' (F)	SKee
- 'Ironsides' (F)	SKee
- 'Kassins Frühe Herz' (F)	SKee
- 'Kentish Red' (F)	SKee
- 'Kordia' (D) 🏆H5	EPom NOra SKee WHar
§ - 'Lapins' (F) 🏆H5	CAgr CDul CFGn CLnd CTho CTri ECrN EMOT EPfP EPom MAsh MRav NLar NOra SDea SKee SSFT WHar WJas WWct
- 'May Duke'	see *P.* × *gondouinii* 'May Duke'
- 'Merchant' (F) 🏆H5	NOra SKee SSFT WWct
- 'Merton Bigarreau' (F)	CArg NOra SKee WHar
- 'Merton Crane' (F)	SKee
- 'Merton Glory' (F)	CAgr CSBt EMOT EPfP IArd NOra SEWo SKee SLim WHar WWct
- 'Merton Premier' (F)	ELan SVic
- 'Merton Reward'	see *P.* × *gondouinii* 'Merton Reward'
- 'Nabella' (F)	MAsh SDea WJas
- 'Napoléon'	see *P. avium* 'Bigarreau Napoléon'
- 'Noir de Guben' (F)	SKee WHar
- 'Noir de Meched' (D)	SKee
- 'Old Black Heart' (F)	SKee
- 'Penny'PBR (F) 🏆H5	CAgr EPom MCoo NOra SKee WHar WWct
- 'Petit Noir' (F)	CLnd NOra
§ - 'Plena' (d) 🏆H6	Widely available
§ - 'Preserving' (F)	CTho
- 'Regina' (F)	EPom NLar NOra SKee WHar
- 'Ronald's Heart' (F)	SKee
- 'Roundel Heart' (F)	SKee WHar
- 'Sasha' (F)	MCoo
- 'Skeena'PBR (F)	MCoo NOra
- 'Small Black' (F)	CHab CTho
- STARDUST ('13-7-70, Stardust') (F) **new**	LRHS NOra
- 'Stella' (F) 🏆H5	Widely available
- 'Stella Compact' (F)	ECrN LSRN SDea WHar
- 'Strawberry Heart' (F)	SKee
- 'Summer Sun' (D) 🏆H5	CAgr CLnd CMac CTho CTri EMOT EPom ERea ESps LBuc LRHS MAsh MCoo MGos NLar NOra SCoo SDea SKee SLim SPoG SSFT WHar WWct
- 'Summit' (F)	CLnd SKee
- 'Sunburst' (D)	Widely available
- 'Sweetheart' (F) 🏆H5	CAgr CLnd CTri EMOT EPom LMaj LRHS LSRN MAsh NOra NRHS SEWo SKee SLim SPoG SVic WHar
- 'Sylvia' (F)	CAgr NOra WHar
- 'Turkish Black' (F)	SKee
- 'Ursula Rivers' (F)	SKee
- 'Van' (F)	CAgr CSBt EPom NLar NOra SKee WHar
- 'Vanda'PBR (F)	NOra
- 'Vega' (F)	CAgr EMOT ERea NOra SKee WHar WJas
- 'Waterloo' (F)	NOra SKee
- 'White Heart' (F)	CHab ECrN EMOT SKee
§ 'Beni-tamanishiki' 🏆H6	NOra WHar
'Beni-yutaka' 🏆H6	CCVT CTho EMOT EWTr MAsh MRav MSwo NOra NRHS SCob SCoo SLim WHar
'Blaze'	see *P. cerasifera* 'Nigra'
× ***blireana*** (d) 🏆H6	CDul CEnd CLnd CTri EMOT EPfP ESps MGos MRav MSwo NLar SCoo SPer SPoG WHar
- 'Moseri' (d)	WTSh
BLUSHING BRIDE	see *P.* 'Shōgetsu'
campanulata 'Felix Jury'	EBee NOra
CANDY FLOSS	see *P.* 'Matsumae-beni-murasaki'
caroliniana **new**	LMaj LPra SArc
cerasifera (F)	CAgr CDul CFGn CHab CPer CTri ECrN EPfP EPom LBuc SDea SKee SPer SVic WHar

	- 'Countess' (F)	EPom NOra
	- CRIMSON POINTE ('Cripoizam')	EBee LRHS NOra SPoG
	- 'Golden Sphere' (F)	CAgr CArg CFGn CLnd CTho CTri ECrN EPom NOra SDea SKee SPer WHar
	- 'Gypsy' (F)	CAgr CLnd CTho LRHS NOra SKee WHar
	- 'Hessei' (v)	MRav NRHS SEle SPoG
	- 'Kentish Red' (F)	MMuc SEND
§	- Myrobalan Group (F)	ECrN MRav SDea SPre SVic
§	- 'Nigra' ♀H6	Widely available
	- 'Pendula'	ECrN SWvt
§	- 'Pissardii'	ECrN EPfP ESps LCro LSRN SCob SCoo SLon SWvt WJas WMou
	- 'Ruby' (F)	CAgr CFGn EPom ERea SPer
	- 'Woodii'	CSBt
	cerasus 'Meteor Korai'	LCro LOPS LRHS MCoo NOra
	- 'Montmorency' (F)	NOra SKee
	- 'Morello' (C) ♀H6	Widely available
	- 'Nabella' (F)	SKee
	- 'Rhexii' (d)	CDul ECrN MAsh
	- 'Semperflorens'	CLnd
	'Cheal's Weeping'	EBar
	CHOCOLATE ICE	see *P.* 'Matsumae-fuki'
§	× ***cistena*** ♀H6	CBcs CDul CRos EBee ELan EPfP ESps LRHS MAsh MGos MSwo NRHS SCoo SGol SPoG SWvt WCFE
	- 'Crimson Dwarf'	see *P.* × *cistena*
	'Collingwood Ingram' ♀H6	EBee EBtc EPfP ESps LRHS MBlu NOra SLim SPoG
	'Cot-N-Candy' (Aprium Series)	CAgr EPom
	'Daikoku'	EBee NOra
	davidiana	SPlb
	'Delma'PBR (F)	NOra WHar
	domestica (D/C)	CPer IRob SPre
	- 'Allgroves Superb' (D)	ERea
	- 'Angelina Burdett' (D)	CHab SDea SKee
	- 'Ariel' (C/D)	SDea SKee
	- 'Avalon' (D)	CAgr CCVT CLnd EMOT LBuc NOra SDea SKee WHar
	- 'Belgian Greengage' (F)	CHab SKee
	- 'Belgian Purple' (C)	SKee
	- 'Belle de Louvain' (C)	CDul CHab CLnd CTho CTri EMOT NOra SDea SKee WHar WWct
	- 'Birchenhayes' (F)	CEnd
	- 'Black Diamond'	see *P. salicina* 'Black Diamond'
	- 'Blaisdon Red' (C)	CTho NOra SKee WHar
	- 'Blue Imperatrice' (C/D)	SKee
	- 'Blue Rock' (C/D) ♀H5	SKee
	- 'Blue Tit' (C/D) ♀H5	CAgr CTho EMOT EPom ERea LSRN MAsh MMuc NOra SDea SEND SKee WHar WWct
	- 'Bohemian' (C)	SKee
	- 'Bonne de Bry' (D)	SKee
	- 'Brandy Gage' (C/D)	SKee
	- 'Bryanston Gage' (D)	CTho SKee
	- 'Burbank's Giant'	see *P. domestica* 'Giant Prune'
	- 'Burcombe' (F)	CEnd
	- 'Cambridge Gage' (D) ♀H5	Widely available
	- 'Chrislin' (F)	CTho
	- 'Coe's Golden Drop' (D)	CAgr CArg CFGn CHab CLnd ECrN EPom ERea IArd MGos MRav NOra SDea SKee SPer WHar WWct
	- 'Count Althann's Gage' (D)	CHab ERea SDea SKee WWct
	- 'Cox's Emperor' (C)	SKee
	- 'Crimson Drop' (D)	SKee
	- 'Cropper'	see *P. domestica* 'Laxton's Cropper'
	- 'Curlew' (C)	SDea SKee
	- 'Czar' (C) ♀H6	Widely available
	- 'Delicious'	see *P. domestica* 'Laxton's Delicious'
	- 'Denbigh' (C)	CHab WGwG
	- 'Denniston's Superb'	see *P. domestica* 'Imperial Gage'
	- 'Des Bejonnieres' (D)	SKee
	- 'Diamond' (C)	SKee
	- 'Dittisham Black' (C)	CTho
	- 'Dittisham Ploughman' (C)	CTho SKee
	- 'Drap d'Or d'Esperen' (D)	SKee
	- 'Dunster Plum' (F)	CTho CTri
	- 'Early Favourite' (D/C)	SKee
	- 'Early Laxton' (C/D)	CHab MMuc SDea SEND SKee
	- 'Early Prolific'	see *P. domestica* 'Early Rivers'
§	- 'Early Rivers' (C)	CAgr CDul CHab CSBt CTho CTri ELan EMOT EPom ERea ESps LRHS LSRN NOra SCoo SDea SKee SPer WHar WWct
	- 'Early Transparent Gage' (C/D)	CAgr CEnd CMac CSBt CTho ECrN EMOT ERea IArd LBuc LRHS MCoo NOra SCoo SDea SKee WHar
	- 'Early Victoria' (C/D)	SDea
	- 'Edda' (D)	NOra WHar
	- 'Edwards' (C/D)	CTri SDea SKee
	- 'Excalibur' (D)	CAgr EMOT EPom IArd LBuc LSRN NOra SDea SKee WHar
§	- German Prune Group (C)	CFGn MCoo NOra SDea SKee
§	- 'Giant Prune' (C)	ECrN EMOT MMuc SDea SEND SKee WHar
I	- 'Godshill Big Sloe' (F)	SDea
	- 'Godshill Blue' (C)	SDea
	- 'Godshill Minigage' (F)	SDea
	- 'Golden Transparent' (D)	MCoo SKee
	- 'Goldfinch' (D)	MCoo MMuc SEND SKee
	- 'Gordon Castle'	NLar SKee WHar
	- Green Gage Group	see *P. domestica* Reine-Claude Group
	- - 'Lindsey Gage' (F)	SKee
	- 'Grey Plum' (F)	CTho
	- 'Grove's Late Victoria' (D)	WWct
	- 'Guinevere' (C)	CAgr CEnd EPom LRHS MCoo NOra SKee WHar
	- 'Guthrie's Late Green' (D)	SKee
	- 'Hackman' (F)	SKee
	- 'Haganta'PBR (F) ♀H5	CAgr ERea MCoo NOra WHar
	- 'Herman' (D)	CAgr CEnd CMac EMOT EPom LRHS MAsh MCoo NOra SDea SKee WHar
	- 'Heron' (C)	NOra SKee WHar WWct
	- 'Impérial Épineuse' (D)	SKee
§	- 'Imperial Gage' (D) ♀H5	CAgr CArg CFGn CLnd CMac CSBt CTho CTri EPom LRHS MAsh MMuc NOra SDea SEND SKee SSFT WHar
	- 'Jan James' (F)	CEnd
	- 'Jefferson' (D) ♀H5	CAgr CHab CLnd EMOT NOra SDea SKee SVic WHar
*	- 'Jubilaeum' (D)	CAgr CFGn CLnd CMac EPom LBuc LRHS NOra SCoo SEWo SKee WHar
	- 'Kea' (C)	CLnd CTho SKee
	- 'Kirke's' (D)	CHab CTho ELan ERea NOra SDea SKee WHar
	- 'Landkey Yellow' (F)	CTho
	- 'Langley Gage' (D)	CAgr ERea SDea
	- 'Late Muscatelle' (D)	SKee
	- 'Late Transparent Gage' (D)	SKee

§ - 'Laxton's Cropper' (C) CHab EMOT SKee WHar
§ - 'Laxton's Delicious' (D) CHab
- 'Laxton's Gage' (D) SDea SKee
- 'Laxton's Jubilee' (C/D) CEnd CSBt EMOT
I - 'Liegel's Apricot' SKee
- 'Madeleine Nomblot' (F) SKee
- 'Mallard' (D) ♀H6 NOra SKee WHar
- 'Manaccan' (C) CTho
- 'Manns No. 1' (C/D) SKee
- 'Marjorie's Seedling' (C) ♀H5 Widely available
- 'McLaughlin' (D) SKee
- 'Meritare' (F) MWat NOra
- 'Merton Gage' (D) SKee
- 'Merton Gem' (D) SKee
- 'Monarch' (C) SKee
- 'Monsieur Jaune' (C/D) SKee
- (Myrobalan Group) 'Myrobalan B' (F) WTSh
- 'Newark' (F) SKee
- Old English gage CLnd ECrN EPom ERea
- 'Olympia' (C/D) SKee
- 'Ontario' (D) SKee
- 'Opal' (D) ♀H6 CAgr CCVT CDul CLnd CMac CRos CTri ECrN EMOT EPom IRob LBuc LRHS LSRN MGos MMuc MWat NLar NOra SCoo SDea SEND SKee SLim SPer SSFT WHar WTSh WWct
- 'Orleans' (C) SKee
- 'Oullins Gage' (C/D) ♀H5 Widely available
- 'Pershore' (C) CAgr CHab EMOT ERea LRHS NOra SDea SKee WHar WWct
- 'Pershore Emblem' (F) WWct
- 'Pond's Seedling' (C) CSBt SDea SKee
- 'Pozegaca' (D) SKee
- 'President' (C) CHab LMaj MMuc SDea SEND SKee
- 'Prince Englebert' (C) SKee
- 'Priory Plum' (D) SDea
- 'Purple Pershore' (C) ♀H5 CAgr CHab CTri IArd NEgg NOra SDea SKee WHar WWct
- 'Quetsche d'Alsace' see *P. domestica* German Prune Group
- 'Reeves' (C) NOra SKee WHar
- 'Reine-Claude' (RHS) (D) SKee
- 'Reine-Claude Dorée' see *P. domestica* Reine-Claude Group
§ - Reine-Claude Group (D) ELan MMuc NOra SDea SEND SKee SLim SPer
- - 'Ingall's Grimoldby Green Gage' (D) SKee
- - 'Old Green Gage' see *P. domestica* (Reine-Claude Group) 'Reine-Claude Vraie'
- - 'Reine-Claude de Brahy' (D) SKee
- - 'Reine-Claude de Bavais' (D) CArg CLnd CTri NOra SDea SKee WHar
- - 'Reine-Claude de Moissac' (D) SKee
- - 'Reine-Claude de Vars' (D) SKee SVic
- - 'Reine-Claude Précoce Léon Hisse' (D) SKee
- - 'Reine-Claude Reforma' (D) SKee
- - 'Reine-Claude Rosée' (D) SKee
- - 'Reine-Claude Tardive de Chambourcy' (D) SKee
- - 'Reine-Claude Violette' (D) SKee
§ - - 'Reine-Claude Vraie' (C/D) CAgr CMac CSBt EMOT EPfP EPom LBuc LRHS LSRN MAsh NOra NPri SDea SKee SPoG SSFT WJas
§ - - 'Willingham Gage' (C/D) EMOT ERea LRHS LSRN NOra SKee WHar
- 'Royale de Vilvoorde' (D) SKee
- 'Sanctus Hubertus' (D) CTri EMOT SDea SKee WHar WWct
- 'Seneca' (D) EPom NOra WHar
- 'Stanley' (C/D) LMaj SVic
- 'Stella' CCVT ELan LOPS LSRN NEgg NPri SLim WHar
- 'Stella's Star' MCoo NOra
- 'Stint' (C/D) SKee
- 'Swan' (C) ERea NOra SKee WHar WWct
- 'Syston White' MGos
- 'Thames Cross' (D) CLnd NOra SKee
- 'Transparent Gage' (D) CFGn SKee
- 'Utility' (D) SKee
- 'Valor' (D) ♀H5 NOra WHar
- 'Verity' (C/D) SKee
- 'Victoria' (D) ♀H5 Widely available
- 'Violetta'PBR (D) CAgr EMOT WHar
- 'Wangenheimer Frühzwetsche' (F) SKee
- 'Warwickshire Drooper' (C) CAgr CHab CTho EMOT ERea ESps IArd MAsh NOra SDea SKee SLon WHar WWct
- 'Washington' (D) SDea SKee
- 'White Magnum Bonum' (C) SDea
- 'Willingham' see *P. domestica* (Reine-Claude Group) 'Willingham Gage'
- 'Woolaston Black' (D) SKee
- 'Zwetschen' SDea
§ ***dulcis*** CAco CHab CLnd CTri ELan EMOT EPfP EPom ESps LRHS MGos MMuc SCoo SDea SEND SWvt
- 'Ai' (F) CAgr
- 'Ardéchoise' (F) CAgr
- 'Ferraduel' (F) CAgr MRai
- 'Ferragnès' (F) CAgr MRai
* - 'Phoebe' (F) CAgr
- 'Princesse' (F) SKee
- 'Sultane' (F) SKee
- 'Supernova' (F) CCCN MRai
- 'Tuono' (F) CCCN
EASTER BONNET ('Comet'PBR) CTri LRHS
'Flavor King' (Pluot Series) (D) CAgr
'Flavour Supreme' (F) EPom
FRAGRANT CLOUD see *P.* 'Shizuka'
FRILLY FROCK ('Fpmspl') (v) EBee LRHS LSRN NLar NOra SLim SPoG
fruticosa new LPra
'Fugenzō' CSBt NOra
glandulosa 'Alba Plena' (d) CDul CEnd CMac CSBt EBee ETMg MAsh SGol SPlb SRms SWvt WCFE
- 'Rosea Plena' see *P. glandulosa* 'Sinensis'
§ - 'Sinensis' (d) CDul CEnd CExl CSBt SGol SRms
§ × ***gondouinii*** 'May Duke' (F) SKee WHar
§ - 'Merton Reward' (F) SKee
grayana B&SWJ 10903 WCru
'Gyoikō' CEnd CLnd EBee NOra
'Hally Jolivette' CEnd MAsh NOra SPoG
§ 'Hanagasa' ♀H6 CEnd EMOT LRHS NLar NOra WMou
'Hillieri' LPra
'Hillieri Spire' see *P.* 'Spire'

	'Hilling's Weeping'	EBee LCro LOPS SLon
	himalaica	LRHS NLar NOra WPGP
	'Hokusai' ♀H6	CDul EMOT EPfP LRHS NOra SGol
	HOLLYWOOD	see *P.* 'Trailblazer'
	'Horinji'	EMOT LRHS NLar NOra SCoo
	'Ichiyo' (d) ♀H6	CDul CLnd EBee ECrN EPfP ESps NOra SCoo
	ilicifolia subsp. ***lyonii***	WPGP
	× ***incam*** 'Okamé' ♀H6	Widely available
	- 'Shosar' ♀H6	CEnd ECrN SCoo SPer
	incisa	CTri NEgg
	- 'Beniomi'	MRav
	- 'February Pink'	CJun SGol
	- 'Fujimae' ♀H6	NLar WAvo
	- 'Kojo-no-mai' ♀H6	Widely available
	- 'Mikinori'	CEnd CJun CMac CSBt EPfP MAsh MBlu MJak NLar NOra SCoo WSpi
	- 'Oshidori' (d) ♀H6	CMac CSBt EBee ELon EPfP LRHS MMrt MRav NOra NQui SRms WSpi
	- 'Paean'	NLar WAvo WFar
	- 'Pendula' ♀H6	LCro LOPS NOra SCoo
	- 'Praecox'	CHGN CSBt CTho EPfP SCoo
§	- f. ***yamadei*** ♀H6	CJun MAsh WSpi
	insititia (F)	MWht
	- 'Abergwyngregin' (C)	NOra
	- 'Andrierez' (F)	SKee
	- 'Aylesbury Prune' (C)	NOra
	- 'Black Bullace' (F)	ERea
	- 'Blue Violet Damson' (F)	CAgr CFGn ERea MCoo NOra SKee WHar
§	- 'Bradley's King Damson' (C)	MCoo NLar NOra SKee WHar
	- bullace (C)	ERea LEdu SDea
	- 'Countess' (C)	CTri
	- 'Dittisham Damson' (C)	CTho
	- 'Farleigh Damson' (C) ♀H6	CAgr CArg CDul CHab CLnd ECrN EMOT EPfP EPom ERea ESps IArd LBuc LEdu MJak NLar NOra SDea SKee SPer SVic WHar WJas WWct
	- 'Godshill Damson' (C)	SDea
	- 'King of Damsons'	see *P. insititia* 'Bradley's King Damson'
	- 'Langley Bullace' (C)	CAgr CTri ERea LEdu NOra SDea SKee WHar
	- 'Lisna' (C)	CTri
	- 'Merryweather Damson' (C)	Widely available
	- 'Mirabelle Countess' (C)	EPom
	- 'Mirabelle de Metz' (C) **new**	SKee
	- 'Mirabelle de Nancy' (C)	CAgr CDul CLnd CTho EPom ERea NOra SDea SEWo SKee WHar
	- 'Mirabelle de Nancy' red (C)	SDea
	- 'Mirabelle Ruby' (C)	CArg ERea LRHS NOra SPoG
§	- 'Prune Damson' (C) ♀H6	CAgr CArg CDul CHab CLnd CMac CRos CTho CTri EMOT EPom ERea IArd LBuc LCro LRHS MAsh MMuc NEgg NLar NOra SDea SEND SEWo SKee SPer WHar WJas WWct
	- 'Shepherd's Bullace' (C)	CTho ERea MCoo SKee
	- 'Shropshire Damson'	see *P. insititia* 'Prune Damson'
	- 'Small Bullace' (C)	SKee
	- 'Westmorland Prune' (C)	CHab NLar
	- 'Yellow Apricot' (C)	ERea SKee
	'Jacqueline' **new**	EBee NOra SPoG
	'Jō-nioi'	CDul CEnd CLnd CTho LRHS
§	'Kanzan' (d) ♀H6	Widely available
§	'Kiku-shidare-zakura'	Widely available
	'Kobuku-zakura'	EWTr NOra SPoG

	Korean hill cherry	see *P. verecunda*
	'Kursar'	CDul CLnd CSBt CTri EMOT EPfP ESps EUJe GKin LRHS LSRN MAsh SCoo SLim SLon SPer SPoG SWvt
	laurocerasus	CBcs CCVT CDul CFGn CMac EBee ECrN ELan EPfP EShb ESps GKin IBoy LMaj LPra MGos MHed MRav NPri SArc SCob SGol SPer WMoo WMou WTSh
	- 'Angustifolia'	IBoy
	- 'Camelliifolia'	CMac CTri MBlu
	- 'Castlewellan' (v)	CDul CTri ELon EMOT EPfP EShb MGos MRav MSwo NLar NWad SCob SPer SPoG SSta WAvo WMoo WRHF
	- 'Caucasica'	CEnd ECrN ESps LMaj NLar SCob SEND SGol
	- 'Cherry Brandy'	SCob SGol
	- ETNA ('Anbri'PBR) ♀H5	CMac EMOT ESps GMcL LBuc LRHS MAsh NRHS SCob SWvt
	- GENOLIA ('Mariblon'PBR)	LMaj SGol
	- 'Green Marble' (v)	CTri EHoe
	- 'Greentorch'PBR	NRHS
	- 'Ivory'PBR	WMoo
§	- 'Latifolia'	LMaj MNHC NRHS WCFE
	- 'Magnoliifolia'	see *P. laurocerasus* 'Latifolia'
	- 'Mano'	LMaj
	- 'Marbled White'	see *P. laurocerasus* 'Castlewellan'
	- 'Miky'	CJun
	- 'Mount Vernon'	CTri MBlu SCob
	- 'Novita'	CBod ECrN EPfP GMcL LMaj LSRN NLar NPri WMoo
	- 'Otto Luyken' ♀H5	CBcs CCVT CDul CMac CTri EBee EHoe ELan EPfP ESps GMcL IBoy LBuc MAsh MGos MJak MSwo NEgg NLar SArc SCob SGol SPer SPlb WFar WHar
	- 'Piranha'PBR	NEoE
	- 'Reynvaanii'	CJun
	- 'Rotundifolia' ♀H5	Widely available
	- 'Schipkaensis'	GMcL
	- 'Variegata' misapplied	see *P. laurocerasus* 'Castlewellan'
	- 'Variegata' ambig. (v)	SRms
	- 'Whitespot'	MMuc
	- 'Zabeliana'	CDul CMac CTri ESps GMcL MJak MSwo NEgg SCob SPer SRms WHar
	litigiosa	EBee EMOT EMil NOra
	'Little Pink Perfection'	NLar NOra SCoo SPoG
	lusitanica ♀H5	Widely available
	- subsp. ***azorica***	CExl EBee LRHS WPGP
	- 'Myrtifolia' ♀H5	CBar CRos CTri EPfP EShb ESps GMcL LMaj LRHS MRav NLar NOra SCob SGol SLon SPoG SWvt WCFE WMoo
	- 'Variegata' (v)	CBar CMac CTri ELan ELon ESps MGos MRav MSwo SCob SGol SPer SPoG SSta SWvt WFar WMoo
	maackii	EMOT ESps WMou
	- 'Amber Beauty'	CBcs CDul CLnd EBee EPfP EUJe GKin LMaj MMuc MRav NOra SEND SGol SLon
§	'Matsumae-beni-murasaki'	EBee EMOT NLar NOra WHar
	'Matsumae-beni-tamanishiki'	see *P.* 'Beni-tamanishiki'
§	'Matsumae-fuki' ♀H6	EBee EMOT LSRN NLar NOra NRHS SLim SPoG WHar
	'Matsumae-hanagasa'	see *P.* 'Hanagasa'
	maximowiczii B&SWJ 10967	WCru
	'Mount Fuji'	see *P.* 'Shirotae'

mume	CMen ELon MMrt
- 'Beni-chidori' ♀H5	CBcs CEnd CMac EBee ELan EPfP LCro LOPS LRHS MAsh MBlu NLar NOra SCob SCoo SPoG WCot WJas
§ - 'Omoi-no-mama' (d)	CEnd CMen SAko
- 'Omoi-no-wac'	see *P. mume* 'Omoi-no-mama'
myrobalana	see *P. cerasifera* Myrobalan Group
nipponica var. ***kurilensis*** 'Brillant'	CBcs CSBt ELon LRHS MAsh MMrt NLar NRHS SPoG
- - 'Ruby'	LSRN NEgg
'Okame Harlequin' (v)	EMOT
'Oku-miyako' misapplied	see *P.* 'Shōgetsu'
'Orange Beauty'	LRHS
padus	CArg CCVT CDul CFGn CHab CLnd CMac CPer CSBt CTri ECrN ESps EWTr LBuc MGos MJak MMuc MSwo NLar SCob SEND SEWo WMou WTSh
- 'Albertii'	CCVT EBee NOra
- 'Colorata' ♀H6	CArg CDul CEnd CMac CTho EBee ECrN ELan EWTr MGos MMuc MRav NLar NPri SEND SGol SPer SWvt
- 'Grandiflora'	see *P. padus* 'Watereri'
- 'Le Thoureil'	MMrt
- 'Purple Queen'	ECrN SCob SGol
§ - 'Watereri' ♀H6	CArg CCVT CDul CEnd CLnd CMCN CMac CTho ECrN ELan EMOT EPfP ESps LMaj LPra MMuc SEND SEWo SGol SPer WMou
'Pandora' ♀H6	CCVT CDul CLnd CSBt EBee ECrN EMOT EPfP ESps EWTr LCro LMaj LOPS LRHS MAsh MGos MMuc MRav MSwo NOra SCob SCoo SEND SEWo SLim SPer SPoG WMou
§ ***pendula*** f. ***ascendens*** 'Rosea' ♀H6	LRHS MRav NOra
- 'Pendula Plena Rosea' (d)	NOra
§ - 'Pendula Rosea'	CDul CEnd CLnd CTri EPfP ESps MAsh SCob SPer WJas
§ - 'Pendula Rubra' ♀H6	CCVT CDul CLnd CMac CSBt EBee ELan EMOT EPfP LRHS MSwo NOra SCoo SLim SPer SPoG
§ - 'Stellata' ♀H6	EPfP NOra SPer
persica	ESps SPre
- 'Advance' (F)	SDea
- 'Amsden June' (F)	CLnd EBtc ERea LEdu NOra NRog SDea SKee WHar
- 'Avalon Pride' (F)	CAgr CRos EPfP EPom ERea MCoo NOra NRog SKee SPoG
- 'Barrington' (F)	ERea
- 'Bellegarde' (F)	CFGn ERea NOra NRog SDea SKee
- 'Black' (F)	ERea
- 'Bonanza' (F)	EPom ERea LRHS LSRN
- 'Carman' (F)	ERea
- 'Champion' (F)	CLnd NRog SDea
- 'Crimson Bonfire' (F)	EPom
- 'Crimson Cascade' (F)	ELan
- 'Darling' (F)	SVic
- 'Diamond' (F)	EPom
- 'Dixi Red' (F)	CAgr ERea
- 'Doctor Hogg' (F)	ERea SDea
- 'Duke of York' (F) ♀H4	CTri ERea SDea SKee
- 'Dymond' (F)	ERea SDea
- 'Early Alexander' (F)	ERea
- 'Foliis Rubris' (F)	CDul
- 'Francis' (F)	SKee
- 'Frost' (F)	ERea NRog
- 'Garden Lady' (F)	EPom NOra SLim WHar
- 'Gorgeous' (F)	NOra SKee
- 'Hale's Early' (F)	MMuc MRav NOra NRog SKee SLim SPer WHar
- 'Harken' (F)	ERea
- 'Hylands' (F)	SDea
- 'Jalousia' (F)	EPom NRog
- 'Johnny Brack' (F)	ERea NRog
- 'Kestrel' (F)	ERea SKee
- 'Lacrima' (F) **new**	EPom
- 'Madison' (F)	ERea
- 'Mesembrine'PBR (F)	EPom ERea NOra
- 'Natalia' (F)	SDea
- var. ***nectarina*** CRIMSON GOLD (F)	SDea
- - 'Earliglo' (F)	LRHS NOra
- - 'Early Gem' (F)	ERea SDea
- - 'Early Rivers' (F) ♀H4	ERea LSRN SDea
- - 'Elruge' (F)	ERea SDea
- - 'Fantasia' (F)	EPfP SDea
- - 'Fire Gold' (F)	ERea SDea
- - 'Flavortop' (F)	EPfP ERea
- - 'Garden Beauty' (F/d)	SPoG
- - 'Honey Kist'PBR (F)	EPom
- - 'Humboldt' (F)	CAgr CDul CFGn EMOT ERea SDea WHar
- - 'John Rivers' (F)	SDea SPer
- - 'Lord Napier' (F) ♀H4	CAgr CDul CRos CSBt CTri EMOT EPfP EPom ERea LRHS MAsh MGos MJak MWat NOra SDea SEND SKee SLim SPer SPoG SSFT SVic WHar
- - 'Madame Blanchet' (F)	SDea
- - 'Nectarella' (F)	EPom ERea LRHS LSRN NOra SLim WHar
- - 'Pineapple' (F)	CAgr CTri ERea NOra SDea SKee WHar
- - RUBIS ('Necta Zee'PBR) (F)	EPom
- - 'Ruby Gold' (F)	SDea
- - 'Sauzee Bel' (F)	EPom
- - 'Sauzee King' (F)	EPom
- - 'Snow Baby' (F)	EPom
- - 'Terrace Ruby' (F)	MGos
- 'Oriane'PBR (F)	NRog
- 'Pallas' (F)	ERea
- 'Peregrine' (F) ♀H4	CAgr CDul CLnd CSBt CTri EMOT EPfP EPom ERea ESps EWTr LRHS LSRN MAsh MGos MJak MMuc MWat NLar NOra NRog SDea SEND SKee SLim SPer SPoG SSFT WHar WJas
- 'Raritan Rose' (F)	ERea
- 'Red Top' (F)	EPfP
- 'Redhaven' (F)	CAgr EMOT ERea NOra NRog SDea SKee SVic WHar
- 'Redwing' (F)	CAgr
- 'Reliance' (F)	SDea
- 'Robin Redbreast' (F)	CAgr SDea
- 'Rochester' (F) ♀H4	CAgr CDul CFGn CLnd CSBt CTri EMOT EPom ERea LRHS LSRN MGos NLar NOra NRog SDea SKee SLim SPer SSFT WHar
- 'Royal George' (F)	NRog
- 'Rubira' (F)	NRog
- 'Sanguine de Savoie' (F)	EPom LRHS NOra NRog
- 'Saturne' (F)	CAgr CLnd EMOT EPom ERea MAsh NOra NRog SDea SKee WHar
- 'Springtime' (F)	SDea
- 'Terrace Amber' (F)	SPoG
- 'Terrace Garnet' (F)	MGos
- 'Wassenberger' (F)	SDea

	× ***persicoides*** 'Ingrid' (F)	CAgr CDul CEnd CFGn ECrN EMOT ERea ESps LRHS MCoo MGos NOra SCoo SKee WHar
	- 'Pollardii'	WJas
	- 'Robijn' (F)	CAgr EPom LBuc LEdu NOra SKee SVic
	- 'Spring Glow'	CCVT CDul CEnd CLnd EMOT EMil EPfP MSwo NOra SCoo SEND SLim SLon WJas
	'Petite Noir'	CLnd
	phaeosticta NJM 10.072	WPGP
	'Pink Candy' (F) **new**	EPom
	PINK PARASOL	see *P.* 'Hanagasa'
	'Pink Perfection' ♀H6	CBcs CDul CLnd CSBt ECrN ELan ELon EMOT EPfP ESps EUJe LPra LRHS MGos MSwo NOra SCob SPer WHar WJas WMou
	'Pink Shell'	CLnd EPfP ESps EWTr NOra SPer
	pissardii	see *P. cerasifera* 'Pissardii'
	'Pissardii Nigra'	see *P. cerasifera* 'Nigra'
	pumila var. ***depressa***	MRav SAko
	'Red Dwarf'	LRHS
	'Royal Burgundy' (d) ♀H6	Widely available
	rufa	CDul CJun CLnd EBtc GKin LLHF NOra SLon
	salicina 'Abundance' (F)	ERea
	- 'Beauty' (F)	ERea
§	- 'Black Diamond' (F)	SDea
	- 'Elephant Heart' (F)	MRai
	- 'Golden Japan' (F)	MRai
	- 'Howard Miracle' (F)	ERea
	- 'Lizzie' (F)	EPom
	- 'Mariposa' (F)	ERea
	- 'Methley' (D)	CAgr ERea MRai NOra SPoG WHar
	- 'Ozark Premier' (F)	ERea
	- 'Santa Rosa' (F)	ERea MRai
	- 'Satsuma' (F)	ERea
	- 'Sierra' (F)	ERea
	- 'Sun Gold' (F)	MRai
	sargentii	Widely available
	- 'Charles Sargent' ♀H6	CMCN LMaj LSRN MBlu
	- 'Rancho'	CLnd IArd LMaj MAsh SCoo SLim SPer
	× ***schmittii***	CCVT EBee ECrN ESps LMaj NOra SPer WJas
	'Sekiyama'	see *P.* 'Kanzan'
§	***serrula***	Widely available
	- 'Branklyn' ♀H6	EBee EPfP MGos NOra SCob
	- 'Princesse Sturdza'	MBlu
	- var. ***tibetica***	see *P. serrula*
	serrula × ***serrulata***	WPGP
	serrulata (d)	CAco LPra
	- 'Erecta'	see *P.* 'Amanogawa'
	- 'Grandiflora'	see *P.* 'Ukon'
	- 'Longipes'	see *P.* 'Shōgetsu'
	- 'Miyako' misapplied	see *P.* 'Shōgetsu'
	- var. ***pubescens***	see *P. verecunda*
	- 'Rosea'	see *P.* 'Kiku-shidare-zakura'
	'Shidare-zakura'	see *P.* 'Kiku-shidare-zakura'
	'Shimizu-zakura'	see *P.* 'Shōgetsu'
	'Shiro' (D)	ERea
	'Shirofugen' ♀H6	Widely available
§	'Shirotae' ♀H6	Widely available
§	'Shizuka' ♀H6	CDul EBee ECrN ELon EMOT LRHS MSwo NLar NOra SCob SCoo SLim SPer SPoG WHar WMou
§	'Shōgetsu' ♀H6	CBcs CDul CEnd CLnd CMCN CMac CSBt CTho ELan EMOT EPfP ESps LMaj LRHS LSRN MAsh MMuc NEgg NLar NOra SCob SEWo SLim SPer SPoG WHar WMou
	'Snow Goose'	CMac EBee ELan EMOT EPfP ESps EUJe LRHS MBlu MMuc NEgg NLar NOra SCoo SGol SPoG WHar
	'Snow Showers'	CCVT CEnd CMac ELan EMOT LCro LRHS LSRN MAsh MGos NOra NPri SEND SLim SPer SPoG WHar
	spinosa	Widely available
	- 'Plena' (d)	CEnd CTho MBlu
	- 'Purpurea'	CDul CTho EGFP MBlu WMou
§	'Spire' ♀H6	Widely available
	SPRING SNOW	see *P.* 'Beni-tamanishiki'
	'Spring Snow' ambig.	EMOT
	× ***subhirtella***	ESps LPra
	- var. ***ascendens***	see *P. pendula* f. *ascendens*
	- 'Autumnalis'	Widely available
	- 'Autumnalis Rosea'	Widely available
§	- 'Dahlem'	LPra
	- 'Falling Stars'	SLon
	- 'Fukubana'	CLnd CMac ELon EMOT EPfP MAsh
	- 'Pendula' misapplied	see *P. pendula* 'Pendula Rosea'
	- 'Pendula Rosea'	see *P. pendula* 'Pendula Rosea'
	- 'Pendula Rubra'	see *P. pendula* 'Pendula Rubra'
	- 'Plena'	see *P.* × *subhirtella* 'Dahlem'
	- 'Rosea'	see *P. pendula* f. *ascendens* 'Rosea'
	- 'Stellata'	see *P. pendula* 'Stellata'
	'Sunset Boulevard' ♀H6	CCVT CLnd ELan EMOT EPfP LMaj LSRN MGos NLar NOra WHar
	'Tai-haku' ♀H6	Widely available
	'Taoyame' ♀H6	CLnd
	tenella	ECha WCot
	- 'Fire Hill'	CSBt ELan EPfP LRHS MGos NLar SPer WCot WJas WSpi
	'The Bride' ♀H6	CBcs CDul CEnd CJun CTho EBee EMOT EPfP LCro LOPS LRHS MAsh NOra SChF SCoo SEWo
	tibetica	see *P. serrula*
	'Tiltstone Hellfire'	EBee EMOT GBin NOra
	tomentosa	EBee
§	'Trailblazer' (C/D)	CDul CEnd CLnd CMac ECrN EMOT EMil MRav MSwo SCob SLon WMou
	triloba	CBcs ECha ESps LCro LOPS MBlu MGos
	- 'Multiplex' (d)	SRms WAvo WJas
§	'Ukon' ♀H6	CBcs CDul CLnd CMCN CMac CTho CTri EBee ECrN EMOT EPfP ESps EWTr IRob LCro LOPS LRHS MAsh MGos MRav NLar NOra SGol SLim SPer WFar WHar
	'Umineko'	CCVT CDul CLnd ECrN ESps LMaj MGos MMuc SEND SEWo SPer WHar
§	***verecunda***	CLnd WJas
	- 'Autumn Glory' ♀H6	CTho
	virginiana 'Schubert'	ECrN EMOT MMuc WMou
	'White Cloud'	CDul
	'Woodfield Cluster'	IArd
	yamadae	see *P. incisa* f. *yamadei*
	× ***yedoensis***	CCVT CDul CLnd EMOT ESps LMaj MRav NOra SEWo SLon SPer WHar
	- 'Ivensii'	CAco CDul CSBt EMOT ESps LMaj SCoo SPer
	- 'Pendula'	see *P.* × *yedoensis* 'Shidare-Yoshino'
	- 'Perpendens'	see *P.* × *yedoensis* 'Shidare-Yoshino'
§	- 'Shidare-Yoshino'	CCVT CDul CLnd CSBt EBee ECrN EMOT ESps EUJe LRHS MAsh MGos MRav MSwo SLim SLon

§ - 'Somei-Yoshino' ♀H6	CCVT CMCN CTho CTri EPfP SLim WHar WJas
'Yoshino'	see *P.* × *yedoensis* 'Somei-Yoshino'
'Yoshino Pendula'	see *P.* × *yedoensis* 'Shidare-Yoshino'

Pseudocydonia (*Rosaceae*)

§ ***sinensis***	CBcs CMen SSta WHil

Pseudofumaria see *Corydalis*

alba	see *Corydalis ochroleuca*

Pseudogynoxys (*Asteraceae*)

§ ***chenopodioides***	CCCN CSpe ECre EWld SVen

Pseudolarix (*Pinaceae*)

amabilis ♀H6	CMen CTho EPfP IRob MBlu MPkF SLim SMad
kaempferi (Lamb.) Gordon	see *Larix kaempferi*

Pseudomuscari see *Muscari*

Pseudopanax ✿ (*Araliaceae*)

(Adiantifolius Group) 'Adiantifolius'	CBcs EBee SVen
- 'Cyril Watson' ♀H3	CBcs ELan LRHS SVen
arboreus	see *Neopanax arboreus*
chathamicus	SArc
crassifolius	CBrP CCCN CDTJ ELon EUJe GBin IDee LRHS NLos SArc WCot
- var. ***trifoliolatus***	WPGP
discolor	LEdu
ferox	CBcs CBrP CDTJ CTsd EUJe GBin IDee LRHS NLos SCob SVen
laetus	see *Neopanax laetus*
lessonii	CBcs CBrP
- 'Gold Splash' (v) ♀H3	CBcs EPfP LRHS SEND SVen
- 'Rangitira'	CBcs
'Linearifolius'	LEdu
'Moa's Toes'	CAbb EUJe NLos SCob SEND
'Purpureus' ♀H3	CDTJ EBee IDee SEND SVen
'Sabre'	CBcs CDTJ EBee EPfP EUJe LRHS SEND
'Trident' ♀H3	LRHS SBig SLim SVen
'Tuatara'	CAbb CCht EUJe GBin NLos SCob

Pseudosasa (*Poaceae*)

sp.	CAco
amabilis misapplied	see *Arundinaria gigantea*
§ ***japonica*** ♀H5	CAbb CAgr CBcs CBdn CBod CSBt CTsd ENBC EPfP ESps EUJe GBin GMcL LCro LOPS LRHS MMoz MMuc MWht NLar NRHS SArc SCob SEND SEWo SPoG WCFE WMoo
§ - 'Akebonosuji' (v)	CBdn MWht WPGP
I - var. ***pleioblastoides***	MWht
- 'Tsutsumiana'	ELon ERod EUJe GMcL MMoz MWht NLar SBig
- 'Variegata'	see *P. japonica* 'Akebonosuji'
viridula	ERod MWht

Pseudotaxus (*Taxaceae*)

chienii new	WPGP

Pseudotsuga (*Pinaceae*)

§ ***menziesii***	CAco CBcs CDul CLnd CPer ECrN EPfP LPra MBlu MMuc WTSh
- 'Bhiela Lhota'	CKen
- 'Blue Wonder'	CKen
- 'Densa'	CKen
- 'Fastigiata'	CKen
- 'Fletcheri'	CKen
- var. ***glauca***	CAco
- 'Glauca Pendula'	CDul CKen MBlu
I - 'Gotelli's Pendula'	CKen
- 'Graceful Grace'	CKen
- 'Hillside Pride'	NLar
- 'Idaho Gem'	CKen NLar
- 'Julie'	CKen
- 'Knaphill'	LRHS
- 'Little Jamie'	CKen
- 'Lohbrunner'	CKen
- 'McKenzie'	CKen
- 'Nana'	CKen
- 'Serpentine'	MBlu
- 'Stairii'	CKen
- 'Uwes Golden'	SLim
- 'Vladstein'	NLar
taxifolia	see *P. menziesii*

Pseudowintera (*Winteraceae*)

§ ***colorata***	CBcs CCCN CExl CMac CPla GAbr GKin LRHS MRav NLar SCob SEle WSHC
- 'Marjorie Congreve'	CBcs GKin IArd LRHS
- 'Moulin Rouge'	CBcs LRHS SEle
- 'Red Glow'	CBcs
- 'Red Leopard'	CAby CBcs LRHS NLar SEle

Psidium (*Myrtaceae*)

cattleyanum	see *P. littorale* var. *longipes*
guajava (F)	CCCN CMCN SPlb XBlo
littorale (F)	CPne
§ - var. ***longipes*** (F)	CCCN XBlo

Psoralea (*Papilionaceae*)

aphylla	SVen
* ***fleta***	SPlb
glabra	SPlb
glandulosa	SBrt SPlb WSHC
oligophylla	SPlb
onobrychis	SPhx
pinnata	CExl

Psychotria (*Rubiaceae*)

capensis	CExl

Psylliostachys (*Plumbaginaceae*)

suworowii new	SPhx

Ptelea (*Rutaceae*)

trifoliata	CAby CBcs CDul ELan EPfP MBlu SChF SPer SRms WPGP
- 'Aurea' ♀H5	CBcs CBot CDul CExl CJun ELan EPfP LRHS MBlu MMuc SMad SPer WBor WPGP

Pteracanthus see *Strobilanthes*

Pteridium (*Dennstaedtiaceae*)

aquilinum	XLum

Pteridophyllum (*Papaveraceae*)

racemosum	GEdr WCru

Pteris ✿ (*Pteridaceae*)

§ ***actiniopteroides***	CFil
cretica ♀H1c	CTsd
- var. ***albolineata*** ♀H1c	EShb LLWG LRHS MBel NRHS SAko WCot XBlo

- 'Mayi' (v)	LRHS NRHS
- 'Ouvradii'	SPlb
- 'Parkeri'	CBdn LRHS NRHS
- 'Rowei'	LRHS NRHS XBlo
- 'Wimsettii'	LRHS NRHS
ensiformis 'Victoriae'	EShb
henryi	see *P. actiniopteroides*
* ***staminea***	XBlo
tremula	EShb
tricolor	EShb
umbrosa	CAby CBdn CHid LLWG LRHS NLos NRHS WPGP
vittata	CBdn
wallichiana	CFil WCot WPGP

Pterocactus (*Cactaceae*)

hickenii F&W 10240	WCot

Pterocarya ✿ (*Juglandaceae*)

fraxinifolia	CBcs CCVT CDul CMCN CTho EBee ECrN EPfP IArd IDee LMaj LPra LRHS MBlu MCoo MMuc MRav SAko SChF WTSh
- NJM 13.007	WPGP
- PAB 13.052	LEdu
- 'Abbotsbury Giant'	WPGP
macroptera var. ***insignis***	CExl CFil WPGP
× ***rehderiana***	CTho MBlu
rhoifolia	CDul CMCN IArd
stenoptera	CBcs CDTJ CDul CMCN CTho NLar
- 'Fern Leaf' ♀H6	CExl CFil CHid LRHS MBlu WPGP
tonkinensis	WPGP

Pterocephalus (*Caprifoliaceae*)

parnassi	see *P. perennis*
§ ***perennis***	CMea IRob MHer SRms WAbe WHoo
spathulatus	WAbe

Pterostylis (*Orchidaceae*)

curta ♀H2	CBro CTal

Pterostyrax (*Styracaceae*)

corymbosa	CBcs CMCN GBin MBlu NLar SMad
- CWJ 12838	WCru
hispida ♀H5	CAby CBcs CDul CHGN CMCN CTsd EPfP GBin IDee LRHS MBlu MRav NLar SAko WFar WGrn WHar WHor
psilophyllus	CMCN WPGP
- var. ***leveillei*** **new**	WPGP
- trilobed	EBee WPGP

Ptilostemon (*Asteraceae*)

§ ***diacantha***	EPfP IFoB LRHS NRHS

Ptilotrichum see *Alyssum*

Ptilotus (*Amaranthaceae*)

exaltatus	SPlb

Puccinellia (*Poaceae*)

distans	EBWF

Pulicaria (*Asteraceae*)

§ ***dysenterica***	CHab EBWF LLWG NMir WHer WSFF

Pulmonaria (*Boraginaceae*)

angustifolia ♀H7	CTri EPfP ESps GKev GMaP MNrw NPnk SHeu SRms
- 'Azurea'	CElw ELan EPPr EPfP GAbr GBin GMaP LRHS MCot MMuc MRav NBro NLar NRHS SRms WSpi
- 'Blaues Meer'	EBee ECtt LRHS MNrw NRHS NSti SGbt SHeu WSpi
- 'Munstead Blue'	CElw MCot MRav NRya SRms
'Apple Frost'	LRHS NRHS SHeu
'Barfield Regalia'	NChi NSti
'Benediction'	EBee MAvo MNrw NSti WBrk WCot WSHC
'Beth Chatto'	CElw
'Beth's Pink'	GAbr
'Blake's Silver'	CBre CDor ECtt GAbr MAvo MHol MNrw NEgg NSti WBrk WCot WGrn WHoo WPGP WWFP
'Blauer Hügel'	NSti
'Blue Crown'	CElw EWes WBrk
'Blue Ensign' ♀H6	Widely available
'Blue Moon'	see *P. officinalis* 'Blue Mist'
'Blue Pearl'	LRHS NRHS XEll
'Blueberry Muffin'	CSpe
'Bubble Gum'PBR	CBod CDor CWCL LRHS NRHS SHeu
Cally hybrid	GCal
'Cedric Morris'	CElw
'Cleeton Red'	MNrw
'Coral Springs'	NLar WCAu
'Cotton Cool'	CTal EBee ECha ECtt EShb LRHS MAvo MBNS MBel MCot MRav MSpe MWat NEgg NPnk NRHS NSti NWad SGbt SHeu SPer SSut WCAu WMoo WWtn
'Dark Vader'	CWCL ECtt LRHS MNrw NRHS SHeu
'Darkling Thrush'	WBrk
'De Vroomen's Pride' (v)	CBod
'Diana Clare' ♀H6	Widely available
'Excalibur'	ECtt LRHS NLar NRHS SHeu SRms
'Gavin Compton' (v)	MNrw
'Glacier'	EPfP NChi WCot
'High Contrast'	ECtt LRHS NRHS SHeu
'Highdown'	see *P.* 'Lewis Palmer'
'Ice Ballet' (Classic Series)	CDor EBee ECtt EPfP MNrw NLar SCob SHar SHeu WCAu
'Joan Curtis' **new**	EWld MNrw
§ 'Lewis Palmer' ♀H7	CBro CDor CTri CWCL GCal GMaP IRob LRHS MAvo MNrw SRGP SRms WAvo WBrk WHoo
'Little Star'	CElw EBee ECha LRHS MAvo NRHS NSti SHeu SRGP WFar
longifolia	ECha EHoe ELan EPfP GAbr GKev LRHS NLar NRHS NSti SCob SRms
§ - 'Ankum'	CElw WCot
- 'Ballyrogan Blue'	LRHS NRHS
- 'Bertram Anderson'	EBee ECtt GMaP IBoy IRob LRHS NLar NRHS SCob SHeu SPer SRGP SRms SWvt
- subsp. ***cevennensis***	ILea LRHS NLar NRHS SHeu WBrk WFar WSpi
- 'Coen Jansen'	see *P. longifolia* 'Ankum'
- 'Howard Eggins'	WAvo WBrk
'Mado'	ECha
'Majesté'	CBod CBot CDor ECha EHrv ELan EPfP EWes GMaP IFro LRHS MBel MRav NGdn NLar NRHS NSti SCob SHeu SMad SPer SPoG SRms WCot WFar
'Marchant's Spotted Dick' **new**	SMHy
'Margery Fish'	CDor LRHS NChi SHeu WAvo WBrk

	'Mary Mottram'	ECtt NSti SHeu WCot
	'Mawson's Blue' ♀H6	EWes NChi SWvt WMoo WSHC
	'Milky Way'	ECtt EPfP SHeu SPoG
	mollis	CBod EPed GBin GCal IMou LRHS MNrw NRHS NSti WCAu
	- 'Royal Blue'	MRav
	'Monksilver'	CElw
	'Moonshine'[PBR]	ECtt EPfP LRHS MAsh NRHS SHeu
	'Moonstone'	CElw
	'Mournful Purple'	ELon
	'Mrs Kittle'	CWCL GPSL IMou LRHS MRav NGdn NRHS NSti SHeu SSut
	'Nürnberg'	CDor
	officinalis	CHby EPed IFoB NChi WBrk
	- 'Alba'	WBrk
§	- 'Blue Mist'	GMaP WCot WMoo
	- 'Bowles's Blue'	see *P. officinalis* 'Blue Mist'
	- Cambridge Blue Group	CWCL EPfP LRHS MRav NGdn NRHS WCot WWtn
	- 'White Wings'	EBee NLar
	'Oliver Wyatt's White'	SRGP
	OPAL ('Ocupol')	Widely available
	'Pierre's Pure Pink'	EBee LRHS NRHS SBee SHeu
	'Pink Haze'[PBR]	EBee ECtt LRHS MHol MPie NLar NRHS NSti SCob SWvt
	'Raspberry Ice'	EBee
	'Raspberry Splash'[PBR]	CBod CPla CWCL ECtt EPfP ETMg GKev LCro LOPS LRHS MBel MMuc MNrw NLar NRHS SCob SHeu SWvt
*	'Rowlatt Choules'	MNrw
	'Roy Davidson'	CDor ECtt EPfP IRob LRHS NChi NRHS NSti SMHy SRms SWvt
	rubra	CBcs CElw CWCL ECha ELan EPPr GAbr LCro LOPS MJak MMuc MNrw NBid NChi NSti SHeu SRms WBrk WCAu
	- var. ***alba***	see *P. rubra* var. *albocorollata*
§	- var. ***albocorollata***	CBre GAbr NBid
	- 'Ann'	GBin
	- 'Barfield Pink'	GCal IFro SHeu
	- 'Bowles's Red'	CBod EHrv EPed GPSL IFoB LRHS MNrw MRav NGdn NLar NRHS WFar WGwG WHoo WWtn
	- 'David Ward' (v)	CBod CWCL ECha ECtt EHrv ELan EShb GMaP LPmr LRHS MBel MRav NRHS NSti SHeu SMad SPer SPoG WCAu WCFE WCot
	- 'Rachel Vernie' (v)	WAvo
	- 'Redstart'	CBod CDor CSam ECtt GMaP ILea LEdu LRHS MNrw MRav NGdn NLar SHeu SRms SWvt WBrk WFar WMoo
§	***saccharata***	ECha GMaP IFro MMuc SRms
	- 'Alba'	CElw IFro MMuc SRms
	- Argentea Group ♀H7	CTri ELan EPfP GMaP LRHS MMuc MRav NGdn NRHS
	- 'Clent Skysilver'	WAvo WBrk
	- 'Dora Bielefeld'	CTal CWCL ECha EPfP GMaP LRHS MNrw MRav NChi NEgg NGdn NRHS NSti SHeu SPer SRGP SWvt
	- 'Frühlingshimmel'	CDor IRob LPla MRav NSti
	- 'Glebe Cottage Blue'	CElw
	- 'Leopard'	CDor CSam CWCL ECha ECtt EPed GBin GMaP LRHS MBel NGdn NRHS NSti SBod SHeu SWvt WCot WGwG WHoo WSpi
	- 'Mrs Moon'	CBod CTri ECtt EPfP GMaP NLar SHeu SPer SWvt WCAu WHar
	- 'Picta'	see *P. saccharata*
	- 'Pink Dawn'	NLar
	- 'Reginald Kaye'	ECha MAvo
	- 'Silverado'[PBR]	ECtt LRHS NGdn NRHS SHeu SWvt
	- 'Stanhoe'	EWes
	'Saint Ann's'	LRHS NRHS NSti
	'Samurai'	CWCL LRHS MAvo NRHS NSti SHeu WFar
	'Silver Bouquet'[PBR]	CElw ECtt EPfP LCro LOPS LSou NHpl SHeu
	'Silver Lance'	SHeu
	'Silver Shimmers'[PBR]	SHeu
	'Sissinghurst White' ♀H7	Widely available
	'Smoky Blue'	ECtt MRav SCob SHeu
	'Spilled Milk'	SHeu
	'Stillingfleet Meg'	ECtt EPfP LRHS LSou MBNS NGdn NRHS NSti NWad SHeu SRGP WCAu WCot WGwG WWFP WWtn
	'Tim's Silver'	GBin
	'Trevi Fountain'	CBod CDor CHid CWCL EBee ECha ECtt ELon EPfP EShb ETMg EUJe GKev LCro LOPS LPla LRHS LSun MHol NDov NRHS NSti SHeu SPoG WCAu WCot WFar WHoo WPnP WSpi
	'Vera May' ♀H7	MNrw
	'Victorian Brooch'[PBR]	CBod CWCL ECtt EPau EPfP GKev GMaP IBoy LRHS MHol MNrw NCou NPri NRHS SHeu SPad SPoG WSpi
	'Weetwood Blue'	LRHS MNrw NRHS
	'Wendy Perry'	LRHS NRHS

Pulsatilla (*Ranunculaceae*)

	albana	CBro LLHF LRHS NPnk NRHS
	- 'Lutea'	EBee LLHF
	- red-flowered **new**	GKev
	alpina	SPlb SRms WArt
§	- subsp. ***apiifolia***	GKev IFro NRya WAbe
	- subsp. ***sulphurea*** misapplied	see *P. alpina* subsp. *apiifolia*
	ambigua	GEdr GKev LLHF
	'Blue Select' (Pr/Prim)	IBoy
	bungeana	GKev SBrt
	campanella	EWld GEdr
	caucasica	CBro EWld LRHS NRHS
	halleri ♀H5	EBee GKev NPnk WHal
*	- ***alba***	EPPr
	- subsp. ***slavica*** ♀H5	LLHF
	- subsp. ***taurica***	GEdr
	lutea	see *P. alpina* subsp. *apiifolia*
	montana	CPla SPlb XEll
	occidentalis	GEdr
§	***patens***	CPla EDAr GKev NGdn
	- SDR 8136	GKev
	- subsp. ***flavescens***	EBee GEdr GKev
	pratensis	GPoy SRms
	- subsp. ***nigricans***	CFis GEdr WAbe
I	- 'Semiplena'	MMoz
	regeliana	LLHF
	rubra	CMea ELan EPfP GBin GMaP LRHS MHer NGdn NLar NPnk NRHS SPad SPer SPoG SRms SRot WHoo WTor
*	***serotina***	GKev
	turczaninovii	LLHF NSla WArt
*	***turkestanica***	GEdr
§	***vernalis***	CSma EPot GEdr NLar NSla WAbe XEll
	violacea	CBcs LLHF
§	***vulgaris*** ♀H5	Widely available
	- 'Alba'	CAby CBod CBro CMea CRos CTsd CWCL EBee ECha ELan EPfP EShb

		GBin GCal IBoy LRHS MBel MHer NGdn NRHS SCob SPad SPer SPoG SWvt WFar WGwG XEll XLum
	- 'Barton's Pink'	CBro CRos LLHF LRHS NPnk NRHS
	- 'Blaue Glocke'	CAby CBod GEdr IBoy LRHS NRHS SHar SWvt
	- 'Eva Constance'	CBro CRos LLHF LRHS NRHS
	- 'Gotlandica'	LLHF
	- subsp. ***grandis***	CRos EPot GEdr LRHS NRHS NSla
	- - 'Papageno'	CDor CSpe ELon GBin GCrg GEdr IPot MAvo MBel MHol NHpl NLar NSla
	- Heiler hybrids	CBod EShb LLHF MArl MRav MWat NEgg NGdn NSla SVic WGwG
	- 'Perlen Glocke'	EDAr GEdr GJos LPmr LRHS MMrt NLar NRHS WArt
	- pink-flowered	CMea GKev LLHF NSla WFar
	- (Pinwheel Series) PINWHEEL BLUE VIOLET SHADES **new**	CRos NRHS
	- - PINWHEEL DARK RED SHADES **new**	CRos NRHS
	- - PINWHEEL WHITE **new**	CRos NRHS
	- RED CLOCK	see *P. vulgaris* 'Röde Klokke'
	- red-flowered	CTsd EBee GAbr IBoy SCob SGbt WFar
§	- 'Röde Klokke'	CAby CBod EAJP ECtt EPfP GBin GEdr GJos GWyn IBoy LRHS MCot NRHS SHar SWvt WHil XEll XLum XSen
	- 'Rosen Glocke' **new**	GJos
	- ROTE GLOCKE	see *P. vulgaris* 'Röde Klokke'
	- 'Violet Bells'	WHil
	- violet-blue-flowered	EPfP LRHS MWat NRHS
§	- 'Weisse Schwan'	EBee EPfP GEdr GMaP SRot
	- 'White Bells'	GEdr
	- WHITE SWAN	see *P. vulgaris* 'Weisse Schwan'

Pultenaea (*Papilionaceae*)

daphnoides	SVen
juniperina	SPlb SVen

pummelo see *Citrus maxima*

Punica (*Lythraceae*)

granatum	CBcs CBod CCCN CMen ELan EPfP ESps LMaj SCob SEND SPre SVic SWvt
- 'Chico' (d)	CBcs
- 'Fina Tendral' (F)	CCCN
- 'Legrelleae' (F/d)	SEND
- 'Maxima Rubra' (d)	EShb XSen
- var. ***nana*** ♀H3	CCCN CMen EPfP EShb LEdu LRHS MHer SRms SVen SVic
- f. ***plena*** (d)	CBcs LRHS MRav WCFE
- - 'Flore Pleno Luteo' (d)	LRHS
- 'Provence' (F)	EPom XSen
- 'Wonderful' (F)	CAgr

Puschkinia (*Asparagaceae*)

scilloides var. ***libanotica*** ♀H5	EPot ERCP GKev LAma LCro LOPS LRHS MPie NRHS SDeJ SEND WRHF WShi
- - 'Alba'	EPot GKev LAma SDeJ

Puya ✿ (*Bromeliaceae*)

	RH 1809	WCot
	RH 2910A	WCot
	RH 2961C	WCot
	RH 3425B	WCot
	alpestris	CCCN CFil CPla EShb SBig SPlb
	- subsp. ***zoellneri***	CAbb CBcs CCCN CDTJ EShb SPlb SVen WCot
	assurgens	WCot
	boliviensis	WCot
	castellanosii	NLos WCot
	chilensis	CAbb CBcs CBlu CCCN CDTJ CPla LRHS NLos SPlb SVen WCot
	coerulea	CCCN CDTJ CPla CTsd LRHS MGil NLos SPlb
	- var. ***monteroana***	WCot
§	- var. ***violacea***	CBlu
	dyckioides	LRHS WCot
	- red-bracted	WCot
	ferruginea	EUJe NLos SPlb WCot
	gilmartiniae F&W 8697	WCot
	harmsii	NLos WCot
	hromadnikii	SPlb
	laxa	SPlb WCot
	mirabilis	CAbb CDTJ EUJe GBin NLos
	raimondii	CFil WCot
	venusta	CCCN CDTJ CPla LRHS NLos SPlb SVen WCot
	violacea	see *P. coerulea* var. *violacea*
	yakespala	WCot

Pycnanthemum (*Lamiaceae*)

curvipes	LEdu
muticum	LEdu SBrt WPGP
pilosum	MHer SPhx XLum
tenuifolium	NLar SBrt SPhx
virginianum	EBee SPhx

Pycnostachys (*Lamiaceae*)

urticifolia	EWes SDys

Pygmea see *Chionohebe*

Pyracantha (*Rosaceae*)

	ALEXANDER PENDULA ('Renolex')	MRav MSwo SRms
	angustifolia	WCFE
	- KR 2481	WPGP
§	***atalantioides***	SPlb WCFE
	'Brilliant'	SCoo
	coccinea 'Lalandei'	CMac
	- 'Red Column'	Widely available
	- 'Red Cushion'	ELan ESps GMcL MJak MRav SArc SCob SRms
	crenulata	WCFE
	DART'S RED ('Interrada')	CSBt
	'Fiery Cascade'	CRos EPfP LRHS NRHS SPoG
	gibbsii	see *P. atalantioides*
	'Golden Charmer'	CMac EPfP ESps IBoy IRob LBuc LRHS MGos MSwo NEgg NLar SCob SCoo SGol SPoG SRms SWvt WFar
	'Golden Glow'	SGol
	'Golden Paradise'	NEoE SCob SHar
	'Golden Sun'	see *P.* 'Soleil d'Or'
	'Harlequin' (v)	SCob SGol WFar
	'Knap Hill Lemon'	MBlu
	koidzumii 'Victory'	ECrN NLar
	'Mohave'	CMac CRos CTri ECrN ELan ELon EMOT ESps GMcL IBoy LRHS MAsh NRHS SCob SGol SLim SRms SWvt
	'Mohave Silver' (v)	CMac ELan EShb LRHS NRHS
	'Navaho'	LMaj
	'Orange Charmer'	CDul CMac CTri EBee ELan ESps LRHS MGos MJak NLar SCob SGol SPer SPlb WFar WHar WMoo
	'Orange Glow' ♀H6	Widely available

* 'Red Pillar'	EUJe
'Red Star' **new**	NRHS
rogersiana	CDul
- 'Flava' ♀H6	CDul CSBt EPfP LRHS MAsh NEgg NRHS SPoG SWvt WAvo
'Rosedale'	LRHS
SAPHYR JAUNE ('Cadaune'PBR)	CBcs CCVT CEnd CSBt EBee ECrN EPfP LCro LOPS LRHS MGos MJak MRav NPri SCob SGol SPer WHar
SAPHYR ORANGE ('Cadange'PBR) ♀H6	CBcs CCVT CEnd CMac CSBt EBee ECrN EPfP ESps LCro LOPS LRHS MGos MJak MRav NEgg NPri NRHS SCob SCoo SGol SPer WHar
SAPHYR PANACHE ('Cadvar'PBR) (v)	MJak
SAPHYR ROUGE ('Cadrou'PBR) ♀H6	CBcs CCVT CChe CEnd CMac CSBt EBee ECrN ELan EPfP LCro LOPS LRHS MGos MJak MMuc MRav MSwo NPri NRHS SCob SCoo SEND SGol SPer SRms SWvt WFar WHar
'Shawnee'	CMac MSwo
§ 'Soleil d'Or'	Widely available
'Sparkler' (v)	CMac EHoe LRHS NRHS SCob SMad SPoG
'Teton' ♀H6	CMac CRos ELan EPfP GMcL LRHS MAsh MGos MJak MSwo NRHS SCob SGol SPoG SRms WFar
'Watereri'	WSpi
'Yellow Sun'	see *P.* 'Soleil d'Or'

× *Pyracomeles* (*Rosaceae*)

vilmorinii	SAko

Pyrethropsis see *Rhodanthemum*

Pyrethrum see *Tanacetum*

+ *Pyrocydonia* (*Rosaceae*)

'Danielii' (F)	SAko

Pyrola (*Ericaceae*)

rotundifolia	LEdu WHer

× *Pyronia* (*Rosaceae*)

veitchii	SAko

Pyrrocoma (*Asteraceae*)

clementis	EBee

Pyrrosia (*Polypodiaceae*)

calvata **new**	CFil
hastata	CMen WCot
- 'Harima Jishi'	CMen
- 'Ryujin'	CMen
- 'Shikoku Jishi'	CMen
- 'World Champion'	CMen
linearifolia 'Urakoryu Jishi'	CMen
lingua	CMen WPGP
- 'Hiryu'	CMen
- 'Ōgon Nishiki' (v) **new**	WCot
- 'Tachiba Koryu'	CMen
polydactyla	CMen

Pyrus ✿ (*Rosaceae*)

amygdaliformis	CMCN
- W&B B-10	WCot
- var. ***cuneifolia***	CLnd
calleryana	LPra SGol
- 'Bradford'	CLnd
- 'Chanticleer'	Widely available
- 'Chanticleer' variegated (v)	CDul MAsh
- 'Redspire'	CCVT EMOT
communis (F)	CCVT CDul CTri ECrN LBuc SPer SPlb WMou WTSh
- 'Abbé Fétel' (D)	SKee
- 'Bambinella' (D)	SKee
- 'Barland' (Perry)	CHab
- 'Barnet' (Perry)	CHab
- 'Baronne de Mello' (D)	CTho NOra
- 'Beech Hill' (F)	CDul EBee ECrN ESps LMaj LPra SGol SPer
- 'Belle Guérandaise' (D)	SKee
- 'Belle Julie' (D)	SKee
- 'Bellissime d'Hiver' (C)	SKee
- BENITA ('Rafzas') (F)	LCro LOPS LRHS MCoo
- 'Bergamotte d'Automne' (D)	SKee
- 'Bergamotte Esperen' (D)	SKee
- 'Beth' (D) ♀H6	CAgr CHab CMac CSBt CTri EBee ECrN EMOT EPfP EPom IArd LBuc LRHS MGos NLar NOra NPri SCob SDea SKee SLim SPer SSFT WHar
- 'Beurré Alexandre Lucas' (D)	SKee
- 'Beurré Bedford' (D)	SKee
- 'Beurré Clairgeau' (C)	SKee
- 'Beurré d'Amanlis' (D)	SKee
- 'Beurré d'Anjou' (F)	SKee
- 'Beurré d'Avalon' (D)	SKee
- 'Beurré de Beugny' (D)	SKee
- 'Beurré de l'Assomption' (D)	SKee
- 'Beurré Diel' (D)	SKee
- 'Beurré Dumont' (D)	CAgr
- 'Beurré Giffard' (D)	CAgr
- 'Beurré Hardy' (D) ♀H6	Widely available
- 'Beurré Mortillet' (D)	SKee
§ - 'Beurré Précoce Morettini' (D)	SDea
- 'Beurré Six' (D)	SKee
- 'Beurré Superfin' (D) ♀H6	CFGn SKee WHar
- 'Bianchettone' (D)	SKee
- 'Bishop's Thumb' (D)	SDea SKee
- 'Black Worcester' (C)	CDul CHab ESps NOra SDea SKee WHar WJas WWct
- 'Blakeney Red' (Perry)	CHab NOra SDea SKee WHar
- 'Blickling' (D)	SKee
- 'Brandy' (Perry)	CAgr CHab CTho NOra SDea SKee SVic WHar
- 'Bristol Cross' (D)	CAgr CHab SDea SKee
- 'Butt' (Perry)	CHab
- 'Calebasse Bosc' (D)	NOra SKee
- 'Canal Red' (D)	SKee
- 'Cannock' (F)	SKee
- 'Catillac' (C)	CAgr CHab ECrN NOra SKee WHar
- 'Charneaux' (F)	LMaj
- 'Chaumontel' (D)	SKee
- 'Clapp's Favourite' (D)	CHab CTho ECrN LMaj NOra SKee SVic
- 'Comte de Lamy' (D)	SKee
- 'Concorde'PBR (D) ♀H6	Widely available
- 'Conference' (D) ♀H6	Widely available
- 'Deacon's Pear' (D)	SDea
- 'Devoe' (D)	SDea
- 'Docteur Jules Guyot' (D)	CAgr SDea SKee
- 'Doyenné d'Été' (D)	ERea MCoo SKee
- 'Doyenné du Comice' (D) ♀H6	Widely available

	– 'Doyenné Georges Boucher' (D)	SKee
	– 'Duchesse d'Angoulême' (D)	SKee
	– 'Durondeau' (D)	ERea NOra SDea SKee
	– 'Easter Beurré' (D)	SKee
	– 'Emile d'Heyst' (D)	MCoo SKee WHar
	– 'Eva Baltet' (D)	SKee
	– 'Fertility' (D)	CLnd
	– 'Fertility Improved'	see *P. communis* 'Improved Fertility'
	– 'Fondante d'Automne' (D)	CAgr CTho NOra SKee WHar
	– 'Forelle' (D)	ERea SKee
	– 'Gansel's Bergamot' (D)	SKee
	– 'Gieser Wildeman' (F) **new**	LMaj
	– 'Gin' (Perry)	CHab
	– 'Glou Morceau' (D)	CAgr CArg ECrN ERea MCoo MWat NOra SDea SKee SSFT WHar
	– 'Gorham' (D) ♀^{H6}	CAgr CDul CTho NOra SKee SSFT WHar
	– 'Green Horse' (Perry)	CHab SKee
	– 'Hacon's Incomparable' (D)	SKee
	– 'Harley Gum' (F)	WHar
	– 'Harrow Delight' (D)	SDea
	– 'Harvest Queen' (D/C)	CAgr SDea
	– 'Hellen's Early' (Perry)	CHab ERea SKee WHar
	– 'Hendre Huffcap' (Perry)	CAgr CHab CTho EPom NOra SKee WHar
	– 'Hessle' (D)	CAgr CHab SDea SKee
	– HUMBUG ('Pysanka') (D)	EPom LRHS NOra SSFT WHar
§	– 'Improved Fertility' (D)	CAgr ERea SDea SKee
	– INVINCIBLE ('Delwinor') (D/C)	CAgr CArg CDul CFGn CTho EPom LBuc LRHS MAsh MCoo NOra SLim SSFT WHar
	– 'Jargonelle' (D)	CAgr CDul CFGn CHab CTho SDea SKee WHar
	– 'Joséphine de Malines' (D) ♀^{H6}	CAgr ERea IArd NOra SDea SKee WHar
	– 'Judge Amphlett' (Perry)	CTho EPom NOra SKee WHar
	– 'Laxton's Foremost' (D)	CAgr SKee
	– 'Le Lectier' (D)	SKee
	– 'Légipont' (F)	CAgr
	– 'Louise Bonne of Jersey' (D) ♀^{H6}	CAgr CFGn CMac CTri ECrN EPfP EPom ERea IArd MGos NOra SDea SKee WHar WWct
	– 'Lübecker Prinzessin Birne' (F)	MRai
	– 'Magyar Kobak' (C)	SKee
	– 'Marguérite Marillat' (D)	SDea SKee
	– 'Marie-Louise' (D)	SKee WHar
	– 'Merrylegs' (Perry)	CHab
	– 'Merton Pride' (D)	CAgr CFGn CLnd CTho EPom IArd MCoo NOra SDea SKee WHar
	– 'Merton Star' (D)	SKee
	– 'Monsieur le Curé'	see *P. communis* 'Vicar of Winkfield'
	– 'Moonglow' (F)	CAgr ERea NOra SDea SKee
	– 'Moorcroft' (Perry)	SKee
	– 'Morettini'	see *P. communis* 'Beurré Précoce Morettini'
	– 'Mrs Seden' (D)	SKee
	– 'Nouveau Poiteau' (C/D)	CAgr SKee
	– 'Nye Russet Bartlett' (F)	CAgr
	– 'Oldfield' (Perry)	CHab
	– 'Onward' (D) ♀^{H6}	CAgr CArg CDul CHab CLnd CTho CTri ECrN EMOT EPom ERea ESps IArd LRHS MAsh NOra SDea SKee SSFT WHar WWct
	– 'Ovid' (D)	CAgr
§	– 'Packham's Triumph' (D)	CAgr CDul CTri ECrN EMOT EPom ESps NOra SDea SKee WHar
	– 'Parsonage' (Perry)	CHab
	– 'Passe Crassane' (D)	SKee
	– 'Pear Apple' (D)	CHab SDea
	– 'Penrhyn' (D)	WGwG
I	– 'Petite Poire' (D)	EPom
	– 'Pitmaston Duchess' (C/D) ♀^{H6}	ECrN ERea MCoo SDea SKee WHar WWct
	– 'Précoce de Trévoux' (D)	WHar
	– 'Red Beurre Hardy' (C)	SKee
	– 'Red Comice' (D/C)	SKee
	– 'Red Pear' (Perry)	CHab
	– 'Red Sensation Bartlett' (D/C)	EMOT EPom LBuc NOra SKee SSFT
	– 'Robin' (C/D)	ERea SDea SKee
	– 'Roosevelt' (D)	SKee
	– 'Santa Claus' (D)	SDea
	– 'Schweizer Hose' (F)	MRai
	– 'Seckel' (D)	NOra
	– 'Shipova'	see × *Sorbopyrus auricularis* 'Shipova'
	– 'Sierra' (D)	CAgr
	– 'Snowdon Queen' (D)	CHab WGwG
	– 'Sommer Blutbirne' (D)	SAko
	– 'Starkrimson' (D)	SKee
	– 'Swan's Egg' (D)	SKee
	– 'Taynton Squash' (Perry)	NOra
	– 'Tettenhall Dick' (C/D)	WHar
	– 'Thorn' (Perry)	CAgr CHab EPom SKee WHar
	– 'Triumph'	see *P. communis* 'Packham's Triumph'
	– 'Uvedale's St Germain' (C)	SKee
	– 'Verdi' (F)	EPom
§	– 'Vicar of Winkfield' (C)	ECrN MRai SDea SKee
	– 'Williams' Bon Chrétien' (D/C) ♀^{H6}	Widely available
	– 'Williams' Red' (D/C)	NPri SKee
	– 'Williams' Rouge Delbard' (F)	EPom
	– 'Winnal's Longdon' (Perry)	EPom WHar
	– 'Winter Nelis' (D)	CAgr CHab CTri ECrN EMOT NLar NOra SDea SKee WHar WWct
	cordata	CDul CTho
	elaeagnifolia	LMaj MAsh
	– var. ***kotschyana***	CDul SLim
	– 'Silver Sails'	CLnd CMac EBee EMOT EMil NOra SCoo WHar WPGP
	× ***michauxii***	SVen
	nivalis	CDul CLnd CTho EBee ECrN EPfP LEdu LMaj SPer
	– 'Catalia'	MAsh
	pashia	CBcs CMCN EBee LEdu NLar
	pyraster	CDul CHab CPer WCot
	pyrifolia '20th Century'	see *P. pyrifolia* 'Nijisseiki'
	– 'Chojuro' (F)	CAgr LEdu
	– 'Hosui' (F)	CAgr LEdu MRai SVic
	– 'Kosui' (F)	SVic
	– 'Kumoi' (F)	CAgr CFGn EPom ERea LRHS MAsh MCoo MRai SDea SKee WHar
§	– 'Nijisseiki' (F)	CDul MRai SKee SVic
	– 'Shinko' (F)	CAgr LEdu
	– 'Shinseiki' (F)	CAgr CFGn CLnd CTri EMOT ERea MAsh SDea SKee WHar
	– 'Shinsui' (F)	SDea SKee
	salicifolia **new**	LMaj LPra
*	– var. ***orientalis***	CTho
	– 'Pendula' ♀^{H6}	Widely available

Q

Qiongzhuea see *Chimonobambusa*

Quercus ✿ (*Fagaceae*)

NJM 05.013A	WPGP
acerifolia	EPfP
acherdophylla	SBir
§ ***acuta***	CBcs
acutifolia	SBir
acutifolia* × *mexicana	SBir
acutissima	CAco CBcs CDul CMCN EPfP LMaj NLar SBir SGol
- PAB 7957	LEdu
- subsp. ***kingii*** NJM 13.077	WPGP
aegilops	see *Q. ithaburensis* subsp. *macrolepis*
affinis ♀H5	CMCN EPfP SBir
agrifolia	CMCN EBtc LMaj
ajudaghiensis	see *Q. hartwissiana*
alba	CMCN WPGP
* ***alentejana***	CMCN
aliena	CDul CMCN
- NJM 13.075 <u>new</u>	WPGP
- PAB 13.383 <u>new</u>	LEdu
- PAB 8972	LEdu
anatolica	see *Q. pubescens* subsp. *crispata*
arkansana	CDul SBir
× ***atlantica***	SBir
aucheri NJM 12.009 <u>new</u>	WPGP
austrina	SBir
× ***beadlei***	see *Q.* × *saulii*
'Bear Creek Ranch' <u>new</u>	MBlu
× ***benderi***	SBir
berberidifolia	CMCN SBir
bicolor	CAco CDul CMCN EPfP IArd IDee LMaj MBlu WPGP
× ***bimundorum***	SBir
§ - 'Crimschmidt'	CDul CLnd EPfP MBlu SAko SBir SGol
borealis	see *Q. rubra*
brantii	CMCN
breweri	see *Q. garryana* var. *breweri*
buckleyi	CMCN EPfP SBir
- 'Dazzling Red' <u>new</u>	MBlu
× ***bushii***	CMCN EPfP MBlu SBir
- 'Seattle Trident'	EPfP MBlu SAko WPGP
canariensis ♀H5	CDul CMCN CTho EPfP SGol WPGP
canbyi	CMCN
candicans	SBir
× ***capesii***	SBir
castaneifolia	CDul CMCN
- NJM 13.004 <u>new</u>	WPGP
- NJM 13.006 <u>new</u>	WPGP
- NJM 13.008 <u>new</u>	WPGP
- 'Green Spire' ♀H6	CDul CMCN EBee EPfP MBlu SEND
cerris	CArg CBcs CCVT CDul CMCN CPer ECrN EMOT EPfP ESps LMaj LPra MGos SCob SEND SGol SPer
- 'Afyon Lace'	MBlu SBir
§ - 'Argenteovariegata' (v)	CEnd CMCN EBee ELan EPfP MAsh MBlu SBir WCot
- 'Athena'	MBlu
- 'Curly Head'PBR	SMad
- 'Variegata'	see *Q. cerris* 'Argenteovariegata'
- 'Wodan'	MBlu

chenii	CDul CMCN SBir
chrysolepis	CBcs CMCN EPfP
coccifera	CAco CMCN EPfP SGol SVen WCot WPGP
- NJM 12.006 <u>new</u>	WPGP
- subsp. ***calliprinos***	CMCN
coccinea	CBcs CDul CLnd CMCN CTho CTri ECrN EPfP ESps LMaj LPra MBlu MWht NEgg SBir SEWo SPer WTSh
- 'Splendens' ♀H6	CDul CEnd CJun CMCN CTri ELan EPfP IArd MBlu NLar SGol SPer
aff. ***coccinea***	EMOT
crassifolia	WPGP
crassipes	SBir
CRIMSON SPIRE	see *Q.* × *bimundorum* 'Crimschmidt'
crispipilis	SBir
dalechampii	SBir
dentata	CMCN IArd
- 'Carl Ferris Miller'	CBcs CDul CMCN EPfP LLHF MBlu SBig SBir SCob WCot WHor WPGP
- 'Pinnatifida'	CMCN EPfP LLHF LMaj MBlu MPkF NLar WCot
- 'Sir Harold Hillier'	CDul CMCN MBlu WHor
- subsp. ***yunnanensis***	MBlu SBir
dolicholepis	CMCN SBir
'Doring's Zweizack'	SBir
douglasii	CDul CMCN
durata	CMCN EGFP
ellipsoidalis	CDul CMCN NLar SBir SGol
- 'Hemelrijk' ♀H6	CMCN EPfP MBlu SBir
emoryi	SBir
engleriana	WPGP
NJM 11.028 <u>new</u>	
× ***exacta***	SBir
fabrei	SBir
faginea	CDul CMCN WPGP
- subsp. ***broteroi***	CMCN
falcata	CMCN EBtc SBir WPGP
- var. ***pagodifolia***	see *Q. pagoda*
× ***fernaldii***	CMCN EPfP MBlu
'Fire Water' <u>new</u>	MBlu
frainetto	CDul CMCN CTho EBee EPfP ESps LMaj LPra SGol SPer WMou
- 'Hungarian Crown' ♀H6	CMCN EPfP MBlu SBir
- 'Trump'	CDul CMCN
franchetii	WPGP
fruticosa	see *Q. lusitanica* Lam.
fusiformis	SBir
gambelii	CMCN EBtc MPkF
garryana	CMCN EPfP
§ - var. ***breweri***	CMCN
- var. ***fruticosa***	see *Q. garryana* var. *breweri*
georgiana	CDul CMCN SBir
germana	CFil WPGP
gilva	CMCN SBir
glabra	see *Lithocarpus glaber*
glabrescens	WPGP
glandulifera	see *Q. serrata* Thunb.
glauca	CDul CMCN EPfP NLar
- from Korea <u>new</u>	WPGP
gravesii	EPfP SBir
greggii	CFil WPGP
grisea	CMCN
§ ***hartwissiana***	EPfP
× ***hastingsii***	CMCN SBir
× ***hawkinsiae***	SBir
× ***haynaldiana***	SBir
hemisphaerica	CDul CMCN EPfP SBir

	× ***heterophylla***	CMCN EPfP SBir
	× ***hickelii***	CMCN EPfP SBir
	hirtifolia	WPGP
	× ***hispanica***	EUJe
	- 'Ambrozyana'	CDul CMCN NLar
	- 'Diversifolia'	CDul CMCN EPfP MBlu
	- 'Fulhamensis'	CDul CMCN MBlu MMuc SBir SEND SGol WMou
§	- 'Lucombeana' $\mathbb{Y}^{H6}$	CBcs CDul CMCN CSBt CTho EBee ELan EPfP MBlu MMuc SBir SPer
	- 'Suberosa'	CTho
	- 'Waasland Select'	NLar SGol WMou
	- 'Wageningen'	CDul CMCN LMaj SBir
	hypoleucoides	CMCN EPfP
	ilex	Widely available
	- 'Fordii'	SBir
	ilicifolia	CMCN EPfP SBir
	imbricaria	CAco CBcs CDul CMCN EPfP SBir WPGP
	incana Roxb.	see *Q. leucotrichophora*
§	***incana*** Bartram	CMCN
	insignis	CFil
	ithaburensis	CDul
§	- subsp. ***macrolepis***	CMCN LEdu SBir
	- - 'Hemelrijk Silver'	EPfP MBlu SBir WCot WPGP
	× ***jackiana***	SBir
	kelloggii	CBcs CDul CMCN EPfP
	× ***kewensis*** $\mathbb{Y}^{H6}$	CMCN SBir SEND
	laevigata	see *Q. acuta*
	laevis	CMCN EPfP SBir
	'Langtry'	SBir
§	***laurifolia***	CDul CMCN EPfP SBir
	laurina	SBir WPGP
	× ***leana***	CMCN
§	***leucotrichophora***	LEdu SBir
	liaotungensis	see *Q. wutaishanica*
	× ***libanerris***	SBir
	- 'Rotterdam'	CMCN SBir
	libani	CDul CMCN EPfP
	lobata	CBcs CDul CMCN
	× ***lucombeana***	see *Q.* × *hispanica* 'Lucombeana'
	- 'William Lucombe'	see *Q.* × *hispanica* 'Lucombeana'
	× ***ludoviciana***	EPfP SBir
§	***lusitanica*** Lam.	SBir
	lyrata	CMCN SGol
	- 'Arnold'	MBlu
	'Macon'	CDul
	macranthera	CDul CMCN EPfP
	- PAB 13.002	LEdu
	macrocarpa	CAco CDul CMCN EPfP IDee WPGP
	macrocarpa × ***robur*** × ***virginiana***	SBir
	macrolepis	see *Q. ithaburensis* subsp. *macrolepis*
	marilandica	CDul CMCN EPfP MBlu SBir
	'Mauri'	CDul IArd LMaj MBlu SBir
	mexicana	CMCN IArd SBir
§	***michauxii***	CMCN EPfP MBlu
	mohriana	SBir
	mongolica	CBcs CDul EPfP MBlu SBig
	- subsp. ***crispula***	CMCN
	'Monument' **new**	WCot
	muhlenbergii	CDul CMCN MBlu MPkF SBir
	- 'Dallas'	EPfP
	myrsinifolia	CBcs CMCN LMaj NLar SArc
	myrtifolia	SBir WPGP
	nigra	CDul CMCN EBtc EPfP SBir
	- 'Beethoven'	MBlu SBir
I	- 'Nyewoodii'	SBir
	- 'Thierry' **new**	MBlu
	nuttallii	see *Q. texana*
	obtusa	see *Q. laurifolia*
	oglethorpensis	CMCN SBir
	oxyodon	LEdu
§	***pagoda***	CAco CDul CMCN EGFP SBir WPGP
	palustris $\mathbb{Y}^{H6}$	CAco CArg CCVT CDul CLnd CMCN CTho ECrN ELan EMOT EPfP EWTr LMaj LPra MBlu MMuc NEgg NLar SBir SCob SEWo SGol SPer WMou WTSh
*	- 'Compacta'	CJun
	- 'Flaming Suzy'	MBlu
	- 'Green Dwarf'	CMCN LCro LMaj LOPS MBlu NLar SLim
	- GREEN PILLAR ('Pringreen')	CTho EMOT EPfP MAsh MBlu NLar NOra SGol WMou
	- 'Isabel'	EPfP WHor
	- 'Pendula'	CEnd CMCN
	- 'Silhouette'	SBir
	- 'Swamp Pygmy'	CMCN EBee EPfP EUJe MBlu SCob
	- 'Windischleuba'	MBlu
	pannosa	SBir
	parvula var. ***parvula***	SBir
§	× ***pauciloba***	CMCN
	pedunculata	see *Q. robur*
	pedunculiflora	see *Q. robur* subsp. *pedunculiflora*
§	***petraea***	CArg CDul CHab CLnd CPer CTri ECrN EPfP ESps LMaj LPra MBlu SCob SGol SPer WMou WTSh
	- 'Acutiloba'	SBir
	- 'Laciniata'	see *Q. petraea* 'Laciniata Crispa'
§	- 'Laciniata Crispa'	CEnd CMCN EPfP MBlu
	- Mespilifolia Group	CDul
	- subsp. ***polycarpa*** NJM 13.025 **new**	WPGP
§	- 'Purpurea'	CMCN EPfP MBlu
	- 'Rubicunda'	see *Q. petraea* 'Purpurea'
§	***phellos***	CAco CDul CLnd CMCN EBee EBtc EPfP EUJe LMaj MBlu NLar SBir
	- HIGHTOWER ('Qpsta')	SGol
	- var. ***latifolia***	see *Q. incana* Bartram
	aff. ***phellos***	ECrN
	phillyreoides	CBcs CDul CLnd CMCN EPfP
	polymorpha	CDul CMCN MPkF SBir WPGP
	Pondaim Group	CMCN EBee NOra WMou
	- 'Pondaim Giant' **new**	MBlu
	pontica	CMCN EPfP LLHF LMaj MBlu
	prinoides	CMCN
	prinus misapplied	see *Q. michauxii*
§	***prinus*** L.	CMCN
	pubescens	CDul CMCN EGFP LMaj MMuc SEND
§	- subsp. ***crispata*** NJM 12.016	WPGP
	- - NJM 12.017 **new**	WPGP
	pumila Michx.	see *Q. prinus* L.
	pumila Walt.	see *Q. phellos*
	pungens	CMCN
	pyrenaica	CMCN EBtc MMuc SBir SEND
	- NJM 12.001 **new**	WPGP
	- 'Pendula' $\mathbb{Y}^{H6}$	CMCN EPfP
	rhysophylla	CMCN EPfP IArd MBlu SBir WPGP
	- 'Maya' $\mathbb{Y}^{H5}$	CBcs CDul CJun EBee ELan EPfP EUJe LLHF NLar SBig SBir SGol SLim WHor WMou WPGP
	× ***riparia***	SBir
§	***robur***	Widely available
	- 'Argenteomarginata' (v)	CDul CMCN MBlu

- 'Atropurpurea'	EBtc MPkF
- 'Blue Gnome'	MBlu
- 'Compacta'	MBlu
- 'Concordia'	CBcs CEnd CMCN EBtc ELan EPfP MBlu NLar
- Cristata Group	CMCN
- 'Dissecta'	CMCN
- 'Facrist'	CDul SBir
- Fastigiata Group	CAco CDul CLnd EBee ESps IArd LPra MGos SBir SCob SGol SLim SPer
- - 'Koster' ♀H6	CDul CMCN CMac CTri EMOT EPfP LMaj LPra MBlu MRav SCob SPoG
- - 'Zeeland'	SBir
- 'Filicifolia' misapplied	see *Q. robur* 'Pectinata'
- 'Filicifolia' Hort. ex Loud.	CEnd
- var. ***haas***	CDul
- 'Irtha'	EPfP MBlu
- 'Menhir'	CMCN LLHF MAsh MBlu
§ - 'Pectinata'	EPfP MBlu
§ - subsp. ***pedunculiflora***	CMCN
- 'Pendula'	CEnd CMCN MBlu
- 'Purpurascens'	CDul CEnd CMCN
- 'Purpurea'	MBlu
- 'Raba'	CMCN
§ - 'Salfast'	MBlu NLar
- 'Salicifolia Fastigiata'	see *Q. robur* 'Salfast'
- 'Strypemonde'	CMCN
- 'Timuki'	MBlu
- 'Totem'	WHor
- 'Tromp Dwarf'	MBlu
- (Variegata Group) 'Fürst Schwarzenburg' (v)	MBlu
× ***rosacea*** 'Columna'	WMou
rotundifolia	CAgr CMCN EPfP WPGP
§ ***rubra***	Widely available
- 'Aurea'	CEnd CMCN EPfP MBlu WHor
- 'Bolte's Gold'	MBlu NOra SMad WHor
- 'Cyrille'	SBir
- 'Magic Fire' ♀H6	CMCN EPfP MBlu SBig SBir
- 'Red Queen'	EPfP MBlu
* - 'Sunshine'	CMCN MBlu WCot
× ***rudkinii***	EPfP
rugosa	CFil
× ***runcinata***	SBir
sadleriana	CDul CMCN WPGP
salicina	WPGP
× ***sargentii*** 'Thomas'	CDul EPfP MBlu
sartorii	CMCN SBir
§ × ***saulii***	CMCN SBir
× ***schochiana***	EPfP MBlu SBir
schottkyana	WPGP
× ***schuettei***	SBir
semecarpifolia	CBcs CMCN MBlu WPGP
§ ***serrata*** Thunb.	CDul CMCN EPfP SBir
- 'Herkenrode'	MBlu
sessiliflora	see *Q. petraea*
shumardii	CAco CDul CLnd CMCN EPfP LMaj MBlu NLar SBir SGol
- 'Del Rio'	MBlu
sinuata subsp. ***breviloba***	SBir
stellata	CMCN EPfP SBir
× ***sternbergii***	SBir
suber	CAgr CBcs CDul CFil CMCN CPer CTsd ELan EMOT EPfP EUJe IArd LEdu LMaj MBlu MGos SArc SEND SPer WPGP
- 'Sopron'	CDul EPfP MBlu
§ ***texana***	CAco CMCN EPfP IArd NOra SBir WPGP
- 'New Madrid'	CDul CTho EPfP LLHF MBlu SBig SBir SPer WHor WMou WPGP
tomentella	SBir
trojana	CDul CMCN SBir WPGP
turbinella	CMCN
× ***turneri***	CDul CMCN CTho EPfP WSpi
- 'Pseudoturneri' ♀H6	CBcs CDul EBee ELan MBlu SGol WMou
undulata Torr.	see *Q.* × *pauciloba*
vacciniifolia	CMCN
variabilis	CMCN EPfP MPkF SGol
velutina	CBcs CDul CMCN CTho EPfP NLar SBir
- 'Albertsii'	MBlu
- 'Oakridge Walker'	MBlu
- 'Rubrifolia'	CMCN EPfP
'Vilmoriana'	CMCN IArd
virginiana	CBcs CMCN SBir
× ***warburgii***	EPfP
× ***warei***	CMCN
- 'Chimney Fire'	EPfP MBlu
- KINDRED SPIRIT	see *Q.* × *warei* 'Nadler'
§ - 'Long'	EBee EMOT EPfP IArd MAsh MBlu MPkF NLar NOra
§ - 'Nadler'	SGol
- REGAL PRINCE	see *Q.* × *warei* 'Long'
- 'Riverbank Lodge'	SBir
- 'Windcandle'	LMaj MBlu SBir
wislizeni	CMCN NLar SBir
§ ***wutaishanica***	SBir

Quillaja (*Quillajaceae*)

saponaria	CBcs CCCN IDee SPlb

quince see *Cydonia oblonga*

Quisqualis (*Combretaceae*)

indica	CCCN

R

Rabiea (*Aizoaceae*)

albinota new	CCac
difformis	CCac

Racosperma see *Acacia*

Radermachera (*Bignoniaceae*)

sinica ♀H1b	EShb

radish see AGM Vegetables Section

Ramonda (*Gesneriaceae*)

§ ***myconi*** ♀H5	CPla EWes LLHF NSla SRms WAbe
- var. ***alba***	WThu
- 'Jim's Shadow'	WAbe
- 'Rosea'	LLHF
nathaliae ♀H5	WAbe WThu
- 'Alba'	NSla WAbe XEll
pyrenaica	see *R. myconi*
serbica	WThu

Ranunculus (*Ranunculaceae*)

aconitifolius	EBee EHrv GMaP NLar SHar WFar WHal WMoo WSHC
- 'Flore Pleno' (d) ♀H7	Widely available
acris	CHab EBWF NMir NPer WSFF

- subsp. ***acris*** 'Stevenii'	WHal
- 'Citrinus'	CElw EAJP EHrv LLWG LSun MHol WCot WHal WHrl WMoo
- 'Flore Pleno' (d) ♀H7	CAby CDor CElw CWCL EBee ECha EHrv ELan EPfP LEdu LLWG MCot MRav NBid NBro NGdn NRya SRms WFar WMoo WSHC XLum
- 'Hedgehog'	MMrt MNrw
- 'Sulphureus'	CBre EBee WHal
alpestris	GCrg GEdr LLHF NSla WFar
- 'Flore Pleno' (d)	GEdr
amplexicaulis	ELon NSla WCot
aquatilis	CWat LLWG MSKA MWts WMAq WSFF
asiaticus	ERCP
- 'Aviv Orange'	GKev SDeJ SDir
- 'Aviv Red'	GKev LCro LOPS
- 'Aviv Rose'	LCro LOPS
- 'Aviv White'	GKev LCro LOPS
- 'Bloomingdale Pink Shades' (Bloomingdale Series)	SDeJ
- var. ***flavus***	GKev
- peony-flowered **new**	GKev
- pink-flowered **new**	GKev
§ ***bulbosus*** 'F.M. Burton'	CElw NRya WCot
- ***farreri***	see *R. bulbosus* 'F.M. Burton'
- 'Speciosus Plenus'	see *R. constantinopolitanus* 'Plenus'
calandrinioides ♀H4	EWes IFoB SBrt WAbe WThu
§ ***constantinopolitanus*** 'Plenus' (d)	GCal GMaP MNrw MRav NBid NBro NLar WCot WMoo WSHC
cortusifolius	CPla ECre SBrt
crenatus	GEdr
ficaria	see *Ficaria verna*
flammula	CBen CHab CWat EBWF EWat LLWG MSKA MWts
- 'Golden Tower'	EBee
- subsp. ***minimus***	EWat
gouanii	NRya
'Gowrie'	GEdr
gramineus ♀H5	EBee GEdr GMaP LRHS NRHS NRya SRms XEll
- 'Pardal'	WCot
hederaceus	LLWG
illyricus	WHal
kochii	CTal GEdr GKev MNrw NRya WCot
lanuginosus	EPPr
lapponicus	GEdr
lingua	SPlb WSFF
- 'Grandiflorus'	CBen LLWG MSKA NPer WHal WMAq WPnP
millefoliatus	CPBP WAbe
montanus double-flowered (d)	SHar WCot
- 'Miss Austria' (d)	NHpl
- 'Molten Gold' ♀H5	EBee GCrg GEdr GMaP MMrt MRav NRya WFar
nivicola	WCot
parnassiifolius	GEdr MNrw WAbe WCot
'Pauline Violet'	IFro
platanifolius	EBee LRHS NRHS
× ***prietoi*** 'Moonlight'	CElw LEdu MMrt WCot
'Purple Heart' (d)	EPfP LCro LOPS SDeJ
repens 'Buttered Popcorn' (v)	EBee
- 'Cat's Eyes' (v)	EBee
- 'Gloria Spale'	CBre
- var. ***pleniflorus*** (d)	CBre LLWG SRot
- 'Snowdrift' (v)	EBee
- 'Timothy Clark' (d)	CBre
sceleratus	EBWF
seguieri	GEdr LLHF LRHS NRHS WAbe
speciosus 'Flore Pleno'	see *R. constantinopolitanus* 'Plenus'
uniflorus **new**	GEdr

Ranzania (*Berberidaceae*)

japonica	GEdr WCru

Raoulia (*Asteraceae*)

australis misapplied	see *R. hookeri*
australis ambig.	EPot GAbr GBin GMaP NHpl SMad WCot WTor
australis Hook.f. ex Raoul	ITim MAsh
§ - Lutescens Group	ECha SRot
bryoides	EPot
§ ***hookeri***	CMea CTal ECha EPot EWes MAsh SPlb SRms WAbe
× ***loganii***	see × *Leucoraoulia loganii*
lutescens	see *R. australis* Lutescens Group
petriensis	SPlb WAbe
× ***petrimia*** 'Margaret Pringle'	EPot WAbe
tenuicaulis	ECha SPlb

raspberry see *Rubus idaeus*

Ratibida (*Asteraceae*)

columnifera	CBod ELan EPfP LRHS NRHS
- f. ***pulcherrima***	CSpe EPfP LRHS NRHS XLum
- - 'Red Midget'	CBod CSpe EBee LRHS NRHS
mexicana	CSam ELan SPhx
pinnata	CSam CSpe EPfP LRHS SBee SPhx SPlb WCot

Ravenala (*Strelitziaceae*)

madagascariensis	SPlb XBlo

Ravenea (*Arecaceae*)

rivularis	CCCN XBlo

Rechsteineria see *Sinningia*

redcurrant see *Ribes rubrum* (R)

Regelia (*Myrtaceae*)

velutina	SPlb

Rehderodendron (*Styracaceae*)

indochinense	CFil
- B&SWJ 12115	WCru
- WWJ 11869	WCru
kwangtungense WWJ 11940	WCru
kweichowense WWJ 12019	WCru
macrocarpum	CBcs CFil EBee WPGP
- B&SWJ 11841	WCru
- KWJ 12310	WCru
- WWJ 11952	WCru

Rehmannia (*Plantaginaceae*)

angulata misapplied	see *R. elata*
§ ***elata*** ♀H2	CBod CPla CSpe ELan EPfP IDee LRHS LSun MNHC NRHS SDys SRms XLum
glutinosa ♀H2	CSpe

henryi new	LRHS
piasezkii	SMHy
WALBERTON'S MAGIC DRAGON ('Walremadra')	CRos EHyd LBuc LRHS NRHS SHar SPoG

Reineckea (*Asparagaceae*)

§ ***carnea***	CAby CDor CExl CHid CHll ECha ELan EPPr GCal GEdr GKev IMou LEdu MMuc MPie NSti SDys SEND SPlb WCot WPGP XLum
- B&SWJ 4808	ELon WCru
- SDR 330	GKev
- 'Baoxing Booty'	IMou WCru
- 'Crûg's Broadleaf'	WCru
- 'Variegata' (v)	EShb WCot
aff. ***carnea*** from Sichuan	WCot
incurva 'Crug's Linearleaf'	WCru
yunnanense	see *R. carnea*

Reinwardtia (*Linaceae*)

§ ***indica***	CCCN CExl CHll SEle
trigyna	see *R. indica*

Remusatia (*Araceae*)

hookeriana	LRHS
- B&SWJ 2529	WCru
pumila	EUJe LRHS MPie
vivipara	EUJe LRHS

Reseda (*Resedaceae*)

alba	MHer
lutea	CWld SRms
luteola	CBod CHab CHby EBWF GPoy MHer MNHC WSFF

Restio (*Restionaceae*)

festuciformis	CPbh
multiflorus	LRHS
paniculatus	CCCN CDTJ CPbh
similis	CPbh LRHS
subverticillatus	CPbh
tetraphyllus	see *Baloskion tetraphyllum*

Retama (*Papilionaceae*)

§ ***monosperma***	SBrt
raetam	SPhx
§ ***sphaerocarpa***	SBrt

Reynoutria see *Fallopia*

Rhamnus (*Rhamnaceae*)

alaternus	XSen
§ - 'Argenteovariegata' (v) ♀H5	Widely available
- 'Variegata'	see *R. alaternus* 'Argenteovariegata'
cathartica	CCVT CDul CHab CLnd CPer CTri ECrN EPfP EShb LBuc MCoo NLar SEWo WMou WSFF WTSh
davurica B&SWJ 12609	WCru
§ ***erythroxyloides***	NLar
frangula	see *Frangula alnus*
ilicifolia new	SBrt
imeretina	WCot WPGP
ludovici-salvatoris	SBrt
lycioides new	SBrt
- subsp. ***oleoides***	XSen
pallasii	see *R. erythroxyloides*
taquetii	NLar

Rhaphidophora (*Araceae*)

decursiva	XBlo

× *Rhaphiobotrya* (*Rosaceae*)

§ 'Coppertone'	LMaj SEND WPGP

Rhaphiolepis (*Rosaceae*)

× ***delacourii***	EPfP SEND
- 'Coates' Crimson'	CTsd EBee ELan EPfP LRHS MAsh MGil SEle WSHC
- ENCHANTRESS ('Moness')	CCCN CTsd ELan EPfP LRHS MAsh MRav SLon
- 'Pink Cloud'	EPfP LRHS
indica	SEND
- B&SWJ 8405	WCru
- 'Coppertone'	see × *Rhaphiobotrya* 'Coppertone'
- SPRINGTIME ('Monme')	CBcs EPfP LCro LOPS LRHS
integerrima	CMCN
umbellata	CBcs CTri EBee ELan EPfP GBin LEdu LRHS MAsh MGil MRav SEND SEle SLon SVen WPGP WSHC
- f. ***ovata*** B&SWJ 4706	WCru

Rhaphithamnus (*Verbenaceae*)

cyanocarpus	see *R. spinosus*
§ ***spinosus***	CBcs EBee EPfP LEdu MGil SPoG

Rhapidophyllum (*Arecaceae*)

hystrix	CBrP CPHo

Rhapis ✿ (*Arecaceae*)

§ ***excelsa*** ♀H1b	CCCN SPlb XBlo

Rhaponticum (*Asteraceae*)

§ ***carthamoides***	XAbr
§ ***centaureoides***	CAby CBWd CBod CBot CDor EBee ECha ELon EWTr GCal IBoy IPot IRob LRHS MAvo MBel MHer MHol MSpe MTis NBid NSti SBrt SEND WCAu WCot WSpi
§ ***exaltata*** new	SPhx

Rhazya (*Apocynaceae*)

orientalis	see *Amsonia orientalis*

Rheum ✿ (*Polygonaceae*)

See also AGM Vegetables Section.

Chen Yi	WCot
GWJ 9329 from Sikkim	WCru
§ 'Ace of Hearts' ♀H6	Widely available
'Ace of Spades'	see *R.* 'Ace of Hearts'
acuminatum HWJCM 252	WCru
- HWJK 2354	WCru
- PAB 2487	LEdu WPGP
alexandrae	CBct EUJe EWes GBin GCal GEdr GKev IRob LEdu MMrt NLar SPlb WFar
- KGB 767 new	WPGP
- SDR 2924	EBee
- SDR 6031	GKev
altaicum PAB 1055	LEdu
§ ***australe***	GCal LRHS NBro NLar NRHS WCot WFar
- CC 7492	GKev
- 'Pink Marble' (v)	WCot
'Cally Dwarf'	GCal
'Cally Giant'	EBee ELon EWes GCal

delavayi	GCal NLar
- BWJ 7592	WCru WFar
emodi	see *R. australe*
'Great Bere'	LEdu WPGP
* ***henryi***	EBee
× ***hybridum*** 'Brandy Carr Scarlet'	CTri LEdu MRav
- 'Cawood Delight'	MCoo
- 'Champagne'	CAgr EPfP EPom LCro LEdu LOPS LRHS NLar NRHS SCob SKee SPer SPoG SRms
* - 'Champagne Rood'	NRHS
- 'Early Victoria'	SRms
- 'Fenton's Special'	CTri LEdu MCoo MRav
- 'Fulton's Strawberry Surprise' ♀H4	EMsh
- 'Glaskin's Perpetual'	CAgr CRos EPfP LBuc LRHS NRHS SRms WHar
- 'Grandad's Favorite' ♀H4	CRos LRHS NRHS
- 'Hawke's Champagne' ♀H4	EMsh WCot
- 'Holsteiner Blut'	NLar SCob SPoG
- 'Livingstone'PBR	EPom LCro LOPS
- 'Pink Champagne'	EPfP
- 'Raspberry Red' ♀H4	CRav CRos EMil EPfP EPom LCro LOPS LRHS SPoG
- 'Red Champagne'	ELan EPfP LBuc SCob WSpi
- 'Stein's Champagne' ♀H4	NRob
- 'Stockbridge Arrow'	CArg CMac CTri ECrN
- 'Strawberry'	LCro LOPS
- 'The Sutton'	EPfP
- 'Thompson's Terrifically Tasty'	EPom
- 'Timperley Early' ♀H4	Widely available
- 'Timperley Early 1'	MJak SRms
- 'Timperley Early 2'	MJak
- 'Timperley Early 30'	MJak
- 'Victoria'	CAgr CMac CRav CRos CSBt CTri ELan EMil EPfP EPom GBin LBuc LCro LEdu LOPS LRHS LSRN MCoo MGos MHer MJak MNHC NLar NRHS SCob SDea SLim SPoG SVic WHar
- 'Victoria 1'	MJak
- 'Victoria 2'	MJak
- 'Victoria 9'	MJak
- 'Vroege Engelse'	LEdu
kialense	EBee LEdu NBid NSti
nobile	GEdr GKev IMou WHil
officinale	CBct GCal
palmatum	CBcs EBee ECha ELan EPfP LRHS MGos MRav NGdn NRHS SCob SHar SRms
- 'Atropurpureum'	see *R. palmatum* 'Atrosanguineum'
- 'Atropurpureum Dissectum'	IBoy
§ - 'Atrosanguineum'	Widely available
- 'Bowles's Crimson' ♀H7	MRav NBid WCot
- 'Ferguson's Red'	WCot
- 'Hadspen Crimson' ♀H7	CBct CGar EBee ECtt EUJe MHol MNrw NBid WCot
- 'Red Herald'	CBct WCot WPGP
- 'Rubrum'	LRHS NChi NRHS
- 'Savill'	MRav
- var. ***tanguticum***	Widely available
rhaponticum	NLar
ribes	WCot WCru
tataricum	EBee LEdu WPGP

Rhexia (*Melastomataceae*)

virginica	SBrt

Rhinanthus (*Orobanchaceae*)

minor	CHab LCro

Rhodanthe (*Asteraceae*)

§ ***anthemoides***	IMou

Rhodanthemum (*Asteraceae*)

'African Eyes'	ELan EPfP MBrN MGos MHol SCoo SPoG SRot SVen
AGADIR (Atlas Daisy Series)	see *R.* MOONDANCE
§ ***atlanticum***	EWes
'Casablanca'PBR (Atlas Daisy Series)	LRHS NRHS SCoo SPoG SRot
§ ***catananche***	CCCN CPBP EPot EWes MBNS SRot WAbe
- 'Tizi-n-Tichka'	CPBP EPot EWes LRHS NRHS WAbe
§ ***gayanum***	CCCN EWes
- 'Flamingo'	see *R. gayanum*
- 'Pretty in Pink'	MHol SPoG
§ ***hosmariense*** ♀H4	CCCN ECha ELan EPfP EPot GCrg GMaP LRHS MCot MHol NRHS NSla SEND SPer SPhx SRms SRot WHoo
'Marrakech' (Atlas Daisy Series)	SCoo SPoG SRot
§ MOONDANCE ('Usrhod0701')	EPfP LRHS NRHS
TANGIER (Atlas Daisy Series)	EPfP LRHS NRHS

Rhodiola (*Crassulaceae*)

SSSE 10	NWad
chrysanthemifolia WJC 13669	WCru
crassipes	see *R. wallichiana*
cretinii HWJK 2283	WCru
§ ***fastigiata***	CSpe GCal WCot WThu
- BWJ 7544	WCru
§ ***heterodonta***	ELan MRav WCot
himalensis misapplied	see *R.* 'Keston'
himalensis (D. Don) Fu	CTri
- WJC 13723	WCru
§ ***integrifolia***	SPlb
- subsp. ***integrifolia***	EDAr
§ 'Keston'	CTri
§ ***kirilovii***	LRHS NRHS
- var. ***rubra***	EPfP LRHS NRHS
§ ***pachyclados***	CTal ECtt EUJe GBin GCrg GJos GKev GMaP GWyn LRHS MHer MMuc NHpl NRHS NRya NWad SEND SPlb SRot SWvt WCot WFar XLum
rhodantha	NLar
§ ***rosea***	CAby CBod CElw EBWF EBee EDAr ELan EPfP EUJe GCal GJos GKev GPoy LRHS MCot MHer MRav NBid NGdn NLar NRHS NWad SPer SRms WCFE WCot WFar XAbr
§ ***saxifragoides***	EPot LRHS NRHS SPlb
semenovii	GKev NLar
sinuata HWJK 2318	WCru
- HWJK 2326	WCru
trollii	see *R. saxifragoides*
§ ***wallichiana***	NBid
- GWJ 9263	WCru
- HWJK 2352	WCru
§ ***yunnanensis*** BWJ 7941	WCru

Rhodochiton (*Plantaginaceae*)

§ ***atrosanguineus*** ♀H2	CBcs CCCN CRav CSpe ELan EPfP IDee LBuc NPri SPer
volubilis	see *R. atrosanguineus*

Rhodocoma (*Restionaceae*)

arida	CCCN
capensis	CAbb CBod CCCN CCht CPbh CTsd LRHS NLos
gigantea	CBod CCCN CCht CPbh LRHS SPlb

Rhododendron ✿ (*Ericaceae*)

sp.	CAco GKin NHim SEWo
'A.J. Ivens'	see *R.* 'Arthur J. Ivens'
aberconwayi	LMil
- 'His Lordship'	GGGa LMil
acrophilum (V)	GGGa
'Addy Wery' (EA)	GKin SPer
adenogynum	GGGa LMil
§ - Adenophorum Group	NHim
adenophorum	see *R. adenogynum* Adenophorum Group
adenopodum	GGGa
adenosum	GGGa
'Admiral Piet Hein'	GGGa SReu SSta
'Adonis' (EA/d) ♀H5	CBcs CMac SLdr
'Advance' (EA)	SLdr
aeruginosum	see *R. campanulatum* subsp. *aeruginosum*
aganniphum	LMil
'Aksel Olsen'	CTri GEdr
'Aladdin' (EA)	SLdr
Aladdin Group	SReu
'Aladdin' (*auriculatum* hybrid)	GGGa SSta
Albatross Group	SReu
- 'Albatross'	SSta
- 'Albatross Townhill Pink'	LMil
'Albert Schweitzer' ♀H5	CDul LMil LRHS LSRN NLar SLdr SLim SPer
albrechtii (A)	CBcs CPne GGGa LMil
- Whitney form (A)	LMil
'Album Grandiflorum' (G) new	MPkF
'Alena'	NHim
'Alexander' (EA) ♀H4	CBcs LMil LSRN NHim SLdr
'Alice' ♀H5	CMac LMil SLdr
Alison Johnstone Group	SLdr SReu
- 'Alison Johnstone'	CAco GGGa LMil WThu
'All Gold'	GGGa
alutaceum	NHim
§ - var. ***alutaceum*** Globigerum Group	GGGa
§ - var. ***russotinctum*** R 158	SLdr
§ - - Triplonaevium Group	GGGa
amagianum (A)	LMil
ambiguum	LMil
- 'Golden Summit'	GGGa
- 'Jane Banks'	LMil
'Ambrosia' (EA)	CSBt
'America'	SCob
amesiae	NHim
'Amity'	LMil MLea MMuc SLdr
Amor Group	SLdr
'Anah Kruschke'	LCro MAsh SPoG
'Analin'	see *R.* 'Anuschka'
'Anchorite' (EA)	SLdr
Angelo Group	GGGa LMil SReu
- 'Angelo'	LMil SLdr SSta
'Ann Lindsay'	NHim SLdr
'Anna Baldsiefen'	GKin SPoG
'Anna Rose Whitney'	CBcs CTri EPfP LRHS LSRN MAsh MJak NPri SLim
'Annabella' (K)	SReu SSta
annae	GGGa LMil LRHS
'Anne Frank' (EA)	NHim WFar
'Anneke' (A)	GMcL LMil MGos MMuc NLar SReu SSta WMoo
'Anniversary Gold'	NLar
anthopogon	LMil NHim
- 'Betty Graham'	GGGa WThu
- subsp. ***hypenanthum*** 'Annapurna'	GGGa ITim LMil WAbe WThu
anthosphaerum	GGGa NHim
'Antilope' (Vs) ♀H6	CBcs LMil LRHS MMuc SLdr SReu SSta
(Antonio Group) 'Antonio'	LMil
§ 'Anuschka'	LMil MAsh
anwheiense	GGGa LMil
aperantum	GGGa
'Aperitif' new	NHim
apodectum	see *R. dichroanthum* subsp. *apodectum*
'Apotrophia'	SLdr
'Apple Blossom' ambig.	CMac GKin
'Appleblossom' (EA)	see *R.* 'Ho-o'
'Apricot Blaze' (A)	SReu SSta
'Apricot Fantasy'	LMil NLar SReu SSta
'Apricot Surprise'	CTri MAsh MMuc
'April Chimes'	WThu
'April Showers' (A)	LMil
'Aquamarin'	NLar
'Arabesk' (EA)	GKin MAsh MGos MPkF NLar
arborescens (A) ♀H6	CTsd GGGa LMil
arboreum	GGGa IDee LMil SLdr SReu
- B&SWJ 2244	WCru
- subsp. ***cinnamomeum*** ♀H4	GGGa LMil SLdr
- - Sch 2049 new	LMil
- - WJC 13821	WCru
- - var. ***album***	GGGa SReu
- - 'Everest Reunion'	LMil
- - var. ***roseum***	GGGa
- - - SDR 749 new	GKev
- - - 'Tony Schilling'	GKin IDee LMil LRHS SReu SSta
- subsp. ***delavayi***	GGGa LMil SLdr
- 'Heligan'	SReu
- 'Rubaiyat'	LMil
§ - subsp. ***zeylanicum***	GGGa
'Arctic Tern' ♀H5	CSBt CTri LCro LMil LOPS MGos MLea NLar NWad SPer WThu
'Ardeur' (EA)	NLar
§ ***argipeplum***	GGGa
- 'Fleurie' new	LMil
(Argosy Group) 'Argosy'	LMil SReu
argyrophyllum	SLdr
- subsp. ***argyrophyllum***	GGGa SLdr
§ - subsp. ***hypoglaucum***	GGGa
- subsp. ***nankingense***	GGGa
- - 'Chinese Silver' ♀H6	IDee LMil NHim SLdr SReu
arizelum	CPne GCal GGGa LMil WPGP
- subsp. ***arizelum*** Rubicosum Group	GGGa LMil
aff. ***arizelum*** KR 10420 new	WPGP
'Arneson Gem' (A) ♀H6	CBcs GGGa LMil LRHS NLar
'Arneson Little Gem' (A) new	NHim
§ (Aronense Group) 'Fumiko' (EA)	CSBt CTsd GMcL LCro LMil MLea NLar SLdr WFar
§ - 'Hanako' (EA)	MLea WFar
§ - 'Kazuko' (EA)	GMcL NLar
§ - 'Satschiko' (EA) ♀H5	CBcs CSBt CTsd ETMg GGGa GMcL LMil LRHS NLar NPri NRHS
'Arpège' (Vs)	LMil NLar SReu

	'Arthur Bedford'	CSBt SReu
§	'Arthur J. Ivens'	SLdr
	'Arthur Stevens'	SLdr
	'Asa-gasumi' (Kurume) (EA)	SLdr
	asterochnoum	GGGa
	'Astrid'	LSRN
	atlanticum (A)	GGGa LMil
	- 'Seaboard' (A)	LMil
	augustinii	CBcs GGGa LMil MLea NLar SLdr SSta
	- 'Bowood Blue'	LMil
	- 'Carolles'	LRHS
§	- subsp. ***chasmanthum***	GGGa
	- compact EGM 293	LMil
	- Electra Group	LMil SLdr
§	- - 'Electra' ♀H3	GGGa
	- Exbury form	GGGa LMil SReu
§	- subsp. ***hardyi***	GGGa NLar
*	- 'Trewithen'	GGGa LMil
I	- 'Werrington'	CExl SLdr SReu
	aureum	GGGa
	auriculatum	GGGa LMil SLdr SSta
	- Reuthe's form	SReu
	auriculatum* × *hemsleyanum	GGGa
	auritum	CPne SLdr
	austrinum (A)	LMil NLar
	- yellow-flowered (A)	LMil
	AUTUMN MAGIC	see *R.* 'Herbstzauber'
	(Avalanche Group) 'Avalanche'	LMil
	Avocet Group	LMil SLdr
	'Award'	LMil
	Azrie Group	SLdr
§	'Azuma-kagami' (Kurume) (EA)	LMil LRHS SLdr
	'Azurika'	MPkF
	'Azurro'	LMil LRHS MMuc NHim SLdr
	'Babette'	see *R.* (Volker Group) 'Babette'
	'Babuschka'	LMil
	'Baden-Baden' ♀H5	CMac CTri GEdr GKin GMcL LCro LMil MAsh MJak NEgg SLdr
	baileyi	NHim SLdr
	balangense	GGGa
	balfourianum	GGGa
	'Baltic Amber' (A)	LRHS NHim SPer
	'Balzac' (K)	GKin LMil MAsh NEgg
	'Bandoola'	SReu
	'Barbara Reuthe'	SSta
	'Barbarella'	LMil
	barbatum	GGGa LMil
	'Barbecue' (K)	LMil
	'Barmstedt'	MAsh
	'Barnaby Sunset'	GGGa LRHS MAsh
	'Bashful' ♀H5	CBcs CSBt MJak
§	***basilicum***	GGGa LMil
	'Bastion'	LMil
	× ***bathyphyllum***	GGGa NHim
	bauhiniiflorum	see *R. triflorum* var. *bauhiniiflorum*
	beanianum	GGGa
	- APA 60	GGGa
	- KC 0122	GGGa
	- compact	see *R. piercei*
	'Beatrice Keir'	LMil SReu SSta
	'Beattie' (EA)	SLdr
	(Beau Brummell Group) 'Beau Brummell'	LMil
	beesianum	GGGa
	'Beethoven' (Vuykiana) (EA)	SLdr
	BELAMI ('Hachbela')	LMil LRHS
	'Belkanto'	CAco GKin MMuc NLar SLdr
	'Bellini'	LMaj LMil
	'Ben Cruachan' (K)	GGGa
	'Ben Lawers' (K)	GGGa
	'Ben Lomond' (K)	GGGa
	'Ben Morrison' (EA)	LMil
	'Ben Vorlich' (K)	GGGa
	'Ben Vrackie' (K)	GGGa
	'Bengal'	GEdr LRHS LSRN MAsh NLar SCob SLdr SLim
	'Bengal Beauty' (EA)	SLdr
	'Bengal Fire' (EA)	CMac SLdr
	benhallii 'Honshu Blue'	GGGa
	- 'Plum Drops'	GGGa
	- 'Slieve Donard'	CMac
	- 'Ylva'	GGGa
	'Beni-giri' (Kurume) (EA)	CMac SLdr
	'Benny Gery' (EA) **new**	CRos
	'Bergensiana'	SReu SSta
	'Bergie Larson' ♀H4	LMil
	'Berg's 10'	MLea
	'Bernard Shaw'	SSta
	'Bernstein'	CAco MAsh MJak
	'Berryrose' (K) ♀H6	CBcs CMac CSBt CTri EPfP GKin GMcL LMil LRHS MAsh MGos MJak MPkF NLar SReu SSta WFar
	Berryrose Group	NHim
	'Bert's Own'	CBcs NHim
	'Beryl Taylor'	GGGa
	'Betty' (Kaempferi) (EA)	SLdr
	'Betty Anne Voss' (EA)	LCro LMil LSRN MAsh SCoo SLdr
	'Betty Wormald'	CMac MLea
	bhutanense	GGGa
	Bibiani Group	LMil
	'Bijou de Ledeberg' (Indian) (EA/v)	CMac
	'Birthday Girl'	LMil LSRN MAsh MLea
	Biskra Group	NHim
	- 'Biskra'	GGGa LMil
	'Blaauw's Pink' (Kurume) (EA) ♀H4	CMac CSBt EPfP ESps GKin GMcL LCro LMil LOPS MMuc SLdr SPer SPlb SPoG SReu
	'Black Hawk' (EA)	CBcs
	'Black Knight' (EA)	SLdr
	'Black Magic'	CAco GKin GMcL LMil MMuc
	'Black Sport'	MLea
	'Black Widow'	SReu SSta
	'Blaney's Blue'	MPkF
	'Blattgold' (v)	LMil
	BLAUE DONAU	see *R.* 'Blue Danube'
	'Blaue Jungs'	EUJe GGGa
	'Blewbury' ♀H5	LMil SReu
	BLOOMBUX ('Microhirs3')	LCro LMil LOPS
	'Blue Boy'	LMil
§	'Blue Danube' (EA) ♀H3	CBcs CMac CSBt CTri EPfP ESps GGGa GKin GMcL LCro LMil LOPS LRHS MAsh MGos MJak NEgg NHim NPri SLdr SLim SPer SPoG SReu SSta WFar
	Blue Diamond Group	CBcs EPfP GMcL SReu
	- 'Blue Diamond'	CSBt LRHS LSRN MAsh MJak NRHS SLdr
	'Blue Monday' (EA)	SLdr
	'Blue Peter' ♀H5	CAco CBcs CSBt LCro LMil LOPS MAsh MLea SPer SReu SSta
	'Blue Pool'	LMil
	Blue Ribbon Group	SLdr
	'Blue Silver'	GGGa LMil MAsh
	'Blue Star'	GMcL

'Blue Steel' see *R. fastigiatum* 'Blue Steel'
Blue Tit Group CBcs CMac EPfP GGGa LMaj LRHS MAsh MGos NLar NRHS SCob SLdr SLim SPer SReu SSta
Bluebird Group CSBt SLdr
'Blueshine Girl' SLdr
'Blutopia' LMil LRHS
'Boddaertianum' LMil
BOHLKEN'S JUDITHA GGGa LMil
BOHLKEN'S KRONJEWEL GGGa LMil
BOHLKEN'S LAURA LMil
BOHLKEN'S LUPINENBERG GGGa LMil
BOHLKEN'S LUPINENBERG LAGUNA LMil NLar
BOHLKEN'S SNOW FIRE GGGa LMil LRHS NLar
boothii GGGa
- HECC 10077 GGGa
Bo-peep Group CBcs
- 'Bo-peep' LMil SLdr
'Boskoop Ostara' LMil
'Boule de Neige' MAsh NLar SPer
'Bouquet de Flore' (G) ♀H6 LMil
Bow Bells Group MLea
- 'Bow Bells' ♀H4 EPfP GEdr GMcL LMil LRHS MAsh MGos NLar SLdr
'Bowjingles' GGGa
brachyanthum subsp. ***hypolepidotum*** GGGa
§ ***brachycarpum*** Dwarf Pink Group GGGa
§ - subsp. ***fauriei*** B&SWJ 4326 WCru
- 'Roseum Dwarf' see *R. brachycarpum* Dwarf Pink Group
'Brambling' GGGa
'Brazier' (EA) SLdr
'Bremen' LMil
Bric-à-brac Group CBcs
'Bright Forecast' (K) MLea SLdr
'Brigitte' LSRN MAsh
'Brilliant Blue' (EA) MAsh
'Britannia' CSBt MJak SReu SSta
'Bronze Fire' (A) SReu SSta
'Brown Eyes' CAco GKin MAsh MMuc
'Bruce Brechtbill' GKin MAsh MMuc
§ 'Bruns Gloria' LMil NLar
'Bruns Schneewitchen' SReu SSta
'Buccaneer' (Glenn Dale) (EA) SLdr
bullatum see *R. edgeworthii*
'Bungo-nishiki' (Wada) (EA/d) CMac WThu
bureavii ♀H5 CBcs GGGa LMil NHim SReu SSta
- 'Wavy' **new** NHim
bureavii* × *yakushimanum SReu
burmanicum CBcs CPne GGGa
Bustard Group LMil
'Busuki' GGGa
'Butter Brickle' LMil MLea NLar
'Butterfly' SLdr
'Buttermint' SLdr
'C.B. van Nes' SLdr
'Caerhays Lavender' (EA) CBcs
calendulaceum (A) GGGa LMil
- red-flowered (A) LMil
- yellow-flowered (A) LMil
(Calfort Group) 'Calfort' GGGa
callimorphum GGGa
calophytum ♀H5 CPne GGGa LMil SLdr
calostrotum 'Gigha' ♀H4 GGGa LMil MAsh SReu WAbe
§ - subsp. ***keleticum*** ♀H4 GCal GEdr GGGa ITim NHim NSla WThu
- - R 58 GGGa LMil
§ - - Radicans Group GEdr GGGa ITim NSla WAbe WThu
- subsp. ***riparioides*** LMil NHim
- subsp. ***riparium*** ITim
§ - - Nitens Group GGGa WThu
caloxanthum see *R. campylocarpum* subsp. *caloxanthum*
'Calsap' GGGa
Calstocker Group LMil
camelliiflorum GGGa
campanulatum GGGa LMil SLdr SReu
- HWJCM 195 WCru
- HWJCM 409 WCru
§ - subsp. ***aeruginosum*** GGGa LMil
'Campfire' J.B. Gable (EA) SLdr
campylocarpum GGGa LMil
§ - subsp. ***caloxanthum*** GGGa
campylogynum GGGa LMil
- SBEC 0519 GGGa
- 'Album' see *R.* 'Leucanthum'
- Charopoeum Group NHim WThu
- - 'Patricia' GEdr NSla
- (Cremastum Group) 'Bodnant Red' GGGa WThu
- Myrtilloides Group ♀H4 GGGa LMil WAbe WThu
- white-flowered **new** NHim
camtschaticum GGGa GKev IDee LMil NHim
- deep red-flowered **new** NHim
- red-flowered GGGa
canadense (A) GGGa
- f. ***albiflorum*** (A) GGGa LMil
- dark-flowered (A) LMil
CANDY LIGHTS ('UMinn's Candy Lights') (A) LRHS
'Candy Striped Pink' SAko
§ ***canescens*** (A) LMil MPkF
'Cannon's Double' (K/d) ♀H6 CBcs GKin LMil LRHS MGos MLea NHim NLar SPer WMoo
'Canzonetta' (EA/d) ♀H5 CEnd EPfP GGGa LMil LRHS MAsh NRHS SAko SLdr
'Captain Jack' GGGa
'Caractacus' SCob
'Carat' (A) NLar
cardiobasis see *R. orbiculare* subsp. *cardiobasis*
(Carita Group) 'Carita Charm' LMil
- 'Golden Dream' LMil
Carmen Group **new** NHim
- 'Carmen' ♀H5 GEdr GGGa GKin LMil MAsh MLea MMuc SLdr
carneum GGGa
'Caroline Allbrook' MAsh MLea NLar SLdr
'Cary Ann' CAco CTri LRHS MAsh
'Casablanca' (EA) SLdr
'Cassley' (Vs) LMil
catawbiense CMCN SLdr
'Catawbiense Album' CAco CTri MAsh
'Catawbiense Boursault' LMaj SLdr
'Catawbiense Grandiflorum' CAco LMil MAsh
caucasicum GGGa
'Caucasicum Pictum' LMil SLdr
'Cayenne' (EA) SLdr
'Cecile' (K) ♀H6 CBcs CMac CTri GKin GMcL LMil LSRN MMuc MPkF SReu
'Celestial' (EA) CMac

	Name	Suppliers
	cephalanthum	GGGa LMil
	- subsp. ***cephalanthum*** SBEC 0751	WThu
	- - Crebreflorum Group	GGGa LMil WAbe WThu
	- - Nmaiense Group	GGGa
	- subsp. ***platyphyllum***	GGGa
	cerasinum	CPne LMil NHim
	- 'Cherry Brandy'	GGGa NHim
	- 'Coals of Fire'	GGGa
	chaetomallum	see *R. haematodes* subsp. *chaetomallum*
	chamaethomsonii	GGGa
	- var. ***chamaethomsonii*** Rock form	GGGa
	championae	GGGa
	'Chanel' (Vs)	SReu SSta
	changii	GGGa NHim
	'Chanticleer' (Glenn Dale) (EA)	SLdr
	chapaense	see *R. maddenii* subsp. *crassum*
	'Chariots of Fire' (EA)	LMil
	charitopes	GCal LMil
	- F 25570	GGGa LMil
§	- subsp. ***tsangpoense***	GGGa NHim
*	'Charlotte de Rothschild' (A)	SLdr
	'Charlotte Foster'	GGGa
	'Charlotte Megan' (A)	LMil
	'Charme La'	GGGa
	chasmanthum	see *R. augustinii* subsp. *chasmanthum*
	'Cheer'	MAsh MMuc NEgg SPer
	'Chelsea Seventy'	SLdr
	'Cherokee' (EA)	SLdr
	'Cherry Cheesecake'	NLar
	'Cherry Drops' (EA)	EPfP MAsh SPoG
	CHERRY KISS ('Hachcher'PBR)	GGGa LMil LRHS SAko
	'Chetco' (A)	LMil MGos
	'Chevalier Félix de Sauvage'	LMil
	'Chikor'	CBcs GGGa GKin MGos NLar
	'Chionoides'	SLdr
	'Chipmunk' (EA/d)	GGGa LRHS MAsh NRHS
	'Chippewa' (Indian) (EA)	CTri LMil SAko
	Choptank River Group (A)	GKev
	(Choremia Group) 'Choremia' ♀H3	LMil NHim
	christi (V)	GGGa
	'Christina' (Vuykiana) (EA/d)	SLdr
	'Christmas Cheer' (*caucasicum* hybrid) ♀H5	CBcs CSBt GGGa GKin IRob LCro LMil LOPS MAsh MGos MLea NLar NPri SCob SLdr SPer SReu
	'Christmas Cheer' (EA/d)	see *R.* 'Ima-shojo'
	'Christopher Loder'	SLdr
	chrysodoron	NHim
	ciliatum	CBcs GGGa SLdr
	ciliipes	GMcL
	Cilpinense Group	CBcs
	- 'Cilpinense' ♀H3	CMac CSBt EPfP LMil LRHS MAsh MMuc NPri SLdr
	cinnabarinum	LMil SLdr
	- subsp. ***cinnabarinum*** BL&M 234	LMil
	- - Blandfordiiflorum Group	GGGa
	- - 'Nepal'	LMil
	- - Roylei Group	GGGa LMil NHim
	- - - 'Vin Rosé'	LMil
	- Cinzan Group	LMil
§	- (Conroy Group) 'Conroy'	LMil
§	- subsp. ***xanthocodon***	CBcs GGGa LMil
§	- - Concatenans Group	CPne GGGa LMil NHim SLdr
	- - - KW 5874	LMil
	- - Purpurellum Group	GGGa SLdr
	'Cinzia' (K)	GGGa
	circinnatum	GGGa
	citriniflorum	LMil
	- R 108	LMil
	- var. ***citriniflorum***	LMil
	- var. ***horaeum***	GGGa
	clementinae	GGGa
	- F 25705	LMil
	'Cliff Garland'	LMil
	'Coccineum Speciosum' (G) ♀H6	CMac GKin LMil SReu SSta
	coeloneurum	GGGa LMil
	- EGM 334	LMil
	collettianum	GGGa
	'Colonel Coen'	GKin MMuc
	Colonel Rogers Group	SLdr SReu
	columbianum	SLdr
	'Colyer' (EA)	SLdr
	Comely Group	SLdr
	comisteum C 6541	GGGa
	concatenans	see *R. cinnabarinum* subsp. *xanthocodon* Concatenans Group
	concinnoides	GGGa
	concinnum	GGGa
	- Pseudoyanthinum Group ♀H5	GGGa
	'Confetti Creeper' **new**	GKev
	'Connie' (Kaempferi) (EA)	SReu SSta
	'Conroy'	see *R. cinnabarinum* (Conroy Group) 'Conroy'
	'Contina'	LMil
	'Conversation Piece' (EA)	CEnd SLdr
	'Cool Haven'	LMil
	'Coral Sea' (EA)	SReu
	'Coral Seas' (V)	GGGa
	'Corany' (A)	LMil NLar
	coriaceum	GGGa LMil NHim
	'Corneille' (G/d)	CSBt LMil NHim
	'Coronation Day'	LMil
	'Cosmopolitan'	CDul GMcL LCro LOPS MGos MMuc NLar SPer SPoG
	'Cotton Candy'	LMil
	'Countess of Athlone'	CMac
	'Countess of Haddington'	CBcs LMil
	Cowslip Group	CTri LMil MAsh MGos MLea NHim
	- 'Cowslip' ♀H4	EPfP LRHS NLar
	coxianum	GGGa
	'Crane' ♀H5	EPfP GGGa LMil LRHS MAsh
	crassum	see *R. maddenii* subsp. *crassum*
	'Cream Crest'	GKin NLar SLim
	'Creamy Chiffon'	CAco MLea
	crenulatum	GGGa
	crinigerum	CPne GGGa LMil
	'Crinoline' (EA)	SLdr
	Crossbill Group	CBcs SLdr
	'Crosswater Belle'	LMil NLar
	'Crosswater Red' (A)	LMil
	cubittii	see *R. veitchianum* Cubittii Group
	cucullatum	see *R. roxieanum* var. *cucullatum*
	cumberlandense (A)	GGGa LMil
	- 'Sunlight'	LMil
	'Cunningham's Blush'	SGol
	'Cunningham's White'	CAco CBcs CDul CTri ELan EPfP ESps EUJe GGGa GMcL LCro LMil LOPS LRHS MAsh MGos MMuc

		NHim NLar NPri SArc SCob SLdr SLim SPer SPoG SReu SSta
	'Cupcake' Delp	see *R.* 'Delp's Cupcake'
	'Cupcake' Thompson	GGGa
	'Curlew' ♀H4	CMac GEdr GKin GMcL LMil MAsh MJak MMuc SLdr WThu
	cyanocarpum	GGGa
	'Cynthia' ♀H5	CMac CSBt GGGa LMil LSRN NEgg SLdr SReu SSta
	'Dagmar'	SAko
	'Dairymaid'	LMil
	'Daisetsuzan' (EA)	MPkF
	(Damozel Group) 'Damozel'	LMil
	'Dartmoor Pixie'	WThu
	'Dartmoor Shepherd's Delight'	SReu SSta
	dauricum 'Album'	see *R. dauricum* 'Hokkaido'
§	- 'Hokkaido'	GGGa
	- 'Mid-winter' ♀H6	GGGa LMil
	davidii	GGGa LMil NEgg
	davidsonianum ♀H3	CMac GGGa LMil
	- Bodnant form	LMil
	- 'Caerhays Blotched'	GGGa
	- 'Ruth Lyons'	LMil
	'Daviesii' (G) ♀H6	CBcs CDul CEnd CSBt CTho CTri ELan EPfP GKin LCro LMil LOPS LRHS MAsh MMuc NHim NLar NPri SPer SPoG SReu SSta WHor WMoo
	'Daybreak' (EA/d)	see *R.* 'Kirin'
	'Dear Barbara'	LSRN
	'Dear Grandad' (EA)	CTri LMil LSRN
	'Dear Grandma' (EA)	LMil LSRN
	'Dearest' (EA)	LMil LRHS MAsh NPri NRHS
	'Debutante'	SReu SSta
	decorum ♀H4	CPne GGGa LMil SLdr
	- subsp. ***cordatum*** C&H 7132	GGGa
§	- subsp. ***diaprepes***	GCal
	- - 'Gargantua'	SLdr
	- late-flowering	LMil
	- pink-flowered	GGGa
	decorum* × *yakushimanum	SReu
§	***degronianum*** subsp. ***degronianum***	LMil
	- subsp. ***heptamerum*** 'Ho Emma'	LMil LRHS
	- 'Rae's Delight'	LMil
	dekatanum	GGGa
	deleiense	see *R. tephropeplum*
	'Delicatissimum' (O) ♀H5	CBcs GGGa GKin LRHS MPkF
§	'Delp's Cupcake'	NHim
	'Delta'	MGos MMuc NHim SCob SLdr SLim
	dendrocharis	LMil NHim
	- C 3016 **new**	NHim
	- Cox 5016	GGGa WAbe
	- GLENDOICK GEM ('Gle002')	GGGa
*	'Denny's Rose' (A)	LMil SReu SSta
	'Denny's Scarlet'	SReu SSta
	'Denny's White' (A)	LMil SReu SSta
	denudatum	LMil
	- EGM 294	LMil
	× ***detonsum***	NHim
	'Devisiperbile' (EA)	SLdr
	Diamant Group lilac-flowered (EA)	LMil MLea
	- pink-flowered (EA)	MLea
§	- purple-flowered (EA)	MLea
§	- red-flowered (EA)	MLea SLdr

	'Diamant Purpur'	see *R.* Diamant Group purple-flowered
	'Diamant Rot'	see *R.* Diamant Group red-flowered
I	'Diana'	SLdr
	'Diana van Herzeele'	SCob
	diaprepes	see *R. decorum* subsp. *diaprepes*
	dichroanthum	GGGa LMil NHim
§	- subsp. ***apodectum***	GGGa LMil NHim
§	- subsp. ***scyphocalyx***	GGGa LMil
	- subsp. ***septentrionale***	GGGa
	didymum	see *R. sanguineum* subsp. *didymum*
	'Diorama' (Vs)	SReu SSta
	discolor	see *R. fortunei* subsp. *discolor*
	diversipilosum 'Milky Way'	GGGa
	'Doc'	CBcs CMac SLdr SReu SSta
	'Doctor Arnold W. Endtz'	SReu
	'Doctor H.C. Dresselhuys'	MMuc
	'Doctor M. Oosthoek' (M)	CSBt GKin SReu
	'Doctor Reiger'	NLar
	'Dominik'	GGGa
	'Don Quixote' (K)	GMcL
	'Donnington' **new**	NHim
	'Dopey' ♀H4	CAco CBcs EPfP GGGa LMil LRHS MAsh MGos MJak MLea NHim NLar SCob SLdr SLim SReu SSta
	'Dora Amateis' ♀H6	CAco CBcs GGGa IDee LMil LRHS MAsh MGos MMuc NPri NRHS SAko SLdr SLim SPer SReu WThu
	Dormouse Group	LMil MAsh
	'Dorothy Hayden' (EA)	SLdr
	'Dörte Reich'	GGGa
	'Dotella'	GGGa SReu SSta
	'Double Beauty' (Vuykiana) (EA/d)	SReu SSta
	Dragonfly Group	SReu SSta
	'Drake's Mountain'	GMcL MJak
	'Dreamland' ♀H5	CBcs EPfP LCro LMil LOPS LRHS MAsh MGos MLea MMuc NLar NRHS SCob SLdr SLim SPoG SReu SSta
	'Dufthecke'	see *R.* WHITE DUFTHECKE
	'Dufthecke Yellow' **new**	LMil
	'Dusty Miller'	LRHS MAsh MJak MPkF NRHS SLdr
	'Earl of Donoughmore'	SReu SSta
	'Easter Parade' (EA)	SLdr
	eastmanii (A)	GGGa NHim
	ebianense NN 904	GGGa
	'Ebony Pearl'	SLdr
	eclecteum	GCal GGGa LMil
§	***edgeworthii*** ♀H3	CBcs GGGa LMil MPkF
	'Edith Bosley'	LRHS NLar SLdr SPer
	'Edna Bee' (EA)	LMil SLdr
	'Egret' ♀H4	GEdr GGGa GMcL LMil MLea NHim NSla SLdr
	'Eider'	GGGa MAsh
	'Eileen'	LMil
	'El Camino'	SLdr
	(Eleanore Group) 'Eleanore'	SLdr
	'Electra'	see *R. augustinii* (Electra Group) 'Electra'
	elegantulum	CPne LMil
	(Elisabeth Hobbie Group) 'Elisabeth Hobbie' ♀H5	IDee LMil NLar SLdr
	'Elizabeth' (EA)	CMac CSBt EPfP SLdr
	Elizabeth Group	CBcs LMil MAsh SLdr SReu
§	- 'Creeping Jenny'	GGGa SLdr
	- 'Elizabeth'	CDul CTri LRHS LSRN NRHS

'Elizabeth Jenny'	see *R.* (Elizabeth Group) 'Creeping Jenny'
'Elizabeth Lockhart'	NHim
'Elizabeth Red Foliage'	CTri GGGa LMil LRHS MAsh NLar NRHS SLdr
'Else Frye'	GGGa
'Elsie Lee' (EA/d) 🏆^{H5}	CEnd CSBt EPfP LMil MAsh SLdr SReu WFar
'Emasculum'	SLdr
'Endsleigh Pink'	LMil
eriocarpum 'Gumpō' (EA)	CMac SLdr
eriogynum	see *R. facetum*
'Eruption'	NLar
'Esmeralda'	CMac
'Esther May' (A)	SReu SSta
'Etna' (EA)	SLdr
'Etta Burrows'	GGGa SLdr
'Euan Cox'	GGGa
'Eucharis' (Glenn Dale) (EA)	SCob
'Eunice Ann' (A)	SReu SSta
'Europa'	SReu SSta
'Eurydice'	LMil
eurysiphon Arduaine form	NHim
'Evelyn Hyde' (EA)	SLdr
'Evening Fragrance' (A)	LMil
'Everbloom' (EA)	SLdr
'Everitt Hershey' (A)	SLdr
EVERRED ('851C'^{PBR})	GGGa
exasperatum	GGGa
- KW 6855	LMil
Exburiense Group	MMuc
'Exbury Calstocker'	LMil
excellens	CPne GGGa LMil
- CW&T 6279 **new**	NHim
eximium	see *R. falconeri* subsp. *eximium*
'Explorer' (EA)	MJak
'Exquisitum' (O) 🏆^{H5}	CBcs CTho GGGa GKin LMil
exquisitum	see *R. oreotrephes* Exquisitum Group
'Extraordinaire'	LMil SReu SSta
faberi	GGGa
(Fabia Group) 'Fabia' 🏆^{H3}	CBcs CMac GGGa GKin LMil SLdr
§ - 'Fabia Tangerine'	CMac MLea
- 'Fabia Waterer'	LMil
§ ***facetum***	GGGa LMil LRHS
'Faggetter's Favourite' 🏆^{H5}	LMil SLdr SReu SSta
Fairy Light Group	LMil LRHS SLdr
faithae CGG 14142	GGGa
falconeri 🏆^{H3}	CPne GGGa LMil NEgg SLdr
§ - subsp. ***eximium***	GGGa GKev LMil
'Falling Snow'	SAko
'Fanal' (K)	NLar
'Fantastica' 🏆^{H6}	CAco ELan EPfP GGGa IDee LMil MAsh MGos MJak MLea MMuc NLar NPri NRHS SLim SPoG
fargesii	see *R. oreodoxa* var. *fargesii*
fastigiatum	GEdr LMil NHim NSla SLdr
- SBEC 0804	GGGa WThu
- SDR 7990	GKev
§ - 'Blue Steel' 🏆^{H6}	CTri GKin LMil LRHS MAsh NHim NPri NRHS SLdr SPlb SReu WAbe
- 'Indigo Steel'	GGGa
'Fastuosum Flore Pleno' (d) 🏆^{H6}	CBcs CMac CSBt GGGa LMil MLea SLdr SPer SReu SSta
faucium	GGGa
fauriei	see *R. brachycarpum* subsp. *fauriei*
'Favorite' ambig. (EA)	SLdr
'Fawley' (K)	SLdr
'Fay Norman' **new**	LMil
'Fedora' (Kaempferi) (EA)	CBcs CTsd
ferrugineum	GGGa LMil LRHS
- f. ***album***	NHim
'Feuerwerk' (K)	GMcL MMuc NHim NLar
fictolacteum	see *R. rex* subsp. *fictolacteum*
'Fire Bird'	SLdr
'Fire Rim'	LRHS MAsh
'Fireball' (K) 🏆^{H6}	CBcs CDul CTri EPfP GGGa GKin GMcL LMil LRHS MAsh MGos MMuc NLar NPri SPer SPoG WMoo
'Fireball' (hybrid)	MJak
'Firecracker' (A)	LRHS MAsh
'Fireglow' (EA)	GKin LMil
'Firelight' (hybrid)	GKin LMil NLar SPer
§ 'Firestorm'	NLar NPri
'Flaming Gold'	LRHS LSRN MAsh SLdr
'Flanagan's Daughter'	LMil MAsh
Flava Group	see *R.* Volker Group
flavidum	GGGa MMuc
fletcherianum 'Yellow Bunting'	GGGa
floccigerum	LMil
- bicoloured	GGGa
'Floriade'	GMcL
floribundum	GGGa LMil
'Florida' (EA/d) 🏆^{H4}	CMac LMil SLdr SReu
'Flower Arranger' (EA)	LMil MAsh SCoo
formosanum	GGGa
formosum	CBcs GGGa
§ - var. ***formosum*** Iteaphyllum Group	GGGa
- - 'Khasia'	GGGa
- var. ***inaequale***	GGGa
forrestii subsp. ***forrestii***	LMil
- - Repens Group	GKev LMil
- - - 'Seinghku'	GGGa
- Tumescens Group	GGGa WThu
Fortune Group	SLdr
fortunei 🏆^{H6}	GGGa LMil SLdr
§ - subsp. ***discolor*** 🏆^{H5}	LMil NLar
- - (Houlstonii Group) 'John R. Elcock'	LMil
- - var. ***kwangfuense*** AC 5208	LMil
- 'Mrs Butler'	see *R.* 'Sir Charles Butler'
fragariiflorum	GGGa
'Fragrance' **new**	SReu
'Fragrant Memories'	LMil
'Fragrant Star' (A)	LRHS MPkF
'Fragrantissimum' 🏆^{H2}	CBcs CEnd CMac CSBt CTsd GGGa LMil LRHS MPkF MRav NHim NLar SLdr
'Fraseri' (M)	LMil
'Fred Peste' 🏆^{H4}	GKin LMil MGos MLea MMuc NHim SLdr SLim
(Fred Wynniatt Group) 'Fred Wynniatt'	LMil
'Fred Wynniatt Stanway'	see *R.* 'Stanway'
'Freya' (R/d)	LMil LSRN
'Fridoline' (EA)	SAko
'Frigate' (EA)	SLdr
'Frilly Lemon' (Ad)	EPfP MPkF
'Frosted Orange' (EA)	LMil MAsh
'Frühlingszauber'	SLdr
'Fulbrook'	LMil
fulgens	GGGa LMil
fulvum 🏆^{H4}	GCal GGGa GKin LMil SReu SSta
'Furnivall's Daughter' 🏆^{H5}	CAco CDul CMac CSBt GGGa LMaj LMil MMuc SLdr SPer SReu SSta
fuyuanense	GGGa

	'Gabrielle Hill' (EA)	MAsh SLdr
	'Gaiety' (Glenn Dale) (EA)	LMil SLdr
	galactinum	GGGa IDee LMil NHim
	'Galathea' (EA)	MMuc
	'Gandy Dancer'	CAco MLea SLdr
	'Garden State Glow' (EA/d)	SLdr
	'Gartendirektor Glocker'	CMac GGGa LMil MGos NHim NLar SLim
	'Gartendirektor Rieger' ♀H5	GGGa LMil NLar SReu
	'Geisha Lilac'	see *R.* (Aronense Group) 'Hanako'
	'Geisha Orange'	see *R.* (Aronense Group) 'Satschiko'
	'Geisha Pink'	see *R.* 'Momoko'
	'Geisha Purple'	see *R.* (Aronense Group) 'Fumiko'
	'Geisha Red'	see *R.* (Aronense Group) 'Kazuko'
	'Geisha White'	see *R.* 'Hisako'
	'Gena Mae' (A/d)	GGGa SLdr
	'General Practitioner'	CMac SLdr
	'General Wavell' (EA)	CMac NHim
	'Gene's Favourite'	SReu SSta
	genestierianum	GGGa
	'Geoffroy Millais'	LMil
	'Georg Arends' (A)	EPfP LMil LRHS MAsh NLar
	'George Hyde' (EA)	EPfP LRHS LSRN MAsh SCoo
§	× ***geraldii***	SLdr
	'Germania'	CBcs GMcL LRHS MAsh MGos NPri SCob SPoG SReu SSta
	Gertrud Schäle Group	CTri GMcL
	Gibraltar Group	LMil WFar
	'Gibraltar' (K) ♀H6	CBcs CDul CSBt CTri EPfP GGGa GKin LMil LRHS MAsh MGos MJak MPkF NLar SLim SPer SReu SSta
	'Gilbert Mullie' (EA)	LMil NLar SLim SReu SSta
	'Gillian Bramley'	SLdr
	'Gill's Crimson'	SReu
	'Ginger' (K)	LMil NHim
	'Ginny Gee' ♀H5	CBcs EPfP GEdr GGGa GKin GMcL LMil LRHS MAsh MGos MLea NEgg NLar NRHS NSla NWad SReu SSta
§	'Girard's Hot Shot' (EA)	GMcL LRHS MPkF NHim NRHS SReu SSta
§	'Girard's Variegated Hot Shot' (EA/v) ♀H4	GGGa MAsh NEgg SLdr SPoG
	'Gislinde' (A)	SAko
	'Glacier' (EA)	SLdr
	'Glamour'	LMil
	glanduliferum	GGGa SLdr
	- EGM 347	LMil
	- 'Peter the Great'	LMil
	glaucophyllum	CPne GGGa LMil
	- Borde Hill form	LMil
	- 'Deer Dell'	LMil
§	- subsp. ***tubiforme***	CPne GGGa
	GLENDOICK BUTTERSCOTCH ('Gle003')	GGGa
	GLENDOICK CRIMSON ('Gle004') (EA)	GGGa
	GLENDOICK DOVE ('Gle025')	GGGa
	GLENDOICK DREAM ('Gle005') (EA)	GGGa
	GLENDOICK ERMINE ('Gle006') (EA)	GGGa
	GLENDOICK FLAMINGO ('Gle026')	GGGa
	GLENDOICK FROLIC ('Gle007')	GGGa
	GLENDOICK GARNET ('Gle008') (EA)	GGGa
	GLENDOICK GLACIER ('Gle009') (EA)	GGGa

	GLENDOICK GOBLIN ('Gle010') (EA)	GGGa
	GLENDOICK GOLD ('Gle011')	GGGa
	GLENDOICK ICE CREAM ('Gle013')	GGGa
	GLENDOICK MYSTIQUE ('Gle014')	GGGa
	GLENDOICK PETTICOATS ('Gle015')	GGGa
	GLENDOICK ROSEBUD ('Gle022') (EA)	GGGa
	GLENDOICK RUBY ('Gle016')	GGGa
	GLENDOICK SHERBET ('Gle029') **new**	GGGa
	GLENDOICK SNOWFLAKES ('Gle001') (EA)	GGGa
	GLENDOICK SORBET ('Gle028') **new**	GGGa
§	'Glendoick Tanager'	GGGa
	GLENDOICK VANILLA ('Gle017')	GGGa
	GLENDOICK VELVET ('Gle018')	GGGa
	'Glenna'	GGGa
	'Gletschernacht'	SAko
	glischrum	GGGa
	- subsp. ***glischroides***	GGGa LMil
§	- subsp. ***rude***	CPne GGGa LMil LRHS
	globigerum	see *R. alutaceum* var. *alutaceum* Globigerum Group
	'Gloria'	see *R.* 'Bruns Gloria'
	'Gloria Mundi' (G)	LRHS
	'Glory of Littleworth' (Ad)	LMil
	'Glory of Penjerrick'	SLdr
	'Glowing Embers' (K)	CTri GKin GMcL LMil LRHS MAsh MGos MLea MMuc NHim NLar SLim SPer SReu SSta
	'Goblin'	SLdr
	'Gog' (K)	CSBt
§	'Goldbukett'	GGGa
	GOLDEN BOUQUET	see *R.* 'Goldbukett'
	'Golden Coach'	CAco
	'Golden Eagle' (K) ♀H6	CBcs GKin GMcL LMil LRHS MGos MJak MLea NHim NLar SLdr SReu WFar
	GOLDEN EVEREST ('Hachgold'PBR)	GGGa LMil SAko
	'Golden Flare' (A)	CBcs GKin GMcL NEgg
	'Golden Fleece'	LMil
	'Golden Gate'	CSBt LRHS MGos MMuc NLar
	(Golden Horn Group) 'Golden Horn'	SLdr
	'Golden Lights' (A)	GKin NEgg NLar
	'Golden Princess'	LMil
	'Golden Ruby'	CBcs
	'Golden Splendour'	LMil
	'Golden Sunset' (K) ♀H6	EPfP LMil LRHS MAsh MLea MPkF WFar
	'Golden Torch' ♀H4	CBcs CDul EPfP IRob LCro LMil LOPS LRHS MAsh MGos MJak MLea NLar NPri SLdr SLim SPer SPoG SReu
	'Golden Wedding'	LMil LRHS LSRN MAsh MJak SLdr SPer
	'Golden Wit'	MAsh MMuc NEgg
	'Golden Wonder'	MAsh
	'Goldflimmer' (v)	EPfP GGGa GKin LRHS MAsh MGos MJak NLar NPri SCob SLim SPoG

(Goldfort Group) 'Goldfort'	SReu
'Goldika'	LMil
'Goldinetta'	GGGa LMil
'Goldkrone' ♀H5	ELon EPfP GGGa LCro LOPS MAsh MLea NHim SPer SPoG SReu SSta
'Goldsworth Orange'	CAco CMac LMil LRHS SLdr
'Goldsworth Yellow'	CSBt
'Goldtopas' (K)	CTri EPfP GGGa GKin LMil LRHS
'Gomer Waterer' ♀H6	CBcs CDul CMac CSBt EPfP GGGa GMcL LCro LMil LOPS LRHS MAsh MGos MJak NLar SCob SLdr SPer SPoG SReu SSta
'Gorbella'	SReu
Gowenianum Group (Ad)	LMil LRHS MGos NHim SPer
'Grace Seabrook' ♀H5	CBcs CSBt CTri GGGa MLea MMuc SLdr SPer SReu
'Graf Lennart'	GGGa
GRAFFITO ('Hachgraf')	GGGa LMil
'Graham Thomas'	LMil
'Grand Slam'	MMuc
grande	GGGa LMil
gratum	see *R. basilicum*
'Graziella'	GGGa LCro LOPS MGos MPkF NHim SPoG SSta
'Greensleeves'	LMil
'Greenway' (Kurume) (EA)	CBcs SLdr
griersonianum	GGGa LMil
- F 30392	LMil
griffithianum B&SWJ 2425	WCru
'Gristede' ♀H5	LMil LRHS NLar SReu SSta
groenlandicum	LMil MLea NLar SPer WSHC
- 'Compactum'	LRHS NLar
- 'Helma'	EBee GBin LRHS NLar
- 'Lenie'	NLar
(Grosclaude Group) 'Grosclaude'	LMil
'Grumpy'	ELan EPfP LMil LRHS MAsh SCob SReu
'Gwenda' (EA)	CTri SLdr
'Gwendoline' (A)	SReu SSta
(Gwillt-king Group) 'Gwillt-king'	CBcs
habrotrichum	GGGa LMil
'Hachmann's Brasilia'	SSta
'Hachmann's Charmant'	EPfP GGGa SAko
'Hachmann's Constanze'	LMil
'Hachmann's Eskimo'	CAco LMil SLdr
'Hachmann's Feuerschein'	SAko
'Hachmann's Junifeuer'	SReu SSta
HACHMANN'S KABARETT ('Hachkaba')	LMil NHim NLar
'Hachmann's Mamamia'	SAko
'Hachmann's Marlis' ♀H6	LMil SReu
§ 'Hachmann's Metallica'	GGGa LCro LMil LRHS
§ 'Hachmann's Orakel'	GGGa LMil SReu SSta
HACHMANN'S PICOBELLO ('Hachpico'PBR)	EPfP GGGa LMil
'Hachmann's Pinguin'	SReu SSta
§ 'Hachmann's Polaris' ♀H7	LMil SReu
'Hachmann's Porzellan' ♀H6	LMil MPkF
§ 'Hachmann's Rokoko' (EA)	CEnd LMil NHim SReu SSta
'Hachmann's Sunny Boy'	LMil LRHS
haematodes	GGGa LMil
§ - subsp. ***chaetomallum***	GGGa LMil
- subsp. ***haematodes***	LMil
'Halfdan Lem' ♀H4	CBcs GGGa GKin LMil LRHS MAsh MGos MLea MMuc NHim NLar SLim SPer SReu SSta

'Halopeanum'	GGGa LMil
'Halton'	LMil
'Hamlet' (M)	LMil
'Hammondii'	LMil
'Hampshire Belle'	LMil LRHS SReu SSta
hanceanum 'Canton Consul'	GGGa
- Nanum Group ♀H5	CBcs GGGa
'Hanger's Flame' (A)	LMil
'Hank Windsor'	CAco
HANS HACHMANN ('Hachhans')	GGGa LMil
'Hansel'	MAsh MMuc NHim
'Hardijzer Beauty' (Ad)	SLdr
'Hardy Gardenia' (EA/d)	SReu SSta
hardyi	see *R. augustinii* subsp. *hardyi*
'Harkwood Red' (EA)	SLdr
Harmony Group	SLdr
'Harry Tagg'	SLdr
Harry White's hybrid (A)	SReu SSta
'Haru-no-sono' (EA) **new**	MPkF
'Harvest Moon' (K)	GMcL NHim NLar SSta
'Hatsu-giri' (EA)	CMac LCro LMil LOPS SPer SReu SSta
(Hawk Group) 'Crest' ♀H3	CBcs GGGa LMil SSta
'Heather Macleod' (EA)	SLdr
heatherae	GGGa LMil
'Heidi'PBR (EA)	SLdr
'Helen Close' (Glenn Dale) (EA)	SLdr
'Helena Evelyn' (A)	LMil NHim
'Helene Schiffner'	SReu
heliolepis	GGGa LMil NHim
- var. ***fumidum***	see *R. heliolepis* var. *heliolepis*
§ - var. ***heliolepis***	GGGa
hemitrichotum SDR 4237 **new**	GKev
hemsleyanum	LMil SLdr
'Herbert' (EA)	CMac MGos NLar SLdr SLim
§ 'Herbstzauber'	MAsh
'High Sheriff'	CBcs
'High Summer'	LMil LRHS NLar
'Hilda Margaret'	SReu
'Hilte' **new**	NHim
'Himmelberg'	GGGa
'Hinamayo'	see *R.* (Obtusum Group) 'Hinomayo'
'Hino-crimson' (Kurume) (EA) ♀H4	CBcs CMac CSBt CTri GKin GMcL LMil MAsh MGos MPkF NHim NLar SLdr SPer SPoG SReu SSta
'Hinode-giri' (EA)	CMac CSBt CTsd SLdr SPer SReu
hippophaeoides	CBcs GKev LMil
- SDR 7919	GKev
- 'Bei-ma-shan'	see *R. hippophaeoides* 'Haba Shan'
§ - 'Haba Shan' ♀H6	GGGa LMil NHim WThu
hirsutum	LMil
hirtipes	GGGa
§ 'Hisako' (EA)	GMcL MAsh
hodgsonii	LMil SLdr
- B&SWJ 2195A	WCru
'Holden'	MAsh
'Homebush' (K/d) ♀H6	CBcs CDul CMac CTri EPfP GBin GMcL LMil LRHS MAsh MGos MJak MMuc NLar SPer SPoG SReu SSta WMoo
'Honey Butter'	LMil MGos NLar SLim
'Honeysuckle' (K)	SReu SSta
§ 'Ho-o' (Kurume) (EA)	SLdr
hookeri	CPne LMil
- Tigh-na-Rudha form	GGGa

'Hoppy'	CBcs LMil MAsh MGos MLea MMuc NLar SLdr SLim SPer
'Horizon Lakeside'	GGGa
'Horizon Monarch' 🏆H4	CAco CBcs GGGa GKin LMil LRHS MGos MLea NHim NLar SLdr SLim SPer SReu SSta WMoo
horlickianum	GGGa
'Hortulanus H. Witte' (M)	CSBt LRHS SReu SSta
'Hot Flush' **new**	LMil
'Hot Shot'	see *R.* 'Girard's Hot Shot'
'Hot Shot Variegated'	see *R.* 'Girard's Variegated Hot Shot' (EA/v)
'Hotei'	CAco CSBt EPfP GKin LMil MAsh MLea NEgg SLdr SReu SSta
(Hotspur Group) 'Hotspur' (K)	MMuc SPer
- 'Hotspur Red' (K) 🏆H6	EPfP GKin GMcL LMil MAsh MMuc MPkF NEgg WMoo
huanum	GGGa LMil
- EGM 316	LMil
'Hugh Koster'	SLdr
huidongense **new**	NHim
aff. ***huidongense***	LMil
'Hullaballoo'	LMil
Humming Bird Group	GEdr LMil SLdr
'Hussar'	LMil
'Hydon Dawn' 🏆H5	CBcs LMil MLea NLar SLdr SReu SSta
'Hydon Hunter' 🏆H5	CBcs SReu SSta
'Hydon Velvet'	CBcs GGGa LMil LRHS MMuc NHim NLar SLdr SReu
hylaeum	NHim
Hyperion Group	SReu
hyperythrum	GGGa LMil
hypoglaucum	see *R. argyrophyllum* subsp. *hypoglaucum*
'Ice Cube'	MLea MMuc SLdr
'Iceberg'	see *R.* (Lodauric Group) 'Lodauric Iceberg'
Idaho Group	LMil
(Idealist Group) 'Idealist'	LMil
'Ightham Yellow'	SLdr SReu
§ 'Ilam Melford Lemon' (A)	LMil
§ 'Ilam Ming' (A)	LMil
'Ilam Violet'	CMac LMil
'Iliad'	LMil
'Imago' (K/d)	LMil
§ 'Ima-shojo' (Kurume) (EA/d)	CMac LRHS SLdr
impeditum	CBcs CSBt ELan GEdr GKev LCro MGos MLea SCob SLdr SReu SSta
- 'Blue Steel'	see *R. fastigiatum* 'Blue Steel'
- 'Indigo'	GKin SReu WAbe
- 'Pygmaeum'	WAbe WThu
- 'Select'	MJak
imperator	see *R. uniflorum* var. *imperator*
(Impi Group) 'Impi'	LMil
indicum (EA)	CTsd
§ - 'Macranthum' (EA)	SLdr
'Ingrid Mehlquist'	GGGa
INKARHO LILAC DUFTHECKE ('Rhodunter 149'PBR)	LMil
insigne 🏆H6	GGGa LMil NHim
- Reuthe's form	SReu
insigne × ***yakushimanum***	SReu
Intrifast Group	GGGa
'Irene Koster' (O) 🏆H5	CTho ELan GGGa GKin LMil LRHS MGos MPkF NHim NLar SLim SPer
'Irohayama' (Kurume) (EA) 🏆H3	CBcs CEnd CMac EPfP LMil LRHS MAsh NPri NRHS
irroratum	LMil SLdr

§ - subsp. ***pogonostylum***	NHim
- 'Polka Dot'	GGGa LMil
- subsp. ***yiliangense*** EGM 339	LMil
'Isabel'	NPri
'Isabel' (EA)	GMcL MAsh
'Isola Bella'	GGGa
iteaphyllum	see *R. formosum* var. *formosum* Iteaphyllum Group
'Ivette' (Kaempferi) (EA)	CMac
Iviza Group	LMil
'Izumi-no-mai' (EA)	SLdr
'J.C. Williams'	CBcs
'J.M. de Montague'	see *R.* 'The Honourable Jean Marie de Montague'
'Jackwill'	SAko
(Jalisco Group) 'Jalisco Janet'	SLdr
- 'Jubilant'	LMil
'James Burchett' 🏆H6	LMil LRHS NLar SReu
'James Gable' (EA)	MAsh SLdr
'Jane Bradish-Ellames' **new**	NHim
Janet Group	LMil
'Janet Rhea' (EA)	SLdr
japonicum (A. Gray) J.V. Suringar	see *R. molle* subsp. *japonicum*
- var. ***pentamerum***	see *R. degronianum* subsp. *degronianum*
jasminiflorum (V)	GGGa
'Jason'	LMil
'Jean Marie Montague'	see *R.* 'The Honourable Jean Marie de Montague'
'Jeff Hill' (EA)	SLdr
'Jenny'	see *R.* (Elizabeth Group) 'Creeping Jenny'
'Jeritsa' **new**	LMil
'Jessica Rose' (A)	LMil
'Jim Russell' (*ciliicalyx* hybrid)	GGGa
'Jingle Bells'	GGGa
'Joanna'	CBcs
'Jock'	SLdr
Jock Group	CBcs
'Jock Brydon' (O)	GGGa LMil NHim
'Johann Sebastian Bach' (EA)	SLdr
'Johanna' (EA) 🏆H5	CEnd CTri EPfP GMcL LMil LRHS MAsh MGos NLar NPri NRHS SLdr SPer
'John Cairns' (Kaempferi) (EA)	CMac SLdr
'John Walter'	SCob
johnstoneanum	CBcs GGGa SLdr
- NJM 12.068 **new**	WPGP
- 'Double Diamond' (d)	LMil
'Jolie Madame' (Vs) 🏆H6	EPfP GKin LMil LRHS MAsh MGos MMuc NHim NLar NPri SPer WFar
'Joseph Hill' (EA)	CEnd NLar
'Jubilee'	SLdr
'July Giant'	SLdr
'June Fire' (A)	GGGa SReu SSta
'Juniduft' (A)	GGGa
kaempferi (EA)	LMil SLdr
§ - 'Mikado' (EA)	LMil SLdr SReu
- orange-flowered (EA)	CMac
'Kali'	GGGa
'Kalinka'	LMil MAsh MGos SPoG
'Karen Triplett'	LMil
'Karin'	MJak
'Karl Naue'	GGGa SReu

KARMINKISSEN ('Hachkarmin') new	LMil
'Kasane-kagaribi' (EA)	SLdr
'Kate Waterer' 🏆H5	SReu
'Kathleen' van Nes (EA)	SLdr
'Katisha' (EA)	SLdr
'Katy Watson'	SReu SSta
'Keija' (EA)	SLdr
keiskei compact	ITim
- Cordifolium Group	CPne WAbe
- var. ***ozawae*** 'Yaku Fairy' 🏆H5	LMil WAbe WThu
keleticum	see *R. calostrotum* subsp. *keleticum*
'Kelsay's Double' (d)	MLea
'Ken Janeck'	GGGa
§ ***kendrickii***	CPne GGGa
aff. ***kendrickii*** KR 10359 new	WPGP
'Kermesinum' (EA)	CTri LRHS MAsh MGos NLar NWad SLdr SLim SReu
I 'Kermesinum Rosé' (EA) 🏆H5	CSBt LMil LRHS NHim NLar SLdr SLim SReu
kesangiae	GGGa LMil NHim
- var. ***album***	GGGa
keysii	CPne GGGa LMil
(Kilimanjaro Group) 'Kilimanjaro'	LMil SReu
'Kimbeth'	GGGa
'King George' Loder	see *R.* (Loderi Group) 'Loderi King George'
kingianum	see *R. arboreum* subsp. *zeylanicum*
'Kings Ride'	LMil
§ 'Kirin' (Kurume) (EA/d)	LMil SLdr
kiusianum (EA)	LMil SReu
I - 'Album' (EA)	LMil NHim SReu WAbe
- 'Hillier's Pink' (EA)	LMil
- var. ***kiusianum*** (EA)	SLdr
'Kleiner Prinz' (EA)	SAko
'Klondyke' (K) 🏆H6	CBcs CSBt CTri EPfP GGGa GKin LCro LMil LOPS LRHS MAsh MGos MMuc NLar NPri SLdr SPer
'Kluis Sensation' 🏆H5	CAco CBcs CMac CSBt SLdr SReu SSta
'Kluis Triumph'	SReu
'Knap Hill Apricot' (K)	LMil
'Knap Hill Red' (K)	LMil
'Koichiro Wada'	see *R. yakushimanum* 'Koichiro Wada'
'Kokardia'	LMil SAko
kongboense	GGGa WAbe
'Königstein' (EA)	LMil MGos SReu SSta
§ 'Koningin Emma' (M)	GKin LMil
'Koningin Wilhelmina' (Vuykiana) (EA)	SLdr
'Koromo-shikibu' (EA)	GGGa LRHS MPkF
'Koromo-shikibu White' (EA)	GGGa
'Koster's Brilliant Red' (M)	LCro LOPS SReu SSta
'Kromlauer Parkperle' new	SAko
§ 'Kure-no-yuki' (Kurume) (EA/d)	CEnd LMil
kyawii	CPne GGGa
'La Ola' (EA) new	SAko
(Lactcombei Group) 'Robert Keir'	SLdr
lacteum	GGGa LMil
'Lady Alice Fitzwilliam' 🏆H3	CBcs CMac ECre GGGa GKin LMil NHim
(Lady Chamberlain Group) 'Salmon Trout'	LMil LSRN

'Lady Clementine Mitford' 🏆H5	CBcs CSBt LMil MLea MMuc SLdr SPer SReu
'Lady Dark' (EA) new	SAko
'Lady de Rothschild'	LMil
'Lady Eleanor Cathcart'	SLdr
'Lady Elphinstone' (Kufume) (EA)	SLdr
'Lady Louise' (EA)	SLdr
'Lady Montagu'	LMil
'Lady Romsey'	LMil
laetum (V)	GGGa
Lamellen Group	LMil
lanatoides	GGGa
lanatum	GGGa LMil NHim
- Flinckii Group new	NHim
'Langworth'	MLea MMuc NHim SReu
lanigerum	LMil SReu
lapponicum	GKev
- Parviflorum Group	GGGa
'Lapwing' (K)	NLar SLdr
'Laramie'	GGGa
* ***laterifolium***	GGGa
'Lavender Brilliant' (EA)	SLdr
'Lavender Girl' 🏆H5	LMil NLar SLdr SReu SSta
'Lavendula'	SAko
'Le Progrès'	LMil LRHS
'Lea Rainbow'	MLea
'Ledifolium'	see *R.* × *mucronatum*
'Ledifolium Album'	see *R.* × *mucronatum*
'Lee's Dark Purple'	CAco LMil MJak
'Lee's Scarlet'	LMil
'Lemon Dream'	LMil LRHS MAsh MGos NHim NLar NPri NRHS SLim
* 'Lemon Drop' (A)	GGGa NHim
'Lemonora' (M)	CBcs GKin
'Lem's 45'	SLdr
'Lem's Cameo' 🏆H3	GGGa LMil LRHS NHim SReu SSta
'Lem's Monarch' 🏆H4	CBcs CDul GGGa LMil MLea MMuc SLdr SReu SSta
'Lem's Tangerine'	LMil
'Lemur' (EA)	GGGa LMil MLea NLar WThu
'Leni'	LRHS MAsh NRHS
'Leo' (EA)	SLdr
'Leo' (hybrid)	CMac
'Leonardslee Giles'	SLdr
'Leonardslee Primrose'	SLdr
'Leonore'	LMil
lepidostylum	CMac GGGa ITim LMil
lepidotum	GGGa
- var. ***album***	GGGa
- yellow-flowered McB 110	WThu
§ ***leptocarpum***	GGGa
§ 'Leucanthum'	GGGa WThu
leucaspis	CBcs SLdr
'Leuchtpolster'	SAko
'Lila Pedigo'	MMuc SLdr
'Lilac Time' (EA)	SLdr
'Lilactina'	SLdr
'Lily Marleen' (EA)	CTri
'Linda' 🏆H5	CMac EPfP GGGa LMil LSRN MAsh MJak MLea SCob SLdr
'Linda Stuart' (EA)	GGGa NHim
lindleyi	CPne GGGa LRHS MPkF NHim
- 'Geordie Sherriff'	GGGa
'Linearifolium'	see *R. stenopetalum* 'Linearifolium'
'Lingot d'Or' (A)	MPkF
'Lionel's First'	LMil
Lionel's Triumph Group	LMil
'Little Beauty' (EA)	SLdr
'Loch Arkaig'	GGGa

'Loch Awe'	GGGa LMil NHim
'Loch Earn'	GGGa
'Loch Faskally'	GGGa
'Loch Laggan'	GGGa NHim
'Loch Leven'	GGGa
'Loch Linnhe'	GGGa SReu
'Loch Lomond'	GGGa
'Loch Morar'	GGGa
lochiae (V)	GGGa
Lodauric Group	SLdr SReu
§ - 'Lodauric Iceberg'	LMil NHim SReu
'Lodbrit'	SReu
Loderi Group	SLdr
- 'Loderi Fairy Queen'	SLdr
- 'Loderi Game Chick'	LMil SLdr
- 'Loderi Georgette'	SLdr
- 'Loderi Helen'	LMil SLdr
§ - 'Loderi King George' 🏆H4	CBcs GGGa GKin LMil LRHS MLea SLdr SPer SReu SSta
- 'Loderi Patience'	SLdr
- 'Loderi Pink Coral'	LMil SLdr
- 'Loderi Pink Diamond' 🏆H4	LMil SLdr
- 'Loderi Pink Topaz'	SLdr
- 'Loderi Pretty Polly'	SLdr
- 'Loderi Princess Marina'	SLdr
- 'Loderi Sir Edmund'	LMil SLdr
- 'Loderi Sir Joseph Hooker'	SLdr
- 'Loderi Titan'	SLdr SReu SSta
- 'Loderi Venus' 🏆H4	LMil SLdr SReu SSta
- 'Loderi White Diamond'	SLdr
'Loder's White' 🏆H3	CMac LMil SReu SSta
longesquamatum	GGGa NHim
longipes	GGGa LMil
- EGM 336	LMil
- var. ***chienianum***	LMil
'Lord Roberts' 🏆H6	CAco CBcs CMac CSBt CTri ELan EPfP GGGa LCro LMil LOPS MAsh MGos MJak MLea MMuc NLar SLdr SLim SPer SReu SSta
'Louis Pasteur'	SCob SReu
'Louisa' (EA)	MAsh NLar
'Louise Dowdle' (Glenn Dale) (EA)	LMil SLdr
'Lovely William'	CMac LMil NLar SLdr
lowndesii	WAbe
'Lucy Lou'	GGGa
ludlowii	GGGa
'Lullaby' (EA)	SLdr
luteiflorum	GGGa NHim
lutescens	CBcs CMac CTsd LMil SLdr SReu
- 'Bagshot Sands' 🏆H3	GGGa LMil SLdr
- 'Exbury'	CExl
luteum (A)	Widely available
- 'Golden Comet' (A)	GGGa NHim
lyi	GGGa
* 'Mac Ovata'	CMac
macabeanum 🏆H3	GGGa GKev GKin LMil LRHS MLea NEgg SLdr SReu SSta
- NAPE 052	GGGa
- Reuthe's form	SReu
macabeanum* × *wardii	GGGa
macgregoriae (V)	GGGa
macranthum	see *R. indicum* 'Macranthum'
macrophyllum B&SWJ 9561	WCru
macrosmithii	see *R. argipeplum*
maculiferum	GGGa
'Madame Ad. van Hecke' (EA)	CTri GKin LMil MAsh MGos SLim

'Madame Albert van Hecke' (EA)	NLar SLdr
'Madame de Bruin'	SLdr
'Madame Galle'	SLdr
'Madame Masson' 🏆H6	CAco CDul CTri ELan LMil LRHS LSRN MAsh MGos MLea MMuc MPkF NLar NPri SPer SReu SSta
maddenii	CBcs LMil SAko
§ - subsp. ***crassum***	CBcs CExl CPne GGGa NHim
§ - subsp. ***maddenii*** Polyandrum Group	CBcs GGGa
'Madleen'	SAko
'Magic Flute' (EA)	LRHS MAsh
I 'Magic Flute' (V)	LMil NRHS SCoo
magnificum	GKev
magniflorum	GGGa
'Maharani'	GGGa
'Mai-ogi' (EA)	SAko
'Maischnee' (EA)	GGGa
'Maja' (G)	SReu SSta
Major Group	LMil
§ ***makinoi*** 🏆H5	GGGa LMil MMuc SReu SSta
- 'Fuju-kaku-no-matsu'	MGos
mallotum	GGGa LMil
'Manda Sue'	NLar
'Mandarin Lights' (A)	NLar
'Manderley'	LMil
maoerense	GGGa NHim
'Maraschino' (EA)	SAko
'Mardi Gras'	MGos NEgg
'Margaret Blain'	SReu
Margaret Dunn Group	CAco
'Maria Elena' (EA/d)	MGos NLar SLdr
'Marie Fortie'	MGos NLar
'Marie Hoffman'	LMil
'Marilee' (EA)	EPfP LRHS MAsh NLar SLdr
(Mariloo Group) 'Mariloo'	LMil
'Marinja' (EA)	LMil
'Marinus Koster'	SReu SSta
'Marion Street'	LMil
'Markeeta's Prize' 🏆H4	CAco EPfP GGGa LMil LRHS MAsh MGos MLea MMuc NHim NLar NPri SLdr SLim SReu
'Marlies' (A)	NLar
'Marmot' (EA)	MLea MMuc
'Marsalla'	LMil SAko
'Martha Isaacson' (Ad)	LMil MLea SLdr SReu
'Martha Wright'	EPfP GGGa MAsh NPri
martinianum	GGGa
'Maruschka' (EA) 🏆H5	GGGa LMil LRHS MAsh NLar SAko SPoG
'Mary Desby' (EA)	CEnd
'Mary Forte'	SCob
'Mary Helen' (Glenn Dale) (EA)	LMil LRHS MAsh MGos NLar NRHS SCoo SLdr SLim SReu
'Mary Poppins' (A)	GKin LMil LSRN MGos MPkF NLar SCoo SLdr SLim SPer WMoo
Matador Group	SReu
- 'Matador'	GGGa LMil SLdr
'Mathie' (A)	SReu SSta
maximum	GGGa
'Maxine Childers'	NHim
§ 'Maxwellii' (EA)	CMac SLdr
May Day Group	CBcs MGos
- 'May Day' 🏆H3	CMac MMuc SLdr
'Mayor Johnstone'	CTri EPfP MAsh NPri
meddianum	LMil
var. ***atrokermesinum*** F 2649	
Medusa Group	SLdr

	megacalyx	GGGa
	'Megan' (EA)	LSRN MAsh SLdr
	megaphyllum	see *R. basilicum*
	megeratum	GGGa
	- KR 9426 **new**	LMil
	- 'Bodnant'	GGGa ITim WAbe WThu
	mekongense	GCal
	- var. ***mekongense*** Rubroluteum Group	see *R. viridescens* Rubroluteum Group
	'Melford Lemon'	see *R.* 'Ilam Melford Lemon'
	'Melina' (EA/d)	LMil
	'Melrose Flash'	GGGa MPkF
	'Melville'	MPkF SSta
	'Merganser' ♀H4	CAco GGGa LMil NHim SLdr
	'Merlin' (Glenn Dale) (EA)	LMil
	METALLICA	see *R.* 'Hachmann's Metallica'
	metternichii	see *R. degronianum*
	var. ***pentamerum***	subsp. *degronianum*
	'Mi Amor'	GGGa LMil
	'Michael Hill' (EA)	CBcs MAsh
	'Michiko' (EA)	SAko
	micranthum	LMil LRHS
	microgynum	GGGa
	microleucum	see *R. orthocladum* var. *microleucum*
	micromeres	see *R. leptocarpum*
	'Midnight Beauty'	EPfP LMil LRHS SAko
	'Midnight Mystique'	GGGa SReu SSta
	'Midsummer'	MMuc SLdr
	'Midsummer Mermaid' (A)	LMil MAsh
	'Mikado' (EA)	see *R. kaempferi* 'Mikado'
	'Millennium Gold'PBR	LMil
	'Milton' (R)	LMil
	'Mimi' (Kaempferi) (EA)	CMac
	'Ming'	see *R.* 'Ilam Ming'
	miniatum CER 9927	GGGa
	minus	CBcs
	- var. ***minus*** (Carolinianum Group) 'Epoch'	LMil
	Mishmiense Group KR 10716 **new**	WPGP
	'Moerheim' ♀H5	CBcs ETMg LRHS MAsh MMuc NPri SLim
§	'Moerheim's Pink'	GGGa LMil SLdr
	(Mohamet Group) 'Mohamet'	LMil
	'Moidart' (Vs)	LMil NLar
	'Moira Salmon' (EA)	SLdr
§	***molle*** subsp. ***japonicum*** (A)	ESps LMil NEgg
	- subsp. ***molle*** (A)	LMil
	Mollis, orange-flowered (M)	GKin SRms
	- pink-flowered (M)	GKin SRms
	- red-flowered (M)	GKin
	- yellow-flowered (M)	GKin SRms
	'Molly Ann'	LSRN
	'Molten Gold' (v)	GGGa LMil LRHS MAsh
§	'Momoko' (EA)	GMcL LRHS WFar
	monanthum	GGGa
	monosematum	see *R. pachytrichum* var. *monosematum*
	'Monsieur Marcel Ménard' ♀H6	CBcs CDul EPfP GGGa LMil LRHS MAsh MGos NLar NPri SCob SLdr SReu SSta
	montroseanum	GGGa LMil SLdr
	- 'Benmore'	NHim
	'Moonstone' (EA) **new**	NHim
	Moonstone Group	CMac MLea
	- 'Moonstone Pink'	SLdr
	- 'Moonstone Yellow'	SLdr
§	'Morgenrot'	MMuc MPkF NLar

	morii	GGGa
	'Morning Cloud'	EPfP LRHS MAsh MGos NLar SLim SReu SSta
	MORNING RED	see *R.* 'Morgenrot'
	'Moser's Maroon'	CBcs GGGa LSRN MMuc MPkF NLar SLdr
	'Mother of Pearl'	SLdr
	'Mother's Day' (Kurume) (EA) ♀H4	CDul CMac CSBt CTri EPfP ESps GKin LCro LMil LOPS LRHS LSRN MAsh MGos MJak NEgg NLar NPri NRHS SCob SLdr SLim SPer SPoG SReu SSta WFar
§	***moulmainense***	CMCN
	'Mount Everest'	LMil LRHS SReu SSta
	'Mount Rainier' (A)	LRHS
	'Mount Saint Helens' (A)	LMil NHim NLar SLim SPer
	'Mount Seven Star'	see *R. nakaharae* 'Mount Seven Star'
	moupinense	GGGa SLdr
	- 'Fulmar'	GGGa
	'Mrs A.T. de la Mare' ♀H6	LMil SReu SSta
	'Mrs Betty Robertson'	CMac GBin SLdr
	Mrs C.Whitner Group	SLdr
	'Mrs Charles E. Pearson' ♀H6	CSBt LMil SLdr SReu SSta
	'Mrs Davies Evans'	LMil SReu SSta
	'Mrs Emil Hager' (EA)	SLdr
	'Mrs Furnivall' ♀H6	GGGa MLea SReu
	'Mrs G.W. Leak'	CSBt GGGa SReu
	'Mrs J.C. Williams' ♀H6	LMil
	'Mrs J.G. Millais'	LMil
	'Mrs James Horlick'	CAco
	'Mrs Lionel de Rothschild'	SReu
	'Mrs Marks'	LMil
	'Mrs P.D. Williams'	SReu
	'Mrs T.H. Lowinsky' ♀H6	CBcs CDul CMac GGGa GKin LMil LRHS MAsh MGos MLea MMuc NHim NLar SLdr SLim SPer SReu
§	× ***mucronatum*** (EA)	MPkF SLdr
	mucronulatum B&SWJ 786	WCru
	- B&SWJ 8657	WCru
	- var. ***albiflorum***	LMil SLdr
	- var. ***chejuense***	see *R. mucronulatum* var. *taquetii*
	- 'Cornell Pink' ♀H5	GGGa
§	- var. ***taquetii***	GGGa
	'Muffet' (EA) **new**	SLdr
	'Mulroy Cream'	LMil
§	***multiflorum*** var. ***purpureum***	GGGa
	'Mum'	LMil
	'Nabucco' (A)	EPfP GGGa MMuc NLar SLdr WMoo
	nakaharae (EA) ♀H5	SLdr SReu
	- 'Mariko' (EA)	EPot WAbe WThu
§	- 'Mount Seven Star' (EA) ♀H5	GGGa ITim LMil NWad SLdr WAbe WThu
§	- orange-flowered (EA)	LMil LRHS MAsh NRHS SLdr SReu
	- pink-flowered (EA)	MPkF SLdr SReu
	'Nakahari Orange'	see *R. nakaharae* orange-flowered
	'Nancy Evans' ♀H4	CSBt EPfP GGGa GKin LMil LRHS LSRN MAsh MGos MLea NLar NPri SLim SReu SSta
	'Nancy of Robinhill' (EA)	SReu
	'Nancy Waterer' (G) ♀H6	SReu
	'Nanki Poo' (EA)	SLdr
	'Naomi' (EA)	SLdr
	(Naomi Group) 'Exbury Naomi'	LMil
	- 'Naomi Nautilus'	LMil
	- 'Naomi Pink Beauty'	LMil
	- 'Naomi Stella Maris'	LMil

	'Narcissiflorum' (G/d) 🏆H6	GKin LMil LRHS MPkF NHim NLar SReu
	'Naselle'	LMil SReu
	'Ne Plus Ultra' (V)	GGGa
	NEGLIGÉ ('Hachneg'^{PBR}) (EA)	LMil
	neriiflorum	GGGa GKev LMil
	- CN&W 906	LMil
§	- subsp. ***phaedropum*** KR 9308 **new**	LMil
	'Newcomb's Sweetheart'	LMil
	'Niagara' (Glenn Dale) (EA) 🏆H5	CMac LMil SLdr
	'Nico' (EA)	CMac LMil LRHS MAsh
	'Nicola' (EA)	LSRN
	'Night Sky' 🏆H5	EPfP GGGa LMil LRHS MAsh MGos NLar SLdr
	'Nightingale'	SReu
	nigroglandulosum	GGGa NHim
	nipponicum	GGGa
	'Nishiki' (EA)	CMac
	nitens	see *R. calostrotum* subsp. *riparium* Nitens Group
	nitidulum var. ***omeiense***	GGGa WThu
	nivale subsp. ***boreale*** Ramosissimum Group	GGGa
§	- subsp. ***nivale***	ITim
	niveum 🏆H4	CPne GGGa IDee LMil SReu
	- B&SWJ 2611	WCru
	- B&SWJ 2659	WCru
	- B&SWJ 2675	WCru
	Nobleanum Group	GGGa LMil SLdr SSta
	- 'Nobleanum Coccineum'	CMac LMil SLdr SReu
	- 'Nobleanum Venustum'	CAco LMil SReu SSta
	Nobleanum Album Group	CMac GGGa LMil NHim SReu SSta
	(Norderney Group) 'Oudijk's Sensation'	MAsh MMuc SLdr
	'Nordlicht' (EA)	SLdr
	'Noriko' (EA)	SLdr
	'Norma' (R/d)	SReu
	'Northern Hi-Lights' (A)	GKin LMil LRHS MGos MPkF NHim NLar SLim SPer
	'Nova Zembla'	CAco CBcs CTri EPfP EUJe GGGa LCro LMil LOPS LRHS MAsh MGos MMuc MPkF NEgg NHim SCob SLim SPer SReu SSta
	'Nuccio's Blue Moon' (EA)	LMil SLdr
	nudiflorum	see *R. periclymenoides*
	nuttallii	GGGa LMil
	nymphaeoides CGG 14027	GGGa
	'Oban'	GEdr ITim NSla
	Obtusum Group (EA)	SLdr
	- 'Amoenum' (EA/d)	CBcs CMac CSBt CTsd ETMg LMil SLdr SPer
	- 'Amoenum Coccineum' (EA/d)	SLdr SReu SSta
§	- 'Hinomayo' (EA) 🏆H5	CMac CTri EPfP GKin LMil SLdr SReu
	occidentale (A)	CDul GKin LMil NHim SLdr
	- SIN 1830	GGGa
	- 'Crescent City Double'	NHim
	ochraceum 🏆H5	GGGa LMil
	- C&H 7042 **new**	LMil
	'Odee Wright'	CAco CTri LRHS MAsh
	'Odoratum' (Ad)	MLea
	'Oh! Kitty'	MLea
	'Oi-no-mezame' (Kurume) (EA)	SLdr
	'Old Port'	LMil
	oldhamii (EA) B&SWJ 3742	WCru
	'Olga' 🏆H5	LMil MPkF SReu SSta
	'Olga Niblett' (EA)	SReu SSta
	oligocarpum	GGGa
	'Opossum' (EA)	GGGa
	ORAKEL	see *R.* 'Hachmann's Orakel'
	'Orange Beauty' (Kaempferi) (EA)	CBcs GGGa MAsh SLdr SReu
	'Orange Bill' **new**	NHim
	'Orange King' (EA) 🏆H5	LMil MGos SLdr SPoG
	'Orangeade' (K)	LRHS MPkF
	orbiculare 🏆H5	GGGa LMil SLdr
§	- subsp. ***cardiobasis***	GGGa
	'Orchid Lights'	MAsh
	'Oregon' (EA)	SLdr
	Oregonia Group	LMil
	oreodoxa	LMil
§	- var. ***fargesii*** 🏆H6	GGGa LMil
	- var. ***oreodoxa***	GGGa LMil
	oreotrephes 🏆H4	LMil NHim
	- SDR 5027	GKev
	- 'Bluecalyptus'	GGGa
§	- Exquisitum Group	SLdr
	- 'Pentland'	GGGa LMil
	'Orion' ambig.	NLar
§	***orthocladum*** var. ***microleucum***	GGGa WThu
	'Osaraku Seedling' (EA)	EPfP LRHS MPkF
	'Osmar' 🏆H5	GGGa
	'Ostara'	CBcs
	'Oudijk's Favorite'	SLdr
§	***pachypodum***	GGGa
	pachysanthum 🏆H6	GGGa GKin LMil SLdr SReu
	- 'Crosswater'	LMil LRHS
	pachysanthum × ***yakushimanum***	SReu
	pachytrichum	GGGa
§	- var. ***monosematum***	NHim
	'Palestrina' (Vuykiana) (EA) 🏆H4	CBcs CDul CMac CSBt EPfP GKin MAsh MJak MMuc SLdr SPer SReu SSta
	paludosum	see *R. nivale* subsp. *nivale*
	'Pancake'	CMac
	'Panda' (EA) 🏆H5	CSBt CTri EPfP GGGa LMil LRHS MAsh MLea NHim SLdr SSta
	'Paprika Spiced'	MLea
	'Parfait' (EA)	LMil
	'Parkfeuer' (A)	GGGa
	parmulatum	LMil
	- KW 5876	LMil
	- 'Ocelot'	GGGa
	parryae AM (*roseatum*)	GGGa
	'Patty Bee' 🏆H5	CBcs CSBt CTri EPfP GEdr GGGa LMil LRHS MAsh MGos MLea NLar NPri NSla SLim SReu SSta
	'Peach Blossom'	see *R.* 'Saotome'
	'Pearl Betteridge'	LMil
	'Peep-bo' (EA)	SLdr
	'Peeping Tom'	SReu SSta
	'Peggy'	LMil
	pemakoense	GGGa WThu
	'Pemakofairy'	WThu
	pendulum	GGGa
	Penelope Group	SReu
	'Penheale Blue' 🏆H5	CTsd GKin LMil
	'Penjerrick'	GGGa
	'Penny Tomlin'	SReu SSta
	pentaphyllum (A)	GGGa
	'Peppermint Candy'	LMil
	'Peppina'	GGGa LMil

	'Percy Wiseman' ♀H5	CBcs CDul EPfP ESps GGGa GKin LCro LMil LOPS LRHS MAsh MGos MJak MLea NEgg NLar SCob SLdr SLim SPer SReu SSta
	'Perfect Lady'	NHim
§	***periclymenoides*** (A)	GGGa GKev LMil
	'Persil' (K) ♀H6	CBcs CSBt CTri ELan EPfP GGGa GKin LMil LRHS MAsh MJak MMuc NEgg NHim NLar SCoo SLdr SPer SReu SSta WFar
	'Peter Bee'	LMil NHim
	'Peter Chapell'	GGGa NHim
	'Peter Gable' (EA)	SLdr
	'Peter Koster' (hybrid)	GKin
	petrocharis	GGGa
	PETTICOAT ('Hachpett') (EA)	LMil
	'Pfauenauge'	GGGa
	phaedropum	see *R. neriiflorum* subsp. *phaedropum*
	phaeochrysum var. ***phaeochrysum*** C 12529	GGGa
	'Phalarope'	GEdr
	'Phyllis Korn'	LMil NLar SAko
§	***piercei***	GGGa LMil
	'Pine Marten' (EA)	GGGa
	pingianum	GGGa
	'Pink and Sweet' (A)	LRHS
	'Pink Bride'	SLdr
	'Pink Cameo'	CAco
	'Pink Cherub' ♀H6	LMil MAsh MLea
I	'Pink Delight' (K)	GKin MMuc
	'Pink Drift'	CSBt GEdr LMil NSla
	'Pink Gin'	LMil
	'Pink Mimosa' (Vs)	SLdr
	'Pink Pancake' (EA) ♀H4	EPfP GKin LMil LRHS MAsh MPkF NPri SLdr
	'Pink Pearl' (EA)	see *R.* 'Azuma-kagami'
	'Pink Pearl' (hybrid) ♀H4	CBcs CDul CMac CSBt CTri EPfP GGGa LCro LMil LOPS MAsh MMuc SLdr SPer SReu SSta
	'Pink Pebble' ♀H5	CExl ELon MAsh MLea
	'Pink Perfection'	CMac SLdr
	'Pink Polar Bear'	LMil
	'Pink Sunset' **new**	LMil
	'Pintail'	GGGa LMil LRHS MAsh
	'Pipit'	GGGa
	'Pippa' (EA)	CMac
	platypodum	LMil
	- CGG 14005	GGGa
	'Pleasant White' (EA)	LCro LMil LOPS NLar
	'Plover'	GGGa
	pocophorum var. ***pocophorum***	GGGa
	pogonostylum	see *R. irroratum* subsp. *pogonostylum*
	'Point Defiance'	MLea SPer
	'Polar Bear' (EA)	CAco SLdr
	Polar Bear Group	LMil MLea
	- 'Polar Bear'	CSBt GGGa GKin LMil LRHS SLdr SReu
	'Polaris' (EA)	MJak NLar
	'Polaris'	see *R.* 'Hachmann's Polaris'
	'Polarnacht'	CBcs GGGa LMil LRHS MPkF NLar SAko SLdr
	poluninii	GGGa
	- KR 8231	LMil
	polyandrum	see *R. maddenii* subsp. *maddenii* Polyandrum Group
§	***polycladum*** Scintillans Group	GGGa
	'Polyroy'	GGGa
	ponticum	CAco CDul CMac CTri ESps WFar
	- 'Filigran'	LMil
	- 'Roseum'	SGol
§	- 'Variegatum' (v)	CAco CMac EPfP ESps MAsh MGos NLar NPri SCob SLdr SPer SPoG SRms
	populare KC 0126	GGGa
	'Praecox' ♀H4	CBcs CSBt EPfP GGGa GKev GKin LCro LMil LOPS LRHS MAsh MGos MJak NLar NPri SLdr SLim SPoG SReu
	Praecox Group	MJak
	praestans	GGGa GKin LMil
	prattii	GGGa
	preptum	GGGa
	'President Roosevelt' (v)	CMac CSBt EPfP ESps GKin MAsh MJak MPkF NPri SLdr SPoG SReu SSta
	'Pridenjoy'	LMil LRHS
	primuliflorum ♀H5	WAbe
	- 'Doker-La'	GGGa LMil NHim WAbe
	'Prince Camille de Rohan'	LMil
	'Princess Alice'	CBcs IDee SLdr
	'Princess Anne' ♀H5	CBcs CMac ELon LCro LMil LOPS MAsh MGos MLea NHpl SLdr SLim SPer SPoG SReu SSta
	'Princess Margaret of Windsor' (K)	LMil
	principis	GGGa LMil
	- 'Lost Horizon'	LMil LRHS
	prinophyllum (A)	GGGa GKin LMil
	'Prins Bernhard' (EA)	MAsh SLdr
	'Prinses Juliana' (Vuykiana) (EA)	SLdr SReu
	'Prinses Máxima'	LMil
	pronum	GGGa
	- R.B. Cooke form	GGGa
	- Towercourt form	GGGa
	proteoides	GGGa NHim
	protistum	GCal GGGa
	pruniflorum	GGGa
	prunifolium (A)	GGGa LMil
	pseudochrysanthum ♀H5	GGGa LMil NHim SReu
	- dwarf	GGGa
	- - RWJ 9807	WCru
	pseudociliipes	CPne GGGa
	Psyche Group	see *R.* Wega Group
	'Ptarmigan' ♀H5	GEdr GGGa LMil WThu
	pudorosum	GGGa
	'Pulchrum Maxwellii'	see *R.* 'Maxwellii'
	pumilum	GGGa WAbe WThu
	- SDR 7413 **new**	GKev
	'Purple Cushion' (EA)	EPfP LMil LRHS MAsh NPri NRHS
	'Purple Diamond'	see *R.* Diamant Group purple-flowered
	'Purple Gem'	MGos
	'Purple Passion' PBR	LMil LRHS LSRN NLar SLdr SPer
	'Purple Queen' (EA/d)	MAsh
	'Purple Splendor' (Gable) (EA)	CMac SGol SLdr
	'Purple Splendour'	CBcs CSBt LMil MGos MLea MMuc NEgg SPer SReu SSta
	'Purple Triumph' (Vuykiana) (EA) ♀H5	LMil SLdr
	'Purpurtraum' (EA) ♀H5	LMil
	qiaojiaense NN 0903	GGGa LMil
	'Quail'	GGGa

'Queen Alice'	NLar
QUEEN EMMA	see *R.* 'Koningin Emma'
'Queen Mary'	SReu SSta
'Queen Souriya'	SReu
'Quentin Metsys' (R)	SReu
quinquefolium (A)	GGGa LMil SLdr
RABATZ ('Hachraba')	GGGa LMil SAko
racemosum ♀H4	LMil NHim
- BWJ 7811	WCru
- SDR 3336	GKev
- 'Rock Rose' ♀H5	EPfP LMil SLdr
'Racine' (G)	SReu
'Racoon' (EA)	GGGa
radicans	see *R. calostrotum* subsp. *keleticum* Radicans Group
'Raimunde' (K)	SAko
'Ramapo' ♀H6	GGGa LMil LRHS MAsh MGos NRHS SLdr SLim SPer SReu
'Ramster's Summer Pearl' **new**	LMil
'Ramster's Summer Pink' **new**	LMil
'Raphael de Smet' (G/d)	SReu
'Rasputin'	EUJe NHim SReu SSta
'Razorbill' ♀H4	GGGa GKin LMil NLar SLim
recurvoides	GGGa LMil SLdr SReu
- Keillour form	GGGa
'Red and Gold'	EPfP GGGa LRHS NPri
'Red Dawn'	LRHS MLea NRHS
'Red Delicious'	LMil SLdr
'Red Diamond'	see *R.* Diamant Group red-flowered
'Red Jack'	MGos MMuc SCob SPoG SReu SSta
'Red Panda' (EA)	GGGa
'Red Pimpernel' (EA)	SLdr
'Red Wood'	GGGa
'Redwing' ambig.	MAsh
'Redwings' (EA)	SLdr
'Reich's Signifikant'	SAko
Remo Group	CMac
'Rennie' (A)	GKin MMuc
'Renoir' ♀H5	CSBt LMil SReu
reticulatum (A)	LMil LRHS SReu
'Reuthe's Purple'	SReu WAbe WThu
'Rêve d'Amour' (Vs)	SReu SSta
Review Order Group	NHim
'Rex' (EA)	MAsh
rex ♀H4	GGGa GKev GKin LMil NHim SLdr
- EGM 295	LMil
- SDR 7924	GKev
§ - subsp. ***fictolacteum*** ♀H4	GGGa GKin LMil SLdr
rex* × *yakushimanum	SReu
'Rhododendronpark Graal-Müritz'	SReu SSta
'Ria Hardijzer' (Ad)	LMil
'Ribbon Candy' (A)	LRHS
rigidum	GGGa
- 'Album'	LMil
'Ring of Fire'	LMil MLea
'Ripe Corn'	LMil
ririei	GGGa
'Robert Croux'	SLdr
'Robert Seleger'	GGGa GKin LMil MAsh SReu
'Robert Whelan' (A)	SReu SSta
'Robin Hill Frosty' (EA)	SLdr
'Robin Hill Gillie' (EA)	SLdr
'Robinette'	MAsh
'Rocket'	CAco CTri LMil MAsh MGos MLea MMuc SLim SPer SPoG
'Roehr's Peggy Ann' (EA)	LMil

'Rokoko'	see *R.* 'Hachmann's Rokoko'
Rosalind Group	CMac
- 'Rosalind'	WFar
'Rosalinda' (EA)	SLdr
'Rosata' (Vs) ♀H5	GGGa GKin SReu SSta
'Rose Bud'	CSBt CTri WThu
'Rose Elf'	WThu
'Rose Glow' (A)	SReu SSta
'Rose Gown'	SReu
'Rose Greely' (Gable) (EA) ♀H5	NLar SLim SPer SReu
'Rose Haze' (Vs)	SReu SSta
'Rosebud' (EA/d)	CMac SLdr SReu SSta
'Rosemary Hyde' (EA)	SLdr
roseum	see *R. canescens*
'Roseum Elegans'	CAco LCro LMaj LOPS LRHS MAsh MMuc NLar SCob SLim
ROSINETTA ('Hachrosi') (EA)	LMil
'Rosy Dream'	MAsh MMuc
'Rosy Fire' (A)	LMil SReu
'Rosy Lea'	MLea
rothschildii	GGGa LMil SLdr
rousei (V)	GGGa
roxieanum	GGGa LMil
§ - var. ***cucullatum***	GGGa
- var. ***oreonastes*** ♀H5	GGGa LMil
- - Nymans form	SReu
- var. ***parvum***	GGGa
'Royal Command' (K)	CBcs CTri GKin LMil
'Royal Lodge' (K)	LRHS MPkF
'Royal Windsor'	LMil
'Roza Stevenson'	SLdr
'Rubicon'	GGGa SLdr
rubiginosum ♀H4	GGGa LMil
- pink-flowered	LMil
rubroluteum	see *R. viridescens* Rubroluteum Group
'Ruby Hart'	GGGa LSRN
RUBY WEDDING	see *R.* 'Firestorm'
rude	see *R. glischrum* subsp. *rude*
rufum	GGGa
rugosum Sinclair 240 (V)	GGGa
rushforthii	GGGa
russatum ♀H5	GGGa LMil SLdr
- blue-black-flowered	LMil
Russautinii Group	SLdr
russotinctum	see *R. alutaceum* var. *russotinctum*
'Rwain'	LMil NLar
'Sabina' (EA)	SLdr
'Sacko'	GGGa LMil NLar SLim
'Saffron Queen'	CBcs CTsd LMil MPkF
'Sahara' (K)	SLdr
'Saint Breward'	MLea
'Saint Kew'	SLdr
'Saint Merryn' ♀H5	CBcs GEdr MJak
'Saint Tudy'	SLdr
'Saint Valentine' (V)	GGGa
'Sakata Red' (EA)	SLdr
'Salmon Sander' (EA)	SLdr
'Salmon's Leap' (EA/v)	CMac ELan LMil LRHS MAsh SReu SSta
saluenense	LMil SLdr WThu
'Sammetglut'	CAco
'Samuel Taylor Coleridge' (M)	GKin
sanguineum	LMil
§ - subsp. ***didymum***	GGGa SLdr
- subsp. ***sanguineum*** var. ***haemaleum***	GGGa LMil

	– – var. ***sanguineum*** F 25521	LMil
	'Santa Maria' (EA) ♀H5	GMcL LMil LSRN NLar SReu SSta
	santapaui (V)	GGGa
§	'Saotome' (EA)	SLdr
	'Sapphire'	GMcL
	'Sappho'	CAco CBcs CDul CMac GGGa GKin LMil LRHS MLea MPkF NEgg NLar SLdr SPer SReu SSta
	sargentianum	GGGa WAbe WThu
	– 'Whitebait'	ITim NHim
	(Sarled Group) 'Sarled' ♀H5	GGGa ITim LMil NHim WThu
	'Satan' (K) ♀H6	LMil LRHS NLar SReu SSta
	Satsuki Group (EA)	ITim SLdr
	– 'Gumpo Pink' (EA)	SLdr
	– 'Gumpo Pink & White' (EA)	SLdr
	– 'Gumpo White' (EA)	LRHS MAsh NHim NRHS SPoG
	– white-flowered (EA) **new**	NHim
	'Saturnus' (M)	GKin
§	***scabrifolium*** var. ***spiciferum***	CMac SLdr
	'Scarlet Wonder' ♀H5	CBcs CDul CSBt EPfP GEdr GGGa GKev GKin LMil LRHS MAsh MGos MJak MMuc NHpl NPri SPer SReu
	schlippenbachii (A)	CBcs CMCN CPne GGGa LMil SLdr
	'Schneekrone' ♀H6	GGGa LMil
	SCHNEEPERLE ('Hachschnee') (EA) ♀H5	LMil LRHS
	'Schneespiegel'	GGGa
	scintillans	see *R. polycladum* Scintillans Group
	'Scintillation' ♀H6	ELan GGGa LMil MAsh MGos MLea MMuc NHim NLar SLdr SPer
	scopulorum	GGGa SLdr
	'Scotian Bells'	GGGa
	scottianum	see *R. pachypodum*
	'Scottish Marmalade'	GGGa
	'Scout' (EA)	MAsh SLdr
	scyphocalyx	see *R. dichroanthum* subsp. *scyphocalyx*
	searsiae	NHim
	'Seaview Sunset'	GGGa MGos
	'Second Honeymoon'	MLea
	seinghkuense	GGGa LMil
	– CCH&H 8106	LMil
	selense subsp. ***jucundum***	GGGa
	semibarbatum	NHim
	semnoides	GGGa LMil
	'Sennocke'	LMil
	'September Red'	LMil
	'September Song' ♀H4	GGGa LMil MAsh MLea
	serotinum	GGGa IDee LMil LRHS
	serpyllifolium (A)	CBcs CTsd NHim
	Seta Group	SReu
	'Seven Stars'	NHim
	'Shamrock' ♀H5	ELon EPfP GEdr LRHS MAsh MGos MLea NEgg NSla SLim SPoG WThu
	'Sheila' (EA)	CSBt MAsh NPri
	'Shelley' (EA)	LMil LSRN
	shepherdii	see *R. kendrickii*
	sherriffii	GGGa
	'Shiko' (EA)	MAsh
	'Shiko Lavender' (A)	SPoG
	Shilsonii Group	LMil
	'Shin-sekai' (Kurume) (EA/d)	SLdr
	'Show Girl' (EA) **new**	NHim
	'Shrimp Girl'	GKin

	sichotense	NHim
	sidereum	CPne GCal GGGa
	siderophyllum	GGGa NHim
	sikangense	GGGa
	– SDR 7932	GKev
	– var. ***exquisitum***	GGGa GKev
§	'Silberwolke' ♀H6	LMil MAsh
	SILVER CLOUD	see *R.* 'Silberwolke'
	'Silver Edge'	see *R. ponticum* 'Variegatum'
	'Silver Glow' (EA)	CMac
	'Silver Jubilee' ♀H4	LMil
	'Silver Moon' (Glenn Dale) (EA)	SLdr
	'Silver Queen' (EA)	MPkF SPoG
	'Silver Sixpence'	EPfP LRHS LSRN MJak MLea MMuc SLdr
	'Silver Skies'	LMil
	'Silver Slipper' (K) ♀H6	CBcs GKin LCro LMil LOPS MLea SReu SSta WFar
	'Silver Sword' (EA/v)	EPfP SPoG
	'Silverwood' (A)	LMil
	'Silvester' (Kurume) (EA)	CTri GMcL LMil LRHS MAsh SLdr SReu
	'Simona'	SAko
	simsii (EA)	CMac SLdr
	sinofalconeri	GGGa LMil NHim
	– KR 7342	LMil
	– NJM 09.137 **new**	WPGP
	– SEH 229	LMil
	sinogrande ♀H3	ELon GCal GGGa GKev GKin LMil NEgg
	– APA 106	GGGa
	– KR 4027	LMil
§	'Sir Charles Butler'	LMil
	'Sir Charles Lemon' ♀H3	CBcs GGGa LMil MAsh
	'Sir Robert' (EA)	MAsh
	'Sleeping Beauty'	WAbe
	'Sleepy'	CBcs MAsh MLea
	smirnowii	GGGa IDee LMil LRHS
	smithii	see *R. argipeplum*
	'Sneezy' ♀H5	CBcs EPfP GGGa IRob LCro LMil LOPS LRHS MAsh MGos MJak MMuc MPkF SLdr SLim SSta
	'Snipe'	CTri GEdr LMil LRHS MAsh MGos MMuc NLar NRHS SLdr SLim SPer SReu WThu
	'Snow Crown' (*lindleyi* hybrid)	MAsh
	'Snow Hill' (EA) ♀H5	CEnd LMil
	'Snow Lady'	CBcs CTsd EPfP GEdr GKin MAsh SLdr SReu
	'Snow Pearl'	EPfP MAsh NPri
	Snow Queen Group	LMil SReu
	– 'Snow Queen'	LMil
	'Snowbird' (A)	CDul CTho
	'Snowflake' (EA/d)	see *R.* 'Kure-no-yuki'
	'Snowstorm'	MLea
	'Snowwhite' (EA)	MGos NLar SLdr
	'Soir de Paris' (Vs) ♀H6	CEnd CSBt GGGa GKin LMil SReu SSta WFar
	'Soldier Sam'	SReu
	(Solent Group) 'Drury Lane' (K)	LMil
	'Solidarity'	CAco CBcs MLea SLdr SReu SSta
	'Solway' (Vs)	LMil
	'Sonata'	GGGa NHim SReu
	'Sonatine'	LMil LRHS
	'Songbird'	GEdr LMil SLdr
	sororium (V)	LMil
	– KR 3085	LMil

	souliei	LMil
	- deep pink-flowered	GGGa
	'Souvenir de D.A. Koster'	SLdr
	'Souvenir de Doctor S. Endtz'	SReu
	'Souvenir of Anthony Waterer'	SReu SSta
	'Souvenir of W.C. Slocock'	MMuc NLar
	'Spek's Orange' (M)	GKin
	sperabile	GGGa
	sphaeranthum	see *R. trichostomum*
	sphaeroblastum	GGGa
	- var. ***wumengense***	GGGa
	spiciferum	see *R. scabrifolium* var. *spiciferum*
	spilotum	NHim
	'Spinner's Glory'	MAsh
	spinuliferum	CBcs GGGa
	'Spitfire'	SReu SSta
	'Spring Beauty' (EA)	SReu
	'Spring Morning'	SReu SSta
	'Spring Pearl'	see *R.* 'Moerheim's Pink'
	'Spring Rose'	SLdr
	'Spring Sunshine'	LMil
	'Squirrel' (EA) ♀H5	GGGa GKin GMcL LMil MAsh MLea NLar SLdr SLim SReu
	'Stadt Essen'	LMil SLdr
	'Stadt Westerstede'	LMil
	stamineum	GGGa
§	'Stanway'	LMil
	'Starbright Champagne'	MAsh SReu SSta
	'Statuette'	SAko
	stenaulum	see *R. moulmainense*
§	***stenopetalum***	CBcs CMac GBin LMil MPkF NHim
	'Linearifolium' (EA)	SLdr
	stenophyllum	see *R. makinoi*
	stewartianum	CPne GGGa
	'Stewartstonian' (EA)	CMac LCro LOPS SReu
	'Stoat' (EA)	NLar
	Stonefield hybrids	ESps
	'Stopham Girl' (A)	LMil
	'Stopham Lad' (A)	LMil
	'Strategist'	SLdr
	'Strawberry Cream'	EPfP GGGa LRHS
	'Strawberry Ice' (K) ♀H6	CBcs CDul CSBt ELan EPfP GGGa GKin MMrt SReu
	'Strawberry Sundae'	MLea MMuc NEgg SLdr
	strigillosum	GGGa
	- Reuthe's form	SReu
	subansiriense	GGGa NHim
	suberosum	see *R. yunnanense* Suberosum Group
	'Suga-no-ito' (Kurume) (EA)	SLdr
	'Summer Blaze' (A)	SLdr
	'Summer Dawn'	LMil
	'Summer Flame'	SReu
	'Summer Fragrance' (A) ♀H6	LMil SReu SSta
	'Summer Snow'	SAko
	'Summer Sorbet'	LMil
	'Summer Sunshine' (A) **new**	NHim
	'Summer Wind'	GGGa
	'Sun Chariot' (K)	CBcs
	'Sun Star' (EA)	GGGa
I	'Sun Star' (A) **new**	LMil
	Sunkist Group	SLdr
	'Sunset Pink' (K)	CDul
	'Sunspray'	SReu SSta
	'Sunte Nectarine' (K) ♀H6	GKin NLar
	suoilenhensis	CMCN
	- NVD 18	GGGa
	'Surprise' ambig. (EA)	CTri SLdr
	'Surprise' B.Y. Morrison (EA)	LMil
	'Surrey Heath'	CBcs EPfP LMil LRHS MGos MJak MMuc SLdr SLim SPer
	'Susan' (EA)	NLar SSta
	'Susan' J.C. Williams	LMil SReu
	'Susannah Hill' (EA)	SLdr
	sutchuenense	GGGa LMil
	- var. ***geraldii***	see *R.* × *geraldii*
	'Swamp Beauty'	MLea MMuc SLdr
	'Swansong' (EA)	CMac
	'Swift' ♀H4	EPfP GEdr GGGa LMil LRHS MAsh MMuc NRHS
	'T.S. Black' (EA)	SLdr
	taggianum	GGGa
	'Talavera'	LMil NHim
	taliense	LMil
	- SBEC 0350	GGGa
	- 'Honigduft'	LMil NLar
	Tally Ho Group	LMil
	TANAGER	see *R.* 'Glendoick Tanager'
	'Tangerine'	see *R.* (Fabia Group) 'Fabia Tangerine'
	tapetiforme	GGGa
	'Taurus' ♀H5	CAco CBcs GKin LMil LRHS MAsh MLea MMuc SAko SLdr SReu
	taxifolium (V)	GGGa
	'Teal'	GEdr
	'Ted Millais'	LMil
	'Teddy Bear'	LMil MLea NHim SReu SSta
	Temple Belle Group	GEdr NHim SLdr
	'Teniers' (R)	SReu
§	***tephropeplum***	CPne GGGa
	- Deleiense Group	see *R. tephropeplum*
	'Tequila Sunrise'	LRHS NLar
I	'Tequila Sunrise' USA	LMil
	'Terracotta'	LMil LRHS NLar
	'Terra-cotta Beauty' (EA)	NWad WThu
	(Tessa Group) 'Tessa'	CMac
	thayerianum	GGGa
§	'The Honourable Jean Marie de Montague' ♀H4	GGGa GKin LMil MAsh MGos MLea MMuc NHim NLar SPer SReu SSta
	'The Marquis of Lansdowne' **new**	LMil
	'Thingy KS' **new**	NHim
	'Thomas David' (A)	LMil
	thomsonii	GGGa GKin LMil SReu
	- B&SWJ 2638	WCru
	- subsp. ***lopsangianum***	GGGa
	'Thor'	GGGa SReu
	'Thunderstorm'	SReu
	'Tibet'	LMil
	'Tidbit' ♀H3	CMac GGGa LMil MLea SLdr
	'Tinkerbird'	EPfP GGGa LMil MAsh MGos NHim NLar NPri SPer
	'Tinner's Blush'	CBcs
	titapuriense	GGGa
	'Titian Beauty'	CBcs CSBt ELan EPfP GGGa LMil LRHS MAsh MGos MMuc NEgg NLar NRHS SAko SLim SPer SPoG
	'Titness Park'	LMil
	'Tit-Willow' (EA)	LRHS MAsh NRHS SCoo
	tomentosum	WThu
	'Too Bee'	GEdr
	'Torchlight' (EA) ♀H5	LMil MGos SLdr
	'Toreador' (EA)	SLdr
	'Torridon' (Vs)	LMil
	Tortoiseshell Group	NLar SCob
	- 'Champagne' ♀H3	CBcs CSBt LMil MAsh NLar NPri SLdr SPer SReu

	- 'Tortoiseshell Orange' ♀^{H3}	CBcs CDul CSBt LMil LRHS MGos MPkF NLar SCob SLim SPer SReu SSta
	- 'Tortoiseshell Salome'	NHim
	- 'Tortoiseshell Wonder' ♀^{H3}	EPfP LMil LRHS MAsh
	'Toucan' (K)	CSBt LMil LRHS MPkF
	'Tower Dainty' (A)	GGGa
	'Tower Daring' (A)	GGGa
	'Tower Dragon' (A)	LMil
	traillianum	LMil
	'Tree Creeper'	GGGa GKin LMil LRHS SLdr
	'Tregedna Red'	SReu
	'Trewithen Orange'	SLdr
	trichanthum	GGGa
	- 'Honey Wood'	LMil NHim SLdr
	trichocladum	CPne GKev
§	***trichostomum***	GGGa WAbe
	- Ledoides Group	LMil
	- pink-flowered **new**	NHim
	triflorum	GGGa LMil
§	- var. ***bauhiniiflorum***	CMac
	- var. ***triflorum*** Mahogani Group	GGGa
	trilectorum	CPne GGGa
	triplonaevium	see *R. alutaceum* var. *russotinctum* Triplonaevium Group
	'Tromba'	GGGa LMil SAko
	tsangpoense	see *R. charitopes* subsp. *tsangpoense*
	tsariense	CPne GGGa LMil NHim
	- var. ***trimoense***	LMil
	- - KW 8288	LMil
	aff. ***tsariense***	CPne
	tubiforme	see *R. glaucophyllum* subsp. *tubiforme*
	'Tuffet' (EA)	LMil SLdr
	'Tunis' (K)	EPfP MAsh NPri
	'Turnstone'	GGGa NHim
	ungernii	GGGa
§	***uniflorum*** var. ***imperator***	GGGa
	'Unique' (G)	EPfP GGGa MMuc SPer
	'Unique' (*campylocarpum* hybrid)	MAsh SLdr SReu
	'Unique Marmalade'	MLea
	uvariifolium	GKev
	SDR 5149 **new**	
	- 'Reginald Childs'	IDee LMil
	valentinianum	GGGa SLdr WAbe
	- var. ***oblongilobatum***	GGGa
	'Van'	LMil LRHS MGos NHim NLar SLim
	'Van Houttei Flore Pleno' (G/d)	SReu
	'Van Nes Sensation'	LMil
	Vanessa Group	LMil
	- 'Vanessa Pastel' ♀^{H3}	CMac GGGa LMil NHim SReu SSta
	vaseyi (A) ♀^{H5}	CBcs GGGa LMil
	- 'White Find'	GGGa
	- white-flowered (A)	LMil
	'Vayo' (EA)	SLdr
§	***veitchianum*** Cubittii Group	CBcs GGGa
	- 'Doi Inthanon'	GGGa
	venator	GGGa NHim
	'Venetia' (K)	SReu SSta
	'Venetian Chimes'	MJak
	vernicosum	GGGa
	vernicosum × ***wardii*** SDR 5026	GKev
	'Vida Brown' (Kurume) (EA/d)	CMac SLdr SReu WThu
	'Vinecourt Dream' (M)	GKin NLar SLdr
	'Vinecourt Duke' (A/d)	GKin MMuc NEgg NLar
	'Vineland Dream' (K/d)	GKin
	'Vintage Rosé' ♀^{H5}	LMil MMuc SSta
	'Violetta' (Glenn Dale) (EA)	SLdr
	'Violette Funken'	LMil
	'Virginia Richards'	MAsh SCob SLdr
	viridescens 'Doshong La'	GGGa LMil NHim
§	- Rubroluteum Group	SLdr
	viscidifolium	GGGa
	viscosum (A) ♀^{H6}	CBcs CMac CTho GGGa LMil LRHS MGos MMrt MMuc NLar SLdr SPer SReu
	- 'Grey Leaf' (Vs)	LMil
	- f. ***rhodanthum*** (A)	LMil
	- 'Roseum' (Vs)	LMil
	'Viscount Powerscourt'	SLdr
	'Viscy' ♀^{H5}	CDul GKin LMil LRHS MMuc SLdr
§	Volker Group	EPfP LMil LRHS MAsh NLar NRHS
§	- 'Babette'	LMil
	'Vollblut'	SReu SSta
	'Vulcan' ♀^{H4}	GGGa LMil LRHS MLea SCob
	'Vuyk's Rosyred' (Vuykiana) (EA) ♀^{H4}	CBcs CDul CMac CTri GKin LMil MAsh NWad SLdr SPer SPoG SReu WFar
	'Vuyk's Scarlet' (Vuykiana) (EA) ♀^{H4}	CBcs CDul CMac CSBt CTri CTsd ESps GKin LRHS MAsh NHim NPri NRHS NWad SLdr SPer SPlb SReu SSta
	'W B I'	SReu
	'W.E. Gumbleton' (M)	SReu
	'W.F.H.' ♀^{H3}	LMil SLdr
	'Wagtail'	GGGa
	WALKÜRE ('Hachwalk')	LMil LRHS
	wallichii	GGGa LMil NHim
	- Heftii Group	GGGa
	'Wallowa Red' (A)	MMuc MPkF
	'Wally Miller'	MAsh
	walongense	GGGa
	'Walter's Pinwheel' (EA)	GGGa
	'Wanna Bee'	LMil
	wardii	GGGa LMil LRHS NHim
	- L&S 5679	GGGa SLdr
	- var. ***puralbum***	GGGa
	'Ward's Ruby' (EA)	SLdr
	wasonii	LMil
	- yellow-flowered	GGGa
	'Water Baby' (A)	LMil
	'Water Girl' (A)	GGGa LMil
	'Waterfall'	SLdr
	watsonii	NHim
	var. ***wenchuanense*** C 5046 **new**	
	'Wee Bee' ♀^{H5}	CBcs EPfP GEdr GKin GMcL LMil MAsh MGos MJak MLea NLar SAko SLim SReu SSta WThu
§	Wega Group	SLdr
	'Weinlese'	SAko
	'Wendy'	MAsh
	'Westminster' (O)	LMil
	'Weston's Pink Diamond' (d)	LMil
	'What a Dane'	GGGa
	'Whidbey Island'	LMil NHim
	'Whisperingrose'	GMcL LMil
	'White Brocade'	SReu SSta
§	WHITE DUFTHECKE ('Rhodunter 48'^{PBR})	LMil
	'White Frills' (EA)	LRHS MPkF SLdr
	'White Glory'	SLdr

'White Gold'	GGGa
'White Jade' (EA)	SLdr
'White Lady' Indian (EA)	SLdr
'White Lights' (A) 🏆^{H7}	CTri SAko
'White Pearl' (EA)	LSRN
'White Perfume' (A)	SReu SSta
'White Prince' (EA/d)	MPkF
'White Rosebud' (EA)	SReu SSta
'White Swan' (hybrid)	LMil SReu
'White Wings'	SLdr
'Whitestone'	GGGa SReu SSta
'Whitethroat' (K/d) 🏆^{H6}	EPfP IRob LMil LRHS MMrt MMuc NHim SReu SSta
'Whitney's Dwarf Red'	MMuc
'Whitney's Orange' **new**	SLdr
'Wigeon'	LMil NHim
wightii	GGGa
'Wild Ginger'	GGGa
'Wilgen's Ruby'	CSBt MGos SLdr SLim SPer
'Wilgen's Surprise'	SCob
'Willbrit'	CBcs MAsh MMuc SLdr
'William Fortescue' **new**	LMil
williamsianum 🏆^{H4}	CMac GGGa GMcL LMil MLea NHim SLdr SReu
- Caerhays form	CExl
'Willy' (Kaempferi) (EA)	LMil SLdr
wiltonii 🏆^{H5}	GGGa LMil NHim
'Wind River' **new**	NHim
'Windsor Lad'	SReu
'Wine and Roses'^{PBR}	CBcs GGGa
Winsome Group	CMac GGGa MAsh
- 'Winsome' 🏆^{H3}	CBcs GKin MGos NLar NPri SLdr SSta
'Winston Churchill' (M)	SReu SSta
'Winter Spice'	GGGa
'Witchery'	GGGa
'Wombat' (EA) 🏆^{H5}	CTri EPfP GGGa LMil LRHS MAsh MGos NHim NLar NPri SLdr SReu
wongii	CMac GGGa
'Woodcock'	SLdr
'Wren' 🏆^{H5}	GEdr GGGa GMcL LMil MAsh MLea SReu WThu
xanthocodon	see *R. cinnabarinum* subsp. *xanthocodon*
xanthostephanum	GGGa
'XXL'	SReu SSta
'Yaku Angel'	LMil SAko
'Yaku Incense'	LMil MAsh MLea MMuc
'Yaku Prince'	MAsh MLea MMuc SLdr
yakushimanum 🏆^{H5}	CBcs ESps GKin LMil MAsh MLea SArc SLdr SPer SReu SSta
- from Exbury	CMac SReu
- FCC form	see *R. yakushimanum* 'Koichiro Wada'
§ - 'Koichiro Wada' 🏆^{H6}	CExl CMac ELan GGGa IDee LMil LRHS NHim NLar SAko SLdr SReu
- 'Schneekissen'	SAko
yaoshanense	GGGa
'Yellow Hammer' 🏆^{H4}	CAco CBcs CMac ELan GGGa GKin NLar SLdr
Yellow Hammer Group	SPer SReu SSta
'Yellow Petticoats'	SReu SSta
yuefengense	GGGa LMil NHim
yunnanense	GGGa GKev LMil
- SDR 4217	GKev
- SDR 4957	GKev
- SDR 4960	GKev
- 'Openwood' 🏆^{H3}	LMil NHim
- pink-flowered	GGGa
- 'Red Throat'	SLdr
- red-blotched	LMil
§ - Suberosum Group	SLdr
- white-flowered	GGGa
zaleucum	CBcs GGGa LMil SLdr
- Flaviflorum Group	GGGa
zeylanicum	see *R. arboreum* subsp. *zeylanicum*

Rhodohypoxis ✿ (*Hypoxidaceae*)

'1000 Cranes'	CTal IBal LEdu
'Alice'	CTal
'Andromeda'	CTal EWes IBal
'Ann Brazier'	NWad
'Annelies'	CTal
baurii 🏆^{H4}	CAvo CCCN CPne IBal IRob LRHS NSla SPoG WAbe WAvo
- 'Alba'	CTal EWes IBal IRob LRHS NRHS WFar
- 'Albrighton'	CTal CTri EWes GEdr NHpl NWad WAbe
- 'Apple Blossom'	CTal EWes GKev IBal IRob ITim LBee LEdu NWad SRot WFar
- 'Badger'	CTal ITim NWad
- var. ***baurii***	EWes LRHS
- 'Bridal Bouquet' (d)	CTal EWes GEdr IBal WFar
- 'Caro'	CTal EWes
- 'Charlotte'	EWes
- 'Coconut Ice'	CTal EWes IBal LEdu
- var. ***confecta***	CElw CPbh CTal EWes GEdr IBal IRob WFar WTor
- 'Daphne Mary'	EWes
- 'David Scott'	EWes
- 'Dawn'	CAby CPla CTal EWes GEdr GKev IBal SDys WAbe
- 'Douglas'	CTal EPfP EWes GEdr GKev IBal LEdu NHpl WAvo WPGP
- 'Dulcie'	CTal EWes GEdr IBal
- 'Emily Peel'	CTal EWes GKev IBal ITim
- 'Eva-Kate'	CTal EWes IBal ITim
- 'Fred Broome'	CTal EWes GEdr GKev IBal LEdu NWad WFar
- 'Goliath'	CTal EWes IBal
- 'Harlequin'	CAby CTal EWes GEdr IBal IRob ITim NWad SRot
§ - 'Helen'	CTal EWes GEdr IBal IRob LEdu NHpl WAbe WPGP
- 'Jacqueline Potterton'	CTal
- 'Jeanette'	EWes IBal
- 'Kitty'	CTal EWes IBal WFar
- 'Komadori'	CTal
- 'Lily Jean' (d)	CAby CPla CTal CTri EPfP EWes GEdr GKev IBal ITim LRHS NHpl NWad XEll
- 'Luna'	EWes
- 'Margaret Rose'	CTal EWes GKev IBal
- 'Mars'	CTal EWes IBal LEdu LRHS NRHS WFar WPGP
- 'Monique'	EWes
- 'Pearl'	CTal LRHS
- 'Pearl' × ***thodiana***	CTal
- 'Perle'	EWes GEdr IBal IRob NWad
- 'Picta' (v)	CTal EWes GKev IBal LEdu NHpl NWad
- 'Pink Pearl'	CTal EWes IBal WAbe
- var. ***platypetala***	CTal CWCL EPfP EWes GEdr GKev IBal IRob NHpl NWad WAvo XEll
- - Burtt 6981	EWes
- var. ***platypetala*** × ***milloides***	IBal LLHF NWad
- 'Rebecca'	EWes
- 'Red King'	CTal EWes IBal

- red-flowered	SPlb
- 'Ruth'	ELon EWes GEdr GKev IBal IRob SDeJ
- 'Susan Garnett-Botfield'	CTal EWes GEdr IBal LRHS NHpl WAbe
- 'Tetra Pink'	CAby EWes GEdr IBal NWad
- 'Tetra Red'	CTal EWes GEdr GKev IBal NWad SDeJ SRot WFar
- 'The Bride'	EWes GEdr
- white-flowered	LRHS
baurii* × *milloides	SRot
'Betsy Carmine'	CCCN CTal GEdr IBal NWad WAbe WFar
'Bright Eyes' (d)	EWes
'Burgundy'	CTal IBal
'Butterfly Wings'	CTal NWad
'Candy Stripe'	CTal EWes GEdr NWad
'Carina'	CTal EWes
'Caroline'	EWes IBal WFar
'Cathy'	CTal EWes IBal
'Confusion'	CTal EWes LEdu NHpl NWad WAbe
'Dainty Dee' (d)	EWes
deflexa	CMen CPbh CTal EPot EWes GKev IBal IRob ITim LEdu LRHS NHpl NRHS NSla NWad WAbe WFar WPGP WTor
- 'Janette'	CTal
'Donald Mann'	CTal EWes GEdr IBal ITim LLHF SRot
'Drakensberg Dusk'	CTal
'Dusky'	CTal EWes GEdr GKev IBal
'E.A. Bowles'	CTal EWes IBal NHpl NRHS NSla WFar
'Ellicks'	CTal IBal
'Flashing Ruby'	CTal GEdr IBal
'Forge Robies'	EWes
'Garnett'	EWes IBal WAbe WFar
'Gemma'	EWes
'Goya' (d)	CAby IBal NHpl
'Great Scot'	EWes GEdr GKev IBal NHpl
'Heather'	CTal
'Hebron Farm Biscuit'	see *Hypoxis parvula* var. *albiflora* 'Hebron Farm Biscuit'
'Hebron Farm Cerise'	see × *Rhodoxis* 'Hebron Farm Cerise'
'Hebron Farm Pink'	see × *Rhodoxis hybrida* 'Hebron Farm Pink'
'Hinky Pinky'	GEdr
'Holden Rose' (d)	CTal IBal NWad WFar
'Hope' (d)	CTal IBal
'Indy'	IBal
'Jap Double'	CTal
'Jupiter'	CTal GEdr NWad
'Kiwi Joy' (d)	CMen CTal EWes GEdr GKev IBal LLHF NHpl NWad SDeJ
'Knockdolian Red'	GEdr IBal NWad WFar
'Lily Fan'	CTal
'Lisette'	EWes
'Louise'	CTal IBal
'Midori'	CTal EWes GEdr IBal NWad SDys
milloides	CAby CMen CPbh CPla CPne CTal CWCL EPot EWes GEdr IBal IRob ITim LBee LEdu LRHS NHpl NRHS NWad WFar WPGP XEll
- 'Claret'	CAby CElw CMen CSam CTal ELon EWes GEdr GKev IBal IRob ITim LLHF LRHS SDys SRot WFar WTor
- 'Claudia' **new**	CRos NRHS
- 'Damask'	CTal EWes GKev IBal LRHS SDys SRot
- 'Donaldson'	CTal SRot
- 'Drakensberg Snow'	CTal EWes
- giant	CMen
- pink-flowered	CMen
- 'Susan'	EWes
'Monty'	EWes GEdr IBal NWad WAbe
'Mystery'	EWes IBal
'Naomi'	EWes
'New Look'	CTal EWes GEdr GKev IBal LLHF NHpl NWad
'Ori Zuru'	CTal GEdr
'Origami'	CTal IBal LEdu
'Pat Lacey'	CTal EWes IBal
'Paula'	IBal
'Pink Ice'	CTal GEdr IBal NWad
'Pinkeen'	CTal EWes LLHF
'Pinkie'	CTal IBal SDys WFar
'Pintado'	CAby CTal EWes GEdr IBal LEdu LRHS NRHS NWad SDys
'Pretty in Pink'	CTal
'Raspberry Ice'	CTal IBal NWad WFar
'Roman'	CTal
'Rosalie'	IBal
'Rosie Lee'	CTal EWes
'Ruby Giant'	GEdr LRHS
'Shell Pink'	CTal EWes IBal NWad
Slack Top hybrids	NSla
'Snow'	EWes
'Snow White'	EWes
'Starlett'	CTal EWes
'Starry Eyes' (d)	CTal EWes IBal WFar
'Stella'	CCCN CTal EWes GEdr GKev IBal IRob LRHS NHpl NWad SDys
'Sunburst'	GEdr NWad
'Telios'	IBal
'Tetra Rose'	GEdr
'Tetra White'	see *R. baurii* 'Helen'
thodiana	CPbh CTal EWes GEdr IBal NHpl NWad WAbe WFar
'Twinkle Star Mixed'	LRHS
'Two Tone'	EWes
'Venetia'	CMea CTal IBal IRob NWad
'Westacre Picotee'	EWes
'White Prince'	CTal
'White Wings'	CTal
'Wild Cherry Blossom'	CTal EWes IBal

Rhodohypoxis × *Hypoxis* see × *Rhodoxis*

R. baurii* × *H. parvula	see × *Rhodoxis hybrida*

Rhodoleia (*Hamamelidaceae*)

championii B&SWJ 11603	WCru
- FMWJ 13155 **new**	WCru
- WWJ 11858	WCru
aff. ***henryi*** B&SWJ 11782	WCru
- DJHV 0640	WCru
parvipetala	WCru
FMWJ 13422 **new**	
- WWJ 11866	WCru
- WWJ 11943	WCru

Rhodophiala (*Amaryllidaceae*)

sp.	WHil
§ ***advena***	NRog
araucana	NRog
§ ***bifida***	CFil NRog
- pink-flowered	NRog
chilensis	NRog
phycelloides	NRog
pratensis	CPne

	rhodolirion	SPlb

Rhodora see *Rhododendron*

Rhodothamnus (*Ericaceae*)

	sessilifolius	WThu

Rhodotypos (*Rosaceae*)

	kerrioides	see *R. scandens*
§	***scandens***	CExl CTri EBee ELan EPfP IDee LEdu LRHS MGil MMrt MMuc MNrw NLar NQui SBrt SEND SLon SPoG WAvo WCru WHar WSHC

× *Rhodoxis* ✿ (*Hypoxidaceae*)

	'Abigail'	EWes IBal WFar
	'Anne Crock'	EWes IBal
	'Aurora'	CTal EWes IBal WFar
	'Betsy'	CTal EWes
	'Bianca'	CTal
	'Bloodstone'	CTal EWes IBal NWad
	'Evelien'	CTal
	FAIRYTALE ('Hil200802'[PBR]) **new**	SPad
	'Fanny'	EWes
	'Hebron Farm Biscuit'	see *Hypoxis parvula* var. *albiflora* 'Hebron Farm Biscuit'
§	'Hebron Farm Cerise'	CCCN CMen CTal EWes GEdr GKev IBal IRob LEdu LRHS NRHS SDys SRot
	'Hebron Farm Rose'	IBal IRob LLHF
§	***hybrida***	EWes WAbe
	- 'Aya San'	CTal EWes GKev IBal LRHS WFar
§	- 'Hebron Farm Pink'	CAby CElw CMen CPla EWes GEdr GKev IBal SRot WAbe
	- 'Hebron Farm Red Eye'	CCCN CMen CTal EWes GKev IBal IRob WAbe
	- 'Hebron Farm Red Eye' seedling	CMen
	- 'Pink Stars'	CTal IBal
	- 'Ruby Giant'	CTal EWes GEdr IBal
	- 'White Knight'	CTal
	- 'White Stars'	CTal EWes
	'Jenny'	EWes
	large red-flowered	CMen
	'Little Pink Pet'	CTal EWes IBal WFar
	'Nippon'	CTal
	'Otterlo Ruby'	EWes WFar
	'Pink Glow'	IBal
	'Pink Tips'	CTal IBal
	'Red Flyer'	CTal EWes IBal
	'Ria'	EWes
	'Sandra'	CTal EWes
	'Sandy'	CTal EWes
	'Sonja'	CTal
	'Sue'	EWes WFar
	'Summer Pink'	IBal

Rhoeo see *Tradescantia*

Rhoicissus (*Vitaceae*)

	digitata **new**	EShb

Rhopalostylis (*Arecaceae*)

	sapida	CBrP
	- 'Chatham Island'	CBlu

rhubarb see *Rheum* × *hybridum*; also AGM Vegetables Section

Rhus (*Anacardiaceae*)

	ambigua B&SWJ 3656	WCru
	- large-leaved B&SWJ 10884	WCru
	aromatica	CAgr CDul EBtc MMrt NLar
	chinensis	CMCN IDee
	copallinum	EBtc
	coriaria	NLar
	cotinus	see *Cotinus coggygria*
	glabra	CBcs EBtc EPfP SPer
	hirta	see *R. typhina*
	incisa	SPlb
	potaninii	EPfP NLar WPGP
	× ***pulvinata*** (Autumn Lace Group) 'Red Autumn Lace' 🏆H5	LRHS MBlu MRav SPer
	punjabensis	EGFP
§	***radicans***	GPoy WHer
	succedanea	CDTJ EGFP
	- NJM 10.154	WPGP
	toxicodendron	see *R. radicans*
	typhina	CAgr CBcs CDul CLnd CMac ELan EMOT EPfP ESps GKin GMcL LCro LMaj LOPS MAsh MGos MMuc NEgg NLar SCob SEND SGol SLim SPer SSta WFar
§	- 'Dissecta' 🏆H6	CBar CBcs CDul CLnd ELan EPfP ESps EUJe GMcL LMaj MGos MJak MMuc MRav NEgg NLar SArc SCob SEND SGol SLim SPer WFar
	- 'Laciniata' hort.	see *R. typhina* 'Dissecta'
	- RADIANCE ('Sinrus') 🏆H6	LRHS MAsh MBlu NLar SPoG
	- TIGER EYES ('Bailtiger'[PBR]) 🏆H6	ELan EPfP EUJe GKin GMcL LBuc MAsh MGos SCob SGol SMad SPoG SWvt
	verniciflua	EGFP NLar
	virens	CFil

Rhynchospora (*Cyperaceae*)

	colorata	LLWG NPer
	latifolia	CKno

Ribes ✿ (*Grossulariaceae*)

	alpinum	CExl EPfP MRav MWht SPer SRms WSpi
	- 'Aureum'	EHoe NEgg
	americanum 'Variegatum' (v)	EHoe NWad
	aureum misapplied	see *R. odoratum*
	aureum ambig.	CAgr IFro
§	× ***beatonii***	CBot CDul CExl CWld EBee ECrN ELon EShb LEdu LRHS MAsh MMuc NLar SBrt SGol SLim SMad SPer SPoG SRms WCot WFar WHar
	'Ben Hope'[PBR] (B)	CAgr CSBt EPom MCoo NPri SCoo SWvt WHar
	'Black Velvet' (D)	CAgr MCoo
	californicum	SBrt
	cereum	GEdr SBrt WCot
	× ***culverwellii*** (F)	CAgr CCCN CTri EPom LBuc LCro LEdu LOPS NLar SDea SVic SWvt WHar
	divaricatum	CAgr LEdu
	gayanum	LEdu NLar
	glaciale PAB 3004	LEdu
	× ***gordonianum***	see *R.* × *beatonii*
	griffithii	WCot
	- GWJ 9331	WCru
	- PAB 4871	LEdu

jostaberry	see *R.* × *nidigrolaria*
laurifolium	CBcs CDul CEnd CExl CHGN CTho CTri EBee ELan EWTr EWes IDee LRHS MMuc MRav NLar SChF SCob SEND SPer WCFE WFar WSHC
- (f)	CMac EPfP SBrt SRms
- (m)	EPfP SBrt
- 'Mrs Amy Doncaster'	CBcs CMac LEdu NLar SEle SRms WBor WCot WPGP WSpi
- Rosemoor form	ELan EPfP LRHS NLar SPoG WCot
longeracemosum	GGGa SBrt
magellanicum new	LRHS
menziesii	CHll EWes NQui WCot
§ × ***nidigrolaria***	CSBt
nigrum (B) PAB 3755	LEdu
- 'Baldwin' (B)	CFGn CTri EPfP MAsh NLar SDea SKee SLim SPer
- 'Barchatnaja' (B)	CAgr
- 'Ben Alder' (B)	CAgr EPom SCoo SDea
- 'Ben Connan'PBR (B) ♀H6	Widely available
- 'Ben Gairn'PBR (B)	CAgr MCoo MMuc
- 'Ben Lomond'PBR (B)	CAgr CFGn CSBt CTri EMOT EPfP LBuc LEdu LSRN MAsh MGos MJak MNHC MRav NEgg NLar NPri SDea SKee SPer SRms SVic
- 'Ben More' (B)	CAgr NPri
- 'Ben Nevis' (B)	CAgr CTri EMOT SDea SKee SPer
- 'Ben Sarek' (B)	Widely available
- 'Ben Tirran' (B)	CAgr CSBt EPom ERea LBuc LRHS LSRN MAsh MGos NLar NPri SCoo SDea SRms SWvt WHar
- 'Big Ben'PBR (B) ♀H6	CArg CFGn CRav CRos EHyd EPfP EPom ERea LBuc LCro LOPS LSRN MNHC SPer SPoG
- 'Black Reward' (B)	CAgr
- 'Boskoop Giant' (B)	CAgr ELan NEgg SLim WHar
- 'Byelorussian Sweet' (B)	CAgr
- 'Cassis Blanc' (B) new	CAgr
- 'Ebony' (B)	CArg CMac CRos EPom ERea LEdu LRHS NPri NRHS SVic
- 'Hystawneznaya' (B)	CAgr LEdu
- 'Jet' (B)	CAgr NEgg
- 'Karaka Black' (B)	ERea
- 'Kosmicheskaya' (B)	CAgr
- 'Loch Ness' (B)	ERea
- 'Pilot Alexander Mamkin' (B)	CAgr
- 'Polar' (B) new	CAgr
- 'Ruben'PBR (B)	ERea
- 'Seabrook's' (B)	CAgr
- 'Titania' (B)	CPer EMOT LRHS MCoo NLar
- 'Vertti' (B) new	CAgr
- 'Wellington XXX' (B)	CAgr CMac EMOT LBuc LEdu
§ ***odoratum***	CBcs CDul CMac CSBt CTho EBee ECrN ELan ELon EPfP ETMg EWTr LRHS MGos MMuc MNHC MNrw MRav NLar SCob SPer SPoG SRms WHar WWFP
- 'Black Pearl'	SVic
- 'Crandall'	CAgr LEdu
orientale PAB 7066	LEdu
'Pink Perfection'	CMCN
praecox	CBcs MMuc SEND
roezlii	CBot
rubrum	ESps
- 'Blanka' (W)	CAgr CArg CMac CPer ERea
- 'Cascade' (R)	CAgr
- 'Cherry' (R)	CAgr
- 'Gloire de Sablons' (P)	EPom
- 'Jonkheer van Tets' (R) ♀H6	CAgr CRos CSBt EMOT EPfP EPom ESps GQue IArd LRHS LSRN MAsh MCoo NLar NPri NRHS SDea SEND SKee SLim SPer SRms WHar
- 'Junifer' (R)	CAgr EPom ERea LEdu LRHS NRHS SKee
- 'Laxton's Number One' (R)	CAgr CFGn CRos CTri EPfP EPom LCro LEdu LOPS LRHS LSRN NLar SDea SLim SPer SPoG SRms
- 'Red Lake' (R) ♀H6	CAgr CFGn CTri ECrN ELan EPfP EPom ERea LBuc LEdu MGos MJak NEgg NLar NPri SDea SGol SKee SPer SPoG
- 'Redstart' (R)	CAgr CFGn CSBt CTri LBuc MAsh MMuc SKee WHar
- 'Rolan' (R)	CAgr EMOT
- 'Rondom' (R)	CAgr CPer SDea SVic
- 'Rosetta' (R)	CAgr
- 'Rotet' new	LEdu
- 'Rovada' (R)	CAgr CArg CFGn CMac CRav CSBt EMOT EPom ERea LBuc LEdu LRHS LSRN MAsh MNHC NLar NPri NRHS SDea SKee SPoG SVic WHar
- 'Roxby Red' (R)	LEdu
- 'Stanza' (R) ♀H6	CAgr EMOT SDea SEND
§ - 'Versailles Blanche' (W/C)	CAgr CFGn CSBt CTri EPfP EPom ERea GQue LBuc LCro LOPS LRHS LSRN MGos MJak MMuc NPri NRHS SDea SKee SLim SPer WHar
- 'Weisse Langtraubige' (W)	CAgr
- 'White Dutch' (W)	EMOT
- 'White Grape' (W) ♀H6	CTri LEdu
- 'White Pearl' (W)	ELan EMOT SDea SVic
- WHITE VERSAILLES	see *R. rubrum* 'Versailles Blanche'
sanguineum	CDul ESps NEgg WMoo
- 'Albescens'	CBot EPfP
- 'Brianjou'	SRms
- 'Brocklebankii'	CExl CMac EBee LRHS MRav NLar SChF SCob SPer SRms WCFE WSHC
- 'Carneum'	LRHS NRHS
- double-flowered	see *R. sanguineum* 'Plenum'
- 'Elkington's White'	CRos ECrN EPfP LBuc LCro LRHS LSRN MAsh MGos NLar NRHS NSti SCoo SLon SRms WBor WSpi
- 'Flore Pleno'	see *R. sanguineum* 'Plenum'
- 'King Edward VII'	Widely available
- 'Koja' ♀H6	CBod CBot CRos EBee ELon EPfP GBin LEdu LRHS LSRN MAsh MGos MMuc NLar NRHS SCoo SEle SGol SPoG SRms WCot
- 'Lombartsii'	EPfP LRHS MRav NRHS
- 'Pink Rain'	LRHS
§ - 'Plenum' (d)	EPfP
- 'Poky's Pink'	ECrN EWTr LLHF LRHS MAsh MRav SPoG SRms
- 'Pulborough Scarlet' ♀H6	Widely available
- 'Red Bross'	EPfP LRHS MAsh SWvt
- 'Red Pimpernel'	EPfP LRHS MAsh MBNS NRHS SRms SWvt WFar
- 'Somerset White'	LRHS MAsh
- 'Taff's Kim' (v)	IRob
- 'Tydeman's White'	CExl CSBt ELan EPfP NLar WSpi
- var. ***variegata***	CMac
- WHITE ICICLE ('Ubric') ♀H6	CBcs CBot CDul CTri EBee ECtt EPfP EWTr GBin GMcL IRob LRHS MAsh MBlu MHer MRav MSwo NLar NRHS SCob SPer SPoG SRms SWvt WCFE WCot WFar WMoo
speciosum ♀H4	Widely available
uva-crispa 'Annelii' (F)	CAgr

- 'Captivator' (C)	CFGn CRos CSBt EMOT EPom LBuc LRHS MAsh MCoo MNHC NLar NRHS SDea SGol SKee SPoG WHar
- 'Careless' (C/D) ♀H6	CFGn CMac CSBt CTri EPom LSRN MAsh MGos MJak SDea SPer WHar
- 'Early Sulphur' (D)	ELan SDea
- 'Greenfinch' (C) ♀H6	CAgr
- 'Hinnonmäki' (F)	CAgr ECrN LBuc NPri SDea SPer
- 'Hinnonmäki Grön' (D)	CAgr CMac CPer CSBt EMOT EMil EPfP LSRN MAsh MRav NPri SDea SKee WHar
- 'Hinnonmäki Gul' (D)	CAgr CMac CSBt EMil EPfP EPom ERea LBuc LEdu LRHS MAsh MGos SDea SKee SPer SPoG SVic WHar
- 'Hinnonmäki Röd' (C/D)	CAgr CFGn CMac CPer CRos EMOT EMil EPfP EPom ERea LBuc LCro LEdu LOPS LRHS LSRN MAsh MCoo MNHC MRav NLar NRHS SDea SKee SPer SPoG SVic WHar
- 'Howard's Lancer' (C/D)	SDea
- 'Invicta' (C/D) ♀H6	Widely available
- 'Jubilee' (C/D)	LBuc
- 'Jubilee Careless' (C/D)	EPom
- 'Keepsake' (C/D)	SDea
- 'Langley Gage' (D)	MCoo
- 'Larell' (C/D)	CAgr
- 'Leveller' (D) ♀H6	CTri ECrN MCoo SDea SPer WHar
- 'Martlet' (F)	MCoo SLim
- 'May Duke' (C/D)	SDea
- 'Mucurines' (D) new	CAgr
- 'Pax'PBR (D)	CAgr EPfP SDea SLim SVic
- 'Pixwell' (C) new	SGol
- 'Redeva'PBR (D)	CAgr
- 'Rokula'PBR (C/D)	ELan MCoo
- 'Snow' (F)	EPfP
- 'Spinefree' (C)	CAgr
- 'Whinham's Industry' (C/D) ♀H6	CRos CSBt CTri ELan LBuc LSRN MGos MMuc NEgg NPri SDea SEND SPer WHar
- 'Whitesmith' (C/D)	CTri LSRN MCoo SDea
- 'Xenia' (D)	CArg CFGn CRav EPfP EPom ERea LEdu LRHS MCoo MNHC NRHS SPoG
valdivianum	WCot
- 'Kathleen'	EPfP
viburnifolium	LRHS NLar SBrt SEND
'Worcesterberry' (C)	CHab IDee SDea

Richea (*Ericaceae*)

dracophylla	CBrP

Ricinus (*Euphorbiaceae*)

communis	CDTJ SPlb
- 'Carmencita' ♀H1c	NGBl SDys
- 'Carmencita Pink'	CDTJ
- 'Carmencita Red'	CDTJ
- 'Dominican Republic'	CDTJ
- 'Gibsonii'	CDTJ
- 'Impala'	CDTJ
- 'New Zealand Black'	CDTJ CSpe SDys
- 'Zanzibariensis' ♀H1c	CDTJ

Ridolfia (*Apiaceae*)

segetum	LRHS SPhx

Rigidella see *Tigridia*

orthantha	see *Tigridia orthantha*

Riocreuxia (*Apocynaceae*)

torulosa	CCCN SPlb

Robinia (*Papilionaceae*)

§ ***hispida***	CDul CEnd ELan EMOT EPfP EWTr MBlu SPer
- var. ***fertilis***	SBrt
- var. ***kelseyi***	CDul EWes WSpi
- 'Macrophylla'	CEnd
§ - var. ***rosea***	LSRN
- 'Rosea' misapplied	see *R. hispida*, *R. hispida* var. *rosea*
- 'Rosea' ambig.	CBcs EBee
× ***margaretta*** CASQUE ROUGE	see *R.* × *margaretta* 'Pink Cascade'
§ - 'Pink Cascade'	CDul CEnd CMac CTri ELan EMOT EPfP LPra MAsh MGos NOra SCoo SEND SGol SLim SPer
pseudoacacia	CAgr CCVT CDul CPer ELan EMOT ESps LBuc LPra MCoo MMuc SCob SEND SGol SPlb
- 'Bessoniana'	CDul EBee ELan EMOT EPfP LPra
- 'Fastigiata'	see *R. pseudoacacia* 'Pyramidalis'
- 'Frisia'	Widely available
- 'Inermis' hort.	see *R. pseudoacacia* 'Umbraculifera'
§ - 'Lace Lady'PBR	CSBt ECrN ELan EPfP LBuc LRHS MAsh MGos MJak NLar SCoo SPoG
- 'Monophylla Fastigiata' new	LPra
§ - 'Pyramidalis'	LPra
- 'Rozynskiana'	CDul
- 'Tortuosa'	CEnd EBee EBtc LPra SPer
- 'Twisty Baby'	see *R. pseudoacacia* 'Lace Lady'
§ - 'Umbraculifera'	CDul ECrN LMaj LPra LSRN SArc SCob
× ***slavinii*** 'Hillieri' ♀H5	CDul CEnd CLnd EBee ECrN ELan EMOT EPfP EUJe LSRN MAsh MBlu NLar SLon SPer SPoG WSpi

Rochea see *Crassula*

Rodgersia ✿ (*Saxifragaceae*)

CLD 1432	CExl
aesculifolia ♀H7	Widely available
- SSSE 36 new	SMHy
- green bud	IBlr
- var. ***henrici***	GCal GLog IBoy LRHS MRav NBro NRHS SGbt SPer WBor WHoo WMoo
- - KW 21015	WCru
- - 'Cherry Blush'	EPfP GWyn MSCN SPad WFar WHar
- - hybrid	ITim NLar XLum
- 'Red Dawn'	IBlr
- 'Red Leaf'	GCal IFoB
'Badenweiter'	ECha LRHS NRHS
'Blickfang' ♀H7	IBlr LRHS MMrt NRHS
'Bloody Mary'	ECtt IMou LLWG SCob WFar
'Borodin'	EBee EWTr
'Bronze Peacock'	CAby CBWd CPla EBee ECtt EUJe GBin LCro LLWG LOPS LRHS MHol MJak MPkF NEoE NLar SCob SEle SPoG WTor
Cally strain	GCal
'Dark Pokers'	EBee ECtt NLar SRms WFar
'Die Anmutige'	IMou
'Die Schöne'	EBee NLar
'Die Stolze'	IMou IRob LEdu LLWG MBrN
'Elfenbeinturm'	IBlr
'Fascination'	IBlr
'Grande Blanche' new	CRos NRHS
'Herkules'	EBee ECha ECtt EHoe ELon EUJe GBin GMaP GMcL GWyn IFoB LEdu

	LRHS LSou MBNS MMuc NLar NQui NRHS WCot WPnP
'Irish Bronze' ♀H7	CBod ECtt ELan EPed EPfP EShb GPSL GQue ILea LEdu LRHS LSRN MBel MWts NPnk NRHS SMad WMoo WPnP
'Koriata'	IBlr
'Kupfermond'	EBee IBlr SMHy
'La Blanche'	EBee ECtt ELon LEdu LRHS MHol NLar NRHS WPnP
'Maigrün'	IBlr
nepalensis	EBee LEdu LRHS NRHS WPGP
- EMAK 713	IBlr
- HWJK 2140	WCru
- 'High Flier'	WCru
'Parasol'	CBro CMac IBlr LRHS NRHS NWad WWtn
pinnata	CAby CHid CTri EBee EHrv EPau EPfP GMaP IBlr IBoy IFoB ITim LEdu LRHS LSRN MBel MGos MRav SCob SMad SRms WMoo WPnP WWtn XLum
- B&SWJ 7741A	CBcs WCru
- L 1670	CExl ELan IBlr
- 'Alba'	GCal IBlr LRHS NRHS
- 'Buckland Beauty' ♀H7	EBee IBlr LRHS NRHS WMoo
- 'Cally Coral'	EBee GCal
- 'Cally Salmon'	EWes GCal IBlr IMou
- 'Candy Clouds' (d)	EBee NLar
- 'Chocolate Wing'	Widely available
- 'Crûg Cardinal'	EBee GCal LRHS NRHS WCru
- 'Elegans'	CBWd CBod CDor EBee EHoe ELan EPed EPfP GKev GMaP IBlr IRob LEdu LRHS MHol MRav NEgg NRHS NWad SPoG SRms SWvt WCFE
- 'Fireworks' PBR	CHid EBee ECtt ELan EPfP GMcL IMou IRob NLar SPer
- hybrids	GNew LRHS NRHS
- 'Jade Dragon Mountain'	EBee GCal IBlr
- 'Maurice Mason'	CExl EBee ECtt IBlr NLar
- 'Mont Blanc'	IBlr
- Mount Stewart form	IBlr
- 'Panache'	IBlr
- 'Perthshire Bronze'	IBlr
- 'Pink Beauty'	EBee
- pink-flowered	WCru
- 'Rosea'	IBlr
- 'Shangri-La'	WCru
- 'Snow Clouds'	EBee
- 'Superba' ♀H7	Widely available
- white-flowered	WCru
pinnata* × *sambucifolia	IBlr
podophylla	CAby CExl CMac CMea ECha ELon EPPr EPfP EUJe GAbr GKev GMaP GMcL GQue LEdu LLWG LRHS MMuc NBid NEgg NLar NRHS NRya NSti NWad SMad WCru WHoo WMoo WWtn
- B&SWJ 10818	WCru
- B&SWJ 10823	WCru
- 'Braunlaub'	EUJe NBro WMoo
- 'Bronceblad'	IBlr
- 'Crûg's Colossus'	WCru
- Donard selection	IBlr
- 'Rotlaub' ♀H7	EBee IBlr IMou LLWG MMoz WBor WMoo
- 'Smaragd'	EShb GCal IBlr LRHS MRav NLar NRHS
purdomii hort.	CMac GCal LRHS NRHS WCot WPGP
'Reinecke Fuchs'	IBlr
'Rosenlicht'	LRHS NRHS
'Rosenzipfel'	IBlr
sambucifolia	CBcs CMac GCal IBoy ILea LEdu LRHS MMuc NEgg NLar NRHS NSti SEND SPer WArt WFar WMoo WPnP XLum
- B&SWJ 7899	WCru
- dwarf, pink-flowered	IBlr
- dwarf, white-flowered	IBlr
- 'Mountain Select'	EBee GCal
'Stoke Gabriel'	EBee
tabularis	see *Astilboides tabularis*

Roemeria (*Papaveraceae*)

hybrida	CSpe

Rohdea (*Asparagaceae*)

delavayi new	WCot
japonica	CMac WCot WPGP
- B&SWJ 4853	WCru
- B&SWJ 5091	WCru
- 'Godaishu' (v)	WCot
- 'Gunjaku' (v)	WCot
- 'Lance Leaf'	LEdu WPGP
- long-leaved	WCot
- 'Miyakonojo' (v)	WCot
- 'Talbot Manor' (v)	CBct WCot WPGP
- 'Tama-jishi' (v)	WCot
- 'Tuneshige Rokujo' (v)	WCot
tonkinensis HWJ 562	WCru
watanabei	IMou
- B&SWJ 1911	WCru

Roldana (*Asteraceae*)

§ ***cristobalensis***	CSpe WCot
§ ***petasitis***	CFil WCot

Romanzoffia (*Boraginaceae*)

californica	EBee
§ ***sitchensis***	CTri
suksdorfii Greene	see *R. sitchensis*
unalaschcensis	SRms

Romneya (*Papaveraceae*)

coulteri ♀H5	Widely available
§ - 'White Cloud' ♀H5	CExl EBee EPfP MRav SChF WPGP WSpi
× ***hybrida***	see *R. coulteri* 'White Cloud'

Romulea (*Iridaceae*)

atrandra	CTal NRog
bulbocodium	CTal
- var. ***crocea***	EPot
- var. ***leichtliniana***	GKev
diversiformis	CTal
engleri	CTal
ligustica var. ***rouyana***	GKev
linaresii subsp. ***graeca***	GKev
nivalis	CTal
ramiflora	CExl CTal
tempskyana	EPot GKev
tetragona	CTal
* ***zahnii***	CTal

Rorippa (*Brassicaceae*)

amphibia	LLWG MSKA
palustris new	EBWF

Rosa ✿ (*Rosaceae*)

NJM 11.048 from Guizhou, China	WPGP
NJM 11.077 from Guizhou, China	WPGP
NJM 11.079 from Guizhou, China	WPGP
'À Longs Pédoncules' (Ce) **new**	EBls
'A. Mackenzie' (S) **new**	EBls
A SHROPSHIRE LAD ('Ausled'PBR) (S) ♀H6	CKel CRos CTri EPfP ESps LBuc LRHS MAus NEgg NLar NRHS SCob SPer SPoG SSea
A WHITER SHADE OF PALE ('Peafanfare'PBR) (HT) ♀H6	CKel CSBt ECnt ESps ESty LSRN MAus MJak MRav MWat SPer SSea SWCr
'Abbotswood' (*canina* hybrid)	EBls
ABIGAILE ('Tanelaigib') (F)	LSRN
ABRACADABRA ('Korhocsel') (HT)	ESty
ABRAHAM DARBY ('Auscot') (S)	CBod CKel CTri ELan EPfP EShb ESps IBoy LRHS LSRN MAsh MAus MJak MRav MWat NEgg NLar SCob SEND SPer SWCr
ABSENT FRIENDS ('Dicemblem'PBR) (F)	ESty IBoy SRGP SWCr WBor
ABSOLUTELY FABULOUS ('Wekvossutono'PBR) (F) ♀H6	CBod CGro CSBt EBls ECnt EPfP ESps ESty IRob LBuc LRHS LSRN MAsh MJak MRav NPri SCoo SPad SPer SPoG SWCr
abyssinica	LEdu
acicularis	EBls
var. ***nipponensis***	
'Adam' (ClT)	EBls LSRN
'Adam Messerich' (Bb)	EBls NLar
ADAM'S ROSE ('Wekromico') (F)	LSRN
'Adélaïde d'Orléans' (Ra) ♀H6	CRHN EBls IRob MAus NLar SEND SPer
'Agatha' (G) **new**	EBls
AGATHA CHRISTIE ('Kormeita'PBR) (ClF)	EPfP LBuc LRHS LSRN MAsh
'Agathe Incarnata' (D × G)	EBls
'Aglaia' (Ra)	CPou EBls MAus
'Agnes' (Ru)	EBls EPfP EWTr IArd MAus MRav NLar SPer SRGP
'Aimée Vibert' (N)	CBWd EBee EBls ELon MAus MRav NLar SPer SRGP
'Alain Blanchard' (G)	CPou EBls MAus
ALAN TITCHMARSH ('Ausjive'PBR) (S)	LCro LOPS LRHS LSRN MAus SPer
× ***alba*** (A)	EBls ESps
§ - 'Alba Maxima' (A) ♀H7	EBee EBls EWTr GBin MAus MRav NLar SEND SPer WFar WHer
§ - 'Alba Semiplena' (A) ♀H7	EBls EPfP GBin LRHS MAus NLar SPer SWCr WHer
- CELESTIAL	see *R.* 'Céleste'
- 'Maxima'	see *R.* × *alba* 'Alba Maxima'
'Albéric Barbier' (Ra) ♀H5	CRHN CSBt CTri EBee EBls ECnt ELan EPfP ESps LCro LOPS MAus MRav MSwo MWat NLar SCob SEND SMad SPer SWCr WHer
'Albertine' (Ra) ♀H6	Widely available
'Alchymist' (ClS)	CKel CPou CRHN CRos EBee EBls ELon EPfP ESty LRHS MAus MRav NLar SPer
ALEC'S RED ('Cored') (HT)	CBcs CKel CTri EBls ESps IBoy LSRN MAsh MAus MJak MRav SPer SPoG SRGP SWCr
ALEXANDER ('Harlex') (HT) ♀H6	CGro EBls ESps GBin IBoy LSRN MAus MRav SPer SSea SWCr
'Alexander Hill Gray' (T)	EBls
ALEXANDER'S ISSIE ('Dicland'PBR) (F)	IDic
'Alexandre Girault' (Ra) ♀H6	CBod CRHN EBls LBuc LRHS MAus NRHS SPer SWCr WHer
'Alfred Colomb' (HP)	EBls
'Alfred de Dalmas' misapplied	see *R.* 'Mousseline'
ALFRED SISLEY ('Delstrijor'PBR) (S)	CBod ESty MRav NLar
'Alfresco'PBR (ClHT)	MSwo
§ 'Alibaba'PBR (Cl) ♀H6	CSBt ECnt EPfP ESty EUJe LRHS LSRN MAsh MRav NPri SPer SPoG SSea SWCr
ALICE FAYE ('Seaodd') (Min)	ESty
'Alida Lovett' (Ra)	CRHN EBls MAus
ALISON ('Coclibee'PBR) (F)	LSRN
'Alison Wheatcroft' (F)	EBls
ALISSAR, PRINCESS OF PHOENICIA ('Harsidon'PBR) (S)	CPou GBin NLar
'Alister Clark' (F) **new**	EBls
§ 'Alister Stella Gray' (N) ♀H5	EBee EBls EPfP ESty MAus MMuc NEgg NLar SLon SPer SSea WBor
ALL AMERICAN MAGIC ('Meiroylear'PBR) (HT)	ESty
ALL MY LOVING ('Fryrisky') (HT) **new**	LRHS MAsh
'Allen Chandler' (ClHT)	EBls MAus
'Allgold' (F)	EBls SCob
ALNWICK CASTLE	see *R.* THE ALNWICK ROSE
'Aloha' (ClHT) ♀H7	CBcs CGro CKel CTri EBee EBls EPfP ESps ESty EWTr LRHS MAsh MAus MCot MJak MRav NLar SCob SPer SWCr
alpina	see *R. pendulina*
'Alpine Sunset' (HT)	CTri EBls ELon ESty MRav SCob SPer SWCr
altaica misapplied	see *R. spinosissima* 'Grandiflora'
altaica Willd.	see *R. spinosissima*
ALTISSIMO ('Delmur') (Cl)	CBod CKel EBls EWTr MAsh MAus SPer SSea SWCr
ALWAYS YOU ('Webalways') (HT)	ESty
'Amadis' (Bs)	EBls MAus
AMANDA ('Beesian') (F)	EBls ESty LSRN
'Ambassador Nogami' (S)	EBls
AMBER COVER ('Poulbambe'PBR) (Towne & Country Series) (GC)	EUJe
AMBER QUEEN ('Harroony') (F) ♀H6	CKel CSBt CTri EBls ELan ESps IArd IBoy LBuc LRHS MAsh MAus MRav SPer SSea SWCr
AMBER SWEET DREAM ('Fryritz') (Patio)	CKel MRav MWat
amblyotis RBS 0262	NLar
AMBRIDGE ROSE ('Auswonder') (S)	MAus
'Amélia'	see *R.* 'Celsiana'
AMELIA ('Poulen011'PBR) (Renaissance Series) (S)	ECnt LSRN
'American Pillar' (Ra)	CGro CKel CRHN CRos CSBt CTri EBee EBls ECnt ELan EPfP IBoy

		LRHS MAsh MAus MMuc MRav MSwo NLar SCob SPer SWCr WBor
	'Amy Robsart' (RH)	EBls MAus
	ANABELL ('Korbell') (F)	LSRN
	'Anaïs Ségalas' (G)	MAus
	'Andersonii' (*canina* hybrid)	EBls
§	'Anemone' (Cl)	CPou EBls EWTr MAus NLar
	anemoniflora	see *R.* × *beanii*
	anemonoides	see *R.* 'Anemone'
	ANGELA ('Grifgela')	LSRN
	ANGELA RIPPON ('Ocaru') (Min)	CSBt
	'Angela's Choice' (F)	LSRN
	'Angèle Pernet' (HT)	EBls
	ANISLEY DICKSON ('Dickimono') (F)	SPer
	ANN ('Ausfete'[PBR]) (S)	LSRN
	ANN HENDERSON ('Fryhoncho') (F)	LSRN
	ANNA FORD ('Harpiccolo') (Min/Patio) ♕H5	ESps SPer
	'Anna Olivier' (T)	EBls
	'Anna Pavlova' (HT)	EBls
	ANNA ZINKEISEN ('Harquhling') (S)	EBls
	ANNE BOLEYN ('Ausecret'[PBR]) (S)	CRos EPfP IBoy LBuc LRHS MAsh MAus NEgg NRHS SCoo
	'Anne Dakin' (ClHT)	MAus
	ANNE HARKNESS ('Harkaramel') (F)	MAus SPer
	ANNE MARIE LAING ('Jospink') (F)	EBls
	'Anne of Geierstein' (RH)	EBls
	'Anne Watkins' (HT)	EBls
	'Anne-Marie de Montravel' (Poly) **new**	EBls
	ANNIVERSARY WALTZ ('Raw237') (HT) **new**	ESty
	'Anthony' (S)	EBls
	ANTIQUE '89 ('Kordalen'[PBR]) (ClF)	EBls MAsh
	ANTIQUE ('Antike') (F)	CBod CPou
	APHRODITE ('Tan00847'[PBR]) (S) ♕H6	ELon ESty LSRN MRav SWCr
	apothecary's rose	see *R. gallica* var. *officinalis*
	'Apple Blossom' (Ra)	EBls SHar
	APPLE BLOSSOM ('Noamel') (GC)	EShb
	'Applejack' (S)	EBls
	'Apricot Nectar' (F)	MAus
	'Apricot Silk' (HT)	CTri EBls SPer
	APRICOT SUNBLAZE ('Savamark') (Min)	CSBt
	'Archduke Charles' (Ch) **new**	EBls
	'Archiduc Joseph' misapplied	see *R.* 'Général Schablikine'
	'Archiduchesse Elisabeth d'Autriche' (HP)	EBls
	ARCHIE MOSS ('Dickumon') (S) **new**	IDic
	'Ardoisée de Lyon' (HP)	EBls
	'Ards Rover' (ClHP)	EBls
	'Arethusa' (Ch)	EBls NLar
§	***arkansana*** var. ***suffulta***	EBls
	ARMADA ('Haruseful') (S)	EBls
	'Arthur Bell' (F) ♕H7	CGro CRos CSBt CTri EBls ELon EPfP ESps ESty EUJe IArd IBoy LRHS LSRN MAsh MAus MJak MRav MSwo MWat NEgg NPri SCob SPer SPoG SRGP SSea SWCr WBor
	'Arthur de Sansal' (DPo)	EBls MAus NLar
	arvensis	CCVT CHab CPer EBls LBuc MAus MMuc SCob WTSh
§	'Aschermittwoch' (Cl)	EBls
	ASH WEDNESDAY	see *R.* 'Aschermittwoch'
	'Assemblage des Beautés' (G)	MAus
	'Astra Desmond' (Ra)	EBls MNrw
	ATTLEBOROUGH ('Beaat') (ClHT)	EBls
	AUDREY WILCOX ('Frywilrey') (HT)	ESty
	'Auguste Gervais' (Ra)	EBls MAus
	'Auguste Roussel' (Cl) **new**	EBls
	'Augustine Guinoisseau' (HT)	EBls
	Austrian copper rose	see *R. foetida* 'Bicolor'
	Austrian yellow	see *R. foetida*
	'Autumn' (HT)	LSRN
	'Autumn Delight' (HM)	EBls NLar
	AUTUMN FIRE	see *R.* 'Herbstfeuer'
	'Autumn Sunset' (ClS)	EBls MCot
	'Autumnalis'	see *R.* 'Princesse de Nassau'
	AVEC AMOUR ('Tan04341') (HT)	ESty
	'Aviateur Blériot' (Ra)	CRHN EBls
	'Avon' (HT)	CBod
	AVON ('Poulmulti'[PBR]) (GC)	EBls ELan MRav SPer
	AWAKENING ('Probuzení') (ClHT)	EBee EBls LRHS MAsh MSwo NLar SWCr
	'Ayrshire Splendens'	see *R.* 'Splendens'
	'Baby Albéric' (Poly) **new**	EBls
	'Baby Faurax' (Poly)	EBls MAus
	BABY GOLD STAR (Min)	see *R.* 'Estrellita de Oro'
	BABY LOVE ('Scrivluv'[PBR]) (Min/Patio)	MAus
	BABY MASQUERADE ('Tanba') (Min)	CBod CGro MRav SPer
	BABYFACE ('Rawril'[PBR]) (Min)	ESty
	'Ballerina' (HM/Poly) ♕H6	Widely available
	'Baltimore Belle' (Ra)	CPou EBls MAus NLar
	banksiae (Ra)	CPou SNig SRms WAvo
	- ***alba***	see *R. banksiae* var. *banksiae*
§	- var. ***banksiae*** (Ra/d)	CBod CBot CDul CHll CKel CPou CRHN CRos CSBt CTri CWld EBls ELan EPfP LCro LOPS LRHS MAus MNHC SCob SEND SLon SPer SPoG WCot XSen
	- 'Lutea' (Ra/d) ♕H5	Widely available
	- 'Lutescens' (Ra)	CBot EBls WPGP
	- var. ***normalis*** (Ra)	CSBt CSam EBls EPfP MAus SLon WCot WHer WPGP
I	- 'Rosea' (Ra)	CBot NLar SPer
	'Bantry Bay' (ClHT)	CBod CSBt EBee EBls ELan ESps LSRN SCob SLon SPer SWCr
	BARAKURA ('Beajap') (GC/S) **new**	EBls
	BARBARA ANN	see *R.* SCENT FROM HEAVEN
	BARBARA AUSTIN ('Austop'[PBR]) (S)	MAus SCob
	BARBARA ('Raw1050') **new**	LSRN
	BARKAROLE ('Tanelorak'[PBR]) (HT)	CSBt ESty
	'Baron de Wassenaer' (CeMo)	EBls
	'Baron Girod de l'Ain' (HP)	EBls ELon LRHS LSRN MAus NEgg NLar SPer SWCr

	Name	Suppliers
	'Baroness Rothschild' (HT)	see *R.* BARONNE EDMOND DE ROTHSCHILD
	'Baroness Rothschild' ambig.	see *R.* BARONNE EDMOND DE ROTHSCHILD, CLIMBING BARONNE EDMOND DE ROTHSCHILD
§	'Baronne Adolph de Rothschild' (HP)	EBls
§	BARONNE EDMOND DE ROTHSCHILD ('Meigriso') (HT)	MAus
	'Baronne Prévost' (HP)	EBls MAus
	BAROQUE FLOORSHOW ('Harbaroque'[PBR]) (S)	CKel MRav
	BARRY STEPHENS ('Horcabellero') (HT)	LSRN
§	× ***beanii*** (Ra)	EBls
	BEATRIX POTTER ('Beafolly') (S)	EBls
	'Beau Narcisse' (G) ♀H7	MAus
	BEAUTIFUL BRITAIN ('Dicfire') (F)	EBls ESps SCob
	'Beauty of Rosemawr' (ClT)	EBls
	'Belinda' (HM)	EBls LSRN
	BELLA CHRISTINA ('Mandella') (F) **new**	LSRN
	BELLA DIANA ('Mandiana') (F) **new**	LSRN
§	BELLA ('Pouljill'[PBR]) (Renaissance Series) (S)	CPou
	'Belle Amour' (A × D)	CBod CPou EBls GBin MAus
	'Belle de Crécy' (G)	CPou CTri EBls MAsh MAus MNrw NLar NPri SMad SPer
	'Belle des Jardins' misapplied	see *R.* × *centifolia* 'Unique Panachée'
	BELLE EPOQUE ('Adasilthe'[PBR]) (HT)	SCob
	BELLE EPOQUE ('Fryyaboo'[PBR]) (HT)	ESty SCob
	BELLE HAPPINESS ('Meileodevin'[PBR]) (Cl)	ESty SSea
	'Belle Isis' (G)	EBls MAus
	'Belle Lyonnaise' (ClT)	EBls
	'Belle Poitevine' (Ru)	CPou EBee
	'Belle Portugaise' (ClT)	EBls MAus
	'Belle Vichyssoise' (N) **new**	EBls
	BELMONTE ('Harpearl'[PBR]) (F)	ESty
§	'Belvedere' (Ra) ♀H6	CPou EBee IBoy MAus NLar SPer
	BENITA ('Dicquarrel') (HT)	IDic
	BENJAMIN BRITTEN ('Ausencart'[PBR]) (S)	CSBt EPfP ESty IBoy LBuc LRHS MAus NEgg NRHS SCob
§	'Bennett's Seedling' (Ra)	EBls
	BERKSHIRE ('Korpinka'[PBR]) (GC) ♀H6	EBls SCob SSea
	BERYL JOYCE ('Tan96145'[PBR]) (HT)	CKel ESty LSRN MRav
	BEST OF FRIENDS ('Pouldunk'[PBR]) (HT)	LSRN
	BEST WISHES ('Chessnut'[PBR]) (ClHT/v)	ESps LSRN SRGP
	'Betty Sherriff' (Cl)	GBin
	'Betty Uprichard' (HT)	EBls
	'Betty's Smile' (HT)	LSRN
	'Bewitched' (HT)	LSRN MAsh
§	BEWITCHED ('Poulbella'[PBR]) (Castle Series) (F)	SWCr
	BIANCO ('Cocblanco') (Patio/Min)	MAus MWat
	BIENVENUE ('Delrochipar') (Cl)	ESty

	Name	Suppliers
	BIG PURPLE ('Stebigpu') (HT)	ECnt
	BILLET DOUX ('Delrosar') (S)	ESty
	BIRTHDAY BOY ('Tan97607'[PBR]) (HT)	CBod ESps ESty LSRN MRav MWat SCob SCoo SPoG SWCr
	BIRTHDAY GIRL ('Meilasso'[PBR]) (F)	CBod CGro CKel CSBt EPfP ESps ESty LSRN MAsh MJak MRav MWat SCoo SPoG SRGP SVic SWCr
	BIRTHDAY SURPRISE ('Guesyoga') (F) **new**	ESty
	BIRTHDAY WISHES (Patio)	see *R.* SHRIMP HIT (Patio)
	BIRTHDAY WISHES ('Guesdelay') (HT)	CTri LRHS LSRN SSea
	'Bishop Darlington' (HM)	EBls
	BLACK BEAUTY ('Korfleur') (HT)	MAus
	'Black Jack' (Ce)	see *R.* 'Tour de Malakoff'
	'Black Prince' (HP)	EBls
	BLACKBERRY NIP ('Somnip'[PBR]) (HT) **new**	ELon
	'Blairii Number One' (Bb)	EBls
	'Blairii Number Two' (ClBb)	CSam EBls MAus NEgg NLar SPer
	'Blanche de Belgique' (A) **new**	EBls
	'Blanche Double de Coubert' (Ru) ♀H7	CBcs CBod CDul CKel CSBt CTri EBee EBls ECnt ELan EPfP ESps GBin LBuc LCro LOPS LSRN MAus MSwo NEgg NLar SCob SEND SPer SWCr WKif
	'Blanche Moreau' (CeMo)	EBls MAus SPer
	'Blanchefleur' (Ce × G)	CPou EBls MAus
	blanda	EBls
	'Blaze' (Cl) **new**	EBls
	'Blesma Soul' (HT)	CSBt
	'Blessings' (HT)	CBcs CSBt CTri EBls ESps LBuc LSRN MAsh MAus MGos MJak MRav SCob SPer SWCr
	'Bleu Magenta' (Ra) ♀H7	CBod CRHN EBee EBls ELan GBin IArd MAus NLar SEND SWCr
	BLOOM OF RUTH ('Harmedley'[PBR]) (HT)	CSBt ECnt
	'Bloomfield Abundance' (Poly)	CPou EBls MAus MMuc NLar SPer
	'Bloomfield Courage' (Ra) **new**	CBod EBls
	'Bloomfield Dainty' (HM)	EBls
	'Blossomtime' (Cl)	SPer
	BLUE FOR YOU ('Pejamblu'[PBR]) (F) ♀H6	CGro CRos CWld EBls ECnt ELan EPfP ESty GBin LBuc LRHS MAsh MAus NPri SCob SCoo SMad SPoG SSea SWCr
	BLUE MOON ('Tannacht') (HT)	CTri EBls ELan EPfP ESps IBoy MGos MJak MRav SCob SPer SPoG SRGP
	BLUE PETER ('Ruiblun') (Min)	ESty IBoy
	BLUEBERRY HILL ('Wekcryplag') (F) **new**	EBls
	BLUESETTE ('Lenmau') (F) **new**	EBls
	'Blush Boursault' (Bs)	EBls MMuc
	'Blush Damask' (D)	EBls
	'Blush Hip' (A)	MAus
	'Blush Noisette'	see *R.* 'Noisette Carnée'
	'Blush Rambler' (Ra)	CSBt EBls EPfP EWTr LBuc MAsh MAus MMuc SPer
	'Blushing Lucy' (Ra) ♀H6	CPou CRHN EWTr MNrw NLar
	BLYTHE SPIRIT ('Auschool'[PBR]) (S)	MAsh MAus NEgg SCob

	'Bobbie James' (Ra) 🏆H6	CRos CTri EBee EBls EPfP EWTr LBuc LRHS MAus MNrw MRav MSwo NEgg NLar NRHS SCob SPer SSea SWCr WFar
	'Bobby Charlton' (HT)	LSRN
	BOBBY DAZZLER ('Smi133-02') (F)	ESty MRav
	'Bon Silène' (T)	EBls
	BONICA ('Meidomonac') (GC) 🏆H6	Widely available
§	BONITA ('Poulen009'PBR) (Renaissance Series) (S)	ECnt
	BOOGIE-WOOGIE ('Poulyc006'PBR) (Courtyard Series) (ClHT)	ECnt LRHS MAsh SWCr
	BORN AGAIN	see *R.* RENAISSANCE
	BOSCOBEL ('Auscousin'PBR) (S)	CRos ECnt EPfP ESty LBuc LRHS MAus NRHS SCob SWCr
	'Botzaris' (D)	EBls
	'Boule de Neige' (Bb)	CBWd CBcs CTri EBls ECnt ELan EPfP IBoy LCro LOPS LRHS LSRN MAus MRav NLar NRHS SPer SWCr
	'Bouquet d'Or' (N)	EBee EBls MAus NLar
	'Bouquet Tout Fait' misapplied	see *R.* 'Nastarana'
	BOWLED OVER ('Tandolgnil'PBR) (F) 🏆H6	ESty SWCr
§	***bracteata*** (S)	CRHN EBls ECre EWes MAus SSea
	BRAVE HEART ('Horbondsmile') (F)	MAus MRav
	BREATH OF LIFE ('Harquanne'PBR) (ClHT)	EBee EBls ELan ESps LBuc MAus MRav SPer SWCr
	BREATHTAKING ('Hargalore'PBR) (HT)	ESty
	'Breeze Hill' (Ra)	EBls
	'Brenda Colvin' (Ra)	EBls
	'Brian's Star' (F)	LSRN
	BRIDE AND GROOM ('Smi10-98') (HT)	CKel ESty LSRN MRav SCoo
	BRIDE ('Fryyearn'PBR) (HT)	LSRN MRav
	BRIDGE OF SIGHS ('Harglowing'PBR) (Cl)	ECnt ESty LBuc LRHS MAsh SPoG SWCr
	BRIGHT AND BREEZY ('Dicjive') (F)	ECnt
	BRIGHT AS A BUTTON ('Chewsumsigns'PBR) (S)	CKel CSBt CSam EBee ESty ETMg GBin LRHS MAsh NLar SLon SPer SWCr
	BRIGHT FIRE ('Peaxi'PBR) (ClHT)	CKel MSwo SPer SWCr
	BRIGHT FUTURE ('Kirora'PBR) (Cl)	ESty
	BRIGHT IDEAS ('Horcoffdrop') (Cl)	CWld EBls LRHS MAsh NPri
	BRIGHT SMILE ('Dicdance') (F/Patio)	MAus
	BRILLIANT SWEET DREAM ('Frysassy') (Patio)	ECnt SWCr
	BROADLANDS ('Tanmirsch'PBR) (GC)	NLar
	BROTHER CADFAEL ('Ausglobe'PBR) (S)	CKel CRos CTri EBee ESps LRHS MAsh MAus NEgg NLar NRHS SCob SCoo SPer SSea SWCr
	BROWN VELVET ('Maccultra') (F)	SPer
	BROWNIE	see *R.* CHOCOLATE RIPPLES
§	***brunonii*** (Ra)	CExl CPou EBls EWes MAus
	- CC 7290	EWld
	- KR 10350	WPGP
	- PAB 3083	LEdu
§	- 'La Mortola' (Ra)	EBls MAus NLar SPer

	BRUSH-STROKES ('Guescolour') (F)	ESty SWCr
	'Buff Beauty' (HM) 🏆H6	CGro CKel CSBt CTri EBee EBls ECnt ELan EPfP ESps IBoy LCro LOPS MAsh MAus MCot MRav MSwo NEgg NLar SCob SEND SPer SWCr WCFE WFar
	'Bullata'	see *R.* × *centifolia* 'Bullata'
§	'Burgundiaca' (G)	EBls MAus
	Burgundian rose	see *R.* 'Burgundiaca'
§	BURGUNDY ICE ('Prose'PBR) (F)	CBod CKel CRav CSBt EBee EBls ECnt EPfP ESty LBuc LCro LOPS LRHS MAsh MRav MSwo NRHS SCob SCoo SMad SPer SSea SWCr
	'Burgundy Iceberg'	see *R.* BURGUNDY ICE
	'Burgundy Rose'	see *R.* 'Burgundiaca'
	burnet, double pink	see *R. spinosissima* double, pink-flowered
	burnet, double white	see *R. spinosissima* double, white-flowered
	BUTTERCUP ('Ausband'PBR) (S)	CRos EPfP LBuc LRHS MAus
	BUXOM BEAUTY ('Korbilant'PBR) (HT) 🏆H6	EPfP LRHS LSRN MAsh SSea
	'C.F. Meyer'	see *R.* 'Conrad Ferdinand Meyer'
§	***caesia*** subsp. ***vosagiaca***	LEdu
	CAFÉ AU LAIT ('Simgrey') (F) **new**	ESty
	californica (S)	MAus
	- 'Plena'	see *R. nutkana* 'Plena'
	'Callisto' (HM)	MAus
	'Camayeux' (G)	CPou EBls ECnt MAus NLar SPer
	CAMBRIDGESHIRE ('Korhaugen'PBR) (GC)	CBod CTri EBls MAus NLar SPer SSea SWCr
	CAMELOT ('Tan05372'PBR) (Cl)	ESty
	'Cameo' (Poly)	EBls
	CAMILLE PISARRO ('Destricol') (F)	ESty
	'Canary Bird'	see *R. xanthina* 'Canary Bird'
	CANDY LAND ('Wekrosopela'PBR) (Cl)	ECnt ESty SWCr
	canina (S)	Widely available
	'Cantabrigiensis' (S) 🏆H6	EBls MAus NLar SPer
	CANZONETTA ('Noa84497d') (F)	MAsh
	CAPEL MANOR ('Beajammie') (Cl) **new**	EBls
	'Capitaine Basroger' (CeMo)	MAus
	'Capitaine John Ingram' (CeMo)	EBls MAus NLar
	CAPRICIA ('Poulren024'PBR) (S) **new**	NLar
	'Captain Christy'	see *R.* 'Climbing Captain Christy'
	'Captain Hayward' (HP)	EBls
	'Captain Scarlet' (ClMin)	ESty
	'Cardinal de Richelieu' (G)	CBcs CPou CSam CTri EBls EPfP ESps IBoy LCro LOPS LRHS MAsh MAus MCot MRav MSwo NEgg NLar SCob SMad SPer SPoG
	CAREFREE DAYS ('Meirivoui'PBR) (Patio) 🏆H6	EPfP ESps IBoy LBuc LRHS MAsh NPri NRHS SPoG SSea
	CARIAD ('Auspanier'PBR) (HM)	MAus
	CARIBBEAN DAWN ('Korfeining'PBR) (Patio)	MAsh
	CARING FOR YOU ambig.	LSRN

	'Carmen' (Ru)	EBls
	'Carmenetta' (S)	EBls
	'Carol' (F)	see *R.* 'Carol Amling'
§	'Carol Amling' (F)	LSRN
	CAROL ANN ('Peapost') (F)	LSRN
	'Caroline Testout'	see *R.* 'Madame Caroline Testout'
	CAROLINE VICTORIA ('Harprior'[PBR]) (HT)	LSRN
	CAROLYN KNIGHT ('Austurner'[PBR]) (S)	CRos EPfP LCro LOPS LRHS MAsh MAus NRHS
	CARRIS ('Harmanna'[PBR]) (HT)	MAsh
§	CASINO ('Macca') (ClHT)	CTri EBls ELon MRav SPer
	'Castle Apricot'	see *R.* LAZY DAYS
	'Castle Cream'	see *R.* PERFECT DAY
	'Castle Fuchsia Pink'	see *R.* BEWITCHED ('Poulbella')
	'Castle Peach'	see *R.* IMAGINATION ('Pouldron')
	'Castle Shrimp Pink'	see *R.* FASCINATION ('Poulmax')
	'Castle Yellow'	see *R.* SUMMER GOLD
	'Catherine Mermet' (T)	EBls
	'Catherine Seyton' (RH)	EBls
§	'Cécile Brünner' (Poly) ♀H6	CKel CTri EBee EBls ELan LRHS LSRN MAus MCot MMuc NLar SPer SSea
	CECILY GIBSON ('Evebright') (F)	ESty
	CELEBRATION 2000 ('Horcoffitup'[PBR]) (S)	MAus
	CELEBRATION TIME	see *R.* CINCO DE MAYO
§	'Céleste' (A) ♀H7	CTri EBls GBin MAus NLar SEND SPer
	'Célina' (CeMo)	EBls GBin LSRN
	'Céline Forestier' (N)	CPou EBee EBls EWTr MAus NLar SEND SPer
§	'Celsiana' (D) ♀H7	CPou CSam EBls LSRN MAus NLar SPer
	CENTENAIRE DE LOURDES ('Delge') (F)	EBls
	CENTENARY ('Koreledas'[PBR]) (F)	MAsh
§	× ***centifolia*** (Ce)	EBls MAus SPer
§	- 'Bullata' (Ce)	EBls MAus
§	- 'Cristata' (Ce) ♀H7	CBWd EBls ELon LEdu LRHS MAus NLar SPer
§	- 'De Meaux' (Ce)	EBls MAus NLar SPer
§	- 'Muscosa' (CeMo)	EBls LEdu MAus
	- 'Parvifolia'	see *R.* 'Burgundiaca'
§	- 'Shailer's White Moss' (CeMo)	CBod EBls MAus
	- 'Spong' (Ce)	EBls MAus
§	- 'Unique' (Ce)	EBls MAus NLar
§	- 'Unique Panachée' (Ce)	CPou EBls MAus
	'Centifolia Variegata'	see *R.* × *centifolia* 'Unique Panachée'
	CENTRE STAGE ('Chewcreepy'[PBR]) (S/GC) ♀H6	MAsh MAus
	'Cerise Bouquet' (S) ♀H7	EBls MAus NLar SPer
§	CHAMPAGNE MOMENT ('Korvanaber'[PBR]) (F) ♀H6	CBcs CGro CRos CSBt CSam EBee EBls ECnt ELan ELon EPfP ESty IRob LBuc LRHS LSRN MAsh MAus MGos MJak MRav MWat NPri NRHS SMad SPer SPoG SRGP SSea SWCr
	'Champion of the World' (Bb) **new**	EBls
	'Champneys Pink Cluster' (China hybrid)	EBls MAus SCob
	CHANDOS BEAUTY ('Harmisty'[PBR]) (HT) ♀H6	CGro CKel CRos ECnt EPfP ESty LBuc LRHS LSRN MAsh MRav MWat SSea SWCr
	'Chanelle' (F)	EBls SPer
	Chapeau de Napoléon	see *R.* × *centifolia* 'Cristata'
	'Chaplin's Pink Climber' (Cl)	EBls
	CHARISMA ('Jelroganor') (F) **new**	ETMg LRHS MAsh NPri
	CHARLES AUSTIN ('Ausles') (S)	MRav
	CHARLES DARWIN ('Auspeet'[PBR]) (S)	CGro EPfP LBuc LRHS MAsh MAus NEgg NLar NRHS SCob SCoo SPer
	'Charles de Mills' (G) ♀H7	CBWd CKel CSam CTri EBls ECnt ELan EPfP ESps EWTr GBin LCro LOPS LRHS LSRN MAus MCot MRav MSwo MWat NLar SMad SPer SWCr WHer
	'Charles Gater' (HP)	EBls
	'Charles Lefèbvre' (HP)	EBls
	'Charles Mallerin' (HT)	EBls
	CHARLES RENNIE MACKINTOSH ('Ausren') (S)	CSBt MAus NEgg
	CHARLIE'S ROSE ('Tanellepa') (HT) ♀H6	ESty LSRN
	CHARLOTTE ('Auspoly'[PBR]) (S) ♀H6	CRos EBee ELan EPfP ESty LBuc LCro LOPS LRHS LSRN MAus MJak NEgg NLar NRHS SCob SCoo SPer SPoG SWCr
	CHARLOTTE VIELI ('Diclooker') (F)	IDic
	CHARMANT ('Korpeligo'[PBR]) (Min)	MAsh
	CHARTERED ('Diclingo') (F)	IDic
	CHARTREUSE DE PARME ('Delviola') (S)	CPou ESty MRav NLar
	CHATSWORTH ('Tanotax'[PBR]) (Patio/F) ♀H6	SPer
	CHECKMATE ('Diclanky') (Cl)	IDic MRav
§	CHEEK TO CHEEK ('Poulslas'[PBR]) (Courtyard Series) (ClMin)	LRHS MAsh SWCr
	CHEERFUL CHARLIE ('Cocquimmer'[PBR]) (F)	LSRN MRav
	CHERIE	see *R.* SONGS OF PRAISE
	CHERRY BONICA ('Meipeporia') (S)	ESty
	CHERRY BRANDY '85 ('Tanryrandy'[PBR]) (HT)	CSBt
	CHESHIRE ('Korkonopi'[PBR]) (County Rose Series) (S)	MAus
	'Cheshire Life' (HT)	MAus
	'Chevy Chase' (Ra)	EBls MAsh
	'Chewton Rose' (S) **new**	EBls
	CHIANTI ('Auswine') (S)	EBls MAus NLar
	CHICAGO PEACE ('Johnago') (HT)	EBls SCob
	CHILD OF ACHIEVEMENT	see *R.* BELLA
	CHILD OF MY HEART ('Beapeace') (HT)	EBls
	CHILTERNS ('Kortemma'[PBR]) (GC)	SWCr
	'Chinatown' (ClF) ♀H7	CTri EBls ESps IBoy LRHS MAsh MAus MRav NPri SCob SPer
	chinensis misapplied	see *R.* × *odorata*
	chinensis Jacq. (S)	EBls
	- 'Minima' *sensu stricto* hort.	see *R.* 'Rouletii'
	- 'Mutabilis'	see *R.* × *odorata* 'Mutabilis'

	Name	Suppliers
	- 'Old Blush'	see *R.* × *odorata* 'Pallida'
	- 'Semperflorens'	EBls
	- var. ***spontanea***	WPGP
	- 'White Beauty' **new**	WCot
	CHLOE ('Poulen003'[PBR]) (Renaissance Series) (S)	CBod CPou ECnt EWTr LSRN NLar SWCr
	'Chloris' (A)	MMuc
	CHOCA MOCHA ('Simcho') (F) **new**	ESty
§	CHOCOLATE RIPPLES ('Simstripe') (Cl)	ESty
	CHRIS ('Kirsan'[PBR]) (ClHT)	CGro CSam ESty LSRN MAus
	CHRISTIAN DIOR ('Meilie') (HT)	EBls
	CHRISTOPHER ('Cocopher') (HT)	LSRN
	CHRISTOPHER MARLOWE ('Ausjump'[PBR]) (S)	MAsh MAus
§	'Chromatella' (N)	EBls MAus
	'Chrysler Imperial' (HT)	EBls
	'Chuckles' (F)	ESty
	CIDER CUP ('Dicladida') (Min/Patio)	IBoy IDic MAus
§	CINCO DE MAYO ('Wekcobeju'[PBR]) (F)	CKel LRHS MRav
	'Cinderella' (Ra)	MAsh
	'Cinderella' (Min)	CSBt NLar
	CINDERELLA ('Korfobalt') (ClS)	CPou EUJe
	cinnamomea misapplied	see *R. majalis*
	'Circus' (F)	EBls
	CITY LIGHTS ('Poulgan'[PBR]) (Patio)	CSBt
	CITY LIVERY ('Harhero 2000') (F)	EPfP LBuc MAsh
	CITY OF BELFAST ('Macci') (F)	EBls
	CITY OF CARLSBAD	see *R.* HANKY PANKY
	'City of Leeds' (F)	SPer
	CITY OF LONDON ('Harukfore') (F)	CSBt EBls SPer
	CITY OF YORK	see *R.* 'Direktör Benschop'
	CLAIR MATIN ('Meimont') (ClS)	CPou EBls MAus NLar
	CLAIRE AUSTIN ('Ausprior'[PBR]) (S)	CRos EBee EPfP ESty LBuc LRHS MAus NLar NRHS SCob SCoo SPoG SWCr
	'Claire Jacquier' (N)	EBls MAus SPer SWCr
	CLAIRE MARSHALL ('Harunite'[PBR]) (F)	ESty
	CLAIRE ROSE ('Auslight'[PBR]) (S)	LSRN
	'Clarence House' (Cl)	CWld EBls ELan LRHS MAsh
	CLARET ('Frykristal'[PBR]) (HT) 🏆H6	ECnt ESty MAsh MRav
	CLAUDE MONET ('Jacdesa') (HT)	ESty
	'Clementina Carbonieri' (T)	CPou EBls NLar
	CLEO ('Beebop') (HT)	LSRN
	CLEOPATRA ('Korverpea'[PBR]) (HT)	MAsh SWCr
	'Cliff Richard' (F)	ESty LSRN
	'Climbing Alec's Red' (ClHT)	ELon SPer
	'Climbing Allgold' (ClF)	EBls
	'Climbing Arthur Bell' (ClF)	CGro CSBt CTri ESty IBoy MAsh MSwo NPri SCob SPer SPoG SSea SWCr
	'Climbing Ballerina' (Ra)	CSBt
§	CLIMBING BARONNE EDMOND DE ROTHSCHILD ('Meigrisosar') (ClHT)	CSBt
	CLIMBING BETTINA ('Mepalsar') (ClHT)	EBls
	'Climbing Blessings' (ClHT)	EBls
	'Climbing Blue Moon' (ClHT)	ELan ELon SWCr
§	'Climbing Captain Christy' (ClHT)	EBls MAus
	'Climbing Cécile Brünner' (ClPoly) 🏆H6	CSBt CTri EBls ECnt EPfP LSRN MAus MRav NLar SCob SEND SPer SSea SWCr
	'Climbing Christine' (ClHT)	MAus
	'Climbing Château de Clos-Vougeot' (ClHT)	EBls MAus
§	'Climbing Columbia' (ClHT)	EBls EShb SPer
	'Climbing Crimson Glory' (ClHT)	CBod CPou EBls EPfP MAus
§	'Climbing Devoniensis' (ClT)	CPou EBls
	'Climbing Ena Harkness' (ClHT)	CRos CTri EBls MAus MRav SEND SPer SPoG SWCr
	'Climbing Étoile de Hollande' (ClHT) 🏆H6	CGro CKel CSBt CTri CWld EBls EPfP EUJe IBoy LBuc LCro LOPS MAus MJak MRav NPri SMad SPer SSea SWCr WBor
	'Climbing Fashion' (ClF)	EBls
	CLIMBING FRAGRANT CLOUD ('Colfragrasar') (ClHT)	ELan
	'Climbing Frau Karl Druschki' (ClHP)	EBls
	'Climbing General MacArthur' (ClHT)	EBls
§	'Climbing Golden Dawn' (ClHT)	EBls
	'Climbing Home Sweet Home' (ClHT)	LSRN
	'Climbing Iceberg' (ClF) 🏆H7	Widely available
	'Climbing Jazz'	see *R.* THAT'S JAZZ
	'Climbing Josephine Bruce' (ClHT)	EBls
§	'Climbing Lady Hillingdon' (ClT) 🏆H4	CKel CWld EBls ELan EPfP EShb ESps EUJe LBuc LRHS LSRN MAus MRav NEgg NLar SPer SWCr WBor
	'Climbing Lady Sylvia' (ClHT)	CKel CSBt EBls EPfP LRHS LSRN MAus NRHS SPer
	'Climbing Little White Pet'	see *R.* 'Félicité Perpétue'
	'Climbing Madame Abel Chatenay' (ClHT)	MAus
	'Climbing Madame Butterfly' (ClHT) 🏆H6	EBls MAus
	'Climbing Madame Caroline Testout' (ClHT)	CPou CTri EBls MAus MRav SPer
§	'Climbing Madame Edouard Herriot' (ClHT)	MAus
	'Climbing Masquerade' (ClF)	CBod CGro CPou CTri EBls MAus MRav NEgg SCob SPer SSea SWCr
	'Climbing Mrs Aaron Ward' (ClHT)	EBls
	'Climbing Mrs Herbert Stevens' (ClHT)	EBls EPfP LRHS MAus MRav SEND SPer SWCr
	'Climbing Mrs Sam McGredy' (ClHT)	CSBt EBls MAus NLar
	'Climbing Niphetos' (ClT)	EBls MAus
	'Climbing Ophelia' (ClHT)	EBee EBls MAus SPer

CLIMBING ORANGE SUNBLAZE ('Meiji Katarsar'PBR) (ClMin) SPer
§ 'Climbing Paul Lédé' (ClT) EBls EWTr LRHS MAus
'Climbing Peace' (ClHT) SPer
'Climbing Picture' (ClHT) EBls
§ 'Climbing Pompon de Paris' (ClMinCh) CTri EBls MAus MNrw MRav SEND SPer
'Climbing Roundelay' (Cl) EBls
'Climbing Ruby Wedding' (ClHT) LSRN
'Climbing Shot Silk' (ClHT) ♀H6 CKel EBls SPer
§ 'Climbing Souvenir de la Malmaison' (ClBb) CPou EBls MAus SPer
'Climbing Talisman' (ClHT) EBls
'Climbing The Queen Elizabeth' (ClF) EBls MAsh
'Climbing White Cloud' see *R.* WHITE CLOUD ('Korstacha')
'Cloth of Gold' see *R.* 'Chromatella'
'Clytemnestra' (HM) **new** EBls
COCO ('Korferse') (F) LSRN
'Coconut Ice' (HT) SCob
COLCHESTER BEAUTY ('Cansend') (F) ECnt
§ 'Colonel Fabvier' (Ch) EBls MAus NLar
colonial white see *R.* 'Sombreuil'
'Columbia' (HT) CPou
'Columbian' see *R.* 'Climbing Columbia'
'Commandant Beaurepaire' (Bb) CPou EBls MAus SMad
common moss see *R.* × *centifolia* 'Muscosa'
'Compassion' (ClHT) ♀H6 Widely available
* 'Compassionate' (F) MRav
'Complicata' (G) CPou CTri EBls EPfP LRHS MAus MCot MRav NLar SCob SEND SMad SPer SWCr
'Comte de Chambord' misapplied see *R.* 'Madame Boll'
COMTE DE CHAMPAGNE ('Ausufo'PBR) (S) MAus
'Comtesse Cécile de Chabrillant' (HP) CPou EBls MAus
'Comtesse de Lacépède' misapplied see *R.* 'Du Maître d'Ecole'
§ 'Comtesse de Murinais' (DMo) EBls MAus
'Comtesse d'Oxford' (HP) **new** EBls
§ 'Comtesse du Caÿla' (Ch) EBls MAus
'Comtesse O'Gorman' (HP) **new** EBls
'Comtesse Vandal' (HT) EBls
'Conditorum' (G) EBls LEdu
CONGRATULATIONS ('Korlift') (HT) CBcs CBod CKel CSBt EBls ECnt IArd IBoy LSRN MAus MGos MRav MWat SCob SPer SVic SWCr
§ 'Conrad Ferdinand Meyer' (Ru) EBee EBls SPer
CONSERVATION ('Cocdimple') (Min/Patio) MJak
'Constance Spry' (ClS) ♀H6 CBod CRav CTri EBls EPfP ESps EWTr LCro LOPS LRHS MAus MMuc MRav MSwo MWat NEgg NLar NRHS SCob SEND SPer
§ 'Cooperi' (Ra) CRHN EBls EWTr MAus SSea WKif WPGP
Cooper's Burmese see *R.* 'Cooperi'
'Copenhagen' (ClHT) EBls
COPPER LIGHTS ('Simhigh') (HT) ESty
'Coral Cluster' (Poly) EBls MAus
'Coral Creeper' (ClHT) CRHN EBls
'Coral Dawn' (ClHT) EBls
CORAL GEM ('Simplan') (HT) ESty
CORAL PALACE see *R.* IMAGINATION ('Pouldron')
'Coralie' (D) EBls
CORDELIA ('Ausbottle'PBR) (S) MAus
'Cornelia' (HM) ♀H6 CBcs CBod CGro CTri EBee EBls EPfP IArd LRHS LSRN MAsh MAus MCot MRav NLar SCob SMad SPer SRGP SWCr
CORONATION STREET ('Wekswetrup') (F) LSRN
CORVEDALE ('Ausnetting'PBR) (S) MAus
'Coryana' (S) EBls
corymbifera (S) EBls
'Cosimo Ridolfi' (G) EBls
COSMOPOLITAN ('Simgrid') (HT) ESty
cottage maid see *R.* × *centifolia* 'Unique Panachée'
COTTAGE MAID ('Poulspan') (S) MAus
COTTAGE ROSE ('Ausglisten'PBR) (S) LSRN MAus
COUNTESS CELESTE see *R.* IMAGINATION ('Pouldron')
COUNTESS OF WESSEX ('Beacream') (S) EBls LRHS MAsh SWCr
COUNTY OF YORKSHIRE ('Korstarnow'PBR) (GC) ♀H6 ELan ESty
'Coupe d'Hébé' (Bb) EBls MAus
COURAGE ('Poulduf'PBR) (HT) ECnt
COURVOISIER ('Macsee') (F) CSBt
'Cramoisi Picotée' (G) MAus
'Cramoisi Supérieur' (Ch) EBls MAus
CRAZY FOR YOU ('Wekroalt'PBR) (F) ♀H6 EBls ESty LBuc LRHS LSRN MAsh SWCr
CREAM ABUNDANCE ('Harflax'PBR) (Abundance Series) (F) SSea SWCr
CREAM DREAM ('Koromtar') (HT) CTri
'Cream of the Crop' (Patio) CGro
CREAMCRACKER ('Dicorigin') (F) **new** IDic
CRÈME DE LA CRÈME ('Gancre'PBR) (ClHT) CKel CRos CSBt EBls ECnt ELan ESty IRob LRHS MAus MRav SPer SPoG SRGP SSea SWCr
CRÈME DE LA CRÈME ('Tan02525'PBR) (HT) **new** IRob
'Crépuscule' (N) EBee EBls EWTr MAus NLar
crested moss see *R.* × *centifolia* 'Cristata'
CRICRI ('Meicri') (Min) MAus
CRIMSON CASCADE ('Fryclimbdown'PBR) (ClHT) ♀H6 ESty EUJe LBuc LRHS MAsh MRav MSwo SPer SPoG SSea
crimson damask see *R. gallica* var. *officinalis*
'Crimson Descant' (ClHT) ECnt
'Crimson Glory' (HT) CTri EBls
'Crimson Shower' (Ra) CBod CKel CRos CTri ELan EWTr LBuc LRHS MAus MBNS MMuc

		MRav MSwo NEgg NLar NRHS SEND SPer WHer
	CRIMSON SWEET DREAM ('Frynogo') (Patio)	ECnt ESty SWCr
	'Cristata'	see *R.* × *centifolia* 'Cristata'
	CROCUS ROSE ('Ausquest'[PBR]) (S) ♀H6	CBod CKel CRos EPfP LCro LOPS LRHS MAus MRav NEgg NLar NRHS SCob SPer SWCr
	CROWN PRINCESS MARGARETA ('Auswinter'[PBR]) (S)	CRos ELan EPfP EShb ESty LBuc LRHS MAus NEgg NLar NRHS SCob SCoo SPer SPoG SWCr
	cuisse de nymphe	see *R.* 'Great Maiden's Blush'
	'Cupid' (ClHT)	EBls EWTr MAus SPer
I	'Cutie' (Patio)	ESty
	cymosa **new**	EBls
	- 'Rebecca Rushforth'	WPGP
	'Cynthia Brooke' (HT)	EBls
	DACAPO ('Poulcy012'[PBR]) (Courtyard Series) (ClPatio)	ECnt
	'D'Aguesseau' (G)	MAus
	'Daily Mail'	see *R.* 'Climbing Madame Edouard Herriot'
	'Dainty Bess' (HT)	EBls MAus
	'Dainty Maid' (F)	EBls
	'Daisy Hill' ('Macrantha' hybrid) ♀H7	EBls
	× ***damascena*** var. ***bifera***	see *R.* × *damascena* var. *semperflorens*
	- 'Kazanlik' (D) **new**	EBls
§	- 'Professeur Émile Perrot' (D)	LEdu MAus WFar
§	- var. ***semperflorens*** (D) ♀H7	CPou EBls EWTr MAus MCot NLar SSea
	- 'Trigintipetala' misapplied	see *R.* × *damascena* 'Professeur Émile Perrot'
§	- 'Versicolor' (D)	EBls MAus SPer SSea
	'Dame Edith Helen' (HT)	EBls
	DAME WENDY ('Canson') (F)	MAus
	'Danaë' (HM)	EBls MAus
	DANCING QUEEN ('Fryfeston') (ClHT) ♀H6	CGro ECnt EUJe LSRN MAsh MRav SWCr
	DANIEL ('Webwhite') (HT)	ESty
	DANNY BOY ('Dicxcon'[PBR]) (Patio)	IDic LSRN
	DANSE DES SYLPHES ('Malcair') (Cl)	EBls
	'Danse du Feu' (ClF)	CBcs CKel CSBt CTri EBls ELan ESps EUJe IBoy LRHS MAsh MAus MRav SCob SPer SWCr
	'Daphne' ambig.	EBls LSRN
	DAPPLE DAWN ('Ausapple') (S)	MAus
	DARCEY BUSSELL ('Ausdecorum'[PBR]) (S) ♀H6	CGro CRos CSBt ECnt EPfP ESty IRob LBuc LCro LOPS LRHS LSRN MAsh MAus MGos NLar NRHS SCob SPer SWCr
	'Darling Jenny' (HT)	LSRN
	DAVID WHITFIELD ('Gana'[PBR]) (F)	LSRN
	davidii (S)	EBls MAus
	DAVID'S STAR ('Hordadstar') (HT)	LSRN
	DAWN CHORUS ('Dicquasar'[PBR]) (HT) ♀H6	CGro CSBt EPfP ESty IBoy MAsh MJak MRav SCob SPer SPoG SSea SWCr
	'Daybreak' (HM)	CTri EBls MAus NLar
	'De la Grifferaie'	EBls
	'De Meaux'	see *R.* × *centifolia* 'De Meaux'
	'De Meaux, White'	see *R.* 'White de Meaux'
§	'De Resht' (DPo) ♀H7	CBod CKel CPou CRav CTri CWld EBls ECnt EPfP LBuc LRHS MAsh MAus MCot MRav MWat NLar NPri SPer SWCr
	DEAR BARBARA ('Rawbar') **new**	LSRN
	'Dear Daughter' (F)	ESty
	DEAR JOAN ('Rawjo') **new**	LSRN
§	DEAR MARGARET ('Raw293') **new**	LSRN
	DEAR MICHAEL ('Raw1065') **new**	LSRN
	'Dearest' (F)	CTri SCob SPer SWCr
	'Debbie Thomas' (HT)	LSRN
	DEB'S DELIGHT ('Legsweet'[PBR]) (F)	LSRN
	'Debutante' (Ra) ♀H7	CBod CRHN EBls EWTr LRHS MAus
	'Deep Secret' (HT)	CBcs CGro CKel CSBt CTri EBls ECnt ELan ELon EPfP ESps ESty LBuc LRHS MAsh MCot MJak MRav NPri SCob SPer SRGP SSea SWCr
	'Deidre Hall' (HT)	LSRN
	'Delambre' (DPo)	MAus
	DELLA BALFOUR ('Harblend'[PBR]) (ClHT)	EBls
	DENTELLE DE MALINES ('Lenfiro') (S)	MAus
	'Deschamps' (N)	EBls
	DESDEMONA ('Auskindling') (HM) **new**	CRos LRHS MAus
	'Designer Sunset' (Patio)	MAsh
§	'Desprez à Fleur Jaune' (N)	EBls IArd LRHS MAus MCot NEgg SPer
	'Deuil de Paul Fontaine' (Mo)	EBls
	'Devoniensis' (ClT)	see *R.* 'Climbing Devoniensis'
	DIAMOND ANNIVERSARY ('Morsixty') (Min)	CRos LBuc LSRN
	'Diamond Celebration' (HT)	LSRN
	DIAMOND DAYS FOREVER ('Fryjess'[PBR]) (F)	ECnt LSRN
	DIAMOND DAYS ('Hartribe'[PBR]) (HT)	ESty MRav
	DIAMOND EYES ('Wekwibypur') (Min)	ECnt ESty
	'Diamond Jubilee' (HT)	CSBt EBls SWCr
	DIAMOND ('Korgazell'[PBR]) (Patio) ♀H6	EPfP LRHS LSRN NRHS
	'Diamond Wishes'	see *R.* MISTY HIT
	DIANA ('Tananaid'[PBR]) (HT)	LSRN
	DICK'S DELIGHT ('Dicwhistle') (GC)	LSRN
	DIENIE STEWART ('Dicpraise') (F)	IDic
	DIORESSENCE ('Deldiore') (F)	ESty
§	'Direktör Benschop'	EBls MCot
	DISCO QUEEN ('Tan08171'[PBR]) (Patio)	ESty
	DIXIELAND LINDA ('Beadix') (ClHT)	EBls LRHS MAsh
	DIZZY HEIGHTS ('Fryblissful'[PBR]) (ClHT) ♀H6	MAus MRav SPer
	'Docteur Grill' (T)	EBls
	'Doctor Edward Deacon' (HT)	EBls

	'Doctor Huey' (Cl) **new**	CRHN EBls
	'Doctor W. Van Fleet' (Ra)	EBls MAus
	DOLCE VITA ('Delcentoran') (F) **new**	ESty
	DOLLY ('Poulvision') (F)	LSRN
	'Don Charlton' (HT)	NEgg
	'Donald Prior' (F) **new**	EBls
	'Doncasteri'	EBls MAus
	DONNA ('Pekcoupamaple') (HT)	LSRN
	'Doreen' (HT)	LSRN
	'Doris Tysterman' (HT)	CTri EBls MAus SPer
	DOROTHY ('Cocrocket'PBR) (F)	LSRN MRav
	'Dorothy Perkins' (Ra)	CBod CRHN CTri EBls ESps IRob LBuc LRHS MAsh MAus MRav NPer SCob SPer SRGP WHer
	'Dorothy Wilson' (F)	EBls
	'Dortmund' (S) ♀H7	EBls EWTr MAus NLar SPer SWCr
	DOUBLE DELIGHT ('Andeli') (HT)	CBod EBls ESty IBoy LSRN SPer SSea SWCr
	DOUGLAS ('Cocfresco') (F)	LSRN
	'Dream Catcher' (F)	ESty
	DREAM LOVER ('Peayetti'PBR) (Patio)	ESty SWCr
	'Dreaming Spires' (Cl)	MSwo SPer
	'Dresden Doll' (MinMo)	EBls
§	'Du Maître d'Ecole' (G)	EBls MAus WHer
	DUBLIN BAY ('Macdub') (ClF) ♀H6	CBod CGro CKel CSBt CSam CTri EBls ECnt ELan ELon EPfP ESps EUJe IArd IBoy IRob LRHS LSRN MAsh MRav MSwo MWat NLar NPri SPer SPoG SSea SWCr WBor
	'Duc de Guiche' (G) ♀H7	EBls ESps MAus MMuc NLar SPer WHer
	DUCHESS OF CORNWALL ('Tan97157') (HT) ♀H6	CKel CSBt EBls ESty LCro LOPS MRav SCob SWCr
	'Duchess of Portland'	see *R.* 'Portlandica'
	DUCHESS OF YORK	see *R.* SUNSEEKER
	'Duchesse d'Angoulême' (Ce × G) ♀H7	EBls MAus
	'Duchesse d'Auerstädt' (N)	EBls
	'Duchesse de Brabant' (HT) **new**	EBls
	'Duchesse de Buccleugh' (G)	EBls MAus
§	'Duchesse de Montebello' (G) ♀H7	CBod CPou EBls EWTr GBin MAus NLar SPer
	'Duchesse de Rohan' (Ce × HP)	EBls
	'Duchesse de Verneuil' (CeMo)	MAus
	'Duke of Edinburgh' (HP)	EBls MAus
	DUKE OF EDINBURGH (Patio)	see *R.* THE GOLD AWARD ROSE
	'Duke of Wellington' (HP)	CPou EBls
	'Duke of Windsor' (HT)	SPer
	'Dundee Rambler' (Ra)	MAus
	DUNHAM MASSEY ('Beajelly') (S) **new**	EBls LRHS
	'Dunwich Rose' (SpH)	CBod EBls EPfP MAus NLar SCob SPer WCot
§	'Duplex' (S)	EBls MAus
	'Dupontii' (S) ♀H6	EBls EWTr MAus NLar SPer
	'Dupuy Jamain' (HP)	EBls
	'Dusky Maiden' (F)	CBod EBls EWTr MAus SWCr
	'Dutch Gold' (HT)	MAus SPer
	DWARF FAIRY ('Korweenu') (Min)	MAsh

	DYNAMIC DUO ('Fryvogue') (F)	ECnt ESty
	'E.H. Morse'	see *R.* 'Ernest H. Morse'
	'Easlea's Golden Rambler' (Ra) ♀H6	EBls ESty LRHS MAus MRav NEgg NLar
	EAST PARK ('Harjope'PBR) (HT)	ESty
§	EASY DOES IT ('Harpageant'PBR) (F) ♀H6	CBod CKel ECnt ESty MAsh MRav MWat NLar SWCr
	EASY GOING ('Harflow'PBR) (F) ♀H6	IArd LBuc MAsh SWCr
§	EBB TIDE ('Weksmopur'PBR) (F)	CBod CSBt CWld ECnt ESty LRHS MAsh SWCr
	ecae (S)	EBls MAus
	'Éclair' (HP)	EBls WBor
	'Eddie's Crimson' (*moyesii* hybrid)	LSRN
	'Eddie's Jewel' (*moyesii* hybrid)	EBls LSRN MAus
	EDEN ROSE '88 ('Meiviolin') (ClHT)	CPou EBee EBls SPer SWCr
	'Edith Bellenden' (RH)	EBls
	EDITH HOLDEN ('Chewlegacy') (F)	EBls
	'Edward Hyams' (*persica* hybrid)	MAus
	EDWARD'S ROSE ('Smi73/7/97') (F)	ESty LSRN MRav
	eglanteria	see *R. rubiginosa*
	EGLANTYNE ('Ausmak'PBR) (S)	CKel CRos CSBt ELan ELon EPfP LCro LOPS LRHS MAus MRav MWat NRHS SCob SPer SSea SWCr
	ELAINE PAGE ('Poulht008'PBR) (HT)	LRHS MAsh SWCr
	'Eleanor' (Patio)	LSRN
	ELEANOR ('Poulberin'PBR) (S)	CPou ECnt LSRN
	'Elegance' (ClHT)	EBls
§	***elegantula*** 'Persetosa' (S)	EBls MAus NLar SPer
§	ELINA ('Dicjana') (HT) ♀H6	EBls ECnt MAus MJak MRav SPer SWCr
	'Elizabeth Harkness' (HT)	EBls MAus SPer
	'Elizabeth Harwood' (Cl) **new**	EBls
	ELIZABETH OF GLAMIS ('Macel') (F)	CTri EBls SPer
	ELIZABETH STUART ('Maselstu') (Generosa Series) (S)	LSRN
	ELLE ('Meibderos'PBR) (HT)	LSRN
	ELLEN ('Auscup') (S)	LSRN
	'Ellen Willmott' (HT)	EBee EBls SPer
	'Elmshorn' (S)	EBls
	ELOISE ('Kirsandra'PBR) (HT)	LSRN
	EMILIA MARIA	see *R.* LA ROSE DE MOLINARD
	EMILY ('Ausburton') (S)	LSRN
	'Emily Gray' (Ra)	CRHN EBls LBuc LSRN MAsh MAus MRav NLar NPri SCob SPer WHer
	EMILY VICTORIA ('Boshipeacon') (F)	LSRN
	'Empereur du Maroc' (HP)	EBee EBls IBoy MAus
	'Ena Harkness' (HT)	CKel CTri EBls ELan ESps LBuc LRHS NRHS SRGP
§	'Enfant de France' (HP)	EBls LSRN
	ENGLAND'S ROSE ('Auslounge'PBR) (S)	CGro MAus
	ENGLISH GARDEN ('Ausbuff') (S)	CTri LSRN

'English Miss' (F)	CKel CPou EBls ECnt ELon ESps IBoy LRHS MAsh MAus MJak MRav SPer SPoG SWCr
ENGLISH SONNET	see *R.* SAMARITAN
'Eos' (*moyesii* hybrid)	EBls MAus
'Erfurt' (HM)	EBee EBls MAus SPer
§ 'Ernest H. Morse' (HT)	CSBt CTri EBls IBoy SPer
ESCAPADE ('Harpade') (F) ♀H6	EBls MAus
ESPECIALLY FOR YOU ('Fryworthy'PBR) (HT) ♀H6	CKel CSBt ESps ESty LSRN SCob SSea SWCr
ESSEX ('Poulnoz'PBR) (GC)	CKel EBls SCob SPer
§ 'Estrellita de Oro' (Min)	SPer
'Etain' (Ra)	ECnt
§ 'Étendard' (ClHT)	EBls MRav NLar SPer SPoG
ETERNAL FLAME ('Korassenet'PBR) (F)	MAsh SWCr
ETERNALLY YOURS ('Macspeego'PBR) (HT)	ESty
ETERNITY ('Moai150097') (F)	CGro
ETERNITY ('Twoetern') (HT)	LRHS MAsh
'Ethel' (Ra)	CPou EBls LSRN NLar
'Étoile de Hollande' (HT)	CBod CTri EBls ELan ELon ESps EUJe EWTr LBuc LRHS MAsh MBNS MCot MJak MMrt NEgg NLar SCob
'Étoile de Lyon' (T)	EBls
'Eugène Fürst' (HP)	EBls
'Eugénie Guinoisseau' (Mo)	CPou EBls
EUPHRATES ('Harunique') (*persica* hybrid)	EBls
'Euphrosyne' (Ra)	MAus
'Eva' (HM)	EBls
'Evangeline' (Ra)	EBls MAus
EVELYN ('Aussaucer'PBR) (S)	CKel CRos CSBt EPfP ESps ESty LSRN NEgg NLar SLon SPer
§ EVELYN FISON ('Macev') (F)	CSBt CTri EBls IBoy LSRN MAus SPer
'Evelyn May' (HT)	EBls LRHS MAsh SWCr
'Everest Double Fragrance' (F)	EBls
'Excelsa' (Ra)	CBod CSBt CSam CTri EBls EPfP ESps IArd IBoy IRob LBuc MAsh MRav SCob SPoG WBor
EYE OF THE TIGER ('Chewbullseye') (S) **new**	CRos ESty ETMg LRHS MAsh NRHS SPoG
EYEOPENER ('Interop') (S/GC)	EBls
EYES FOR YOU ('Pejbigeye') (F) ♀H6	CGro CKel CSBt CWld EBee ESty ETMg GBin LRHS MAsh NLar NPri SLon SPer SWCr WKif
'F.E. Lester'	see *R.* 'Francis E. Lester'
§ 'F.J. Grootendorst' (Ru)	CBod EBls IBoy NEgg SPer WHer
FAB AT 50 ('Woraunt') (F)	LSRN
FABULOUS AT 40 ('Webcountry') **new**	LSRN
FABULOUS AT 50 ('Rawfabsal') (F)	LSRN
FABULOUS AT 65 ('Raw1041') **new**	LSRN
FABULOUS AT 70	LSRN
FABULOUS AT 80 ('Rawcox') (F)	LSRN
FAB-U-LOUS! ('Forfab') (HT) **new**	ESty
'Fabvier'	see *R.* 'Colonel Fabvier'
FAIR EVA ('Seaeva') (Ra/GC)	ESty
'Fairy Rose'	see *R.* 'The Fairy'
FAITHFUL FRIEND ('Beachallenge') (S)	EBls LSRN
FALSTAFF ('Ausverse'PBR) (S)	CRos CSBt EPfP IBoy LCro LOPS LRHS LSRN MAus MBNS MJak MRav MSwo MWat NEgg NLar NRHS SCob SMad SPer SSea SWCr
'Fantin-Latour' (Ce) ♀H7	CTri EBls ECnt ELan EWTr IBoy LEdu LRHS MAus MMuc MRav NEgg NLar SEND SMad SPer
fargesii hort.	see *R. moyesii* var. *fargesii*
farreri f. ***persetosa***	see *R. elegantula* 'Persetosa'
§ FASCINATION ('Poulmax'PBR) (F) ♀H6	ELon IBoy MAsh SPer SWCr
'Fashion' (F) **new**	EBls
FATHER'S FAVOURITE ('Gandoug'PBR) (F)	LSRN
fedtschenkoana misapplied	MAus SPer
fedtschenkoana Regel	EBls
FÉE DES NEIGES	see *R.* ICEBERG
'Felicia' (HM) ♀H6	CKel CRav CSBt CSam CTri EBee EBls ECnt ELan LRHS MAsh MAus MCot MMuc MRav MSwo MWat NLar SEND SPer SSea SWCr WKif
'Félicité Parmentier' (A × D) ♀H7	EBls EPfP MAus NLar SPer SWCr
§ 'Félicité Perpétue' (Ra) ♀H7	CBcs CBod CTri EBls ELan EPfP IBoy LRHS MAus MRav MSwo NEgg NLar SEND SPer SSea SWCr
'Fellemberg' (ClCh)	EBee EBls MAus
FELLOWSHIP ('Harwelcome'PBR) (F) ♀H6	EBls MAus SCob SSea SWCr
'Ferdinand Pichard' (Bb) ♀H7	Widely available
FERDY ('Keitoli'PBR) (GC)	EBls SPer
ferruginea	see *R. glauca* Pourr.
FESTIVAL ('Kordialo'PBR) (Patio)	IBoy MRav SPer
FESTIVE JEWEL ('Beacost') (S)	EBls LRHS MAsh
FIGHTING TEMERAIRE ('Austrava'PBR) (S)	CRos EBee EPfP LBuc LRHS MAus NRHS SSea SWCr
§ ***filipes*** 'Kiftsgate' (Ra) ♀H6	CBcs CBod CGro CKel CSBt CTri EBee EBls ECnt ELan EPfP ESps GKin IBoy LEdu LRHS MAus MRav MWat NEgg NLar NRHS SCob SEND SMad SPer SPoG SSea SWCr WKif
filipes* × *glauca	MAus
§ 'Fimbriata' (Ru)	CPou EBee EBls LEdu MAus NLar SPer
FIONA ('Meibeluxen') (S/GC)	EBls LSRN MSwo
'Firecracker' (F)	EBls
FIRESTAR	see *R.* EASY DOES IT
FIRST GREAT WESTERN ('Oracharpam'PBR) (HT)	ESty
'First Love' (HT)	EBls
'Fisher and Holmes' (HP)	EBls MAus
FLAMINGO ('Simref') (F)	ESty
FLASH GORDON ('Simgord') (F)	ESty
FLIRT ('Korkopapp'PBR) (F)	MAsh
'Flora' (HT)	MAus
'Flora' (Ra) **new**	EBls
'Flora McIvor' (RH)	EBls

FLOWER CARPET AMBER ('Noa97400a'^{PBR}) (GC) 🏆^{H6}	CGro CRos CSBt EBls ELan EPfP EUJe IBoy LBuc LRHS MAsh NPri NRHS SPoG SWCr
'Flower Carpet Coral'^{PBR} (GC) 🏆^{H6}	CRos CSBt EBls EPfP IBoy LBuc LRHS MAsh NPri NRHS SPer SWCr
FLOWER CARPET GOLD ('Noalesa'^{PBR}) (GC)	CGro CRos EBls ECnt IBoy LBuc LRHS MAsh NPri NRHS SPoG
FLOWER CARPET PINK	see *R.* PINK FLOWER CARPET
FLOWER CARPET PINK SUPREME ('Noa168098f') (GC) **new**	EBls
FLOWER CARPET RED VELVET ('Noare'^{PBR}) (GC/S) 🏆^{H6}	CGro CRos EBls ELan EPfP IBoy LBuc LCro LOPS LRHS MAsh NPri NRHS SCoo SPer SSea
FLOWER CARPET RUBY (GC)	CRos EBls EUJe LBuc LRHS LSRN MAsh NPri NRHS SPoG
FLOWER CARPET SCARLET ('Noa83100b'^{PBR}) (GC) 🏆^{H6}	CRos EBls LBuc LRHS MAsh NRHS SWCr
FLOWER CARPET SUNSET ('Deseo') (S)	CGro CRos EPfP LRHS MAsh NPri SWCr
§ FLOWER CARPET SUNSHINE ('Noason'^{PBR}) (GC) 🏆^{H6}	CBod CRos EBee EBls LCro LOPS LRHS MAsh NPri NRHS SCoo SPer SSea
FLOWER CARPET WHITE ('Noaschnee'^{PBR}) (GC) 🏆^{H6}	CGro CRos CTri EBee EBls ECnt EPfP IBoy IRob LCro LOPS LRHS LSRN MAsh MAus NPri NRHS SCoo SMad SPer SPoG SSea SWCr
FLOWER POWER ('Frycassia'^{PBR}) (Patio) 🏆^{H6}	CKel CSBt ECnt ESty IBoy LRHS MAsh MAus MRav MWat NPri SPoG SWCr
FLOWER POWER GOLD ('Fryneon') (Patio)	ECnt ESty LRHS MAsh NPri NRHS SPoG SWCr
§ ***foetida*** (S)	EBls MAus SPer
§ - 'Bicolor' (S)	EBls MAus NLar SPer
§ - 'Persiana' (S)	EBls MAus
foliolosa	EBls
'Follette' (Cl)	EBls
FOND MEMORIES ('Kirfelix'^{PBR}) (Patio)	ESty LSRN SCoo
FOR YOU WITH LOVE ('Fryjangle') (Patio)	LSRN MAsh
FOR YOUR EYES ONLY ('Cheweyesup') (S)	CBod CGro CKel CRos CSBt EBee ECnt ESty ETMg GBin LBuc LCro LOPS LRHS LSRN MAsh MRav MWat NLar NPri NRHS SCoo SPer SPoG SWCr
FORGET ME NOT ('Coccharm'^{PBR}) (HT)	ESty
forrestiana (S)	EBls MAus
× ***fortuneana*** (Ra)	EBls
Fortune's double yellow	see *R.* × *odorata* 'Pseudindica'
'Fountain' (S)	EBls MAus
FOXY LADY ('Simmem') (HT)	ESty
FRAGONARD ('Delparviro'^{PBR}) (HT) **new**	ESty
FRAGRANT BEAUTY ('Smi152-1-4') (HT) **new**	ESty
FRAGRANT CLOUD ('Tanellis') (HT)	CBcs CRos CTri EBls ELan ELon EPfP IBoy LBuc LRHS MAsh MAus MGos MRav SPer SPoG SWCr
'Fragrant Delight' (F) 🏆^{H6}	CKel CSBt EBls ELan ESps MAus MJak MRav SCob SPer
FRAGRANT DREAM ('Dicodour') (HT)	ESty IBoy SSea
FRAGRANT MEMORIES ('Korpastato'^{PBR}) (HT)	CSBt
'Fragrant Silk' **new**	SSea

'Francesca' (HM)	EBls EWTr LSRN MAus NLar SPer
FRANCINE AUSTIN ('Ausram') (S/GC)	MAus NEgg SPer
'Francis Copple' (S) **new**	EBls
'Francis Dubreuil' (T)	EBls
§ 'Francis E. Lester' (HM/Ra) 🏆^{H6}	CBWd CRHN CSam EBls ELan EPfP EWTr LRHS MAus MCot MMuc NLar NRHS SEND SPer SRGP SSea SWCr
× ***francofurtana*** misapplied	see *R.* 'Impératrice Joséphine'
- 'Empress Josephine'	see *R.* 'Impératrice Joséphine'
'François Juranville' (Ra) 🏆^{H6}	CHll CRHN EBee EBls EPfP IBoy LRHS MAus MMuc MRav NLar SEND SLon SPer WFar WHer
§ 'Frau Karl Druschki' (HP)	EBls MAus
'Fred Loads' (F) 🏆^{H7}	EBls MAus MCot
FREDDIE MERCURY ('Batmercury') (HT)	ESty LSRN NEgg
FREE SPIRIT ('Fryjeru'^{PBR}) (F) 🏆^{H6}	ECnt
FREEDOM ('Dicjem') (HT) 🏆^{H6}	CKel CTri EBls ECnt MAus MJak MRav SCob SPer
FREEDOM ('Tan97544') (HT)	CKel
'Frensham' (F)	CBcs EBls SSea
FRIEND FOR LIFE ('Cocnanne'^{PBR}) (F) 🏆^{H6}	LSRN MRav
FRIENDS FOREVER ('Korapriber') (F) 🏆^{H6}	CSBt EPfP LSRN MAsh SWCr
FRIENDSHIP OF STRANGERS ('633D9') (Cl) **new**	EBls
FRILLY CUFF ('Beajingle') (S) **new**	EBls
'Fritz Nobis' (S) 🏆^{H7}	CPou EBls MAus NLar SPer
FROTHY ('Macfrothy'^{PBR}) (Patio)	ECnt ESty
'Fru Dagmar Hastrup' (Ru) 🏆^{H7}	CBcs CBod CDul CKel CSBt CTri EBee EBls ECnt ELan EPfP ESps IBoy IRob LBuc LRHS MAsh MAus MSwo NEgg NLar SCob SEND SPer SWCr
'Frühlingsanfang' (SpH)	EBls
'Frühlingsduft' (SpH)	EBls
'Frühlingsgold' (SpH) 🏆^{H7}	EBls ELan ESps EWTr MAus NLar SPer
'Frühlingsmorgen' (SpH) 🏆^{H7}	EBls MAus SMad SPer
'Frühlingsschnee' (SpH)	EBls
'Frühlingszauber' (SpH)	EBls
'Fulgens'	see *R.* 'Malton'
§ ***gallica*** (G)	EBls
§ - var. ***officinalis*** (G) 🏆^{H7}	CBod CRos CTri EBls EPfP GPoy LEdu LRHS MAsh MAus MHer MNHC MRav NLar SPer SRms SSea SWCr WHer
- 'Velutiniflora' (G)	EBls
§ - 'Versicolor' (G) 🏆^{H7}	CKel CSBt CTri EBee EBls ECnt ELan EPfP EWTr GPoy IBoy IRob LEdu LRHS LSRN MAsh MAus MCot MHer MNHC MRav MWat NLar NRHS NSti SPer SSea WBor WKif
GALWAY BAY ('Macba') (ClHT)	CBod CPou EBls IBoy IRob LRHS MAsh NLar SPer SWCr
GARDEN OF ROSES	see *R.* JOIE DE VIVRE
GARDEN PARTY ('Kormollis') (F)	EBls
'Gardeners Glory'^{PBR} (ClHT) 🏆^{H6}	CSBt ECnt EPfP ESty EUJe MAsh MRav NPri SPoG SWCr

GARDENERS' JOY ('Beadrum') (S)	EBls
'Gardenia' (Ra)	EBee EBls MAus MMuc MSwo NLar SPer
'Garnette Carol'	see *R.* 'Carol Amling'
'Garnette Pink'	see *R.* 'Carol Amling'
'Gaujard'	see *R.* ROSE GAUJARD
'Gelbe Dagmar Hastrup'	see *R.* YELLOW DAGMAR HASTRUP
GEMINI ('Jacnepal') (HT) **new**	ESty
'Général Jacqueminot' (HP)	EBls MAus
'Général Kléber' (CeMo) ♀H7	EBls MAus
§ 'Général Schablikine' (T)	EBls MAus MCot NLar
GENESIS ('Fryjuicy'[PBR]) (Patio)	CGro ECnt MRav SWCr
gentiliana misapplied	see *R.* 'Polyantha Grandiflora'
gentiliana H. Lév. & Variot	see *R. multiflora* var. *cathayensis*
GENTLE HERMIONE ('Ausrumba'[PBR]) (S)	CGro CRos ELan EPfP IBoy LBuc LRHS MAsh MAus NLar NRHS SCob SPer SPoG
GENTLE TOUCH ('Diclulu') (Min/Patio)	CKel CSBt ESps MRav SPer
GEOFF HAMILTON ('Ausham'[PBR]) (S)	EBee EPfP IBoy LSRN MAsh MAus MBNS NEgg SCob SPer SSea
'Geoffrey Smith' (Cl)	LSRN NDal
'Georg Arends' (HP)	EBls MAus
GEORGE BEST ('Dichimanher'[PBR]) (Patio) ♀H6	ESty IDic LSRN
'George Dickson' (HT)	EBls
GEORGE ('Simetna') (F) **new**	ESty
'George Vancouver' (S)	EBls
'Georges Vibert' (G)	EBls MAus
'Geranium' (*moyesii* hybrid) ♀H7	CBcs CDul CKel CTri EBee EBls ELan EPfP ESps IArd IBoy MAus MRav MWat NLar SCob SPer SWCr
GERBE D'OR	see *R.* CASINO
'Gerbe Rose' (Ra)	EBls MAus WHer
GERTRUDE JEKYLL ('Ausbord'[PBR]) (S) ♀H6	Widely available
'Ghislaine de Féligonde' (HM) ♀H6	CBod CKel CSam EBee EBls EPfP ESty LBuc LRHS MAsh MAus MCot NLar SEND SPer SWCr WBor
GHITA	see *R.* MILLIE
GIARDINA ('Tan08576'[PBR]) (HT) **new**	SWCr
§ GIARDINA ('Tan97289'[PBR]) (Cl)	ESty
gigantea	WPGP
gigantea* × *longicuspis	WPGP
GIGGLES ('Frynoodle'[PBR]) (Patio)	SCoo
GINGER SYLLABUB ('Harjolina'[PBR]) (ClHT)	CKel CPou ECnt ELon ESty MRav SPer SPoG SRGP
GIPSY BOY	see *R.* 'Zigeunerknabe'
giraldii (S)	EBls
GISELA'S DELIGHT ('Horpink') (S) **new**	EBls
GLAD TIDINGS ('Tantide') (F)	CTri EBls IBoy MRav SPer SWCr
GLAMIS CASTLE ('Auslevel'[PBR]) (S)	CBcs CTri EBee IBoy LCro LOPS NEgg SCob SCoo SPer SWCr
glauca Vill. ex Lois.	see *R. caesia* subsp. *vosagiaca*
glauca ambig.	ESps EWTr GMcL MHer MSwo SCob
§ ***glauca*** Pourr. (S) ♀H7	CBWd CDul CMea CSBt CTri EBee EBls ECnt ELan ELon EPfP GBin LCro LEdu LOPS LRHS MAus MMuc MRav NEgg NLar SEND SGol SPer SPoG SSea SWCr WCot WMoo
'Glenfiddich' (F)	CSBt CTri ESps LSRN MAus SPer
'Glenn Dale' (Cl)	CPou
GLOBAL BEAUTY ('Tan 94448') (HT)	ECnt MRav SWCr
'Gloire de Bruxelles' (HP)	EBls
'Gloire de Dijon' (ClT)	CGro CKel CSBt CTri EBee EBls ECnt ELan IBoy LCro LOPS LRHS LSRN MAus MRav MWat NEgg NLar SCob SPer SRGP
'Gloire de Ducher' (HP)	EBls MAus
'Gloire de France' (G) ♀H7	EBls MAus NLar WHer
'Gloire de Guilan' (D)	MAus
'Gloire des Mousseuses' (CeMo)	CPou EBls IRob MAus
'Gloire du Midi' (Poly)	MAus
'Gloire Lyonnaise' (HP)	EBls MMuc
'Gloria Mundi' (Poly)	EBls NEgg
GLORIANA ('Chewpope'[PBR]) (ClMin)	CGro CKel ECnt ESty EUJe MAsh MAus MRav MWat SPer SPoG SSea SWCr
'Glory of Edzell' (SpH)	MAus
'Glory of Seale' (S)	SSea
GLOWING AMBER ('Manglow') (Min)	ESty
'Goethe' (Mo) **new**	EBls
GOLD CHARM ('Chewalbygold') (Cl)	CGro ESty MAsh
'Goldbusch' (RH)	EBls
'Golden Anniversary' (Patio)	ESps IBoy SSea
'Golden Autumn' (HT)	LSRN
GOLDEN BEAUTY ('Clebeau') (Min)	CKel
GOLDEN BEAUTY ('Korberbeni'[PBR]) (F) ♀H6	CKel CPou MAsh SWCr
GOLDEN BERYL ('Manberyl') (Min)	LSRN
GOLDEN CELEBRATION ('Ausgold'[PBR]) (S) ♀H6	CBod CKel CRos CSBt CTri EBee ECnt EPfP ESps ESty IBoy LCro LOPS LRHS LSRN MAsh MAus MMuc MRav MSwo MWat NLar NRHS SCob SLon SMad SPer SPoG SSea SWCr
'Golden Chersonese' (S)	EBls MAus
'Golden Dawn' (HT)	MAsh
'Golden Dawn' (ClHT)	see *R.* 'Climbing Golden Dawn'
GOLDEN FUTURE ('Horanymoll'[PBR]) (ClHT) ♀H6	MAus
GOLDEN GATE ('Korgolgat'[PBR]) (ClHT) ♀H6	ECnt EPfP LRHS MAsh MAus NRHS SSea
'Golden Glow' (Cl)	EBls
GOLDEN JEWEL ('Tanledolg'[PBR]) (F/Patio)	ESty
GOLDEN JUBILEE ('Cocagold') (HT)	EBls MRav
GOLDEN MELODY ('Irene Churruca') (HT)	EBls
GOLDEN MEMORIES ('Korholesea'[PBR]) (F) ♀H6	CSBt EBls ESps LBuc MAsh MGos MJak MRav NPri SCoo SPer SWCr
GOLDEN MOMENT ('Smi-99-2-04') (HT)	ESty MRav
'Golden Moss' (Mo)	EBls
'Golden Rambler'	see *R.* 'Alister Stella Gray'

	'Golden Salmon Supérieur' (Poly)	EBls
	'Golden Showers' (Cl)	Widely available
§	GOLDEN SMILES ('Frykeyno'[PBR]) (F) 𝕐H6	CKel ECnt ESty LSRN MAsh NPri SPoG SWCr
	GOLDEN WEDDING ANNIVERSARY (F)	IRob LSRN
	GOLDEN WEDDING ('Arokris'[PBR]) (F)	Widely available
	'Golden Wedding Celebration' (F)	IRob LSRN
	'Golden Wings' (S)	CPou CTri EBls ELan GBin IBoy MAus MCot MRav MSwo NLar SPer SWCr
	'Goldfinch' (Ra)	CBod EBls ELan EPfP ESps EWTr LRHS MAsh MAus MRav NEgg NLar SEND SPer SPoG WFar
	GOLDSTAR ('Candide') (HT)	ECnt
	GOOD AS GOLD ('Chewsunbeam'[PBR]) (ClMin)	CSBt ECnt ESty SPer
	GORDON SNELL ('Dicwriter') (F)	IDic
	GORGEOUS ('Poulpmt009'[PBR]) (HT) **new**	LRHS MAsh NPri
	'Grace Abounding' (F)	LSRN
	GRACE ('Auskeppy'[PBR]) (S) 𝕐H6	CGro CRos CSBt EPfP EShb ESty LBuc LRHS LSRN MAus NEgg NLar NRHS SCob SMad SPer SSea SWCr
	'Grace Darling' (T)	EBls
	GRACE DE MONACO ('Meimit') (HT)	EBls
	'Graciously Pink' (Min)	MAsh SPoG
	GRAHAM THOMAS ('Ausmas') (S) 𝕐H6	Widely available
I	'Granada' Lindquist (HT)	EBls
	GRANDE AMORE ('Korcoluma'[PBR]) (HT) 𝕐H6	CSBt LSRN
	'Grandma' (F)	LSRN
	GRAND-MÈRE JENNY ('Grem') (HT)	EBls
	'Grandpa Dickson' (HT)	EBls IBoy MAsh MAus SPer
	GRANNY'S FAVOURITE (Patio/F)	LSRN
	GREAT EXPECTATIONS ambig.	EBee
	GREAT EXPECTATIONS ('Lanican') (HT)	CBcs
	GREAT EXPECTATIONS ('Mackalves'[PBR]) (F)	EPfP ESps IArd MRav SPer
§	'Great Maiden's Blush' (A) 𝕐H7	EBls LEdu MRav NLar
	'Great Ormond Street' (F)	EBls
	'Great Western' (Bb)	EBls
	GREENALL'S GLORY ('Kirmac') (F/Patio)	CKel MAus MRav MWat
	GREETINGS ('Jacdreco'[PBR]) (F)	ESps LBuc MAsh
	'Grimpant Cramoisi Supérieur' (ClCh)	EBls
	'Grootendorst'	see *R.* 'F.J. Grootendorst'
	'Grootendorst Supreme' (Ru)	MMrt
	'Gros Chou de Hollande' (Bb)	EBls
	'Grosvenor House Rose' (S) **new**	LRHS MAsh
	GROUSE 2000 ('Korteilhab') (GC) 𝕐H6	MAus
	GROUSE ('Korimro') (S/GC)	EBls MAus NLar SEND SPer
	'Gruss an Aachen' (Poly) 𝕐H6	EBls EPfP MCot MJak NLar SPer
	'Gruss an Teplitz' (China hybrid)	EBls MAus NLar SPer
	'Guinée' (ClHT)	CBod CKel CRos CSBt CTri EBee EBls ELan EPfP ESps EWTr MAus MRav MSwo NLar SPer SRGP WCot WKif
	GUIRLANDE ROSE ('Velwichba') (Ra) **new**	EBls
	'Gustav Grünerwald' (HT)	EBls
	GUY SAVOY ('Delstrimen'[PBR]) (F)	EBls ESty MRav
	GUY'S GOLD ('Harmatch'[PBR]) (HT)	LRHS MAsh
	GWENT ('Poulurt'[PBR]) (GC)	CSBt EBls ELan SCob SEND SPer SSea
	gymnocarpa **new**	EBls
	GYPSY BOY	see *R.* 'Zigeunerknabe'
	'Hakuun' (F/Patio)	MAus
	'Hamburger Phönix' (Ra)	EBls SPer
	HAMPSHIRE ('Korhamp'[PBR]) (GC)	MAus
	HÄNDEL ('Macha') (ClHT)	CBcs CBod CGro CKel CSBt CTri EBls ELan EPfP ESps IBoy LBuc MAsh MRav NEgg NLar NPri SPer SPlb SSea SWCr
§	HANKY PANKY ('Wektorcent'[PBR]) (F)	CGro EBls ESty MAsh MRav SWCr
	HANNAH GORDON ('Korweiso') (F)	EBls MAsh SPer SWCr
	'Hansa' (Ru)	EBls LBuc MAus NLar SPer SWCr
	'Happenstance' (GC) **new**	EBls
	HAPPY 70TH BIRTHDAY ('Rawday') (F)	LSRN
	HAPPY ANNIVERSARY ambig.	EPfP SSea
	HAPPY ANNIVERSARY ('Bedfranc'[PBR]) (F)	ESps LSRN MWat NPri SWCr
	HAPPY ANNIVERSARY ('Delpre') (F)	CRos CTri LRHS MAsh MRav NRHS SPoG
	'Happy Birthday' (Min/Patio)	ESps ESty IBoy LCro LOPS LSRN SSea SWCr
	HAPPY DAYS ('Harquad'[PBR]) (S)	MRav
	HAPPY GOLDEN WEDDING	see *R.* GOLDEN SMILES
	'Happy Memories' (F)	EBls MAsh
	HAPPY RETIREMENT ('Tantoras'[PBR]) (F) 𝕐H6	CBcs EBls EPfP ESty IRob LBuc LSRN MAsh MRav NPri SCoo SPoG SSea SWCr
	HAPPY RUBY WEDDING ('Frynoble'[PBR]) (HT)	CBcs MAsh NPri SWCr
	HAPPY SILVER WEDDING ('Frysilva') (F)	EPfP MAsh SWCr
	× ***harisonii*** (SpH)	EBls
§	- 'Harison's Yellow' (SpH)	MAus
§	- 'Lutea Maxima' (SpH)	MAus
§	- 'Williams' Double Yellow' (SpH)	EBls MAus
	HARLOW CARR ambig.	CKel CRos LRHS MWat NRHS SCob
	HARLOW CARR ('Aushouse'[PBR]) (S)	CKel CRos EPfP IBoy LBuc LSRN MAsh MAus MRav SCob SCoo SPer
	'Harry Edland' (F)	SMad
	'Harry Maasz' (GC/Cl)	EBls
	'Harry Wheatcroft' (HT)	IBoy SPer
	HARVEST FAYRE ('Dicnorth'[PBR]) (F)	SPer

	HAVANA HIT ('Poulpah032'[PBR]) (Patio)	EPfP MAsh NPri
	'Havering Rambler' (Ra)	ELon
	'Hazel Le Rougetel' (Ru)	EBls WFar
	'Headleyensis' (S)	EBls MAus SPer
	HEART OF GOLD ('Coctarlotte'[PBR]) (HT) ♀H6	ECnt ESty MRav
	HEATHCLIFF ('Ausnipper'[PBR]) (S)	CRos CSBt EPfP ESty LBuc LRHS MAsh MAus NLar NRHS
	'Heather Muir' (*sericea* hybrid) (S)	EBls
§	'Hebe's Lip' (D × RH)	MAus
	'Helen Knight' (*ecae* hybrid) (S)	EBls ESty MAsh MAus
	HELEN ROBINSON ('Harlevel'[PBR]) (HT)	ESty
	'Helen Traubel' (HT)	EBls
	helenae	CTri EBls GBin GLog MAus NLar SPer WPGP
	HELEN'S TRUST ('Taytrust') (HT)	LSRN
	hemisphaerica (S)	EBls MAus
§	'Henri Martin' (CeMo) ♀H7	CBod CTri EBls IBoy IRob LEdu MAus NEgg NLar SLon SPer
	HENRI MATISSE ('Delstrobla') (HT)	ESty MRav SPoG
	'Henry Kelsey' (Cl/S) **new**	EBls
	'Henry Nevard' (HP)	EBls MAus
	'Her Majesty' (HP)	EBls
§	'Herbstfeuer' (RH)	CPou EBls NLar
	'Here's Sam' (HT)	LSRN
	HERITAGE ('Ausblush') (S)	CBod CGro CKel CRos CTri EBee ELan EPfP IRob LRHS MAus MJak MRav MWat NEgg NLar SCob SPer
	'Hermosa' (Ch)	EBls MAus NLar
	HERO ('Aushero') (S)	MAus
	HERTFORDSHIRE ('Kortenay'[PBR]) (GC) ♀H6	ELan IRob MAus SCob SEND SPer
	'Hiawatha' (Ra)	EBls
	× ***hibernica***	EBls IRob MAus
	'Hidcote Gold' (S)	EBls MAus
§	'Hidcote Yellow' (Cl)	EBls SPer
	HIGH HOPES ('Haryup'[PBR]) (ClHT)	CGro EPfP EUJe IBoy LBuc MAsh MAus SPer SSea
	'Highdownensis' (*moyesii* hybrid) (S)	EBls ELan MAus
	HIGHFIELD ('Harcomp') (ClHT)	MAus
	HIGHGROVE ('Hornightshade') (Cl)	EBls LRHS MAsh NPri
	'Hillieri' (*moyesii* hybrid)	EBls MAus
	'Hippolyte' (G)	MAus
	HOLE-IN-ONE ('Horeagle') (F)	LSRN
	holodonta	see *R. moyesii* f. *rosea*
	holy rose	see *R.* × *richardii*
	'Home Sweet Home' (HT)	EBls
	'Homère' (T)	EBls
	HOMMAGE À BARBARA ('Delchifrou'[PBR]) (HT)	CBod EBee ESty MRav WKif
	HONEY BUNCH ('Cocglen'[PBR]) (F)	CKel ELon MRav MWat SPer SRGP
	HONEY DIJON ('Weksproulses'[PBR]) (F)	ESty
	HONEYBUN ('Tan98264'[PBR]) (Patio)	ESty
	HONEYMOON	see *R.* 'Honigmond'
§	'Honigmond' (F)	CBcs
	'Honorine de Brabant' (Bb) ♀H6	CPou EBls EWTr LEdu MAus NLar SPer
	'Horace Vernet' (HP)	EBls
	HORATIO NELSON ('Beahor') (S)	EBls
	horrida	EBls
	'Horstmanns Rosenresli' (F)	EBls
	HOT CHOCOLATE ('Wekpaltlez') (F) ♀H6	CGro CKel CRos CSBt CWld EBee EBls ECnt ELan ELon EPfP ESps ESty ETMg GBin IBoy LBuc LRHS MAsh MJak MRav MWat SMad SPad SPer SPoG SRGP SSea SWCr WBor
	HOT PRINCESS ('Tantocnirp') (HT) **new**	ESty
	HOUSE BEAUTIFUL ('Harbingo') (Patio)	MRav
	'Hovyn de Tronchère' (HT) **new**	EBls
	'Hugh Dickson' (HP)	CPou EBls LSRN MAus NLar
	hugonis	see *R. xanthina* f. *hugonis*
	- 'Plenissima'	see *R. xanthina* f. *hugonis*
	HUMANITY ('Harcross'[PBR]) (F)	MRav
	Hume's blush	see *R.* × *odorata* 'Odorata'
	HUMMINGBIRD ('Tynpam') (F)	ESty
	'Hunter' (Ru)	EBls
	HYDE HALL ('Ausbosky'[PBR]) (S)	CRos MAus SCob
	ICE CREAM ('Korzuri'[PBR]) (HT) ♀H6	ECnt ESty IBoy MAus MRav SCob SPer SPoG SWCr
§	ICEBERG ('Korbin') (F) ♀H6	Widely available
	'Ilse Krohn Superior' (Cl)	EBls
§	IMAGINATION ('Pouldron'[PBR]) (F)	MAsh
	IMPÉRATRICE FARAH ('Delivour') (HT)	ESty
§	'Impératrice Joséphine' (Gn) ♀H7	EBls EWTr IBoy NLar
	IN MEMORY OF	LSRN
	IN MEMORY OF MY CAT ('Webyum') (HT)	LSRN
	IN MEMORY OF MY DOG ('Rawbark') (F)	LSRN
	INDIAN SUMMER ('Harwigwam') (ClMin)	MJak
	INDIAN SUMMER ('Peaperfume'[PBR]) (HT) ♀H6	CKel CSBt ESps LBuc MAsh MRav MWat SPoG SWCr
	INDIANNA MAE ('Beacrunch') (S)	EBls
	'Indigo' (DPo)	CPou EBls EWTr MAus
	INFINITY ('Frytropic') (HT)	ESty LRHS MAsh
	INGRID BERGMAN ('Poulman'[PBR]) (HT) ♀H6	CBod CTri EBls ECnt EPfP ESps IBoy LRHS LSRN MAsh MGos MRav MWat SPer SPoG SWCr
	'Inspiration' (ClHT)	EPfP MAsh SWCr
	INSPIRE ('Frytempo') (HT) **new**	ECnt
	'Intermezzo' (HT)	EBls
	'Ipsilanté' (G)	EBls MAus
	'Irene Av Danmark' (F)	EBls
	'Irène Watts' (Ch)	CPou EBee EBls LSRN NLar SWCr
	'Irene's Delight' (HT)	ESty LSRN
	IRIS ('Coczero') (HT)	LSRN
	IRIS ('Ferecha') (HT)	LSRN
	IRISH EYES ('Dicwitness'[PBR]) (F) ♀H6	CGro ESps ESty IArd IBoy MAsh MJak MRav SCoo SPer SWCr

IRISH WONDER	see *R.* EVELYN FISON
'Isabel' **new**	LSRN
ISABELLA ('Poulisab'[PBR]) (Renaissance Series) (S)	CPou CTri ECnt NLar SWCr
'Isabella Sprunt' (HT) **new**	EBls
ISIS (HT)	see *R.* SILVER ANNIVERSARY ('Poulari')
ISN'T SHE LOVELY ('Diciluvit'[PBR]) (HT) ♀H6	EBls ELan ESty IDic LSRN SWCr
'Ispahan' (D) ♀H7	EBls EPfP GBin LRHS MAus NEgg NLar SPer WFar
IVOR'S ROSE ('Beadonald') (S)	EBls LRHS MAsh
'Ivory Silk' (Min)	LSRN
'Jack Hume' (ClHT)	ESty
JACK'S WISH ('Kirsil') (HT)	LSRN
§ × ***jacksonii*** 'Max Graf' (GC/Ru)	MAus NLar
- RED MAX GRAF	see *R.* ROTE MAX GRAF
§ - WHITE MAX GRAF ('Korgram') (GC/Ru)	ECrN
'Jacky's Favorite' (F)	LSRN
Jacobite rose	see *R.* × *alba* 'Alba Maxima'
JACQUELINE DU PRÉ ('Harwanna') (S) ♀H6	CKel EBls ECnt ESty LSRN MAus MCot MRav MWat NLar SEND SLon SPer SSea SWCr
'Jacques Cartier' misapplied	see *R.* 'Marchesa Boccella'
JAM AND JERUSALEM ('Frymojo'[PBR]) (F)	CGro CKel LRHS MAsh MRav MWat
'James Bourgault' (HP)	EBls
JAMES GALWAY ('Auscrystal'[PBR]) (S)	CSBt EPfP ESty IBoy LBuc LRHS LSRN MAsh MAus NEgg NRHS SCob SCoo SSea SWCr
'James Mason' (G)	EBls MAus
'James Mitchell' (CeMo)	EBls MAus
'James Veitch' (DPoMo)	MAus
JANET ('Auspishus'[PBR]) (S)	LSRN MAus
'Janet B. Wood' (Ra) **new**	EBls
'Janet's Pride' (RH)	EBls
§ 'Japonica' (CeMo)	MAus
§ JARDINS DE BAGATELLE ('Meimafris') (HT)	LSRN MRav
JASMINA ('Korcentex'[PBR]) (ClHT)	CBod CPou CWld EBee ESty LBuc MAsh
'Jaune Desprez'	see *R.* 'Desprez à Fleur Jaune'
JAYNE AUSTIN ('Ausbreak'[PBR]) (S)	CSBt MAus SPer
JAZZ (ClF)	see *R.* THAT'S JAZZ
'Jazz' (F)	LSRN
JEAN ('Cocupland'[PBR]) (Patio)	LSRN
'Jean Mermoz' (Poly)	MAus
'Jean Rosenkrantz' (HP)	EBls
'Jeanne de Montfort' (CeMo)	EBls MAus
JEANNE MOREAU ('Meidiaphaz') (HT)	CSBt ESty
'Jenny Duval' misapplied	see *R.* 'Président de Sèze'
'Jenny Wren' (F)	EBls
JENNY'S ROSE ('Cansit') (F)	ECnt LSRN
'Jens Munk' (Ru)	EBls NLar
'Jersey Beauty' (Ra)	EBls
JILL'S ROSE ('Ganjil'[PBR]) (F)	LSRN
JILLY JEWEL ('Benmfig') (Min)	LSRN
JIVE ('Poulyc009'[PBR]) (Cl)	LSRN
JOAN BEALES ('Beaagile') (S)	EBls

JOAN ('Raw1019') **new**	LSRN
'Joanna Hill' (HT)	EBls
'Jocelyn' (F)	LSRN
JOHANN WOLFGANG VON GOETHE ROSE	see *R.* PURE POETRY
'John Cabot' (S)	EBls
JOHN CLARE ('Auscent'[PBR]) (S)	MAus
'John Gwilliam'	MAvo MHCG
'John Hopper' (HP)	EBls MAus SWCr
JOHN INNES ('Beafickle') (S)	EBls
§ JOIE DE VIVRE ('Korfloci 01'[PBR]) (Patio/S) ♀H6	CGro CPou CSBt EBee EBls ELan EPfP ESty EWTr GBin IBoy LRHS MAsh MRav NLar NPri SPer SPoG SWCr
'Josephine Bruce' (HT)	CBcs CTri EBls LSRN
§ JOSEPHINE ('Weksiamia') (HT) **new**	LSRN
'Joseph's Coat' (ClS)	CBod CKel EBls ESps IArd SWCr
JOY VIELI ('Dickaramel') (F)	IDic
'Jubilee Celebration' (F)	CBod EPfP LRHS NRHS
JUBILEE CELEBRATION ('Aushunter'[PBR]) (S)	CKel CRos CSBt EBee LBuc LRHS MAus NLar NRHS SPer SPoG
JUDE THE OBSCURE ('Ausjo'[PBR]) (S)	EPfP ESty LBuc LRHS MAus MGos NEgg NRHS SCob SPer SWCr
'Julia's Rose' (HT)	EBls LSRN MAus SPer
'Juliet' (HP)	EBls
JULIO IGLESIAS ('Meistemon'[PBR]) (F)	ESty LSRN
'Juno' (Ce)	EBls NLar
'Juno' (Ch)	CPou MAus
JUST FOR YOU ('Moryou') (Min)	LSRN
'Just Jenny' (Min)	LSRN
'Just Joey' (HT) ♀H6	CBcs CBod CGro CKel CSBt CTri EBls ECnt ELan ELon ESps IArd IBoy LSRN MAus MJak MRav MWat NEgg SCob SPer SPoG SRGP SSea SWCr
JUST STEVE ('Raw890') **new**	LSRN
'Karlsruhe' (Cl)	EBls
'Kassel' (ClF)	EBls
'Kasteel Hex' (S) **new**	EBls
'Katharina Zeimet' (Poly)	CKel CTri EBee EBls MAus
'Kathleen' (HM)	EBls LSRN
'Kathleen Ferrier' (F)	EBls
'Kathleen Harrop' (Bb)	CKel EBls ESps EWTr LRHS MAus MMuc MSwo NLar SEND SPer SRGP SWCr
KATHLEEN JANE ('Horcoed') (S/F)	LSRN
KATHLEEN'S ROSE ('Kirkitt') (F)	LSRN
KATHRYN ('Rawkat') **new**	LSRN
'Katie' (ClF)	LSRN
'Kazanlik' misapplied	see *R.* × *damascena* 'Professeur Émile Perrot'
KEEP SMILING ('Fryflorida') (HT) ♀H6	CGro EBls MAsh MRav SPoG
KEEPSAKE ('Kormalda') (HT)	ESty
'Keith Maughan' (Cl)	EBls LRHS MAsh
§ KENT ('Poulcov'[PBR]) (Towne & Country Series) (S/GC) ♀H6	CBod CKel CSBt EBls ECnt ELan EPfP ESty EWTr GBin IBoy LCro LOPS LSRN MMuc MRav MSwo NLar SCob SEND SPer SPoG SSea SWCr
KEW GARDENS ('Ausfence'[PBR]) (S) ♀H6	CBod CKel EBee EPfP LBuc LRHS MAus MRav MWat NLar SCob SPer SSea

'Kew Rambler' (Ra)	CBod CRHN CSam EBls MAus NLar SLon SPer
'Kiftsgate'	see *R. filipes* 'Kiftsgate'
'Kiftsgate Superior' (S) **new**	EBls
'Killarney' (HT) **new**	EBls
'Kim' (Patio)	LSRN
KIND REGARDS ('Peatiger') (F)	LSRN
KING'S MACC ('Frydisco'^{PBR}) (HT) 🏆^{H6}	MAus
'King's Ransom' (HT)	CSBt EBls MRav SPer SPoG
KISSES OF FIRE ('Chewmultiseek') (Cl)	CGro ECnt MRav NLar
KITTY ('Beaarty') (S)	EBls
× ***kochiana***	EBls
KOLO ('Poulcy033') (Courtyard Series) (Cl) **new**	ECnt
§ 'Königin von Dänemark' (A) 🏆^{H7}	CBod EBls EPfP IBoy LCro LOPS LRHS LSRN MRav MWat NEgg NLar SPer
§ 'Kordes' Magenta' (S/F)	EBls
'Kordes' Robusta'	see *R.* ROBUSTA
'Kordesii' (S) **new**	EBls
KORONA ('Kornita') (F)	SPer
'Korresia' (F) 🏆^{H7}	CBod CSBt CTri EBls ECnt EPfP ESps IBoy LRHS MAsh MAus MJak MRav SCob SPer SPoG SWCr
KRONENBOURG ('Macbo') (HT)	EBls
'Kronprinzessin Viktoria von Preussen' (Bb)	EBls MAus
L.D. BRAITHWAITE ('Auscrim'^{PBR}) (S)	CBcs CBod CTri ELan EPfP ESps IBoy LRHS MAus MBNS MJak MWat NLar SCob SPer SSea
'La Belle Sultane'	see *R.* 'Violacea'
'La France' (HT)	EBls
'La Mortola'	see *R. brunonii* 'La Mortola'
'La Noblesse' (Ce)	EBls
'La Perle' (Ra)	CRHN
'La Reine' (HP)	EBls
'La Reine Victoria'	see *R.* 'Reine Victoria'
§ LA ROSE DE MOLINARD ('Delgrarose'^{PBR}) (S) 🏆^{H6}	CPou ESty EWTr MRav MWat NLar
LA ROSE DE PETIT PRINCE ('Delgramau') (F)	EBee ESty
'La Rubanée'	see *R.* × *centifolia* 'Unique Panachée'
LA SÉVILLANA ('Meigekanu') (F/GC)	EBls MSwo SPer WCot
'La Ville de Bruxelles' (D) 🏆^{H7}	CSam EBls MAus NLar SPer
'Lady Alice Stanley' (HT)	EBls
'Lady Anne' (F)	LSRN
'Lady Barnby' (HT)	EBls
'Lady Belper' (HT)	EBls
'Lady Curzon' (Ru)	EBls
'Lady Elgin'	see *R.* THAÏS
LADY EMMA HAMILTON ('Ausbrother'^{PBR}) (S) 🏆^{H6}	CGro CRos EPfP ESty IBoy LBuc LRHS MAus NRHS SCob SCoo SPer SWCr
'Lady Gay' (Ra)	CBod EBee WBor
'Lady Godiva' (Ra)	MAus
'Lady Hillingdon' (T)	EBls MAsh
'Lady Hillingdon' (ClT)	see *R.* 'Climbing Lady Hillingdon'
LADY MARMALADE ('Hartiger') (F)	CGro CKel CSBt ECnt ESty LBuc LRHS MAsh MRav MWat NPri SCoo SMad SPer SPoG SWCr

'Lady Mary Fitzwilliam' (HT)	EBls
LADY MITCHELL ('Haryearn') (HT)	ECnt
LADY OF MEGGINCH ('Ausvolume'^{PBR}) (S)	MAus
LADY OF SHALOTT ('Ausnyson'^{PBR}) (S) 🏆^{H6}	CRos ECnt EPfP IRob LBuc LCro LOPS LRHS MAsh MAus NLar NRHS SCob SSea SWCr
LADY PENELOPE ('Chewdor'^{PBR}) (ClHT)	CSBt
§ 'Lady Penzance' (RH)	EBls SPer
'Lady Romsey' (F)	EBls
LADY ROSE ('Korlady') (HT)	MAsh
LADY SALISBURY ('Auscezed'^{PBR}) (S)	CRos EPfP LBuc LRHS MAus NRHS SCob SCoo
'Lady Sylvia' (HT)	EBls LSRN MAus NEgg SPer
'Lady Waterlow' (ClHT)	EBee EBls MAus
laevigata (Ra)	EBls MAus MMuc
- 'Anemonoides'	see *R.* 'Anemone'
'Lafter' (S)	EBls
'Lagoon' (F)	EBls
LAGUNA ('Koradigel'^{PBR}) (ClHT)	MAsh
L'AIMANT ('Harzola'^{PBR}) (F) 🏆^{H5}	CGro MAus MRav SWCr
LALANDE DE POMAROL ('Delcherot') (F) **new**	ESty
L'ALHAMBRA (Cl)	see *R.* GIARDINA ('Tan97289') (Cl)
'Lamarque' (N)	CPou EBee EBls MAus
LANCASHIRE ('Korstesgli'^{PBR}) (GC) 🏆^{H6}	CKel ECnt ELan ESty LSRN MAus MRav MSwo SSea SWCr
LANCELOT ('Tan03542'^{PBR}) (Cl)	ESty
§ 'Lanei' (CeMo)	EBee EBls
latibracteata **new**	EBls
LAURA FORD ('Chewarvel'^{PBR}) (ClMin) 🏆^{H5}	CKel CTri EBls ELan ESps IBoy LRHS MAsh MAus MGos MRav MWat SPer SPoG SSea
'Laura Louisa' (Cl)	EBee EBls LRHS MAsh
'Laure Davoust' (Ra)	CPou EBee EBls MMuc NLar
LAVENDER ICE ('Tan04249'^{PBR}) (F)	ESty MAsh SWCr
'Lavender Jewel' (Min)	MAus
'Lavender Lassie' (HM)	CPou CSam EBls EWTr MAus NLar SPer SWCr
'Lavender Pinocchio' (F)	EBls WKif
LAVINIA	see *R.* LAWINIA
§ LAWINIA ('Tanklewi') (ClHT) 🏆^{H6}	CSBt EBee LRHS MAsh SPer
'Lawrence Johnston'	see *R.* 'Hidcote Yellow'
laxa **new**	EBls
§ LAZY DAYS ('Poulkalm'^{PBR}) (F)	ECnt MAsh SWCr
'Le Rêve' (Cl)	EBls EWTr
LE ROUGE ET LE NOIR ('Delcart') (HT)	ESty
'Le Vésuve' (Ch)	CPou EBls MAus
LEAH TUTU ('Hornavel') (S)	CWld EBls ESty LRHS MAsh SWCr
LEANDER ('Auslea') (S)	MAus
LEAPING SALMON ('Peamight'^{PBR}) (ClHT) 🏆^{H6}	CGro CSBt EBee ELon ESps ESty LSRN MAus MRav SPer SRGP SWCr
'Leda' (D)	EBls EWTr MAus SPer
LEGENDS	see *R.* JOSEPHINE
'Lemon Pillar'	see *R.* 'Paul's Lemon Pillar'
LÉONARDO DE VINCI ('Meideauri'^{PBR}) (F)	CSBt

LEONIDAS ('Meicofum'[PBR]) (HT) EŚty
'Léonie Lamesch' (Poly) EBls
'Léontine Gervais' (Ra) CRHN EBls LRHS MAus
'Leo's Eye' (Ra) CPou EPfP NLar
LESLIE'S DREAM ('Dicjoon') (HT) IDic
LET THERE BE LOVE ('Frysoda') (F) **new** MAsh
LET'S CELEBRATE ('Fryraffles'[PBR]) (F) EPfP ESty LBuc LRHS MAsh MRav NPri NRHS SPoG SWCr
'Leverkusen' (ClF) ♀H7 CBod CKel EBls EWTr LRHS MAus MRav NLar SEND SPer SWCr
'Leveson-Gower' (Bb) EBls
'Ley's Perpetual' (ClT) EBls
× ***lheritieriana*** (Bs) EBls
LICHFIELD ANGEL ('Ausrelate'[PBR]) (S) ♀H6 EBee EPfP LBuc LRHS MAsh MAus NLar NRHS SCob SCoo
LICHTKÖNIGIN LUCIA ('Korlillub') (S) EBls SSea
LIFE BEGINS AT 40! ('Horhohoho') (F) LSRN
LIGHT FANTASTIC ('Dicgottago') (F) ♀H6 EPfP IDic MAsh
LIGHTNING STRIKE ('Raw967') (F) **new** ESty
'Lilac Charm' (F) EBls
LILAC WINE ('Dicmulti') (F) CGro IDic MRav
LILIANA ('Poulsyng'[PBR]) (S) CPou ECnt LSRN SLon SWCr
LILLI MARLENE ('Korlima') (F) CSBt CTri EBls ESps IBoy SPer
LINCOLN CATHEDRAL ('Glanlin'[PBR]) (HT) MJak SPer
LINCOLNSHIRE POACHER ('Glareabit') (HT) NEgg
'Lincolnshire Yellow Belly' (F) ESty
LION'S FAIRY TALE see *R.* CHAMPAGNE MOMENT
LISA ('Kirdisco') (F) LSRN
LITTLE AMY ('Battamy') (Min) LSRN
LITTLE DUET ('Guesbliss') (F) ESty
'Little Flirt' (Min) ELan MAus
'Little Gem' (DPMo) EBls MAus
LITTLE JACKIE ('Savor') (Min) LSRN
LITTLE MISS SUNSHINE ('Dicgungho') (F) ECnt
LITTLE RAMBLER ('Chewramb'[PBR]) (MinRa) ♀H6 CSBt EBls ECnt ELan ESty LRHS MAus MGos MMuc MRav MWat NRHS SCoo SPer SSea SWCr
'Little White Pet' see *R.* 'White Pet'
LOCHINVAR ('Ausbilda'[PBR]) (S) MAus
'Lolabelle' CPou EWTr
'Long John Silver' (Cl) EBls ELan MAus SSea
longicuspis misapplied see *R. mulliganii*
§ ***longicuspis*** Bertol. var. ***sinowilsonii*** (Ra) EBls GCal MAus
LOOK GOOD... FEEL BETTER ('Poulcas034'[PBR]) (Castle Series) (Poly) EPfP LRHS MAsh
LORD BYRON ('Meitosier') (ClHT) ESty
'Lord Penzance' (RH) EBls NLar SPer
LORNA ('Cocringer') (F) LSRN
LOTS OF LOVE ('Forchriso') (F) **new** ESty
'L'Ouche' misapplied see *R.* 'Louise Odier'
'Louis Gimard' (CeMo) MAus
'Louis Philippe' (Ch) EBls
'Louis XIV' (Ch) CBod EBls MCot
LOUISE CLEMENTS ('Clelou') (S) EBls
'Louise D'Arzens' (N) **new** EBls
§ 'Louise Odier' (Bb) CBWd CBod CKel CTri EBls ECnt EPfP IArd LRHS LSRN MAus MCot MRav NLar SPer SRGP SWCr
LOVE & PEACE ('Baipeace'[PBR]) (HT) ♀H6 ESty SWCr
LOVE KNOT ('Chewglorious'[PBR]) (ClMin) ♀H6 CRos CSBt ECnt EPfP ESps ESty LRHS MAsh MRav SSea SWCr
§ LOVELY BRIDE ('Meiratcan'[PBR]) (Patio) CGro CRos EPfP LRHS MAsh NRHS SPoG SWCr
LOVELY LADY ('Dicjubell'[PBR]) (HT) ♀H6 CKel CSBt EBls ECnt ESty LSRN MAus MRav SSea SWCr
LOVELY MEIDILAND see *R.* LOVELY BRIDE
'Lovers' Meeting' (HT) MJak MRav SPer
LOVING MEMORY ('Korgund81') (HT) CBod CGro CKel CSBt EBls ECnt ESty IArd LSRN MAsh MGos MRav NPri SPer SPoG SSea SVic SWCr
LOVING MUM see *R.* SHOWSTAR
LOWTHORPE DELIGHT ('Dicgoofy') (F) IDic
luciae EBls
LUCKY! ('Frylucy') (F) ♀H6 CSBt EBls EPfP ESty LBuc LSRN MAsh MGos MRav NPri NRHS SCoo SPer SPoG
LUCY ('Kirlis') (F) LSRN
LULLABY ('Kenfrilpin') (Cl) ESty
LUSCIOUS LUCY ('Tucklucy') (Patio) LSRN
'Lutea Maxima' see *R.* × *harisonii* 'Lutea Maxima'
LYDA ROSE ('Letlyda') (S) EBls
'Lykkefund' (Ra) CKel EBls MAus
'Ma Perkins' (F) EBls
'Mabel Morrison' (HP) EBls MAus
Macartney rose see *R. bracteata*, *R.* THE MCCARTNEY ROSE
MACMILLAN NURSE ('Beamac') (S) CWld EBee EBls ELan ESty LRHS MAsh
'Macrantha' (Gallica hybrid) EBls MAus
macrophylla (S) MAus
- B&SWJ 2603 WCru
- GWJ 9306 WCru
§ - 'Master Hugh' (S) EBls MAus
'Madame Abel Chatenay' (HT) EBls
'Madame Alfred Carrière' (N) ♀H5 Widely available
'Madame Alice Garnier' (Ra) CPou CRHN EBee EBls SPer
'Madame Antoine Mari' (T) CPou EBls
'Madame Bérard' (ClT) **new** EBls
§ 'Madame Boll' (DPo) CBWd CKel CWld EBls ESty EWTr MAsh MRav MSwo NLar SMad
'Madame Butterfly' (HT) EBls LRHS
§ 'Madame Caroline Testout' (HT) CTri EBls LRHS SPoG SRGP
'Madame de la Roche-Lambert' (DPMo) CPou EBls MAus
'Madame de Sancy de Parabère' (Bs) EBls MAus
'Madame Driout' (ClT) CPou
'Madame Ernest Calvat' (Bb) CPou EBls

'Madame Eugène Résal' misapplied	see *R.*'Comtesse du Caÿla'
§ 'Madame Grégoire Staechelin' (ClHT) ♀H6	CTri EBls ECnt ELan EPfP EWTr IBoy LCro LOPS LRHS LSRN MAsh MAus MRav MSwo NEgg NLar NRHS SCob SPer SPlb
'Madame Hardy' (D) ♀H7	CPou CSBt EBls ECnt EPfP LRHS LSRN MAus MCot MRav MSwo NEgg NLar SCob SPer SWCr WFar
'Madame Isaac Péreire' (ClBb)	CSBt CTri EBls ECnt EPfP ESps GBin IBoy LCro LOPS MAus MCot MRav MSwo NLar SCob SMad SPer SPoG SWCr WBor WFar
'Madame Jules Gravereaux' (ClT)	EBls MAus
'Madame Knorr' (DPo) ♀H7	CPou ECnt ELon EPfP SPer
'Madame Knorr' misapplied	see *R.*'Madame Boll'
'Madame Laurette Messimy' (Ch)	CPou
'Madame Lauriol de Barny' (Bb)	EBls MAus MRav NLar
'Madame Legras de Saint Germain' (A × N)	CPou EBls EWTr MAus NLar SPer
'Madame Louis Laperrière' (HT)	EBls
'Madame Louis Lévêque' (DPMo)	CPou EBls EWTr NLar
'Madame Pierre Oger' (Bb)	CTri EBls ECnt MAus NLar SPer
'Madame Plantier' (A × N)	CPou EBee EBls MAus NLar SCob SPer WFar
'Madame Scipion Cochet' (HP)	CPou
'Madame Victor Verdier' (HP)	EBls
'Madame Zöetmans' (D)	MAus
'Madeleine Seltzer' (Ra)	EBls
'Magenta' (S/F)	see *R.* 'Kordes' Magenta' (S/F)
MAGIC CARPET ('Jaclover'[PBR]) (S/GC) ♀H6	CKel EBls ELan ESps IBoy MAus MRav MSwo MWat SPer SWCr
MAGIC MOMENT ('Forrusty') (HT)	ESty
'Magna Charta' (HP)	EBls
'Magnifica' (RH)	EBls
MAID MARION ('Austobias'[PBR]) (HM)	EPfP MAsh MAus
'Maid of Kent'[PBR] (Cl)	LSRN MAus NLar SCob SCoo SMad SPer SWCr
'Maiden's Blush' (A)	CBWd CSam CTri ELan EWTr LEdu MAsh MAus SPer WHer
'Maiden's Blush, Great'	see *R.* 'Great Maiden's Blush'
'Maigold' (ClPiH) ♀H7	CBcs CBod CGro CRos CTri EBls ELan EPfP ESps LRHS MAsh MAus MCot MRav MSwo NLar SCob SPer SWCr WBor
§ ***majalis***	EBls
Maltese rose	see *R.*'Cécile Brünner'
§ 'Malton' (China hybrid)	EBls
MALVERN HILLS ('Auscanary'[PBR]) (Ra)	CGro CRos CSBt EBee EPfP ESty LRHS MAus NLar SCob SPer SWCr
MALVERNS ('Kordehei') (GC)	IRob
'Maman Cochet' (T)	EBls
MAMMA MIA! ('Fryjolly'[PBR]) (HT) ♀H6	ECnt EPfP ESty LRHS MAsh MRav SPoG SWCr
MAMY BLUE ('Delblue') (HT)	ESty
'Mandarin' (F)	CKel SSea
MANDARIN ('Korcelin'[PBR]) (Min)	ESty IBoy MRav
'Manettii' (N)	EBls
'Manning's Blush' (RH)	EBls MAus
'Mannington Cascade' (Ra)	EBls
'Mannington Mauve Rambler' (Ra)	EBls ESty
MANY CONGRATULATIONS ('Forshelly') (F) **new**	ESty
MANY HAPPY RETURNS ('Harwanted'[PBR]) (F) ♀H6	CBod CKel CRos CSBt EBls ECnt ELan EPfP ESps IBoy IRob LRHS LSRN MAsh MGos MJak MRav MWat NPri NRHS SCob SPer SPoG SSea SVic SWCr
'Marbrée' (DPo)	MAus
'Märchenland' (F)	MAus
§ 'Marchesa Boccella' (DPo) ♀H7	CPou CSam CTri EBls EPfP LRHS MAsh NLar NPri SPer SSea WHer
'Marchioness of Salisbury' (HT) **new**	EBls
'Maréchal Davoust' (CeMo)	LEdu MAus
'Maréchal Niel' (N)	EBls EShb MAus NLar SPer
'Margaret' (HT)	LSRN
MARGARET MERRIL ('Harkuly') (F)	CBcs CGro CKel CSBt CTri EBee EBls ELan EPfP ESps ESty IArd IBoy LCro LOPS LRHS LSRN MAsh MAus MJak MRav MWat NPri SCob SPer SPoG SRGP SSea SWCr
MARGARET	see *R.* DEAR MARGARET
'Marguerite Hilling' (S)	CTri EBls MAus MSwo NLar SPer
'Marie Bugnet' (Ru) **new**	EBls
'Marie Louise' (D)	EBee EBls MAus
'Marie Pavič' (Poly)	CPou EBee MAus NLar
'Marie van Houtte' (T)	EBls
'Marie-Jeanne' (Poly)	EBls MAus
MARIGOLD SWEET DREAM ('Fryprospa') (Patio)	ECnt
MARINETTE ('Auscam'[PBR]) (S)	MAus
MARJORIE FAIR ('Harhero') (Poly/S) ♀H6	EBls ELan MAus MRav SWCr
'Marlena' (F/Patio)	MAus
MARRY ME ('Dicwonder'[PBR]) (Patio) ♀H6	ESty SWCr
'Martha' (Bb)	EBls LSRN
'Martin Frobisher' (Ru)	EBls MAus
I 'Mary' (Poly)	LSRN
MARY MAGDALENE ('Ausjolly'[PBR]) (S)	MAus
'Mary Manners' (Ru)	EBls
MARY ROSE ('Ausmary') (S)	CKel CRos CSBt CTri EBee ELan EPfP ESps IBoy IRob LRHS LSRN MAsh MAus MJak MRav NLar NRHS SCob SLon SPer SPoG SSea SWCr WKif
'Mary Wallace' (Cl)	EBls MAus
'Masquerade' (F)	CTri EBls ELan ESps MRav NLar SPer SWCr
'Master Hugh'	see *R. macrophylla* 'Master Hugh'
MATAWHERO MAGIC	see *R.* SIMPLY THE BEST
MATCHMAKER ('Dicnarrow') (F) **new**	IDic
'Maude Elizabeth' (GC)	EBls
'Maurice Bernardin' (HP)	EBls
MAURICE UTRILLO ('Delstavo') (HT)	ESty
'Max Graf'	see *R.* × *jacksonii* 'Max Graf'
'Maxima'	see *R.* × *alba* 'Alba Maxima'
MAXIMA ROMANTICA ('Meikerira'[PBR]) (HT)	ESty
'May Queen' (Ra)	CBod CPou CRos EBee EBls MAus MRav NLar SEND SPer SWCr

	'McCartney Rose'	see *R.* THE MCCARTNEY ROSE
	'McGredy's Sunset' (HT)	EBls
	'McGredy's Yellow' (HT)	EBls
§	MEDLEY RUBY ('Noa140715'PBR) (Min)	MAsh
	'Meg' (ClHT)	CKel EBls LRHS LSRN MAus MCot MMuc NLar SPer SRGP
	'Meg Merrilies' (RH)	EBls
	MELINA	see *R.* SIR HARRY PILKINGTON
	MELODY MAKER ('Dicqueen'PBR) (F)	IBoy
	MEMORY LANE ('Peavoodoo'PBR) (F)	LSRN
	'Mermaid' (Cl) 🏆H5	CBcs CDul CSBt CTri EBls EPfP ESps MAus NLar SCob SEND SPer SSea SWCr
§	'Mevrouw Nathalie Nypels' (Poly)	CTri EBee EBls MAus MMuc MRav NLar SPer
	'Michèle Meilland' (HT)	EBls MAus
	× ***micrugosa***	EBls MAus
	- 'Alba'	EBls MAus
	MIDDLESBOROUGH FOOTBALL CLUB ('Horflame') (HT)	LSRN
	MIDNIGHT BLUE ('Wekfabpur') (S)	EBls ESty
	MIDNIGHT ROSE ('Simdamo') (F)	ESty
§	MILLIE ('Poulren013'PBR) (Renaissance Series) (S) 🏆H6	CBcs EBls ECnt ELan ESty LBuc LCro LOPS LRHS LSRN MAsh NLar NRHS SPoG
	MILLIE ROSE ('Wekblunez'PBR) (HT)	SWCr
	MILLIONAIRE ('Peazara') (F)	LSRN
	MIND GAMES ('Dickylie') (F)	IDic
	MINERVA ('Visancar') (F) new	ESty
	'Minnehaha' (Ra)	EBls MAus SSea
	mirifica stellata	see *R. stellata* var. *mirifica*
	MISCHIEF ('Macmi') (HT)	LSRN SPer
	MISS ALICE ('Ausjake'PBR) (S)	LSRN MAus
	'Miss Edith Cavell' (Poly)	EBls MAus
	MISS SCARLET ('Forbright') (Cl)	ESty
§	'Mister Lincoln' (HT)	EBls MJak SPer
§	MISTY HIT ('Poulhi011'PBR) (PatioHit Series) (Patio)	EBls ECnt LSRN MAsh
	MITSOUKO ('Delnat') (HT)	ESty
	MOLINEUX ('Ausmol'PBR) (S) 🏆H6	CRos EPfP IRob LRHS LSRN MAsh MAus NRHS SCob SPer SWCr
	'Molly Sharman-Crawford' (HT) new	EBls
	MOMENT IN TIME ('Korcastrav'PBR) (F) 🏆H6	CSBt EBee ECnt MAsh MRav MWat NPri SPer SPoG SWCr
	MONICA BELLUCCI ('Meimonkeur'PBR) (HT)	ESty
	'Monique' (HT)	EBls
	MONSIEUR PÉLISSON	see *R.* 'Pélisson'
	MOODY BLUE ('Fryniche') (HT)	ECnt ESty IBoy MAsh MRav MWat SWCr
	'Moonlight' (HM)	CKel CTri EBls EWTr GBin MAus MRav MSwo SPer SWCr
	MOORCROFT ('Guesyearn') (F) new	ESty
	'Morletii' (Bs)	EBls EWTr MMuc SEND
	'Morning Jewel' (ClF) 🏆H7	SPer SWCr
	MORNING MIST ('Ausfire') (S)	EPfP LBuc LRHS MAsh MAus SPer SSea SWCr
§	'Morsdag' (Poly/F)	LSRN SCob SPer SVic
	MORTIMER SACKLER ('Ausorts'PBR) (S) 🏆H6	CKel EPfP LBuc LRHS MAus MMuc NRHS SCob SCoo SPer SSea SWCr
	moschata (Ra)	CPou EBls MAus SSea
	- 'Autumnalis'	see *R.* 'Princesse de Nassau'
	- var. ***nepalensis***	see *R. brunonii*
	MOTHER'S DAY	see *R.* 'Morsdag'
I	'Mother's Day'	MJak SRGP
	MOTHER'S JOY ('Horsiltrop') (F)	LSRN
	MOUNT AORANGI ('Sanaran') (HT)	ESty
	MOUNTAIN SNOW ('Aussnow') (Ra)	LRHS MAus
	MOUNTBATTEN ('Harmantelle') (F) 🏆H6	CKel EBls ELan ESps MAus MRav SPer SPoG SWCr
§	'Mousseline' (DPoMo)	CPou EBls MAus MCot SPer
	'Mousseuse du Japon'	see *R.* 'Japonica'
	moyesii (S)	CTri EBls ELan ESps EWTr GKev MAus MWat NEgg SPer
§	- var. ***fargesii*** (S)	EBls
	- ***holodonta***	see *R. moyesii* f. *rosea*
§	- f. ***rosea*** (S)	EBls
	'Mozart' (HM)	ETMg
	'Mr Bluebird' (MinCh)	MAus
	'Mr Lincoln'	see *R.* 'Mister Lincoln'
	'Mrs Anthony Waterer' (Ru)	EBls MAus NLar SPer
	'Mrs Arthur Curtiss James' (ClHT)	MMuc NLar
	MRS DOREEN PIKE ('Ausdor'PBR) (Ru)	MAus
	'Mrs F.W. Flight' (ClF) new	EBls
	'Mrs Honey Dyson' (Ra)	CPou EWTr
	'Mrs John Laing' (HP)	EBee EBls MAus NLar SPer SWCr
	'Mrs Oakley Fisher' (HT)	EBls EWTr MAus MCot SMad SPer SWCr
	'Mrs Paul' (Bb)	EBls MAus
	'Mrs Sam McGredy' (HT)	CPou EBls NEgg
	'Mrs Yamada' (Bb)	EBls
§	***mulliganii*** (Ra)	EBls EPfP GKin MAus SPer
	multibracteata (S)	CBcs EBls GLog MAus
	multiflora (Ra)	EBls MAus
	- 'Carnea' (Ra)	EBls
§	- var. ***cathayensis*** (Ra)	EBls
§	- 'Grevillei' (Ra)	EBls MAus MCot MMuc SPer
	- 'Platyphylla'	see *R. multiflora* 'Grevillei'
	- var. ***watsoniana***	see *R. watsoniana*
	MUM IN A MILLION	see *R.* MILLIE
	MUMMY	see *R.* NEWLY WED
	mundi	see *R. gallica* 'Versicolor'
	MUNSTEAD WOOD ('Ausbernard'PBR) (S) 🏆H6	CBod CGro CRos CTri ECnt EPfP EShb ESty LBuc LCro LOPS LRHS LSRN MAus MBNS NLar NRHS SCob SPer SPoG SSea SWCr
	murielae new	EBls
	'Murjami'	EBls
	'Muscosa Alba'	see *R.* × *centifolia* 'Shailer's White Moss'
	'Mutabilis'	see *R.* × *odorata* 'Mutabilis'
	MY BROTHER ('Raw1056') (F) new	ESty
	MY DAD ('Boselftay'PBR) (F)	CBcs CBod EBls LSRN SWCr
	'My Darling Husband' (F)	LSRN
	'My Darling Wife' (F)	LSRN
	'My Joy' (HT)	LSRN
	MY MUM ('Webmorrow'PBR) (F)	CBcs CGro ESty LSRN SCob SWCr

	MY SISTER ('Raw1052') (F) **new**	ESty
	MY VALENTINE ('Mormyval') (Min)	EBls LSRN MAsh
	MYRIAM ('Cocgrand') (HT)	LSRN
	MYSTERIOUS ('Simpansy') (F)	ESty
	MYSTERY GIRL ('Dicdothis'^{PBR}) (HT)	ECnt
	'München' (HM)	EBls
	NANCY ('Poulninga') (Renaissance Series) (S)	CPou LSRN
	'Naomi' (HT)	CPou LSRN
	'Narrow Water' (Ra) 𝕐H6	CPou EBls EWTr GBin SWCr
§	'Nastarana' (N)	EBls NLar
	NATALIE ('Poulren014'^{PBR}) (Renaissance Series) (S)	ECnt LSRN
	NATASHA RICHARDSON ('Harpacket'^{PBR}) (F)	CKel MRav
	'Nathalie Nypels'	see *R.* 'Mevrouw Nathalie Nypels'
	'National Trust' (HT)	CTri EBls ESps IArd IBoy MJak SPer
	NATURAL BEAUTY ('Rogscriv') (HT) **new**	SSea
	NELSON'S JOURNEY ('Beaflirt') (S) **new**	EBls
	'Nelson's Pride' (F)	EBls
	'Nestor' (G)	EBls MAus
	'Nevada' (S)	CSBt CTri EBls ECnt EPfP ESps GBin IArd IBoy LEdu MAus MRav NLar SPer
	NEVER FORGOTTEN ('Gregart') (HT)	LSRN
	NEW ARRIVAL	see *R.* 'Red Patio'
	NEW BEGINNINGS ('Korprofko'^{PBR}) (F)	CBod LSRN MAsh SWCr
§	'New Dawn' (Cl) 𝕐H7	Widely available
	'New Home'	LSRN
	NEW ZEALAND ('Macgenev'^{PBR}) (HT)	SWCr
§	NEWLY WED ('Dicwhynot'^{PBR}) (Patio) 𝕐H6	LSRN SSea SWCr
	NEWS ('Legnews') (F)	MAus
	NEWSFLASH ('Kendutch'^{PBR}) (F)	CBod ESty SWCr
	NICE DAY ('Chewsea'^{PBR}) (ClMin)	CTri EPfP ESty IBoy MAsh MRav MWat SPer SPoG SSea
	'Nicola' (F)	LSRN
	NIGHT LIGHT ('Poullight'^{PBR}) (Courtyard Series) (Cl)	ECnt
	NIGHT OWL ('Wekpurosot') (Cl)	ECnt ESty EWTr GBin LRHS MRav NLar SPer SPoG
	NINA ('Mehnina'^{PBR}) (S)	LSRN
	NINA ('Poulren018'^{PBR}) (Renaissance Series) (S)	ECnt
	nitida	EBls ESps GMcL MAus SPer
	NOBLE ANTONY ('Ausway'^{PBR}) (S)	EPfP MAus SCob
§	'Noisette Carnée' (N) 𝕐H7	CKel CPou CTri EBee EBls EPfP LEdu LRHS MAsh MBNS MCot MRav MWat NLar NRHS SPer SSea WBor
	NORFOLK ('Poulfolk'^{PBR}) (GC)	CBod CKel CTri EBls ESty MSwo NLar SCob SPer
	NORTHAMPTONSHIRE ('Mattdor'^{PBR}) (GC)	EBls
	'Norwell' **new**	MNrw
	'Norwich Castle' (F)	EBls
	NORWICH CATHEDRAL ('Beacath') (HT)	EBls
	'Norwich Pink' (S)	MAus
	NORWICH THEATRE ROYAL ('Beacalm') (S)	EBls
	'Norwich Union' (F)	EBls
	NOSTALGIA ('Savarita') (Min)	CBod CGro EPfP LBuc LRHS MAsh MAus
§	NOSTALGIA ('Taneiglat'^{PBR}) (HT) 𝕐H6	CSBt CWld EBee EBls ECnt ESty MRav SPoG SSea SWCr
	NOSTALGIE	see *R.* NOSTALGIA
	'Notre-Dame de Calais' (Cl) **new**	EBls LRHS MAsh
	'Nova Zembla' (Ru)	EBls
	'Nozomi' (ClMin/GC)	CBod CKel CSma CTri EBls ELan ESty MAus NLar SPer
	'Nuits de Young' (CeMo) 𝕐H7	EBls EPfP LRHS MAus NLar
	'Nur Mahal' (HM)	EBls MAus
	NURSE TRACEY DAVIES ('Frykookie'^{PBR}) (F) 𝕐H6	MAsh SWCr
	nutkana (S)	EBls MAus
§	- var. ***hispida*** (S)	EBls
§	- 'Plena' (S/D) 𝕐H7	EBls MAus NLar WHer
	'Nymphenburg' (HM)	EWTr SPer
	'Nyveldt's White' (Ru)	EBls MAus
	OCTAVIA HILL ('Harzeal'^{PBR}) (F)	CBod MRav NLar SPer SWCr
§	× ***odorata***	CPou EBls
*	- 'Burmese Crimson'	CBot
	- 'Fortune's Double Yellow'	see *R.* × *odorata* 'Pseudindica'
	- 'Hume's Blush Tea-scented China' (Cl) **new**	EBls
§	- 'Mutabilis' (Ch) 𝕐H5	CBod CKel CPou CRHN CTri EBls ECnt ECre ELan EPfP GBin LCro LOPS LRHS MAus MCot MRav MWat NLar NRHS SEND SPer SPoG SSea SWCr WAvo WCFE WCot XSen
§	- 'Ochroleuca' (Ch)	CPou
I	- 'Odorata' (Ch)	EBls
	- old crimson China (Ch)	EBls
§	- 'Pallida' (Ch)	CPou EBls EPfP EWTr LRHS MAus MCot NLar SPer SSea
§	- 'Pseudindica' (ClCh)	EBls IArd MAus
§	- Sanguinea Group (Ch)	EBls SEND
	- - 'Bengal Crimson' (Ch) 𝕐H5	CPou CRos ECre EPfP EWTr LRHS LSRN NRHS SLon SPoG WAvo WCot WKif
	- - 'Bob's Beauty' (Ch)	WCot
§	- 'Viridiflora' (Ch)	CPou EBls LEdu MAus SLon SMad SPer SSea WCot WHer
	ODYSSEY ('Franski'^{PBR}) (F)	ESty
	'Oeillet Flamand'	see *R.* 'Oeillet Parfait'
§	'Oeillet Parfait' (G)	MAus
	officinalis	see *R. gallica* var. *officinalis*
	OH WOW! ('Wekspitrib'^{PBR}) (Cl)	ECnt ESty
	old blush China	see *R.* × *odorata* 'Pallida'
	old cabbage	see *R.* × *centifolia*
	OLD JOHN ('Dicwillynilly') (F)	LSRN
	old pink moss rose	see *R.* × *centifolia* 'Muscosa'
	OLD PORT ('Mackati'^{PBR}) (F)	ESty IArd
	old red moss	see *R.* 'Henri Martin'
	old velvet moss	see *R.* 'William Lobb'
	'Old Velvet Rose'	see *R.* 'Tuscany'
	old yellow Scotch (SpH)	see *R.* × *harisonii* 'Williams' Double Yellow'
	OLIVIA ROSE AUSTIN ('Ausmixture') (S)	EPfP ESty LCro LOPS MAus
	OLIVIA ('Wekquahofa') (HT)	LSRN

	'Olympic Flame' (F)	EPfP MAsh
	'Omar Khayyám' (D)	EBls MAus NLar
	omeiensis	see *R. sericea* subsp. *omeiensis*
	OPEN ARMS ('Chewpixcel'^{PBR}) (ClMin) ♀H6	CRos EBls ESps ESty LBuc MAsh MAus MMuc SMad SPer SSea SWCr
	'Ophelia' (HT)	EBls NLar
	ORANGE BLOSSOM SPECIAL ('Smi52/02') (ClMin)	ESty
	'Orange Sensation' (F)	CTri MAus
§	ORANGE SUNBLAZE ('Meijikatar'^{PBR}) (Min)	CSBt SPer
	'Orange Triumph' (Poly)	EBls
	'Orangeade' (F)	SCob
	ORANGES AND LEMONS ('Macoranlem'^{PBR}) (F)	CBod CSBt EBls ESty IBoy MAus SSea SWCr
	OTHELLO ('Auslo'^{PBR}) (S)	SPer
	OUR BETH ('Beacarol') (S)	EBls LRHS LSRN MAsh SWCr
	'Our Dream' (Patio)	MAsh
	OUR GEORGE ('Kirrush') (Patio)	LSRN
	OUR HILDA ('Lancoro') (F)	LSRN
	OUR JUBILEE ('Coccages') (HT)	ESty
	OUR MOLLY ('Dicreason') (GC/S)	IDic LSRN SPer
	OUT OF THE BLUE ('Simblue') (F) **new**	ESty
	OXFORDSHIRE ('Korfullwind'^{PBR}) (GC) ♀H6	IRob SCob SSea
	'Pablito' (Min) **new**	MMuc
	PANACHE ('Poultop'^{PBR}) (Patio/Min)	ECnt IBoy LRHS NPri
	'Papa Gontier' (T)	CPou
	PAPA MEILLAND ('Meisar') (HT)	CSBt CTri EBls SPer SSea
	PAPER ANNIVERSARY (Patio)	LBuc LSRN
	PAPI DELBARD ('Delaby') (ClHT)	EBee EWTr LSRN MRav NLar
	'Papillon' (Ch) **new**	EBls
I	'Parade' (Cl) ♀H6	CKel EBls LSRN MAus NLar SWCr
	'Parkdirektor Riggers' (ClF)	CBod EBls GBin MAus NLar SCob SPer
	Parks's yellow China	see *R.* × *odorata* 'Ochroleuca'
	Parson's pink China	see *R.* × *odorata* 'Pallida'
	PARTRIDGE ('Korweirim') (GC)	EBls MAus SPer
	parvifolia	see *R.* 'Burgundiaca'
	PAS DE DEUX ('Poulhult'^{PBR}) (Courtyard Series) (ClF)	MAsh
	PASCALI ('Lenip') (HT)	CBcs CTri EBls IBoy MAus MJak SCob SPer
	PAT AUSTIN ('Ausmum'^{PBR}) (S)	CBod CRos CSBt CTri EPfP IBoy LRHS LSRN MAsh MAus MBNS MRav NEgg NLar NRHS SCob SEND SPer SWCr
	'Paul Crampel' (Poly)	EBls
	'Paul Lédé' (ClT)	see *R.* 'Climbing Paul Lédé'
	PAUL MCCARTNEY (HT)	see *R.* THE MCCARTNEY ROSE
	'Paul Neyron' (HP)	EBls EWTr MAus SPer
	'Paul Noël' (Ra)	CRos MAus
	'Paul Ricault' (Ce × HP)	EBls MAus
	PAUL SHIRVILLE ('Harqueterwife'^{PBR}) (HT)	CKel EBls ESps MAus SPer SWCr
	'Paul Transon' (Ra) ♀H6	CPou CRHN CRos EBls EPfP LRHS MMuc NEgg NLar SEND SPer SRGP WHer

	'Paul Verdier' (Bb)	EBls
	'Paula's Rose' (Patio)	LSRN
§	'Paulii' (Ru/GC)	EBls MAus
	'Paulii Alba'	see *R.* 'Paulii'
	'Paulii Rosea' (Ru/GC)	MAus
	'Paul's Early Blush' (HP)	EBls
	'Paul's Himalayan Musk' (Ra) ♀H6	Widely available
§	'Paul's Lemon Pillar' (ClHT)	CKel EBls ELon EPfP LRHS MAus NLar SPer
	'Paul's Scarlet Climber' (Cl/Ra)	EBee EBls ELan ELon ESps IBoy IRob LBuc LRHS MAsh MAus MJak MRav MSwo NPri SPer SRGP WBor
	'Paul's Single White Perpetual' (Ra)	CTri EBls NLar
	PAWS ('Beapaw') (S)	EBls
	'Pax' (HM)	CPou EBls MAus WKif
	PEACE ('Madame A. Meilland') (HT) ♀H6	CBcs CKel CRos CSBt CTri EBls ECnt ELan EPfP ESty IBoy LCro LOPS LRHS LSRN MAsh MAus MRav MWat NEgg NPri NRHS SCob SPer SPoG SRGP SSea SWCr
	'Peach Grootendorst' (Ru)	CPou
	PEACHY ('Macrelea') (HT)	MAsh SPoG
	PEARL ANNIVERSARY ('Whitston'^{PBR}) (Min/Patio)	CBod CKel CSBt ESps ESty LBuc LSRN MRav SSea SWCr
	PEARL DRIFT ('Leggab') (S)	EBee EBls MAus MCot MSwo SPer SWCr
	PEARL ('Korterschi'^{PBR}) (F) ♀H6	MAsh MRav SWCr
	PEAUDOUCE	see *R.* ELINA
	PEGASUS ('Ausmoon'^{PBR}) (S)	MAus
§	'Pélisson' (CeMo)	EBls
§	***pendulina***	EBls MAus WOut
	- 'Nana'	NWad
	'Penelope' (HM) ♀H5	CKel CRav CSBt CTri EBls ECnt ELan EPfP ESps EWTr IBoy LRHS LSRN MAus MCot MNrw MRav MWat NLar SCob SPer SRGP SSea SWCr
	'Penelope Hobhouse' (HM) **new**	EBls
	PENNY LANE ('Hardwell'^{PBR}) (ClHT) ♀H6	CGro CSBt EBee EBls ECnt ELon EPfP ESps EUJe IBoy LBuc LRHS MAsh MAus MRav NLar SCoo SPer SPoG SSea SWCr
	PENNY LANE ('Talpen') (Min)	EWTr MSwo
	× ***penzanceana***	see *R.* 'Lady Penzance'
	PEPPERMINT SPLASH	see *R.* RACHEL LOUISE MORAN
	PERENNIAL BLUE ('Mehv9601') (Ra) ♀H6	CSam EBls ESty MRav SCob SSea SWCr
	PERENNIAL BLUSH ('Mehbarbie'^{PBR}) (Ra) ♀H6	CKel ESty MRav SWCr
§	PERFECT DAY ('Poulcrem') (F)	ECnt
	PERFECT HARMONY ('Tangustedv') (HT)	ESty
	PERFECT MATCH ('Hartie') (F)	ESty
	PERFECT PET ('Smi122-2-04') (F)	ESty SWCr
	'Pergolèse' (DPo) **new**	EBls
	'Perle des Jardins' (T)	EBls
§	'Perle d'Or' (Poly) ♀H6	EBls MAus NLar SLon SPer
	PERPETUALLY YOURS ('Harfable'^{PBR}) (Cl)	CGro MRav
	Persian yellow	see *R. foetida* 'Persiana'

Name	Suppliers
PETER BEALES ('Cleexpert') (S)	EBls
PETER PAN ('Chewpan'[PBR]) (Min) ♀H6	EPfP MAus SWCr
PETER PAN ('Sunpete') (Patio)	MAsh
'Petite de Hollande' (Ce)	EBls MAus NLar SPer
'Petite Lisette' (Ce × D)	MAus NLar
'Petite Orléannaise' (Ce)	EBls
'Pharisäer' (HT)	EBls
PHEASANT ('Kordapt') (GC)	EBls MAus SPer
PHILLIPA ('Poulheart'[PBR]) (S)	LSRN
PHOEBE (Ru)	see *R.* 'Fimbriata'
phoenicea	EBls
'Phyllis Bide' (Ra) ♀H6	CKel EBee EBls ELan EPfP EWTr IArd LCro LOPS LRHS MAus MCot MSwo NLar SPer SRGP SSea SWCr WKif
PICCADILLY ('Macar') (HT)	CSBt CTri IBoy SPer SWCr
PICCOLO ('Tanolokip') (F/Patio)	SWCr
'Picture' (HT)	EBls SPer
PIERRE CARDIN ('Meilolipo'[PBR]) (HT)	ESty
PIGALLE '84 ('Meicloux') (F)	SCoo SWCr
'Pilgrim'	see *R.* THE PILGRIM
pimpinellifolia	see *R. spinosissima*
- 'Altaica'	see *R. spinosissima* 'Grandiflora'
- double yellow-flowered	see *R.* × *harisonii* 'Williams' Double Yellow'
- 'Harisonii'	see *R.* × *harisonii* 'Harison's Yellow'
- 'Lutea'	see *R.* × *harisonii* 'Lutea Maxima'
PINK BELLS ('Poulbells') (GC)	CGro EBls SPer
'Pink Bouquet' (Ra)	CRHN
PINK CHAMPAGNE ('Forchamp') (Cl) **new**	ESty
PINK CHAMPAGNE ('Frysamba') (F) **new**	MAsh SWCr
'Pink Cloud' (ClHT)	ELan
'Pink Favorite' (HT)	SCob SPer
PINK FIZZ ('Poulycool') (ClPatio)	ECnt
§ PINK FLOWER CARPET ('Noatraum'[PBR]) (GC) ♀H6	CGro CRos CSBt CTri EBee EBls ECnt ELan EUJe IBoy IRob LCro LOPS LRHS LSRN MAsh NPri NRHS SCoo SEND SPer SPoG SSea SWCr
'Pink Garnette'	see *R.* 'Carol Amling'
'Pink Grootendorst' (Ru)	EBee EBls EPfP LEdu MAus NEgg NLar SPer
'Pink Gruss an Aachen' (F) **new**	EBls
§ PINK HIT ('Poultipe'[PBR]) (Min/Patio)	EBls ECnt LRHS LSRN MAsh NRHS
PINK MARTINI ('Tan04608'[PBR]) (HT)	ESty MRav
pink moss	see *R.* × *centifolia* 'Muscosa'
'Pink Parfait' (F)	EBls SPer
PINK PERFECTION ('Korpauvio'[PBR]) (HT)	CSBt ECnt EPfP LRHS MAsh SSea SWCr
'Pink Perpétué' (Cl)	CBod CSBt CTri EBls ECnt ELan ELon EPfP ESps IBoy LBuc MAus MRav NLar SPer SPoG SSea SWCr
'Pink Prosperity' (HM)	EBls MAus
'Pink Showers' (ClHT)	MSwo
PINK SKYLINER ('Franwekpink'[PBR]) (ClS)	EBls
PINOCCHIO ('Rosenmärchen') (F)	EBls
PIPPIN ('Beajaffa') (S) **new**	EBls LRHS MAsh
PIROUETTE ('Poulyc003'[PBR]) (ClS)	ECnt MAsh
PLAYTIME ('Morplati') (F)	MAus
PLEINE DE GRÂCE ('Lengra') (S)	EBls LEdu MAus
'Plentiful' (F)	EBls
POETRY IN MOTION ('Harelan'[PBR]) (HT)	EBls
POLAR STAR ('Tanlarpost') (HT)	CSBt EBls ECnt ESps SPer SWCr
'Polly' (HT)	EBls LSRN
§ 'Polyantha Grandiflora' (Ra)	EBls MAus SVic
pomifera	see *R. villosa* L.
POMPADOUR ('Deldour') (F) **new**	ESty
'Pompon Blanc Parfait' (A)	EBls MAus
'Pompon de Bourgogne'	see *R.* 'Burgundiaca'
'Pompon de Paris' (ClMinCh)	see *R.* 'Climbing Pompon de Paris'
'Pompon de Paris' (MinCh)	SCob SSea WAbe
'Pompon Panaché' (G)	MAus
POMPONELLA ('Korpompan'[PBR]) (F)	CWld MAsh
PORT SUNLIGHT ('Auslofty'[PBR]) (HM) ♀H6	CRos EPfP ESty IBoy LRHS MAus NLar NRHS
Portland rose	see *R.* 'Portlandica'
§ 'Portlandica' (Po)	CTri EBls SPer
prairie rose	see *R. setigera*
prattii	EBls
'Precious Amber' (F)	MAsh
'Precious Gold'	MAsh SPoG
PRECIOUS LOVE ('Kirlowo'[PBR])	MAsh
'Precious Memories' (Min)	LSRN
PRECIOUS MEMORIES ('Dichello'[PBR]) (F)	ESty
'Precious Platinum' (HT)	MJak SPer
PRECIOUS TIME ('Oramarpa'[PBR]) (HT)	ESty
§ 'Président de Sèze' (G) ♀H7	CPou EBls MAus NLar SPer
'President Herbert Hoover' (HT)	EBls
PRETTY IN PINK ('Dicumpteen'[PBR]) (GC) ♀H6	ECnt
PRETTY JESSICA ('Ausjess') (S)	CGro LSRN MRav MWat
PRETTY LADY ('Scrivo'[PBR]) (F) ♀H6	MAus
PRETTY POLLY ('Meitonje') (Min) ♀H6	CKel EPfP ESps ESty IBoy LRHS MAsh MRav MWat SPer SPoG SSea SWCr
PRIDE OF ENGLAND ('Harencore'[PBR]) (HT)	EBls
'Pride of Reigate' (HP) **new**	EBls
'Prima Ballerina' (HT)	CTri EBls EPfP ESps LRHS MAsh SPer SWCr
primula	EBls MAus NLar SPer
primula* × *rugosa	MJak
'Prince Camille de Rohan' (HP)	CBod EBls MAus
'Prince Charles' (Bb)	EBls MAus WKif
PRINCE JARDINIER ('Meitroni'[PBR]) (HT) ♀H6	ESty LSRN SWCr

Princess Alexandra of Kent ('Ausmerchant'[PBR]) (S)	CRos EPfP EShb ESty LRHS MAus NRHS SPer
Princess Alexandra ('Pouldra'[PBR]) (Renaissance Series) (S) ♀H6	CTri ECnt ESty NLar SWCr
Princess Alice ('Hartanna') (F)	LSRN
Princess Anne ('Auskitchen'[PBR]) (S) ♀H6	CSBt ECnt EPfP LBuc LRHS MAus NRHS SCob
Princess ('Korspobux'[PBR]) (HT)	ECnt
'Princess Louise' (Ra) **new**	EBls
Princess of Wales ('Hardinkum'[PBR]) (F) ♀H6	EBls MJak MRav SPer SWCr
§ 'Princesse de Nassau' (Ra)	CPou EBls MAus
'Princesse Louise' (Ra)	EBls
'Princesse Marie' misapplied	see *R.* 'Belvedere'
'Princesse Marie' Jacques (Ra) **new**	EBls
'Pristine' (HT)	MAus
'Prolifera de Redouté' misapplied	see *R.* 'Duchesse de Montebello'
Proper Job ('Tan02733'[PBR]) (HT)	ECnt ELon ESty SWCr
'Prosperity' (HM) ♀H6	CTri EBee EBls GBin LRHS MAus MCot MRav NLar SPer SWCr
Prospero ('Auspero') (S)	NLar
§ Pure Poetry ('Tan04179') (HT)	ESty
'Purezza' (Ra)	EBls NLar
'Purity' (ClHT)	CBod
Purple Eden	see *R.* Ebb Tide
Purple Moon ('Dicmover') (F)	IDic
Purple Prince ('Simpurple') (HT)	ESty
Purple Skyliner ('Franwekpurp'[PBR]) (ClS)	EBls LRHS MAsh MCot NPri SPer SWCr
Purple Tiger ('Jacpurr'[PBR]) (F)	ESty
quatre saisons	see *R.* × *damascena* var. *semperflorens*
'Quatre Saisons Blanche Mousseuse' (DMo)	CPou EBls MAus NLar
Queen Anne ('Austruck'[PBR]) (S)	CSBt EPfP ESty MAus
Queen Elizabeth	see *R.* 'The Queen Elizabeth'
Queen Mother ('Korquemu'[PBR]) (Patio) ♀H6	CSBt EBls ELan EPfP ESps MAus MJak MRav SPer SWCr
'Queen of Bourbons' (Bb)	EBls LEdu NLar
Queen of Denmark	see *R.* 'Königin von Dänemark'
Queen of Sweden ('Austiger'[PBR]) (S)	CGro CRos ECnt EPfP LBuc LRHS MAus NRHS SCob SPer SPoG SWCr
'Rachel' (HT)	CPou LSRN MAsh NLar NPri
§ Rachel Louise Moran ('Jacdrama'[PBR]) (HT)	ESty
Rachel ('Tangust'[PBR]) (HT) ♀H6	CSBt EBls ESty MRav SPoG SSea SWCr
Rainbow Magic ('Dicxplosion'[PBR]) (Patio)	MJak
'Rambling Rector' (Ra) ♀H6	Widely available

Rambling Rosie ('Horjasper'[PBR]) (Ra) ♀H6	CBod CKel CRos CSBt EBee EBls ECnt EPfP ESty EWTr LRHS LSRN MAus MSwo NLar NRHS SSea SWCr
'Ramona' (Ra)	EBls
'Raspberry Royale' (F/Patio) ♀H6	EPfP MAsh SPoG
'Raubritter' ('Macrantha' hybrid)	CBod CPou EBls EWTr MAus SPer SWCr
Raymond Blanc ('Delnado') (HT)	LSRN MRav NLar
'Raymond Carver' (S)	EBls LRHS MAsh
Rebecca (Patio)	ESty LSRN
'Rebecca Claire' (HT)	LSRN
Rebecca Mary ('Dicjury'[PBR]) (F)	IDic
Reconciliation ('Hartillery'[PBR]) (HT)	SWCr
Red Abundance	see *R.* Songs of Praise
Red Bells ('Poulred') (Min/GC)	EBls
Red Blanket ('Intercell') (S/GC)	EBls MAus SPer
Red Coat ('Auscoat') (F)	MAus
Red Collection ('Pang607') (F) **new**	GRid
Red Devil ('Dicam') (HT)	IBoy
Red Eden Rose ('Meidrason'[PBR]) (Cl)	ESty
Red Fairy ('Moredfor') (Poly) **new**	ETMg
Red Finesse ('Korvillade'[PBR]) (F) ♀H6	MAsh SWCr
'Red Grootendorst'	see *R.* 'F.J. Grootendorst'
Red Letter Day ('Beajackdaw') (S) **new**	EBls
'Red Max Graf'	see *R.* Rote Max Graf
red moss	see *R.* 'Henri Martin'
Red New Dawn	see *R.* 'Étendard'
Red Parfum de Provence ('Meiafone'[PBR]) (HT)	ESty
§ 'Red Patio' (F/Patio)	LSRN
Red Rascal ('Jacbed') (S/Patio)	CKel CSBt
red rose of Lancaster	see *R. gallica* var. *officinalis*
'Red Wing' (S)	EBls MAus
Redova ('Poulcy030') (Courtyard Series) (Cl) **new**	ECnt
Regensberg ('Macyoumis'[PBR]) (F/Patio)	EBls IBoy LEdu MAus SPer SWCr
'Reine des Violettes' (HP) ♀H7	CBWd CPou EBls ELon EPfP EWTr GBin IArd LCro LOPS LRHS LSRN MAsh MAus MCot NLar NPri SMad SPer SRGP SWCr
'Reine Marie Henriette' (ClHT)	CPou EBls
'Reine Olga de Wurtenberg' (N)	EBls
§ 'Reine Victoria' (Bb)	EBls LCro LOPS MAus NLar SPer
§ Remember ('Poulht001'[PBR]) (HT) ♀H6	EBls ECnt EPfP LRHS MAsh NRHS SPoG
Remember Me ('Cocdestin') (HT) ♀H6	CGro CSBt EBls ECnt EPfP ESps ESty IArd IBoy LCro LOPS LRHS LSRN MAsh MAus MGos MRav MWat NEgg SCob SPer SPoG SWCr
Remembrance ('Harxampton'[PBR]) (F)	CRos EBls EPfP ESps ESty LBuc LRHS LSRN MAsh MJak MRav MWat NPri NRHS SCob SPer SPoG SSea SWCr

§ RENAISSANCE ('Harzart'[PBR]) (HT)	CKel CSBt MJak SWCr
'René André' (Ra)	CPou CRHN EBee EBls MAus NLar
'René d'Anjou' (CeMo)	MAus
RÉPUBLIQUE DE MONTMARTRE ('Delparfrou') (F) **new**	ESty
'Rescht'	see *R.* 'De Resht'
'Rêve d'Or' (N)	EBls MAus MCot MMuc SPer
'Réveil Dijonnais' (ClHT)	EBls MAus
RHAPSODY IN BLUE ('Frantasia'[PBR]) (S) ♀H6	Widely available
RICHARD PORSON ('Beajuniper') (S) **new**	EBls
§ × ***richardii***	EBls EWTr MAus NLar
RICK STEIN ('Tan96205'[PBR]) (HT)	LSRN
'Rival de Paestum' (T)	MAus
'River Gardens'	NPer
ROB ROY ('Cocrob') (F)	EBls SPer
ROBBIE BURNS ('Ausburn') (SpH)	MAus
'Robert le Diable' (Ce × G)	EBls MAus SPer
'Robert Léopold' (Mo)	EBls
'Robin Hood' (HM)	CBod EBls
ROBIN REDBREAST ('Interrob') (Min/GC)	EBls
§ ROBUSTA ('Korgosa') (Ru)	EBls
ROCK & ROLL ('Wekgobnez') (HT)	CSBt ESty
'Roger Lambelin' (HP)	CPou EBls MAus SPer
ROMANCE ('Tanezamor'[PBR]) (S)	IBoy LSRN
'Rosa Mundi'	see *R. gallica* 'Versicolor'
ROSARIUM UETERSEN ('Kortersen') (ClHT)	EBls
'Rose à Parfum de l'Haÿ' (Ru)	CTri EBls
'Rose Ball' (S)	EBls LRHS MAsh
§ 'Rose d'Amour' (S) ♀H6	EBls
'Rose de Meaux'	see *R.* × *centifolia* 'De Meaux'
'Rose de Meaux White'	see *R.* 'White de Meaux'
'Rose de Rescht'	see *R.* 'De Resht'
ROSE DES CISTERCIENS ('Delarle') (HT)	ESty
'Rose des Maures' misapplied	see *R.* 'Sissinghurst Castle'
'Rose d'Hivers' (D)	EBls
'Rose du Maître d'Ecole'	see *R.* 'Du Maître d'Ecole'
'Rose du Roi' (HP/DPo)	EBls ELon MAus
'Rose du Roi à Fleurs Pourpres' (HP)	EBls MAus
ROSE FOR ELAINE ('Rawdenqueen') (HT)	LSRN
§ ROSE GAUJARD ('Gaumo') (HT)	EBls MAsh
ROSÉE DE MATIN ('Evematch'[PBR]) (S) **new**	EBls
'Rose-Marie Viaud' (Ra)	CPou EBee EBls MAus MMuc
ROSEMARY HARKNESS ('Harrowbond') (HT)	ESps ESty MJak SPer SRGP
'Rosemary Rose' (F)	EBls SPer
ROSEMOOR ('Austough'[PBR]) (S) ♀H6	CRos LBuc LRHS MAsh MAus NRHS SPer
'Roseraie de l'Haÿ' (Ru) ♀H7	Widely available
ROSIE ('Benros') (Min)	LSRN
'Rosy Cheeks' (HT)	MAsh SWCr
ROSY CUSHION ('Interall') (S/GC)	CKel EBls LRHS MAus MCot NLar SPer WKif

'Rosy Mantle' (ClHT)	CSBt EBls SPer SWCr
§ ROTARY SUNRISE ('Fryglitzy') (HT)	CSBt
§ ROTE MAX GRAF ('Kormax') (GC/Ru)	CBod CDul CKel EBls NLar
§ 'Rouletii' (Min)	ITim
'Roundelay' (HT)	EBee EBls
roxburghii	CBcs LEdu MAus
- L 817 **new**	GKev
- PAB 7331	LEdu
- var. ***hirtula*** (S)	EBls
- f. ***normalis*** (S)	EBls
- 'Plena'	see *R. roxburghii* f. *roxburghii*
§ - f. ***roxburghii*** (d)	MAus
'Royal Air Force' (HT)	ELan
§ ROYAL BROMPTON ROSE ('Meivildo') (HT)	ESty
ROYAL COPENHAGEN	see *R.* REMEMBER
'Royal Gold' (ClHT)	EBls SSea
'Royal Highness' (HT)	EBls
ROYAL JUBILEE ('Auspaddle'[PBR]) (S)	CSBt EPfP LCro LOPS MAus SCob SPer
'Royal Occasion' (F)	SPer
ROYAL WILLIAM ('Korzaun') (HT) ♀H6	CSBt CTri EBls ELan ESps LBuc LRHS LSRN MAsh MAus MJak MRav MWat NPri SCob SPer SWCr
§ ***rubiginosa***	CCVT CDul CPer CTho EBls ESps GPoy IFro LBuc MAus MRav SPer WMoo WMou WTSh
rubra	see *R. gallica*
rubrifolia	see *R. glauca* Pourr.
'Rubrotincta'	see *R.* 'Hebe's Lip'
rubus (Ra)	MAus
RUBY ANNIVERSARY ('Harbonny'[PBR]) (Patio)	CGro CKel CRos CSBt EBls ELon ESps ESty LBuc LCro LOPS LSRN MAsh MRav MSwo MWat SCob SCoo SPer SPoG SSea SVic SWCr
RUBY CELEBRATION ('Peawinner'[PBR]) (F) ♀H6	CBod CKel EBls ESps ESty IRob MRav SWCr
RUBY ROMANCE	see *R.* MEDLEY RUBY
RUBY RUBY	see *R.* RUBY SLIPPERS
§ RUBY SLIPPERS ('Weksactrumi') (Min)	LRHS MAsh NRHS SPoG
'Ruby Wedding' (HT)	CBcs CKel CRos CSBt CTri EBls ECnt ELan EPfP ESps IArd IBoy LRHS LSRN MAsh MAus MGos MJak MRav NRHS SCob SPer SPoG SVic SWCr
'Ruby Wedding Anniversary' (F)	LSRN
rugosa (Ru)	CArg CBod CDul CFGn CGro CLnd CPer CRos CTri ECrN EPfP EPom ESps LBuc MAus MRav SCob SGol SPlb SVic SWCr WHar WMou WTSh
- 'Alba' (Ru)	Widely available
- 'Rubra' (Ru)	CBcs CBod CCVT CDul CGro CTho CTri EBee ELan EPfP EPom ESps ETMg GMcL LBuc LCro LOPS SCob SEWo SPer SPoG SSea SVic WHar
- var. ***ventenatiana*** (Ru)	EBls
'Rugosa Atropurpurea' (Ru)	EPom
'Ruhm von Steinfurth' (HP)	EBls
'Rumba' (F)	CBod ELan
'Rural England' (Ra)	EBls LRHS MAsh SWCr
RUSHING STREAM ('Austream') (GC)	MAus
'Russelliana' (Ra)	CBod EBls MAus NLar
'Sadler's Wells' (S)	EBls
'Safrano' (T)	EBls

SAINT ALBAN ('Auschesnut'PBR) (S)	MAus
SAINT BONIFACE ('Kormatt') (F/Patio)	CSBt
SAINT EDMUNDS ROSE	see *R.* BONITA
SAINT ETHELBURGA ('Beabimbo') (S)	EBls LRHS MAsh SWCr
Saint John's rose	see *R.* × *richardii*
Saint Mark's rose	see *R.* 'Rose d'Amour'
'Saint Nicholas' (D)	EBls MAus
'Saint Prist de Breuze' (Ch)	EBls
SAINT SWITHUN ('Auswith'PBR) (S)	EPfP ESty LRHS MAsh MAus NLar NRHS SCob SPer SSea SWCr
'Salet' (DPMo)	CPou EBls MAus NLar
'Sally Holmes' (S) ♀H7	CPou EBee EBls ECnt EPfP EWTr LRHS MAus MRav MWat NLar SEND SLon SPer SWCr
SALLY KANE ('Frygroovy'PBR) (HT)	MRav
SALLY'S ROSE ('Canrem') (HT)	ECnt LSRN
SALSA	see *R.* CHEEK TO CHEEK
SALVATION ('Harlark'PBR) (F)	ESty
§ SAMARITAN ('Harverag'PBR) (HT)	CSBt ESty SWCr
sancta	see *R.* × *richardii*
'Sander's White Rambler' (Ra) ♀H7	CRHN CRos CSam CTri EBee EBls EPfP EWTr IRob LRHS MAus MSwo NRHS SPer SWCr WFar
SANDRA ('Koreinek') (HT)	LSRN
SANDRA ('Poulen055'PBR) (Renaissance Series) (S)	LSRN NLar
SANDRINGHAM ('Beamolly') (S) **new**	EBls
'Sandringham Centenary' (HT)	EBls
'Sanguinea'	see *R.* × *odorata* Sanguinea Group
SARAH (HT)	see *R.* JARDINS DE BAGATELLE
'Sarah van Fleet' (Ru)	CBWd CBod CTri EBls ESps GBin IArd IBoy MAus MMuc MRav MSwo NEgg NLar SMad SPer
SARAH, DUCHESS OF YORK	see *R.* SUNSEEKER
SAVOY HOTEL ('Harvintage') (HT)	EBls ESps MAus SPer SWCr
'Scabrosa' (Ru) ♀H7	CBod EBls ECnt EPfP LBuc LRHS MAsh MAus NLar SPer
SCARBOROUGH FAIR ('Ausoran') (S) ♀H6	LBuc MAus MMuc
SCARLET FIRE	see *R.* 'Scharlachglut'
SCARLET GLOW	see *R.* 'Scharlachglut'
SCARLET HIT ('Poulmo'PBR) (PatioHit Series) (Min/Patio)	EBls ECnt IBoy LRHS LSRN NRHS
SCARLET PATIO ('Kortingle'PBR) (Patio)	CRos MAsh MWat SPoG
SCARLET QUEEN ELIZABETH ('Dicel') (F)	EBls
§ SCENT FROM HEAVEN ('Chewbabaluv') (Cl) **new**	ECnt ESty
SCENTED CARPET ('Chewground'PBR) (GC) ♀H6	ECnt ELan MAus SWCr
SCENTED GARDEN ('Chewscentity') (S)	CSBt ESty SSea
SCENTED MEMORY ('Poulht002'PBR) (HT)	ECnt
SCENTIMENTAL ('Wekplapep'PBR) (F)	CBod EBls EPfP ESty MAsh MRav MWat SSea SWCr
'Scentsation' (Min)	CKel
SCENT-SATION ('Fryromeo'PBR) (HT)	CKel MRav SPoG SWCr
SCEPTER'D ISLE ('Ausland'PBR) (S)	CRos CSBt EPfP LBuc LCro LOPS LRHS MAsh MAus NLar NRHS SCob SCoo SPer SPoG SWCr
§ 'Scharlachglut' (ClS)	CPou EBls EPfP EWTr MAus SPer
SCHLOSS BAD HOMBURG	see *R.* ALIBABA
SCHNEEWITTCHEN	see *R.* ICEBERG
§ 'Schneezwerg' (Ru) ♀H7	EBee EBls MAus NLar SPer
'Schoolgirl' (ClHT)	CBcs CBod CTri EBee EBls ELan EPfP ESps EUJe IBoy LBuc LRHS MAsh MMrt MRav MSwo MWat NEgg NPri SPer SSea SWCr
'Scintillation' (S/GC)	MAus
Scotch rose	see *R. spinosissima*
Scotch yellow (SpH)	see *R.* × *harisonii* 'Williams' Double Yellow'
'Sea Foam' (S)	ETMg
'Seagull' (Ra) ♀H6	CBWd CRos CTri EBls ECnt EPfP ESps IBoy LEdu LRHS LSRN MAsh MRav NLar SCob SLon SMad SPer SWCr WHer
'Seale Pink Diamond' (S)	SSea
SEALED WITH A KISS ('Simwhat') (HT)	ESty
'Sealing Wax' (*moyesii* hybrid)	CPou EBls EWTr NLar
'Semiplena'	see *R.* × *alba* 'Alba Semiplena'
sempervirens (Ra)	EBls
sericea (S)	MAus
- var. ***morrisonensis*** B&SWJ 7139	WCru
§ - subsp. ***omeiensis***	LEdu WPGP
- - BWJ 7550	WCru
- - PAB 2883	LEdu
- - f. ***pteracantha*** (S)	CBcs CDul CKel CTri EBls ELan EPfP EWTr IDee LEdu MAus NLar SBrt SCob SPer
- - SDR 8371 **new**	GKev
'Serratipetala' (Ch)	EBls
§ ***setigera***	EBls MAus
setipoda	EBls MAus
seven sisters rose	see *R. multiflora* 'Grevillei'
SEXY REXY ('Macrexy') (F)	CBcs EBls ESps IBoy LSRN MAsh MAus MRav SCob SMad SPer SRGP SWCr
'Shailer's White Moss'	see *R.* × *centifolia* 'Shailer's White Moss'
SHARIFA ASMA ('Ausreef'PBR) (S)	CBod CSBt EBee ELan LSRN MAus MSwo NEgg NLar SPer
SHEILA'S PERFUME ('Harsherry') (F) ♀H6	CGro EBls ECnt EPfP ESty IBoy LSRN MAsh MRav SPer SPoG SWCr
SHINE ON ('Dictalent'PBR) (Patio) ♀H6	CSBt ECnt IBoy SWCr
'Shot Silk' (HT)	CKel EBls EWTr
SHOWMEE MUSIC ('Chewdaybell') (GC)	MAsh
SHOWMEE SUNSHINE ('Kenveron') (GC)	MAsh
§ SHOWSTAR ('Smi36-1-02') (HT)	CSBt ESty
'Showtime' Lindquist (HT) **new**	EBls
SHOWTIME ('Baitime') (ClS)	MAsh SPoG SWCr
§ SHRIMP HIT ('Poulshrimp'PBR) (Patio)	EBls ECnt MAsh SPoG
'Shropshire Lass' (S)	MAus SPer

	SHROPSHIRE STAR ('Chewsummit')	ESty SSea
	'Silver 25th Anniversary' (F)	CGro
	SILVER ANNIVERSARY ambig.	CGro LSRN
	SILVER ANNIVERSARY ('Jaclav') (HT)	CKel MJak
	SILVER ANNIVERSARY ('Meiborfil') (HT)	ELon
§	SILVER ANNIVERSARY ('Poulari'PBR) (HT) ♀H6	CBod CRos CSBt EBls ECnt ELan LCro LOPS LRHS LSRN MAsh MAus MGos MRav MWat NPri NRHS SCoo SPer SPoG SSea SVic SWCr
	'Silver Jubilee' (HT)	CBcs CTri EBls IArd IBoy LRHS MAsh MAus MRav NRHS SCob SPer SWCr
	'Silver Lining' (HT)	CKel
	'Silver Moon' (Cl)	EBls
	SILVER SHADOW ('Frystereo') (HT)	ECnt ESty MAsh SWCr
	'Silver Wedding' (HT)	CBcs CKel CTri EBls ELan IArd MJak MRav MSwo NEgg SCob SPer SVic SWCr
	'Silver Wedding Celebration' (F)	ESty LSRN
	SILVER WISHES	see *R.* PINK HIT
	SIMBA ('Korbelma') (HT)	LSRN
	'Simone' (HT)	CPou EBee
	'Simplex Multiflora'	CBot
	SIMPLY GORGEOUS ('Formaui') (HT)	ESty
	SIMPLY SALLY ('Harpaint'PBR) (Patio)	LSRN
§	SIMPLY THE BEST ('Macamster'PBR) (HT) ♀H6	CGro CKel CSBt EBls ELan EPfP ESty LRHS LSRN MAsh MAus MGos MJak MRav MWat NPri NRHS SCob SCoo SPer SPoG SWCr
	sinowilsonii	see *R. longicuspis* var. *sinowilsonii*
	'Sir Cedric Morris' (Ra)	EBls NLar SSea
	'Sir Frederick Ashton' (HT)	EBls
	'Sir Galahad' deep pink-flowered (F)	CKel
I	'Sir Galahad' white-flowered (F)	CKel MRav
§	SIR HARRY PILKINGTON ('Tanema') (HT) **new**	EBls
	SIR HENRY CECIL ('Webpegasus') (F) **new**	LSRN
	SIR JOHN BETJEMAN ('Ausvivid'PBR) (S)	EPfP LBuc LRHS MAus NRHS
	SIR JOHN MILLS ('Beadaffy') (Cl)	EBls
	'Sir Joseph Paxton' (Bb)	CPou EWTr MAus
	SIR PAUL SMITH ('Beapaul') (ClHT)	EBls LRHS MAsh SWCr
	SIR WALTER RALEIGH ('Ausspry') (S)	MRav
	SIR WALTER SCOTT ('Ausfalcon') (S) **new**	MAus
§	'Sissinghurst Castle' (G)	EBls MAus
	SISTER ELIZABETH ('Auspalette'PBR) (S)	LRHS LSRN MAus NRHS
	SKYLARK ('Ausimple'PBR) (S) ♀H6	LBuc MAsh MAus SCob
	'Skyrocket'	see *R.* 'Wilhelm'
	SMARTY ('Intersmart') (S/GC)	EBls MAus SPer
	SNAZZEE ('Wekzazette'PBR) (F) **new**	ECnt ESty
	SNOW CARPET ('Maccarpe') (Min/GC)	EBls MAus
	'Snow Dwarf'	see *R.* 'Schneezwerg'
	SNOW GOOSE ('Auspom'PBR) (ClS)	CSBt EPfP LRHS MAus NLar NRHS SPer SSea SWCr
	SNOW HIT ('Poulsnows'PBR) (Min/Patio)	ECnt
	'Snow Queen'	see *R.* 'Frau Karl Druschki'
	SNOW QUEEN ('Simseen') (HT)	ESty
	SNOW SUNBLAZE ('Meigovin') (Min)	SPer
	SNOWBALL ('Macangeli') (Min/GC)	LSRN
	SNOWCAP ('Harfleet'PBR) (Patio)	ESty
	'Snowdon' (Ru)	EBls MAus
	SOEUR EMMANUELLE ('Delamo'PBR) (S)	CBod EBee ESty LSRN MRav
	'Soldier Boy' (Cl)	CBod CPou EBee EBls NLar
	'Soleil d'Or' (S) **new**	EBls
	SOLEIL VERTICAL ('Delsov') (Cl) **new**	ESty
§	SOLO MIO ('Poulen002'PBR) (Renaissance Series) (S)	CTri EBee ECnt NLar
§	'Sombreuil' (ClT)	EBee EBls EPfP IArd LRHS MAus MRav NEgg NLar SPer SWCr
	SOMETHING DIFFERENT ('Simsodiff') (HT)	ESty
	SOMETHING SPECIAL ('Macwyo'PBR) (HT)	ESty
§	SONGS OF PRAISE ('Harkimono'PBR) (Abundance Series) (F)	EBls
	SONIA	see *R.* SWEET PROMISE
	'Sophia'	see *R.* SOLO MIO ('Poulen002')
	'Sophie's Perpetual' (ClCh)	CPou CTri EBls MAus SLon SPer
	SOPHY'S ROSE ('Auslot'PBR) (S)	CRos LBuc LRHS LSRN MAus MBNS NEgg SPer SWCr
	SORBET FRUITÉ ('Meihestries'PBR) (ClF)	SSea
	soulieana (Ra/S)	EBls MAus
	'Soupert et Notting' (DPoMo)	CPou MAus NLar SPer
	'Southampton' (F) ♀H6	EBls LSRN SPer SSea
	SOUTHERN BEAUTY ('Forauty') (F)	ESty
	'Souvenir d'Alphonse Lavallée' (ClHP)	EBls
	'Souvenir de Claudius Denoyel' (ClHT)	CPou EBls SPer
	'Souvenir de François Gaulain' (T)	EBls
	'Souvenir de Jeanne Balandreau' (HP)	CPou EBls
	'Souvenir de la Malmaison' (ClBb)	see *R.* 'Climbing Souvenir de la Malmaison'
	'Souvenir de la Malmaison' (Bb)	EBls EWTr MAus MRav NLar SPer
	'Souvenir de Madame Auguste Charles' (Bb) **new**	EBls
	'Souvenir de Madame Léonie Viennot' (ClT)	EBee EBls MAus MRav NLar
	'Souvenir de Pierre Vibert' (DPMo)	CPou
	'Souvenir de Saint Anne's' (Bb)	EBls MAus NLar
	'Souvenir d'Elise Vardon' (T)	EBls
	'Souvenir du Docteur Jamain' (ClHP)	CBWd CPou CSBt EBls ELan ELon EPfP ESty GBin LCro LOPS LRHS

	LSRN MAus MCot MRav MWat NLar SPer SPoG SSea SWCr WFar WKif
'Souvenir d'un Ami' (T)	EBls
spaldingii	see *R. nutkana* var. *hispida*
'Spanish Beauty'	see *R.* 'Madame Grégoire Staechelin'
SPARKLE ('Frymerlin'^{PBR}) (HT)	ECnt ESty MAsh SWCr
SPARKLER	see *R.* KENT
SPARKLING BURGUNDY ('Raw1007') (F)	ESty
SPARKLING SCARLET ('Meihati') (ClF)	MAsh
SPECIAL ANNIVERSARY ('Whastiluc'^{PBR}) (HT) ♀^{H6}	CBcs CGro CKel CRos CSBt EBee EBls ECnt ELon EPfP ESty LCro LOPS LRHS LSRN MAsh MJak MRav NPri NRHS SCoo SPoG SSea SWCr
SPECIAL CHILD ('Taniripsa'^{PBR}) (F/Patio) ♀^{H6}	MRav SPoG SSea SWCr
'Special Dad' (HT)	CGro
SPECIAL EVENT ('Meibrelon') (HT)	ESty
SPECIAL FRIEND ('Kirspec'^{PBR}) (Patio)	ESty LSRN SCob SWCr
'Special Grandad' **new**	LSRN
SPECIAL GRANDCHILD ('Flimika') (F) **new**	ESty
SPECIAL GRANDMA (F) **new**	ESty LSRN
SPECIAL GRANDPA (F) **new**	ESty
SPECIAL MEMORIES ('Fortop') (F) **new**	ESty
'Special Mum' (F) **new**	LSRN
SPECIAL OCCASION ('Fryyoung'^{PBR}) (HT)	MAsh MRav MWat SNig SWCr
SPECIAL SON (F)	ESty
'Spectabilis' (Ra)	CBod CPou EBls
'Spek's Yellow' (HT)	EBls
'Spencer' (HP) **new**	EBls
'Spencer' misapplied	see *R.* 'Enfant de France'
SPICE OF LIFE ('Diccheeky'^{PBR}) (F/Patio)	EBls
§ ***spinosissima***	CArg CCCN CDul CPer EBls LBuc MAus MMuc SCob SGol SPer WTSh
- 'Andrewsii' ♀^{H7}	EBls MAus MRav
§ - double, pink-flowered	EBls WBor
§ - double, white-flowered ♀^{H7}	EBls ECha LEdu MAus
- 'Falkland'	EBls ECha MAus
§ - 'Grandiflora'	EBls
- 'Marbled Pink'	MAus
- 'Mary, Queen of Scots'	CPou EBls EWTr GBin MAus NLar SRms
- 'Mrs Colville'	EBls MAus
- 'Ormiston Roy'	MAus
- 'Single Cherry'	EBls MAus
- 'William III'	EBls EWes GCal MAus
SPIRIT OF FREEDOM ('Ausbite'^{PBR}) (S)	EPfP LBuc LRHS MAus NEgg NRHS
§ 'Splendens' (Ra)	EBls GBin MMuc
SPLISH SPLASH ('Raw1020') (F)	ESty
ST CLARE ('Horbamber') (F) **new**	EBls
ST HELENA ('Canlish') (F)	ECnt
STAMFORD'S SANCTUARY ('Beajealous') (Cl) **new**	EBls
'Stanwell Perpetual' (SpH) ♀^{H7}	CTri EBls ELan EPfP EWTr IBoy MAus MRav MWat NLar SPer SSea
STAR DUST ('Morstar') (Min)	ELon
'Star Performer'^{PBR} (ClPatio)	CSBt ECnt EPfP ESty MAsh SPoG SSea SWCr
STARDUST ('Devstar') (HT)	WBor
STARDUST ('Peavandyke'^{PBR}) (Patio/F)	CPou ESty
STARLIGHT EXPRESS ('Trobstar'^{PBR}) (Cl)	IBoy LBuc LRHS MAsh NPri SPer
STARRY EYED ('Horcoexist') (Patio)	MMrt
'Stars 'n' Stripes' (Min)	MAus
STELLA (HT)	LSRN
stellata	MAus
§ - var. ***mirifica***	MAus
'Stephen' **new**	LSRN
STRAWBERRIES AND CREAM ('Geestraw') (Min/Patio)	ESty
STRAWBERRY FAYRE ('Arowillip'^{PBR}) (Min/Patio)	CGro CKel ESty MRav MWat SPoG SWCr
STRAWBERRY HILL ('Ausrimini'^{PBR}) (S) ♀^{H6}	CSBt ESty IRob LRHS MAsh MAus MMuc NRHS SCoo
STRIKE IT RICH ('Wekbepmey'^{PBR}) (HT) ♀^{H6}	ESty MRav SWCr
§ SUE HIPKIN ('Harzazz'^{PBR}) (HT)	ESty MRav
'Suffolk' (HT)	SCob
SUFFOLK ('Kormixal'^{PBR}) (S/GC) ♀^{H6}	CSBt EBls ELan MAus MJak MRav SCob SPer SSea
suffulta	see *R. arkansana* var. *suffulta*
SUGAR AND SPICE ('Peaallure'^{PBR}) (Patio)	SPoG
SUGAR BABY ('Tanabagus'^{PBR}) (Patio)	ESty
SUGAR 'N' SPICE ('Tinspice') (Min)	MRav
SUMA ('Harsuma') (GC)	EBls ESty
SUMMER BEAUTY ('Kororbe'^{PBR}) (F) ♀^{H6}	MAsh
SUMMER BREEZE ('Korelasting'^{PBR}) (ClS)	CSam MAsh
SUMMER FRAGRANCE ('Tanfudermos') (Castle Series) (HT)	EBls ELon
§ SUMMER GOLD ('Poulreb'^{PBR}) (F)	MAsh SWCr
'Summer Holiday' (HT)	SPer
SUMMER LOVE ('Franluv') (F)	CBcs
SUMMER MEMORIES ('Koruteli'^{PBR}) (Palace Series) (F)	CKel
SUMMER SONG ('Austango'^{PBR}) (S)	CRos EPfP ESty LBuc LCro LOPS LRHS LSRN MAsh MAus NRHS SCob SWCr
'Summer Sunrise' (GC)	EBls
'Summer Sunset' (GC)	EBls
SUMMER WINE ('Korizont'^{PBR}) (ClHT) ♀^{H6}	CSBt EBls ECnt EPfP LRHS MAsh SPer SWCr
SUMMERTIME ('Chewlarmoll'^{PBR}) (ClPatio) ♀^{H6}	CGro CSBt EBls ECnt ELan EPfP IBoy LBuc LRHS MAsh MAus MRav MWat NPri SPer SPoG
SUN HIT ('Poulsun'^{PBR}) (PatioHit Series) (Min/Patio)	CSBt ECnt ESps MRav
'Sunblaze'	see *R.* ORANGE SUNBLAZE

	Name	Suppliers
	SUNBLEST ('Landora') (HT)	MAsh MRav SCob
	SUNFIRE ('Jacko') (F)	ECnt
	SUNNY DAY ('Savasun') (S)	CBod
	SUNNY SKY ('Koraruli'^{PBR}) (HT)	CGro CSBt ECnt ESty LBuc LCro LOPS LRHS MAsh NPri NRHS SCoo SPoG SWCr
	SUNNY SKY ('Korvestavi') (HT) **new**	MWat
	SUNRISE ('Kormarter'^{PBR}) (S)	CGro EPfP ESty MAsh SPoG SWCr
§	SUNSEEKER ('Dicracer'^{PBR}) (F/Patio) 𝒴H6	MAsh MRav SPoG
	SUNSET BOULEVARD ('Harbabble'^{PBR}) (F)	ESps MAsh MAus MRav SPer SWCr
	SUNSET CELEBRATION	see *R.* WARM WISHES
	SUNSET GLOW	see *R.* ALIBABA
	SUPER DOROTHY ('Heldoro') (Ra) 𝒴H6	LSRN MAus SSea SWCr
	SUPER ELFIN ('Helkleger'^{PBR}) (Ra)	CRos LBuc LRHS MAus MRav NLar SCob SPer SSea SWCr
	SUPER EXCELSA ('Helexa') (Ra) 𝒴H6	EBls IBoy IRob MAus SCob SSea SWCr
	SUPER FAIRY ('Helsufair'^{PBR}) (Ra) 𝒴H6	CKel EBee EBls ECnt MAus MRav SMad SPer SSea SWCr
	SUPER SPARKLE ('Helfels'^{PBR}) (Ra)	SCob SSea
§	SUPER STAR ('Tanorstar') (HT)	CKel EBls ESps MRav SWCr
	SUPER TROUPER ('Fryleyeca'^{PBR}) (F) 𝒴H6	CBod CGro CSBt ECnt ESty IBoy LRHS LSRN MAsh MRav MWat SCoo SPer SWCr WBor WCot
	'Surpasse Tout' (G)	EBls MAus
§	'Surpassing Beauty of Woolverstone' (ClHP)	EBls
	SURREY ('Korlanum') (GC) 𝒴H6	CKel CSBt CTri EBls ELan ESty LCro LOPS LSRN MAus MRav MSwo MWat NLar SCob SPer SSea SWCr
	SUSAN HAMPSHIRE ('Meinatac') (HT)	EBls
	SUSAN ('Poulsue') (S)	EBee ECnt LSRN NLar SLon SWCr
	SUSAN WILLIAMS-ELLIS ('Ausquirk'^{PBR}) (S)	CRos EPfP LBuc LRHS MAus NLar NRHS SCob
	SUSIE ('Harwhistle') (ClPatio) **new**	ECnt ESty
	SUSSEX ('Poulave'^{PBR}) (GC)	CSBt EBls MSwo SCob SPer SSea
	'Sutter's Gold' (HT)	EBls
	SWAN LAKE ('Macmed') (Cl)	CPou EBee EBls ECnt EPfP IBoy MRav NLar SPer
	SWANY ('Meiburenac') (Min/GC)	EBls ECrN ESps ESty EWTr MAus MJak MMuc MSwo SPer SWCr
	'Sweet Ballymaloe' (S)	IBoy
	SWEET CAROLINE ('Micaroline') (Min)	LSRN
	SWEET CHILD OF MINE (HT)	ESty
	SWEET DREAM ('Fryminicot') (Patio) 𝒴H6	CGro CRos CSBt CTri EBee EBls ELan EPfP ESps IBoy LRHS LSRN MAsh MAus MJak MRav MWat SPer SPoG SRGP SSea SWCr
	'Sweet Fairy' (Min)	CSBt
	'Sweet Harmony' (HT) **new**	EBls
	SWEET HAZE ('Tan97274'^{PBR}) (F) 𝒴H6	CKel CSBt IBoy MRav SPer
	SWEET JULIET ('Ausleap'^{PBR}) (S)	CSBt ELan IBoy MAus MSwo SPer SWCr
*	'Sweet Lemon Dream' (Patio)	CTri
	SWEET MAGIC ('Dicmagic'^{PBR}) (Min/Patio) 𝒴H6	CTri EBls ESps IBoy MRav SPoG
	SWEET MEMORIES ('Whamemo') (Patio)	CKel CTri EBls ECnt ELan EPfP ESps ESty IBoy LRHS MAsh MRav NPri NRHS SCoo SPer SPoG SWCr
	SWEET PARFUM DE PROVENCE ('Meiclusif'^{PBR}) (HT) 𝒴H6	ELan ESty LSRN
§	SWEET PROMISE ('Meihelvet') (GC)	EBls
	SWEET REMEMBRANCE ('Kirr') (HT)	SCoo
	'Sweet Repose' (F)	EBls
	'Sweet Revelation'	see *R.* SUE HIPKIN
	'Sweet Wonder' (Patio)	EPfP MAsh
	sweginzowii	GCal GLog MAus
	- 'Macrocarpa'	EBls
	'Sydonie' (HP)	CPou
	'Sylvia Dot' (F)	LSRN
	'Sympathie' (ClHT)	MAsh SPer
	'Talisman' (HT)	EBls
	TALL STORY ('Dickooky') (F) 𝒴H6	EBee EBls MWat NLar SWCr
	TAM O'SHANTER ('Auscerise'^{PBR}) (S)	MAus
	TANGO SHOWGROUND ('Chewpattens'^{PBR}) (GC)	ESty
	TATTON ('Fryentice'^{PBR}) (F)	EBls ESty MAus MRav
§	'Tausendschön' (Ra)	EBls
	TEA CLIPPER ('Ausrover'^{PBR}) (S)	MAus
	TEAR DROP ('Dicomo') (Min/Patio)	SCob SSea SWCr
	TEASING GEORGIA ('Ausbaker'^{PBR}) (S) 𝒴H6	CKel CRos ECnt EPfP ESty IBoy LBuc LRHS LSRN MAus MMuc NLar NRHS SCob SCoo SWCr
	TEMPTRESS ('Korramal') (ClS) 𝒴H6	CPou EPfP EUJe MAsh
	TENACIOUS ('Macblackpo'^{PBR}) (F)	ESty
	TEQUILA SUNRISE ('Dicobey') (HT) 𝒴H6	CGro CKel CTri EBls ELan EPfP ESps ESty IBoy LBuc MAsh MAus MJak MRav SPer SSea SWCr
	TERRACOTTA ('Meicobuis') (HT)	ESty
	TESS OF THE D'URBERVILLES ('Ausmove'^{PBR}) (S)	CRos EBee ELan EPfP EShb ESps ESty IBoy LCro LOPS LRHS LSRN MAus NEgg NLar NRHS SCob SCoo SPer SSea SWCr
	'Tessa' (F)	LSRN
	'Texas Centennial' (HT)	EBls
§	THAÏS ('Memaj') (HT)	EBls
	'Thalia' (Ra)	EBls
	THANK YOU ('Chesdeep'^{PBR}) (Patio)	ESps ESty LBuc
§	THAT'S JAZZ ('Poulnorm'^{PBR}) (Courtyard Series) (ClF)	CSam ECnt LSRN SWCr
	THE ALBRIGHTON RAMBLER ('Ausmobile'^{PBR}) (Ra)	CGro CRos EPfP LRHS MAus NLar NRHS SWCr
	THE ALEXANDRA ROSE ('Ausday'^{PBR}) (S)	EPfP LBuc LRHS MAsh MAus SPer
§	THE ALNWICK ROSE ('Ausgrab'^{PBR}) (S)	CRos EPfP LBuc LRHS MAus MGos NLar NRHS SCob SCoo SPer SSea
	THE ANCIENT MARINER ('Ausoutcry') (S) **new**	MAus
I	'The Anniversary Rose'	CRos EBls EPfP LBuc LRHS MAsh NRHS SWCr
	THE BIRTHDAY ROSE (F)	CGro
	'The Bishop' (Ce × G)	MAus

	THE BOSWORTH ROSE ('Raw1014') (F)	ESty
	THE CHURCHILL ROSE ('Horoften') (S) **new**	EBls LRHS MAsh SWCr
	THE COUNTRYMAN ('Ausman') (S)	EBee IBoy MAus SCob SSea
	THE COVENTRY CATHEDRAL ROSE ('Smi72-02') (F)	ESty
	THE DARK LADY ('Ausbloom'[PBR]) (S)	MAus NEgg SPer
	THE DIAMOND WEDDING ROSE (HT)	EBls LSRN MAsh SWCr
	'The Doctor' (HT)	EBls
§	'The Fairy' (Poly) 𝕐[H7]	CKel CSBt CTri EBee EBls ECnt ELan ESps EWTr IBoy LEdu MAsh MAus MRav MWat NLar SCob SMad SPer SSea SWCr WBor WCFE WHer
	'The Garland' (Ra) 𝕐[H6]	EBee EBls EPfP LBuc LRHS MAus MMuc NLar NRHS SPer SWCr
	THE GENEROUS GARDENER ('Ausdrawn'[PBR]) (S) 𝕐[H6]	CKel CRos CSBt CTri ELan EPfP EShb ESty LBuc LRHS LSRN MAus MGos MJak NLar NRHS SCob SCoo SPer SSea SWCr
§	THE GOLD AWARD ROSE ('Poulac008') (Palace Series) (Patio)	ECnt
	THE HERBALIST ('Aussemi') (S)	MAus
	THE INGENIOUS MR FAIRCHILD ('Austijus'[PBR]) (S)	EPfP MAus SCoo
	THE JACK DUCKWORTH ROSE ('Korlutmag'[PBR]) (Patio)	MAsh
	THE JUBILEE ROSE ('Poulbrido'[PBR]) (F)	ECnt
	THE LADY GARDENER ('Ausbrass'[PBR]) (S)	CRos EPfP LRHS MAsh MAus NRHS SWCr
	THE LADY OF THE LAKE ('Ausherbert') (Ra)	CRos EPfP LCro LOPS LRHS MAus NLar NRHS SCob SCoo SWCr
	THE LADY'S BLUSH ('Ausoscar'[PBR]) (S)	EPfP LRHS MAsh MAus
	THE LAKELAND ROSE ('Harspiral') (Cl)	MAsh
	THE LARK ASCENDING ('Ausursula'[PBR]) (S)	LBuc LCro LRHS MAus NRHS SCob SCoo SSea
	'The Margaret Coppola Rose'	see *R.* WHITE GOLD
	THE MAYFLOWER ('Austilly'[PBR]) (S) 𝕐[H6]	CSBt ELon IBoy LBuc LRHS MAus MSwo SCob SPer
§	THE MCCARTNEY ROSE ('Meizeli'[PBR]) (HT)	SPer
	'The New Dawn'	see *R.* 'New Dawn'
	'The One and Only' (HT)	LRHS MAsh SWCr
	THE PAINTER ('Mactemaik'[PBR]) (F)	LSRN
	THE PERSE ROSE ('Beajargon') (S) **new**	EBls
§	THE PILGRIM ('Auswalker'[PBR]) (S) 𝕐[H6]	CKel CRos CSBt CTri EPfP ESps LBuc LRHS MAsh MAus MBNS MJak NLar NRHS SCob SPer SPoG SSea SWCr
	THE POET'S WIFE ('Auswhisper') (S)	CRos ECnt EPfP ESty LRHS MAus NRHS SCoo
	THE PRINCE ('Ausvelvet'[PBR]) (S)	NLar SPer
	THE PRINCE'S TRUST ('Harholding'[PBR]) (Cl)	EBee LBuc MAsh MAus SSea
§	'The Queen Elizabeth' (F)	CBod CSBt CTri EBls ELan ESps IBoy LCro LOPS LSRN MAsh MAus MRav SCob SPer SRGP SSea SWCr WBor

	THE QUEEN'S JUBILEE ROSE ('Beajubilee') (S) **new**	EBls MAsh
	THE ROTARIAN	see *R.* ROTARY SUNRISE
	'The Royal Brompton Rose'	see *R.* ROYAL BROMPTON ROSE
I	'The Rugby Rose' (HT)	LSRN
	THE SHEIKH KHALIFA ROSE ('Dickoolkid') (Patio)	IDic
	THE SHEPHERDESS ('Austwist'[PBR]) (S)	IBoy MAus
	THE SIMPLE LIFE ('Hartrifle') (Cl)	MRav SSea
	THE TIMES ROSE ('Korpeahn') (F) 𝕐[H6]	ECnt MAus SCob SPer SWCr
	THE WEDGWOOD ROSE ('Ausjosiah'[PBR]) (ClS)	EPfP LBuc LRHS MAus NRHS SCob
	THE WREN ('Kormamtiza'[PBR]) (F/Patio)	EPfP MAsh
	'Thelma' (Ra)	EBls MAus
	'Thérèse Bugnet' (Ru) 𝕐[H7]	EBls MAus
	THINKING OF YOU ('Frydandy'[PBR]) (HT) 𝕐[H6]	CGro EBls EPfP ESps ESty IBoy LSRN MAsh MAus SRGP SSea SWCr
	'Thisbe' (HM)	CPou EBls MAus SPer
	THOMAS À BECKET ('Auswinston'[PBR]) (S)	CRos EPfP ESty LCro LOPS LRHS MAsh MAus NRHS
	'Thoresbyana'	see *R.* 'Bennett's Seedling'
	THOUSAND BEAUTIES	see *R.* 'Tausendschön'
	'Threave' (Bb)	CPou
	threepenny bit rose	see *R. elegantula* 'Persetosa'
	THUMBS UP ('Hornothing') (S)	EBls
	TICKLED PINK ('Fryhunky'[PBR]) (F) 𝕐[H6]	CKel CSBt CTri EBls ELon IRob LRHS LSRN MAsh MRav MWat SPer SPoG SSea
	TIMES PAST ('Harhilt'[PBR]) (ClHT)	CKel MRav SPoG SRGP SWCr
	'Tina Turner' (HT)	LSRN
	TINTINARA ('Dicuptight'[PBR]) (HT) 𝕐[H6]	ECnt
	'Tipo Ideale'	see *R.* × *odorata* 'Mutabilis'
	'Tipsy Imperial Concubine' (T)	EBls
	TITANIC ('Macdako'[PBR]) (F)	ESty
	'Toby Tristam' (Ra)	EBls
	TOGETHER FOREVER ('Dicecho'[PBR]) (F)	MAsh SWCr
	TOGMEISTER ('Beahappy') (F) **new**	EBls LRHS MAsh
	'Tom Marshall' (Ra)	LSRN
	'Tony Jacklin' (F)	LSRN
	TOP MARKS ('Fryministar'[PBR]) (Min/Patio)	CGro EPfP ESps MJak MRav SCoo SPer SWCr
	TOPAZ JEWEL	see *R.* YELLOW DAGMAR HASTRUP
	'Topsi' (F/Patio)	SPer
§	'Tour de Malakoff' (Ce)	CPou EBls IBoy NLar SPer
	TOYNBEE HALL ('Korwonder') (F)	MAsh
	TRADESCANT ('Ausdir'[PBR]) (S)	SCob
	TRADITION	see *R.* TRADITION '95
§	TRADITION '95 ('Korkeltin'[PBR]) (ClHT)	GBin MAsh NLar
	TRANQUILITY ('Barout') (HT)	EPfP LRHS NRHS
	TRANQUILLITY ('Ausnoble'[PBR]) (S)	CRos CSBt ECnt ESty LBuc MAus NLar SCob SCoo SPer SWCr

	'Treasure Trove' (Ra)	CRHN EBls MAus
	'Tricolore' (G) **new**	EBls
	'Tricolore de Flandre' (G)	EBls MAus
	'Trier' (Ra)	CPou EBls MAus NLar
	'Trigintipetala' misapplied	see *R.* × *damascena* 'Professeur Émile Perrot'
	'Triomphe de Laffay' (Ch) **new**	EBls
	'Triomphe de l'Exposition' (HP)	MAus
	triphylla	see *R.* × *beanii*
	'Triple Delight' (S)	LSRN
I	'Trish's Rose'	LSRN
	TROIKA ('Poumidor') (HT)	IBoy MAsh MAus SPer SWCr
	'Tropicana'	see *R.* SUPER STAR
	'Truly Loved' (F)	MAsh
	TRULY SCRUMPTIOUS ('Smi35-4-02') (HT)	ESty MRav
	TRUMPETER ('Mactru') (F) ♀H6	CTri EBee ECnt ESps IArd IBoy LBuc MAsh MAus MRav MWat SPer SPoG SWCr
§	'Tuscany' (G)	EBls MAus SPer
	'Tuscany Superb' (G) ♀H7	CBWd CBod CPou CRav CRos CSBt CTri EBls ELan EPfP EWTr LCro LEdu LOPS LRHS MAus MCot MRav NLar SPer SSea SWCr WBor WFar WHer WKif
	TWENTY-FIFTH ('Beatwe') (F)	EBls
	TWENTY-ONE AGAIN! ('Meinimo'[PBR]) (HT)	LSRN
	TWICE IN A BLUE MOON ('Tan96138'[PBR]) (HT) ♀H6	CGro CKel CSBt EBee EBls ECnt ELon ESps ESty IBoy MRav MWat SCob SCoo SPoG SSea SWCr
	TWIGGY'S ROSE ('Harteam'[PBR]) (F)	MAsh
	TWIST ('Poulstri'[PBR]) (Courtyard Series) (ClPatio)	ECnt
	TYNWALD ('Mattwyt') (HT)	EBee SPer
	'Ulrich Brünner'	see *R.* 'Ulrich Brünner Fils'
§	'Ulrich Brünner Fils' (HP)	EBls MAus
	'Una' (Ra) **new**	WKif
	'Uncle Bill' (HT)	EBls
	UNCLE WALTER ('Macon') (HT)	EBls
	'Unique Blanche'	see *R.* × *centifolia* 'Unique'
	VALENCIA ('Koreklia'[PBR]) (HT)	MAus SPer
	VALENTINE HEART ('Dicogle'[PBR]) (F) ♀H6	CSBt ELon ESps ESty IArd LSRN MAsh MAus MRav SPoG SWCr
	'Vanguard' (Ru)	EBls
	'Vanity' (HM)	EBls MAus
	'Variegata di Bologna' (Bb)	EBls EPfP LRHS MAus SWCr
	'Vatertag' (Min)	LSRN
	'Veilchenblau' (Ra) ♀H7	Widely available
	VELVET FRAGRANCE ('Fryperdee') (HT)	CSBt ECnt ELon EPfP ESty MAus MRav SPoG SSea SWCr
	VELVET LUSTRE ('Simpalno') (HT)	ESty
	'Venusta Pendula' (Ra)	MAus
	'Verschuren' (HT/v)	ESty
	versicolor	see *R. gallica* 'Versicolor'
	'Vick's Caprice' (HP)	EBls MAus NLar
	'Vicomtesse Pierre du Fou' (ClHT)	EBls MAus
	VICTORIA JOY ('Diciwill') (F)	IDic
	VICTORIA ('Simlast') (HT) **new**	ESty
	VIKING PRINCESS	see *R.* IMAGINATION ('Pouldron')
	'Village Maid'	see *R.* × *centifolia* 'Unique Panachée'
§	***villosa*** L.	EBls
	- subsp. ***villosa***	MAus
§	'Violacea' (G)	EBls MAus
	VIOLET CLOUD ('Harquick'[PBR]) (Min)	CKel ESty MRav
	'Violette' (Ra)	CPou CRHN CRos EBls ESps ESty EWTr MAus SPer WFar WHer
	'Violinista Costa' (HT)	EBls
	virginea	SPer
	virginiana ♀H7	EBls GCal MAus WMoo
	- 'Plena'	see *R.* 'Rose d'Amour'
	'Viridiflora'	see *R.* × *odorata* 'Viridiflora'
	'Vivid' (Bourbon hybrid)	EBls
	vosagiaca	see *R. caesia* subsp. *vosagiaca*
	'Vuosaari' (Ru) **new**	EBls
	WALTZ ('Poulkrid'[PBR]) (Courtyard Series) (ClPatio)	ECnt
	wardii var. ***culta***	MAus
	WARM WELCOME ('Chewizz'[PBR])	CGro CKel CRos EBls ECnt ELan EPfP ESty EUJe IBoy LCro LOPS LRHS LSRN MAsh MAus MRav NRHS SMad SPer SPoG SSea SWCr WCot
§	WARM WISHES ('Fryxotic'[PBR]) (HT) ♀H6	CSBt EBls ECnt EPfP ESps IBoy LBuc LRHS LSRN MAsh MAus MJak MRav MWat NRHS SCob SSea SWCr
	'Warrior' (F)	SPer
	WARWICKSHIRE ('Korkandel'[PBR]) (GC)	EBls
§	***watsoniana*** (Ra)	EBls
	WB YEATS ('Dicoodles') (F) **new**	IDic
	webbiana	MAus
	WEDDING BELLS ('Korsteflali'[PBR]) (HT)	LSRN MAsh SWCr
	WEDDING CELEBRATION ('Poulht006'[PBR]) (HT)	EBls ECnt LBuc MAsh NRHS
	'Wedding Day' (Ra)	Widely available
	WEE JOCK ('Cocabest') (F/Patio)	IBoy
	'Weetwood' (Ra)	CRHN
	WEISSE WOLCKE	see *R.* WHITE CLOUD ('Korstacha')
	WELL-BEING ('Harjangle'[PBR]) (S)	ELon
	'Wendy Cussons' (HT)	CTri EBls MRav SCob SPer
	WENLOCK ('Auswen') (S)	SPer
	WESTERLAND ('Korwest') (S) ♀H6	CBod EBls MRav NLar SWCr
	WHERE THE HEART IS ('Cocoplan'[PBR]) (HT)	ESty
	WHISKY MAC ('Tanky') (HT)	CBcs CSBt CTri EBls ELan ESps LBuc LSRN MRav SCob SPer SRGP
	'White Bath'	see *R.* × *centifolia* 'Shailer's White Moss'
	WHITE BELLS ('Poulwhite') (Min/GC)	EBls
	'White Cécile Brünner' (Poly)	EBls
§	WHITE CLOUD ('Korstacha'[PBR]) (ClHT)	ESty SWCr
	'White Cockade' (ClHT)	CPou EBls MSwo SPer SWCr
	WHITE COVER	see *R.* KENT
§	'White de Meaux' (Ce)	EBls MAus
	WHITE DIAMOND ('Interamon'[PBR]) (S)	ECnt

	Name	Suppliers
§	WHITE GOLD ('Cocquiriam'PBR) (F) ♀H6	CSBt
	'White Grootendorst' (Ru)	EBls NLar
	'White Maman Couchet' (HT) **new**	EBls
	WHITE MAX GRAF	see *R.* × *jacksonii* WHITE MAX GRAF
	WHITE MEIDILAND ('Meicoublan') (S/GC)	LRHS MAsh
	white moss	see *R.* × *centifolia* 'Shailer's White Moss', *R.* 'Comtesse de Murinais'
	'White New Dawn' **new**	EBls
	'White Patio' (Min/Patio)	CRos MAsh
	WHITE PERFUMELLA ('Meicalanq'PBR) (HT)	ELon ESty LSRN SWCr
§	'White Pet' (Poly) ♀H7	CKel CTri EBee EBls ECnt ELan EPfP EWTr MAus MCot MRav NLar SEND SPer SSea SWCr WKif
	white Provence	see *R.* × *centifolia* 'Unique'
	'White Queen Elizabeth' (F)	SCob
	white rose of York	see *R.* × *alba* 'Alba Semiplena'
	WHITE SKYLINER ('Franwekwhit'PBR) (ClS)	EBls SSea
	WHITE STAR ('Harquill') (ClHT)	ECnt MRav SSea
	'White Wings' (HT)	EBls IBoy SPer WKif
	wichurana (Ra)	EBls GCal MAus
	- 'Cally Anemone' (Ra)	MAus
	'Wickwar' (Ra) ♀H6	EBls EWTr GCal NLar
	WILD EDRIC ('Aushedge'PBR) (Ru) ♀H6	ECnt LBuc LRHS MAus MMuc SCob SCoo
	WILD ROVER ('Dichirap'PBR) (F) ♀H6	EBls ESty
	WILD THING ('Jactoose'PBR) (S) ♀H6	MAsh
	WILDEVE ('Ausbonny'PBR) (S) ♀H6	LBuc LCro LOPS LRHS MAus NRHS
	WILDFIRE ('Fryessex') (Patio)	CGro ECnt ESty IBoy LRHS MAsh MAus MRav SPoG SWCr
§	'Wilhelm' (HM)	CPou EBls MAus SPer
	'Will Scarlet' (HM)	MAus
	'William Allen Richardson' (N)	EBls MAus
	WILLIAM AND CATHERINE ('Ausrapper'PBR) (S)	CRos CSBt ESty LCro LOPS LRHS MAsh MAus SCob
	'William Baffin' (S) **new**	EBls
	'William Cobbett' (F)	SSea
§	'William Lobb' (CeMo) ♀H7	CBod CGro CKel CPou EBls EPfP IBoy LRHS MAus MCot MNrw MRav MWat NEgg NLar NRHS SMad SPer WHer WKif
	WILLIAM MORRIS ('Auswill'PBR) (S)	CRos CSBt MAus NEgg SCob SPer
	'William R. Smith' (T)	EBls
	WILLIAM SHAKESPEARE 2000 ('Ausromeo'PBR) (S)	CBod CGro CKel CRos CSBt ECnt ELan EShb ESty IBoy LCro LOPS MAus MBNS MJak MSwo NEgg NLar SCob SSea SWCr
	WILLIAM SHAKESPEARE ('Ausroyal') (S)	IBoy MCot MJak SCob SPer
	'William Tyndale' (Ra)	CBod CPou
	'Williams' Double Yellow'	see *R.* × *harisonii* 'Williams' Double Yellow'
	willmottiae	EBls MAus
	WILTSHIRE ('Kormuse'PBR) (S/GC) ♀H6	CBod CSBt CTri EBls ECnt ELan ESty IBoy IRob MRav MWat NLar SCob SEND SLon SSea SWCr
	WINCHESTER CATHEDRAL ('Auscat'PBR) (S)	Widely available
	'Windermere' (Ra) **new**	EBls
	WINDFLOWER ('Auscross') (S)	LBuc MAus
	WINDRUSH ('Ausrush') (S)	MAus SPer
	WINE AND DINE ('Dicuncle') (GC)	EBls
	WISLEY 2008 ('Ausbreeze'PBR) (S)	CRos CSBt IBoy LBuc LRHS MAsh MAus NRHS SCob SCoo
	WITH THANKS ('Fransmoov'PBR) (HT)	MJak
	'Woburn Abbey' (F)	EBls
	WOLLERTON OLD HALL ('Ausblanket'PBR) (S)	CRos CSBt EPfP EShb ESty LBuc LRHS MAus NLar NRHS SCob SCoo SPer SSea SWCr
	'Wolley-Dod'	see *R.* 'Duplex'
	WONDERFUL HUSBAND ('Raw982') (F)	ESty
	WONDERFUL NEWS ('Jonone'PBR) (Patio)	CGro ESty MWat
	WONDERFUL WIFE ('Raw1025') (HT)	ESty
	WONDERFUL YOU ('Smi 170-2-4') **new**	ESty
	woodsii (S)	EBls MAus
	- var. ***fendleri*** **new**	EBls
	- var. ***ultramontana*** **new**	EBls
	'Woolverstone Church Rose'	see *R.* 'Surpassing Beauty of Woolverstone'
	WORCESTERSHIRE ('Korlalon'PBR) (GC) ♀H6	MAus MJak MRav SPer SWCr
	'Wretham Rose' (Ce) **new**	EBls
	WYMONDHAM ABBEY ('Beadevil') (ClHT)	EBls LRHS MAsh
§	***xanthina*** 'Canary Bird' (S) ♀H7	CBcs CGro CKel CSBt CTri EBee EBls ECnt ELan EPfP ESps ESty EWTr GKin IBoy LRHS LSRN MAsh MAus MNrw MRav NEgg NLar SPer SPoG SSea SWCr SWvt
§	- f. ***hugonis***	CBod CTri EBls ELan MAus NLar SPer
	- - 'Flore Pleno' **new**	EBls
	'Xavier Olibo' (HP)	EBls
	YARDLEY BAROQUE ('Beayar') (HT) **new**	EBls
	YELLOW BRICK ROAD ('Baload') (S) **new**	ETMg
	'Yellow Cécile Brünner'	see *R.* 'Perle d'Or'
§	YELLOW DAGMAR HASTRUP ('Moryelrug'PBR) (Ru)	CBod CPou EBls MMrt NLar SCob SPer
	YELLOW FLOWER CARPET	see *R.* FLOWER CARPET SUNSHINE
	'Yellow Mutabilis'	EBls
	'Yellow Patio' (Min/Patio)	CRos LRHS MAsh SPoG
	yellow Scotch	see *R.* × *harisonii* 'Williams' Double Yellow'
	YELLOW SUNBLAZE ('Meitrisical') (Min)	CSBt
	'Yesterday' (Poly/FCl) ♀H6	CKel EBee EBls MAus NLar
	YOKOHAMA ('Keihayokoki') (HT)	EBls
	'Yolande d'Aragon' (HP)	EBls
	York and Lancaster	see *R.* × *damascena* 'Versicolor'
	YORK MINSTER ('Harquest') (F)	MRav
	YORKSHIRE ('Korbarkeit'PBR) (GC)	EBls ELan MRav
	'Yorkshire Lady' (HT)	NEgg
	YORKSHIRE PRINCESS ('Dicmouse') (Patio)	IDic MRav

YOU ARE MY SUNSHINE ('Frykwango'PBR) (HT) ♀H6	SWCr
YOUNG AT HEART ('Raw922') (F) new	ESty
YOUNG LYCIDAS ('Ausvibrant'PBR) (S)	CSBt EPfP IBoy LBuc LRHS LSRN MAus NRHS SCob
'Your Wedding Day' (F)	CGro
YOU'RE BEAUTIFUL ('Fryracy'PBR) (F)	CGro CKel CSBt EBee ECnt ESty LBuc LCro LOPS LRHS MAsh MRav NRHS SPer SPoG SWCr
YVES PIAGET	see *R.* ROYAL BROMPTON ROSE
'Yvonne Rabier' (Poly) ♀H7	EBls EWTr MAus MRav NLar SPer
'Zéphirine Drouhin' (Bb)	Widely available
§ 'Zigeunerknabe' (S)	CBod EBls MAus NLar SPer WFar

Roscoea ✿ (*Zingiberaceae*)

sp.	CMac SDir
alpina	CAby CBro CExl EBee EPot GEdr GKev ILea WCru XLum
- CC 1820	IBlr
- pink-flowered	IBlr
- purple-flowered	IBlr
- short	WCru
alpina* × *cautleyoides	IBlr
§ ***auriculata*** ♀H5	CAby CAvo CBct CBro EHrv EPfP EPot GCal GEdr GKev IBlr IFoB ILea IRob LEdu MAsh MPie NWad SChF SDeJ SDir SPer WCru WHil
- B&SWJ 2594	WCru
- B&SWJ 2687	WCru
- GWJ 9230	WCru
- 'Anorexia'	IBlr
- brown-stemmed × ***purpurea***	CJun IBlr
- early-flowering	IBlr WCru
- 'Floriade'	CJun EBee IBlr LPla WSHC
- green-stemmed × ***purpurea***	CJun IBlr
- late-flowering	WCru
- 'White Cap'	CJun EBee GKev
auriculata* × *australis	IBlr
auriculata* × *cangshanensis	WCru
auriculata* × *capitata	IBlr
auriculata* × *purpurea	WCru
australis	CSam CTal EBee ELon GEdr LLHF MAsh MNrw WCru WThu
- pink-flowered KW 22124	IBlr
- purple-flowered KW 22124	IBlr
australis* × *humeana	IBlr
'Ballyrogan Lavender'	IBlr
'Ballyrogan White'	IBlr
× ***beesiana*** ♀H5	CAvo CBod EPfP EUJe ILea MAsh SMHy
- 'Ballyrogan Purple'	CJun IBlr
- Cream Group	CBct CJun CTal EBee EPfP EPot IBlr LEdu MMrt SDeJ WCru
- Dark Group	IBlr
- Gestreept Group	CBro CMea CTal EPot EUJe GEdr GKev IBlr LAma LRHS MPie NRHS SDir SPer WCru WHil
- - white-flowered	GKev
- 'Lemon and Lavender'	CJun IBlr
- 'Monique'	CDTJ CJun EBee EPfP IBlr
- 'Moonlight'	CJun IBlr
- 'Petite Purple'	IBlr
bhutanica PAB 3826	LEdu
Blackthorn strain	IBlr WCru WHil
brandisii misapplied	see *R. tumjensis*
brandisii (King ex Baker) K. Schum.	IBlr
cangshanensis	CTal MAsh
- BWJ 7848	WCru
capitata	IBlr
cautleyoides	CAby CAvo CBro CWCL ECha EHrv ELon EPot GEdr GKev IBlr IFoB ILea IRob LAma LRHS MNrw NBid NGdn NPnk NRHS SPer SRot WCot WCru XEll
- CLD 772	GEdr IBlr
I - 'Alba'	CTal
- var. ***cautleyoides*** f. ***atropurpurea***	IBlr
- - - 'Giraffe'	IBlr
- - white-flowered	CAby
- 'Crûg's Late Lemon'	WCru
- 'Doge Purple'	IBlr
- 'Early Purple'	CJun
- 'Early Yellow'	CTal EBee
- 'Himalaya' ♀H5	WHil
- 'Jeffrey Thomas' ♀H5	CJun CSam CTal EBee ELan GCal GEdr IBlr IRob WHil
- 'Last Emperor'	CTal
- late, lavender-flowered	IBlr
- late, yellow-flowered	IBlr
- 'Lemon Giraffe'	CJun IBlr
- mauve-flowered	WHil
- 'Pennine Purple'	IBlr
- plum-flowered	IBlr
- var. ***pubescens***	CJun IBlr
- 'Purple Giant'	CJun EBee WHil
- 'Purple Queen' ♀H5	EBee GKev
- purple-flowered	CAby IBlr
- 'Reinier'	CJun CTal GCal IBlr
- f. ***sinopurpurea***	GKev IBlr
- 'Stephanie Bloom' ♀H5 new	EBee
- 'Vanilla'	CJun CTal LEdu
- 'Washfield Purple'	IBlr
- 'Wine Red'	WHil
- 'Yeti'	CJun CTal WHil
aff. ***cautleyoides***	MAsh NChi SPlb
cautleyoides* × *humeana	IBlr LRHS NRHS
cautleyoides* × *praecox	IBlr
cautleyoides* × *scillifolia* f. *atropurpurea	IBlr
debilis var. ***debilis***	CTal IBlr
forrestii ♀H5	NHim
- f. ***forrestii***	IBlr
- - pubescent	IBlr
- 'Ice Maiden'	IBlr
- f. ***purpurea***	IBlr
- f. ***purpurea* × *humeana***	IBlr
'Harvington Evening Star'	CJun EBee LLHF LRHS MAsh NRHS
'Harvington Raw Silk' ♀H5	CJun EBee LLHF LRHS NRHS WFar WHil
'Harvington Royale'	CJun EBee LLHF LRHS NRHS
humeana	CAby CBro EPot GEdr GKev LAma LRHS NPnk NRHS WThu
- ACE 2539	IBlr
- from Cruickshank Botanic Garden	IBlr
- f. ***alba***	CJun IBlr WHil
- Forrest's form	IBlr
- 'Guincho White Stripe'	IBlr
- lavender-flowered	IBlr
- 'Long Acre Sunrise'	CJun EBee WHil
- f. ***lutea*** ♀H5	CJun GEdr IBlr
- pink-flowered	IBlr

- 'Purple Streaker'	CJun WHil
- purple-flowered	EBee
- 'Rosemoor Plum'	CAby CJun WCot WHil
- 'Snowy Owl'	CJun GEdr
- 'Two Tone'	CJun IBlr
- f. ***tyria*** ♀H5	CJun IBlr WHil
'Ice Maiden'	CJun IBlr
'Kew Beauty' ♀H5	CAby CBod CBro CExl CJun CMea CTal EPfP GCal LRHS NGdn NPnk NRHS SMHy SPoG WGwG WHil
'Lavender Mist'	IBlr
'McBeath's Pink'	LLHF LRHS NRHS
nepalensis	CJun WHil
'Pallid Sun'	IBlr
'Pinky'	CMea
praecox	GEdr IBlr
procera misapplied	see *R. auriculata*
procera Wall.	see *R. purpurea*
'Purple King'	CJun
§ ***purpurea***	CAvo CBod CBro CTal ECha ELan ELon EPfP EPri EUJe GCal GKev IBal IBlr IBoy IFoB ILea LAma LRHS MAsh MMuc NGdn NRHS SPer SPlb SPoG WArt WCru WGwG WHer
- CC 1757	IBlr
- CC 3628	CExl IBlr
- HWJK 2020	WCru
- HWJK 2169	WCru
- HWJK 2175	WCru
- HWJK 2400	WCru
- HWJK 2407	WCru
- KW 13755	IBlr
- MECC 2	CJun IBlr
- MECC 10	CJun IBlr
- 'Ant Marian'	EBee GKev
- 'Bronzed Albino'	IBlr
- bronze-leaved	CAby
- 'Brown Peacock'	CAvo CFil CJun CTal GKev IBlr MMoz SDir WCot WCru
- 'Butterfly'	GEdr GKev
- 'Cinnamon Stick'	CAbb CJun CWGN ECtt GEdr MAsh MMrt
- 'Dalai Lama' ♀H4	GEdr GKev WHil
- var. ***gigantea***	WHil
- - CC 1757	IBlr
- 'Himalayan Delight'	IBlr
- 'Julie's Glory'	EBee GKev WFar
- 'Late Lavender'	IBlr
- 'Nico'	CJun ELan IBlr
- 'Peacock'	CJun EPot GKev IBlr WHil
- 'Peacock Eye'	CJun GEdr GKev IBlr
- 'Petticoat Pink'	GKev
- var. ***procera***	see *R. purpurea*
- 'Purple Dwarf'	IBlr
- 'Purple Tower'	IBlr
- 'Red Foot'	EBee
- 'Red Gurkha'	see *R. purpurea* f. *rubra*
- 'Red Riding Hood'	GEdr GKev WFar
- Royal Purple hybrids	CJun MAsh WHil
§ - f. ***rubra*** ♀H4	CAby CBro CJun CTal EBee GKev IBlr LLHF LRHS MAsh MMoz NRHS WCot WFar WPGP WSHC
- - 'Gurkha Redstem'	CJun MMoz WCru
- 'Salt 'n' Pepper'	EBee GEdr GKev
- short	IBlr
- 'Slender Wisp'	IBlr
- 'Spice Island'	CAbb CJun CSpe CWGN EBee ECtt GEdr MAsh SPad WFar
- 'Summer Snow'	EBee GEdr GKev
- tall	WCru
- 'Twin Towers'	GKev
- 'Typico'	IBlr
- 'Vannin'	CJun LEdu WCru
- 'Vincent'	CJun EBee EPot GKev MMoz
- 'Wisley Amethyst'	CBro CJun CTal EBee IBlr LLHF LRHS MAsh MNrw NRHS WFar
'Red Neck' ♀H4	EBee IBlr
schneideriana	CJun GKev IBlr WThu
- robust form	IBlr
scillifolia	CBro GEdr LAma LRHS NRHS SDeJ
- f. ***atropurpurea***	CAby EBee EPot GCal GKev IBal IBlr WCru WThu
- black-flowered	NHpl
- f. ***scillifolia***	EBee IBlr IFoB NHpl WCru WHil WThu
aff. ***scillifolia*** purple-flowered	GEdr IBlr NPnk
'Summer Deep Purple' ♀H5	CJun EBee LRHS NRHS
tibetica	EBee GEdr GKev IBlr LEdu LLHF SPlb WCru WThu
- ACE 2538	IBlr WCru
- BWJ 7878	WCru
- aff. f. ***albo-purpurea***.	IBlr
- f. ***atropurpurea*** BWJ 7640	WCru
- f. ***rosea***	WCru
aff. ***tibetica***	IBlr
§ ***tumjensis***	CTal IBlr
'Two Tone'	CJun
wardii ♀H5	CExl IBlr WHil

rosemary see *Rosmarinus officinalis*

Rosenia (*Asteraceae*)

humilis	CPBP

Rosmarinus ✿ (*Lamiaceae*)

'Barwinnock Dwarf Blue'	WHer
corsicus 'Prostratus'	see *R. officinalis* Prostratus Group
× ***lavandulaceus*** misapplied	see *R. officinalis* Prostratus Group
× ***noeanus***	XSen
officinalis	Widely available
- f. ***albiflorus***	CBod ENfk EPfP ESps GPoy LEdu LRHS MHer MNHC NPol SDow SLim SPlb SPoG SRms WCFE WGwG XSen
- - 'Lady in White'	CRos CSBt ELan EPfP ESps LRHS MAsh NRHS SGol SLim SPer SRms WGwG
- 'Alderney'	WGwG
- 'Almondsbury' **new**	WGwG
- 'Amethyst Beauty' **new**	SDow
§ - var. ***angustissimus*** 'Benenden Blue' ♀H4	CSBt ELan GPoy LRHS MBNS SGol SPer SPlb SPoG SRms WGwG WSpi XSen
- - 'Corsican Blue'	CBod EBee ELan GPoy MHer MHol MNHC SGol SPer SRms WGwG
- 'Arp'	CBod ENfk EWes SPad WGwG XSen
- 'Aureovariegatus'	see *R. officinalis* 'Aureus'
§ - 'Aureus' (v)	CBcs SRms WHer
- 'Avicenna'	WGwG
- 'Barbecue'PBR	EBee ENfk LEdu SRms
- 'Blue Lagoon'	CBod ENfk LRHS MHer MNHC SAko SRms WGwG WHer
- 'Blue Rain'	CBar CBod EPfP MHer MSwo NQui WGwG WHer
- 'Capercaillie'	SDow WGwG
- 'Charlotte' **new**	WGwG

- 'Collingwood Ingram'	see *R. officinalis* var. *angustissimus* 'Benenden Blue'
- 'Cottage White'	WGwG WHer
- 'Farinole'	MNHC SRms WGwG
- 'Fota Blue'	IArd MHer MNHC NPol SAko SDow SGol SRms SVen SWvt WGwG
- 'Foxtail'	CBod ENfk LRHS SRms
- 'Frimley Blue'	see *R. officinalis* 'Primley Blue'
- 'Genges Gold' (v)	WGwG
- 'Gold Dust' (v)	ENfk
- 'Golden Rain'	see *R. officinalis* 'Joyce DeBaggio'
- 'Gorizia'	CBcs CBod LRHS SDow SRms
- 'Green Ginger' ♀H4	CBod CRos EBee ELan EPfP GBin LEdu LRHS MGos MHer MNHC MRav MSCN NPer NRHS SAko SCob SDow SPer SPoG SRms SVen WGwG
- 'Guilded'	see *R. officinalis* 'Aureus'
- 'Haifa'	CBod ENfk NQui SRms WGwG
- 'Heavenly Blue'	WGwG WHer
- 'Huntington Carpet'	ECtt
- 'Iden Pillar'	WGwG
- Israeli	XAbr
§ - 'Joyce DeBaggio' (v)	MHer SDow WGwG WHer
- 'Ken Taylor'	WGwG
- 'Kevock' **new**	WGwG
- 'Knightshayes Blue'	CRos LRHS NRHS
- 'Lady in Blue'	WGwG
- ***lavandulaceus***	see *R. officinalis* Prostratus Group
- 'Lilies Blue'	GPoy WGwG
- 'Lockwood Variety'	see *R. officinalis* (Prostratus Group) 'Lockwood de Forest'
- 'Madeline Hill'	LRHS
- 'Majorca Pink'	CBcs CSBt CSpe ENfk LRHS MHer MNHC SDow SPer WGwG WHer XLum XSen
- 'Marenca'	CHll MNHC SRms WGwG
- 'Margaret of Pershore'	WGwG
- 'McConnell's Blue' ♀H4	ELan EPfP LRHS MGos MNHC NRHS SCob SDow SRms WGwG WHer WPGP
- 'Miss Jessopp's Upright' ♀H4	Widely available
- 'Pointe du Raz'	CBod ELan EPfP MAsh SChF SLim SRms WGwG WSpi
§ - 'Primley Blue'	CBcs CBod CSam ECtt MNHC MRav SGol SRms WGwG
§ - Prostratus Group	Widely available
- - 'Capri'	CBod EPfP LRHS SCob SRms WFar
- - 'Freda'	WGwG
- - 'Gethsemane'	WGwG
§ - - 'Lockwood de Forest'	WGwG WHer
- - 'Rampant Boule'	CBod SDow SRms WGwG XLum XSen
- - 'Sea Level'	MHer WGwG
- - 'Sheila Dore'	SPlb SVen
- - white-flowered	GPoy
- - 'Whitewater Silver'	LRHS
- 'Punta di Canelle'	XSen
§ - 'Pyramidalis' **new**	XSen
- f. ***pyramidalis***	see *R. officinalis* 'Pyramidalis'
- ***repens***	see *R. officinalis* Prostratus Group
- 'Rex'	WGwG XSen
- 'Roman Beauty'PBR	CBcs CSBt EBee EHoe EPfP LRHS LSRN MHol MTin NRHS SAko SCob SLim SRms SWvt WHer WSpi
- 'Roseus'	CBot ELan ENfk EPfP GPoy LRHS MAsh MHer MNHC SDow SEND SLim SPoG SRms SVen WAvo WGwG XAbr
- 'Salem'	CBod MHer
- 'Severn Sea' ♀H4	CBod CRos CSBt CTri ECtt ELan ENfk EPfP ESps GPoy LRHS MGos MNHC MRav MSwo SLon SPer SRms SVen WAvo WCFE WGwG WSpi
- 'Shimmering Stars'	SDow WGwG
- 'Silver Sparkler'	WFar WGwG WHer
- SILVER SPIRES ('Wolros')	WGwG
- 'Sissinghurst Blue' ♀H4	CBod CRos EBee ECha ECrN ELan EPfP ESps LRHS MAsh MHer MNHC MRav SDow SGol SLim SPer SPlb SPoG SRms SWvt WGwG XAbr
- 'Sissinghurst White'	WGwG
- 'Sorcerer's Apprentice'	SDow
- 'South Downs Blue'	WGwG
- 'Spanish Snow'	WGwG
- 'Spice Island'	CBod LRHS SPer XSen
- 'Sudbury Blue'	EBee ENfk MNHC SAko SDow SGol SRms WGwG
- 'Sunkissed'PBR	SRms
- 'Trusty'	WGwG
- 'Tuscan Blue'	CBcs CBod CExl ECha ECrN ECtt ELan EPfP ESps EUJe LRHS MHer MNHC MSwo NEgg NRHS SDow SGol SPer SRms WAvo WGwG WPGP XSen
- 'Variegatus'	see *R. officinalis* 'Aureus'
- 'Wisley Blue'	WGwG
repens	see *R. officinalis* Prostratus Group
Salcombe form	CHll
'Sappho'	CHll

Rostrinucula (*Lamiaceae*)

dependens	CMCN EBee EPfP EWes LRHS NLar SBrt SMad SPad WCFE
sinensis	CExl

Rosularia (*Crassulaceae*)

§ ***aizoon***	CRos EDAr LRHS NRHS SRms
alba	see *R. sedoides* var. *alba*
§ ***chrysantha***	CRos EDAr LRHS NHpl NRHS SPlb SRms
crassipes	see *Rhodiola wallichiana*
libanotica RCB RL 20	WCot
§ ***muratdaghensis***	SPlb
pallida A. Berger	see *R. chrysantha*
pallida Stapf	see *R. aizoon*
pallida ambig.	EPot
platyphylla misapplied	see *R. muratdaghensis*
rechingeri	SRms
§ ***sedoides*** var. ***alba***	EDAr EPot NHpl SRms XLum
sempervivum	ESps EWes WThu
§ - subsp. ***glaucophylla***	LRHS NRHS SRms WHal WThu
spatulata hort.	see *R. sempervivum* subsp. *glaucophylla*

Rotheca (*Lamiaceae*)

§ ***myricoides*** 'Ugandense' ♀H1b	CCCN CCse CHll EShb WSFF

Rubia (*Rubiaceae*)

peregrina	EBWF GPoy
tinctorum	CHab CHby GPoy MNHC SRms WSFF

Rubus ✿ (*Rosaceae*)

RCB/Eq C-1	WCot
SDR 4635	GKev
acuminatus	CBot LEdu SBrt

alceifolius Poir.	SDys
- B&SWJ 1833	WCru
arcticus	EBee ECtt EPPr LEdu MGil SHar SRot WThu XLum
bambusarum	CBot EBee EShb MRav WCFE WCru
'Benenden' ♀H5	CAby CBcs CDul CExl CTri CTsd EBee ECrN ELan EPfP EWTr GKin LRHS LSRN MBNS MMuc MRav NEgg NLar SCob SPer SPhx WAvo WBor WCFE WHar WMoo WSpi
'Betty Ashburner'	CAgr CBcs CDul EBee EPPr EWTr GLog GMcL MCoo MGos MRav SCob SPer SPoG WMoo XLum
biflorus ♀H5	LEdu LRHS MBlu MMuc NRHS SEND WPGP
'Boatsberry'	SDea
'Boysenberry' (F)	CArg ERea LEdu LRHS NPri
boysenberry, thornless (F)	CMac ESps LBuc LSRN NPri SDea SPer
buergeri B&SWJ 5555	WCru
caesius	WCot
calophyllus	CBcs CFil WPGP
- PAB 13.171	LEdu
calycinoides Hayata ex Koidz.	see *R. rolfei*
calycinoides Kuntze	GKev SGol
chamaemorus	GPoy
'Clarke's Velvet Night'	SBrt
cockburnianus (F)	CBcs CTri ELan EPfP GKev GKin GMcL IFoB LBuc LCro LOPS MMuc MRav MSwo NLar NSti SCob SMad SPer SPlb SRms WHar WSpi
- 'Goldenvale' ♀H5	CBcs CBot CDul EBee EHoe ELon EPfP ESps GMcL IFro LRHS MAsh MBlu MGos MMuc MRav MSwo NEgg NLar NSti SCob SEND SLon SPer SPoG SRms WFar
crataegifolius	MRav
'Emerald Spreader'	WMoo
fockeanus misapplied	see *R. rolfei*
formosensis	SBrt
- B&SWJ 1798	WCru
fruticosus agg.	CArg EMOT ESps WSFF
- 'Adrienne' (B)	CAgr CFGn CHab CSBt LEdu MAsh SRms WHar
- 'Apache' (B)	CHab CRos SPoG
- 'Ashton Cross' (B)	LBuc
- 'Asterina' (B)	EMil
- 'Bedford Giant' (B)	CHab CSBt LSRN MAsh MGos SEND SLim WHar
- 'Black Butte' (B)	CHab EPom SDea SLon SVic
- 'Black Satin' (B)	CAgr ECrN EMOT NLar NPri SDea SVic
- 'Čačanska Bestrna' (B)	MCoo
- 'Chester' (B)	CRos EPom ERea LEdu LRHS NRHS SKee
- 'Godshill Goliath' (B)	SDea
- 'Helen' (B)	CAgr MAsh SDea
- 'Himalayan Giant' (B)	CHab EMOT NEgg NLar SDea
- 'Karaka Black'PBR (B)	CHab CRos ERea LBuc LRHS NRHS SPoG SVic
- 'Loch Maree'PBR (B/d)	CHab CMac EPom LEdu MCoo NPri SLon
- 'Loch Ness'PBR (B) ♀H6	CAgr CArg CHab CRos EMOT EPom ESps IArd LCro LOPS LRHS LSRN NPri NRHS SCoo SDea SKee SPer SVic
- Loch Tay'PBR (B)	CArg CHab CMac CRos EPom LRHS NRHS SPoG
- 'Merton Thornless' (B)	CSBt CTri ECrN EMOT GBin LEdu LSRN MAsh MGos NPri SRms WHar
- 'Natchez'PBR (B)	SPer
- 'Navaho' (B)	CHab CRos ERea LRHS NRHS
- 'No Thorn' (B)	SDea
- 'Obsidian' (B)	LEdu
- 'Oregon Thornless' (B)	CAgr CFGn CSBt ECrN EPfP ESps LCro LOPS LRHS LSRN MAsh MJak MRav NLar SCoo SDea SKee SLim SPoG SRms SVic
- 'Ouachita'PBR (B)	CFGn LCro LOPS LRHS NRHS SKee SPer SPoG
- 'Parsley Leaved' (B)	SDea
- 'Reuben' (B)	CFGn CHab CRos EPom LBuc LCro LOPS LRHS MCoo MNHC NRHS SKee SPoG
- 'Thornfree' (B)	CAgr CFGn CTri EPfP NLar NPri SDea SKee SLim
- 'Triple Crown' (B)	CHab CMac MCoo
- 'Variegatus' (v)	CMac MBlu WCot
- 'Waldo' (B)	CAgr CFGn CRos CSBt LBuc LSRN MAsh MGos NPri SDea SRms WHar
'Glencoe' (F)	MCoo
henryi	CBcs LRHS NLar WCot
- var. ***henryi***	WCru
ichangensis	CBot CFil
idaeus	CPer GPoy
- 'All Gold' (F) ♀H6	CFGn CMac CPer EMOT EMil EPom ERea LBuc LRHS MAsh NLar NPri SCoo SPer SPoG SRms SVic WHar
- 'Alpengold'PBR (F) **new**	LCro LOPS
- 'Aureus' (F)	ECha LEdu MRav NBid WCot
- 'Autumn Bliss' (F) ♀H6	Widely available
- 'Autumn Treasure'PBR (F)	EMil EPom ERea NPri SLon SVic
- 'Black Jewel' (F)	EPfP LCro LOPS
- 'Cascade Delight' (F)	CSBt EPom LBuc LCro LOPS LRHS MAsh NRHS
- 'Chemainus' (F)	LCro LOPS
- 'Erika'PBR (F)	LCro LOPS LRHS NLar NRHS
- 'Fallgold' (F)	LSRN MMuc SKee
- 'Glen Ample'PBR (F) ♀H6	CAgr CMac CRav CRos CSBt CTri ECrN ELan EMil EPfP EPom ERea LBuc LCro LOPS LRHS LSRN MAsh MCoo NLar NRHS SCoo SDea SKee SLim SPer SPoG SRms SVic WHar
- 'Glen Clova' (F)	CAgr CFGn CSBt CTri EMOT LRHS LSRN MAsh MGos NLar NPri NRHS SKee SLim SPer SPoG SRms WHar
- 'Glen Doll'PBR (F)	CAgr MAsh NLar NRHS SCoo
- 'Glen Fyne'PBR (F)	CAgr
- 'Glen Lyon'PBR (F)	ECrN LBuc MAsh MJak NPri SCoo WHar
- 'Glen Magna'PBR (F) ♀H6	CAgr CArg CMac CSBt ERea MAsh NPri SCoo SDea SKee SLim
- 'Glen Moy'PBR (F)	CAgr CArg CTri EMOT MAsh MGos MJak SCoo SDea SKee SLim
- 'Glen Prosen'PBR (F)	CAgr CSBt EMOT EPfP ERea LRHS LSRN MAsh MGos NPri SCoo SDea SKee SLim SPlb SPoG WHar
- 'Glen Rosa' (F)	ERea SDea
- 'Heritage' (F)	MAsh SCoo SGol SRms
- 'Joan J'PBR (F) ♀H6	EPom ERea LSRN SPer
- 'Leo'PBR (F) ♀H6	CSBt CTri LSRN MAsh SCoo SKee SPer SRms WHar
- 'Malling Admiral' (F) ♀H6	CSBt CTri EMOT EPom LSRN MAsh SCoo SKee SPer WHar
- 'Malling Delight' (F)	ELan SCoo SPlb
- 'Malling Jewel' (F) ♀H6	CAgr CSBt CTri EPfP EPom LBuc LSRN MAsh MJak NPri SDea SKee SRms

- 'Malling Minerva' (F)	CAgr EPom SPer SVic
- 'Malling Promise' (F)	MJak SGol
- 'Octavia'PBR (F)	CAgr CArg CSBt CTri EMil EPom GQue LBuc MAsh MCoo NLar NRHS SLim WHar
- 'Polka'PBR (F) ♀H6	CRos EPfP EPom ESps LBuc LCro LOPS LRHS LSRN MAsh MCoo MRav NRHS SCoo SKee SLim SPer SRms WHar
- RUBY BEAUTY ('Nr7') (F) **new**	LBuc LCro LOPS LSRN MGos NRHS SPoG
- 'Rubyfall'PBR (F) **new**	LCro LOPS
- 'Sugana'PBR (F)	MAsh
- 'Tadmor'PBR (F)	CArg CFGn ERea LCro LOPS LRHS NRHS SKee
- 'Tulameen' (F) ♀H6	CAgr CSBt ELan EMil EPfP EPom LBuc LCro LOPS LRHS LSRN MAsh MMuc NPri NRHS SCoo SEND SKee SLim SPer SPoG SRms SVic WHar
- 'Zeva' (F) **new**	SGol
- 'Zeva Herbsternte' (F)	MAsh
idaeus* × *ursinus	EMOT
illecebrosus (F)	LEdu XLum
irenaeus	CBot LEdu LRHS SEND WHal
Japanese wineberry	see *R. phoenicolasius*
'Kenneth Ashburner'	NLar
lambertianus PAB 8931	LEdu
lineatus	CBot CDTJ EPfP EWes GBin LEdu LRHS MCot NLar WCru WPGP
- B&SWJ 11261 from Sumatra	WCru
- PAB 13.163	LEdu
- HWJ 892 from Vietnam	WCru
- HWJK 2045 from Nepal	WCru
× ***loganobaccus*** (F)	CFGn EMOT GBin MJak
- 'Brandywine' (F)	SDea
- 'Ly 59' (F)	ECrN EPfP MMuc SDea SEND SKee SRms
- 'Ly 654' (F) ♀H5	CRos CSBt EPom ERea LBuc LRHS NEgg NPri NRHS SDea SPer WHar
- thornless (F)	CAgr CTri EPfP EPom LEdu MJak SDea SPoG SVic
ludwigii	SBrt
'Margaret Gordon'	MRav
microphyllus 'Variegatus' (v)	MRav
§ ***nepalensis***	CAgr CFGn GKev LEdu WPGP
nutans	see *R. nepalensis*
odoratus	CAgr CBcs CDul CExl ELan EPPr EPfP EWTr LEdu MBlu NBid NLar SPer WBor
palmatus var. ***coptophyllus***	MMuc
parkeri PAB 6891	LEdu
parviflorus	IFro
- 'Bill Baker'	LEdu
- double-flowered (d)	EPPr
- 'Sunshine Spreader'	EHoe LEdu
parvus	LEdu
pectinellus var. ***trilobus***	SBrt
- - B&SWJ 1669B	NLar WCru
peltatus	CFil NLar
pentalobus	see *R. rolfei*
§ ***phoenicolasius***	CAgr CBcs CCCN CDul CFGn CHGN ELan EMOT EPPr EPfP ERea GNew LCro LEdu LRHS MBlu MCoo MHer MRav SDea SPer SPoG SVic WBor WPGP XAbr
reflexus var. ***hui***	EShb
§ ***rolfei***	CDul CTri MCoo NWad
- B&SWJ 3546 from Taiwan	WCru
- B&SWJ 3878 from the Philippines	WCru
- 'Emerald Carpet' ♀H5	CAgr NLar
rosifolius NJM 10.142	WPGP
- 'Coronarius' (d)	ECrN LSou WCot
rubrisetulosus PAB 9532	LEdu
'Rushbrook Redleaf'	SBrt
saxatilis	LEdu
- PAB 3912	LEdu
setchuenensis	CMCN EPPr NLar
'Silvan' (F)	MMuc SEND
spectabilis	CBcs ELan EPPr EWTr LEdu MMuc MRav WSHC
- 'Flore Pleno'	see *R. spectabilis* 'Olympic Double'
§ - 'Olympic Double' (d)	Widely available
splendidissimus B&SWJ 2361	WCru
squarrosus	SMad
'Sunberry' (F)	CCCN LEdu SDea
swinhoei B&SWJ 1735	WCru
taiwanicola B&SWJ 317	WCru
- CWJ 12400	WCru
- 'Buckingham'	NPer
Tayberry Group (F)	CSBt CTri LRHS LSRN MGos NLar NPri NRHS SPer SRms SVic WHar
- 'Buckingham' (F)	CArg EMil EPom ERea LBuc LCro LOPS LRHS NLar SVic
- 'Medana Tayberry' (F)	CAgr CRos CTri ECrN EMOT EPfP LEdu LRHS MNHC NLar SDea SKee SPoG WHar
§ ***thibetanus*** ♀H5	CBcs CBod CDul CEnd CRos EBee EHoe ELan EPfP EWTr GBin GKin LRHS LSRN MAsh MGos MMuc MRav MSwo NEgg NLar SCob SEND SPer SPoG SWvt WMoo WSpi
- 'Silver Fern'	see *R. thibetanus*
treutleri B&SWJ 2139	WCru
tricolor	CAgr CBcs CBod CDul CSBt CTri ECrN GKev GKin GMcL MBlu MCoo MMuc MRav MSwo NLar SCob SGol SPer WHar WMoo
trilobus B&SWJ 9096	WCru
'Tummelberry' (F)	GQue LRHS MCoo SVic
ulmifolius 'Bellidiflorus' (d)	EPPr MRav NLar
ursinus	SVic
xanthocarpus	LEdu NLar XLum
'Youngberry' (F)	SDea

Rudbeckia ✿ (*Asteraceae*)

alpicola	EBee
AUTUMN SUN	see *R. laciniata* 'Herbstsonne'
'Berlin'	CDor CWGN EBee ECtt GMaP LRHS LSou LSun MHol NLar NRHS SCob SPer
californica	EBee LRHS NRHS
- B&SWJ 14105 **new**	WCru
'Copper Kettle' **new**	WHlf
deamii	see *R. fulgida* var. *deamii*
'Dublin'	CWGN ECtt IBoy LSou MBNS MBel MHol SCob SPer
fulgida	SWvt WFar
- 'City Garden'	CKno ECtt GBin LRHS NLar SRms
§ - var. ***deamii*** ♀H7	Widely available
- 'Early Bird Gold'	CRos CWGN EBee ECtt ETMg GBin GMaP IBoy IRob LCro LOPS MHol NLar NRHS SAko WFar
- var. ***fulgida***	CMea EBee EPfP LEdu SPhx SPoG
- 'Little Goldstar'PBR	CBod CKno CRos EBee ECtt ELan EPfP LCro LOPS LRHS MAsh MHol

		NDov NPnk NPri NRHS SCob SLon SPoG SRms WFar
§	- var. ***speciosa*** ♀H7	CWCL EBee ECha ECtt ELan EPfP GBin GWyn LRHS MMuc NRHS SEND SHar SPlb SPtp SRms SWvt WFar WMoo WOld WPtf XLum
	- var. ***sullivantii*** 'Goldsturm' ♀H7	Widely available
	- VIETTE'S LITTLE SUZY ('Blovi')	CBod EBee SRms WFar
	gloriosa	see *R. hirta*
	grandiflora	LRHS NRHS
	- 'Sundance'	EBee SPhx
§	***hirta***	SVic
	- 'Autumn Colours' (mixed)	CMea ELan LOPS LRHS SPhx
	- 'Cappuccino'	ELan EPfP LRHS
	- CHEROKEE SUNSET mixed (d)	CSpe EPfP
	- 'Cherry Brandy'	CRav CSBt CSpe ETMg LRHS NGBl NRHS SPhx
	- CHIM CHIMINEE mixed	MSCN NGBl SCob SPoG
	- 'Goldilocks'	SVic
	- 'Indian Summer' ♀H3	CRos EPfP LRHS MHol MNHC NRHS SPav SPhx
	- 'Irish Eyes'	SPav SPhx SVic
	- 'Marmalade'	EPfP LRHS NRHS SPhx SVic
	- MOROCCAN SUN mixed (d) **new**	MSCN
	- 'Prairie Sun'	CMea CRos ELon EPfP LRHS NGBl NRHS SPhx
	- 'Sonora'	NGBl
	- 'Tiger Eye'	SPoG
	- 'Toto' ♀H3	EPfP ETMg SPav SWvt
	JULY GOLD	see *R. laciniata* 'Juligold'
	laciniata	CKno CMac CSpe EBee ELan EPPr GCal GQue LEdu LRHS MSpe NDov NGBl NLar NRHS SMHy SPhx SRms WArt WCot WMoo WOld WPGP WWtn XLum
	- var. ***digitata***	IMou
	- 'Golden Glow'	see *R. laciniata* 'Hortensia'
	- 'Goldkugel' (d) ♀H7	MSpe MWat
	- 'Goldquelle' (d)	CBod CRos EBee ECha ECtt ELan EPed EPfP GMaP GWyn LRHS MSCN MTis NGdn NRHS SCob SMad SPer SPoG SRms SWvt WFar WGwG XLum
§	- 'Herbstsonne' ♀H7	Widely available
§	- 'Hortensia' (d)	EBee MAvo MRav NGBl WBrk WCot WFar WHoo WOld
§	- 'Juligold'	CBod EBee ECtt LRHS MBNS MPie NEgg NGdn NPnk NRHS WBrk WSpi WWFP
	- 'Starcadia Razzle Dazzle' ♀H7	EWld MAvo NPnk SAko WCot WFar
	maxima	CAby CBWd CBod CKno CSpe EBee ECha ELon GBin GQue IBoy IFoB ILea LEdu LRHS LSun MBel MHol MMuc NDov NGBl NLar NSti SBrt SMad SPhx SPlb WCot WFar XLum
	missouriensis	CMea EBee GBin LRHS MMuc MNrw NPnk NRHS SPhx WArt
	mollis	EBee LRHS NRHS
	newmannii	see *R. fulgida* var. *speciosa*
	nitida	IBoy WSpi
	occidentalis	LRHS NChi NRHS
	- 'Black Beauty'PBR	EPfP EUJe WSpi
	- 'Green Wizard'	CBod CMac EBee ECtt ELan EPed EPfP EShb EWTr GBin GWyn IBoy LRHS NRHS NSti SPav SPer SRms WHar WSpi
*	***paniculata***	CDor EBee LLHF NGBl WCot
	'Peking'PBR	CBod CWGN EBee ECtt EPfP MBNS NSti SCob SPer
	purpurea	see *Echinacea purpurea*
	speciosa	see *R. fulgida* var. *speciosa*
	subtomentosa	CBWd CSam EWes GCal IRob LEdu LRHS MMuc MSpe NDov NPnk NRHS NSti SCob SMHy WCot WOld WSpi XLum
	- 'Henry Eilers'	Widely available
	- 'Little Henry'PBR	CBod CKno CSpe EBee ECtt EPed IRob LCro LOPS LRHS MBNS MHol NRHS SCob SPoG
	Summerina Series	LRHS SCob
	- SUMMERINA BROWN ('Et Rdb 03'PBR)	CKno CMea LRHS LSou MBNS MHol NGBl NPnk NRHS NSti SPoG WCot
	- SUMMERINA ORANGE ('Et Rdb 01'PBR)	IBoy LPla LRHS LSou MBNS MHol NPnk NRHS SPad SPoG SRkn WCot
	- SUMMERINA YELLOW ('Et Rdb 02'PBR)	CMea IPot LRHS LSou MBNS MHol NGBl NPnk NRHS SPoG SRkn WCot
	triloba ♀H7	CRos CSpe ECha ELon EPfP IBoy LRHS MBel MNrw MWat NGBl NGdn NPnk NRHS SCob SPhx WMoo WPGP WSpi
	- 'Prairie Glow'	CBot CDor CSpe EAJP ELon IBoy ILea LRHS MSCN NPnk SCob SPer SPhx SRkn WCot

rue see *Ruta graveolens*

Ruellia (*Acanthaceae*)

	amoena	see *R. brevifolia*
§	***brevifolia***	ECre EShb WFib
	humilis	EBee EShb GEdr SBrt SPhx
	macrantha	CCCN EShb
	makoyana ♀H1a	EShb
	- pink-flowered	WHil
	- white-flowered	EShb
	strepens	EBee
	tweediana	EShb WFib

Rumex (*Polygonaceae*)

acetosa	CAgr CHab CHby EBWF ENfk GPoy MCoo MHer MJak MMuc MNHC SRms WHer WSFF WTre XAbr
- 'Abundance'	LEdu
- subsp. ***acetosa*** 'Saucy' (v)	LEdu WCot
- 'Profusion'	GPoy MHer
acetosella	CAgr CHab EBWF WSFF
alpinus	EBee LEdu WCot WPGP
flexuosus	CSpe EPPr GCal
hydrolapathum	CBod CHab EBWF MMuc MSKA SEND SPlb WCot WSFF
patientia	CHab
sanguineus	ENfk EShb LEdu MSKA NLar NQui SRms XLum
- var. ***sanguineus***	CHby ELan GQue IFoB MHer MNHC NBro WHer
scutatus	CBod CHby ENfk GPoy MNHC SPlb SRms
- subsp. ***induratus***	SEND
- 'Silver Shield'	EPPr LEdu MHer SRms

Rumohra (*Dryopteridaceae*)

adiantiformis ♀H1c	CBdn CCCN EBee LRHS NLos NRHS SEND WFib

Rupicapnos (Papaveraceae)

africana	GKev
- subsp. ***gaetula*** new	GKev

Ruschia (Aizoaceae)

putterillii	SPlb
spinosa	SPlb
tumidula	SPlb

Ruscus ✿ (Asparagaceae)

aculeatus	CBcs CDul CMac ELan EPfP GPoy LEdu MGil MGos NLar SPlb SRms SWvt WMou WRHF
- (f)	SCob WSpi
- hermaphrodite	EPfP GCal MMuc SEND SMad
- var. ***aculeatus*** 'Lanceolatus' (f)	GCal
- var. ***angustifolius*** PAB 254	LEdu
- 'John Redmond'PBR ♀H5	CBcs ELan ELon EPfP EShb LRHS NLar NWad SCob SLon SPer SWvt WBor WFar WSpi
* - 'Wheeler's Variety' (f/m)	CJun MRav
colchicus 'Trabzon' new	LEdu
hypoglossum	CMac IMou MMuc SEND WCot WSpi
× ***microglossum*** (f) B&SWJ 14041 new	WCru
racemosus	see *Danae racemosa*

Ruspolia (Acanthaceae)

hypocrateriformis	CCCN

Russelia (Plantaginaceae)

§ ***equisetiformis*** ♀H1c	WFib
- 'Lemon Falls' ♀H1c	WFib
- 'Tangerine Falls'	WFib
juncea	see *R. equisetiformis*

Ruta (Rutaceae)

chalepensis	SPhx XLum
corsica	XLum
graveolens	CBod CDul CHab ENfk GPoy LSun MJak MNHC XAbr XLum
- 'Jackman's Blue'	CBcs CTri EHoe EPfP GMaP GPoy MGos MHer MNHC MRav MSwo SRms SWvt WSpi XLum
- 'Variegata' (v)	MNHC MPie NPer SRms

Ruttya (Acanthaceae)

fruticosa	CCCN

× Ruttyruspolia (Acanthaceae)

lutea	CCCN
'Phyllis van Heerden'	CCCN

Rytidosperma (Poaceae)

* ***arundinaceum***	EShb

S

Sabal (Arecaceae)

minor	CPHo NLos SBig SPlb
uresana	LRHS

Saccharum (Poaceae)

arundinaceum	CKno
brevibarbe var. ***contortum***	WCot
officinarum	SPlb
ravennae	SMad SPlb

sage see *Salvia officinalis*

sage, annual clary see *Salvia viridis*

sage, biennial clary see *Salvia sclarea*

sage, pineapple see *Salvia elegans*

Sageretia (Rhamnaceae)

§ ***thea***	CMen
theezans	see *S. thea*

Sagina (Caryophyllaceae)

subulata	EHoe LRHS SVic XLum
- var. ***glabrata***	MAsh
§ - - 'Aurea'	CMea ECha ECtt EDAr GMaP MHer NHpl SPoG SRms

Sagittaria (Alismataceae)

australis	EWat
'Bloomin' Babe'	EWat
graminea	LLWG SBrt
- 'Crushed Ice' (v)	EWat
japonica	see *S. sagittifolia*
lancifolia	EWat LLWG
latifolia	NPer
§ ***sagittifolia***	CWat LLWG MSKA MWts WMAq WPnP XLum
- 'Flore Pleno' (d)	CWat EWat WMAq XLum
- var. ***leucopetala***	WMAq
- - 'Flore Pleno' (d)	NPer

Saintpaulia ✿ (Gesneriaceae)

'Aca's Pink Delight'	WDib
'Aca's Red Ember' (v)	WDib
'Aca's Ronnie Redhead'	WDib
'Ae-Amur Elit'	WDib
'Ae-Armageddon'	WDib
'Ae-Cosmic Jaguar'	WDib
'Ajohn's Fruit Cocktail'	WDib
'Ajohn's Shimmering Star'	WDib
'Alan's Fallen Angel' (d/v) new	WDib
'Alan's White Feather'	WDib
'Allegro Appalachian Trail'	WDib
'Always Pink'	WDib
'Aly's Rosy Baby'	WDib
'Amazing Grace'	WDib
'Amethyst'	WDib
'Anouk'	WDib
'Anthoflores Edith'	WDib
'An-Yablochnyi Spas'	WDib
'Apache Thunderbolt'	WDib
'Arctic Frost' (d)	WDib
'Aussie Magic'	WDib
'Baby Brian'	WDib
'Baby's Breath'	WDib
'Ballet Snowcone' (d)	WDib
'Beacon Trail'	WDib
'Beatrice Trail'	WDib
'Black Ace' (d)	WDib
'Blackie Bryant'	WDib
'Bliznecy'	WDib
'Bloomlover's Cat' (d)	WDib

'Bloomlover's Chimpy'	WDib
'Blue Dragon' (d)	WDib
'Blue Tail Fly'	WDib
'Blushing Ivory'	WDib
'Blushing Trail'	WDib
'B-Man's Taormina'	WDib
'Bob Serbin' (d)	WDib
'Bob's Omega'	WDib
'Bol's Evening Holger' **new**	WDib
'Bol's Evening Irja'	WDib
brevipilosa	WDib
'Buckeye Carioca'	WDib
'Buffalo Hunt' (d)	WDib
'Bylina'	WDib
'Calico Beauty'	WDib
'Candy Fountain'	WDib
'Candy Swirls'	WDib
'Cathedral'	WDib
'Chantamara'	WDib
'Chantaspring'	WDib
'Cherries 'n' Cream'	WDib
'Chiffon Fiesta'	WDib
'Chiffon Pageant'	WDib
'Chiffon Vesper'	WDib
'Cirelda'	WDib
'Colette'	WDib
'Country Romance' (d)	WDib
'Crimson Ice'	WDib
'Cupid's Jewel'	WDib
'Deep Sky'	WDib
'Deer Trail'	WDib
'Delft' (d)	WDib
'Desir'	WDib
'Dibleys Kaarina'	WDib
'Dibleys Mercedes'	WDib
'Dibley's Pat'	WDib
'Ek Lubasha'	WDib
'Ek-Vrata Raia'	WDib
'Electric Dreams'	WDib
'Emerald Love'	WDib
'Falling Raindrops'	WDib
'Favorite Child'	WDib
'Festive Holiday' (d)	WDib
'Fire Mountain'	WDib
'Flashy Angel' (v)	WDib
'Flower Drum'	WDib
'Gecko's Vespa Vino'	WDib
'Genetic Blush'	WDib
'Gillian' (d)	WDib
'Golden Dawn'	WDib
'Golden Eye'	WDib
'Golden Glow' (d)	WDib
'Goluboi Tuman'	WDib
'Grandmother's Halo'	WDib
'Green Dragon'	WDib
'Green Lace' (d)	WDib
'Happy Cricket'	WDib
'Heinz's Moonrays'	WDib
'Hot Summer Day'	WDib
'In The Pink'	WDib
'Indigo Ruffles'	WDib
ionantha subsp. ***grotei***	WDib
– subsp. ***ionantha***	WDib
– subsp. ***rupicola***	WDib
– subsp. ***velutina***	WDib
'Irish Flirt' (d)	WDib
'Irish Laughter'	WDib
'Island Breezes'	WDib
'Joli Concerto'	WDib
'Jolie Madame'	WDib
'Jolly Cutie Pie'	WDib
'Jolly Fairy'	WDib
'Jolly Fire'	WDib
'Jolly Imp'	WDib
'Jolly Orchid' (d)	WDib
'Jolly Texan' (d)	WDib
'Kamennyi Tsvetoz'	WDib
'Kazumi'	WDib
'Kosmicheskaia Legenda 2'	WDib
'Kostina Fantaziia'	WDib
'Lemon Drop' (d)	WDib
'Lemon Whip' (d)	WDib
'Letnaya Noch'	WDib
'Letnie Sumerki'	WDib
'Lil Bit O'Irish'	WDib
'Lilla Blaklockan'	WDib
'Little Axel'	WDib
'Little Seagull'	WDib
'Lollipop'	WDib
'Looking Glass'	WDib
'Louisiana Lagniappe'	WDib
'Louisiana Lullaby' (d)	WDib
'Love Spots'	WDib
'Lubimaia Dochka'	WDib
'Lucky Lee Ann' (d)	WDib
'Luminescence'	WDib
'Lyon's Minnie-HaHa'	WDib
'Lyon's Paprika'	WDib
'Lyon's Plum Pudding'	WDib
'Mac's Black Jack'	WDib
'Mac's Blowing Bubbles'	WDib
'Mac's Carnival Clown'	WDib
'Mac's Cheery Cherry'	WDib
'Mac's Circus Clown'	WDib
'Mac's Coral Cutie'	WDib
'Mac's Glacial Grape'	WDib
'Mac's Just Jeff' (d/v)	WDib
'Mac's Nocturne' (d)	WDib
'Mac's Rouge Rogue'	WDib
'Mac's Southern Springtime' (d)	WDib
'Mac's Strawberry Sundae'	WDib
'Mac's Will-o'-th'-Wisp'	WDib
'Mair'	WDib
'Ma's Ching Dynasty' (d)	WDib
'Ma's Corsage'	WDib
'Ma's Easter Parade'	WDib
'Ma's Lily Pad'	WDib
'Ma's Midnight Rain'	WDib
'Ma's Prince Froggie'	WDib
'Masked Man'	WDib
'Midget Lilian' (v)	WDib
'Midnight Flame' (d)	WDib
'Midnight Magic' (d) ambig.	WDib
'Midnight Rascal' (d)	WDib
'Midnight Waltz' (d)	WDib
'Milky Way Trail'	WDib
'Mindi Brooke'	WDib
'Minstrel's Mary Ruth'	WDib
'Munchkin Kisses' (d)	WDib
'Ness' Antique Red'	WDib
'Ness' Bangle Blue'	WDib
'Ness' Blueberry Puff'	WDib
'Ness' Cherry Smoke'	WDib
'Ness' Crinkle Blue' (d)	WDib
'Ness' Dynomite'	WDib
'Ness' Jesse' (d)	WDib
'Ness' Midnight Fantasy'	WDib
'Ness' Orange Pekoe'	WDib
'Ness' Satin Rose'	WDib

'Ness' Sheer Peach' WDib
'Newtown Ohio' WDib
nitida WDib
'Nortex's Razzmatazz Haven' WDib
'Number 32' WDib
'Ode to Beauty' WDib
'Okie Easter Bunny' WDib
'Oksana' WDib
'Optimara Chico' WDib
'Optimara Dali' WDib
'Optimara Hiroshige' WDib
'Optimara Little Moonstone' WDib
'Optimara Little Ruby' WDib
'Optimara Little Seneca' WDib
'Otoe' (d) WDib
'Parnikovyi Effekt' WDib
'Pat Tracey' WDib
'Peppermint Doll' WDib
'Pink Wink' WDib
'Pixie Blue' WDib
'Pixie Pink' WDib
'Pixie Show-off' WDib
'Podvenechnaia' (d) WDib
'Powder Keg' (d) WDib
'Powwow' (d/v) WDib
'Prancing Pony' WDib
'Purple Passion' WDib
'Rainbow's Limelight' (d) WDib
'Rainbow's Quiet Riot' WDib
'Ramblin' Amethyst' WDib
'Ramblin' Angel' (d) WDib
'Ramblin' Dots' WDib
'Ramblin' Lassie' WDib
'Ramblin' Sunshine' WDib
'Rare Tapestry' WDib
'Raspberry Crisp' WDib
'Rebel's Amy' WDib
'Rebel's Splatter Kake' WDib
'Red Lantern' (d) WDib
'Red Summit' WDib
'Reflections of Spring' (d) WDib
'Rhapsodie Clementine' WDib
'Rhapsodie Rosalie' WDib
'Robert Mayer' WDib
'Rob's Argyle Socks' (d) WDib
'Rob's Bamboozle' (d) WDib
'Rob's Blue Cat' WDib
'Rob's Blue Socks' WDib
'Rob's Boo Hoo' WDib
'Rob's Boogie Woogie' WDib
'Rob's Chilly Willy' (d/v) WDib
'Rob's Dandy Lion' (d/v) WDib
'Rob's Dust Storm' (d) WDib
'Rob's Fuzzy Navel' WDib
'Rob's Hallucination' WDib
'Rob's Heebie Jeebie' WDib
'Rob's Hot Tamale' WDib
'Rob's Ice Ripples' (d) WDib
'Rob's Jitterbug' WDib
'Rob's Love Bite' (d) WDib
'Rob's Mad Cat' (d) WDib
'Rob's Peedletuck' WDib
'Rob's Pewter Bells' WDib
'Rob's Pink Buttercups' (v) WDib
'Rob's Rinky Dink' (d) WDib
'Rob's Ruff Stuff' WDib
'Rob's Sarsparilla' (d) WDib
'Rob's Scarecrow' WDib
'Rob's Scooter' WDib
'Rob's Scrumptious' WDib
'Rob's Seduction' (d/v) WDib
'Rob's Shadow Magic' (d/v) WDib
'Rob's Smarty Pants' (d) WDib
'Rob's Sticky Wicket' (d) WDib
'Rob's Toorooka' (d) WDib
'Rob's Twinkle Blue' (d) WDib
'Rob's Twinkle Pink' (d) WDib
'Rob's Vanilla Trail' (d) WDib
'Rob's Wooloomooloo' (d) WDib
'Roll Along Blue' (d) WDib
'RS-Bog Solntsa' (d) **new** WDib
'RS-Boyarinya' WDib
'RS-Gertsogninea' WDib
'RS-Kabaret' WDib
'RS-Korrida' WDib
'RS-Strast' WDib
'Ruffled Skies' WDib
'Ruffles 'n' Lace' WDib
'Saint Paul' WDib
'Santa Anita' WDib
'Sapphire Halo' WDib
'Scarlet Ribbons' WDib
'Senk's Arctic Fox' WDib
'Senk's Beanstalk' WDib
'Shirl's Hawaiian Lei' WDib
shumensis WDib
'Shy Blue' WDib
'Silly Girl' WDib
'Silverglade Beads' WDib
'Silverglade Dolls' WDib
'Silverglade Dreams' WDib
'Silverglade Gems' WDib
'Silverglade Jingles' WDib
'Silverglade Meadows' WDib
'Sky Bells' (v) WDib
'Sky Trail' WDib
'Snow Leopard' WDib
'Sparkleberry' WDib
'Special Treat' WDib
'Sultan' (d) WDib
'Sun Sizzle' WDib
'Sunkissed Rose' WDib
'Sweet Amy Sue' (d) WDib
'Swifty Thriller' WDib
'Taffeta Blue' (d) WDib
'The Madam' WDib
'Tiger' (v) WDib
'Tina's April Fantasy' WDib
'Toy Castle' WDib
'Tula' WDib
'Twist 'n' Shout' WDib
'Two-w Miss Sophie' (d) WDib
'Vallartas Campanas Moradas' WDib
'Warm Sunshine' WDib
'Whirligig Star' WDib
'Wild Irish Rose' WDib
'Winnergreen' WDib
'Wisteria' (d) WDib
'Witch Doctor' (d) WDib
'Wrangler's Jealous Heart' WDib
'Yesterday's Child' WDib

Salicornia (*Amaranthaceae*)

europaea SVic

Salix ✿ (*Salicaceae*)

sp. GWyn LPra

	acutifolia 'Blue Streak' (m) ♀H5	CEnd CWiW EPfP EWes MBlu NLar WMou
	- 'Pendulifolia' (m)	SGol
	'Aegma Brno' (f)	WMou
	aegyptiaca	CBot CLnd EBtc ECrN MBlu WMou
	alba	CCVT CDul CHab CLnd CPer CWiW ECrN EMOT ESps LBuc LMaj LPra MAsh SEWo SGol WMou WTSh XAbr
	- f. ***argentea***	see *S. alba* var. *sericea*
	- 'Aurea'	WMou
	- var. ***caerulea***	CDul CLnd WMou
	- - 'Wantage Hall' (f)	CWiW
	- 'Cardinalis' (f)	CWiW
	- 'Chermesina' hort.	see *S. alba* var. *vitellina* 'Britzensis'
	- 'Golden Ness' ♀H6	CRos LRHS MAsh MBlu NOra NRHS SPoG WFar
	- 'Hutchinson's Yellow'	NLar
	- 'Liempde' (m)	LPra
	- 'Raesfeld' (m)	CWiW
§	- var. ***sericea*** ♀H6	CDul CLnd CTho EPfP MBlu MRav NLar SPer WCot WMou
	- 'Splendens'	see *S. alba* var. *sericea*
	- 'Tristis' misapplied	see *S.* × *sepulcralis* var. *chrysocoma*
§	- 'Tristis' ambig.	CAco CLnd CTri ELan IBoy LMaj LRHS MGos MRav MSwo NLar NOra SEWo WHar
	- var. ***vitellina***	CDul CPer CTri EMOT EPfP ESps IRob LBuc MBNS MMuc NLar SGol SLon SRms
§	- - 'Britzensis' (m)	Widely available
§	- var. ***vitellina*** 'Yelverton' ♀H6	CRos EBee EPfP LRHS NOra NRHS SPoG WFar
	- 'Vitellina Tristis'	see *S. alba* 'Tristis' ambig.
§	***alpina***	GEdr
	'Americana' (m)	CWiW
	amplexicaulis 'Pescara' (m)	CWiW
	amygdaloides	CWiW
	'Aokautere'	see *S.* × *sepulcralis* 'Aokautere'
§	***arbuscula***	XEll
	arenaria	see *S. repens* var. *argentea*
	aurita	MMuc
	babylonica	CDul CEnd CPer LPra WMou
	- 'Annularis'	see *S. babylonica* 'Crispa'
	- 'Bijdorp'	NLar
§	- 'Crispa'	CDul ELan GBin LRHS MMrt NQui NSti SMad SPoG WBor WFar WGrn
	- 'Pan Chih-kang'	CWiW NLar
	- var. ***pekinensis*** 'Pendula'	IArd
§	- - 'Tortuosa' (f)	CBcs CDul CLnd CSBt ECrN ELan EMOT EPfP GMcL IBoy LPra LRHS MGos MMuc NPer NRHS SCob SEND SGol SLon SPer SPlb SPoG SRms WFar
*	- 'Tortuosa Aurea'	CAco IBoy LMaj LPra SGol SWvt
	'Blackskin' (f)	CWiW
	bockii	EBtc LRHS SDys
§	'Bowles's Hybrid'	WMou
	'Boydii' (f) ♀H7	CMea EPfP EPot GAbr GCrg GKev GMaP ITim LEdu LRHS MGos NPoe NRya NSla SAko WAbe WFar WThu
	candida	WFar
	caprea	CArg CBcs CCVT CDul CHab CLnd CPer CTri EPfP ESps LBuc MJak SCob SEWo SPer WMou WSFF WTSh
	- 'Black Stem'	CDul
§	- 'Kilmarnock' (m)	CBcs CCVT CDul CMac CSBt CTri ECrN ELan EMOT EPfP ESps LBuc LRHS MAsh MGos MJak MMuc NLar NPri SCob SGol SLim SPer SPoG SWvt WFar WJas
	- var. ***pendula*** (m)	see *S. caprea* 'Kilmarnock' (m)
	capusii	EBee WPGP
	cashmiriana	GEdr
	'Chrysocoma'	see *S.* × *sepulcralis* var. *chrysocoma*
	cinerea	CBcs CDul CPer CTri SEWo WMou WTSh
	- 'Tricolor' (v)	NEoE
	'Coire Kander'	GKev
	daphnoides	CBcs CCVT CDul CLnd CMac CPer ELan EPfP ESps MGos MMuc MSwo SEND SGol SPer SRms WMou WSFF
	- 'Aglaia' (m) ♀H6	CDul CTri
	- 'Meikle' (f)	CWiW
	- 'Netta Statham' (m)	CWiW
	- 'Ovaro Udine' (m)	CWiW
	- 'Stewartstown'	CWiW
§	× ***doniana*** 'Kumeti'	CWiW
	'E.A. Bowles'	see *S.* 'Bowles's Hybrid'
	× ***ehrhartiana***	CNat
§	***elaeagnos***	CCVT CTho CTri ECrN EPfP GMcL MBrN MMuc MSCN SLon SMHy SPer WMou
§	- subsp. ***angustifolia*** ♀H5	CBcs CDul ELan EPfP MMuc MRav MSwo NLar SCob SEND SRms
	eriocephala 'American Mackay' (m)	CWiW
	- 'Kerksii' (m)	CWiW
	- 'Mawdesley' (m)	CWiW
	- 'Russelliana' (f)	CWiW
	exigua ♀H5	CBcs CDul CLnd CTho EBee ELan EPfP EWes IDee LBuc LEdu LRHS MBlu MBrN MGos MSwo NLar SChF SCob SMad SPer WMou WPGP
	fargesii ♀H6	CAby CBcs CBot CDul CEnd CExl CFil CMac EBee ELan EPfP GBin LEdu LRHS MBlu MGos MMuc MRav NBid SBrt SCob SMad SPer SPoG WCot WCru WFar
	fargesii × ***magnifica***	CFil
§	× ***finnmarchica***	WAbe
	formosa	see *S. arbuscula*
§	× ***fragilis***	CCVT CDul CHab CLnd CPer EMOT WMou WTSh
	- 'Basfordiana' (m)	CDul CLnd CTho CWiW MBNS WMou
	- 'Bouton Aigu'	CWiW
	- var. ***bullata***	LMaj
	- 'Farndon'	CWiW
	- 'Flanders Red' (f)	CWiW XAbr
	- 'Fransgeel Rood' (m)	CWiW
§	- var. ***furcata***	CTri GCrg GKev NWad
	- 'Glaucescens' (m)	CWiW
	- 'Golden Willow'	CWiW
	- 'Jaune de Falaise'	CWiW
	- 'Jaune Hâtive'	CWiW
	- 'Laurina'	CWiW
	- 'Natural Red' (f)	CWiW
	- 'Parsons'	CWiW
	- 'Rouge Ardennais'	CWiW
	- 'Rouge Folle'	CWiW
	- 'Russet' (f)	CWiW
	× ***fruticosa*** 'McElroy' (f)	CWiW
	fruticulosa	see *S. fragilis* var. *furcata*
	'Fuiri-koriyanagi'	see *S. integra* 'Hakuro-nishiki'
	furcata	see *S. fragilis* var. *furcata*

	glauca	CNat
	'Golden Curls'	see *S.* × *sepulcralis* 'Erythroflexuosa'
	gracilistyla	WMou
§	- 'Melanostachys' (m) ♀H5	CAby CBot CDul EBee ECrN ELan EPfP EWTr MAsh MBNS MBlu MBrN MGos MMuc MRav NEgg NLar SBrt SGol SPer SRms WBor
	- 'Mount Aso'	EBee NLar WPGP
	× ***greyi***	NEoE
	hastata 'Wehrhahnii' (m) ♀H6	CBcs CDul CMea EBee ELan EPfP ESps GKev GMcL MAsh MBlu MJak MMuc MRav MSwo NLar SPer
	helvetica ♀H7	CBcs CDul CMac CMea EBee ELan EPfP GMcL IRob MAsh MBlu MRav NEgg NLar SPer WFar
	herbacea	GEdr WAbe
	hibernica	see *S. phylicifolia*
	hookeriana	CDul CExl CFil ELan MBlu MBrN MCoo NLar WCFE WMou
	incana	see *S. elaeagnos*
	integra 'Albomaculata'	see *S. integra* 'Hakuro-nishiki'
	- 'Flamingo'PBR	EBee ELan NLar SPoG WTSh
§	- 'Hakuro-nishiki' (v) ♀H5	Widely available
	- 'Pendula' (f)	CEnd MAsh
	irrorata ♀H5	CDul EPfP MBlu MSwo NOra SCob
	'Jacquinii'	see *S. alpina*
	kinuyanagi (m)	NSti
§	***koriyanagi***	CWiW
	'Kumeti'	see *S.* × *doniana* 'Kumeti'
	'Kuro-me'	see *S. gracilistyla* 'Melanostachys'
	lanata ♀H7	CBcs CBot CMac CMea ELan ELon EPfP GKev GMcL IRob MAsh MGos MJak NEgg NLar SBrt SPer WCFE
	lapponum	LEdu MMuc NLar SRms
	- compact	GKev
	magnifica	CAby CBot CDul CEnd CExl CFil EBee ELan EPfP EUJe IArd LEdu LRHS MMuc NLar SMad SPoG WCot WFar WHer WHor WMou WPGP WSpi
	'Mark Postill' (f)	CAby CBot ELon EWTr GBin LRHS MBNS MMuc NLar SAko WWFP
	matsudana 'Tortuosa'	see *S. babylonica* var. *pekinensis* 'Tortuosa'
	- 'Tortuosa Aureopendula'	see *S.* × *sepulcralis* 'Erythroflexuosa'
	'Melanostachys'	see *S. gracilistyla* 'Melanostachys'
	× ***meyeriana*** 'Lumley' (f)	CWiW
	× ***mollissima***	CWiW
	var. ***hippophaifolia*** 'Jefferies' (m)	
	- - 'Notts Spaniard' (m)	CWiW
	- - 'Trustworthy' (m)	CWiW
	- var. ***undulata*** 'Kottenheider Weide' (f)	CWiW
	moupinensis	LRHS
	aff. ***moupinensis*** from Vietnam	CFil
§	***myrsinifolia***	ELan MBlu MMuc NLar
	- 'Black Knight'	EPfP
	myrsinites var. ***jacquiniana***	see *S. alpina*
	myrtilloides 'Pink Tassels' (m)	SBrt
	myrtilloides × ***repens***	see *S.* × *finnmarchica*
	nakamurana var. ***yezoalpina***	CBot EBee ELan EWes GKev LRHS MBlu MMuc MRav NLar SBrt WFar
	nigra	CDul XAbr
	nigricans	see *S. myrsinifolia*
	nivalis	see *S. reticulata* subsp. *nivalis*
	pentandra	CBot CDul LMaj WMou
	- 'Patent Lumley'	CWiW
§	***phylicifolia***	WMou
	- 'Malham' (m)	CWiW
§	***purpurea***	CCVT CDul CPer GMcL SCob WMou XAbr
	- 'Brittany Green' (f)	CWiW
	- 'Continental Reeks'	CWiW
	- 'Dark Dicks' (f)	CWiW NLar WSFF
	- 'Dicky Meadows' (m)	CWiW
	- 'Goldstones'	CWiW NLar
	- f. ***gracilis***	see *S. purpurea* 'Gracilis'
§	- 'Gracilis'	MMuc SCob WCot
	- 'Green Dicks'	CWiW
	- 'Helix'	see *S. purpurea*
	- 'Howki' (m)	WMou
	- 'Irette' (m)	CWiW
	- 'Jagiellonka' (f)	CWiW
	- var. ***japonica***	see *S. koriyanagi*
	- subsp. ***lambertiana***	CWiW
	- 'Lancashire Dicks' (m)	CWiW
	- 'Leicestershire Dicks' (m)	CWiW
	- 'Light Dicks'	CWiW
	- 'Lincolnshire Dutch' (f)	CWiW
	- 'Nancy Saunders' (f) ♀H6	CTho CWiW EHoe EWld GLog LEdu MBNS MBlu MBrN MRav NLar NSti SMHy WCot WGrn
	- 'Odeta'	LEdu
	- 'Pendula' ♀H6	CCVT CEnd CMac ECrN MAsh MSwo
	- 'Read' (f)	CWiW
	- 'Reeks' (f)	CWiW
	- 'Richartii' (f)	CWiW
	- 'Uralensis' (f)	CWiW
	pyrenaica	EWes
	radinostachya KR 7622 new	WPGP
	repens	SRms WAbe
§	- var. ***argentea***	ELan EWes LRHS MMuc MRav SPer
	reticulata ♀H7	EBee EPot GCrg NSla WAbe WFar
§	- subsp. ***nivalis***	EPot
	retusa	CTri GEdr
	rosmarinifolia misapplied	see *S. elaeagnos* subsp. *angustifolia*
	rosmarinifolia L.	EPfP NLar
	× ***rubens***	see *S.* × *fragilis*
	× ***rubra***	CWiW
	- 'Abbey's Harrison' (f)	CWiW
	- 'Continental Osier' (f)	CWiW
	- 'Eugenei' (m)	CDul ECrN MBlu
	- 'Fidkin' (f)	CWiW
	- 'Harrison's' (f)	CWiW
	- 'Harrison's Seedling A' (f)	CWiW
	- 'Mawdesley'	CWiW
	- 'Mawdesley Seedling A' (f)	CWiW
	- 'Pyramidalis'	CWiW
I	'Salix Red'	WJPR
§	× ***sepulcralis*** 'Aokautere' (m)	CWiW
	- 'Caradoc'	CWiW
§	- var. ***chrysocoma*** ♀H5	Widely available
	- 'Dart's Snake' (m)	ELan EPPr EShb MAsh MBrN MRav NLar WCot
§	- 'Erythroflexuosa' (m) ♀H5	CBcs CDul CEnd EBee ELan EMOT EPPr EPfP ESps MAsh MGos MMuc MRav NOra SCob SEND SGol SLim SPer SPoG WCFE
	serpyllifolia	CTri GKev WThu
	- 'Chamonix'	NSla
	serpyllum	see *S. fragilis* var. *furcata*
	'Setsuka'	see *S. udensis* 'Sekka'

'Stuartii'	GAbr
subopposita	EBtc ELan MGil MMuc SBrt WAbe
× ***tetrapla*** 'Hutchinson's Nigricans'	CNat
triandra	WMou
- 'Black German' (m)	CWiW
- 'Black Hollander' (m)	CWiW NLar
- 'Black Maul'	CWiW
- 'Grisette de Falaise'	CWiW
- 'Grisette Droda' (f)	CWiW
- 'Long Bud'	CWiW
- 'Noir de Challans'	CWiW
- 'Noir de Touraine'	CWiW
- 'Noir de Villaines' (m)	CWiW WJPR
- 'Rouge d'Orléans'	EBtc
- 'Sarda d'Anjou'	CWiW
- 'Whissander'	CWiW
udensis 'Golden Sunshine'	EBee EMil LRHS MAsh MMrt MPkF NEoE NRHS SPer SPoG WCot
§ - 'Sekka' (m)	CBcs MBlu MMuc WMou
uva-ursi	WAbe
viminalis	CCVT CLnd CMac CPer EPfP GMcL LBuc MMuc SEWo SVic WJPR WMou WSFF
- 'Green Gotz'	CWiW
vitellina 'Pendula'	see *S. alba* 'Tristis' ambig.
'Yelverton'	see *S. alba* var. *vitellina* 'Yelverton'

Salpiglossis (*Solanaceae*)

sinuata Royale Series ♀H3 new	ETMg

Salvia ✿ (*Lamiaceae*)

CD&R 1141	SPin
CD&R 1162	SPhx
CD&R 1458	SPin
CD&R 1495	SPin
PC&H 226	SPin
from Catamarca, Argentina	SDys
absconditiflora	SPin
acerifolia	SDys SPin
acetabulosa	see *S. multicaulis*
adenophora	SPin
aethiopis	EWes SPav SPhx WOut
I 'African Sky'	CBod CElw CSam CSpe MPie SDys SMHy SPhx SPin WGrn WOut
§ ***africana***	EBee SPin
africana-caerulea	see *S. africana*
africana-lutea	see *S. aurea*
agnes	SDys SPin
'Alegría'	SDys SPin
algeriensis	SPhx
'Alice' new	SPin
altimitrata	see *S. lasiantha*
amarissima	SPin
'Amber'	IMou LPla SBrt SPin
ambigens	see *S. guaranitica* 'Blue Enigma'
'Amistad'PBR	Widely available
ampelophylla	SDys
- B&SWJ 10751	SPin
§ ***amplexicaulis***	CBod LPla MMuc NLar SRms WHrl XSen
angustifolia Cav.	see *S. reptans*
angustifolia Mich.	see *S. azurea*
'Anna'	SDys
'Anthony Parker'	CSam WOut
apiana	EWld SPin SPlb SRms SVen XAbr XSen
argentea ♀H4	CBcs CBod CDor CSpe ECha ELan EPfP EWld LRHS MSpe NRHS NSti SMad SPer SPhx WHar WKif WOut XSen
arizonica	CSam EBee EWld GCal MAsh SDys SPin WSHC
atrocyanea	CSam CSpe EBee ECre EWes MAsh MAvo MGil MSpe SDys SMHy SPin WHal WKif
atropatana	WCot
aucheri	SPin
§ ***aurea***	CBot CHll CSpe SPin SPlb SVen XLum
- 'Kirstenbosch'	CAby ECtt EWld NSti SDys SPin WCot WKif WOut
aurita	SPin
- var. ***galpinii***	SPin
austriaca	SPin
§ ***azurea***	CPla SBrt SPhx SPin XSen
- var. ***grandiflora***	SPin WCot
bacheriana	see *S. buchananii*
§ ***barrelieri***	EBee SPhx SPin
'Bee's Bliss'	XSen
'Belhaven'	EBee GCal
benthamiana	SDys
bertolonii	see *S. pratensis* Bertolonii Group
bicolor	see *S. barrelieri*
'Black Knight'	MAsh SDys SPin WOth
blancoana	see *S. lavandulifolia* subsp. *blancoana*
blepharophylla	ECtt MHer MSCN
- 'Diablo'	ECtt
- 'Painted Lady'	CBot ECtt MAsh SDys SPin
'Bleu Armor'PBR	SPhx
'Blue Merced' new	SDys
'Blue Moon'	SDys
'Blue Note'PBR	CAby CBod CBot CMea CSpe CWGN CWld EBee ECtt ELan EUJe LLWG LRHS MAvo MBel MHol MTis NDov NRHS SCob SEND SPoG SRkn WCot WHil WHlf
'Blue Sky'	EWld
bogotensis	SPin
bowleyana	SPin
brandegeei	SPin
brevilabra	SPin
brevipes	SPin
'Bright Eyes'	CWGN SCob
broussonetii	EBee SPin
§ ***buchananii*** ♀H2	CSam ECtt MAsh MHer MRav SDys SPin SRkn WKif
bulleyana misapplied	see *S. flava* var. *megalantha*
bulleyana Diels	CBcs CExl EWes GPSL MMuc NQui WHil
- 'Blue Lips'	CWld EBee ECtt LSou SCob WHil
bullulata	SPin
- pale-blue-flowered	CBot CSpe SDys SPin
cacaliifolia ♀H2	CExl CWCL ECtt EWld GCal MAsh MHer MPie SDys SPin SRkn WAvo
cadmica	SPin
caerulea misapplied	see *S. guaranitica*
caerulea L.	see *S. africana*
calolophos new	SPin
campanulata	SPin
- B&SWJ 9232	WCru
- GWJ 9294	SPin WCru
- var. ***hirtella*** GWJ 9397	WCru
canariensis	SEND SPin WCot
- f. ***albiflora***	EBee SVen
- f. ***candidissima***	SBrt SPin
candelabrum ♀H3	CSpe ECre EWes MHer SPav SPhx SPin SVen WKif XSen

	candidissima	XSen
	canescens	XSen
	cardinalis	see *S. fulgens*
	cardiophylla	SPin
	carnea	MAsh SPin
	- from Valle de Bravo, Mexico	SDys
	castanea	EWld
	caudata	SPin
	'Cavalieri d'Alto'	SPhx WHil
	'Cavaliero Celeste'	SDys
§	***chamaedryoides***	CFil ELan MAsh SBrt SPin XSen
	- var. ***isochroma***	MAsh MAvo SDys SPin WPGP XSen
	- 'Marine Blue'	MAsh MCot
	- silver-leaved	CAby CSpe SPin XLum
	aff. ***chamaedryoides*** B&SWJ 9032 from Guatemala	SPin
	chamelaeagnea	EPPr SBrt SDys SPin
	'Cherry Queen'	CWGN MAsh WOut
	chiapensis	MAsh SDys SPin
	chionophylla	CElw SPin
	'Christine Yeo'	CElw EBee ECtt ELon EPri MAsh SDys SEND SPin WAvo WHil WHlf WSHC XSen
	'Christopher Fairweather'	ECtt
	chrysophylla **new**	SDys
	- from Akdağ, Turkey **new**	SBrt
	cinnabarina	SPin
	cleistogama misapplied	see *S. glutinosa*
	clevelandii	SPav SPin
	- 'Winnifred Gilman'	SDys
	clinopodioides	EBee SDys SPin
	'Clotted Cream'	LRHS
	coahuilensis misapplied	see *S. greggii* × *serpyllifolia*
	coahuilensis ambig.	EBee LSou MAsh SLon SPin SRkn WSHC XLum
	coccinea (Nymph Series) 'Coral Nymph'	SPav
	- - 'Lady in Red' ♀H3	SPav
	- (Summer Jewel Series) 'Summer Jewel Pink'	LRHS NRHS
	concolor misapplied	see *S. guaranitica*
	concolor Lamb. ex Benth.	CAby EBee EWld GCal SDys SPin WSHC
	confertiflora	CAby CBcs CBod CBot CExl CSam CSpe CWCL EBee ECre ECtt GCal IPot MAsh MHer MSCN NSti SDys SPhx SPin SPlb SRkn SVen WKif WOth WPGP
	corrugata	CBcs CElw EBee ECtt GBin GCal LRHS MAsh MHer SDys SPhx SPin
	'Crazy Dolls' **new**	SDys
	'Crème Caramel'	EBee ECtt MAsh MCot SDys WHil
	cruickshanksii	SPin
	cuatrecasana	SPin
	curviflora	CBot CElw CSam CSpe IPot LSvl MAsh SBch SDys SEle SPin
	cyanescens	CFis CMea EPot SPin XSen
	cyanicalyx	SDys SPin
	cyclostegia	CExl
	daghestanica	EBee SPin
	'Dancing Dolls'	CWGN EWTr LRHS NRHS SCob
I	***dangitalis***	SPin
	- SDR 4332	CExl
	darcyi misapplied	see *S. roemeriana*
	darcyi J. Compton	CBot CExl CHll ELan EWes MCot SDys SPin WSHC XLum
	davidsonii	SPin
	'Dayglo'	ECtt
	deserta	SPhx WCot
	desoleana	EBee SPin
	'Didi'	NDov
	digitaloides BWJ 7777	SPin
	discolor	CHll CSpe ECtt EWld GCal MAsh MHer SCob SDys SPin WAvo WOth
*	- ***nigra***	CCse
	disermas	SPin SPlb
	disjuncta	CElw SPin
	- 'Chimbango'	SPin
	dolichantha	CTsd NLar SPin WMoo
	dolomitica	SPav SPin
	dombeyi	CAby CSam SDys SPin WPGP
	dominica	SPin
	dorisiana	MAsh MHer SDys SPin SVen
	'Dorset Wonder'	IPot NDov
	durifolia	SPin
	'Dyson's Crimson'	CAby CSpe ELan IPot MCot SDys WAul
	'Dyson's Gem'	SDys
	'Dyson's Joy' ♀H3	CBot MAvo MCot SDys WHil WKif
	'Edith Piaf' **new**	SPin
	eigii	SPin
	eizi-matudae	CSam SDys SPin
§	***elegans***	CBot CPla EWes GCal IDee NPol NWad SPhm WHer WOth WOut WSHC XLum XSen
	- 'Golden Delicious'	CAby CBod ENfk EWes MHer NEoE SPin SRms WFar WOut
	- 'Honey Melon'	ENfk MAsh SBee SDys
	- 'Scarlet Pineapple'	CBod CExl ELan ENfk EWld GPoy MCot MHer MNHC SDys SRms SVen
	- 'Sonoran Red'	SDys
	- 'Tangerine'	CBod ENfk MHer MNHC NQui SPin SRms
	EMBER'S WISH ('Sal 0101')	CBcs CBod CBot ECtt IPot LCro MAsh MNrw MSpe NDov SDys SEle SPad SPin SPoG SRkn WAvo WGrn WHil
	'Endless Love'	EBee LSou NDov SAko SRms
	evansiana	SPin
	'Eveline'	CBWd CKno CMac CWGN EBee ECtt EPfP IPot LRHS NLar NRHS SHar SRms STPC WHar WTor
	excelsa	SPin
	exserta	EBee
	fallax	see *S. roscida*
	farinacea 'Midnight Candle'	LRHS NRHS
	- 'Rhea'	SPoG
	- 'Strata'	SPoG
	- 'Violet Candle' **new**	CWCL
§	***flava*** var. ***megalantha***	CAby CBod EPfP LRHS LSRN MSpe NRHS SPin XSen
	'Flower Child'	SDys
	forreri	EBee MAsh NDov SDys SPin
	- 'Karen Dyson'	SDys
§	***forsskaolii***	CBod CElw CExl CSam ELan GKev MMuc MNrw MRav NChi NLar NQui NSti SAko SEND SPav SPin SPtp WCot WHil WKif WMoo XLum XSen
	- white-flowered	EBee
§	***fruticosa***	LRHS SLon SPhx SPin SRms XAbr XSen
§	***fulgens*** ♀H3	GCal MAsh SDys SPin SRkn
	- from Mount Popocatépetl, Mexico	SPin
	gachantivana	SPin
	gesneriiflora	ECtt EWld SPin

	– mountain form	ECre SDys
	– 'Tequila'	SPin WOut
	gilliesii	SPin
	glabrescens B&SWJ 11152	WCru
*	– var. ***robusta*** B&SWJ 11147	WCru
	glechomifolia	SPin
§	***glutinosa***	CBod CMac CSpe EBee EWld GCal GWyn IMou LRHS MMuc MNrw NBro NLar NRHS NSti SPav SPin SPtp WHil XLum XSen
	gracilis	SPin
	grahamii	see *S. microphylla* var. *microphylla* 'Newby Hall'
	'Great Comp'	NDov SDys
	greggii	EPfP EWes LRHS NRHS SPlb SRms WKif XLum XSen
	– CD&R 1148	SDys
	– 'Alba'	CSpe WHil XLum XSen
	– 'Blush Pink'	see *S. microphylla* 'Blush Pink'
	– 'Caramba' (v)	LRHS WHil
§	– 'Desert Blaze' (v)	CWGN EAJP ECtt ELan EPfP LRHS MAsh MRav NRHS SDys SLon SPin WAvo WGrn XLum
	– 'Devon Cream'	see *S. greggii* 'Sungold'
	– 'Diane'	MAsh
	– 'Emperor'	CWGN EWTr MAvo SEle
	– 'Flame'	CWGN WHil
	– 'Icing Sugar'PBR	CBod CNor CWGN EBee ECtt ELan ENfk EPfP LCro LOPS LRHS MAsh MCot MSpe NDov NRHS SCob SDys SEle SRkn WBor WHil WKif WSHC
	– 'Lara'	MAvo WHil
	– 'Lipstick'	CExl ECtt GWyn LCro LOPS MAsh
	– 'Magenta'	SPin WHil
	– 'Peach' misapplied	see *S.* × *jamensis* 'Pat Vlasto'
	– 'Peach'	CWGN EPfP MAsh SDys SPin XLum XSen
	– 'Pink Preference'	MAsh SDys
	– 'Raspberry Red'	XLum
	– 'Sierra San Antonio'	see *S.* × *jamensis* 'Sierra San Antonio'
	– 'Sparkler'	see *S. greggii* 'Desert Blaze'
	– 'Stormy Pink'	CAby CHll CSam CSpe ECtt IPot MAsh MAvo MCot NDov WHil WOth
§	– 'Sungold'	CWGN ECtt EPfP LRHS MAsh MAvo MPie SDys SPhx XSen
	– variegated (v)	XSen
	– yellow-flowered	XLum
	greggii × ***lycioides***	see *S. greggii* × *serpyllifolia*
§	***greggii*** × ***serpyllifolia***	CSam CSpe MAsh SDys SPin SVen
	guadalujarensis	SPin
§	***guaranitica***	ECtt MHer SPin WHil WKif WPGP XLum XSen
	– 'Argentina Skies'	CAby CHGN ECtt EPPr SDys SPin
	– 'Black and Blue'	Widely available
§	– 'Blue Enigma' ♀H4	CAby CBod CBot CExl CWGN EBee ECha ECtt EHrv ELan EPfP GCal LRHS MAsh MBel MGos MRav MSpe NRHS SDys SPin WGwG WSpi XLum XSen
	– 'Costa Rica Blue'	SDys
	– 'Indigo Blue'	EPfP MAsh SPin
	– 'Midnight'	CSpe
	– 'Purple Emperor'	CBot
	– 'Purple Splendor'	MHer
	– purple-flowered	CSam SDys
	– small form **new**	CBct

	– 'Super Trouper'	SDys SPoG
	– violet-flowered **new**	SDys
	'Guarini' **new**	SDys
	haematodes	see *S. pratensis* Haematodes Group
	haenkei	CElw SPin
	– 'Prawn Chorus'	MAsh
	heldreichiana	SMHy XSen
	henryi	SPin
	hians	CFis GCal ILea SRms WArt
	– CC 1787	CExl
	hierosolymitana	EBee LRHS NRHS SPhx SPin XSen
	hispanica misapplied	see *S. lavandulifolia*
	holwayi	SDys SPin
	horminum	see *S. viridis* var. *comata*
§	'Hot Lips' ♀H4	Widely available
	'I Cavalieri del Tau'	SDys
	inconspicua	SPin
	'Indiansummer' **new**	SDys
	indica	SPhx
	'Indigo Spires'	CBot CExl CHll CSam CSpe CWGN ECre ECtt EPfP IMou MAsh MCot NDov SDys SEle SPhx SPin WAvo WFar WKif WOth XLum
	interrupta	EWld MCot SPin WOut
	involucrata ♀H3	CAby IPot MCot NBro SDys SPin SVen WSHC
	– 'Bethellii' ♀H3	CBod CBot EBee ECtt ELan EPfP EWld LRHS MAsh MHer MNrw NSti SDys SPin SRkn WFar WGrn WKif WOth WSpi XLum
	– 'Boutin' ♀H3	CTsd LPla MAsh SDys SEle SPin
§	– 'Hadspen'	CBot CHll CRHN CSam CSpe EWes GCal SBch SPin WAvo WOth WOut
	– 'Mrs Pope'	see *S. involucrata* 'Hadspen'
	– 'Pink Icicles'	SDys
	involucrata × ***wagneriana***	SDys
	iodantha	SPin
	iodochroa B&SWJ 10252	WCru
	× ***jamensis***	EWes MAsh SPin
	– 'Amarillo' **new**	SDys
	– 'Blue Amor'	CSpe
	– 'California Sunset'	MAsh SDys
	– 'Dark Dancer'	MAsh SDys WHil
	– 'Devantville'	XLum
	– 'Dysons' Orangy Pink'	CSpe NDov SDys
	– 'Flammenn'PBR	LRHS NRHS
	– 'Golden Girl'	CWGN EBee WHil WSHC
	– HEATWAVE BLAZE ('Eggben005') **new**	EBee
	– 'Heatwave Glimmer'PBR **new**	MCot SPin
	– 'Javier' ♀H4	CSpe EWld MAsh SDys SPin WHil
	– 'Kentish Pink'	SDys
	– 'La Luna'	CSam CSpe MAsh MHer MRav NDov WOth WSHC XLum XSen
	– 'La Siesta'	MAsh XSen
	– 'La Tarde'	CTri MAsh
	– 'Los Lirios'	CTri MCot SPin WHil
	– 'Maraschino'	EPfP LRHS MAsh SDys SPin SRms WHil XLum
	– 'Melen'PBR	EBee SPin
	– 'Moonlight Over Ashwood' (v)	MAsh SPin WSHC
	– 'Moonlight Serenade'	MAsh SDys
§	– 'Pat Vlasto'	SPin
	– 'Peter Vidgeon' ♀H4	CWGN EBee EPPr EPfP LRHS MAsh MCot NRHS SBee SDys SPhx SPin WPGP WSHC
	– 'Pleasant Pink'	MAsh

	- 'Pluenn'PBR	LRHS NRHS
	- 'Plum Wine'	WHil
	- 'Raspberry Royale'	ECtt EPfP LRHS MAsh MHer MPie NRHS SDys SPin XLum XSen
	- 'Red Velvet'	EBee ECtt MAsh MCot SDys SPhx WAvo WHrl WSHC
	- 'Señorita Leah'	CWGN MAsh MAvo MCot NDov SDys
§	- 'Sierra San Antonio'	EPfP LRHS MAsh NRHS SDys WHil XLum XSen
	- 'Snow White'	SPin
	- 'Stormy Sunrise'	SDys
§	- 'Trebah'	CAby CBod ECre MAsh MCot SDys SPin WHil WKif WSHC
	- 'Trenance'	CBod ECre ELon MHer SPin WHil
	- VIOLETTE DE LOIRE ('Barsal'PBR)	LRHS
	'Jean's Jewel'	SDys SPin
	'Jean's Purple Passion'	MAsh SDys SPin
	'Jezebel' ♀H4	EPfP LRHS NRHS SDys SPin
	'Joan'	CSam CWGN MAsh MAvo MCot SDys SPin WHil
	judaica	CMac SPhx SPin WGrn
	jurisicii	CFis EPfP LRHS NRHS SBrt SPav WArt WHil XLum XSen
	karwinskyi	SDys SPin
	karwinskyi* × *univerticillata	SDys
	keerlii	SPin
	koyamae	EBee SPin
	- B&SWJ 10919	WCru
	'Krystle Pink' **new**	WHlf
	'La Mancha' **new**	SDys
	'Lalarsha'	CElw ELan MAsh MCot NDov SDys
	lanceolata	SPin WOut
§	***lasiantha***	SPin
§	***lavandulifolia***	EBee ELan EPPr EPfP EWes GPoy LRHS MAsh MHer MNHC MRav SPin SRms WHoo WKif XLum XSen
§	- subsp. ***blancoana***	ECha SPhx SPin XSen
	- subsp. ***gallica***	XSen
	- subsp. ***pyrenaeorum***	XSen
	- 'Roquefure'	XSen
	- subsp. ***vellerea***	XSen
	lavanduloides	SPin
	'Lavender Dilly Dilly'	LRHS MAvo
	lemmonii	see *S. microphylla* var. *wislizeni*
	'Lemon Pie'	SDys SPin
	leptophylla	see *S. reptans*
	leucantha ♀H2	CBot CSpe ECre ELan EWld MAsh MCot MHer MNrw MRav SPin SPlb SRkn SVen WKif WOth WOut XSen
	- DANIELLE'S DREAM ('Ferpink')	SPin
	- 'Eder' (v)	MAsh SDys
	- 'Midnight'	CSam
	- 'Purple Velvet'	CAby CSpe EBee ECtt MAsh MHer SDys SPin
	- 'San Marcos Lavender'	SPin
	- 'Santa Barbara'	CBot CHll ECtt MAsh SDys
	- 'White Mischief'	SPin
	leucocephala	SDys SPin
	leucophylla NNS 01-375	SPin
	libanensis **new**	SDys
	littae	SDys SPin
	'Little Azur' **new**	SDys
	longispicata	SPin
	longistyla	CFil SDys SPin SVen
	LOVE AND WISHES ('Serendip6')	CBcs CBod CBot CHll CPla CRav CWGN ECtt IPot LCro LRHS MAsh MCot MSpe NCou SDys SPhm SPoG SRkn WAvo WHil
	lycioides misapplied	see *S. greggii* × *serpyllifolia*
	lycioides A. Gray	CHll SDys
	lyrata 'Burgundy Bliss'	see *S. lyrata* 'Purple Knockout'
§	- 'Purple Knockout'	EPfP LRHS NRHS SPin XSen
	- 'Purple Vulcano'	see *S. lyrata* 'Purple Knockout'
	macellaria misapplied	see *S. microphylla*
	macellaria Epling	CSam
	macrophylla	SDys SPin
	- purple-leaved	SDys
	macrosiphon	SPin
	'Madeline'PBR	CWGN EPfP GBin IBoy LCro LOPS LRHS LSou MHol MNrw NRHS SPer SPin STPC WHil
	madrensis	SDys SPin
	- 'Dunham'	EWld GCal
	'Magenta Magic'	SDys SPin
	'Magic Potion'	CWGN
	mellifera	SPin
	mexicana	SPin
	- var. ***minor***	EWld SDys SPin
I	***miahuatlanensis***	SPin
§	***microphylla***	CBod CMac CTri EWes GMcL LRHS MHer NRHS SVen WOut XLum
	- CD&R 1141	SPin
	- 'Belize'	IPot MAsh WHil
	- 'Blue Monrovia'	LRHS NRHS
§	- 'Blush Pink'	MAvo SDys
	- 'Cerro Potosí' ♀H4	CElw CSpe EBee ECtt ELan ELon EShb LRHS MAsh MAvo MCot MHer MSCN SDys SHar SPhx SPin WCFE WHil WOth WOut XLum
	- 'Chalk White' **new**	SMHy
	- 'Hot Lips'	see *S.* 'Hot Lips'
	- 'Kew Red'	CBot MNrw SPin WHil
I	- 'Lutea'	MAsh SDys
	- 'Maroon'	SDys WHlf
	- 'Mauve'	NDov
§	- var. ***microphylla***	CRHN CTri ECtt ELan ENfk LSRN MCot MHer MNHC MRav SEND SPin SRkn XLum XSen
	- - 'La Foux'	SPhx
§	- - 'Newby Hall'	CBot ECtt EWes LRHS NWad SPhx WSHC
	- var. ***neurepia***	see *S. microphylla* var. *microphylla*
	- 'Norwell'	MNrw
	- 'Orange Door'	SDys
	- orange-red-flowered	MRav
	- 'Oregon Peach'	EPfP LRHS NRHS
	- 'Oxford'	SPin
	- 'Pink Blush'	CAby EAJP ECtt ELan EPfP LCro LRHS MAsh MCot MHer MNHC MSpe SEND SPin SRkn WHil WHoo WKif WSHC XSen
	- 'Pleasant View'	WHil
	- 'Robin's Pride'	SDys WHil
	- 'Rodbaston Red'	WHil
	- 'Rosy Cheeks'	WOut
	- 'San Carlos Festival'	MAsh SDys SPin
	- 'Trelawny Rose Pink'	see *S.* 'Trelawney'
	- 'Trelissick Creamy Yellow'	see *S.* 'Trelissick'
	- 'Trewithen Cerise'	see *S.* 'Trewithen'
	- 'Wendy's Surprise'	EWld LSvl MCot SDys
	- 'Wild Watermelon'	CWGN EBee ECtt EWes GPSL MAsh MAvo MCot MHer NQui SDys WGrn WHil WHrl WWFP XSen
§	- var. ***wislizeni***	CElw SPhx
	- 'Wollerton White'	MCot MRav SDys
	- 'Zaragoza'	SPin

miltiorrhiza	CSpe EBee SPhx SPin WArt WHer XLum XSen
miniata	SPin
misella	SPin
mocinoi	SPin
mohavensis	SPhx
moorcroftiana	SPin
moschata	SPin
muelleri misapplied	see *S. greggii* × *serpyllifolia*
muelleri ambig.	CSpe NDov WOth
'Mulberry Jam'	CAby CBot CHGN CHll CSam EAJP ECtt ELan EPfP EWes MAsh MCot MSCN SDys SEle SPin SRkn WHil WKif WOth WSHC
§ ***multicaulis*** ♀H3	MAsh XSen
munzii	SDys SPin
MYSTIC SPIRES BLUE ('Balsalmisp'PBR)	CSpe CWGN EPfP MCot SCob SPin SPoG
'Nachtvlinder' ♀H4	Widely available
namaensis	SPin
nana B&SWJ 10272	SPin
- 'Curling Waves'PBR	CBod ECtt MHol
napifolia	EBee EWes LRHS MMuc MNrw NLar SPav
- 'Baby Blue'	EBee
'Nazareth'	SPin
'Nel'	EBee
nemorosa	LSRN NPol SPin SRms XLum XSen
- 'Amethyst' ♀H7	CBod CRos EBee ELon EPfP GBin IBoy LCro LOPS LRHS MBel MHol MPie MRav MSpe MTis NDov NRHS SCob SPer SPhx SPin SRms WCAu WCot WKif XSen
- 'Blue Marvel' **new**	MHol
- BLUE MOUND	see *S.* × *sylvestris* 'Blauhügel'
- 'Bordeau Steel Blue'	EBee ELon LRHS NRHS SRms
- 'Caradonna' ♀H7	Widely available
- EAST FRIESLAND	see *S. nemorosa* 'Ostfriesland'
- 'Experimental Pink'	LRHS NRHS
- 'Experimental Rose Compact'	LRHS NRHS
- 'Experimental White'	LRHS NRHS
- 'Grace'	NDov
- 'Little Friesland' **new**	CRos NRHS
- 'Lubecca' ♀H7	CBod ECtt EHrv EPed EPfP LRHS LSou MAsh MPie NDov NEgg NGdn NLar NRHS SPer WFar XSen
- LYRICAL SILVERTONE ('Balyricsil'PBR)	CBod WFar
- MARCUS ('Haeumanarc'PBR)	CBod EBee ECtt ELan EPed EPfP ETMg EUJe LRHS LSRN MBNS MRav MTin NDov NRHS SAko SDys SPoG WFar
- 'New Dimension Blue'	EPfP WHil
- 'New Dimension Rose'	EBee
§ - 'Ostfriesland' ♀H7	Widely available
- 'Pink Beauty'	LRHS NRHS
- 'Pink Friesland'PBR	CAby ECtt EHoe EPfP GBin GMaP LSou NGdn NRHS SAko WSpi
- 'Plumosa'	see *S. nemorosa* 'Pusztaflamme'
§ - 'Pusztaflamme' ♀H7	EBee ECha ECtt EPfP MRav SAko XSen
- 'Rose Queen'	CBod CSBt EHoe ELon GMaP GWyn IBoy MSpe MTis SCob SPhx WArt WCot WFar XLum XSen
- 'Rosenwein'	CDor GWyn IBoy LRHS NGdn NRHS SGbt SPhx XSen
- 'Royal Distinction'	ECtt
- 'Schwellenburg'	CBod ECtt LCro LRHS MHol NLar NRHS SAko SCob
- (Sensation Series) SENSATION BLUE IMPROVED	CRos LRHS NRHS
- - SENSATION DEEP BLUE ('Florsaldblue')	CBod EBee GBin LRHS NRHS
- - SENSATION DEEP ROSE ('Flor Sal Roz'PBR) **new**	CNor LRHS NRHS
- - SENSATION DEEP ROSE IMPROVED	CRos IBoy LRHS NRHS
- - SENSATION PINK	LRHS
- - SENSATION ROSE	CBod LCro LLHF LOPS LRHS LSRN LSou MHol NRHS SHar SRms
- - SENSATION WHITE ('Florsalwhite')	CWGN LRHS MHol NRHS
§ - subsp. ***tesquicola***	CBod NLar SPhx WFar
- 'Theodor'	ECtt MTis
- 'Wesuwe'	ELon MTis NDov
'Neon'	SPin
neurepia	see *S. microphylla* var. *microphylla*
* ***nevadensis***	SPin
nilotica	SPin
nipponica	EBee SBrt
- B&SWJ 5829	SPin WCru
- 'Fuji Snow' (v)	EBee
- var. ***trisecta***	SPin
nubicola	CExl GPoy WHil XSen
- CC 4607	EBee
'Nuchi'	SDys SPin
nutans	CBod SPhx SPin XSen
officinalis	Widely available
- 'Albiflora'	SPin WArt XSen
- 'Aurea' ambig.	GPoy
- 'Berggarten' ♀H4	CBod CBot ECha GBin GCal MHer MRav SCob SPhx SPin WHer WHil WKif XLum XSen
- 'Bicolor'	SPin
- 'Blackcurrant'	CBod
§ - broad-leaved	ESps MHer
- 'Crispa'	SPin XSen
- 'Extrakta'	GCal
- 'Grete Stolze'	SEND XSen
- 'Grower's Friend'	CTsd
§ - 'Icterina' (v) ♀H4	CBcs CBod CTri EBee ECha ECrN EHoe ELan ENfk ESps MAsh MGos MHer MMuc MNHC MRav MSwo SCob SEND SGol SPer SPin SPoG SRms WFar WHar WKif XLum XSen
- ***latifolia***	see *S. officinalis* broad-leaved
- narrow-leaved	see *S. lavandulifolia*
- 'Nazareth'	XSen
- ***prostrata***	see *S. lavandulifolia*
- 'Purpurascens' ♀H5	Widely available
- 'Purpurascens Variegata' (v)	ESps
- 'Robin Hill'	EPed LRHS NRHS WGwG
- 'Rosea'	XSen
- 'Tricolor' (v)	CBcs CBod CTri EBee ELan ENfk EPfP ESps GMcL GPoy MAsh MHer MNHC MRav SCob SGol SPer SPhm SPin SPoG SRms WHar XSen
- 'Variegata'	see *S. officinalis* 'Icterina'
- variegated (v)	MHer
- 'Würzburg'	XSen
ombrophila	SPin
omeiana BWJ 8062	SPin WCru
- 'Crûg Thundercloud'	WCru
oppositiflora misapplied	see *S. tubiflora*
oppositiflora ambig.	ELan SDys SPin
'Orchid Glow'	CWGN
'Othello' **new**	SDys

oxyphora	CAby CSpe ELan MAsh MPie SDys SPin WFar WOth
pachyphylla	LRHS NRHS XSen
'Pakhuis Pass'	SPin
pallida	SPin
'Pam's Purple'	MAsh
'Pasadena' **new**	SDys
§ ***patens*** ♀H4	CAby CBod CSpe EBee ECha ECtt EPfP IFro LCro LOPS LPmr LRHS MAsh MHer MNHC MRav NGdn SDys SEND SPer SPhx SPin SPoG SRms WFar WHil WKif WOth WSHC WSpi
- 'Alba' misapplied	see *S. patens* 'White Trophy'
- 'Blue Angel'	CCht EPfP EWTr EWes GPSL LEdu SPad
- 'Cambridge Blue' ♀H3	CAby CBod CExl CRos CSpe CWGN EBee ECtt EHrv ELan EPfP LRHS MAsh MHer MRav MSpe NLar NPer NRHS SDys SPer SPhm SPhx SPin WOth WOut WSHC
- 'Chilcombe'	CAby SDys SPin WOut
- 'Dot's Delight'	CExl CSpe ECtt LRHS MAsh SDys SHar
- 'Guanajuato'	CAby CBod CBot CExl CRav CSBt CSam ECtt EWes MAsh MCot NLar SDys SPin SRot WHil WKif WOth WOut WSHC
- 'Holbrook'	CSam
- large	CSpe
- light blue-flowered	LRHS NRHS
- OCEANA BLUE	EBee
- 'Oxford Blue'	see *S. patens*
- (Patio Series) 'Patio Deep Blue'	CWGN EPfP WHil
- - 'Patio Pink'	LRHS NRHS
- - 'Patio Sky Blue'	WHil WSpi
- - 'Patio White'	LRHS NRHS
- 'Pink Ice'	EBee ECtt SDys WOut
- pink-flowered	SPin
- 'Regal Blue' **new**	CBod
- 'Royal Blue'	see *S. patens*
§ - 'White Trophy'	CExl ECtt EWld LRHS LSvl SBee SDys SPin WOut
pauciserrata	SPin
'Peach Parfait'	EShb MAvo SDys
pennellii	SPin
'Penny's Smile'	CAby CBot CElw CMac ELon IPot MAsh MCot SDys SPhx SPin WGrn WHil WKif
'Peru Blue'	EBee SDys
'Peter Vider'	EPfP
'Phyllis' Fancy'	CAby CBot CSam CSpe EBee EWld LPla MAsh MCot MHer NDov NSti SDys SPhx SPin SPlb SRms WHlf WOth
pinguifolia	SPin
'Pink Icing'	SPin
'Pink Lace' **new**	SDys
pisidica	SPin XSen
polystachya	SPin
pratensis	EBWF EPfP GJos MNHC MRav SPin SRms WCot WOut XSen
- W&B BGH-3	WCot
§ - Bertolonii Group	SPin
- 'Dear Anja'	see *S.* × *sylvestris* 'Dear Anja'
§ - Haematodes Group ♀H7	MNrw SPin SRms
- 'Indigo' ♀H7	ECtt ELon EPed GMaP LRHS MPie MRav NEgg NLar NRHS SPhx SPin SPoG WCot WPGP
- 'Lapis Lazuli'	EBee EWTr EWes LPla LRHS
- 'Pink Delight'[PBR]	EBee ECtt EPfP LRHS MPie MSCN NDov NRHS SRms

- 'Rose Rhapsody' (Ballet Series)	CBod CDor EBee EPPr EPfP MMrt NLar SPhx WArt WKif XSen
- 'Rosea'	ECha SPin
- 'Sky Dance' (Ballet Series) **new**	CBod
- 'Swan Lake' (Ballet Series)	CBod CDor EBee EPPr GWyn NLar SPhx SPlb XSen
- 'Sweet Esmeralda' (Ballet Series)	CDor EBee NGdn SPhx XSen
- 'Twilight Serenade' (Ballet Series)	CBod CDor EBee ECtt EPfP SPhx WOut XSen
procurrens	EBee SPin XSen
przewalskii	CExl EBee LRHS NRHS SPin
- ACE 1157	WCru
- BWJ 7920	WCru XLum
pulchella	ELan SPin
'Purple Majesty'	CHll CSam ECtt SDys WKif WSpi XLum
'Purple Queen'	CAby CBod EBee LRHS LSou MAvo MCot NRHS SBee SDys SEle WHil
purpurea	LSRN
quitensis	SPin
radula	EBee SPin
'Raspberry Truffle'	SDys SPin
raymondii subsp. ***mairanae***	SPin
recognita	LRHS NRHS XSen
recurva	SPin
'Red Swing'[PBR]	CBod LRHS NRHS
reflexa	SPin
regeliana misapplied	see *S. virgata* Jacq.
regla	MAsh SDys SPin WPGP XSen
- 'Jame'	SPin
- 'Royal'	SPin
repens	SPin
§ ***reptans***	SBrt SPin
- from Mexico	SPhx
- from western Texas	CAby SDys WCot
rhinosima	WHil
'Ribambelle' ♀H3	EAJP IPot MAsh XLum
ringens	SPin XSen
riparia misapplied	see *S. rypara*
roborowskii	SPin
§ ***roemeriana***	CSpe IFoB WOut
- 'Arriba'	CDor LRHS NRHS
- 'Hot Trumpets'	CBod LRHS NRHS
'Rolando'	SDys SPin
§ ***roscida***	SPin
'Royal Bumble' ♀H4	Widely available
'Royal Crimson Distinction'[PBR]	EBee LSou
rubescens	SPin
- B&SWJ 14368 **new**	WCru
rubiginosa	SPin
runcinata	SPin
rutilans	see *S. elegans*
§ ***rypara***	SPin
sagittata	EBee GCal SPin WOut
'Salmon Dance'	CBod CWGN ECtt LRHS NRHS SPhm WHlf
'Savannah Red' (Savannah Series)	EPfP
scabra	EBee SPin WOut
schlechteri	EBee SPin
sclarea	CBod CHby ECtt ENfk GPoy MNHC SRms XAbr XLum XSen
- var. ***turkestanica*** hort.	CBot CDor CSpe EAJP ECha EHrv EPfP LRHS LSRN LSun MRav MSpe NEgg NGdn NRHS SEND SPav SPer

		SPhx SPtp SRkn WBrk WHar WKif XAbr XSen
§	- 'Vatican White'	CBot CSpe EAJP EBee EWTr LRHS LSun MSpe NRHS SPhx SPtp XSen
	- white-bracted	SWvt
	scutellarioides	SPin
	- B&SWJ 14273 **new**	WCru
	semiatrata misapplied	see *S. chamaedryoides*
	semiatrata ambig.	EWld
	semiatrata Zucc.	SPin
	serboana	EBee GBin SAko WPGP
	- B&SWJ 10236	WCru
	'Serenade'	CBWd CBod ELon MHol MTis NDov WCot
	serpyllifolia	SPin XSen
	- white-flowered	SPin
	sessei	SPin
	setulosa	SPin
	'Shame'	NDov
	'Shy Ruby'	SPin
	sikkimensis	SPin
	'Silas Dyson'	CFil CSam ECre ECtt EPfP IPot LRHS MAsh MAvo MCot NDov NRHS SBch SDys SPin SPoG WHil WKif WSHC
	'Silke's Dream'	CFil CSam ECtt EPfP LRHS MAsh MCot MPie SDys SHar SPin SPoG XSen
	'Silke's Red'	MCot SDys SPin
	sinaloensis	SPin
	'Smoke'	SDys
	somalensis	CSam EBee SPin SVen
	'Southern Belle'	SDys SPin
	spathacea ♀^{H4}	WOut
	- 'Avis Keedy'	SPin
	sphacelioides	SPin
	splendens 'Blaze of Fire' **new**	ETMg
	- 'Jimi's Good Red'	CSpe SDys WOth
	- 'Red Indian'	SDys
	- 'São Borja'	SDys
	- 'Vanguard' ♀^{H3}	NPri
§	- 'Van-Houttei' ♀^{H3}	EBee SDys SVen
	squalens	SPin
	stachydifolia	SPin WHil WPGP
	- CDPR 3071	WPGP
	- dark blue calyx **new**	WPGP
	- lavender calyx **new**	WPGP
§	***staminea***	SPin
	'Stephanie'	SDys SPin
	stolonifera	CAby CSam ECre MAsh MHer SDys SMHy SPin
	striata	SDys SPin
	- red-flowered	SPin
	styphelus	SDys SPin
	subpalmatinervis	SPin
	subpatens	SPin
	subrotunda	SDys SPin
	'Sunset Strip'	SDys
	× ***superba***	CBod CSBt EBee ECha ECtt ELan EPfP ESps LRHS LSRN NRHS SRms WCAu WGwG WHar WHoo
	- 'Adora Blue'	LRHS NRHS
	- 'Adrian'	CBod EBee ECtt EPed EPfP LRHS LSRN LSou NRHS WCot
	- 'Merleau'	LRHS
	- 'Merleau Blue'	SAko
	- 'Merleau Pink'	LRHS
	- 'Merleau Rose'	EBee MRav NDov SRms
*	- 'Rosea'	EBee
	- 'Rubin' ♀^{H7}	ECtt NBre
I	- 'Superba'	ECtt MRav SPhx SRkn
	× ***sylvestris***	LSRN SPin
§	- 'Blauhügel' ♀^{H7}	CBod CGar CRos EAJP ECha ECtt ELan EPfP GBin GCal LRHS MArl MHol MRav MSpe NDov NPri NRHS SPer SPhx SRms WCAu WGwG WHoo XSen
§	- 'Blaukönigin'	CBod CDor CNor EPfP GMaP LBuc LRHS NGBl NLar NRHS SCob SPer SPlb SPoG SRms SWvt WCot WHil XLum
	- BLUE QUEEN	see *S.* × *sylvestris* 'Blaukönigin'
§	- 'Dear Anja'	CBWd EBee ECtt IPot LCro MHol NDov WCot
	- 'Deep Blue Field'^{PBR} **new**	IPot
	- 'Lye End'	MRav MWat WCot
§	- 'Mainacht' ♀^{H7}	Widely available
	- MAY NIGHT	see *S.* × *sylvestris* 'Mainacht'
	- 'Negrito'	EBee ECtt GQue NLar
	- 'Rhapsody in Blue'^{PBR}	LLWG MBNS MHol MTis NLar WCot
	- 'Rose Queen'	CBWd CBod CMac ECha ELan ELon EPed EPfP EShb ESps LCro LOPS LRHS MHol MJak MRav NGBl NRHS SCob SCoo SPer SPhm SPhx SPoG SRms SWvt WHar XLum XSen
	- 'Rügen'	ELon GQue LRHS NRHS SAko
	- 'Schneehügel'	Widely available
	- 'Superba'	ESps
	- 'Tänzerin' ♀^{H7}	EBee ECtt ELon LRHS MTis NDov NLar SAko SPhx XSen
	- 'Viola Klose'	CBod EBee ECha ECtt ELan EPed EPfP EShb LCro LOPS LRHS LSRN MAvo MCot MSpe NDov NGdn NLar NRHS SAko SPin SRms WAul XSen
	tachiei hort.	see *S. forsskaolii*
	taraxacifolia	SPin XSen
	tesquicola	see *S. nemorosa* subsp. *tesquicola*
	'Theresia'	SDys
	thymoides	SPin WHil
	tianschanica	SPin
	tiliifolia	SPav SPin SRms
	tingitana	SPin
	tomentosa	EBee SPin XSen
	tortuosa	SPin
	transcaucasica	see *S. staminea*
	transsylvanica	IMou SPav SPin SRms XSen
	- 'Blue Spire'	SRkn
	'Trebah Lilac White'	see *S.* × *jamensis* 'Trebah'
§	'Trelawney'	CBod ECtt EWld LRHS MAvo MPie MSpe NRHS WHil
§	'Trelissick'	CBod MAsh MAvo MCot MSpe NPnk SDys SEND SEle SPhx SPin SRkn WHil
§	'Trewithen'	CBod CExl ECre MAvo MSpe SPin WHil XLum
	trijuga	SPin
	triloba	see *S. fruticosa*
	tubifera	SPin
§	***tubiflora*** ♀^{H2}	MAsh SPin
	uliginosa ♀^{H4}	Widely available
	- 'African Skies'	CChe MCot SPin WOth
	- 'Ballon Azul'	CBot CSpe EBee ELan EWes MAsh SDys SEle SPin SPoG WPGP WSHC
	'Ultra Violet'	CWGN
	univerticillata	SPin
	urica	SPin
	- short	SDys

	'Valerie'	SDys
	'Valle de Bravo'	SPin
	'Van-Houttei'	see *S. splendens* 'Van-Houttei'
	variana	SPin
	'Vatican City'	see *S. sclarea* 'Vatican White'
	vazquezii	SPin WOut
	verbenaca	EBWF MHer SPin WOut XSen
	- pink-flowered	WOut
	verticillata	EPfP LEdu NLar SPin
§	- 'Alba'	CBod EBee EPed EPfP GJos GQue LRHS MRav NGdn NLar NRHS SPer SPin XSen
	- 'Hannay's Blue'	EPPr GMaP LPla MAvo SBee SMHy WCAu
	- 'Hannay's Purple'	ECtt EPPr
	- 'Purple Rain'	Widely available
	- 'Smouldering Torches'	EBee NDov SCob SMad SPhx
	- 'White Rain'	see *S. verticillata* 'Alba'
	villicaulis	see *S. amplexicaulis*
	'Violin Music' PBR	CBod CSpe CWGN EBee ECtt LRHS NRHS WTor
§	***virgata*** Jacq.	EBee SPin XSen
	viridis	CBod CHby CRav MNHC SPin
	- Claryssa Series	SRms
§	- var. ***comata***	MCot
	- 'Marble Arch Blue' (Marble Arch Series)	CSpe
	viscosa Jacq.	SPin
	vitifolia	CSpe SDys WOut
	- B&SWJ 10236	SPin
	wagneriana	SPin
	'Waverly'	CBod CBot EBee EWTr EWld MAsh MHer SDys SEle SPoG WOut
	'Wendy's Wish' PBR	CAby CBod CBot CSpe EBee ECtt IPot LCro LRHS LSou MAsh MSCN MSpe NDov NRHS SCob SDys SPin SPoG SRkn SRms WGrn WHil WHoo WNPC
	× ***westerae***	SPin
	- 'Petra'	SDys
	willeana	SPin
	yunnanensis	SPin
	- BWJ 7874	WCru
	aff. ***yunnanensis***	SPin

Salvinia (*Salviniaceae*)

natans	LLWG MSKA XBlo

Sambucus ✿ (*Adoxaceae*)

	'Black Diamonds'	NPri
	caerulea	see *S. nigra* subsp. *caerulea*
	coraensis	see *S. williamsii* subsp. *coreana*
	ebulus	EBee EPPr LEdu NSti SMad WCot WWtn
	formosana	WCot
*	***himalayensis***	WCot
	mexicana B&SWJ 10349	WCot WCru
	miquelii	WCot
	nigra	CArg CBcs CCVT CDul CFGn CPer ECrN EPom ESps GMcL GPoy IBoy LBuc SEWo SPer SVic WMou WSFF WTSh
	- 'Albomarginata'	see *S. nigra* 'Marginata'
	- 'Ardwall'	CAgr GBin GCal WCot
	- 'Aurea'	CBcs CDul CMac ELan EPom ESps GMcL MMuc SPer WCot WMoo
	- 'Aureomarginata' (v)	ECrN ELan EPPr MMuc MRav SEND WCot
	- 'Bont Oosterwoldë'	WCot
	- 'Bradet'	CAgr WCot WFar

	- 'Broadway' (v)	WCot
	- 'Cae Rhos Lligwy'	CAgr WCot WHer
§	- subsp. ***caerulea***	EBee WCot WPGP
	- subsp. ***canadensis***	SPhx
	- - 'Adams' (F)	WCot
	- - 'Aurea'	WCot WHar
	- - 'Johns'	CAgr WCot
	- - 'Maxima'	SMad WCot
	- - 'Rubra'	WCot
	- - 'York' (F)	CAgr WCot
	- 'Castledean'	WCot
	- 'Dart's Greenlace'	WCot
	- 'Dolomite' (v)	WCot
	- 'Donau'	CAgr WCot
	- 'Frances' (v)	EPPr WCot
	- 'Franzi'	CAgr WCot
	- 'Fructuluteo'	NLar WCot
	- 'Godshill' (F)	CAgr SDea WCot
	- GOLDEN TOWER ('Jdeboer001') **new**	SPoG
	- 'Haidegg 17' (F)	CAgr
	- 'Haschberg'	CAgr WCot
	- 'Heterophylla'	see *S. nigra* 'Linearis'
	- 'Hillier's Dwarf'	WCot
	- 'Ina'	CAgr WCot
	- 'Körsör' (F)	WCot
	- f. ***laciniata*** ♀H6	CBcs CDul CRos EBee ELan EPPr EPfP GCal LRHS MBlu MMuc MRav SLon SPer SPoG WCFE WCot WFar
§	- 'Linearis'	ELan MRav NLar WCot
	- 'Long Tooth'	CDul WCot
	- 'Lutea Punctata'	WCot WFar
	- 'Madonna' (v)	CMac LEdu LRHS MBlu MRav NLar NPol NQui SPer SPoG WAvo WCot
§	- 'Marginata' (v)	CDul CMac EHoe MHer MRav SPer WCot WFar WMoo
	- 'Marion Bull' (v)	CDul NLar WCot
I	- 'Marmorata'	NLar WCot
	- 'Mint Julep'	WCot
I	- 'Monstrosa'	WCot
	- 'Nana'	WCot
	- 'Naomi'	WCot
	- 'Norfolk Speckled' (v)	WCot
	- 'Pingo Trail'	WCot
	- 'Plena' (d)	WCot
	- f. ***porphyrophylla*** 'Black Beauty'	see *S. nigra* f. *porphyrophylla* 'Gerda'
	- - 'Black Lace'	see *S. nigra* f. *porphyrophylla* 'Eva'
	- - BLACK TOWER ('Eiffel 1' PBR)	Widely available
	- - 'Blue Sheen'	CRos EPfP GBin LRHS NRHS SCoo WCot
§	- - 'Eva' PBR ♀H6	Widely available
§	- - 'Gerda' PBR ♀H6	Widely available
§	- - 'Guincho Purple'	CBcs CDul CMac CTri EPPr EPfP GMcL LRHS MRav NLar SPlb WCot WFar WMoo
	- - 'Purple Pete'	CDul WCot
	- - 'Thundercloud' ♀H6	CDul ECrN ELon EWes GCal MAsh MNrw NEoE NLar SPhx WCot WFar WMoo
	- 'Pulverulenta' (v)	EPPr GCal MRav NLar NQui SRms WCot
	- 'Purpurea'	see *S. nigra* f. *porphyrophylla* 'Guincho Purple'
	- 'Pyramidalis'	MRav SMad WCot
	- 'Riese aus Vossloch'	WCot
	- 'Robert Piggin' (v)	WCot

- var. ***rotundifolia***	WCot
- 'Sambu' (F)	CAgr WCot
- 'Samdal' (F)	CAgr WCot WFar
- 'Samidan' (F)	CAgr WCot
- 'Samnor' (F)	CAgr WCot
- 'Sampo' (F)	CAgr WCot
- 'Samyl' (F)	CAgr WCot
- 'Serenade' **new**	CRos NEoE NRHS
- 'Urban Lace'	CAgr WCot
- 'Variegata'	see *S. nigra* 'Marginata'
- f. ***viridis***	CAgr WCot
'Ocean Depths'	GBin NEoE
palmensis	WCot
racemosa	EPfP GBin WCot
- 'Altamont'	WCot
- 'Aurea'	EHoe EPfP IBoy WFar
- var. ***callicarpa***	WCot WFar
- 'Goldenlocks'	EWes
- subsp. ***kamtschatica***	WCot
- var. ***melanocarpa***	WCot
- 'Plumosa Aurea'	CDul ELan EPfP ESps GMcL MGos MJak MRav MSwo NLar SLim SRms WAvo WCot
- var. ***pubens***	WCot
§ - var. ***sieboldiana***	WCot
- 'Sutherland Gold' ♀H7	Widely available
- 'Tenuifolia'	WCot
sieboldiana	see *S. racemosa* var. *sieboldiana*
'Sunny Days'	CBod LRHS NRHS
tigranii	WCot WFar
WELSH GOLD ('Walfinb'PBR)	LRHS MAsh SPoG WCot
§ ***williamsii*** subsp. ***coreana***	WCot

Samolus (*Primulaceae*)

valerandi	EBWF LLWG

Sandersonia (*Colchicaceae*)

aurantiaca	CAvo EPot GKev LAma SDeJ SDir

Sanguinaria (*Papaveraceae*)

canadensis	CBct CBot CPla EPfP EPot EWTr GEdr GKev GPoy LAma LEdu LRHS MMuc NHpl NRHS NRya SDir SEND SMHy SPer WAbe WPnP
- 'Jerry Flintoff' **new**	GEdr
- f. ***multiplex*** (d)	CTal EPot IFro LRHS NRHS SPhx
- - 'Plena' (d) ♀H5	CBct CWCL EBee ECha ELon EPfP GEdr GKev GPoy GQue IRob LAma LRHS MMoz NHpl NLar NPoe NRHS NRya NSla NSti SDeJ SPer WAbe WCot WFar WPnP XEll
- pink	GEdr

Sanguisorba ✿ (*Rosaceae*)

from Japan	EBee MAvo
§ ***albiflora***	CKno EBee ELan EPfP EShb EWTr ILea LCro LEdu LOPS LRHS MAvo MMuc MRav MSpe NDov NEoE NGdn SEND SPhx SRkn WMoo
'All Time High'	NDov
alpina	GLog MMuc SEND
'Ankum's Thums' **new**	MTis
applanata	WCot
armena	CElw EBee EWes IMou MNrw MPie WWtn XEll
'Autumn Bliss'	EBee GMaP
'Autumn Red' **new**	MAvo
'Beetlewings'	MAvo MTis
'Blacksmith's Burgundy'	LEdu MAvo
'Blackthorn'	CBWd CKno CMea EBee ECtt GMaP LPla MTis NDov NLar SMHy SPhx WCot WHoo
'Burr Blanc'	SMHy SPhx
canadensis	CBWd CBod CKno CMac CMea EBee ECha ECtt EPPr EPfP GCal GMaP GPoy GQue GWyn ILea LCro MAvo MNrw MRav NLar NSti SPer SPhx SRms WCot WMoo WOld WWtn XEll
- hybrid	MAvo
'Cangshan Cranberry'	CSpe EBee ECtt GMaP LPla MAvo MHol NDov SMHy WCot WWtn
* ***caucasica***	GBin LEdu SPhx
'Ccc'	MAvo
'Chocolate Tip'	CDor EBee ECtt ILea IPot LRHS MAvo
'Coen's Cranberry'	NDov
dodecandra	EBee IPot MAvo MTis
'Foxtail'	MAvo
hakusanensis	CBWd CBod CKno EBee GBin GCal GKev IBoy IFro IPot LEdu LRHS MAvo MMuc MNrw NBro NChi NDov NEoE NGBl NLar NRHS WArt WCot WFar WHoo
- B&SWJ 8709	WCru
- 'Lilac Squirrel'	CKno EBee ECtt ILea IPot LEdu LRHS MAvo MBNS MBel MNrw MSpe MTis NDov NLar WTor
'Ivory Towers'	MAvo SBee WFar
'John Coke'	EBee NLar
'Joni'	CKno MAvo
'Little Angel'	CAby CBod CKno EBee ECtt LLWG LRHS MAvo MBNS MBel MHol NRHS SMad SPad SPoG WCot WFar
magnifica	EWes GCal LEdu
- ***alba***	see *S. albiflora*
menziesii	Widely available
- 'Dali Marble' (v)	EBee ECtt NLar WMoo
- 'Fathoms Deep' **new**	MAvo
- 'Wake Up'	IRob NDov
§ ***minor***	CAgr CHby GPoy LEdu MHer MJak MNHC NMir NPol SCob SPhx SPlb SRms WHar WHer WMoo XAbr XLum
- subsp. ***minor***	CHab EBWF
'Misbourne Pink'	LPla
'Nettlesworth Wand'	SMHy
obtusa	Widely available
- 'Chatto'	MAvo NLar WPGP
- silver-leaved	MNrw SMHy
- white-flowered	EBee EWTr GPSL MAvo MBel MTis WPGP
officinalis	CBWd CHab CKno EBWF EHoe GKev GQue MHer NEoE NMir NPol SPer SPhx SRms WMoo WOut WTre
- CDC 262	EPPr LEdu SMHy SPhx
- CDC 282	CSpe SPhx
- CDC 292	MAvo WCot
- DJHC 535	LEdu
- from Mongolia	EBee
- 'Arnhem'	CCse CDor CKno EBee ECtt EHrv EPPr ILea LEdu LRHS MTis NDov SBee SMHy SPhx WCot
- 'Crimson Queen'	EBee ECtt GQue IPot MTis NLar
- dark-flowered	MAvo
- early-flowering	GWyn
- 'False Tanna'	WFar
- 'Lemon Splash' (v)	EBee ECtt LEdu MAvo MMrt WCot WFar

- 'Lum'	MAvo
- 'Martin's Mulberry'	CKno EBee EWes GCal GMaP LEdu MAvo MNrw NDov
- subsp. ***microcephala***	SPer
- 'Morning Select'	EBee ECtt EPPr GMaP NLar
- 'Red Buttons'	MAvo NDov
- 'Red Thunder'	CBWd CSpe CWld ECtt EPPr GMaP ILea IPot IRob LCro LEdu LOPS LRHS MAvo MTis NDov NLar NRHS WCAu WCot WGwG WPGP
- 'Shiro-fukurin' (v)	CBot EBee ECtt EWes GMaP LEdu LSun MBel MCot MHol MNrw NLar WCot WFar WHer WOut WSHC
- 'Tsetseguun'	LEdu LRHS MAvo WPGP
- 'White Tanna' **new**	MBel
parviflora	see *S. tenuifolia* var. *parviflora*
pimpinella	see *S. minor*
'Pink Brushes'	CKno ECtt GBin GQue IMou IPot MAvo MTis NLar
'Pink September'	MAvo
'Pink Tanna'	Widely available
'Purple Tails'	MAvo
'Raspberry Coulis'	MAvo
'Raspberry Mivvi'	SPhx
'Rock and Roll'	ECtt EPPr MBNS MSpe MTis NLar WOut
'Sangria' **new**	MAvo
'Scapino' **new**	MAvo
sitchensis	see *S. stipulata*
§ ***stipulata***	CMac EBee GCal LEdu LPla LRHS MNrw NRHS
'Tanna'	Widely available
'Tanna' seedling	EShb
tenuifolia	EHrv GCal IFro LRHS MCot NChi NGBl NLar NRHS SPhx WCot
- RBS 0266	GKev
- from Ernst Pagels	MAvo
- var. ***alba***	Widely available
- - CDC	GCal MRav
- - 'Korean Snow'	CCse GMaP LEdu LRHS SMHy SPhx SSut
- 'Big Pink'	MAvo MNrw WFar WOut
- 'Bordeaux'	EBee ECtt EWTr MAvo
- 'Henk Gerritsen'	EBee MAvo NLar
§ - var. ***parviflora***	EBee LEdu MAvo MNrw NLar WPGP
- 'Pieters'	MAvo
- 'Pink Elephant'	CKno EBee ECtt EPPr GJos GMaP GQue ILea LEdu LRHS MAvo MBel MSpe MTis NLar SMad WCAu WMoo WOut
- pink-flowered **new**	SMHy
- var. ***purpurea***	EBee GBin
- 'Purpurea'	CBWd CKno EBee EPPr GQue ILea LEdu MAvo MTis SPhx WCAu WCot WPGP
- 'Stand Up Comedian'	IMou LEdu MAvo NDov NLar
- 'Strawberry Frost'	MAvo
- 'Strawberry Fruli'	LEdu
- 'Sturdy Guard'	LEdu
- 'The Invisible'	MAvo
- 'White Elephant'	ELan
- 'White Tanna'	CKno EBee EPPr GQue LEdu MTis

Sanicula (*Apiaceae*)

europaea	CEls EBWF GPoy IMou

Sansevieria (*Asparagaceae*)

bacularis 'Mikado' **new**	LCro
cylindrica	ELan EShb
- 'Boncel' **new**	LToo
trifasciata var. ***laurentii*** (v) ♀H1b	LOPS
- 'Moonshine' ♀H1b	EShb

Santolina (*Asteraceae*)

sp.	CPla
'Apple Court'	LRHS
benthamiana	XSen
§ ***chamaecyparissus***	Widely available
- var. ***corsica*** misapplied	see *S. chamaecyparissus* 'Nana'
- subsp. ***insularis***	XSen
- 'Lambrook Silver'	CFis CRos EBee ECtt ENfk EPfP LRHS MAsh NLar SCoo SLim XSen
- 'Lemon Queen'	CRos ENfk EPfP EWTr LRHS MAsh MSwo NLar SRms XSen
- subsp. ***magonica***	XSen
§ - 'Nana' ♀H5	CRos EPfP ESps LRHS MAsh MHer MRav MSwo SCob SPoG SRms XSen
- 'Pretty Carroll' ♀H5	CBod CBot EBee EBtc ELan EPfP EWTr LRHS LSRN MAsh NLar SPoG WFar
- 'Small-Ness'	CSma ELan EPfP EWes LRHS MHer NLar SWvt WHer XSen
impressa	XSen
incana	see *S. chamaecyparissus*
* ***lindavica***	XSen
pectinata	see *S. rosmarinifolia* subsp. *canescens*
pinnata	CTri MHer
§ - subsp. ***neapolitana*** ♀H5	CSBt ECha ELan ENfk EPfP MRav SEND
- - cream-flowered	see *S. pinnata* subsp. *neapolitana* 'Edward Bowles'
§ - - 'Edward Bowles'	CBod EBee EHoe EPfP EWTr GMaP LRHS LSRN MAvo MHer MNHC MRav MSwo NLar NPer SCob SLim SPoG SRGP SRms SVen SWvt WCFE WHer WHoo XSen
- - 'Sulphurea'	CBot EPfP LRHS MAsh SPer SPhx WKif XSen
rosmarinifolia	CRos GPoy IRob LRHS LSun MRav NRHS SCob SEND SLon SPlb SRms WHoo
§ - subsp. ***canescens***	XSen
- 'Green Fizz' **new**	WFar
- 'Lemon Fizz' ♀H5	CBod CPla EBee ECrN EHoe ELan ELon ENfk EPfP GMaP LRHS LSou MAvo MHer NLar NRHS SCob SCoo SPer SPoG SRms SWvt WFar WHar WHer XSen
§ - subsp. ***rosmarinifolia***	ECha ECrN ELan ENfk EPfP MHer MRav SCob SPer SRms SWvt WFar WGwG XLum XSen
- - 'Primrose Gem' ♀H5	CBcs CBod CSBt CTri EAJP ECha EPfP LRHS MAsh MAvo MNHC MSwo SCob SEND SGbt SPer SRms SWvt XSen
- - white-flowered	WHer
SHADES OF JADE ('Sant101')	ECrN SRms
tomentosa misapplied	see *S. pinnata* subsp. *neapolitana*
virens	see *S. rosmarinifolia* subsp. *rosmarinifolia*
viridis	see *S. rosmarinifolia* subsp. *rosmarinifolia*

Sapindus (*Sapindaceae*)

saponaria var. ***drummondii***	EGFP

Saponaria (*Caryophyllaceae*)

	× ***boissieri***	EPot
	'Bressingham' 🏆H5	ECtt EPfP EPot GCrg MHol WAbe
	Bressingham hybrid	MAsh
	caespitosa	EDAr EPot EWes
§	***intermedia***	NDov WCot
	× ***lempergii*** 'Fritz Lemperg'	NDov WCot
	- 'Max Frei'	CSam EBee ECtt ELon EPPr LCro LOPS LPla MCot MRav NDov SBch SPhx WCot WOld XLum
	ocymoides 🏆H5	CMea EBee ECha ECtt EDAr ELan EPfP GMcL MAsh MHol MNHC MSCN NHpl NPnk SEND SPlb SPoG SRms SRot XLum
	- 'Alba'	ECha NSla
	- 'Snow Tip'	EDAr NGdn WRHF
	officinalis	CBod CBre EBWF ENfk GBin GPoy MHer MNHC SPlb SRms WHer WMoo WPtf WSFF XAbr
	- 'Alba'	CSam
	- 'Alba Plena' (d)	CBre MMuc NLar SEND WFar XLum
	- 'Betty Arnold' (d)	CAby EBee ECtt EPPr EWes MHer WCot
	- 'Flore Pleno' (d)	CBod WOut
	- 'Rosea Plena' (d)	CAby CBre CMac ELan EPfP LEdu MHer MMuc NBid NGdn NPnk SCob SEND SPer WFar WGwG WMoo WPtf
	- 'Rubra Plena' (d)	ELan EPPr EWes MMuc
	× ***olivana*** 🏆H5	CPBP ECtt EPot GCrg GMaP MAsh NLar XLum
	'Rosenteppich'	CPBP
	sicula subsp. ***intermedia***	see *S. intermedia*
*	× ***sundermannii*** new	CPBP
	zawadskii	see *Silene zawadskii*

Sanvitalia (*Asteraceae*)

procumbens misapplied	see *Melampodium montanum*

Saposhnikovia (*Apiaceae*)

divaricata	SPhx

Sarcococca ✿ (*Buxaceae*)

	confusa 🏆H5	Widely available
	hookeriana	ELon GKin IFoB LSRN MBlu MSwo NLar NWad SCob SGbt SWvt WFar WPGP WSpi
	- B&SWJ 2585	WCru
	- HWJK 2393	WCru
	- HWJK 2428	WCru
	- 'Daman'	CExl
	- var. ***digyna***	Widely available
	- - SDR 7816	GKev
	- - 'Purple Stem' 🏆H5	CEnd CExl CJun CTri EBee EPfP ESps EUJe GKin LCro LOPS LRHS MGos MNrw NLar NPnk SCob SCoo SPer SPoG SRkn SWvt WCru WSpi
	- - 'Schillingii'	see *S. hookeriana* var. *digyna* 'Tony Schilling'
§	- - 'Tony Schilling'	CExl CJun NLar WCru
	- var. ***hookeriana***	CJun LSRN
	- - GWJ 9222	WCru
	- - GWJ 9344	WCru
	- - GWJ 9369	WCru
	- - HWJK 2102	WCru
	- - HWJK 2366	WCru
	- - HWJK 2393	WCru
	- - 'Ghorepani' 🏆H5	CRos LCro LOPS LRHS NRHS
	- var. ***humilis***	Widely available
	- WINTER GEM ('Pmoore03'PBR)	CRos CSBt EMil EPfP LCro LOPS LRHS LSRN MAsh MGos MSwo NRHS SLon SPoG
	orientalis	CBct CExl CJun CMCN CRos EBee ELan ELon EPfP IMou LEdu LRHS MAsh NLar NRHS NWad SPoG WPGP WSpi
	'Roy Lancaster'	see *S. ruscifolia* var. *chinensis* 'Dragon Gate'
	'Rudolph'	EPfP LLHF LRHS
	ruscifolia	Widely available
	- var. ***chinensis***	CJun NLar SLon WCru WPGP
§	- - 'Dragon Gate' 🏆H5	CBct CExl CJun CRos EBee ELan ELon EPfP LEdu LLHF LRHS LSRN MAsh MGos NRHS SLim SLon SPoG SWvt WCru WPGP WSpi
	saligna	CBcs CJun EBtc ELan EPfP LRHS MRav SLon WCru
	- HWJK 2428	WCru
	- MF P2056	WCru
	- NJM 12.043	WPGP
I	***taiwaniana*** RWJ 9999 new	WCru
	trinervia B&SWJ 9500	WCru
	vagans B&SWJ 7285	WCru
	- B&SWJ 9760 from Vietnam	WCru
	- B&SWJ 9766 from Vietnam	WCru
	aff. ***vagans*** B&SWJ 7265 from north Thailand	WCru
	wallichii	CBcs CExl CHll ELon EWTr LEdu MBlu SPoG WPGP
	- B&SWJ 2291	CJun WCru WSHC
	- GWJ 9427	WCru
	- HWJK 2425	WCru
	- HWJK 2428	WCru
	- PAB 13.077 new	LEdu
	zeylanica B&SWJ 10199	WCru
	- var. ***brevifolia*** GWJ 9480	WCru
	- - GWJ 9483	WCru

Sarcopoterium (*Rosaceae*)

spinosum	SPhx SVen

Sarmienta (*Gesneriaceae*)

repens 🏆H2	CExl CFil WAbe

Sarothamnus see *Cytisus*

Sarracenia ✿ (*Sarraceniaceae*)

× ***ahlesii***	NLos
alata	EECP SHmp WSSs
- from Deer Park, Alabama, pubescent	NLos
- from Desoto National Forest, Mississippi	NLos
- from Robertson County, Texas	NLos
- from Stone County, Mississippi	NLos
- all green	SHmp
- 'Black Tube' 🏆H3	WSSs
- heavily veined	SHmp WSSs
- var. ***nigropurpurea***	WSSs
- var. ***ornata***	WSSs
- pubescent	EECP NLos WSSs
- 'Red Lid'	EECP NLos WSSs
- 'Red Lid' × ***flava*** red pitcher	EECP
- 'Red Lid' all red clone × ***flava*** var. ***rubricorpora***	NLos

- var. ***rubrioperculata***	WSSs
- wavy lid	SHmp WSSs
- white-flowered	WSSs
alata × ***flava***	NLos
alata × ***flava*** var. ***maxima***	NLos WSSs
alata × ***leucophylla***	NLos
(***alata*** red tube × ***flava*** 'Burgundy') × (***leucophylla*** × ***purpurea***)	NLos
× ***areolata***	NLos WSSs
'Barbapapa'	NLos
× ***catesbaei***	NLos SHmp WSSs
- 'Johnny Marr'	SHmp
- RV clone × ***oreophila***	NLos
× ***catesbaei*** × ***leucophylla***	NLos
× ***catesbaei*** × ***oreophila***	NLos
× ***courtii***	SHmp
× ***courtii*** × ***minor***	NLos
'Dixie Lace' ♀H3	NLos
'Eva'	NLos SHmp WSSs
× ***excellens***	WSSs
- 'Judy'	NLos
× ***excellens*** × (***minor*** × ***rubra*** subsp. ***rubra***)	NLos
× ***excellens*** × (× ***rehderi***)	NLos
× ***exornata***	SPlb SRms
'Fiona'	SHmp
flava	LOPS WSSs
- from Bay County, Florida	NLos
- from Carteret County, North Carolina	NLos
- from Dorchester County, South Carolina	NLos
- from Jedbury, Dorchester County, South Carolina	NLos
- from Marston Exotics	NLos
- from McClellanville, South Carolina	NLos
- from Santee Coastal Reserve, South Carolina	NLos
- from SB Creek Road	NLos
- from Shallotte, North Carolina	NLos
- all green giant	see *S. flava* var. *maxima*
- all red tube	NLos
- var. ***atropurpurea***	EECP SHmp WSSs
- - from Blackwater, Florida	NLos
- 'Claret'	WSSs
- var. ***cuprea***	SHmp WSSs
- var. ***flava***	EECP WSSs
- - from Hurleyville, South Carolina	NLos
- - very tall, from Dahlia Bog, Virginia	NLos
- giant red tube	NLos
§ - var. ***maxima***	EECP NLos SHmp WSSs
- - from North Carolina	NLos
- var. ***maxima*** × (× ***moorei*** Brooks's hybrid)	NLos
- var. ***ornata***	EECP NLos SHmp WSSs
- var. ***rubricorpora***	EECP SHmp SPlb WSSs
- - from Apalachicola National Forest, Florida	NLos
- - 'Burgundy'	NLos WSSs
- var. ***rugelii***	EECP NLos SHmp SPlb WSSs

- - from Homerville Airport, Ware County, Georgia	NLos
- stocky, from Appalachicola National Forest, Florida	NLos
((***flava*** × ***leucophylla***) × ***leucophylla***) × (***flava*** × ***rubra***)	NLos
(***flava*** × ***purpurea***) × (***purpurea*** subsp. ***purpurea***)	NLos
leucophylla	NLos SHmp SPlb SRms WSSs
- from Bens Bog, Baldwin County, Alabama	NLos
- from Citronelle, Alabama	NLos
- from Ctenium Fields, Perdido, Alabama	NLos
- from gas station site, Perdido, Alabama	NLos
- from Hosford, Liberty County, Florida	NLos
- from Okaloosa Co., Florida	NLos SHmp
- from Southern Eglin Reserve, Oskaloosa County, Florida	NLos
- var. ***alba***	WSSs
- 'Deer Park Alabama'	NLos SHmp
- green	WSSs
- green and white	NLos WSSs
- pubescent	WSSs
- pubescent from Deer Park, Alabama	SHmp
- from Perdido, Alabama	NLos
- 'Schnell's Ghost' ♀H3	SHmp WSSs
- 'Tarnok'	WSSs
- f. ***viridescens***	WSSs
leucophylla × ***oreophila***	EECP
leucophylla × (***minor*** × ***rubra*** subsp. ***rubra***)	NLos
leucophylla × (× ***popei***)	EECP
(***leucophylla*** × ***purpurea***) × (***minor*** × ***oreophila***)	NLos
leucophylla × ***rubra*** subsp. ***alabamensis***	NLos
'Lynda Butt' ♀H3	SHmp WSSs
'Maroon'	NLos
× ***miniata***	EECP SHmp WSSs
minor	EECP SHmp WSSs
- from Berkeley County, South Carolina	NLos
- from Fitzgerald, Ben Hill County, Georgia	NLos
§ - 'Okee Giant'	NLos WSSs
- 'Okefenokee Giant'	see *S. minor* 'Okee Giant'
- var. ***okefenokeensis***	WSSs
minor × ***rubra***	NLos
× ***mitchelliana***	NLos SHmp WSSs
- 'Juthatip Soper' ♀H3	NLos SHmp WSSs
- 'Rita Soper'	SHmp
× ***moorei***	NLos SHmp WSSs
- 'Adrian Slack' **new**	WSSs
- 'Brooks's Hybrid' ♀H4	EECP NLos WSSs
- 'Leah Wilkerson' **new**	WSSs
- 'Marston Clone'	NLos
× ***moorei*** × ***purpurea*** subsp. ***venosa***	NLos
oreophila	SHmp WSSs
- purple throat	NLos
oreophila × ***purpurea***	NLos
oreophila × ***rubra*** subsp. ***wherryi*** 'Chatom Giant'	NLos

× ***popei*** NLos WSSs
'Pseudo-Judy' NLos
psittacina EECP NLos SHmp SRms WSSs
purpurea NLos SPlb
- subsp. ***purpurea*** SHmp WSSs
- - f. ***heterophylla*** ♀H6 WSSs
- subsp. ***venosa*** NLos SHmp WSSs
- - var. ***burkii*** SHmp WSSs
× ***readei*** EECP NLos SHmp WSSs
× ***rehderi*** SHmp WSSs
rubra EECP WSSs
- subsp. ***alabamensis*** ♀H3 SHmp WSSs
- subsp. ***gulfensis*** SHmp WSSs
* - - f. ***heterophylla*** WSSs
* - - - from Yellow River, North Florida NLos
- subsp. ***jonesii*** EECP NLos SHmp WSSs
* - - f. ***heterophylla*** WSSs
- subsp. ***rubra*** SHmp WSSs
- subsp. ***wherryi*** EECP WSSs
- - from near Perdido, Baldwin County, Alabama NLos
- - 'Chatom Giant' NLos
- - giant WSSs
- - yellow-flowered WSSs
× ***swaniana*** SHmp SRms
'Velvet' NLos
'Vogel' ♀H3 NLos SHmp WSSs
× ***wrigleyana*** NLos SRms

Saruma (*Aristolochiaceae*)

henryi CAby CPla CTal EWld GEdr GKev GLog LEdu LPla MMoz SBrt SPad WCot WCru WFar WSHC

Sasa (*Poaceae*)

disticha 'Mirrezuzume' see *Pleioblastus pygmaeus* 'Mirrezuzume'
glabra f. ***albostriata*** see *Sasaella masamuneana* 'Albostriata'
kurilensis MWht
§ - 'Shima-shimofuri' (v) ERod EShb MMoz
- 'Shimofuri' see *S. kurilensis* 'Shima-shimofuri'
nana see *S. veitchii* f. *minor*
§ ***palmata*** EHoe LCro LOPS MMuc SArc
- f. ***nebulosa*** CBcs ENBC MMoz MWht NLar SArc WMoo
tessellata see *Indocalamus tessellatus*
tsuboiana CBcs MJak MWht NLar SBig SGol WMoo
§ ***veitchii*** CBcs CBdn EHoe ENBC GQue MJak MMoz MMuc MRav MWht NLar SCob SGol WFar WMoo
§ - f. ***minor*** MMuc WMoo

Sasaella (*Poaceae*)

§ ***masamuneana*** 'Albostriata' (v) CAco ENBC ERod LEdu MJak MMuc MWht SBig WMoo
§ ***ramosa*** MWht

Sassafras (*Lauraceae*)

albidum CBcs CMCN ELan EPfP LRHS MAsh NLar SChF SLon SPoG

satsuma see *Citrus reticulata*

Satureja ✿ (*Lamiaceae*)

coerulea ♀H5 EWes XSen
douglasii CBod
- 'Indian Mint'PBR ENfk MHer SRms
hortensis CBod ENfk LCro LOPS MHer MNHC SRms SVic
montana CHby EBee ENfk GPoy LEdu MHer MNHC SEND SRms SVic XAbr XSen
* - ***citriodora*** GPoy MHer XAbr XSen
§ - subsp. ***illyrica*** SPhx XLum XSen
- 'Purple Mountain' GPoy MHer
- ***subspicata*** see *S. montana* subsp. *illyrica*
repanda see *S. spicigera*
§ ***spicigera*** CBod ENfk EPot IMou LEdu MHer MMuc SPhx SRms XLum
spinosa XSen
thymbra SPhx SRms

Sauromatum (*Araceae*)

gaoligongense WCot
giganteum GKev
guttatum see *S. venosum*
§ ***venosum*** CExl EBee EShb LAma LEdu LRHS MMoz NLos NRHS WCot XLum

Saururus (*Saururaceae*)

cernuus CBen CBod CWat ELan LLWG MSKA WMAq WWtn XLum
- 'Hertford Streaker' (v) **new** WCot
chinensis LLWG SBrt

Saussurea (*Asteraceae*)

costus GPoy
japonica B&SWJ 12672 WCru
leucophylla **new** GKev
prostrata **new** CPBP
pseudoalpina WCot

savory, summer see *Satureja hortensis*

savory, winter see *Satureja montana*

Saxegothaea ✿ (*Podocarpaceae*)

conspicua CBcs NLar
- weeping form **new** WPGP

Saxifraga ✿ (*Saxifragaceae*)

JJH 9309174 NMen
McB 1475 **new** EPot
TJR 615/01 (7) EPot
acerifolia (5) GCal GEdr
§ 'Afrodite' (*sempervivum*) (7) WAbe
aizoides (9) GKev
aizoon see *S. paniculata* subsp. *paniculata*
× ***akinfievii*** (7) NMen
'Aladdin' (× *borisii*) (7) NMen
'Alan Hayhurst' (8) CPBP NSla WAbe
'Alan Martin' (× *boydilacina*) (7) EPot EWes
'Alba' ambig. LRHS NRHS
'Alba' (× *apiculata*) (7) ♀H5 NMen NRya SPlb
'Alba' (*oppositifolia*) (7) ELan EWes GCrg ITim NWad WAbe
'Albert Einstein' (× *apiculata*) (7) ♀H5 CTal NMen
'Albertii' (*callosa*) see *S.* 'Albida'
§ 'Albida' (*callosa*) (8) CTal NWad WAbe
'Albrecht Dürer' (Lasciva Group) (7) NMen
'Aldo Bacci' (Milford Group) (7) NMen NSla
'Alexander Humboldt' (Expedition Group) (7) **new** EPot

'Alfons Mucha' (7)	EPot
'Alice Longbottom' (*fortunei*) (5)	SAko
'Allendale Acclaim' (× *lismorensis*) (7)	NMen
'Allendale Accord' (7)	NMen
'Allendale Andante' (× *arco-valleyi*) (7)	NMen
'Allendale Angel' (× *kepleri*) (7)	NMen WAbe
'Allendale Argonaut' (7)	NMen
'Allendale Ballad' (7)	NMen
'Allendale Bamby' (× *lismorensis*) (7)	EPot WAbe
'Allendale Banshee' (7)	NMen
'Allendale Baron' (7)	NMen
'Allendale Beau' (× *lismorensis*) (7)	CTal
'Allendale Beauty' (7)	NMen WAbe
'Allendale Betty' (× *lismorensis*) (7)	EPot NMen
'Allendale Billows' (7)	NMen
'Allendale Bonny' (7)	EPot NSla WAbe
'Allendale Boon' (× *izari*) (7)	NMen
'Allendale Bounty' (7)	NMen
'Allendale Bravo' (× *lismorensis*) (7)	WAbe WHoo
'Allendale Cabal' (7)	NMen
'Allendale Carol' (7)	NMen
'Allendale Celt' (× *novacastelensis*) (7)	NMen
'Allendale Charm' (Swing Group) (7)	EPot GKev ITim NMen WAbe WHoo WThu
'Allendale Chick' (7)	EPot
'Allendale Citation' (7)	NMen WAbe
'Allendale Czech' (7)	NMen
'Allendale Delight' (7)	NMen
'Allendale Divine' (7)	NMen
'Allendale Dream' (7)	EPot NMen
'Allendale Duo' (7)	NMen
'Allendale Eden' (7)	NMen
'Allendale Elegance' (7)	NMen WAbe
'Allendale Elf' (7)	EPot NMen WAbe WHoo
'Allendale Elite' (7)	NMen WAbe
'Allendale Enchantment' (7)	NMen
'Allendale Envoy' (7)	ITim WAbe
'Allendale Epic' (7)	NMen
'Allendale Fairy' (7)	WHoo
'Allendale Fame' (7)	NMen
'Allendale Fancy' (7)	NMen
'Allendale Frost' (7)	NMen
'Allendale Ghost' (7)	NMen
'Allendale Goblin' (7)	NMen WAbe
'Allendale Grace' (7)	NMen
'Allendale Host' (7)	NMen
'Allendale Ice' (7)	NMen
'Allendale Imp' (7)	NMen
'Allendale Ina' (7)	NMen WAbe
'Allendale Jinn' (7)	CPBP NMen NSla
'Allendale Jo' (7)	CPBP NMen
'Allendale Joy' (× *wendelacina*) (7)	NMen
'Allendale King' (7)	NMen
'Allendale Magic' (7)	WAbe
'Allendale News' (7) **new**	NMen
'Allendale Noon' (7)	NMen
'Allendale Ruby' (7)	NMen
'Allendale Snow' (× *rayei*) (7)	EPot NMen
'Alpenglow' (7)	NMen
alpigena (7)	WAbe
ALPINO EARLY LIME ('Sax20007') (15) **new**	WFar
'Amberglow' (× *anglica*) (7)	NMen
'Amberine' (× *anglica*) (7)	EPot WHoo
'Amedeo Modigliani' (7)	NMen
'Amerigo Vespucci' (Continent Group) (7)	NMen
andersonii (7)	GKev
'Andrea Cesalpino' (Renaissance Group) (7)	EPot NMen
× ***andrewsii*** (8 × 11)	XLum
angustifolia Haw.	see *S. hypnoides*
'Anna' (× *fontanae*) (7)	EPot
'Anne Beddall' (× *goringiana*) (7)	NMen
'Anneka Hope' (8)	GKev
'Antonín Dvořák' (× *arco-valleyi*) (7)	NMen
'Antonio Vivaldi' (7)	EPot NMen
'Aphrodite' (*sempervivum*)	see *S.* 'Afrodite'
× ***apiculata*** (7)	MAsh
× ***apiculata*** *sensu stricto* hort.	see *S.* 'Gregor Mendel'
'Apple Blossom' (Mossy Group) (15)	ECtt EPfP NEoE NRya
'Arabella' (× *edithae*) (7)	NMen
'Aramis' (7)	NMen
× ***arendsii*** purple-flowered (15)	MMuc SPlb
'Šárka' (7)	CPBP NMen
'Artemis' (× *megaseiflora*) (7) **new**	NMen
'Arthur' (× *anglica*) (7)	NMen
'Asahi' (*fortunei*) (5)	SAko
aspera L. (10)	WAbe
'Assimilis' (× *petraschii*) (7)	EPot NMen
'Athena' (7)	NMen
'Atropurpurea' (*paniculata* subsp. *cartilaginea*) (8)	GAbr GMaP WHoo XLum
'Aufheitern von Eri' (*fortunei*) (5)	SAko
'August Hayek' (× *leyboldii*) (7)	NMen
'Aurea Maculata' (*cuneifolia*)	see *S.* 'Aureopunctata'
'Aurea' (*umbrosa*)	see *S.* 'Aureopunctata'
§ 'Aureopunctata' (× *urbium*) (11/v)	CMac CTri ECha ELan EPfP GKev GMaP LEdu LRHS MHer MPnt MRav NRHS SPer SPlb SPoG SRms WFar WMoo XLum
'Autumn Tribute' (*fortunei*) (5)	GEdr WAbe
'Aya' (*fortunei*) (5)	SAko
'Ayer's Rock' (7)	WAbe
'Balcana' (*paniculata*) (8)	EPot NSla WAbe
'Baldensis'	see *S. paniculata* var. *minutifolia*
'Balkan' (*marginata* subsp. *marginata* var. *rocheliana*) (7) ♀H5	ITim
'Beatles' (Beat Group) (7)	EPot NSla
§ 'Beatrix Stanley' (× *angelica*) (7)	CRos LRHS NMen NRHS NWad
'Bedřich Smetana' (*marginata*) (7)	NMen
'Beinn Eighe' (× *concinna*) (7)	NMen
'Beinne Alligin' (× *concinna*) (7)	NMen
'Ben Loyal' (× *concinna*) (7)	NMen WAbe
'Beni-tsukasa' (*fortunei*) (5) **new**	GEdr

'Benibana' (*fortunei*) (5) SAko
'Beni-komachi' (*fortunei*) (5) SAko
'Berenika' (× *bertolonii*) (7) EPot
'Berounka' (Prominent Group) (7) NMen
'Bertramka' (Holenka's Miracle Group) (× *megaseiflora*) (7) NMen
'Beryl Bland' (Sugestivo Group) (7) WAbe
'Bettina' (× *paulinae*) (7) NMen
× ***biasolettoi*** *sensu stricto* hort. see *S.* 'Phoenix'
'Birch Yellow' see *S.* 'Pseudoborisii'
'Bizourtouse' (× *luteopurpurea*) (7) **new** NSla
'Black Beauty' (15) ECtt GCrg MHer NWad
BLACK RUBY (*fortunei*) (5) Widely available
'Blackberry and Apple Pie' (*fortunei*) (5) ♀H4 CExl CRos ECtt EPfP GEdr LRHS NRHS SBch SWvt WMoo
'Blush' (*fortunei*) (5) LLHF
'Bob Hawkins' (Mossy Group) (15/v) NWad
'Bohdalec' (× *megaseiflora*) (7) NMen
'Bohemia' (7) EPot NSla
'Bohemian Karst' (Prominent Group) (7) NMen
'Bohemian Paradise' (Region Group) (7) NMen
'Bohnice' (× *megaseiflora*) (7) NMen
'Bohunka' (7) NMen
× ***borisii*** *sensu stricto* hort. see *S.* 'Sofia'
'Boston Spa' (× *elisabethae*) (7) ECtt GCrg LRHS MHer NLar NRHS NWad SPlb
'Boží Dar' (Sessile Group) (7) **new** EPot
'Brailes' (× *poluanglica*) (7) NMen
'Brian Arundel' (Magnus Group) (7) NMen
'Bridget' (× *edithae*) (7) CMea LRHS NRHS
'Brno' (× *elisabethae*) (7) EPot NMen
'Brookside' (*burseriana*) (7) EPot
'Bryn Llwyd' (Vanessa Group) (7) NMen WAbe
× ***burnatii*** (8) CRos LRHS NRHS NSla
burseriana (7) NMen WAbe
'Buster' (× *hardingii*) (7) EPot NMen
'Bychan' (*fortunei*) (5) **new** WAbe
× ***caesia*** misapplied (× *fritschiana*) see *S.* 'Krain'
× ***caesia*** L. (8) SRms WAbe
§ ***callosa*** (8) ♀H5 EDAr GKev LRHS MHer MMuc NRHS SEND WAbe
§ - subsp. ***callosa*** var. ***australis*** (8) CTal
§ - subsp. ***catalaunica*** (8) WAbe
- var. ***lantoscana*** see *S. callosa* subsp. *callosa* var. *australis*
- ***lingulata*** see *S. callosa*
'Candy Floss' (7) NMen
× ***canis-dalmatica*** see *S.* 'Canis-dalmatica'
§ 'Canis-dalmatica' (× *gaudinii*) (8) ECtt GAbr GCrg GJos GKev LRHS NRHS NWad WTor
§ 'Carmen' (× *elisabethae*) (7) WAbe
'Carniolica' (× *engleri*) (8) WAbe
§ 'Carniolica' (*paniculata*) (8) NBro NWad WOld
carolinica see *S.* 'Carniolica' (*paniculata*)

cartilaginea see *S. paniculata* subsp. *cartilaginea*
'Castor' (× *bilekii*) (7) NMen
catalaunica see *S. callosa* subsp. *catalaunica*
'Cathy Read' (× *polulacina*) (7) NMen
cebennensis (15) EPot NRya
- dwarf (15) WAbe
'Celebration' WAbe
cespitosa (15) WAbe
'Chambers' Pink Pride' see *S.* 'Miss Chambers'
'Charles Chaplin' (7) EPot NMen WAbe
'Charles Darwin' (7) NMen
CHEAP CONFECTIONS (*fortunei*) (5) ECtt GEdr IFoB LLHF MMrt MPnt NLar SBch SPoG WBor WFar WMoo WOld
CHERRY PIE (*fortunei*) (5) GEdr LLHF NHpl
'Cherrytrees' (× *boydii*) (7) NMen
'Chodov' (Holenka's Miracle Group) (× *megaseiflora*) (7) EPot NMen
cinerea (7) WAbe
- McB 1376 NWad
'Cio-Cio-San' (Vanessa Group) (7) EPot WAbe
'Circe' (5) SAko
'Citronella' (7) NMen WAbe
'Claire Felstead' (7) WAbe
* 'Clare' (*paniculata*) (8) NSla
'Clare' (× *anglica*) (7) ECtt GPSL
§ 'Clarence Elliott' (London Pride Group) (*umbrosa*) (11) ♀H5 CTri ECtt EWTr EWes GAbr GBin GCal GJos GKev GMaP LSun MHer NDov NLar NRya NWad
'Claude Monet' (Impressio Group) (7) CPBP EPot NMen WAbe
'Cleo' (× *boydii*) (7) NMen
'Cloth of Gold' (*exarata* subsp. *moschata*) (15) CRos ECha ECtt ELan EPfP GCrg GWyn LRHS MAsh NEoE NHpl NRHS NRya NWad SPlb SPoG SRms WAbe
cochlearis (8) CTri LRHS MAsh NBro NRHS NSla SBch WAbe
'Cockscomb' (*paniculata*) (8) ECtt EPot NLar NWad WAbe
columnaris × ***juniperifolia*** (7) **new** NMen
'Combrook' (× *poluanglica*) (7) NMen
'Conwy Snow' (*fortunei*) (5) ♀H4 WAbe WFar WMoo
'Conwy Star' (*fortunei*) (5) GEdr WAbe WFar
'Coolock Gem' (7) EPot NMen WAbe WHoo
'Coolock Jean' (7) WAbe
'Coolock Kate' (7) ♀H5 NSla WAbe WHoo
'Corennie Claret' see *S.* 'Glowing Ember'
'Corona' (× *boydii*) (7) NMen
* × ***correvensis*** GWyn
'Correvoniana' misapplied see *S.* 'Lagraveana'
'Correvoniana' Farrer (*paniculata*) (8) EDAr EPot MHer MMuc SEND XLum
cortusifolia (5) EBee
- var. ***stolonifera*** (5) CBct GCal XLum
COTTON CROCHET (*fortunei*) (5/d) ECtt GEdr SHeu WBor WFar WMoo WOld
cotyledon (8) CTal LRHS NRHS WAbe WCFE
cotyledon × ***cuneifolia*** (8 × 11) NSla
§ 'Cranbourne' (× *anglica*) (7) ♀H5 CMea CTal EPot GCrg LRHS MAsh NMen NRHS NSla WAbe
'Cream Seedling' (× *elisabethae*) (7) NMen

	'Crenata' (*burseriana*) (7) ♀^{H5}	CMea LRHS NRHS
	'Crimscote-love' (*poluanglica*) (7)	EPot NMen
	'Crimson Rose' (*paniculata*)	see *S.* 'Rosea' (*paniculata*)
	'Crinoline' (7)	NMen NSla WAbe
§	***crustata*** (8)	CPBP WAbe WThu XLum
	- var. ***vochinensis***	see *S. crustata*
	CRYSTAL PINK (*fortunei*) (5/v)	CBct CBod CExl EBee ECtt GEdr GPSL IFoB MBNS MHol NHpl WCot WFar
	'Crystalie' (× *biasolettoi*) (7)	LRHS NRHS
	'Cultrata' (*paniculata*) (8)	NBro
	'Cumulus' (7) ♀^{H5}	EPot NMen WAbe
§	***cuneifolia*** (11)	IMou MHer NWad WMoo XLum
	- var. ***capillipes***	see *S. cuneifolia* subsp. *cuneifolia*
§	- subsp. ***cuneifolia*** (11)	ECtt GJos
	'Cuscutiformis' (*stolonifera*) (5)	CAby CElw CExl CHid EWld GEdr MAvo MBel MMoz MSCN SBch SRms WBor WCru XLum
	dahurica	see *S. cuneifolia*
	'Dainty Dame' (× *arco-valleyi*) (7)	ECtt LRHS NRHS
	'Dana' (Prichard's Monument Group) (× *megaseiflora*) (7)	NMen
	'David' (7)	NMen
	'Dawn Frost' (7)	EPot NMen
	'Delia' (× *hornibrookii*) (7)	EPot
	'Demeter' (× *petraschii*) (7)	NMen
§	'Dentata' (London Pride Group) (× *polita*) (11)	ECha GCal MPnt WBor WMoo
	'Dentata' (× *urbium*)	see *S.* (London Pride Group) 'Dentata' (× *polita*)
I	'Diana' (× *lincolni-fosteri*) (7)	NMen
	diapensioides (7)	WAbe
	dinnikii (7)	WAbe
	'Dobruška' (× *irvingii*) (7)	NMen
	'Doctor Clay' (*paniculata*) (8)	CRos CTal ECtt EPot GCrg GKev LRHS NRHS NRya NSla SPlb WAbe
	'Doctor Ramsey' (8)	CRos EWes LRHS NRHS NWad WAbe
	'Doctor Watson' (7) **new**	EPot
	'Dolores Umbridge' (*fortunei*) (5)	SAko
	'Donald Mann' (15)	EWes
	'Donatello' (7)	NMen
	'Donnington Chalice' (7)	NMen
	'Donnington Gold' (7)	NMen
	'Dora Ross' (× *baccii*) (7)	NMen
	'Drakula' (*ferdinandi-coburgi*) (7)	CPBP LRHS NMen NRHS
	'Dulcimer' (× *petraschii*) (7)	NMen
	'Edgar Irmscher' (7)	NMen
	'Edith' (× *edithae*) (7)	CTal LRHS NMen NRHS
	'Elegance'	SAko
	'Elf' (7)	see *S.* 'Beatrix Stanley'
	'Elf' (*exarata* subsp. *moschata*) (15)	ECtt MAsh SRms
	'Elf Rose' (15)	CRos EPfP LRHS NEoE NRHS
	'Eliot Hodgkin' (× *millstreamiana*) (7)	NMen
	× ***elisabethae*** *sensu stricto* hort.	see *S.* 'Carmen'
	'Ellie Brinckerhoff' (× *hornibrookii*) (7)	WAbe
	'Elliott's Variety'	see *S.* 'Clarence Elliott' (*umbrosa*)
	'Emil Holub' (Ethography Group) (7)	EPot NMen
	'Emile Burnat' (× *burnatii*) (8) ♀^{H5}	CTal
	× ***engleri*** (8)	CTal
	epiphylla (5) BWJ 8177	WCru
§	'Ernst Heinrich' (× *heinrichii*) (7)	NMen
	'Esther' (× *burnatii*) (8)	CMea CRos ECtt GMaP LRHS NRHS WAbe WHoo
§	'Eulenspiegel' (× *geuderi*) (7)	EPot NWad
	'Eva Hanzliková' (× *izari*) (7)	EPot
	'Excellent' (Exclusive Group) (7)	EPot NSla
	'Exhibit' (Exclusive Group) (7)	NMen
	fair maids of France	see *S.* 'Flore Pleno'
	'Fairy Dust'	SAko
	'Fairy' (*exarata* subsp. *moschata*) (15)	ECtt NEoE
	'Faldonside' (× *boydii*) (7)	MAsh
	'Falstaff' (*burseriana*) (7)	NMen
	× ***farreri*** hort.	see *S.* 'Reginald Farrer'
	'Favorit' (× *bilekii*) (7)	NMen
§	***federici-augusti*** subsp. ***grisebachii*** (7) ♀^{H5}	GCrg GKev LRHS NRHS NSla WAbe
	'Felicity' (× *anglica*) (7)	NMen
	ferdinandi-coburgi (7)	ECtt WAbe
§	- subsp. ***chrysosplenifolia*** var. ***rhodopea*** (7)	LRHS NRHS
	- var. ***pravislavii***	see *S. ferdinandi-coburgi* subsp. *chrysosplenifolia* var. *rhodopea*
	- var. ***radoslavoffii***	see *S. ferdinandi-coburgi* subsp. *chrysosplenifolia* var. *rhodopea*
	ferdinandi-coburgi × ***scardica*** (7) **new**	EPot
	'Findling' (Mossy Group) (15)	ECtt EPfP GCrg NWad SPoG WAbe
	'Firebrand' (× *kochii*) (7)	WAbe
	FIVE COLOR (*fortunei*)	see *S.* 'Go-nishiki'
§	***flagellaris*** (1)	WAbe
	'Flavescens' misapplied	see *S.* 'Lutea' (*paniculata*)
	'Fleece' (15)	NHpl
§	'Flore Pleno' (*granulata*) (15/d)	CElw EWes
	'Flowers of Sulphur'	see *S.* 'Schwefelblüte'
	fortunei (5) ♀^{H4}	CMac NPnk SRms WAbe WFar
	- B&SWJ 6346	WCru
	- from John Fielding (5)	WCot
	- f. ***alpina*** from Hokkaido (5)	WCru
	- var. ***koraiensis*** (5) B&SWJ 8688	WCru
	- var. ***obtusocuneata*** (5)	GEdr GPSL LLHF WAbe
	- f. ***partita*** (5)	WCru
	- var. ***pilosissima*** (5) B&SWJ 8557	WCru
	- pink-flowered (5)	WAbe
	'Forum' (× *megaseiflora*) (7) **new**	NMen
	'Foster's Gold' (× *elisabethae*) (7)	EPot NMen
	'Four Winds' (Mossy Group) (15)	EWes SPoG
	'Francis Cade' (8)	GAbr WAbe
	'Franz Liszt' (7)	CPBP EPot NMen
	'Franzii' (× *paulinae*) (7)	NMen
	'Freckles'	GCrg GKev NHpl
	'Frederik Chopin' (7)	EPot

'Friesei' (× *salmonica*) (7) CTal NMen
'Fumiko' (*fortunei*) (5) WCru
'Funkii' (× *petraschii*) (7) NMen
'Gaiety' (15) ECtt LRHS NEoE NRHS SPoG
'Galaxie' (× *megaseiflora*) (Holenka's Miracle Group) (7) EPot NMen
'Ganymede' (*burseriana*) (7) EPot NMen
× ***gaudinii*** (8) XLum
'Gelber Findling' (7) NMen
'Gelbes Monster' (*fortunei*) (5) WCot
'Gem' (× *irvingii*) (7) CTal LRHS NRHS
'Gemma' (× *megaseiflora*) (7) LRHS NRHS
genesiana (15) EWes
'Geoff Wilson' (× *biasolettoi*) (7) EPot
'Geoffrey Gould' (7) NMen
georgei (7) EPot WAbe
'Gertie Pritchard' see *S.* 'Mrs Gertie Prichard'
× ***geuderi*** *sensu stricto* hort. see *S.* 'Eulenspiegel'
§ × ***geum*** (11) MRav WFar WMoo
- Dixter form (11) CElw ECha EWes LEdu NDov SMHy SPhx
'Gleborg' (Mossy Group) (15) SPoG
'Gloria' (*burseriana*) (7) EPot LRHS MAsh NMen NRHS NSla
§ 'Glowing Ember' (Mossy Group) (15) ECtt EWes
'Glückliches Mädchen' (*fortunei*) (5) SAko
'Gold Dust' (× *eudoxiana*) (7) GCrg NRya
'Golden Eye' (× *poluanglica*) (7) NMen
'Golden Falls' (Mossy Group) (15/v) EWes SPlb SPoG
GOLDEN PRAGUE (× *pragensis*) see *S.* 'Zlatá Praha'
§ 'Go-nishiki' (*fortunei*) (5) GEdr
'Gorges du Verdon' (8) EWTr
'Goring White' (7) NMen
'Gothenburg' (7) EPot WAbe
'Grace Farwell' (× *anglica*) (7) GAbr NLar
granulata (15) EBWF EWes GJos NMir NRHS
'Gratoides' (× *grata*) (7) NMen
'Grébovka' (× *megaseiflora*) (7) NMen
'Greensleeves' (*fortunei*) (5) LLHF
§ 'Gregor Mendel' (× *apiculata*) (7) ♀H5 CMea CRos CTal ECtt EPot LRHS NLar NRHS NSla NWad SRms WAbe WHoo
'Gregor' (× *poluanglica*) (7) NMen
grisebachii see *S. federici-augusti* subsp. *grisebachii*
'Haagii' (× *eudoxiana*) (7) CTri
'Hare Knoll Beauty' (8) CRos EPot GCrg LRHS NHpl NRHS NSla WAbe
'Harlow Car' (× *anglica*) (7) EPot NSla
'Harlow Car' (× *anglica* × ***poluniniana***) (7) NMen
'Harold Bevington' (*paniculata*) (8) CTal
'Harold Lloyd' (7) NMen
'Harry Marshall' (× *irvingii*) (7) NWad
'Harry Smith' (× *cimgani*) (7) NMen
'Harvest Moon' (*stolonifera*) (5) WBor WFar WHer
× ***heinreichii*** *sensu stricto* hort. see *S.* 'Ernst Heinrich'
'Heisel Kurenai' (*fortunei*) (5) SAko
'Henri Rousseau' (Conspecta Group) (7) NMen
'Hi-Ace' (Mossy Group) (15/v) NHpl SPlb
'Highlander Red' (Mossy Group) (15) ECtt GWyn
'Highlander White' (Mossy Group) (15) GWyn
'Hime' (*stolonifera*) (5) SRms WCru
'Hindhead Seedling' (× *boydii*) (7) CRos LRHS NMen NRHS WAbe
hirsuta (11) EHrv EWld LEdu MMuc WCot WCru
'Hirsuta' (× *geum*) see *S.* × *geum*
'Hirtella' Ingwersen (*paniculata*) (8) EPot
'Hirtifolia' (*paniculata*) (8) CTal
'His Majesty' (× *irvingii*) (7) NMen
'Hiten' (*fortunei*) (5) EBee GKev
'Holden Seedling' (Mossy Group) (15) ECtt
I 'Holden Variety' (*oppositifolia*) (7) NWad
'Honeybunch' (Safran Group) (7) NMen WAbe
'Honington' (× *poluanglica*) (7) NMen
hostii (8) EDAr GKev NWad XLum
- subsp. ***hostii*** (8) WAbe XLum
- - var. ***altissima*** (8) XLum
- subsp. ***rhaetica*** (8) NBro WThu XLum
'Hsitou Silver' (*stolonifera*) (5) WCot
'Hunscote' (× *poluanglica*) (7) NMen
§ ***hypnoides*** (15) WAbe
hypostoma (7) WAbe
'Iceland' (*oppositifolia*) (7) EWes WAbe
imparilis (5) EHrv GEdr WCru
'Ingeborg' (Mossy Group) (15) CElw ECha
iranica (7) EPot NMen
'Irena' (7) NMen
'Irene Bacci' (× *baccii*) (7) EPot NMen
'Iris Prichard' (× *hardingii*) (7) CTal NMen
× ***irvingii*** *sensu stricto* hort. see *S.* 'Walter Irving'
× ***jaccgiana*** **new** NSla
'James' (7) NMen NSla
'Jan Amos Kómenský' (× *anglica*) (7) NMen
'Jan Neruda' (× *megaseiflora*) (7) EPot NMen
'Jan Palach' (× *krausii*) (7) EPot NMen WAbe
'Jan Preisler' (Conspecta Group) (7) EPot
'Jaromir' (8) GCrg NMen
'Jaroslav Horný' (maginata) (7) NMen
'Jason' (× *elisabethae*) (7) NMen
'Jenkinsiae' (× *irvingii*) (7) CMea CTal EPot LRHS MAsh MMuc NLar NMen NRHS NSla NWad SEND WAbe

'Joachim Barrande' (× *siluris*) (7)	NMen
'Jocelynne Bacci' (7)	NMen
'Johanka' (7) **new**	NMen
§ 'Johann Kellerer' (× *kellereri*) (7)	NMen
'Johann Wolfgang Goethe' (7)	EPot
'John Byam-Grounds' (Honor Group) (7)	EPot WAbe
'John Tomlinson' (*burseriana*) (7)	NSla
'Jorg' (× *biasolettoi*) (7)	EPot
'Josef Čapek' (Holenka's Miracle Group) (× *megaseiflora*) (7)	EPot NMen
'Joy'	see *S.* 'Kaspar Maria Sternberg'
'Joy Bishop' (7)	NMen
'Joyce Carruthers' (7)	NMen
'Judith Shackleton' (× *abingdonensis*) (7)	CPBP
'Juliet'	see *S.* 'Riverslea'
§ ***juniperifolia*** (7)	CMea GCrg SRms XLum
'Jupiter' (Holenka's Miracle Group) (× *megaseiflora*) (7)	EPot NMen
× ***karacardica*** (7) **new**	NSla
karadzicensis* × *scardica (7)	EPot
'Karasin' (7)	NMen
'Karel Čapek' (Prichard's Monument Group) (× *megaseiflora*) (7)	EPot LRHS NMen NRHS WAbe
'Karlštejn' (× *borisii*) (7)	EPot NMen
§ 'Kaspar Maria Sternberg' (× *petraschii*) (7) Y^{H5}	LRHS NRHS
'Kath Dryden' (7)	ECtt ITim NMen
'Kathleen Pinsent' (8)	WAbe
'Kathleen' (× *polulacina*) (7)	EPot NMen
'Kath's Delight' (8)	GKev
'Katrin' (× *borisii*) (7)	NSla
'Kbley'	NMen
× ***kellereri*** *sensu stricto* hort.	see *S.* 'Johann Kellerer'
'Ken McGregor' (7)	NMen
'Kestoniensis' (× *salmonica*) (7)	NMen
'Kineton' (× *poluanglica*) (7)	NMen
'King Lear' (× *bursiculata*) (7)	CTal LRHS NRHS
'Kinki Purple' (*stolonifera*) (5)	EHrv EPri EShb GBin GWyn WCru WPnP
'Kirke' (7)	EPot NMen
'Klondike' (× *boydii*) (7)	EPot NMen
'Knapton Pink' (Mossy Group) (15)	ECtt EPfP NEoE SPoG WAbe
'Kokaku' (*fortunei*) (5)	LLHF
'Kon Tiki' (7)	EPot NMen
kotschyi (7)	NSla
kotschyi* × *wendelboi (7)	EPot NMen
§ 'Krain' (× *fritschiana*) (8)	WOld
'Krákatit' (Prichard's Monument Group) (× *megaseiflora*) (7)	NMen
'Krasava' (Prichard's Monument Group) (× *megaseiflora*) (7)	NMen
'Labe' (× *arco-valleyi*) (7)	CMea EPot LRHS NMen NRHS
'Lady Beatrix Stanley'	see *S.* 'Beatrix Stanley'
§ 'Lagraveana' (*paniculata*) (8) Y^{H5}	EDAr GCrg GKev LRHS NRHS
'Laka' (7)	EPot NMen
× ***landaueri*** *sensu stricto* hort.	see *S.* 'Leonore'
'Lantoscana Superba' (*callosa* subsp. *callosa* var. *australis*) (8)	WOld
'Laura Sinclair' (× *fallsvillagensis*) (7)	NMen
'Lenka' (× *byam-groundsii*) (7)	EPot NMen
'Leo Gordon Godseff' (× *elisabethae*) (7)	LRHS NRHS NSla
'Leonardo da Vinci' (7)	WAbe
§ 'Leonore' (× *landaueri*) (7)	CRos LRHS NRHS
'Letchworth Gem' (× *urbium*) (London Pride Group) (11)	GAbr GCal LRHS NRHS
'Libuse' (7)	NMen
'Lidice' (7)	EPot NMen WAbe WHoo
'Lilac Time' (× *youngiana*) (7)	EPot
lilacina (7)	NMen WAbe
'Lily Potter' (5)	SAko
'Limelight' (*callosa* subsp. *callosa* var. *australis*) (8)	NWad
'Lincoln Foster' (8)	NWad
lingulata	see *S. callosa*
'Lismore Carmine' (× *lismorensis*) (7)	EPot NMen
'Lismore Mist' (× *lismorensis*) (7)	EPot
'Lissadell' (*callosa*) (8)	GKev IFoB IRob
* 'Little Piggy' (*epiphylla*) (5)	WCru
'Lizzy' (7)	NMen
llonakhensis (1)	WAbe
'Lohmuelleri' (× *biasolettoi*) (7)	GKev
lolaensis (7)	WAbe
longifolia (8)	EPot GEdr GKev LRHS NHpl NRHS NSla
- var. ***aitanica*** (8)	WAbe
'Louis Armstrong' (Blues Group) (7)	EPot NMen WAbe
LOVE ME	see *S.* 'Miluj Mne'
lowndesii (7)	WAbe
'Loxley' (× *poluanglica*) (7)	NMen
'Lužnice' (× *poluluteopurpurea*) (7)	CTal
'Lutea' (*aizoon*)	see *S.* 'Lutea' (*paniculata*)
'Lutea' (*diapensioides*)	see *S.* 'Wilhelm Tell'
§ 'Lutea' (*paniculata*) (8)	EDAr EHoe GMaP MMuc NBro NRya NSla NWad
§ 'Luteola' (× *boydii*) (7)	NMen
macedonica	see *S. juniperifolia*
'Magna' (*burseriana*) (7)	NMen
'Maigrün' (*fortunei*) (5)	EBee SMad
'Major Lutea'	see *S.* 'Luteola'
'Mangart' (*burseriana*) (7)	NMen
'Marcela' (× *megaseiflora*) (7)	NMen
'Marco Polo' (7)	NMen
marginata (7) Y^{H5}	WAbe
- var. ***balcanica***	see *S. marginata* subsp. *marginata* var. *rocheliana*
- var. ***bubakii*** (7)	NMen NSla
- subsp. ***marginata*** var. ***boryi*** (7)	EPot LRHS NRHS WAbe
§ - - var. ***rocheliana*** (7)	LRHS NRHS

'Maria Callas' (× *poluanglica*) (7) CPBP WAbe
'Maria Luisa' (× *salmonica*) (7) NMen
'Marianna' (× *borisii*) (7) CMea
'Marie' (7) NMen
'Marilyn Monroe' (Vanessa Group) (7) WAbe
'Maroon Beauty' (*stolonifera*) (5) EBee ECtt EPPr MCot NBid NBre WCot
'Martin Luther' (Wittenberg Group) (7) **new** EPot
'Mary Golds' (Swing Group) (7) ITim NLar NMen
'Masami' (*fortunei*) (5) SAko
'Medea' (5) SAko
× ***megaseiflora*** *sensu stricto* hort. see *S.* 'Robin Hood'
'Merlin' (7) SAko
mertensiana (6) EHrv WCru WSHC
'Meteor' (7) NRya NSla
'Michelangelo' (Rutil Group) (7) NMen
'Michle' (× *megaseiflora*) (7) NMen
'Millstream Cream' (× *elisabethae*) (7) NMen
§ 'Miluj Mne' (× *poluanglica*) (7) CSma CTal WAbe WHoo
'Minor' (*cochlearis*) (8) 🏆H5 CTal GCrg LRHS NRHS NWad
'Mirko Webr' (Harmonia Group) (7) NMen
§ 'Miss Chambers' (London Pride Group) (11) ECtt EWes GCal LPla SMHy WCot WMoo WSHC
'Moderne Zeit' (5) SAko
'Mollie Broom' (7) NMen WAbe
'Molly Weasley' (5) SAko
'Momo Sekisui' (*fortunei*) (5) SAko
'Momo Tarou' (*fortunei*) (5) SAko
'Momobenkei' (*fortunei*) (5) SAko
'Mona Lisa' (× *borisii*) (7) NWad
'Monarch' (8) 🏆H5 EPot EWes GAbr GCrg GKev LRHS NHpl NRHS NWad WAbe
§ 'Mondscheinsonate' (× *boydii*) (7) NMen WAbe
'Monika' (*webrii*) (7) NMen
'Moon Beam' (× *boydilacina*) (7) NMen
'Moonlight Sonata' (× *boydii*) see *S.* 'Mondscheinsonate'
'Moonlight' (× *boydii*) see *S.* 'Sulphurea'
'Morava' (7) CPBP EPot NMen
Mossy Group pink-flowered (15) GAbr MMuc SPoG
- red-flowered (15) SPoG
- white-flowered (15) MMuc
'Mossy Triumph' see *S.* 'Triumph'
'Mother of Pearl' (× *irvingii*) (7) CMea NMen
'Mother Queen' (× *irvingii*) (7) NMen
'Mount Nachi' (*fortunei*) (5) 🏆H4 EPfP EWes GAbr GEdr GMaP LRHS NBro NHpl NRHS SPlb WAbe WFar WMoo WSpi
§ 'Mrs Gertie Prichard' (Prichard's Monument Group) (× *megaseiflora*) (7) NMen
'Mrs Helen Terry' (× *salmonica*) (7) 🏆H5 LRHS NMen NRHS
'Myra Cambria' (× *anglica*) (7) NMen NWad
'Myra' (× *anglica*) (7) NMen WHoo
'Myriad' (7) WAbe
'Myriad Seedling' (7) EPot NMen
'Naarden' (7) NMen
'Nancye' (× *goringiana*) (7) EPot
'Neride' (7) NMen
'Nicholas' (8) GKev NHpl
'Nimbus' (*iranica*) (7) NMen
'Niobe' (× *pulvilacina*) (7) EPot NMen
'Norvegica' (*cotyledon*) (8) IRob ITim
'Nottingham Gold' (× *boydii*) (7) EPot NMen NWad
§ ***obtusa*** (7) EPot MHer NMen
'Oh Yes' (*cochlearis*) (8) WAbe
'Olsany' (× *megaseiflora*) (7) NMen
'Olympus' (× *boydilacina*) (7) NMen
'Omar Khayyám' (7) EPot NMen
'Ontake-san' (5) SAko
'Opalescent' (7) NMen
'Opatov' (× *megaseiflora*) (7) NMen
oppositifolia (7) GCrg MAsh MWat NSla SPlb SRms WAbe WSHC
'Orava' (7) NMen
'Ottone Rosai' (Toscana Group) (7) NMen
'Pablo Picasso' (Conspecta Group) (7) NMen
paniculata (8) EDAr EHoe EPot GKev GMaP MHer MWat NSla SPlb SRms WAbe WHoo
- from Gorges du Verdon GKev
§ - subsp. ***cartilaginea*** (8) GCrg
- subsp. ***kolenatiana*** see *S. paniculata* subsp. *cartilaginea*
§ - var. ***minutifolia*** (8) CPBP LRHS NBro NHpl NRHS NRya NSla SPlb WAbe
§ - subsp. ***paniculata*** (8) MAsh
paradoxa (15) EPot LRHS NRHS NWad
'Parcevalis' (× *finnisiae*) (7 × 9) WAbe
'Paul Gaughin' (7) EPot
'Paul Rubens' (7) EPot WAbe
'Peach Blossom' (7) NMen
'Peach Melba' (7) 🏆H5 CPBP CSma CTal LRHS NHpl NLar NMen NRHS NSla WAbe WHoo
'Peachy Head' (7) NMen WAbe
'Pearl Rose' (× *anglica*) (7) EPot NMen
'Pearly Gates' (× *irvingii*) (7) CTal NMen
'Pearly King' (Mossy Group) (15) ECtt GMaP WAbe
'Pearly King' variegated (15/v) CBod GKev
× ***pectinata*** Schott, Nyman & Kotschy see *S.* 'Krain'
'Penelope' (× *boydilacina*) (7) CTal EPot LRHS NLar NMen NRHS NSla WHoo WThu
pensylvanica (4) CAby EBee GCal IMou
'Perikles' (7) NMen
'Peter Burrow' (× *poluanglica*) (7) EPot NMen
'Peter Pan' (Mossy Group) (15) CRos ECtt EDAr EPfP GCrg GMaP LRHS MAsh MHer NLar NRHS NWad SPoG WSHC
§ 'Phoenix' (× *biasolettoi*) (7) LRHS NRHS
'Pierantonio Micheli' (Renaissance Group) (7) NMen
'Pilatus' (× *boydii*) (7) NMen
'Pink Cloud' (*fortunei*) (5) EPri GEdr WAbe

'Pink Haze' (*fortunei*) (5) ♀H4	GEdr WAbe
'Pink Mist' (*fortunei*) (5)	GEdr WAbe WFar WMoo
'Pink Pagoda' (*nipponica*) (5)	EBee WCot WCru
'Pink Ray' (*fortunei*) (5)	LLHF
'Pink Star' (× *boydilacina*) (7)	EPot NLar NMen
'Pixie' (15)	CTal ECtt GCrg MAsh NRya NWad SPoG SRms
'Pixie Alba'	see *S.* 'White Pixie'
'Plena' (*granulata*)	see *S.* 'Flore Pleno'
'Polar Drift'	LRHS NRHS NSla WAbe
'Pollux' (× *boydii*) (7)	EPot
poluniniana × 'Winifred' (× *poluanglica*) (7)	EPot
'Pompadour' (15)	NEoE
'Popelka' (*marginata* subsp. *marginata* var. *rocheliana*) (7)	LRHS NMen NRHS
porophylla (7)	GKev
aff. ***porophylla*** (7)	EPot
'Portae' (× *fritschiana*) (8)	XLum
'Precious Piggy' (*epiphylla*) (5)	WCru
'Primulaize Salmon' (9 × 11)	GCrg WHoo
'Primuloides' (*umbrosa*) (11)	EDAr MMuc SRms SWvt
'Primuloides' variegated (*umbrosa*) (11v) **new**	SRms
'Prince Hal' (*burseriana*) (7)	EPot LRHS NRHS NSla
'Princess' (*burseriana*) (7)	LRHS NMen NRHS NSla
'Probynii' (*cochlearis*) (8)	EPot NWad WAbe
'Prometheus' (× *prossenii*) (7)	NMen
'Prosek' (× *megaseiflora*) (7) **new**	NMen
× ***prossenii*** *sensu stricto* hort.	see *S.* 'Regina'
§ 'Pseudoborisii' (× *borisii*) (7)	NMen
'Pseudo-valdensis' (*cochlearis*) (8)	WAbe
pubescens (15)	WAbe
'Punctatissima' (*paniculata*) (8)	NWad
'Pungens' (× *apiculata*) (7)	EPot
'Purple Piggy' (*epiphylla*) (5)	WCru
'Purpurea' (*fortunei*)	see *S.* 'Rubrifolia'
'Purpurea' (*marginata*) (7) **new**	NMen
'Pygmalion' (× *webrii*) (7)	NMen
'Pyramidalis' (*cotyledon*) (8)	EPfP GKev XLum
'Quarry Wood' (× *anglica*) (7)	NMen
'Rachael Young' (× *borisii*) (7)	NMen
'Rachel' (8) **new**	GKev
'Radka' (× *megaseiflora*) (7) **new**	NMen
'Rainsley Seedling' (8)	EPot GKev NBro
'Ray Woodliffe' (× *dinninaris*) (7)	WAbe
'Red Poll' (× *poluanglica*) (7)	GAbr NHpl NMen
* 'Regent'	WAbe
§ 'Regina' (× *prossenii*) (7)	NMen
§ 'Reginald Farrer' (Silver Farreri Group) (8) ♀H5	WAbe
'Rembrandt van Rijn' (7)	EPot NMen WAbe
retusa (7)	WAbe
'Rex' (*paniculata*) (8)	CMac NWad
'Risa' (5)	SAko
'River Thame' (× *polulacina*) (7)	NMen
§ 'Riverslea' (× *hornibrookii*) (7)	CPBP NMen
§ 'Robin Hood' (× *megaseiflora*) (7)	EPot NMen WHoo
'Rockrose'PBR (× *arendsii*) (15)	WTor
'Rokujō' (*fortunei*) (5) ♀H4	NEoE NLar NPnk SHeu
'Rosa Tubbs' (8)	EWTr
§ 'Rosea' (*paniculata*) (8) ♀H5	CBod GMaP GWyn MMuc NBro NRya NSla SEND SRms
'Rosemarie' (7)	NMen
'Rosina Sündermann' (× *rosinae*) (7)	LRHS NRHS
rotundifolia (12)	CElw EBee ECha MPnt
'Roztyly' (× *megaseiflora*) (7)	NMen
'Rubella' (× *irvingii*) (7)	NMen
'Rubin' (× *hornbrookii*) (7)	NMen
'Rubra' (*aizoon*)	see *S.* 'Rosea' (*paniculata*)
§ 'Rubrifolia' (*fortunei*) (5) ♀H4	CMac CSpe ECha ECtt GAbr GEdr GMcL NHpl NPnk SMad SWvt WBor WCot WCru WFar WMoo WPnP
* 'Ruby Red'	NEoE
rufescens (5) BWJ 7510	EHrv WCru
- BWJ 7684	GEdr WCru
'Rufina' (7)	NMen
'Rusalka' (× *borisii*) (7)	NMen
'Russell V. Prichard' (× *irvingii*) (7)	NMen NWad
'Ruth Draper' (*oppositifolia*) (7) ♀H5	GCrg WAbe
'Ruth McConnell' (15)	CMea
'Ruzný' (× *megaseiflora*) (7)	NMen
'Saint John's' (8)	GKev WAbe
'Saint Kilda' (*oppositifolia*) (7)	GCrg NWad
× ***salmonica*** *sensu stricto* hort.	see *S.* 'Salomonii'
'Salome' (× *lincolni-fosteri*) (7)	NMen
§ 'Salomonii' (× *salmonica*) (7)	SRms
sancta (7)	LRHS NMen NRHS SRms
- subsp. ***pseudosancta***	see *S. juniperifolia*
- - var. ***macedonica***	see *S. juniperifolia*
'Sara Sinclair' (× *arco-valleyi*) (7)	CMea
sarmentosa	see *S. stolonifera*
'Satchmo' (Blues Group) (7)	EPot NMen WAbe
'Saturn' (× *megaseiflora*) (7)	NMen
'Saxony Red'	EPfP
'Sázava' (× *poluluteopurpurea*) (7)	CTal
§ ***scardica*** (7)	EPot NBro NMen
- var. ***dalmatica***	see *S. obtusa*
§ 'Schelleri' (× *petraschii*) (7)	EPfP NMen
§ 'Schwefelblüte' (15)	GMaP LRHS NRHS
'Seissera' (*burseriana*) (7)	NMen
sempervivum (7)	NGdn WAbe
- f. ***sempervivum*** (7)	WAbe
sendaica (5)	WCru
'Seren y Gwanwyn' (*oppositifolia*) (7)	WAbe
'Setomidori' (*fortunei*) (5)	SAko
'Sherlock Holmes' (7)	CTal NMen
'Shimmy'	WAbe
'Shiranami' (*fortunei*) (5) ♀H4 **new**	WCot

§ 'Silver Cushion' (15/v)	CMea CRos CTri ELan LRHS NHpl NRHS SPlb SPoG WAbe
'Silver Edge' (× *arco-valleyi*) (7)	EPot
'Silver Hill' (*paniculata*) (8)	NSla
'Silver Maid' (× *engleri*) (8)	GCrg NSla
'Silver Mound'	see *S.* 'Silver Cushion'
'Silver Velvet' (*fortunei*) (5/v)	CSpe EBee ECtt EUJe GEdr GMcL IFoB MBNS MBel MNrw NHpl NPnk SHeu SMad WBor WCot
'Sir Douglas Haig' (15)	NWad
'Sissi' (7)	CPBP CTal EPot NMen WAbe
'Slack's Ruby Southside' (Southside Seedling Group) (8) YH5	NRHS NSla NWad
'Slack's Supreme' (8)	NSla WCot
'Slavia' (7)	NMen
'Slzy Coventry' (× *proximae*) (7)	WAbe
'Smíchov' (× *megaseiflora*) (7)	NMen
'Sněhurka' (Fenomen Group) (7)	NMen
'Snowcap' (*pubescens*) (15)	EPot NWad WAbe
'Snowflake' (Silver Farreri Group) (8) YH5	WAbe
§ 'Sofia' (× *borisii*) (7)	EPot NMen
Southside Seedling Group (8)	CMea CRos CTal EDAr EPfP EPot EWTr GAbr GKev GMaP LRHS MAsh MAvo MMuc NBro NHpl NRHS NWad SAko SEND SPoG SRms WAbe WHoo XLum
- 'Southside Star' (8) YH5	IRob NHpl WAbe
spathularis (11)	WCot WHoo
'Spinners Snow-storm' (*fortunei*) (5)	SAko
'Splendens' (*oppositifolia*) (7) YH5	EPfP GAbr GCrg MMuc NRHS SRms WAbe
'Spotted Dog'	see *S.* 'Canis-dalmatica'
'Sprite' (15)	SPoG
spruneri (7)	LRHS NRHS
'Stansfieldii' (*rosacea*) (15)	GCrg SPlb SPoG
'Starfire' (8)	GKev
'Starlight' (8)	GKev
startorii	see *S. scardica*
'Štásek' (*dinnikii*) (7)	WAbe
stellaris (4)	WAbe
stenophylla subsp. ***stenophylla***	see *S. flagellaris*
§ ***stolonifera*** (5) YH2	CRos CSpe CTsd EShb NBro NPnk SWvt WCot WFar WMoo WWtn
- large-flowered (5)	WCot WGrn
'Strawberry Melba' (7)	NMen
'Sturmiana' (*paniculata*) (8)	SRms WOld
'Sue Drew' (*fortunei*) (5) YH4	LLHF
'Sue Tubbs' (8)	EWTr GKev
'Suendermannii Major' (× *kellereri*) (7)	CRos LRHS NRHS
'Suendermannii' (× *kellereri*) (7)	CRos LRHS NMen NRHS
SUGAR PLUM FAIRY ('Toujya') (*fortunei*) (5) YH4	EBee ECtt EShb
§ 'Sulphurea' (× *boydii*) (7)	CMea CRos EPot LRHS MAsh NRHS NSla NWad WHoo
'Superba' (*callosa* subsp. *callosa* var. *australis*) (8)	NSla
'Symons-Jeunei' (8)	NWad WAbe
'Tamatsuzuri' (*fortunei*) (5)	SAko
tangutica (1) **new**	LLHF
'Tankei' (5)	SAko
'Tenerife' (Swirly Group) (7)	EPot EWes NMen WAbe
'Tetín' (Teta Group) (7)	NMen
'Thalia' (7)	NMen
'Theoden' (*oppositifolia*) (7)	CMea EWes
'Theresa Cooper' (7)	EPot
'Thór Heyerdahl' (Ocean Group) (7) **new**	EPot
tombeanensis (7)	EPot
'Torrisholme Rose' (7) **new**	EPot NMen
TOURAN DEEP RED ('Rockred') (Mossy Group) (15)	LBuc LRHS NRHS
TOURAN LARGE WHITE ('Rocklarwhi'PBR) (Mossy Group) (15)	EPfP LBuc LRHS NRHS
'Tricolor' (*stolonifera*) (5) YH2	EBak
trifurcata (15)	ECtt
'Tristan' (*stribrnyi*)	WAbe
§ 'Triumph' (× *arendsii*) (15)	CBod ECtt EPfP GMaP MAsh NEgg SPoG
'Tully' (× *elisabethae*) (7)	NMen
'Tumbling Waters' (8) YH5	CRos EPot LRHS MRav NHpl NPnk NRHS NSla NWad WAbe
§ 'Tvoje Píseň' (× *poluanglica*) (7)	CTal WHoo WThu
§ 'Tvůj Úsměv' (× *poluanglica*) (7) YH5	NHpl
§ 'Tvůj Úspěch' (× *poluanglica*) (7)	EPot NMen NWad
'Tycho Brahe' (× *doerfleri*) (7)	WAbe
'Tysoe' (7)	EPot
'Tysoe Pink-Perfection' (Blues Group) (7) **new**	NSla
'Tysoe Splendour' (Blues Group) (7) **new**	NSla
umbrosa (11)	CMac EDAr ESps GAbr LEdu LRHS LSun MMuc MRav NRHS SBod SCob SEND SPlb SPoG SRms SWvt WFar WMoo XLum
* - ***subinteger***	MMuc
× ***urbium*** (11) YH5	CBod CTri ELan EPfP EWTr GMaP IRob LEdu LRHS MBel MCot NRHS NSti SPer SRms WBor WCAu WHoo WSpi WTor
'Vaccariana' (*oppositifolia*) (7)	EPot SHar
'Václav Hollar' (× *gusmusii*) (7)	NMen
'Vahlii' (× *smithii*) (7)	NMen
'Valborg'	see *S.* 'Cranbourne'
'Valentine'	see *S.* 'Cranbourne'
'Valerie Keevil' (× *anglica*) (7)	NMen
I 'Variegata' (*cuneifolia*) (11/v)	CBod ECtt EPfP ESps LRHS NHpl NRHS NRya NWad SPlb SPoG WHoo WMoo
I 'Variegata' (*exarata* subsp. *moschata*) (15/v)	GMaP
'Variegata' (*umbrosa*)	see *S.* 'Aureopunctata'
I 'Variegata' (× *urbium*) (11/v)	CBod EBee EPfP GPSL LRHS MBel MSpe NLar NRHS SBod SCob SMad SRms WHoo WTor
'Večerní Hvezda' (7)	CPBP WAbe
veitchiana (5)	NBro XLum
'Vesna' (× *borisii*) (7)	NMen
'Vikos Gold' (7)	NMen

'Vincent van Gogh' (× *borisii*) (7)	EPot NMen
virginiensis (4) new	EWTr
'Vítkov' (× *megaseiflora*) (7)	NMen
'Vladana' (× *megaseiflora*) (7)	CMea EPot LRHS NMen NRHS NSla
'Vlasta' (7)	NMen
'Wada' (*fortunei*) (5)	CAby CBod CSpe ECtt ELon EPri GKev GMaP LRHS MBel MNrw MSpe NRHS SRms WAul WBor WCot WFar WOld WSHC WWtn
'Walpole's Variety' (8)	NWad
'Walter Ingwersen' (*umbrosa*) (11)	SRms
§ 'Walter Irving' (× *irvingii*) (7) ♀^{H5}	NSla WAbe
'Walton' (× *poluanglica*) (7)	NMen
'Wasperton' (× *poluanglica*) (7)	NMen
'Welsh Dragon' (15)	WAbe
'Welsh Red' (15)	WAbe
'Welsh Rose' (15)	WAbe
wendelboi (7)	CTal EPot NMen WThu
'Wendrush' (× *wendelacina*) (7)	NMen
'Wendy' (× *wendelacina*) (7)	NMen
'Wetterhorn' (*oppositifolia*) (7)	GCrg
'Whatcote' (7)	NMen
'Wheatley Lion' (× *borisii*) (7)	NMen
'Wheatley Rose' (7)	CRos LRHS NRHS
'White Cap' (× *boydii*) (7)	NMen
'White Delight' (× *megaseiflora*) (7)	LRHS NRHS NSla
'White Imp' (7)	NMen
§ 'White Pixie' (15)	ECtt EDAr EPfP GCrg MAsh MHer NEoE NRya NWad SPlb SPoG SRms
'White Star' (*fortunei*) (5)	CRos LLHF LRHS NMen NRHS
'White Star' (× *petraschii*)	see *S.* 'Schelleri'
'Whitehill' (8) ♀^{H5}	CMea CRos ELan EPot GMaP LRHS NRHS NRya NSla NWad SBch WHoo WRHF
§ 'Wilhelm Tell' (× *malbyana*) (7)	NMen
'William Boyd' (× *boydii*) (7)	NMen WAbe
'William Shakespeare' (Blues Group) (7)	CPBP EPot NMen WAbe
'Winifred Bevington' (8 × 11)	CRos CSma CTal EDAr GCrg GMaP LRHS NBro NHpl NLar NRHS NRya NWad SBch SRms WAbe WHoo WOld WRHF WTor
'Winifred' (× *anglica*) (7)	CTal EPot NMen WAbe
'Winston Churchill' (15)	CRos LRHS NEoE NRHS NWad
WINTER FIRE	see *S.* 'Winterfeuer'
§ 'Winterfeuer' (*callosa*) (8)	ECtt
'Winton' (× *paulinae*) (7)	EPot NMen
'Wisley' (*federici-augusti* subsp. *grisebachii*) (7) ♀^{H5}	GKev
'Yellow Rock' (7)	NMen NRya
YOUR GOOD FORTUNE	see *S.* 'Tvůj Úspěch'
YOUR SMILE	see *S.* 'Tvůj Úsměv'
YOUR SONG	see *S.* 'Tvoje Píseň'
YOUR SUCCESS	see *S.* 'Tvůj Úspěch'
'Yunagi' (*fortunei*) (5)	SAko WOld
'Zbraslav' (× *megaseiflora*) (7)	NMen
'Ziva' (7)	NMen
§ 'Zlatá Praha' (× *pragensis*) (7)	NMen WAbe
'Zlatý Kůň' (× *laeviformis*) (7)	EPot

Scabiosa (*Caprifoliaceae*)

africana	CElw EWes
- 'Jocelyn'	EWes SHar
alpina L.	see *Cephalaria alpina*
argentea	EWes WPGP
- PAB 1229	LEdu
atropurpurea	CRav LCro LOPS SPav
- 'Ace of Spades'	ELan EPfP SCob SPav SPhx
- 'Beaujolais Bonnets'	EAJP EPed EPfP LRHS NGBl NRHS SPer WHar
- 'Black Knight'	CSpe LCro LOPS SPav
- 'Blue Beau'	LRHS NRHS
- 'Chat Noir'	CRav
§ - 'Chile Black'	CAby CBcs CPla EAJP EHoe ELan EPfP EUJe EWTr EWes GWyn IBoy LRHS NRHS SCob SPav SPer SPoG SRkn SWvt WHar
§ - 'Chilli Pepper'	LRHS
- 'Derry's Black'	CSpe SPtp
- 'Fata Morgana'	LCro SPav
- 'Fire King'	LCro
- 'Snowmaiden'	SPav
- tall double mixed (d) new	CRav
banatica	see *S. columbaria*
'Barocca'	CNor CSpe EPfP LRHS NRHS SRms WCot
'Black PomPom'	CSpe NLar
'Blackberry Fool' (Dessert Series)	EPfP
'Blue Diamonds'	EBee GJos IBoy LRHS MHol NRHS WFar WHar
'Blueberry Muffin' (Dessert Series)	WHlf
BURGUNDY BONNETS ('Scabon'^{PBR})	CBod EPfP LCro LOPS
§ 'Butterfly Blue'	Widely available
'Cambridge Blue'	EPfP
caucasica	CMac EPfP GKev LEdu LRHS NRHS XSen
- var. ***alba***	CBcs EPfP ILea NGBl WHoo
- 'Blauer Atlas'	NDov
- 'Blausiegel'	CBod MRav MWat
- 'Clive Greaves' ♀^{H4}	CBod EBee ECha ELon GMaP IBoy LRHS LSun MBNS MSpe NDov NRHS SCob SGbt SPad SPer SPoG SRms SWvt WCAu WFar WHil WTor
- 'Deep Waters'	CSpe LRHS
- 'Fama'	CSpe MSpe NGBl NLar SPlb SRms WFar WHoo
- 'Fama Deep Blue'	LRHS NRHS
- 'Fama White'	LRHS NRHS
- 'Goldingensis'	NGdn WHil
- House's hybrids	CSBt MHol NGdn SRms
- 'Isaac House'	WFar XLum
- 'Kompliment'	NDov WFar
- 'Miss Willmott' ♀^{H4}	CBod CMac CSam EBee ECha ECtt EHoe EHrv GBin IBoy IRob LRHS MArl MRav MSpe MWat NDov NLar NRHS SGbt SPer SPoG SWvt WCAu
- Perfecta Series	GBin GMcL ILea LRHS NGdn NLar NRHS SPoG WHar
- - 'Perfecta Alba'	CDor CRav ELan ELon EPfP GBin GMaP LRHS MBel MHer MHol NLar NRHS SCob SPad SPer SPoG WArt WCAu WHar XLum XSen
- - 'Perfecta Blue'	CDor CMac CRav ELan ELon EPfP GMaP MBel MHer MHol WCot XLum

- - 'Perfecta Lilac Blue'	EPfP SPer
- 'Stäfa'	EBee ECha IRob LRHS MWat NDov NEgg NLar NRHS SPoG WHoo
- 'Thorp's Variegated' (v)	WCot
'Cherry Pie' (Dessert Series)	WHlf
'Chile Black'	see *S. atropurpurea* 'Chile Black'
'Chile Pepper'	see *S. atropurpurea* 'Chilli Pepper'
cinerea	SPhx
§ ***columbaria***	CFis CHab CWld EBWF EBee LRHS NEgg NMir NRHS SPhx WArt WHer WSFF
* - ***alpina***	GKev
- 'Blue Note'[PBR]	CBod EBee MHol NPri
- blue-flowered	NHpl
- FLUTTER DEEP BLUE ('Balfluttdelu') **new**	MHol
- FLUTTER ROSE PINK ('Balfluttropi') **new**	CBod MHol
- 'Mariposa Blue'[PBR]	CBod LRHS MHol NPri
- 'Misty Butterflies'	CAby ECtt EPfP GJos MHol NCou NEgg NGdn NLar SRms WFar
- 'Nana'	EBee EPfP GWyn LRHS NGdn NLar NRHS SBch WCFE XLum
§ - subsp. ***ochroleuca***	CDor CKno CSpe ECha EHrv LRHS MBel MCot MSpe NGBl NLar NRHS SCob SHar SPhx SPoG SRms SSut WBrk WCAu
- - MESE 344	EBee
- - 'Moon Dance'	CDor CMea CSam GBin GPSL LLHF LRHS LSun MSpe MTis NLar NRHS SAko SGbt WCot WHoo
- - 'Pixie Yellow'	LRHS NRHS
- 'Pincushion Blue'	EDAr LRHS NRHS
- 'Pincushion Pink'	EDAr GJos GWyn LRHS NGdn NRHS
- pink-flowered	MMuc
cretica	XLum
drakensbergensis	CHid ELan EWTr EWes GBin GKev ILea LRHS SLon WCot WPtf
gigantea	see *Cephalaria gigantea*
graminifolia	GKev LRHS NRHS SBch SPhx SRms XLum
- ***rosea***	EWes
'Helen Dillon'	ECre EWes
incisa	CPla WHlf WOut
- 'Kudo' **new**	CBWd CKno MHol NSti SPad SPoG
'Irish Perpetual Flowering'	see *S.* 'Butterfly Blue'
japonica var. ***acutiloba***	SPhx
- var. ***alpina***	EBee EPfP GKev MMuc NGdn SEND SPhx WCot WHoo XLum
- - 'Blue Star'	EBee NBre SGbt
- - 'Ritz Blue'	CMea EPfP
lachnophylla	GCal SPhx WCot
- 'Blue Horizon'	EBee WArt
'Little Cracker'	LRHS LSou SCob SLon
'Little Emily'	ELon LSou
lucida	EPfP IPot LRHS MMuc MRav NRHS SEND WCAu XLum
MAGIC ('Pmoore02')	EBee LCro LSou
'Midnight'	CMea
'Miss Havisham'	CElw EWes MNrw
montana Mill.	see *Knautia arvensis*
ochroleuca	see *S. columbaria* subsp. *ochroleuca*
parnassi	see *Pterocephalus perennis*
'Perpetual Flowering'	see *S.* 'Butterfly Blue'
PINK BUTTONS ('Walminipink')	CBod MBel
'Pink Diamonds'	EBee ELan EPfP MHol WFar WHar
'Pink Mist'[PBR]	CBod CRos EBee ECtt ELan EPfP GBin IBoy LRHS MAsh NDov NHpl NLar NRHS SCob SCoo SPer SPoG SRms WTor
'Plum Pudding' (Dessert Series)	WHlf
pterocephala	see *Pterocephalus perennis*
'Raspberry Sorbet' (Dessert Series)	WHlf
rhodopensis	EBee
'Ritz Pink' **new**	NRHS
'Rosie's Pink'	ECtt
rumelica	see *Knautia macedonica*
'Satchmo'	see *S. atropurpurea* 'Chile Black'
stellata	SPhx
'Strawberry Parfait' (Dessert Series)	EPfP WHlf
succisa	see *Succisa pratensis*
tatarica	see *Cephalaria gigantea*
'Vivid Violet'	CAbb CDor CSpe EBee ECtt LBuc LRHS LSRN LSou MHol MMuc MNrw NDov NHpl NLar NRHS SAko WBrk WCot

Scadoxus ✿ (*Amaryllidaceae*)

membranaceus	WCot
multiflorus	CCCN GKev LAma SDeJ SDir
§ - subsp. ***katherinae*** [H1b]	CPne WCot
§ - subsp. ***multiflorus***	WCot
natalensis	see *S. puniceus*
§ ***puniceus***	CPne WCot

Scaevola (*Goodeniaceae*)

aemula 'Blue Fan'	see *S. aemula* 'Blue Wonder'
- BLUE PRINT ('Kingscablin'[PBR])	LSou
§ - 'Blue Wonder'[PBR]	NPer SWvt
- WHITE WONDER ('Scax0226')	CRav
- 'Zig Zag'[PBR]	CCCN
BLAUER FACHER ('Saphira'[PBR])	CCCN NLar
'Dream Blue' **new**	LSou
'Mini Blue'	CCCN
'Topaz Pink'	LSou

Sceletium (*Aizoaceae*)

tortuosum	SPlb

Schefflera ✿ (*Araliaceae*)

alpina	CFil
- B&SWJ 8247	WCru
- B&SWJ 11827	WCru
- HWJ 936	WCru
- NJM 09.140	WPGP
- NJM 09.157	WPGP
- large-leaved WWJ 11999	WCru
arboricola [H1c]	SEND XBlo
- 'Gold Capella' [H1c]	SEND XBlo
- 'Kalahari'	XBlo
brevipedicellata HWJ 870	WCru
- KWJ 12224	WCru
§ ***chapana*** B&SWJ 11833	WCru
- B&SWJ 11848	WCru
- HWJ 983	WCru
delavayi	CFil CPne WCru WPGP
enneaphylla HWJ 1018	WCru
fantsipanensis	CFil
- B&SWJ 11666	WCru
- B&SWJ 11671	WCru
- NJM 10.137	WPGP
gracilis HWJ 622	WCru

- HWJ 878	WCru
- NJM 10.102 **new**	WPGP
gracilis × taiwaniana	WCru
hoi B&SWJ 11747	WCru
kornasii B&SWJ 11830	WCru
- HWJ 918	WCru
macrophylla B&SWJ 8210	WCru
- B&SWJ 9788	WCru
- B&SWJ 11842	WCru
- PAB 2788	LEdu
- WWJ 11681	WCru
microphylla B&SWJ 3872	WCru
multinervia B&SWJ 11727	WCru
aff. ***myriocarpa*** B&SWJ 11828	WCru
nova NJM 13.128 **new**	WPGP
rhododendrifolia	CBct CExl CFil WPGP
- GWJ 9375	WCru
shweliensis PAB 13.216	LEdu
taiwaniana 🏆^{H4}	CBct CFil CPne WPGP
- B&SWJ 3575	WCru
- B&SWJ 3788 **new**	WCru
- B&SWJ 7096	WCru
- RWJ 10000	WCru
- RWJ 10016	WCru
vietnamensis	see *S. chapana*

Schima (*Theaceae*)

argentea	CBcs CCCN CExl EPfP WPGP
aff. ***argentea*** NJM 13.042 **new**	WPGP
khasiana	WPGP
- PAB 3447	EBee LEdu
wallichii	CBcs CExl

Schinus (*Anacardiaceae*)

lentiscifolius	SPlb SVen
molle	SPlb
montanus	SPlb
polygamus	MGil SPlb

Schisandra (*Schisandraceae*)

arisanensis	EBee MBlu NLar WPGP
- B&SWJ 3050	WCru
chinensis	CAgr CBcs CRHN GKev GPoy LEdu MSwo NLar SBrt
- B&SWJ 4204	WCru
- B&SWJ 4611A	WCru
- B&SWJ 4611B	WCru
- 'Bere'	LEdu WPGP
- 'Sadova No.1'	ETho
grandiflora 🏆^{H5}	CBcs CBot CWCL EBee ELan EPfP GBin IMou LRHS MBlu SBrt SNig SPer
- B&SWJ 2245	WCru WSHC
- PAB 3673	LEdu
- WJC 13666 **new**	WCru
- var. *cathayensis*	see *S. sphaerandra*
- 'Jamu' (m)	WCru
- 'Lahlu' (f/F)	WCru
aff. ***grandiflora*** WJC 13817 **new**	WCru
grandiflora × rubriflora	MMuc WCru
henryi subsp. ***yunnanensis*** B&SWJ 6546	WCru
incarnata BWJ 7898	WCru
incarnata × rubriflora	WCru
lancifolia	MBlu
nigra	see *S. repanda*
perulata FMWJ 13100	WCru
aff. ***plena*** HWJ 664	WCru
propinqua	WSHC
- subsp. ***sinensis***	CBot CMac CRHN LEdu NLar WPGP
- - BWJ 8148	WCru
§ ***repanda*** B&SWJ 5897	WCru
- B&SWJ 11455	WCru
rubriflora 🏆^{H5}	CBcs CTri EPfP ETho IMou LRHS MBlu MGos NLar SBrt SLon SPoG WCFE
- BWJ 7557	WCru
- (f)	WSHC WSpi
- 'Bodnant Redberry' (f)	WCru
§ ***sphaerandra***	MBlu
- BWJ 7739	WCru
- BWJ 8082	WCru
sphenanthera	EBee LRHS MBlu NLar WSHC
- BWJ 8151	WCru

Schizachyrium (*Poaceae*)

§ ***scoparium***	CBWd CBod CKno EBee EHoe EPfP LRHS NRHS XLum
- 'Blue Heaven'	CKno ELon IPot NDov
- 'Prairie Blues'	CBod CSpe ELon EPfP LRHS NRHS WCot

Schizocarphus (*Asparagaceae*)

nervosus	WCot

Schizocodon see *Shortia*

Schizophragma (*Hydrangeaceae*)

corylifolium	NLar
§ ***fauriei***	NLar
- B&SWJ 1701	WCru
- B&SWJ 6831	WCru
- B&SWJ 7052	WCru
- CWJ 12405	WCru
- CWJ 12433	WCru
hydrangeoides	CBcs CCCN CDul CRHN CRos EBee ELan EPfP GKin LCro LOPS LRHS MBlu MGos NRHS SGol SLim SLon SPer SWvt WCFE WSpi
- 'Brookside Littleleaf'	see *Hydrangea anomala* subsp. *petiolaris* var. *cordifolia* 'Brookside Littleleaf'
- var. ***concolor*** B&SWJ 5954	WCru
- - 'Moonlight' 🏆^{H5}	CBcs CDul CKel CMac CWGN ELan EPfP LEdu LRHS MBlu MGil MGos MMuc NLar NRHS SGol SLon SPer SPoG SWvt WCru WPGP
- var. ***hydrangeoides*** B&SWJ 5489	WCru
- - B&SWJ 5732	WCru
- - 'Iwa Garami'	NLar
- - 'Roseum' 🏆^{H5}	CArg CBcs CDul CMac ELan EPfP EWes IArd LRHS MBlu MGil MGos NLar SGol SLon SPer SWvt WCru WPGP
* - f. ***quelpartensis***	LRHS
- 'Rose Sensation'	CCCN EPfP LRHS NRHS SGol SLon SPoG
- var. ***taquetii*** B&SWJ 8771	WCru
- - 'Cheju's Early'	WCru
- var. ***ullungdoense*** B&SWJ 8505	WCru
- - B&SWJ 8522	WCru
- var. ***yakushimense*** B&SWJ 6119	WCru

integrifolium ♀H5	CBcs CBot CCCN CDul CRHN ELan EPfP LRHS MBlu MMuc NLar SPer WKif WPGP
- BWJ 8150	WCru
molle HWJ 1011	WCru
- WWJ 11905	WCru

Schizostylis see *Hesperantha*

Schoenoplectus (*Cyperaceae*)

§ ***lacustris***	CWat LLWG MMuc MSKA MWts
§ - subsp. ***tabernaemontani***	CSpe LLWG
- - 'Albescens' (v)	CBen CWat MMuc MNrw MSKA MWts WHal WWtn XLum
- - 'Zebrinus' (v)	CBen CWat ELan MNrw MSKA NPla SPlb WMAq WWtn XLum

Schoenoxiphium (*Cyperaceae*)

lanceum	XBlo

Schoenus (*Cyperaceae*)

nigricans new	EBWF
pauciflorus	LLWG WMoo

Sciadopitys (*Sciadopityaceae*)

verticillata ♀H6	CAco CDul CKen CMac CPne EPfP GKin LRHS MBlu MGil MGos MMuc MPkF NRHS SAko SArc SCoo SEND SLim SMad SPoG SWvt WHar
- 'Beauty Green'	NLar
- 'Dutch Mill' new	NLar
- 'Firework'	CKen
- 'Globe'	CKen
- 'Gold Star'	CKen
- 'Golden Rush'	CKen MAsh
- 'Goldmahne'	CKen
- 'Grüne Kugel'	CKen MAsh NLar
- 'Jeddeloh Compact'	CKen
- 'Koja Maki'	NLar
- 'Kugelblitz'	NLar
- 'Kupferschirm'	CKen
- 'Mecki'	CKen
- 'Megaschirm'	CKen
- 'Ossorio Gold'	CKen NLar
- 'Perlenglanz'	CKen NLar
- 'Picola'	CKen MAsh NLar
- 'Pygmy'	CKen
- 'Richie's Cream'	CKen
- 'Richie's Cushion'	CKen
- 'Shorty'	CKen
- 'Speerspitze'	CKen
- 'Star Wars'	CKen
- 'Starburst'	CKen
- 'Sternschnuppe'	CKen MAsh NLar
- 'Tsai Cheng'	NLar
- 'Wiels Beauty'	NLar
- 'Wintergreen'	CKen

Scilla (*Asparagaceae*)

adlamii	see *Ledebouria cooperi*
× ***allenii***	see × *Chionoscilla allenii*
amethystina	see *S. litardierei*
amoena	GKev
autumnalis	CAvo CPla EBWF EPot GKev LAma LLHF LRHS NRHS NRog WShi WThu
- white-flowered	NRog
bifolia ♀H5	CAvo CTca EPot GKev LAma SDeJ SPhx WShi
- 'Alba'	GKev SPhx
- 'Rosea'	ERCP GKev LAma LRHS NRHS SDeJ
bithynica ♀H5	EPot GKev WCot WShi
I - 'Alba'	CAvo
campanulata	see *Hyacinthoides hispanica*
chinensis	see *S. scilloides*
cilicica	CAvo
greilhuberi	EPPr EPri LLHF SBch WCot
hohenackeri	GKev LLHF SPhx WCot WThu
- BSBE 811	WCot
§ ***hughii***	EBee
hyacinthoides	EBee ERCP GKev SDir WCot
ingridiae	GKev
- var. ***taurica***	GKev
italica	see *Hyacinthoides italica*
japonica	see *S. scilloides*
latifolia	WCot
liliohyacinthus	CAvo CBro GKev IBlr WShi
- 'Alba'	CAvo
lingulata	see *Hyacinthoides lingulata*
§ ***litardierei*** ♀H5	EPPr EPfP EPot EPri ERCP GKev LAma MMuc SDeJ SEND SPhx WShi
lutea hort.	see *Ledebouria socialis*
madeirensis	WCot
- from Madeira	CHll
melaina	GKev WCot
mesopotamica	GKev
messeniaca	GKev
- MS 38 from Greece	WCot
mischtschenkoana ♀H5	CAby CAvo CHid EPot IFro IRob LAma LCro LOPS LRHS NRHS SDeJ SDir WShi
§ - 'Tubergeniana' ♀H5	CMea GKev SPhx WCot
monophyllos	GKev WArt WCot
morrisii	GKev
natalensis	see *Merwilla plumbea*
non-scripta	see *Hyacinthoides non-scripta*
nutans	see *Hyacinthoides non-scripta*
obtusifolia subsp. ***intermedia***	WCot
persica ♀H4	GKev WCot
peruviana	Widely available
- SB&L 20/1	WCot
- 'Alba'	CBro CTal CTca CWCL EPot EPri EWes NHpl WCot XLum
- Carribean Jewels Series new	CBod
- 'Hughii'	see *S. hughii*
- var. ***venusta*** S&L 311/2	WCot
- 'White Moon'	ERCP GKev
pratensis	see *S. litardierei*
ramburei	GKev
rosenii	CWCL
- 'Cloudy Sky'	WCot
§ ***scilloides***	NRog
- B&SWJ 8812	WCru
* - 'Alba'	SDeJ
siberica ♀H5	CAby CAvo CPla CRos CTca ELan EPfP EShb GKev LAma LCro LOPS LRHS MMuc MWat NGBl NRHS SCob SDir SPer SPhx WBor WShi
- 'Alba'	EPfP EPot GKev LAma LRHS NRHS SDeJ WArt WShi
- subsp. ***armena***	GKev
- 'Enem'	GKev
- 'Spring Beauty'	CMea EPot ERCP GKev LAma LRHS NRHS SDeJ SPhx SRms
'Tubergeniana'	see *S. mischtschenkoana* 'Tubergeniana'
verna	EBWF GKev WShi WThu
vicentina	see *Hyacinthoides vincentina*
violacea	see *Ledebouria socialis*

Scirpoides (*Cyperaceae*)

§ ***holoschoenus***	EBWF

Scirpus (*Cyperaceae*)

cernuus	see *Isolepis cernua*
'Green Mist'	WCot
holoschoenus	see *Scirpoides holoschoenus*
lacustris	see *Schoenoplectus lacustris*
- 'Spiralis'	see *Juncus effusus* f. *spiralis*
maritimus	see *Bolboschoenus maritimus*
tabernaemontani	see *Schoenoplectus lacustris* subsp. *tabernaemontani*

Scleranthus (*Caryophyllaceae*)

biflorus	CPla CSma EDAr EWes GBin LEdu LRHS MAsh NRHS SPlb XLum
uncinatus new	EUJe
uniflorus	CPla EPot EUJe LEdu NHpl SMad SPlb SRot XLum
- 'Selected Bronze'	SMad

Sclerochiton (*Acanthaceae*)

harveyanus	EShb

Scoliopus (*Liliaceae*)

bigelowii	CAby GCal
hallii	CTal GBin LEdu MNrw

Scolopendrium see *Asplenium*

Scopolia (*Solanaceae*)

anomala HWJK 2252	WCru
- PAB 4925 new	LEdu
carniolica	CAvo EBee EPPr EWld GBin GPoy ILea LEdu MPhe NChi NLar NSti SPlb WCru WPGP WSHC XLum
- from Poland	LEdu
§ - var. ***brevifolia***	EBee EHrv EPPr EPfP EWld LEdu LRHS MNrw NRHS SPhx WCot WPGP
- - WM 9811	MPhe
- 'Zwanenburg'	EHrv EPPr EWes LEdu NLar SPhx WPGP WSHC XLum
hladnikiana	see *S. carniolica* var. *brevifolia*

Scorzonera (*Asteraceae*)

hispanica	SVic

Scrophularia (*Scrophulariaceae*)

aquatica misapplied	see *S. auriculata*
§ ***auriculata***	CHab EBWF LLWG NMir NPer WHer
§ - 'Variegata' (v)	CAby CBcs ECha EHoe ELan EPfP GCal GLog LLWG LRHS MHer NRHS SHar SPer
buergeriana 'Lemon and Lime' misapplied	see *Teucrium viscidum* 'Lemon and Lime'
- 'Lemon and Lime' (v)	EBee NEgg
macrantha	GJos SPhx
nodosa	EBWF GPoy NMir WHer
- ***variegata***	see *S. auriculata* 'Variegata'
vernalis	CBgR

Scutellaria (*Lamiaceae*)

albida	EBee
§ ***alpina***	GJos SPlb SRms SRot
- 'Arcobaleno'	LLHF
altissima	CFis CPla ECha ELan ELon GPSL MMuc MSpe NBro SPlb WPtf WWtn XSen
'Amazing Grace'	EWes
baicalensis	GJos GPoy
canescens	see *S. incana*
costaricana	CCCN
diffusa	SBch
galericulata	CBod CHab EBWF ENfk GPoy LLWG MHer SPhx WHer
hastata	see *S. hastifolia*
§ ***hastifolia***	CTri ECtt
§ ***incana***	ELan ELon IPot LCro LOPS LRHS MAvo MHol MPie NRHS SPhx WCot
indica var. ***japonica***	see *S. indica* var. *parvifolia*
§ - var. ***parvifolia***	EWes GJos GMaP ITim SRot WAbe
- - 'Alba'	LLHF WAbe
lateriflora	GJos GPoy SRms XAbr
- PAB 3921	LEdu
maekawae	EBee
- B&SWJ 557A	WCru
minor	EBWF
orientalis	ECtt WAbe
- subsp. ***bicolor***	ECtt
pontica	SPhx
red-flowered new	CCCN
scordiifolia	CFis ECha NRya NWad SRms WFar
- 'Seoul Sapphire'	CSpe LEdu SPtp WPGP WPtf
sevanensis	WCot
'Sherbert Lemon'	CMea MCot WTor
suffrutescens	EBee GJos XSen
- 'Texas Rose'	CMea CSpe GJos LLHF MCot NHpl SBch SRot WAbe WHoo WTor
supina	see *S. alpina*
tournefortii	EBee ECtt LRHS NRHS WOut
* ***zhongdianensis***	WPtf

seakale see *Crambe maritima*

Sebaea (*Gentianaceae*)

rehmanii	SPlb
thomasii	WAbe
- 'Bychan'	WAbe

Securigera (*Papilionaceae*)

§ ***varia***	CDor GJos LEdu MMuc SEND SRms XLum

Sedastrum see *Sedum*

× *Sedeveria* (*Crassulaceae*)

'Harry Butterfield'	WCot
'Letizia'	SChr

Sedum ✿ (*Crassulaceae*)

'Abbey Dore'	CBod ECtt ELan ELon EPfP LRHS LSou MSCN MTis SPhx WCAu WHar
acre	CRos CTri EBWF EPfP ESps GPoy LEdu LRHS MNHC NMir NRHS SCob SPlb XLum
- 'Aureum'	EDAr EHoe ELan EPfP NHpl NLar NRya SCob SPoG SRms WCot XLum
- 'Elegans'	ECtt GCrg
- 'Golden Queen'	CRos LRHS MSCN NRHS SPlb SPoG SRms
- 'Helvetica'	WCot
- 'Minus'	CRos LRHS NRHS SRms
§ - subsp. ***neglectum*** var. ***majus***	EPfP NLar
- 'Oktoberfest'	GJos
aizoon	CPla GCal NBre SPlb WFar XLum
- 'Aurantiacum'	see *S. aizoon* 'Euphorbioides'

§	- 'Euphorbioides'	ECha ECtt ELan MHer MMuc MRav NLar SEND SPer SPlb
§	- subsp. ***maximowiczii***	NWad
	alatum	WFar
	albescens	see *S. forsterianum* f. *purpureum*
	alboroseum	see *S. erythrostictum*
§	***album***	CRos EBWF GJos LRHS MMuc NBro NMir NRHS SEND SRms XLum
	- 'Coral Carpet'	ECtt EDAr EPPr EPfP GCrg GJos GKev GWyn MRav NHpl NLar NRya SBod SPoG XLum
	- subsp. ***teretifolium*** var. ***micranthum*** 'Chloroticum'	XLum
§	- - var. ***murale***	CTri LRHS NHpl NRHS XLum
	alpestre	XLum
	altissimum	see *S. sediforme*
*	***altum***	NBre SRms
	AMBER ('Florseamb')	EBee WCot
	anacampseros	GQue MHer MMuc NWad SEND XLum
	anglicum	EBWF
	'Aquarel'	GBin GWyn
	athoum	see *S. album*
	'Autumn Charm'	see *S.* (Herbstfreude Group) 'Lajos'
	'Autumn Delight' **new**	MAvo
	AUTUMN JOY	see *S.* (Herbstfreude Group) 'Herbstfreude'
	beauverdii	WCru
	subsp. ***vietnamense*** HWJ 824	
	'Bertram Anderson' ♀H7	Widely available
	beyrichianum misapplied	see *S. glaucophyllum*
	'Birthday Party' (Birthday Party Series)	EBee SPoG
	BLACK BEAUTY ('Florseblab')	ECtt LRHS MNrw NDov NLar NRHS
	'Blade Runner'	LRHS LSou
	'Blue Pearl' (SunSparkler Series)	CAbb EBee LCro LOPS LRHS SPoG WHil
	brevifolium	EWes
	burrito	EShb
	'Carl' ♀H7	Widely available
	cauticola ♀H5	EDAr EPot GCal MAvo MMuc MRav NWad SRms SRot WAbe XLum
	- 'Coca-Cola'	CBod CMac CWGN ECtt EHoe GBin GJos GMcL GWyn LRHS MAvo MCot MRav NDov NHpl NRHS NWad SPhx SPoG SWvt WHoo
	- 'Lidakense' ♀H5	CMea CSpe CTal CTri ECha ECtt EPot GBin GCrg MHer NLar NRHS NWad SBch SPlb SRot XLum XSen
	- 'Robustum'	see *S.* 'Ruby Glow'
	'Cherry Tart'^{PBR} (SunSparkler Series)	ECtt
	'Chocolate Drop'^{PBR}	CWGN ECtt NLar SDys SPoG SRms WHlf
	'Chocolate Sauce'	MAvo
	chrysicaulum	EPot
	'Class Act'^{PBR}	ECtt LRHS MAvo MNrw NLar NRHS SPoG SRms
	clavatum ISI 1161 **new**	NWad
	'Cloud Walker'^{PBR}	ECtt MNrw SPoG WFar
	compressum	see *S. palmeri* subsp. *palmeri* tetraploid
	confusum Hemsl.	SEND
	crassipes	see *Rhodiola wallichiana*
	crassularia	see *Crassula setulosa* 'Milfordiae'
	'Crazy Ruffles'	ECtt WCot
	cryptomerioides B&SWJ 054	WCru
	cyaneum 'Sakhalin'	LRHS NRHS WCot
	'Dark Jack'	ECtt EPfP MTis NGdn WCot
	dasyphyllum	NRya SPlb SRms
	'Dazzleberry'^{PBR} (SunSparkler Series) **new**	EPfP LCro LOPS
	'Diamond Edge' (v)	EBee ECtt
	divergens	GKev XLum
	douglasii	see *S. stenopetalum* 'Douglasii'
	drymarioides	IRob NBre
	'Dudley Field'	MHer
	'Eleanor Fisher'	see *S. telephium* subsp. *ruprechtii*
	ellacombeanum	see *S. kamtschaticum* var. *ellacombeanum*
	'Elworthy Rose'	CElw
§	***erythrostictum***	GBin XLum
	- 'Frosty Morn' (v)	Widely available
§	- 'Mediovariegatum' (v)	CDor EBee ELan LRHS MHer MNrw NLar SWvt WFar WMoo XLum
	ewersii	ECtt EDAr GCrg MMuc NBro NLar SPhx SPlb WTor
	- CC 5288	GKev
	- var. ***homophyllum*** 'Rosenteppich'	EPPr EPfP GWyn LBuc LRHS NRHS SPoG SRms SWvt WAvo WMoo
	fabaria	see *S. telephium* subsp. *fabaria*
	fastigiatum	see *Rhodiola fastigiata*
	'Firecracker' (SunSparkler Series) **new**	LCro LOPS
	floriferum	see *S. kamtschaticum* var. *floriferum*
	forsterianum	SEND SPlb XLum
	subsp. ***elegans***	
	- - 'Silver Stone'	GJos MMuc WRHF
§	- f. ***purpureum***	NRya
	'Frosted Fire'	EBee LSou NSti SRms WFar
	furfuraceum	GCrg GEdr NHpl SPlb WAbe
§	***glaucophyllum***	EDAr GJos XLum
	'Gold Mound'	CPla EUJe GWyn NHpl SWeb
	'Green Expectations'	GBin MRav NBre
	Herbstfreude Group	EHrv EPed ETMg IBoy LRHS NRHS NWsh WAvo
	- 'Autumn Fire'	EBee MAsh
	- 'Beka' (v)	ETMg LSou
	- 'Elsie's Gold' (v)	EBee ECtt EPfP LRHS MAvo MNrw SRms
§	- 'Herbstfreude' ♀H7	Widely available
	- 'Jaws'^{PBR}	CKno EBee ECtt NLar WCot WFar XLum
§	- 'Lajos' (v)	LSou MAsh NEoE SPoG WCot WFar
	- 'Mini Joy'	ELon GKev LRHS MHol MNrw NRHS
	hernandezii FO -199 **new**	NWad
	heterodontum	see *Rhodiola heterodonta*
	hidakanum	ECtt EHoe EPot GMaP NBro NWad WHoo
	himalense misapplied	see *Rhodiola* 'Keston'
	hispanicum	LPmr SPlb WArt
	- 'Blue Carpet'	EPPr MSCN NHpl WGrn
	- ***glaucum***	see *S. hispanicum* var. *minus*
§	- var. ***minus***	ECtt MMuc SEND SPlb WCot WMoo
	humifusum	NHpl
§	***hybridum***	XLum
	- 'Czar's Gold'	NGdn
	'Ice Ruffles' (v)	WFar
	'Indian Chief'	see *S.* (Herbstfreude Group) 'Herbstfreude'
	indicum var. ***yunnanense***	EShb

	integrifolium	see *Rhodiola integrifolia*
	'José Aubergine'PBR	CKno EBee ECtt EPfP IPot IRob LRHS MAvo MBel MRav MTis MWat NDov NLar NRHS NSti SCob SPoG SRms WCAu WPGP
	'Joyce Henderson'	CDor CElw ELan EPfP LRHS MCot MNrw MRav MTis NChi NLar NRHS SPer SRGP SRms WAvo WBrk WCot WMoo WOld
	kamtschaticum ♀H5	EDAr GJos IRob
	- B&SWJ 10870	WCru
§	- var. ***ellacombeanum*** ♀H5	MMuc SEND WCot XLum
	- - B&SWJ 8853	WCru
§	- var. ***floriferum***	XSen
§	- - 'Weihenstephaner Gold'	CTri ECtt ELan EPfP GEdr GJos GKev GMaP MHer MMuc MRav NSla SPlb SPoG SRms XLum
	- var. ***kamtschaticum*** 'Variegatum' (v) ♀H5	CMea EHoe ELan EPfP GCrg LRHS MHer MJak MMuc NHpl NRHS SBod SPoG SRms SRot SWvt XLum
	'Katharine's Gold'	MNrw
	kirilovii	see *Rhodiola kirilovii*
	'Knight Rider'	EBee
	lanceolatum	NBre
	'Lime Zinger'PBR (SunSparkler Series)	ECtt LCro LOPS
	lineare 'Variegatum' (v)	SBch XLum
	'Little Dove'	SBch
	'Little Missy' (v)	NEoE WFar
§	***lydium***	CTri MHer SPlb
	- 'Bronze Queen'	see *S. lydium*
	'Manoir de Gaudon' **new**	WCot
I	'Marchants Best Red' ♀H7	LRHS MNrw MRav SPhx WCot
	'Matrona' ♀H7	Widely available
	maweanum	see *S. acre* subsp. *neglectum* var. *majus*
	maximowiczii	see *S. aizoon* subsp. *maximowiczii*
	middendorffianum	GCrg MBrN MHer MMuc SRms SRot WHoo XLum
§	***montanum***	MMuc
	moranense	MMuc XLum
	morganianum ♀H2	EBak EShb
	morrisonense B&SWJ 7078	WCru
	'Mr Goodbud'PBR ♀H7	CAby CBct CKno ECtt LRHS LSun MAvo MHol MNrw NEgg NRHS SAko SPoG SRms WCAu WCot WSpi WTor
	'Munstead Red'	CBod CDor CWCL EBee ECha ECtt ELon EPfP GBin LRHS MNrw MRav MTis MWat NLar NRHS SBch SPer SPhx SPoG SRms WCAu WFar WHar WKif WMoo
	murale	see *S. album* subsp. *teretifolium* var. *murale*
	nevii misapplied	see *S. glaucophyllum*
	nevii ambig.	SPlb
	nicaeense	see *S. sediforme*
	obtusatum misapplied	see *S. oreganum*
§	***obtusatum*** A. Gray	NBro NSla
	obtusifolium var. ***listoniae***	EDAr GEdr GJos
	ochroleucum	NBre WCot
	- subsp. ***montanum***	see *S. montanum*
	oppositifolium	see *S. spurium* 'Album'
§	***oreganum***	ECha GAbr GCrg GMaP MHer SPlb SRms SRot XLum
	- 'Procumbens'	see *S. oreganum* subsp. *tenue*
§	- subsp. ***tenue***	NRya NWad
§	***oregonense***	LRHS MHer NRHS
	pachyclados	see *Rhodiola pachyclados*
	pachyphyllum	SAll
	palmeri	MRav SChr XLum
§	- subsp. ***palmeri*** tetraploid	SEND
	'Parish Plum'	SBch
	'Pink Dove'	SBch
	'Pinky'	EBee
§	***pluricaule***	GCrg LRHS NRHS SPlb SRms
	polytrichoides 'Chocolate Ball'	ECtt LSou MSCN
	'Pool Party'PBR (Party Hardy Series)	EPfP LRHS NLar NRHS
	populifolium	ECha GCal GJos IMou MHer MMuc NLar XLum
	praealtum	SChr SEND
	pulchellum	ECtt WFar
	'Red Cauli' ♀H7	Widely available
	'Red Rum'	GBin GWyn
	'Red Setter'	EBee SAko WPGP
	'Red Star'	MAvo
	reflexum L.	see *S. rupestre* L.
	- red-leaved	NHpl
	rhodiola	see *Rhodiola rosea*
	rosea	see *Rhodiola rosea*
	rubroglaucum misapplied	see *S. oregonense*
	rubroglaucum Praeger	see *S. obtusatum* A. Gray
	× ***rubrotinctum*** ♀H2	SEND
§	'Ruby Glow' ♀H5	Widely available
	'Ruby Port'	CSpe
§	***rupestre*** L.	EBWF ELan GJos MMuc MNHC SEND SPhx SPlb XLum
	- 'Angelina'	CKno CTal ECtt EPPr EWes IMou MAvo MHer NDov NEoE NWad SPoG SRGP WCot WGrn XLum
	- 'Aureum'	WFar
	- 'Blue Cushion'	ESps LRHS NRHS
	- 'Green Cushion'	LRHS NRHS
	- 'Monstrosum Cristatum'	SMad WCot XLum
	- 'Yellow Cushion'	LRHS NRHS
	ruprechtii	see *S. telephium* subsp. *ruprechtii*
	sarcocaule hort.	see *Crassula sarcocaulis*
	sarmentosum	XLum
§	***sediforme***	MMuc SEND XSen
	- B&F MA 25	WCot
	- ***nicaeense***	see *S. sediforme*
	selskianum	GJos NBre NLar SBch XLum
	- 'Goldilocks'	GJos
	sexangulare	ELon EPot MHer MMuc NRya SPlb SRms XLum
	sibiricum	see *S. hybridum*
	sieboldii	GPSL
	- 'Dragon'	MHCG
	- 'Mediovariegatum' (v) ♀H3	EHoe GMcL MHer MRav SPlb XLum
	'Silvermoon'	NWad
	spathulifolium	CTri ECha EPot
	- Atropurpureum Group	SRot
	- 'Aureum'	ECtt WAbe
	- 'Cape Blanco' ♀H5	Widely available
	- 'Purpureum' ♀H5	CPla CRos CTri ECtt EDAr EHoe ELan EPfP EPot ESps GAbr GMaP GWyn LBee LRHS MBel MHer NHpl NRHS NRya NWad SPlb SPoG WAbe WMoo XLum
	- subsp. ***yosemitense***	WTor
	- - 'Red Raver'	CPBP
	spectabile ♀H7	CBod CTri ELan EPfP GJos GMaP LRHS MCot MHer MRav NGdn NRHS SCob SPlb SRms WBor WBrk WFar WSFF
	- Brilliant Group	CBar ESps MJak MSpe SRms WHar

	- - 'Brilliant' ♀H7	CBcs CBod CSBt CTri CTsd ECha ECtt ELan EPfP LCro LOPS LRHS MAvo MGos MRav NGdn NLar NWsh SCob SPer SPoG SWvt WFar WMoo WSpi
	- - 'Carmen'	XLum
	- - 'Hot Stuff'	CAby ECtt ELan ELon EPfP LRHS LSRN NCou NPri NRHS SPoG SPtp SRms SRot WCot
	- - 'Lisa'	GBin GWyn NLar
	- - 'Meteor'	MRav MWat NLar
	- - 'Neon'	EBee EPfP LRHS MAsh MAvo NRHS
	- - 'Pink Fairy'	MNrw
	- - 'Rosenteller'	CKno EBee GBin NBre
§	- - 'Septemberglut'	LRHS NBre NRHS WSpi XLum
	- - 'Steven Ward'	CKno EWes SRGP
	- 'Crystal Pink' PBR	LRHS MNrw NLar NRHS
	- 'Humile'	XLum
	- 'Iceberg'	CBod EBee ECha ECtt EHrv EPfP ESps EWTr GBin LRHS MCot MGos MRav NGdn NRHS SCob SPer SPhx SPtp SWvt WBrk WFar WMoo WSFF WSpi XLum
	- 'Nordlicht'	GWyn
	- 'Pink Chablis' (v)	WCot
	- SEPTEMBER GLOW	see *S. spectabile* (Brilliant Group) 'Septemberglut'
	- 'Stardust'	CRos CTri EBee EPfP GKev GMaP LCro LRHS MRav MTis NRHS SGol SPer SRms WFar XLum
	- 'Variegatum'	see *S. erythrostictum* 'Mediovariegatum'
	- WALBERTON'S PIZAZZ	EPfP LRHS NRHS SPoG
	spinosum	see *Orostachys spinosa*
	spurium	ESps GJos MMuc SEND SRms XSen
§	- 'Album'	NRya XLum
	- 'Atropurpureum'	ECha WMoo XLum
	- 'Coccineum'	GJos MMuc SEND
	- DRAGON'S BLOOD	see *S. spurium* 'Schorbuser Blut'
	- 'Erdblut'	CTri
	- 'Fuldaglut'	CTri ECtt EHoe EPPr GCrg GMaP LRHS MAvo MNrw NRHS NRya SBee SRms WMoo
	- 'Green Mantle'	ECha EPfP LRHS NRHS
	- 'John Creech'	ECtt
	- PURPLE CARPET	see *S. spurium* 'Purpurteppich'
	- 'Purpureum'	SRms SRot
§	- 'Purpurteppich'	ECtt GJos MJak MRav NBro NLar NWad SRms SVen
	- 'Roseum'	SRms
	- 'Ruby Mantle'	GKev GMcL MSCN NBro NEoE SBch SPoG SRGP SRms SWvt WMoo XLum
§	- 'Schorbuser Blut' ♀H5	CBod CMea ECtt ELan EPau EPfP GJos GKev LRHS MCot MWat NDov NRHS NRya NSla SPlb SRGP SRms WHoo XLum
I	- 'Splendens Roseum'	XLum
	- 'Summer Glory'	NLar
§	- 'Tricolor' (v)	CTri EBee ECha EHoe EPfP GEdr GJos GKev MHer MRav NRya NWad SPlb SPoG WMoo XLum
	- 'Variegatum'	see *S. spurium* 'Tricolor'
	- 'Voodoo'	ECtt EPfP EWes LRHS MBel MHer NBro NDov NGdn NRHS XLum
	stefco	XLum
	stenopetalum	SPlb
§	- 'Douglasii'	MHer SRms
	'Stewed Rhubarb Mountain'	CBod CKno EBee ECha ECtt ELan EPfP LRHS MBNS MRav NLar NRHS SGbt WMoo
	stribrnyi	see *S. urvillei* Stribrnyi Group
	'Sunset Cloud'	EBee ECtt EWes GCal LPla MRav
	takesimense	XLum
	- B&SWJ 8493	WCru
	- B&SWJ 8518	WCru
	tatarinowii	WCot
	telephium	IFro SRms WSFF XLum
§	- Atropurpureum Group	MRav NLar SWvt
	- - 'African Pearl'	GWyn WCFE
	- - 'Arthur Branch'	EBee GWyn LRHS NRHS
	- - 'Bon Bon'	CBod EPfP MBNS MTis NLar SPoG
	- - 'Bressingham Purple'	EBee LRHS NRHS
	- - 'Chocolate'	EBee ECtt GPSL NLar
	- - 'Dark Knight'	EPfP LRHS NRHS
	- - 'El Cid'	EWes
	- - 'Karfunkelstein' ♀H7	CKno EBee ECha ECtt GBin GLog GQue IRob LCro LOPS LRHS MAvo MHol MTis MWat NDov NRHS SPhx WCot XLum
	- - 'Leonore Zuuntz'	NBre
	- - 'Lynda et Rodney'	EWes
	- - 'Lynda Windsor'	ECtt EPfP NLar NPnk SWvt
	- - 'Möhrchen'	GMaP GMcL MHer MRav NGdn NLar SPhx WMoo
	- - 'Picolette'	ECtt EPfP EWTr LRHS MNrw MSCN NGdn NRHS SPoG SRms WCot WMoo
	- - 'Postman's Pride' PBR	CWGN ECtt EPfP GBin GWyn MNrw NGdn NQui
§	- - 'Purple Emperor' ♀H7	Widely available
	- - 'Purple Moon'	SPhx
	- - 'Ringmore Ruby'	EBee MHer MNrw SPhx WCot WPGP
	- - 'Xenox' PBR ♀H7	CBct CWGN EBee ECtt EHoe EPfP GBin IPot LRHS MAvo MBNS MCot MNrw NLar NRHS SCob SPoG SRGP SRms WCAu
	- 'Coral Reef' PBR	EBee
	- Emperor's Waves Group	ELan MNHC NGdn NWad WRHF
§	- subsp. ***fabaria***	ECtt MRav NWsh WCot
	- - var. ***borderei***	CElw LPla SBch SPhx
	- 'Jennifer'	CAby EBee ECtt IRob LLWG MBel MPie SBch WHoo WRHF
	- subsp. ***maximum*** 'Atropurpureum'	see *S. telephium* Atropurpureum Group
	- - 'Gooseberry Fool'	CMea EBee ECtt ELan EPfP GMaP LRHS NEoE SBch SPhx
	- 'Moonlight Serenade' PBR	EBee ECtt EPfP LRHS NRHS SRms
	- 'Orange Xenox' PBR **new**	EPfP LPla
	- 'Rainbow Xenox' PBR	SCob
	- 'Raspberry Truffle'	LRHS SDys
§	- subsp. ***ruprechtii***	CDor ECha ECtt EHoe EPPr EPed EPfP GMaP GMcL LRHS MCot MRav NDov NLar NRHS NSti SPer SPhx WMoo WWtn
	- - 'Citrus Twist'	EBee ECtt EPed LRHS MRav NPnk NRHS
	- - 'Hab Gray'	CSpe EBee ECtt EWes EWld LRHS NLar SAko SBch
	- - 'Pink Dome'	ECha
	- 'Strawberries and Cream'	CMac EBee ECha ECtt ELan ELon EPfP EShb EWTr GMaP LCro LRHS MBNS MBel MMuc MRav NEoE NGdn NLar NRHS SGbt SPer WMoo WPtf
	- 'Sunkissed' PBR	ECtt LPla LRHS NLar NRHS
	- 'Twinkling Star' PBR	ECtt MNrw NLar
	- YELLOW MATRONA ('Eline') **new**	LCro LOPS WHlf

- 'Yellow Xenox'PBR	EBee ECtt LRHS LSou NLar NRHS SCob
ternatum	MHer
tetractinum 'Coral Reef'	CSpe SRms XLum
'Thundercloud'PBR	EPfP LBuc LRHS MTin NRHS SCob SRms WMoo
'Touchdown Teak' **new**	LOPS WTor
trollii	see *Rhodiola saxifragoides*
urvillei Sartorianum Group	MHer XLum
§ - Stribrnyi Group	XLum
ussuriense	EPfP GCal GPSL
- 'Chuwangsan'	EWld WCru
valens	SPlb
'Veluwse Wakel'	ECtt GBin GWyn
'Vera Jameson' 🏆H5	CMac CRos ECha ECtt EHoe ELan EPfP EShb GKev LRHS LSRN MBel MCot MRav NRHS NSti NWsh SArc SBch SPer SRms SWvt WHoo WKif WMoo WSpi
viviparum	NLar
- B&SWJ 8662	WCru
WALBERTON'S PINK WHISPER	EPfP LRHS NRHS SPoG
'Washfield Purple'	see *S. telephium* (Atropurpureum Group) 'Purple Emperor'
'Weihenstephaner Gold'	see *S. kamtschaticum* var. *floriferum* 'Weihenstephaner Gold'
weinbergii	see *Graptopetalum paraguayense*
yezoense	see *S. pluricaule*
yunnanense	see *Rhodiola yunnanensis*

Seemannia see *Gloxinia*

Selaginella (*Selaginellaceae*)

apoda	CTsd LRHS NLos
braunii	WCot
helvetica	EBee IMou XLum
kraussiana 🏆H2	CKel CTsd NWad
- 'Aurea'	CBod CCCN LRHS NRHS
- 'Bronsiana'	NLos
- 'Brownii' 🏆H2	CCCN
- 'Gold Tips'	CCCN CKel LRHS NRHS
lepidophylla	GKev SVic
martensii 🏆H1b	CKel
- 'Jori' (v)	NLos
moellendorfii	LRHS NRHS
uncinata 🏆H1b	CKel LRHS NRHS
wallichii **new**	SMad

Selinum (*Apiaceae*)

CC 6869	EBee
KWJ 12281 from northern Vietnam	WCru
candollei HWJK 2329	WCru
carvifolium	CExl CMac CSam CSpe EBWF ELan LEdu LLWG MNrw SPhx SPtp
- HWJK 2347 **new**	WCru
- PAB 2676	LEdu
cryptotaenium FMWJ 13250	WCru
- PAB 8948	LEdu
filicifolium **new**	LLWG MBel MTis WCot WRHF
tenuifolium	see *S. wallichianum*
§ ***wallichianum*** 🏆H7	Widely available
- CC 6869	GKev
- EMAK 886	EBee GPoy
- HWJK 2347	WCru
- PAB 3579	LEdu WPGP
- PAB 8969	LEdu WPGP
- from Sikkim WJC 13656	WCru

Selliera (*Goodeniaceae*)

radicans	GAbr

Semele (*Asparagaceae*)

androgyna	CRHN WCot

Semiaquilegia (*Ranunculaceae*)

§ ***adoxoides***	GKev
- double-flowered (d)	GKev
§ ***ecalcarata*** 🏆H5	CPla CSpe CWCL GCal GKev MNrw NGdn NHpl SRms WHal
simulatrix	see *S. ecalcarata*
'Sugar Plum Fairy'	CSma EPfP LBuc LRHS NRHS SPoG

Semiarundinaria (*Poaceae*)

§ ***fastuosa*** 🏆H4	CBcs CBdn CBod CJun CTsd ENBC EPfP ERod EUJe IMou MMoz MMuc MWht SArc SEND SPlb
- var. ***viridis***	ERod MWht SBig WCru
kagamiana	ENBC EPfP IMou MMuc MWht SBig
§ ***lubrica***	MWht
makinoi	MWht
I ***maruyamana***	MWht
nitida	see *Fargesia nitida*
§ ***okuboi***	ERod MMoz MWht
villosa	see *S. okuboi*
yamadorii	ERod MWht
yashadake	ERod MWht
- f. ***kimmei***	CBod ENBC EPfP ERod GMcL LCro LRHS MJak MMoz MMuc MWht NLar NRHS SBig SPoG WMoo WPGP

Semnanthe see *Erepsia*

Sempervivella see *Rosularia*

Sempervivum ✿ (*Crassulaceae*)

'Aalrika'	NMen
'Aaroundina'	NMen
'Abba'	CMea EDAr NMen WHal
'Achalm'	NMen
acuminatum	see *S. tectorum* var. *glaucum*
'Adelaar'	NMen
'Adelmoed'	NMen
'Ageet'	NMen
'Aladdin'	GEdr MSCN NMen SRms
'Alchimist'	NMen XLum
'Aldo Moro'	CTal EDAr LBee NMen XLum
'Alenco'	NMen
'Alesia'	NMen
'Alfons-Roelands'	NMen
'Alice'	MSCN
allionii	see *Jovibarba allionii*
'Alluring'	GAbr NMen
'Alpha'	CMea LBee NMen SRms WHal XLum
altum	CRos LRHS NMen NRHS SPlb SRms XLum
'Amanda'	EDAr MBrN NMen SRms WHoo
'Ambergreen'	NMen
andreanum	see *S. tectorum* var. *alpinum*
'Andrenor'	NMen
'Andrenor' sport	NMen
'Apache' Haberer	NMen
'Apollo'	XLum
'Apple Blossom'	NMen
'Apricot'	NMen

	arachnoideum ♀H5	CMea CRos CTri EDAr ELan ELon EPfP EUJe GAbr GMaP GWyn LBee LRHS LSun MAsh MSCN NEgg NHpl NRHS SEND SPlb SPoG SRms WAbe WHal WHoo WOld XLum
	- from Zermatt, Switzerland	XLum
	- subsp. ***arachnoideum*** new	CPla
	- 'Ararat'	SDys
	- var. ***bryoides***	CRos LLHF LRHS NRHS SRms
	- 'Clärchen'	MSCN WAbe XLum
	- cristate	XLum
*	- ***densum***	EDAr EPPr GAbr WAbe
	- subsp. ***doellianum***	see *S. arachnoideum* subsp. *tomentosum* var. *glabrescens*
	- 'Gorges d'Héric' new	EPot
	- 'Laggeri'	see *S. arachnoideum* subsp. *tomentosum* (C.B. Lehm. & Schnittsp.) Schinz & Thell.
	- 'Opitz'	NMen SRms
	- 'Peña Prieta'	XLum
	- 'Red Wings'	NMen XLum
	- 'Rheinkiesel'	XLum
	- 'Rubin'	CBod NHpl
	- 'Rubrum'	CRos ELon EUJe GMaP LRHS NRHS SPlb XLum
	- subsp. ***tomentosum*** misapplied	see *S.* × *barbulatum* 'Hookeri'
	- subsp. ***tomentosum*** ambig.	EPot XLum
§	- subsp. ***tomentosum*** (C.B. Lehm. & Schnittsp.) Schinz & Thell. ♀H5	GCrg LRHS NPer NRHS NWad SPlb SRms WAbe
§	- - var. ***glabrescens***	SDys XLum
	- - 'Minus'	EPfP LRHS NRHS
§	- - 'Stansfieldii'	CRos EPPr LRHS NRHS SRms WHal
§	- 'White Christmas'	MHer NMen
	arachnoideum* × *montanum	see *S.* × *barbulatum*
	arachnoideum* × *nevadense	SDys
	arachnoideum* × *pittonii	NMen SRms WAbe
	arenarium	see *Jovibarba arenaria*
	'Arlet'	EDAr
	'Arondina'	NMen
	'Aross'	CMea NMen
	'Arrowheads Red'	NMen
	'Artist'	NMen
	'Ashes of Roses'	MSCN NMen WAbe XLum
	'Astrid'	NMen
	'Atlantic'	SRms
	atlanticum	CTal MMuc NMen SRot
	- from Oukaïmeden, Morocco	NMen SRms
	- 'Edward Balls'	NMen SDys SRms WFar
	'Atlantis' ambig.	NMen SRms
	'Atlantis' Adams	NWad
	'Atropurpureum' ambig.	EDAr GAbr GEdr MBrN NMen
	'Attraction'	NMen
	'Aureum'	see *Greenovia aurea*
	'Averil'	NMen
	'Aymon Correvon'	NMen
	'Baby Skrocki'	NMen
	balcanicum	CTal EDAr NMen SRms XLum
	ballsii	LLHF LRHS NMen NRHS SRms
	- from Smólikas, Greece	NMen
	- from Tschumba Petzi, Greece	SDys XLum

	'Banderi'	NMen
	'Banjo'	NMen
	'Banyan'	CRos CTal LRHS NMen NRHS SRms
§	× ***barbulatum***	GAbr LBee NMen SDys WHoo
§	- 'Hookeri'	CTri GCrg WAbe WHoo XLum
	'Baronesse'	NMen
	'Bascour Zilver'	CMea LBee MSCN SRms WHal
	'Be Mine'	MSCN
	'Beatles Memory'	NMen
	'Beaute'	NMen
	'Bedazzled'	NMen
	'Bedivere'	LBee NMen SRms
	'Bedivere Crested'	NMen
	'Bella Meade'	EDAr NMen SRms
	'Bellotts Pourpre'	NMen
	'Bennerbroek'	NMen
	'Bernstein'	EDAr GKev MSCN NMen NWad WHal XLum
	'Beta'	NMen WAbe XLum
	'Bethany'	CMea NMen NWad WHal
	'Bianca'	NMen
	'Bicolor' ambig.	EPfP
	'Big Slipper'	NMen
	'Bijou'	NMen
	'Birchmaier'	NMen
	'Björn' new	NMen
	'Black Beauty'	EPot NMen
	'Black Knight'	CRos LRHS MHer NRHS SPlb SRms WHal
	'Black Mini'	GCrg GKev NMen SRms
	'Black Mountain'	LBee NMen
	'Black Rose'	NMen
	'Black Velvet'	NMen
	'Blood Tip'	CMea CRos CTal ELon EPfP GAbr GKev LRHS LSun MHer MMuc MSCN NMen NRHS NRya NWad SEND SPlb SPoG SRms WHal WHoo
	'Bloody Goose'	NMen
	'Blue Bird'	NMen
	'Blue Boy'	CTal ELon EPPr EPot GAbr GCrg LBee LRHS MSCN NMen NRHS SPlb SRms
	'Blue Knight'	NMen
	'Blue Time'	GCrg LLHF WHoo XLum
	'Blush'	EDAr NMen
	'Boissieri'	see *S. tectorum* subsp. *tectorum* 'Boissieri'
	'Bold Chick'	NMen
	'Bombardier'	EDAr
	'Booth's Red'	NMen
	borisii	see *S. ciliosum* var. *borisii*
	borissovae	EPot NMen SDys
	'Boromir'	EDAr NMen XLum
	'Boule de Neige'	GCrg GEdr NMen NRya
	'Bowles's Variety'	NMen
I	'Braunella'	NMen
	'Britta'	SDys
	'Brock'	CRos LLHF LRHS NMen NRHS SRms
	'Bronco' ♀H5	CRos CTal ELon EPfP GAbr GBin GCrg LBee LRHS MMuc NMen NRHS NRya NWad SEND SRms WBrk WCot WPGP WRHF XLum
	'Bronze Beauty'	EDAr
	'Bronze Pastel'	EDAr MSCN NHpl NMen NSla SRms SRot
	'Brown Owl'	SRms
	'Brownii'	GAbr NMen

	'Brunette'	GAbr
	'Brunhilde'	NMen
	bungeanum hort.	NMen
	'Burgundy'	NMen
	'Burgundy Velvet'	NMen
	'Burnatii'	see *S. montanum* subsp. *burnatii*
	'Burnished Bronze'	NMen
	'Butterbur'	NMen
	'Butterfly'	NMen
	'Café'	ELon MSCN NMen SRms
	calcareum	CMea CRos CTal ECtt EUJe GKev LRHS MAsh MMuc NBro NHpl NMen NRHS SArc SBod SEND SPlb SPoG SRms SRot XLum
	- GDJ 92.16 from Petite Ceüse, France	SRms
	- from Cleizé, France	see *S. calcareum* 'Limelight'
	- from Col Bayard, France	GAbr NMen
	- from Colle St Michel, France	SRms
	- from Petite Ceüse, France	SRot
	- from Queyras, France	NMen
	- from Triora, Italy	NMen
	- 'Benz'	SDys
	- 'Extra' ♀H5	CTal GAbr GCrg GEdr MSCN NMen SRms SRot
	- 'Greenii'	CRos ECtt LRHS MSCN NMen NRHS SPlb SRms
§	- 'Grigg's Surprise'	NMen SPlb
	- 'Guillaumes' ♀H5	CRos CTal LBee LRHS MSCN NMen NRHS SRms SRot WHoo
§	- 'Limelight'	CMea CRos EDAr LBee LRHS NMen NRHS WHal WHoo
	- 'Monstrosum'	see *S. calcareum* 'Grigg's Surprise'
	- 'Mrs Giuseppi'	CTal GAbr GCrg GEdr LBee LSun MHer NHpl NMen SBch SRms WAbe XLum
	- 'Nigricans'	NMen
	- 'Pink Pearl'	MSCN NMen SDys SPlb XLum
	- 'Sir William Lawrence' ♀H5	CMea CRos ECtt EDAr LBee LRHS NMen NRHS SRms WAbe WHal WHoo WThu XLum
	'Campagha'	NMen
	'Canada Kate'	NMen
	'Cancer'	XLum
	'Candy Floss'	NMen
	cantabricum	MMuc NMen XLum
	- from Navafria, Spain	NMen
	- from San Glorio, Spain	GAbr
	- from Ticeros	XLum
	- from Valvanera, Spain	NMen
	- subsp. ***cantabricum*** from Leitariegos, Spain	GAbr
I	- subsp. ***gredense*** GDJ 95.04	CTal
	- subsp. ***guadarramense***	see *S. vicentei* subsp. *paui*
	- - from Pico del Lobo, Spain, No 1	SRms SRot
	- subsp. ***urbionense***	GEdr SRms
	'Caramel'	NMen
	'Carmen'	GAbr NMen
	'Carneum'	NMen
	'Carnival'	NMen
	'Casablanca'	NMen
	'Caspara'	NMen
	caucasicum	CRos LRHS NMen NRHS SRms XLum
	'Cavo Doro'	NMen
	'Celon'	NMen
	'Centennial'	NMen
	charadzeae	LBee XLum
	'Chartbury'	EDAr
	'Cherry Frost'	NMen XLum
	'Cherry Glow'	see *Jovibarba heuffelii* 'Cherry Glow'
	'Cherry Tart'	SPlb
	'Chilli Pepper'	MSCN
	'Chocolate'	NHpl WAbe
	'Cholie'	GKev
	× ***christii*** 'Peter Lotter'	NMen
	ciliosum ♀H4	NMen NRya SPlb SRms
	- from Alí Butús, Bulgaria	SDys
§	- var. ***borisii***	CFis EPPr EPfP GCal NMen NRya WAbe WHal
	- var. ***ciliosum*** × ***ciliosum*** var. ***borisii***	CTri
	- var. ***galicicum***	CTal
	- - 'Mali Hat'	NMen
	ciliosum × ***grandiflorum***	NMen
	'Cindy'	SRms
	'Circlet'	NMen
	'Claey's Fluweel'	NMen
	'Clara Noyes'	NMen
	'Clare'	NMen
	'Cleveland Morgan'	NMen XLum
	'Climax' ambig.	EPfP
	'Climax' Ford	NMen
	'Cobweb Capers'	NMen
	'Cobweb Centres'	EWes NMen
	'Colchicum'	SRms
	'Collecteur Anchisi'	CTal SDys
	'Commander Hay'	CTal CTri EDAr EPfP EWes GMaP MSCN NHpl NMen NPer NRya SRGP SRms WHal XLum
	'Comte de Congae'	NMen
	'Concorde'	LBee
	'Congo'	NMen XLum
	'Corio'	NMen
	'Corona'	NMen
	'Coronet'	NMen
	'Corsair'	CTal ELon EPPr GEdr MBrN MMuc SRms WBrk WOld
	'Cotopaxi'	NMen
	'Crimson Velvet'	CMea GCrg LBee XLum
	'Cripello'	NMen
§	'Crispyn' ♀H5	CRos CTal EPot LBee LRHS MHer MMuc MSCN NMen NRHS SEND SRms
	'Crucify'	NMen
	'Cupream'	NMen SRms
	'Cyclops'	NMen
	'Dakota'	EDAr NMen
	'Dallas'	GCrg NMen SRms
	'Damask'	LBee MSCN NMen
	'Dancer's Veil'	NMen
	'Darjeeling'	NMen
	'Dark Beauty'	CMea CRos LRHS MSCN NRHS SRms WAbe WCot WHal
	'Dark Cloud'	GAbr LBee WHoo XLum
	'Dark Point'	MSCN NMen
	davisii	NMen
	'De Kardijk'	NMen
	'Deep Fire'	NMen SRms
	× ***degenianum***	GAbr NMen XLum
	'Delta' ♀H5	NMen WHoo
	densum	see *S. tectorum*
	'Devil's Teeth'	MSCN
	'Devon Glow'	MSCN
	'Diane'	NMen
	'Diavolo'	NMen

'Director Jacobs'	EDAr NHpl NMen
'Dolle Dina's'	NMen
dolomiticum	NMen XLum
dolomiticum* × *montanum	NBro NMen
'Donarrose'	NMen
'Dornröschen'	NMen
'Downland Queen'	NMen
'Dr Fritz Köhlein'	NMen
'Dragoness'	NMen
'Dream Catcher'	NMen
'Dyke'	CTri EDAr GAbr GCrg NMen WHal
dzhavachischvilii	NMen XLum
'Edge of Night'	SRms
'Edwardine'	NMen
'Eefje'	NMen
'El Greco'	NMen
'El Toro'	MSCN NHpl NMen
'Electra'	GBin
'Elva'	NMen
'Elvis'	NMen
'Emerald Giant'	SRms
'Emerson's Giant'	NMen SRms
'Emmchen'	NMen
'Engle's'	CMea CRos CTri GCrg GKev LRHS MHer MMuc MSCN NMen NRHS SEND SPlb SRms WHal
'Engle's 13-2'	NMen
'Engle's Rubrum'	CTal LBee NMen
'Eos'	NMen
erythraeum	LLHF LRHS NHpl NMen NRHS SPlb SRms WHal
- from Mesta Valley, Bulgaria	NMen
- from Pirin, Bulgaria	NMen
- 'Red Velvet'	NMen
'Eureka'	NMen
'Excalibur'	NMen
'Exhibita'	EPPr NMen SDys SRms
'Exorna'	EDAr NMen
'Fair Lady'	NMen
'Fairy'	EPot NMen
'Fame'	SPlb
'Faramir'	NMen
'Fat Jack'	NMen
× ***fauconnetii***	CTal EDAr
- 'Rubellum'	NMen
- 'Thompsonii'	SRms
'Feldmaier'	NMen WFar
'Fernwood'	CTal NMen
'Festival'	EDAr NMen
'Fiery Furness'	NMen
'Fiesta' ambig.	NMen WHal
fimbriatum	see *S.* × *barbulatum*
'Finerpointe'	NMen
'Fire Glint'	GCrg GEdr NMen SRms
'Firgrove Big Bronze'	NMen
'First Try'	NMen
flagelliforme	XLum
'Flaming Heart'	EDAr MBrN NMen
'Flamingo'	NMen
'Flammenschwert' **new**	NMen
'Flanders Passion'	EWes LBee NMen SRms
'Flasher'	GCrg NMen
'Fluweel'	MSCN NMen
'Forden'	MSCN NMen
'Ford's Amiability'	SDys
'Ford's Giant'	XLum
'Ford's Shadows'	SDys

'Ford's Spring'	NMen SRms
'Freckles'	NMen
'Fronika'	NMen
'Frosty'	NMen SRms
'Fuego' 🏆H5	LRHS NMen NRHS SRms
'Fuji'	NMen
× ***funckii***	EDAr MBrN NMen XLum
'Fuzzy Wuzzy'	EDAr NMen
'Gabrielle' **new**	NMen
'Gallivarda' 🏆H5	LRHS MSCN NMen NRHS
'Gambol'	NWad
'Gamma'	LBee NMen SRms
'Garnet'	NMen
'Gay Jester'	CTal CTri NMen WHoo
'Gazelle'	XLum
'Georgette'	NMen XLum
'Georgia Rowan'	NMen
'Gilosum'	EDAr
'Ginnie's Delight'	NMen
'Gipsy'	NMen
giuseppii 🏆H5	LBee LRHS MMuc NMen NRHS SRms
- from Coriscao, Spain	CTal LBee
- from Peña Espigüete, Spain	SDys SRms
'Gizmo'	NMen
'Glaucum'	see *S. tectorum* var. *glaucum*
globiferum subsp. ***globiferum*** 'Minor'	XLum
'Gloriosum' ambig.	EDAr MSCN NMen
'Glowing Embers'	NMen WHal XLum
'Godaert'	MMuc SEND XLum
'Goldie'	NMen
'Granada'	EDAr GAbr NMen
'Granat'	GBin GWyn LBee MHer NMen SRms XLum
'Granby'	LBee SDys
grandiflorum	CTal NMen WThu XLum
- 'Fasciatum'	NMen
'Grannie's Favourite'	NMen
'Grapetone'	NMen SDys WHal
'Graupurpur'	XLum
'Green Apple'	GAbr NMen SDys
'Green Caro'	NMen
'Green Disk'	SRms
'Green Dragon'	CRos CTal LRHS MSCN NMen NRHS SRms
'Green Gables'	EDAr
'Green Ice'	NMen
'Greenwich Time'	EDAr NMen
* ***greigii***	EPot MSCN
'Grey Dawn'	CRos LRHS NMen NRHS SRms XLum
'Grey Ghost'	NMen
'Grey Lady'	NMen
'Grey Owl'	CRos LRHS MSCN NMen NRHS SRms
'Grey Velvet'	LBee NMen
'Greyfriars'	CMea CRos CTal EDAr LBee LRHS MSCN NMen NRHS SRms WOld
'Greyolla'	NMen
'Grünschnabel'	XLum
'Gulle Dame'	CMea NMen SRms
'Gumby'	NMen
'Gwiazda'	GBin
'Halemaumau'	NMen
I 'Hall's Hybrid'	MSCN NBro NMen SRms
'Happy'	CTal NMen SRms

'Harriet'	NMen
'Hart'	NMen
'Havana'	NMen
'Havendijks Pride'	NMen
'Hayling'	LRHS NMen NRHS NWad SRms XLum
'Heigham Red'	CRos EPPr LBee LRHS NMen NRHS SRms
'Heike'	NMen
'Helen'	EDAr GCrg GEdr
'Heliotroop'	NMen SDys SRot
helveticum	see *S. montanum*
'Hermann Näpfel'	NMen
'Hester'	MBrN NBro NMen
'Hey-hey'	CTal ELon EPot LBee LRHS MBrN NMen NRHS SPlb WCot XLum
'Hidde'	NMen SPlb
'Hirsutum'	see *Jovibarba allionii*
hirtum	see *Jovibarba hirta*
'Honymoon'	NMen
'Hookeri'	see *S.* × *barbulatum* 'Hookeri'
'Hopi'	NMen
'Hortulanus Smit'	XLum
'Hot Boyz'	NMen
'Hot Peppermint'	NMen
'Hullabaloo'	EDAr GAbr NMen
'Hurricane'	GCrg NMen
'Icicle'	CMea ELon LRHS MSCN NBro NMen NRHS SRms
imbricatum	see *S.* × *barbulatum*
'Impact'	NMen
'Imperial'	NMen SPlb
'Inge'	see *Jovibarba heuffelii* 'Inge'
ingwersenii	CTal NMen XLum
ingwersenii* × *pumilum	NMen SRms
'Iophon'	LBee
iranicum	NMen
'Irazu'	CTal EPot GCrg LRHS MSCN NMen NRHS SDys SRms
'Isaac Dyson'	SDys SRot
'Isabelle'	NMen
italicum	XLum
'Itchen'	NMen
'Ivonne'	NMen
'Iwo'	NMen
'Jack Frost'	NBro NMen XLum
'Jacquette'	NMen
'Jadestern'	NMen
'Janis'	NMen
'Jelly Bean'	NMen
'Jet Stream' ♀^{H5}	ELon LRHS MSCN NMen NRHS SDys SPlb SRms
'Jewel Case'	CTal LRHS NMen NRHS SRms
I 'John Hobbs seedling No. 2'	NMen
'John T' × 'Saffron'	NMen
'Jolly Green Giant'	NMen
'Jo's Spark'	NMen
'Jubilee'	CMea EDAr ELan GCrg GEdr MAsh MHer NMen SRms XLum
'Jubilee Tricolor'	GCrg GEdr NMen WAbe
'Jungle Fires'	CMea ELon EPot NMen SDys SRms WHoo
'Jungle Shadows'	EDAr NMen NWad XLum
'Jupiter'	XLum
'Jurrina'	NMen
'Justine's Choice'	NMen SRms
'Kappa'	NBro NMen SDys SRot
'Katmai'	NMen
'Keiko'	NMen
'Kelly Jo'	NBro WBrk
'Kelut'	NMen
'Kermit'	NMen
'Kiara'	NMen
'Kibo'	NMen
'Kidlington'	NMen
'Kim'	NMen
'Kimba'	NMen
'Kimble'	NMen
'Kimono'	NMen NWad
kindingeri	NMen SRms XLum
'King George'	CTal CTri LBee MMuc NMen SEND SRms WHal WHoo XLum
'King Lear'	GBin
'Kip'	CMea NMen
'Kismet'	NMen
'Knight Hawk'	NMen
'Koko Flanel'	CTal NMen SRms
'Korspel Beauty'	NMen
'Korspel Prince'	NMen
'Korspel Sport'	NMen
'Korspelsegietje'	GAbr NMen SRms
kosaninii	NMen
- from Koprivnik, Slovenia	MSCN NMen WAbe XLum
- 'Hepworth'	SPlb
'Krakeling'	NMen
'Kramer's Spinrad'	CMea CTal EPPr GEdr LBee MBel NMen SPlb SRms WHoo WThu
'Krankii'	XLum
'Krater'	NMen
'Lady Kelly'	CMea
'Lancer'	NMen
'Laura Lee'	MMuc NMen SEND
'Lavender and Old Lace'	EPot LBee LRHS MSCN NMen NRHS SPlb SRms XLum
'Le Congai'	NMen
'Legolas'	NMen
'Leneca'	NMen
'Lennik's Glory'	see *S.* 'Crispyn'
'Lennik's Glory No. 2'	NMen
'Lennik's Sport'	XLum
'Leocadia's Nephew'	NMen
leucanthum	XLum
'Lilac Queen'	NMen
'Lilac Time' ♀^{H5}	CMea CTal ELon EPPr GAbr LRHS MBrN MHer MSCN NMen NRHS SPlb SRms WFar WHal XLum
'Limbo'	NMen
'Lion King'	CTal MSCN NMen
'Lioness'	NMen
'Lipari'	SRms WCot XLum
'Lipstick'	GQue NMen
'Little Flirt'	MSCN
'Lively Bug'	EDAr EPPr LBee LRHS MSCN NMen NRHS SDys SRms XLum
'Lloyd Praeger'	see *S. montanum* subsp. *stiriacum* 'Lloyd Praeger'
'Long Shanks'	MSCN
'Lonzo'	NMen SRms
'Lord Alan'	GKev NMen
'Lord Morton'	NMen
'Louisse-Marie'	NMen
'Lovely Roset'	NMen
'Lucy Liu'	NMen
'Ludmila'	NMen
'Lynn's Choice'	GAbr NMen NWad WHal
macedonicum	NMen SPlb SRms XLum
'Magic Spell'	NMen
'Magical'	NMen
'Magnificum'	NMen XLum

	'Mahogany'	CTal CTri EDAr GKev LBee MHer MSCN NMen SRms WHal XLum
	'Maigret'	GCrg NMen
	'Majanka'	NMen
	'Majestic'	LBee NMen
	'Malby's Hybrid'	see *S.* 'Reginald Malby'
	'Maria Laach'	GCrg NMen
	'Marijntje'	NMen
	'Marjorie Newton'	NMen
	'Marland Ruby'	NMen
	'Marmalade'	NMen
§	***marmoreum***	EPot LBee LRHS NMen NRHS SRms WHal
	- from Börzöny, Hungary	XLum
	- from Kanzan Gorge, Bulgaria	XLum
	- from Okol, Albania	NMen
	- 'Brunneifolium'	CTal GAbr LBee NMen XLum
	- subsp. ***marmoreum*** var. ***dinaricum***	MHer NMen
§	- - 'Rubrifolium'	XLum
	- monstrose	MSCN
	'Marshall'	NMen
	'Mary-Beth'	NMen
	'Mauna Kea'	NMen
	'Mauvine'	NMen XLum
	'Mayfair'	EDAr NMen
	'Medallion'	NMen
	'Meelah'	NMen
	'Meisse'	NMen
	'Melanie'	MBrN NMen
	'Mercury'	GAbr GCrg LRHS NBro NMen NRHS SRms
	'Merlin'	MSCN NMen
	mettenianum	NMen
	'Mickey Mouse'	NMen
	'Midas'	CTal LRHS NMen NRHS SRms
	'Minaret'	NMen
	'Mini Frost'	NMen
	'Minuet'	NMen
	'Mira'	GBin MHol
	'Mixed Spice'	CMea NMen
	'Moerkerk's Merit'	CTal GAbr LRHS NMen NRHS XLum
	'Mohair'	NMen
	'Mona Lisa'	NMen
	'Mondstein'	MSCN SRms
	'Monseigneur Desmet'	GQue
	'Montage'	NMen
§	***montanum***	XLum
	- from Haute-Loire, France	XLum
	- from Mont Aigoual, France	XLum
	- from Monte Tirone, Italy	LBee
	- from the Pyrenees	XLum
	- from Vallée d'Estaing, France	XLum
§	- subsp. ***burnatii***	NMen
	- 'Caesar'	MSCN
	- subsp. ***carpaticum*** 'Cmiral's Yellow'	WAbe WFar
	- 'Rubrum'	see *S.* 'Red Mountain'
	- subsp. ***stiriacum***	EPot NMen SRms XLum
	- - from Mauterndorf, Austria	NMen
§	- - 'Lloyd Praeger'	CTal NMen SDys
	montanum* × *tectorum var. ***boutignyanum***	NMen
	'More Honey'	NMen
	'Morning Glow'	NMen WHal
	'Mount Hood'	ELon LRHS NMen NRHS SRms WHal
	'Mount Skippet'	NMen
	'Mount Usher'	NMen
	'Mulberry Wine'	LBee NMen SRms WHoo
	'Mystic'	MBrN NMen
	'Naemi'	NMen
	'Neon'	NMen
*	***netaginatum***	XLum
	nevadense	CTal NMen SRms
	- 'Hirtellum'	SRms
	'New Rose'	WFar XLum
	'Nico'	NMen NWad SRms
	'Night Raven'	NMen
	'Nigrum'	see *S. tectorum* 'Nigrum'
	'Niobe'	NMen WHal
	'Nocturno'	XLum
	'Noir'	EDAr EPfP GKev LRHS MSCN NBro NMen NRHS WFar XLum
	'Norbert'	CTal EDAr NMen SRms XLum
	'Nörtofts Beauty'	NMen
	'Nouveau Pastel'	CFis CMea NMen WHal XLum
	'Oberon'	NMen
	'Ockerwurz' **new**	WFar
	'Octet'	NMen
	octopodes	XLum
	- var. ***apetalum***	CTal EPPr GAbr MSCN NMen WHoo
	'Oddity'	GBin MBrN MHer NMen WHal
	'Ohio Burgundy'	LRHS MSCN NMen NRHS SRms WAbe
	'Old Man Sage' **new**	SPlb
	'Old Rose'	NMen
	'Olivette'	NMen
	'Omega'	NMen
	'Ornatum'	MHer WAbe WHal
	ossetiense	CTal EDAr GAbr NMen XLum
	'Othello' 🏆H5	CTri EPfP GAbr GCrg NMen SRms WCot WPGP XLum
	'Pachamama'	NMen
	'Pacific Charm'	NMen
	'Pacific Devils Food'	NMen
	'Pacific Hazy Embers'	NMen
	'Pacific Hep'	NMen
	'Pacific Opal'	NMen
	'Pacific Purple Shadows'	NMen
	'Pacific Sexy'	NMen
	'Pacific Sunset'	NMen
	'Pacific Thunder'	NMen
	'Packardian'	NMen NWad
	'Painted Lady'	NMen
	'Palissander'	EDAr GAbr NMen SPhm XLum
	'Pallas'	XLum
	'Pam Wain'	NMen
	'Passionata'	NMen
	'Pastel'	CTri MHer
	patens	see *Jovibarba heuffelii*
	'Patrician'	LBee SRms
	'Pavilion'	NMen
	'Peggy'	NMen
	'Pekinese'	CTal EDAr GEdr LRHS MBrN NBro NMen NRHS SRms WBrk XLum
	'Peterson's Ornatum'	SDys
	'Petsy'	NMen SRms
	'Phoebe'	NMen
	'Pilatus'	EPfP GAbr LRHS NRHS SRms WFar XLum
	'Pine Cone'	NMen
	'Pink Astrid'	NMen

	'Pink Cloud'	NMen
	'Pink Delight'	MSCN
	'Pink Flamingoes'	NMen
	'Pink Grapefruit'	NMen
	'Pink Lemonade'	NMen
	'Pink Mist'	SRms
	'Pink Puff'	NMen
	'Pippin'	CMea CTal NMen SRms
	pittonii ♀H5	CMea EPot NMen WHal XLum
	'Pixie'	NMen
	'Plum Frosting'	MSCN
	'Plum Mist'	NWad
	'Plumb Rose'	NMen
	'Pluto'	NMen XLum
	'Polaris'	GBin NMen
	'Poldark'	NMen
	'Ponderosa'	NMen
I	'Powellii'	NMen
	'Prairie Sunset'	NMen
	'President Arsac'	XLum
	'Probus'	NMen
	'Procton'	GCrg NMen
	'Proud Zelda'	EDAr GAbr MSCN NMen
	'Průhonice'	NMen
	'Pseudo-ornatum'	LBee SRms
	pulchellum	XLum
	'Pumaros'	SDys
	pumilum	LRHS NMen NRHS SRms
	- from Techensis, Caucasus Mountains	SRms
	- 'Sopa'	MSCN
	'Purdy'	NHpl NMen WAbe
	'Purdy's 50-6'	GAbr NMen
	'Purdy's 70-40'	NMen
	'Purdy's Big Red'	NMen
	'Purple Beauty'	NMen
	'Purple Dazzler'	NMen
	'Purple Haze'	NMen
	'Purple King'	CMea SDys
	'Purple Passion'	NMen
	'Purple Queen'	EDAr ELon EPPr LRHS NMen NRHS SRms
	'Purple Shadows'	NMen
	'Purple Violet'	NMen
	'Pygmalion'	NMen
	'Quax'	NMen
	'Queen Amalia'	see *S. reginae-amaliae*
	'Quintessence'	MSCN NMen SRms
	'Ramses'	SDys
	'Raspberry Ice'	CMea LBee MSCN NBro NHpl NMen
	'Rauer Kulm'	NMen
	'Rauhreif'	ECtt XLum
	'Ravenheart'	MSCN
	'Red Ace'	GCrg GEdr MBel NBro NEoE NMen
	'Red Beam'	LRHS NMen NRHS
	'Red Chief'	XLum
	'Red Chips'	EDAr
	'Red Delta'	NMen WCot WPGP
	'Red Devil'	ELon LLHF LRHS NMen NRHS SPlb SRms WHoo
	'Red Knight'	NMen
	'Red Lion'	NMen
§	'Red Mountain'	LBee LSun MMuc NMen SRms
	'Red Pink'	CMea NMen
	'Red Pluche'	NMen
	'Red Robin'	EDAr NMen
	'Red Shadows'	LBee
	'Red Spider'	EPot GCrg NBro NMen
	'Red West'	NMen
	'Regal'	NMen
	reginae	see *S. reginae-amaliae*
§	***reginae-amaliae***	LRHS NMen NRHS SRms XLum
	- from Kambeecho, Greece, No 2	SDys
	- from Sarpun, Turkey	NMen SDys
§	'Reginald Malby'	LRHS NMen NRHS SRms
	'Reinhard' ♀H5	CMea CTal EDAr ELon EPot GCrg GEdr GMaP LRHS MAsh MBrN MHer MSCN NHpl NMen NRHS NRya SPlb SRms WBrk WHal WHoo
	'Remus'	ELan NMen SRms
	'Rex'	NMen
	'Rhöne'	LBee NMen
	'Rich 'n' Fruity'	MSCN
	'Rio de Janeiro'	NMen
	'Risque'	LBee
	'Rita Jane'	NMen
	'Robin'	GCrg NBro NMen SRms XLum
	'Ronny'	NMen
	'Roosemaryn'	EDAr
	'Rosa Mädchen'	NMen
	× ***roseum***	NMen
	'Rosie'	CMea ELon EPot GAbr GEdr GMaP LBee LRHS MAsh MMuc MSCN NMen NRHS SRms WBrk WHal WHoo
	'Rotkopf' ♀H5	CTal LRHS MSCN NMen NRHS NWad XLum
	'Rotmantel'	NMen
	'Rotund'	GEdr MSCN
	'Rouge'	NMen
	'Royal Opera'	EDAr NMen
	'Royal Ruby'	GCrg
	'Rubikon Improved'	NMen
	'Rubin'	CBod CMea CTal CTri EPfP MAsh MMuc NEgg NHpl NMen SPoG SRms WAbe XLum
I	'Rubra Ash'	NMen
I	'Rubra Ray'	EDAr MMuc NMen SEND
	'Rubrifolium'	see *S. marmoreum* subsp. *marmoreum* 'Rubrifolium'
*	'Ruby Glow'	EDAr
	'Ruby Heart'	EDAr
	'Russian River'	WHoo
	ruthenicum	CTal EPPr LLHF LRHS NRHS NRya SRms XLum
	- 'Regis-Fernandii'	XLum
	'Samwise'	NMen
	'Sando'	NMen
	'Sanford's Hybrid'	NMen
	'Santis'	NMen
	'Sarah'E	DAr NMen
	'Sarotte'	NMen
	'Sassy Frass'	NMen
	'Saturn'	GEdr MSCN NMen SRms
	schlehanii	see *S. marmoreum*
	schnittspahnii	XLum
	seguieri	XLum
	'Seminole'	NMen
	'Seren'	GBin
	'Serendipity'	EDAr
	'Sharon's Pencil'	NMen
	'Sha'uri'	NMen
	'Sheila'	GAbr
	'Shirley Moore'	EDAr NMen
	'Shirley's Joy'	NMen XLum
	'Show Baby'	NMen

	'Sideshow'	NMen
	'Sigma'	NMen
	'Silberkarneol' misapplied	see *S.* 'Silver Jubilee'
	'Silberkarneol' ambig.	MMuc
	'Silberspitz'	CTal ELon LRHS MHer NBro NMen NRHS SPlb SRms
	'Silver Andre'	NMen
§	'Silver Jubilee'	CMea EDAr GBin GQue LRHS NBro NMen NRHS NRya SPlb SRms XLum
	'Silver Shadow'	MSCN
	'Silver Thaw'	EDAr GMaP LRHS NMen NRHS
	'Silverine'	EDAr
	'Simonkaianum'	see *Jovibarba hirta*
	'Sioux'	CTal GAbr LBee MBrN NMen WHal
	'Sirius'	GBin MHol NMen
	'Skrocki's Beauty'	GAbr NMen SRms
	'Skrocki's Bronze'	LRHS NMen NRHS
	'Smaragd'	LBee LRHS NRHS XLum
	'Smit's Seedling'	NMen
	'Smokey Jet'	NMen
	'Snowberger'	CTal MSCN NMen SRms WHal
	soboliferum	see *Jovibarba sobolifera*
	'Solist'	NMen
	'Sombrero'	NMen
	'Soothsayer'	NMen
	sosnowskyi	NMen XLum
	'Soul'	NMen
	'Space Dog'	NMen
	'Spangle'	NMen
	'Spangle' sport	NMen
	'Spanish Dancer'	NMen
	'Sparkler'	CTal
	'Spherette'	EDAr MBrN MSCN NMen WAbe
	'Spice'	NMen
	'Spider's Lair' ♀H5	EDAr NMen SRms
	'Spinellii'	NMen WThu
	'Spiver's Velvet'	NMen
	'Sponnier'	XLum
	'Springmist'	LRHS NMen NRHS SRms
	'Sprite'	GEdr LRHS MBel NMen NRHS SDys SRms
	'Squib'	CTal MSCN NMen
	stansfieldii	see *S. arachnoideum* subsp. *tomentosum* 'Stansfieldii'
	'Starburst'	CMea LRHS NRHS
	'Starion'	NMen
	'Starshine'	NMen
	'State Fair'	EDAr NMen
	'Steerosentern'	NMen
*	***stoloniferum***	GAbr
	'Strawberry Sundae'	NMen
	'Strider'	GAbr NMen
	'Stuffed Olive'	NMen SDys SRms SRot
	'Sugary'	NMen
	'Sun Waves'	NMen SDys
	'Super Dome'	NMen
	'Superama'	NMen
	'Syston Flame'	NMen
	'Tamberlane'	EDAr
	'Tarita'	NMen
	'T'Boz'	NMen
	'Teck'	NMen
§	***tectorum*** ♀H5	CHby CTal CTri EDAr ELan EPfP EUJe GPoy LBee MHer MNHC SPlb XAbr XLum
§	- var. ***alpinum***	LRHS NBro NMen NRHS SRms
	- var. ***andreanum***	XLum
	- 'Atropurpureum'	ELan SRms

	- 'Atroviolaceum'	EDAr NMen SPlb XLum
*	- 'Aureum'	NMen
	- var. ***boutignyanum*** GDJ 94.04 from Route de Tuixén, Spain	SRms
§	- var. ***glaucum***	NMen XLum
	- 'Marin'	NMen
	- 'Mettenianum'	XLum
	- monstrose	SPlb SRms
	- 'Murale'	XLum
§	- 'Nigrum'	LBee MHer NBro SDys XLum
	- 'Red Flush'	EDAr EPPr MBrN NMen
	- 'Royanum' ♀H5	MSCN SRms
*	- subsp. ***sanguineum***	EDAr
	- 'Sunset'	CMea EDAr GAbr GCrg SDys WHal
	- subsp. ***tectorum***	GEdr NMen
§	- - 'Boissieri'	NMen
	- - 'Triste'	LBee NHpl NMen XLum
	- 'Violaceum'	NMen SPlb SRms
	'Teddy Bear'	MSCN
	'Tederheid'	GCrg NMen
	'Telfan'	NMen
	'Tenburg'	NMen
	'Terlamen'	NMen
	'Terracotta Baby'	CTal ELon GCrg NMen
	'Thayne'	NMen
	'The Platters'	NMen
	'Thunder'	NMen
	'Tiger Bay'	NMen
	'Tintenblut'	NMen
	'Tintinabulum'	NMen
	'Tip Top'	GEdr NMen
	tissieri	XLum
	'Titania'	NBro NMen WHal
	'Tjabine'	NMen
	'Tommella'	XLum
	'Topaz'	LBee NMen SRms XLum
	'Tordeur's Memory'	GCrg MMuc NMen SEND SRms
I	'Tourmalyi'	NMen
	'T'Pol'	NMen
	'Tracy Sue'	EDAr XLum
	'Trail Walker'	LBee NMen SRms
	transcaucasicum	XLum
	'Tree Beard'	NMen
	'Trine'	NMen
	'Tristesse' ♀H5	ECtt EDAr GAbr LBee MBrN NMen
	'Troika'	NMen
	'Truva'	NMen
	'Twilight Blues'	LRHS NMen NRHS SRms
	'Twizzler'	MSCN
	'U4'	NMen
	'Undine'	NMen
	'Unicorn'	NMen
	'Ualturmalin'	NMen
	'Uranus'	XLum
	× ***vaccarii***	XLum
	'Van der Steen'	NMen
	'Vanbaelen'	GAbr NMen SDys
	'Vasi Petru'	NMen
	'Vega'	CPla GBin MHol
	'Venus'	XLum
	× ***versicolor***	CPla
	'Veughelen'	NMen
	vicentei	NMen
	- from Gaton, Spain	LBee LRHS NMen NRHS
§	- subsp. ***paui***	NSla
	'Video'	NMen
	'Vignola'	NMen

	'Violet Queen'	NMen
	'Virgil'	EDAr GAbr GCrg MBrN MSCN NMen NWad SDys SPlb WAbe WCot
I	'Virginius'	GAbr NMen
	'Vulcano'	NMen
	'Waldalina'	NMen
	'Warrior'	EDAr
	'Wasti'	NMen
	'Waterlily'	NWad
	'Watermelon Rind'	NMen
	webbianum	see *S. arachnoideum* L. subsp. *tomentosum* (C.B. Lehm. & Schnittsp.) Schinz & Thell.
	'Webby Flame'	NMen
	'Webbyola'	NMen
	'Weirdo'	NMen
	'Wendy'	NMen
	'Westerlin'	NMen
	'Wheel of Fire'	NMen
	'White Bouquet'	NMen
	'White Christmas'	see *S. arachnoideum* 'White Christmas'
	'White Ladies'	NMen
	'Whitening'	EDAr EPot GAbr GEdr
	'Whitney'	NMen
	× ***widderi***	NMen
	'Wilhelm Tell'	NMen
	'Winsome'	NWad
	'Winter Beauty'	NMen
	'Wok'	NMen
I	'Woolcott's Variety'	MSCN NMen SRms
	wulfenii	NMen XLum
	- subsp. ***juvanii***	XLum
*	- ***roseum***	EDAr
	'Xaviera'	NMen
	'Xerxes'	NMen
	'Yanisha'	NMen
	'Yarnton'	NMen
	'Yolanda'	NMen
	'Yvette'	NMen
	'Zaccour'	NMen
	'Zackenkrone'	NMen
	zeleborii	NMen WHal
	'Zenith'	EDAr GAbr NMen SRms
	'Zenocrate'	WHal
	'Zepherin'	NMen
	'Zilver Moon'	NMen
	'Zilver Snowflake'	NMen
	'Zilverprinsesje'	NMen
	'Zircon'	EDAr NMen
	'Zone'	NMen
	'Zorba'	NMen
	'Zulu'	NMen

Senecio (*Asteraceae*)

	aquaticus	see *Jacobaea aquatica*
	articulatus	see *Curio articulata*
§	***barbertonicus***	EShb
	candicans misapplied	see *Jacobaea maritima*
	chrysanthemoides misapplied	see *Euryops chrysanthemoides*
	cineraria	see *Jacobaea maritima*
	cinerascens	SVen
	coccinilifera hort.	see *Kleinia grantii*
	compactus	see *Brachyglottis compacta*
	confusus	see *Pseudogynoxys chenopodioides*
	crassissimus	EShb
	cristobalensis	see *Roldana cristobalensis*
	doria	EShb MMuc SAko WHrl
	elegans	SVen
	ficoides	see *Curio ficoides*
	formosoides B&SWJ 10736	WCru
	formosus B&SWJ 10700	WCru
	gerberifolius B&SWJ 10357	WCru
	- B&SWJ 10361	WCru
	glastifolius	CPne
	'Gregynog Gold'	see *Ligularia* 'Gregynog Gold'
	greyi misapplied	see *Brachyglottis* (Dunedin Group) 'Sunshine'
	greyi Hook. f.	see *Brachyglottis greyi* (Hook. f.) B. Nord.
	haworthii	see *Caputia tomentosa*
	heritieri DC.	see *Pericallis lanata* (L'Hér.) B. Nord.
	kleiniiformis	EShb
	laxifolius hort.	see *Brachyglottis* (Dunedin Group) 'Sunshine'
	leucostachys misapplied	see *S. viravira*
	macroglossus	CHll EShb
	maritimus	see *Jacobaea maritima*
	mikanioides	see *Delairea odorata*
	monroi	see *Brachyglottis monroi*
	niveoaureus B&SWJ 14320 **new**	WCru
	petasitis	see *Roldana petasitis*
	polyodon var. ***polyodon***	GBin MMuc WWFP
	- var. ***subglaber***	CCCN CSpe EAJP EWes GLog GQue LRHS MHol MNrw MPie MSpe SBee SPhx WArt WCAu WCFE WCot WFar WPGP WSHC
	przewalskii	see *Ligularia przewalskii*
	pulcher	CDTJ SBch SHar WPGP
	reinoldii	see *Brachyglottis rotundifolia*
	rowleyanus	see *Curio rowleyanus*
	scandens	see *Delairea odorata*
	seminiveus	EBee
	serpens	see *Curio repens*
§	***smithii***	ELan LLWG NBid WWtn
	'Sunshine'	see *Brachyglottis* (Dunedin Group) 'Sunshine'
	talinoides	see *S. barbertonicus*
	subsp. ***cylindricus*** 'Himalaya'	
	tanguticus	see *Sinacalia tangutica*
§	***viravira***	EPri MCot WSHC

Senna (*Caesalpiniaceae*)

	alexandrina	CCCN EShb WPGP
	artemisioides [H1c]	WCot
§	***candolleana***	EBee
§	***corymbosa***	CBcs CCCN CRHN CTri ECre
	didymobotrya	WArt
	hebecarpa	SBrt
§	***marilandica***	EBee ELan MGil
	multiglandulosa	WPGP
	obtusa Clos	see *S. candolleana*
	septemtrionalis	CCCN LRHS SEND

Sequoia (*Cupressaceae*)

	sempervirens [H6]	CAco CBcs CCVT CDul CLnd CMCN CMen CPer CTho CTsd ECrN EPfP EWTr LMaj LPra MBlu MMuc NOra SEND SGol WMou WTSh
	- 'Adpressa'	CAco CDul MGos SCoo
	- 'Cantab'	WMou
	- 'Henderson Blue'	SLim
	- 'Mount Loma Prieta Spike'	NLar

Sequoiadendron (*Cupressaceae*)

giganteum 🏆H6 CBcs CCVT CDul CLnd CMCN CPer CTho CTri CTsd ELan EPfP ESps EWTr GMcL LPra LRHS MBlu MGos MMuc NEgg NOra SEND SEWo SGol SLim SPlb WMou WTSh
- 'Barabits Requiem' MBlu NLar SMad
- 'Beautiful Jop' NLar
- 'Blauer Eichzwerg' NLar
- 'Bultinck Yellow' MBlu
- 'Cannibal' NLar
- 'Desperado' **new** NLar
- 'Glaucum' CDul MBlu SLim
* - 'Glaucum Compactum' MBlu
- 'Greenpeace' MBlu
- 'Little Stan' NLar SLim
- 'Pendulum' CCVT CDul CKen ERod MBlu SLim SMad
- 'Petticoat' NLar
- 'Powdered Blue' WPGP
- 'Yellow Stone' **new** NLar

Serapias (*Orchidaceae*)

lingua SChF

Seriphidium see *Artemisia*

Serratula (*Asteraceae*)

bulgarica see *Klasea bulgarica*
coronata subsp. ***insularis*** see *Klasea coronata* subsp. *insularis*
gmelinii see *Klasea radiata* subsp. *gmelinii*
lycopifolia see *Klasea lycopifolia*
shawii see *S. tinctoria* var. *seoanei*
tinctoria NLar NMir SPhx
§ - var. ***seoanei*** CKno CMea CSam EBee ELan LEdu MCot MHer MNrw MPie MRav NBid NDov SHar SPhx SRms WCot WPGP WTor

Serruria (*Proteaceae*)

florida SPlb
phylicoides SPlb

Sesamothamnus (*Pedaliaceae*)

lugardii LToo

Sesamum (*Pedaliaceae*)

indicum XAbr

Sesbania (*Papilionaceae*)

punicea CCCN

Seseli (*Apiaceae*)

elatum MAvo
- PAB 9228 LEdu SPhx
gummiferum CHid CSam CSpe EAJP MAvo SPhx
hippomarathrum CSpe LEdu MAvo MNrw SBrt SPhx WCot WHal WHrl WPGP WWtn
lehmannii SPhx
§ ***libanotis*** CBod CPla CSam EBee EPPr GBin LEdu LRHS MAvo NLar NPnk SPhx
montanum CSam CSpe EBee IMou LPla MAvo NDov SBrt WPGP

Sesleria (*Poaceae*)

§ ***albicans*** SCob
§ ***argentea*** EHoe LPla
autumnalis CBWd CKno EBee EHoe ELon EShb EWes IMou LCro LEdu NDov SCob SPhx XLum
caerulea CBod CKno EBWF EHoe ELan ELon EPfP IMou LEdu LRHS MBrN NDov NRHS SPhx SPoG WPtf XLum XSen
- subsp. ***calcarea*** see *S. albicans*
- 'Malvern Mop' EBee WHrl
* ***candida*** EPPr
cylindrica see *S. argentea*
glauca CPla EHoe
'Greenlee' CKno
heufleriana EHoe EPPr GEdr IMou LPla MBel NRya SPhx SPlb WCot
insularis EBee EPPr EShb
'Morning Dew' EBee GCal
nitida CKno EBee EHoe EUJe IMou LEdu LRHS MBrN NDov NRHS SPhx WCot XLum XSen
rigida EHoe
sadleriana EBee EPPr EWes

Setaria (*Poaceae*)

italica 'Red Jewel' CSpe
macrostachya SPhx
palmifolia 🏆H2 CBot CPla EShb EUJe MPie NLos SPlb
- BWJ 8132 WCru
viridis CSpe WCot

Setcreasea see *Tradescantia*

shaddock see *Citrus maxima*

Sharon fruit see *Diospyros kaki*

Shepherdia (*Elaeagnaceae*)

argentea NLar

Shibataea (*Poaceae*)

kumasaca 🏆H5 CAbb CBcs CBdn ENBC ERod EUJe GCal LEdu MJak MWht SBig SGol

Shortia (*Diapensiaceae*)

soldanelloides var. ***magna*** EPot
uniflora GKev

Sibbaldia (*Rosaceae*)

procumbens GKev

Sibbaldiopsis (*Rosaceae*)

§ ***tridentata*** SBrt
- 'Nuuk' EWTr

Sibthorpia (*Plantaginaceae*)

europaea CExl

Sidalcea (*Malvaceae*)

'Brilliant' CBcs CBod CNor GBin IBoy ILea MJak MNrw MSCN WCAu WMoo
campestris from Oregon EPPr
candida CSam EBee ECtt ELan EPfP GMaP GWyn IBoy ILea LRHS MBNS MMuc MRav MTis NChi NGdn NLar NRHS NSti SCob SPer WCAu WCot
- 'Bianca' EBee EPfP NLar WFar WMoo WOut

'Candy Girl'	CBod EBee IRob NLar SCob WCot WFar
'Crimson King'	WFar
'Croftway Red'	EBee ELan EWld LRHS MBel NBro NGdn NRHS NWad SPer SWvt WFar
'Elsie Heugh' 🏆H7	Widely available
LILAC CANDICE ('Midawioha') **new**	WFar
'Little Princess' PBR	CRos EBee EPfP EWes IRob LRHS MHol MNrw NCou NGdn NLar NRHS SCob SPoG WCot
'Loveliness'	CBod EBee ECtt ELan EShb LRHS MRav NBro NDov NRHS NWad WFar WGwG WMoo WWtn
malviflora	SBrt SRms
- 'Crimson Beauty'	EBee
- subsp. ***purpurea***	LRHS NRHS
'Monarch'	WFar
'Moorland Rose Coronet'	WFar WMoo
'Mr Lindbergh'	EBee MPie NLar WCFE
'Mrs Borrodaile'	CMac MBel MRav NBro NEoE NGdn WMoo
'Mrs Galloway'	LRHS NRHS
'My Love'	EBee NDov
'Oberon'	EBee LRHS MRav NRHS
oregana	NGdn
- subsp. ***spicata***	WFar WMoo
'Party Girl'	CMac CRos CSBt CSam ELan EPfP GJos IBoy LRHS MNHC MPie MRav NBro NGdn NLar NRHS SPlb SPoG WBor WFar WMoo WWtn XLum
'Purpetta'	EBee ELan EPfP NEoE NGBl NLar
reptans	WFar
'Reverend Page Roberts'	MRav WCot
'Rosaly'	CSam EAJP IFoB LRHS MPie NLar NRHS WFar WWtn
'Rosanna'	CSam EAJP EPfP GMaP LRHS NLar NRHS
'Rose Bud'	EBee ELan WFar
'Rose Queen'	CBod EBee ECha EPPr LRHS MRav NBro NRHS SHar SPer SRms WFar
Stark's hybrids	LRHS NRHS SRms
'Sussex Beauty'	CSam EBee LRHS MBel MRav NEgg NGdn NRHS WCot WFar WMoo
'Wensleydale'	EBee LRHS NRHS WFar
'William Smith' 🏆H7	CSam EBee ECha ECtt EPfP EWes GBin LRHS MArl MMuc MRav NGdn NLar NRHS SEND SPer WFar WWtn
'Wine Red'	CBod EBee EShb LRHS MMrt NEgg NGdn NRHS SPoG SWvt WGwG WTor

Sideritis (*Lamiaceae*)

cypria	EBee
syriaca	MHer XAbr XSen
- RCB UA 2 **new**	WCot

Sieversia (*Rosaceae*)

§ ***pentapetala***	GEdr
reptans	see *Geum reptans*

Silaum (*Apiaceae*)

silaus	NMir

Silene (*Caryophyllaceae*)

RBS	EPPr
from Uzbekistan	GCal
acaulis	EDAr GJos SRms WAbe WArt
§ - subsp. ***acaulis***	SPlb SRms
- 'Alba'	EWes WAbe
- 'Blush'	EDAr GCrg NRHS NSla WAbe WOld
§ - subsp. ***bryoides***	NLar
- 'Correvoniana'	NLar
- subsp. ***elongata***	see *S. acaulis* subsp. *acaulis*
- subsp. ***exscapa***	see *S. acaulis* subsp. *bryoides*
- 'Frances'	CPBP EDAr EPot GCrg ITim NLar NRHS NRya NSla WAbe
- 'Mount Snowdon'	EWes NHpl NLar SPlb SPoG SRms SRot WHoo
- 'Pedunculata'	see *S. acaulis* subsp. *acaulis*
aegyptiaca **new**	SPhx
alba	see *S. latifolia* subsp. *alba*
§ ***alpestris***	SRms SRot WArt WMoo WThu
- 'Flore Pleno' (d) 🏆H5	CMea CPBP EWes NRHS NSla
- 'Starry Dreams'	LRHS NPnk NRHS
araratica	CMea WAbe
× ***arkwrightii***	see *Lychnis* × *arkwrightii*
armeria	SDys
- 'Electra'	CSpe MNHC
asterias	EBee EPPr GCal MNrw SBrt
atropurpurea	see *Lychnis viscaria* subsp. *atropurpurea*
californica	SBrt
catholica	EBee
ciliata	GEdr
'Confetti'	CWld EAJP EPPr NSti
'Country Comet'	NChi
§ ***davidii***	GKev
§ ***dioica***	CBre CHab CWld EBWF GJos LOPS MHer MNHC NLar NMir SPhx SPoG SRms WMoo WOut WSFF WShi
- 'Clifford Moor' (v)	ECtt MHer MSCN NSti SCoo
- 'Compacta'	see *S. dioica* 'Minikin'
- 'Firefly' PBR (d)	CDor CMac CSpe CWCL ECtt NSti SHar SRkn SWvt WSHC
§ - 'Flore Pleno' (d)	MHer MRav NBid NBro NGdn WHoo
- 'Inane'	ELon WBor WPGP WRHF WSHC
- 'Innocence'	NChi
§ - 'Minikin'	MTis NGdn
- 'Purple Prince'	CBre MMuc SEND WMoo WPtf
I - 'Ray's Golden Campion'	NWad SHar
- 'Rollie's Favorite' PBR	CRos EBee ECtt EPfP LRHS MAsh MHol MNrw MSCN NDov NPnk NPri NRHS NSti SPoG WBor
- 'Rosea Plena' (d)	WSHC
- 'Rubra Plena'	see *S. dioica* 'Flore Pleno'
- 'Thelma Kay' (d/v)	NGdn WMoo
- 'Valley High' (v)	EBee ECtt EWes MHol WCot
elisabethae	NSla
falcata	CPBP
§ ***fimbriata***	CSpe EHrv ELan EPPr EShb GQue GWyn ILea MCot MMrt MNrw MRav NChi NLar NSti WArt WCot WKif WMoo WPGP WPtf WRHF WWtn
frivaldskyana	SBrt
gallica	EBWF
hookeri	GBin GKev SPlb
- subsp. ***bolanderi*** **new**	SBrt
- Ingramii Group	GKev WAbe
kantzeensis	see *S. davidii*
keiskei	CPBP
- var. ***akaisialpina***	NSla
- - f. ***leucantha***	NSla

	- var. ***minor***	EWes LRHS NRHS WAbe
	laciniata 'Jack Flash'	MSCN
	latifolia	CHab MHer MNHC NMir WOut
§	- subsp. ***alba***	SEND SPhx
	mariana new	GAbr
	maritima	see *S. uniflora*
	multifida	see *S. fimbriata*
	noctiflora	CHab EBWF WSFF
	nutans	EBWF SBrt SRms WSFF
	pusilla	NHpl NLar
	quadridentata	see *S. alpestris*
	regia	EBee SBrt SPhx
	- 'Prairie Fire'	WCot
	rubra	see *S. dioica*
	schafta ♀H5	CTri ECha EPfP GJos GKev LPmr MAsh MMuc MRav NBid SEND SRms WHoo XLum
	- 'Abbotswood'	see *Lychnis × walkeri* 'Abbotswood Rose'
	- 'Shell Pink'	CPBP CSam ECha ECtt EPfP EPot EWes GJos LRHS MMuc NBid NRHS SEND WHoo
	sieboldii	see *Lychnis coronata* var. *sieboldii*
	stellata	SPhx
§	***uniflora***	CHab EBWF EPfP MMuc NBro SPlb SRms SRot WMoo WOut
	- 'Alba Plena'	see *S. uniflora* 'Robin Whitebreast'
I	- 'Compacta'	WArt WMoo
§	- 'Druett's Variegated' (v)	CRos ECtt ELon EPot EWes GJos LRHS MAsh MHer MHol MSCN NBid NHpl NRHS SPlb SPoG SRms XLum
	- 'Flore Pleno'	see *S. uniflora* 'Robin Whitebreast'
§	- 'Robin Whitebreast' (d)	ECha ECtt EPfP GBin LRHS NBid NBro NRHS NWad SPhx SRms SRot WMoo WSHC XLum
	- 'Rosea'	ECtt GCrg GJos MHol MMuc NHpl SPlb SRot
	- 'Variegata'	see *S. uniflora* 'Druett's Variegated'
	- WEISSKEHLCHEN	see *S. uniflora* 'Robin Whitebreast'
	- 'White Bells'	CTri WKif
	viridiflora	SPhx
§	***vulgaris***	CAgr CHab EBWF MMuc MNHC NMir SPhx SRms WHer WMoo WOut
	- subsp. ***maritima***	see *S. uniflora*
	wallichiana	see *S. vulgaris*
	'Wisley Pink'	ECtt
	yunnanensis	SPhx WSHC
§	***zawadskii***	GKev MMuc NWad SBrt SEND

Siler (*Umbelliferae*)

	montanum	see *Laserpitium siler*

Silphium (*Asteraceae*)

	integrifolium	NBre SMad SPhx WCot WOld XLum
	laciniatum	CMac LEdu NBre SBrt SPhx WHal XLum
	perfoliatum ♀H7	EBee GPoy IMou LPla LRHS MMuc NBre NDov NLar NRHS SEND SPhx WCot WFar XLum
	- from Great Dixter	IMou
	- var. ***connatum***	SPhx
	terebinthinaceum	SBrt SPhx WCot XLum
	trifoliatum	EPPr SPhx WCot

Silybum (*Asteraceae*)

	marianum	ELan GPoy LRHS MNHC NRHS SPav SPhx SRms WArt WOut XAbr

Sinacalia (*Asteraceae*)

§	***tangutica***	CSam GQue ILea MBel NBid NLar NSti WCot WOld WWtn

Sinapis (*Brassicaceae*)

	alba	SVic

Sinarundinaria (*Poaceae*)

	anceps	see *Yushania anceps*
	jaunsarensis	see *Yushania anceps*
	maling	see *Yushania maling*
	murielae	see *Fargesia murielae*
	nitida	see *Fargesia nitida*

Sinningia (*Gesneriaceae*)

	aggregata new	LToo
*	***caerulea***	WDib
	calcaria	WDib
	canescens ♀H1c	LToo
§	***cardinalis***	EBak WDib
	- 'Innocent'	WDib
	conspicua	WDib
	nivalis	WDib
	speciosa 'Blanche de Méru'	SDeJ
	- 'Hollywood'	SDeJ
	- 'Kaiser Friedrich'	SDeJ
	- 'Kaiser Wilhelm'	SDeJ
	- 'Mont Blanc'	EShb SDeJ
	tubiflora	CSpe LEdu WCot WKif XLum

× *Sinocalycalycanthus* see *Calycanthus*

Sinocalycanthus see *Calycanthus*

Sinocrassula (*Crassulaceae*)

	yunnanensis	CPla EUJe NHpl SPlb

Sinofranchetia (*Lardizabalaceae*)

	chinensis	CRHN IArd MGil SAko WPGP WSHC
	- DJHS 4117	WCru

Sinojackia (*Styracaceae*)

	xylocarpa	CBcs CMCN NLar

Sinopanax (*Araliaceae*)

	formosanus	CFil

Sinopodophyllum (*Berberidaceae*)

§	***hexandrum***	CBct CBro CWCL EBee ELan EPot GBin GKev GMaP GPoy GQue ILea LPla MNrw MRav NBid NChi NLar SPlb WAvo WCot WPnP WSHC
§	- var. ***chinense***	GCal LEdu WCru
	- - BWJ 7908	WCru
	- - SDR 4409	CExl
	- 'Chinese White'	CExl
§	- var. ***emodi***	EPfP ITim MMoz
	- - 'Majus'	EWTr GBin WCot WHal

Sinowilsonia (*Hamamelidaceae*)

	henryi	CBcs NLar

Siphocranion (*Lamiaceae*)

§	***macranthum***	EWes WPGP WSHC

Sison (*Apiaceae*)

	amomum	CBre

Sisyrinchium (*Iridaceae*)

	× ***anceps***	see *S. angustifolium*
§	***angustifolium***	CWCL ECha LSun MCot NChi SChF SPlb SRms WBrk
	- f. ***album***	MCot NChi NLar
§	***arenarium***	CWCL
	bellum hort.	see *S. idahoense* var. *bellum*
	bermudiana	see *S. angustifolium*
	'Biscutella'	CBod CKno EPfP GMaP ITim LEdu MHCG SPad SPlb SRot WHal WHoo WKif
	'Blue Ice'	GPSL ITim LRHS NLar WAbe WMoo
	'Blue Skies'	ITim
	boreale	see *S. californicum*
	brachypus	see *S. californicum* Brachypus Group
	'Californian Skies'	CAby CBro CElw CExl CKno CRos EAJP ECha ECtt GMaP LRHS NDov NRHS NSla SRms SRot SWvt WAvo WKif WMoo
§	***californicum***	CBen GWyn IMou LLWG LRHS WMAq XLum
§	- Brachypus Group	CPla EPfP MAsh NLar SPlb SWvt WMoo
	- 'Yellowstone'	CSBt EPfP GMcL SRms
*	***capsicum***	CExl
	convolutum	NDov
	- B&SWJ 9117	WCru
	cuspidatum	see *S. arenarium*
	depauperatum	MNrw
	'Devon Skies'	CElw CPBP CPla CRos CWCL ECtt GCrg LRHS MNrw NLar NRHS SBch SRms SWvt WAbe
	'Doctor Bailey'	EBee
	douglasii	see *Olsynium douglasii*
	'Dragon's Eye'	CElw CKno CMea CPBP EAJP ECtt EHoe EWes MBrN MHer SCob
	'E.K. Balls'	CAby CPBP CRos CTal ECtt EDAr EHoe ELan EPot GCrg GMaP LRHS MAsh NHpl NRHS NRya NSla SMad SPoG SRGP SRms SRot SWvt WAbe WHar WMoo
	graminoides	GWyn IFoB
	grandiflorum	see *Olsynium douglasii*
	'Hemswell Sky'	ECtt EHoe GAbr NLar NRya
	'Iceberg'	CAby CElw CKno ECha EWes
	idahoense	CPla ECha ECtt GAbr MHer NDov NHpl NRya SPlb SRms
§	- var. ***bellum***	CKno EPfP LPmr SRms WMoo XLum
	- - pale-flowered	CKno SMHy
	- - 'Rocky Point'	CKno EBee EPfP EWes LRHS NRHS SPoG WFar
	- var. ***macounii***	GEdr GPSL SPlb
§	- - 'Album' 🏆^{H5}	CAby CElw CMea ECtt EWes GAbr GCrg GEdr WAbe
	'Janet Denman' (v)	EWes LLHF MAvo SRot
	junceum	see *Olsynium junceum*
	littorale	CExl
	macrocarpon misapplied	see *S. macrocarpum*
§	***macrocarpum***	EWld
	'Marchants Seedling'	SMHy
	'Marion'	CMea ECtt MBrN WHoo
	'May Snow'	see *S. idahoense* var. *macounii* 'Album'
	montanum	NHpl
	montanum × ***nudicaule***	GAbr NRHS NWad SRot
	'Mrs Spivey'	CSpe
	'North Star'	see *S.* 'Pole Star'
	nudicaule	NWad
	palmifolium	CAby CSpe EBee LEdu MHer MNrw SBch SMad SPad WFar WSHC XLum
	patagonicum	CExl CPla CTal GKev
§	'Pole Star'	NLar
	'Quaint and Queer'	CCCN CExl EAJP ECha EHoe MBrN MCot MNrw WAvo WSHC
	'Raspberry'	CKno CMea
	'Sapphire'	CAby CBod CCCN CKno ECha ECtt EDAr EHoe ELan GCrg GPSL LRHS MHol NHpl NLar NRya SCob SPoG WGrn WMoo
§	***striatum***	Widely available
§	- 'Aunt May' (v)	CBcs CBod CCCN CMac ECha EHoe EPed EPfP GMaP LRHS LSRN MBel MGos MRav MSpe NHpl NLar NRHS NSti SCob SPer SPoG SRms SWvt WCot WPGP
	- 'Variegatum'	see *S. striatum* 'Aunt May'
	'Stripey'^{PBR} (v)	CSpe WCot
	aff. ***unispathaceum*** B&SWJ 10683	WCru

Sium (*Apiaceae*)

sisarum	GPoy LEdu MAvo MHer NDov

Skimmia ✿ (*Rutaceae*)

	anquetilia	CMac
	- (f)	WCru
	- (m)	WCru
	arborescens B&SWJ 11799	WCru
	- PAB 8774	LEdu
	- subsp. ***nitida*** B&SWJ 8239	WCru
	arisanensis B&SWJ 7114	WCru
	- CWJ 12417	WCru
	black-fruited B&SWJ 8259 from northern Vietnam (f/m)	WCru
	× ***confusa*** 'Kew Green' (m) 🏆^{H5}	Widely available
	japonica	CMac CTho MGos NPla SCob SSta WFar
	- (f)	CMac CTri ELan EPfP GMcL SRms
	- - B&SWJ 5053	WCru
	- (m) B&SWJ 5053	WCru
	- 'Alba'	see *S. japonica* 'Wakehurst White'
	- 'Attraction' **new**	MGos
	- 'Bowles's Dwarf Female' (f)	CEnd MRav MWht SLim
	- 'Bowles's Dwarf Male' (m)	NWad SLim
	- 'Bronze Knight' (m)	CMac MAsh MRav NLar NWad SRms
	- 'Carberry' (f)	CMac
	- 'Chameleon' (f)	GMcL NLar
	- 'Dad's Red Dragon' (f)	CMac MAsh SRms
	- 'Emerald King' (m)	WFar
	- 'Finchy'^{PBR} (m)	NLar
	- 'Foremanii'	see *S. japonica* 'Veitchii'
§	- 'Fragrans' (m) 🏆^{H5}	CMac CRos CSBt CTri EBee EPfP LRHS LSRN MAsh MGos MJak MRav NLar NRHS SCob SLim SPer SPoG SRms SWvt WFar WGwG
	- 'Fragrant Cloud'	see *S. japonica* 'Fragrans'
	- 'Fructu Albo'	see *S. japonica* 'Wakehurst White'
	- 'Godrie's Dwarf' (m)	CRos EPfP LRHS NLar NRHS WFar
	- 'Humpty Dumpty' (f)	WFar
	- var. ***intermedia*** f. ***repens*** B&SWJ 5560	WCru
	- - B&SWJ 11165	WCru
	- 'John Turner' (f)	GBin

- 'Kew White' (f)	CAby CBcs CRos ELan EPfP GMcL IArd LRHS MAsh MGos MRav NRHS NWad SLon SPer SSta SWvt WCFE
- LUWIAN ('Wanto') (m)	CRos LRHS NRHS
- 'Macpenny Dwarf' (m)	CMac SRms
- 'Magic Marlot'PBR (m/v)	CRos EBee EPfP GMcL LRHS LSRN MAsh MGos MRav NHpl NLar NRHS SCob SPoG
- 'Marlot' (m)	CRos EPfP LRHS NLar NRHS SPoG
- 'Nymans' (f) ♀H5	CEnd CRos CTsd ELan EPfP GBin GMcL LCro LRHS MAsh MGos MRav NRHS SCob SLim SPer SPoG SRms SWvt
- OBSESSION ('Obsbolwi'PBR) (m/f)	CRos GMcL LRHS LSRN MAsh MGos NRHS SCob
- 'Olympic Flame' (f)	CRos EPfP IArd LRHS MAsh MBlu MJak NRHS SPoG
- 'Pabella'PBR (f)	LRHS MAsh SPoG
- 'Pigmy' (f)	CExl
- 'Red Diamonds'	CRos LRHS NRHS SPoG
- 'Red Princess' (f)	MAsh WAvo
- 'Red Riding Hood' (f)	CRos ELan ELon LRHS MAsh NRHS NWad SLon
- 'Redruth' (f)	CBcs CMac CSBt CTsd ELon MAsh SEND WAvo
§ - subsp. ***reevesiana***	CBcs CMac CRos CSBt CTri ELan EPfP ESps GBin GMcL LCro LOPS LRHS MGos MRav MSwo NLar SCob SPoG SRms SWvt WHar
- - B&SWJ 3763	MAsh WCru
- - 'Chilan Choice' (f/m)	LRHS WPGP
- - 'Godries Little Ruby'PBR	EPfP NLar
- - var. ***reevesiana***	MJak NRHS
- - - B&SWJ 3544	WCru
§ - Rogersii Group	CMac CTri
- - 'George Gardner' (m)	EPfP LRHS
- - 'Nana Mascula' (m)	CTri
- - 'Rogersii' (f)	CMac
- 'Rubella' (m) ♀H5	Widely available
- 'Rubinetta' (m)	CBar EPfP IArd MAsh SCob SEND
- 'Ruby Dome' (m)	LRHS NWad
- 'Ruby King' (m)	CSBt IArd LSRN NLar
- 'Scarlet Dwarf' (f)	WAvo
- SEDUCTION ('Redbolwi'PBR)	LRHS MGos
- 'Snow White'PBR (m)	WAvo
- 'Tansley Gem' (f)	CRos LRHS MAsh MWht SPoG
- 'Temptation'PBR (f)	CRos ELan EPfP LRHS NRHS SCob
- 'Thereza'PBR (m)	EBee EPfP LRHS
§ - 'Veitchii' (f)	CBar CBcs CDul CMac CRos CSBt CTri ELan EPfP LRHS LSRN MAsh MGos MJak MMuc MRav NLar NRHS SCob SEND SLim SPer SPoG SRms SWvt WCFE
§ - 'Wakehurst White' (f)	CBcs CMac CSBt CTri EPfP LRHS MAsh MRav NWad SLim SPoG SRms WFar
- 'White Bella' (m)	CRos LRHS NRHS
- 'Winifred Crook' (f)	EBee LRHS
- 'Wisley Female' (f)	CTri
laureola	CExl MRav SRms WCFE WSHC
- GWJ 9364	WCru
- 'Kew Green'	CEnd NWad
- subsp. ***laureola*** HWJK 2095	WCru
- subsp. ***multinervia*** GWJ 9374	WCru
reevesiana	see *S. japonica* subsp. *reevesiana*
rogersii	see *S. japonica* Rogersii Group
'Snowman' **new**	WCFE

Sloanea (*Elaeocarpaceae*)

sinensis	WPGP

Smallanthus (*Asteraceae*)

sonchifolius	LEdu
- 'Morado'	LEdu WPGP

Smilacina see *Maianthemum*

Smilax (*Smilacaceae*)

sp.	WBor
B&SWJ 6628 from Thailand	WCru
CC 6826 **new**	MMoz
aspera	CMac LEdu WCru WPGP WSHC
china B&SWJ 4427	WCru
discotis	SEND
glaucophylla B&SWJ 2971	WCru
nipponica B&SWJ 4331	WCru
rotundifolia	LEdu
sieboldii	LEdu MRav
- B&SWJ 744	WCru

Smyrnium (*Apiaceae*)

olusatrum	CHab CSpe MNHC SPhx SRms WHer WSFF XAbr
perfoliatum	CSpe EHrv ELan ELon EWes GBin LCro LEdu LOPS SPhx WCot WHal WSHC
rotundifolium	WCot
- PAB 6714	LEdu

Solandra (*Solanaceae*)

grandiflora misapplied	see *S. maxima*
hartwegii	see *S. maxima*
§ ***maxima***	CCCN

Solanum (*Solanaceae*)

aerial-rooting climbing species B&SWJ 14398 **new**	WCru
aethiopicum **new**	WHil
atropurpureum	CDTJ CSpe SPlb WCot
betaceum (F)	CCCN EUJe SVic
- yellow-fruited (F)	SPlb
burchellii	SPlb
capsicastrum	SPlb
conchifolium hort.	see *S. linearifolium*
crispum	CBot
- 'Autumnale'	see *S. crispum* 'Glasnevin'
§ - 'Glasnevin' ♀H4	Widely available
dulcamara	EBWF GPoy
- 'Lucia' (v)	CNat
- 'Variegatum' (v)	CMac MAsh
jasminoides	see *S. laxum*
laciniatum	CCCN CDTJ CExl IDee SBig SEND SPav SPlb
§ ***laxum***	CRav CRos EBee LRHS MAsh NRHS SPer SRms SWvt WSHC
- 'Album' ♀H4	Widely available
- 'Album Variegatum' (v)	SCob
* - 'Aureovariegatum' (v)	CMac EBee NEgg SPlb
- 'Coldham'	MNrw
- 'Creche ar Pape'	ECha LRHS SRms
§ ***linearifolium***	CSpe WPGP WSHC
muricatum (F)	CCCN CHll EShb SPlb
pinnatum	SPlb
pseudocapsicum variegated (v)	WCot
pyracanthum	CDTJ SPlb
quitoense (F)	CDTJ SBig SPlb

rantonnetii	see *Lycianthes rantonnetii*
rigescentoides	SPlb
sisymbriifolium	SPlb
aff. ***stenophyllum*** B&SWJ 10744	WCru
wendlandii	CCCN CHll

Solaria (*Alliaceae*)

sp.	GCal

Soldanella (*Primulaceae*)

alpina	CPBP CTal EBee GKev LLHF NSla SRms WAbe
- SDR 6332	GKev
I - 'Alba'	NSla WAbe
carpatica	CTal LEdu LLHF SPlb WAbe
- 'Alba'	GEdr LEdu WAbe
carpatica* × *pusilla	ITim MNrw NRya NWad WAbe WSHC
carpatica* × *villosa	LEdu
cyanaster	EBee GAbr GBin GJos GKev GLog LEdu LLHF NHpl NQui NRya WAbe
dimoniei	CTal EBee ITim LEdu WAbe
hungarica	GEdr WAbe
minima	GEdr GJos LEdu NSla WAbe
montana	CFis CPla GBin GJos GKev LEdu LLHF NLar SBch WBor
pindicola	CTal GEdr LEdu
pusilla	NWad
'Spring Symphony'	CTal GCrg GEdr GMaP ITim LEdu LLHF SAko SPoG
'Sudden Spring'	CElw CTal GEdr LEdu NWad WAbe
villosa ♀H5	CTal EBee GAbr GBin GEdr GKev GLog GPSL LEdu NRya NWad SBch WMoo WSHC

Soleirolia (*Urticaceae*)

soleirolii	CBod CTri EUJe LLWG MMuc NLos SCob SEND SMad SPer SVic SWvt WHer XLum
- 'Argentea'	see *S. soleirolii* 'Variegata'
§ - 'Aurea'	EUJe NHpl SVic SWvt
- 'Golden Queen'	see *S. soleirolii* 'Aurea'
- 'Silver Queen'	see *S. soleirolii* 'Variegata'
§ - 'Variegata' (v)	EUJe LLWG SCob SVic

Solenopsis (*Campanulaceae*)

axillaris	see *Isotoma axillaris*

Solenostemon ✿ (*Lamiaceae*)

'Autumn Rainbow'	WDib
'Beauty of Lyons'	EShb WDib
'Brilliant' (v)	WDib
'Bronze Pagoda'	WDib
'Chamaeleon' (v)	WDib
'City of Sunderland'	WDib
'Combat' (v) ♀H1c	WDib
'Crimson Ruffles' (v) ♀H1c	WDib
'Dazzler' (v)	WDib
'Durham Gala' ♀H1c	WDib
'Firelight' (v)	WDib
GIANT EXHIBITION PALISANDRA (Giant Exhibition Series)	CSpe
HENNA ('Balcenna'PBR) (v) ♀H1c	ECtt
'Illumination'	WDib
'Inky Fingers' (v)	WDib
'Juliet Quartermain' ♀H1c	EShb EUJe WDib
'Jupiter'	WDib
'Kentish Fire' (v)	WDib
'Kiwi Fern' (Stained Glassworks Series) (v)	WDib
'Lemon Chiffon'	WDib
'Lord Falmouth' (v) ♀H1c	WDib
'Mrs Pilkington' (v)	WDib
'Muriel Pedley' (v)	WDib
'Paisley Shawl' (v)	EShb WDib
'Peter Wonder' (v)	WDib
'Pineapple Beauty' (v) ♀H1c	WDib
'Pink Chaos' (v) ♀H1c	WDib
'Red Angel' (v)	WDib
'Red Velvet' (v)	WDib
REDHEAD ('Uf0646'PBR) ♀H1c	NPri
'Rose Blush' (v)	WDib
'Roy Pedley' (v) ♀H1c	WDib
'Royal Scot' (v) ♀H1c	WDib
'Saturn' (v)	WDib
scutellarioides CAMPFIRE ('Uf12823') **new**	LSou NPri
'Timotei'	WDib
'Walter Turner' (v) ♀H1c	ECtt WDib
'Winsome' (v) ♀H1c	WDib
'Winter Sun' (v)	WDib
'Wisley Tapestry' (v) ♀H1c	WDib

Solidago (*Asteraceae*)

'Autumn Blaze' **new**	WFar
BABYGOLD	see *S.* 'Goldkind'
'Ballardii' **new**	SRms
brachystachys	see *S. cutleri*
caesia	EBee EWes LRHS NRHS SMHy WFar
canadensis	CTri ELan SEND SPlb WBrk WHer WMoo WOld WWtn XAbr XLum
- var. ***salebrosa***	EBee LRHS NRHS
- var. ***scabra***	MMuc
'Citronella'	ECtt GQue
'Cloth of Gold'	CMac ECtt EPfP ESps NEoE SPoG SWvt WGwG
§ 'Crown of Rays'	ECtt ELon EPfP GBin LRHS MRav NRHS SCob WFar
§ ***cutleri***	NLar SPlb SRms WFar
- 'Goldrush'	LRHS NRHS
'Dennis Strange' **new**	MAvo
'Ducky'	SCob
'Early Bird'	NLar WFar
flabelliformis	WCot
§ ***flexicaulis***	GMaP SPhx WCot XLum
- 'Variegata' (v)	EBee ELan EShb GMaP LRHS NLar NRHS WMoo XLum
'Foxbrook Gold'	MAvo WFar
'Gardone' ♀H7	WFar
gigantea	WFar
glomerata	MMuc NLar SEND
GOLDEN BABY	see *S.* 'Goldkind'
§ 'Golden Dwarf'	SPoG SRms WPtf XLum
'Golden Fleece'	see *S. sphacelata* 'Golden Fleece'
'Golden Thumb'	see *S.* 'Queenie'
'Golden Wings'	CBre MWat
'Goldenmosa' ♀H7	CSBt EWes GMaP SPer WFar
'Goldilocks'	SRms
§ 'Goldkind'	CBre CRos CSBt CTri EBee ECtt ELan EPfP ESps GAbr GMcL IBoy LRHS NEgg NRHS SRms SWvt WBrk WFar WHar WWtn
GOLDZWERG	see *S.* 'Golden Dwarf'
'Hiddigeigei' (v)	WCot
hybrida	see *S.* × *luteus*
latifolia	see *S. flexicaulis*

'Laurin'	NLar XLum
'Ledsham'	CBod ECtt GBin LEdu LRHS NBre NRHS SPoG
'Lena'	SRms
'Linner Gold'	NBre
'Little Lemon'^{PBR}	EBee ELan LRHS LSou NEoE NRHS SCob
§ × ***luteus***	EBee EWTr GBin SRms WFar XLum
- 'Lemore' 🏆^{H7}	CAby CBod CDor EBee ECha ELan EPfP GMaP IRob LSou MSpe NSti SPer SPhm SPhx SPoG SRms WCot WFar XLum
* ***minutissima*** subsp. ***minuta***	MHol
ohioensis	XLum
- 'Four Seasons'	GBin
§ ***ptarmicoides***	EBee MMuc XEll XLum
§ 'Queenie'	ECha MHer
riddellii	XLum
rigida	WMoo
- 'Upright Rod'	GBin
rugosa	ECha MBNS MMuc SEND SPhx WCot WWtn
- 'Fireworks' 🏆^{H7}	CAby CBod CBre CMac CMea CSam EBee ECha ECtt ELon GBin GQue IBoy ILea LRHS MAvo MSpe MWat NLar NRHS SDys SPhx WBrk WCot WFar WHoo WOld WWFP XLum
- 'Loydser Crown'	NDov
sciaphila	SPhx
sempervirens	EBee IMou LRHS NRHS WFar WOld
'Septembergold'	CSam
shortii 'Solar Cascade'	EBee
'Sonnenschein'	NBre
speciosa	SPhx WCot
spectabilis var. ***confinis*** KM 27-01	EBee
§ ***sphacelata*** 'Golden Fleece'	CBcs EPfP IMou NBre SRms
spiraeifolia	EBee
STRAHLENKRONE	see *S.* 'Crown of Rays'
'Super'	WCot
SWEETY ('Barseven'^{PBR})	LRHS NRHS
'Tom Thumb'	MRav SRms
uliginosa	EShb
ulmifolia	EBee
virgaurea	EBWF GPoy MHer MMuc MNHC NLar SRms WHer XAbr
- subsp. ***alpestris*** var. ***minutissima***	GEdr IMou
- var. ***cambrica***	see *S. virgaurea* subsp. *minuta*
§ - subsp. ***minuta***	GBin GCrg
§ - 'Variegata' (v)	CBre EHoe NEoE WOut
vulgaris 'Variegata'	see *S. virgaurea* 'Variegata'
'Yellow Springs'	GJos
'Yellow Stone'	EBee

× *Solidaster* see *Solidago*

hybridus	see *Solidago* × *luteus*

Sollya (*Pittosporaceae*)

fusiformis	see *S. heterophylla*
§ ***heterophylla*** 🏆^{H3}	Widely available
- 'Alba'	CBcs CCCN CFlo CKel CRos ELan EPfP LRHS NRHS SEle SLon SPoG SWvt
- 'Pink Charmer'	CBcs ELan EPfP LRHS SEle SPoG
- pink-flowered	CCCN SWvt

Sonchus (*Asteraceae*)

pinnatus	SPlb

Sophora (*Papilionaceae*)

cassioides NJM 08.008	WPGP
- 'Goldilocks'	WPGP
- 'Goughensis'	WPGP
§ ***davidii***	CAby CBcs CExl EBee ELon EPfP LRHS MBlu SBrt SEND SPoG WCot WGrn WPGP WSHC
- dark blue-flowered	WPGP
flavescens	SBrt
fulvida	EBee WPGP
howinsula	EUJe WCot
japonica	see *Styphnolobium japonicum*
§ 'Little Baby'	ELan EPfP EUJe LSRN MGil MGos MNHC SEle SPoG SWvt WGrn
macrocarpa	SWvt
microphylla	CTri LEdu MGil WPGP
molloyi 'Dragon's Gold'	CBcs EBee ELan ELon EPfP EUJe LRHS MAsh SCob SCoo SEND SEle SPoG SSta SWvt WPGP
- 'Early Gold'	WPGP
prostrata misapplied	see *S.* 'Little Baby'
prostrata Buchanan	CMac
SUN KING ('Hilsop'^{PBR}) 🏆^{H4}	CBcs CBot CDul CRos CWGN ELan EPfP EUJe EWes LRHS LSRN MGos NLar NRHS SCob SCoo SLon SPer SPoG SWvt WCot
tetraptera	CBcs CDul CTsd EPfP LRHS MMuc SEND SWvt WCFE WPGP
viciifolia	see *S. davidii*

Sorbaria (*Rosaceae*)

aitchisonii	see *S. tomentosa* var. *angustifolia*
arborea	see *S. kirilowii*
§ ***kirilowii***	CExl CMac MRav NLar SMad WOut
sorbifolia	CBcs CMCN ELan GMcL MGil MMuc SCob SEND SPer SPlb WFar WSpi
- 'Sem'^{PBR} 🏆^{H5}	Widely available
- var. ***stellipila*** B&SWJ 776	WCru
§ ***tomentosa*** var. ***angustifolia*** 🏆^{H5}	CDul CTri EBee ELan EPfP LRHS MMuc MRav NBid SCob SEND SLon

× *Sorbaronia* (*Rosaceae*)

fallax	EPfP NLar
- 'Ivan's Beauty'	ECrN

× *Sorbopyrus* (*Rosaceae*)

auricularis	MCoo
§ - 'Shipova' (F)	CAgr MAsh NOra WHar

Sorbus ✿ (*Rosaceae*)

sp.	CMen ESps LPra
NJM 09.203	WPGP
SDR 7808	GKev
adamii	CMCN
alnifolia	CLnd CMCN EPfP MBlu
- B&SWJ 8461	WCru
- B&SWJ 10948	WCru
- 'Red Bird'	EPfP MBlu
'Amber Light'	EBee LRHS NOra
americana	CLnd
anglica	CDul
'Apricot'	CEnd
'Apricot Queen'	CDul CLnd EBee ECrN EMOT MJak SGol WFar
aria	CAco CCVT CDul CHab CLnd CPer CTri ECrN EMOT ESps IBoy LBuc

		LPra MGos MMuc SCob SEND SEWo SGol WHar WMou WTSh
	- 'Aurea'	CLnd SPer
	- 'Chrysophylla'	CDul CSBt ECrN
	- 'Decaisneana'	see *S. aria* 'Majestica'
	- 'Lutescens' ♀H6	Widely available
	- 'Magnifica'	CLnd ECrN ELan EMOT LPra NEgg NLar SEWo WJas
§	- 'Majestica' ♀H6	CCVT CDul CLnd CMac EBee ECrN EMOT ESps LMaj LPra MRav SCob WFar WHar WJas
	- 'Mitchellii'	see *S. thibetica* 'John Mitchell'
	- 'Quercoides'	CDul
	aria* × *pseudovilmorinii	EBee WPGP
	arnoldiana 'Golden Wonder'	see *S.* 'Lombarts Golden Wonder'
	aronioides misapplied	see *S. caloneura*
	aronioides Rehder	GKev
	arranensis	CDul
§	***aucuparia***	Widely available
	- 'Aspleniifolia'	CBcs CCVT CDul CMCN CMac CSBt EBee ECrN EMOT ERea ESps EUJe IBoy LRHS MGos MJak MRav NLar NOra NRHS SCob SLim WFar WJas WMou
§	- 'Beissneri'	CAgr CDul MRav
	- CARDINAL ROYAL ('Michred')	CCVT CDul CLnd ECrN EMOT ESps EWTr MMuc NEgg SCoo SEWo SLon
	- 'Dirkenii'	SGol WJas
§	- var. ***edulis*** (F)	CArg CDul CLnd ECrN LBuc LPra MGos MMuc SCob SPer
	- - 'Rossica' misapplied	see *S. aucuparia* var. *edulis* 'Rossica Major'
§	- - 'Rossica Major'	CDul ECrN SEWo
§	- 'Fastigiata'	CEnd CTri ELan EPfP GKin LMaj LPra SCob
	- 'Fingerprint'[PBR] **new**	EMOT
	- 'Hilling's Spire'	CTho
	- subsp. ***maderensis***	LPra MBlu
	- ***pluripinnata***	see *S. scalaris* Koehne
	- var. ***rossica*** Koehne	see *S. aucuparia* var. *edulis*
	- 'Sheerwater Seedling' ♀H6	CBcs CCVT CDul CMCN CSBt EBee ECrN ELan EMOT EPfP GKin IBoy LMaj LPra MGos MMuc MRav MSwo SCob SEND SGol SPer WFar
	- var. ***xanthocarpa***	ELan
	aucuparia* × *scalaris	EMOT
	AUTUMN SPIRE ('Flanrock') ♀H6	CBcs CDul CEnd CLnd EBee ELan EMOT EPfP ERea IBoy LRHS LSRN MAsh MGos MJak NLar NOra NPri SCoo SEWo SLim SLon SPoG SWvt WHar
	bissetii Yu 14299	WCru
*	***bomiensis*** **new**	GKev
	brevipetiolata B&SWJ 11771	WCru
	bulleyana MF 96170 **new**	GKev
§	***caloneura***	EBee EPfP LEdu LRHS MBlu WPGP
	- Guiz 80	WCru
	carmesina B&L 12545	EBee EPfP GKev WCru
	- 'Emberglow'	EBee EPfP NOra
	cashmiriana Hedl. ♀H6	CBcs CCVT CDul CMCN CMac CTri EBee ECrN ELan EPfP ESps GKev IBoy LRHS MBlu MGos MMuc MRav MSwo NEgg NLar NRHS SGol SPer SPoG WCFE WHar WJas WMou
	aff. ***cashmiriana***	EMOT GKev IBoy IRob LCro LOPS MAsh MJak NOra WFar WTSh
	- B 751	WCru
	chamaemespilus	WThu
	'Chinese Lace'	Widely available
§	***commixta***	CBcs CDul CEnd CLnd CMCN EBee ECrN EMOT ESps IBoy LCro LMaj MBlu MGos MJak MMuc MSwo NLar SCob SEND SGol SLim SPer WJas
	- B&SWJ 10839	WCru
	- B&SWJ 11043	WCru
	- B&SWJ 12640 from Ulleungdo, South Korea	WCru
§	- 'Dodong' ♀H6	CEnd EBee EMOT EPfP ERea GBin IArd LBuc LRHS LSRN MBlu NLar NOra NPri SCoo SEWo SLim SPer SPoG WHCr WHar WMou
	- 'Embley' ♀H6	CBcs CCVT CDul CLnd CMCN CSBt CTho CTri ECrN ELan EPfP LCro LOPS MBlu MGos MMuc MRav NEgg SCob SEND SGol SPer SPoG
	- OLYMPIC FLAME	see *S. commixta* 'Dodong'
	- 'Ravensbill'	EBee EPfP LRHS NLar NOra SCoo WHar
	- var. ***rufoferruginea*** B&SWJ 11486	WCru
	- var. ***sachalinensis*** B&SWJ 8515	WCru
	- 'Serotina'	LPra
	aff. ***commixta***	IBoy WTSh
	conradinae Koehne	see *S. esserteauana*
	'Copper Kettle' ♀H6	EBee EPfP MAsh MBlu NLar NOra SCoo WHar WMou
	'Coral Beauty'	CLnd
	corymbifera WWJ 11860	WCru
	'Covert Gold'	CEnd
	croceocarpa	CDul
	cuspidata	see *S. vestita*
*	***decora*** 'Grootendorst'	CDul
	- var. ***nana***	see *S. aucuparia* 'Fastigiata'
	devoniensis	CDul CTho
	- 'Devon Beauty'	CAgr
	discolor misapplied	see *S. commixta*
	discolor (Maxim.) Maxim.	ESps MBlu MJak WJas
	- MF 96172	MAsh
	- MF 97103	WCru
	domestica	CDul CLnd CPer EPfP MMuc SEND
	- 'Maliformis'	see *S. domestica* f. *pomifera*
§	- f. ***pomifera***	LEdu
§	- f. ***pyrifera***	LEdu
	- 'Pyriformis'	see *S. domestica* f. *pyrifera*
	- 'Rosie'	CAgr
	dunnii	WPGP
	'Eastern Promise' ♀H6	CDul EMOT EPfP ESps LCro MAsh MBlu MSwo NLar NOra SCob SCoo SLim WHCr WHar WMou
§	***eburnea***	GKev
	- Harry Smith 12799	WPGP
	ellipsoidalis C 288 **new**	GKev
	eminens	CDul CNat
§	***esserteauana***	CLnd CTho
	fansipanensis NJM 09.176	WPGP
	'Fastigiata'	see *S. aucuparia* 'Fastigiata', *S.* × *thuringiaca* 'Fastigiata'
	aff. ***filipes***	GKev
	- KR 5095	GKev
	- KR 6844	GKev

	folgneri 'Emiel' ♀H6	EPfP IArd MBlu NOra
	- 'Lemon Drop'	CDul CEnd CJun CLnd EBee EPfP MAsh NHim NOra SCoo
	foliolosa	CLnd
	forrestii ♀H6	CBcs CMCN EBee EPfP GKev IArd NLar
*	***fosteri*** MF 97103 **new**	GKev
§	***frutescens*** ♀H6	NWad
	- R 14987 **new**	EBee GKev
	fruticosa 'Koehneana'	see *S. koehneana* C.K. Schneid.
	'Ghose'	CEnd CTho
	glabrescens	LEdu
	'Glendoick Spire'	EBee EMOT LRHS NLar NOra
	'Glendoick White Baby'	LRHS NLar
	glomerulata	LLHF
	'Golden Wonder'	see *S.* 'Lombarts Golden Wonder'
	gonggashanica	EPfP GEdr LRHS WPGP
*	***gorrodini***	CLnd
	granulosa HWJ 1041	WCru
	harrowiana	LEdu LLHF WPGP
	- KW 21009 **new**	WPGP
	Harry Smith	NRHS
	hedlundii	CExl EBee EBtc EPfP NLar WPGP
	- GWJ 9363	WCru WPGP
	- KR 1687	WPGP
	- KR 1810	WPGP
	- WJC 13806	WCru
	helenae	WPGP
	- EN 3088	EBee GKev WPGP
	hemsleyi	CBcs CDul CExl CLnd WPGP
	- 'John Bond' ♀H6	EMOT LRHS NLar NOra WHCr
	× ***hostii***	CLnd
	hugh-mcallisteri CLD 310	GKev
	hupehensis misapplied	see *S. pseudohupehensis*
	- 'November Pink'	see *S. pseudohupehensis* 'Pink Pagoda'
	- var. ***obtusa*** misapplied	see *S. pseudohupehensis* 'Pink Pagoda'
	- 'Rosea'	see *S. pseudohupehensis* 'Pink Pagoda'
	aff. ***hupehensis***	ECrN EMOT WFar WTSh
	hybrida misapplied	see *S.* × *thuringiaca*
	hybrida L.	ECrN
	- 'Gibbsii' ♀H6	ELan EPfP ESps MAsh NOra
	insignis	LLHF WPGP
	intermedia	CAco CBcs CCVT CDul CLnd CPer CTho CTri ECrN ELan ESps LMaj LPra MMuc SEND SGol WHar WMou
	- 'Brouwers'	CLnd ELan LPra
	japonica	CDul EBee
	- B&SWJ 10813	WCru
	- B&SWJ 11048	WCru
	'Joseph Rock'	Widely available
	aff. ***karchungii*** AGS/ES 347	EBee WPGP
I	***keenanii*** KR 7746	EBee WPGP
	- NJM 13.050	WPGP
I	***keenanii*** × ***wattii*** NJM 13.123 **new**	WPGP
	keissleri NJM 11.004	WPGP
	- NJM 11.056	WPGP
	- NJM 11.060	WPGP
	- PAB 7916	LEdu
	'Keith Rushforth'	WCru
§	× ***kewensis***	CDul CLnd SPlb
	khumbuensis	GKev
	'Kirsten Pink'	CCVT
	koehneana misapplied	see *S. frutescens*

§	***koehneana*** C.K. Schneid.	CLnd CMCN ELan GKev MMrt WCru
	aff. ***koehneana*** C.K. Schneid.	see *S. eburnea*, *S. tenuis*
	aff. ***koehneana*** ambig.	GEdr
	lanata misapplied	see *S. vestita*
	latifolia 'Henk Vink'	CCVT
	'Leonard Messel' ♀H6	EPfP MAsh NLar NOra WHCr
	'Likjornaja'	EPfP LRHS
§	'Lombarts Golden Wonder'	CDul MMuc SEND
*	***maculata*** KR 5334	EBee GKev
	'Maidenblush'	NRHS
	matsumurana misapplied	see *S. commixta*
	matsumurana (Makino) Koehne	IDee WPGP
	megalocarpa	CJun CMCN EBee WPGP
	- var. ***cuneata***	WPGP
	meliosmifolia B&SWJ 11709	WCru
	microphylla agg.	CMCN GKev
	- GWJ 9252	WCru
	- SICH 1009	EBee
	monbeigii (Cardot.) N.P. Balakr.	CLnd MGil
	moravica 'Laciniata'	see *S. aucuparia* 'Beissneri'
	muliensis F 22177	EBee GKev
§	***munda***	WCFE
	needhamii NJM 11.005	WPGP
	- PAB 9853	LEdu
	'Nevezhinskaja' **new**	MBlu
	olivacea	EPfP GKev
	aff. ***ovalis*** H 1948	EBee
	paniculata NJM 13.067	WPGP
	- NJM 13.092	WPGP
	- PAB 9831	LEdu
	parvifructa	EBee GKev WPGP
	'Pearly King'	CTho MAsh WJas
§	'Pink Pearl'	CDul EPfP
	'Pink-Ness'	EPfP MBlu NOra SCoo
	pohuashanensis misapplied	see *S.* × *kewensis*
	porrigentiformis	CDul
	poteriifolia ♀H5	EBee GEdr GKev
	prattii misapplied	see *S. munda*
	matsumurana Koehne var. ***subarachnoidea***	see *S. munda*
§	***pseudohupehensis*** ♀H6	CDul CLnd CMCN CMac CTho CTri EPfP GLog MMuc SEND SGol SPer WHar WJas
§	- 'Pink Pagoda' ♀H6	CCVT CDul EBee EMOT EPfP ESps EWTr IBoy LCro LOPS LRHS LSRN MAsh MBlu MGos MMuc MRav MSwo NLar NOra SCob SCoo SEND SEWo SLim SLon SPer SPoG WHCr WMou
	pseudovilmorinii	CBcs CDul GKev LRHS NLar NOra WCru
	- SBEC 974	WPGP
	randaiensis	EBee SPlb WPGP
	- B&SWJ 156	WPGP
	- B&SWJ 3202	EPfP WCru
	'Red Robin'	IBoy
	'Red Tip'	CDul
	reducta ♀H5	GBin GCal GKev MMuc NLar NSla SPer
	aff. ***reducta***	SRms
	reflexipetala misapplied	see *S. commixta*

rehderiana misapplied	see *S. aucuparia*
rosea	GEdr GKev
- SEP 492	WCru WPGP
- 'Rosiness' ♀H6	EBee EPfP LRHS
rubescens	GKev
rushforthii KR 5789	EBee GKev
'Salmon Queen'	CLnd
sambucifolia	EBee GKev
sargentiana ♀H6	CBcs CCVT CDul CEnd CLnd CMCN CMac CTho CTri EBee ECrN ELan EMOT EPfP ESps MBlu MGos MRav MSwo NLar NOra SLim SPer SPoG
- EGM 291	WCru
'Savill Orange'	MMuc
scalaris ambig.	CBcs CMCN ELan MAsh MSwo NOra SPoG WHCr WHar WMou
§ ***scalaris*** Koehne	CCVT CDul CEnd CTho CTri EPfP ESps MBlu SPer WJas
'Schouten'	ECrN MMuc
scopulina misapplied	see *S. aucuparia* 'Fastigiata'
(sect. *Discolores*)	GKev
- KR 5585	WCru WPGP
- KR 6308	WCru
setschwanensis	CMCN
'Showa' **new**	GKev
subulata HWJ 925	WCru
- KWJ 12272	WCru
'Sunshine'	CCVT CDul CLnd EMOT ESps EWTr LMaj MAsh MGos MMuc SEND WJas
§ ***tenuis***	GKev
§ ***thibetica*** 'John Mitchell' ♀H6	CAgr CBcs CDul CEnd CLnd CMCN EBee ECrN EPfP ESps MBlu MGos NLar NOra SLim SPoG
aff. ***thibetica*** BWJ 7757a	WCru
thomsonii GWJ 9363	WCru
- HWJ 984	WCru
- WWJ 12004	WCru
§ × ***thuringiaca*** 'Fastigiata'	CCVT CDul CLnd EBar EBee EPfP LPra NEgg SCoo WJas
tianschanica	WCru
'Titan'	EPfP
× ***tomentella***	CLnd
torminalis	CAgr CBcs CCVT CDul CHab CLnd CMCN CMac CPer CTho CTri EBee ELan EPfP ESps LPra LRHS MGos MMuc MRav NLar SCoo SEND SEWo SPer SPoG WHar WMou WSpi WTSh
* ***ullungdoensis*** B&SWJ 12640 **new**	WCru
§ ***vestita***	CLnd CMCN CTho EPfP WCru
vexans	CDul
vilmorinii ♀H6	Widely available
- 'Pink Charm'	EPfP NOra
- 'Robusta'	see *S.* 'Pink Pearl'
aff. ***vilmorinii***	EMOT ESps GKin IBoy MJak
- KR 5095 **new**	GKev
- KR 6453	WCru WPGP
wardii	CBcs CDul CLnd CTho EPfP MBlu
- KR 21127	EBee WPGP
'White Wax'	CCVT CDul EMOT EWTr MGos SPer SPoG
'Wilfrid Fox'	CCVT MGos
wilmottiana	CDul
wilsoniana	CLnd LRHS
'Wisley Gold' ♀H6	EBee EMOT LRHS MAsh NOra SCoo SLim
yuana	EBee WPGP
- clone 1	WPGP
- clone 2	WPGP

Sorghastrum (*Poaceae*)

avenaceum	see *S. nutans*
§ ***nutans***	CBod
- 'Indian Steel'	CBod EBee XLum

sorrel, common see *Rumex acetosa*

sorrel, French see *Rumex scutatus*

Souliea see *Actaea*

Sparaxis (*Iridaceae*)

sp.	CRav
'Bright Star'	GKev
bulbifera	NRog
caryophyllacea	NRog
elegans	NRog SPlb
'Fire King'	GKev NRog
fragrans **new**	NRog
grandiflora	CPbh NRog
subsp. ***acutiloba***	
- subsp. ***fimbriata***	NRog
- subsp. ***grandiflora***	CGrW CPbh NRog
- subsp. ***violacea*** **new**	NRog
maculosa **new**	NRog
metelerkampiae	NRog
'Moonlight'	GKev LAma NRog
'Red Reflex'	GKev NRog
'Skyline' **new**	GKev
'Sunshine'	GKev LAma NRog
tricolor	CAby CGrW CPbh GKev NRog SDeJ
villosa	NRog

Sparganium (*Sparganiaceae*)

§ ***erectum***	CWat EBWF NMir NPer WMAq WSFF XLum
ramosum	see *S. erectum*

Sparrmannia (*Malvaceae*)

africana ♀H1c	CCCN CHll ELan EShb SEND SPlb SVen

Spartina (*Poaceae*)

pectinata	SGol XLum
- 'Aureomarginata' (v)	CBod CWCL EBee EHoe ELan EPfP GMaP GMcL GNew LRHS MMuc NRHS NWsh SEND SPer WMoo WWtn XLum

Spartium (*Papilionaceae*)

junceum ♀H5	CAco CBcs CDul CEnd CMac CWld EBee ECrN ELan ELon EPfP ESps LRHS MGos MMuc SCob SEND SPer SRms WAvo XAbr XSen
- 'Brockhill Compact'	ELan EPfP LRHS

Spartocytisus see *Cytisus*

Spathantheum (*Araceae*)

orbignyanum	GKev WCot

Spathipappus see *Tanacetum*

Spathiphyllum (*Araceae*)

wallisii	LCro NGBl SPre

Spathodea (*Bignoniaceae*)

campanulata SPlb

spearmint see *Mentha spicata*

Speirantha (*Asparagaceae*)

§ ***convallarioides*** CDTJ CTal EBee EHrv ELon EPPr EPfP IMou LEdu MNrw WCru WHil WPGP
gardenii see *S. convallarioides*

Spergularia (*Caryophyllaceae*)

rupicola EBWF

Sphacele see *Lepechinia*

Sphaeralcea (*Malvaceae*)

ambigua SPlb XSen
'Childerley' CSpe EBee ECtt MBNS SPad SPoG WCot
coccinea EBee SPlb
fendleri CCCN CHll CSam
fulva 'La Luna' new WKif
'Hopleys Lavender' CCCN LSou SWvt
incana CCCN CSpe LSou MGil
- 'Sourup' CBod CSpe EBee ECtt ELan SMHy WCot
malviflora CDTJ
miniata CCCN CHll
munroana CCCN CDTJ ECtt ELan SRkn
- pale-pink-flowered CSam ECtt
'Newleaze Coral' CBod CCCN ELan LRHS MAsh MGil MNrw SPad SPoG SRkn SWvt WBor WCot WWFP
'Newleaze Pink' SRkn
remota CExl LPla SPlb
umbellata see *Phymosia umbellata*

Sphagneticola (*Asteraceae*)

§ ***trilobata*** LLWG

Sphenomeris (*Dennstaedtiaceae*)

chinensis B&SWJ 6108 WCru

Spigelia (*Loganiaceae*)

marilandica EBee GKev ILea SMad WHil WSHC

Spiloxene see *Pauridia*

spinach see AGM Vegetables Section

Spiraea (*Rosaceae*)

sp. ESps
alba var. ***latifolia*** MMuc
albiflora see *S. japonica* 'Albiflora'
arborea see *Sorbaria kirilowii*
§ 'Arguta' ♀H6 Widely available
× ***arguta*** 'Bridal Wreath' see *S.* 'Arguta'
aff. 'Arguta' ESps GMcL
betulifolia CDul MRav SCob WFar
- var. ***aemiliana*** MMuc SCob
- 'Tor' EPPr
- 'Tor Gold'PBR CBcs LRHS NEoE SPoG
× ***billardii*** misapplied see *S.* × *pseudosalicifolia*
blumei CWJ 12829 WCru
× ***bumalda*** 'Wulfenii' see *S. japonica* 'Walluf'
callosa 'Alba' see *S. japonica* 'Albiflora'
canescens CExl GKin
- CC 7281 EWld
- var. ***glaucophylla*** MMuc
chamaedryfolia GKev
× ***cinerea*** 'Grefsheim' ♀H6 CAco CBcs CSBt EBee ELan LBuc MMuc NLar SCob SGol SLim SPer SPlb
crispifolia misapplied see *S. japonica* 'Bullata'
densiflora GKev
- var. ***splendens*** SBrt
DOUBLE PLAY BIG BANG see *S.* 'Tracy'
douglasii CMac GKev SCob
FIRST EDITIONS SUPERSTAR ('Denistar') NEoE
formosana B&SWJ 1597 CExl WCru
fritschiana CMac
hayatana GKev
- RWJ 10014 WCru
hendersonii see *Petrophytum hendersonii*
henryi GKev
japonica ESps
§ - 'Albiflora' CMac CSBt CTri ECrN ELan ELon GMcL LRHS MRav MSwo NEgg NRHS NWad SCob SGbt SGol SLim SPad SPer SRms SWvt WMoo
- 'Alpina' see *S. japonica* 'Nana'
- 'Alpine Gold' NEoE
- 'Anthony Waterer' (v) Widely available
§ - 'Bullata' CMac GCrg NLar NRHS WAbe
- 'Candlelight' ♀H6 CSBt ELan EPfP ESps GBin GKin GMcL LRHS LSou MAsh NEgg NLar SCob SCoo SGol SLim SPer SPoG SWvt WMoo
- 'Crispa' CAco EPfP NEoE NWad WFar WGrn WMoo
- 'Dart's Red' ♀H6 CDul ELan EPfP ESps GKin WMoo
- DOUBLE PLAY ARTISAN ('Galen') new SPoG
- DOUBLE PLAY GOLD ('Yan') new SPoG
- 'Firelight' Widely available
- 'Froebelii' GMcL
§ - 'Genpei' CMac MAsh MJak MMuc SGol SPer SPoG SRms
- 'Gold Mound' CBar CExl CMac EBee EHoe ELan EPfP ESps GMcL MAsh MGos MJak MMuc MRav MSwo NLar SCoo SGol SLim SPlb SRms WFar WHar
- GOLDEN PRINCESS ('Lisp') ♀H6 CMac CRos CTri ELan EPfP ESps GMcL IBoy IRob LBuc LRHS MAsh MGos NEgg NLar NRHS SCoo SGol SRms SSta WFar WMoo
- 'Goldflame' Widely available
- 'Little Princess' CBcs CMac CRos EBee ELan EShb ESps GMcL LRHS MAsh MRav MSwo NLar NRHS SCob SCoo SGol SLim SPer SRGP SRms SWvt WFar WHar WMoo
- MAGIC CARPET ('Walbuma'PBR) (v) ♀H6 CBcs CRos EPfP ETMg GMcL LBuc LRHS MAsh MMuc NLar NRHS SCob SCoo SPoG SRms
§ - 'Nana' ♀H6 CMac CSBt MAsh SRms
- 'Nyewoods' see *S. japonica* 'Nana'
- 'Shiburi' see *S. japonica* 'Albiflora'
- 'Shirobana' misapplied see *S. japonica* 'Genpei'
- 'Shirobana' see *S. japonica* 'Albiflora'
- 'Stanton Gold' WCFE
§ - 'Walluf' CMac CTri GBin
- 'White Gold'PBR CBod CMac CSBt ELan EPfP ESps GMcL LRHS MAsh NEoE NRHS

NWad SCoo SLim SPer SPoG SRms SWvt WMoo
× ***margaritae*** SPer SWvt
micrantha CExl
nipponica CAco CBcs
- 'Halward's Silver' MRav NEoE
§ - 'Snowmound' ♀H6 Widely available
- var. ***tosaensis*** misapplied see *S. nipponica* 'Snowmound'
palmata 'Elegans' see *Filipendula purpurea* 'Elegans'
prunifolia (d) CBod CMac ELan EPfP ESps LRHS MRav SPer WAvo WCFE WFar
× ***pseudosalicifolia*** 'Triumphans' CDul MMuc SPer
SPARKLING CHAMPAGNE ('Lonspi'[PBR]) CSBt LBuc LCro LOPS LSRN NEoE NWad SLim SLon
tarokoensis CMCN
thunbergii ♀H6 CBcs CDul CMac CTri EPfP MMuc MRav SBrt SCob SEND SGol SLim SPer SRms WHar
- 'Golden Times' LRHS SPoG
- 'Mount Fuji' CMac MRav NEoE WFar
* - 'Variegata' (v) SRms
§ 'Tracy' new NEoE
trilobata ESps
ulmaria see *Filipendula ulmaria*
× ***vanhouttei*** CBcs CBod CTri ELan EPfP ESps MMuc MRav MSwo SEND SLim SPer SRms WFar WMoo
- 'Gold Fountain' CMac ELan EMil EPfP EShb ESps IRob LSRN MMuc NLar SCoo SEND SPer WFar WMoo
- 'Pink Ice' (v) EHoe EPfP ESps LRHS MAsh MMuc MRav NLar SPer SPlb SPoG SWvt WFar
veitchii GLog MRav
venusta 'Magnifica' see *Filipendula rubra* 'Venusta'

Spiranthes (*Orchidaceae*)

cernua NGdn
odorata LSou
- 'Chadd's Ford' ♀H4 CExl EBee GKev LAma LEdu LRHS MNrw WSHC

Spirodela (*Araceae*)

§ ***polyrrhiza*** EWat

Spodiopogon (*Poaceae*)

sibiricus CBWd CKno EBee EHoe EPPr GBin LRHS MBNS NDov NLos NRHS SMad WPtf XLum
- 'West Lake' IMou

Sporobolus (*Poaceae*)

airoides CBod CKno EBee EHoe EPPr EShb SMad
heterolepis CBWd CFis CKno CSpe EBee EHoe EPfP GBin LRHS NDov SMHy WCot
- 'Blue Dust' NDov
I - 'Wisconsin Strain' CFis EBee EPPr IMou SPhx
wrightii CKno EPPr SMad

Sprekelia (*Amaryllidaceae*)

formosissima EShb GKev LAma LEdu SDeJ SDir SPav

squashes see AGM Vegetables Section

Stachys (*Lamiaceae*)

aethiopica 'Danielle' see *S. thunbergii* 'Danielle'
§ ***affinis*** GPoy LEdu SPlb SVic XAbr
balcanica GKev
- MESE EBee
'Bello Grigio' CAby LPla MHol WCot
betonica see *S. officinalis*
§ ***byzantina*** Widely available
§ - 'Big Ears' EBee ECha ELan EPfP ESps GMaP GQue LCro LRHS LSRN MCot MGos MMuc MRav MWat NLar NRHS SCob SPer SPhx SPoG SRkn SRms SWvt WCAu WCFE WCot WFar WHoo
§ - 'Cotton Boll' CRos ECha GBin GCal LRHS SRms WFar
- 'Countess Helen von Stein' see *S. byzantina* 'Big Ears'
- 'Fuzzy Wuzzy' CBod WFar
- gold-leaved see *S. byzantina* 'Primrose Heron'
- large-leaved see *S. byzantina* 'Big Ears'
- 'Limelight' ECtt WCot XLum
§ - 'Primrose Heron' EBee ECha GBin GKev LRHS MBel MRav NLar NRHS SPer SWvt WCAu XLum
- 'Sheila McQueen' see *S. byzantina* 'Cotton Boll'
- 'Silky Fleece' CBod ECha ELan EPfP GWyn LRHS MMuc NBre SRms XSen
- 'Silver Carpet' Widely available
chamissonis var. ***cooleyae*** GBin
citrina CMea GCal XSen
coccinea ECtt EWld GEdr WMoo
cretica XSen
densiflora see *S. monieri* (Gouan) P.W. Ball
§ ***discolor*** CFis CMea EWes LRHS NLar SBrt WCAu WCot
germanica CNat EBWF NBre
grandiflora see *S. macrantha*
'Hidalgo' CSpe SRms
lanata Jacq. see *S. byzantina*
lavandulifolia WAbe
- from Bolkar Dag, Turkey new SBrt
'Lilac Falls' see *Lamium* × *Stachys*, 'Lilac Falls'
§ ***macrantha*** CKno CMac CTri ECha GKev GLog LEdu LRHS LSRN NChi NLar NRHS NSti SPhx SRms WArt WCAu WCFE WCot
* - 'Alba' ECha IRob
- 'Ben' (v) LEdu
- 'Hummelo' see *S. officinalis* 'Hummelo'
- 'Morning Blush' CAby GEdr SPhx WFar
* - 'Nivea' CSam ELan
- 'Pink Barrels' IRob
- 'Robusta' ♀H7 ELan ELon GCal LEdu MAvo MMuc NBro NGdn WCot
- 'Rosea' CElw ELan GMaP IRob LRHS MArl MAvo NRHS SCob SPlb WCAu
- 'Superba' ♀H7 CSpe ECtt EPfP ESps GKev GMaP IBoy IRob LEdu MAvo MRav NEgg NLar SCob SPer SRms SWvt WBor WCAu WCot WFar WMoo XLum
- 'Violacea' ♀H7 GKev MBrN NChi WCot WOut
mexicana misapplied see *S. thunbergii*
monieri misapplied see *S. officinalis*
monieri ambig. GKev NLar NSti WOut
§ ***monieri*** (Gouan) P.W. Ball LEdu
* - 'Rosea' CBre EBee LEdu NBre NDov NLar SRms
nivea see *S. discolor*
obliqua NBre WOut
§ ***officinalis*** CHab CWld EBWF EBee ESps GPoy ILea LEdu MHer MMuc MNHC

	NMir NRya SRms WCot WHer WOut WTre XAbr
- 'Alba'	EBee LEdu MArl MAvo MMuc NBro SCob SMHy XAbr
- 'Cally Bicolor'	GCal
- 'Cally Pink'	GCal
- dwarf, white-flowered	CBre GCal
§ - 'Hummelo'	Widely available
- 'Marchant's Pink'	SMHy
- 'Pink Cotton Candy'	EBee STPC WNPC
- 'Rosea'	GCal NBro SCob WFar
- 'Rosea Superba'	ECha GWyn NBre WCot
- 'Saharan Pink'	EPfP IPot LSRN NLar WOut
- 'Spitzenberg'	LPla
- 'Wisley White'	CAby CBre ECtt EPau LBuc LEdu LRHS MHol NHpl NRHS SRms WCot WFar WOut
olympica	see *S. byzantina*
ossetica	CFis EBee GEdr
palustris	CBod CHab EBWF EBee EWat LLWG MMuc NLar NMir SEND SRms XAbr
- from Islay, Hebrides	MMuc SEND
- pale-flowered	WOut
recta	EBee WCAu
setifera	NBre XLum
spicata	see *S. macrantha*
sylvatica	CHab EBWF NMir WHer WOut WSFF
thirkei	WCot XSen
§ ***thunbergii***	MBrN MNHC WHal WHrl
§ - 'Danielle'	CElw ECtt EPfP GJos LRHS NLar NRHS SDys SPhx SRkn SRms WOut
tuberifera	see *S. affinis*

Stachyurus (*Stachyuraceae*)

chinensis	CBcs CJun CMCN CTri MGos NLar WCFE
- 'Celina' ♀H4	CJun ELon EPfP GKin LRHS MGos NLar NRHS SPoG
- 'Goldbeater'	NLar
- 'Joy Forever' (v) ♀H4	CBcs CBot CEnd CMac EBee EPfP IArd LLHF LRHS LSRN MGos NLar NRHS SPer SPoG SSta SWvt
- 'Senna'	NLar
- 'Wonderful Image'	NLar
himalaicus	CBcs NLar
- HWJCM 009	WCru
- HWJK 2035	WCru
- pink-flowered	see *S. himalaicus* subsp. *purpureus*
§ - subsp. ***purpureus*** HWJK 2052	WCru
'Magpie' (v)	LRHS WFar
praecox ♀H5	Widely available
- B&SWJ 8898	WCru
- B&SWJ 10899	IDee LCro WCru
- var. ***leucotrichus***	CJun NLar
- var. ***matsuzakii***	CJun NLar
- - B&SWJ 2817	WCru
- - B&SWJ 11229	WCru
- - 'Issai'	LRHS NRHS
- 'Petra'	CJun
retusus	CExl LRHS
'Rubriflorus'	CJun EPfP LRHS MAsh NLar WPGP
salicifolius	CBcs CExl CFil CJun CTho EBee EPfP NLar WPGP
sigeyosii	CBcs CExl CFil
- B&SWJ 6915	WCru
- CWJ 12420	WCru
- RWJ 10094	WCru
aff. ***szechuanensis***	CExl
- BWJ 8153	WCru
yunnanensis	CBcs CFil CJun IArd NLar WPGP WSHC

Stapelia (*Apocynaceae*)

flavopurpurea new	LToo

Staphylea ✿ (*Staphyleaceae*)

bolanderi	CBcs NLar
bumalda	CJun LEdu LRHS NLar
- B&SWJ 11053	WCru
- B&SWJ 12744 from Korea	WCru
colchica	CBcs CDul CHll CMCN ELan EPfP EWTr EWes LEdu LPra LRHS MGos MMrt MRav NLar SPer WKif WSHC
holocarpa	CBcs CJun EPfP
- 'Innocence'	CBcs LRHS
- var. ***rosea***	CJun CMCN EPfP LRHS MBlu NLar SAko SMad SWvt
pinnata	CAgr CBcs CJun EBtc EPfP MCoo NLar SEND
- PAB 8427	LEdu
trifolia	CAgr CBcs EBee WWFP

Statice see *Limonium*

Stauntonia (*Lardizabalaceae*)

sp.	CKel
from northern Vietnam FMWJ 13177	WCru
- NJM 09.198	WPGP
- NJM 10.133	WPGP
- NJM 10.153	WPGP
aff. ***chinensis*** DJHV 06175	WCru
hexaphylla	CBcs CCCN CHll CTri CWGN EBee EPfP EUJe LEdu LRHS MAsh MGil NLar SAdn SNig SPer SPoG SSta
- B&SWJ 4858	WCru
aff. ***libera*** KWJ 12218	WCru
aff. ***maculata*** FMWJ 13055	WCru
obovata CWJ 12353	WCru
obovatifoliola B&SWJ 3685	WCru
purpurea	WPGP
- B&SWJ 3690	WCru
yaoshanensis B&SWJ 8223	WCru
- HWJ 1024	WCru WPGP

Stegnogramma (*Thelypteridaceae*)

pozoi	EFer

Stellaria (*Caryophyllaceae*)

graminea	CHab EBWF
holostea	CHab CWld EBWF MMuc NMir WHer WPtf WShi

Stemmacantha see *Rhaponticum*

Stenanthium (*Melanthiaceae*)

gramineum	CFil EBee EWes

Stenochlaena (*Blechnaceae*)

palustris	CBdn

Stenomesson (*Amaryllidaceae*)

coccineum	see *Clinanthus coccineus*
incarnatum	see *Clinanthus incarnatus*

	pearcei	NRog
	variegatum	see *Clinanthus variegatus*

Stenotaphrum (*Poaceae*)

	secundatum 'Variegatum' (v) 🏆H1c	EShb LSou XLum

Stephanandra (*Rosaceae*)

	incisa	CBcs CExl SCob
§	- 'Crispa'	CDul CMac CTri EBee ELan EPfP EWTr GKin GMcL MBlu MJak MRav NEgg SCob SPer SRms WMoo
	- 'Prostrata'	see *S. incisa* 'Crispa'
	tanakae	CBcs CDul CExl CTri EBee ELan EPfP EWTr MBlu MGil MRav NEgg SLon SPer SRms

Stephania (*Menispermaceae*)

	japonica CWJ 12823	WCru
	longa KWJ 12163	WCru
	rotunda	EUJe
	aff. ***tetrandra*** WWJ 11896	WCru

Stephanotis (*Apocynaceae*)

	floribunda 🏆H1b	CBcs CCCN

Sterculia (*Malvaceae*)

	rupestris	see *Brachychiton rupestris*

Sternbergia (*Amaryllidaceae*)

	candida	CBro NRog
	colchiciflora	NRog
	fischeriana	CBro NRog
	greuteriana	GKev NRog
	lutea 🏆H4	CAvo CBro CTal CTri ECha EPot ERCP EWes GKev LAma LOPS LRHS NRHS NRog SBch SCob SDeJ WHoo XLum
	- Angustifolia Group	CBro CMea WCot
	sicula	CBro EPot GKev NRog
	- 'Arcadian Sun'	GKev NRog
	- 'Dodona Gold'	NRog
	- var. ***graeca***	CTal NRog
	- 'John Marr'	WThu

Stevia (*Asteraceae*)

	rebaudiana	CBod CGro CPla ENfk GPoy SPre SRms WCot XAbr

Stewartia ✿ (*Theaceae*)

	gemmata	see *S. sinensis*
	'Korean Splendor'	see *S. pseudocamellia* Koreana Group
	koreana	see *S. pseudocamellia* Koreana Group
	monadelpha	CBcs CJun CMen GKev MBlu MPkF NLar
	pseudocamellia 🏆H5	Widely available
	- B&SWJ 11044 from North Japan	WCru
§	- Koreana Group 🏆H5	CDul CEnd CJun CMCN EPfP GKin LRHS NLar SLim
	- 'Ogisu'	NHim NLar
	pteropetiolata B&SWJ 11726	WCru
	- NJM 10.107	WPGP
	- WWJ 11939	WCru
	rostrata	CBcs CJun CLnd LRHS MBlu MPkF NLar
	- 'Hulsdonk Pink'	CJun
	serrata	CJun CMCN MPkF WCru
§	***sinensis*** 🏆H5	CBcs CCCN CJun EPfP IArd IDee IMou LMaj MBlu MPkF NLar SAko WPGP

Stigmaphyllon (*Malpighiaceae*)

	ciliatum	CCCN
	littorale	CCCN

Stipa (*Poaceae*)

	F&M 248	EBee
	arundinacea	see *Anemanthele lessoniana*
	barbata	CKno CSpe EAJP ECha EPPr ETod EWes GBin SCob WKif XSen
	- 'Silver Feather'	CBot ETod
	brachytricha	see *Calamagrostis brachytricha*
§	***calamagrostis***	Widely available
	- 'Allgäu'	WCot
	- 'Lemperg'	CRos IMou LRHS NRHS
	capillata	CBod CFis EPPr GBin GCal IBoy LRHS MBel MNrw MSpe NRHS SMHy SPhx XSen
	- 'Brautschleier'	CBod
*	- 'Lace Veil'	WAvo WHar
	elegantissima	CPla NLos
	extremiorientalis	EPPr SEND
	gigantea 🏆H7	Widely available
	- 'Gold Fontaene'	CKno CRos EPPr EPfP EWes LRHS MAvo MNrw NDov NRHS SMHy SMad WCot WMoo
	- 'Goldilocks' **new**	LEdu
	- 'Pixie'	CRos EBee LRHS NRHS
	grandis	EPPr WMoo
	ichu	CKno CRos LRHS MAvo NDov NLos NRHS SMad
	- F&M 32	CFil
	joannis	GCal
	lasiagrostis	see *S. calamagrostis*
	lessingiana	CExl CPla EMFm EPPr EPed ETod LRHS NLos SEND SPhx WMoo
	pennata	EPPr ETod XSen
	pseudoichu	CBod CFil CSpe EMFm EPPr ETod GBin GCal LPla LRHS MAvo MBNS MBel MSpe SMad SPtp WCot WRHF
	- RCB/Arg Y-1	EBee ELon
	pulcherrima	EPPr GCal
	robusta	EPPr
	splendens misapplied	see *S. calamagrostis*
	splendens Trin.	ECha GCal SAko
	stenophylla	see *S. tirsa*
	tenacissima	CTri GMcL IBoy MAsh
	tenuifolia misapplied	see *S. tenuissima*
	tenuifolia Steud.	CMea EBee EPfP ESps LRHS MRav NBro NSti WHal WMoo XLum XSen
§	***tenuissima***	Widely available
	- 'Wind Whispers'	CBod CExl CSpe LEdu LRHS MBel SBee
§	***tirsa***	EWes GCal WPGP
	turkestanica	NDov

Stoebe (*Asteraceae*)

	alopecuroides	SPlb

Stokesia ✿ (*Asteraceae*)

	cyanea	see *S. laevis*
§	***laevis***	ECha EPfP LRHS NLar NRHS SCob SPlb SRms WCAu WMoo

- 'Alba'	ECha ELan EPfP EPri LEdu LRHS MRav NLar NRHS WCAu
- 'Blue Star'	Widely available
- 'Color Wheel'	ECtt LRHS NRHS SCob
- 'Honeysong Purple'	NLar
- 'Klaus Jelitto'	CRos ECtt LEdu LRHS MAvo NRHS SPoG WHrl WMoo
- 'Mary Gregory'	CAby CBod CMac CNor CSam EBee ECtt EHrv ELan EPfP LEdu LRHS LSou MBel MNrw MRav MSCN NLar NPnk NRHS SPer SPhx SRGP SWvt WGwG WHrl
- 'Mel's Blue'	ECtt LRHS NPri NRHS WTor
- mixed	CPou
- 'Omega Skyrocket'	CPou SRms
- 'Peach Melba'	ECtt WMoo
- 'Peachie's Pick'	EBee ECtt
- 'Purple Parasols'	CDor CMac CWGN ECtt EPfP LEdu LRHS LSou MBel NPnk NRHS SCob SPoG SWvt WGwG WHrl WMoo
- 'Purple Pixie'PBR	ECtt
- 'Silver Moon'	ECtt EPfP GBin LRHS MBel NPnk NRHS SPer
§ - 'Träumerei'	CBod CWGN EBee ECtt EPfP LRHS NLar NPnk NRHS WHrl WMoo XLum
- 'White Star'	see *S. laevis* 'Träumerei'

Stranvaesia see *Photinia*

× ***Stranvinia*** see *Photinia*

Stratiotes (*Hydrocharitaceae*)

aloides	CBen CWat EWat LLWG MWts NPer SVic WMAq WPnP

strawberry see *Fragaria*

Strelitzia (*Strelitziaceae*)

alba	CCCN
juncea	XBlo
nicolai	CCCN NPer SPlb XBlo
reginae 🏆H1c	CAbb CBcs CCCN CTsd ELan EShb ETod EUJe LCro LOPS NPer NPla SBig SChr SPlb XBlo
- 'Kirstenbosch Gold'	XBlo

Streptocarpella see *Streptocarpus*

Streptocarpus ✿ (*Gesneriaceae*)

'Adele'	WDib
'Albatross'	CTsd WDib
'Alissa'	WDib
'Amanda' Dibley	WDib
'Ambiente' 🏆H1c	WDib
'Amy' **new**	WDib
'Anne' (d)	CTsd WDib
'Anwen' **new**	WDib
'Awena'	WDib
baudertii	WDib
'Bella'	WDib
'Bethan' 🏆H1c	CTsd WDib
'Bianca'	WDib
'Black Gardenia'	CTsd
'Black Panther'	CTsd WDib
'Blue Frills' 🏆H1c	WDib
'Blue Gem'	WDib
'Blue Leyla'	see *S.* 'Leyla'
'Blue Moon'	WDib
'Blue Nymph'	WDib
'Boysenberry Delight'	WDib
'Branwen'	CTsd WDib
'Bristol's Black Bird'	WDib
'Bristol's Very Best'	WDib
caeruleus	WDib
'Caitlin'	CTsd WDib
candidus	WDib
'Cappuccino'	WDib
'Cariad'	WDib
'Carol'	WDib
'Carys' 🏆H1c	CTsd WDib
caulescens	WDib
- var. ***pallescens***	WDib
'Celebration'	WDib
'Charlotte' 🏆H1c	WDib
'Chloe'	WDib
'Chorus Line'	CTsd WDib
'Constant Nymph'	WDib
'Crystal Beauty'	WDib
'Crystal Blush'	WDib
'Crystal Charm'	WDib
'Crystal Dawn'	WDib
'Crystal Ice'PBR 🏆H1c	LCro LOPS WDib
'Crystal Snow'	WDib
'Crystal Wonder'	WDib
cyaneus	WDib
- subsp. ***polackii***	WDib
'Cynthia'	WDib
'Daphne'	WDib
'Dee'	WDib
'Delia'	WDib
'Denim'	WDib
denticulatus	WDib
'Diana'	WDib
'Dinas'	WDib
'Ds-Horus'	WDib
dunnii	WDib
'Elsi'	CTsd WDib
'Emily'	WDib
'Eve'	NWad WDib
'Falling Stars' 🏆H1c	CTsd WDib
'Festival Wales'	WDib
'Fiesta' **new**	WDib
'Fiona'	WDib
floribundus	WDib
'Franken Alayana'	WDib
'Franken Isabella'	WDib
'Franken Skye'	WDib
'Franken Strawberry Fondant'	WDib
'Freya' **new**	WDib
'Frosty Diamond' 🏆H1c	CTsd WDib
'Full Moon'	WDib
gardenii	WDib
glandulosissimus 🏆H1c	WDib
'Gloria' 🏆H1c	CTsd WDib
'Gwen'	WDib
'Hannah' 🏆H1c	WDib
'Harlequin Blue'PBR 🏆H1c	WDib
'Harlequin Damsel'	WDib
'Harlequin Dawn'	WDib
'Harlequin Delft'	WDib
'Harlequin Lace'PBR 🏆H1c	WDib
'Harlequin Purple'	WDib
'Harlequin Rose' **new**	WDib
'Harriet'	WDib
'Hayley'	WDib
'Heidi'	CTsd WDib
'Helen'	CTsd WDib
'Hope'	WDib

'Iona'	WDib
'Isabella'	WDib
'Jacquie'	WDib
'Jennifer' ♀H1c	WDib
'Jessica' ♀H1c	WDib
'Joanna'	CTsd WDib
johannis	WDib
'Joy'	WDib
'Karen'	WDib
'Katie'PBR ♀H1c	WDib
kentaniensis	WDib
'Kim' ♀H1c	WDib
kirkii	WDib
'Laura' ♀H1c	WDib
§ 'Leyla'PBR	WDib
'Louise'	WDib
'Lucy'	WDib
'Lyndee'	WDib
'Lynne'	WDib
'Maassen's White'	WDib
'Margaret' Gavin Brown	WDib
'Marie'	WDib
'Marion'	WDib
'Matilda' **new**	WDib
'Megan'	WDib
'Melanie' Dibley	WDib
'Menai' **new**	WDib
meyeri	WDib
'Midnight Flame'	CTsd
modestus	WDib
'Myfanwy'	WDib
'Natalie'	WDib
'Nerys'	CTsd WDib
'Nia'	CTsd WDib
'Nicola'	CTsd WDib
'Olivia'	WDib
'Padarn'	WDib
'Paula'	WDib
'Pearl' ♀H1c	WDib
pentherianus	WDib
'Pink Leyla'PBR ♀H1c	WDib
'Pink Souffle'	WDib
'Polka-Dot Purple'	WDib
'Polka-Dot Red' **new**	WDib
polyanthus subsp. ***dracomontanus***	WDib
primulifolius	WDib
- subsp. ***formosus***	WDib
prolixus	WDib
'Purple Velvet' **new**	WDib
rexii	WDib
'Rhiannon'	CTsd WDib
'Rose Halo'	WDib
'Rosebud'	WDib
(Roulette Series) 'Roulette Azur'PBR ♀H1c	WDib
- 'Roulette Cherry'	WDib
'Rubina'PBR	WDib
'Rubina Pink' ♀H1c	WDib
'Ruby'	CTsd WDib
'Ruth'	WDib
'Sally'	WDib
'Sandra'	WDib
'Sarah'	WDib
saxorum	CCCN CTsd WDib
- compact ♀H1c	CCCN WDib
'Scarlett'	WDib
'Seren'	WDib
'Sian'	WDib
silvaticus	WDib
'Sioned' ♀H1c	WDib
'Snow White' ♀H1c	WDib
I 'Stella'PBR Dibleys ♀H1c	WDib
§ 'Stella' Fleischle (Marleen Series) ♀H1c	WDib
'Stephanie'	WDib
stomandrus	WDib
'Susan' ♀H1c	CTsd WDib
'Sweet Melys'	WDib
'Tanga'	see *S.* 'Stella' Fleischle
'Tanya'	WDib
'Teleri'	WDib
'Texas Hot Chili'	CTsd WDib
thompsonii	WDib
'Tina' ♀H1c	WDib
'Tracey'	WDib
'Valor' **new**	WDib
vandeleurii	WDib
variabilis	WDib
'Wawel' **new**	WDib
wendlandii	WDib
'Wendy'	WDib
'White Butterfly' ♀H1c	WDib
'Wiesmoor Red'	WDib
'Winifred'	WDib

Streptopus (*Liliaceae*)

amplexifolius	EBee EHrv GBin MNrw WCru
roseus	WCru
streptopoides	EBee EPPr EPfP LEdu LRHS MMrt NRHS

Streptosolen (*Solanaceae*)

jamesonii ♀H1c	CCCN CHll EBak EShb SWvt

Strobilanthes (*Acanthaceae*)

CC 4071	CExl
CC 4573	CExl
anisophylla	EShb SDys WSpi
atropurpurea misapplied	see *S. attenuata*
atropurpurea Nees	see *S. wallichii*
§ ***attenuata***	CBct CBod CWld EBee ECtt EPfP GCal IBoy ILea ITim LEdu LRHS MBel MRav NChi NRHS NSti SPoG WCot WCru WMoo WOut
- 'Blue and White' **new**	EBee
- 'Blue Carpet'	EBee NDov
- 'Cally Bicolor'	GCal
- 'Latham's Form' **new**	WHil
- subsp. ***nepalensis***	CHll XLum
- 'Out of the Ocean'	WOut
dyeriana ♀H1b	EBak SPlb WCot
flexicaulis	MHer
- B&SWJ 354	WCru
aff. ***inflata*** B&SWJ 7754	WCru
* ***lactea***	EShb
nutans	CPou EBee EWld NSti SBrt XLum
pentstemonoides	GCal
rankanensis	EBee EPPr ILea SDys SHar XLum
- B&SWJ 1771	WCru
violacea misapplied	EShb IArd
§ ***wallichii***	CMac EBee EPfP EWes EWld ILea MMuc NSti SEND WCru WMoo
- PAB 8440	LEdu

Stromanthe (*Marantaceae*)

sanguinea 'Triostar'PBR (v)	XBlo

Strophanthus (*Apocynaceae*)

speciosus	CCCN CHll EShb

Strumaria (*Amaryllidaceae*)

chaplinii	NRog
discifera	NRog WCot
subsp. ***bulbifera***	
gemmata	NRog
karooica	NRog
salteri	NRog
tenella subsp. ***orientalis***	NRog
truncata	NRog
watermeyeri	NRog
subsp. ***watermeyeri***	

Stuartia see *Stewartia*

Stylidium (*Stylidiaceae*)

graminifolium	CTsd SPlb
- LITTLE SAPHIRE ('St116')	SRot

Stylophorum (*Papaveraceae*)

diphyllum	CPou EWld GCal IMou LEdu MPie WCru WPGP WPnP WWtn
lasiocarpum	CExl CSpe EBee EPPr EWes EWld GEdr MMrt NBid WArt WCot WCru

Styphelia (*Ericaceae*)

colensoi	see *Leucopogon colensoi*

Styphnolobium (*Papilionaceae*)

§ ***japonicum***	CBcs CDul CHab CLnd CMCN CMac CTho EPfP LMaj LPra SCob SPlb WTSh
- 'China Gold' **new**	SPoG
- 'Flavirameum'	LRHS
- 'Pendulum'	CDul LPra NPri
- 'Regent'	LPra

Styrax ✿ (*Styracaceae*)

NJM 11.013 from Guizhou, China	WPGP
NJM 11.085 from Guizhou, China	WPGP
americanus Kankakee form **new**	WPGP
confusus	CExl
dasyanthus	CExl
faberi	CExl
formosanus	CBcs CExl CFil CJun EBee EPfP
var. ***formosanus***	MBlu WPGP
- - B&SWJ 3803	WCru
- - B&SWJ 6786	WCru
- var. ***hayatiana*** B&SWJ 6823	WCru
grandiflorus	CExl
hemsleyanus ♀H5	CBcs CExl CTho EPfP LEdu MBlu NHim NLar SPer
hookeri	CExl
japonicus	CAco CBcs CDul CEnd CExl CMCN CTho CTri ELan EPfP ESps GKin LMaj LRHS MAsh MBlu MGos MMuc MRav NLar SPer SPoG SReu WPGP
- B&SWJ 4405	WCru
- B&SWJ 8770	WCru
- B&SWJ 11078	WCru
- Guiz 216	CExl WPGP
- PAB 8366	LEdu
§ - Benibana Group	SChF WPGP
- - 'Pink Chimes'	CBcs CExl CJun CMCN ELan GKin IDee MBlu MMrt MPkF NLar NOra SAko SMad WGob
- 'Carillon'	CJun
- 'Evening Light'	CBcs LCro LOPS
- 'Fargesii' ♀H5	CBcs CDul CExl CJun CTho
- 'Fragrant Fountain'	MBlu
- 'Herkenrode'	LRHS
- MARLEY'S PINK PARASOL ('JLWeeping') **new**	LCro LOPS LRHS
- 'Pendulus'	EBee EPfP LRHS NHim NLar NRHS SMad WPGP
I - 'Pink Snowbell'	LRHS
- 'Purple Dress' ♀H5	CJun MBlu NLar
- 'Roseus'	see *S. japonicus* Benibana Group
- 'Snowfall'	CJun NLar
- 'Sohuksan' ♀H5	CExl CFil CJun LRHS MBlu NRHS WPGP
limprichtii	CExl CFil
obassia	CBcs CDul CMCN CTho EPfP LRHS MBlu NLar WGob WPGP
- B&SWJ 6023	WCru
- B&SWJ 10890	WCru
odoratissimus	CExl
officinalis	CJun
platanifolius var. ***mollis***	CFil
redivivus	SBrt
serrulatus	CExl
shiraianus	CExl CFil WPGP
tonkinensis FMWJ 13134	WCru
wilsonii	CExl
wuyuanensis	CBcs WPGP

Succisa (*Caprifoliaceae*)

§ ***pratensis***	CAby CBod CDor CHab CMac CWld EBWF EPri EWld GWyn LEdu LLWG MAvo MHer MPie MWts NLar SBch SMHy SPhx SRms WCAu WHer WHoo WPGP WPtf WSFF WWFP XAbr XLum
- 'Alba'	EWes
- 'Buttermilk'	CDor
- 'Cassop'	NRya
- 'Derby Purple'	CSpe WPtf
- early-flowering	LEdu SPhx
- 'Peddar's Pink'	EWes LLWG SPhx

Succisella (*Caprifoliaceae*)

inflexa	LEdu LRHS MSpe SPhx WFar
- 'Frosted Pearls'	CDor CElw CFis LEdu LRHS LSun MAvo MMuc NLar

sunberry see *Rubus* 'Sunberry'

Sutera (*Scrophulariaceae*)

cordata	see *Chaenostoma cordatum*
microphylla	see *Jamesbrittenia microphylla*
neglecta	see *Chaenostoma neglectum*

Sutherlandia ✿ (*Papilionaceae*)

frutescens	CBod CSpe GDun SPlb
- fine-leaved	GDun
montana	CPbh CSpe SBrt

Swainsona (*Papilionaceae*)

galegifolia	CHll

swede see AGM Vegetables Section

sweet cicely see *Myrrhis odorata*

sweet corn see AGM Vegetables Section

sweet pepper see *Capsicum*; also AGM Vegetables Section

Swertia (*Gentianaceae*)

bimaculata PAB 8845	LEdu
perennis	GEdr
petiolata CC 7335	GKev

Swietenia (*Meliaceae*)

mahogani	SPlb

Syagrus (*Arecaceae*)

botryophora	XBlo
§ ***romanzoffiana***	EUJe LRHS XBlo

× *Sycoparrotia* (*Hamamelidaceae*)

semidecidua	CBcs CCCN CJun MBlu NLar
- 'Purple Haze'	CJun NLar
- 'Variegata' (v)	CJun

Sycopsis (*Hamamelidaceae*)

sinensis	CAby CBcs CExl EBee EPfP GBin GCal LEdu LMaj LRHS MGil MMuc NLar SPoG SWvt WPGP WSHC

Symphoricarpos (*Caprifoliaceae*)

albus	CDul CMac CPer MSwo SCob WTSh
- 'Constance Spry'	SRms
§ - var. ***laevigatus***	LBuc
× ***chenaultii***	SRms
- 'Hancock'	CBar CMac EBee ELan EPfP ESps GMcL MMuc MRav MSwo SCob SGol SLim SPer WCFE
× ***doorenbosii*** 'Magic Berry'	EBee MRav SGol
- 'Mother of Pearl'	CDul ELan EPfP ESps LCro LOPS MMuc MRav SCob SPer SRms
- 'White Hedge'	GMcL LBuc MMuc SPer SPlb
guatemalensis B&SWJ 1016	WCru
MAGICAL CANDY ('Kolmcan'PBR)	ELan EPfP LRHS NEoE NRHS SPoG
MAGICAL GALAXY ('Kolmgala'PBR)	ELan EPfP LRHS NEoE NRHS SPoG
MAGICAL SWEET ('Kolmaswet'PBR)	LRHS NRHS SPoG
orbiculatus	SLon
- 'Albovariegatus'	see *S. orbiculatus* 'Taff's Silver Edge'
- 'Argenteovariegatus'	see *S. orbiculatus* 'Taff's Silver Edge'
- 'Bowles's Golden Variegated'	see *S. orbiculatus* 'Foliis Variegatis'
§ - 'Foliis Variegatis' (v)	CMac CTri EHoe ELan MRav SGol SPer
- 'George Gardiner'	CMac
§ - 'Taff's Silver Edge' (v)	SGol
- 'Variegatus'	see *S. orbiculatus* 'Foliis Variegatis'
rivularis	see *S. albus* var. *laevigatus*

Symphyandra see *Campanula*

asiatica	see *Hanabusaya asiatica*

Symphyotrichum (*Asteraceae*)

§ × ***amethystinum***	MNrw WCot
- 'Freiburg'	MNrw
'Anja's Choice'	EBee MTis WOld
'Ann Leys'PBR	EBee SCob WCot XEll
'Aqua Compact' (Autumn Jewels Series)	CBod EUJe LSou
'Blue Butterfly'	SPhx WOld XLum
'Blütenregen'	WArt WCot XEll
chilense 'Purple Haze' **new**	EPPr
§ ***ciliolatum***	SPhx
'Claudia'	WOld
'Climax' Vicary Gibbs	MNrw WOld
'Coombe Fishacre' ♀H7	CBot EBee ECtt ELan ELon EWTr GCal ILea LEdu LRHS MNrw NDov NLar SPhx SRGP SWvt WArt WCAu WCot WHoo WOld WSpi
§ ***cordifolium***	SPhx XLum
- from Piney Fork	EPPr
- 'Aldebaran'	WOld
- 'Blue Heaven'	SAko
- 'Chieftain' ♀H7	LEdu MHCG MNrw SMHy SPhx WOld
- 'Elegans'	CSam EBee WOld
- 'Ideal'	NLar SPhx XLum
- 'Silver Spray'	CKno CRos ECtt ELon GMaP ILea MWat SRGP WOld XLum
- 'Sweet Lavender' ♀H7	CRos EBee LRHS NRHS WOld
- 'White Chief'	WOld
drummondii	SPhx
§ ***dumosum***	CExl
- 'Biteliness'	NLar
- 'Early Blue'	IBoy ILea
- SAPPHIRE ('Kiesapphire'PBR) (Autumn Jewels Series)	CBod CChe ELon EWTr LRHS LSRN MHol NCou NEgg SRGP SRkn SWvt XLum
§ ***ericoides***	ESps NBre WOld
- 'Blue Star' ♀H6	CDor CRos LRHS NLar NRHS WOld
- 'Blue Wonder'	XLum
- 'Brimstone' ♀H6	MRav WOld
- 'Cinderella'	CRos EBee LRHS NRHS NSti WOld
- 'Constance'	WOld
- 'Deep Danziger'	SPhx
- 'Erlkönig'	EBee ELon EPri EShb GCal GQue LEdu NGdn NLar SWvt WCot WOld XLum
- 'Esther'	ECha ECtt ELan IRob MNrw SBee WOld
- 'First Snow'	WCot WFar
- 'Golden Spray' ♀H6	EBee ECtt ELon EPfP EWes GMaP GQue NLar SPer WOld
- 'Herbstmyrte'	CRos LRHS NRHS
- 'Hon. Edith Gibbs'	WOld
- 'Pink Cloud' ♀H6	CBod CBot CRos ECtt EPfP EPri EShb GCal LEdu LRHS MSpe NRHS NWad SAko SPhm SPhx WCot WOld
- 'Monte Cassino'	see *S. pilosum* var. *pringlei* 'Monte Cassino'
- f. ***prostratum***	CBod CRos EPot MRav SAko XEll XSen
§ - - 'Snow Flurry' ♀H6	CMea ECha ECtt ELon IMou LEdu LPla MAvo MHol MNrw MWat NLar SAko SPhx SWvt WCot WHoo WOld WOut XLum
- 'Rosy Veil'	NGdn WOld
- 'Schneegitter'	CRos LRHS NRHS SPhx WCot XSen
- 'Schneetanne'	ETMg SAko
- 'Sulphurea'	MWat
- 'Vimmer's Delight'	ECtt WArt WCot
- 'White Heather'	ECtt NLar WOld
- 'Yvette Richardson'	CSam ECtt SMHy WOld
§ ***falcatum***	WCot

	– var. ***commutatum***	WCot WOld
	foliaceum from Montana	EPPr
	– var. ***parryi***	EBee
	GRANAT ('Kiastgranat') (Autumn Jewels Series) **new**	NCou SPad
§	***greatae***	EBee
	'Herfstweelde'	EBee SPhx WOld
	'Hill Close Blue'	MHCG
	'Hon. Vicary Gibbs' (*ericoides* hybrid)	WOld WOut
§	***laeve***	CDor GNew LEdu NLar SPhx
	– 'Anneke Van der Jeugd'	MNrw SAko
§	– 'Arcturus'	CElw LEdu MAvo MBel MNrw MTis WCot WOld XLum
	– 'Blauschleier'	EBee
	– 'Blue Bird'	WOld
§	– 'Calliope'	Widely available
	– 'Cally Compact'	GQue NLar WOld
	– 'Climax'	CElw EBee ELan GCal MMuc MRav NBid NSti SEND WBrk XLum
	– var. ***geyeri***	MNrw
	– 'Glow in the Dark'	EBee EPPr MAvo MSpe MWat NLar WBrk WCot WHoo WOld
	– 'Les Moutiers'	CMea EBee EPPr LEdu MAvo MNrw WBrk WOld
	– 'Nightshade'	EPPr MAvo MNrw MTis WOld WRHF
	– 'Orpheus'	LEdu MAvo MNrw WBrk
	– 'Vesta'	ECtt MTis WOld
§	– 'White Climax'	CSam MNrw WCot
	– white-flowered	WBrk WOld
	lanceolatum 'Edwin Beckett'	CBre MNrw SWvt WOld
§	***lateriflorum***	SWvt WOld
	– 'Bleke Bet'	WCot WFar WOld
	– 'Buck's Fizz'	ELan WOld
	– 'Chloe'	CDor CSam SPhx WCot WFar WOld
	– 'Datschi'	XLum
	– var. ***horizontalis*** $\mathcal{P}^{H7}$	CRos CSam EBee ECha ECtt EHoe ELan EPfP LRHS MRav MWat NBro NGdn NRHS NWad SCob SPer SPlb SRms SRot SWvt WCAu WMoo WOld WSpi XEll
	– 'Lady in Black'	Widely available
	– 'Lovely'	CSam WArt WCot
	– 'Prince'	Widely available
	'Little Carlow' (*cordifolium* hybrid) $\mathcal{P}^{H7}$	Widely available
	'Little Dorrit' (*cordifolium* hybrid)	ECtt NWsh
	(Newstars Series) 'Newstars Fantasy'	WArt WCot WOld
	– 'Newstars Glory'	ECtt WArt WCot
	'Nicholas'	ECtt WCot WFar WOld
	'Noreen'	MAvo MHCG MTis WOld
§	***novae-angliae***	GKev WOld
	– 'Abendsonne'	SAko
	– 'Alex Deamon'	ELon MAvo WBrk WOld
	– 'Anabelle de Chazal'	ECtt ELon WBrk WOld
	– 'Andenken an Alma Pötschke'	Widely available
	– 'Andenken an Paul Gerber'	ECtt ELon MAvo MNrw MTis NLar SRGP WOld
	– 'Augusta'	ELon MAvo NLar SPhx WBrk WOld
	– AUTUMN SNOW	see *S. novae-angliae* 'Herbstschnee'
	– 'Badsey Pink'	WCot
	– 'Barr's Blue'	CMac EBee ECtt ELan ELon EPfP IPot MAvo MMuc MTis MWat NLar NWsh SEND SPer SRms WBrk WCAu WMoo WOld
	– 'Barr's Pink'	CBot CMac EBee ECtt ELan ELon EPfP IBoy MCot MMuc MPie MTis MWat NLar SEND SRGP SRms WBrk WFar WOld WSFF
	– 'Barr's Purple'	ECtt WBrk WCFE WOld
	– 'Barr's Violet'	ECtt MAvo NSti SRms WBrk WCot WHal WHoo WMoo WOld
	– 'Bishop Colenso'	EPPr SPhx WBrk
	– 'Blackheart' **new**	ELon
I	– 'Blue Eyes'	MAvo
I	– 'Brightness'	MAvo WCot
	– 'Brockamin'	EPPr MNrw WBrk WOld
	– 'Brunswick'	WFar WOld
	– 'Christopher Harbutt'	LEdu
	– 'Colwall Century'	MAvo WBrk WOld
	– 'Colwall Constellation'	ELon MAvo WBrk WOld
	– 'Colwall Galaxy'	WBrk WOld
	– 'Colwall Orbit'	ECtt ELon MAvo NWsh WBrk WOld
	– 'Connie'	MNrw MSpe
	– 'Constanze'	EBee ECtt ELon MAvo MTis
	– 'Crimson Beauty'	ECtt ELon MAvo MHCG MHer MNrw MWat SAko WBrk WOld
	– 'Dapper Tapper'	ECtt ELon MAvo WCot WOld
	– 'Early Bird' **new**	ELon
	– 'Evensong'	ECtt LEdu MAvo MNrw MPie WBrk WOld
	– 'Festival'	MAvo WBrk
	– 'Foxy Emily'	ECtt MAvo MHCG WBrk WOld
	– 'Harrington's Pink' $\mathcal{P}^{H7}$	Widely available
	– 'Helen Picton'	CDor CSam ECtt ELon EWld LEdu MAvo MBrN MHer MPie MWat NLar NWsh SAko WBrk WFar WHoo WOld
§	– 'Herbstschnee'	Widely available
	– 'James'	MAvo
	– 'James Ritchie'	CSam ECtt ELon WHoo WOld
	– 'John Davis'	MNrw SBch WOld
	– 'John Dickinson'	WBrk
	– 'Jon Baker'	CBot MAvo WBrk
	– 'Kate Deamon'	ECtt WOld
	– 'Kylie'	CBot ECtt EPPr LEdu LSRN MAvo MNrw MTis SPhx SRGP WBor WBrk WCot WFar WOld
	– 'Lachsglut'	ELon EPPr LEdu NLar SAko WCot WOld
	– 'Ladies Day'	WOld
	– 'Little Bella'	ECtt MWat WOld
	– 'Lou Williams'	ECtt ELon MAvo MNrw MWat NLar WFar WOld
I	– 'Lucida'	MAvo SPhx SRms WOld
	– 'Lucinda'	ECtt
	– 'Lye End Beauty'	CDor ECtt ELon MAvo MHer MNrw MPie MWat SRGP WBrk WCot WFar WHoo WMoo WOld
	– 'Mabelle'	MAvo NDov
	– 'Mandie's Choice'	WCot
	– 'Marina Wolkonsky'	CAby CBWd ECtt ELon EWes IPot LEdu MAvo MMrt MNrw MTis MWat NLar SAko SPhx SRms WBrk WCot WKif WOld
	– 'Millennium Star'	ECtt ELon WBrk WOld
	– 'Miss K.E. Mash'	ECtt MAvo NLar SRGP WBrk WFar WOld
	– 'Mrs S.T. Wright'	CAby CTri ECtt EWes LEdu MAvo MBrN MNrw NWsh SRGP WBrk WFar WOld
	– 'Mrs S.W. Stern'	WBrk WOld

	- 'Nachtauge'	SAko
	- 'Naomi'	MAvo WBrk WOld
	- 'Percy Picton' **new**	LEdu
	- 'Pink Parfait'	CSam ECtt MPie NGdn SRms WBrk WCot WFar WOld
	- 'Pink Victor'	EPPr SRms WMoo
	- 'Pride of Rougham'	ECtt EWes MAvo WBrk
	- 'Primrose Upward'	CAby ECtt MNrw NDov NWsh SPhx WCot WOld
	- 'Purple Cloud'	CAby CSam ECtt ELon MAvo MHer MWat NGdn WBrk WHal WOld
I	- 'Purple Dome'	Widely available
	- 'Quinton Menzies'	CAby ELon MAvo WOld
	- 'Red Cloud'	ECtt ELon LEdu MAvo MHer WBrk WOld
	- 'Rosa Sieger' ♀H7	CAby CBre CSam ECtt ELon GMaP LEdu MAvo MNrw MTis NGdn NLar SRGP WBor WBrk WFar WHoo WOld XLum
	- 'Rose Williams'	LEdu MAvo MPie WBrk
	- 'Röter Stern'	ECtt MAvo MPie WBrk WOld
	- 'Röter Turm'	SAko
	- 'Rougham Pink'	MAvo WBrk
	- 'Rougham Purple'	EWes
	- 'Rougham Violet'	EPPr WBrk
	- 'Rubinschatz'	EBee ECtt ELon MAvo MTis MWat NWsh SRms WOld XLum
	- 'Rudelsburg'	EBee ECtt ELon MAvo SHar WBrk
	- 'Rudolph'	ECtt EWes
	- 'Saint Michael's'	MAvo MWat WBrk WFar WOld
	- 'Sayer's Croft'	ECtt ELon MAvo MWat WBrk WCot WFar WHoo WOld
§	- 'Septemberrubin'	CAby CMea EBee ECtt ELan ELon EPfP IFoB LEdu LPla LSou MAvo MBel MMuc MRav MTis NSti NWsh SAko SEND SRGP SRms WFar WOld WSpi XLum
	- SEPTEMBER RUBY	see *S. novae-angliae* 'Septemberrubin'
	- 'Treasure'	CBre CRos ECtt ELon EPPr EWes LRHS MAvo NBre NRHS SPhx SRGP WBrk WMoo WOld
	- 'Vibrant Dome' PBR	CRos LRHS MNrw MTis NLar NRHS
	- 'Violet Dusk'	ELon WBrk
	- 'Violet Haze'	CMea ELon WBrk
	- 'Violetta'	CBot CRos ECtt ELon GMaP ILea LCro LEdu LRHS LSou MAvo MNrw MTis NRHS SCob SPhx WBrk WHoo WKif WOld
	- 'W. Bowman'	ECtt MNrw WBrk WOld
	- 'Wineflower' **new**	MTis
	- 'Wow'	ELon
§	***novi-belgii***	ESps WHer WMoo
	- 'Ada Ballard'	CBod CFis CMac CRos CWld EBee EHoe LRHS LSRN NEgg NRHS SRGP WFar WMoo WOld
	- 'Albanian'	WOld
	- 'Alderman Vokes'	WOld
	- 'Algar's Pride'	ECtt WFar WOld
	- 'Alice Haslam'	CMac CRos EBee ECtt ELan ESps LRHS MHol MSCN NLar NRHS SRGP SRms WFar WOld
	- 'Angela Peel'	CRos LRHS NRHS
	- 'Anita Ballard'	WOld
	- 'Anita Webb'	WOld
	- 'Anneke'	NLar SRGP WOld
	- 'Apollo'	CRos EWTr ILea LRHS MSCN MWat NLar NRHS WFar WOld
	- 'Apple Blossom'	MWat WFar WOld
	- 'Aramis Rose'	EBee
	- 'Audrey'	CMac CRos EWTr GMaP LRHS LSRN MBNS NGdn SRGP SRms WFar WOld
	- 'Autumn Beauty'	WOld
	- 'Autumn Days'	WOld
	- 'Autumn Glory'	WOld
	- 'Autumn Rose'	WOld
	- 'Baby Climax'	WOld
	- BAHAMAS ('Dasone') (Island Series)	CBod CRos EPfP IRob LRHS NEgg NLar NRHS NWsh SPoG SRms SWvt WCot
	- BARBADOS ('Dastwo') (Island Series)	CBod EPfP LRHS NLar NRHS SPoG SWvt WCot WFar
	- 'Beauty of Colwall'	WOld
	- 'Beechwood Beacon'	WFar
	- 'Beechwood Challenger'	MHCG MPie WBrk WOld
	- 'Beechwood Charm'	WFar WOld
	- 'Beechwood Rival'	CDor CTri WOld XEll
	- 'Blandie'	MWat SRGP WOld
	- 'Blauglut'	WFar WOld
	- 'Blaukuppel' **new**	MAvo
	- 'Blue Baby'	CMac MPie
	- 'Blue Bouquet'	CTri EWTr SRms WFar WOld
	- 'Blue Boy'	WOld
	- 'Blue Danube'	WOld
	- 'Blue Eyes' **new**	WOld
	- 'Blue Gown'	CCse GCal IRob WOld WOut
	- 'Blue Lagoon'	CDor CFis CMea ELan GMcL LSRN NPnk WBrk WOld
	- 'Blue Lapis'	EBee WFar
I	- 'Blue Moon'	EWTr MWat WFar WOld
	- 'Blue Patrol'	WOld
	- 'Blue Radiance'	WOld
	- 'Blue Spire'	WOld
	- 'Blue Whirl'	WOld
	- 'Boningale Blue'	WOld
	- 'Boningale White'	MHCG WFar WOld
	- 'Bridesmaid'	WOld
	- 'Bridgette'	NPnk
	- 'Bright Eyes'	SRGP WOld
	- 'Brightest and Best'	WOld
	- 'Brigitte'	CBod CDor EWTr NLar
	- 'Cameo'	WOld
	- 'Cantab'	WOld
	- 'Carlingcott'	WOld
	- 'Carnival'	CMac CRos EBee ECtt LRHS NRHS SRGP WOld
	- 'Cecily'	MWat WOld
	- 'Charles Wilson'	CFis WOld
	- 'Chatterbox'	CRos EBee ELan EPfP EWTr LRHS MRav MWat NEgg NLar NRHS SRGP SRms WFar WHar WOld
	- 'Chelwood'	WFar WOld
	- 'Chequers'	CElw EBee MBNS MHer NEgg SRGP WFar WOld
	- 'Christina'	see *S. novi-belgii* 'Kristina'
	- 'Christine Soanes'	WOld
	- 'Cliff Lewis'	WFar WOld
	- 'Climax Albus'	see *S. laeve* 'White Climax'
	- 'Cloudy Blue'	WOld
	- 'Colonel F.R. Durham'	WOld
	- 'Coombe Gladys'	WOld
	- 'Coombe Margaret'	WOld
	- 'Coombe Radiance'	WOld
	- 'Coombe Ronald'	WOld
	- 'Coombe Rosemary'	ECtt NLar WBor WOld
	- 'Coombe Violet'	MWat WOld
	- 'Countess of Dudley'	CFis WFar WOld
	- 'Court Herald'	WOld

– 'Crimson Brocade'	CDor CRos ECtt ELan EPfP EWTr LRHS NLar NRHS SAko SPoG SRGP SRms SWvt WFar
– 'Dandy'	CMac CRos ELan EPfP LRHS NGdn NRHS SRGP WFar WOld
– 'Daniela'	SRms WBrk WFar WOld
– 'Daphne Anne'	WOld
– 'Dauerblau'	EBee WOld
– 'Davey's True Blue'	CTri WFar WOld XLum
– 'David Murray'	WOld
– 'Dazzler'	ECtt WFar WOld
– 'Destiny'	WOld
– 'Diana'	ECtt NWsh
– 'Diana Watts'	WOld
– 'Dietgard'	MWat WOld
– 'Dolly'	SRms WOld
– 'Dora Chiswell'	WOld
– 'Dusky Maid'	ELon WFar WOld
– 'Elizabeth Hutton'	SRGP WFar WOld
– 'Elsie Dale'	WOld
– 'Elta'	WOld
– 'Erica'	CElw MWat WOld
– 'Ernest Ballard'	WOld
– 'Eva'	ELon SRms WOld
– 'Eventide'	CDor CTri LSRN WOld
– 'Fair Lady'	MWat WOld
– 'Faith'	WFar WOld
– 'Farncombe Lilac'	MAvo
– 'Feckenham Rival'	WOld
– 'Fellowship' 🏆^{H6}	CAby CBod CBot CDor CRos EAJP EBee ECtt ELon EPfP LEdu LRHS MAvo MBel MMuc MNrw NLar NRHS SAko SEND SHar SRGP SRms SWvt WCot WFar WOld
– 'Flamingo'	CRos EBee LRHS NRHS WOld
– 'Freda Ballard'	CRos ECtt GMaP LRHS MWat NRHS SRGP WFar WOld
– 'Freya'	CElw LSRN MWat WOld WSHC
– 'Fuldatal'	MWat WFar WOld
– 'Gayborder Blue'	WFar WOld
– 'Gayborder Royal'	WOld
– 'Goliath'	MWat WOld
– 'Grey Lady'	WFar WOld
– 'Guardsman'	WOld
– 'Gulliver'	WBrk WFar WOld
– 'Gurney Slade'	WFar WOld
– 'Guy Ballard'	WOld
– 'Harrison's Blue'	MWat WOld
– 'Heinz Richard'	CFis ECha MHer NGdn SRGP SRms WOld
– 'Helen'	ELon WOld
– 'Helen Ballard'	NBid SRms WFar WOld
– 'Herbstgruss vom Bresserhof'	CRos LRHS NBre NLar NRHS SAko WOld
– 'Hilda Ballard'	WOld
– 'Ibiza'	WCot
– 'Ilse Brensell'	WOld
– 'Irene'	WOld
– 'Janet Watts'	WOld
– 'Jean'	ELon SRms WFar WOld
– 'Jean Gyte'	WOld
– 'Jeanette'	SRms WFar WOld
– 'Jenny'	CBod CRos CSBt ECtt EHoe ELan EPPr EPfP GBin GMaP IBoy LRHS LSRN MRav MWat NEgg NGdn NPnk NRHS SBod SGol SPer SRGP SRms SWvt WCAu WFar WHar WMoo WOld
– 'Jollity'	WOld

– 'Jugendstil'	XLum
– 'Julia'	WOld
– 'Karminkuppel'	ETMg IPot
– 'Kassel'	SRms WFar WOld
– 'King of the Belgians'	WFar WOld
– 'King's College'	WOld
§ – 'Kristina'	CRos ECha GMcL ITim LRHS MNrw MRav NPnk NRHS WFar WOld
– 'Lady Frances'	EBee SRms WOld
– 'Lady in Blue'	CRos CSBt ECtt EHoe ELan EPfP ESps GWyn LEdu LRHS MBNS MGos MWat NEgg NGdn NRHS NWad SBod SGbt SPer SPoG SRGP SRms SWvt WCAu WFar WHar WMoo WOld
– 'Lassie'	EWTr MWat NWsh WFar WOld
– 'Lavender Dream'	WOld
– 'Lawrence Chiswell'	WFar WOld
– 'Lederstrumpf'	NDov
– 'Lisa Dawn'	WOld
– 'Lisette' **new**	LEdu
– 'Little Boy Blue'	CBod CDor SRms WOld XLum
– 'Little Man in Blue'	EWTr WOld
– 'Little Pink Beauty'	CRos ECtt ELan EPfP ESps GMcL IBoy ITim LEdu LRHS MBNS NGdn NRHS NWad SBod SPer SRGP SRms WCAu WHar WOld
– 'Little Pink Lady'	MHCG SRms WFar WOld
– 'Little Pink Pyramid'	SRms WOld
– 'Little Red Boy'	WOld
– 'Little Treasure'	WOld
– 'Madge Cato'	SRms WOld
– 'Mammoth'	WOld
– 'Margery Bennett'	WOld
– 'Marie Ann Neil'	SRms WOld
– 'Marie Ballard'	CMac CRos CSBt GMaP LEdu LRHS MHer MRav MWat NGdn NLar NPer NPnk NRHS SGol SPer SRGP SRms SWvt WCAu WOld XLum
– 'Marie's Pretty Please'	WOld
– 'Marie-Theres'	SAko
– 'Marjorie'	LSRN SRGP WOld XLum
– 'Mauve Magic'	CRos MWat NRHS SRms WFar WOld
– 'Melbourne Belle'	WOld
– 'Melbourne Magnet'	WOld
– 'Midget'	WOld
– 'Mistress Quickly'	ECtt WFar WOld
– 'Mittelmeer'	CRos LRHS NRHS WOld XLum
– 'Mount Everest'	CDor SRGP WOld
– 'Mrs Leo Hunter'	WOld
– 'Nachtlicht'	SAko
– 'Neron'	IMou MNrw MPie NDov SPhx
– 'Nesthäkchen'	WOld
– 'Niobe'	WOld
– 'Norman's Jubilee'	CRos EBee EPfP ESps LRHS MHer NRHS SRGP WFar WOld
– 'Nursteed Charm'	WOld
– 'Oktoberschneekuppel'	CRos WOld
– 'Pamela'	WOld
– 'Patricia Ballard' (d)	CBcs CBod CBot CDor CMac CRos CSBt EBee ELan EPfP GMaP LCro LOPS LRHS MHer MWat NLar NPer NRHS NWad SGol SPer SRGP WFar WMoo WOld
– 'Peace'	MWat WOld
– 'Percy Thrower'	WOld
– 'Peter Chiswell'	SRms WOld
– 'Peter Harrison'	CRos EBee GMaP LRHS MHol NRHS WOld XLum

- 'Peter Pan'	EWTr NLar
- 'Pink Lace'	MBNS WOld
- 'Pink Topas'	LRHS
- 'Plenty'	WOld
- 'Porzellan'	CBod CElw CFis CMea EBee ECtt LEdu MAvo MBNS MNrw NGdn NLar SRGP WCot WHal WOld
- 'Pride of Colwall'	SRms WOld
- 'Priory Blush'	CElw MWat WOld
- 'Professor Anton Kippenberg'	CFis CRos EAJP ELan EPfP EWTr GMaP LRHS MNrw MRav NDov NLar NRHS SAko SRGP SRms SWvt WFar WOld XLum
- 'Prosperity'	WOld
- 'Purple Dome'	CDor CFis ECha ELan EWTr LEdu LOPS LSRN MHer MWat SCob SHar SRkn WOld WOut
- 'Ralph Picton'	WFar WOld
- 'Red Robin'	MWat
- 'Red Star' **new**	SPhx
- 'Red Sunset'	SRms WOld
- 'Rembrandt'	ECtt MArl NGdn SRGP
- 'Remembrance'	MWat SRms WFar WOld
- 'Reverend Vincent Dale'	WOld
- 'Richness'	WOld
- 'Rosa Perle' **new**	ETMg
- 'Rose Bonnet'	CRos CSBt LRHS MWat NRHS SPlb WFar WOld
- 'Roseanne'	WOld
- 'Rosebud'	WOld
- 'Rosenquartz'	NLar WFar
- 'Rosenwichtel'	CDor ILea NLar WOld
- 'Royal Blue'	WOld
- 'Royal Ruby'	CFis CRos EBee ECtt IPot LRHS NLar NRHS WOld
- 'Royal Velvet'	WOld
- 'Rozika'	MNrw WOld
- 'Rufus'	NWsh WFar WOld
- 'Saint Egwyn'	WOld
- 'Sam Banham'	MNrw WOld
- SAMOA ('Dasthree') (Island Series)	CRos EPfP EUJe IRob LRHS LSou NEgg NLar NRHS SPad SPoG SRms WCot
- 'Sandford White Swan'	EWTr MHer MWat WFar WOld
- 'Sarah Ballard'	CRos LRHS NLar NRHS SRGP WBrk WOld
§ - 'Schneekissen'	CBod CRos ECtt ELan EPfP GMaP LRHS MBNS MHer NRHS SRGP SRms SWvt WHar WOld XLum
- 'Schneezicklein'	GBin GWyn
- 'Schöne von Dietlikon'	CKno IPot LEdu MWat WFar WOld XLum
- 'Schoolgirl'	WOld
- 'Sheena'	WFar WOld
- 'Silberblaukissen'	WOld
- SNOW CUSHION	see *S. novi-belgii* 'Schneekissen'
- 'Snowsprite'	CBod CSBt ELan ESps LRHS MWat NLar NRHS SGbt SGol SRGP SRms WOld
- 'Sonata'	GMaP WOld
- 'Sophia'	MWat WOld
- 'Starlight'	CBod CDor ECtt GMcL IBoy ILea LRHS NLar WFar WRHF
- 'Steinebrück'	WOld
- 'Sterling Silver'	WOld
- 'Sun Queen'	WOld
- 'Sunset'	WOld
- 'Susan'	SRGP WOld
- 'Sweet Briar'	WOld
- 'Tapestry'	WOld
- 'Terry's Pride'	SRGP WFar WOld
- 'The Archbishop'	ECtt WOld XEll
- 'The Bishop'	WOld
- 'The Cardinal'	WOld
- 'The Dean'	WOld
- 'The Sexton'	WOld
- 'Thundercloud'	MWat WOld
- 'Timsbury'	SRms WOld
- TONGA ('Dasfour') (Island Series)	CRos EPfP EWTr LRHS MHol NLar NRHS NWsh SPoG SRms SWvt WCot
- 'Tovarich'	WOld
- 'Trudi Ann'	WOld
- 'Twinkle'	WOld
- 'Victor'	WOld
- 'Vignem'	NSti
- 'Violet Lady'	WOld
- 'Waterperry'	MWat WBrk WOld
- 'White Ladies'	CBcs CRos ECtt GMaP IMou LCro LOPS LRHS MMuc MNrw MWat NLar NRHS SRGP XLum
- 'White Swan'	ECtt
- 'White Wings'	MWat WOld
- 'Winston S. Churchill'	CAby CDor CRos EAJP ELan EPfP GMaP LEdu LRHS MHer MPie MWat NEgg NRHS SPer SPlb SPoG SRGP WOld WTor
- 'Zwergenhimmel'	SAko
§ ***oblongifolium***	NWsh WOld XSen
§ - 'Fanny's'	ECtt GCal MMuc NGdn NWad SEND SRGP WOld
- 'October Skies'	CSpe EBee EWes LRHS MNrw
'Ochtendgloren' (*pilosum* var *pringlei* hybrid) ♀H4	CSam EBee ECtt ELon EPPr EWes MNrw NLar WHal WHoo WOld
§ 'Oktoberlicht'	CRos EPPr LRHS MNrw NRHS WHoo WOld
§ ***oolentangiense***	MMuc NLar SPhx WOld
'Orchidee'	CMea ECtt EPPr EPri EWTr EWes MAvo MWat WOld
'Photograph' ♀H7	CRos CSam ECtt EWes LEdu LRHS NPnk NRHS WOld WPGP
§ ***pilosum***	WCot WFar
§ - var. ***pringlei*** ♀H7	ECha EWes MMuc MRav NWad WOld
§ - - 'Monte Cassino'	CAby CBot CSBt EPfP LRHS MBNS MRav MWat NBro SPhx SRGP SRms WOld WSpi XLum
- - 'October Glory'	CCse ECtt MMuc WFar
- - 'Phoebe'	WOld
'Pink Star'	CBot CRos EBee ECtt ELon GMaP LEdu LRHS MRav MWat NRHS NSti SPhx WOld XLum
'Pinwheel'	WCot
'Pixie Dark Eye' (*ericoides* hybrid)	EBee ECtt SMHy WCot
'Pixie Red Eye' (*ericoides* hybrid)	EBee LEdu WCot
'Prairie Lavender'	WOld
'Prairie Pink'	WOld
'Prairie Purple'	CDor ECtt MTis MWat SMHy SPhx WCot WOld
'Prairie Violet'	WOld
'Primrose Path'	CDor ECtt LEdu MNrw SPhx WBrk WCot WOld
§ ***puniceum***	MMuc NLar XLum
'Ringdove' (*ericoides* hybrid) ♀H6	MAvo NSti SRGP SWvt WCot WOld
'Rosa Star'	WOld
'Rose Quartz' (Autumn Jewels Series) **new**	NCou

§ × ***salignum*** WOld
- Scottish form WOld
'Sea Spray' WCot
§ ***sericeum*** SBrt SPhx
shortii SPhx
'Soft Lass' WCot WOld
'Speyerer Herbstwoge' **new** MAvo
'Star of Chesters' MWat WOld
'Sunhelene' EBee ECtt WCot
SUNPLUM ('Danasplum'^{PBR}) SRGP
'Superstar' WHoo WOld
§ ***tradescantii*** ELan MBNS MRav NSti SMad WBrk WCot WOld
'Treffpunkt' IBoy IMou MAvo SAko
§ ***turbinellum*** ambig. EWTr
turbinellum misapplied 🏆^{H6} CFis CKno EPfP EWes LRHS MMuc NGdn SMHy SPhx SRkn SWvt WArt
turbinellum Lindl. CSam EBee EPfP EWTr MWat NLar NQui SSut WCot WOld
- 'El Fin' EWld MNrw
- hybrid WOld WSpi
'Vasterival' IMou LEdu MPie MSpe MTis NDov SBee WOut XLum
'Wood's Blue' CRos EPPr LRHS NRHS
'Wood's Pink' CRos LRHS MTis NRHS
'Wood's Purple' CRos EBee LRHS NRHS

Symphytum (*Boraginaceae*)

'Angela Whinfield' CMea EBee LPla
asperum ECha EPPr MRav NLar WMoo
* ***azureum*** LPla MBel NChi WCAu
'Belsay' IRob
'Belsay Gold' NBid WBor
bulbosum PAB 4886 LEdu
caucasicum CElw EBee ECha GPoy IFro LEdu NLar NSti SPer SRms WHil WMoo WOut WWtn XLum
- 'Norwich Sky' CExl WBor
cordatum EPPr LEdu MNrw
§ 'Goldsmith' (v) CBod CMea EBee ECha ELan EPfP MHol MPie NBid NEgg NLar NPer SPer WFar
grandiflorum CMac CTri GKev GPoy LEdu LRHS NRHS SPer
I - 'Miraculum' EBee
- 'Sky-blue-pink' IFro
'Hidcote Blue' CBre CTri ECha ECtt EPPr EPed EPfP IBoy LRHS MMuc NBro NEgg NRHS SCob SEND SPer SPoG SRms WGwG WMoo WOut WPnP WWtn
§ 'Hidcote Pink' CBod CBre ECha ECtt EPPr LRHS MMuc MNrw NRHS SEND SPer SPoG SRms WCAu WFar WGwG WMoo WPnP WWtn XLum
'Hidcote Variegated' (v) CMac SRms
ibericum CAgr CBod CSam ECha EHrv EWTr GKev GMaP GPoy LRHS MMuc NRHS NSti SEND SRms WGwG WMoo WOut WWtn
- 'All Gold' ECha LRHS MHer MNrw NRHS WMoo
- 'Blaueglocken' ECha WMoo
- dwarf IFro WMoo
- 'Gold in Spring' WFar
- 'Jubilee' see *S.* 'Goldsmith'
- 'Lilacinum' CFis WHer
- 'Variegatum' see *S.* 'Goldsmith'
- 'Wisley Blue' CBcs ILea LRHS NRHS SCob WFar WMoo
'Icy-Ness' **new** GKev
'Lambrook Sunrise' CMac LEdu NBro SRms WCot WMoo
'Langthorns Pink' ELan GCal
officinale CAgr CHab EBWF ENfk GPoy MHer MNHC MNrw NPer NPri SPoG SRms WHer XAbr XLum
- var. ***ochroleucum*** WHer
orientale EPPr GCal MBel
peregrinum see *S.* × *uplandicum*
'Roseum' see *S.* 'Hidcote Pink'
'Rubrum' CBod EHrv ELan EPed EPfP EWes LEdu LRHS MBel MHer MMuc NBro NLar NRHS SPer WCAu WGwG WWtn XLum
'Sera Howys' WOut
tuberosum CBre CElw CFis CSam EPPr GPoy LEdu LPla MHer MMuc NWad WBor WCot WFar WHer XAbr
§ × ***uplandicum*** CTri ELan GPoy MMuc SVic
- 'Axminster Gold' (v) CMea EWes NChi WCot
- 'Bocking 14' CAgr CBod CFGn CHby EOHP EShb GAbr LEdu MHer MNHC SRms WSFF XLum
- 'Droitwich' (v) WCot
- 'Moorland Heather' CDor EBee LEdu LPla MHer MMrt MNrw MPie SPhx WBor WMoo
- purple-flowered MMuc
- 'Variegatum' (v) CBot ECha ECtt ELan EWes GCal LRHS NGdn NRHS WAvo WMoo WSpi

Symplocarpus (*Araceae*)

foetidus CHid

Synadenium (*Euphorbiaceae*)

grantii 'Rubrum' EShb

Syncarpha (*Asteraceae*)

vestita SPlb

Syncolostemon (*Lamiaceae*)

'Candy Kisses' WCot

Syneilesis (*Asteraceae*)

aconitifolia GEdr MAvo WCot WHal
- B&SWJ 879 EHrv LEdu WCru
palmata GEdr
- B&SWJ 1003 WCru
- B&SWJ 11226 WCru
- 'Aka-fu' GEdr
- 'Kikkou-fu' GEdr
- 'Kiko' GEdr
subglabrata B&SWJ 298 WCru
aff. ***tagawae*** B&SWJ 11191 WCot

Syngonium (*Araceae*)

podophyllum 🏆^{H1b} XBlo

Synnotia see *Sparaxis*

Synsepalum (*Sapotaceae*)

dulcificum SCit

Synthyris (*Plantaginaceae*)

laciniata EBee LLHF
missurica subsp. ***missurica*** EBee WFar
- subsp. ***stellata*** CAby CBod EBee ECre ECtt EPfP EPri EWes GAbr GBin GCal LEdu LRHS MMrt NHpl NPnk NRHS NSti

		SPoG WGwG WHal WMoo WSHC WTor
	platycarpa	EBee

Synurus (*Asteraceae*)

	pungens	SBrt

Syringa ✿ (*Oleaceae*)

	afghanica misapplied	see *S. protolaciniata*
	BLOOMERANG DARK PURPLE ('Smsjbp7')	LCro LOPS MAsh SGol SPoG
	BLOOMERANG PINK PERFUME	see *S.* 'Pink Perfume'
	BLOOMERANG PURPLE ('Penda')	LRHS NRHS
	× ***chinensis***	EPfP
	- 'Alba'	see *S.* 'Correlata'
	- 'Bicolor'	WGob
	- 'Saugeana'	MBlu MMuc SPer
§	'Correlata' (graft-chimaera)	EPfP
	× ***diversifolia***	NLar
	emodi 'Aureovariegata'	see *S. emodi* 'Variegata'
	- 'Elegantissima' (v)	CBcs CEnd CMac EBtc ELan EPfP LRHS MAsh NEgg SPoG
§	- 'Variegata' (v)	CBot EMil LRHS NLar
	× ***hyacinthiflora*** 'Clarke's Giant'	NLar SGol
	- 'Dark Night' **new**	WGob
	- 'Esther Staley' ♀H6	EPfP MRav WGob
	- 'Maiden's Blush' ♀H6	SGol WGob
	- 'Pocahontas' ♀H6	LRHS WGob
	- 'Sweetheart' (d)	NOra
	JOSÉE ('Morjos 060f')	ELan ELon EPfP LSou MAsh SCob SGol SWvt WFar WGob
	× ***josiflexa***	CExl
	- 'Agnes Smith'	EBee LRHS NLar
	- 'Bellicent' ♀H6	CBot CEnd CMac ELan EMil EPfP GMcL IFro LRHS MAsh MMuc MRav NPri NRHS SMad SPer SPoG SRms SWvt WAvo WCFE WFar WSpi
	- 'Lynette'	NEoE
	- 'Redwine'	NLar
§	- 'Royalty'	NLar
	josikaea	CAco CMCN CSBt EBee EWTr NLar SPer
	komarowii	GGGa MGil WSHC
§	- subsp. ***reflexa***	CDul EPfP EWTr MBlu NLar SLon WPGP
§	× ***laciniata*** Mill.	CDul CJun CWCL EBee ELan EPfP LRHS MRav NLar SPer SPoG WAvo WCFE WHar WPGP
	'Lark Song'	NLar
	meyeri	SVen
	- 'Inge'	NLar
§	- 'Palibin' ♀H5	Widely available
	'Minuet'	CBcs LBuc LRHS SGol
	'Miss Canada'	LRHS NLar
	MISS JAPAN	EBee LRHS
	oblata	CMCN
	palibiniana misapplied	see *S. meyeri* 'Palibin'
	patula misapplied	see *S. meyeri* 'Palibin'
	patula (Palib.) Nakai	see *S. pubescens* subsp. *patula*
	pekinensis	see *S. reticulata* subsp. *pekinensis*
	× ***persica*** ♀H6	CExl CJun CTri EPfP EWTr MGos MRav NLar SLon SPer WFar WGob WHar
	- 'Alba' ♀H6	CJun MRav WAvo WFar WGob
	- var. ***laciniata***	see *S.* × *laciniata* Mill.
§	'Pink Perfume'[PBR]	EPfP LCro LOPS MAsh NRHS SGol SPoG

	pinnatifolia	CBcs CBot EBee GBin LRHS NLar SAko WPGP
	× ***prestoniae*** 'Desdemona'	EBtc LRHS MMuc
	- 'Elinor' ♀H6	CBot ELan EMil EPfP LRHS MRav
	- 'Minuet'	NLar
	- 'Miss Poland'	LRHS
	- 'Nocturne'	WFar
	- 'Royalty'	see *S.* × *josiflexa* 'Royalty'
§	***protolaciniata***	IDee LRHS NLar SLim
	pubescens subsp. ***julianae*** 'George Eastman'	MRav
	- subsp. ***microphylla*** 'Superba' ♀H6	Widely available
§	- subsp. ***patula***	CMac EPfP LRHS MMuc MRav NRHS SLim SVen
	- - 'Miss Kim' ♀H6	Widely available
	'Red Pixie'	CMac CRos EPfP LCro LOPS LRHS MAsh MGos MMrt NRHS SCoo WGob
	'Red Prince'	NPri
	reflexa	see *S. komarowii* subsp. *reflexa*
	reticulata	CMCN EGFP MBlu
	- 'Ivory Silk'	EBtc EPfP
§	- subsp. ***pekinensis***	CMCN LRHS
	- - 'Yellow Fragrance'	NLar
	× ***swegiflexa***	CDul CExl EPfP
	tomentella	EBee EWTr SRms WPGP
	- subsp. ***sweginzowii***	CBcs CWCL EBee EBtc GKin LLHF MMuc NLar SPer WSpi
	- - 'Superba'	SGol
	- subsp. ***yunnanensis***	CExl GGGa
	velutina Kom.	see *S. pubescens* subsp. *patula*
	villosa	SPlb
	vulgaris	CAco CDul EPfP ESps
§	- 'Andenken an Ludwig Späth' ♀H6	Widely available
	- 'Aucubifolia' (d/v)	SEND WGob
	- 'Aurea'	MRav NEoE WAvo
	- BEAUTY OF MOSCOW	see *S. vulgaris* 'Krasavitsa Moskvy'
	- 'Belle de Nancy' (d)	CCCN CDul CLnd CMac ECrN ELan ELon EMOT EWTr GMcL MAsh MMuc MRav NGdn NLar SCob SEND SGol SWvt WGob
	- CARPE DIEM	see *S. vulgaris* 'Evert de Gier'
	- 'Charles Joly' (d) ♀H6	Widely available
	- 'Comtesse d'Harcourt'	EPfP SEND WGob
	- 'Congo'	LSRN WGob
	- 'Dark Koster' **new**	WGob
	- 'Dwight D. Eisenhower' **new**	WGob
	- 'Edward J. Gardner' (d) ♀H6	SEND
	- 'Etna'	WGob
§	- 'Evert de Gier'[PBR]	CBcs EBee
	- 'Firmament' ♀H6	ELan MRav SEND SPer WGob WSpi
	- 'G. J. Baardse'	EWTr
	- 'Hope'	see *S. vulgaris* 'Nadezhda'
	- 'Hugo de Vries'	IArd
	- 'Katherine Havemeyer' (d) ♀H6	Widely available
§	- 'Krasavitsa Moskvy' (d) ♀H6	CTri CWCL EPfP EWes GMcL LRHS MAsh MRav NLar NOra NPri SEND SGol
	- 'Lee Jewett Walker'	SSta
	- 'Lila Wonder'[PBR]	EPfP SPoG
	- 'Madame Florent Stepman'	CMac CWCL ELon GMcL NGdn NLar WFar WGob
	- 'Madame Lemoine' (d) ♀H6	Widely available
	- 'Michel Buchner' (d)	CBcs CDul CLnd EBee ECrN ELan EMOT EWTr GMcL MBlu MGos

	NLar NOra SCob SCoo SLim SPer WHar
- 'Miss Ellen Willmott' (d)	IArd NLar
- 'Mrs Edward Harding' (d) ♀H6	ECrN EMOT EPfP ESps GMcL MRav NLar SPer WGob
§ - 'Nadezhda' (d)	GAbr WGob
- 'Pat Pesata'	WGob
- 'Paul Thirion' (d)	WGob
- 'Pavlinka' (d)	IArd
- 'Président Grévy' (d)	CBar CWCL EPfP MAsh NPri SGol SLim SPer SPoG
- 'President Lincoln'	WGob
- 'Président Poincaré' (d)	WGob
- 'Primrose' ♀H6	CBcs CCCN CMac CRav EBee ELan ELon EPfP LRHS MAsh MGos MJak NLar NOra SCoo SEND SGol SPer SPoG WGob WSpi
- 'Prince Wolkonsky' (d)	ECrN ELon EPfP LSRN MAsh SEND SPer WFar WGob
- 'Princesse Sturdza'	ELon
- 'Professor Hoser'	WGob
- ROSE DE MOSCOU ('Minkarl'PBR)	EPfP
- 'Saint Margaret' new	WGob
- 'Sarah Sands'	WGob
- 'Sensation' ♀H6	Widely available
- 'Souvenir d'Alice Harding' (d) ♀H6	IBoy
- 'Souvenir de Louis Spaeth'	see *S. vulgaris* 'Andenken an Ludwig Späth'
- variegated (v)	EWes
- variegated double (d/v)	WCot
- 'Vesper'	IArd
- 'Victor Lemoine' (d)	WGob
- 'Viviand-Morel' (d)	CMac
- 'Wedgewood Blue' new	WGob
- 'William Robinson' (d)	WGob
wolfii	EBtc NLar

Syzygium (*Myrtaceae*)

luehmannii	EShb
paniculatum	CExl

T

Tabernaemontana (*Apocynaceae*)

coronaria	see *T. divaricata*
§ ***divaricata***	CCCN WFib

Tacca (*Taccaceae*)

chantrieri	CCCN

Taccarum (*Araceae*)

weddellianum	WCot

Tacitus see *Graptopetalum*

Taenidia (*Apiaceae*)

integerrima new	SPhx

Tagetes (*Asteraceae*)

'Cinnabar'	CSpe
erecta 'French Vanilla' new	ETMg
lemmonii 'Martin's Mutant'	WCot
lucida	ENfk LEdu MHer SRms WTre
minuta new	MSCN
patula 'Dainty Marietta' ♀H2 new	LCro
- 'Harlequin'	see *T. patula* 'Old Scotch Pride'
§ - 'Old Scotch Pride'	SPav
- Safari Series new	NPri
- - 'Safari Red' new	LCro
- 'Strawberry Blonde' new	ETMg
- 'Tall Scotch Prize' new	CRav
tenuifolia 'Golden Gem' new	LOPS
Zenith Series new	ETMg

Taiwania (*Cupressaceae*)

cryptomerioides	CAco IArd IDee SAko WPGP

Talbotia (*Velloziaceae*)

§ ***elegans***	SBrt

Talinum (*Portulacaceae*)

'Zoe'	CPBP

tamarillo see *Solanum betaceum*

tamarind see *Tamarindus indica*

Tamarindus (*Caesalpiniaceae*)

indica (F)	SPlb

Tamarix (*Tamaricaceae*)

gallica	SArc SEND SWeb WSHC
hampeana	SEND
§ ***parviflora*** ♀H5	CDul CMac CRos EPfP LRHS NLar NRHS SCob SPoG
pentandra	see *T. ramosissima* 'Rosea'
ramosissima	CCCN CTri EBee ECrN ELan EPfP EWTr MAsh SCob SEWo SLim SLon SRms WAvo WHar
- 'Hulsdonk White'	CBcs SPer
- 'Pink Cascade' ♀H5	CAco CBcs CCCN CDul CMac CWCL EBee EPfP ESps LCro LOPS LRHS MBlu MGos MRav NEgg NRHS SCob SEND SGbt SGol SPer SPoG SWvt
§ - 'Rosea'	CBcs
§ - 'Rubra'	EPfP GMcL SEND SLon SPer
- 'Summer Glow'	see *T. ramosissima* 'Rubra'
tetrandra ♀H5	CBcs CCVT CDul CTsd EBee ELan EPfP ESps LRHS MAsh MBlu MGil MGos MRav MSwo NPer SEND SGol SPad SPlb SRms SWvt WAvo WHar
- var. ***purpurea***	see *T. parviflora*

Tanacetum ✿ (*Asteraceae*)

§ ***argenteum***	MRav
- subsp. ***canum***	LRHS SLon
§ ***balsamita***	CBod CHby EBee ELan ENfk GPoy LEdu MHer MMuc MNHC SEND SRms WHer WSFF XLum XSen
§ - subsp. ***balsamita***	GPoy
§ - subsp. ***balsamitoides***	CBod MHer SRms
- var. ***tanacetoides***	see *T. balsamita* subsp. *balsamita*
- ***tomentosum***	see *T. balsamita* subsp. *balsamitoides*
camphoratum	SBrt
§ ***cinerariifolium***	CBod GPoy MNHC
§ ***coccineum***	SVic WFar
- 'Alfred'	MNrw
- 'Bees' Pink Delight'	ECtt NEgg
- 'Duro'	LRHS NRHS
- 'Eileen May Robinson'	CBod EPfP LSRN

	- 'Garden Treasure'	EBee ECtt
	- 'H.M. Pike'	EBee
	- 'James Kelway'	ECtt EPfP
	- 'Laurin'	EBee ECtt LRHS NRHS
	- 'Red Dwarf'	ECtt
	- Robinson's crimson-flowered	LRHS NRHS
	- Robinson's giant-flowered	CTsd LRHS NRHS SRms
	- Robinson's pink-flowered	EBee EPfP GMaP MHol SCob WHar XLum
	- Robinson's red-flowered	CSBt EAJP EPfP GMaP GMcL GWyn LRHS MHol NRHS SPlb SWvt WHar XLum
	- Robinson's rose-flowered	CSBt
	- 'Snow Cloud'	ECtt EPfP
	- 'Vanessa'	MNrw
§	***corymbosum***	EBee GCal LRHS NLar NRHS WCot
	- 'Bukke'	LEdu
	- 'Festtafel'	LEdu LPla
	densum	WCFE
	- subsp. ***amani***	ECha GMaP LRHS SEND XSen
§	***haradjanii***	MCot SBch WKif
	macrophyllum misapplied	see *Achillea grandifolia* Friv.
§	***macrophyllum*** (Waldst. & Kit.) Sch.Bip.	CAby EBee ECtt EPPr GWyn SPhx WBor
	- 'Cream Klenza'	WCot
	niveum	ECha WCot
	- 'Jackpot'	CBot EPfP EWes SWvt
§	***parthenium***	CBod CHab CHby ENfk GPoy LOPS MHer MNHC NPer SRms SVic WHer WTre XLum
	- 'Aureum'	CBod CHid ECha ELan ENfk EWes GPoy LEdu MHer MNHC SPer SPlb SRms SWvt WCot WHer WMoo XLum
	- double white-flowered (d)	NPer SRms
	- 'Golden Ball'	EPfP
	- 'Golden Moss'	XLum
	- 'Malmesbury'	WHer
	- 'Plenum' (d)	MNrw
§	- 'Rowallane' (d)	MMuc SEND WCot
	- 'Selma Star' (d) **new**	WHer
	- 'Sissinghurst White'	see *T. parthenium* 'Rowallane'
	- 'Snowball' (d)	EPfP
	- 'White Bonnet' (d)	WHer
	poteriifolium	EBee LRHS NRHS
	ptarmiciflorum 'Silver Feather'	SRms SVen
*	***tommansii***	EBee LRHS NRHS
	vulgare	CHab CHby CMac EBWF ECha ECtt ENfk GBin GPoy GWyn IRos LCro LOPS MHer MNHC SRms SVic WFar WMoo WSFF WTre XAbr XSen
	- 'All Gold'	SMad SRms
	- var. ***crispum***	EBee ENfk MHer MRav SMad SRms WFar
	- 'Gold Sticks'	CBod
	- 'Golden Fleece'	ECtt EWes GMcL LEdu LSou NSti WCot WGrn
	- 'Isla Gold' (v)	CDor ECtt EWes LEdu MHer MMuc MRav NBid SEND WCAu WCot WFar WMoo
	- 'Silver Lace' (v)	CBre EBee EWes WFar WMoo

Tanakaea (*Saxifragaceae*)

	radicans	GEdr WCru
	- B&SWJ 11407	WCru

tangelo see *Citrus* × *aurantium* Tangelo Group

tangerine see *Citrus reticulata* Tangerine Group

tangor see *Citrus* × *aurantium* Tangor Group

tarragon see *Artemisia dracunculus*

Taraxacum (*Asteraceae*)

	faeroense	NPoe NWad WCot
	officinale agg.	CHab
	- 'Nettleton'	CNat
	pseudoroseum	MMuc NPoe SBee
	rubrifolium	CBre EPPr

Tasmannia (*Winteraceae*)

§	***lanceolata***	Widely available
	- (f)	EUJe MCot SPer
	- (m)	SPer
	- 'Mount Wellington'	GCal
	- 'Red Spice'	EPfP LSRN SEle
	- 'Suzette' (v)	LRHS MBlu SRms

Taxodium ✿ (*Cupressaceae*)

	ascendens 'Nutans'	see *T. distichum* var. *imbricarium* 'Nutans'
	distichum	Widely available
	- 'Cascade Falls'	CDul MBlu MGos NLar NOra SAko SLim
	- 'Cave Hill'	NLar
	- 'Falling Waters'	SGol
	- var. ***imbricarium***	CMCN EPfP
§	- - 'Nutans'	CAco EPfP IArd MBlu SGol SLim
	- 'Little Twister'	SLim
	- 'Minaret'	MBlu
*	- 'Pendulum'	IDee
	- 'Peve Minaret'	CMen MGos SAko SArc SCob SGol SLim SPoG
	- 'Peve Yellow'	MBlu SLim
	- 'Schloss Herten'	NLar
	- 'Secrest'	MBlu
	- SHAWNEE BRAVE ('Mickelson')	MBlu SBig
	mucronatum	CExl CFil
	- NJM 09.037	WPGP

Taxus ✿ (*Taxaceae*)

	baccata ♀H6	Widely available
	- 'Adpressa Aurea' (v)	GMil
	- 'Adpressa Variegata' (m/v)	GMil
	- 'Aldenham Gold'	CKen
	- 'Amersfoort'	GMil NLar NWad
	- 'Argentea Minor'	see *T. baccata* 'Dwarf White'
	- 'Arngost' **new**	NLar
	- Aurea Group	ELan SRms
I	- 'Aureomarginata' (v)	CBcs NEgg SWvt
	- 'Autumn Shades'	CBcs NLar
	- 'Bridget's Gold'	CKen
	- 'Bultinck Orange Beauty' **new**	NLar
	- 'Corleys Coppertip'	CKen EBtc EMOT GMil LRHS MMuc MRav NLar SLim
	- 'Cristata'	CKen GMil MBlu NLar
	- 'David'	GMil IArd IBoy IRob LRHS MGos NLar SLim SPoG SWvt
	- 'Dorothea'	NLar
	- 'Dovastoniana' (m or f)	CAco CDul CMac LPra NLar
	- 'Dovastonii Aurea' (m or f/v)	CAco CBcs GKin GMil LPra MBlu NLar SGol SMad SRms

	– 'Drinkstone Gold' (v)	EMOT SLim
§	– 'Dwarf White' (v)	GMil NLar
	– 'Elegantissima' (f/v)	EMOT EPfP NEgg SCoo SPoG
§	– 'Fastigiata' (f) ♀H6	Widely available
	– Fastigiata Aurea Group	CLnd CMac CTho EPfP ESps GMcL GQue IArd LMaj LPra LRHS MGos MJak NLar NRHS SArc SCob SGol SRms WHar
	– 'Fastigiata Aureomarginata' (m/v) ♀H6	CDul CMac CSBt CTri EPfP GMil LBee LPra LRHS MGos MSwo NRHS SCoo SLim SLon SPer SPoG SWvt WTSh
	– 'Fastigiata Robusta' (f)	CAco CSBt EBtc ELan EMOT EPfP EUJe GMcL LMaj LRHS MAsh MGos NLar NRHS SCoo SLim SPoG
	– 'Goldener Zwerg'	MBlu NLar
	– 'Graciosa'	NLar
	– 'Great Column'	MBlu
	– 'Green Column'	CKen
	– 'Green Diamond'	CKen MBlu NLar SBod
	– 'Hibernica'	see *T. baccata* 'Fastigiata'
	– 'Icicle' ♀H6	CBcs GMil MAsh NLar NWad SBod
	– 'Itsy Bitsy'	CKen
	– 'Ivory Tower'	CAco CBcs CKen ELan EUJe LRHS NLar NRHS NWad
	– 'Klitzeklein'	CKen
	– 'Lakatos' **new**	CAco
	– 'Luca' **new**	NLar
	– 'Micro'	CKen MAsh
	– 'Nutans'	CKen GMil
	– 'Papageno' **new**	NLar
	– 'Prostrata'	CMac
	– 'Pygmaea'	CKen
	– 'Repandens' (f) ♀H6	CDul ESps GMcL IArd WSpi
I	– 'Repens Aurea' (v) ♀H6	CDul CKen CMac EMOT EPfP NLar SCoo SLim SRms WSpi
	– 'Rushmore'	NLar
	– 'Semperaurea' (m) ♀H6	CBcs CMac GMil LBuc LPra LRHS MAsh NLar SCoo SGol SLim SPoG WSpi
	– 'Standishii' (f) ♀H6	CBcs CDul CKen CMac CSBt ELan EMOT EPfP ESps EUJe GKin GMcL GMil IArd LBee LRHS MAsh MGos MMuc MRav NEgg NLar NOra NRHS NWad SLim SMad SPoG SWvt
	– 'Stove Pipe'	CKen
	– 'Summergold' (v)	ELan EMOT ESps GMcL GMil LRHS MRav NLar NRHS SCoo WSpi
	cuspidata	CAco CMen GMil
	– 'Aurea' **new**	GMil
	– 'Aurescens' (v)	CKen
	– 'Minuet'	CKen
	– 'Straight Hedge'	SLim
	× ***media*** 'Hicksii' (f)	CDul ESps GMcL GMil LBuc LMaj LPra SGol
	– 'Hillii'	LBuc
	wallichiana	LEdu

tayberry see *Rubus* Tayberry Group

Tecoma (*Bignoniaceae*)

capensis ♀H1c	CHll CRHN GCal MGil SVen
– 'Apricot'	CBcs
– 'Lutea'	CBcs EPfP
ricasoliana	see *Podranea ricasoliana*

Tecomanthe (*Bignoniaceae*)

speciosa	CRHN

Tecomaria see *Tecoma*

Tecophilaea (*Tecophilaeaceae*)

	cyanocrocus ♀H3	EPot GKev LAma LLHF LRHS NRHS SDir
	– 'Leichtlinii' ♀H3	CAvo EPot GKev LAma LLHF LRHS NRHS SDeJ SDir
	– 'Purpurea'	see *T. cyanocrocus* 'Violacea'
	– Storm Cloud Group	EPot GKev LLHF SDir
§	– 'Violacea'	CAvo EPot GKev LLHF LRHS NRHS SDir

Telekia (*Asteraceae*)

§	***speciosa***	CMac CRos CSam CSpe ELan EPfP GAbr GLog LEdu LRHS MMuc NBro NChi NLar NRHS NSti SEND SPlb WBrk WHer WMoo

Telesonix see *Boykinia*

Teline see *Genista*

Tellima (*Saxifragaceae*)

	grandiflora	Widely available
	– 'Bob's Choice'	WCot
	– 'Delphine' (v)	EPPr WCot XLum
	– 'Forest Frost'	CBod CFis CMac EHoe ELan EPPr EPed EShb LRHS MBNS MBel MMoz MPnt NLar NRHS SCob SWvt WCot WGwG WMoo WOut
	– Odorata Group	CBre ECha WCot WMoo
	– 'Purpurea'	see *T. grandiflora* Rubra Group
	– 'Purpurteppich'	ECha EPPr GPSL LRHS MPnt MRav NRHS SWvt WCot WMoo WPnP
§	– Rubra Group	CBre CBro CMac CSam CTri ECha EHoe ELan EPfP GMaP GQue LRHS MCot NChi NEgg NLar NPer NRHS NSti SCob SPer SPlb SRms SWvt WCAu WCot WHoo WMoo WPnP
	– 'Silver Select'	EPPr

Telopea (*Proteaceae*)

'Emperor's Torch'	LRHS MPkF
oreades	SPlb
'Shady Lady Crimson'	CCCN
'Shady Lady White'	CCCN
'Shady Lady Yellow'	CCCN
speciosissima	CCCN LRHS SPlb
truncata	CCCN SPlb WCru

Temu see *Blepharocalyx*

Tephroseris (*Asteraceae*)

integrifolia subsp. ***capitata***	SPlb

Ternstroemia (*Pentaphylacaceae*)

chapaensis WWJ 11918	WCru
gymnanthera	WCru
kwangtungensis FMWJ 13402 **new**	WCru
luteoflora FMWJ 13360	WCru

Tetracentron (*Trochodendraceae*)

§	***sinense***	CBcs CMCN EPfP IArd MBlu
	– WJC 13818 from the Himalaya **new**	WCru
	– var. ***himalense***	see *T. sinense*

Tetradium (*Rutaceae*)

	austrosinense NJM 09.215	WPGP
§	***daniellii***	CBcs CDul CMCN CTho EBee EPfP IArd LEdu SAko SPtp WGob WHar WPGP
	- from Korea **new**	WPGP
§	- Hupehense Group	CMCN CTho MCoo NLar SEND WPGP
	fraxinifolium PAB 9101	LEdu
	- WJC 13750 **new**	WCru
	aff. ***fraxinifolium*** WWJ 11615	WCru
	glabrifolium B&SWJ 6882	WCru
	- CWJ 12364	WCru
	ruticarpum	LEdu WPGP
	- B&SWJ 3541	WCru

Tetragonolobus see *Lotus*

Tetraneuris (*Asteraceae*)

§	***grandiflora***	CSma GKev SPlb
	scaposa	EPot

Tetrapanax ✿ (*Araliaceae*)

	sp.	ETod
§	***papyrifer*** ♀H4	CBrP CDTJ CHGN ELan NLos SBig SEND SVen XBlo
	- B&SWJ 7135	WCru
	- 'Empress'	WCru
	- 'Rex'	Widely available
	- 'Steroidal Giant'	CDTJ SBig

Tetrapathaea see *Passiflora*

Tetrastigma (*Vitaceae*)

	obtectum	CCCN ECre EShb EWes SEND WAvo WCFE

Teucrium (*Lamiaceae*)

*	***ackermannii*** ♀H5	CMea LRHS MHer WAbe WHoo XSen
	aroanium	CTal EPot XSen
	asiaticum	XSen
	aureum	XSen
	botrys	MHer
	chamaedrys misapplied	see *T.* × *lucidrys*
	chamaedrys L.	CBar CRos ENfk GJos GMaP GPoy GQue LEdu LRHS LSRN MCot MNHC MRav MSwo NWad SCob SEND SLim SPer SPlb SRms SVen SWvt WBrk WHar XSen
	- f. ***albiflora***	LPla
	- 'Nanum'	GMaP
	- 'Rose'	SRms
	- 'Spring Gold'	LRHS
	- 'Summer Sunshine'	CRos LRHS
§	***creticum***	SPhx
	dunense	XSen
	flavum	EBee EDAr EPPr GCal SBrt XSen
	fruticans	Widely available
	- 'Azureum' ♀H3	CBcs CBod CTsd EBee ELan EPfP EWTr LRHS LSRN MRav SBrt SEND SPer SPoG SRms SWvt WAvo WCFE WKif XSen
	- 'Compactum'	ELan EWTr LRHS LSRN SLim SLon SPer SPoG SWvt WAvo WCFE WPGP
	- 'Drysdale'	CSBt ELan LRHS SWvt
	hircanicum	CAby CElw CSam ECha ECtt ELan GJos IFro LRHS LSRN MMuc MNrw NWad SEND SPhx SRkn WArt WCFE WMoo XSen
	- PAB 13.341 **new**	LEdu
	- 'Paradise Delight'	ECtt GWyn
	- 'Purple Tails'	CBod CSpe CTsd CWld EPfP LSou MHol MNHC MRav SPoG SRms WFar
	lamiifolium W&B BGB-7	WCot
§	× ***lucidrys***	CChe CMea CRos ECha ECrN ELan ENfk EPfP EWTr GBin IRob LPla LRHS LSRN MHer MNHC MPie MRav SPer SPoG SRms SWvt WCFE WFar WHar WHoo XSen
	- 'Lucky Gold'PBR	SPoG SRms
	lucidum	GCal SLon
	marum	CTri LEdu SRms XSen
	massiliense misapplied	see *T.* × *lucidrys*
	montanum	XSen
	orientale	WAbe XSen
	polium	SPhx WThu XSen
	pyrenaicum ♀H5	CMea CPBP EPot EWes GEdr SBch XSen
	rosmarinifolium	see *T. creticum*
	scorodonia	CBod CHab EBWF MCot MHer MNHC NLar NMir SRms WHer XSen
	- 'Binsted Gold'	MMoz NSti
	- 'Crispum'	LEdu LRHS MHer MMuc NBro NLar NRHS SBod SPer SRms WAvo WGrn WKif WMoo WOut WSHC
	- 'Crispum Marginatum' (v)	EBee ECha EHoe EPPr EPfP EWld LEdu LSou MRav
	- 'Winterdown' (v)	SBch
	subspinosum	LLHF WHoo WThu
§	***viscidum*** 'Lemon and Lime' (v)	EBee NSti

Thalia (*Marantaceae*)

	dealbata	CBen EUJe EWat LLWG MSKA SBig WMAq XLum

Thalictrum ✿ (*Ranunculaceae*)

	CC 4576	CExl
	CC 6859	MMoz
	CC 7077	MMoz
	Cox 6118	ITim
	from Afghanistan	see *T. isopyroides*
	actaeifolium B&SWJ 4664	WCru
	- B&SWJ 6310	WCru
	- var. ***brevistylum*** B&SWJ 8819	WCru
	- - 'Twinkling Star'	ECtt
	- compact B&SWJ 4946	WCru
	- 'Perfume Star'	CPar EBee ECtt GBin ILea MMrt NDov NLar SCob SMad WSpi
	adiantifolium	see *T. minus* 'Adiantifolium'
	alpinum	EBWF EDAr EPPr GJos
	angustifolium	see *T. lucidum*
	'Anne'PBR	CAby CDor CKno CPar EBee ECtt EMFm EWTr ILea IPot LRHS MAvo MBel MHol MNrw MTis NDov NGBl NLar SAko SMad SPoG WCot WSpi
	aquilegiifolium	Widely available
	- 'Album'	CBot CWCL EBee ECha ELan EPfP GBin GKin IPot LRHS MBel MCot MMuc NBid NRHS SEND SPer SPhx SWvt WArt WCAu WFar WSpi
*	- 'Hybridum'	WMoo

- var. ***intermedium*** B&SWJ 10965	WCru
- 'Purpureum'	NLar NQui WWtn
- var. ***sibiricum***	IMou
- - B&SWJ 11007	WCru
- 'Small Thundercloud'	GCal SMHy
- 'Thundercloud' ♀H5	Widely available
baicalense	EPPr
'Black Stockings'	Widely available
calabricum	NLar
chelidonii	EPPr MMoz
- HWJK 2216	WCru
clavatum	CAby WPGP
coreanum	see *T. ichangense*
cultratum	EBee LRHS NRHS WPGP
dasycarpum	EPPr GJos LPla WCot WPnP
§ ***delavayi*** ♀H7	Widely available
- BWJ 7800	WCru
- BWJ 7903	WCru
- var. ***acuminatum***	MBel
- - BWJ 7535	WCru
- - BWJ 7971	WCru
- 'Album'	Widely available
- 'Ankum'	EBee IPot LRHS MNrw NLar NRHS
- var. ***decorum***	CElw ECtt EPPr MBel WCot WCru WPGP
- - BWJ 7770	WCru
- aff. var. ***decorum***	CExl
- 'Gold Laced'	EBee NLar
- 'Hewitt's Double' (d) ♀H7	Widely available
- 'Hinkley'	IPot
- var. ***mucronatum***	MBel WCru
- - DJHC 473	WCru
- purple-stemmed BWJ 7748	WCru
- 'White Cloud'	GBin
aff. ***delavayi***	CBod ESps GKin IBoy
diffusiflorum	EWld IMou IPot MBel WAbe WCru
dipterocarpum misapplied	see *T. delavayi*
dipterocarpum Franch.	CMac EBee LRHS NRHS XLum
'Elin'	Widely available
fendleri	GBin
- var. ***polycarpum***	IMou WOut
filamentosum	EPPr IMou MBel WCot
- B&SWJ 777	WCru
- B&SWJ 4145	WCru
flavum	CBod CHab CMac EBWF ELan EWld GKin LLWG NBro NMir WFar WShi
- 'Chollerton'	see *T. isopyroides*
§ - subsp. ***glaucum*** ♀H7	Widely available
- - Brown's strain	WCot
- - dwarf	WPGP
- - 'Silver Sparkler' (v)	WCot
- - 'True Blue'	SGbt
- 'Illuminator'	CDor CElw CTri EPfP IBoy LRHS MArl MRav NLar NRHS WCot WFar XEll
flexuosum	see *T. minus* subsp. *minus*
honanense BWJ 7962	WCru
§ ***ichangense***	CBot CHid CSpe EBee ECtt EPri EUJe GAbr GEdr IPot LEdu LRHS LSou MBel MHol MTis NRHS NSti NWad WCot WRHF
- B&SWJ 8203	WCru
- Evening Star strain (v)	CAby CSpe ECtt GBin MHol SCob SPad
- var. ***minus*** 'Chinese Chintz'	WCru
- 'Purple Marble'	CWGN GEdr LEdu NPnk WCot
integrilobum B&SWJ 11151	WCru
§ ***isopyroides***	EBee GBin GCal GKev GKin LRHS MBel MHol MRav NLar NPnk NRHS NWad SHar WCot
javanicum	LEdu WPGP
- B&SWJ 9506	WCru
- PAB 9431	LEdu
- var. ***puberulum*** B&SWJ 6770	WCru
johnstonii B&SWJ 9127	WCru
kiusianum	CAby CTal EBee ECha EHoe ELan EPfP EPot EWes GBin GMcL ITim LLWG LRHS MBel MHer MHol NHpl NLar NPnk NSla SMad SRot SWvt WAbe WCot WFar WPnP XEll
- Kew form	WSHC
koreanum	see *T. ichangense*
§ ***lucidum***	CBod CElw CExl EBee ECtt EHoe ELan EShb GBin GCal GKin IMou LEdu LRHS MHol MMuc MPie MTis NGBl NLar NRHS NSti SEND SPhx WCot WPnP
minus	EBWF GBin LEdu LRHS NRHS SEND XAbr
§ - 'Adiantifolium'	GBin IPot MBel MRav NGdn SRms WSpi XLum
- var. ***hypoleucum*** B&SWJ 8634	WCru
- subsp. ***kemense***	EBee
§ - subsp. ***minus***	NBre
- var. ***sipellatum*** B&SWJ 5051	WCru
morisonii	EBee LRHS NBid NRHS
'Nishiki'	GEdr
omeiense BWJ 8049	WCru
orientale	EBee LRHS NRHS
osmundifolium	WCru
petaloideum	EPPr
platycarpum B&SWJ 2261	WCru
podocarpum B&SWJ 14297 **new**	WCru
polygamum	see *T. pubescens* Pursh
przewalskii	WCru
§ ***pubescens*** Pursh	EBee ECha GJos GMaP LRHS NDov NLar NRHS SHar SPhx WCot
punctatum B&SWJ 1272	WCru
ramosum BWJ 8126	WCru
reniforme	LEdu
- GWJ 9311	WCru
- HWJK 2403	WCru
- WJC 13761	WCru
rochebruneanum	Widely available
rubescens B&SWJ 10006	WCru
rugosum	EBee LRHS NRHS
sachalinense	WPGP
- RBS 0279	EBee EPPr NLar
shensiense	CExl
simplex var. ***brevipes*** B&SWJ 4794	WCru
speciosissimum	see *T. flavum* subsp. *glaucum*
* ***sphaerostachyum***	CBod CElw EBee EPPr GPSL LRHS MBel MNrw MPie NDov NRHS WHal WHil
'Splendide'	Widely available
SPLENDIDE WHITE ('Fr21034'PBR)	CBot CSpe CWGN EBee ECtt IBoy ILea IPot LCro LOPS LRHS MBel

	MCot MNrw NDov NLar NPnk NRHS SAko SHar STPC WHil
squarrosum	EBee WPGP
tenuisubulatum BWJ 7929	WCru
tuberiferum var. ***yakusimense*** B&SWJ 6094	WCru
tuberosum	CElw CPla CSpe EPot LLHF NDov SBrt WCot
- 'Rosy Hardy'	WCot
tubiferum B&SWJ 10999	WCru
'Tukker Princess'	EBee ECtt EWTr GBin ILea MBel MHol NDov NLar WCot
uchiyamae	EBee EWld WCot WPGP
urbainii B&SWJ 7085	WCru
'Yubari Mountains'	GEdr
yunnanense	WCru

Thamnocalamus (*Poaceae*)

crassinodus	SBig
- 'Gosainkund'	CDTJ ERod MMoz MWht
- 'Kew Beauty' ♀H3	CDTJ EPfP ERod EUJe MBrN MMoz MWht SBig WCot WPGP
- 'Langtang'	CBdn ERod MWht WPGP
- 'Merlyn'	CDTJ EPfP ERod MWht WPGP
khasianus	see *Drepanostachyum khasianum*
maling	see *Yushania maling*
spathaceus misapplied	see *Fargesia murielae*
§ ***spathiflorus***	EUJe
- subsp. ***nepalensis***	ERod MWht
tessellatus	see *Bergbambos tessellata*

Thamnochortus (*Restionaceae*)

bachmannii	LRHS
cinereus	CPbh LRHS
insignis ♀H2	CPbh CSpe MPkF SPlb
lucens	SPlb
pluristachyus	LRHS
rigidus	CCCN

Thapsia (*Apiaceae*)

decipiens	see *Melanoselinum decipiens*
garganica	SBrt
villosa	SHar

Thea see *Camellia*

Thelypteris (*Thelypteridaceae*)

kunthii	CBdn EBee
limbosperma	see *Oreopteris limbosperma*
noveboracensis	see *Parathelypteris novae-boracensis*
palustris	CBdn CKel EBee EShb MMoz NBro NHim NLar SRms WFib WPnP XLum
phegopteris	see *Phegopteris connectilis*

Themeda (*Poaceae*)

triandra	SMad

Thermopsis (*Papilionaceae*)

caroliniana	see *T. villosa*
chinensis	EAJP EBee ELon LPla LRHS MHer MMuc NRHS
fabacea	see *T. lupinoides*
lanceolata	CAby CMea EBee ELon EPfP LRHS MMuc NQui NRHS SHar SPad WCot WFar
§ ***lupinoides***	CDor ECha EHrv
macrophylla	EBee
mollis	CExl NBid
montana var. ***montana***	CBod CWCL EBee ELan EPfP GAbr GMaP LRHS MMuc NPnk NRHS NSti NWad SEND SPer
- - NNS 99-480 new	WCot
§ ***villosa***	LPla LRHS MRav NGdn NLar NRHS WCot

Therorhodion see *Rhododendron*

Thladiantha (*Cucurbitaceae*)

dubia	EBee SBrt WCot

Thlaspi (*Brassicaceae*)

sp.	NGdn
bellidifolium	CPla
biebersteinii	see *Pachyphragma macrophyllum*
§ ***cepaeifolium*** subsp. ***rotundifolium***	WAbe
- - SDR 8406 new	GKev
rotundifolium	see *T. cepaeifolium* subsp. *rotundifolium*
stylosum	CPla

Thryptomene (*Myrtaceae*)

baeckeacea	CCCN

Thuja ✿ (*Cupressaceae*)

'Extra Gold'	see *T. plicata* 'Irish Gold'
§ ***koraiensis***	NLar SLim
occidentalis	ESps LPra SEND SWeb
- 'Amber Glow'	CKen CSBt EMOT GMcL GMil LRHS MAsh NLar NWad SCoo SLim SPoG SRms
- 'Anniek'PBR	CKen LRHS SPoG
- 'Bateman Broom'	CKen
- 'Beaufort' (v)	CKen
- 'Brabant' ♀H6	GMcL GMil LPra MGos MJak NLar SCob SCoo SLim WHar WMou
- 'Brobeck's Tower' ♀H6	CKen GMil NLar SLim
- 'Caespitosa'	CKen
- 'Columbia' (v) new	LPra
- 'Cuprea'	CKen
- 'Danica' ♀H6	CDul CMac EMOT ESps GKin GMcL GMil IBoy LCro LOPS MAsh MGos MJak NRHS SCob SCoo SLim SPoG SRms WCFE
- 'Danica Gold'	SLim
- 'Degroot's Spire'	CKen ELan LRHS NLar
- 'Douglasii Aurea' (v)	CKen
- EMERALD	see *T. occidentalis* 'Smaragd'
- 'Ericoides'	ESps GMil SRms
- 'Europa Gold' ♀H6	NLar SGol
- 'Fastigiata'	ESps
- 'Filiformis'	CKen SLim
- 'Filips Magic Moment'PBR	LRHS SPoG
- FIRE CHIEF ('Congabe'PBR)	CKen NLar SPoG
- 'Globosa'	ELan
I - 'Globosa Variegata' (v)	CKen
- 'Gold Drop'	CKen
- 'Golden Anne'PBR	SPoG
- 'Golden Globe'	GMil IBoy MJak SCoo SLim
- GOLDEN SMARAGD ('Janed Gold'PBR)	CCVT GMil LRHS SLim SPoG
- 'Golden Tuffet' ♀H6	CKen ELan EMOT GKin LBee MPkF NLar NWad SCob SCoo SLim SPoG
- 'Hetz Midget' ♀H6	CKen EMOT ESps GKin GMil IBoy NRHS NWad SCob SCoo SLim SPlb

- 'Holmstrup' ♀H6	CDul CMac ESps GMil MAsh MGos NRHS SGol SLim SRms WHar
- 'Hoveyi'	CTri
- 'Jantar'PBR	LRHS NRHS SLim SPoG
- 'Konfettii' (v)	EMOT SLim SPoG
- 'Linesville'	CKen
- 'Little Champion'	IBoy
- 'Little Gem'	SRms
- 'Lutea Nana'	ESps
- 'Malonyana Holub'	SLim
- 'Maria Wn' **new**	CKen
- 'Meineke's Zwerg' (v)	CKen
- 'Miky'	LRHS
- 'Milleri'	CKen
- 'Mirjam'PBR (v)	CKen
- 'Mr Bowling Ball'	NLar
- 'Ohlendorffii'	CKen
- 'Perk Vlaanderen' (v)	LRHS
I - 'Pygmaea'	CKen
- 'Pyramidalis Aurea'	ECrN GMcL
- 'Recurva Nana'	NWad
- 'Rheingold' ♀H6	CBcs CDul CMac CSBt CTri ELan EMOT ESps GKin GMcL GMil IBoy LBee LRHS MAsh MGos MJak MMuc NEgg NRHS SCob SEND SGol SLim SPer SPlb SPoG SRms WCFE WFar
§ - 'Smaragd' ♀H6	Widely available
* - 'Smaragd Variegated' (v)	CKen MAsh
- 'Smokey'	CKen
- 'Spiralis'	NLar
- 'Starstruck'	SPoG
§ - 'Stolwijk' (v)	GMil SLim
- 'Sunkist' ♀H6	CKen CMac EMOT ESps GMcL GMil MGos MJak NEgg NRHS SCoo SGol SRms WFar
- 'Teddy'	EMOT EPfP LBee LRHS MAsh SCoo SPoG
- 'Tiny Tim'	CMac IBoy NRHS SGol SLim
- 'Trompenburg'	NLar
- 'Wansdyke Silver' (v)	CMac
- 'Wareana'	CMac
- 'Waterfield'	NLar NWad
- 'Yellow Ribbon'	CDul CKen CSBt GMcL GMil LPra MJak SCob SGol SRms
orientalis	see *Platycladus orientalis*
plicata	CAco CBcs CCVT CDul CMac CPer CTho ELan EPfP ESps SCob SPer SWeb WHar WMou WTSh
- 'Atrovirens' ♀H6	CDul CTri ECrN ESps GMcL GMil LBee LBuc LCro LOPS LPra LRHS MAsh MGos MMuc NOra NRHS SCob SCoo SEND SEWo SGol SRms SWvt WAvo WHar WMou
* - 'Atrovirens Aurea'	ESps
- 'Aurea' ♀H6	LMaj MAsh SRms
- 'Can-can' (v)	ELan EMOT GMil NRHS
I - 'Cole's Variety'	CDul
- 'Collyer's Gold'	CDul SRms
- 'Copper Kettle'	CKen GKin GMil LRHS SLim
- 'Cuprea'	CKen
- 'Doone Valley'	CKen NWad
- 'Excelsa'	CDul LMaj LPra WMou
- 'Fastigiata'	CDul
- 'Gelderland' ♀H6	ELan EMOT EPfP GMil NEgg SCoo SLim WHar
- GOLDY ('4ever'PBR)	EMOT GMcL GMil LRHS NLar NRHS SLim SPoG
- 'Gracilis Aurea'	ESps
- 'Hillieri'	CDul
- 'Holly Turner'	SLim
§ - 'Irish Gold' (v)	CDul CMac
- 'Martin'	GMcL SRms SWvt
- 'Rogersii' ♀H6	CKen CMac EMOT ESps GMil MAsh SCoo SPoG SRms WThu
- 'Semperaurescens' (v)	CMac
- 'Stolwijk's Gold'	see *T. occidentalis* 'Stolwijk'
- 'Stoneham Gold' ♀H6	CMac ESps GKin GMil MAsh MGos SRms WCFE
- VERIGOLD ('Courtapli')	CCVT MMuc SEND
- 'Whipcord' ♀H6	CAco CBcs CKen ELan EMOT EPfP EUJe GMcL LRHS MPkF NLar NRHS SCoo SLim SPoG
- 'Winter Pink' (v)	CKen
- 'Zebrina' (v) ♀H6	CAco CBcs CDul CMCN CMac CTri ELan EMOT EPfP ESps GMil LRHS MAsh MGos MMuc NLar SCob SCoo SEND SLim SPer SPoG SWvt WAvo WHar
standishii	WThu

Thujopsis (*Cupressaceae*)

dolabrata ♀H6	CAco CBcs CDul GKin MMuc NEgg SEND SWvt
- 'Aurea' (v)	CKen LRHS NLar
- var. ***hondae***	IArd SLim
- 'Laetevirens'	see *T. dolabrata* 'Nana'
§ - 'Nana'	CKen CMac LRHS NLar NRHS SLim SRms
- 'Solar Flare' **new**	SLim
- 'Variegata' (v)	CMac GKin NLar SRms
koraiensis (Nakai) hort.	see *Thuja koraiensis*

Thunbergia ✿ (*Acanthaceae*)

alata	EPfP SPoG
- 'African Sunset'	CRav CSpe EShb
- 'Lemon Queen'	CHll SWvt
- 'Orange Beauty'	LBuc SWvt
- 'Sunny Suzy Red-Orange'	EPfP
- 'Suzie White Black Eye' (Suzie Series) **new**	CRav
* ***arborea***	CCCN
battiscombeii	CCCN EShb WCot
coccinea	CCCN
erecta	CCCN
fragrans GWJ 9441	WCru
grandiflora ♀H1a	CCCN CHll WFib WSFF
- 'Alba'	CCCN CHll
gregorii ♀H1c	CCCN CHll EShb WFib
laurifolia B&SWJ 7166	WCru
'Lemon Star'	EPfP LBuc
'Moonglow'	CCCN
natalensis	CCCN EShb
'Orange Wonder'	CCCN

Thymbra (*Lamiaceae*)

capitata	LLHF WAbe
spicata	SPhx

thyme, caraway see *Thymus herba-barona*

thyme, garden see *Thymus vulgaris*

thyme, lemon see *Thymus citriodorus*

thyme, wild see *Thymus serpyllum*

Thymus ✿ (*Lamiaceae*)

from Turkey	EWes LEdu
§ 'Alan Bloom'	LRHS NRHS

	'Albus'	ENfk
	'Anderson's Gold'	see *T. pulegioides* 'Bertram Anderson'
	'Aureus' ambig.	MJak
	azoricus	see *T. caespititius*
	'Bressingham'	CBod CMea CTri ECtt ELon GCrg GMaP LEdu LRHS MHer MMuc MNHC NRHS SPlb SRms
	'Caborn Wine and Roses'	ENfk SRms
§	***caespititius***	GPoy MHer NRya SPlb SRms SRot
	caespitosus	CTri LEdu
	camphoratus	ENfk EWes GCrg MHer NHpl
§	***carnosus*** Boiss.	MHer XSen
	'Carol Ann' (v)	ENfk EWes MNHC SRms
	ciliatus	CBod XSen
	cilicicus misapplied	see *T. caespititius*
	cilicicus ambig.	MNHC SRms
	cilicicus Boiss. & Bail.	WAbe
	citriodorus misapplied	see *T.* 'Culinary Lemon'
	citriodorus ambig.	CTal CTsd MMuc SRms XLum
	citriodorus (Pers.) Schreb.	LEdu
	- 'Archer's Gold'	see *T. pulegioides* 'Archer's Gold'
	- 'Aureus'	see *T. pulegioides* 'Aureus'
	- 'Bertram Anderson'	see *T. pulegioides* 'Bertram Anderson'
	- 'Silver Posie'	see *T.* 'Silver Posie'
	'Coccineus'	see *T.* Coccineus Group
§	Coccineus Group 🏆H5	CBod CTal CTri ECha ECtt ELan ENfk ESps GMaP LCro LRHS MHer MMuc MNHC NHpl NRHS NRya NSla NWad SPer SPoG SRms SRot WAbe WHoo XSen
	- 'Atropurpureus' Schleipfer	see *T.* (Coccineus Group) 'Purple Beauty'
§	- 'Purple Beauty'	ECtt EPot GCrg LRHS MHer NRHS SRms XSen
§	- 'Red Elf'	CBod GAbr GCrg MHer
	'Coccineus Major'	CMea LRHS MHer MNHC NRHS SCob SRms
	'Creeping Lemon' misapplied	see *T. pulegioides* 'Kurt'
	'Creeping Orange'	CRav
§	'Culinary Lemon'	CBod CHby ENfk GPoy MBrN MHer MNHC NPri XLum XSen
	'Dartmoor'	CBod
	'Desboro'	see *T. serpyllum* 'Desborough'
	'Dillington'	ENfk
	doerfleri	XSen
	'Doone Valley' (v)	CBod CMea CTri ECha ELan ENfk EPfP ESps EUJe GMaP LRHS MAsh MHer MJak MMuc MNHC NRHS SCob SPer SPhm SPlb SPoG SRms
	drucei	see *T. polytrichus* A. Kern. ex Borbás subsp. *britannicus* (Ronniger) Kerguélen
	'Duftkissen'PBR	XSen
	'E.B. Anderson'	see *T. pulegioides* 'Bertram Anderson'
	'Elfin Pink Carpet'	MHol
	erectus	see *T. carnosus* Boiss.
	'Fragrantissimus'	ENfk GPoy MHer MNHC SPhx SPlb XSen
	'Golden King' (v)	ECha ELan ENfk LSRN MAsh MHer SRms XSen
	'Golden Lemon' misapplied	see *T. pulegioides* 'Aureus'
	'Golden Queen' (v)	MHol SRms WFar XSen
§	'Hartington Silver' (v)	CMea CTri ECha ECtt ENfk EPot EWes GCrg GKev LRHS MAsh MHer NHpl NRHS SPlb SPoG SRms WHoo
	herba-barona	CBod ENfk GPoy LEdu MHer MMuc MNHC SRms
	- ***citrata***	see *T. herba-barona* 'Lemon-scented'
§	- 'Lemon-scented'	ECha GPoy LEdu MHer SRms XSen
	'Highdown'	ECtt
	'Highland Cream'	see *T.* 'Hartington Silver'
	hirsutus	XSen
	hyemalis	XSen
§	'Iden'	CBod
	'Jekka'	CBod MHer SRms
	'Kurt'	see *T. pulegioides* 'Kurt'
	'Lavender Sea'	EWes
	'Lemon Caraway'	see *T. herba-barona* 'Lemon-scented'
	'Lemon Curd'	ENfk MNHC SPlb SPoG SRms
*	'Lemon Variegated' (v)	ENfk EPfP MNHC SPer SPoG XSen
	leucotrichus	XSen
	'Lilac Time'	ECtt ENfk EWes MHer SPlb SRms
	'Lime'	LEdu
	linearis	XSen
	longicaulis	CBod ECha MHer MMuc SRms
	longiflorus	XSen
	'Magic Carpet'	WArt
	marschallianus	see *T. pannonicus*
	mastichina	SPhx XSen
	- 'Didi'	MHer
	membranaceus	WAbe
	micans	see *T. caespititius*
	minus	see *Calamintha nepeta*
	neiceffii	CMea ECha SBch XSen
	nitens	XSen
	'Orange'	CBod LEdu SRms
§	ORANGE SPICE ('Tm95')	XSen
§	***pannonicus***	MHer
	- PAB 9021 **new**	LEdu
	'Peter Davis'	ENfk GBin GCrg LRHS LSRN NRHS SPoG SRms WAbe WTor XSen
§	'Pinewood'	CTal MHer XSen
	'Pink Ripple'	CBod CMea CTal ECtt ENfk EWes LEdu MHer MNHC SRms WHal WHoo
	polytrichus misapplied	see *T. praecox*
	polytrichus A. Kern. ex Borbás	EBWF
§	- subsp. ***britannicus***	CBod CTri ECha EUJe GBin GJos GMaP GPoy LEdu MBNS MHer MMuc NEoE SEND SPlb SRms WHoo XLum XSen
§	- - 'Thomas's White' 🏆H5	CTri
	'Porlock'	CBod CMea CSam CTri EPfP MHer SRms WHoo
§	***praecox***	CWld ESps GJos MHer NMir WArt
	- 'Albiflorus'	MRav XSen
	- subsp. ***arcticus***	see *T. polytrichus* A. Kern. ex Borbás subsp. *britannicus*
	- - 'Albus'	see *T. polytrichus* subsp. *britannicus* 'Thomas's White'
	prostrate	CBod
	'Provence'	XSen
	pulegioides	CBod CHby CTri ENfk GPoy MHer MNHC NHpl SRms SRot WArt WSFF XAbr
§	- 'Archer's Gold'	ECtt EHoe ENfk EPfP EPot ESps LRHS LSRN MAsh MHer MHol MNHC MRav NHpl NRHS SCob SRms XSen
§	- 'Aureus' 🏆H5	ENfk EPot ESps GMaP MAsh MHer SPer SPlb SRms WHoo

§ – 'Bertram Anderson' 🏆[H5]	CMea CTal ECha ECtt ENfk EPfP GCrg GMaP MAsh MHer NRya SCob SPer SPoG SRms WHoo XSen
– 'Foxley' (v)	CBod EHoe ELon ENfk EPfP MHer MNHC SPlb SPoG SRms XSen
– 'Golden Dwarf'	XSen
§ – 'Kurt'	ENfk LEdu MHer SRms
– 'Sir John Lawes'	MHer
– 'Tabor'	CBod ENfk MNHC SRms XSen
'Rainbow Falls' (v)	EPfP SRms
'Rasta' (v)	MHer XSen
'Redstart'	CBod ECha ECtt ENfk LEdu MHer SRms
richardii subsp. ***nitidus*** 'Compactus Albus'	see *T. vulgaris* 'Snow White'
rotundifolius misapplied	see *T. vulgaris* 'Elsbeth'
'Ruby Glow'	ECtt EWes GCrg MHer
serpyllum ambig.	SCob SVic XLum
serpyllum L.	GJos IRob LBuc MMuc SPlb SRms WRHF
– var. ***albus***	CTal ECha ELon GMaP GPoy LRHS MNHC NRHS SPer SRms WHoo
– 'Albus Variegatus'	see *T.* 'Hartington Silver'
– 'Amadé'	XSen
– 'Annie Hall'	CTal EPfP LRHS MAsh MHer MNHC NRHS SRms WCFE
– 'Atropurpureus'	see *T.* (Coccineus Group) 'Purple Beauty'
– ***coccineus*** 'Minor' misapplied	see *T.* Coccineus Group
– – 'Minor' Bloom	see *T.* 'Alan Bloom'
– 'Conwy Rose'	CPBP WAbe
§ – 'Desborough'	MHer
– 'East Lodge'	MHer MNHC SRms
– 'Elfin'	ECtt EWes GCrg MRav NSla SPlb SRms SRot WAbe XSen
– 'Goldstream' (v)	ENfk LRHS MHer NRHS SPlb SRms WRHF
– 'Iden'	see *T.* 'Iden'
– 'Minimalist'	see *T. serpyllum* 'Minor'
– 'Minimus'	see *T. serpyllum* 'Minor'
§ – 'Minor'	CMea CTal CTri ECha ECtt ENfk GCrg LRHS MHer MMuc MNHC NChi NRHS NSla SEND SPlb SRms SRot WAbe WHoo
– 'Minus'	see *T. serpyllum* 'Minor'
– 'Pink Chintz' 🏆[H5]	CBod ECha ECtt ENfk EPfP EPot GMaP GPoy LCro LEdu LRHS MHer MNHC NRHS SPer SPlb SPoG SRms
– 'Purple Beauty'	see *T.* (Coccineus Group) 'Purple Beauty'
– 'Red Carpet'	ECtt GCrg NWad SRot
– 'Red Elf'	see *T.* (Coccineus Group) 'Red Elf'
– 'Russetings'	CBod CTsd CWld ECtt ENfk EPfP GKev MHer MNHC SCob SPoG SRms
– 'September'	MHer
– 'Snowdrift'	CMea ECtt EPfP LEdu MHer MNHC NWad SPlb SRms WCFE
– 'Variegatus'	see *T.* 'Hartington Silver'
– 'Vey'	CBod CTal EWes LRHS MHer NRHS SRms
– 'Wirral White'	XSen
'Silver King' (v)	ENfk
§ 'Silver Posie'	CBar CHby CTri ECtt EHoe ELan ENfk EPfP ESps EWTr LCro LOPS LRHS MHer MJak MNHC MRav NHpl NRHS SCob SPer SPlb SPoG SRms XSen
'Silver Queen' (v) 🏆[H5]	CBcs CBod CSam ECha ELan ENfk EPfP ESps GCrg GMaP MHer MNHC SCob SPer SPhm SPlb SRms XSen
'Spicy Orange'	see *T.* ORANGE SPICE
striatus	LEdu
§ ***vulgaris***	CBod CHab CHby CTri CTsd ECha ENfk ESps GAbr GBin GMaP GPoy LCro LOPS MHer MJak MNHC NPri SArc SCob SEND SPer SPhx SPlb SPoG SRms SVic XAbr XLum XSen
* – 'Compactus'	ENfk GPoy LEdu MHer MNHC MRav SPhx SRms XSen
– 'Deutsche Auslese'	see *T. vulgaris*
– 'Dorcas White'	MHer
§ – 'Elsbeth'	MHer
– English, winter	SRms
– French	see *T. vulgaris*
– 'Golden Pins'	MHer
– 'Lucy'	MHer
– 'Pinewood'	see *T.* 'Pinewood'
§ – 'Snow White'	EWes
zygis	GJos XSen

Tiarella ✿ (*Saxifragaceae*)

'Angel Wings' (Fox Series) **new**	MPnt WNPC
'Appalachian Trail'	CBcs ELan LSou MPnt NPnk NWad SHeu SPoG
'Black Snowflake'	MPnt SHeu
'Black Velvet'	MBel MPnt SHeu
'Braveheart'	EPfP MPnt SHeu SPoG
'Butter and Sugar'	MPnt
'Butterfly Wings'	MPnt
'Candy Striper'	MPnt SHeu
'Cascade Creeper'[PBR]	LRHS LSou MPnt NWad SHeu
collina	see *T. wherryi*
cordifolia 🏆[H5]	CBcs CBod CMac CRav CTri ECha ELan EPed EPfP GAbr GMaP LAma LEdu LRHS MCot MGos MPnt MRav NDov NRHS SCob SPer SRms SWvt WHoo WMoo XLum
– 'Glossy'	MPnt
– 'Milk Chocolate'	MMoz MPnt
– 'Oakleaf'	MPnt NBro SHeu
– 'Rosalie'	see × *Heucherella alba* 'Rosalie'
– 'Running Tapestry'	MPnt SHeu
– 'Slick Rock'	EPPr
'Crow Feather'[PBR]	MPnt NWad SHeu
'Cygnet'	CDor GBin GMcL MPnt SHeu
'Dunvegan'	MPnt
'Elizabeth Oliver'	MPnt
'Emerald Ellie' (Fox Series) **new**	MPnt WNPC
'Freckles'	MRav
'Happy Trails'[PBR]	EBee MPnt NPnk NWad SHeu WCot
'Hidden Carpet'	CHid
'Inkblot'	ELan LRHS MPnt NBro SHeu WMoo
'Iron Butterfly'[PBR] (v)	CBod CMac EBee ECha EHoe EPfP EUJe GMaP LRHS LSRN MPnt MRav SCob SGbt SHeu SPer SPoG SRms SRot
'Iron Cross'	SPlb
'Jeepers Creepers'[PBR]	CHid ECha LRHS MJak MPnt NWad SHeu WNPC
'Martha Oliver'	EBee MPnt
'Mint Chocolate'	EHrv ELan LRHS MNrw MPnt MRav NGdn NLar NRHS SHeu SWvt WNPC
'Moorgrün'	EPPr GCal SHeu

MORNING STAR ('Tntia042')	CHid GMcL MPnt SHeu SRkn SRot WHoo
'Mystic Mist'PBR (v)	CBod CDor CHid CWGN ECtt EPed LSou MPnt NPnk NWad SHeu SPad SPoG WNPC
'Neon Lights'PBR	CHid ELan MPnt NWad SCob SHeu SPer SWvt WNPC
§ 'Ninja'	CHid EHrv ELan GMcL LRHS MPnt NLar NRHS SWvt
'Oregon Trail'	MNrw MPnt NPnk NWad SHeu WNPC
'Pacific Crest'PBR	EBee MPnt NWad SHeu WNPC
'Pink Bouquet'	CMac CSpe EHrv ELan MBel MPie MPnt NBro NLar SHeu WGwG WMoo WPnP
'Pink Brushes'PBR	MPnt SHeu WPnP
'Pink Skyrocket'PBR	CBWd CDor ELan EPau LLHF LSRN LSun MBel MPnt NGdn NWad SHeu SPad SPer SWvt WCot WPnP
'Pinwheel'	MPnt
'Pirate's Patch'PBR	LLHF MPnt SHeu
polyphylla	MPnt SHeu WCru
- 'Baoxing Pink'	MPnt WCru
- 'Filigran'	ELan EPfP IBoy MPnt NLar NWad SHar SHeu
'Running Tiger'	MPnt
'Sea Foam'	MPnt SHeu
'Simsalabim'	MPnt
'Skeleton Key'	MPnt
'Skid's Variegated' (v)	ECtt MNrw MPnt SHeu SPoG SWvt
'Skyrocket'	NLar
'Spanish Cross'	MPnt SHeu
'Spring Symphony'PBR	CBod CDor EShb GBin GKev GMcL GWyn LCro LOPS LRHS MBel MPnt NPer NRHS NWad SHar WSHC
STARBURST ('Tntia041'PBR)	MPnt NWad SHeu
'Sugar and Spice'PBR	CWGN EPed EPfP LRHS MBrN MPnt NDov NRHS NWad SHeu WNPC
'Sunset Ridge'PBR	EBee MPnt NWad SHeu
'Tiger Stripe'	EPfP LRHS MPnt NBro SHeu
'Timbuktu'	MAsh MPnt SHeu WFar
trifoliata	MPnt MRav
- var. ***unifoliata***	MPnt
'Viking Ship'	see × *Heucherella* 'Viking Ship'
§ ***wherryi*** 🏆H5	CBcs CBod ELan ELon EPfP ESps IBoy LRHS MPnt NBro NRya SCob SPer SPlb SWvt WArt WHar WPnP XLum
- 'Bronze Beauty'	MPnt SHeu
- bronze-leaved	SCob
- 'Green Velvet'	ECha MPnt SHeu
- 'Heronswood Mist' (v)	ECtt ELan MMoz MNrw MPnt SHeu SWvt

Tibouchina (*Melastomataceae*)

grandifolia	CCCN
'Groovy Baby' new	SPhm
heteromalla	CCCN
organensis	CBcs CBod CCCN CHII EUJe SEle SHeu SPoG SWvt
paratropica	CRHN GCal
semidecandra misapplied	see *T. urvilleana*
§ ***urvilleana*** 🏆H1c	CBcs CBod CCCN CEnd CSBt CTri CTsd EBak EMdy IDee NLos SPer SRkn SWvt
- 'Compacta'	CCCN
- 'Edwardsii' 🏆H1c	CRHN SAdn WCot
- 'Rich Blue Sun'	CBod
- variegated (v)	CBcs CCCN EMdy SPer SWvt WCot

Tigridia (*Iridaceae*)

sp.	EShb
chiapensis	CPla GKev
immaculata B&SWJ 10393	WCru
§ ***orthantha***	CPla
- 'Red-Hot Tiger'	WCot WCru
pavonia	CAby CExl SDeJ SDir WSHC
- 'Alba Grandiflora'	GKev SDeJ SDir
- 'Aurea'	GKev SDir
- 'Canariensis'	GKev SDeJ SDir
- 'Lilacea'	CPla GKev SDeJ SDir
- 'Speciosa'	GKev SDeJ SDir
van-houttei	GKev

Tilia ✿ (*Malvaceae*)

sp.	LPra
HRS 2808	WPGP
americana	CLnd CMCN LPra
- 'Dentata'	CDul
- 'Nova'	LPra
amurensis from Korea new	WPGP
argentea	see *T. tomentosa*
begoniifolia	see *T. dasystyla* subsp. *caucasica*
callidonta	WPGP
§ ***caroliniana***	CDul CMCN EBee ELan EPfP MBlu
subsp. ***heterophylla***	WPGP
chinensis	CMCN WPGP
- F 30558	WPGP
chingiana	CDul CMCN EBee EBtc SLon WPGP
concinna new	WMou WPGP
cordata	Widely available
§ - 'Böhlje'	CDul ECrN LPra
- 'Dainty Leaf'	CDul
- 'Erecta'	see *T. cordata* 'Böhlje'
- Erecta Group new	LPra
- 'Greenspire' 🏆H6	CArg CCVT CDul CLnd EBar ECrN EPfP ESps IBoy LPra MRav SCob SEWo WMou
- 'Len Parvin'	EBee WPGP
- 'Rancho'	EMOT LPra
- 'Roelvo'	CDul
- 'Swedish Upright'	CDul
- 'Winter Orange' 🏆H6	CBcs CBod CDul CEnd EBee ECrN ELan EPfP ESps MBlu MSwo SBir SCoo SEWo WHar
dasystyla	CMCN
§ - subsp. ***caucasica***	CMCN EBee WPGP
- - A&L 16	WPGP
- - NJM 13.029 new	WPGP
endochrysea	WPGP
× ***euchlora***	CArg CCVT CDul CLnd CMCN EBee ECrN EMOT EPfP ESps LMaj LPra SCob SEWo SPer
§ × ***europaea***	CBcs CDul CLnd ELan ESps EWTr LPra MMuc SCob SEND
- 'Koningslinde'	CDul
- 'Pallida'	CDul CLnd LMaj LPra MBlu
- 'Wratislaviensis' 🏆H6	CDul MBlu
× ***flavescens*** new	LPra
§ 'Harold Hillier'	CMCN MBlu WPGP
henryana	CBcs CDul CEnd CLnd CMCN EBee ELan EPfP ERod ESps IArd IDee MBlu MMuc SBir SEND WMou WPGP
- 'Kerdalo'	WPGP
- large	WPGP
'Hillieri'	see *T.* 'Harold Hillier'
insularis misapplied	see *T. japonica*

	intonsa	CMCN
§	***japonica***	CDul CMCN EBee EPfP WPGP
	- 'Ernest Wilson' ♀H6	CMCN MBlu
	- large-leaved, from China	WPGP
	kiusiana	CDul CMCN EBee MBlu WMou WPGP
	mandshurica	CDul CMCN EBee WPGP
	maximowicziana	CMCN EBee EPfP MBlu WPGP
	mexicana	WPGP
	- CD&R 1318	EBee WPGP
	miqueliana	CMCN MBlu
	× ***moltkei***	CMCN EBee IArd WPGP
	mongolica	CBcs CDul CMCN EBee EPfP MBlu WMou WPGP
	- 'Harvest Gold'	CBcs MBlu
	monticola	see *T. caroliniana* subsp. *heterophylla*
	nobilis KR 226	WPGP
	oliveri	CBcs CDul CMCN EBee MBlu WMou WPGP
	paucicostata	WPGP
	platyphyllos	CAco CAgr CCVT CDul CFGn CHab CLnd CMCN CPer CSBt CTho CTri ECrN EMOT EPfP ESps EWTr LBuc LPra MMuc SCob SCoo SEND SPer WMou WTSh
	- 'Aurea'	CDul CTho ECrN MBlu
	- 'Corallina'	see *T. platyphyllos* 'Rubra'
	- 'Erecta'	see *T. platyphyllos* 'Fastigiata'
§	- 'Fastigiata'	CDul
	- 'Laciniata'	CDul CMCN CTho MBlu
§	- 'Rubra' ♀H6	CCVT CDul CLnd CTho EBar EMOT ESps IBoy LPra SEWo
	- 'Tortuosa'	LMaj MBlu
	× ***stellata*** new	WPGP
§	***tomentosa***	CAco CDul CLnd CMCN ESps LPra MMuc SCob SCoo SEND
	- 'Brabant' ♀H6	CDul ELan EMOT EPfP LMaj LPra
	- 'Petiolaris' ♀H6	CArg CBcs CCVT CDul CEnd CLnd CMCN ECrN ELan EMOT EPfP ESps LPra MBlu MSwo SCob SPer WMou
	tuan	WPGP
	- var. ***chenmoui***	CMCN EPfP MBlu WPGP
I	'Varsaviensis' new	WPGP
	× ***vulgaris***	see *T.* × *europaea*

Tilingia (*Apiaceae*)

	ajanensis B&SWJ 11202	IMou WCru

Tillaea see *Crassula*

Tillandsia (*Bromeliaceae*)

	sp.	XBlo
	abdita	NCft
	aeranthos	NCft SChr
	- 'Bronze' new	NCft
	- var. ***rosea*** new	NCft
	aizoides new	NCft
	albertiana	NCft
	albida	NCft SPlb
	andicola new	NCft
	andreana	NCft
	argentea ♀H1b	NCft
	argentina	NCft
	ariza-juliae new	NCft
	baileyi	NCft
	baileyi × ***ionantha*** new	NCft
	balbisiana	NCft
	bandensis	NCft
	bartramii	NCft
	bergeri	NCft SChr SPlb
	brachycaulos	NCft
	- var. ***multiflora***	NCft
	brachycaulos × ***schiedeana*** new	NCft
	bryoides new	NCft
	bulbosa	NCft NLos SPlb
	butzii	NCft
	cacticola	NCft
	caerulea new	NCft
	'Califano' new	NCft
	caliginosa	NCft
	capillaris	NCft
	capitata	NCft NLos
	- 'Peach' new	NCft
	- red-leaved	NCft
	caput-medusae	NCft NLos
	caput-medusae × ***flabellata*** new	NCft
	caulescens × ***tenuifolia*** new	NCft
	chusgonensis new	NCft
	concolor	NCft
	'Cotton Candy'	NCft
	crocata	NCft
	- 'Copper Penny' new	NCft
	cyanea ♀H1a	NCft
	diaguitensis	NCft
	duratii	NCft
	dyeriana	NCft
	elongata new	NCft
	espinosae new	NCft
	fasciculata	NCft
	festucoides	NCft
	filifolia	NCft
	flabellata	NCft SPlb
	flavobracteata new	NCft
	flexuosa new	NCft
	floribunda new	NCft
	× ***floridana***	NCft
	fresnilloensis new	NCft
	fuchsii var. ***fuchsii*** new	NCft
	- f. ***gracilis***	NCft
	funckiana	NCft
	gardneri	NCft
	geminiflora	NCft
	grao-mogolensis new	NCft
	harrisii	NCft NLos
	'Heather's Blush'	NCft
	heteromorpha	NCft
	hondurensis	NCft
	incarnata new	NCft
	intermedia	NCft
	ionantha	NLos
*	- 'Fuego'	NCft
	- 'Haselnuss' new	NCft
	- var. ***ionantha*** new	NCft
	- var. ***maxima*** 'Huamelula'	see *T. ionantha* var. *stricta*
	- 'Ron' new	NCft
I	- 'Rosea' new	NCft
	- 'Rubra'	NCft
	- 'Peach' new	NCft
	- var. ***scaposa***	see *T. kolbii*
	- 'Silver' new	NCft
§	- var. ***stricta***	NCft
	- var. ***vanhyningii***	NCft
	ixioides	NCft
	'Jackie Loinaz'	NCft
	jucunda	NCft
	juncea	NCft NLos

kammii new NCft
karwinskyana new NCft
kautskyi new NCft
'Kimberly' new NCft
§ ***kolbii*** NCft
lautneri new NCft
leonamiana NCft
loliacea NCft
lorentziana NCft
magnusiana NCft NLos
mallemontii NCft
marconae new NCft
'Maria Teresa' new NCft
mitlaensis new NCft
montana new NCft
mooreana NCft SPlb
myosura NCft
neglecta NCft
I - 'Rubra' new NCft
oaxacana NCft
paleacea NCft
paucifolia new NCft
plagiotropica NCft
pohliana new NCft
polystachia NCft
pruinosa NCft SPlb
pseudobaileyi NCft
pueblensis new NCft
punctulata NCft
purpurea new NCft
× ***rectifolia*** new NCft
recurvata NCft
reichenbachii NCft
schiedeana NCft
- 'Major' NCft
I - 'Minor' new NCft
schreiteri new NCft
seideliana new NCft
seleriana NCft SPlb
stellifera new NCft
straminea new NCft
streptocarpa NCft
streptophylla NCft
stricta var. ***albifolia*** NCft
I - 'Amethyst' new NCft
- 'Grey' new NCft
tectorum NCft
- caulescent new NCft
tenuifolia new NCft
I - 'Minima' new NCft
tricholepis NCft
tricolor var. ***melanocrater*** NCft NLos
usneoides NCft NLos SHmp SPlb WSFF
utriculata subsp. ***pringlei*** NCft
xerographica NCft NLos
xiphioides new NCft
zecheri new NCft
- var. ***cafayatensis*** new NCft

Tinantia (*Commelinaceae*)

pringlei EWld GEdr LEdu MNrw MPie SBrt SDys WPGP
- AIM 77 EBee MAvo MNrw WCot
- variegated (v) WCot

Titanopsis (*Aizoaceae*)

calcarea ♀H2 CCCN

Titanotrichum (*Gesneriaceae*)

oldhamii GEdr SBrt

Tithonia (*Asteraceae*)

rotundifolia 'Torch' CRav CSpe SPav
'Torchlight' LRHS

Tofieldia (*Tofieldiaceae*)

coccinea CTal GCal GEdr WCot WCru
furusei GEdr
japonica GEdr
- 'Rosea' GEdr

Tolmiea (*Saxifragaceae*)

menziesii CMac EWld MCot XLum
- 'Goldsplash' see *T. menziesii* 'Taff's Gold'
- 'Maculata' see *T. menziesii* 'Taff's Gold'
§ - 'Taff's Gold' (v) CBod EHoe GMaP LRHS NBid NRHS SPlb XLum
- 'Variegata' see *T. menziesii* 'Taff's Gold'

Tolpis (*Asteraceae*)

barbata IMou

tomato see AGM Vegetables Section

Toona (*Meliaceae*)

§ ***sinensis*** CAgr CBcs CDul CTho EBee ELan EPfP LEdu SEND WPGP
- 'Flamingo' (v) CTho EPfP GKin LCro LEdu LOPS LRHS MAsh MGos NLar NRHS SGol SPoG SWvt
- 'Lisa' CMCN

Torenia (*Linderniaceae*)

(Moon Series) PURPLE MOON ('Dantopur'PBR) LSou
- YELLOW MOON ('Danmoon20'PBR) CRav
Summer Wave Series CCCN

Torilis (*Apiaceae*)

japonica CBre EBWF

Townsendia (*Asteraceae*)

alpigena CPla
§ - var. ***alpigena*** GKev
condensata WAbe
eximia × ***parryi*** new GKev
formosa CPBP NHpl
hookeri CPBP
incana WAbe
mensana GKev
montana see *T. alpigena* var. *alpigena*
parryi GKev
spathulata CPBP SPlb
- 'Cotton Ball' new CPBP

Toxicodendron see *Rhus*

Trachelium (*Campanulaceae*)

§ ***asperuloides*** SPlb WAbe
caeruleum 'Black Knight' CSpe WCot
lanceolatum WCot

Trachelospermum ✿ (*Apocynaceae*)

from Nanjing, China EShb
§ ***asiaticum*** ♀H4 Widely available
- 'Copper Tips' MGil WAvo
- 'Golden Memories' CBcs CExl CKel CRHN CWCL CWGN EBee ELan ELon EPfP LRHS

	LSRN NLar NRHS SLon SNig SPoG SSta SWvt
- 'Goshiki' (v)	EShb SEle
- 'Kulu Chirimen'	WCot
- 'Ōgon-nishiki' (v)	LRHS SEle SMad SPoG
- 'Summer Sunset'	CWCL ELan ELon EPfP LRHS MGos SRms WCot
- 'Theta'	LRHS WCot WFar WPGP
'Chameleon'	ELan
'Christabel Bielenberg'	LRHS
jasminoides ♀^{H4}	Widely available
- 'Major'	CMac CWCL EBee ELan EWTr MAsh SNig
§ - var. ***pubescens*** 'Japonicum'	CRHN LRHS NPri SLon SPoG WBor WSHC
- STAR OF TOSCANA ('Selbra'^{PBR})	ECtt LCro LOPS LRHS NLar NRHS SCob
- 'Tricolor' (v)	LRHS SCob SEle SGol SWvt
- 'Variegatum' (v) ♀^{H4}	Widely available
- 'Waterwheel'	CKel CMac CWCL EBee ELan ELon EUJe LRHS NLar SCob SMad SPoG SWvt WPGP WSHC
- 'White Wings'	LRHS
- 'Wilsonii'	CExl CMac CWCL ELan ELon EPfP EUJe LRHS LSRN MRav NLar SAdn SEND SLim SNig SPer SPoG SWvt WAvo WCot WCru WPGP
majus misapplied	see *T. jasminoides* var. *pubescens* 'Japonicum'
majus Nakai	see *T. asiaticum*

Trachycarpus ✿ (*Arecaceae*)

sp.	LPra
from Manipur	CPHo
§ ***fortunei*** ♀^{H5}	Widely available
geminisectus	NLos
latisectus	CBlu NLos
oreophilus	NLos
princeps	CBlu CBrP
wagnerianus	CBlu CBrP CCCN CDTJ CExl CPHo EPfP ETod EUJe LRHS NLos SArc SBig SChr WPGP

Trachymene (*Apiaceae*)

coerulea	CSpe

Trachystemon (*Boraginaceae*)

orientalis	Widely available

Tradescantia (*Commelinaceae*)

albiflora	see *T. fluminensis*
× ***andersoniana*** W. Ludwig & Rohw. nom. inval.	see *T.* Andersoniana Group
§ Andersoniana Group	WHar WWtn
- 'Angelic Charm' (Charm Series)	CWGN ECtt SHeu
- 'Baby Doll'	XLum
- 'Baerbel'	XLum
- 'Bilberry Ice'	CDor CMac CWCL ECtt EPfP GMaP LRHS MBel NBro NGBl NGdn NLar NPnk NRHS SCob SGbt SPad SWvt WHar WWtn XLum
- 'Blanca'	WWtn
- 'Blue and Gold'	CBcs EBee ECtt ELon EPfP EUJe LRHS MHol MRav NCou NRHS NSti WCot WFar WGrn WHil
- 'Blue Stone'	CCse CDor CMea CSBt ECha ECtt MAvo MRav SRkn SRms WHoo XLum
- 'Bridal Veil'	CHll SChr WDib
- 'Caerulea Plena'	see *T. virginiana* 'Caerulea Plena'
- CARMINE GLOW	see *T.* (Andersoniana Group) 'Karminglut'
- 'Charlotte'	CDor ECha ECtt ELan LRHS LSRN NBro NGdn NLar NRHS WWtn XLum
- 'Concord Grape'	Widely available
- 'Danielle'	EPfP
- 'David's Blaby Blue'	MMoz
- 'Domaine de Courson'	ECtt XLum
- 'Euridice' **new**	MBel
- 'Good Luck'^{PBR}	MHol
- 'In the Navy'	NLar
- 'Innocence'	CAby CDor CSBt CTri ECha ECtt ELan EPfP GMaP GWyn IBoy LRHS MBel MMuc NGdn NPnk NRHS NSti SCob SPer SWvt XLum
- 'Iris Prichard'	EBee ELan GLog GMaP NLar
- 'Isis'	CBWd EBee ECtt ELan EPfP GMaP LRHS MMuc MRav NGdn NRHS SPer SWvt WGwG WKif WWtn
- 'J.C. Weguelin'	EPfP SRms WCAu WWtn XLum
§ - 'Karminglut'	EBee ECtt ELan EPfP GLog GMaP IBoy NGdn NPnk WHoo XLum
- 'Leonora'	CBod EPfP MBel MMuc NLar SCob WHar XLum
- 'Little Doll'	CDor ECtt EPfP LRHS MPie NBro NLar NRHS XLum
- 'Little White Doll'	ECtt EPfP
- 'Lucky Charm' (Charm Series)	EBee NLar SHeu
- 'Mac's Double' (d)	EBee
- 'Mariella'	EBee
- 'Melissa'	XLum
- 'Merlot Clusters'	LSun SCob
- 'Ocean Blue'	EPfP
- 'Osprey'	CBWd CBcs CDor ECha ECtt ELan GCal LRHS MBel MRav NGdn NRHS NSti SPer SRms WCAu WGwG WHoo WKif WWtn XLum
- 'Pauline'	MRav NLar XLum
- 'Perinne's Pink'	CWCL ECtt EPfP LRHS NRHS NSti WCAu
- 'Pink Chablis'	CWCL ECtt EPfP LRHS MHol NBro NLar NRHS XLum
- 'Purewell Giant'	CMac CTri GLog LRHS NBro NLar NRHS SWvt WKif
- 'Purple Dome'	ECtt EPfP GMaP LRHS MMuc MRav NBro NGdn NRHS SPoG
- 'Red Grape'	LRHS NRHS NSti SCob XLum
- 'Regal Charm' (Charm Series)	EBee SHeu
- 'Rosi'	EBee
- 'Rubra'	SCob SRms XLum
- 'Satin Doll'^{PBR}	CBcs ECtt EPfP
- 'Snowbank'	EBee
- 'Sunshine Charm'^{PBR} (Charm Series)	CWCL EBee LRHS NCou NLar NRHS SHeu WHil
- 'Sweet Kate'	CMac CWCL ECtt LRHS LSRN MBNS NBro NLar NRHS SGbt SPoG SRms XLum
- 'Sylvana'	EBee
- 'Valour'	CSBt EBee EPfP LRHS NRHS
- 'Zwanenburg Blue'	ECha ECtt ELan GLog LRHS NLar NRHS SPlb SPoG XLum
blossfeldiana 'Variegata'	see *T. cerinthoides* 'Variegata'
bracteata	SBrt
canaliculata	see *T. ohiensis*
§ ***cerinthoides*** 'Variegata' (v) ♀^{H1c}	EShb
crassifolia	CFil

	- F&M 258	WPGP
§	***fluminensis***	SChr WDib
§	- 'Aurea' ♀H1c	SChr
	- 'Maiden's Blush' (v)	CSpe CWCL EShb EUJe SChr SPlb SVen
	- 'Quicksilver' (v) ♀H1c	EShb NGBl
	- 'Variegata'	see *T. fluminensis* 'Aurea'
	'Green Hill' new	LCro
§	***ohiensis***	SBrt
	pallida 'Kartuz Giant'	EShb MPie WCot
	- 'Pale Puma'	EShb
§	- 'Purpurea' ♀H1c	CBcs EOHP EShb EUJe NGBl SPlb
	pendula	see *T. zebrina*
	'Purple Sabre'	see *T. pallida* 'Purpurea'
	purpurea	see *T. pallida* 'Purpurea'
	sillamontana ♀H1c	EShb MPie SChr
I	- 'Variegata' (v) new	EShb
	spathacea	EShb EUJe
	- 'Versicolor'	EShb
	tricolor	see *T. zebrina*
	virginiana	ESps NChi
	- 'Alba'	CMac GCal SRms
*	- 'Brevicaulis'	EBee ECha NBro
§	- 'Caerulea Plena' (d)	ELan EPfP MRav NLar SPer XLum
	- 'Rubra'	SPlb
§	***zebrina*** ♀H1c	EShb NGBl
	- *pendula*	see *T. zebrina*
	- 'Purpusii' ♀H1c	EShb WDib

Tragopogon (*Asteraceae*)

crocifolius	CSpe LRHS SPhx
porrifolius	CFis EBWF GCal MCot NGBl SPhx SVic WCot WTre
pratensis	EBWF NMir

Trautvetteria (*Ranunculaceae*)

carolinensis	CBot IMou WSHC
- var. ***japonica***	EWld GEdr WCru
- - B&SWJ 10861	WCru
- var. ***occidentalis***	EBee LEdu WCru

Triadica (*Euphorbiaceae*)

sebifera	SBrt WCru WPGP
- CWJ 12819	WCru

Trichilia (*Meliaceae*)

hirta	SMad

Trichodiadema (*Aizoaceae*)

intonsum	SPlb

Trichopetalum (*Asparagaceae*)

§	***plumosum***	CBro

Trichostema (*Lamiaceae*)

'Blue Bonnets'	MMuc

Tricuspidaria see *Crinodendron*

Tricyrtis (*Liliaceae*)

	B&SWJ 3229 from Taiwan	WCru
	'Abdane'	GKev
	'Adbane'	ELan EWes WGwG
	affinis B&SWJ 2804	WCru
	- B&SWJ 5645	WCru
	- B&SWJ 6182	WCru
	- B&SWJ 11169	WCru
	- B&SWJ 11442	WCru
	- 'Early Bird'	WCru
	bakeri	see *T. latifolia*
	'Blue Wonder'	CBod ELon LBuc LRHS SPad SPer WHar WWtn XLum
	dilatata	see *T. macropoda*
	'Empress'	CAby CBct CDor CExl CPla ECha ELon EPfP EThi EWTr EWes LRHS LSou MAvo MJak NEgg NWad SRkn SRot WHar WWtn
	flava	EBee LRHS NRHS WCru
	formosana	CAby CAvo CMea CTri ECha EHrv ELan EPfP GKev GLog GMaP IBoy LEdu LRHS MCot MMuc MNrw SDys SRms SRot WAvo WKif
	- B&SWJ 355	WCru
	- B&SWJ 3073	WCru
	- B&SWJ 3616	CExl WCru
	- B&SWJ 3712	WCru
	- B&SWJ 6741	WCru
	- B&SWJ 6970	WCru
	- RWJ 10109	WCru
	- 'Autumn Glow' (v)	WFar
	- 'Dark Beauty'	CAby CBot CDor CExl CWCL ECtt EHrv ELan GAbr LCro LPmr MBel MNrw MPnt SCob WCAu WFar WPGP
	- 'Emperor' (v)	EBee
	- 'Gilt Edge' (v)	CBct CExl ECtt ELan EPfP EThi LPmr LSou MBNS NEgg NLar NWad SWvt
	- f. ***glandosa*** B&SWJ 7084	WCru
	- aff. f. ***glandosa*** 'Blu-Shing Toad'	MAvo WCru
	- var. ***grandiflora*** 'W-Ho-ping Toad'	WCru
	- 'Kestrel' (v)	CBct WCot
	- pale-flowered	EThi
	- 'Purple Beauty'	LPmr MNrw
	- 'Samurai' (v)	CWCL EWes NPnk
	- 'Seiryu'	EBee
	- 'Small Wonder'	WCru
	- 'Spotted Toad'	LEdu WCru
§	- Stolonifera Group	CAvo CBcs CBod CDor CMac EHrv ELan EPfP LEdu LRHS MCot NRHS NWad SHar
	- - B&SWJ 7046	WCru
	- 'Taiwan Toad'	CExl
	- 'Taroko Toad'	WCru
	- 'Tiny Toad'	MAvo WCru
	- 'Variegata' (v)	LEdu SRms WCru
	- 'Velvet Toad'	WCru
	'Golden Leopard'	EBee
	'Harlequin'	LEdu
§	***hirta***	CBcs CDor CHid CMac CTri CTsd IBoy ILea LCro LOPS LRHS MCot MJak NBro NRHS SGbt SPlb SWvt WSHC
	- B&SWJ 5971	WCru
	- B&SWJ 11182	WCru
	- B&SWJ 11227	WCru
	- 'Alba'	CMac WAvo
	- 'Albomarginata' (v)	CBod CMac LRHS NEgg NRHS NSti SPoG SWvt WWtn
	- 'Golden Gleam'	WCot
	- var. ***masamunei***	WCru
	- 'Matsukaze'	CExl EWes
	- 'Miyazaki'	CMac ECha ECtt EPfP IFoB LPmr LRHS MHer MNrw NRHS NSti SPoG WSHC WWtn XLum
	- 'Taiwan Atrianne'	CDor ECtt ELan EPed LRHS MNrw MPie NEgg NRHS NWad SGbt SPoG WCAu WWtn

- 'Variegata' (v)	CTri EBee EWes GKev GMcL LRHS NRHS WCot
Hototogisu	CExl ECha ECtt ELan EPed LRHS MHer NLar NPnk NRHS SPoG WWtn
'Imperial Banner' (v)	CWCL
ishiiana	CTal EBee EHrv MMoz WCot WCru WSHC
- var. ***surugensis***	LEdu WCru WFar
japonica	see *T. hirta*
'Kohaku'	EBee
lasiocarpa	EHrv LEdu MAvo XLum
- B&SWJ 3635	CAby CExl WCru
- B&SWJ 6861	WCru
- B&SWJ 7013	WCru
- B&SWJ 7103	WCru
- 'Royal Toad'	WCru
§ ***latifolia***	ELan GLog GPSL IRob LEdu LLHF LRHS NRHS WCru WFar
- B&SWJ 10996	CBct
- 'Saffron'	WCru
'Lightning Strike' (v)	CDor EBee ECha ECtt LEdu WCot
'Lilac Towers'	WCru
macrantha	GAbr GLog WCru WSHC
§ - subsp. ***macranthopsis***	CAby CBct CExl WCot WCru
- - 'Juro' (d)	WCru
macranthopsis	see *T. macrantha* subsp. *macranthopsis*
* ***macrocarpa***	XLum
macropoda	GLog ILea LEdu LRHS MAvo MBNS
- B&SWJ 1271 from Korea	WCru
- B&SWJ 5013	WCru
- B&SWJ 5556	WCru
- B&SWJ 5847 from Japan	WCru
- B&SWJ 6209	WCru
- B&SWJ 8700	WCru
- B&SWJ 8829 from Korea	WCru
maculata HWJCM 470	WCru
- HWJK 2010	WCru
- HWJK 2411	WCru
- PAB 3188	LEdu
'Moonlight Treasure'PBR	CExl EBee IBoy WCot
nana	WCru
- B&SWJ 11399	WCru
ohsumiensis	CAby ECha EHrv WCru
perfoliata	LEdu WCru
- 'Spring Shine' (v)	WCru
pilosa	GKev LEdu
PINK FRECKLES ('Innotripf'PBR)	CBct CDor ELon EThi GMcL LSou MPnt NCou SRot SWvt
'Raspberry Mousse'	CWCL EPfP IFoB MBNS
ravenii	CTal
- B&SWJ 3229	WCru
- RWJ 10012	WCru
setouchiensis	WCru
'Shimone'	CExl CHid ECha
'Sinonome'	EBee IPot MNrw
stolonifera	see *T. formosana* Stolonifera Group
suzukii RWJ 10111	WCru
'Taipei Silk'PBR	IFoB LCro LOPS
'Tojen'	ECha ECtt ELon EPfP EWTr EWes GKev GMcL GPSL LRHS MNrw NPnk NRHS SPer WHar WWtn
'Washfields'	EBee
'White Towers'	CAby CAvo CBro CExl CHid CWCL ECha ECtt IFoB LRHS LSou MRav NEgg NLar NPnk NRHS NSti SRms XLum

Trifolium (*Papilionaceae*)

arvense PAB 7952	LEdu
barnebyi	CPBP
dubium	EBWF SPre
fragiferum	EBWF
incarnatum	CSpe MHer
macrocephalum	EBee
medium	EBWF
ochroleucon	CAby EAJP EBWF ECha ECtt EHrv ELon EWTr GBin GMaP ILea LEdu MAvo MCot MPie NPnk NSti SBch SHar SMad SPhx WAul WCAu WFar WMoo WPGP
pannonicum	CMea GCal IRob MNrw WOut WWFP
- 'White Tiara'	GBin MMrt
pratense	CHab EBWF MHer NMir WOut WSFF
- 'Dolly North'	see *T. pratense* 'Susan Smith'
- 'Ice Cool'	see *T. repens* 'Green Ice'
§ - 'Susan Smith' (v)	CCCN
repens	EBWF LCro LOPS SPhx SVic WSFF
- 'Debbie'	LEdu
- 'Dragon's Blood'	CBod CMea EPPr GMcL GWyn LEdu LLWG MMuc MPie NRHS SPer WPGP WTor
- 'Gold Net'	see *T. pratense* 'Susan Smith'
§ - 'Green Ice'	LLWG NSti WHal
- 'Harlequin' (v)	WCot WMoo WOut
- 'Isabella'PBR	LEdu WPGP
- 'Pentaphyllum'	see *T. repens* 'Quinquefolium'
- 'Purpurascens'	CBre EPfP LLWG LRHS MBNS MHer MPie NRHS NSti SPoG WFar
§ - 'Purpurascens Quadrifolium'	CAby CBod CMea ECha EHoe EPau EWes GAbr GMcL GWyn LEdu MCot NMir NPer NRHS SPer SPlb WFar WRHF WTor
§ - 'Quinquefolium'	XLum
- 'Tetraphyllum Purpureum'	see *T. repens* 'Purpurascens Quadrifolium'
- 'Wheatfen'	CNat LEdu NDov NPer
- 'William'	CBre LEdu MMuc NDov WCot WFar
rubens	Widely available
- 'Drama'	ELon LEdu MNrw
- 'Peach Pink'	ELon EPPr MAvo MMrt SPhx WCot WHrl
- 'Red Feathers'	ELon EPPr EWes GBin GQue LSun MHol SHar SMad
'Spring'	LEdu
trichocephalum	EPPr

Triglochin (*Juncaginaceae*)

maritima	EBWF

Trigonella (*Papilionaceae*)

foenum-graecum	WSFF XAbr

Trillidium see *Trillium*

Trillium ✿ (*Melanthiaceae*)

albidum ♀H5	EBee GEdr LAma LLHF LRHS NRHS
amabile	GEdr
angustipetalum	EPot GEdr GKev
apetalon	GEdr GKev
camschatcense	CExl GEdr GKev
§ ***catesbyi***	CExl CWCL EBee EPot GEdr GKev ILea IRob LAma LLHF MNrw NChi NWad SDir

	catesbyi × sulcatum	GKev
	cernuum	CWCL EBee GKev GMaP LAma
	chloropetalum	CBro CElw CPla GAbr GEdr LPla LRHS NRHS NWad
§	- var. ***giganteum*** ♀H5	CExl GBin LEdu SPhx WCru
	- var. ***rubrum***	see *T. chloropetalum* var. *giganteum*
	- white-flowered	GKev
	cuneatum	CBcs CBct CExl CWCL EHrv EPot GEdr GKev GMcL GWyn IRob LAma LEdu LRHS MCot MNrw NChi NHpl NRHS NWad SDeJ SDir WPnP
	decipiens	GEdr
	decumbens	GEdr
	discolor	GEdr
	erectum ♀H5	Widely available
	- f. ***albiflorum***	CMea ECha MMoz MNrw NRHS NWad
	- - Harvington clone	LRHS
	- 'Beige'	GKev
	- Harvington dark form	EBee
	- f. ***luteum***	GEdr
	- red-flowered	GKev
	erectum × flexipes	EBee EHrv GKev MNrw
	flexipes	CBct CWCL EHrv EPot GEdr GKev LAma LRHS MNrw NHpl NPnk NRHS NWad
	- 'Harvington Dusky Pink'	LRHS NRHS
I	- 'Harvington Selection'	EBee LRHS NRHS
	foetidissimum	GEdr
	govanianum	GEdr GKev LAma LRHS
	gracile	GEdr
	grandiflorum ♀H5	Widely available
	- Gothenburg pink	GEdr
	- pale-pink-flowered	LRHS NRHS
	- f. ***polymerum*** 'Flore Pleno' (d)	CWCL GEdr LLHF LRHS NRHS SDir
	- - 'Snowbunting' (d)	EWes GKev LAma LEdu LRHS NRHS WThu
	- f. ***roseum***	CWCL EBee GEdr GKev LRHS MNrw NRHS
	- white-flowered	MAvo
	kurabayashii	CExl CPne CTal CWCL EBee EHrv EPot GEdr GKev LRHS MNrw NRHS WCru
	lancifolium	GEdr GKev
	ludovicianum	GEdr
	luteum ♀H5	CBcs CBro CExl CWCL EBee EHrv EPfP EPot GAbr GEdr GKev ILea IRob LAma LCro LEdu LOPS LRHS MAvo MNrw NBid NChi NHpl NPnk NRHS NWad SDeJ SDir WCru WPnP
	maculatum	GEdr
	nivale	CBct GEdr
	ovatum 'Roy Elliott'	CExl
	parviflorum	GEdr MNrw
	pusillum	CExl EBee EPot GEdr GKev ILea LAma LLHF MNrw NHpl
	recurvatum	CBcs CWCL EBee EHrv EPot EUJe GEdr GKev ILea IRob LAma LEdu NChi NHpl NWad SDir WPnP
	reliquum	GEdr
	rivale ♀H4	CExl GEdr GKev LEdu SCob
	- Purple Heart Group	GEdr
	rugelii	EBee EHrv EWes GEdr GKev MNrw WSHC
	- Askival hybrids	GAbr MNrw
	rugelii × vaseyi	EBee EHrv EWes MNrw
	sessile	CExl CWCL GEdr GKev GWyn IRob LAma MAvo MCot MNrw NChi NPnk NWad SDeJ WCot WKif WPnP WSHC WShi
	- 'Rubrum'	see *T. chloropetalum* var. *giganteum*
	simile	EBee GEdr GKev LLHF LRHS MNrw NRHS
	smallii	GEdr GKev
	stamineum	CWCL GEdr LAma
	stylosum	see *T. catesbyi*
	sulcatum	CExl CWCL EBee EHrv GAbr GEdr GKev GMaP LAma LEdu LRHS MNrw NRHS WSHC
	- yellow-flowered	GKev
	taiwanense B&SWJ 3411	WCru
	tschonoskii	GEdr
	underwoodii	GEdr
	undulatum	MNrw
	vaseyi	CWCL EBee EHrv EWes GEdr GKev IRob LAma LRHS MNrw NRHS
	viridescens	GEdr LAma

Triosteum (*Caprifoliaceae*)

	erythrocarpum	EWTr SMad
	himalayanum	GCal GEdr GKev IMou WPnP WSHC
	- BWJ 7907	WCru
	pinnatifidum	EBee EWld GCal IMou

Tripleurospermum (*Asteraceae*)

§	***maritimum***	WHer

Tripogandra (*Commelinaceae*)

	serrulata 'Purple Scimitars' **new**	EShb

Tripolium (*Asteraceae*)

§	***pannonicum***	EBWF WHer

Tripsacum (*Poaceae*)

	dactyloides	EPPr

Tripterospermum (*Gentianaceae*)

	japonicum	GEdr
	lanceolatum RWJ 9918	WCru

Tripterygium (*Celastraceae*)

	doianum B&SWJ 11467	WCru
	aff. ***doianum*** CWJ 12852	WCru
	regelii	CBcs
	- B&SWJ 5453	WCru
	- B&SWJ 8666 from Korea	WCru
	- B&SWJ 10921	WCru
	wilfordii	EBee LEdu
	- BWJ 7852 from China	WCru
	- NJM 11.029 from China	WPGP
	- WWJ 12009	WCru

Trisetum (*Poaceae*)

	flavescens	EBWF

Tristagma (*Alliaceae*)

	nivale	EBee

Triteleia (*Asparagaceae*)

	'4U'	EBee GKev
	'Aquarius'	ERCP GKev
	californica	see *Brodiaea californica*
§	'Corrina'	CAvo EBee EPot ERCP GKev
	'Crystal Pink'	SDeJ
	'Double Touch' (d)	EBee GKev SDeJ WCot
	'Foxy'	EBee EPot

grandiflora	WCot
hendersonii	GKev
hyacinthina	EBee GEdr GKev WCot
- NNS 06-560 **new**	WCot
ixioides 'Starlight'	CTri EPot ERCP GKev SDeJ
§ ***laxa***	ECha
- 'Allure'	EBee
§ - 'Koningin Fabiola'	EBee GKev LAma MNrw SCob SDeJ WCot
- QUEEN FABIOLA	see *T. laxa* 'Koningin Fabiola'
lemmoniae	GKev
'Ocean Queen'	EBee ERCP
§ ***peduncularis***	GKev WCot
'Rudy'	CAvo CBro CHid CMea CWCL EBee ERCP GKev SCob SDeJ WCot
'Silver Queen'	EBee EPot ERCP GKev SDeJ XEll
'Twilight'	GKev
uniflora	see *Ipheion uniflorum*
'White Cloud' **new**	GKev
'White Sweep'	EBee

Trithrinax (*Arecaceae*)

brasiliensis	SBig
campestris	CBrP LRHS SBig

Tritoma see *Kniphofia*

Tritonia (*Iridaceae*)

crocata ♀H2	GKev
- 'Baby Doll'	LEdu
- 'Serendipity'	EPri
deusta	EPri
disticha	SMad
§ - subsp. ***rubrolucens***	Widely available
laxifolia	CTca EPot GKev NRog
lineata	EBee EPri LEdu
- 'Parvifolia'	GKev
pallida	SPlb
rosea	see *T. disticha* subsp. *rubrolucens*
securigera	CTal LEdu
squalida	EPri

Trixis (*Asteraceae*)

sp.	NPri

Trochocarpa (*Ericaceae*)

clarkei	WThu
gunnii	WThu
thymifolia	WThu
- white-flowered	WThu

Trochodendron (*Trochodendraceae*)

aralioides	CAby CBcs CMac CSam CTho CTsd EBee ELan EPfP GBin GKin MBlu MGos MMuc NLar SAko SArc SLon SMad SPer SReu SSta WCot WPGP
- B&SWJ 1651 from Taiwan	WCru
- B&SWJ 6080 from Japan	WCru
- CWJ 12357 from Taiwan	WCru
- RWJ 9845 from Taiwan	WCru
- from Taiwan	CFil

Trollius (*Ranunculaceae*)

ACE 1187	CExl
acaulis	EWes GAbr
altaicus	EBee LRHS NRHS
asiaticus	GKev
buddae	CWCL EWes MRav WFar
§ ***chinensis***	ECha GCal GKev GWyn
- 'Golden Queen' ♀H7	Widely available
- 'Imperial Orange'	GWyn
- 'Morning Sun'	CBct
- wild-collected	GBin
× ***cultorum***	CAby
- 'Alabaster'	Widely available
- 'Baudirektor Linne'	MRav NGdn
- 'Byrne's Giant'	ECtt GBin
- 'Canary Bird'	GCal NGdn SRms WSpi
- 'Cheddar'	see *T.* × *cultorum* 'Taleggio'
- 'Earliest of All'	CSam CWCL NGdn NLar WSHC WSpi
- 'Etna'	GMcL IRob
§ - 'Feuertroll'	ECha ECtt MRav NEoE NGdn WSpi
- FIREGLOBE	see *T.* × *cultorum* 'Feuertroll'
- 'Golden Cup'	GWyn NGdn
- 'Goldquelle' ♀H7	EBee GBin GWyn
- 'Goliath'	GWyn NLar
- 'Helios'	CSam GBin
- 'Lemon Queen'	CBod CWCL CWat ECtt EHrv EPfP EWTr GKev GMaP GWyn IRob LRHS MRav NLar NQui NRHS SCob SGol SPer
- 'New Moon'	CAby CBcs CBct CDor CWCL EBee EShb GBin GWyn LRHS NChi NPnk NQui NRHS SPad WWtn
- 'Orange Crest'	CBod EBee ECtt ELon EPfP GCal
- 'Orange Globe'	GMaP
- 'Orange Princess' ♀H7	CDor CWCL CWat GMcL GWyn LRHS NBro NLar NRHS SPer SRms
- 'Orange Queen'	SWvt
- 'Prichard's Giant'	ECtt ELan ELon NBro WCFE WSpi
§ - 'Superbus' ♀H7	CBod CWCL ELan ELon EPfP GBin GMaP GWyn LRHS MHol NGdn NRHS SPer WFar
- 'T. Smith'	ECtt IRob NBro
§ - 'Taleggio'	CWCL ECtt ELon EPfP GMaP IBoy ILea LEdu LRHS MBNS MBel MRav NBro NEoE NRHS SWvt WFar WPnP WSpi
- 'Yellow Beauty'	GBin
'Dancing Flame'	CMac LCro LOPS LRHS NEoE SHar SPoG SRms
europaeus	CAby CBod CWCL EBWF ECha ELan EPfP ESps GBin GCal GJos GMcL GWyn LEdu LLWG LRHS MHol MRav MWat NGdn NRHS SRms SRot WCFE WHar
- SDR 6306	GKev
- subsp. ***europaeus***	WFar
- 'Lemon Supreme'	EBee GKev LRHS NRHS WWtn
- 'Superbus'	see *T.* × *cultorum* 'Superbus'
farreri	GKev
- var. ***major*** SDR 2713 **new**	GKev
hondoensis	LLHF NEoE
ircuticus	EWes GKev
laxus 'Albiflorus'	CExl
ledebourii misapplied	see *T. chinensis*
macropetalus	EBee GKev
pumilus	ECha ELan EPfP LLHF LRHS NLar NPnk NRHS SPer
- ACE 1818	CExl MHer
- 'Double Jeopardy'	EBee
ranunculoides	GEdr GKev
vaginatus	EBee GEdr LLHF
yunnanensis ♀H6	EBee GBin LRHS NRHS
- orange-flowered	CExl

Tropaeolum (*Tropaeolaceae*)

azureum	CCCN CExl CFil CPla CPne
brachyceras	CCCN CPne SDir

ciliatum	CCCN CFil CPla EWld NBid WCot WCru WPGP
hookerianum	CExl
- subsp. ***austropurpureum***	CExl CFil
- subsp. ***hookerianum***	CFil
incisum	CCCN CFil
lepidum	CPla
majus	ENfk GPoy SVic
- Alaska Series (v) ♀H3	ENfk LCro LOPS MNHC
- 'Black Velvet' (Tom Thumb Series)	CRav LCro LOPS
- 'Crimson Beauty'	CSpe
§ - 'Darjeeling Double' (d) ♀H3	GCal
- 'Darjeeling Gold'	see *T. majus* 'Darjeeling Double'
- 'Empress of India'	MNHC
- 'Hermine Grashoff' (d)	CSpe GCal
- Jewel Series	ENfk
- 'Margaret Long' (d)	CSpe GCal
- 'Red Wonder'	CCCN CSpe EPfP WCot
- Tom Thumb Series	MNHC
nubigenum* × *polyphyllum	CFil
pentaphyllum	CExl CFil CPne CRHN CSpe EBee GCal
polyphyllum ♀H3	CCCN CWCL EBee EPot SMHy WCot
sessilifolium	CFil EBee
smithii	GCal WPGP
speciosum ♀H5	Widely available
sylvestre	EWld
tricolor ♀H2	CAvo CCCN CFil CRHN CWCL GCal GKev SBrt SDir XEll
tuberosum	CAgr CEnd GKev GPoy SDeJ
- var. ***lineamaculatum*** 'Ken Aslet' ♀H3	CAbb CAvo CBro CCCN CKel CWCL ECha ELan EPfP EPot GKev GMcL IFro LAma LEdu LRHS NLar NRHS SPer

Tsuga ✿ (*Pinaceae*)

canadensis	CAco CDul EPfP ESps LMaj LPra
- 'Abbott's Dwarf'	CKen
§ - 'Abbott's Pygmy'	CKen
- 'Bacon Cristate'	CKen
- 'Beehive'	GMil NLar
- 'Bennett'	NLar
- 'Betty Rose' (v)	CKen
- 'Birkett's White'	CKen
- 'Brandley'	CKen
§ - 'Branklyn'	CKen WCFE
- 'Cappy's Choice'	CKen
- 'Cinnamonea'	CKen
- 'Coffin'	CKen
- 'Cole's Prostrate' ♀H7	CKen GMil LRHS MAsh NRHS SLim
- 'Creamey' (v)	CKen
- 'Curley'	CKen
- 'Curtis Ideal'	CKen
- 'Dr Hornbeck'	see *T. canadensis* 'Hornbeck'
- 'Eisburg'	SLim
- 'Essex'	CKen
* - 'Everitt's Dense Leaf'	CKen
- 'Everitt's Golden'	CKen NLar
- 'Fantana'	GMcL
- 'Greenwood Lake'	WThu
- 'Hedgehog'	NLar
§ - 'Hornbeck'	CKen
- 'Horsford'	CKen
- 'Horstmann' No 1	CKen
- 'Hussii'	CKen
- 'Jacqueline Verkade'	CKen NLar
- 'Jeddeloh' ♀H7	ESps GEdr GMcL GMil LRHS MAsh NEgg NLar NRHS SCob SGol SLim
- 'Jervis'	CKen NWad
- 'Julianne'	CKen
- 'Kingsville Spreader'	CKen
- 'Little Joe'	CKen
- 'Livingston'	SLim
I - 'Lutea'	CKen
- 'Many Cones'	CKen
- 'Minima'	CKen
- 'Minuta' ♀H7	CKen
- 'Nana'	SPoG
- 'Palomino'	CKen
- 'Pendula' ♀H7	CKen LRHS NRHS
- 'Pincushion'	CKen
- 'Prostrata'	see *T. canadensis* 'Branklyn'
- 'Pygmaea'	see *T. canadensis* 'Abbott's Pygmy'
- 'Rugg's Washington Dwarf'	CKen
- 'Snowflake'	CKen
- 'Stewart's Gem'	CKen
- 'Verkade Petite'	CKen
- 'Verkade Recurved'	CKen
- 'Von Helms' Dwarf'	CKen
- 'Warnham'	CKen
caroliniana 'La Bar Weeping'	CKen NLar
- 'Planting Fields Broom'	CKen
chinensis	CKen
diversifolia 'Gotelli'	CKen
dumosa	CKen
heterophylla ♀H6	CAco CBcs CCVT CDul CPer EPfP ESps GMil MMuc SCob SEWo SGol WMou WTSh
- 'Iron Springs'	CKen NLar
- 'Laursen's Column'	CKen
- 'Ray Godfrey'	NLar
- 'Thorsens Weeping'	CKen NLar SLim
menziesii	see *Pseudotsuga menziesii*
mertensiana	CAco
- 'Blue Star'	CKen
- 'Elizabeth'	CKen
- 'Glauca'	CKen
I - 'Glauca Nana'	CKen
I - 'Horstmann'	CKen
- 'Quartz Mountain'	CKen
sieboldii 'Baldwin'	CKen
- 'Green Ball'	CKen
- 'Honeywell Estate'	CKen
- 'Nana'	CKen

Tuberaria (*Cistaceae*)

lignosa	WAbe

Tulbaghia ✿ (*Alliaceae*)

acutiloba	CTca LEdu MHom
alliacea	EPri LEdu WCot
alliacea* × *violacea	CAvo
* ***allioides***	CBro
'Bob Brown'	LEdu
capensis	CPou LEdu WAvo
'Cariad'	LEdu WPGP
cernua CD&R 199	EBee LEdu
- hybrid	EPri
§ ***coddii***	MHom
cominsii	CExl CPla EPri LEdu SBch
cominsii* × *violacea	CAvo CExl EPri MHom
'Cornish Beauty' **new**	CTca
'Cosmic'	CPou EBee EPPr EPri LEdu WPGP
'Fairy Snow'	LEdu WCot

'Fairy Star'	CKno CTca CWGN EBee EPri EShb LEdu LSou SMHy SPoG WCot WHlf
fragrans	see *T. simmleri*
- 'Alba'	ELan EPot SDeJ
'Hazel'	CPou EBee LEdu MHer SMHy
'John May's Special'	EShb LEdu MHom WCot WHoo WPGP
leucantha ♀H2	CTca EPri LEdu MHom NWad
- H&B 11996	LEdu
ludwigiana	CPne MHer
maritima	see *T. violacea* var. *maritima*
Marwood seedling	LEdu MHer MHom
montana	EBee LEdu MHer MPie
'Moshoeshoe'	LEdu WPGP
natalensis ♀H2	CBro CPrp GKev
- B&V 421	EPri
- B&V 421 clone 2 pink-flowered	LEdu
- Burtt 6949	CPne
- pink-flowered	CTca LPla MHom
- white-flowered	CTca
poetica	see *T. coddii*
'Purple Eye' ♀H2	CBro CCht CKno CPne EBee LEdu SBee SPoG WCot WHlf
§ ***simmleri*** ♀H2	CPrp EBee EPri EWes GKev LAma LEdu SDeJ
- 'Cheryl Renshaw'	WCot
- 'Snow Queen'	CPrp
- white-flowered	CPrp GKev
'Snow White'	WCot
verdoorniae	LEdu
violacea ♀H2	CAvo CBcs CBlu CBro CKno CMea CPou CPrp CSpe CTca ECha EHrv EPfP EPot EPri ERCP GKev LAma LEdu MHom MSCN SEND SPlb WHoo WPGP WPnP XSen
- from RBGE	MHom
* - 'Alba'	CKno EBee EPri MHer SChF WKif WPnP
I - 'Fine Form'	CKno WKif
- 'Harry Hay' **new**	SMHy
- 'John Rider'	EPri
* - var. ***maritima***	CPne EShb LEdu MHer MHom
- 'Pallida'	CAvo CBro CCse CTca LEdu WPGP
- 'Peppermint Garlic'	LEdu
- var. ***robustior***	CAby ECha EWes
- 'Seren'	LEdu
§ - 'Silver Lace' (v) ♀H2	Widely available
- 'Variegata'	see *T. violacea* 'Silver Lace'
- 'White Drooper' **new**	SMHy

Tulipa ✿ (*Liliaceae*)

sp.	NRHS
(4) **new**	CArg
'Abba' (2)	CArg LAma SCob SDeJ SDir
'Abigail' (11) **new**	SDir
'Absalon' (9)	CRav GKev LAma SDir
'Abu Hassan' (3)	CAvo CRav ERCP LAma SDeJ
acuminata (15)	CTca ERCP GKev LAma SCob SDeJ SDir
'Ad Rem' (4) ♀H6	SDeJ
'Addis' (14)	LAma
'Affaire' (3) **new**	GKev
'Aguila'	SDir
aitchisonii	see *T. clusiana*
'Akebono' (11)	GKev LAma SDeJ SDir
'Akela' (5)	LAma
'Akita' (6)	GKev
'Alabaster' (5)	LAma
'Aladdin' (6)	CArg GKev LAma LCro LOPS SDeJ
'Aladdin's Record' (6)	LAma SDeJ SDir
'Alba Regalis' (1)	LAma
'Albert Heijn' (13)	GKev SDeJ
albertii (15)	LAma
ALBION STAR ('Mieke Telkamp') (13)	CArg EPfP SDeJ SPer
'Aleppo' (7)	SDeJ
'Alexander Pushkin'PBR (3)	LAma
'Alfred Cortot' (12) ♀H6	LAma SDeJ
'Alibi' (3)	EPfP GKev SDeJ
'Alice Leclercq' (2)	LAma
'Allegretto' (11)	LAma
altaica (15) ♀H6	LAma
amabilis	see *T. hoogiana*
'American Dream' (4)	LAma SDir
'American Eagle' (7)	LAma SDeJ
'Ancilla' (12) ♀H6	GKev LAma SDeJ SDir WShi
'André Rieu' (5)	LCro LOPS
'Angélique' (11) ♀H6	CAvo CRav CTca EPfP ERCP GKev LAma LCro LOPS SCob SDeJ SDir SPer
'Angels Wish' (5) ♀H6	CAvo EPfP LAma SDeJ SDir
'Annie Schilder' (3)	CRav ERCP LAma
'Antarctica'PBR (3)	LAma
'Anthony Eden' (2)	LAma SDir
'Antoinette'PBR (5)	CAby EPfP LAma LCro LOPS SDeJ SDir
'Antraciet' (11)	CRav ERCP LAma LCro LOPS
'Apeldoorn' (4)	CArg GKev LAma LCro LOPS SCob SDeJ
'Apeldoorn's Elite' (4) ♀H6	LAma SDeJ
'Apricot Beauty' (1) ♀H6	CAvo CRav CTca ERCP GKev LAma LCro LOPS MCot SDeJ SDir
'Apricot Delight' (4)	GKev
'Apricot Emperor' (13)	GKev SDeJ
'Apricot Foxx' (3)	CArg EPfP GKev LAma SDeJ
'Apricot Impression'PBR (4)	LAma
'Apricot Jewel'	see *T. linifolia* (Batalinii Group) 'Apricot Jewel'
'Apricot Parrot' (10) ♀H6	ERCP GKev LAma MCot SDeJ SDir
'Aquilla' (11)	LAma SDeJ
'Arabian Mystery' (3)	GKev LAma SDeJ
'Aria Card' (7)	LAma SDeJ
'Arjuna' (3) **new**	CRav
'Arma' (7) ♀H6	ERCP
armena (15) **new**	GKev
'Artist' (8) ♀H6	CRav ERCP GKev LAma SDeJ SDir
'Atlantis' (5)	CArg CRav ERCP LAma SDeJ
'Attila' (3)	CAvo GKev LAma
aucheriana (15) ♀H5	EPot LAma LLHF
'Avignon' (5)	SDeJ
aximensis (15)	EPot GKev LAma
'Bacchus' (7)	LAma
bakeri	see *T. saxatilis* Bakeri Group
'Ballade' (6) ♀H6	CAvo ERCP GKev LAma LCro LOPS MCot SDeJ
BALLADE DREAM ('Sonnet') (6)	LAma SDeJ
'Ballade Gold' (6)	LAma
'Ballerina' (6) ♀H6	CArg CAvo CMea CRav CTca EPfP ERCP GKev LAma LCro LOPS MCot SCob SDeJ SDir SPer
'Banja Luka' (4)	GKev LAma MJak SDeJ
'Barbados' (7)	LAma SCob SDeJ
'Barcelona' (3) ♀H6	ERCP GKev LAma LCro LOPS
'Baronesse' (5)	SDeJ
'Bastogne' (3)	LAma SCob
'Bastogne Parrot' (10)	LAma
batalinii	see *T. linifolia* Batalinii Group
'Beau Monde' (3) ♀H6	SDeJ
'Beauty of Apeldoorn' (4)	LAma SDir
'Beauty of Bath' (9)	LAma

'Beauty of Spring' (4) GKev LAma
'Beauty Queen' (1) GKev LAma SDeJ
'Beethoven's Memory' (19) GKev
'Belcanto' (3) LAma
'Belicia' (2) GKev LAma
'Bell Song' (7) GKev
'Bellflower' (7) LAma
'Bellona' (3) LAma SDeJ
'Berlioz' (12) LAma SDeJ
'Bessie' (5) LAma
'Bestseller' (1) SDeJ
§ ***biflora*** (15) EPot ERCP GKev LAma SDeJ SDir
- var. ***major*** (15) GKev
bifloriformis (15) GKev LAma LLHF
I - 'Maxima' (15) SPhx
- 'Starlight' (15) ♀H6 GKev
'Big Chief' (4) ♀H6 LAma
'Big Smile' (5) SDir
'Black and White' (9) LAma
'Black Charm' (3) CAby
'Black Hero' (11) CAby CAvo CRav ERCP GKev LAma LCro LOPS MCot SDeJ SDir
'Black Horse' (5) LAma
'Black Jewel' (7) ERCP GKev SDeJ SDir
'Black Parrot' (10) ♀H6 CAby CArg CAvo CRav EPfP ERCP GKev LAma LCro LOPS SCob SDeJ SDir SPer
'Black Stallion' (11) SDir
'Black Swan' (5) SDeJ
'Blackjack' (3) GKev LAma
'Bleu Aimable' (5) CAvo ERCP GKev LAma SDeJ
'Blue Beauty' (3) **new** LCro LOPS
'Blue Burst' (11) **new** SDir
'Blue Diamond' (11) CArg CAvo ERCP LAma SDeJ SDir
'Blue Heron' (7) ♀H6 ERCP LAma LCro LOPS MCot SDeJ
'Blue Parrot' (10) CArg CRav EPfP ERCP LAma LCro LOPS SCob SDeJ SPer
'Blue Ribbon' (3) CAvo LCro LOPS
'Blue Spectacle' (11) GKev
BLUEBERRY RIPPLE see *T.* 'Zurel'
'Blumex Favourite'PBR (10) SCob
'Blushing Apeldoorn' (4) LAma
'Blushing Beauty' (5) LAma SDeJ
'Blushing Bride' (5) SDeJ
'Blushing Girl' (5) LAma SDeJ SDir
'Blushing Lady' (5) GKev LAma
'Border Legend' (13) LAma
'Boston' (3) LAma SDir
'Boutade' (14) NPer
'Bridesmaid' (5) LAma
'Bright Parrot' (10) LAma
'Brilliant Star' (1) LAma
'Brooklyn' (11) **new** NPer
'Brown Sugar' (3) CRav ERCP GKev
'Bruine Wimpel' (5) CRav GKev LAma
'Buddy' (14) SCob
'Bulldog' (7) CAvo SDeJ
'Burgundy' (6) CAvo CTca ERCP GKev LAma LCro LOPS SDeJ SDir SPer
'Burgundy Lace' (7) GKev LAma LCro LOPS SDeJ
'Burning Heart' (4) ♀H6 CArg GKev LAma SDeJ
butkovii (15) GKev
'Buttercup' (14) SDeJ
'Café Noir' (5) ERCP LAma LCro LOPS SDir
'Cairo' (3) CRav LOPS
'Calgary' (3) ♀H6 CAvo GKev LAma LCro LOPS SCob SDeJ SDir
'Calibra' (7) LAma
'Californian Sun' (14) LAma
'Calypso' (14) ♀H6 LAma LRHS NRHS
'Camargue' (5) **new** SDeJ
'Canasta' (7) ♀H6 LAma SDeJ
'Candela' (13) ♀H6 LAma SDeJ
'Candy Apple Delight' (4) **new** SDir
'Candy Cane' (3) **new** CRav
'Candy Clouds' (2) LAma
'Candy Club' (5) LAma SDeJ
'Candy Prince'PBR (1) CArg LAma SDeJ SDir
'Canova' (7) SDeJ
'Cantata' (13) LAma
'Cape Cod' (14) CAvo LAma SDeJ
'Cape Town' (1) ♀H6 SDeJ
'Caractère' (3) **new** CArg
'Caravelle' (5) **new** SDeJ
'Cardinal Mindszenty' (2) ERCP LAma LRHS NRHS SDeJ SDir
'Caribbean Parrot' (10) **new** GKev
'Carlton' (2) LAma
'Carnaval de Nice' (11/v) ♀H6 CAby CTca ERCP GKev LAma LCro LOPS SDeJ SDir SPer
'Carrousel' (7) SDeJ
'Cartouche' (11) LAma SDeJ
'Cassini' (3) LAma SDeJ
'Catherina' (5) **new** LOPS
§ ***celsiana*** (15) GKev LAma
'Charmeur'PBR (3) SDeJ
'Charming Beauty' (11) GKev
'Charming Lady' (11) ERCP
'Chato' (11) **new** CRav
'China Lady' (14) SDeJ
'China Pink' (6) ♀H6 CAvo CRav CTca ERCP GKev LAma LCro LOPS MCot SDeJ SDir
'China Town' (8) ♀H6 ERCP GKev LAma LCro LOPS SDeJ SDir SPer
'Chopin' (12) LAma
'Christmas Dream' (1) GKev LAma SDeJ SDir
'Christmas Marvel' (1) SDeJ
'Christmas Sweet' (1) CArg
chrysantha see *T. montana*
'Cilesta' (2) LAma MJak
'Cistula' (6) SDeJ
'City Flower' (14) LAma
'City of Vancouver' (5) LAma SDeJ
'Claudia' (6) CArg LAma SDeJ SDir
'Clearwater'PBR (5) LAma SDeJ
§ ***clusiana*** (15) EPfP ERCP GKev LAma SPer
- var. ***chrysantha*** (15) ♀H5 CExl GKev LAma WShi
- - 'Tubergen's Gem' (15) EPot GKev LAma SDir
- 'Cynthia' (15) ♀H6 CAby CTca EPot ERCP GKev LAma SDeJ SDir WShi
- 'Sheila' (15) GKev LAma
§ - var. ***stellata*** (15) ♀H6 GKev LAma
'Colour Spectacle'PBR (5) CAby LAma
'Columbine' (5) CRav GKev LAma SDir
'Comedian' (14) LAma
'Concerto' (13) LAma NPer SDeJ
'Conqueror'PBR (4) **new** SDir
'Continental' (3) GKev LAma
'Cool Crystal' (7) GKev LAma
'Coquette' (1) SDeJ
'Corona' (12) SDeJ
'Corsage' (14) ♀H6 LAma SDeJ
'Cortina' (9) SDeJ
'Cottage Boy' (1) LAma SDir
'Couleur Cardinal' (3) CAvo ERCP GKev LAma LCro LOPS LRHS NRHS SDeJ SDir
'Cream Perfection' (3) LAma
'Creme Upstar' (11) ERCP GKev LAma LCro LOPS SDeJ SDir
cretica (15) LAma LLHF

	- 'Archanes' (15) **new**	GKev
	- 'Chania' (15) **new**	GKev
	'Crystal Beauty' (7) ♀H6	LAma
	'Crystal Star' (7) **new**	CArg
	'Cuban Night' (7)	LAma
	'Cum Laude' (5)	LAma SDeJ
	'Cummins' (7)	CAvo ERCP GKev LAma LOPS SDir
	'Curly Sue' (7)	ERCP LAma LCro LOPS MCot SDir SPer
	'Czaar Peter' (14) ♀H6	GKev NPer SDeJ
	'Dallas' (7)	LAma
	'Dance' (13)	SDeJ
	'Danceline' (11) **new**	GKev
	'Dancing Show' (8)	LAma
	dasystemon (15)	GKev LAma LLHF
	'Davenport' (7)	ERCP
	'David Teniers' (2)	ERCP LAma SDeJ
	'Daydream' (4) ♀H6	CArg GKev LAma SCob SDeJ SDir SPer
	'Daytona' (7)	CAvo LAma
	'Deep River' (5)	LAma
	'Deshima' (3)	LAma
	'Design Impression' (4)	CRav LAma
	'Diana' (1)	CArg
	'Dior' (2)	LCro LOPS
	'Doll's Minuet' (8)	CAvo CRav EPfP ERCP LAma LCro LOPS SPer
	'Dom Pedro' (5)	LAma SDir
	'Don Quichotte' (3) ♀H6	ERCP LAma LCro LOPS SDeJ
	'Donauperle' (14)	SDeJ
	'Donna Bella' (14)	SDeJ
	'Dordogne' (5) ♀H6	LAma SDeJ SDir
	'Double Dazzle' (2)	LAma
	'Double Flaming Parrot' PBR (10)	LAma
	'Double Princess' PBR (2)	LAma
	'Double Red Riding Hood' (14v)	GKev LAma MCot SCob SDeJ SDir
	'Double Sugar' (11)	LAma
	'Double You' (11)	EPfP SPer
	'Dragon King' (3)	SDeJ
	'Dream Touch' (11)	GKev LAma LCro LOPS
	'Dreamboat' (14)	EPfP LAma
	'Dreaming Maid' (3)	LAma
	'Dreamland' (5) ♀H6	LAma SDeJ
	dubia 'Beldersai' (15)	GKev
	'Duc van Tol' (1)	SDir
	'Duc van Tol Aurora' (1)	LAma
	'Duc van Tol Max Cramoisie' (1)	LAma SDir
	'Duc van Tol Primrose' (1)	LAma
	'Duc van Tol Red and Yellow' (1)	GKev LAma SDir
	'Duc van Tol Rose' (1)	LAma SDir
	'Duc van Tol Salmon' (1)	LAma
	'Duc van Tol Scarlet' (1)	LAma
	'Duc van Tol Violet' (1)	GKev LAma SDir
	'Duc van Tol White' (1)	LAma
	'Early Glory' (3)	LCro LOPS
	'Early Harvest' (12) ♀H6	CAvo GKev LAma SDeJ SDir
	'Early Star' (14)	LAma
	'Easter Parade' (13)	LAma
	'Easter Surprise' (14) ♀H6	GKev LAma SDeJ SDir
	'Ego Parrot' (10)	LCro LOPS
	eichleri	see *T. undulatifolia*
	'El Niño' (5)	SDir
	'Electra' (5)	LAma
	'Elegans Alba' (6)	LAma
	'Elegant Lady' (6)	CAvo GKev LAma MCot MJak SDeJ
	'Erna Lindgreen' (10)	LAma

	'Escape' PBR (3)	LAma
	'Esperanto' (8/v) ♀H6	GKev LAma NPer SDeJ SDir
	'Esprit' (7)	LAma
	'Estella Rijnveld' (10)	ERCP GKev LAma LCro LOPS SDeJ SDir
	'Esther' (5)	LAma
	'Eternal Flame' (2)	GKev LAma LCro LOPS SDir
	'Evergreen' (3) **new**	GKev
	'Exotic Emperor' (13)	CAvo CRav GKev LAma LCro LOPS SDeJ SDir SPer
	'Eye Catcher' (8)	LAma SDir
	'Fabio' (7)	LRHS NRHS
	'Fairy Nymph' (5)	LAma
	'Fancy Frills' (7) ♀H6	ERCP GKev LAma SDeJ SDir
	'Fancy Parrot' (10) **new**	SDeJ
	'Fantasy' (10) ♀H6	LAma
	'Fashion' (12)	LAma SDeJ
	ferganica (15)	GKev LAma WCot
	'Fidelio' (3) ♀H6	SDeJ
	'Fiery Club' (5) **new**	GKev
*	'Finola' (11)	GKev
	'Fire of Love' (14)	LAma SDir
	'Fire Queen' (3) ♀H6	ERCP LAma
	'First Impression' (14)	LAma
	'Flair' (1)	LAma LRHS NRHS SDeJ
	'Flamenco' (7)	SDeJ
	'Flaming Club' (5)	LAma
	'Flaming Evita' PBR (2)	SDeJ
	'Flaming Flag' (3) **new**	LCro LOPS
	'Flaming Jewel' (4)	LAma
	'Flaming Parrot' (10)	CAby CAvo ERCP GKev LAma LCro LOPS SDeJ SDir
I	'Flaming Purissima' (13)	CAvo GKev LAma SDeJ SDir
	'Flaming Springgreen' (8)	CAvo CRav ERCP GKev LAma LCro LOPS SDeJ SDir
	'Flashback' (10)	ERCP LAma
	'Flig Flag' (3)	ERCP
	'Florette' PBR (5)	LAma
	'Florijn Chic' (6)	LAma
	'Florosa' (8)	CRav ERCP GKev LCro LOPS SDeJ
	'Flower Power' (10)	GKev
	'Fontainebleau' (3)	GKev LAma SDeJ
	'Formosa' (8)	EPfP LAma
	'Foxtrot' PBR (2) ♀H6	EPfP ERCP GKev LAma MCot SDir
	'Françoise' (3)	CRav LAma SDeJ
	'Franz Léhar' (12)	SDeJ
	'Freeman' (11)	LAma
	'Fringed Elegance' (7) ♀H6	LAma LCro LOPS SDir
	'Fringed Family' (7)	SDeJ
	'Fringed Golden Apeldoorn' (7)	LAma
	'Fritz Kreisler' (12)	LAma SDeJ
	'Fulton' (5)	LAma
	'Für Elise' (14)	GKev LRHS NRHS SDeJ
	'Gabriella' (3)	GKev LAma
	'Gaiety' (12)	SDeJ
	'Gander's Rhapsody' (3)	LAma
	'Garanza' (2)	LAma
	'Garden Party' (3)	LAma SDeJ
	'Garden Show' (14)	LAma
	'Gavota' (3) ♀H6	CAvo GKev LAma MJak SCob SDeJ
	'Generaal de Wet' (1)	LAma SDeJ
	'Gentle Giants' (4) **new**	CRav
	'Georges Grappe' (5)	LAma
	'Georgette' (5)	GKev LAma
	'Gerbrand Kieft' (11) ♀H6	ERCP GKev
	'Gipsy Love' (7)	SDeJ
	'Girlfriend' (15)	GKev
	'Giuseppe Verdi' (12)	GKev LAma LRHS NRHS

	'Gloria Nigrorum' (9) new	GKev
	'Glück' (12) ♀H6	EPfP LAma
	'Golden Apeldoorn' (4)	CArg ESps GKev LAma LCro LOPS SCob SDeJ SDir
	'Golden Artist' (8)	GKev LAma LCro LOPS SDeJ SDir
	'Golden Emperor' (13)	GKev LAma SDeJ SDir
	'Golden Melody' (3)	SDeJ
	'Golden Nizza' (11)	LAma
	'Golden Oxford' (4)	IRob LAma
	'Golden Parade' (4)	LAma
	'Goldwest' (14)	SDeJ
	'Gordon Cooper' (4)	LAma SDeJ
	'Gorilla' (7)	LAma
	'Goudstuk' (12)	LAma
	'Goya' (2)	LAma
	'Graceland' (3) new	CRav
	'Grand Perfection'PBR (3) ♀H6	CAvo LCro LOPS
	'Grand Style' (5) ♀H6	LAma
	'Granny Award' (11)	LAma
	'Green Eyes' (8)	SDeJ
	'Green River' (8)	LAma SDeJ
	'Green Unique' (11)	LAma
	'Green Wave' (10)	CRav ERCP GKev LAma LCro LOPS SDeJ SDir
	'Greenstar' (6)	LAma SDir
	greigii (14)	GKev LAma
	grengiolensis (15)	GKev
	'Greuze' (5)	LCro LOPS
	'Groenland' (8)	CAvo GKev LAma LCro LOPS MCot SDeJ SDir
	'Gudoshnik' (4)	LAma
	hageri (15)	CRav GKev LAma LLHF SDir
	- 'Splendens' (15)	GKev LAma SDeJ SPhx
	'Hakuun' (4)	LAma SDir
	'Halcro' (5) ♀H6	LAma
	'Hamilton' (7)	GKev LAma SDeJ
	'Hans Dietrich Genscher' (3)	GKev
	'Happy Family' (3)	LAma
	'Happy Generation' (3)	GKev LAma LCro LOPS
	'Happy Hour' (7)	ERCP
	'Havran' (3)	CAvo CRav ERCP GKev LAma LCro LOPS SDir
	'Heart's Delight' (12)	CArg GKev LAma SDeJ
	'Helmar' (3) ♀H6	LAma SDeJ
	'Hemisphere' (3)	CArg EPfP GKev LAma SDeJ SDir
	'Hermitage' (3)	ERCP LAma SDir
	heweri (15)	EPot GKev LAma
	'Hocus Pocus' (5)	LAma SDeJ
	'Holland Baby' (2)	LAma SDeJ
	'Holland Beauty'PBR (3) new	MCot
	'Holland Bouquet' (3)	LAma
	'Holland Chic' (6)	LAma MCot SDeJ
	'Holland Happening' (10)	LAma
	'Holland Queen'PBR (3)	LAma SDeJ
	'Holland Sun' (3)	LAma
	'Hollandia' (3)	LAma
	'Hollands Glorie' (4)	LAma SDeJ
	'Hollywood' (8)	LAma
	'Hollywood Star' (8)	LAma
	'Honeymoon' (7)	LAma
	'Honky Tonk' (15) ♀H6	CAvo GKev LAma LCro LOPS
§	***hoogiana*** (15)	GKev
	'Hotpants' (3)	LAma MCot SCob
	'Huis Ten Bosch' (7)	LAma
§	***humilis*** (15)	CRav GKev LAma LRHS NRHS SDeJ SDir WShi
	- 'China Carol' (15)	GKev LAma SDeJ
	- 'Eastern Spice' (15)	LAma
	- 'Eastern Star' (15)	GKev LAma
§	- 'Lilliput' (15)	CAby EPot GKev LAma LRHS NRHS
	- 'Magenta Queen' (15)	LAma
	- 'Odalisque' (15)	CRav EPot ERCP GKev LAma LRHS NRHS
	- 'Persian Pearl' (15)	CAvo EPfP EPot ERCP GKev LAma LCro LOPS SCob SDeJ SDir WTor
*	- 'Pink Charm' (15)	GKev
	- var. ***pulchella*** Albocaerulea Oculata Group (15)	EPot ERCP GKev SDir
	- 'Rosea' (15)	GKev
	- 'Tête-à-tête' (15)	LAma SDir
§	- Violacea Group (15)	CMea LRHS NRHS
	- - black base (15)	EPot ERCP GKev LAma
	- - yellow base (15)	EPot GKev LAma
	'Humming Bird' (8)	LAma
	hungarica	GKev
	'Ice Cream' (11)	GKev LAma SDeJ SDir
	'Ice Stick' (12)	GKev SDeJ
	'Ice Wonder' (11)	SDir
	'Ile de France' (5)	ERCP LAma LCro LOPS SDeJ
	iliensis (15)	CMea EPot GKev LAma LLHF
	'India' (3)	LAma
	'Indian Velvet' (5)	LCro LOPS
	ingens (15)	GKev LAma
	'Innuendo' (3)	LRHS NRHS SPer
	'Insulinde' (9)	GKev LAma SDir WCot
	'Inzell' (3)	GKev LAma SDir
	'Ivory Floradale' (4) ♀H6	GKev LAma SDeJ SDir
	'Jackpot' (3)	EPfP LAma SCob
	'Jacqueline' (6)	LAma LCro LOPS
	'Jan Reus' (3)	CAvo CRav ERCP LAma LCro LOPS
	'Jazz' (6)	ERCP
	'Jenny' (1) new	CRav
	'Jewel of Spring' (4)	LAma
	'Jimmy' (3)	LAma
	'Johann Strauss' (12)	CArg LAma MJak
	'Juan' (13) ♀H6	CAvo GKev LAma
	'Judith Leyster' (3)	LAma SDir
	'Juliet' (5)	GKev
	'Juliette' (4)	LAma
	'Karel Doorman' (10)	LAma
	'Kathleen Truxton' (5)	LAma SDir
	kaufmanniana (12)	EPot SDir
	'Keizerskroon' (1)	LAma SDeJ
	'Kiev' (14) ♀H6 new	SDir
	'Kikomachi' (3)	LRHS NRHS
	'Kingsblood' (5) ♀H6	ERCP LAma SDeJ SDir
	'Kleurenpracht'	see *T.* 'Princess Margaret Rose'
	kolpakowskiana (15) ♀H6	EPot ERCP GKev LAma LLHF WShi
	kurdica (15)	LAma
	'La Belle Époque' (2)	CAvo CRav ERCP GKev LAma LCro LOPS SCob SDeJ SDir
	'La Courtine' (5)	LAma
	'La Douceur' (5)	LAma SDir
	'Lac van Rijn' (1)	GKev LAma SDir
*	'Lady Diana' (14)	GKev
	'Lady Jane' (15) ♀H6	CMea GKev LAma SDir SPer SPhx WShi
	'Lalibela' (4) new	GKev
	'Lambada' (7) ♀H6	SDeJ
	lanata (15)	GKev WCot
	'Large Copper' (14)	LAma
	'Lasting Love' (3)	LAma SDir
	'Latvian Gold' (15)	GKev
	'Le Mogol' (5)	LAma
	'Leen van der Mark' (3)	LAma

'Libretto Parrot' (10)	LAma SDeJ
'Light and Dreamy' (4)	CAvo CRav ERCP GKev LCro LOPS SDeJ
'Lighting Sun' (4)	LAma
'Lilac Crystal' (7) **new**	LCro LOPS
'Lilac Perfection' (11)	CTca ERCP GKev LAma SDeJ
'Lilac Time' (6)	LAma SDir
'Lilac Wonder'	see *T. saxatilis* (Bakeri Group) 'Lilac Wonder'
'Lilliput'	see *T. humilis* 'Lilliput'
'Lilybeauty' (6)	LAma
'Lilyfire' (6)	GKev LAma SDeJ
'Limelight' (3)	LAma
'Lingerie' (7)	LAma
linifolia (15) ♀H5	CAvo EPot ERCP GKev LAma SDeJ WShi
§ - Batalinii Group (15) ♀H5	GKev SDir
§ - - 'Apricot Jewel' (15)	EPot ERCP GKev LAma
- - 'Bright Gem' (15) ♀H5	EPot GKev LAma NPer SPhx WCot WHoo
- - 'Bronze Charm' (15)	CAvo CMea EPot GKev LAma SDeJ SPhx WTor
- - 'Red Gem' (15)	GKev WCot
- - 'Red Hunter' (15) ♀H6	ERCP GKev LAma
- - 'Red Jewel' (15)	LAma SDir
- - 'Salmon Jewel' (15)	GKev
- - 'Yellow Jewel' (15)	GKev LAma WShi
§ - Maximowiczii Group (15)	GKev LAma
'Lipgloss' (3)	LAma
'Little Beauty' (15) ♀H6	CAby CAvo EPfP EPot GKev LAma LCro LOPS LRHS NRHS SDeJ SPhx WCot WHoo
'Little Girl' (14)	EPfP GKev
'Little Princess' (15) ♀H6	CAvo EPot GKev LAma LRHS NRHS SDeJ SPhx
'Little Star' (15) ♀H6	GKev LAma
'Long Lady' (5)	LAma MCot
'Louvre' (7) ♀H6	LAma
'Love Song' (12)	LAma SDeJ
'Lovely Surprise' (14)	SDeJ
§ 'Lustige Witwe' (3)	LAma SDeJ
'Lydia' (3)	LAma
'Mabel' (9)	LAma
§ 'Madame Lefeber' (13)	LAma LCro LOPS SDeJ SDir
'Madonna' (10)	EPfP LAma
'Magic Lavender' (3)	GKev
'Maja' (7)	LAma
'Makassar' (3)	LAma
'Mango Charm' (3)	GKev LAma SDir
'Margarita' (2)	GKev LAma LCro
'Marie José' (14)	SDeJ
'Marie Louise' (5)	LAma
'Mariette' (6)	CAby GKev LAma SDeJ
'Marilyn' (6)	ERCP GKev LAma SDeJ
'Marjolein' (6)	LAma
marjolletii (15)	GKev LAma
'Mary Ann' (14)	GKev LAma SPer
'Mata Hari' (3)	LAma
'Match' (3) **new**	LCro LOPS
'Matchpoint' (7/d)	LAma SDeJ
'Maureen' (5) ♀H6	CAvo ERCP GKev LAma LCro LOPS SDeJ SDir
'Maureen Double' (11)	CRav LOPS
mauritiana 'Cindy' (15)	GKev LAma
maximowiczii	see *T. linifolia* Maximowiczii Group
'Maytime' (6)	GKev LAma LCro LOPS MCot SDeJ
'Melody d'Amour' (5)	LAma
'Melrose' (2)	LAma
'Menton' (5) ♀H6	CRav ERCP GKev LAma LCro LOPS SDeJ SDir
'Menton Exotic' (11)	ERCP
'Merlot' (6)	CAvo CRav ERCP GKev LAma LCro LOPS
'Merry Christmas' (1)	LAma
'Merry Christmas Design' (1)	LAma
MERRY WIDOW	see *T.* 'Lustige Witwe'
'Mickey Mouse' (1)	LAma LCro LOPS
'Miranda' (11)	LAma
'Miskodeed' (14)	SDeJ
'Miss Elegance' (3)	LAma
'Mistress' (3)	LAma LCro LOPS
'Mistress Grey' (3) **new**	CRav
'Modern Style' (5)	LAma
'Mona Lisa' (6)	LAma SDeJ
'Mondial'PBR (2)	LAma
'Moneymaker' (6) ♀H6	ERCP
'Monsella' (2)	GKev LAma
§ ***montana*** (15)	CTca EPot LAma SDir
- yellow-flowered (15)	GKev LAma
'Monte Carlo' (2) ♀H6	CArg LAma LOPS SDeJ SDir
'Montreux' (2)	LAma SDir
'Moonlight Girl' (6) ♀H6	CRav
'Moonshine' (6)	LAma
'Moonwalker' (4)	LAma
'Mount Tacoma' (11)	CAvo ERCP GKev LAma LCro LOPS SDeJ SDir
'Mr Van der Hoef' (2)	LAma SDeJ
'Mrs John T. Scheepers' (5)	LAma SDeJ
'Muriel' (10)	ERCP
'National Velvet' (3)	CRav LCro LOPS SDir SPer
'Negrita' (3)	CArg ERCP GKev LAma LCro LOPS MCot SCob SDeJ SDir
neustruevae (15)	EPot GKev LAma
'New Design' (3/v)	GKev LAma LCro LOPS
'Nicholas Heyek' (3)	LCro
'Night Club' (5)	CRav
'Nightrider' (8)	ERCP GKev LAma LCro LOPS MCot SDeJ SDir
'Noranda' (7)	LAma
'Ollioules' (4) ♀H6	GKev LAma SDeJ
'Olympic Flame' (4) ♀H6	LAma LCro LOPS SDeJ
'Orange Angelique' (11)	SDir XEll
'Orange Bouquet' (3) ♀H6	GKev LAma SDeJ
'Orange Brilliant' (13)	LAma
'Orange Cassini' (3)	LAma
'Orange Emperor' (13) ♀H6	CAvo CRav ERCP GKev LAma MCot SDeJ SDir
'Orange Favourite' (10)	CRav ERCP GKev LAma
'Orange Lion' (4)	LAma
'Orange Monarch' (3)	LAma
'Orange Princess' (11) ♀H6	CTca ERCP GKev LAma LCro LOPS SCob SDeJ SDir
'Orange Queen' (4)	LAma
'Orange Sun'	see *T.* 'Oranjezon'
'Orange Toronto' (14)	LAma
'Oranje Nassau' (2) ♀H6	LRHS NRHS
§ 'Oranjezon' (4) ♀H6	ERCP LAma
'Oratorio' (14) ♀H6	LAma SDeJ
'Oriental Beauty' (14) ♀H6	LAma
orithyioides	GKev
'Orleans' (3) **new**	GKev
orphanidea (15)	GKev LAma
- 'Flava' (15)	GKev LAma
§ - Whittallii Group (15) ♀H6	CRav EPot ERCP GKev LCro LOPS SDeJ SPhx WCot WShi
'Oscar' (3)	LAma
ostrowskiana (15)	LAma
'Oxford' (4) ♀H6	LAma
'Oxford's Elite' (4)	LAma
'Page Polka' (3)	SDeJ

	'Palestrina' (3)	LAma SPer
	'Panorama' (5)	LAma
	'Papillon' (9)	LAma
	'Parade' (4) ♀H6	LAma
	'Parrot King' (10)	SDeJ
	'Passionale' (3) ♀H6	EPfP LAma LCro LOPS SDeJ SPer
	'Paul Scherer' (3) ♀H6	CAvo ERCP LAma LCro LOPS SDeJ
	'Peach Blossom' (2)	CArg ERCP GKev LAma LCro LOPS LRHS NRHS SCob SDeJ
	Peacock Group	SDeJ SDir
	'Peppermintstick' (15) ♀H6	CAvo CRav CTca GKev LAma SCob SDeJ
	'Perestroyka' (5)	GKev LAma SDeJ
	persica	see *T. celsiana*
	'Philippe de Comines' (5)	SDir
	'Piccolo' (15)	LAma
	'Picture' (5)	ERCP LAma SDeJ SDir
	'Pieter de Leur' (6)	LAma
	'Pimpernel' (8/v)	LAma SDeJ
	'Pink Diamond' (5)	CAvo ERCP GKev LCro LOPS SDeJ SDir
	'Pink Dwarf' (12)	SDeJ
*	'Pink Emperor' (13)	GKev
	'Pink Impression' (4) ♀H6	CArg GKev LAma LCro LOPS SDeJ SDir
	'Pink Sensation' (14)	SDeJ
	'Pink Star' (11)	GKev
	'Pinkeen' (13)	LAma
	'Pinocchio' (14)	CArg GKev LAma LRHS MJak NRHS SDeJ
	'Pirand' (13) ♀H6	SDeJ
	'Pittsburg' (3)	LCro LOPS
	'Plaisir' (14) ♀H6	LAma
	platystigma (15)	LAma
	'Poco Loco' (13)	GKev SDeJ
	polychroma	see *T. biflora*
	praestans (15)	GKev SDir SPer WShi
	- 'Bloemenlust' (15)	GKev
	- 'Fusilier' (15) ♀H6	CExl EPot GKev LAma SDeJ SDir
	- 'Moondance' (15)	GKev
	- 'Shogun' (15)	ERCP GKev SDeJ SPer
	- 'Unicum' (15/v)	EPot ERCP GKev LAma SDeJ
	- 'Van Tubergen's Variety' (15)	GKev LAma NPer SDir
	- 'Zwanenburg Variety' (15)	GKev
	'Pretty Princess' (3)	CRav ERCP SDeJ
	'Pretty Woman' (6)	LAma SDir SPer
	'Princeps' (13)	LAma SDeJ
§	'Princess Margaret Rose' (5)	SDir
	'Princess Unique'[PBR] (11)	LAma
	'Princesse Charmante' (14) ♀H6	LAma LCro LOPS
	'Prinses Irene' (3) ♀H6	CArg CAvo CMea CRav CTca EPfP ERCP GKev LAma LCro LOPS LRHS MCot NRHS SDeJ SDir
	'Prinses Margriet' (3)	ERCP LAma
	'Professor Einstein' (3)	LAma
	'Professor Röntgen' (10)	ERCP GKev LAma LCro LOPS SDeJ SDir
	'Professor Schotel' (15)	LAma
	pulchella humilis	see *T. humilis*
	'Purified' (3)	GKev
§	'Purissima' (13) ♀H6	CAvo CRav GKev LAma LCro LOPS SCob SDeJ SDir SPer
	'Purple Bouquet' (3)	LAma SDeJ
	'Purple Dream' (6)	LAma SDeJ
	'Purple Flag' (3)	LAma LCro LOPS
	'Purple Jacket' (11)	LOPS MCot
	'Purple Prince' (5)	LAma LCro LOPS LRHS NRHS SDeJ SDir
I	'Purple Prince' (1) **new**	CArg
	'Purple Rain' (3)	LAma
	'Purple Tower' (7)	CRav
	'Quebec' (14)	LAma MJak SDeJ SDir
	'Queen of Marvel' (2)	LAma SDeJ
	'Queen of Night' (5)	CArg CAvo CMea CTca EPfP ERCP ESps GKev LAma LCro LOPS MCot MJak SCob SDeJ SDir SPer SPhx
	'Queensday' (11)	CRav LAma SDeJ
	'Queensland' (7)	LAma
	'Quest' (3)	LAma
	'Rai' (10)	LAma
	'Rajka' (6)	GKev
	'Real Time' (7)	LAma SDir
	'Recreado' (5)	CAvo CRav ERCP LAma SDeJ
	'Red Baby Doll' (2)	LAma
	'Red Emperor'	see *T.* 'Madame Lefeber'
	'Red Georgette' (5) ♀H6	CAby CRav GKev LAma
	'Red Hat' (7) ♀H6	LCro LOPS
	'Red Impression'[PBR] (4) ♀H6	EPfP LAma LCro LOPS SDir
	'Red Mark'[PBR] (3)	SDir
	'Red Present' (3)	LAma
	'Red Princess' (11) ♀H6	ERCP LAma NRHS SDir
	'Red Revival' (1)	GKev LAma
	'Red Riding Hood' (14) ♀H6	CArg CAvo CMea EPfP ESps GKev LAma LRHS NRHS SCob SDeJ SDir SPer
	'Red Rover' (3)	LCro LOPS SDir
	'Red Shine' (6) ♀H6	CAvo ERCP GKev LAma LCro LOPS SDeJ
	'Red Springgreen' (8)	GKev LAma LCro LOPS SDeJ
	'Red Wing' (7) ♀H6	LAma SDeJ
	'Redwood' (14)	SDeJ
	(Rembrandt Group) 'Saskia' (15)	LAma SDir
	'Rems Favourite' (3)	CAvo CRav LCro LOPS SDeJ
	'Renown' (5)	LAma SDeJ
	'Renown Unique' (11)	LAma SDir
	'Request' (3)	CRav LAma
	'Rex Rubrorum' (2)	LAma
	rhodopea	see *T. urumoffii*
	'Robert Schuller' (14)	LAma
	'Rockery Master' (14)	LAma
	'Rococo' (10)	CAvo CRav ERCP LAma LCro LOPS SDeJ
	'Roi du Midi' (5)	LAma SDeJ
	'Ronaldo' (3)	CRav ERCP GKev LAma LCro LOPS SDir
	'Rosalie' (3)	ERCP LAma SDeJ
	'Rose des Dames' (5)	LAma
	'Rosy Dream' (13)	LAma SDeJ
	'Roulette' (3)	LAma
	'Royal Acres' (2)	LAma
	'Royal Anthos' (14)	SDeJ
	'Royal Elegance' (7)	LAma
	'Royal Gift' (6) ♀H6 **new**	SDir
	'Ruud Lubbers' (14)	LAma
	'Salmon Impression'[PBR] (4)	GKev LAma SDeJ
	'Salmon Parrot' (10)	LAma
	'Sanne' (3) ♀H6	CAvo ERCP LAma SDeJ
	'Sapporo' (6)	CRav ERCP GKev LAma LCro LOPS
	'Sarah Raven' (6) **new**	CRav
	saxatilis (15)	EPfP GKev LAma LCro LOPS SDeJ SDir
§	- Bakeri Group (15)	CRav MPie SCob SDir SEND
§	- - 'Lilac Wonder' (15) ♀H6	CAby CAvo CExl EPot ERCP GKev LAma LCro LOPS NPer SCob SDeJ SDir SPhx WShi WTor

'Scarlet Baby' (12)	EPfP GKev LAma
'Schoonoord' (2)	LAma
schrenkii (15)	EPot ERCP GKev LAma SDir
'Seadov' (3) ♀H6	LAma LCro LOPS SDeJ SDir
'Sensual Touch' (7) ♀H6	LAma SDeJ SDir
'Sexy Lady' (10)	LAma
'Shakespeare' (12)	ESps LAma SDeJ
'Shirley' (3)	CAvo CRav ERCP GKev LAma LCro LOPS SCob SDeJ SDir SPer
'Shirley Dream' (3)	LAma SDeJ
'Shirley Flame' (3)	LAma
'Showtime' (14)	SDeJ
'Showwinner' (12) ♀H6	CAvo GKev LAma SDeJ SDir
'Sihouette Bouquet' (3)	LAma
'Silk Road' (2) **new**	GKev
'Silver Dollar' (3)	LAma
'Silver Parrot' (10)	CRav GKev LAma SDir
'Silver Standard' (1)	GKev
'Silverado' (5)	LAma
'Silverstream' (4)	GKev LAma
'Sinopel' (8)	LAma
'Snow Crystal' (11)	SDir
'Snow Parrot' (10)	CRav ERCP
'Snowboard' (3)	LAma
'Snowpeak' (5)	LAma
sogdiana (15)	GKev LAma LLHF
'Sorbet' (5) ♀H6	GKev LAma SDeJ
sosnowskyi (15)	GKev
sprengeri (15) ♀H6	CAvo CBro CExl CSpe CTca ECha ERCP GKev IRob LAma LLHF WHal WShi
- Trotter's form (15)	WCot
'Spring Green' (8) ♀H6	CArg CAvo CRav CTca EPfP ERCP GKev LAma LCro LOPS MCot SCob SDeJ SDir SPer SPhx
'Spryng' (3) ♀H6	SDeJ
'Starfighter' (7)	SDeJ
stellata	see *T. clusiana* var. *stellata*
'Stockholm' (2) ♀H6	LAma
'Stresa' (12) ♀H6	GKev LAma LRHS NRHS SDeJ
'Striped Sail' (3)	LAma
'Strong Gold' (3) ♀H6	LAma SDeJ
'Stunning Apricot' (5)	LAma LCro LOPS SDir
subpraestans (15)	LAma
'Sun Dance' (14)	LAma
'Sun Lover' (11)	LAma
'Sunny Prince'PBR (1)	SDeJ
'Sunset Tropical' (11) **new**	GKev
'Super Parrot' (10)	LAma
'Survivor' (5)	SDeJ
'Swan Wings' (7)	ERCP GKev LAma LCro LOPS SDeJ
'Sweet Desire' (2)	SDeJ
'Sweet Flag' (3) **new**	GKev
'Sweet Lady' (14)	LAma SDeJ
'Sweetheart' (13)	GKev LAma LCro LOPS SDeJ
'Sweety' (3)	LAma
sylvestris (15)	CAby CAvo CRav CSpe CTca EPfP EPot ERCP GKev LAma LCro LOPS SDeJ SDir SPhx WCot WShi
'Sylvia Warder' (14)	LAma
'Synaeda King' (6) ♀H6	LAma MJak
'Synaeda Orange' (6)	LAma
systola (15)	GKev LAma
'Taco' (15)	GKev LAma
'Talisman' ambig.	LAma
'Talisman' (5)	GKev
'Talisman' (9)	SDir
'Tambour Maître' (3) **new**	CRav
'Tarafa' (14)	LAma
tarda (15) ♀H5	CAvo CExl EPfP ERCP GKev LAma LCro LOPS LRHS NRHS SDeJ SDir SPhx WShi
- 'Kazakhstan' (15)	GKev
'Temple of Beauty' (5) ♀H6	GKev LAma SDeJ
'Temple's Favourite' (5)	CRav
'Tender Whisper' (3) **new**	GKev
'Tennessee' (3)	LAma
'Tequila Sun' (3)	LAma
tetraphylla (15)	GKev LAma
'Texas Flame' (10)	GKev LAma SDeJ
'Texas Gold' (10)	LAma SDeJ
'The First' (12)	GKev LAma SDir
'The Lizard' (9)	GKev LAma SDir
'Theeroos' (2)	LAma SDir
'Tinka' (15) ♀H6	GKev LAma SCob SDir
'Tiny Timo' (15)	GKev LLHF
'Tom Pouce' (3)	LCro LOPS
'Toplips' (11)	LAma SDeJ
'Topparrot' (10)	LAma SDeJ
'Toronto' (14) ♀H6	LAma MJak SCob SDeJ
'Toronto Double' (2)	GKev LAma SDeJ
'Toucan' (3)	LAma
'Toyota' (5)	SDeJ
'Très Chic' (6)	CAvo CTca EPfP GKev LAma LCro LOPS SPer
'Trinket' (14) ♀H6	LAma
'Tropical Dream' (3)	LAma
'Tropical Lady' (3)	LAma
tschimganica (15)	GKev LAma WCot
turkestanica (15) ♀H5	CAby CExl CHid CTca EPfP EPot ERCP GKev LAma NPer SDeJ WHoo WShi
'Turkish Delight' (14)	NPer
'Typhoon' (3)	CMea GKev LAma
'Uncle Tom' (11)	CAvo ERCP GKev LAma SDeJ SDir
§ ***undulatifolia*** (15)	GKev
- 'Clare Benedict' (15)	GKev
- 'Excelsa' (15)	GKev
'Unique de France'PBR (3)	CAvo
'United States' (14) ♀H6	LAma NPer SDir
'Up Rosar' (11)	ERCP
'Upstar' (11)	LAma
urumiensis (15) ♀H5	CHid EPot GKev LAma SDeJ SPhx
§ ***urumoffii*** (15)	LAma
'Valentine' (3)	LAma SDeJ
'Valery Gergiev' (7)	ERCP LAma SDeJ
'Van der Neer' (1)	GKev SDeJ
'Van Eijk'PBR (4)	LAma SCob
'Vanilla Cream' (14)	SDeJ
'Velvet Lily' (6)	GKev
'Verona' (2)	GKev LAma SDeJ
'Véronique Sanson' (3)	CRav ERCP LCro LOPS SDeJ
'Victoria's Secret' (3)	CRav GKev
'Viking' (2)	LAma
'Vincent van Gogh' (7) ♀H6	LAma SDir
violacea	see *T. humilis* Violacea Group
'Violet Beauty' (5)	GKev LAma LCro LOPS SDeJ
'Violet Bird' (8)	LAma LCro LOPS SDeJ
'Virichic' (8)	ERCP GKev LAma LCro LOPS MCot SDir
vvedenskyi (15)	EPot GKev
- 'Bernadette' (15)	LAma
- 'Tangerine Beauty' (15) ♀H6	GKev LAma
'Wallflower' (5)	LAma SDir
'Wapen van Leiden' (1)	LAma
'Warbler' (7)	LAma SDeJ
'Washington' (3)	GKev LCro LOPS

'Weber's Parrot' (10) LAma LOPS MCot
'Weisse Berliner' (3) GKev LAma
'West Point' (6) CAvo CTca GKev LAma LCro LOPS SDeJ SDir
'Whispering Dream' (3) new CAvo
* 'White Bouquet' (5) LAma
'White Dream' (3) CArg GKev LAma LCro LOPS SDeJ
'White Elegance' (6) LAma
'White Emperor' see *T.* 'Purissima'
'White Fire' (14) GKev
'White Lieberstar' (5) ERCP
'White Marvel' (3) GKev LAma LRHS NRHS
'White Parrot' (10) CAvo ERCP GKev LAma LCro LOPS SDeJ SDir
'White Sea' (13) LAma
'White Touché' (11) new CRav
'White Triumphator' (6) ♀H6 CArg CAvo CMea CRav ERCP GKev LAma LCro LOPS SDeJ SDir SPhx
whittallii see *T. orphanidea* Whittallii Group
'Wildhof' (3) ♀H6 ERCP SDir
'Wilja' (5) GKev
§ 'Willem van Oranje' (2) LAma LRHS NRHS SDeJ
'Willemsoord' (2) LAma LRHS NRHS SDeJ
WILLIAM OF ORANGE see *T.* 'Willem van Oranje'
wilsoniana see *T. montana*
'Winterberg' (3) LAma
'Wisley' (5) ♀H6 LCro LOPS SCob
'World Expression' (5) ♀H6 LAma SDeJ
'Yellow Crown' (3) LAma
'Yellow Emperor' (5) SDir
'Yellow Flight' (3) LAma SDeJ
'Yellow Pompenette'PBR (11) ♀H6 SDeJ
'Yellow Present' (3) LAma
I 'Yellow Purissima' (13) ♀H6 LAma SDir
'Yellow Springgreen' (8) ERCP GKev LAma SDeJ
'Yellow Wave' (4) LAma SDir
'Yoko Parrot' (10) SDeJ
'Yokohama' (3) GKev LAma SCob SDeJ SPer
'Yonina' (6) CArg LAma LCro LOPS
'Zampa' (14) ♀H6 LAma
'Zombie' (13) LAma
'Zomerschoon' (5) LAma
§ 'Zurel' (3) CArg ERCP GKev LAma MCot SCob SDir

tummelberry see *Rubus* 'Tummelberry'

Tunica see *Petrorhagia*

Tupistra (*Asparagaceae*)

aurantiaca GEdr LEdu
- B&SWJ 2267 WCot WCru
- B&SWJ 2401 WCru
chinensis 'Eco China Ruffles' WCot
grandistigma WCot
- B&SWJ 11773 WCru
jinshanensis WCot
urotepala HWJ 562 WCru
wattii B&SWJ 8297 WCru

turnip see AGM Vegetables Section

Turpinia (*Staphyleaceae*)

ternata CWJ 12360 new WCru

Turritis (*Brassicaceae*)

glabra EBWF

Tussilago (*Asteraceae*)

farfara EBWF GPoy MHer NMir WHer WSFF

Tweedia (*Apocynaceae*)

§ ***coerulea*** ♀H1c CBcs CCCN CDTJ CFlo CKel CSpe SChF SPad SPer SWvt

Typha (*Typhaceae*)

angustifolia CBen CKno CWat LLWG MMuc MSKA NPer SPlb WMAq WPnP
latifolia CBen CWat LLWG MSKA NPer SVic WMAq XLum
- 'Variegata' (v) CWat LLWG MSKA MWts NPla WBor WMAq
§ ***laxmannii*** CBen LLWG MSKA WMAq WPnP XLum
lugdunensis MWts
minima CBen CWat EHoe LLWG MSKA MWts NPer WMAq WPnP XLum
shuttleworthii CBen LLWG
stenophylla see *T. laxmannii*

Typhonium (*Araceae*)

giganteum CAby WCot
horsfieldii LEdu MPie WCot
roxburghii WFar
trilobatum WCot
venosum EUJe

Typhonodorum (*Araceae*)

lindleyanum XBlo

U

Uapaca (*Euphorbiaceae*)

kirkiana (F) XBlo

Uccerodendron (*Hamamelidaceae*)

* ***whartonii*** B&SWJ 11706 WCru

ugli see *Citrus* × *aurantium* (Tangelo Group) 'Ugli'

Ugni ✿ (*Myrtaceae*)

candollei SVen
§ ***molinae*** CBcs CBod CCCN CCht CDul CExl CHll CRos EBee ELan EPfP EShb GMcL IDee LEdu LRHS MGil MGos MHer MMuc SAdn SChF SEle SPer SWvt WAvo WBor WGwG WHar
- PAB 1347 LEdu SBrt
- 'Butterball' CBcs EBee EPfP LRHS LSou SPoG SWvt
- 'Flambeau' (v) CAgr CBcs CBod CCht CDul CExl CMac CRos EBee ELan EPfP EShb LEdu LRHS MAsh MGil NLar NRHS SEle SLon SPoG SRms SWvt WHar
- 'Ka-Pow' LCro SCob
- 'Variegata' (v) LEdu
- 'Villarica Strawberry' WPGP

Ulex (*Papilionaceae*)

europaeus CBcs CCVT CDul CHab CMac CPer CTri EBWF ECrN ELan ELon EPfP ESps GMcL IRob LBuc MCoo MGil MGos MMuc SCob SEWo SPer WHar

§ - 'Flore Pleno' (d) ♀H4 CBcs CBod CDul CMac CSBt CTri ELan ELon EPfP GCal IArd MBlu MMuc SCob SPer WFar WHer
- 'Irish Double' (d) NLar
- 'Plenus' see *U. europaeus* 'Flore Pleno'
gallii NLar
- 'Mizen Head' GCal

Ullucus (*Basellaceae*)

tuberosus LEdu

Ulmus ✿ (*Ulmaceae*)

americana 'Princeton' SEWo
bergmanniana new WPGP
carpinifolia var. ***suberosa*** CDul LPra
chenmoui IArd WPGP
'Columella' SAko
davidiana WPGP
- var. ***davidiana*** new WPGP
- var. ***japonica*** WPGP
'Dodoens' IArd MBlu
'Frontier' SGol WPGP
§ ***glabra*** CDul CPer EGFP EPfP SCob WTSh
- 'Camperdownii' CMac ECrN ELan ESps WMou
- 'Lutescens' CTho CTri EBee NOra SEWo
× ***hollandica*** EGFP
§ - 'Dampieri Aurea' ♀H6 CDul CTho EBee ELan ELon EPfP LBuc MAsh MBlu MGos MJak MRav NLar SCob SPer SPoG
- 'Jacqueline Hillier' CDul CMac CSpe EBee ELan LRHS MMuc NLar SEND SGol WCFE WFar
- 'Major' EGFP
- 'Wredei' see *U.* × *hollandica* 'Dampieri Aurea'
'Homestead' WPGP
laevis CPer WPGP
'Lobel' CCVT LMaj
LUTÈCE ('Nanguen') CDul SGol
minor 'Dampieri Aurea' see *U.* × *hollandica* 'Dampieri Aurea'
montana see *U. glabra*
parvifolia CAco CMen EShb WPGP
- 'Geisha' (v) ELan
§ - 'Hokkaido' CMen EPot EWes SMad WAbe WFar
- 'Pygmaea' see *U. parvifolia* 'Hokkaido'
- 'Yatsubusa' GEdr MRav
plotii EGFP
procera CDul EMOT MCoo MGos SLon WSFF
- 'Argenteovariegata' (v) NLar
pumila 'Beijing Gold' ELan NLar
'Regal' PBR WPGP
'Sapporo Autumn Gold' CCVT MRav SGol WCFE
szechuanica WPGP
uyematsui WPGP
VADA ('Wanoux' PBR) SGol
villosa EBee WPGP

Umbellularia (*Lauraceae*)

californica IDee WPGP

Umbilicus (*Crassulaceae*)

§ ***oppositifolius*** ♀H5 CAby CElw CRos CSam CTri EBee ECha EDAr ELan EPfP GAbr GCrg GJos GKev GLog IRob ITim LRHS MMuc MRav NBid NRHS NSla SPlb SRms WKif WMoo WSHC XLum
- 'Jane's Reverse' (v) WCot
§ - 'Jim's Pride' (v) ECha EHoe EWes GKev GMaP MHer MPie MRav NHpl NPer NWad SPlb SRGP SRms SRot WFar WKif WMoo WSHC WTor
rupestris SChr SPhx WHer WShi

Uncinia (*Cyperaceae*)

egmontiana CPla EPfP LRHS NRHS NWad WGrn WMoo
erinacea GCal
rubra CBod CEnd CSBt EHoe ELan EMOT EPfP EShb ESps GCal GMaP GMcL IBoy LRHS MGos MRav NRHS NSti NWad SCob SGol SPad SPlb SPoG WFar WMoo
§ - 'Belinda's Find' PBR CKno EBee ELan IBoy LRHS MAsh MHol NLar NRHS SPoG SRms
- EVERFLAME see *U. rubra* 'Belinda's Find'
uncinata CBcs ECha
* - ***rubra*** CBod CKno CTri ESps IFro MAsh SCob SLim SRms SWvt

Uniola (*Poaceae*)

latifolia see *Chasmanthium latifolium*

Urginea (*Asparagaceae*)

maritima see *Charybdis maritima*
ollivieri CTal

Urospermum (*Asteraceae*)

dalechampii CCCN CSam

Ursinia (*Asteraceae*)

alpina CPBP

Urtica (*Urticaceae*)

dioica EBWF
- 'Bradfield Purpler' CNat
- 'Chedglow 2' (v) CNat
- 'Good as Gold' CNat
- OGG mutant CNat
- 'Vicky' new CNat

Utricularia (*Lentibulariaceae*)

sp. EECP
alpina SHmp
bisquamata SHmp
calycifida SHmp
exoleta R. Brown see *U. gibba*
§ ***gibba*** EECP
intermedia EECP
livida ♀H2 NLos SHmp
longifolia SHmp
praelonga SHmp
reniformis SHmp
sandersonii ♀H2 EECP NLos SHmp
tricolor SHmp

Uvularia (*Colchicaceae*)

grandiflora ♀H5 Widely available
- gold-leaved CAby CBct MAvo
- 'Lynda Windsor' CTal LEdu
- var. ***pallida*** CAby CAvo CBct CTal EBee EHrv EPPr EPfP EPot GBin GCal GEdr IBlr ILea LEdu LRHS MRav NPnk NRHS WCru WFar WPnP
- 'Susie Lewis' WCru
perfoliata CAby CBct CBot CExl EBee ECha EPPr EPfP EPot GKev IBlr IMou LEdu MRav NChi NHpl NPnk SPlb WCru
- tall EPPr

sessilifolia	CBcs CBct CBot CExl CTal EPfP GEdr GKev IMou LEdu LRHS MMrt NRHS WCru
- 'Cobblewood Gold' (v)	EPPr LEdu WCru
- 'Variegata' (v)	EBee

V

Vaccaria (*Caryophyllaceae*)

§ ***hispanica***	SPhx
segetalis	see *V. hispanica*

Vaccinium ✿ (*Ericaceae*)

arctostaphylos	SWvt
'Berkeley' (F)	CAgr CCCN CEnd GKin LSRN MBlu NPla SDea SPre WHar
BLUE SUEDE ('Th-682') (F)	LCro SPoG
'Bluejay' (F)	CFGn CRos ELan LRHS MAsh NRHS SCoo SLon SPoG WHar
'Blueray' (F)	GKin SDea
'Brigitta' (F)	CEnd CMac CTrh EMil EPom NPla SPoG SPre
chaetothrix	WAbe WThu
'Chandler' (F)	CAgr CArg CEnd CMac CRos CTrh EPom GKin LCro LOPS NPla SKee SPer
consanguineum B&SWJ 10486	WCru
corymbosum (F)	CBcs MNHC SCoo SSta
- 'Aurora' PBR (F)	LCro LOPS
- 'Blauweiss-Goldtraube' (F)	CAgr CSBt EPfP ESps GKin MAsh NLar NPri SDea SPoG SVic WHar WTSh
- 'Blue Duke' (F)	LSRN
- 'Bluecrop' (F)	Widely available
- 'Bluegold' (F)	CFGn CRos LRHS MAsh NRHS SPoG
- 'Bluetta' (F)	CAgr CTri ELan SCoo SPoG
- 'Darrow' (F)	CAgr NPla NRHS
- 'Dixie' (F)	CSBt NLar NPla SDea
- 'Duke' (F) 🏆H6	CArg CMac CTrh ELan EPfP EPom IBoy LCro LOPS MGos NPla SDea SPre SRkn WHar
- 'Elliott' (F)	LSRN SPer
- 'Hardyblue' (F)	CAgr
- 'Jersey' (F)	CAgr CEnd CRos EPfP LRHS MAsh MGos MMuc NPla NRHS SCoo SDea SPer SPoG SVic WHar
- 'Liberty' PBR (F) **new**	CRos LRHS NRHS
- 'Nelson' (F)	NPla SCoo
- 'Nui' (F)	CEnd EPom LSRN MRav
- 'Patriot' (F)	CAgr CEnd CRos CSBt CTrh ECrN EMOT EPom ESps GKin LBuc LRHS MGos MRav NLar NPla NPri NRHS SCoo SDea SPer SPre
- 'Polaris' (F)	CEnd
- 'Reka' (F)	CAgr NPer
- 'Spartan' (F) 🏆H6	CTrh EPom LCro LOPS LSRN MGos NPla SKee
- 'Stanley' (F)	CRos EPfP LRHS NRHS SPoG
- 'Toro' (F)	CRos NPla SPre
- 'Weymouth' (F)	SDea
crassifolium	LRHS MAsh
subsp. ***sempervirens*** 'Well's Delight' (F)	
cylindraceum 🏆H5	CBcs CEnd EBee NLar WPGP
- 'Tinkerbell'	ITim
delavayi	CRos LRHS MAsh NLar WThu
dunalianum var. ***caudatifolium*** B&SWJ 1716	WCru
- var. ***megaphyllum*** HWJ 515	WCru
'Earliblue' (F)	CAgr CFGn CMac CRos CSBt GKin LBuc LRHS NPla NRHS SDea SPer SPoG
floribundum	CBcs GMcL LRHS MAsh
glaucoalbum 🏆H5	CMac EBee EPfP LRHS MAsh MBlu MRav NRHS SPoG WPGP
'Goldtraube 71'	EMOT MAsh NPla
griffithianum	SSta
'Herbert' (F)	CAgr CMac EPom LBuc
macrocarpon (F)	CRos ELan LRHS MAsh NRHS SDea SPre SRms XAbr
- 'CN' (F)	NLar
- 'Early Black' (F)	ELan EMOT EPom GKin IDee NLar SVic WTSh
- 'Hamilton'	WThu
- 'Langlois' (F)	NLar
- 'Olson's Honkers' (F)	CAgr NLar
- 'Pilgrim' (F)	CAgr CFGn CMac CSBt EMOT GKin LCro LEdu LOPS LRHS MAsh MCoo NPri SDea SPoG WHar
- 'Red Star' (F)	CTrh
- 'Stevens' (F)	CAgr
moupinense	GEdr LRHS MAsh WThu
myrtillus	CAgr EPom GPoy SVic XAbr
'Northland' (F)	CRos CSBt EMOT EPfP EPom NLar NPla NPri NRHS SCoo SDea SPoG
nummularia	GEdr LRHS NLar WAbe WThu
ovatum	CBcs CMac CTsd GKin WThu
- 'Thundercloud'	EPfP LRHS MAsh NRHS
§ ***oxycoccos*** (F)	CAgr GPoy MCoo WThu
'Ozarkblue' (F)	EPom LCro LOPS LSRN
pallidum	IBlr
palustre	see *V. oxycoccos*
'Pink Lemonade' (F)	CRos ELan EPom LCro LOPS LRHS NPri NRHS SPer
'Pinkberry' (F)	LRHS
praestans	WThu
retusum	WThu
'Spring Surprise'	WAbe WThu
'Sunshine Blue' (F)	CAgr CEnd CTrh ELan EPom LBuc LRHS SDea SPoG
'Tophat' (F)	CCCN LEdu
vitis-idaea	EPfP EWes GPoy SVic
- 'Aalshorst'	NLar
- 'Autumn Beauty'	NLar
- 'Compactum'	EWes
- 'Erntetraum'	NLar
- 'Ida'	LBuc
- Koralle Group 🏆H5	CAgr EPot GKin GMcL NLar NWad
- 'Leucocarpa'	NLar
- subsp. ***minus***	GEdr NLar WThu
- 'Red Candy' PBR	ELan EPfP LCro LOPS LRHS MSCN NLar NRHS SCob
- 'Red Pearl'	CSBt EPom MAsh
- 'Red Shank'	ITim

Vachellia (*Leguminosae*)

§ ***karroo***	CDTJ SPlb

Valeriana (*Caprifoliaceae*)

'Alba'	see *Centranthus ruber* 'Albus'
alliariifolia	CSam GCal GQue MSpe NBro SPhx
- PAB 3001	LEdu WPGP
'Coccinea'	see *Centranthus ruber*
dioica	EBWF LLWG

hardwickii PAB 8999	LEdu
jatamansi	GPoy SRms
- PAB 6846	LEdu WPGP
montana	LEdu MMuc NBro NRya SRms
officinalis	Widely available
- subsp. ***sambucifolia***	EPPr GCal MNrw MSpe SHar
phu 'Aurea'	CBod CDor CHby CMac EBee ECha EHoe ELan EPfP GKin GQue LRHS MRav NBid NBro NEgg NLar NRHS NSti NWad SPer SPoG SRms WCAu WMoo
pyrenaica	EBee ECha EHrv EPPr EWTr GCal LRHS MMuc MNrw SEND SHar SPhx WCot WHrl WMoo
wallrothii	WCot

Valerianella (*Caprifoliaceae*)

§ ***locusta***	CBod GPoy SVic
olitoria	see *V. locusta*

Vallea (*Elaeocarpaceae*)

stipularis	CTsd

Vallisneria (*Hydrocharitaceae*)

americana	XBlo
asiatica var. ***biwaensis***	XBlo
gigantea	XBlo
spiralis	LLWG XBlo
- 'Tortifolia'	XBlo

Vallota see *Cyrtanthus*

Vancouveria (*Berberidaceae*)

chrysantha	CExl CFil CTal EPPr EPfP GEdr GLog MMoz MRav NRya WMoo WPGP
hexandra	CExl CFil CMac CTal ECha EPPr EPfP EWld GEdr GKev GLog ILea LEdu MMoz NSti WCru WMoo WPGP
planipetala	CTal IMou MMoz WCru

Vania see *Thlaspi*

Vasconcellea (*Caricaceae*)

§ ***pubescens***	SPlb

Vellozia (*Velloziaceae*)

elegans	see *Talbotia elegans*

Veltheimia ✿ (*Asparagaceae*)

§ ***bracteata*** ♀H2	CCse CPne EPri LRHS NRog SDir SRms
- 'Lemon Flame'	NRog SDir
- yellow-flowered	CPne NRog
§ ***capensis*** ♀H2	CBlu NRog
viridifolia misapplied	see *V. capensis*
viridifolia Jacq.	see *V. bracteata*

× *Venidioarctotis* see *Arctotis*

Venidium see *Arctotis*

Veratrilla (*Gentianaceae*)

baillonii	GEdr

Veratrum (*Melanthiaceae*)

album ♀H7	CBot EBee ECha GKev GPoy ILea MAvo MNrw MRav NBid WCot WCru WSHC
- PAB 537	LEdu
- 'Auvergne White'	EBee GCal LEdu MNrw
- var. ***flavum***	CAby MNrw SPhx WCot WCru
- - 'Primrose Warburg' new	GEdr
- subsp. ***lobelianum***	GCal LEdu
- 'Lorna's Green'	EBee GCal MNrw WCot
- var. ***oxysepalum***	WCru
californicum	CAby EBee ECha GCal LEdu MNrw NBid SMad WCru WWFP
formosanum	CAby EBee MNrw
- B&SWJ 1575	WCru
- RWJ 9806	WCru
grandiflorum B&SWJ 4416	WCru
longebracteatum	WCru
maackii	EBee GCal MNrw
- B&SWJ 5875	WCru
- green-flowered	EBee GCal LEdu
- var. ***japonicum***	MNrw WCru
- var. ***maackii***	MNrw
- - B&SWJ 5831	WCru
nigrum ♀H7	CAby CBct CBro EBee ECha GCal GEdr GKev GMaP ILea LEdu LRHS MAvo MNrw MRav NBid NRHS SMad SPhx SPlb WCot WCru WWFP
- B&SWJ 4450 from South Korea	WCru
schindleri	GEdr MNrw
- B&SWJ 4068	WCru
stamineum	WCru
viride	EBee EWes GCal LEdu MNrw NBid WCot WCru

Verbascum (*Scrophulariaceae*)

'Apricot Sunset'	SPhx
'Arctic Summer'	see *V. bombyciferum* 'Polarsommer'
arcturus	SVen
'Argentina'	WHer
blattaria	EBWF GJos SPav WHer
- f. ***albiflorum***	CPla CSpe GJos IFro NDov NGBl SPlb WHer WMoo
- yellow-flowered	SPav
'Blue Lagoon'	CSpe CWGN EBee EPfP SCob
'Blushing Bride'PBR	LLHF
§ ***bombyciferum***	CBod CBre ECha ELan GMaP LRHS NGBl SCob SEND SRms
* - 'Arctic Snow'	SPav SPoG
§ - 'Polarsommer'	CSpe EPfP GJos LRHS SPer
- 'Silver Lining'	NPer
'Broussa'	see *V. bombyciferum*
'Buttercup'	CRos LRHS NRHS
'Camelot'	LRHS NRHS
'Caribbean Crush'	CDor ECtt ELan GJos IBoy LRHS MBNS NRHS SPer SPoG WSpi WTor
chaixii	CSam ECha EPPr GAbr MArl MMrt WFar WMoo
- 'Album'	Widely available
- 'Sixteen Candles'	CBod GJos IPot WFar
- 'Wedding Candles'	CBod ELan GWyn NGdn SPtp WFar
'Cherry Helen'PBR	CDor GMcL LCro LOPS LRHS LSRN MBNS NLar SCob
'Christo's Yellow Lightning' ♀H7	CBod CSpe EBee ECha ECtt MAvo MHol MPie SMad SPoG WCot WRHF
'Clementine'	CBcs CBod CRos EBee ECtt EPfP ILea LCro LOPS LRHS MHol NPnk NRHS SBee SCob SPhx SPoG
'Coneyhill Yellow'	ECtt EPPr
(Cotswold Group) 'Cotswold Beauty'	CRav CSam CSpe ECtt EPfP LRHS LSun MRav NDov NGdn NRHS SHar SPer WHoo

	- 'Cotswold Cream' **new**	IBoy
	- 'Cotswold Queen'	CBod CSam ECtt EPPr EPed EPfP LCro LOPS LRHS MNHC MRav MWat NDov NRHS SHar SPer SPhm SWvt WSpi
	- 'Gainsborough' ♀H6	CBod CDor ECha ECtt EPed EPfP GMaP GMcL IBoy LCro LOPS LRHS MArl MJak MRav NLar NRHS NSti SCob SGbt SPer SPoG SWvt WCAu WSpi
	- 'Mont Blanc'	LRHS NRHS
	- 'Pink Domino' ♀H6	CBod CSam ECtt EPPr EPfP GMaP LCro LOPS LRHS MJak MRav NPnk NRHS NSti SPer SWvt WSpi WWFP
	- 'Royal Highland'	CSam ECtt EPed EPfP LRHS MBNS NRHS SWvt
	- 'White Domino'	SPer WSpi
	'Cotswold King'	see *V. creticum*
§	***creticum***	CSpe WCot
	'Dark Eyes'PBR	CWGN ECtt GMcL LRHS MCot NHpl SCob
	delphicum **new**	GKev
§	***densiflorum***	GJos
	dumulosum ♀H4	WAbe
	epixanthinum ♀H5	EBee
	'Firedance' **new**	CBod CWld ECtt IPot LLHF LRHS LSou NDov NPnk NRHS SHar
	'Golden Wings' ♀H4	WAbe
	'Guinevere'	CRos LRHS NRHS
	'Helen Johnson'	CDor CRav CWCL ECtt ELan EUJe GMcL LRHS LSRN MGos MRav NDov NLar NRHS SCob SCoo SPer SRkn SWvt WSpi
	× ***hybridum*** 'Banana Custard'	NGBl WSpi
	- 'Copper Rose'	EBee LRHS
	- 'Snow Maiden'	CTri EPfP
	'Hyde Hall Sunrise'	EPfP
	'Jackie'	ECtt GMcL LRHS LSRN NRHS SCob SCoo SPer
	'Jackie in Pink'	LRHS NRHS
	'Jester'	CBcs CDor ECtt GMcL LRHS MBNS MCot NRHS SCob SPoG WSpi
	'Jolly Eyes'	ILea
	'June Johnson'	ECtt LRHS NPnk NRHS
	'Kynaston'	CBcs ECtt LRHS MBNS NPnk NRHS
	'Lavender Lass'	GMcL MHol WSpi
	'Letitia' ♀H4	CRos ECtt EPot EWes GCal LRHS NRHS SWvt WAbe WCot WTor
	levanticum	GJos
	'Linda'	ECtt
	longifolium var. ***pannosum***	see *V. olympicum*
	lychnitis	NGBl SPhx
	lydium	EBee
	'Megan's Mauve'	WSpi
	'Merlin'PBR	CBod ECtt EPed LRHS MBNS NDov NRHS
	nigrum	CHab EBWF EBee NGdn NLar WMoo
	- var. ***album***	GJos NGdn NLar WArt WMoo WSpi
§	***olympicum***	CBcs CBod ELan EPfP ESps ETMg GJos IBoy LRHS MArl MBNS NGBl NRHS SCob WCot WHar
	'Petra'	LRHS SPhx
	phlomoides	SPhx
	phoeniceum	CBcs CSBt EBee ELan EPfP GJos NBro SPlb SPoG WFar WMoo WSpi
*	- 'Album'	CSpe
	- 'Flush of White'	CBot CDor CRav EAJP EPfP EWTr GMcL NGBl NGdn NLar NPnk SCob WArt WHar WHil WMoo
	- hybrids	GMaP NEgg NGdn SRms WFar
	- 'Rosetta'	CBod EPfP GWyn NGBl NGdn WArt
	- 'Temptress White' **new**	CBod
	- 'Violetta'	CBWd CBod CBot CSpe CTsd CWld EAJP EPPr EPfP GBin IBoy LRHS MHol MSpe MWat NChi NEgg NGBl NGdn SGbt SPav SPer SPhx WArt WCFE WHil WMoo
	'Pink Kisses'	LRHS LSRN MBNS NRHS SPoG
	(Pixie Series) 'Pixie Apricot'	SBee
	- 'Pixie Blue'	EBee LRHS NRHS
	'Plum Smokey'PBR	ECtt IBoy LLHF
	'Primrose Path'	EPfP GMcL LRHS MBNS NLar NRHS
	pyramidatum	SPhx
	'Queen of Hearts'	LRHS NRHS
	'Raspberry Ripple'	GWyn LLHF MAvo MRav
	roripifolium	GJos
	'Rosie'	ECtt NHpl SCob
	'Sierra Sunset'	LRHS NLar
	'Southern Charm'	EPfP GJos GMaP LPmr NQui WHar WHil
	'Spica'	CBot LRHS
	'Sugar Plum'PBR	CRav ECtt GMcL LCro LLHF LOPS NPnk SPoG
	'Summer Sorbet'	CBcs ECtt MNrw SPoG
	'Temptress Purple'	CBod
	thapsiforme	see *V. densiflorum*
	thapsus	CHab EBWF ENfk GJos GPoy GQue MArl MNHC NMir SEND SRms
	'Tropic Sun' ♀H5	SPhx WHoo
	'Ventnor Giant' **new**	SVen
	'Wessex'	LRHS NRHS
	Verbena (_Verbenaceae_)	
	(G)	see *Glandularia*
§	***bonariensis*** ♀H4	Widely available
	- 'Little One'	EBee
	- 'Lollipop'PBR	Widely available
	brasiliensis misapplied	see *V. bonariensis*
	chamaedrifolia	see *V. peruviana*
	hastata	CAby CSpe EBee ECtt EPfP IBoy LEdu LRHS MArl MNHC MNrw NRHS NSti SCob SEle SPer SPhx SPlb SRms SWvt WCAu WFar WMoo WOut XLum
*	- 'Alba'	CAby CTsd EBee ELan EPfP GCal IBoy MBel NLar NSti SCob WFar WMoo XLum
	- 'Blue Spires'	CNor EPfP IPot SCob WHar
	- f. ***rosea***	CAby CBre CElw CMea CSpe EHoe ELan EPfP IPot LEdu LRHS MNrw MRav NDov NSti SPer SPhx WBor WCAu WFar WMoo WSHC XLum
	- - 'Pink Spires'	CBWd EBee ECtt ELan EPfP LRHS SCob
	- 'White Spires'	EPfP GQue
	lasiostachys	EBee
	macdougalii 'Lavender Spires'	CSpe IPot LRHS NDov SPhx
	officinalis	EBWF EBee ENfk GPoy MHer MNHC SRms WHer WSFF WTre XAbr
	- var. ***grandiflora*** 'Bampton'	Widely available
§	***rigida*** ♀H3	Widely available
	- f. ***lilacina*** 'Lilac Haze'	CMac EPfP LRHS NRHS SRkn

- - 'Polaris'	CMea CSam EBee ELan ELon EPfP EShb GWyn LRHS LSRN MNrw MPie NRHS SCob SHar SPer SPoG
- 'Santos'	LRHS MHol NRHS
scabridoglandulosa	see *Junellia succulentifolia*
serpyllifolia	see *Junellia micrantha*
stricta	EBee EWes NDov NLar SPhx
venosa	see *V. rigida*

Verbesina (*Asteraceae*)

alternifolia	EBee
- 'Goldstrahl'	EPPr
helianthoides	CSam

Vernicia (*Euphorbiaceae*)

fordii	SPlb

Vernonia (*Asteraceae*)

angustifolia new	SPhx
angustifolia* × *missurica	WCot
§ ***arkansana***	CHGN CSam EBee ECha ECtt EPPr EWTr EWes GLog IPot LEdu LRHS NLar NRHS SPhx WFar
- 'Alba'	EBee ECtt EWTr
- 'Betty Blindeman'	EBee LEdu MNrw
- 'Mammuth'	CKno EBee ECtt ELon EWTr EWes ILea IPot LEdu LRHS MNrw MTis SBee SMad SPhx SPoG WCot WTor
baldwinii	EBee MAvo SPhx
crinita	see *V. arkansana*
fasciculata	EWes LRHS MAvo MRav NLar SPhx WCot
gigantea	ELon EWes MMuc MNrw NLar SMad
glauca	SPhx WCot
lettermannii 'Iron Butterfly'	EBee IPot SCob SMad
missurica	LEdu SPhx
noveboracensis	EBee LEdu MAvo NLar SMad XLum
- 'Albiflora'	EPPr EWes MTis
- 'White Lightning'	EBee EPPr ILea MAvo

Veronica (*Plantaginaceae*)

amethystina	see *V. spuria* L.
anagallis-aquatica	LLWG
'Anna' PBR	MTis
armena	EDAr EWes MHer MMuc SBch SRot XSen
'Atomic Hot Pink'	EBee WFar
'Atomic Lilac'	LSou
'Atomic Pink'	LSou
'Atomic Pink Ray' PBR	EBee
'Atomic Sky Ray' PBR	LSou
'Atomic Violet Ray' PBR	LSou
§ ***austriaca***	EWTr NBre WMoo
- dark blue-flowered	NChi
- var. ***dubia***	see *V. prostrata*
- 'Ionian Skies'	CMea ECha ECtt EPPr EWTr GBin NPnk NWad SHar SPer WKif WSHC
- 'Jacqueline'	XSen
§ - subsp. ***teucrium***	CSam EBee SRms WKif
- - 'Blue Fountain'	LRHS NRHS
- - 'Crater Lake Blue' 🏆H6	CBod CDor CRos CTri EBee ECtt ELan EPfP EWld GWyn LEdu LRHS MArl MAsh MAvo MBel MHol MRav NChi NRHS SPhm SPhx SPlb SRms WCot WFar WGwG WSHC
- - 'Kapitän'	CRos ECha ECtt GCrg LRHS NGdn NRHS WFar
- - 'Knallblau'	EAJP WFar
- - 'Lapis Lazuli'	EBee
- - 'Mammuth'	CBWd
- - 'Royal Blue' 🏆H6	CRos EAJP EBee EPfP GMaP LRHS MHol NRHS NSti SRms WArt WFar WKif WMoo XLum XSen
- subsp. ***vahlii***	LLHF
'Baby Doll' PBR	MBNS
beccabunga	CHab CWat EBWF EWat GPoy LLWG MMuc MSKA MWts NMir NPer SEND WMAq WSFF WSpi
'Bergen's Blue'	NLar SHar WSHC
BLUE BOUQUET	see *V. longifolia* 'Blaubündel'
'Blue Indigo'	MAvo MNrw NBre NGdn
'Blue Spire'	WSpi
bombycina	ITim WAbe
- subsp. ***bolkardaghensis***	WAbe
bonarota	see *Paederota bonarota*
caespitosa subsp. ***caespitosa***	WAbe
candida	see *V. spicata* subsp. *incana*
× ***cantiana*** 'Kentish Pink'	WAul WCFE WMoo XLum
caucasica	XSen
chamaedrys	EBWF NMir XLum
'Christa Bubblegum'	EPfP
CHRISTY ('Henslerone' PBR)	ECtt EPfP LBuc MHol NEoE SCob SRot
cinerea 🏆H5	SBch SBrt WHoo WSHC XSen
'Dark Martje'	IBoy
'Darwin's Blue'	NLar
'Ellen Mae'	ECtt EWes MNrw WCAu WCot
'Eveline' PBR	ECtt EPfP LRHS MHol NDov NHpl NLar NRHS SPer
exaltata (d)	NChi WSpi
'Fairytale' PBR	LRHS MBNS NGdn NRHS
'Fantasy'	NDov
filiformis	XLum
'First Love'	CMea ECtt EPfP LRHS LSou MNrw NGdn NRHS SPad SRms WHil
formosa	see *Parahebe formosa*
§ ***fruticans***	GJos
fruticulosa	CPla
gentianoides	Widely available
- 'Alba'	CMea GCal LEdu NBre
- 'Barbara Sherwood' 🏆H7	EBee LRHS NGdn NRHS
- 'Blue Streak'	EPfP XLum
- 'Mountain Breeze' new	CRos LBuc NRHS
- 'Pallida'	GAbr GKev MBrN MMuc MRav SCob SPlb WBor XLum
- 'Robusta'	CAby CBod ECtt GBin GMaP GWyn LRHS MAvo MWat NGdn NRHS WFar WHoo
- 'Tissington White'	CBod CRos EAJP ECtt EPfP GMaP GNew IRob LEdu LRHS MCot MHol MPie MPnt MSpe MTis NBro NEgg NGdn NLar NRHS NWad SHar SPoG SRms WCAu WFar
- 'Variegata' (v)	EBee ECha ECtt ELan GMaP GWyn LRHS MHer MRav MSCN NEgg NRHS NWad SPer WRHF
'Giles van Hees'	ECtt
grandis	EBee IFro LEdu MMuc NChi NLar SBee SEND WArt WHrl WMoo WPtf XLum
'Hocus Pocus'	ECtt LRHS NRHS
incana	see *V. spicata* subsp. *incana*
* - 'Candidissima'	GCal
'Inspiration'	CCse NBre
'Inspire Blue'	CBod LBuc LRHS MMuc MPnt NRHS
'Inspire Pink'	CBod LRHS MPnt NRHS
kellereri	see *V. spicata*

	kiusiana	CMea EBee ECtt LEdu NLar NWad
*	- var. ***maxima***	CAby WPtf
	kotschyana	XSen
	liwanensis	EPot MNrw WHal XSen
	longifolia	CMac CSBt ECha ELan ESps EWTr MBel MSpe NSti WMoo XLum
	- 'Alba'	ELan MArl MMuc SEND WArt WMoo XEll XLum
	- 'Antarctica'	EBee EWTr
	- 'Blaubart'	XLum
§	- 'Blaubündel'	CCse LRHS NGdn NRHS
	- 'Blauer Sommer'	EBee EPfP LRHS NEgg NGdn NRHS SPer
§	- 'Blauriesin'	ELan EPfP GBin GMaP GWyn NLar NPnk NSti SAko SPer SRms WSpi XEll
	- BLUE GIANTESS	see *V. longifolia* 'Blauriesin'
	- 'Blue John'	ECtt EPfP LSou MPie NBre NDov NSti
	- blue-flowered	CBod WHar
	- 'Candied Candle' **new**	ETMg
	- 'Charlotte'PBR (v)	CDor CWGN EBee ECtt EHoe GBin GWyn LCro LOPS LRHS MBel MHol MTis NDov NGBl NRHS SCob SHar SPer SPoG WCot WHil
	- 'Charming Pink'	CDor LRHS NDov NPnk SAko
	- 'Christa'PBR	ECtt EPfP
	- 'Fascination'	CBod ECtt EHoe NEoE NGdn
	- 'First Glory'	CMea LRHS LSou MHol NRHS WHil
	- 'First Lady'	CMea LRHS LSou NRHS
	- 'Foerster's Blue'	see *V. longifolia* 'Blauriesin'
	- 'Incarnata'	EBee LRHS NRHS
	- 'Joseph's Coat' (v)	NBre
	- 'Lilac Fantasy'	MRav NSti
	- 'Marietta'PBR	CBot CDor ECtt LCro LOPS LRHS MAvo MBel MHol MTis NCou NRHS SPer WCot WHil WHoo WPnP WRHF
	- 'Melanie White'	SPer WHil WPnP
	- 'Oxford Blue'	CBar CBod
	- 'Pink Eveline'PBR	EBee ECtt EPfP LRHS MHol NDov NGdn NLar NRHS SPad STPC
	- pink-flowered	CBod CMac
	- 'Rose Tone'	GJos WMoo
	- 'Schneeriesin'	CBod EBee ECha ECtt EPfP GBin GMaP LRHS MRav MTis NLar NPnk NRHS SAko SPer
	lyallii	see *Parahebe lyallii*
	'Martje'	XLum
	montana 'Corinne Tremaine' (v)	SRms
	officinalis	EBWF GJos XLum XSen
	oltensis	CPBP EPot EWld ITim MHer WAbe
	orchidea	see *V. spicata* subsp. *orchidea*
	ornata	MAvo
	'Pacific Ocean'	ECtt NLar
	pectinata	ECtt
	- 'Rosea'	ECtt EWes XSen
	peduncularis 'Oxford Blue'	see *V. umbrosa* 'Georgia Blue'
	perfoliata	see *Parahebe perfoliata*
	petraea 'Madame Mercier'	SRot XLum
	'Pink Damask'	CSpe ECtt ELan ELon EPfP GMaP MAvo MCot MRav MSpe MTis NGdn NLar SDys SRms WHoo
	'Pink Harmony'	MHol NGBl
	pinnata	SBrt
	- 'Blue Feathers'	WArt WOut
	piroliformis	WAbe
	(Plumosa Series) PLUMOSA AMETHYST PLUME	MHol WFar
	- PLUMOSA BLUE PLUME **new**	MHol
	- PLUMOSA LAVENDER PLUME	CWGN EBee EPfP
	porphyriana	CBod EBee MMuc NLar SAko
	prenja	see *V. austriaca*
§	***prostrata*** ♀H5	CBod CMea CSpe CTri ECtt EDAr EPfP GCrg GEdr GJos LRHS MHol NEgg SRms WHoo WMoo
	- 'Alba'	XSen
	- 'Aztec Gold'PBR	CMac
§	- 'Blauspiegel'	CPBP
	- BLUE MIRROR	see *V. prostrata* 'Blauspiegel'
	- 'Blue Sheen'	ECtt EPfP LRHS NRHS
	- 'Goldwell'	EBee ECtt EPPr SRot
	- 'Lavender Mist'	LRHS NRHS
	- 'Lilac Time'	ECtt LRHS NRHS SBch SRms WHil WRHF WTor
	- 'Little Nell'	ECtt
	- 'Loddon Blue'	SRms WCot
	- 'Mrs Holt'	ECtt GCrg LRHS MHer NLar NRHS NWad SRms WHoo
	- 'Nana'	CPBP ECtt EPot EWes GCrg MWat WAbe
	- 'Nestor'	CTri ECtt SRms WHar WPtf XLum
	- 'Rhapsody in Blue' **new**	CRos NRHS
	- 'Rosea'	XSen
	- 'Spode Blue' ♀H5	CMac CMea CTri ECtt EUJe GCrg GMaP GWyn LRHS MHer MMuc NRHS SPoG SRms
	- 'Trehane'	ECtt EPfP GBin GCrg LEdu LRHS MHer MHol NEgg NRHS NRya NWad SPlb SPoG SRms
	'Purpleicious Harmony'PBR	EBee EPfP GBin MTis SPer WFar WHil
	repens	EPfP NEoE SPlb
	'Rosalinde'	NGdn
	'Royal Pink'	MRav NLar
	rupestris	see *V. prostrata*
	saturejoides	SRms
	saxatilis	see *V. fruticans*
	schmidtiana	CPla
	- 'Nana'	GAbr GKev
	selleri	see *V. wormskjoldii*
	'Shirley Blue' ♀H6	ELan EPfP ESps ILea LCro LOPS LSRN MHer MJak MMuc MWat SEND SPer SPhx SRms WCAu WCFE WSpi
§	***spicata***	CSam ELan EPfP GJos LRHS MRav NBid NRHS SCob SRms WBrk WFar WMoo WShi XLum
	- 'Alba'	CBod EBee EPfP GJos LRHS MRav NLar WFar XLum
§	- 'Blaufuchs'	CSam
	- BLUE FOX	see *V. spicata* 'Blaufuchs'
§	- 'Erika'	ECtt EPfP GBin IBoy NBid NGdn
	- 'Foxy Lady' **new**	MTis
§	- 'Glory'PBR	CDor CWGN ECtt ELan ELon ETMg GMcL LOPS LRHS MMrt MPie MTis NPri NRHS SCob SPad SPer SPoG WCot WHar WHoo
	- 'Heidekind'	CBod EBee ECha ELan EPot GCrg GKev NGdn NPnk SRms SRot WHil WHoo XLum
	- 'High Five'PBR	EBee
	- subsp. ***hybrida***	WHer
I	- - 'Elaine's Form'	WCot
§	- 'Icicle'	EBee SCob WCAu
§	- subsp. ***incana*** ♀H4	EHoe ELan EPfP GMcL MMuc SPlb SRms WCFE WMoo XSen

- - 'Nana'	SRms
- - 'Silver Carpet'	ECtt LRHS MRav NRHS SPer WSpi
- - 'Wendy'	GCal
- 'Nana Blauteppich'	NLar
- 'Pink Goblin'	EAJP EDAr ELan EPfP WArt
§ - subsp. ***orchidea***	SRms
- 'Pink Panther'PBR	LSou WCot
- RED FOX	see *V. spicata* 'Rotfuchs'
- 'Romiley Purple'	WSpi
- 'Rosalind'	NLar
- ***rosea***	see *V. spicata* 'Erika'
§ - 'Rotfuchs'	CBod ECtt EHoe ELan ELon EPfP GMcL GWyn LRHS LSou MBel MHer MRav NBid NGdn NPnk NRHS SCob SPer SPoG SRms WCAu WCFE WFar WMoo
- 'Royal Candles'	see *V. spicata* 'Glory'
- 'Sightseeing'	GJos SRms
- subsp. ***spicata*** 'Nana'	XSen
- 'Twilight'PBR	ECtt EPfP LRHS NLar NRHS
- 'Ulster Blue Dwarf'	EBee EPfP EWTr GMaP IBoy IMou LRHS LSou MAvo NBid NGdn NRHS XLum
- YOUNIQUE BABY BLUE	CBod
§ ***spuria*** L.	SEND
stelleri	see *V. wormskjoldii*
subsessilis 'Blaue Pyramide'	WPtf
'Sunny Border Blue'	EPfP GWyn MHol NLar
tauricola	XSen
teucrium	see *V. austriaca* subsp. *teucrium*
thessalica	WHal
§ ***umbrosa*** 'Georgia Blue' 🏆H5	Widely available
urticifolia	SBrt
virginica	see *Veronicastrum virginicum*
'White Icicle'	see *V. spicata* 'Icicle'
whitleyi	MMuc
§ ***wormskjoldii***	GCrg MBrN MMuc SRms

Veronicastrum ✿ (*Plantaginaceae*)

'Adoration'	EBee ECtt ELon EPPr GBin IPot LCro LOPS LRHS MAvo MBel MTis NDov NRHS SMHy SPhx WSpi
axillare	IMou
brunonianum	GCal WSHC
japonicum var. ***australe*** B&SWJ 11009	WCru
latifolium	WCot
- BWJ 8158	EPPr NWad WCru WSHC
'Red Arrows'	Widely available
sibiricum	CKno CSpe EBee ECha EPfP EShb GCal ILea LRHS MMuc NRHS SEND SHar SRms WMoo WWtn XLum
- BWJ 6352	NLar WCru WFar
- 'Kobaltkaars'	SMHy
- var. ***yezoense***	IMou WHoo
- - RBS 0290	EPPr NEoE
villosulum	EBee EWes IMou NBid NBro WSHC XLum
§ ***virginicum***	CKno CTri EBee ECtt GPoy MAvo NLar SRms WFar WHar WMoo WSpi WWtn XLum
- 'Album' 🏆H7	Widely available
- 'Apollo'	Widely available
- 'Cupid'	EBee ECtt EPfP EWTr EWes GMaP ILea LEdu MNrw NDov SHar SPad WSpi
- 'Diane'	CBod EBee ECtt ELon EPPr EPfP GMaP IBoy ILea IPot LRHS MCot MPie MTis NDov NLar SHar SPhx SWvt WCAu WMoo
- 'Erica'	Widely available
- 'Fascination'	Widely available
- var. ***incarnatum***	see *V. virginicum* f. *roseum*
- 'Klein Erica' new	CBod
- 'Lavendelturm'	Widely available
- 'Pointed Finger'	CMea GCal GMaP LEdu NLar SPhx
§ - f. ***roseum***	CBWd CBod ECha ELan EPPr GMaP GQue IRob LRHS MHol MJak MRav NBro NDov NRHS SGbt SPhx SWvt WBor WHrl WKif WMoo WSpi XLum
- - 'Pink Glow'	Widely available
- 'Spring Dew'	CBre EWTr GBin ILea LEdu LRHS MBel MNrw NBid NBro NEoE NGBl SPhx WSpi
- 'Temptation'	EBee EPPr EWTr GMaP ILea IPot LEdu MAvo MRav MTis NBro NEoE NLar SPhx

Verschaffeltia (*Arecaceae*)

splendida	XBlo

Vesalea (*Caprifoliaceae*)

§ ***floribunda*** 🏆H5	CBcs CBot CDul CExl CMac CRos ECre EHyd ELan ELon EPfP LRHS MAsh MGil MRav NLar SAko SBrt SGbt SGol SPer SPoG SRms

Vestia (*Solanaceae*)

§ ***foetida***	CBcs CCCN CExl CTsd EBee ELan ELon EPfP LRHS MGil MNrw MPie SBig SBrt SEND WSHC
lycioides	see *V. foetida*

Viburnum ✿ (*Adoxaceae*)

sp.	LPra
acerifolium	LLHF NWad
atrocyaneum	CExl CJun NWad SBrt
- B&SWJ 7272	EPfP WCru
- HIRD 113	WPGP
betulifolium	CBcs CExl CJun CMCN EBee ELan EPfP EWes GKev GKin SAko WPGP
- f. ***aurantiacum***	CJun
- 'Hohuanshan'	SSta WCru
bitchiuense	CJun NLar
× ***bodnantense***	CMac CTri EBee WFar
- 'Charles Lamont' 🏆H6	Widely available
- 'Dawn' 🏆H6	Widely available
- 'Deben' 🏆H6	EPfP NLar SPer
brachyandrum B&SWJ 5784	WCru
bracteatum	NLar
buddlejifolium	CMac EBee EBtc EPfP EWes LRHS MMuc WCru
× ***burkwoodii***	Widely available
- 'Anika'	NLar
- 'Anne Russell'	Widely available
- 'Chenaultii'	MRav
- 'Compact Beauty'	CJun
- 'Conoy'	CJun LRHS MAsh
- 'Fulbrook'	CRos EPfP LEdu LRHS MAsh NLar
- 'Mohawk' 🏆H6	CEnd CJun CRos ELan EPfP LCro LEdu LOPS LRHS MAsh MGos NLar NRHS SCob SCoo SWvt WSpi
- 'Park Farm Hybrid' 🏆H6	CExl CMac CRos CTri EBee ELan ELon EPfP ESps LEdu LRHS MAsh

	MGos MRav NLar SPer SPoG SRms SWvt WKif WSpi
calvum	CExl
aff. ***calvum*** WWJ 12012	WCru
× ***carlcephalum*** ♀H6	Widely available
- 'Cayuga' ♀H5	ELon MAsh
- 'Van der Maat'	NLar
carlesii	CBcs CCVT CDul CMac CTri ELon EPfP ESps GKin GMcL IRob LSRN MBlu MGos MRav MSwo NRog SCob SEWo SGol SLim SPer SRms WFar
- B&SWJ 8838	WCru
- 'Aurora' ♀H6	Widely available
- 'Charis'	CJun LRHS NLar WKif WPGP
- 'Compactum'	CJun MAsh NLar SSta
- 'Diana' ♀H6	CAby CEnd CJun CMac CRos ELon EMil EPfP LRHS LSRN MAsh MBlu NLar NRHS SCob SPer SPoG SSta WCFE WPGP
- 'Marlou'	CJun NLar
cassinoides	CJun WPGP
- 'Sear Charm'	WPGP
'Chesapeake'	CJun EWes MMuc NLar SEND
chingii	CFil CJun WCru WPGP
'Chippewa'	CJun
cinnamomifolium ♀H5	CBcs CBot CExl ELan EPfP EWTr LMaj LRHS MAsh NLar SArc SBrt SCob SEND SLon SPer SPoG WCot WSHC
costaricanum B&SWJ 10477	WCru
cotinifolium	CExl CTho
- CC 4541	CExl NLar
cylindricum	CBot EPfP LEdu LRHS NLar WCru WPGP
- B&SWJ 6479 from Thailand	WCru
- B&SWJ 7239	WCru
- B&SWJ 9719 from Vietnam	WCru
- HWJCM 43 from Nepal 4	WCru
- Yu 13557 **new**	CFil
- 'Chino-Crûg'	WCru
davidii ♀H5	Widely available
- (f)	CAby CBcs CMac CSBt EBee ELan EPfP EWTr MAsh NRog SPer SPoG SRms WCFE WHar
- (m)	CAby CBcs CMac CSBt ELan EPfP SGbt SPer SPoG SRms WHar
- 'Angustifolium'	CBar CJun NLar WPGP
dentatum	EBtc
- AUTUMN JAZZ	see *V. dentatum* 'Ralph Senior'
- BLUE MUFFIN ('Christom')	LRHS SGol
- CHICAGO LUSTRE	see *V. dentatum* 'Synnestvedt'
- 'Moonglow'	NLar
§ - 'Ralph Senior'	NLar
§ - 'Synnestvedt'	NLar
- 'White and Blue'	CJun NLar
dilatatum B&SWJ 5844	WCru
- B&SWJ 8734	WCru
- B&SWJ 10830	WCru
- PAB 6831	LEdu
- CARDINAL CANDY ('Henneke')	NLar
- 'Erie'	EPfP
- 'Michael Dodge'	MBlu
- 'Sealing Wax'	NLar
'Emerald Triumph'	CJun
erosum B&SWJ 11083	WCru
- B&SWJ 8735	WCru
- B&SWJ 8893	WCru
erubescens	CJun NLar SBrt
- HWJK 2163	WCru
- VdL 4122 **new**	WPGP
- var. ***gracilipes***	CJun LLHF
- 'Ward van Teylingen'	NLar
'Eskimo' ♀H5	CBcs CCVT CMac CRos CSBt EBee ELan EPfP GMcL LRHS MAsh MBNS MBlu MGos NRog SAko SCob SCoo SGol SLim SPoG SRms SSta SWvt
fansipanense B&SWJ 8302	WCru
- KWJ 12239	WCru
§ ***farreri*** ♀H6	CBcs CBod CDul CRos CSBt CTri EBee ELan EPfP EWTr GMcL LBuc LEdu LRHS LSRN MGos MRav MSwo NLar NRog SCob SGol SPer SWvt
- 'Album'	see *V. farreri* 'Candidissimum'
§ - 'Candidissimum'	CBot CDul CExl CMac EBee ELan EPfP LRHS MRav NLar SGol SPer SRms SWvt WAvo
- 'December Dwarf'	CJun GMcL MMrt NLar
- 'Farrer's Pink'	CExl CJun NLar
- 'Nanum'	CJun CMac EBtc ELan EPfP LRHS MAsh MBrN MRav WAvo
foetens	see *V. grandiflorum* f. *foetens*
foetidum	IArd
- var. ***ceanothoides***	NLar
- var. ***rectangulatum*** B&SWJ 1888	WCru
- - B&SWJ 3451	WCru
formosanum CWJ 12460	WCru
fragrans Bunge	see *V. farreri*
'Fragrant Cloud'	ECrN SWvt
furcatum ♀H6	CBot EPfP GKin IArd IDee LRHS NLar SAko
- B&SWJ 5939	WCru
- B&SWJ 10880	WCru
× ***globosum*** 'Jermyns Globe'	CJun CMac EPfP ETMg MRav NLar SCob SEND SGol SLon SPoG WFar
grandiflorum	CJun NLar
- 'De Oirsprong'	NLar
§ - f. ***foetens***	CJun LRHS
- f. ***grandiflorum*** **new**	SPoG
- 'Snow White'	CJun
harryanum	EBtc EWTr IArd IDee NLar WCru WPGP WSHC
henryi	CJun EPfP IArd IDee SBrt WCFE
× ***hillieri***	CHGN
- 'Winton' ♀H5	CBcs CJun CMac CRos EBee EPfP IArd IDee LRHS LSRN MGos NLar NRHS SGol SLon SPoG SVen WFar WPGP
hoanglienense B&SWJ 8281	WCru
- HWJ 934	WCru
- KWJ 12283	WCru
- PAB 7833 **new**	LEdu
'Huron'	NLar
ichangense	CJun NLar
japonicum	CExl EBee EPfP SLon
- B&SWJ 5968	WCru
× ***juddii***	Widely available
kansuense	CExl
- BWJ 7737	WCru
koreanum B&SWJ 4231	WCru
lantana	CCVT CDul CHab CLnd CPer CTho CTri ECrN ELan EPfP EShb ESps EWTr LBuc MMuc SCob SEWo SPer SVic WMou WTSh
- 'Aureum'	CBot EHoe EPfP MAsh MBlu NLar

	- var. ***discolor***	NLar
	- 'Mohican'	NLar
	- 'Xanthocarpum'	SWvt WFar
	aff. ***lautum*** B&SWJ 10290	WCru
	'Le Bois Marquis' PBR	CRos EBee EMil EPfP EShb EUJe LOPS LRHS MAsh MGos SGol SPoG WCot
	lentago	CMac EPfP
	lobophyllum	NLar
	luzonicum	CJun
	- B&SWJ 3637	WCru
	- var. ***formosanum*** B&SWJ 3585	WCru
	- var. ***oblongum***	LLHF
	- - B&SWJ 3549	WCru
	- var. ***sinuatum*** B&SWJ 4009	WCru
	macrocephalum	CJun SLon
	- 'Sterile'	CJun
	mariesii	see *V. plicatum* f. *tomentosum* 'Mariesii'
	mullaha B&SWJ 2251A	WCru
	- GWJ 9227	WCru
	- KR 10609 new	WPGP
	aff. ***mullaha*** GWJ 9388	WCru
	nervosum HWJK 2241	WCru
	- HWJK 2373	WCru
	nudum	ECrN IDee
	- BRANDYWINE ('Bulk')	LRHS WPGP
	- 'Pink Beauty'	CJun CRos ECrN EPfP LCro LOPS LRHS LSRN MMrt NRHS SGol SWvt WFar WPGP
	- 'Winterthur'	CJun NLar
	odoratissimum misapplied	see *V. odoratissimum* var. *awabuki*
	odoratissimum Ker Gawl.	EBee
	- RWJ 10046	WCru
	- var. ***arboricola*** B&SWJ 6913	WCru
§	- var. ***awabuki***	CExl ELon EPfP EUJe EWTr LEdu LRHS MBlu MGos NLar SEND SGol SLim SPer WCot
	- - B&SWJ 8404	WCru
	- - B&SWJ 11374 from Wabuka, Japan	WCru
	- - 'Emerald Lustre'	CBcs LRHS
	aff. ***odoratissimum*** B&SWJ 3913 from the Philippines	WCru
	oliganthum 'Kyo Kanzashi'	WPGP
	'Oneida'	CJun
	opulus	Widely available
§	- var. ***americanum***	NLar
	- - 'Phillips'	CAgr
	- - 'Spring Red'	NLar
	- - 'Wentworth'	CAgr
	- 'Amy's Magic Gold'	NLar
	- 'Apricot'	NLar
	- 'Aureum'	CMac CRos EHoe ELan EPfP ESps EWTr LRHS MAsh MGos MMuc MRav NEgg NLar SCob WCFE WMoo
	- var. ***calvescens*** B&SWJ 10544	WCru
	- 'Compactum' ♀H6	Widely available
	- 'Fructuluteo'	SCob SGol
*	- 'Harvest Gold'	MAsh SCoo SGol SLim
	- 'Lady Marmalade'	NLar
	- 'Nanum'	CBcs ELan EPfP EShb GBin GMcL MRav NLar
	- 'Notcutt's Variety' ♀H6	MAsh
	- 'Park Harvest'	CAby EBee EBtc EPfP LRHS MAsh NLar SMad SPoG SWvt
§	- 'Roseum' ♀H6	Widely available
	- 'Sterile'	see *V. opulus* 'Roseum'
*	- 'Sterile Compactum'	SWvt
	- 'Sylvie'	NLar
	- 'Xanthocarpum' ♀H6	CBcs CDul CExl CMac CTho EBee ELan EPfP EShb ESps GBin LRHS MAsh MGos MMuc MRav MSwo NLar SCob SGol SLon SPer SRms SWvt WAvo WFar WSpi WWtn
	parviflorum new	LLHF
	parvifolium	EPfP NLar
	- B&SWJ 3375	WCru
	- B&SWJ 6768	WCru
	phlebotrichum B&SWJ 11058	WCru
	- B&SWJ 11470	WCru
	pichinchense B&SWJ 10660	WCru
	plicatum	CTri ESps
	- 'Nanum'	see *V. plicatum* f. *tomentosum* 'Nanum Semperflorens'
§	- f. ***plicatum***	EWTr SChF
	- - 'Grandiflorum'	CBcs CMac EPfP LRHS NLar NPnk SCob SPer SPoG WCFE WFar
	- - 'Mary Milton'	CJun ELan IArd NLar
	- - NEWPORT ('Newzam')	LRHS NRHS
	- - 'Pink Sensation'	CJun GBin
	- - 'Popcorn' ♀H5	CExl CJun CMac CRos EBee ELan ELon EPfP EShb EUJe LRHS LSRN MAsh NLar SGol SLim SPoG SSta
	- - 'Rosace'	EPfP LLHF LRHS MBlu NLar NRHS SAko
	- - 'Rotundifolium'	CRos IArd LRHS MAsh MGos MRav NLar NRHS WFar
	- - TRIUMPH ('Trizam')	NLar
	- 'Sterile'	see *V. plicatum* f. *plicatum*
§	- f. ***tomentosum***	IBal SGol
	- - 'Cascade' ♀H5	CJun EWTr LRHS NLar SAko WSpi
	- - 'Dart's Red Robin'	ECtt LLHF MAsh
	- - 'Elizabeth Bullivant'	EPfP LRHS MAsh NRHS SPoG
	- - 'Fireworks' new	NLar
	- - KILIMANJARO ('Jww1' PBR)	EPfP GBin GMcL LCro LOPS LRHS LSRN MBlu MGos NEoE NLar NPnk NRHS SGol SPer WMoo WSpi
	- - KILIMANJARO SUNRISE ('Jww5') new	CBcs ETMg LCro LOPS LRHS MGos NRHS SCoo WHlf
	- - 'Lanarth'	CBar CBcs CDul CExl CMac CRos CSBt CTri ELan EPfP EShb ESps EWTr LRHS LSRN MAsh MBlu MGos MJak NLar NSti SCob SCoo SGol SLim SPer SWvt WSpi
§	- - 'Mariesii' ♀H5	Widely available
	- - 'Mariesii Great Star'	LRHS
	- - 'Molly Schroeder'	CJun EBee NLar
§	- - 'Nanum Semperflorens'	CBcs CDul CMac CMea ECtt EMOT EPfP EShb LRHS MGos NLar NRHS SGol SPoG WFar
	- - 'Pink Beauty' ♀H5	Widely available
	- - 'Rowallane'	NLar
	- - 'Saint Keverne'	ELan GKin
	- - 'Shasta'	CDul CJun CMCN EMOT EPfP EWTr GMcL LRHS MMrt NLar SGol WFar WSpi
	- - 'Shoshoni'	NLar SGol WPGP
	- - 'Summer Snowflake' ♀H5	CEnd CRos CWGN EMOT EPfP EShb GMcL LRHS MAsh MSwo NLar NPnk NRHS SGol SLim SPer SPoG WFar

- 'Watanabe'	see *V. plicatum* f. *tomentosum* 'Nanum Semperflorens'
'Pragense' 𝕐^{H6}	CBcs CBot CDul CJun CMCN EPfP LRHS MGos NLar SPer
propinquum CWJ 12395	WCru
- CWJ 12426	WCru
- var. ***propinquum*** Guiz 222 **new**	WPGP
prunifolium	EBtc SGol WCru
- 'Mrs Henry's Large'	CJun EPfP NLar
× ***rhytidophylloides***	IBoy
- 'Alleghany'	NLar
- DART'S DUKE ('Interduke')	WCFE
- 'Willowwood'	ELan LRHS MAsh NLar SCob SPer
rhytidophyllum	CBcs CDul CMac EBee ECrN EPfP ESps GMcL LMaj LRHS MGos MJak MMuc MSwo NEgg NLar SCob SEND SGol SPer SRms SWvt WCFE WHar WSFF
- 'Roseum'	CBot CExl SWvt
- 'Variegatum' (v)	CJun
- 'Wisley Pink'	MAsh
'Royal Guard'	CJun
sambucinum HWJ 838	WCru
- var. ***tomentosum*** HWJ 733	WCru
sargentii B&SWJ 8695	WCru
- f. ***flavum***	NLar
- 'Onondaga' 𝕐^{H6}	Widely available
semperflorens	see *V. plicatum* f. *tomentosum* 'Nanum Semperflorens'
§ ***setigerum***	EBee EPfP IDee NLar WCFE
- BWJ 8409	WCru
- 'Aurantiacum'	NLar
sieboldii B&SWJ 2837	WCru
- CWJ 12808	WCru
- 'Seneca'	CJun LRHS NLar
subalpinum	NLar
sympodiale	CFil
taitoense CWJ 12406	WCru
taiwanianum B&SWJ 3009	WCru
- CWJ 12467	WCru
theiferum	see *V. setigerum*
tinoides B&SWJ 10612	WCru
tinus	Widely available
- 'Bewley's Variegated' (v)	EBee SCob SPer
I - 'Compactum'	SWvt
- 'Eve Price' 𝕐^{H4}	Widely available
- 'French White' 𝕐^{H4}	CDul CMac CPer ELan EMOT EPfP EWTr IBoy LCro LOPS MGos MRav NLar SAko SCob SCoo SLim SPoG SRms SWvt WFar WHar
- 'Gwenllian' 𝕐^{H4}	Widely available
- 'Israel'	LRHS MBNS
- 'Lisarose'^{PBR}	CBar CBcs CRos EBee EPfP LCro LOPS LRHS LSRN MAsh MGos NLar NRHS SPoG SWvt WSpi
- 'Little Bognor'	NLar
- 'Lucidum'	CBcs ECrN EPfP LMaj LPra NLar SGol
- 'Lucidum Variegatum' (v)	CMac SLim WFar
* - 'Macrophyllum'	EPfP LRHS NLar SPoG SWvt
- 'Peter's Purple'	EPfP LRHS NRHS SPoG
- 'Pink Prelude'	SCob
- 'Purpureum'	CBcs CJun CSBt ECrN EHoe ELon EMOT EPfP ESps MAsh MGos MSwo NEgg NLar SCob SCoo SGol SLim SPer SPoG
- SPIRIT ('Anvi'^{PBR})	CRos CSBt ELan EPfP ESps LRHS LSou MAsh MMrt NEoE NLar NRHS NWad SCob SCoo SPoG SWvt
- 'Spring Bouquet'	CJun MAsh
- subsp. ***subcordatum***	see *V. treleasei*
- 'Variegatum' (v)	CBot CMac CRos CTri EBee EHoe ELan ELon EPfP ESps LRHS MAsh MGos NEgg NLar NPol NRHS SCob SGol SLim SPoG SRms SWvt WFar
tomentosum	see *V. plicatum* f. *tomentosum*
§ ***treleasei*** B&SWJ 12544	WCru
trilobum	see *V. opulus* var. *americanum*
triphyllum B&SWJ 10757	WCru
- B&SWJ 14298 **new**	WCru
utile	WThu
aff. ***venustum*** B&SWJ 10477	WCru
wrightii	EPfP IArd IDee MRav NLar
- B&SWJ 5871	WCru
- var. ***stipellatum*** B&SWJ 5856	WCru
- - B&SWJ 8780A	WCru

Vicia (*Papilionaceae*)

americana	EBee
cracca	CHab CWld EBWF NMir WSFF
oroboides	EBee
sativa	CHab EBWF
sepium	EBWF

Vigna (*Papilionaceae*)

caracalla	see *Cochliasanthus caracalla*

Villaresia see *Citronella*

Viminaria (*Papilionaceae*)

juncea	SBrt

Vinca (*Apocynaceae*)

difformis	CFis CTri ECha IDee LPla SRms WAvo WHer XLum
- 'Alba'	CBot CSam
- Greystone form	CExl EPPr SEND
- 'Jenny Pym'	CBod CChe CDor CExl CMac CRos CSam EBee EPPr EPfP EWes EWld LRHS MBNS NLar SBch SEND SPoG SRms WAvo WOut WRHF
- 'Ruby Baker'	EPPr EWes NChi WAvo WFar
- subsp. ***sardoa***	CBot EPPr EWes LRHS WCot
- 'Snowmound'	CSBt LRHS MRav NLar SPoG SWvt WAvo
herbacea RCB UA 21	WCot
'Hidcote Purple'	see *V. major* var. *oxyloba*
major	CBcs CBod CDul CFGn CSBt ELan EShb ESps ETMg GMcL GPoy LBuc LCro LRHS MAsh MGos MJak MSwo NPol SCob SGbt SGol SLim SPer SRms WFar WMoo XLum XSen
- 'Alba'	CMac
- subsp. ***balcanica***	IMou XLum
- 'Elegantissima'	see *V. major* 'Variegata'
- var. ***hirsuta*** misapplied	see *V. major* var. *oxyloba*
§ - subsp. ***hirsuta*** (Boiss.) Stearn	CMac WCot XLum
§ - 'Maculata' (v)	CBcs CSBt ECrN EHoe EShb ESps GMcL GWyn LRHS MSwo SCob SEND SGol SLim SPer SPoG SWvt WAvo WMoo WOut
§ - var. ***oxyloba***	CExl CFis CTri ECha ELan EPfP EPri EWld LRHS MRav SCob SRms WAvo WHer
- var. ***pubescens***	see *V. major* subsp. *hirsuta* (Boiss.) Stearn
- 'Surrey Marble'	see *V. major* 'Maculata'

§	- 'Variegata' (v) ♀H6	Widely available
	- 'Wojo's Jem' (v)	CBod CBot CMac CPla CRos ELan EPfP EWes LRHS MGos NCou NLar NRHS SCob SLim SPoG SWvt WAvo WCot WMoo
	minor	CBar CBcs CDul CRos CSBt ELan ESps GAbr GBin GKin GMcL GPoy LCro LOPS LRHS MAsh MGos MJak NRHS SCob SLim SVic XLum
	- f. ***alba***	CBcs CBod CDul CMac ECha EMOT EPPr EPfP ESps EWTr LCro LOPS LRHS LSRN MAsh MBel NLar SCob SGol SPer WCot WFar WHar WOut XLum
§	- - 'Alba Variegata' (v)	CBar CExl EHoe GMcL IFro LSRN NEoE NWad SPer SRms WCot WFar WHoo WOut WWtn
	- - 'Gertrude Jekyll'	Widely available
	- 'Alba Aureovariegata'	see *V. minor* f. *alba* 'Alba Variegata'
§	- 'Argenteovariegata' (v) ♀H6	CBcs CDul CMac CRos CSBt CSam CTri ECha ELan ELon EMOT EPfP GMcL LBuc LRHS MGos MJak MMuc MSwo NChi NRHS SCob SGol SLim SPer SRms WFar
§	- 'Atropurpurea' ♀H6	Widely available
	- 'Aurea'	CBod
I	- 'Aureomarginata' (v)	WMoo
§	- 'Aureovariegata' (v)	CBcs CMac CRos EBee ELan EPPr EPfP ESps GAbr LRHS MGos MJak MRav NChi NRHS SGol SLim SPer SPlb WRHF
	- 'Azurea'	CHid
§	- 'Azurea Flore Pleno' (d) ♀H6	CBot CMac CTri ECha EPPr EPfP GAbr GBin IFro LRHS MAsh MRav NChi NLar NRHS SLim SPer SPoG SRms SWvt WFar WHar WHoo WKif WMoo XLum
*	- 'Blue and Gold'	EPPr SCob
	- 'Blue Drift'	EWes MSwo
	- 'Bowles's Blue'	see *V. minor* 'La Grave'
	- 'Bowles's Purple'	CBod CTsd GMaP NCou SPer
	- 'Bowles's Variety'	see *V. minor* 'La Grave'
	- 'Burgundy'	SRms
	- 'Caerulea Plena'	see *V. minor* 'Azurea Flore Pleno'
	- 'Dartington Star'	see *V. major* var. *oxyloba*
	- 'Double Burgundy'	see *V. minor* 'Multiplex'
	- 'Evelyne'PBR **new**	CBod WFar
	- 'Flower Power'	EPPr
	- GREEN CARPET	see *V. minor* 'Grüner Teppich'
§	- 'Grüner Teppich'	SGol
	- 'Halstenbek'	XLum
	- 'Illumination' (v)	Widely available
	- 'Josefine'	MHol NLar
§	- 'La Grave' ♀H6	Widely available
	- 'Marie'	EPPr MBel NLar
	- 'Mrs Betty James' (d)	WCot
§	- 'Multiplex' (d)	EPPr GBin MSwo SGol SLim SRms WOut
	- 'Purpurea'	see *V. minor* 'Atropurpurea'
	- 'Ralph Shugert' (v) ♀H6	CBot CExl CMac CRos ECtt ELon EMOT EPPr EPfP ESps EWTr EWes GMcL LCro LOPS LRHS MAsh MGos NLar NPri NRHS SCob SCoo SEle SGol SPoG SRms WFar WMoo
	- 'Rubra'	see *V. minor* 'Atropurpurea'
	- 'Sabinka'	CHid EPPr
	- 'Silver Service' (d/v)	CHid MRav
	- 'Snowdrift'	EPPr
	- 'Variegata'	see *V. minor* 'Argenteovariegata'
	- 'Variegata Aurea'	see *V. minor* 'Aureovariegata'
	- 'White Gold'	NEoE
	- 'White Power'	EPPr EWes

Vincetoxicum (*Apocynaceae*)

cretaceum PAB 3432	LEdu
forrestii	CExl
fuscatum	IMou
hirundinaria	EBee EPPr GEdr GPoy LEdu
nigrum	EBee GCal NChi WCot

Viola ✿ (*Violaceae*)

	'Ada Segre' (Vt)	CGro
	'Admiral Avellan'	see *V.* 'Amiral Avellan'
	'Admiration' (Va)	WGoo
	adunca var. ***minor***	see *V. labradorica* ambig.
§	***alba***	EWes
	'Alethia' (Va)	SDys WGoo
	'Alice Kate' (Va)	WGoo
	'Alice Witter' (Vt)	CGro LLHF SHar
*	'Alison' (Va)	NDov WGoo
	altaica	GJos
	'Amelia' (Va)	WGoo
§	'Amiral Avellan' (Vt)	CGro
	'Amy' (Va) **new**	EVic
	'Annaleisia' (Vt)	CGro
	'Annette Ross' (Va)	GWyn NDov WGoo
I	'Annie' (Vt)	CGro LLHF
	'Ardross Gem' (Va)	WGoo
	'Arkwright's Ruby' (Va)	MAsh
	arvensis	CHab GJos
	'Ashvale Blue' (dPVt)	CGro
	'Aspasia' (Va) ♀H5	GAbr GWyn MAsh WGoo
	'Avril Lawson' (Va)	GBin GKev SHar WGoo
	'Baby Blue'	GMcL
	'Barbara' (Va)	ECtt WGoo
	'Baroness de Rothschild' misapplied	see *V.* 'Baronne Alice de Rothschild'
	'Baroness de Rothschild' ambig. (Vt)	CGro WHer
§	'Baronne Alice de Rothschild' (Vt)	CDor WCot
	'Beatrice' (Vtta)	WGoo
	'Becky Groves' (Vt)	CGro EWTr
	'Beetroot' (Vt)	CGro
§	'Belmont Blue' (C)	CSam CTri EBee ELon EWes GAbr GBin GCal GMaP IPot IRob LCro LOPS LRHS MAsh MCot MHer MRav NDov SCob SHar SPer SPhx WCAu WFar WGoo WSpi
§	***bertolonii***	NRHS WGoo
	'Beshlie' (Va) ♀H5	ECtt WGoo
	biflora	EWld MNrw
	'Blackout'PBR (C)	ECtt MHol
	'Blue Butterfly' (C)	GWyn
	'Blue Horns' (C)	ELon
	'Blue Moon' (C)	MAsh WGoo
	BLUE MOON ('Smev1') (Va)	GWyn
	'Blue Moonlight' (C)	IRob MPie
	'Blue Sails' (Va) **new**	EVic
	'Blue Tit' (Va)	ECtt
	'Bonny' (Va) **new**	EVic
	'Boughton Blue'	see *V.* 'Belmont Blue'
	'Bournemouth Gem' (Vt)	CDor CGro
§	'Bowles's Black' (T)	CSpe EPfP LEdu NBro SRms WArt
	brevistipulata var. ***hidakana***	GEdr
	- var. ***laciniata***	GEdr
	'Bruneau' (dVt)	EBee ECtt LEdu WCot WFar
*	'Bryony' (Vtta)	WGoo

	Name	Suppliers
	bubanii	GJos GKev
	'Bullion' (Va)	WGoo
	'Burncoose Yellow'	WGoo
	'Buttercup' (Vtta)	ECtt GWyn MHol SDys SPhx SPoG WGoo
	'Butterpat' (C)	MAsh NDov SPhx WFar WGoo
	'Buxton Blue' (Va)	WGoo
	'Candy' (Vt)	EBee
	canina	NBro NMir
	'Carol' (Vt)	CGro
	'Carol Loxton' (Vt)	EBee
	'Catalina'	CGro
	CELESTIAL TWILIGHT ('Smev3') (C) **new**	MHol
	chaerophylloides var. ***chaerophylloides***	GEdr
§	- var. ***sieboldiana***	SBrt
	- - pink-flowered	SBrt
	'Charles William Groves' (Vt)	CGro ELon
	'Charles Winston Groves' (Vt)	CGro
	'Charlotte' (Va)	GWyn WGoo
	'Chloe' (Vtta)	CGro
	'Christie's Wedding' (Vt)	CGro
	'Christmas' (Vt)	CGro
	'Clementina' (Va) ♀H5	MRav WGoo
	'Cleo' (Va)	GWyn WGoo
	'Clive Farrell' (Vt)	MNrw
	'Clive Groves' (Vt)	CGro ELon
	'Coeur d'Alsace' (Vt)	CGro EBee ECtt GBin GMaP NLar SHar SRms WHal XLum
	'Colette' (Va)	WGoo
	'Colombine' (Vt)	CAby MAsh
	'Columbine' (Va)	ECtt EPfP GMaP GWyn LRHS MHer MHol NDov NRHS SPer SPoG WCot WFar WGoo WTor
§	'Conte di Brazza' (dPVt)	CGro GWyn NLar SHar WHer
	'Copperfield' (P) **new**	CRos NRHS
	'Cordelia' (Vt)	CDor
	cornuta ♀H5	CAby CElw CMea GKev GWyn LRHS MMuc MNrw NBro SCob SRms WGoo WHoo
	- Alba Group (C) ♀H5	CAby CElw CMac CSpe CTri ECha ELan ELon EPfP GBin GMaP LRHS MBel MCot MHer MMuc MNrw NBro NDov NRHS SCob SPer SPhx SRms WGoo WHoo WKif
	- 'Alba Minor' (C)	CMea EPfP EWes MTin NBro NDov NRHS NSla SPhx
	- 'Blaue von Paris' (C)	GWyn
	- blue-flowered	MHer WMoo
	- 'Brimstone' (C)	GAbr
	- 'Cleopatra' (C)	MNrw MPie SPhx
	- 'Clouded Yellow' (C)	GWyn MNrw
	- 'Gypsy Moth' (C)	GWyn SPhx
	- 'Icy But Spicy' (C)	GWyn IPot MAsh MCot MRav NDov WGoo
	- Lilacina Group (C)	ECha MRav WPtf
	- 'Maiden's Blush' (C)	WFar
	- 'Mark's Dainty' (C)	MPie
	- 'Minor' (C)	CSam EPfP MAsh NBro NDov NSla WGoo
	- 'Netta Statham' (C)	MPie WGoo
	- 'Pale Apollo' (C)	SPhx
	- Purpurea Group (C)	CMea ECha
	- 'Rosea' (C)	ECha
	- 'Spider' (C)	GWyn MAsh MPie SDys WFar WGoo
	- 'Swallowtail' (C) **new**	GWyn
	- 'Ulla' (C)	WHer
	- 'Victoria's Blush' (C)	CElw ELon EWTr GMaP LRHS MAsh MPie NDov SHar SPhx WGoo
	- 'Violacea' (C)	MAsh
	corsica	CMea CSpe EPPr GJos SBch SPhx WOut
	'Covent Garden' (Vt) **new**	CGro
§	***cucullata*** ♀H5	SRms
§	- 'Alba' (Vt)	CBro CGro SRms
*	- 'Striata Alba'	NBro
	'Curlylocks'	ECtt
	curtisii	see *V. tricolor* subsp. *curtisii*
	'Czar'	see *V.* 'The Czar'
§	'Czar Bleu' (Vt)	CGro
	'Daisy Smith' (Va)	WGoo
	'Danielle Molly'	WGoo
	'Dawn' (Vtta)	CAby CBod CMea ECtt EPfP GBin GMaP GWyn NDov NLar SPoG WFar WGoo WTor
	'Delicia' (Vtta)	GWyn NDov SPhx WGoo
	'Desdemona' (Va)	GWyn IRob WGoo
	'Devon Cream' (Va)	WGoo
	'Diana Groves' (Vt)	CGro
	'Dick o' the Hills' (Vt)	CGro
	dissecta var. ***sieboldiana***	see *V. chaerophylloides* var. *sieboldiana*
	'Donau' (Vt)	CGro WCot
	'Double White' (dVt)	CGro WHer
	dubyana	GJos
	'Duchesse de Parme' (dPVt)	CGro GMaP GWyn IFro NLar SRms WHer
	'D'Udine' (dPVt)	CGro ECtt SRms WCot WHer
	'Dusk'	WGoo
	'E.A. Bowles'	see *V.* 'Bowles's Black'
	'Eastgrove Blue Scented' (C)	SDys WGoo WOut
	'Eastgrove Ice Blue' (C)	WGoo WOut
	'Elaine Quin'	ECtt GWyn MCot NDov NEgg NLar SPoG WGoo WKif
§	***elatior***	EPPr MNrw SBrt WArt
	'Eliza May Groves' (Vt) **new**	CGro
	'Elizabeth' (Va)	WGoo
	'Elizabeth Lee'	WCot
	'Elliot Adam' (Va)	WGoo
	'Emperor Blue Vein'	EPfP
	'Emperor Magenta Red'	LEdu
	erecta	see *V. elatior*
	'Eris' (Va)	WGoo
	'Etain' (Va)	CAby CBod ECtt ELan EPfP GMaP GWyn IPot LRHS MAsh MHol NDov NEgg NLar NRHS SCob SPoG WFar WGoo
*	'Fantasy'	WGoo
	'Fee Jalucine' (dVt)	CGro
	'Fiona' (Va)	MCot SPhx WGoo
	'Fiona Lawrenson' (Va)	WGoo
	'Florence' (Va)	GWyn NDov WGoo
	'Foxbrook Cream' (C)	MAsh WGoo
	'Francesca' (Va)	WGoo
	'Freckles'	see *V. sororia* 'Freckles'
	'Fred Morey' (Vt)	CGro
	glabella	SBrt
	'Gladys Findlay' (Va)	WGoo
	'Glanmore'	WCot WFar
*	'Glenda'	WGoo
	'Glenholme'	GWyn IRob MAsh
	'Gloire de Verdun' (PVt)	CGro
	'Governor Herrick' (Vt)	CGro EBee ECtt EHrv LLHF NLar WCot WFar
	gracilis 'Lutea'	CSam
	- 'Major'	WGoo
	'Green Goddess'PBR (P)	CRav EPfP

	'Grey Owl' (Va)	WGoo
	'Grovemount Blue' (C)	CMea EPfP WTor
	grypoceras var. ***exilis*** 'Sylettas'	LEdu
	'Gustav Wermig' (C)	MAsh WGoo
	'Heartthrob' (v)	ECtt GEdr LSou MNrw NHpl SPoG SWeb WNPC
*	'Heaselands'	SMHy
§	***hederacea***	CExl CTsd GQue GWyn IFoB SCob SRms
§	'Helen Mount' (T)	GWyn
	'Helena' (Va)	GWyn WGoo
	'Hespera' (Va)	WGoo
	heterophylla subsp. ***epirota***	see *V. bertolonii*
*	'Hetty Gatenby'	WGoo
	hirta	EBWF
	'Holdgate'	WGoo
	'Hopleys White' (PVt) **new**	CGro
	'Hudsons Blue'	CElw MNrw
	'Huntercombe Purple' (Va) ♀H5	LRHS MAsh NRHS SCob WGoo WHal WKif
	'Iden Gem' (Va)	ECtt WGoo
	'Inverurie Beauty' (Va) ♀H5	GAbr GBin GMaP GWyn SDys WGoo WKif
	'Irish Elegance'	see *V.* 'Sulfurea'
	'Irish Molly' (Va)	CRav CSpe ECtt ELan EPfP GWyn MAsh NEgg SPer SPoG WFar WGoo WTor
	'Isabel'	SRms WGoo
	'Isabella' (Vt)	CGro EBee
	'Isobel'	MAsh
	'Ivory Queen' (Va)	GWyn IRob MRav SPhx WGoo
	'Jack Sampson' (Vt)	EBee
	'Jackanapes' (Va) ♀H5	EBee ECtt ELan EPfP GWyn LRHS MAsh NRHS SPer SPoG WGoo WTor
	'Janet' (Va)	EBee GWyn LSRN SDys SPoG
	'Janette' (Va)	NDov WGoo
	'Jean Jeannie' (Va)	GWyn NDov WGoo
	'Jeannie Bellew' (Va)	ECtt WGoo
	'Jennifer Andrews' (Va)	GWyn WGoo
	'Jenny Dickson'	CElw
	'Joanna' (Va)	WGoo
	'Johnny Jump Up'	see *V.* 'Helen Mount'
	jooi	EPfP WAbe WPtf WThu
	'Josephine' (Vt)	CGro
	'Josie' (Va)	GWyn WGoo
	'Joyce Gray' (Va)	WGoo
	'Joyce Mary Paul' (Vt)	CGro
	'Judy Goring' (Va)	ECtt SPhx
	'Julian' (Va)	ECtt GWyn WGoo
	'Jupiter' (Va)	GWyn WCot
	'Karpatenfrühling' (C)	WArt
	'Katerina' (Va)	WGoo
	'Kerry Girl' (Vt)	CGro
	'Kim'	CGro
	'Kitten'	MAsh SDys SPhx WGoo
	'Kitty White' (Va)	GWyn SDys SPhx
§	'Königin Charlotte' (Vt)	CGro EPfP GBin GMaP LRHS MHer NLar SRms WCot WMoo
	labradorica misapplied	see *V. riviniana* Purpurea Group
	- ***purpurea***	see *V. riviniana* Purpurea Group
§	***labradorica*** ambig.	CBod CSBt EHrv GJos GWyn NHpl SCob WCAu WHer
	'Lady Hume Campbell' (dPVt)	CGro WHer
	'Lady Jane' (Vt)	CGro
	'Lavender Lady' (Vt)	CGro
	'Lees Blue' (Vt) **new**	CGro
	'Lees Peachy Pink' (Vt)	CGro MNrw
	'Letitia' (Va)	MAsh MNrw MRav SDys WGoo
	'Lianne' (Vt)	LLHF SRms WCot
	'Lindsay'	WGoo
	'Lisa Tanner' (Va)	GWyn WGoo
	'Little Angel'	ECtt
	'Little David' (Vtta) ♀H5	CSam CTri ECtt MCot NDov WGoo
	'Lord Plunket' (Va)	WGoo
§	'Lord Primrose'	ECtt MHol
	'Lorna Cawthorne' (C)	MAsh SDys WGoo
	'Louisa' (Va)	GWyn WGoo
	'Lucy' (Va)	MAsh
§	***lutea***	SHar WGoo
	- subsp. ***elegans***	see *V. lutea*
	'Luxonne' (Vt)	CGro
	'Lydia Groves' (Vt)	CBod CDor CGro ECtt LLHF SRms WCot
	'Lydia's Legacy' (Vt)	CGro
	'Madame Armandine Pagès' (Vt)	CGro
	'Madeleine Mary Groves' (Vt) **new**	CGro
	'Maggie Mott' (Va) ♀H5	CSma ECha ECtt GWyn IRob MAsh MRav WGoo
	'Magic'	NDov WGoo
	mandshurica	GJos
	- f. ***albiflora***	SBrt
	- 'Fuji Dawn' (v)	GWyn WCot
	- f. ***plena*** (d)	GEdr
	- - white-flowered	GEdr
	mandshurica × ***patrinii***	SBrt
	'Margaret' (Va)	ECtt WGoo
	'Marie-Louise' (dPVt)	CGro GWyn SHar
	'Mars' (Va)	LEdu
I	'Mars'	LSRN WSpi
	'Martin' (Va) ♀H5	CAby CBod CMea CRav ECha ECtt EPfP GMaP GWyn LRHS LSRN MAsh MAvo MHer MHol MPie NDov SPer SPoG WGoo
	'Mary Mouse'	WGoo
	'Mauve Haze' (Va)	WGoo
	'Mauve Radiance' (Va)	WGoo
	'May Mott' (Va)	WGoo
	'Mayfly' (Va)	ECtt
	'Melinda' (Vtta)	WGoo
	'Mercury' (Va)	WGoo
	'Milkmaid' (Va)	ELon
	(Miracle Series) 'Miracle Barley Pink' (Vt) **new**	LCro LOPS
	- 'Miracle Bride White' (Vt)	CBod MHol SHar WFar
	- 'Miracle Classy Blue' (Vt) **new**	LCro LOPS
	- 'Miracle Classy Pink' (Vt)	CBod LCro LOPS MHol SHar WFar WHlf
	- 'Miracle Ice White' (Vt)	CBod NLar SHar WHlf
	- 'Miracle Intense Blue' (Vt)	NLar WFar WHlf
	- 'Miracle Vanilla White' (Vt)	SHar
	'Miss Brookes' (Va)	WGoo
	'Misty Guy' (Vtta)	MAsh WGoo
	'Molly Sanderson' (Va) ♀H5	CAby CPla ECha ECtt ELan EPfP GWyn LRHS MAsh MHer NEgg NRHS SCob SPer SPlb SPoG SRms WFar WGoo
	'Moonlight' (Va) ♀H5	ELan LRHS NRHS WGoo
	'Morwenna' (Va)	ECtt GWyn MAsh MCot NDov WGoo
	'Mrs Lancaster' (Va)	EBee ECtt ELan GMaP GWyn LSRN NLar NWad SDys SPoG WGoo WTor
	'Mrs Pinehurst' (Vt)	CGro EBee GMaP GWyn SRms
	'Mrs R. Barton' (Vt)	CDor CGro SHar SRms

	'Myfawnny' (Va)	LRHS NDov NRHS SDys WFar WGoo WSpi
	'Neapolitan'	see *V.* 'Pallida Plena'
	'Netta Statham'	see *V.* 'Belmont Blue'
	'Nora' (Va)	ECtt NDov WGoo
	'Norah Leigh' (Va)	WGoo
	obliqua	see *V. cucullata*
	odorata (Vt)	CBcs CBod CGro CHab EPfP GPoy LCro LRHS MRav NMir SEND SRms SVic WOut XAbr
	- 'Alba' (Vt)	CGro EBee ELan EPfP LEdu MHer SEND SRms WMoo
	- 'Alba Plena' (dVt)	EHrv
	- 'Albiflora' (Vt)	EPfP
	- 'Amethyst Witch' (Vt)	CGro
	- apricot-flowered	see *V.* 'Sulfurea'
	- 'Bethan Davies' (d/Vt)	WCot
	- 'Christopher William Groves' (Vt)	CGro
	- 'Copper Pennies' (Vt)	CGro
	- 'Cyclops' (Vt)	CGro
	- 'Dawnie' (Vt)	CGro EBee
	- 'Double Rose' (d)	WCot
	- var. ***dumetorum***	see *V. alba*
	- 'Elsmeer' (Vt)	ECtt WCot
	- 'Empress Augusta' (Vt)	CGro
	- 'Explorateur Dybowski' (Vt)	CGro
	- 'Hungarian Beauty' (Vt)	EBee LCro LOPS
	- 'King of Violets' (dVt)	ECtt SHar SPer
	- 'Lees Ivory' (Vt)	CGro
	- 'Little Plum' (Vt)	CGro
	- 'Melanie' (Vt)	CDor CGro MNrw WArt WCot
	- 'Mrs R.O. Barlow' (Vt)	WCot WSHC
	- 'Piddle Pink' (Vt)	CGro
	- pink-flowered	see *V. odorata* Rosea Group
	- 'Princess Thirza' (Vt)	CGro
	- ***rosea***	see *V. odorata* Rosea Group
§	- Rosea Group (Vt)	CBod CDor IFoB MRav SEND SPer SRms WCot
	- 'Stonehill Shadow' (Vt) **new**	WOut
	- 'Sulphurea'	see *V.* 'Sulfurea'
	- 'Vin d'André Thorp' (Vt)	ECtt LEdu WCot
I	- 'Violett Charm' (Vt)	WCot
	- 'Wismar' (Vt)	WCot
	'Olive Edwards' (Va)	WGoo
	'Opéra' (Vt)	LLHF
	'Orchid Pink' (Vt)	CGro EBee GMaP LEdu MNrw
	orientalis	GEdr
§	'Pallida Plena' (dPVt)	CGro WHer
	palustris	EBWF EWat LLWG WHer WSFF WShi
	'Pamela Zambra' (Vt)	SHar WSHC
	PANOLA YELLOW AND PURPLE ('Pas 341442') (Panola Series) (P) **new**	LRHS NRHS
	papilionacea	see *V. sororia*
	'Parchment' (Vt)	CGro EBee GWyn
	'Parme de Toulouse' (dPVt)	CGro EWTr GWyn NLar WHer XLum
	'Pasha' (Va)	ECtt GWyn SDys
	'Pat Creasy' (Va)	NDov WGoo
	'Pat Kavanagh' (C)	MAsh WGoo
	'Patience'	WGoo
	'Patricia Lillington' (Va)	GWyn
	pedata	CBro MPie WAbe
	- f. ***alba***	GEdr
	- 'Bicolor'	WAbe
	pedatifida	IFoB
	- white-flowered	WArt
	pensylvanica	see *V. pubescens* var. *eriocarpa*
	'Peppered-palms'	EHrv
	'Perle Rose' (Vt)	CGro EHrv SHar
	persicifolia **new**	EBWF
	'Petra' (Vtta)	GWyn SPhx WGoo
	phalacrocarpa	SBrt
	'Phyl Dove' (Vt)	WCot
	'Pickering Blue' (Va)	WGoo
	pinnata	SBrt
	'Primrose Dame' (Va)	ECtt WGoo
	'Primrose Pixie' (Va)	WGoo
	'Prince Henry' (T)	MNHC
	'Prince John' (T)	MNHC
	'Princess Diana' (Vt)	EBee
	'Princess Mab' (Vtta)	WGoo
	'Princess of Prussia' (Vt)	CGro WCot
	'Princess of Wales'	see *V.* 'Princesse de Galles'
§	'Princesse de Galles' (Vt)	CGro CTri
	prionantha	GEdr
§	***pubescens*** var. ***eriocarpa***	SRms
	'Purple Wings' (Va)	WGoo
	QUEEN CHARLOTTE	see *V.* 'Königin Charlotte'
	'Raven'	LRHS SPhx WGoo
	'Rebecca' (Vtta)	CAby CBod CDor CPla CSam ECtt ELan EPfP GMaP GWyn IPot LRHS LSRN MAsh MCot MHer MHol NDov NEgg NLar NRHS SDys SPer SPoG WFar WGoo WHer
	'Red Charm' (Vt)	CGro
	'Red Giant' (Vt)	CGro EHrv LEdu MBNS
	'Red Lion' (Vt)	CGro
	reichenbachiana	GJos
	'Reine des Blanches' (dVt)	EBee ECtt LEdu SPer SRms WCot WOut
	'Reine des Neiges' (Vt)	CDor CGro
	reniforme	see *V. hederacea*
	riviniana	EBWF GJos MHer MMuc WHer WOut WSFF WShi
	- dark pink-flowered	MMuc WOut
§	- Purpurea Group	CBcs CBod CMac EBee ECha EHoe EPfP EWes GAbr MHer MPie MRav NDov NRya NSti SPer SPhx SPlb SRms WFar WMoo
	- white-flowered	EWes
	'Roem van Aalsmeer'	GBin
	'Roscastle Black'	CMea CSma EPfP GWyn IRob MAsh NDov WGoo WSpi
	'Royal Elk' (Vt)	CGro
	'Rubra' (Vt)	EPfP GJos WArt WOut XLum
*	***rupestris rosea***	IFro WHer WPtf
	'Saint Helena' (Vt)	CGro WCot
	'Sally' (Vtta)	CGro
	selkirkii Pursh ex Goldie	WThu
	- 'Variegata' (v)	XEll
	sempervirens	SBrt
	septentrionalis	see *V. sororia*
	'Serena' (Va)	WGoo
	'Sherbet Dip'	WGoo
	'Sidborough Poppet'	EWes
	'Silver Samurai'	WCot
	'Smugglers' Moon'	ECtt GWyn WGoo
	somchetica	WCot
	'Sophie' (Vtta)	WGoo
	'Sorbet Series'	NPri
§	***sororia***	CBod ECha EPPr GWyn MNrw NBro SCob SPhx WGwG
*	- 'Albiflora' ♀H6	CHid EPPr EPfP EWTr LEdu LRHS LSun MRav SCob SPhx WCFE
	- 'Dark Freckles'	CGro EBee EWTr NLar NRya SPhx

§ - 'Freckles'	CBod CBro CMac CSBt CSam EBee ECha ECtt EPfP EWTr GKev LEdu LRHS LSun MAsh MHer MPie MRav NHpl NLar NRya SCob SPer SPhx SPlb SRkn WArt WCAu WFar WSHC
- 'Priceana'	CBod CMea EWTr LEdu MRav SHar SPlb WCot
- 'Sorority Sisters'	GJos NChi
- 'Speckles' (v)	WCot
- 'Sweet Emma'	SPhx
* 'Spencer's Cottage'	WGoo
STARRY NIGHT	see *V.* 'Lord Primrose'
'Steyning' (Va)	WGoo
stojanowii	GJos LLHF
§ 'Sulfurea' (Vt)	CDor EHrv MRav WCot
'Sundowner'	ECtt
'Sunny Jim' (Va) new	EVic
'Susanne Lucas' (Vt)	CGro
'Susie' (Va)	GWyn MCot WFar WGoo
'Swanley White'	see *V.* 'Conte di Brazza'
'Sweetheart' (Va) new	EVic
'Sybil' (SP)	WGoo
TEARDROPS MIXED (P) new	ETMg
'Thalia' (Vtta)	GWyn
§ 'The Czar' (Vt)	CBre SHar WCot
'Tiger Eyes' (Va)	CMea SPoG
'Titania' (Va)	EBee
'Tom Tit' (Va)	ECtt WGoo
'Tony Venison' (C/v)	ELon EPfP GWyn MHol NEgg NLar WFar WGoo WHer
tricolor	CBod CHab EBWF ENfk EPfP GPoy LCro LOPS MHer MNHC SRms XAbr
§ - subsp. ***curtisii***	EBWF
- 'Sawyer's Black'	ENfk
vaginata	GEdr
verecunda B&SWJ 604a	WCru
§ - var. ***yakusimana***	WThu
'Victoria'	see *V.* 'Czar Bleu'
'Victoria Cawthorne' (C)	IRob MAsh MHer NDov WFar WGoo
'Violacea' (C)	GAbr
'Virginia' (Va)	GWyn WGoo
'Vita' (Va)	ECtt SRms WGoo
'Wasp' (Va)	ECtt
'White Ladies'	see *V. cucullata* 'Alba'
'White Pearl' (Va)	SPhx WGoo
'White Perfection' (C)	GWyn
'White Swan' (Va)	MAsh
'Winifred Jones' (Va)	WGoo
'Wisley White'	LRHS
× ***wittrockiana*** BALLERINA MIXED (P) new	ETMg
- 'Deltini Rose Pink' (Deltini Series) (P) new	LRHS NRHS
- 'Dynamite Purple' (Dynamite Series) (P) new	XAbr
- FROU FROU mixed (P) new	ETMg
- Matrix Series (P)	ETMg NPri
- SORBET XP T&M MIX (Sorbet Series) (P) new	ETMg
- TEA PARTY mixed (P) new	ETMg
- 'Viking Northern Lights' (Viking Series) (P) new	MHol
- WATERFALL MIXED (P) new	ETMg
'Woodlands Cream' (Va)	GWyn MHer WGoo
'Woodlands Lilac' (Va)	WGoo
yakusimana	see *V. verecunda* var. *yakusimana*
yezoensis	SBrt
'Zara' (Va)	WGoo
'Zoe' (Vtta)	CBod ECtt EPfP GWyn MAsh NEgg SPoG WFar WGoo

Viscaria (*Caryophyllaceae*)

vulgaris	see *Lychnis viscaria*

Visnaga (*Apiaceae*)

§ ***daucoides***	CBre CHby CRav CSpe LRHS MNHC SPav SPhx SRms WCot WHal
- 'Green Mist' new	LCro MAvo

Vitaliana (*Primulaceae*)

§ ***primuliflora***	GKev NRya NSla
- subsp. ***praetutiana***	GCrg NWad WThu

Vitex (*Lamiaceae*)

agnus-castus	CAgr CBcs CMCN EPri EShb GPoy LEdu LRHS MRav NLar SLon SMad SPer SPoG WSHC XAbr XSen
- f. ***alba***	LRHS MBlu NLar NRHS SPoG XSen
- - PAB 9281	LEdu
- - 'Silver Spire'	CBot EBee ELan EMil EPfP NLar SRms WPGP
- f. ***latifolia*** ♀H5	CBot ECre ELan EPfP LRHS LSRN MGos MHer NLar NRHS SEND SPoG WHlf WPGP
chinensis	see *V. negundo* var. *heterophylla*
incisa	see *V. negundo* var. *heterophylla*
lucens	CPla
negundo	LEdu
§ - var. ***heterophylla***	EWes SBrt XSen
trifolia 'Purpurea'	LRHS

Vitis ✿ (*Vitaceae*)

amurensis	EPfP WSpi
- B&SWJ 4138	WCru
- B&SWJ 4299	WCru
- B&SWJ 12568	WCru
§ 'Aurore' (W)	CAgr
'Baco Noir' (O/B)	CAgr SDea
'Bata'	SDea
'Beauty Seedless' (B/S)	SDea
betulifolia	EPfP
BLACK HAMBURGH	see *V. vinifera* 'Schiava Grossa'
* 'Black Strawberry' (B)	CAgr SDea
'Blanc Seedless' (W/S)	SDea
§ 'Boskoop Glory' (O/B) ♀H5	CMac EMOT ERea ETod LBuc SCob SCoo SDea WHar
'Brant' (O/B) ♀H5	Widely available
californica (F)	EPfP NLar
'Canadice' (O/R/S)	SDea
'Cascade'	see *V.* SEIBEL 13053
CLARET CLOAK ('Frovit'PBR) ♀H5	CBot ELan EPfP EUJe GBin LRHS LSRN MAsh MBlu NLar SCoo SPer SPtp WPGP WSpi
coignetiae ♀H5	Widely available
- B&SWJ 4550 from Korea	WCru
- B&SWJ 4744	WCru
- B&SWJ 8553 from Korea	WCru
- B&SWJ 10882 from Japan	WCru
- B&SWJ 10908 from Japan	WCru
- var. ***glabrescens*** B&SWJ 8537	WCru
- 'Purple Cloak'	SCob
- Sunningdale form	NLar WGrn
ficifolia	see *V. thunbergii*
flexuosa B&SWJ 5568	WCru
- B&SWJ 6304	WCru
- var. ***choii*** B&SWJ 4101	WCru

- var. ***parvifolia***	NLar
- - B&SWJ 1946	WCru
'Fragola' (O/R)	CAgr CDul CFGn CMac CTri ECha EPfP EPom ERea LRHS MCoo MRav NLar SDea SLim SRms WSpi
'Gagarin Blue' (O/B)	CAgr EPom SDea SVen
'Glenora' (F/B/S)	CAgr
henryana	see *Parthenocissus henryana*
'Himrod' (O/W/S)	CCCN ELan ERea SDea
inconstans	see *Parthenocissus tricuspidata*
'Interlaken' (O/W/S)	CAgr ERea SDea
'Johanniter' (W)	SPre
'Kempsey Black' (O/B)	CAgr
'Léon Millot' (O/G/B)	CAgr CSBt LSRN SDea
'Maréchal Joffre' (O/R)	CAgr
'Muscat Bleu' (O/B)	CCCN CFGn EPom LRHS NLar SKee SLim SPoG
'Nero'[PBR]	CAgr
'Phönix' (O/W)	CAgr CCCN EPom LBuc LCro LOPS LRHS LSRN MAsh MGos NLar NPla NRHS SKee SLim SPer SPoG SPre SVic
piasezkii var. ***pagnuccii***	WCru
'Pirovano 14' (O/B)	SDea
'Poloske Muscat' (W)	CCCN CFGn EPom ERea NLar
pulchra	WCru
purpurea 'Spetchley Park' (O/B)	CAgr
quinquefolia	see *Parthenocissus quinquefolia*
'Regent'[PBR] (O/B)	CAgr CCCN CFGn CTri EPom ERea LCro LOPS LRHS MCoo MGos NLar SKee SLim SPoG SPre SVic
'Reliance' (O/R/S)	CAgr ERea
'Rembrant' (R)	CAgr
riparia	NLar
'Rondo' (O/B)	CAgr CFGn LRHS NPla SDea SPre SVic
'Saturn' (O/R/S)	CAgr
'Schuyler' (O/B)	CAgr
SEIBEL (F)	EPfP SDea
SEIBEL 5279	see *V.* 'Aurore'
§ SEIBEL 13053 (O/B)	CMac LRHS NRHS SDea SEND SRms
§ 'Seyval Blanc' (O/W)	CAgr MAsh SDea SEND SVic
SEYVE VILLARD 20.473 (F)	NPer
SEYVE VILLARD 5276	see *V.* 'Seyval Blanc'
SEYVE VILLARD ambig.	LRHS NPer
'Solaris' (O/W)	LRHS MCoo NLar
'Suffolk Seedless' (B/S)	ERea
'Tereshkova' (O/B)	CAgr SDea
§ ***thunbergii*** B&SWJ 4702	WCru
'Triomphe d'Alsace' (O/B)	CAgr CSBt LRHS MCoo NPer NRHS SDea
'Trollinger'	see *V. vinifera* 'Schiava Grossa'
'Vanessa' (O/R/S)	EPom SDea
vinifera	EUJe LMaj
§ - 'Alicante' (G/B)	CBcs CMac SDea
- 'Bacchus' (O/W)	CAgr CFGn ERea LRHS NLar SDea SLim SVic
- 'Baresana' (G/W)	EMOT NPla SRms
- 'Beauty'	CAgr
- 'Black Alicante'	see *V. vinifera* 'Alicante'
- 'Black Beauty' (B)	SDea
- 'Black Corinth' (G/B/S)	ERea
- BLACK HAMBURGH	see *V. vinifera* 'Schiava Grossa'
- 'Black Prince' (G/B)	CAgr
- 'Buckland Sweetwater' (G/W)	SDea SLim
- 'Cabernet Sauvignon' (O/B)	EPfP EUJe LRHS MAsh MGos NPer NRHS SDea SVic
- 'Chardonnay' (O/W)	CAgr CCCN LRHS LSRN MAsh NPer SDea SPre SVic
§ - 'Chasselas' (G/O/W)	LRHS SDea
- 'Chasselas de Fontainebleau' (G/O/W)	SVic
- 'Chasselas d'Or'	see *V. vinifera* 'Chasselas'
- 'Chasselas Rosé' (G/R)	CAgr
- 'Chasselas Rosé Royal' (O/R)	CCCN SVic
- 'Chenin Blanc' (O/W)	SVic
- 'Ciotat' (F)	ERea EShb MRav SDea
- 'Crimson Seedless' (R/S)	ERea
- 'Dattier Saint Vallier' (O/W)	SVic
- 'Dornfelder' (O/R)	CCCN CFGn ERea NLar SLim SPoG SVic
- 'Exalta' (G/W/S)	CCCN
- 'Excelsior' (W)	SDea
- 'Flame' (R/S)	CAgr CFGn NPla SPoG SVic WHar
- 'Flame Red' (O/D)	CCCN EPom
- 'Flame Seedless' (G/O/R/S)	CMac EPom
- 'Foster's Seedling' (G/W)	SDea SVic
- 'Gamay Noir' (O/B)	SVic
- 'Gewürztraminer' (O/R)	LRHS MAsh NRHS SDea SVic
- 'Glory of Boskoop'	see *V.* 'Boskoop Glory'
- 'Golden Chasselas'	see *V. vinifera* 'Chasselas'
- 'Huxelrebe' (O/W)	SVic
- 'Incana' (O/B)	EBee ELon LRHS MRav SVen WCFE WCot WPGP WSHC
- 'Italia' (O/W)	NPla
- 'King's Ruby' (F/S)	ERea
- 'Lady Hastings' (G/B)	ERea
- 'Lakemont' (O/W/S)	CAgr CCCN CFGn CMac CTri ELan EMOT EPfP EPom ERea LRHS MGos NLar NPla NRHS SDea SEWo SKee SLim SPoG SPre SVic WHar
- 'Madeira Frontignan' (G/R)	ERea
- 'Madeleine Angevine' (O/W)	CAgr LRHS LSRN MAsh NPer NRHS SDea SVen SVic
- 'Madeleine Silvaner' (O/W)	CSBt LRHS MAsh NPer NRHS SDea
- 'Merlot' (G/B)	EPfP EUJe LRHS NRHS SDea SVic
§ - 'Meunier' (B)	SVic
- 'Mireille' (F)	SDea
- 'Mrs Pearson' (G/W)	ERea
§ - 'Müller-Thurgau' (O/W)	LRHS LSRN MAsh SDea SVic
- 'Muscat Blanc à Petits Grains' (O/W)	SWvt
- 'Muscat Cannon Hall' (G/W)	CHll
- 'Muscat Hamburg' (G/B)	LRHS LSRN MAsh SDea SWvt
- 'Muscat of Alexandria' (G/W)	CBcs CCCN CMac CRHN CTri ERea LRHS MRav NRHS SDea SLim SPer SRms SVic WHar
- 'Ortega' (O/W)	CCCN
- 'Perlette' (O/W/S)	CCCN EPom ERea LRHS
- 'Pinot Blanc' (O/W)	CCCN LCro LOPS LRHS MAsh SVic
- 'Pinot Gris' (O/B)	SDea SVic
- 'Pinot Noir' (O/B)	CCCN SDea SVic
- 'Précoce de Malingre' (O/W)	CAgr SDea
- 'Purpurea' (O/B) ♀H5	Widely available
- 'Queen of Esther' (B)	SLim
- 'Reichensteiner' (O/G/W)	CAgr SDea SVic
- 'Riesling' (O/W)	CCCN LRHS MAsh SVic
- RIESLING-SILVANER	see *V. vinifera* 'Müller-Thurgau'
- 'Saint Laurent' (G/O/W)	SVic
- 'Sauvignon Blanc' (O/W)	CCCN LRHS NRHS SVic
§ - 'Schiava Grossa' (G/B/D)	CRHN CSBt CTri ECrN ELan EMOT EPfP EPom ERea LCro LOPS LRHS LSRN MAsh MRav NPer NPla NRHS

		SCob SDea SLim SPer SPoG SPre SVic SWvt WHar
	- 'Schönburger' (O/W)	SDea SVic
	- 'Schwarzriesling'	see *V. vinifera* 'Meunier'
	- 'Sémillon' (G/O/W)	LRHS LSRN MAsh SVic
	- 'Siegerrebe' (O/W/D)	CAgr LBuc LRHS MAsh NPer SDea SPoG SVic
	- 'Spetchley Red' (O/B) ♀H5	CKel CRHN EBee NLar WAvo WCot WCru WMou WPGP WSpi
	- strawberry grape	see *V.* 'Fragola'
	- 'Suffolk Red' (G/R/S)	ERea SDea
§	- 'Sultana' (W/S)	CAgr NPla SDea
	- 'Theresa' (O/W)	SLim
	- 'Thompson Seedless'	see *V. vinifera* 'Sultana'
*	- 'Triomphe' (O/B)	SVic
	- 'Vroege van der Laan' (O/W)	EMOT ETod NLar SRms
	- 'Wrotham Pinot' (O/B)	SDea
	'Zalagyöngye' (W)	CAgr

Vriesea (*Bromeliaceae*)

'Era'PBR	NLos
gigantea 'Nova'	NLos
splendens ♀H1a	NLos SPlb XBlo

W

Wachendorfia (*Haemodoraceae*)

multiflora	CTal SVen
paniculata	CTal
thyrsiflora	CBcs CBod CExl EBee LEdu NLos SBrt SVen WPGP

Wahlenbergia (*Campanulaceae*)

congesta	NWad
pumilio	see *Edraianthus pumilio*
serpyllifolia	see *Edraianthus serpyllifolius*

Waldsteinia (*Rosaceae*)

	fragarioides	EBee IMou
	geoides	EPPr MGil MMuc NEoE SPer WMoo XLum
	- 'Goldkäfer'	IMou
	ternata	Widely available
§	- 'Mozaick' (v)	EBee EPPr EShb EWes NEoE
	- 'Variegata'	see *W. ternata* 'Mozaick'

walnut, black see *Juglans nigra*

walnut, common see *Juglans regia*

Wasabia (*Brassicaceae*)

wasabi	see *Eutrema japonicum*

Washingtonia (*Arecaceae*)

× ***filibusta*** ♀H1c	CCCN CPHo SArc SBig SEND SPlb
robusta	EUJe SPlb XBlo

Watsonia (*Iridaceae*)

	aletroides	CPbh CPrp EBee GBin GCal GKev SDeJ SVen
	amatolae	IBlr
	angusta	CExl CPrp CTal EBee IBlr SPlb
	'Apricot Queen'	CPla
	ardernei	see *W. borbonica* subsp. *ardernei* (Sander) Goldblatt 'Arderne's White'
	'Ballyrogan Early Pink'	IBlr
	beatricis	see *W. pillansii*
§	***borbonica***	CPne CPrp EBee NRHS
	- subsp. ***ardernei*** misapplied	see *W. borbonica* subsp. *ardernei* (Sander) Goldblatt 'Arderne's White'
§	- subsp. ***ardernei*** (Sander) Goldblatt 'Arderne's White'	CBre CExl CPrp GBin GCal IBlr
	- subsp. ***borbonica***	CTal IBlr
	- 'Peach Glow'	EBee ERCP GKev SDeJ
	brevifolia	see *W. laccata*
	brick red-flowered	EBee LEdu WPGP
	coccinea Herb. ex Baker	CBlu CPbh
	'Curly Blooms'	CPbh
	'Dart Sea Trout'	EBee
	densiflora	CTal
	early pink-flowered	CPne
	fourcadei	ECre GCal
	fulgens	LEdu
	galpinii lavender-flowered	IBlr
	- pink-flowered	IBlr
	galpinii × ***knysnana***	IBlr
I	'Gigantea'	LRHS
§	***humilis***	CPrp EBee GCal
	knysnana	EBee IBlr
§	***laccata***	CPbh CPne
	- orange-flowered	CTal
	- pink-flowered	EBee
	latifolia	IBlr
	lepida	CPbh SPlb
	× ***longifolia*** dark red-flowered	GCal
	marginata	CPbh CPrp EBee
	meriana	CPne EBee ERCP GBin GKev IBlr MPie MWat SDeJ
	- var. ***bulbillifera***	CPrp CTal EBee GAbr GBin GCal IBlr WSHC
	'Peachy Pink Orphan'	EBee
§	***pillansii***	CAbb CCCN CExl CPrp CTal EBee ECre EPri EWld GBin IBlr ILea LEdu LRHS SVen
	- apricot-flowered	CAbb
	- peach-flowered	CExl
	- pink-flowered	CExl CPrp
	- red-flowered	CExl
	- soft pink-flowered	EPri
	pink-flowered	EBee
	pyramidata	see *W. borbonica*
	roseoalba	see *W. humilis*
	'Stanford Scarlet'	CAby CExl CPrp EBee ELon
	tabularis	CPrp IMou
	transvaalensis	EBee
	'Tresco Dwarf Pink'	CExl CPrp EBee LEdu WPGP
	Tresco hybrids	CAbb CAby CBcs CExl CPbh EPri SRkn
	vanderspuyae	CExl CPrp CTal EPri
	wilmaniae	CExl CPrp EBee IBlr WFar
	wordsworthiana	GCal
	zeyheri	EBee

Wattakaka see *Dregea*

Wedelia (*Asteraceae*)

trilobata	see *Sphagneticola trilobata*

Weigela ✿ (*Caprifoliaceae*)

	CC 1231	CExl
	'Abel Carrière'	CMac CTri ECtt SRms WCFE WSpi
§	ALL SUMMER RED ('Slingco 1'PBR)	EPfP LCro LOPS LRHS NRHS SPoG
	'Avalanche' misapplied	see *W.* 'Candida'

'Avalanche' Lemoine	EPfP
'Avant Garde'	MAsh
BLACK AND WHITE ('Courtacad1'[PBR])	CBcs CBot CWGN EBee EPfP LRHS LSRN NEoE NLar NRHS SCob SEle SGol SPoG
'Boskoop Glory'	SPer
§ BRIANT RUBIDOR ('Olympiade') (v)	CAby CBot CMac CRos ECrN EHoe EMOT ESps GMcL LRHS MAsh MGos MMuc MRav NEgg NLar NQui SCob SGol SLim SPer SPlb SPoG WAvo WHar WSpi
'Bristol Ruby'	Widely available
'Bristol Snowflake'	CDul CMac EPfP MBlu MHer MSwo NLar SLon SRms
§ 'Candida'	CTri ELan EWTr MRav NLar SGol SPer WSpi
CAPPUCCINO ('Verweig 2'[PBR])	MBlu NLar SGol
CARNAVAL ('Courtalor'[PBR]) ♀H6	CBcs GMcL MRav NLar SCob
'Chameleon'	MPkF NEoE
coraeensis ♀H6	CHll EPfP IArd IDee MBlu MGil MMrt MNrw NLar SBrt SPer
- 'Alba'	CHll
CRIMSON KISSES	see *W.* ALL SUMMER RED
decora B&SWJ 10834	WCru
EBONY AND IVORY ('Velda'[PBR])	CRos LCro LOPS LRHS NRHS
'Eva Rathke'	NLar
'Evita'	IBoy MBlu
floribunda B&SWJ 10831	WCru
florida	CMac ESps
- B&SWJ 8439	WCru
- f. ***alba***	CBcs
* - 'Albovariegata' (v)	CExl
- 'Bicolor'	CMac ELan
- 'Foliis Purpureis'	Widely available
- 'Gustave Malet'	CMCN
- MAGICAL FANTASY	see *W.* SUNNY FANTASY
- MAGICAL RAINBOW ('Kolmagira'[PBR])	LBuc LCro LOPS LRHS MJak MPkF NEoE NRHS SGol SPoG
- 'Milk and Honey'	LRHS NRHS
- MINOR BLACK ('Verweig 3'[PBR])	EPfP GMcL LRHS MGos MPkF NBro NEoE NLar SGol SPoG WMoo
- MONET ('Verweig'[PBR]) (v)	CDul CMac CRos EBee EHoe EPfP EShb ESps ETMg GMcL IBoy LBuc LCro LOPS LRHS LSRN MAsh MGos MJak MMrt NBro NLar NRHS SCob SGol SLim SPer SPoG SRms WHar
- MOULIN ROUGE ('Brigela'[PBR])	CRos ELan EPfP LCro LOPS LRHS MAsh MGos SLim WCot
- 'Pink Princess'	LRHS MSwo WHar
- RUBIGOLD	see *W.* BRIANT RUBIDOR
§ - SUNNY FANTASY ('Kolsunn')	MPkF NEoE WHil
- 'Versicolor'	CExl SLon SRms
- WINE AND ROSES ('Alexandra'[PBR]) ♀H6	CDul CExl CRos CSBt EHoe ELan EMil EPfP ESps GKin IBoy LRHS LSRN MAsh MGos MRav NBro NEgg NLar NRHS SCob SEle SPoG SRGP SRkn SWvt WGrn
- 'Wings of Fire'[PBR]	LBuc LRHS NRHS SCob
'Florida Variegata' (v) ♀H6	Widely available
'Gold Rush'	NLar
'Golden Candy'	NEoE SCob
hortensis	CExl
- B&SWJ 10808	WCru
'Hulsdonk'	NLar
japonica 'Dart's Colourdream'	CAby EHoe EWes MMrt MMuc SCob SEND SGol WGrn
- 'Variegated Dart's Colourdream' (v)	ELon
'Jean's Gold'	ELan MBlu MRav
'Kosteriana Variegata' (v)	CSBt EBee EPfP ESps LRHS MAsh MMuc NEgg SEle SRms
'Little Red Robin'	NEoE SCob
'Looymansii Aurea'	CBot CExl CTri ELan EPfP NLar SGol SPer SRms
LUCIFER ('Courtared'[PBR])	WSpi
maximowiczii	CExl LLHF
§ ***middendorffiana***	CBcs CBot CExl CMCN CMac CTri EBee ELan EPfP GMcL LRHS MAsh MBlu MGil MMuc MRav NEgg NLar NSti NSum SBrt SChF SCob SCoo SPer SPoG WCru WHar WPGP WSHC
- 'Mango'	LCro LOPS LRHS NRHS
'Minuet'	LRHS MRav MSwo NEoE SGol
'Mont-Blanc'	MAsh MMrt
NAIN ROUGE ('Courtanin'[PBR])	CTri NLar
'Nana Variegata' (v)	CExl ECrN ELon EPfP ETMg GMcL LCro LRHS MJak NLar NRHS SCob
NAOMI CAMPBELL ('Bokrashine'[PBR])	EBee EShb GKin MMrt NEgg NLar SGol WMoo
'Newport Red'	see *W.* 'Vanicek'
PINK POPPET ('Plangen'[PBR])	CBot CRos CSBt ELan EMOT EPfP ESps GBin GKin LCro LOPS LRHS LSRN LSou MAsh MGos MPkF NLar NRHS SCob SCoo SLim SPoG SRkn SWvt
praecox	ECrN
- B&SWJ 8705	WCru
'Praecox Variegata' (v) ♀H6	CMac CTri EPfP ESps LRHS MAsh MRav NRHS SPer SPoG SRms WCFE WKif
'Red Prince' ♀H6	CWCL EBee ELan EMOT EPfP ESps GMcL LRHS MAsh MMrt MSwo NLar SCob SGol SPoG
RUBIDOR	see *W.* BRIANT RUBIDOR
RUBIGOLD	see *W.* BRIANT RUBIDOR
'Ruby Anniversary'	CBcs LBuc LRHS SLon
'Ruby Queen'[PBR]	CMac EPfP
RUBY WEDDING	LSRN
'Rumba'	CMac MRav
sessilifolia	see *Diervilla sessilifolia*
'Snowflake'	SRms
'Stelzneri'	MMuc
subsessilis B&SWJ 1056	WCru
- B&SWJ 4206	WCru
'Suzanne' (v)	EPPr MAsh
'Tango'	LRHS MAsh NEoE WAvo
§ 'Vanicek'	GMcL MBNS
'Victoria'	CDul CMac ECrN EHoe ELan EPPr EPfP ESps LRHS MGos MSwo NWad SCob SGol SPer WHar WMoo
WHITE LIGHTNING ('Wf-2009') (v) **new**	NEoE

Weldenia (*Commelinaceae*)

candida	GEdr IBlr LLHF SChF WCot

Westringia (*Lamiaceae*)

brevifolia	SVen
- 'Grace'	LRHS
§ ***fruticosa*** ♀H1c	CBcs CCCN CHll SRms SVen
- 'Smokie' (v)	CCCN CTsd
- 'Variegata' (v)	CCCN CPbh SRms SVen
longifolia	CCCN

	rosmariniformis	see *W. fruticosa*
	'Wynyabbie Gem'	CAbb CCCN EBee LRHS SEND SPoG SVen

whitecurrant see *Ribes rubrum* (W)

Wigandia (*Boraginaceae*)

	caracasana	CHll

Wikstroemia (*Thymelaeaceae*)

	gemmata	see *Daphne gemmata*

wineberry see *Rubus phoenicolasius*

Wisteria ✿ (*Papilionaceae*)

	'Betty's Dwarf Blue'	NLar
§	***brachybotrys***	CRos ERea NRHS SCob WSpi
§	- Murasaki-kapitan	CEnd CRos CTri CWGN EBtc EMil EPfP LRHS MGil SEND
	- 'Okayama' ♀^{H5}	EPfP ERea LRHS NOra NRHS SLau
§	- 'Shiro-kapitan' ♀^{H5}	CAby CBcs CEnd CFlo CRHN CTri CWGN EPfP LSRN MAsh MGil MGos MMuc MRav NLar SEND SLau SLim SPer WPGP WSpi
	- 'Showa-beni' ♀^{H5}	CEnd CFlo CKel CRHN CTri CWGN EMil EPfP LRHS MGil MGos MMuc NLar SCoo SEND SLau SLim WPGP WSpi
*	- 'White Silk'	CBcs CKel CRos EPfP LRHS LSRN MGos NPla SLon SPoG WSpi
§	'Burford' ♀^{H5}	CEnd CFlo CKel CWGN EBee EMil EPfP ERea LRHS LSRN MAsh NLar NOra SCob SCoo SEND SLau SLim SRms WHar WPGP WSpi
	'Caroline'	CBcs CCCN CFlo CRos CWCL CWGN EMil EPfP ERea IBoy LRHS LSRN MAsh MGos MJak MRav NLar NOra NRHS SCob SLau SMad SNig SPer SPoG SRms WHar WPGP
	floribunda	CBcs CRHN ELan ESps IBoy SCob SEWo SGol
	- B&SWJ 12748 from South Korea	WCru
§	- 'Alba' ♀^{H5}	Widely available
	- 'Black Dragon'	see *W. floribunda* 'Russelliana'
	- 'Burford'	see *W.* 'Burford'
	- 'Cascade'	CBcs SNig
§	- 'Domino' ♀^{H5}	CBcs CKel CMac CRos CWGN ELon EPfP ESps IArd LRHS LSRN MAsh MGos MMuc MRav MSwo NLar NPla SCoo SEND SGol SLau SLim SPer SSta WHar
	- 'Ed's Blue Dragon' (d)	NPla
	- 'Fragrantissima'	see *W. sinensis* 'Jako'
	- 'Geisha'	CAby CBcs CEnd CFlo CKel CRos ELon LRHS NRHS SEND SNig SRms WPGP
	- 'Golden Dragon'	EPfP
	- 'Harlequin'	CBcs CFlo CRos CWCL EHyd ELon LRHS MMuc NPla SEND
	- 'Hocker Edge'	SLau
	- 'Hon-beni'	see *W. floribunda* 'Rosea'
	- 'Honey Bee Pink'	see *W. floribunda* 'Rosea'
	- 'Honko'	see *W. floribunda* 'Rosea'
	- 'Issai Perfect'	CRos EHyd LRHS LSRN NLar SCoo SLon
	- 'Issai-naga'	ESps NLar
	- 'Jakohn-fuji'	see *W. sinensis* 'Jako'
	- 'Kimono'	SLau
§	- 'Kuchi-beni'	CBcs CEnd CKel CRHN CRos ELan GBin IBoy LCro LOPS LRHS LSRN MGos MRav NLar SEND SLau SMad SPer SPoG SRms WHar
	- 'Lawrence' ♀^{H5}	CBcs CEnd CFlo CKel CRos CWCL CWGN EBtc LRHS NLar SLau SPoG
	- 'Lipstick'	see *W. floribunda* 'Kuchi-beni'
	- 'Longissima'	see *W. floribunda* 'Multijuga'
	- 'Longissima Alba'	see *W. floribunda* 'Alba'
	- 'Macrobotrys'	see *W. floribunda* 'Multijuga'
	- 'Magenta'	LRHS NPla
§	- 'Multijuga' ♀^{H5}	Widely available
	- MURASAKI-NAGA	see *W. floribunda* 'Purple Patches'
	- 'Nana Richin's Purple'	CEnd LRHS SLau
	- 'New Pink'	LRHS NRHS
	- 'Peaches and Cream'	see *W. floribunda* 'Kuchi-beni'
	- 'Pink Ice'	see *W. floribunda* 'Rosea'
§	- 'Purple Patches'	WSpi
	- REINDEER	see *W. sinensis* 'Jako'
§	- 'Rosea' ♀^{H5}	Widely available
	- 'Royal Purple' ♀^{H5}	CEnd EMil EPfP IArd NLar SGol SLau SPoG
§	- 'Russelliana'	CFlo CKel GBin
	- 'Shiro-naga'	see *W. floribunda* 'Alba'
	- 'Shiro-nagi'	see *W. floribunda* 'Alba'
	- 'Shiro-noda'	see *W. floribunda* 'Alba'
	- 'Snow Showers'	see *W. floribunda* 'Alba'
	- 'Variegata' (v)	CWGN
	- 'Violacea Plena' (d) ♀^{H5}	CArg CBcs CMac MRav SNig SWvt
	- 'Yae-kokuryū' (d)	Widely available
	× ***formosa***	CEnd LCro LOPS SLau SLim
	- 'Black Dragon'	see *W. floribunda* 'Russelliana'
	- 'Domino'	see *W. floribunda* 'Domino'
	- 'Issai' Wada *pro parte*	see *W. floribunda* 'Domino'
	- 'Kokuryū'	see *W. floribunda* 'Russelliana'
	- 'Yae-kokuryū'	see *W. floribunda* 'Yae-kokuryu'
	frutescens	EBee EPfP
	- 'Alba'	see *W. frutescens* 'Nivea'
	- 'Amethyst Falls'^{PBR}	CBcs CEnd CWGN ELan EShb ESps IArd LCro LRHS LSRN MGos SCoo SLon SPoG WHlf
	- 'Longwood Purple'	LRHS NRHS SNig SPoG
§	- 'Nivea'	LRHS NRHS
	Kapitan-fuji	see *W. brachybotrys*
	'Lavender Lace'	CBcs CKel EPfP LRHS LSRN MAsh MJak NLar SLau
	macrostachya 'Aunt Dee'	CWGN NLar
	- 'Blue Moon'	GMcL NOra WHar
	- 'Clara Mack'	CWGN
	multijuga 'Alba'	see *W. floribunda* 'Alba'
	sinensis	Widely available
	- 'Alba'	CAco CBcs CMen CRos ELan EMOT EPfP ESps IBoy LCro LOPS LRHS LSRN MAsh MGil MGos MSwo NPla SCob SLau SPer SPoG SRms SWeb
	- 'Amethyst' ♀^{H5}	CAco CArg CBcs CEnd CKel CRav CRos EPfP LCro LOPS LRHS LSRN MAsh MGil MGos MJak NPla NRHS SLau SLim SPer SWeb WSpi
	- 'Consequa'	see *W. sinensis* 'Prolific'
	- 'Cooke's Special'	CWGN
§	- 'Jako' ♀^{H5}	CEnd
	- 'Oosthoek's Variety'	see *W. sinensis* 'Prolific'
I	- 'Pink Ice'	SRms
	- 'Prematura'	see *W. floribunda* 'Domino'
	- 'Prematura Alba'	see *W. brachybotrys* 'Shiro-kapitan'
§	- 'Prolific' ♀^{H5}	Widely available
	- 'Rosea'	CAco LSRN SCob SWvt
	- 'Shiro-capital'	see *W. brachybotrys* 'Shiro-kapitan'

'Tiverton' CBcs MJak NPla
venusta see *W. brachybotrys* 'Shiro-kapitan'
- 'Alba' see *W. brachybotrys* 'Shiro-kapitan'
- var. ***violacea*** misapplied see *W. brachybotrys* Murasaki-kapitan

Withania (*Solanaceae*)

somnifera GPoy XAbr

Wittsteinia (*Alseuosmiaceae*)

vacciniacea GEdr SBrt WCru

Wodyetia (*Arecaceae*)

bifurcata XBlo

Wollemia (*Araucariaceae*)

nobilis CDTJ CTho EPfP EUJe GBin LRHS MGos SArc

Woodsia ✿ (*Woodsiaceae*)

ilvensis NLos
obtusa CBdn CDTJ CKel CWCL EBee EFer EPfP IBal LRHS MMuc NBro NRHS SGol SPoG SRms SRot XLum
polystichoides SRms
pseudopolystichoides NLos

Woodwardia ✿ (*Blechnaceae*)

fimbriata ♀H3 CAby CBdn CBod CCCN CTal CWCL EFer EMOT EPfP ERod EUJe EWTr GCal GMcL IBal LCro LEdu LLWG LRHS NBro NLar NRHS SBig SEND SPlb WBor WCot WFib WMoo
japonica ESps
orientalis LEdu LRHS NLos NRHS WFib WPGP
- var. ***formosana*** B&SWJ 6865 WCru
radicans ♀H3 CHid CKel EShb EWes WFib XBlo
unigemmata ♀H4 CBdn CHid EFer EShb EWes LRHS NLos NRHS WAbe WFib WHal WPGP
virginica CBdn LRHS NRHS

Worcesterberry see *Ribes* 'Worcesterberry'

Wulfenia (*Plantaginaceae*)

amherstiana GEdr GKev LEdu
baldaccii EBee GKev SBrt
carinthiaca CPla CTal EBee GAbr GEdr GKev LEdu NLar WCot XLum
- 'Alba' GKev
orientalis CTal
× ***schwarzii*** EBee IMou LEdu WSHC

Wurmbea (*Colchicaceae*)

§ ***stricta*** WCot

Wyethia (*Asteraceae*)

angustifolia SBrt
helianthoides SBrt
mollis B&SWJ 14067 new WCru

X

Xanthisma (*Asteraceae*)

§ ***coloradoense*** LLHF NRHS NSla

Xanthoceras (*Sapindaceae*)

sorbifolium ♀H5 CAgr CBcs CLnd CMCN ELan EPfP IMou MBlu NLar SBrt WSpi

Xanthocyparis (*Cupressaceae*)

§ ***nootkatensis*** LPra
- 'Aurea' CAco
- 'Boyko's Sundown' NLar
- 'Glauca' CAco
- 'Golden Waterfall' NLar
- 'Green Arrow' ♀H6 CKen NOra SLim
- 'Jubilee' SLim WCFE
- 'Pendula' ♀H6 CAco CCVT CDul CKen ELan EPfP GKin LPra LRHS MAsh MBlu NEgg NRHS WCFE
- 'Sparkling Arrow' NLar
- 'Strict Weeper' CKen NLar SLim
vietnamensis WPGP

Xanthorhiza (*Ranunculaceae*)

simplicissima CBcs CDul EPfP LEdu MGil NLar SDys WCot WPGP

Xanthorrhoea (*Xanthorrhoeaceae*)

australis SPlb
fulva SPlb
glauca CCCN
johnsonii CKel SPlb
preisii SPlb

Xanthosoma (*Araceae*)

violaceum EUJe

Xerochrysum (*Asteraceae*)

sp. CPla
§ ***bracteatum*** SVen
§ - 'Coco' CSpe
§ - 'Dargan Hill Monarch' CHll CSpe SRms
'Sundaze Flame' CPla

Xeronema (*Xeronemataceae*)

callistemon CBcs CBrP CCCN LRHS

Xerophyllum (*Melanthiaceae*)

tenax CAco LRHS

Xerophyta (*Velloziaceae*)

viscosa new CPla

Y

Youngberry see *Rubus* 'Youngberry'

Ypsilandra (*Melanthiaceae*)

cavaleriei CExl GEdr WCot
thibetica CBct CExl CHid CSpe EBee EPfP GCal GEdr IRob LEdu LRHS MNrw NHim NLar SChF WCot WCru WSHC
- narrow-leaved WCru

Yucca ✿ (*Asparagaceae*)

aloifolia CBlu CCCN CDTJ ETod SArc SBig SCob SPlb
§ - f. ***marginata*** (v) SBig
- 'Purpurea' EBee

– 'Variegata'	see *Y. aloifolia* f. *marginata*
angustifolia	see *Y. glauca*
arizonica	CDTJ
baccata	CAco CAgr CCCN ETod NLos SPlb XSen
campestris	CDTJ XSen
carnerosana	CBlu CDTJ
cernua	WCot
constricta	CDTJ
decipiens	XSen
§ ***elata***	CCCN CTsd XSen
§ ***elephantipes*** ♀H2	CDTJ ETod EUJe LCro SEND
– 'Jewel' (v)	EUJe SEND
– 'Puck' (v)	SEND
– variegated (v)	SEND
faxoniana	CDTJ EUJe SPlb
filamentosa	CAco CBcs CCCN CDul CMac CTri EBee ELan EPfP ESps ETod EUJe LCro LRHS LSun MCri MGos MJak MMuc MSwo SBod SCob SEND SGol SLim SPer SPlb SRms XSen
– 'Antwerp'	GCal
– 'Bright Edge' (v) ♀H3	CBcs CDul CMac CTri ELan ELon EPfP ESps EUJe LCro LOPS LRHS LSRN MRav MSwo SChr SCob SGol SLim SPer SWvt
– 'Color Guard' (v) ♀H5	EPfP EUJe LRHS MJak SChr
– 'Garland's Gold' (v)	CBcs CCCN MJak SBig
– 'Variegata' (v)	CBcs ESps SCob SRms
filifera	EUJe SPlb
flaccida	SCob XSen
– 'Golden Sword' (v) ♀H3	CBcs CMac CTsd EBee ELan EPfP ESps GMaP GMcL LRHS LSRN MAsh MGos MJak MSwo SCob SGol SLim SPer SRms SWvt
– 'Ivory' ♀H5	CEnd CTsd ELan ELon ESps GBin GCal GMaP LSRN MRav NLar SPer SRms
× ***floribunda***	SArc
§ ***glauca***	EPfP SPlb WCot XSen
gloriosa ♀H5	CBcs CMac CTri ESps ETod EUJe NPla SArc SCob SEND SPer SPlb SPoG SWeb SWvt
– 'Aureovariegata'	see *Y. gloriosa* 'Variegata'
– BRIGHT STAR ('Walbristar'PBR)	SCob SPoG WCot
§ – 'Variegata' (v) ♀H5	CBcs CDul CMac CSBt CTsd ECrN ELan ELon EPfP ESps EUJe GMaP LRHS MRav NLos SArc SCob SEND SLim SPer SPlb SPoG SRms SWvt WCFE
guatemalensis	see *Y. elephantipes*
harrimaniae	WCot
linearifolia	WCot
linearis	see *Y. thompsoniana*
mexicana	CDTJ XSen
queretaroensis	CDTJ
radiosa	see *Y. elata*
recurvifolia ♀H5	EPfP ETod SArc
– BANANA SPLIT ('Monvil') (v)	EBee EPfP LBuc LRHS MAsh SPoG WCot
– 'Gold Stream' (v)	WCot
rigida	CDTJ WCot XSen
rostrata	CBlu CCCN CDTJ ETod EUJe SArc SPlb WCot XSen
– 'Sapphire Skies'	CMac EUJe LRHS NLos WCot
rupicola	WCot
schottii	EShb
§ ***thompsoniana***	CDTJ EUJe XSen
torreyi	CDTJ
'Vittorio Emanuele II'	SMad
whipplei	CCCN ELan EPfP LRHS SBig WPGP XSen
– subsp. ***whipplei*** NJM 11.001	WPGP

Yushania (*Poaceae*)

KR 7698	ERod MWht
§ ***anceps***	CAgr CBcs CDul CExl ENBC MMoz MMuc MWht SBig SEND WMoo
– 'Pitt White'	CAgr CBdn CExl MWht
– 'Pitt White Rejuvenated'	ERod
brevipaniculata	ERod
chungii	CBdn CExl ERod MWht
maculata	CAgr CBdn CDul CExl ERod MMoz MWht SBig
§ ***maling***	CBdn CExl ERod MMoz
Yunnan 5	CExl MWht

Z

Zabelia (*Caprifoliaceae*)

§ ***triflora***	CExl CRos CTho LRHS MMuc NLar SEND WPGP WSHC

Zaluzianskya (*Scrophulariaceae*)

JCA 15665	WAbe
elongata	SPlb
microsiphon	SPlb
ovata	CElw CPbh CSpe CTal CWCL EPfP EPot EWld GBin GKev LCro LOPS MHer NRHS NSla SPlb SPoG SPtp XEll
– 'Orange Eye'	CPBP CPbh CTal ECtt EWes GKev NHpl NRHS NSla
– 'Star Balsam'	CPla GWyn
pulvinata	SPlb
'Semonkong'	GCal SWvt

Zamia (*Zamiaceae*)

furfuracea 'Super'	NLos
pumila	SPlb

Zamioculcas (*Araceae*)

zamiifolia	CCCN LOPS

Zantedeschia (*Araceae*)

sp.	NRHS
§ ***aethiopica***	Widely available
– 'Childsiana'	LRHS NRHS
– 'Crowborough' ♀H4	Widely available
– 'Glencoe'	CBct CBod EBee ECtt GCal SPad WCot WRHF WSHC
– 'Glow'	CExl CMac ECtt IRob WAvo WGwG
– 'Green Goddess' ♀H2	Widely available
– 'Little Gem'	SMad
– 'Luzon Lovely'	WCru
– 'Marshmallow'	CAby ECtt ELan EPfP LLWG LRHS MAsh NRHS WAvo WFar WGwG
– 'Mr Martin'	CCCN ECtt ELon SBig SMad SWvt WCot WFar
– 'Pershore Fantasia' (v)	CExl WAvo WCot WFar
– 'Pink Mist'	GKev

- 'Spotted Giant' new	CDTJ
- 'White Gnome'	WCot
- 'White Sail'	ECtt ELan LRHS MRav NGdn NRHS WGwG
albomaculata	CTca GKev LAma SPlb WPGP
'Allure'PBR new	GKev
'Anneke'	CCCN SDeJ
'Apricot Glow'	CHll GKev
'Ascari'PBR	CCCN
'Auckland'PBR	GKev SDeJ
'Black Eyed Beauty'	GKev
'Black Magic'	CCCN CMac GKev
'Black Pearl'	LAma
'Black Star'	see *Z.* 'Edge of Night'
'Cameo'	CCCN LAma SDeJ
(Captain Series) 'Captain Florida'	SDir
- 'Captain Murano'PBR	SPoG
- 'Captain Prado'PBR	CRos EPfP LRHS NRHS SPoG
- 'Captain Reno'PBR	EPfP
- 'Captain Romance'PBR	LOPS
- 'Captain Tendens'PBR	SDeJ
'Chianti'	GKev SDeJ
'Crystal Blush'	LAma SDeJ SDir WHar
'Dark Eyes' new	CBod WHar
§ 'Edge of Night'	CCCN GKev SDeJ
'Elegant Swan'PBR	SCob
elliottiana ♀H1c	CBcs CTri EUJe LAma
'Flame'	CBcs CBod CCCN GKev
'Flamingo'PBR	GKev
'Garnet Glow'	SDir WHar
'Helen O'Connor'	CExl
jucunda	GKev
'Kiwi Blush'	CAby CBod CBro CCCN CExl CSpe CTca ELan ELon EPfP IRob LLWG LRHS NRHS WFar WGwG
'Lime Lady'	ECha EWat
'Majestic Red'	GKev
'Mango'	EPri EShb LAma MPie SRms
'Mercedes'PBR	LRHS NRHS
'Mozart'	CCCN SDeJ
'Odessa'PBR	CBod LOPS SPad WHar
'Orania'PBR new	LRHS NRHS
'Philomena'	LRHS NRHS
'Picasso'PBR	CBcs CCCN EPfP GKev SDeJ SDir SPad WCot WHar
'Pink Mist'	LAma LLWG SMad
'Pink Persuasion'	LAma
'Pink Royalty' new	CRos NRHS
'Red Alert'PBR	LRHS NRHS SPad SPoG
'Red Sox'PBR	CCCN SDeJ
rehmannii ♀H1c	GKev LAma SDeJ SRms
'San Remo'PBR	GKev LRHS NRHS
'Sapporo'PBR	LRHS NRHS
'Schwarzwalder'PBR	EShb GKev SDir
'Serrada' new	SPoG
'Summer Sun'PBR	LRHS NRHS
'White Giant'	EPri EWat WPGP
'White Pixie'	EPfP

Zanthorhiza see *Xanthorhiza*

Zanthoxylum (*Rutaceae*)

acanthopodium GWJ 9287	WCru
- PAB 8760	LEdu
- WJC 13653	WCru
ailanthoides B&SWJ 11115 from Japan	WCru
- B&SWJ 11394 from Japan	WCru
- from Taiwan new	WPGP
- f. ***inermis*** RWJ 10048	WCru
americanum	ELan LEdu
armatum	CAgr
- B&SWJ 12753	WCru
- CWJ 12824 new	WCru
- FMWJ 13091 new	WCru
- NJM 11.080	WPGP
- PAB 8902 new	LEdu
bungeanum BWJ 8040	WCru
clava-herculis	CFil
dissitum FMWJ 13498	WCru
fauriei B&SWJ 11080	WCru
aff. ***fauriei*** B&SWJ 11371	WCru
- B&SWJ 11523	WCru
laetum	CFil
- FMWJ 13175	WCru
- WWJ 11678	WCru
myriacanthum B&SWJ 11844	WCru
oxyphyllum	CMCN LEdu
- GWJ 9428	WCru
- HWJK 2131	WCru
piperitum	CAgr GPoy LEdu WPGP
- B&SWJ 8543	WCru
- B&SWJ 11377	WCru
- purple-leaved	CBcs CExl CFil EBee LEdu WPGP
schinifolium	CAgr LEdu
- B&SWJ 8593	WCru
- B&SWJ 11080	WCru
- B&SWJ 11391	WCru
simulans	CAgr CBcs CDul CExl LEdu MBlu WPGP
stenophyllum	CMCN
tomentellum B&SWJ 13903 new	WCru

Zauschneria (*Onagraceae*)

arizonica	see *Z. californica* subsp. *latifolia*
§ ***californica***	CHll CTri MBrN SLon SWvt XLum
§ - 'Dublin' ♀H4	Widely available
- 'Ed Carman'	ECha ECtt EUJe MGil MMuc
* - subsp. ***garrettii***	SDys XLum
- 'Glasnevin'	see *Z. californica* 'Dublin'
§ - subsp. ***latifolia***	XLum
§ - subsp. ***mexicana***	SRms
- 'Olbrich Silver'	ECha EWes WHoo WKif XSen
- 'Western Hills' ♀H5	CFis CRos CSpe CTri ECha EPfP EPot EWld LRHS LSou MHer MMuc MRav NRHS SEND SPhx SRms SWvt WHoo XLum
§ ***cana***	ECha
- from Santa Lucia Mountains, California new	SBrt
- 'Sir Cedric Morris'	EPfP
- ***villosa***	see *Z. californica* subsp. *mexicana*
I 'Pumilio'	EPot NRHS
§ ***septentrionalis***	WAbe

Zebrina see *Tradescantia*

Zehneria (*Cucurbitaceae*)

scabra	SVic

Zelkova ✿ (*Ulmaceae*)

abelicea	CMCN MBlu
carpinifolia	CDul CMCN SPlb WPGP

- PAB 13.047	LEdu
- NJM 13.014 from Azerbaijan	WPGP
- NJM 13.016 from Azerbaijan	WPGP
'Kiwi Sunset'	EPfP
serrata 🏆H6	CBcs CCVT CDul CLnd CMCN CMen EBee ECrN ELan EPfP EShb GQue LMaj LPra MGos MMuc SEND SGol WHCr WMou
- B&SWJ 8491 from Korea	WCru
- 'Goblin'	CJun MBlu NLar
- 'Green Vase'	LMaj MBlu SCob
- 'Kiwi Sunset'^{PBR}	CDul MGos NOra
- 'Luminifera' **new**	MBlu
- 'Musashino'	SGol
- 'Ogon'	EPfP SGol
- 'Urban Ruby'	LMaj
- 'Variegata' (v)	CJun CMac MBlu NLar SGol
× ***verschaffeltii***	CMCN EPfP IArd MBlu

Zenobia (*Ericaceae*)

pulverulenta	CBcs CMac ELan EPfP LRHS MAsh MBlu MGil MGos SCob SLon SSta WSHC
- 'Blue Sky'	CBcs CBct CDul CMCN EBee EPfP GKin LRHS MAsh MBlu MGos MPkF NLar SCob SMad SPer SPoG SSta WPGP
- f. ***nitida***	CMac NLar
- 'Raspberry Ripple'	CBcs LRHS MAsh NLar NRHS SSta
- 'Viridis'	NLar

Zephyranthes (*Amaryllidaceae*)

candida	CAby CBro CRos CTal EBee EPot EShb EWld GKev LAma LRHS NRHS NRog SChF SDeJ WAvo
- 'Lemon Drops'	NRog
citrina	CExl GKev LAma SDeJ
drummondii	NRog
'Ivory Crocus'	NRog
katherinae	NRog
'Krakatau'	WCot
La Bufa Rosa Group	CExl WCot
lindleyana	NRog
minima	NRog
minuta 🏆H2	NRog
primulina	NRog
robusta	see *Habranthus robustus*
rosea	GKev SDeJ
traubii from San Carlos	NRog
versicolor	NRog

Zigadenus (*Melanthiaceae*)

elegans	CPla EBee ECha EPri LEdu LRHS MAvo MHer NRHS WSHC
nuttallii	CTal

Zingiber ✿ (*Zingiberaceae*)

clarkei	CTsd
mioga	CAgr CFil CTsd EBee GPoy IMou LEdu SChr SPlb SRms WPGP
- 'Crûg's Zing'	CFil LEdu SBrt WCru WPGP
- 'Dancing Crane' (v)	CFil CMac EUJe LEdu SRms WPGP
- 'White Feather'	CFil CTsd LEdu WPGP
officinale	SPlb SPre

Zinnia (*Asteraceae*)

(Benary's Giants Series)	CRav
'Benary's Giant Coral' **new**	
- 'Benary's Giant Lime' **new**	CRav
- 'Benary's Giant Purple' **new**	CRav
- 'Benary's Giant White' **new**	CRav
- 'Benary's Giant Wine' **new**	CRav
DAHLIA-FLOWERED MIXED **new**	LCro
elegans	SVic
- 'Oklahoma White' (Oklahoma Series) **new**	CRav
- 'Sprite Mix' **new**	CRav
'Envy' (d)	CSpe
GIANT DAHLIA mixed **new**	CRav
GIANT DAHLIA ORANGE **new**	CRav
'Red Spider'	CSpe
Zahara Series	CRav

Zizia (*Apiaceae*)

aptera	SPhx
aurea	SBrt SPhx WSHC XLum

Ziziphus (*Rhamnaceae*)

§ ***jujuba*** (F)	CBcs MBlu
- 'Lang' (F)	CAgr
- 'Li' (F)	CAgr
sativa	see *Z. jujuba*

Zosima (*Apiaceae*)

absinthifolia **new**	WCot

RHS Award of Garden Merit Vegetables

AWARD OF GARDEN MERIT VEGETABLES

This is a directory of vegetables offered by nurseries participating in *RHS Plant Finder 2016* that have been awarded an RHS Award of Garden Merit (AGM). It does not represent a complete list of AGM vegetables.

Entries are accompanied by a short description and the relevant hardiness rating for the UK. **Hardiness ratings** are explained on p.11. The figures to the left of the rating indicate the year the Award of Garden Merit was made.

Vegetables present some nomenclatural peculiarities that may require explanation. Cultivars that are repeatedly raised by different growers, while retaining their essential characteristics, can become recognisably different. These strains are referred to as maintenances and are often distinguished by the use of **maintenance names** which exist separately from the cultivar name. Here maintenance names appear after the cultivar name separated by a dash following The Vegetable Seed (England) Regulations 2002.

ASPARAGUS (*Asparagus officinalis*)

01 H4 **'Backlim'**
F_1 hybrid; consistently high yield of large spears.
ECrN EMsh EPom

9 H4 **'Connover's Colossal'**
Early; heavy yield of good quality spears. Reconfirmed after trial 2001 and 2012.
CSBt EKin ELan EUnw LCro LOPS LSRN MCtn MNHC NRob SEND SVic

12 H4 **'Dariana'**
Bred in France. Sound yield of straight, green spears and tight buds of excellent flavour.
SDea

01 H4 **'Gijnlim'**
F_1 hybrid; early. Consistently high yield of mid-green spears with purple tips. Reconfirmed after trial 2012.
CRav ECrN EKin EMsh EPom LCro LOPS NRob SDea

12 H5 **'Guelph Millennium'**
Bred in Canada. Excellent cold tolerance. Lateness helps to avoid frost damage. Sound yield of slender stems with pleasing flavour.
CRav EPom LCro LOPS NRob

AUBERGINE (*Solanum melongena*)

95 H1c **'Bonica'**
F_1 hybrid. Early cropping, good quality, attractive glossy black fruits are a good size. Plants are tall, but also strong and vigorous. Reconfirmed after trial 2008.
MCtn MShS

BEANS

BROAD BEANS (*Vicia faba*)

11 H3 **'De Monica'**
Short pods; well filled. Good ratio of seed to pod; excellent cropping.
EMsh MShS

11 H3 **'Giant Exhibition Longpod'**
Smooth, slender pods of good length; long cropping period.
EKin MShS NRHS NRob

11 H3 **'Robin Hood'**
Green-seeded; 3–5 seeds per pod. Good yield. Dwarf cultivar, ideal for containers and small gardens.
MCtn MShS

11 H4 **'Scabiola Verde'**
Early cropping; large seeds of good flavour. Long-podded 'Aguadulce' type.
EMsh

11 H3 **'Statissa'**
Upright podded mid-size pods; 4–5 beans per pod.
EUnw

BROAD BEANS (NOVEMBER SOWN)

95 H5 **'Aguadulce'**
Dark green foliage, showing some variability. Long pods; the highest yielding in the trial. May also be sold as 'Aquadulce'.
CHby EHyd LSds

BROAD BEANS (SPRING SOWN)

93 H5 **'Aquadulce Claudia'**
Not too tall; a good compact plant. An early crop when spring-sown; one of the most reliable cultivars for overwintering. Reconfirmed after trial 1999, 2011.

EKin EMsh EUnw LCro MCtn MShS NRHS NRob

93 H3 **'Express'**
Quick to mature, with well-filled pods.
EKin EUnw MCtn

93 H3 **'Imperial Green Longpod'**
Green-seeded, with long smooth pods; good green colour and flavour; particularly good for freezing. Reconfirmed after trial 1999, 2011.
EKin MCtn MShS

99 H3 **'Jubilee Hysor'**
Good yield; uniform, well-filled, smooth, long-podded pods; reconfirmed after trial 2011.
EMsh EUnw

99 H3 **'Masterpiece Green Longpod'**
Slender, well-filled pods; stands well; good green colour and flavour; suitable for freezing; reconfirmed after trial 2011.
EKin EMsh EUnw LCro MCtn MShS

93 H4 **'Meteor'**
An early crop with well-filled, even pods; good flavour. Reconfirmed after trial 1999.
EMsh EUnw

93 H3 **'The Sutton'**
Dwarf compact plants, with nice flavour; ideal for smaller gardens/containers and windy situations. Reconfirmed after trial 1999, 2011.
EKin EMsh LCro MShS NRob

99 H4 **'Witkiem' - Manita**
Traditional 'Witkiem' type; sets well. Good early yield, with uniform pods; reconfirmed after trial 2011.
CHby EKin MCtn NRHS

BEANS – CLIMBING FRENCH (*Phaseolus vulgaris*)

93 H2 **'Algarve'** (flat)
High yield; uniform mid-green stringless pods. Reconfirmed after trial 2000 and 2008.
EMsh

00 H2 **'Cobra'** (round)
Very high early yield; long, fleshy; very attractive; reconfirmed after trial 2008.
CHby EKin EMsh LCro MCtn MShS NRob

93 H2 **'Eva'** (round)
Very early. Long straight fleshy pods, wider-podded than other round varieties. Reconfirmed after trial 2000 and 2008.
CHby

08 H2 **'Golden Gate'** (flat)
Good crop of golden, fleshy, flat pods with a sweet, fresh flavour.
CHby

93 H2 **'Hunter'** (flat)
Attractive long stringless pods. Slow to show seed development. Reconfirmed after trial 2000 and 2008.
EKin EUnw MCtn MShS NRob

08 H2 **'Limka'** (flat)
Consistently high yields of good quality, flat, light green pods with a good flavour.
CHby

BEANS – DWARF FRENCH

93 H2 **'Annabel'**
Dark green colour, compact habit, fine foliage, tender fleshy tasting pods. Reconfirmed after trial 1996 and 2010.
EKin MCtn

02 H2 **'Berggold'** (wax podded)
Attractive, clear golden, medium to long beans with slightly curved and flattened pods.
LSds

93 H2 **'Delinel'**
Strong-growing with long, dark green pods. Reconfirmed after trial 2001 and 2010.
EMsh

02 H2 **'Golddukat'** (wax podded)
Very early; high yield of pale yellow beans with some greening. Slightly curved and flattened pods. Reconfirmed after trial 2010.
EMsh

01 H2 **'Safari'**
Short, slim, mid-green, round, attractive pods. Low yields.
EKin EMsh MCtn MShS NRHS

02 H2 **'Sonesta'** (wax podded)
Early. High yield of bright yellow, fairly long, straight, slightly flattened pods. A compact plant. Reconfirmed after trial 2010.
EUnw

93 H2 **'Sprite'**
Heavy yield, with long, dark green pods.
EHyd EKin MCtn MShS NRHS

10 H2 **'Stanley'**
Mid to dark green colour; tender and sweet. Taller plant. Uniform and picks over long period.
EUnw MCtn

96 H2 **'The Prince'**
Excellent yield; straight pale green pods.
EKin EMsh MShS NRob

BEANS – RUNNER (*Phaseolus coccineus*)

93 H2 **'Achievement'**
Maincrop with long, smooth, slender pods.
MCtn MShS

06 H2 **'Aintree'**
Mid-season. Red-flowered, producing attractive, good quality, slim, straight, long pods with sweet flavour. Reconfirmed after trial 2013.
EMsh

06 H2 **'Benchmaster'**
Long, fairly straight beans, good yield; reconfirmed after trial 2013.
EKin EMsh MShS

06 H2 **'Celebration'**
High yield of attractive, straight, smooth, good quality, fleshy pods with good colour and flavour. Flowers are a decorative pink. Reconfirmed after trial 2013.
EKin EMsh MShS

99 H2 **'Desiree'**
Stringless pods with thick fleshy walls.
EKin MCtn

99 H2 **'Enorma'**
Late; long, smooth, slender pods.
CHby CRos EHyd EKin EMsh EUnw MShS NRHS

13 H2 **'Firestorm'**
Hybrid of runner and French bean parentage. Excellent yield, slender, smooth-skinned, fleshy pods. Self-setting.
EKin EMsh MShS

99 H2 **'Lady Di'**
Attractive, blemish-free, long, slender pods.
CHby EKin LCro MCtn MShS

93 H2 **'Liberty'**
Very long pods; a popular show variety.
MShS NRob

13 H2 **'Moonlight'**
Hybrid of runner and French bean parentage; grown commercially. Very high yielding. Easy to pick; leaves pedicel behind on picking. Smooth, fleshy pods, of good length. Self-setting.
EHyd EKin EMsh EUnw MCtn MShS NRHS

99 H2 **'Red Rum'**
Good early and late yield; slim, straight, stringless pods, of medium length. Reconfirmed after trial 2006, 2013.
EKin EMsh EUnw MCtn

06 H2 **'St George'**
Bicolour variety; prized for ornamental value. Some French bean parentage. Popular commercial variety; easy to pick, leaving pedicel behind. Slender beans, straight, pale green. Reconfirmed after trial 2013.
CHby EMsh

13 H2 **'Stardust'**
Hybrid of runner and French bean parentage. Very smooth, fairly fleshy. High yield, long, straight pods.
EMsh

99 H2 **'White Emergo'**
Late; smooth, tender, uniform pods, with good colour.
CHby EUnw

99 H2 **'White Lady'**
Late; very fleshy pods. Reconfirmed after trial 2006, 2013.
CHby EKin EMsh EUnw LCro MCtn MShS NRHS

Beetroot (*Beta vulgaris*)

With long red root

93 H3 **'Cheltenham Green Top'**
Good crop of uniformly shaped roots for late harvest; smooth skins and smooth shoulders. Good internal colour and sweet flavour. Reconfirmed after trial 2005.
MShS

93 H3 **'Forono'**
Open-pollinated. Cylindrical, with fairly smooth skins and roots of moderate uniformity; good internal colour. Slow to bulk up. Reconfirmed after trial 2005.
EKin MShS

With round red root

93 H3 **'Action'**
F_1 hybrid; early. Smooth uniform roots with good flesh colour and freedom from rings. Appears to have good bolting resistance. Bulks up quickly. Reconfirmed after trial 2001 and 2005.
EMsh MShS

05 H3 **'Alto'**
F_1 hybrid; early. Cylindrical, uniform, smooth roots with very good internal colour. Potential to bulk up well.
EKin

93 H3 **'Boltardy'**
Good bolting resistance.
CRav EHyd EKin EMsh EUnw LCro MCtn MShS NRHS

93 H3 **'Pablo'**
F_1 hybrid; very early. Uniform roots with very smooth skins; very good internal colour and freedom from internal rings. Appears to have good bolting resistance. Widely used as a show cultivar. Reconfirmed after trial 2001 and 2005.
EHyd EKin EMsh MCtn MShS NRHS NRob

01 H3 **'Red Ace'**
F_1 hybrid; uniform roots with good flesh colour and no rings.
EKin MShS NRob

05 H3 **'Solo'**
F_1 hybrid; monogerm. Round to slightly flattened shape. Bulks up well; smooth roots of good internal colour.
EMsh MShS

Borecole or curly kale (*Brassica oleracea* Acephala Group)

00 H5 **'Afro'**
Medium height; mid-green leaves, curled to the edge. Winters well.
EMsh

99 H5 **'Redbor'**
F_1 hybrid. Tall plants with open habit; strongly curled purple-green leaves. Winters well.
EKin EMsh LCro MCtn MShS NRob

93 H5 **'Winterbor'**
F_1 hybrid. Tall plants with finely curled blue-green leaves; winters well. Reconfirmed after trial 1999.
EKin MCtn MShS

Broccoli (*Brassica oleracea* Italica Group)

Purple sprouting

13 H5 **'Cardinal'**
Tidy upright plants, some variability in height, as expected for open-pollinated cultivars. Dense

spears of deep purple. Good for late crop.
EKin EMsh MShS

95 H5 **'Claret'**
F_1 hybrid. Very tall; heavy yield of dark purple spears from March through April. Reconfirmed after trial 2013.
EMsh MShS NRHS

95 H5 **'Red Arrow'**
Early to mid-season; long cropping period. Good winter hardiness; bushy, vigorous plants. Reconfirmed after trial 2003, 2013.
EKin MCtn MShS

WHITE SPROUTING

95 H5 **'White Star'**
Good weight; late white spears for cutting in April.
EKin

BRUSSELS SPROUTS (*Brassica oleracea* Gemmifera Group)

99 H5 **'Bosworth'**
F_1 hybrid; late. Oval, mid to dark green, solid, closely spaced sprouts. Easy to pick; plants stand well. Quality still good in February.
EUnw MShS

99 H5 **'Cascade'**
F_1 hybrid; late. Smooth, clean, well-spaced, fairly round sprouts. Uniform plants which stand and yield well.
EKin MShS

99 H5 **'Clodius'**
F_1 hybrid; midseason. Good quality, round, smooth, solid, sweet sprouts. Plants stand and yield well.
EMsh

93 H5 **'Igor'**
F_1 hybrid. Mid to late season; attractive, vigorous, uniform plants producing well-spaced, solid, round, mid-green sprouts. Reconfirmed after trial 2006.
NRob

06 H4 **'Maximus'**
F_1 hybrid; early to mid-season. Uniform plants, producing a good crop of mid to dark green, smooth, solid sprouts.
EKin EUnw LCro MShS

06 H5 **'Montgomery'**
F_1 hybrid. Mid to late season; tall, uniform plants that stand well, producing a good crop of clean, smooth, round mid to dark green, well-spaced sprouts.
EMsh EUnw MCtn

06 H5 **'Petrus'**
F_1; late season. Tall, vigorous plants that stand well. Good crop of clean, round, dark green sprouts; well-spaced and easy to pick.
EUnw

99 H5 **'Revenge'**
F_1 hybrid; late. Very uniform plants producing a good yield of solid, round, clean, mid-green sprouts. Can be hard to pick.
EUnw

CABBAGE (*Brassica oleracea* Capitata Group)

JANUARY KING – NOVEMBER TO MARCH

08 H5 **'Deadon'**
Uniform, attractive 'January King' type with a flattened, round head.
EKin EMsh MShS

08 H5 **'January King 3'**
Open-pollinated. Attractive heads that develop a good colour. Good yield and long spread of cut.
EKin MCtn MShS

93 H5 **'Marabel'**
F_1 hybrid; mid-green leaves with good, deep red colour; round well-filled heads with good standing ability. Reconfirmed after trial 2000 and 2007.
EMsh

SAVOY – SEPTEMBER TO MARCH

00 H5 **'Alaska'**
F_1 hybrid; mid-season to late. Dark green, well-blistered leaves; small to medium heads. Could be grown at closer spacing for small heads. Reconfirmed after trial 2007.
EMsh EUnw

01 H5 **'Endeavour'**
F_1 hybrid; late. Attractive, mid-green, well-blistered, medium-sized heads with good internal quality and sweet taste. Long stems.
EMsh

08 H5 **'Rigoléto'**
Dense, dark green Savoy type with medium-large blister and a leafy, large frame.
MCtn

08 H5 **'Traviata'**
Uniform Savoy type.
MShS

01 H5 **'Tundra'**
F_1 hybrid; dark green, slightly blistered leaf; heads solid and attractive. Sweet-tasting; overwinters well. Reconfirmed after trial 2007.
EKin EMsh EUnw MCtn

01 H5 **'Wintessa'**
F_1 hybrid; late. Dark green well-blistered leaves, with uniform well-filled heads of good quality and flavour. Plants stand well.
EKin

AUTUMN – SEPTEMBER TO NOVEMBER

09 H3 **'Castello'**
F_1 hybrid. Spread of maturity within rows is useful to the gardener. Ready from the end of August and standing well to the end of September. Cut and cooked when just ready, it will have a little yellow at the centre and good flavour, or can be left to mature fully for dense

white cabbage that shreds well.
MShS

09 H3 **'Minicole'**
F_1 hybrid. Good early autumn cultivar with attractive round heads.
EHyd NRHS NRob

09 H3 **'Picador'**
F_1 hybrid. Good quality dense round heads with a shorter core. Flexible; can be sown from February to May for July to November cropping.
EMsh MShS

09 H3 **'Red Jewel'**
F_1 hybrid. Attractive, solid, round-headed red cabbage with upright foliage and a short core. Could be grown at a closer spacing.
NRob

Early red, non-storing – September to October

96 H3 **'Rookie'**
F_1 hybrid; early. Round to slightly flat heads.
EMsh

Spring – pointed or summer, June to August

93 H5 **'Duncan'**
F_1 hybrid. Mid to dark green uniform heads with well-closed bases. A good early yield; compact neat habit; plants heart slowly to produce small, solid, well-filled heads. Reconfirmed after trial 2001, 2011 as spring greens and hearted cabbage.
EMsh MShS NRHS

01 H5 **'Durham Elf'**
As a hearted cabbage; dark blue-green leaf; short-stemmed.
EMsh MShS

93 H5 **'Pixie'**
Mid-green with good basal quality, producing small well-hearted heads. Reconfirmed after trial 2001 as a very early hearted cabbage.
EUnw

94 H5 **'Pyramid'**
F_1 hybrid. Very uniform, medium-sized, well-filled, compact, solid pointed heads, with short core, quite slow to mature; reconfirmed after trial 2001, 2011 as a hearted cabbage, and after trial 2002 as a summer cabbage.
MShS

Spring

11 H5 **'Advantage'**
Good heart. Compact, uniform. Little bolting; withstood the dry, hot weather in April.
MShS

11 H5 **'Spring Hero'**
Distinctive round-headed spring cabbage for overwintering. Large, dense ball-shaped heads. Blue-grey, rugose leaves. Showing excellent winter survival.
EKin MShS NRHS

11 H5 **'Winterjewel'**
Ideally grown as greens. Can be left to bulk slowly to give loose hearts. Uniform, dark green, leafy habit. Excellent winter hardiness.
EMsh EUnw

Summer, June to August

04 H2 **'Candisa'**
F_1 hybrid; early. Uniform, medium green, well-filled heads.
EMsh

93 H2 **'Derby Day'**
Early. Bright, round, mid-green, well-filled heads. Reconfirmed after trial 1998.
CHby EUnw MShS

02 H2 **'Greyhound'**
Early-maturing; pointed; pale to mid-green; medium to large frame.
EKin EMsh EUnw MCtn MShS NRHS

02 H2 **'Hispi'**
F_1 hybrid; early. Smooth, pointed, dark green outer leaves, with good uniformity and well-filled heart.
CHby EKin LCro MShS NRHS NRob

08 H3 **'Huzaro'**
Red cabbage; good crop of well-filled, uniform heads. Could also be used for storage.
MShS

08 H3 **'Kilaton'**
Late-season, large, white cabbage with claimed resistance to club-root.
EKin EMsh EUnw MShS

93 H2 **'Stonehead'**
F_1 hybrid; late. Uniform, round, mid-green heads. Also useful for cropping into the autumn from later planting.
EKin MShS NRHS NRob

CALABRESE (*Brassica oleracea* Italica Group)

03 H3 **'Belstar'**
F_1 hybrid; May sown. Mid to late season; uniform medium-sized plants, with attractive heads and medium to small buds.
EHyd NRHS

07 H3 **'Green Magic'**
Autumn-cropping; very good yield of slightly domed, good-sized heads with small beads. Known to make good side shoots. Reconfirmed after trial 2013.
EKin EMsh MCtn MShS NRHS

13 H2 **'Ironman'**
Domed, larger heads of blue-green, tight buds, healthy foliage.
EKin MShS

03 H3 **'Kabuki'**
F_1 hybrid; May sown; early. Short, compact plants, producing a good crop of medium green, deep, well-rounded heads with uniform buds. Average yield of medium-sized secondaries, produced 3 to 5 weeks after the primary heads.

Could be closely spaced to produce baby heads. Reconfirmed after trial 2007, 2013.
EHyd EMsh MCtn MShS NRHS

13 H2 **'Marathon'**
Dome-shaped heads, uniform, mid-size, held high.
EKin EMsh MShS NRHS

CARROT (*Daucus carota*)

06 H3 **'Amsterdam Forcing 3'**
Open-pollinated. Relatively smooth with good flesh and core colour; bulks up well. Strong foliage that does not grow too tall.
EKin EMsh MCtn MShS

93 H4 **'Bangor'**
F_1 hybrid. Blunt, medium-length, smooth roots. Well-filled with good uniform shape and medium orange internal colour. Bulks up well. Can be stored over winter; reconfirmed after trial 2005.
MShS

95 H4 **'Berlikumer 2 - Berjo'**
Maincrop. Heavy yields of smooth cylindrical roots with bright orange flesh. Suitable for storing.
EMsh

05 H5 **'Eskimo'**
F_1 hybrid; medium-length, smooth roots with good colour. Useful size, well-filled. Grows with crowns at or below ground level, so very little crown discoloration. Good overwintering cultivar. Reconfirmed after trial 2014.
EKin MCtn MShS

99 H3 **'Flyaway'**
F_1 hybrid. Maincrop; medium-length, well-filled, stump-ended roots with good flesh and core colour. Good strong tops. Partial resistance (i.e. lack of attraction) to carrot flies. Reconfirmed after trial 2006.
EKin EUnw LCro MCtn MShS

06 H3 **'Ideal Red'**
Open-pollinated. 'Nantes' type; uniform crop of fairly smooth, medium length, well-filled roots with good flesh and core colour. Strong top growth.
EMsh

99 H3 **'Maestro'**
F_1 hybrid. Best lifted before Christmas. Blunt, smooth-skinned, medium to slim, fairly well-filled roots, uniform in size and shape. Mid to pale internal colour with some green shoulders. Widely grown by organic carrot growers. Reconfirmed after trial 2005, 2014.
MShS

10 H3 **'Marion'**
Early to mature; uniform crop of slightly tapered roots with good weight. Smooth skin, deep orange flesh and good core colour. Suitable for containers.
EMsh

93 H3 **'Mokum'**
F_1 hybrid. Early to mature, good weight and sweet flavour. Slightly tapering roots, well-coloured to the tip; smooth skin; almost coreless. Good for bunching. Reconfirmed after trial 2010 as early, suitable for containers.
EHyd MShS NRHS

99 H3 **'Nairobi'**
F_1 hybrid; second early/early maincrop. Strong tops, with uniform, broader-shouldered, cylindrical, stump-ended roots. Heavy yields. Reconfirmed after trial 2006, 2014.
EKin EMsh MShS

93 H3 **'Napoli'**
F_1 hybrid, very early maturing. Slightly tapering; good weight. Smooth skin, core and flesh deep orange. Strong tops for easy pulling; quick to bulk up. Ideal for successional sowings and early sowing in frames. Reconfirmed after trial 2010 as early, suitable for containers.
EKin

06 H3 **'Primo'**
Hybrid; flavoursome crop of good weight. Smooth skin, deep orange colour, with low core–flesh ratio. Reconfirmed after trial 2010 as early, suitable for containers.
EMsh

05 H4 **'Sugarsnax 54'**
F_1 hybrid. Very long, smooth, 'Imperator' type with roots of good internal colour. Suited to deep, light soils. Commercially used, cut into short lengths and sold as pre-packed "baton" carrots.
EMsh MCtn MShS

05 H3 **'Sweet Candle'**
F_1; short, blunt, quite smooth, well-filled, uniform roots. Good internal colour. Reconfirmed after trial 2014.
EKin EMsh LCro MCtn MShS NRob

CAULIFLOWER (*Brassica oleracea* Botrytis Group)

AUTUMN HEADING – SEPTEMBER TO NOVEMBER

02 H3 **'Aviso'**
F_1 hybrid; early cropping, with a short cropping period; high proportion of first-class, smooth white curds.
MShS

02 H3 **'Pavilion'**
F_1 hybrid; early with a short cropping period; very uniform; good white colour, size and depth.
EHyd NRHS

COLOURED AND ROMANESCO

05 H3 **'Graffiti'**
F_1 hybrid. Small to medium, high quality, solid curds of a very attractive amethyst colour. The colour fades a little if boiled, but is retained

better if steamed. The raw curds have a good flavour and would be a colourful addition to a salad or dish of crudités. Midseason. Reconfirmed after trial 2006.
EKin EMsh MShS NRHS

05 H3 **'Veronica'**
F_1 hybrid; appetising light green Romanesco type. Uniform good-sized, solid, well-shaped heads.
EKin EUnw

Summer heading – June to mid July

06 H3 **'Avalanche'**
Hybrid; midseason. Attractive, high quality, medium to large sized, white, solid curds.
EHyd NRHS

06 H3 **'Aviron'**
Hybrid; late. High quality, well-protected, large to medium-sized solid, white heads.
EMsh

97 H3 **'Barcelona'**
F_1 hybrid; mid-season. Deep, round, solid, well-protected curds.
EKin

06 H3 **'Flamenco'**
Hybrid; midseason to late. Very high quality, large to medium-sized, white, solid curds with good depth.
NRob

97 H3 **'Mayflower'**
F_1 hybrid; very early. High quality, medium-sized, white, solid curds Reconfirmed after trial 2006.
EMsh

97 H3 **'Nautilus'**
F_1 hybrid; late. Vigorous plants with deep, white, well-protected curds of excellent quality.
NRHS

Winter for spring heading, maturing from March to May

05 H5 **'Aalsmeer'**
Open-pollinated cultivar; early mid-season. Produces medium to small, cream-coloured, slightly lumpy, well-protected curds that have a good depth. This cultivar produced several multiple heads and side shoots, many of usable quality.
EKin MShS NRob

97 H5 **'Jerome'**
F_1 hybrid; early mid-season. Vigorous plant, producing good quality, well-covered curds. Curds well-rounded, medium to small and cream-coloured. Reconfirmed after trial 2005.
EMsh MShS

Celeriac (*Apium graveolens* var. *rapaceum*)

93 H4 **'Monarch'**
Attractive white-skinned, bold, smooth, deep globes; good interior; healthy foliage. Reconfirmed after trial 2011.
EMsh EUnw

00 H4 **'Prinz'**
Smooth, deep, white-skinned; small to medium, flattened and round; compact plant with healthy foliage. Reconfirmed after trial 2011.
CHby EKin LCro MCtn MShS SVic

Celery (*Apium graveolens* var. *dulce*)

93 H2 **'Celebrity'**
Self-blanching, fairly short plants, with ribbed petioles and good flavour. Reconfirmed after trial 2001.
MCtn MShS NRHS

93 H4 **'Giant Pink' - Mammoth Pink**
Pink-tinged, green variety for blanching or earthing up; solid stems.
NRob

05 H2 **'Granada'**
F_1 hybrid; pale green, reasonably smooth, quite fleshy petioles. Medium to strong flavour. Resistant to celery leaf spot (blight) caused by the *Septoria apiicola* fungus.
EMsh

05 H2 **'Loretta'**
Open-pollinated; early. Uniform, long, well-blanched, attractive petioles. Good sweet flavour.
EMsh

01 H2 **'Tango'**
Open-pollinated; slower-maturing, long, mid-green, fleshy petioles. Reconfirmed after trial 2005.
EHyd NRHS

94 H2 **'Victoria'**
F_1 hybrid. Tall, well-filled plants with medium-green, smooth, fleshy petioles. Widely used for commercial crops. Reconfirmed after trial 2005.
EHyd EKin NRHS

Chard (*Beta vulgaris* subsp. *cicla* var. *flavescens*)

00 H3 Bright Lights
Good colourful mix, including reds, yellows and whites; very ornamental and decorative.
CHby CRav EHyd EMsh MShS NRHS NRob

00 H3 **'Bright Yellow'**
Bright golden-yellow petioles and mid-green puckered leaf; uniform; sweet taste; reconfirmed after trial 2011.
MCtn NRob

11 H3 **'Canary Yellow'**
Green leaves and yellow stem; healthy blister-type attractive glassy leaf. Even stock. Taste is not bitter. No bolting in either sowing.
MShS NRob

00 H3 **'Fordhook Giant'**
Attractive shiny light green, puckered leaf with

white stem and long succulent broad white petioles; old blister-leaf chard type.
EKin EMsh EUnw MCtn NRob

00 H3 **'Rhubarb Chard'**
Dark green leaves and red stem; uniform; blister-type leaf; reconfirmed after trial 2011.
EKin LCro LSds MCtn MShS NRob

11 H3 **'White Silver'**
Dark green leaves and white stem; shiny leaf; broad petiole. Compact habit; good taste.
MShS

CHICORY (*Cichorium intybus*)

LEAFY TYPES – RADICCHIO

02 H4 **'Indigo'**
Dense round heads; very uniform with dark green outer leaves and red hearts.
NRHS

02 H4 **'Palla Rossa'**
Medium to large heads; well-filled red hearts; fairly uniform. No bolting.
CHby EUnw LSds MCtn MShS SRms

LEAFY TYPES – SUGAR LOAF

02 H4 **'Pan di Zucchero'**
Uniform plants with medium to large frames and dark green outer leaves. Hearts blanch well.
CHby EUnw LSds MCtn

CHILLI PEPPER (*Capsicum annuum*)

06 H1c **'Apache'**
Decorative, growing to 45cm; does well in both large and small pots. Produces large crop of small, juicy, hot peppers that ripen from bright green to red and are held outwards from the stems. Reconfirmed after trial 2013.
CCCN CRos EKin EMsh MShS NPri NRHS NRob SPre

13 H1c **'Basket of Fire'**
Multi-branched, open habit, height to c.25cm. Numerous upright fruits, maturing through cream, lemon, yellow, orange to red.
CRos EHyd EKin EMsh EUnw MShS NRHS SPhm SPre SVic

13 H1c **'Bolivian Rainbow'**
Compact plant, height c.32cm, with mid-green foliage. Stumpy, broad-based fruit held erect. Fruit ripening cream through orange to red.
SVic

06 H1c **'Caribbean Antillais'**
Quite small, blocky, bright red fruits; aromatic and very hot, of a type widely used in South American and Caribbean cooking. Later cropping, best sown in January and given a higher temperature to germinate.
SVic

06 H1c **'Demon Red'**
A small, ornamental plant, starred with white flowers, producing an abundant crop of tiny upward-pointing fruits that mature to dark, bright red. Fruits are hot and used in Thai cooking. Reconfirmed after trial 2013.
CRos EKin EUnw MShS NRHS SPre SVic

06 H1c **'Etna'**
Attractive bunches of erect, shiny peppers that mature from bright mid-green to red, carried on compact plants that are suitable for growing in pots. Large crop of very hot peppers.
CRos MCtn NRHS

06 H1c **'Filius Blue'**
Attractive, highly ornamental plants. The young leaves are mid-green, becoming very dark green with a purple flush; the plants are covered with purple, orange and bright red fruits that are spicy and hot.
NRob

06 H1c **'Fresno'**
Fairly short, upright growing plants; very productive. The conical fruits ripen from light green to deep scarlet red, with medium thick flesh that is very hot.
NRHS

06 H1c **'Fuego'**
Good yield of early, easy to harvest, big, red fruits. A hot pepper with thick meaty flesh.
EMsh LSds

06 H1c **'Habanero'**
Very attractive, blocky, orange fruits; very hot. Plants quite compact; good yield; suitable for growing in pots. Later-cropping, it is best sown in January.
EHyd EKin LSds MCtn MShS NRHS NRob

13 H1c **'Hot Thai'**
Bushy yet compact habit, height to 25cm. Dainty dark green foliage. Small, hot fruits (1.5cm in length, and 1cm wide), held erect. Ideal for a windowsill.
CRos EMsh NRHS

06 H1c **'Hungarian Hot Wax'**
Conical fruits ripening from pale yellow to bright red; medium hot; very good for frying, stuffing and using in salads. One of the easiest to grow. Suitable for growing in pots.
CHby EKin LCro LSds MCtn MShS NRob SVic

13 H1c **'Krakatoa'**
Compact, bushy plant, with dark green foliage; height c.20cm. Erect clusters of glossy fruit, 3cm long, and 1cm across the base.
CRos NRHS

13 H1c **'Loco'**
Bushy plant, height c.25cm, cascading habit which looks especially attractive in a basket or container. Numerous oblong fruit, c.2cm long, held erect above the foliage. Ripening purple to red.
CRos EMsh NRHS

14 H1c **'Pot Black'**
Upright plant with branching habit; height c.36cm. Stem, foliage, fruit very dark purple.

Fruit blocky in shape, held erect above the foliage. Interesting and unusual variety.
SVic

06 H1c **'Prairie Fire'**
Very attractive, short (20cm high), spreading plants covered in a mass of very small, very hot, upright peppers that ripen from white, through yellow and orange, to red. Ideal for pots or a windowsill. Reconfirmed after trial 2013.
CCCN CRos NRHS NRob

14 H1c **'Sparkler'**
Bushy plant; height c.29cm. Numerous erect fruit, 2–3cm long, held above the foliage. Masses of fruit and very attractive. Ripening cream, orange and red.
EHyd NRHS

14 H1c **'Spike'**
Bushy plants, height c.33cm, small leaves. Masses of upright, small, long, hot chillies. Fruit ripens lime-green to red.
EHyd NRHS

14 H1c **'Stumpy'**
Small, multi-branched habit, height c.17cm. Massed clusters of tiny 1.5cm pointed fruits held erect above the foliage.
EHyd NRHS

06 H1c **'Super Chili'**
Ornamental plants; well suited to growing in pots. Produces a high yield of very hot, thin-walled fruits that are held upright and ripen from light green to orange-red.
SPre SVic

06 H1c **'Tricolor Variegatum'**
Ornamental foliage an attractive mid-green, splashed cream and purple. Small fruits mature from purple, through orange to red. Plants 70cm high with a rather spreading habit, but can be pruned to shape.
NRob

Chinese cabbage (*Brassica rapa* Pekinensis Group)

03 H3 **'Yuki'**
Barrel-shaped. Medium green, slightly savoyed outer leaves; very short internal stem; medium-sized heavy head; well-blanched.
EKin MCtn MShS

Courgette (*Cucurbita pepo*)

93 H2 **'Defender'**
F_1 hybrid. A high yield of medium-sized, slender, very lightly flecked fruits.
EKin LCro MCtn MShS

93 H2 **'Early Gem'**
F_1 hybrid; a high yield of slender, lightly speckled fruits. Easy to see on the plant.
EKin MCtn

98 H2 **'El Greco'**
F_1 hybrid. Bush type; plant of open habit with mid-green fruits.
MCtn

07 H2 **'Firenze'**
Lovely dark green fruits; smooth and shiny; reconfirmed after trial 2013.
LSds

13 H2 **'Jaguar'**
Open habit, few spines. Uniform, glossy mid-green fruit, which hold flowers well.
EUnw

07 H2 **'Romanesco'**
Distinctive, heavily ribbed fruits that hold their flowers. Popular in Italy; the flowers are used for stuffing. Semi-trailing plants; good yield.
CRav EMsh LCro LSds

07 H2 **'Tuscany'**
Very attractive, smooth glossy fruits; reconfirmed after trial 2013.
EMsh

98 H2 **'Venus'**
F_1 hybrid. Bush type; smooth, spine-free stems with dark green glossy fruits; reconfirmed after trial 2013.
EMsh

Cucumber (*Cucumis sativus*)

02 H1c **'Carmen'**
F_1 hybrid; standard length, dark green, slightly ribbed fruits. Reconfirmed after trial 2009.
EKin MShS NRob

09 H1c **'Cucino'**
Smooth, small, dark green, uniform fruits with good flavour and texture. Highly productive plants.
NRHS

95 H2 **'Marketmore'** (ridge)
Good yield of short, attractive, dark green fruits. Grown in the open garden. Reconfirmed after trial 2001.
CHby EKin EMsh LSds MCtn MShS

09 H1c **'Mini Munch'**
Highly productive plants producing abundant small, crunchy, shiny-skinned fruits with good flavour.
EKin EMsh

Endive (*Cichorium endivia*)

96 H3 **'Pancalieri'** (curled)
Very strong cut-leaf type. Does not blanch well.
CHby EKin LSds MCtn MShS

Fennel – Florence (*Foeniculum vulgare*)

05 H2 **'Orion'**
F_1 hybrid; vigorous foliage; attractive, medium to large bulbs with a good shape, with few side shoots and clean, with a bright white colour.
EKin EMsh

96 H2 **'Zefa Fino'** (bulb)
Quick-maturing. Medium large, round, very uniform bulbs of excellent quality.
EKin MCtn NRob

Garlic (*Allium sativum*)

04 H4 **'Early Wight'**
Very early crop (during May); good fat cloves. Hard neck; best used immediately after harvest.
NRob

04 H4 **'Germidour'**
Late-maturing, virus-free selection. Soft necks; well-packed, purple-skinned cloves.
NRob

04 H4 **'Solent White'**
Late. Soft neck; many purple-skinned, very attractive cloves, with appealing bouquet; high yield; keeps beyond Christmas (up to March). Also performed well at Harlow Carr.
CRav EKin EMsh NRob

Kohlrabi (*Brassica oleracea* Gongylodes Group)

06 H3 **'Kolibri'**
Hybrid; uniform crop of purple, decorative bulbs with crisp flesh and good flavour. Medium-sized tops.
MShS

97 H3 **'Quickstar'**
F_1 hybrid. Uniform crop of juicy, tender bulbs with a mild flavour. Medium-sized tops. Reconfirmed after trial 2006.
MCtn

Leek (*Allium porrum*)

Early maturing

00 H4 **'King Richard'**
Very long shafts with pale green flags; high yields with low levels of bolting.
EHyd NRHS

00 H4 **'Mammoth Blanch'**
A show variety suitable for December sowing. Early-maturing, with high yields of well-shaped leeks with pale green flags, long, heavy shafts and no bolters.
EKin MShS NRob

Late spring

09 H5 **'Blauwgroene Winter' - Atlanta**
Good open-pollinated cultivar. Dark blue-green, erect flags, with healthy foliage. Medium length of blanch.
EKin

09 H5 **'Blauwgroene Winter' - Bandit**
Good open-pollinated cultivar. Dark blue-green flags; reasonable length of blanch.
EKin MCtn

Maincrop

02 H5 **'Apollo'**
F_1 hybrid; smooth, with slightly pale green leaves; high December yield.
EMsh

93 H5 **'Longbow'**
Mid-season. Uniform, medium-length, slightly bulby leeks.
MShS

02 H5 **'Mammoth Pot'**
Uniform, with whole stem blanched and light green flag. High December yield. A good short garden plant.
EKin NRob

02 H5 **'Oarsman'**
F_1 hybrid; erect plant, with very straight shank, uniform, smooth; flag leaf clean.
EKin EMsh MCtn MShS

00 H4 **'Swiss Giant – Jolant'**
For December cropping; high yield; medium to dark green flags; long, solid shafts with little bulbing and very few bolters. Low levels of rust infection. Reconfirmed after trial 2002.
EKin NRob

Lettuce (*Lactuca sativa*)

Cos

12 H2 **'Amaze'**
A 'Red Gem' type; good colour; green heart, red outer leaves. Compact, uniform crop, sweet taste.
EMsh

12 H2 **'Chartwell'**
Neat, mid-size green Cos; dense, crisp heart.
EKin

93 H2 **'Little Gem'**
Small solid heads with mid-green, medium-blistered leaves. Reconfirmed after trial 1999, 2007, 2012.
CHby CRos EHyd EKin EMsh EUnw LCro LSds MCtn MShS NRHS NRob

99 H2 **'Little Leprechaun'**
Semi-Cos with dark red leaves.
MCtn NRob

93 H2 **'Lobjoit's Green Cos'**
Large, rather open heads, with relatively smooth mid-green leaves. Reconfirmed after trial 1999.
EKin EUnw MShS NRob

12 H2 **'Maureen'**
Uniform crop, mid-green leaves. One of the most popular commercial 'Gem' varieties.
EKin

99 H2 **'Parris Island'**
Vigorous with pale green uniform heads; reconfirmed after trial 2007.
EKin MShS

00 H2 **'Winter Density'**
Semi-Cos with leafy, erect habit; dark green, very uniform. Reconfirmed after trial 2007, 2012.
EKin EMsh LCro MCtn MShS NRob

Crisphead

01 H2 **'Robinson'**
Medium to large frame, good quality solid hearts; reconfirmed after trial 2014.
MShS NRob

Leafy

95 H2 **'Black-seeded Simpson Improved'**
Yellow-green leaves with frilled edges. Cos-like in growth.
MCtn

95 H2 **'Catalogna'**
Strong-growing oak-leaved type. Light green slightly blistered leaves.
MCtn

95 H2 **'Cocarde'**
Large oak-leaved type, with bronze green-tinged leaves.
MCtn

95 H2 **'Lollo Rossa'**
Round, medium-sized plants with green-centred leaves and bronzed frilled outer leaves.
CHby CRos EKin LCro MCtn MShS NRHS NRob

95 H2 **'New Red Fire'**
Large, with puckered light bronze outer leaves.
EKin MShS

95 H2 **'Red Salad Bowl'**
Large oak-leaved type. Green leaves flushed with red on the edge.
CHby CRav EKin LCro LSds MCtn MShS NRHS NRob

95 H2 **'Salad Bowl'**
Large open-hearted plants with light green frilled leaves.
CHby CRav EKin EMsh LCro LSds MCtn MShS NRHS NRob

Marrow (*Cucurbita pepo*)

97 H2 **'Badger Cross'**
F_1 hybrid. Later bush variety; small, good shape with dark-striped fruits. Claimed CMV tolerance.
EMsh MShS

97 H2 **'Tiger Cross'**
F_1 hybrid. High yield of pale-striped fruits. Claimed CMV tolerance.
EHyd EKin EUnw MCtn NRHS

Melon (*Cucumis melo*)

09 H1c **'Emir'**
Good crop of netted Charentais type fruits with orange flesh; H2 for outdoor use.
EKin MCtn

93 H1c **'Ogen'**
Oval-round fruit with yellow-green flesh.
EHyd NRHS

93 H1c **'Sweetheart'**
Early ripening; globular, medium-sized, cream-coloured fruit with orange flesh.
MCtn NRob

Onions & shallots (*Allium cepa*)

Bulb grown from sets

02 H3 **'Autumn Gold Improved'**
Uniform, excellent size, with good skin and colour; good yield. Reconfirmed after trial 2013.
EMsh

93 H3 **'Centurion'**
F_1 hybrid. Flattened globe-shaped bulbs with straw-coloured skins of good thickness. Reconfirmed after trial 2002, 2013.
MShS NRob

13 H3 **'Marshalls Red Fen'**
Large bulbs, early; uniform size and shape. Deep red colour.
EMsh

13 H3 **'Rumba'**
Uniform crop; large bulb size, globe-shaped, with brown skin. Stores well.
EKin NRob

02 H3 **'Sturon'**
Very good yield of globe-shaped, slightly high-shouldered bulbs, with good yellow-brown skins. Reconfirmed after trial 2002, 2013.
CHby CRav EKin EMsh LCro NRob

02 H3 **'Stuttgarter'**
High yield, well shaped, deep bulb, good skin.
CRav EKin EMsh LCro LSds NRob

93 H3 **'Turbo'**
Globe-shaped to slightly conical bulbs with brown skins. Some skin splitting. Reconfirmed after trial 2013.
NRob

Maincrop bulb

93 H3 **'Golden Bear'**
F_1 hybrid; early. Thin-skinned, high-shouldered bulbs; do not store well.
MCtn MShS NRob

95 H3 **'Marco'**
F_1 hybrid. Flattened globe-shaped bulbs; store well.
EMsh

95 H3 **'Rijnsburger 5' - Balstora**
Thick-skinned, dark straw-coloured bulbs; store well.
NRob

95 H3 **'Unwins Exhibition'**
An exhibition onion suitable for January sowing under heated conditions.
EUnw

Red, globe, from seed and sets

05 H3 **'Red Baron'**
High yield of attractive, dark-skinned, globe-shaped bulbs with good internal colour. Plants in the trial grown from seed produced a higher

yield and bolder bulbs than those grown from sets. Reconfirmed after trial 2013.
CHby EKin EMsh EUnw LCro LSds MCtn NRHS NRob

05 H3 **'Rossa di Firenze'**
High yield of flattened, top-shaped, solid bulbs with deep-coloured, tight skins and good internal colour; awarded as 'Vernina di Firenze'.
LSds

SALAD – NON-BULBING

96 H3 **'Feast'**
F_1 hybrid. Medium to dark green, erect leaves; well-blanched bases; slow to bolt. Reconfirmed after trial 2004; also performed well at Harlow Carr.
EHyd NRHS

04 H4 **'Guardsman'**
F_1 hybrid: cross between *A. fistulosum* and *A. cepa*. Medium to dark green leaves. Very vigorous; well-blanched with some bulbing. Also performed well at Harlow Carr.
EMsh MShS

96 H3 **'Ishikura'**
Strong-growing; long-stemmed.
MCtn MShS

96 H3 **'Savel'**
Long stems with a good length of blanch.
MCtn

04 H3 **'Summer Isle'**
Late. Erect, vigorous, uniform plants, with a good length of blanch. Also performed well at Harlow Carr.
MCtn

SALAD – TRADITIONAL

04 H3 **'Lilia'**
Dark green leaves with attractive deep red base. Tends to be bulby. Also performed well at Harlow Carr.
EKin

96 H4 **'Ramrod'**
Later-cropping. Versatile cropper with medium-green leaves and a good length of blanch. Reconfirmed after trial 2004.
MCtn MShS

93 H4 **'White Lisbon'**
Medium-green leaves with good length of blanch. Good for early and successional sowing. Reconfirmed after trial 2004.
CHby EHyd EKin EMsh LCro MCtn MShS NRHS NRob SVic

93 H4 **'Winter White Bunching'**
Strong-growing with dark green leaves. Overwinters well.
EKin

93 H4 **'Winter-Over'**
Dark green leaves, with high yields; may become bulby. Overwinters well.
MShS

SHALLOT (*Allium cepa* Aggregatum Group)

01 H3 **'Golden Gourmet'**
Well-shaped, good size; high yield.
EKin EMsh LCro LOPS NRob SVic

01 H3 **'Jermor'**
Good skin, uniform shape and size; suitable for exhibition.
EMsh NRob

01 H3 **'Longor'**
Good yield and shape; also suitable for exhibition.
LCro LOPS NRob

01 H3 **'Matador'**
F_1 hybrid; thick skins, and good yield.
EKin MCtn MShS NRHS SVic

93 H3 **'Santé'**
Attractive, reddish brown, uniform bulbs with smooth skins. Plant a month later than others to avoid bolting.
NRob

PAK CHOI (*Brassica rapa* Chinensis Group)

10 H3 **'Baraku'**
Good germination rate. Little bolting. Compact and uniform, attractive dark green leaf and petiole. Good size for cooking.
MCtn

10 H3 **'Glacier'**
Good germination rate. Little bolting. Good hearting. Compact, clean, healthy and uniform crop.
EMsh

10 H3 **'Red Choi'**
Good germination rate. Very little bolting. Stands well. Attractive purple leaves and tender green stem. Good hearting, uniform clean, healthy crop. Ideal size for cooking.
EKin

10 H3 **'Summer Breeze'**
Good germination rate. Very little bolting. Stands well. Shorter compact type, tight stem, uniform, clean crop. Good hearting. Tender leaves and stem. Mid-green leaves. Ideal size for cooking.
EMsh

PARSNIP (*Pastinaca sativa*)

09 H5 **'Albion'**
Uniform crop of good, smooth-skinned, white roots.
EUnw MShS

09 H5 **'Archer'**
Crops between 'Gladiator' and 'Javelin'. Good smooth-skinned roots.
EMsh

93 H5 **'Cobham Improved Marrow'**
Open-pollinated; wedge- and bayonet-shaped roots with smooth skins; good canker resistance. Reconfirmed after trial 2001 and 2009.
EMsh

01 H5 **'Gladiator'**
F_1 hybrid; very smooth skin, good potential yield, uniform shape, shallow lenticels. Reconfirmed after trial 2009.
EHyd EKin EMsh EUnw LCro MCtn MShS NRHS

93 H5 **'Javelin'**
F_1 hybrid. Wedge-shaped, smooth-skinned roots; yields well. Good canker resistance. Reconfirmed after trial 2009.
EUnw

09 H5 **'Panache'**
Evenly tapered roots with smooth skins.
EMsh

01 H5 **'White Spear'**
Uniform shape, shallow lenticels, smooth skin, good white colour.
EUnw NRob

Pea (*Pisum sativum*)

98 H2 **'Ambassador'**
Maincrop; medium-sized twin pods, easy to pod; good yield with even distribution.
EKin EMsh MShS

93 H2 **'Early Onward'**
Early, high yield of blunt-ended pods borne in pairs.
EHyd EKin EMsh LCro MCtn MShS NRHS NRob

93 H2 **'Hurst Green Shaft'**
Maincrop; heavy yield of dark green, medium-length, pointed pods. Average of nine good-flavoured peas per pod. Reconfirmed after trial 1998, 2005.
EKin EMsh EUnw LCro MCtn MShS

05 H2 **'Jaguar'**
Early maincrop; heavy crop of mainly double pods per node. Medium-length pods have an average of seven peas per pod, with good flavour.
MCtn MShS

97 H2 **'Kelvedon Wonder'**
Early maincrop. Long, dark green pods, with an average of 7–8 peas per pod. Reconfirmed after trial 2004, 2005.
EKin EMsh LSds MCtn MShS NRob

98 H2 **'Onward'**
First of the main crop with a high yield and good flavour.
CRos EKin EMsh EUnw MCtn MShS NRHS NRob

98 H2 **'Rondo'**
Maincrop; large, broad, straight, pointed pods.
EHyd EKin NRHS

05 H2 **'Serge'**
Maincrop; semi-leafless plants produce a heavy crop of easy to pick pods. Medium-length pods have an average of ten peas per pod, with good flavour.
EKin MCtn

98 H2 **'Show Perfection'**
Maincrop; an 'exhibition' pea, very tall with long dark green pods. A high yield over a long period.
MShS NRob

04 H2 **'Spring'**
Early crop from compact plants. Single and double pods per node. Pods evenly set, with average of 6 peas; good flavour.
EMsh

Mangetout

00 H2 **'Delikata'**
Tall, with similar pods to 'Oregon Sugar Pod'. A shade earlier and carries a heavy crop. Pods soon form strings if not picked regularly. Mildew and fusarium resistant.
EMsh EUnw MShS

09 H2 **'Oregon Giant'**
Clean, healthy, mid-height plants. Attractive broad, mid-green pods.
EKin MShS

Sugarsnap

00 H2 **'Delikett'**
Dwarf habit. Young, dark green pods stringless but soon form strings; become fleshier and sweeter with age. Very well cropped and a long season of picking. Reconfirmed after trial 2009.
EKin EUnw MCtn MShS NRob

00 H2 **'Norli'**
Medium height. About the earliest maturing and a heavy cropper but over a short period and so requires successional sowing. Medium height plants; good for garden use. Reconfirmed after trial 2009.
CHby MCtn

00 H2 **'Sugar Ann'**
Medium height. Early to crop and gives a good yield of juicy, sweet pods. Good flavour. Reconfirmed after trial 2009.
CHby CRav EKin EMsh EUnw MCtn

Potato (*Solanum tuberosum*)

1st early

98 H2 **'Accent'**
A super-tasting new potato, with pale creamy-yellow waxy flesh. Eelworm and common scab resistance.
EKin EMsh NRob

98 H2 **'Foremost'**
Originally 'Suttons Foremost'. Ever popular new potato with slightly waxy, firm, white, good-flavoured flesh that does not discolour or disintegrate on cooking.
EKin EMsh NRob

07 H2 **'Orla'**
First early, but can also be used as a second early and maincrop. Good yield of round to oval creamy white tubers; flesh slightly waxy with

good flavour. Popular with organic gardeners.
NRob

98 H2 **'Red Duke of York'**
Oval red sport of 'Duke of York' with moist pale yellow flesh of superb flavour. Excellent roasted but a good all-rounder as tubers bulk up quickly if left to mature as a late second early.
EKin EMsh LCro NRob

07 H2 **'Vales Emerald'**
Very good yield of oval, pale yellow, shallow-eyed tubers with cream-coloured flesh. Reconfirmed after trial 2013 as early for container use.
NRob

07 H2 **'Vivaldi'**
Can be left to bulk up as summer baker. Good yield of oval, pale yellow, smooth-skinned tubers with creamy flesh.
EKin EMsh NRob

98 H2 **'Winston'**
Bulks up quickly to produce large, even-shaped tubers. Creamy moist flesh of excellent flavour which does not discolour on cooking.
CRav EKin NRob

2nd early

98 H2 **'British Queen'**
Heavy and uniform crop of white-skinned and floury-textured tubers of delicious flavour for all cooking purposes.
EMsh NRob

98 H2 **'Charlotte'**
Long oval variety producing yellow-skinned and waxy tubers with creamy yellow flesh of first-class flavour either hot or cold. Reconfirmed after trial 2013 as early for container use.
CRav EKin EMsh LCro NRob

98 H2 **'Kondor'**
Large pale red-skinned oval tubers with tasty, almost waxy, yellow flesh. Very high yields. Excellent for baking.
NRob

98 H2 **'Lady Christl'**
Bulks up very quickly and is almost a first early. Long oval, shallow-eyed, pale yellow-skinned and creamy flesh which remains firm on cooking. Eelworm resistant. Reconfirmed after trial 2007; also in 2013 after trial as early for container use.
EKin EMsh NRob

98 H2 **'Nadine'**
Exceptionally smooth skin and shallow eyes. Cream flesh with a moist, waxy texture that does not discolour on cooking. Heavy uniform yields. An exhibitor's favourite.
EKin NRob

Early in containers

13 H2 **'Casablanca'**
Clean crop, white flesh, uniform size.
EKin LCro NRob

13 H2 **'Maris Bard'**
White flesh, thin skin, good flavour and texture; fairly uniform crop.
EKin EMsh NRob

13 H2 **'Sharpe's Express'**
Heritage variety; white skin, uniform crop size. Slightly waxy, good flavour.
CRav EMsh NRob

Early maincrop

93 H2 **'Maxine'**
Large, smooth, pale red-skinned tubers with white waxy flesh. Uniform tubers so also recommended for exhibitors. Eelworm resistant. Reconfirmed after trial 1998.
NRob

93 H2 **'Picasso'**
One of the heaviest croppers with creamy skin and striking bright red eyes. Waxy fine-flavoured flesh, particularly when boiled. Eelworm resistant and good resistance to common scab. Reconfirmed after trial 1998, 2014.
EMsh NRob

Salad

03 H2 **'Annabelle'**
First early. High yield, oval tubers, shallow eyes, waxy, yellow flesh. Reconfirmed after trial 2007.
EMsh

03 H2 **'Cherie'**
Good yield; pink-skinned, oval tubers. Pale yellow, waxy flesh, good flavour. Reconfirmed after trial 2007.
NRob

03 H2 **'Pink Fir Apple'**
Late main crop (22 weeks from planting). Very vigorous plants, elongated, knobbly tubers; good flavour.
CRav EKin EMsh LCro NRob

03 H2 **'Ratte'**
Early main crop. Oval tubers, waxy, cream flesh; good flavour.
CRav NRob

RADISH (*Raphanus sativus*)

02 H2 **'Flamboyant'**
Cylindrical type; red with small white tip. Uniform, medium-sized tops.
LSds

08 H2 **'Pink Beauty'**
Attractive, shiny pink roots. Crunchy texture and good, sweet flavour. No pithiness.
MCtn MShS

02 H2 **'Rudi'**
Round type; uniform, with good red colour; very short tops. Fairly uniform. Reconfirmed after trial 2008, 2013.
EHyd NRHS

96 H2 **'Scarlet Globe'**
Round medium to large red roots.
EKin MShS

96 H2 **'Sparkler'**
Slightly flattened round roots. Unique colour split: red upper with white lower skin. Reconfirmed after trial 2013.
CHby EKin EMsh EUnw MCtn

RHUBARB (*Rheum × hybridum*)

03 H4 **'Fulton's Strawberry Surprise'**
Maincrop. Very attractive bright red colour. Strong plant, but not too vigorous for the garden.
EMsh

03 H4 **'Grandad's Favorite'**
First early. Vigorous plants, high yield, thick, fairly sweet stem, bright colour, good leaf to stem ratio. Suitable for showing.
CRos LRHS NRHS

03 H4 **'Hawke's Champagne'**
Second early. Compact plants; high yield potential. Attractive, bright red, medium-length, uniform stems.
EMsh WCot

12 H4 **'Raspberry Red'**
First early. High quality, rich red stalks. Crops heavily and reliably.
CRav CRos EMil EPfP EPom LCro LOPS LRHS SPoG

03 H4 **'Stein's Champagne'**
Maincrop. Very bold, bright red stems, with the colour along the full length. Medium vigour.
NRob

03 H4 **'Timperley Early'**
First early. Thick stems, early, high yield. Bred for forcing; performs very well outside, but even better colour when forced.
Widely available

SPINACH (*Spinacia oleracea*)

08 H2 **'Amazon'**
F_1 hybrid; resistant to mildew races 1–10. Vigorous plants that bulk well; leaves are large, round and a good glossy dark green.
EMsh

02 H2 **'Emilia'**
F_1 hybrid. Very uniform plants, with upright habit and good dark green colour; slightly blistered (semi-Savoy) leaves. Resistant to mildew races 1–10. Reconfirmed after trial 2007 and 2008.
EUnw LSds

00 H2 **'Matador'**
F_1 hybrid. Thick, dark green, upright leaf.
EKin LSds

00 H2 **'Medania'**
Open-pollinated; resistant to mildew races 1 and 3. Good yield from slower-growing plants that are slow to bolt. Slightly blistered, large round leaves. Reconfirmed after trial 2008.
EKin MCtn

07 H2 **'Mikado'**
F_1 hybrid; resistant to mildew races 1–4. New slow-bolting, oriental type with glossy, mid-green, pointed leaves with long petioles. Vigorous and high yielding with good flavour. Bulks well; reconfirmed after trial 2008. May also be listed as 'Oriento'.
EMsh EUnw

08 H2 **'Missouri'**
F_1 hybrid; resistant to mildew races 1–10. Heavy yield of bright, medium green leaves with an upright habit.
EKin MCtn

SPINACH BEET (*Beta vulgaris* subsp. *cicla* var. *cicla*)

00 H4 **'Perpetual Spinach'**
Mid to pale green with fairly soft texture, medium vigour; uniform; stable and clean; flat leaf with good green petiole; reconfirmed after trial 2011.
CHby EKin EMsh LCro MCtn MShS NRHS NRob

SQUASH – BUTTERNUT (*Cucurbita moschata*)

08 H2 **'Harrier'**
Early crop of small to medium-sized, bell-shaped fruits, with a small seed cavity.
EUnw

08 H2 **'Hunter'**
A very high yield of uniformly small to medium, long pear-shaped fruits with a small seed cavity. Early ripening with orange-gold flesh.
EHyd EMsh EUnw MCtn MShS NRHS NRob

SQUASH – SUMMER (*Cucurbita pepo*)

06 H2 **'Eight Ball'**
Good yield of round, green fruits; easy to see and pick from the compact, upright plants.
MCtn MShS

06 H2 **'Geode'**
Early and heavy crop of uniform, round, mid to pale green, marbled fruits with smallish blossom end scar. Clean, healthy plants.
NRHS

06 H2 **'Soleil'**
Hybrid; early to crop. Attractive, bright yellow, cylindrical fruits with yellow stalks. Healthy, compact, productive plants.
CRav

06 H2 **'Sunburst'**
Hybrid; attractive yellow, scallop-shaped fruits. Used for "baby veg"; best harvested when small (5–6cm diameter).
EUnw MShS NRob

Squash – winter (*Cucurbita maxima*)

11 H2 **'Crown Prince'**
Large fruits, with blue-grey skin with excellent storage quality. Popular, reliable variety. Fruits have high flesh content, of deep orange colour and excellent flavour.
CHby EKin MCtn MShS NRob

11 H2 **'Honey Bear'**
High sugar variety. Dark green, mini acorn shape fruits of uniform size, typically 8–10cm diameter. Sweet flavour; ideal size for baking whole. Compact, bushy habit, giving a reasonable yield of fruits, with excellent storage qualities. Plant demonstrates good resistance to powdery mildew.
MCtn

11 H2 **'Sweet Dumpling'**
Original sweet dumpling type. Uniform crop of small fruit, approximately 9–10cm diameter; ridged, cream-coloured with green stripes and mottling; sweetly flavoured orange flesh. Trailing habit, producing a good yield of fruits with excellent storage quality.
CHby EKin MCtn NRob

Swede (*Brassica napus* Napobrassica Group)

02 H4 **'Brora'**
Uniform crop; very good smooth shape and colour. Reconfirmed after trial 2014.
EHyd NRHS

Sweet corn (*Zea mays*)

03 H2 **'Earlibird'** (supersweet)
F_1 hybrid; second early. Uniform cobs; good vigour. Reconfirmed after trial 2009.
EHyd MCtn NRHS

03 H2 **'Lark'** (extra tender sweet)
F_1 hybrid; second early. High yield of well-filled cobs with very sweet, clean flavour. Reconfirmed after trial 2009.
EKin EMsh MCtn MShS

09 H2 **'Marshall's Honeydew'** (extra tender sweet)
Mid-season. Good-sized, well-filled cobs.
EMsh

09 H2 **'Seville'**
Mid-season. Tall plants; attractive later-maturing cobs with good shape and straight rows of small grains.
EUnw

93 H2 **'Sundance'** (supersweet)
Early to mid-season. Short plants, with short well-filled cobs.
MCtn

03 H2 **'Swift'** (extra tender sweet)
F_1 hybrid; early. High yield of cobs with excellent eating quality. Good sweet flavour and tender kernels. Reconfirmed after trial 2009.
EKin EMsh MCtn

Sweet pepper (*Capsicum annuum* var. *annuum* Grossum Group)

98 H1c **'Ace'**
F_1 hybrid; productive plants produce uniform, blocky, bell-shaped, fleshy fruits that ripen from mid-green to a bright, attractive red. Reconfirmed after trial 2005.
EMsh

05 H1c **'Corno di Toro Rosso'**
Open-pollinated; later-cropping. Long, horn-shaped, very fleshy fruits that have a good flavour. Maturing from pale green to bright red.
CHby

98 H1c **'Cuneo Giallo'**
Very large fruits; good for stuffing.
LSds

05 H1c **'Diablo'**
F_1 hybrid; very productive plants producing large, pointed, horn-shaped fruits with a very good flavour. Fruits ripen from mid-green to an attractive bright red.
EMsh

05 H1c **'Friggitello'**
Open-pollinated; productive plants with small, long, slim, pointed fruits. Ripening from mid-green to red; the versatile sweet-flavoured fruits have the appearance of a hot pepper and are also suitable for stir-fry and pickling.
LSds

05 H1c **'Mohawk'**
F_1 hybrid. Medium-sized, bell-shaped fruits that ripen from dark green to bright yellow; good flavour. Dwarf-growing plants are well suited to growing in pots.
CRos EKin EUnw NRHS

05 H1c **'Redskin'**
F_1 hybrid; small to medium, blocky, bell-shaped fruits that ripen from dark green to a glossy, dark red. Compact plants give a high yield and are well suited to growing in pots.
CRos EKin MShS NRHS

05 H1c **'Topepo Rosso'**
Open-pollinated; productive, early-cropping plants. Medium-sized, beef tomato shape that is good for stuffing. Attractive fruits mature from dark green to bright red and have a good flavour.
LSds MShS

Tomato (*Solanum lycopersicum*)

97 H1c **'Alicante'**
Good shape; heavy crop of attractive fruits which ripen well. H2 for outdoor use.
EKin EMsh EUnw MShS NRHS NRob

97 H1c **'Golden Sunrise'**
Later-maturing; small yellow fruits.
EKin MCtn MShS NRHS NRob

13 H1c **'Mecano'**
Long trusses of 7–10 fruits; high yield; good flavour.
MShS

93 H1c **'Outdoor Girl'**
Early. Indeterminate, round red fruits with good flavour.
EHyd MCtn NRHS NRob

97 H1c **'Pannovy'**
F_1 hybrid. Thick skin; very high yield.
MShS

13 H1c **'Premio'**
Trusses of 7–10 mid-size fruits, good yield, and nice flavour.
EMsh

93 H1c **'Shirley'**
F_1 hybrid; fairly early. Uniform trusses; nice round red fruit of medium size and average flavour. Reconfirmed after trial 1997.
EKin EMsh EUnw MShS NRHS NRob

93 H1c **'Tigerella'**
Interesting attractive striped fruit with quite good flavour; reconfirmed after trial 1997. H2 for outdoor use.
CHby EKin MCtn MShS NRob

97 H1c **'Vanessa'**
F_1 hybrid. High yield of greenback-free, succulent fruits with very nice flavour.
NRob

93 H1c **'Yellow Perfection'**
Indeterminate, uniform, round, pale, yellow fruit. H2 for outdoor use.
EKin EMsh

Beefsteak

14 H1c **'Beefmaster'**
Multilocular; large fruit; deeply ribbed; light, smooth taste, good yield.
EKin LSds MShS

03 H1c **'Costoluto Fiorentino'**
High yield; medium-sized, attractive bright red, highly ribbed, succulent fruit with good flavour.
CRav LCro LSds MShS

03 H1c **'Marmande'**
High yield; large, bright red, attractive fruits, with solid flesh and good flavour.
CHby EKin EMsh EUnw LSds MCtn MShS

14 H1c **'Supersteak'**
Multilocular; smooth skin; good-sized fruit; nice taste, good yield.
EHyd NRHS

Cherry

07 H1c **'Cherrola'**
High yield, with attractive fruit well spaced on long trusses. Nice flavour.
EHyd NRHS

93 H1c **'Gardener's Delight'**
Indeterminate plants, producing long trusses of fruits of good flavour under glass or outside; reconfirmed after trial 1998. H2 for outdoor use.
CHby CRav EHyd EKin EMsh EUnw MCtn MShS NRHS NRob

98 H1c **'Sun Baby'**
Good trusses of uniform, attractive, yellow fruits. H2 for outdoor use.
MCtn

07 H1c **'Sungold'**
Good yield of attractive round golden-orange fruits. Good flavour.
CHby CRav EKin EMsh MCtn MShS NRHS NRob

98 H1c **'Sweet Million'**
F_1 hybrid. Long trusses of sweet, round, bright red fruits; good yield.
EMsh EUnw MShS NRHS NRob

Plum

04 H1c **'Ildi'**
Vigorous, indeterminate plants; heavy crop of small, attractive, yellow, plum-shaped fruit.
EKin MCtn

04 H1c **'Sweet Olive'**
F_1 hybrid; very early. Very high yield from vigorous, healthy, determinate plants. Small, red, round to plum-shaped fruits, a little difficult to pick, but of good flavour.
EUnw MCtn

Turnip (*Brassica rapa* Rapifera Group)

97 H3 **'Atlantic'**
Early to mid-season. Attractive flattened round roots with a purple top; very quick to mature. Reconfirmed after trial 2004.
EMsh MShS

97 H3 **'Market Express'**
F_1 hybrid; early. Uniform, medium size, smooth, round, pure white, shiny roots. Reconfirmed after trial 2004.
MCtn

04 H3 **'Primera'**
Uniform crop of flat-shaped roots with purple top and attractive smooth skin. Good internal flesh.
EHyd NRHS

04 H3 **'Tiny Pal'**
Attractive round white roots with very smooth skin.
EMsh

93 H3 **'Tokyo Cross'**
F_1 hybrid; early. Uniform, medium size, smooth, round, pure white, shiny roots; reconfirmed after trial 1997 and 2004.
MShS

RHS Perfect for Pollinators

The plants listed below have been selected to help gardeners identify those plants that will provide nectar and pollen for bees and the many other types of pollinating insects.

Key to codes: **T** tree **S** shrub **C** climber **B** bulb / corm **A** annual **Bi** biennial **H** herbaceous perennial † denotes an archaeophyte (a naturalised plant introduced before 1500)

Wildflowers

Short Grass (up to 15cm)

Ajuga reptans bugle	H
Bellis perennis daisy	H
Campanula rotundifolia common harebell	H
Hippocrepis comosa horseshoe vetch	H
Lotus corniculatus bird's foot trefoil	H
Potentilla anserina silverweed	H
Potentilla erecta tormentil	H
Potentilla reptans creeping cinquefoil	H
Primula veris common cowslip	H
Prunella vulgaris selfheal	H
Ranunculus repens creeping buttercup	H
Sanguisorba minor salad burnet	H
Taraxacum officinale dandelion	H
Thymus polytrichus wild thyme	H
Thymus pulegioides large thyme	H
Trifolium pratense red clover	H
Trifolium repens white clover	H
Veronica chamaedrys germander speedwell	H

Hedges, Shrub Borders and Woodland Edges

Acer campestre field maple	S or T
Alliaria petiolata garlic mustard	Bi
Allium ursinum ramsons	B
Aquilegia vulgaris columbine	H
Ballota nigra black horehound	H
Berberis vulgaris barberry †	S
Bryonia dioica white bryony	H/C
Buxus sempervirens common box	S
Campanula trachelium nettle-leaved bellflower	H
Clematis vitalba old man's beard, traveller's joy	C
Clinopodium vulgare wild basil	H
Cornus sanguinea common dogwood	S
Crataegus monogyna common hawthorn	S or T
Cytisus scoparius common broom	S
Digitalis purpurea common foxglove	Bi
Euonymus europaeus spindle	S
Fragaria vesca wild strawberry	H
Frangula alnus alder buckthorn	S
Galium mollugo hedge bedstraw	H
Galium odoratum sweet woodruff	H
Galium verum lady's bedstraw	H
Geranium robertianum herb robert	A/Bi
Geum urbanum wood avens	H
Hedera helix common ivy	C
Helleborus foetidus stinking hellebore	H
Hyacinthoides non-scripta bluebell	B
Ilex aquifolium common holly	T
Lamium album white deadnettle	H
Lamium galeobdolon yellow archangel	H
Ligustrum vulgare wild privet	S
Lonicera periclymenum common honeysuckle	C
Malus sylvestris crab apple	T
Malva sylvestris common mallow	H
Myosotis sylvatica wood forget-me-not	H
Primula vulgaris primrose	H
Prunus avium wild cherry, gean	T
Prunus padus bird cherry	T
Prunus spinosa blackthorn, sloe	S
Ranunculus ficaria lesser celandine	H
Rhamnus catharticus purging buckthorn	S
Rosa canina dog rose	S
Rosa rubiginosa sweet briar	S
Rubus fruticosus blackberry	S
Salix atrocinerea grey willow (male forms best)	S
Salix caprea goat willow (male forms best)	S
Sanicula europaea sanicle	H
Sedum telephium orpine	H
Silene dioica red campion	H
Silene latifolia subsp. *alba* white campion	H
Smyrnium olusatrum alexanders †	Bi
Sorbus aria common whitebeam	T
Sorbus aucuparia rowan, mountain ash	T

Sorbus torminalis wild service tree	T
Stachys officinalis betony	H
Stellaria holostea greater stitchwort	H
Symphytum officinale common comfrey	H
Teucrium scorodonia wood sage	H
Tilia cordata small-leaved lime	T
Viburnum lantana common wayfaring tree	S
Viburnum opulus guelder rose	S
Vicia cracca common tufted vetch	H
Vicia sativa common vetch	H

Disturbed Ground

Agrostemma githago corncockle †	A
Anchusa arvensis bugloss †	A
Anthemis arvensis corn chamomile †	A
Anthemis cotula stinking chamomile †	A
Centaurea cyanus cornflower †	A
Cichorium intybus chicory †	H
Dipsacus fullonum common teasel	Bi
Echium vulgare viper's bugloss	Bi
Glebionis segetum corn marigold †	A
Iberis amara wild candytuft	A
Lamium amplexicaule henbit deadnettle †	A
Matricaria recutita scented mayweed †	A
Mentha arvensis corn mint	H
Myosotis arvensis field forget-me-not †	A/H
Onopordum acanthium cotton thistle †	Bi
Papaver dubium long-headed poppy †	A
Papaver rhoeas common poppy †	A
Sinapis arvensis charlock †	A
Sonchus arvensis perennial sowthistle	H
Tussilago farfara coltsfoot	H
Verbascum thapsus great mullein	Bi

Flower Beds

Calluna vulgaris heather, ling	S
Erica ciliaris Dorset heath	S
Erica cinerea bell heather	S
Erica tetralix cross-leaved heath	S

Long Grass (above 50cm)

Arctium minus lesser burdock	Bi
Carduus crispus welted thistle	Bi
Carduus nutans musk thistle	Bi
Chamaenerion angustifolium rosebay willowherb	H
Cirsium arvense creeping thistle	H
Cirsium vulgare spear thistle	Bi
Conopodium majus pignut	H
Cynoglossum officinale hound's tongue	H
Daucus carota wild carrot	Bi
Geranium pratense meadow cranesbill	H
Heracleum sphondylium hogweed	Bi
Hypericum perforatum perforate St John's wort	H
Knautia arvensis field scabious	H
Lathyrus pratensis meadow vetchling	H
Pastinaca sativa wild parsnip	Bi
Succisa pratensis devil's bit scabious	H
Tanacetum vulgare tansy †	H
Thalictrum flavum meadow rue	H
Tragopogon pratensis goat's beard	Bi
Verbascum nigrum dark mullein	Bi/H

Medium Height Grass (up to 50cm)

Achillea millefolium common yarrow	H
Achillea ptarmica sneezewort	H
Agrimonia eupatoria agrimony	H
Anthyllis vulneraria kidney vetch	H
Armeria maritima thrift, sea pink	H
Blackstonia perfoliata yellowwort	A
Campanula glomerata clustered bellflower	H
Centaurea nigra common knapweed, hardheads	H
Centaurea scabiosa greater knapweed	H
Centaurium erythraea common centaury	Bi
Echium vulgare viper's bugloss	Bi
Erigeron acris blue fleabane	A/H
Filipendula vulgaris dropwort	H
Helianthemum nummularium common rockrose	H
Hypochaeris radicata cat's ear	H
Inula conyzae ploughman's spikenard	H
Leontodon autumnalis autumn hawkbit	H
Leontodon hispidus rough hawkbit	H
Leucanthemum vulgare ox-eye daisy	H
Linaria vulgaris common toadflax	H
Malva moschata musk mallow	H
Ononis repens common restharrow	H
Origanum vulgare wild marjoram	H
Pilosella officinarum mouse-ear hawkweed	H
Ranunculus acris meadow buttercup	H
Ranunculus bulbosus bulbous buttercup	H
Reseda lutea wild mignonette	Bi/H
Rhinanthus minor yellow rattle	A
Scabiosa columbaria small scabious	H
Silene vulgaris bladder campion	H
Solidago virgaurea goldenrod	H

Ponds, Pond Margins & Wet Soils

Alisma plantago-aquatica water plantain	H
Angelica sylvestris wild angelica	Bi
Butomus umbellatus flowering rush	H
Caltha palustris marsh marigold	H
Cardamine pratensis cuckoo flower, lady's smock	H
Cirsium dissectum meadow thistle	H
Epilobium hirsutum great willowherb	H
Eupatorium cannabinum hemp agrimony	H
Filipendula ulmaria meadowsweet	H
Galium palustre marsh bedstraw	H
Geum rivale water avens	H
Hypericum tetrapterum square-stalked St John's wort	H

Iris pseudacorus yellow iris	H
Lotus pedunculatus greater bird's-foot trefoil	H
Lychnis flos-cuculi ragged robin	H
Lycopus europaeus gypsywort	H
Lysimachia nummularia creeping Jenny	H
Lysimachia vulgaris yellow loosestrife	H
Lythrum salicaria purple loosestrife	H
Mentha aquatica water mint	H
Menyanthes trifoliata bogbean	H
Myosotis scorpioides water forget-me-not	H
Nasturtium officinale common watercress	H
Nuphar lutea yellow waterlily	H
Nymphaea alba white waterlily	H
Oenanthe aquatica fine-leaved water dropwort	A/Bi
Oenanthe crocata hemlock water dropwort	H
Persicaria amphibia amphibious bistort	H
Persicaria bistorta common bistort	H
Polemonium caeruleum Jacob's ladder	H
Pulicaria dysenterica common fleabane	H
Ranunculus aquatilis common water crowfoot	A/H
Ranunculus flammula lesser spearwort	H
Ranunculus fluitans river water crowfoot	H
Ranunculus lingua greater spearwort	H
Ranunculus sceleratus celery-leaved buttercup	A
Sagittaria sagittifolia arrowhead	H
Sanguisorba officinalis great burnet	H
Scrophularia auriculata water figwort	H
Scutellaria galericulata common skullcap	H
Stachys palustris marsh woundwort	H
Valeriana officinalis common valerian	H
Veronica beccabunga brooklime	H

Shingle – Gravel Garden

Cakile maritima sea rocket	A
Crambe maritima sea kale	H
Crithmum maritimum rock samphire	H
Eryngium maritimum sea holly	H
Glaucium flavum yellow horned poppy	Bi/H
Sedum acre biting stonecrop	H
Sedum album white stonecrop †	H
Silene uniflora sea campion	H

Garden Plants

Winter (nov – feb)

Clematis cirrhosa Spanish traveller's joy	C
Crocus species crocus (winter-flowering)	B
Eranthis hyemalis winter aconite	B
× *Fatshedera lizei* tree ivy	S
Galanthus nivalis common snowdrop	B
Helleborus species and hybrids hellebore (winter-flowering)	H
Lonicera × *purpusii* Purpus honeysuckle	S
Mahonia species Oregon grape	S
Salix aegyptiaca musk willow	S
Sarcococca confusa sweet box	S
Sarcococca hookeriana sweet box	S
Viburnum tinus laurustinus	S

Spring (mar – may)

Acer campestre Native plant; field maple	S or T
Acer platanoides Norway maple	T
Acer pseudoplatanus sycamore	T
Acer saccharum sugar maple	T
Aesculus hippocastanum horse chestnut	T
Ajuga reptans Native plant; bugle	H
Arabis alpina subsp. *caucasica* alpine rock cress	H
Armeria juniperifolia juniper-leaved thrift	H
Aubrieta species aubretia	H
Aurinia saxatilis gold dust	H
Berberis darwinii Darwin's barberry	S
Berberis thunbergii Japanese barberry	S
Bergenia species elephant ear	H
Buxus sempervirens Native plant; common box	S
Caltha palustris Native plant; marsh marigold	H
Cercis siliquastrum Judas tree	T
Chaenomeles species Japanese quince	S
Cornus mas Cornelian cherry	S
Cotoneaster conspicuus Tibetan cotoneaster	S
Crataegus monogyna Native plant; common hawthorn	S or T
Crocus species crocus (spring-flowering)	B
Doronicum × *excelsum* leopard's bane	H
Enkianthus campanulatus redvein enkianthus	S
Erysimum species wallflower	Bi
Erica carnea alpine heath	S
Erica × *darleyensis* Darley Dale heath	S
Erysimum 'Bredon' wallflower 'Bredon'	H
Euphorbia amygdaloides Native plant; wood spurge	H
Euphorbia characias Mediterranean spurge	H
Euphorbia cyparissias cypress spurge	H
Euphorbia nicaeensis Nice spurge	H
Euphorbia epithymoides cushion spurge	H
Geranium species cranesbill	H
Geum rivale Native plant; water avens	H
Hebe species hebe	S
Helleborus species & hybrids hellebore (spring-flowering)	H
Iberis saxatilis alpine candytuft	H
Iberis sempervirens perennial candytuft	H
Ilex aquifolium Native plant; common holly	T
Lamium maculatum spotted dead nettle	H
Lunaria annua honesty	Bi
Mahonia species Oregon grape (spring-flowering)	S
Malus baccata Siberian crab	T
Malus domestica edible apple	T
Malus floribunda Japanese crab	T

Malus hupehensis Hupeh crab T
Malus sargentii Sargent's crab apple T
Mespilus germanica common medlar T
Muscari armeniacum Armenian grape hyacinth B
Ornithogalum umbellatum common star of Bethlehem B
Pieris formosa lily-of-the-valley bush S
Pieris japonica lily-of-the-valley bush S
Primula veris Native plant; common cowslip H
Primula vulgaris Native plant; primrose H
Prunus avium Native plant; wild & edible cherries T
Prunus domestica wild & edible plums T
Prunus dulcis almond T
Prunus incisa 'Kojo-no-mai' cherry 'Kojo-no-mai' S
Prunus insititia damson T
Prunus laurocerasus cherry laurel S
Prunus mume Japanese apricot T
Prunus padus Native plant; bird cherry T
Prunus pendula f. *ascendens* 'Rosea' flowering cherry T
Prunus persica peach T
Prunus spinosa Native plant; blackthorn S
Prunus tenella dwarf Russian almond S
Prunus × *yedoensis* flowering cherry T
Pulmonaria species lungwort H
Pyrus communis pear T
Ribes nigrum blackcurrant S
Ribes rubrum Native plant; common redcurrant S
Ribes sanguineum flowering currant S
Salix caprea Native plant; goat willow (male form only) S or T
Salix hastata 'Wehrhahnii' halberd willow 'Wehrhahnii' S
Salix lanata Native plant; woolly willow (male form only) S
Skimmia japonica skimmia S
Smyrnium olusatrum Native plant; alexanders † Bi
Stachyurus chinensis stachyurus S
Stachyurus praecox stachyurus S
Vaccinium corymbosum blueberry S

Summer (June – Aug)

Achillea species yarrow H
Actaea japonica baneberry H
Aesculus indica Indian horse chestnut (resistant to leaf-mining moth) T
Aesculus parviflora bottlebrush buckeye S
Agastache species giant hyssop H
Ageratum houstonianum flossflower A
Alcea rosea hollyhock Bi
Allium species ornamental and edibles (when allowed to flower) B
Amberboa moschata sweet sultan A
Amsonia tabernaemontana eastern bluestar H
Anchusa azurea large blue alkanet A
Anchusa capensis Cape alkanet A
Angelica archangelica angelica Bi
Angelica gigas purple angelica Bi
Angelica sylvestris Native plant; wild angelica Bi
Anthemis tinctoria dyer's chamomile H
Antirrhinum majus snapdragon A or H
Aquilegia species columbine H
Argemone platyceras crested poppy A or H
Armeria maritima Native plant; thrift H
Aruncus dioicus goat's beard (male form only) H
Asparagus officinalis common asparagus H
Astrantia major greater masterwort H
Borago officinalis borage A
Brachyglottis (Dunedin Group) 'Sunshine' brachyglottis 'Sunshine' S
Brachyglottis monroi Monro's ragwort S
Buddleja davidii butterfly bush S
Buddleja globosa orange ball tree S
Buphthalmum salicifolium yellow ox-eye H
Bupleurum fruticosum shrubby hare's ear S
Calamintha nepeta Native plant; lesser calamint H
Calendula officinalis common marigold A
Callicarpa bodinieri var. *giraldii* beautyberry S
Callistephus chinensis China aster A
Calluna vulgaris Native plant; heather S
Campanula carpatica tussock bellflower H
Campanula glomerata Native plant; clustered bellflower H
Campanula lactiflora milky bellflower H
Campanula latifolia Native plant; giant bellflower H
Campanula medium Canterbury bells Bi
Campanula persicifolia peach-leaved bellflower H
Campsis radicans trumpet honeysuckle C
Caryopteris × *clandonensis* caryopteris S
Catalpa bignonioides Indian bean tree T
Catananche caerulea blue cupidone H
Centaurea atropurpurea purple knapweed H
Centaurea cyanus cornflower † A
Centaurea dealbata mealy centaury H
Centaurea macrocephala giant knapweed H
Centaurea montana perennial cornflower H
Centaurea nigra Native plant; common knapweed H
Centaurea scabiosa Native plant; greater knapweed H
Centranthus ruber red valerian H
Centratherum punctatum Manaos beauty A
Cerinthe major 'Purpurascens' honeywort 'Purpurascens' A
Cirsium rivulare 'Atropurpureum' purple plume thistle H
Clarkia unguiculata butterfly flower A
Clematis vitalba Native plant; old man's beard, travellers' joy C
Cleome hassleriana spider flower A
Consolida ajacis giant larkspur A
Convolvulus tricolor dwarf morning glory C/A
Coreopsis species tickseed H or A

Cornus alba red-barked dogwood S
Cosmos bipinnatus cosmea A
Cosmos sulphureus yellow cosmos A
Crambe cordifolia greater sea kale H
Crataegus monogyna Native plant; common hawthorn S or T
Cucurbita pepo marrow, courgette A
Cuphea ignea cigar flower A
Cynara cardunculus including Scolymus Group globe artichoke and cardoon H
Cynoglossum amabile Chinese forget-me-not H
Dahlia species dahlia H
Delosperma floribundum ice plant H
Delphinium elatum candle larkspur H
Dianthus barbatus sweet william Bi
Dictamnus albus dittany H
Digitalis species foxglove Bi
Dipsacus fullonum Native plant; common teasel Bi
Echinacea purpurea purple coneflower H
Echinops species globe thistle H
Echium vulgare Native plant; viper's bugloss A
Elaeagnus angustifolia oleaster S
Erica cinerea Native plant; bell heather S
Erica erigena Irish heath S
Erica vagans Native plant; Cornish heath S
Erigeron species fleabane H
Eriophyllum lanatum golden yarrow H
Eryngium × *tripartitum* eryngo H
Eryngium alpinum alpine eryngo H
Eryngium giganteum Miss Willmott's ghost Bi
Eryngium planum blue eryngo H
Erysimum × *allionii* Siberian wallflower H
Erysimum 'Bowles's Mauve' wallflower 'Bowles's Mauve' S
Escallonia species escallonia S
Eschscholzia californica California poppy A
Eupatorium cannabinum Native plant; hemp agrimony H
Eupatorium maculatum Joe Pye weed H
Euphorbia cornigera horned spurge H
Euphorbia sarawschanica Zeravshan spurge H
Ferula communis giant fennel H
Foeniculum vulgare common fennel † H
Fragaria × *ananassa* garden strawberry H
Fuchsia species fuchsia – hardy types S
Gaillardia × *grandiflora* blanket flower H
Gaura lindheimeri white gaura H
Geranium pratense Native plant; meadow cranesbill H
Geranium species cranesbill (summer-flowering) H
Geum species avens (summer-flowering) H
Gilia capitata blue thimble flower A
Glebionis segetum corn marigold † A
Gypsophila elegans annual baby's breath A
Hebe species hebe S
Helenium species Helen's flower H
Helianthus annuus common sunflower A
Helianthus debilis cucumberleaf sunflower A
Heliopsis helianthoides smooth ox-eye H
Heliotropium arborescens common heliotrope A
Heracleum sphondylium Native plant; hogweed Bi
Hesperis matronalis dame's violet H
Hydrangea anomala subsp. *petiolaris* climbing hydrangea C
Hydrangea paniculata paniculate hydrangea (cultivars with many fertile flowers e.g. 'Kyushu', 'Big Ben', 'Floribunda', 'Brussels Lace') S
Hyssopus officinalis hyssop S
Iberis amara Native plant; wild candytuft A
Ilex aquifolium Native plant; common holly T
Inula species harvest daisy H
Jasminum officinale common jasmine C
Kalmia latifolia mountain laurel S
Knautia arvensis Native plant; field scabious H
Knautia macedonica Macedonian scabious H
Koelreuteria paniculata pride of India T
Lathyrus latifolius broad-leaved everlasting pea H
Laurus nobilis bay tree S
Lavandula angustifolia English lavender S
Lavandula × *intermedia* lavandin S
Lavandula stoechas French lavender S
Lavatera olbia tree lavatera S
Lavatera trimestris annual lavatera A
Leucanthemum × *superbum* Shasta daisy H
Leucanthemum vulgare Native plant; ox-eye daisy H
Liatris spicata button snakewort H
Ligustrum ovalifolium garden privet S
Ligustrum sinense Chinese privet S
Limnanthes douglasii poached egg flower A
Limonium platyphyllum broad-leaved statice H
Linaria maroccana annual toadflax A
Linaria purpurea purple toadflax H
Lobularia maritima sweet alyssum A
Lonicera periclymenum Native plant; common honeysuckle C
Lychnis coronaria rose campion Bi or H
Lychnis flos-cuculi Native plant; ragged robin H
Lysimachia vulgaris Native plant; yellow loosestrife H
Lythrum salicaria Native plant; purple loosestrife H
Lythrum virgatum wand loosestrife H
Malope trifida large-flowered mallow wort A
Malva moschata Native plant; musk mallow H
Matthiola incana hoary stock Bi
Mentha aquatica Native plant; water mint H
Mentha spicata spearmint H
Monarda didyma bergamot H
Myosotis species forget-me-not Bi
Nemophila menziesii baby blue eyes A
Nepeta × *faassenii* garden catmint H
Nicotiana alata flowering tobacco A
Nicotiana langsdorffii Langsdorff's tobacco A
Nigella damascena love-in-a-mist A
Nigella hispanica Spanish fennel flower A
Oenothera species evening primrose Bi

Olearia species daisy bush S
Onopordum acanthium cotton thistle Bi
Origanum 'Rosenkuppel' marjoram 'Rosenkuppel' H
Origanum vulgare Native plant; oregano, wild marjoram H
Paeonia species peony H
Papaver orientale oriental poppy H
Papaver rhoeas Native plant; common poppy † A
Parthenocissus tricuspidata Boston ivy C
Penstemon species beard-tongue T
Perovskia atriplicifolia Russian sage S
Persicaria amplexicaulis red bistort H
Persicaria bistorta Native plant; common bistort H
Phacelia campanularia Californian bluebell A
Phacelia tanacetifolia fiddleneck A
Phaseolus coccineus scarlet runner bean A
Phlomis species sage S
Phlox paniculata perennial phlox H
Photinia davidiana stranvaesia S
Phuopsis stylosa Caucasian crosswort H
Pileostegia viburnoides climbing hydrangea C
Polemonium caeruleum Native plant; Jacob's ladder H
Potentilla species cinquefoil H or S
Prostanthera cuneata alpine mint bush S
Ptelea trifoliata hop tree S
Pyracantha species firethorn S
Reseda odorata garden mignonette A
Ridolfia segetum false fennel A
Robinia pseudoacacia false acacia T
Rosa canina Native plant; dog rose S
Rosa rubiginosa Native plant; sweet briar S
Rosa rugosa Japanese rose S
Rosmarinus officinalis rosemary S
Rubus fruticosus agg. Native plant; blackberry S
Rubus idaeus Native plant; common raspberry S
Rudbeckia species coneflower H or A
Salvia species sage A or H
Sanvitalia procumbens creeping zinnia A
Scabiosa atropurpurea sweet scabious A
Scabiosa caucasica garden scabious H
Scabiosa columbaria Native plant; small scabious H
Sedum spectabile & hybrids ice plant H
Sedum telephium Native plant; orpine H
Sidalcea malviflora checkerbloom H
Solidago species goldenrod H
Sorbus aria Native plant; common whitebeam T
Sorbus aucuparia Native plant; mountain ash, rowan T
Spiraea japonica Japanese spiraea S
Stachys byzantina lamb's ear H
Stachys macrantha big sage H
Stokesia laevis Stokes' aster H
Symphoricarpos albus snowberry S
Tagetes patula French marigold A
Tamarix ramosissima tamarisk S
Tanacetum coccineum pyrethrum H
Tanacetum vulgare Native plant; tansy † H
Telekia speciosa yellow ox-eye H
Tetradium daniellii bee-bee tree T
Teucrium chamaedrys Native plant; wall germander H
Thymus species thyme S
Tilia × europaea common lime T
Tilia maximowicziana lime T
Tilia oliveri lime T
Tilia platyphyllos Native plant; broad-leaved lime T
Tithonia rotundifolia Mexican sunflower A
Trachymene coerulea blue lace flower A
Tropaeolum majus garden nasturtium A
Verbascum species mullein Bi
Verbena × hybrida garden verbena A
Verbena bonariensis purple top H
Verbena rigida slender vervain A
Veronica longifolia garden speedwell H
Veronicastrum virginicum Culver's root H
Viburnum lantana Native plant; common wayfaring tree S
Viburnum opulus Native plant; guelder rose S
Vicia faba broad bean A
Weigela florida weigelia S
Zauschneria californica Californian fuchsia S
Zinnia elegans youth and old age A

Autumn (sept – oct)

Aconitum carmichaelii Carmichael's monk's hood H
Actaea simplex simple-stemmed bugbane H
Anemone hupehensis Chinese anemone H
Anemone × hybrida Japanese anemone H
Arbutus unedo strawberry tree S or T
Campanula poscharskyana trailing bellflower H
Ceratostigma plumbaginoides hardy blue-flowered leadwort H
Chrysanthemum species & hybrids chrysanthemum H
Clematis heracleifolia tube clematis C
Colchicum species autumn crocus B
Crocus species crocus (autumn-flowering types) B
Dahlia species & hybrids dahlia H
Elaeagnus pungens silverthorn S
Elaeagnus × ebbingei Ebbinge's silverberry S
Fatsia japonica Japanese aralia S
Hedera colchica Persian ivy C
Hedera helix Native plant; common ivy C
Helianthus × laetiflorus perennial sunflower H
Leucanthemella serotina autumn ox-eye H
Machaeranthera tanacetifolia tansy-leaf aster A
Salvia species sage (autumn-flowering types) H
Symphyotrichum species and hybrids Michaelmas daisy H
Tilia henryana Henry's lime (one of the last to flower) T

Nurseries

Nursery Codes and Symbols

The first letter of each nursery code represents the area of the country in which the nursery is situated.

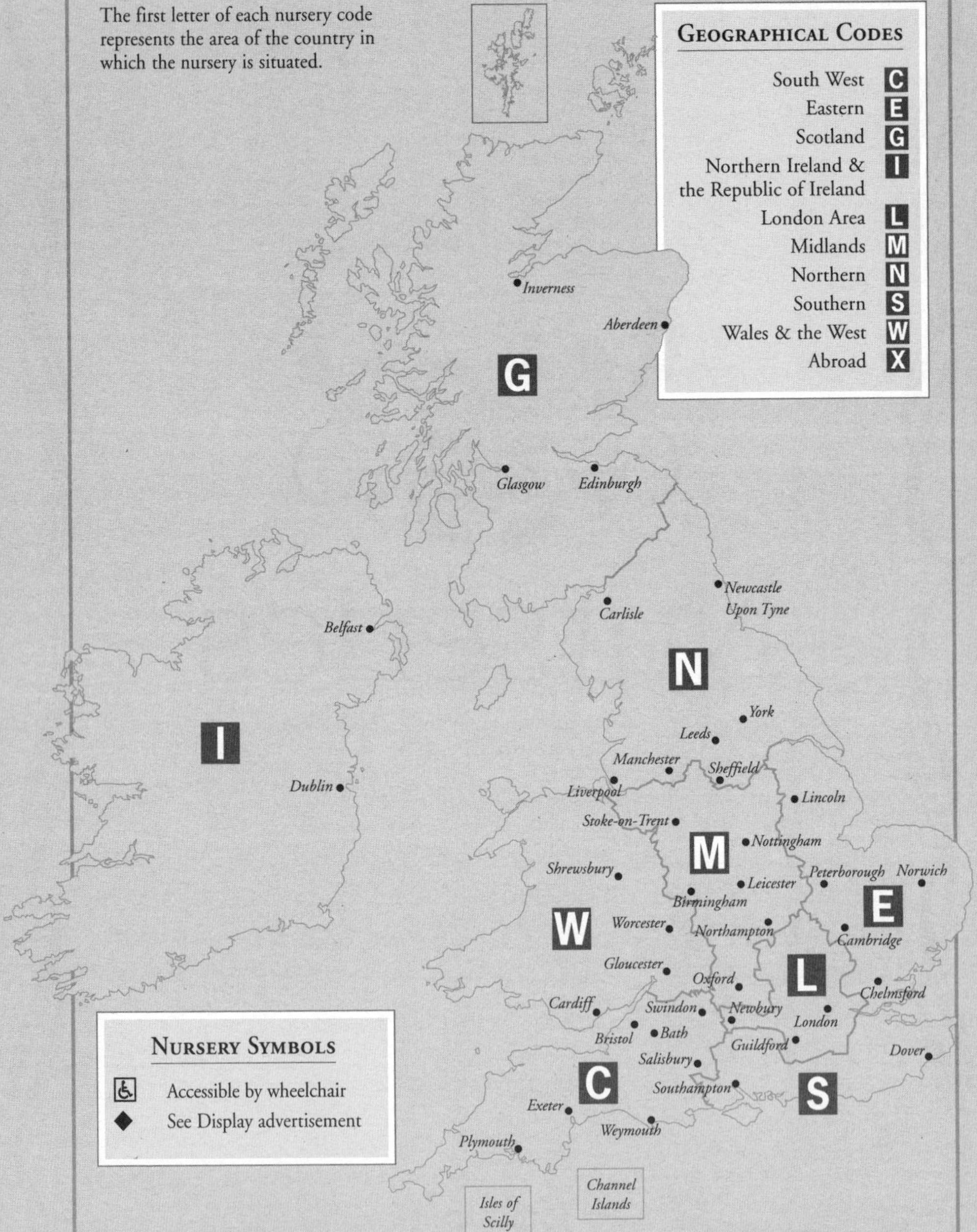

Geographical Codes

South West	C
Eastern	E
Scotland	G
Northern Ireland & the Republic of Ireland	I
London Area	L
Midlands	M
Northern	N
Southern	S
Wales & the West	W
Abroad	X

Nursery Symbols

- ♿ Accessible by wheelchair
- ◆ See Display advertisement

Using the Nursery Listings

Your main reference from the Plant Directory is the Nursery Details by Code listing, which includes all relevant information for each nursery in order of nursery code. The Nursery Index by Name is an alphabetical list for those who know a nursery's name but not its code and wish to check its details in the main list.

1 Nursery Details by Code

Once you have found your plant in the Plant Directory, turn to this list to find out the name, address, opening times and other details of the nurseries whose codes accompany the plant.

KEY
♿ Accessible by wheelchair ◆ See Display advertisement

A geographical code is followed by three letters reflecting the nursery's name

SBig **Big Plant Nursery** ♿ ◆
Hole Street, Ashington, West Sussex
RH20 3DE
Ⓣ (01903) 891466
Ⓕ (01903) 892829
Ⓔ info@bigplantnursery.co.uk
Ⓦ www.bigplantnursery.co.uk
Contact: Bruce Jordan
Opening Times: 0900-1700 Mon-Sat, 1000-1600 Sun & B/hols.
Min Mail Order UK: Please phone for further info.
Cat. Cost: Online only.
Credit Cards: All major credit/debit cards
Specialities: Bamboos, hardy exotics & palms, *Ginkgo*, *Betula*. Architectural plants, evergreens.
Notes: Programme of events & propagation tuition, see website or phone for details. Also sells wholesale. Wheelchair accessible.
Map Ref: S, D3 **OS Grid Ref:** TQ132153

Other information about the nursery

A brief summary of the plants available

The map letter is followed by the map square in which the nursery is located

The Ordnance Survey national grid reference for use with OS maps

2 Nursery Index by Name

If you are looking for a particular nursery, use this alphabetical index to find it, note its code and then turn to the Nursery Details by Code listing for full information.

Beggar's Roost Plants	CBgR
Bennetts Water Gardens	CBen
Bide-A-Wee Cottage Gardens	NBid
Big Plant Nursery	SBig
Binny Plants	GBin
Birchfleet Nurseries	SBir
Birchwood Plants	SBch
Blooming Wild Nursery	CBWd

How to Use the Nursery Listings

The details given for each nursery have been compiled from information supplied to us in answer to a questionnaire. In some case, because of space constraints, the entries have been abbreviated.

Nurseries are not charged for their entries and inclusion in no way implies a value judgement.

Nursery Details by Code (p.840)

Each nursery is allocated a code, for example GPoy. The first letter of each code indicates the region of the British Isles in which the nursery is situated. In this example G = Scotland. The remaining three letters reflect the nursery's name, in this case Poyntzfield Herb Nursery.

In this listing, nurseries are given in alphabetical order of code for quick referral from the Plant Directory. All of the nurseries' details, such as addresses, opening times, etc will be found in this index.

Opening Times

These are published as submitted. It is always advisable, especially if travelling a long distance, to double-check with the nursery before setting out.

Mail Order

Many nurseries offer a mail order service. This is often restricted to certain times of the year or to particular genera. Please check the **Notes** section of the nursery entry for restrictions or special conditions.

In some instances the mail order service extends throughout the European Union. Where this is the case, the minimum charge to the EU will be noted. If this is "Nmc" ("no minimum charge") please note that to send even one plant may involve the nursery in substantial postage and packaging costs. Some nurseries may not be prepared to send tender or bulky plants.

Where a nursery offers a mail order only service, this will be noted under **Opening Times** in the nursery entry. Many nurseries offer a mail order online service with some only operating in this way.

Export

This refers to mail order beyond the EU and indicates nurseries that are prepared to consider this. There is usually a substantial minimum charge and, in addition, all the costs of phytosanitary certificates and Customs have to be met by the purchaser.

Catalogue Cost

Only a small number of nurseries now offer a printed catalogue. Some may not charge or may ask for stamps to bear the cost of postage. If plant lists are available in an electronic format, some nurseries have indicated that they will email them to enquirers.

The majority of nurseries now publish their catalogues only on the internet as this is more cost-effective than producing a printed copy and enables them to reflect stock changes throughout the year.

Specialities

This is where nurseries list the plants or genera in which they specialise and any National Collections that they hold. Please note that some nurseries may charge an entry fee to visit a National Collection. Charges may also be levied to visit any garden to which the nursery is attached.

Nurseries also indicate here if they only have small quantities of individual plants available for sale or if they will propagate to order.

Notes

This section contains: information on restrictions to mail order or export; whether payment in euros is accepted; whether nurseries deliver to shows; details of partial wheelchair access; the nursery site address if this differs from the office address; and any other non-horticultural or general information.

Wheelchair Access ♿

Nurseries are asked to indicate if their premises are suitable for wheelchair users.

We use the wheelchair symbol for those nurseries that tell us their site is fully accessible. Where only partial or restricted access is offered, this is stated in the **Notes** section of the nursery's details and the nursery is not marked with the symbol.

Please note that wheelchair access does not necessarily relate to any gardens to which the nursery may be attached.

The assessment of ease of access is entirely the responsibility of the individual nursery.

Delivers to Shows

Many nurseries will deliver pre-ordered plants to flower shows for collection by customers. Contact the nursery for details of shows that they will be attending.

Payment in Euros

A number of UK nurseries will accept payment in euros. You should check with the nursery concerned before making such a payment, as some will only accept cash and some only cheques, whilst others will expect the purchaser to pay bank charges.

Maps

The approximate locations of nurseries are shown on the relevant maps (p.927) unless the nursery has requested not to be shown. Nurseries are also encouraged to provide their Ordnance Survey national grid reference for use with OS Land Ranger Series maps.

Nursery Index by Name

An alphabetical index of nurseries is included (p.922). Nurseries new to the book and those making a re-entry are shown in embolden type.

Deleted Nurseries

Every year some nurseries ask to be removed from the book. This may be a temporary measure because, for example, they are relocating or because their plant stocks are low due to adverse growing conditions, or it may be permanent following closure, sale, retirement or a change in the way they trade.

Some nurseries miss the deadline for submissions and may ask to re-enter the book in the following edition. Other nurseries do not respond at all and, as we have no current information on their trading status, they are not included in the book.

Please, never use an out of date edition

Nursery Details by Code

Please note that all these nurseries are listed in alphabetical order by their code. All nurseries are listed in alphabetical order by their name in the **Nursery Index by Name** on page 922.

South West

CAbb **Abbotsbury Sub-Tropical Gardens** ♿
Abbotsbury, Nr Weymouth, Dorset DT3 4LA
Ⓣ (01305) 871344
Ⓕ (01305) 871344
Ⓔ info@abbotsburygardens.co.uk
Ⓦ www.abbotsbury-tourism.co.uk/gardens/
Contact: David Sutton
Opening Times: 1000-1800 daily, mid Mar-1st Nov. 1000-1500, Nov-mid Mar.
Credit Cards: Access, Visa, MasterCard, Switch
Specialities: Less common & tender shrubs incl. palms, tree ferns, bamboos & plants from Australia, New Zealand & S. Africa.
Notes: Mail order of some plants is possible upon request, please phone/email for details & a quotation. Wheelchair accessible.

CAby **The Abbey Nursery** ♿
Forde Abbey, Chard, Somerset TA20 4LU
Ⓣ (01460) 220088
Ⓔ theabbeynursery@hotmail.com
Contact: Paul Bygrave
Opening Times: 1000-1700 7 days, 1st Mar-31st Oct.
Cat. Cost: None issued.
Credit Cards: All major credit/debit cards
Specialities: Hardy herbaceous perennials.
Notes: Wheelchair accessible.
Map Ref: C, C4 **OS Grid Ref:** ST359052

CAco **Acorn Trees and Shrubs** ♿
Hilltown Farm, Rackenford, Tiverton, Devon EX16 8DX
Ⓣ (01884) 881633
Ⓜ 07976 807510
Ⓔ goakey101@gmail.com
Ⓦ www.acorntreesandshrubs.co.uk
Contact: Grahame Oakey
Opening Times: Most days & times but by appt. only.
Min Mail Order UK: £50.00 + VAT & delivery.
Min Mail Order EU: £60.00 + VAT & delivery.
Cat. Cost: Full plant listing available by email only.
Credit Cards: All major credit/debit cards
Specialities: Rhododendrons. Conifer specialist, incl. very rare & long needle varieties, incl. *Pinus montezumae, Cedrus atlantica* 'Glauca Pendula' & other pendulous trees.
Notes: Plant specimen procurement, incl. rare/large specimens, delivery & planting service. Also sells wholesale. Wheelchair accessible.
Map Ref: C, B3

CAgr **Agroforestry Research Trust**
46 Hunters Moon, Dartington, Totnes, Devon TQ9 6JT
Ⓕ (01803) 840776
Ⓔ mail@agroforestry.co.uk
Ⓦ www.agroforestry.co.uk
Contact: Martin Crawford
Opening Times: Not open. Mail order only.
Min Mail Order UK: Nmc
Min Mail Order EU: Nmc
Cat. Cost: 4 × 1st class.
Credit Cards: All major credit/debit cards
Specialities: Top & soft fruit, nut trees including *Castanea, Corylus, Juglans, Pinus.* Also seeds. Some plants in small quantities only.
Notes: Euro accepted.

CAni **Anita Allen**
Shapcott Barton Estate, East Knowstone, South Molton, Devon EX36 4EE
Ⓣ (01398) 341664
Contact: Anita Allen
Opening Times: By appt. only. Garden open under NGS & Plant Heritage.
Min Mail Order UK: Nmc
Cat. Cost: 5 × 1st class & state which catalogue: Shasta daisies or *Buddleja.*

Credit Cards: None
Specialities: Nat. Collections of *Leucanthemum* × *superbum* & *Buddleja davidii* & hybrids, 70+ cvs. 80+ accurately named Shasta daisies, a few in very short supply. Also many hardy perennials. Some *Buddleja* propagated to order.
Map Ref: C, B3 **OS Grid Ref:** SS846235

CArg **Ashridge Nurseries**
Grove Cross Barn, Castle Cary, Somerset BA7 7NJ
Ⓣ (01963) 359444
Ⓕ (01963) 359445
Ⓔ support@ashridgetrees.co.uk
Ⓦ www.ashridgetrees.co.uk
Contact: Catherine Young
Opening Times: Not open. Mail order only.
Min Mail Order UK: £20.00
Credit Cards: MasterCard, Visa
Specialities: Trees, hedging & fruit. Roses. Climbers & bulbs.

CAvo **Avon Bulbs**
Burnt House Farm, Mid-Lambrook, South Petherton, Somerset TA13 5HE
Ⓣ (01460) 242177 or 249060
Ⓕ (01460) 249025
Ⓔ info@avonbulbs.co.uk
Ⓦ www.avonbulbs.co.uk
Contact: C Ireland-Jones
Opening Times: Mail order only. Collection of pre-booked orders by arrangement.
Min Mail Order UK: Nmc
Min Mail Order EU: Nmc
Cat. Cost: 4 × 2nd class.
Credit Cards: All major credit/debit cards
Specialities: Some special snowdrops are only available in small quantities.
Notes: Delivers to some shows.
Map Ref: C, B5 **OS Grid Ref:** ST422187

CBar **Barters Plant Centre & Nursery** ♿
Chapmanslade, Westbury, Wiltshire BA13 4AL
Ⓣ (01373) 832694
Ⓕ (01373) 832677
Ⓔ plantcentre@barters.co.uk
Ⓦ www.barters.co.uk
Contact: Andrew Stone
Opening Times: 0900-1700 Mon-Sat, Mar-Oct. 0900-1630 Mon-Sat, Nov-Feb. 1000-1600 Sun (closed Sun Jul-Nov & Jan-Feb), 1000-1600 Sun, Dec only.
Cat. Cost: None issued.
Credit Cards: All major debit/credit cards except American Express
Specialities: Wide range of shrubs. Ground cover, container trees, ferns, half-hardy perennials, grasses, herbaceous & climbers. Hedging, fruit trees, old fashioned roses & bare-root stock.
Notes: Also sells wholesale. Wheelchair accessible.

CBcs **Burncoose Nurseries** ♿
Gwennap, Redruth, Cornwall TR16 6BJ
Ⓣ (01209) 860316
Ⓔ info@burncoose.co.uk
Ⓦ www.burncoose.co.uk
Contact: C H Williams
Opening Times: 0830-1700 Mon-Sat & 1100-1700 Sun.
Min Mail Order UK: Nmc
Min Mail Order EU: Individual quotations for EU sales.
Cat. Cost: Free
Credit Cards: Visa, MasterCard, Maestro
Specialities: Extensive range of over 3500 ornamental trees & shrubs and herbaceous. Rare & unusual *Magnolia, Rhododendron*. Conservatory plants. 30 acre garden.
Notes: Also sells wholesale. Delivers to shows. Wheelchair accessible.
Map Ref: C, D1 **OS Grid Ref:** SW742395

CBct **Barracott Plants** ♿
Old Orchard, Calstock Road, Gunnislake, Cornwall PL18 9AA
Ⓣ (01822) 832234
Ⓜ 07811 207186
Ⓔ geoffandthelma@barracott.eclipse.co.uk
Ⓦ www.barracottplants.co.uk
Contact: Geoff & Thelma Turner
Opening Times: 0900-1700 Thu & Fri, Mar-end Sep. Other times by appt.
Min Mail Order UK: Nmc
Cat. Cost: 1st class stamp.
Credit Cards: None
Specialities: Herbaceous plants: shade-loving, foliage & form. *Acanthus, Aspidistra, Astrantia, Bergenia, Convallaria, Disporum, Liriope, Maianthemum, Polygonatum, Roscoea, Trillium* & *Uvularia*.
Notes: Also sells wholesale. Delivers to shows. Euro accepted. Wheelchair accessible.
Map Ref: C, C3 **OS Grid Ref:** SX436702

CBdn **Bowden Hostas**
Cleave House, Sticklepath, Okehampton, Devon EX20 2NL
Ⓣ (01837) 840989
Ⓔ tim@bowdenhostas.com
Ⓦ www.bowdenhostas.com
Contact: Tim Penrose
Opening Times: 1000-1700 Mon-Sat, Apr-Aug. Sep-Mar, please ring before travelling.
Min Mail Order UK: Nmc
Min Mail Order EU: Nmc

C

Cat. Cost: Free.
Credit Cards: Visa, Access, EuroCard, Switch
Specialities: Hostas, ferns, bamboos. Nat. Collection of modern hybrid *Hosta*.
Notes: Also sells wholesale. Exports beyond EU.

CBen **Bennetts Water Gardens** ♿
Putton Lane, Chickerell, Weymouth, Dorset DT3 4AF
Ⓣ (01305) 785150
Ⓔ orders@waterlily.co.uk
Ⓦ www.waterlily.co.uk
Contact: James Bennett
Opening Times: 1000-1700 Apr-Sep, Sun-Fri.
Min Mail Order UK: Nmc
Min Mail Order EU: Nmc
Credit Cards: Visa, MasterCard, JCB,Maestro
Specialities: Nat. Collection of *Nymphaea* (hardy water lilies).
Notes: Loose plants available by mail order. Potted plants available in store. Wheelchair accessible.
Map Ref: C, C5 **OS Grid Ref:** SY650797

CBgR **Beggar's Roost Plants**
Lilstock, Bridgwater, Somerset TA5 1SU
Ⓣ (01278) 741519
Ⓔ ro@lilstock.eclipse.co.uk
Contact: Lady Rosemary FitzGerald
Opening Times: Not open. Mail order only.
Min Mail Order UK: £10.00
Min Mail Order EU: £15.00
Cat. Cost: 3 × large 2nd class.
Credit Cards: None
Specialities: *Hemerocallis* (incl. heritage) grown in British conditions.
Notes: Mail order for specialities *Hemerocallis*. Ask for list. Euro accepted.
Map Ref: C, B4 **OS Grid Ref:** ST168450

CBlu **Blue Nurseries Ltd**
(Office) Brook Cottage, 2 Bleet, Steeple Ashton, Wiltshire BA14 6EA
Ⓜ 07813 894026
Ⓔ office@bluenurseries.com
Ⓦ www.bluenurseries.com
Contact: Richard Hill
Opening Times: Not open. Mail order only.
Min Mail Order UK: £4.95
Min Mail Order EU: £6.95
Cat. Cost: Online only.
Credit Cards: Paypal
Specialities: South African plants & hardy palms with slowly expanding range of plants but focussed on the architectural & rare.
Notes: Online based but displays at plant and horticultural shows. Also sells wholesale. Euros accepted via Paypal only.

CBod **Bodmin Nursery** ♿
Laveddon Mill, Laninval Hill, Bodmin, Cornwall PL30 5JU
Ⓣ (01208) 72837
Ⓕ (01208) 76491
Ⓔ bodminnursery@aol.com
Ⓦ www.bodminnursery.co.uk
Contact: Mark Lawlor
Opening Times: 0900-1700 Mon-Sat. 1000-1600 Sun.
Credit Cards: All major credit/debit cards
Specialities: Herbs, herbaceous & grasses, hardy geraniums & coastal plants. Interesting shrubs, fruit & ornamental trees.
Notes: Wheelchair accessible.
Map Ref: C, C2 **OS Grid Ref:** SX053659

CBot **The Botanic Nursery**
Coombe Lane, Atworth, Nr Melksham, Wiltshire SN12 8NU
Ⓜ 07850 328756
Ⓔ office@botanicnursery.co.uk
Ⓦ www.botanicnursery.co.uk
Contact: Terence Baker
Opening Times: 1000-1700 Mon-Sat, Sun by arrangement, Mar-Oct. W/ends only in Feb for hellebores & winter-flowering shrubs.
Min Mail Order UK: 5 plants.
Min Mail Order EU: At cost.
Cat. Cost: Online only.
Credit Cards: MasterCard, Visa
Specialities: Specialists in propagation of rare shrubs. All plants are lime-tolerant. Nat. Collection of *Digitalis*. Species & intersectional *Paeonia*, single flowered hollyhocks (*Alcea*), species *Hellebore*.
Notes: Themed events annually incl. foxglove week in May (immediately after Chelsea), peony study days in Apr & hollyhock study days in Aug. Tour of plant collections available for groups. Mail order Oct-Mar. Plugs also available, see website or contact nursery. Delivers to shows. Only partially accessible for wheelchairs.
Map Ref: C, A5 **OS Grid Ref:** ST852655

CBrP **Brooklands Plants**
25 Treves Road, Dorchester, Dorset DT1 2HE
Ⓣ (01305) 265846
Ⓔ cycads@btinternet.com
Ⓦ botanicalgardenphotography.com
Contact: Ian Watt
Opening Times: By appt. only for collection of plants.
Min Mail Order UK: £25.00 + p&p
Cat. Cost: Online only.
Credit Cards: None
Specialities: Cycad nursery specialising in the more cold-tolerant species of *Encephalartos*, *Dioon*, *Macrozamia* & *Cycas*. Also specialist in

cold-tolerant palms as well as plants from New Zealand. Some species available in small quantities only.
Notes: Euro accepted.
Map Ref: C, C5 **OS Grid Ref:** SY682897

CBre **Bregover Plants**
Middlewood, North Hill, Nr Launceston, Cornwall PL15 7NN
Ⓣ (01566) 782661
Ⓔ jenbousfield@gmail.com
Contact: Jennifer Bousfield
Opening Times: 1100-1700 Wed, Mar-mid Oct and by appt.
Min Mail Order UK: Nmc
Cat. Cost: 3 × 1st class. Plant list available as PDF download.
Credit Cards: None
Specialities: Unusual hardy perennials grown in small garden nursery. Available in small quantities only.
Notes: Mail order Oct-Mar only. Delivers to shows.
Map Ref: C, C2 **OS Grid Ref:** SX273752

CBro **Broadleigh Gardens** ♿
Bishops Hull, Taunton, Somerset TA4 1AE
Ⓣ (01823) 286231
Ⓕ (01823) 323646
Ⓔ info@broadleighbulbs.co.uk
Ⓦ www.broadleighbulbs.co.uk
Contact: Christine Skelmersdale
Opening Times: 0900-1600 Mon-Fri for viewing only (charity donation). Orders may be collected if notice given.
Min Mail Order UK: Nmc
Min Mail Order EU: Nmc
Cat. Cost: 2 × 1st class.
Credit Cards: All major credit/debit cards
Specialities: Jan catalogue: bulbs in growth (*Galanthus*, *Cyclamen* etc) & herbaceous woodland plants (trilliums, hellebores etc). Extensive list of *Agapanthus*. June catalogue: dwarf & unusual bulbs, *Iris* (DB & PC). Nat. Collection of Alec Grey hybrid daffodils.
Notes: Delivers to shows. Euro accepted as cash payment only. Wheelchair accessible.
Map Ref: C, B4 **OS Grid Ref:** ST195251

CBur **Burnham Nurseries**
Forches Cross, Newton Abbot, Devon TQ12 6PZ
Ⓣ (01626) 352233
Ⓔ mail@orchids.uk.com
Ⓦ www.orchids.uk.com
Contact: Any member of staff
Opening Times: 1000-1600 Mon-Sun.
Min Mail Order UK: Nmc
Min Mail Order EU: £100.00 + p&p
Cat. Cost: 1 × 2nd class or online.
Credit Cards: Visa, MasterCard, Maestro
Specialities: Many types of tropical orchid species and hybrids.
Notes: Exports beyond EU, please ask for details. Delivers to shows. Euro accepted. Partial wheelchair accessiblity.
Map Ref: C, C4 **OS Grid Ref:** SX841732

CBWd **Blooming Wild Nursery** ♿
At the Oasis Plant Centre, Shaftesbury Road, Child Okeford, Dorset DT11 8EQ
Ⓜ 07525 169662
Ⓔ info@bloomingwild.co.uk
Ⓦ www.bloomingwild.co.uk
Contact: Will Holley
Opening Times: 0900-1700 Mon-Fri, closed Sat & Sun, 28th Mar-30th Sep.
Credit Cards: All major credit/debit cards
Specialities: Small family-run nursery based in North Dorset. Specialises in growing a wide range of herbaceous perennials and ornamental grasses.
Notes: Site at bottom of Oasis Plant Centre (separate nursery). Wheelchair accessible.
Map Ref: C, B5 **OS Grid Ref:** ST838131

CCac **Cactus Shop** ♿
Caldicott, Winkleigh, Devon EX19 8DW
Ⓣ (01837) 83610
Ⓜ 07586 880472
Ⓕ (01837) 83610
Ⓔ ralph@cactusshop.co.uk
Ⓦ www.cactusshop.co.uk
Contact: Ralph Northcott
Opening Times: 1000-1600 daily.
Min Mail Order UK: Nmc
Min Mail Order EU: Nmc
Cat. Cost: Online only.
Credit Cards: All major credit/debit cards
Specialities: Epiphytes. Cacti hardy in the UK. Some stock in very small quantities.
Notes: Also sells wholesale. Exports beyond EU. Euro accepted. Delivers to shows. Wheelchair accessible.
Map Ref: C,C3 **OS Grid Ref:** SS612098

CCCN **Cross Common Nursery**
The Lizard, Helston, Cornwall TR12 7PD
Ⓣ (01326) 290722/290668
Ⓔ info@crosscommonnursery.co.uk
Ⓦ www.crosscommonnursery.co.uk
Contact: Kevin Bosustow
Opening Times: 1000-1700 7 days, Apr, May & Jun. Reduced hours Jul-Sep, please phone for opening times.
Min Mail Order UK: Nmc
Cat. Cost: Online only.
Credit Cards: All major credit/debit cards
Specialities: The most southerly nursery in England, offering a wide rane of unusual

C

plants & shrubs. Tropical/sub-tropical, coastal plants & conservatory plants. Wide range of grapevines and citrus trees. Some plants available in small quantities only.
Map Ref: C, D1 **OS Grid Ref:** SW704116

CChe **CHERRY TREE NURSERY (SHELTERED WORK OPPORTUNITIES PROJECT)** ♿
off New Road Roundabout, Northbourne, Bournemouth, Dorset BH10 7DA
Ⓣ (01202) 593537
Ⓔ contactus@cherrytreenursery.org.uk
Ⓦ www.cherrytreenursery.org.uk
Contact: Stephen Jailler
Opening Times: 0830-1530 Mon-Fri, 0900-1500 Sat, Apr-Sep & 0900-1300 Sat, Oct-Mar. 1000-1500 Sun, Apr to Jul.
Cat. Cost: A4 sae + £2.80 stamps.
Credit Cards: All major debit/credit cards except American Express
Specialities: Hardy shrubs, perennials, climbers, grasses & bamboos.
Notes: A registered charity providing work for adults with severe and enduring mental illness. Also sells wholesale. Wheelchair accessible.
Map Ref: C, C6 **OS Grid Ref:** SZ083965

CCht **CHESTNUT NURSERY (SHELTERED WORK OPPORTUNITIES PROJECT)** ♿
75 Kingland Road, Poole, Dorset BH15 1TN
Ⓣ (01202) 685999
Ⓔ info@chestnutnursery.org.uk
Ⓦ www.chestnutnursery.org.uk
Contact: Angela Mansbridge
Opening Times: 0800-1600 Mon-Fri. 1000-1600 Sat (Mar-Nov) & 1000-1500 Sat (Nov-Xmas). 1000-1500 Sun (Mar-Sep).
Credit Cards: All major credit/debit cards
Specialities: Wide variety of nectar-rich herbaceous perennials, evergreen specimen shrubs, ornamental grasses and annual bedding. Range of exotics for coastal gardens.
Notes: A registered charity providing work for adults with severe and enduring mental illness. Wheelchair accessible.
Map Ref: C, C6 **OS Grid Ref:** SZ018909

CCse **CHASE PLANTS**
Hookswood Cottage, Farnham, Blandford Forum, Dorset DT11 8DQ
Ⓣ (01725) 516394
Ⓔ sales@chaseplants.co.uk
Ⓦ www.chaseplants.co.uk
Contact: Sue Lees & Eddie Wheatley
Opening Times: By appt. only.
Min Mail Order UK: £10.00
Credit Cards: None
Specialities: Hardy perennials, shrubs & some conservatory plants.
Notes: Delivers to shows.

CCVT **CHEW VALLEY TREES** ♿
Winford Road, Chew Magna, Bristol BS40 8HJ
Ⓣ (01275) 333752
Ⓔ info@chewvalleytrees.co.uk
Ⓦ www.chewvalleytrees.co.uk
Contact: S Scarth
Opening Times: 0800-1700 Mon-Fri all year. 0800-1630 Sat. Closed Sun. Closed B/hols & Sats Jul & Aug.
Min Mail Order UK: Nmc
Cat. Cost: Free.
Credit Cards: All major credit/debit cards
Specialities: Native British & ornamental trees, shrubs, fruit trees & hedging.
Notes: Also sells wholesale. Wheelchair accessible.
Map Ref: C, A5 **OS Grid Ref:** ST558635

CDor **DORSET PERENNIALS** ♿
Berkeley Perennials, Holnest, Sherborne, Dorset DT9 5PR
Ⓣ (01963) 210643
Ⓕ (01963) 210643
Ⓔ sales@dorsetperennials.co.uk
Ⓦ www.dorsetperennials.co.uk
Contact: Dawn & Martin Preston
Opening Times: By appt. only during spring & summer. Please check website or contact nursery for any changes.
Min Mail Order UK: Nmc
Cat. Cost: Online only.
Credit Cards: All major credit/debit cards
Specialities: An eclectic mix of hardy perennials grown, the common alongside the unusual. Plants for herbaceous borders & cottage gardens, with a good mix of oddities to tempt the discerning.
Notes: All plants available via website, with larger pot sizes available at nursery. Wheelchair accessible. Delivers to shows.
Map Ref: C, B5 **OS Grid Ref:** ST662090

CDoy **CARADOC DOY**
PO Box 28, Exeter, Devon EX3 0WY
Ⓣ (01392) 877225
Ⓕ (01392) 877225
Ⓔ info@caradocdoy.co.uk
Ⓦ www.caradocdoy.co.uk
Contact: Caradoc Doy
Opening Times: Open by appt. only.
Min Mail Order UK: Nmc
Cat. Cost: Online.
Credit Cards: None
Specialities: Olive trees.

CDTJ **DESERT TO JUNGLE** ♿
Henlade Garden Nursery, Lower Henlade, Taunton, Somerset TA3 5NB
Ⓣ (01823) 443701

Ⓔ plants@deserttojungle.com
Ⓦ www.deserttojungle.com
Contact: Rob Gudge
Opening Times: 1000-1700 Mon, Tues & Thu-Sun (closed Wed), 1st Mar-31st Oct. Thu, Fri & Sat only Nov-Feb. Opening times may vary during RHS shows, so please phone to check.
Min Mail Order UK: Nmc
Cat. Cost: Online only.
Credit Cards: All major credit/debit cards
Specialities: Exotic-looking plants giving a desert or jungle effect in the garden. Incl. *Agave*, *Canna*, aroids, succulents, ferns, tree ferns & bamboos.
Notes: Nursery shares drive with Mount Somerset Hotel. Also sells wholesale. Delivers to shows. Wheelchair accessible.
Map Ref: C, B4 **OS Grid Ref:** ST273232

CDul **DULFORD NURSERIES** ♿
Cullompton, Devon
EX15 2BY
Ⓣ (01884) 266361
Ⓔ dulford.nurseries@virgin.net
Ⓦ www.dulford-nurseries.co.uk
Contact: Paul Rawlings
Opening Times: 0730-1630 Mon-Fri.
Min Mail Order UK: Nmc
Min Mail Order EU: Nmc
Cat. Cost: Free.
Credit Cards: All major credit/debit cards
Specialities: Native, ornamental & unusual trees, hedging & shrubs incl. oaks, maples, beech, birch, chestnut, lime, *Malus*, *Sorbus* & pines.
Notes: Wheelchair accessible.
Map Ref: C, C4 **OS Grid Ref:** SY062062

CEls **ELSWORTH HERBS**
Farthingwood, Broadway,
Sidmouth, Devon
EX10 8HS
Ⓣ (01395) 578689
Ⓔ john.twibell@btinternet.com
Contact: Drs J D & J M Twibell
Opening Times: By appt. only.
Min Mail Order UK: £10.00
Cat. Cost: By email only.
Credit Cards: None
Specialities: Nat. Collection of *Artemisia*. Wide range of *Artemisia*. Stock available in small quantities only. Orders may require propagation from Collection material, for which we are the primary reference source.
Notes: Mail order only on small scale in exceptional situations. Partially accessible for wheelchairs.
Map Ref: C, C4 **OS Grid Ref:** SY119881

CElw **ELWORTHY COTTAGE PLANTS** ♿
Elworthy Cottage, Elworthy, Nr Lydeard St Lawrence, Taunton, Somerset
TA4 3PX
Ⓣ (01984) 656427
Ⓔ mike@elworthy-cottage.co.uk
Ⓦ www.elworthy-cottage.co.uk
Contact: Mrs J M Spiller
Opening Times: 1000-1700 Thu, late Mar-end Aug. Also by appt. Feb-Oct.
Cat. Cost: 3 × 2nd class.
Credit Cards: None
Specialities: Unusual herbaceous plants esp. hardy *Geranium*, *Geum*, *Crocosmia*, *Epimedium*, *Monarda*, *Pulmonaria* & *Viola*. Some varieties only available in small quantities. *Galanthus* available by mail order in Feb.
Notes: Nursery on B3188, 5 miles north of Wiveliscombe, in centre of Elworthy village. Delivers to shows. Wheelchair accessible.
Map Ref: C, B4 **OS Grid Ref:** ST084349

CEnd **ENDSLEIGH GARDENS** ♿
Milton Abbot, Tavistock, Devon PL19 0PG
Ⓣ (01822) 870235
Ⓕ (01822) 870513
Ⓔ info@endsleigh-gardens.com
Ⓦ www.endsleighgardens.co.uk
Contact: Adrian Steele
Opening Times: 0800-1700 Mon-Sat. 1000-1600 Sun.
Min Mail Order UK: Nmc
Cat. Cost: 2 × 1st class.
Credit Cards: Visa, Access, Switch, MasterCard
Specialities: Choice & unusual trees & shrubs incl. *Acer* & *Cornus* cvs. Old apples & cherries. *Wisteria*. Grafting service. Modern fruit trees, soft fruit and good selection of perennials.
Notes: Wheelchair accessible (but no disabled toilets).
Map Ref: C, C3 **OS Grid Ref:** SX398780

CExl **EXCLUSIVE PLANTS NURSERY**
Tretawn, High Cross, Constantine, Falmouth, Cornwall TR11 5RE
Ⓣ (01326) 341496
Ⓜ 07775 811385
Ⓕ (01326) 341496
Ⓔ info@exclusiveplants.com
Ⓦ www.exclusiveplants.com
Contact: Paul Bonavia
Opening Times: W/ends or by appt. only.
Min Mail Order UK: Nmc
Min Mail Order EU: £25.00
Cat. Cost: 2 × 1st class.
Credit Cards: All major credit/debit cards
Specialities: A plantsperson's nursery, offering

C

rare & unusual plants from around the world. Also new introductions & the best form of our better known plants.
Notes: Euro accepted.

CFen **FENTONGOLLAN FARM** ♿
Merther Lane, St Michael Penkivel, Tresillian, Truro, Cornwall
TR2 4AQ
Ⓣ (01872) 520209
Ⓕ (01872) 520606
Ⓔ admin@flowerfarm.co.uk
Ⓦ www.flowerfarm.co.uk
Contact: James Hosking
Opening Times: 0900-1700 7 days, Aug-end Nov.
Min Mail Order UK: Nmc
Min Mail Order EU: Nmc
Cat. Cost: Free.
Credit Cards: All major debit/credit cards except American Express
Specialities: *Narcissus*. Importers of quality Dutch bulbs.
Notes: Also sells wholesale. Delivers to shows. Euro accepted. Wheelchair accessible.
Map Ref: C, D2

CFGn **THE FOREST GARDEN**
Penjerrick Hill, Budock Water, Falmouth, Cornwall TR11 5ED
Ⓣ (01326) 250090
Ⓔ simonmiles@theforestgarden.co.uk
Ⓦ www.theforestgarden.co.uk
Contact: Simon Miles
Opening Times: Not open. Mail order only. Will open for pre-arranged plant order collection.
Min Mail Order UK: £10.00
Specialities: Perennial edible forest garden & agroforestry plants. Top fruit & nut trees, soft fruit, unusual & less common perennial vegetables, tubers, fruits & herbs. Shelter belts & hedging.
Map Ref: C, D1 **OS Grid Ref:** SW178030

CFil **FILLAN'S PLANTS**
Tuckermarsh Gardens, Yelverton, Devon
PL20 7HN
Ⓜ 07813 161276
Ⓔ mail@tuckermarshplants.co.uk
Ⓦ www.tuckermarshplants.co.uk
Contact: Mark Fillan
Opening Times: By appt. only. Please phone or email.
Min Mail Order UK: £20.00
Min Mail Order EU: £50.00
Cat. Cost: 4 × 1st class
Credit Cards: None
Specialities: *Aucuba, Dasylirion, Deutsia, Epimedium, Hydrangea, Mahonia, Nolina, Oreopanax, Philadelphus, Polystichum setiferum, Quercus, Schefflera* & *Yucca*. Also species *Dahlia* & *Narcissus*. Some plants available in small quanitities only.

CFis **MARGERY FISH PLANT NURSERY** ♿
East Lambrook Manor Gardens, East Lambrook, South Petherton, Somerset
TA13 5HH
Ⓣ (01460) 240328
Ⓜ 07710 484745
Ⓔ enquiries@eastlambrook.com
Ⓦ www.eastlambrook.com
Contact: Tom Wild
Opening Times: 1000-1700 Tue-Sat, Feb-Oct, plus B/hol Mons & Suns Feb, May-Jul. Nov-Jan by appt.
Cat. Cost: None issued.
Credit Cards: All major credit/debit cards
Specialities: Hardy geraniums & cottage garden herbaceous plants. Stock available in small quantities only. Major collection of hardy geraniums on site.
Notes: Wheelchair accessible.
Map Ref: C, B5 **OS Grid Ref:** ST431188

CFlo **FLOYDS CLIMBERS AND CLEMATIS**
36 Dowding Drive, Lower Compton, Calne, Wiltshire
SN11 8QL
Ⓣ (01249) 823200
Ⓜ 07762 499416
Ⓔ sales@floydsclimbers.co.uk
Ⓦ www.floydsclimbers.co.uk
Contact: Marcel Floyd
Opening Times: Open w/ends twice a year. See website or phone for dates.
Min Mail Order UK: Nmc
Credit Cards: Paypal
Specialities: *Clematis* and climbers.
Notes: Also sells wholesale. Euro accepted. Delivers to shows.
Map Ref: C, A6

CFst **FOREST EDGE NURSERIES**
Verwood Road, Woodlands, Wimborne, Dorset BH21 8LJ
Ⓣ (01202) 824387
Ⓕ (01202) 829564
Ⓔ info@theheathergarden.co.uk
Ⓦ www.theheathergarden.co.uk
Contact: David Edge
Opening Times: 0900-1630 Mon. Collection available by arrangement on other days.
Cat. Cost: £2.00
Credit Cards: Paypal
Specialities: Heathers: *Calluna, Erica, Daboecia*.
Notes: Also sells wholesale. Euro accepted.
Map Ref: C, B6

CGar **Gardeners Delight Nursery**
Old Bideford Road, Barnstaple, Devon
EX31 2PA
Ⓣ (01271) 861461
Ⓔ g.d.n@hotmail.co.uk
Ⓦ www.gardenplantsandgifts.co.uk
Contact: Nick Wade
Opening Times: 0930-1630 Mon-Sat, 1000-1600 Sun.
Min Mail Order UK: Nmc
Credit Cards: All major credit/debit cards
Specialities: Traditional plant nursery.
Notes: Also sells wholesale. Limited wheelchair access but help available. Delivers to shows.
Map Ref: C, B3

CGro **C W Groves & Son Ltd** ♿
West Bay Road, Bridport, Dorset DT6 4BA
Ⓣ (01308) 422654
Ⓔ garden@grovesnurseries.co.uk
Ⓦ www.grovesnurseries.co.uk
Contact: Becky Groves
Opening Times: 0830-1700 Mon-Sat, 10.00-16.00 Sun.
Min Mail Order UK: Nmc + p&p £5.99 for mainland UK
Min Mail Order EU: £15.00 + p&p
Cat. Cost: Free.
Credit Cards: Visa, Switch, MasterCard
Specialities: Established in 1866, a family-run garden centre with nursery on site specialising in *Viola odorata*, Parma violets & roses.
Notes: Mainly violets, roses, herbs, soft fruit & grapevines by mail order. Main violet display at nursery in Feb, Mar & Apr. Will export violet seeds only beyond EU. Wheelchair accessible.

CGrW **The Great Western Gladiolus Nursery**
17 Valley View, Clutton, Bristol BS39 5SN
Ⓣ (01761) 452036
Ⓔ clutton.glads@btinternet.com
Ⓦ www.greatwesterngladiolus.co.uk
Contact: G F Hazell
Opening Times: Mail order only. Open by appt. only.
Min Mail Order UK: Nmc
Min Mail Order EU: Nmc
Cat. Cost: 4 × 1st class (2 catalogues).
Credit Cards: None
Specialities: *Gladiolus* species & hybrids, corms & seeds. Other South African bulbous plants. Only available in small quantities.
Notes: Also sells wholesale. Euro accepted.

CHab **Habitat Aid Ltd.**
Hookgate Cottage, South Brewham, Somerset
BA10 0LQ
Ⓣ (01749) 812355
Ⓔ info@habitataid.co.uk
Ⓦ www.habitataid.co.uk
Contact: Nick Mann
Opening Times: Not open. Mail order only.
Min Mail Order UK: £50.00, incl. p&p.
Cat. Cost: None issued.
Credit Cards: All major credit/debit cards
Specialities: British trees, wildflowers and seeds. Local provenance seed mixes. Native aquatic plants. Cottage garden perennials. Heritage fruit trees.
Notes: Also sells wholesale. Delivers to shows.

CHby **The Herbary**
161 Chapel Street, Horningsham,
Warminster, Wiltshire
BA12 7LU
Ⓣ (01985) 844442
Ⓔ info@beansandherbs.co.uk
Ⓦ www.beansandherbs.co.uk
Contact: Pippa Rosen
Opening Times: May-Sep strictly by appt. only.
Min Mail Order UK: Nmc
Min Mail Order EU: Nmc
Cat. Cost: Online only.
Credit Cards: None
Specialities: Culinary, medicinal & aromatic herbs organically grown in small quantities.
Notes: Mail order for seed only and all year for organic vegetable seed & large variety of organic bean & herb seed. Also sells wholesale. Euro accepted.

CHGN **High Garden Nurseries** ♿
Chiverstone Lane, Kenton, Exeter, Devon
EX6 8NJ
Ⓣ (01626) 899106
Ⓔ highgarden@highgarden.co.uk
Ⓦ highgardenkenton.wordpress.com
Contact: Chris Britton
Opening Times: 0900-1700 Tue-Fri
Cat. Cost: None issued.
Credit Cards: All major credit/debit cards
Specialities: Quality shrubs, trees & perennials, some unusual & different.
Notes: Wheelchair accessible.
Map Ref: C, C4 **OS Grid Ref:** SX957836

CHid **Hidden Valley Nursery**
Umberleigh, Devon EX37 9BU
Ⓣ (01769) 560567
Ⓜ 07899 788789
Ⓔ plalindley@itsosbroadband.co.uk
Contact: Linda & Peter Lindley
Opening Times: Daylight hours, but please phone first.
Cat. Cost: None issued.
Credit Cards: None
Specialities: Hardy perennials esp. shade

lovers & Chatham Islands forget-me-nots (*Myosotidium hortensia*).
Notes: Nursery not easy to find using Sat Nav or Google Street Map. Delivers to shows. Euro accepted.

CHII **HILL HOUSE NURSERY LTD**
Landscove, Nr Ashburton, Devon TQ13 7LY
Ⓣ (01803) 762273
Ⓔ bluebird@hillhousenursery.com
Ⓦ www.hillhousenursery.com
Contact: Raymond, Sacha & Matthew Hubbard
Opening Times: 1100-1700 7 days, all year. Open all B/hols incl. Easter Sun. Closed Friday before Xmas Eve for two weeks only. Tearoom open 1st Mar-30th Sep.
Min Mail Order UK: Nmc
Cat. Cost: None issued.
Credit Cards: Delta, MasterCard, Switch, Visa, Paypal
Specialities: 3000+ varieties of plants, most propagated on premises, many rare or unusual. The garden, open to the public, was laid out by Edward Hyams. Pioneers of glasshouse pest control by beneficial insects.
Notes: Groups welcome with prior notice. Also sells wholesale. Euro accepted. Tea room & garden wheelchair accessible, access limited in nursery.
Map Ref: C, C3 **OS Grid Ref:** SX774664

CHVG **HIDDEN VALLEY GARDENS** ♿
Treesmill, Nr Par, Cornwall PL24 2TU
Ⓣ (01208) 873225
Ⓔ hiddenvalleygardens@yahoo.co.uk
Ⓦ www.hiddenvalleygardens.co.uk
Contact: Mrs P Howard
Opening Times: 1000-1800 Thu-Mon (closed Tue & Wed), 20th Mar-15th Oct. Please phone for directions. Garden open as nursery.
Cat. Cost: None issued.
Credit Cards: All major credit/debit cards
Specialities: Cottage garden plants, *Dahlia* & many perennials which can be seen growing in the garden. Some stock available in small quantities. Display garden.
Notes: Award-winning Garden In Cornwall 2014. Euro accepted. Wheelchair accessible.
Map Ref: C, D2 **OS Grid Ref:** SX094567

CIri **THE IRIS GARDEN**
Yard House, Pilsdon, Bridport, Dorset DT6 5PA
Ⓣ (01308) 868797
Ⓔ info@theirisgarden.co.uk
Ⓦ www.theirisgarden.co.uk
Contact: Clive Russell
Opening Times: Show garden open by appt. only. Please email or phone for details.
Cat. Cost: None issued.
Specialities: Modern bearded & beardless *Iris* from breeders in UK, USA, France, Italy & Australia. Nat. Collection of Space Age *Iris*. Also Nat. Collection of 6-fall & Novelty Bearded *Iris*.
Notes: No mail order or sales from website. Ordering in garden only. Plants can be ordered on site with a 25% deposit but customers must be prepared to return & collect at a later date.
Map Ref: C, C5 **OS Grid Ref:** SY421988

CJun **JUNKER'S NURSERY LTD.**
Higher Cobhay, Milverton, Somerset TA4 1NJ
Ⓣ (01823) 400075
Ⓔ karan@junker.co.uk
Ⓦ www.junker.co.uk
Contact: Karan Junker
Opening Times: Strictly by appt. only. Contact nursery for directions (do not rely on Sat Nav).
Min Mail Order UK: Nmc
Min Mail Order EU: Nmc
Cat. Cost: Free list available by email.
Credit Cards: None
Specialities: Choice & unusual shrubs & trees incl. grafted *Acer palmatum*, *Betula*, *Cornus*, *Daphne*, *Magnolia* cvs. Also extensive collections of *Euonymus*, *Ilex*, *Liquidambar* & *Viburnum*, all grown on own roots. Many available in larger, more mature sizes. Small quantities only of some hard to propagate plants, esp. daphnes.
Notes: Extensive planted areas showing how the plants look growing in "real world" conditions. Propagate & grow all own plants with an increasing number grown naturally in open ground as well as younger plants in pots, incl. larger sizes. Limited wheelchair access.
Map Ref: C, B4

CKel **KELWAYS PLANTS LTD** ♿
Picts Hill, Langport, Somerset TA10 9EZ
Ⓣ (01458) 250521
Ⓔ sales@kelways.co.uk
Ⓦ www.kelways.co.uk
Contact: Dave Root, Andy Martin
Opening Times: 0900-1700 Mon-Fri & Sat, 0930-1600 Sun.
Min Mail Order UK: £3.95 + p&p
Cat. Cost: Online only.
Credit Cards: Paypal
Specialities: *Paeonia*, *Iris*, herbaceous perennials, roses, *Clematis*, climbers, ferns, trees & shrubs.
Notes: Contract growing & plant sourcing service. Also sells wholesale. Euro accepted. Wheelchair accessible.
Map Ref: C, B5 **OS Grid Ref:** ST434273

CKen **KENWITH CONIFER NURSERY (GORDON HADDOW)** ♿
Blinsham, Nr Torrington, Beaford, Winkleigh, Devon EX19 8NT
Ⓣ (01805) 603274
Ⓕ (01805) 603663
Ⓔ info@kenwithconifernursery.co.uk
Ⓦ www.kenwithconifernursery.co.uk
Contact: Gordon Haddow
Opening Times: 1000-1630 Tue-Sat all year. Closed all B/hols. If travelling a long distance, please phone previous day to ensure nursery will be open.
Min Mail Order UK: £20 + p&p
Cat. Cost: Online only.
Credit Cards: Visa, MasterCard
Specialities: All conifer genera. Grafting a speciality.
Notes: Wheelchair accessible.
Map Ref: C, C3 **OS Grid Ref:** SS518160

CKno **KNOLL GARDENS**
Hampreston, Wimborne, Dorset BH21 7ND
Ⓣ (01202) 873931
Ⓕ (01202) 870842
Ⓔ enquiries@knollgardens.co.uk
Ⓦ www.knollgardens.co.uk
Contact: N R Lucas
Opening Times: 1000-1700 Tue-Sat, Feb-Dec. Open B/hol Mons. See website for further details.
Min Mail Order UK: Nmc
Min Mail Order EU: Nmc
Cat. Cost: None.
Credit Cards: Visa, MasterCard
Specialities: Grasses (main specialism). Flowering perennials. Nat. Collection of *Pennisetum*.
Notes: Also sells wholesale.
Map Ref: C, C6

CLnd **LANDFORD TREES**
Landford Lodge, Landford, Salisbury, Wiltshire SP5 2EH
Ⓣ (01794) 390808
Ⓕ (01794) 390037
Ⓔ trees@landfordtrees.co.uk
Ⓦ www.landfordtrees.co.uk
Contact: C D Pilkington
Opening Times: 0800-1700 Mon-Thu, 0800-1530 Fri.
Cat. Cost: Free.
Credit Cards: All major debit/credit cards except American Express
Specialities: Deciduous ornamental trees.
Notes: Also sells wholesale.
Map Ref: C, B6 **OS Grid Ref:** SU247201

CLoc **C S LOCKYER (FUCHSIAS)** ◆
Lansbury, 70 Henfield Road, Coalpit Heath, Bristol BS36 2UZ
Ⓣ (01454) 772219
Ⓕ (01454) 772219
Ⓔ Stuart@lockyerfuchsias.co.uk
Ⓦ lockyerfuchsias.co.uk
Contact: Mary Lockyer
Opening Times: 1000-1300, 1430-1700 most days, please ring.
Min Mail Order UK: 6 plants + p&p
Min Mail Order EU: £12.00 + p&p
Cat. Cost: 4 × 1st class or online
Credit Cards: All major credit/debit cards
Specialities: *Fuchsia*.
Notes: Many open days & coach parties. Also sells wholesale. Exports beyond EU. Euro accepted. Delivers to shows. Partial wheelchair access.
Map Ref: C, A5

CMac **MAC PENNYS NURSERIES**
154 Burley Road, Bransgore, Christchurch, Dorset BH23 8DB
Ⓣ (01425) 672348
Ⓕ (01425) 673917
Ⓔ office@macpennys.co.uk
Ⓦ www.macpennys.co.uk
Contact: T & V Lowndes & S Lowndes
Opening Times: 0900-1700 Mon-Sat, 1000-1700 Sun & B/hols, except closed Xmas-New Year.
Min Mail Order UK: Nmc
Cat. Cost: A4 sae with 4 × 1st class.
Credit Cards: All major debit/credit cards except American Express
Specialities: General. Plants available in small quantities only.
Notes: Mail order available Oct-Feb incl., UK only. Also sells wholesale. Nursery partially accessible for wheelchairs.
Map Ref: C, C6

CMCN **MALLET COURT NURSERY** ♿
Marshway, Curry Mallet, Taunton, Somerset TA3 6SZ
Ⓣ (01823) 481493
Ⓜ 07713 091521
Ⓕ (01823) 481493
Ⓔ malletcourtnursery@btinternet.com
Ⓦ www.malletcourt.co.uk
Contact: J G S & P M E Harris F.L.S.
Opening Times: 0930-1700 Mon-Fri summer, 0930-1600 winter. Sat & Sun by appt.
Min Mail Order UK: Nmc
Min Mail Order EU: Nmc
Cat. Cost: £1.50
Credit Cards: All major credit/debit cards
Specialities: Maples, oaks, *Magnolia*, hollies & other rare and unusual plants including those from China & South Korea.
Notes: Mail order Oct-Mar only. Also sells wholesale. Exports beyond EU. Euro accepted.

C

Wheelchair accessible.
Map Ref: C, B4

CMea **THE MEAD NURSERY** ♿
Brokerswood, Nr Westbury, Wiltshire BA13 4EG
Ⓣ (01373) 859990
Ⓔ info@themeadnursery.co.uk
Ⓦ www.themeadnursery.co.uk
Contact: Steve & Emma Lewis-Dale
Opening Times: 0900-1700 Wed-Sat & B/hol Mons, 1200-1700 Sun, 1st Feb-10th Oct. Closed Easter Sun.
Cat. Cost: 4 × 2nd class.
Credit Cards: All major credit/debit cards
Specialities: Perennials, alpines, pot-grown bulbs and grasses.
Notes: Wheelchair accessible.
Map Ref: C, B5 **OS Grid Ref:** ST833517

CMen **MENDIP BONSAI STUDIO**
Byways, Back Lane, Downside, Shepton Mallet, Somerset BA4 4JR
Ⓣ (01749) 344274
Ⓜ 07711 205806
Ⓔ john@mendipbonsai.co.uk
Ⓦ www.mendipbonsai.co.uk
Contact: John Trott
Opening Times: Private nursery. Visits by appt. only.
Min Mail Order UK: £15.00
Cat. Cost: None issued. Workshop lists available.
Credit Cards: All major credit/debit cards
Specialities: Bonsai, Potensai, accent plants & garden stock. Acers, conifers, incl. many *Pinus thunbergii* species, *Aciphylla*, *Davallia* & *Pyrrosia*. Many plants available in small numbers only. Can propagate to order. Young trees for garden or bonsai culture. Many rare & unusual ferns from Japan for 'accent' use and gardens.
Notes: Education classes, lectures, demonstrations & club talks on bonsai. Stockist of most bonsai pots, related bonsai sundries & a large range of bronze figures. Mail orders will normally be despatched late Mar-early Apr, late Sep-Oct. Delivers to shows by arrangement.
Map Ref: C, B5

CMil **MILL COTTAGE PLANTS** ♿
Henley Mill, Henley Lane, Wookey, Somerset BA5 1AW
Ⓣ (01749) 676966
Ⓜ 07851 698759
Ⓔ millcottageplants@gmail.com
Ⓦ www.millcottageplants.co.uk
Contact: Sally Gregson
Opening Times: By appt. only. Phone for directions.
Min Mail Order UK: Nmc
Min Mail Order EU: £25.00 + p&p
Cat. Cost: Online only.
Credit Cards: All major credit/debit cards
Specialities: Rare *Hydrangea serrata* cvs, *H. aspera* cvs, *Epimedium*, shade & damp-loving plants.
Notes: Euro accepted. Wheelchair accessible.
Map Ref: C, B5

CMus **MUSGROVE WILLOWS** ♿
Willowfields, Lakewall, Westonzoyland, Bridgwater, Somerset TA7 0LP
Ⓣ (01278) 691105
Ⓕ (01278) 699107
Ⓔ info@musgrovewillows.co.uk
Ⓦ www.musgrovewillows.co.uk
Contact: Ellen Musgrove
Opening Times: 0900-1700 Mon-Fri.
Min Mail Order UK: £12.50
Min Mail Order EU: Nmc
Credit Cards: All major credit/debit cards
Specialities: *Salix* (willow). A family nursery since 1928.
Notes: Exports beyond EU. Euro accepted. Wheelchair accessible. Also sells wholesale.
Map Ref: C, B4

CNat **NATURAL SELECTION**
1 Station Cottages, Hullavington, Chippenham, Wiltshire SN14 6ET
Ⓣ (01666) 837369
Ⓜ 07800 583999
Ⓔ martin@worldmutation.demon.co.uk
Ⓦ www.worldmutation.demon.co.uk
Contact: Martin Barber
Opening Times: Please phone first.
Min Mail Order UK: £9.00 + p&p
Min Mail Order EU: Nmc
Cat. Cost: 1 × 2nd class.
Credit Cards: None
Specialities: Unusual British natives & others. Also seed. Only available in small quantities.
Notes: Euro accepted.

CNMi **NEWPORT MILLS NURSERY**
Wrantage, Taunton, Somerset TA3 6DJ
Ⓣ (01823) 490231
Ⓔ john@newportmillsnursery.net
Ⓦ www.newportmillsnursery.net
Contact: John Barrington
Opening Times: Not open. Mail order only.
Min Mail Order UK: Nmc free p&p
Min Mail Order EU: Nmc. EU postal rate per order.
Cat. Cost: Free.
Credit Cards: All major credit/debit cards
Specialities: *Delphinium elatum* hybrids. English scented perpetual flowering carnations. *Dianthus*. Pinks: Exhibition,

Modern & Old World.
Notes: Mail order Apr-Sep for young delphiniums in 7cm pots. Euro accepted.

CNor **NORTHBROOK NURSERY** ♿
47 Northbrook Road, Broadstone, Dorset BH18 8HD
Ⓣ (01202) 695256
Ⓔ marg@northbrooknursery.co.uk
Ⓦ www.northbrooknursery.co.uk
Contact: Margaret Bailey
Opening Times: 1000-1600, Wed-Fri, Apr-Oct.
Min Mail Order UK: Nmc
Cat. Cost: None issued.
Credit Cards: Paypal
Specialities: Perennials. Plants available in small quantities only.
Notes: Delivers to shows. Wheelchair accessible.
Map Ref: C, C6 **OS Grid Ref:** SZ001947

CPar **PARKS PERENNIALS**
242 Wallisdown Road, Wallisdown, Bournemouth, Dorset BH10 4HZ
Ⓣ (01202) 524464
Ⓜ 07977 878546
Ⓔ parks.perennials@ntlworld.com
Contact: S. Parks
Opening Times: Apr-Oct most days, please phone first.
Cat. Cost: None issued.
Credit Cards: None
Specialities: Hardy herbaceous perennials.
Notes: Delivers to shows.
Map Ref: C, C6

CPbh **PENBERTH PLANTS (FORMERLY TREWIDDEN NURSERY)**
St Buryan, Penzance, Cornwall TR19 6HJ
Ⓣ (01736) 810978
Ⓔ info@penberthplants.co.uk
Ⓦ www.penberthplants.co.uk
Contact: Jeff Rowe
Opening Times: Not open. Mail order & RHS shows. Open Days throughout the year, check website or contact nursery for dates.
Min Mail Order UK: Nmc
Min Mail Order EU: Nmc
Cat. Cost: Online only.
Credit Cards: All major credit/debit cards
Specialities: *Protea*, *Restio*, succulents and other unusual plants.
Notes: Sells at shows around the country and online. Card payments accepted at shows. Mail order through website only.

CPBP **PARHAM BUNGALOW PLANTS**
Parham Lane, Market Lavington, Devizes, Wiltshire SN10 4QA
Ⓣ (01380) 812605
Ⓔ jjs@pbplants.freeserve.co.uk
Contact: Mrs D E Sample
Opening Times: Please ring first.
Min Mail Order UK: Nmc
Min Mail Order EU: Nmc
Cat. Cost: 2 × 2nd class.
Credit Cards: None
Specialities: Alpines.
Notes: Delivers to shows.
Map Ref: C, B6

CPer **PERRIE HALE NURSERY**
Northcote Hill, Honiton, Devon EX14 9TH
Ⓣ (01404) 43344
Ⓕ (01404) 47163
Ⓔ faye@perriehale.co.uk
Ⓦ www.perriehale.co.uk
Contact: Faye Davey
Opening Times: 0800-1730 Mon-Fri, 0900-1230 Sat, Oct-Apr. Please phone first May-Sep.
Min Mail Order UK: £10.50 + VAT
Cat. Cost: Free
Credit Cards: All major debit/credit cards except American Express
Specialities: Broad-leaf trees & conifers; native & evergreen hedging for screening & amenity; soft fruit & shrubs. Family business established 1957, supplying in excess of 700,000 plants per year.
Notes: Sell bare-root stock Oct-Mar, after which pot-grown stock available. Also sells wholesale.
Map Ref: C, C4 **OS Grid Ref:** ST178007

CPhi **ALAN PHIPPS CACTI**
62 Samuel White Road, Hanham, Bristol BS15 3LX
Ⓣ (0117) 9607591
Ⓦ www.cactus-mall.com/alan-phipps/index.html
Contact: A Phipps
Opening Times: 1000-1700 but prior phone call essential to ensure a greeting.
Min Mail Order UK: £5.00 + p&p
Min Mail Order EU: £20.00 + p&p
Cat. Cost: Sae or 2 × IRC (EC only).
Credit Cards: None
Specialities: *Mammillaria*, *Astrophytum* & *Ariocarpus*. Species & varieties will change with times. Ample quantities exist in spring. Limited range of *Agave*.
Notes: Specimen-size plants not available by mail order. Euro accepted as cash only.
Map Ref: C, A5 **OS Grid Ref:** ST644717

CPHo **THE PALM HOUSE**
8 North Street, Ottery St Mary, Devon EX11 1DR
Ⓣ (01404) 815450
Ⓜ 07815 673397

C

Ⓔ george@thepalmhouse.co.uk
Ⓦ www.thepalmhouse.co.uk
Contact: George Gregory
Opening Times: Mail order only. Open by appt. only.
Min Mail Order UK: £5.00
Min Mail Order EU: £10.00
Cat. Cost: 2 × 1st class.
Credit Cards: All major credit/debit cards
Specialities: Palms.
Notes: Also sells wholesale.

CPla **Plant World Botanic Gardens** ♿
St Marychurch Road, Newton Abbot, Devon TQ12 4SE
Ⓣ (01803) 872939
Ⓕ (01803) 875018
Ⓔ raybrown@plant-world-seeds.com
Ⓦ www.plant-world-seeds.com
Contact: Ray Brown
Opening Times: 0930-1700 7 days a week, Apr (Easter if earlier)-Oct.
Min Mail Order UK: Nmc
Min Mail Order EU: Nmc
Cat. Cost: Free.
Credit Cards: Visa, Access, EuroCard, MasterCard
Specialities: Alpines, perennials, small shrubs, succulents, herbaceous & patio plants. 4 acre garden planted as map of the world (entry charge).
Notes: Mail order for seed only (no mail order for plants). Also sells wholesale. Exports beyond EU. Wheelchair access to nursery & café only.
Map Ref: C, C4 **OS Grid Ref:** SX893693

CPne **Pine Cottage Plants** ♿
Pine Cottage, Fourways, Eggesford, Chulmleigh, Devon EX18 7QZ
Ⓣ (01769) 580076
Ⓜ 07718 505053
Ⓔ sales@pcplants.co.uk
Ⓦ www.pcplants.co.uk
Contact: Dick Fulcher
Opening Times: By appt. only. Please phone first.
Min Mail Order UK: £20.00
Min Mail Order EU: £20.00
Cat. Cost: 3 × 1st class.
Credit Cards: Maestro, MasterCard, Visa
Specialities: *Agapanthus* South African bulbus plants, *Rhododendron* species only & other unusual plants.
Notes: Mail order *Agapanthus* from Sep-Jun. Wheelchair accessible.
Map Ref: C, B3 **OS Grid Ref:** SS683099

CPou **Pounsley Plants** ♿
Pounsley Combe, Spriddlestone, Brixton, Plymouth, Devon PL9 0DW
Ⓣ (01752) 402873
Ⓜ 07770 758501
Ⓔ pou599@aol.com
Ⓦ www.pounsleyplants.com
Contact: Mrs Jane Hollow
Opening Times: Normally 1000-1600 Mon-Sat but please phone first.
Min Mail Order UK: £10.00 + p&p
Min Mail Order EU: €20.00 + p&p
Cat. Cost: 2 × 1st class.
Credit Cards: None
Specialities: Unusual herbaceous perennials. Comprehensive range of Old Roses & large selection of modern roses.
Notes: Mail order solely bare-root roses, Nov-Mar. Also sells wholesale. Delivers to shows. Euro accepted. Wheelchair accessible.
Map Ref: C, D3 **OS Grid Ref:** SX521538

CPrp **ProperPlants.com**
Penknight, Edgcumbe Road, Lostwithiel, Cornwall PL22 0JD
Ⓣ (01208) 872291
Ⓔ sarah@penknight.plus.com
Ⓦ www.ProperPlants.com
Contact: Sarah Wilks
Opening Times: By appt. only. Please phone or email first.
Min Mail Order UK: Nmc
Min Mail Order EU: Nmc
Cat. Cost: 2 × 1st class.
Credit Cards: All major credit/debit cards
Specialities: *Agapanthus*, *Crocosmia* & *Hesperantha*.
Notes: Also sells wholesale. Exports beyond EU. Delivers to shows.
Map Ref: C, C2 **OS Grid Ref:** SX093596

CQua **Quality Daffodils**
14 Roscarrack Close, Falmouth, Cornwall TR11 4PJ
Ⓣ (01326) 317959
Ⓜ 07989 243450
Ⓕ (01326) 317959
Ⓔ rascamp@daffodils.uk.com
Ⓦ www.qualitydaffodils.com
Contact: R A Scamp
Opening Times: Not open. Mail order only. Viewing by appt. only.
Min Mail Order UK: Nmc
Min Mail Order EU: Nmc
Cat. Cost: 4 × 1st class.
Credit Cards: All major credit/debit cards
Specialities: *Narcissus* hybrids & species. Some stocks are less than 100 bulbs.
Notes: Exports beyond EU. Euro accepted.
Map Ref: C, D1

CRav **Sarah Raven**
1 Woodstock Court, Blenheim Road, Marlborough, Wiltshire SN8 4AN

Ⓣ 0345 092 0283
Ⓔ info@sarahraven.com
Ⓦ www.sarahraven.com
Contact: Customer Services
Opening Times: Not open. Mail order only. Phone (orders) 0800-2200 Mon-Sat, 0900-2200 Sun; (customer service) 0900-1700 Mon-Fri.
Min Mail Order UK: Nmc
Cat. Cost: Free.
Specialities: A range of trialled & tested bulbs, plants, seedlings & seeds.

CRea **Really Wild Flowers**
H V Horticulture Ltd, Heather Cottage, 23 New Close, Bourton, Gillingham, Dorset SP8 5DL
Ⓣ (01747) 416376
Ⓔ info@reallywildflowers.co.uk
Ⓦ www.reallywildflowers.co.uk
Contact: Grahame Dixie
Opening Times: Not open. Mail order & online only.
Min Mail Order UK: £10 + p&p
Cat. Cost: 3 × 1st class.
Credit Cards: All major debit/credit cards except American Express
Specialities: Native wild flowers for grasslands, woodlands & wetlands. Seeds & bulbs. Hedge plants & trees. Advisory & soil analysis services.
Notes: Credit card payment accepted for online orders only. Also sells wholesale. Delivers to shows.

CRHN **Roseland House Nursery**
Chacewater, Truro, Cornwall TR4 8QB
Ⓣ (01872) 560451
Ⓔ clematis@roselandhouse.co.uk
Ⓦ www.roselandhouse.co.uk
Contact: C R Pridham
Opening Times: 1300-1700 Tue & Wed, Apr-Sep. Other times by appt.
Min Mail Order UK: Nmc
Min Mail Order EU: Nmc
Cat. Cost: Online only.
Credit Cards: All major credit/debit cards
Specialities: Climbing & conservatory plants. Nat. Collections of *Clematis viticella* & *Lapageria rosea*. Named *Lapageria* in short supply but occasionally available.
Notes: Garden open to the public. Credit cards accepted from mail order customers only. Delivers to shows.
Map Ref: C, D1 **OS Grid Ref:** SW752445

CRoa **Roadford Water Gardens**
Higher Goodacre Farm, Broadwoodwidger, Lifton, Devon PL16 0ER
Ⓜ 07790 779991
Ⓔ info@roadfordwatergardens.co.uk
Ⓦ www.roadfordwatergardens.co.uk
Contact: Carolyn Wixon
Opening Times: Not open. Mail order only.
Min Mail Order UK: Nmc
Min Mail Order EU: Nmc
Cat. Cost: Online only.
Credit Cards: Paypal
Specialities: Sells Rowden Iris & other water & moisture-loving *Iris*, *Nymphaea* for small ponds, *Caltha* & candelabra *Primula*. Some stock available in small quantities only. Over 200 varieties of *Iris*. Enquiries welcome.
Notes: Rowden Irises by mail order only (Apr-Aug 2016). Euro accepted.

CRos **Rosemoor Plant Centre (RHS)** ♿ ◆
RHS Garden Rosemoor, Torrington, Devon EX38 8PH
Ⓣ (01805) 626842
Ⓔ rosemooradmin@rhs.org.uk
Ⓦ www.rhs.org.uk/rosemoor
Contact: Emma Van-Huysse or Sam Smith
Opening Times: 1000-1800 Mon-Sat, 11.30-1730 Sun, Apr-Sep (summer). 1000-1700 Mon-Sat, 1030-1630 Sun, Oct-Mar (winter). Closed Easter Sun & Xmas Day.
Cat. Cost: None issued
Credit Cards: All major credit/debit cards
Specialities: Wide range of shrubs, herbaceous plants, roses, climbers, alpines & seasonal lines, reflecting where possible the diversity of planting in the garden. Displays of Curator's Choice, garden favourites, AGM plants & Plants for Pollinators.
Notes: Plant centre attached to RHS Garden Rosemoor. Free entry to plant centre, gift shop & restaurant. Plants subject to seasonal availability but will source plants whenever possible. Accept HTA & RHS vouchers (paper only). Wheelchair accessible.
Map Ref: C, B3 **OS Grid Ref:** SS500176

CSam **Sampford Shrubs** ♿
Sampford Peverell, Tiverton, Devon EX16 7EN
Ⓣ (01884) 821164
Ⓦ www.samshrub.co.uk
Contact: M Hughes-Jones & S Proud
Opening Times: 1000-1700, 25th Mar-9th Sep but closed 30th Jul-16th Aug.
Min Mail Order UK: £25.00 plant value.
Cat. Cost: Online only.
Credit Cards: All major credit/debit cards
Specialities: Plants particularly suitable for naturalistic gardening.
Notes: Mail order only via dedicated ecommerce website. Despatched Oct-Mar. Wheelchair accessible.
Map Ref: C, B4 **OS Grid Ref:** ST043153

C

CSBt **ST BRIDGET NURSERIES LTD** ♿
Old Rydon Lane, Exeter, Devon EX2 7JY
Ⓣ (01392) 873672
Ⓕ (01392) 876710
Ⓔ sales@stbridgetnurseries.co.uk
Ⓦ www.stbridgetnurseries.co.uk
Contact: Sales Dept
Opening Times: 0900-1700 Mon-Sat, 1030-1630 Sun. Closed Xmas Day, Boxing Day, New Year's Day & Easter Sunday.
Min Mail Order UK: Nmc
Cat. Cost: Free.
Credit Cards: All major credit/debit cards
Specialities: General nursery propagating a wide range of genera, with two retail garden centres. Founded 1925.
Notes: Tours of the rose field during the summer. Mail order available, please contact for prices & carriage charges. Also sells wholesale. Wheelchair accessible.
Map Ref: C, C4 **OS Grid Ref:** SX955905

CSgt **STRETE GATE CAMELLIAS**
(Office) 17 Seymour Drive, Torquay, Devon TQ2 8PY
Ⓣ (01803) 770710
Ⓜ 07964 824673
Ⓔ plants@stretegatecamellias.co.uk
Ⓦ www.stretegatecamellias.co.uk
Contact: Jeremy Wilson
Opening Times: Not open. Mail order only. Plant collection may be available by prior arrangement.
Min Mail Order UK: Nmc
Specialities: Over 300 varieties of *Camellia*, many in small quantities not listed.
Notes: Nursery at different site from correspondence address. Also sells wholesale. Delivers to shows.

CSma **PLANTS FOR SMALL GARDENS**
Goosegate, Bridford, Exeter, Devon EX6 7LW
Ⓣ (01647) 252010
Ⓔ sales@plantsforsmallgardens.co.uk
Ⓦ www.plantsforsmallgardens.co.uk
Contact: Sue Hearnden
Opening Times: Not open. Mail order online only.
Min Mail Order UK: £12.50
Cat. Cost: Online only.
Credit Cards: Paypal
Specialities: Dwarf hardy, rockery and alpine plants, all grown on our nursery in Devon. Range to suit all types of gardeners from *Aubrieta* & *Helianthemum* to more specialist plants such as kabschia saxifrages & *Meconopsis*. Good range of hardy geraniums.

CSna **SNAPE COTTAGE**
Chaffeymoor, Bourton, Dorset SP8 5BZ
Ⓣ (01747) 840330 (evenings only).
Ⓔ ianandangela@snapecottagegarden.co.uk
Ⓦ www.snapestakes.com
Contact: Mrs Angela Whinfield
Opening Times: Not open. Mail order only. The garden is closed in 2016.
Min Mail Order UK: Nmc
Cat. Cost: Sae.
Credit Cards: None
Specialities: Snowdrops & "Snape Stakes" plant supports.
Notes: Mail order *Galanthus* only. List issued in Feb. See website or contact nursery for information on group visits.
Map Ref: C, B5 **OS Grid Ref:** ST762303

CSpe **SPECIAL PLANTS**
Hill Farm Barn, Greenways Lane, Cold Ashton, Chippenham, Wiltshire SN14 8LA
Ⓣ (01225) 891686
Ⓔ derry@specialplants.net
Ⓦ www.specialplants.net
Contact: Derry Watkins
Opening Times: 1000-1700 7 days Mar-Oct. Other times please ring first to check.
Min Mail Order UK: £10.00 + p&p
Cat. Cost: 2 × 1st class for seed list.
Credit Cards: All major credit/debit cards
Specialities: Tender perennials, *Pelargonium*, *Salvia*, hardy geraniums, *Anemone*, *Erysimum*, *Papaver* & grasses. Many varieties propagated in small numbers only.
Notes: Mail order Sep-Mar only. Delivers to shows. Euro accepted.
Map Ref: C, A5 **OS Grid Ref:** ST749726

CSta **STADDON FARM NURSERIES** ♿
Staddon Road, Holsworthy, Devon EX22 6NH
Ⓜ 07547 711189
Ⓔ penny.staddonfarm@yahoo.co.uk
Ⓦ www.pennysprimulas.co.uk
Contact: Penny Jones
Opening Times: By appt. only.
Min Mail Order UK: Nmc
Cat. Cost: Online only.
Credit Cards: All major credit/debit cards
Specialities: *Primula*. National Collection of *Primula sieboldii* Japanese cvs.
Notes: Delivers to shows. Wheelchair accessible.

CSto **STONE LANE GARDENS**
Stone Farm, Chagford, Devon TQ13 8JU
Ⓣ (01647) 231311
Ⓔ paul.bartlett@stonelanegardens.com
Ⓦ www.stonelanegardens.com
Contact: Paul Bartlett
Opening Times: Open by appt. only. Not open

to casual visitors. Website ordering available.
Min Mail Order UK: Nmc
Min Mail Order EU: Nmc
Cat. Cost: 6 × 1st class for colour catalogue with photos or online.
Credit Cards: All major credit/debit cards
Specialities: Comprehensive selection of wild origin *Betula* & *Alnus*, both bare-root & in pots. Choice selection of specially grafted cvs. Nat. Collection of Birch & Alder.
Notes: Arboretum open all year with summer sculpture exhibition (charges apply). Planting service available in West Country, details on request. Also sells wholesale. Credit cards accepted online only.
Map Ref: C, C3 **OS Grid Ref:** SX708908

CTal **Tale Valley Nursery**
Barratt's Cottage, Cullompton, Devon EX15 2NQ
Ⓣ (01884) 277614
Ⓜ 07791 676162
Ⓔ contactus@talevalleynursery.co.uk
Ⓦ www.talevalleynursery.co.uk
Contact: Lorraine & Chris Birchall
Opening Times: Not open.
Min Mail Order UK: £10.00 + p&p
Min Mail Order EU: £25.00 + p&p
Credit Cards: None
Specialities: Alpines, shade/woodland herbaceous plants standard dwarf bearded *Iris* & South African bulbs. Nat. Collections of *Rhodohypoxis* & *x Rhodoxis*. Some specialist plants available in small numbers only.
Notes: Mail order for selection of Nat. Collections, other bulbs & a few select plants. Despatch of selected bare-root herbaceous plants in autumn. Delivers to shows.

CTca **Trecanna Nursery**
The Old Barn, Chilsworthy, Cornwall PL18 9PB
Ⓣ (01822) 834680
Ⓜ 07785 242148
Ⓔ mark@trecanna.com
Ⓦ www.trecanna.com
Contact: Mark Wash
Opening Times: Not open. Mail order only.
Min Mail Order UK: £22.00
Min Mail Order EU: £45.00
Cat. Cost: Online only.
Credit Cards: All major credit/debit cards
Specialities: Hardy South African plants. Good collections of *Crocosmia*, *Eucomis*, *Kniphofia*, *Watsonia*, *Crinum*, *Albuca*, nerines, *Zantedeschia*, *Lachenalia* & *Moraea*. Wide range of dry bulbs from around the globe.
Notes: Talks given to garden societies. Exports beyond EU. Delivers to shows.
Map Ref: C, C3 **OS Grid Ref:** SX247733

CTho **Thornhayes Nursery**
St Andrews Wood, Dulford, Cullompton, Devon EX15 2DF
Ⓣ (01884) 266746
Ⓕ (01884) 266739
Ⓔ trees@thornhayes-nursery.co.uk
Ⓦ www.thornhayes-nursery.co.uk
Contact: K D Croucher
Opening Times: 0800-1600 Mon-Fri. 0930-1400 Sat.
Min Mail Order UK: £30
Min Mail Order EU: Price on application.
Cat. Cost: Free.
Credit Cards: All major credit/debit cards
Specialities: A broad range of forms of ornamental, amenity & fruit trees incl. West Country apple varieties and choice shrubs. A particular emphasis on disease-resistant forms for the wet and windy west.
Notes: Also sells wholesale. Euro accepted. Limited wheelchair accessible.
Map Ref: C, C4

CTrh **Trehane Nursery** ♿
Stapehill Road, Hampreston, Wimborne, Dorset BH21 7ND
Ⓣ (01202) 873490
Ⓔ nursery@trehane.co.uk
Ⓦ www.trehane.co.uk
Contact: Lorraine Keets
Opening Times: 0830-1630 Mon-Fri all year (excl. Xmas & New Year). 1000-1600 Sat in spring & by special appt.
Min Mail Order UK: Nmc
Min Mail Order EU: Nmc
Cat. Cost: Free
Credit Cards: All major credit/debit cards
Specialities: Extensive range of *Camellia* species, cultivars & hybrids. Many new introductions. Blueberries.
Notes: Also sells wholesale. Wheelchair accessible.
Map Ref: C, C6 **OS Grid Ref:** SU059000

CTri **Triscombe Nurseries** ♿ ◆
West Bagborough, Nr Taunton, Somerset TA4 3HG
Ⓣ (01984) 618267
Ⓔ info@triscombenurseries.co.uk
Ⓦ www.triscombenurseries.co.uk
Contact: S Parkman
Opening Times: 0900-1730 Mon-Sat.
Min Mail Order UK: Nmc
Cat. Cost: 1 × 1st class.
Credit Cards: None
Specialities: Trees, shrubs, roses, fruit, *Clematis*, herbaceous & rock plants.
Notes: Wheelchair accessible.
Map Ref: C, B4

C

CTsd **TRESEDERS** ♿
Wallcottage Nursery, Lockengate, St. Austell, Cornwall PL26 8RU
Ⓣ (01208) 832234
Ⓔ Treseders@btconnect.com
Ⓦ www.treseders.co.uk
Contact: James Treseder
Opening Times: 0900-1700 Mon-Sat, 1000-1600 Sun. Closed Wed.
Min Mail Order UK: Nmc
Min Mail Order EU: Nmc
Cat. Cost: Online or by email only.
Credit Cards: All major credit/debit cards
Specialities: A wide range of choice & unusual plants grown in peat-free compost. Establishing collection of *Prostanthera*.
Notes: Plants sometimes only available in small quantities. Enquiries welcome. Delivers to shows. Wheelchair accessible.
Map Ref: C, C2 **OS Grid Ref:** SX034620

CWat **THE WATER GARDEN** ♿
Hinton Parva, Swindon, Wiltshire SN4 0DH
Ⓣ (01793) 790558
Ⓕ (01793) 791298
Ⓔ mike@thewatergarden.co.uk
Ⓦ www.thewatergarden.co.uk
Contact: Mike & Anne Newman
Opening Times: 1000-1700 Wed-Sun.
Min Mail Order UK: £10.00 + p&p
Cat. Cost: 4 × 1st class.
Credit Cards: Visa, Access, Switch
Specialities: Water lilies, marginal & moisture plants, oxygenators & alpines.
Notes: Also sells wholesale. Wheelchair accessible.
Map Ref: C, A6

CWCL **WESTCOUNTRY NURSERIES**
Donkey Meadow, Woolsery, Devon EX39 5QH
Ⓣ (01237) 431111
Ⓔ info@westcountry-nurseries.co.uk
Ⓦ www.westcountry-nurseries.co.uk
Contact: Sarah Conibear
Opening Times: 1000-1600 Mar-mid Jul. Closed for lunch 1300-1330. Before travelling at a weekend, please check with nursery.
Min Mail Order UK: Nmc
Cat. Cost: 2 × 1st class + A5 sae for full colour cat.
Credit Cards: All major credit/debit cards
Specialities: *Lupinus*, *Lewisia*, *Hellebore*, *Clematis*, cyclamen, select perennials, grasses, ferns & climbers. Nat. Collection of Lupins.
Notes: Delivers to shows.
Map Ref: C,B2 **OS Grid Ref:** SS351219

CWel **WELLGARTH PLANTS**
(Office) Ravendale, St Lawrence, Bodmin, Cornwall PL30 5JL
Ⓜ 07445 240133
Ⓔ info@wellgarthplants.com
Ⓦ www.wellgarthplants.com
Contact: Cassie Corby
Opening Times: Not open, except by appt. Mail order only.
Min Mail Order UK: Nmc
Cat. Cost: Online only.
Credit Cards: Paypal
Specialities: *Hemerocallis.*
Notes: Stock available in small quantities. Mail order via website only.

CWGN **WALLED GARDEN NURSERY** ♿
Brinkworth House, Brinkworth, Nr Malmesbury, Wiltshire SN15 5DF
Ⓣ (01666) 826637
Ⓜ 07921 436863
Ⓔ sales@clematis-nursery.co.uk
Ⓦ www.clematis-nursery.co.uk
Contact: Fraser Wescott
Opening Times: 1000-1700, 7 days, Mar-Oct. 1030-dusk, Mon-Fri, Nov & Feb. Closed Dec & Jan.
Min Mail Order UK: £15.00
Credit Cards: All major credit/debit cards
Specialities: *Clematis* & climbers, with a selection of unusual perennials & shrubs.
Notes: Mail order UK mainland only. Wheelchair accessible.
Map Ref: C, A6 **OS Grid Ref:** SU002849

CWGr **NATIONAL DAHLIA COLLECTION**
Varfell Farm, Long Rock, Penzance, Cornwall TR20 8AQ
Ⓣ (01736) 711271
Ⓜ 07879 337714
Ⓔ info@national-dahlia-collection.co.uk
Ⓦ www.national-dahlia-collection.co.uk
Contact: Michael Mann
Opening Times: Garden open in summer. See website or contact nursery for details.
Min Mail Order UK: Nmc
Min Mail Order EU: Nmc
Cat. Cost: Online. Contact nursery for hard copy.
Credit Cards: All major debit/credit cards except American Express
Specialities: Nat. Collection of *Dahlia*. 1600+ *Dahlia* cultivars.
Notes: See website for plant availability. Also sells wholesale. Limited wheelchair accessible.
Map Ref: C, D1

CWiW **WINDRUSH WILLOW**
Higher Barn, Sidmouth Road, Aylesbeare, Exeter, Devon EX5 2JJ
Ⓣ (01395) 233669
Ⓕ (01395) 233669
Ⓔ windrushw@aol.com

Ⓦ www.windrushwillow.com
Contact: Richard Kerwood
Opening Times: Mail order only. Open by appt.
Min Mail Order UK: Nmc
Min Mail Order EU: Nmc
Cat. Cost: 2 × 1st class.
Credit Cards: All major credit/debit cards
Specialities: *Salix*. Unrooted cuttings available Dec-Mar.
Notes: Also sells wholesale. Euro accepted. Carrier charge £5.00.

CWld **WILD THYME**
(Office) The Old Orchard, Friggle Street, Frome, Somerset BA11 5LH
Ⓣ (01373) 464417
Ⓜ 07956 888477
Ⓔ jess@wildthymeplants.co.uk
Ⓦ www.wildthymeplants.co.uk
Contact: Monica Ashman
Opening Times: Not open. Mail order only via online shop.
Min Mail Order UK: £15.00
Credit Cards: Visa, MasterCard, Maestro
Specialities: Wildflowers & fragrant plants.
Notes: Delivers to shows.

CWSG **WEST SOMERSET GARDEN CENTRE** ♿
Mart Road, Minehead, Somerset TA24 5BJ
Ⓣ (01643) 703812
Ⓕ (01643) 706476
Ⓔ wsgc@btconnect.com
Ⓦ www.westsomersetgardencentre.co.uk
Contact: Ms J K Webber
Opening Times: 0800-1700 Mon-Sat, 1000-1600 Sun.
Min Mail Order UK: Nmc
Cat. Cost: None issued.
Credit Cards: All major debit/credit cards except American Express
Specialities: Wide general range. *Clematis* & rose varieties change throughout the season.
Notes: Wheelchair accessible.
Map Ref: C, B4

CWVF **WHITE VEIL FUCHSIAS** ♿
Verwood Road, Three Legged Cross, Wimborne, Dorset BH21 6RP
Ⓣ (01202) 813998
Contact: A. C. Holloway
Opening Times: 0900-1300 & 1400-1700 Mon-Sat, Jan-Jul. Closed Sun.
Cat. Cost: Only available at nursery.
Credit Cards: None
Specialities: Fuchsias. Small plants grown from Jan-Apr. Available in small quantities only at the nursery.
Notes: Wheelchair accessible.

EASTERN

EACa **ALPINE CAMPANULAS (BELLFLOWER NURSERY)** ♿
Langham Hall Walled Garden, Langham, Nr Bury St Edmunds, Suffolk IP31 3EE
Ⓜ 07879 644958
Ⓔ campanulas@btinternet.com
Ⓦ www.bellflowernursery.co.uk
Contact: Sue Wooster
Opening Times: 1000-1600 Thu & Fri, mid-Mar to end Oct. Other times by appt.
Min Mail Order UK: £10.00
Cat. Cost: 2 × 1st class A5 sae.
Credit Cards: None
Specialities: *Campanula*. Nat. Collection of Alpine Campanulas. Most stock in small numbers only.
Notes: Hardy plant nursery & Nat. Collection within 1.5 acre Georgian Walled Garden. Groups welcome by appt. Wheelchair accessible but nursery reached by gravel paths through walled garden.
Map Ref: E, C3 **OS Grid Ref:** TL978691

EAJP **A & J PLANTS**
Scenterfields, Chappel Road, Great Tey, Colchester, Essex CO6 1JR
Ⓣ (01206) 212124
Ⓕ (01206) 212124
Ⓔ mail@aandjplants.com
Ⓦ www.aandjplants.com
Contact: Jackie Rhodes
Opening Times: Not open. Mail order only. Orders can be collected from nursery by prior arrangement.
Min Mail Order UK: Nmc
Credit Cards: Visa, MasterCard
Specialities: Wide variety of choice perennials and ornamental grasses propagated on the nursery, some in small quantities.
Notes: Plant Centre at Marks Hall Garden (CO6 1TG) stocked with seasonal selection of perennials & grasses. Also sells wholesale. Delivers to shows.

EBak **B & H M BAKER** ♿
Bourne Brook Nurseries, Greenstead Green, Halstead, Essex CO9 1RB
Ⓣ (01787) 476369
Contact: Clive Baker
Opening Times: 0800-1600 Mon-Fri, 0900-1200 & 1400-1600 Sat & Sun, Mar-Jun.
Cat. Cost: 2 × 1st class + 33p.
Credit Cards: All major credit/debit cards
Specialities: *Fuchsia* & conservatory plants.
Notes: Also sells wholesale. Wheelchair accessible.
Map Ref: E, C2

E

EBar **Barcham Trees PLC**
Eye Hill Drove, Ely, Cambridgeshire
CB7 5XF
Ⓣ (01353) 720950
Ⓜ 07801 917566
Ⓕ (01353) 723060
Ⓔ info@barchamtrees.co.uk
Ⓦ www.barcham.co.uk
Contact: Mike Glover
Opening Times: 0900-1700 Mon-Fri. Visits to the nursery by appt. only.
Min Mail Order UK: Nmc
Min Mail Order EU: Nmc
Cat. Cost: £10.00
Credit Cards: All major debit/credit cards except American Express
Specialities: Large grower of containerised trees. 478 varieties available, from 10-12cm to 40cm girth.
Notes: As trees range from 3-8 metres all are despatched on lorries rather than through the mailing service. Also sells wholesale. Exports beyond EU. Euro accepted.

EBee **Beeches Nursery** ♿
Crown Hill, Ashdon, Saffron Walden, Essex
CB10 2HB
Ⓣ (01799) 584362
Ⓕ (01799) 584421
Ⓔ sales@beechesnursery.co.uk
Ⓦ www.beechesnursery.co.uk
Contact: Alan Bidwell/Kevin Marsh
Opening Times: 0830-1700 Mon-Sat, 1000-1700 Sun & B/hols.
Min Mail Order UK: £15.00
Min Mail Order EU: £20.00
Cat. Cost: Online.
Credit Cards: All major credit/debit cards
Specialities: Herbaceous specialists & extensive range of other garden plants. Rarieties available in limited numbers only.
Notes: Plants dispatched Oct-Feb only. Orders accepted throughout the year. No trees by mail order. Wheelchair accessible.
Map Ref: E, C2 **OS Grid Ref:** TL586420

EBls **Peter Beales Roses** ♿ ◆
London Road, Attleborough, Norfolk
NR17 1AY
Ⓣ (01953) 454707
Ⓔ info@peterbealesroses.com
Ⓦ www.classicroses.co.uk
Contact: Tina Limmer
Opening Times: 0900-1700 Mon-Sat, 1000-1600 Sun & B/hols. Closed 25th Dec-5th Jan.
Min Mail Order UK: Nmc
Min Mail Order EU: Nmc
Cat. Cost: £5.00 outside UK.
Credit Cards: All major debit/credit cards except American Express
Specialities: Large range of perennials, shrubs, *Clematis*, climbers, ornamental trees, fruit, summer & winter bedding. Nat. Collection of Species Roses.
Notes: Display garden, open all year round (free entry). Agent for Classic Garden Element iron work. Also sells wholesale. Exports beyond EU. Wheelchair accessible.
Map Ref: E, C3 **OS Grid Ref:** TM026929

EBoy **J W Boyce**
237 Carter Street, Fordham, Ely,
Cambridgeshire CB7 5JU
Ⓣ (01638) 721158
Ⓔ enquiries@jwboyce.co.uk
Ⓦ www.jwboyce.co.uk
Contact: Roger Morley
Min Mail Order UK: Nmc
Min Mail Order EU: Nmc
Cat. Cost: Free.
Credit Cards: All major debit/credit cards except American Express
Specialities: Pansy & vegetable seed and plants, onion 'Oakey'. Wide range of separate colours for cut flowers, bedding & drying.

EBtc **Botanica**
Chantry Farm, Campsea Ashe, Wickham
Market, Suffolk IP13 0PZ
Ⓣ (01728) 747113
Ⓜ 07887 423964
Ⓕ (01728) 747725
Ⓔ sales@botanica.org.uk
Ⓦ www.botanicaplantnursery.co.uk
Contact: Daniel Everett
Opening Times: 0900-1700 Mon-Fri (0900-1600 in winter), 1000-1600 w/ends. Closed w/ends in Jul.
Min Mail Order UK: £30 + p&p
Cat. Cost: Online only.
Credit Cards: All major debit/credit cards except American Express
Specialities: Range of rare & unusual hardy plants. All stock is English-grown at our nursery and in non-peat based compost.
Notes: Also sells wholesale.
Map Ref: E, C3 **OS Grid Ref:** TM328550

EBWF **British Wild Flower Plants** ♿
Burlingham Gardens, 31 Main Road, North
Burlingham, Norfolk NR13 4TA
Ⓣ (01603) 716615
Ⓕ (01603) 716615
Ⓔ office@wildflowers.co.uk
Ⓦ http://wildflowers.co.uk
Contact: Matt Smith
Opening Times: 1000-1600 Mon-Thu. 1000-1430 Fri. Clsoed for lunch 1230-1330.
Min Mail Order UK: Nmc
Min Mail Order EU: Nmc

Credit Cards: All major credit/debit cards
Specialities: UK native species of wildflowers with 375+ species represented, drawn from own seed collections or from known provenance native sources compliant with the Flora Locale Code of Practice.
Notes: Also sells wholesale. Wheelchair available.
Map Ref: E, B3 **OS Grid Ref:** TG370100

ECha **THE BETH CHATTO GARDENS LTD** ♿
Clacton Road, Elmstead Market, Colchester, Essex CO7 7DB
Ⓣ (01206) 822007
Ⓕ (01206) 825933
Ⓔ info@bethchatto.co.uk
Ⓦ www.bethchatto.co.uk
Contact: David Ward
Opening Times: 0900-1700 Mon-Sat, 1000-1700 Sun, 1st Mar-31st Oct. 0900-1600 Mon-Sat, 1000-1600 Sun, Nov-end Feb.
Min Mail Order UK: Nmc
Min Mail Order EU: Ask for details
Cat. Cost: Online only.
Credit Cards: All major debit/credit cards except American Express
Specialities: Predominantly herbaceous perennials, grasses & ferns. Many unusual for special situations.
Notes: Delivers to shows. Wheelchair accessible.
Map Ref: E, C3 **OS Grid Ref:** TM069238

ECnt **CANTS OF COLCHESTER LTD**
Nayland Road, Mile End, Colchester, Essex CO4 5HA
Ⓣ (01206) 844008
Ⓕ (01206) 855371
Ⓔ enquiries@cantsroses.co.uk
Ⓦ www.cantsroses.co.uk
Contact: Angela Pawsey
Opening Times: 0900-1300, 1400-1630 Mon-Fri. Sat varied, please phone first. Sun closed.
Min Mail Order UK: Nmc
Min Mail Order EU: Nmc
Cat. Cost: Free
Credit Cards: Visa, MasterCard, Delta, Maestro
Specialities: Roses. Unstaffed rose field can be viewed dawn-dusk every day from end Jun-end Sep.
Notes: Celebrated 250 years of rose growing in 2015. Bare-root mail order end Oct-end Mar, containers Apr-Aug. Exports beyond EU. Partial wheelchair access.
Map Ref: E, C3

ECrc **THE CROCOSMIA GARDENS**
9 North Street, Caistor, Lincolnshire LN7 6QU
Ⓣ (01472) 859269
Ⓜ 07434 444924
Ⓔ mark@thecrocosmiagardens.net
Ⓦ www.thecrocosmiagardens.net
Contact: Mark Fox
Opening Times: 1000-1700 Mon, Wed-Sun. Closed Tue.
Min Mail Order UK: £5.00
Min Mail Order EU: £5.00
Cat. Cost: None issued.
Credit Cards: None
Specialities: *Crocosmia*. Nat. Collection of *Crocosmia*. Available in small quantities only.
Notes: Sent bareroot only, Oct-Apr. Exports beyond EU. Euro accepted.
Map Ref: E, A1

ECre **CREAKE PLANT CENTRE** ♿
Leicester Road, South Creake, Fakenham, Norfolk NR21 9PW
Ⓣ (01328) 823018
Ⓜ 07760 762499
Ⓕ (01328) 823018
Ⓔ trevor-harrison@btconnect.com
Ⓦ www.creakeplantcentre.co.uk
Contact: Mr T Harrison
Opening Times: 1000-1300 & 1400-1730 7 days excl. Xmas.
Cat. Cost: None issued
Credit Cards: All major credit/debit cards
Specialities: Unusual shrubs, herbaceous, conservatory plants, old roses. Hellebores. Some plants only available in small quantities.
Notes: Delivers to shows. Wheelchair accessible.
Map Ref: E, A2 **OS Grid Ref:** TF864353

ECrN **CROWN NURSERY** ♿
High Street, Ufford, Suffolk IP13 6EL
Ⓣ (01394) 460755
Ⓕ (01394) 460142
Ⓔ enquiries@crown-nursery.co.uk
Ⓦ www.crown-nursery.co.uk
Contact: Jill Proctor
Opening Times: 0900-1700 (1600 in winter) Mon-Sat.
Min Mail Order UK: Nmc
Credit Cards: All major credit/debit cards
Specialities: Mature & semi-mature native, ornamental & fruit trees. Heritage fruit varieties.
Notes: Mail order for small/young stock only. Also sells wholesale. Wheelchair accessible.
Map Ref: E, C3 **OS Grid Ref:** TM292528

ECtt **COTTAGE NURSERIES** ♿
Thoresthorpe, Alford, Lincolnshire LN13 0HX
Ⓣ (01507) 466968
Ⓔ bill@cottagenurseries.net

E

Ⓦ www.cottagenurseries.net
Contact: W H Denbigh
Opening Times: 0900-1700, 7 days 1st Mar-31st Oct. 1000-1500, Nov-Feb. Closed 15th Dec-6th Jan.
Min Mail Order UK: £15.00
Cat. Cost: Online only.
Credit Cards: Visa, MasterCard, Maestro
Specialities: Hardy perennials. Wide general range.
Notes: Wheelchair accessible.
Map Ref: E, A2 **OS Grid Ref:** TF461776

EDAr **D'Arcy & Everest**
Meadowsweet Nursery, Pidley Sheep Lane (B1040), Pidley, Cambridgeshire
PE28 3FL
Ⓣ (01480) 497672
Ⓜ 07715 374440
Ⓕ (01480) 466042
Ⓔ angela@darcyeverest.co.uk
Ⓦ www.darcyeverest.co.uk
Contact: Angela Whiting
Opening Times: 1000-1500 Wed-Sat, Mar-end Sep. Nursery gardens open Sat only, but close at 1400 if an event on. Winter by appt. Coach parties welcome by appt.
Min Mail Order UK: £15.00 + p&p
Credit Cards: All major credit/debit cards
Specialities: Alpines & sempervivums.
Notes: Delivers to shows. Partial wheelchair access.
Map Ref: E, C2 **OS Grid Ref:** TL338762

EECP **Essex Carnivorous Plants**
12 Strangman Avenue, Thundersley, Essex
SS7 1RB
Ⓣ (01702) 551467
Ⓜ 07957 196391
Ⓔ Mark@essexcarnivorousplants.com
Ⓦ www.essexcarnivorousplants.com
Contact: Mark Haslett
Opening Times: By appt. only.
Min Mail Order UK: Nmc
Min Mail Order EU: Nmc
Cat. Cost: 2 × 1st class or online.
Credit Cards: Paypal
Specialities: Good range of carnivorous plants. *Sarracenia*, *Dionaea*. Some stock available in small quantities only.
Notes: Also sells wholesale. Delivers to shows.
Map Ref: E, D2 **OS Grid Ref:** TQ797875

EFer **The Fern Nursery** ♿
Grimsby Road, Binbrook, Lincolnshire
LN8 6DH
Ⓣ (01472) 398092
Ⓔ rtimm@fernnursery.co.uk
Ⓦ www.fernnursery.co.uk
Contact: R N Timm
Opening Times: 0900-1700 Fri, Sat & Sun Apr-Oct or by appt.
Min Mail Order UK: Nmc
Min Mail Order EU: Nmc
Cat. Cost: 2 × 1st class.
Credit Cards: All major credit/debit cards
Specialities: Ferns. Display garden.
Notes: Only plants in the mail order part of the catalogue can be sent mail order. Also sells wholesale. Euro accepted. Wheelchair accessible.
Map Ref: E, A1 **OS Grid Ref:** TF212942

EFly **The Fly Trap Plants** ♿
Cookes Road, Thurton, Norwich, Norfolk
NR14 6AE
Ⓣ (01508) 480348
Ⓜ 07769 256556
Ⓔ sales@tftplants.co.uk
Ⓦ www.tftplants.co.uk
Contact: Pauline Steward
Opening Times: By appt. only.
Min Mail Order UK: Nmc
Cat. Cost: 1 × 1st class sae
Credit Cards: Paypal
Specialities: All kinds of carnivorous plants, from *Sarracenia*, *Drosera*, *Pinguicula*, to *Utricularia* aquatic plants.
Notes: Delivers to shows. Euro accepted. Wheelchair accessible.
Map Ref: E, B3

EGeo **George's Gorgeous Gardens**
Outlaws Cottage, Lugs Lane, Broome, Norfolk NR35 2HT
Ⓣ (01508) 518559
Ⓜ 07592 491234
Ⓔ georgesgorgeousgardens@gmail.com
Contact: George Gillespie
Min Mail Order UK: £20.00
Min Mail Order EU: £50.00
Cat. Cost: £2.50
Credit Cards: None
Specialities: *Plectranthus*.

EGFP **Grange Farm Plants** ♿
Grange Farm, 38 Fishergate Road, Sutton St James, Spalding, Lincolnshire
PE12 0EZ
Ⓣ (01945) 440240
Ⓜ 07742 138760
Ⓕ (01945) 440355
Ⓔ ellis.family@tinyonline.co.uk
Contact: M C Ellis
Opening Times: Mail order only. Open by appt. only.
Min Mail Order UK: Nmc
Min Mail Order EU: Nmc
Cat. Cost: 1 × 1st class.
Credit Cards: None

Specialities: Rare trees & shrubs, esp. *Juglans*, *Fraxinus*. Some species available in small quantities only.
Notes: Euro accepted. Wheelchair accessible.
Map Ref: E, B2 **OS Grid Ref:** TF382186

EHDe **Harper & Debbage**
33 The Ridgeway, Norwich, Norfolk
NR1 4ND
Ⓣ (01603) 708104
Ⓜ 07889 679444
Ⓔ info@harperanddebbage.co.uk
Ⓦ www.harperanddebbage.co.uk
Contact: Kristopher Harper
Opening Times: Not open except by appt. or on Open Days,
Min Mail Order UK: Nmc
Cat. Cost: Online only.
Credit Cards: None
Specialities: *Fuchsia*. National Collection of Fuchsias introduced by James Lye.
Notes: Sells by mail order, at Open Days or available for collection by appointment only. New online shop to be launched in 2016. Delivers to shows.
Map Ref: E, B3

EHoe **Hoecroft Plants** ♿
Severals Grange, Holt Road, Wood Norton, Norfolk NR20 5BL
Ⓣ (01362) 684206
Ⓔ hoecroft@hotmail.co.uk
Ⓦ www.hoecroft.co.uk
Contact: Jane Lister
Opening Times: 1000-1600 Thu-Sun, 1st Apr-31st Oct or by appt.
Min Mail Order UK: Nmc
Min Mail Order EU: Nmc
Cat. Cost: 5 × 2nd class.
Credit Cards: None
Specialities: An extensive range of coloured & variegated-leaved shrubs & herbaceous perennials. 260 ornamental grasses. Donation to NGS for entry to display gardens.
Notes: Nursery 2 miles north of Guist on B1110. Euro accepted. Wheelchair accessible.
Map Ref: E, B3 **OS Grid Ref:** TG008289

EHrv **Harveys Garden Plants** ♿
Great Green, Thurston, Bury St Edmunds, Suffolk IP31 3SJ
Ⓣ (01359) 233363
Ⓔ admin@harveysgardenplants.co.uk
Ⓦ www.harveysgardenplants.co.uk
Contact: Roger Harvey
Opening Times: 0930-1630 Mon-Sun. Closed 24th Dec-1st Jan incl.
Min Mail Order UK: £20.00
Min Mail Order EU: £20.00
Cat. Cost: None issued.
Credit Cards: All major credit/debit cards
Specialities: *Helleborus*, *Anemone*, *Epimedium*, *Galanthus*, *Astrantia*, *Pulmonaria* & other herbaceous perennials, plus shade & woodland plants.
Notes: Garden design & maintenance service. Customers can buy online. Exports beyond EU. Delivers to shows. Euro accepted. Wheelchair accessible.
Map Ref: E, C2 **OS Grid Ref:** TL951677

EHyd **Hyde Hall Plant Centre (RHS)** ♿ ◆
RHS Garden Hyde Hall, Rettenden, Chelmsford, Essex CM3 8ET
Ⓣ (01245) 402113
Ⓕ (01245) 400013
Ⓔ benmansfield@rhs.org.uk
Ⓦ www.rhs.org.uk
Contact: Any member of staff
Opening Times: 0930-1600 Mon-Sat, 1000-1600 Sun, Nov-Feb. 0930-1800 Mon-Sat, 1100-1700 Sun, Mar-Oct. Closed Xmas Day & Easter Sun.
Credit Cards: All major credit/debit cards
Notes: Wheelchair accessible.
Map Ref: E, D2

EIri **Irisesonline**
Slade Cottage, Petts Lane, Little Walden, Essex CB10 1XH
Ⓣ (01799) 526294
Ⓔ sales@irisesonline.co.uk
Ⓦ www.irisesonline.co.uk
Contact: Clare Kneen
Opening Times: By appt. only.
Min Mail Order UK: Nmc
Cat. Cost: 3 × 1st class or online.
Credit Cards: None
Specialities: *Iris*. Small family-run nursery. Some varieties available in small quantities only.
Map Ref: E, C2 **OS Grid Ref:** TL546416

EKin **E W King & Co. Ltd. (Kings Seeds)**
Monks Farm, Pantling Lane, Coggeshall Road, Kelvedon, Essex CO5 9PG
Ⓣ (01376) 570000
Ⓕ (01376) 571189
Ⓔ sales@kingsseeds.com
Ⓦ www.kingsseeds.com
Contact: Andrew Tokely
Min Mail Order UK: No minimum charge
Cat. Cost: Free
Credit Cards: All major credit/debit cards
Specialities: Vegetable, flower, grass, sweet pea and pea & bean seeds, incl. many hybrid & unusual items.
Notes: Incorporating Suffolk Herbs. Also sells wholesale.

E

ELad **Ladybird Nurseries** ♿
Gromford Lane, Snape, Saxmundham, Suffolk IP17 1RD
Ⓣ (01728) 688289
Ⓦ www.ladybirdnurseries.co.uk
Contact: Mrs M Booker
Opening Times: 0900-1700, Mon-Sat, 1000-1600 Sun.
Credit Cards: All major credit/debit cards
Notes: Wheelchair accessible.
Map Ref: E, C3 **OS Grid Ref:** TM388589

ELan **Langthorns Plantery** ♿
High Cross Lane West, Little Canfield, Dunmow, Essex CM6 1TD
Ⓣ (01371) 872611
Ⓔ info@langthorns.com
Ⓦ www.langthorns.com
Contact: E Cannon
Opening Times: 1000-1700 or dusk (if earlier) 7 days excl. Xmas fortnight.
Min Mail Order UK: £ 20.00
Cat. Cost: Online only.
Credit Cards: Visa, Access, Switch, MasterCard, Delta
Specialities: Wide general range with many unusual plants.
Notes: Mail order any plant under 4ft tall. Mail order not available during spring & summer months. Wheelchair accessible.
Map Ref: E, D2 **OS Grid Ref:** TL592204

ELon **Long House Plants** ♿
The Long House, Church Road, Noak Hill, Romford, Essex RM4 1LD
Ⓣ (01708) 371719
Ⓔ tim@longhouse-plants.co.uk
Ⓦ www.longhouse-plants.co.uk
Contact: Tim Carter
Opening Times: 1000-1700 Fri, Sat & B/hols, 1000-1600 Sun, beginning Mar-end Sep, or by appt.
Cat. Cost: None issued.
Credit Cards: All major credit/debit cards
Specialities: Interesting range of choice trees, shrubs, climbers, roses, grasses, herbaceous perennials & ferns. Many unusual varieties. Specialities incl. *Agapanthus*, *Aster*, *Camellia*, *Hemerocallis*, *Iris sibirica*, *Kniphofia*, *Phlox* & *Symphyotrichum*. Some plants available in small quantities.
Notes: Wheelchair accessible. Disabled toilet.
Map Ref: E, D2 **OS Grid Ref:** TQ554194

EMal **Marshall's Malmaisons** ♿
Hullwood Barn, Shelley, Ipswich, Suffolk IP7 5RE
Ⓣ (01473) 822400
Ⓜ 07768 454875
Ⓔ jim@malmaisons.plus.com
Ⓦ www.malmaisonsandiris.co.uk
Contact: J M Marshall/Sarah Cook
Opening Times: By appt. only.
Min Mail Order UK: £33.00 incl. p&p
Min Mail Order EU: £36.00 incl. p&p
Cat. Cost: 1st class sae.
Credit Cards: None
Specialities: Nat. Collections of Malmaison Carnations & Cedric Morris Irises. *Iris* stock only available in small quantities.
Notes: Also sells wholesale. Wheelchair accessible.
Map Ref: E,C3 **OS Grid Ref:** TM006394

EMdy **Mandy Plants** ♿
(Office) 4 Stevens Road, Little Snoring, Norfolk NR21 0GZ
Ⓣ (01328) 878144
Ⓜ 07432 112245
Ⓔ enquiries@mandyplants.com
Ⓦ www.mandyplants.com
Contact: Liz Spanton
Opening Times: By appt. only.
Min Mail Order UK: Nmc
Min Mail Order EU: £25.00
Credit Cards: Paypal, All major credit/debit cards
Specialities: *Mandevilla* & *Dipladenia* & other tender perennials.
Notes: Nursery is at Little Snoring, Norfolk. Also sells wholesale. Delivers to shows. Wheelchair accessible.

EMFm **Mill Farm Nursery** ♿
(Office) 26 The Brambles, Middle Rasen, Lincolnshire LN8 3NS
Ⓜ 07940 302674 or 07899 905230
Ⓔ linclan@sky.com
Ⓦ www.millfarmnursery.com
Contact: Robert Parry
Opening Times: 1000-1600 Thu-Sun, Mar-Nov.
Min Mail Order UK: Nmc
Cat. Cost: Sae or email for stock list.
Credit Cards: Maestro, Visa, MasterCard, Electron
Specialities: Traditional nursery growing most plants on site. Hardy perennials & unusual types of difficult to find perennials. All perennials are British grown. Ornamental grasses, varied range of *Miscanthus* cvs, trees & specimen plants. Two large display borders. Some stock available in small quantities only.
Notes: Nursery is at Old Gallamore Lane, Middle Rasen, LN8 3US. Mail order: please phone to check seasonal availability. Wheelchair accessible.
Map Ref: E, A1 **OS Grid Ref:** TF091891

EMic **Mickfield Hostas** ♿
The Poplars, Mickfield, Stowmarket, Suffolk
IP14 5LH
Ⓣ (01449) 711576
Ⓕ (01449) 711576
Ⓔ mickfieldhostas@btconnect.com
Ⓦ www.mickfieldhostas.co.uk
Contact: Mr & Mrs R L C Milton
Opening Times: 1000-1600, Thu to Mon. Closed Tue & Wed.
Min Mail Order UK: Nmc
Min Mail Order EU: Nmc
Cat. Cost: Online only.
Credit Cards: All major debit/credit cards except American Express
Specialities: Nat. Collection of *Hosta* containing over 2000 varieties. See website for details of cvs held & latest availability. Operates a waiting list for rarities & some limited quantity plants only available at nursery. Will divide parent plants for collectors if feasible. Expect to pay more for root divisions of mature plants.
Notes: Delivers to shows. Wheelchair accessible.
Map Ref: E, C3 **OS Grid Ref:** TM136619

EMil **Mill Race Garden Centre** ♿
New Road, Aldham, Colchester, Essex
CO6 3QT
Ⓣ (01206) 242521
Ⓔ plantdesk@millracegardencentre.co.uk
Ⓦ www.millracegardencentre.co.uk
Contact: Annette Bayliss
Opening Times: 0900-1730 Mon-Sat, 1000-1630 Sun.
Min Mail Order UK: £9.00
Credit Cards: All major credit/debit cards
Specialities: Stock available in small quantities only.
Notes: Trees & large shrubs not sent by mail order. Wheelchair accessible.
Map Ref: E, C2 **OS Grid Ref:** TL918268

EMOT **Mail Order Trees** ◆
42 Station Road, Fordham, Ely,
Cambridgeshire CB7 5LW
Ⓣ 0800 066 5972
Ⓔ info@mailordertrees.co.uk
Ⓦ www.mailordertrees.co.uk
Contact: Michael Simpson
Opening Times: Not open. Mail order only.
Min Mail Order UK: Nmc
Credit Cards: All major credit/debit cards
Specialities: Specialist fruit & ornamental tree growers, offering a range of home-grown evergreen & deciduous shrubs, climbing plants, conifers, soft fruit bushes & hedging plants to buy online.
Notes: Also sells wholesale.

EMsh **S E Marshall & Co Ltd.**
Alconbury HIll, Huntingdon,
Cambridgeshire
PE28 4HY
Ⓣ (01480) 443390
Ⓕ (01945) 588235
Ⓔ info@marshalls-seeds.co.uk
Ⓦ www.marshalls-seeds.co.uk
Contact: Customer Services
Opening Times: Not open, mail order only.
Min Mail Order UK: Nmc
Min Mail Order EU: Nmc
Cat. Cost: Free
Credit Cards: All major debit/credit cards except American Express. Paypal.
Specialities: Vegetables.
Notes: Also sells wholesale.

ENfk **Norfolk Herbs** ♿
Blackberry Farm, Dillington, Dereham,
Norfolk NR19 2QD
Ⓣ (01362) 860812
Ⓕ (01362) 860812
Ⓔ info@norfolkherbs.co.uk
Ⓦ www.norfolkherbs.co.uk
Contact: Rosemary or Oliver Clifton-Sprigg
Opening Times: 0900-1700 Mon-Sat, 1000-1600 Sun, Apr-Aug. 1000-1600 Fri & Sat, Feb, Oct & Nov. 1000-1600 Wed-Sat, Mar, Sept & Dec. Closed from Xmas to end Jan. To visit at other times, please contact nursery.
Min Mail Order UK: £8.39
Cat. Cost: 2 × 2nd class.
Credit Cards: All major credit/debit cards
Specialities: Established 1986. Growers & suppliers of naturally raised culinary, medicinal & aromatic herb plants. Bay trees & scented pelagoniums.
Notes: Sells from nursery, online & at local shows. A founding member of Norfolk Nursery Network. Also sells wholesale. Delivers to shows. Wheelchair accessible.
Map Ref: E, B2 **OS Grid Ref:** TF967150

ENBC **Norfolk Bamboo Company**
Vine Cottage, The Drift, Ingoldisthorpe,
King's Lynn, Norfolk
PE31 6NW
Ⓣ (01485) 543935
Ⓜ 07970 310880
Ⓔ Lewdyer@hotmail.com
Ⓦ www.norfolkbamboo.co.uk
Contact: Lewis Dyer
Opening Times: 1000-1600 Fri & 1000-1400 Sat, Apr-Sep, or by appt.
Min Mail Order UK: £10.00 + p&p
Cat. Cost: 1 × 1st class sae for price list.
Credit Cards: None
Specialities: Bamboos.
Map Ref: E, B2

E

EOHP **Old Hall Plants**
1 The Old Hall, Barsham, Beccles, Suffolk NR34 8HB
Ⓣ (01502) 717475
Ⓔ info@oldhallplants.co.uk
Ⓦ www.oldhallplants.co.uk
Contact: Janet Elliott
Opening Times: By appt. only. Please phone first.
Min Mail Order UK: Nmc
Min Mail Order EU: Nmc
Cat. Cost: 4 × 1st class.
Specialities: A variety of rare herbs, house plants. Some plants available in small quantities.
Notes: Paypal accepted for overseas orders only. Cheques accepted. Partial wheelchair access.
Map Ref: E, C3 **OS Grid Ref:** TM396904

EPau **Paugers Plants Ltd**
Bury Road, Depden, Bury St Edmunds, Suffolk IP29 4BU
Ⓣ (01284) 850527
Ⓜ 07906 618603
Ⓔ enquiries@paugers-plants.co.uk
Ⓦ www.paugers-plants.co.uk
Contact: Geraldine Arnold
Opening Times: 0900-1730 Wed-Sat, 1000-1700 Sun & B/hols, 1st Mar-30th Nov.
Min Mail Order UK: Nmc
Cat. Cost: None issued.
Credit Cards: All major credit/debit cards
Specialities: Hardy shrubs & perennials in large or small quantities.
Notes: Also sells wholesale.
Map Ref: E, C2 **OS Grid Ref:** TL783568

EPed **Pernewood Plants** ♿
Popes Hall, Fersfield Road, South Lopham, Diss, Norfolk IP22 2JY
Ⓜ 07484 332651
Ⓔ info@pernewoodplants.co.uk
Ⓦ www.pernewoodplants.co.uk
Contact: Kevan Milbourne
Opening Times: Not open. Mail order only. Plants may be collected by arrangement.
Min Mail Order UK: £25.00
Credit Cards: All major debit/credit cards except American Express
Specialities: Small family-run online plant nursery, offering a wide range of hardy perennials, ornamental grasses and shade-loving plants and ferns. Plants UK sourced or raised from own nursery stock specimens.
Notes: Delivers to shows.

EPfP **The Place for Plants** ♿
East Bergholt Place, East Bergholt, Suffolk CO7 6UP
Ⓣ (01206) 299224
Ⓕ (01206) 299229
Ⓔ sales@placeforplants.co.uk
Ⓦ www.placeforplants.co.uk
Contact: Sara Eley
Opening Times: 1000-1700 (or dusk if earlier) 7 days. Closed Easter Sun. Garden open Mar-Oct.
Min Mail Order UK: Nmc
Cat. Cost: Online only.
Credit Cards: All major credit/debit cards
Specialities: Wide range of specialist & popular plants. Nat. Collection of Deciduous *Euonymus*. 20 acre mature garden with free access to RHS members during season (excl. Sun).
Notes: Mail order from Sep-Feb. Delivers to shows. Euro accepted. Wheelchair accessible.
Map Ref: E, C3

EPom **Pomona Fruits Ltd**
Pomona House, 12 Third Avenue, Walton-on-the-Naze, Essex CO14 8JU
Ⓣ (01255) 440410
Ⓕ (01255) 440420
Ⓔ Info@PomonaFruits.co.uk
Ⓦ www.PomonaFruits.co.uk
Contact: Ming Yang/Claire Higgins
Opening Times: Not open. Mail order only.
Min Mail Order UK: Nmc
Cat. Cost: Free.
Credit Cards: All major credit/debit cards
Specialities: Fruit stock.

EPot **Pottertons Nursery** ♿
Moortown Road, Nettleton, Caistor, Lincolnshire LN7 6HX
Ⓣ (01472) 851714
Ⓕ (01472) 852580
Ⓔ sales@pottertons.co.uk
Ⓦ www.pottertons.co.uk
Contact: Robert Potterton
Opening Times: 1000-1600 Tue-Sat, Mar-Oct. By appt. only from Nov-Feb.
Min Mail Order UK: Nmc
Min Mail Order EU: Nmc
Cat. Cost: £2.00 in stamps
Credit Cards: MasterCard, Visa
Specialities: Alpines, dwarf bulbs & woodland plants.
Notes: External talks nationally & internationally to garden clubs & societies. Group nursery tours by arrangement. Delivers to shows. Euro accepted. Wheelchair accessible.
Map Ref: E, A1 **OS Grid Ref:** TA091001

EPPr **The Plantsman's Preference** ♿
Church Road, South Lopham, Diss, Norfolk IP22 2LW

Ⓣ (01379) 710810
Ⓜ 07799 855559
Ⓔ tim@plantpref.co.uk
Ⓦ www.plantpref.co.uk
Contact: Tim Fuller
Opening Times: 0930-1700 Fri, Sat & Sun Mar-Oct. Other times by appt.
Min Mail Order UK: Nmc
Min Mail Order EU: Nmc
Cat. Cost: Online only.
Credit Cards: All major credit/debit cards
Specialities: Hardy geraniums & ornamental grasses. Unusual & interesting perennials incl. shade/woodland. Some choice shrubs esp. *Caprifoliaceae*. Nat. Collection of *Molinia*.
Notes: Mail order all year except Xmas-New Year. Delivers to shows. Wheelchair accessible.
Map Ref: E, C3 **OS Grid Ref:** TM041819

EPri PRIORY PLANTS ♿
1 Covey Cottages, Hintlesham, Nr Ipswich, Suffolk IP8 3NY
Ⓣ (01473) 652656
Ⓜ 07798 627618
Ⓕ (01473) 652656
Ⓔ sue.mann3@btinternet.com
Ⓦ www.prioryplants.co.uk
Contact: Sue Mann
Opening Times: By appt. only. Please ring first to avoid disappointment.
Min Mail Order UK: £15.00 + p&p
Min Mail Order EU: £25.00
Cat. Cost: Online only.
Credit Cards: None
Specialities: Cottage garden perennials, as well as increasing range of South African plants. *Agapanthus, Astrantia, Dierama, Dietes, Geum*, Siberian *Iris, Kniphofia, Nerine, Papaver, Tritonia, Tulbaghia* & *Watsonia*.
Notes: Sells at plant fairs & agricultural shows. Also sells wholesale. Exports beyond EU. Delivers to shows. Wheelchair accessible.
Map Ref: E, C3 **OS Grid Ref:** TM070448

EPts POTASH NURSERY ♿
Cow Green, Bacton, Stowmarket, Suffolk IP14 4HJ
Ⓣ (01449) 781671
Ⓔ enquiries@potashnursery.co.uk
Ⓦ www.potashnursery.co.uk
Contact: M W Clare
Opening Times: Pre-ordered plants can be collected by appt. only.
Min Mail Order UK: £21.00
Cat. Cost: 1 × 1st class.
Credit Cards: Visa, Delta, MasterCard
Specialities: *Fuchsia*.
Notes: Peat free. Delivers to shows. Wheelchair accessible.
Map Ref: E, C3 **OS Grid Ref:** TM055656

ERCP ROSE COTTAGE PLANTS
Bay Tree Farm, Epping Green, Essex CM16 6PU
Ⓣ (01992) 573775
Ⓔ anne@rosecottageplants.co.uk
Ⓦ www.rosecottageplants.co.uk
Contact: Anne & Jack Barnard
Opening Times: By appt. & for special events (see website for details).
Min Mail Order UK: Nmc
Min Mail Order EU: £20.00
Cat. Cost: Online only.
Credit Cards: All major debit/credit cards except American Express
Specialities: Hardy bulbs & dahlias.
Notes: Mail order for bulbs only. Delivers to shows.
Map Ref: E, D2 **OS Grid Ref:** TL435053

ERea READS NURSERY
Douglas Farm, Bungay, Suffolk NR35 2JG
Ⓣ (01986) 895555
Ⓔ plants@readsnursery.co.uk
Ⓦ www.readsnursery.co.uk
Contact: Stephen Read
Opening Times: Not open. Mail order only.
Min Mail Order UK: Nmc
Min Mail Order EU: Nmc
Cat. Cost: Free.
Credit Cards: All major credit/debit cards
Specialities: Ornamental & unusual fruit trees. Soft fruit. *Magnolia*.

ERod THE RODINGS PLANTERY ♿
Anchor Lane, Abbess Roding, Essex CM5 0JW
Ⓣ (01279) 876421
Ⓜ 07790 020940
Ⓔ janeandandy@therodingsplantery.co.uk
Ⓦ www.therodingsplantery.co.uk
Contact: Jane & Andy Mogridge
Opening Times: 1000-1600 Wed & Sat. By appt. only. Occasional open days, please phone for details.
Min Mail Order UK: Nmc
Min Mail Order EU: £500.00 + p&p
Cat. Cost: 3 × 1st class.
Credit Cards: None
Specialities: Bamboos. Rare & unusual trees.
Notes: Also sells wholesale. Delivers to shows. Euro accepted. Wheelchair accessible.
Map Ref: E, D2

ESgl SEAGATE IRISES ♿
A17 Long Sutton By-Pass, Long Sutton, Lincolnshire PE12 9RX
Ⓣ (01406) 365138
Ⓜ 07887 856389
Ⓔ sales@irises.co.uk
Ⓦ www.irises.co.uk

E

Contact: Julian Browse or Wendy Browse
Opening Times: 1000-1700 daily Apr-mid Jul. Please phone for appt. mid-Jul to Mar.
Cat. Cost: £3.50 or €8.00.
Credit Cards: Maestro, Visa, MasterCard
Specialities: Different types of *Iris*, bearded, beardless & species hybrids with about 1000 varieties in all, both historic & modern. Some only available in small quantities. Many container-grown available to callers.
Notes: Wheelchair accessible.
Map Ref: E, B2 **OS Grid Ref:** TF437218

EShb **Shrubland Park Nurseries**
Maltings Farm, Whatfield Road, Elmsett, Ipswich, Suffolk IP7 6LZ
Ⓣ (01473) 657012
Ⓜ 07890 527744
Ⓔ gill@shrublandparknurseries.co.uk
Ⓦ www.shrublandparknurseries.co.uk
Contact: Gill & Catherine Stitt
Opening Times: 1000-1600 daily, 1st Mar-30th Oct & 1000-1600 Wed, Sat & Sun, 1st Nov-1st Mar. Please ring or check website for any changes, especially if travelling a long distance.
Min Mail Order UK: Nmc
Min Mail Order EU: Nmc
Cat. Cost: Online or free by post.
Credit Cards: All major credit/debit cards, Paypal
Specialities: Conservatory plants, succulents, hardy perennials, climbers, shrubs, ferns & grasses.
Notes: Delivers to shows.
Map Ref: E, C3 **OS Grid Ref:** TM052466

ESMi **Straight Mile Nursery Gardens** ♿
Ongar Road, Pilgrims Hatch, Brentwood, Essex CM15 9SA
Ⓣ (01277) 374439
Ⓔ gdlsisley@aol.com
Ⓦ www.straightmile.net
Contact: David Sisley
Opening Times: 1000-1700, 7 days (but closed some Weds, phone first.)
Min Mail Order UK: Nmc
Cat. Cost: Online only.
Credit Cards: All major debit/credit cards except American Express
Specialities: General nursery stock. Japanese maples, *Epimedium*. Some in small quantities only.
Notes: Delivers to shows. Wheelchair accessible.
Map Ref: E, D2 **OS Grid Ref:** TQ571964

ESps **Simpson's Nurseries Ltd** ♿
42 Station Road, Fordham, Ely, Cambridgeshire CB7 5LW
Ⓣ (01638) 720194
Ⓕ (01638) 720961
Ⓔ simpstree@aol.com
Ⓦ www.simpsonsnurseries.com
Contact: Dave Simpson
Opening Times: 0900-1700.
Credit Cards: All major credit/debit cards
Specialities: Family-run business. Specialist plant and tree centre with wide selection of plants. Always fully stocked with over 300 varieties of shrubs & 300 varieties of herbaceous and perennial plants, with over 90% of stock home grown.
Notes: Wheelchair accessible.
Map Ref: E, C2 **OS Grid Ref:** TL623701

EStr **Strictly Daylilies**
2 Primes Corner, Histon, Cambridgeshire CB24 9AG
Ⓣ (01223) 236239
Ⓜ 07765 236880
Ⓔ info@strictlydaylilies.com
Ⓦ www.strictlydaylilies.com
Contact: Paula & Chris Dyason
Opening Times: Mail order only. Open by appt. Open gardens Fri-Sun in Jul, please phone for confirmation.
Min Mail Order UK: Nmc
Min Mail Order EU: Nmc
Cat. Cost: No charge.
Credit Cards: All major credit/debit cards
Specialities: *Hemerocallis*. Some stock available in small quantities only. National Collection of *Hemerocallis* (post 2014 hybrid registrations).
Notes: Also sells wholesale. Delivers to shows. Exports beyond the EU. Euro accepted.

ESty **Style Roses** ♿
(Office) Highworth, 56 Spalding Road, Holbeach, Spalding, Lincolnshire PE12 7HG
Ⓣ (01406) 424089
Ⓜ 07760 626750 or 07780 860415
Ⓕ (01406) 490006
Ⓔ mail@styleroses.co.uk
Ⓦ www.styleroses.co.uk
Contact: Margaret Styles
Opening Times: Opening times vary on workload so customers should phone to make an appt. before visiting. Nursery is at Cackle Hill Farm PE12 8AG.
Min Mail Order UK: Nmc
Min Mail Order EU: Nmc
Cat. Cost: Free in UK.
Credit Cards: MasterCard, Visa
Specialities: Standard & bush roses.
Notes: Bush roses available mail order to mainland UK all year round (Highlands & Islands may be subject to additional courier charges). Standard roses mail order only Nov-

Mar as bare-root plants or by collection in pots from nursery & shows all year round. Export to EU during bare-root season Nov-Mar. Exports beyond EU subject to Plant Health Requirements (not USA). Also sells wholesale. Delivers to shows. Wheelchair accessible.
Map Ref: E, B2

EThi THISTLEFIELD PLANTS AND DESIGN
65 Westgate Street, Shouldham, Kings Lynn, Norfolk PE33 0BL
Ⓣ (01366) 347365
Ⓜ 07899 994071
Ⓕ (01366) 347365
Ⓔ paul@thistlefieldplants.co.uk
Ⓦ www.thistlefieldplants.co.uk
Contact: Paul Welford
Opening Times: Not open. Sells at plant fairs & shows only.
Min Mail Order UK: Nmc
Cat. Cost: Online only.
Credit Cards: None
Specialities: Perennials. *Tricyrtis* available in small quantities only.
Notes: Delivers to shows.

ETho THORNCROFT CLEMATIS LTD ♿
The Lings, Reymerston, Norwich, Norfolk NR9 4QG
Ⓣ (01953) 850407
Ⓔ sales@thorncroftclematis.co.uk
Ⓦ www.thorncroftclematis.co.uk
Contact: Peter Skeggs-Gooch
Opening Times: Not open regularly. Mail order only but orders can be collected by prior arrangement. Telephones manned 0900-1600 Mon-Sat.
Min Mail Order UK: Nmc
Min Mail Order EU: Nmc
Cat. Cost: 6 × 2nd class.
Credit Cards: All major credit/debit cards
Specialities: *Clematis.*
Notes: Events & Open Days held throughout the year. See website or phone for details. Delivers to shows. Toilets available. Wheelchair accessible.

ETMg THOMPSON & MORGAN
Poplar Lane, Ipswich, Suffolk IP8 3BU
Ⓣ 0333 400 0033
Ⓕ (01473) 680199
Ⓔ ccare@thompson-morgan.com
Ⓦ www.thompson-morgan.com
Contact: Customer Care
Opening Times: Mail order only.
Min Mail Order UK: Nmc
Cat. Cost: Free
Credit Cards: All major debit/credit cards except American Express

ETod TODD'S BOTANICS
West Street, Coggeshall, Colchester, Essex CO6 1NT
Ⓣ (01376) 561212
Ⓔ info@toddsbotanics.co.uk
Ⓦ www.toddsbotanics.co.uk
Contact: Mark Macdonald
Opening Times: Not open, except by appt. Mail order only.
Min Mail Order UK: Nmc
Cat. Cost: Online only.
Credit Cards: Paypal, All major credit/debit cards
Specialities: Hardy exotics, herbaceous. Bamboos, palms, ferns, grasses, *Canna* & *Hedychium*. Olives, incl. named varieties. *Citrus*. Drought-resistant plants.
Notes: Not all plants available mail order, contact nursery for details. Also sells wholesale. Delivers to shows. Euro accepted. Nursery partially accessible for wheelchairs.

EUJe URBAN JUNGLE
Ringland Lane, Old Costessey, Norwich, Norfolk NR8 5BG
Ⓣ (01603) 744997
Ⓕ (0709) 2366869
Ⓔ lizzy@urbanjungle.uk.com
Ⓦ www.urbanjungle.uk.com
Contact: Elizabeth Browne
Opening Times: 1000-1700 1st Feb-31st Oct 7 days incl. B/hols. 1000-1600 Nov-Dec Thu, Fri, Sat, Sun. Closed Jan.
Min Mail Order UK: Nmc
Min Mail Order EU: Nmc
Credit Cards: All major credit/debit cards
Specialities: Wide range of choice plants from exotic bedding to hardy evergreens.
Notes: Display gardens & living walls. Delivers to shows. Limited wheelchair access.
Map Ref: E, B3 **OS Grid Ref:** TG153127

EUnw UNWINS SEEDS LTD
Customer Services Dept, Alconbury Hill, Huntingdon, Cambridgeshire PE28 4HY
Ⓔ JRichardson@WestlandHorticulture.com
Ⓦ www.unwins.co.uk
Contact: Jen Richardson
Min Mail Order UK: Nmc
Min Mail Order EU: £15.00
Cat. Cost: Free
Credit Cards: Visa, Access
Specialities: Sweet peas & wide general range.

EVic VICTORIAN VIOLAS
85 Fulmar Road, Lincoln, Lincolnshire LN6 0RX
Ⓣ (01522) 686343
Ⓔ victorianviolasinfo@fsmail.net
Ⓦ www.victorianviolas.co.uk

Contact: Robert Chapman
Opening Times: Not open.
Min Mail Order UK: Nmc
Cat. Cost: 2 × 1st class or online.
Credit Cards: None
Specialities: Hardy perennial violas (summer flowering). Named cultivars of *Viola odorata* (sweet violet).
Notes: Delivers to shows.

G

EWat **WATER GARDEN PLANTS**
Wayside Aquatics, Blackmore Road, Doddinghurst, Brentwood, Essex CM15 0HU
Ⓜ 07517 873206
Ⓔ sales@watergardenplants.co.uk
Ⓦ www.watergardenplants.co.uk
Contact: Anna Robinson
Opening Times: Mail order only. With prior notice, plants may be collected during the following times:1000-1700 Wed-Sun.
Min Mail Order UK: Nmc
Min Mail Order EU: Nmc
Cat. Cost: Online.
Credit Cards: All major credit/debit cards
Specialities: Range of water garden plants: waterlilies; floating plants; oxygenating plants; marginals; marsh plants. Some stock in small quantities.
Notes: Euro accepted.
Map Ref: E, D2 **OS Grid Ref:** TQ585995

EWes **WEST ACRE GARDENS** ♿
Tumbleyhill Road, West Acre, King's Lynn, Norfolk PE32 1UJ
Ⓣ (01760) 755562
Ⓔ info@westacregardens.co.uk
Ⓦ www.westacregardens.co.uk
Contact: J J Tuite
Opening Times: 1000-1700 7 days 1st Feb-30th Nov. Other times by appt.
Cat. Cost: None issued.
Credit Cards: Visa, MasterCard, Delta, Switch
Specialities: Very wide selection of herbaceous & other garden plants incl. *Rhodohypoxis*, *Primula auricula* & *Galanthus*.
Notes: Delivers to shows. Wheelchair accessible.
Map Ref: E, B2 **OS Grid Ref:** TF792182

EWld **WOODLANDS**
Peppin Lane, Fotherby, Louth, Lincolnshire LN11 0UW
Ⓣ (01507) 603586
Ⓔ annbobarmstrong@btinternet.com
Ⓦ www.woodlandsplants.co.uk
Contact: Ann Armstrong
Opening Times: Flexible, but please phone or email to avoid disappointment.
Min Mail Order UK: Nmc
Min Mail Order EU: Nmc
Cat. Cost: None issued.
Credit Cards: None
Specialities: Small but interesting range of unusual plants, esp. woodland, *Codonopsis* and *Salvia*, all grown on the nursery in limited quantity. National Collection of *Codonopsis*.
Notes: Mature garden, art gallery & refreshments. Euro accepted.
Map Ref: E, A2 **OS Grid Ref:** TF322918

EWTr **WALNUT TREE GARDEN NURSERY**
Flymoor Lane, Rocklands, Attleborough, Norfolk NR17 1BP
Ⓣ (01953) 488163
Ⓔ info@wtgn.co.uk
Ⓦ www.wtgn.co.uk
Contact: Jim Paine & Clare Billington
Opening Times: 0900-1800 Tue-Sun Feb-Nov & B/hols.
Min Mail Order UK: Nmc
Cat. Cost: Online.
Credit Cards: All major credit/debit cards
Specialities: Flowering dogwood: *Cornus florida*, *C. kousa* & *C. nuttalli* cvs. Crab apple (*Malus*) cvs.
Map Ref: E, B2 **OS Grid Ref:** TL978973

SCOTLAND

GAbr **ABRIACHAN NURSERIES** ♿
Loch Ness Side, Inverness, Inverness-shire IV3 8LA
Ⓣ (01463) 861232
Ⓔ info@lochnessgarden.com
Ⓦ www.lochnessgarden.com
Contact: Mr & Mrs D Davidson
Opening Times: 0900-1900 daily (dusk if earlier) Feb-Nov.
Min Mail Order UK: Nmc
Cat. Cost: 4 × 1st class.
Credit Cards: All major credit/debit cards
Specialities: Herbaceous perennials, old-fashioned *Primula*, *Helianthemum*, hardy geraniums, *Sempervivum* & *Primula auricula*.
Notes: Delivers to shows. Wheelchair access to nursery only.
Map Ref: G, B2 **OS Grid Ref:** NH571347

GAgs **ANGUSPLANTS**
3 Balfour Cottages, Menmuir, By Brechin, Angus DD9 7RN
Ⓣ (01356) 660280
Ⓜ 07972 026109
Ⓔ alison@angusplants.co.uk
Ⓦ www.angusplants.co.uk
Contact: Dr Alison S. Goldie & Mark A. Hutson
Opening Times: By appt. only. Please phone first.

Min Mail Order UK: Nmc
Min Mail Order EU: Nmc
Cat. Cost: 2 × 2nd large letter stamps.
Credit Cards: None
Specialities: *Primula auricula*, Nat. Collection of Alpine Auriculas.
Notes: Mail order available all year.
Map Ref: G, B3 **OS Grid Ref:** NO528643

GBee **Beeches Cottage Nursery** ♿
High Boreland, Lesmahagow, South Lanarkshire ML11 9PY
Ⓣ (01555) 893369
Ⓜ 07930 343131
Ⓔ thebeeches.nursery@talktalk.net
Ⓦ www.beechescottage.co.uk
Contact: Margaret Harrison, Steven Harrison
Opening Times: 1000-1630 7 days incl. Apr-end Jun. 1000-1630 Wed-Sat, Jul-end Sep.
Cat. Cost: None issued.
Credit Cards: None
Specialities: Traditional & unusual hardy cottage garden perennials which can be seen growing in display gardens at 850ft. Some plants available in small quantities only. Hanging basket specialists. Cottage gardens designed and planted.
Notes: Wheelchair access to nursery only.
Map Ref: G, C2 **OS Grid Ref:** NS837403

GBin **Binny Plants** ♿
Binny Estate, Ecclesmachan Road, Nr Broxburn, West Lothian EH52 6NL
Ⓣ (01506) 858931
Ⓜ 07753 626116
Ⓔ contact@binnyplants.com
Ⓦ www.binnyplants.com
Contact: Billy Carruthers & David Wong
Opening Times: 1000-1700, 7 days. Closed over Xmas & New Year.
Cat. Cost: 4 × 1st class.
Credit Cards: Visa, MasterCard, EuroCard, Maestro
Specialities: Over 250 varieties of *Paeonia*, plus a good range of herbaceous perennials, grasses & ferns incl. *Astilbe*, *Bergenia*, *Geranium*, *Molinia*, *Persicaria* & *Iris*.
Notes: Also sells wholesale. Delivers to shows. Wheelchair accessible.
Map Ref: G, C3 **OS Grid Ref:** NT050732

GCal **Cally Gardens** ♿
Gatehouse of Fleet, Castle Douglas, Kirkcudbrightshire DG7 2DJ
Ⓣ (01557) 815029 recorded information only.
Ⓔ info@callygardens.co.uk
Ⓦ www.callygardens.co.uk
Contact: Michael Wickenden
Opening Times: 1000-1730 Sat-Sun, 1400-1730 Tue-Fri. Easter Sat-last Sun in Sept.
Min Mail Order UK: £15.00 + p&p
Cat. Cost: 3 × 1st class.
Credit Cards: None
Specialities: Unusual perennials & grasses. Some rare shrubs, climbers & conservatory plants. 3500 varieties growing in an 2.7 acre walled garden built in the 1760s.
Notes: Also sells wholesale. Wheelchair accessible.
Map Ref: G, D2 **OS Grid Ref:** NX604549

GCrg **Craigiehall Nursery**
Carnwath, Lanark, Lanarkshire ML11 8LH
Ⓣ (01555) 840027 (answering machine)
Ⓔ sales@craigiehallnursery.co.uk
Ⓦ www.craigiehallnursery.co.uk
Contact: Innes Hogg
Opening Times: Not open. Mail order only.
Min Mail Order UK: Nmc
Cat. Cost: Online only.
Credit Cards: All major credit/debit cards
Specialities: A very wide range of alpine and rock garden plants; over 500 different varieties on the nursery. Some are quite common, others much less so.
Notes: Online sales only, no telephone ordering.

GCro **Croft 16 Daffodils**
16 Midtown of Inverasdale, Poolewe, Achnasheen, Ross-shire IV22 2LW
Ⓣ (01445) 781717
Ⓔ sales@croft16daffodils.co.uk
Ⓦ www.croft16daffodils.co.uk
Contact: Duncan & Kate Donald
Opening Times: Not open. Mail order only.
Min Mail Order UK: Nmc
Min Mail Order EU: Nmc
Cat. Cost: Online. Customers without internet access send 4 × 1st for sales list without pictures.
Credit Cards: Paypal
Specialities: Nat. Collection of Daffodils bred pre-1930. Some stocks only available in small quantities. A waiting list for *desiderata* is in operation.
Notes: Limited availability, so please order by late May if possible. Orders unfulfilled in one season will take priority the following year. Customers outside the EU should contact nursery.
Map Ref: G, A1 **OS Grid Ref:** NG822851

GDun **Dunskey Gardens & Maze** ♿
Portpatrick, Stranraer, Wigtownshire DG9 8TJ
Ⓣ (01776) 810905
Ⓜ 07899 092070
Ⓕ (01776) 810581

Ⓔ gabygardeners@btinternet.com
Ⓦ www.dunskey.com
Contact: Gabrielle Reynolds
Opening Times: 1000-1600 w/ends only Feb, 1000-1700 daily Easter-Oct. See website for details.
Credit Cards: All major credit/debit cards
Specialities: Broad range, propagated from the gardens, incl. bulbs, tender perennials, herbaceous, trees and shrubs. Available in small quantities only. National Collections of *Clianthus*, *Nicotiana* & *Sutherlandia*.
Notes: Dunskey Estate Walled Garden & Maze open to the public. Sells at local plant shows. Wheelchair accessible.
Map Ref: G, D2 **OS Grid Ref:** NX004560

GEdr **EDROM NURSERIES**
Coldingham, Eyemouth, Berwickshire
TD14 5TZ
Ⓣ (01890) 771386
Ⓕ (01890) 771387
Ⓔ info@edrom-nurseries.co.uk
Ⓦ www.edrom-nurseries.co.uk
Contact: Mr Terry Hunt
Opening Times: 0900-1700 Thu, Fri, Sat & Mon (closed Tue & Wed), 1000-1600 Sun.
Min Mail Order UK: Nmc
Min Mail Order EU: Nmc
Cat. Cost: Free.
Credit Cards: All major credit/debit cards
Specialities: *Cypripedium*, *Epimedium*, *Gentiana*, *Primula*, *Meconopsis*, *Rhodohypoxis*, *Trillium* & Japanese *Hepatica*.
Notes: Delivers to shows.
Map Ref: G, C3 **OS Grid Ref:** NT873663

GGGa **GLENDOICK GARDENS LTD** ♿
Glendoick, Perth, Perthshire
PH2 7NS
Ⓣ (01738) 860205
Ⓔ orders@glendoick.com
Ⓦ www.glendoick.com
Contact: Kenneth Cox
Opening Times: Nursery not open to the public. Garden centre open 0900-1730 (summer), 0900-1700 (winter) 7 days. Gardens open Apr & May, details on website.
Min Mail Order UK: £50.00
Min Mail Order EU: £100.00
Cat. Cost: £2.00.
Credit Cards: All major debit/credit cards except American Express
Specialities: Rhododendrons, azaleas and ericaceous, *Primula* & *Meconopsis*. Plants from wild seed. Many catalogue plants available at garden centre. 3 Nat. Collections.
Notes: Exports beyond EU. Wheelchair access to garden centre.
Map Ref: G, C3

GJos **JO'S GARDEN ENTERPRISE** ♿
Easter Balmungle Farm, Eathie Road, by Rosemarkie, Ross-shire
IV10 8SL
Ⓣ (01381) 621006
Ⓔ jos_garden_enterprise@hotmail.co.uk
Contact: Joanna Chance
Opening Times: 1000 to dusk, 7 days.
Cat. Cost: None.
Credit Cards: None
Specialities: Alpines & herbaceous perennials. Selection of native wild flowers.
Notes: Wheelchair accessible.
Map Ref: G, B2 **OS Grid Ref:** NH600742

GKev **KEVOCK GARDEN PLANTS**
16 Kevock Road, Lasswade, Midlothian
EH18 1HT
Ⓣ 0131 454 0660
Ⓜ 07811 321585
Ⓕ 0131 454 0660
Ⓔ sales@kevockgarden.co.uk
Ⓦ www.kevockgarden.co.uk
Contact: Stella Rankin
Opening Times: Not open. Mail order & plant stalls only.
Min Mail Order UK: £25.00
Min Mail Order EU: £25.00
Cat. Cost: 3 × 1st class.
Credit Cards: Visa, MasterCard, Switch
Specialities: Chinese & Himalayan plants. *Androsace*, *Daphne*, *Paeonia*, *Primula*, *Meconopsis*, *Iris*, woodland plants, alpines, rock plants, marginal & bog plants, bulbs, Sino-himalayan trees & shrubs.
Notes: Also sells wholesale. Delivers to shows. Euro accepted.

GKin **KINLOCHLAICH GARDEN PLANT CENTRE**
Appin, Argyll PA38 4BB
Ⓜ 07881 525754
Ⓔ fiona@kinlochlaich.plus.com
Ⓦ www.kinlochlaichgardencentre.co.uk
Contact: Fiona Hutchison
Opening Times: 1000-1700 Mar-mid Oct, 1000-1500 or by appt., mid-Oct-Feb. Happy to open if contacted by phone first.
Cat. Cost: None issued
Credit Cards: All major credit/debit cards
Specialities: Hardy shrubs, trees, azaleas, perennials. Also Gulf Stream plants such as *Tropaeolum*, *Embothrium*, *Eucryphia*, *Drymis* & more. Good selection of hardy seaside plants.
Notes: Do not offer mail order but will post where possible. Limited wheelchair access (gravel paths), toilet wheelchair accessible.
Map Ref: G, C2

GLog **LOGIE STEADING PLANTS** ♿
Forres, Moray IV36 2QN
Ⓣ (01309) 611222 or 611278
Ⓕ (01309) 611300
Ⓔ panny@logie.co.uk
Ⓦ www.logie.co.uk
Contact: Mrs Panny Laing
Opening Times: 1030-1700 hours, 7 days, March-Christmas.
Credit Cards: All major credit/debit cards
Specialities: Unusual hardy plants, grown in Scotland for Scottish gardens. Large range of hardy geraniums, bold herbaceous plants, grasses & marginal plants.
Notes: Logie House Garden open every day. Café, farm shop, art gallery, secondhand books, whisky & wine, river walk, heritage centre. Wheelchair accessible (except river walk).
Map Ref: G, B2 **OS Grid Ref:** NJ006504

GMaP **MACPLANTS** ♿
Berrybank Nursery, 5 Boggs Holdings, Pencaitland, East Lothian EH34 5BA
Ⓣ (01875) 341179
Ⓕ (01875) 340842
Ⓔ sales@macplants.co.uk
Ⓦ www.macplants.co.uk
Contact: Gavin McNaughton
Opening Times: 1030-1700 7 days, Mar-end Sep. 1030-1600 Mon-Fri, Oct. Closed Nov-end Feb unless by appt.
Min Mail Order UK: Nmc
Cat. Cost: 4 × 2nd class.
Credit Cards: MasterCard, Switch, Visa
Specialities: Herbaceous perennials, alpines, hardy ferns, violas & grasses. *Meconopsis*. National Collection of *Sanguisorba*.
Notes: Also sells wholesale. Delivers to shows. Wheelchair accessible.
Map Ref: G, C3 **OS Grid Ref:** NT447703

GMcL **MCLAREN'S NURSERIES**
Lochlibo Road, Uplawmoor, Barrhead, East Renfrewshire G78 4DN
Ⓣ (01505) 850666
Ⓕ (01505) 850706
Ⓔ mclarensplants@aol.com
Contact: Adam McGowan
Opening Times: 0800-1630 Mon-Fri, 0900-1600 Sat & Sun.
Min Mail Order UK: Nmc
Credit Cards: All major credit/debit cards
Specialities: A family-run business that is one of the largest nurseries in the UK, with over 3200 popular & rarer plants.
Notes: Also sells wholesale.

GMil **MILL & BARBAUCHLAW MILL NURSERY** ♿
Mill Road, Armadale, West Lothian EH48 3AP
Ⓣ (01501) 732347
Ⓜ 07725 401864
Ⓔ info@millgardencentre.co.uk
Ⓦ www.millgardencentre.co.uk
Contact: Colin & Kathleen McIndoe
Opening Times: 0900-1700 Mon-Sat, 1000-1700 Sun, Oct-Mar; 0900-1800 Mon-Wed, 0900-2000 Thu, 0900-1700 Fri & Sat, 1000-1700 Sun, Apr-Sep; 0900-2000 Mon-Thu, May & Jun.
Min Mail Order UK: £15.00
Credit Cards: American Express, MasterCard, Visa
Specialities: An independent, family-owned garden centre based in central Scotland. Many unusual conifers along with a wide variety of hedging conifers in a range of sizes. Large collection of Japanese *Acer*, ranging from miniature patio size to large specimens.
Notes: Wheelchair accessible.

GNew **NEWTONAIRDS HOSTAS & GARDEN** ♿
Newtonairds Lodge, Newtonairds, Dumfries DG2 0JL
Ⓣ (01387) 820203
Ⓔ info@newtonairds-hostasandgarden.co.uk
Ⓦ www.newtonairds-hostasandgarden.co.uk
Contact: James & Carol Coutts
Opening Times: 1000-1800, Thu, Fri, Sat, 5th May-27th Aug (nursery & garden). Garden entry Thu for Peter Pan Moat Brae Trust charity.
Min Mail Order UK: Nmc
Cat. Cost: Free list.
Credit Cards: None
Specialities: Hostas, herbaceous perennials & grasses grown in the garden. Also some seed collected from garden. Pesticide & herbicide free plants, National Collection of Fragrant Hostas (*Hosta plantaginea* cultivars and hybrids). Available in small quantities only.
Notes: £4.00 entry fee applies for adults to the garden, children free. Dogs welcome on leads. Coaches by arrangement. Most of garden wheelchair accessible.
Map Ref: G, D2 **OS Grid Ref:** NX882800

GPoy **POYNTZFIELD HERB NURSERY** ♿
Nr Balblair, Black Isle, Dingwall, Ross-shire IV7 8LX
Ⓣ (01381) 610352. Phone between 1200-1300 & 1800-1900 Mon-Sat only.
Ⓔ info@poyntzfieldherbs.co.uk
Ⓦ www.poyntzfieldherbs.co.uk
Contact: Duncan Ross
Opening Times: 1300-1700 Mon-Sat 1st Mar-30th Sep, 1300-1700 Sun May-Aug.
Min Mail Order UK: £10.00 + p&p
Min Mail Order EU: £20.00 + p&p
Cat. Cost: 4 × 1st class.

Credit Cards: All major credit/debit cards
Specialities: Over 400 popular, unusual & rare herbs esp. medicinal. Also seeds.
Notes: Mail order operates in the spring & autumn. Wheelchair accessible.
Map Ref: G, B2 **OS Grid Ref:** NH711642

GPSL **Plants, Shoots and Leaves**
Dovecot Bungalow, Haddington, East Lothian EH41 4HA
Ⓣ (01620) 823536
Ⓜ 07885 444241
Ⓔ karen.leys@btinternet.com
Ⓦ www.plantsshootsandleaves.co.uk
Contact: Karen Payne
Opening Times: 1000-1700 1st Apr-1st Oct. Closed Mon.
Min Mail Order UK: £3.50
Min Mail Order EU: £6.60
Cat. Cost: Online only.
Specialities: *Epimedium.* Perennials and some shrubs. Some available in small quantities only.
Notes: Euro accepted. Mostly accessible for wheelchairs.
Map Ref: G, C3 **OS Grid Ref:** NT500730

GQue **Quercus Garden Plants Ltd**
Whitmuir Farm, Lamancha, West Linton, Scottish Borders EH46 7BB
Ⓣ (01968) 660708
Ⓔ rona@quercusgardenplants.co.uk
Ⓦ www.quercusgardenplants.co.uk
Contact: Rona Peddie
Opening Times: 1000-1700 Wed-Sun.
Cat. Cost: Online only.
Credit Cards: All major credit/debit cards
Specialities: Easy & unusual plants for Scottish gardens.
Notes: Wide range of plants, including old favourites and many unusual varieties of herbaceous perennials, grasses, trees, shrubs & plants for shade. Plants are grown at 850ft above sea level so are tough and well acclimatised to Scottish growing conditions. The majority of plants are propagated on site and grown on for a least a season.
Map Ref: G, C3 **OS Grid Ref:** NT192512

GRid **J & I Cruickshanks** ♿
Ridgeview Nursery, Crossroad by Longridge, Fauldhouse, West Lothian EH47 9AB
Ⓣ (01501) 771144
Ⓔ enquiries@ridgeviewnursery.co.uk
Ⓦ www.ridgeviewnursery.co.uk
Contact: Alice Kyle & Andrew Cruickshanks
Opening Times: 0900-1600, 7 days.
Min Mail Order UK: Nmc
Credit Cards: None
Specialities: Rooted *Dahlia* cuttings.
Notes: Wheelchair accessible.

GWyn **Wyndford Farm Plants Ltd**
Wyndford Farm, Ecclesmachan, West Lothian EH52 6NW
Ⓜ 07871 496732
Ⓔ info@wyndfordfarmplants.com
Ⓦ www.wyndfordfarmplants.com
Contact: Adam Fleming
Opening Times: 1000-1700, 7 days.
Min Mail Order UK: Nmc
Cat. Cost: Online only.
Credit Cards: All major debit/credit cards except American Express
Specialities: Large range of perennials & shrubs, incl. large collection of violas.
Notes: Also sells wholesale. Delivers to shows.
Map Ref: G, C2 **OS Grid Ref:** NT059731

N. Ireland & Republic

IArd **Ardcarne Garden Centre** ♿
Ardcarne, Boyle, Co. Roscommon, Rep. of Ireland
Ⓣ +353 7196 67091
Ⓕ +353 7196 67341
Ⓔ ardcarne@indigo.ie
Ⓦ www.ardcarneplantsplus.ie
Contact: James Wickham, Mary Frances Dwyer, Kirsty Ainge
Opening Times: 0900-1800 Mon-Sat, 1300-1800 Sun & B/hols.
Credit Cards: Access, Visa, American Express
Specialities: Native & unusual trees, choice perennials, roses, plants for coastal areas, fruit trees, incl. heritage Irish apple trees, vegetable plants, specimen plants & semi-mature trees. Wide general range.
Notes: Café. Groups & tours welcome. Ample free parking. Garden design & landscape service available. Euro accepted. Wheelchair accessible.
Map Ref: I, B2

IBal **Bali-Hai Mail Order Nursery**
42 Largy Road, Carnlough, Ballymena, Co. Antrim, N. Ireland BT44 0EZ
Ⓣ 028 2888 5289
Ⓜ 07708 257164
Ⓕ 028 2888 5289
Ⓔ balihainursery@btinternet.com
Ⓦ www.mailorderplants4me.com
Contact: Mrs M E Scroggy
Opening Times: Mon-Sat by appt. only.
Min Mail Order UK: Nmc
Min Mail Order EU: Nmc
Cat. Cost: Online only.
Credit Cards: All major credit/debit cards
Specialities: Nat. Collection of *Hosta*, part planted in 1.5 acres, open to the public by appt. *Agapanthus*, *Crocosmia*, *Rhodohypoxis*, tree ferns & other perennials. Hostas grown to order.

Notes: Also sells wholesale. Export beyond EU restricted to bare-root perennials, no grasses. Euro accepted.
Map Ref: I, A3 **OS Grid Ref:** D287184

IBlr **BALLYROGAN NURSERIES** ♿
The Grange, Ballyrogan, Newtownards, Co. Down, N. Ireland BT23 4SD
Ⓣ 028 9181 0451 (evenings)
Ⓔ gary.dunlop@btinternet.com
Contact: Gary Dunlop
Opening Times: Only open by appt.
Min Mail Order UK: £10.00 + p&p
Min Mail Order EU: £20.00 + p&p
Cat. Cost: 2 × 2nd class.
Credit Cards: None
Specialities: Choice herbaceous. *Agapanthus*, *Crocosmia*, *Rodgersia*, *Dierama*, *Erythronium*, *Roscoea* & *Watsonia*.
Notes: Also sells wholesale. Euro accepted. Wheelchair accessible.
Map Ref: I, B3

IBoy **BOYNE GARDEN CENTRE**
Ardcalf, Slane, Co. Meath
C15 P92W,
Rep. of Ireland
Ⓣ +353 419 824350
Ⓜ +353 8724 01156
Ⓔ boynegardencentre@eircom.net
Ⓦ www.boynegardencentre.com
Contact: Aileen Muldoon Byrne
Opening Times: 0930-1800 Mon-Sat, 1400-1800 Sun, Mar-Sep (incl. B/hols). W/ends only Oct-Feb with week days by appt. only.
Min Mail Order UK: Nmc
Cat. Cost: Online only.
Credit Cards: All major credit/debit cards
Specialities: Award winning growers of hardy herbaceous perennials, specialising in planting for pollinators. David Austin & Harkness roses. Trees, shrubs, climbers, grasses, bamboos & ferns.
Notes: Complimentary tea/coffee. Gift vouchers. Pre-ordered plants delivered to shows. Euro accepted.
Map Ref: I, B3 **OS Grid Ref:** N93791 78126

IDee **DEELISH GARDEN CENTRE**
Deelish, Skibbereen, Co. Cork,
Rep. of Ireland
Ⓣ +353 28 21374
Ⓕ +353 28 21374
Ⓔ deel@eircom.net
Ⓦ www.deelish.ie
Contact: Bill & Rain Chase
Opening Times: 1000-1800 Mon-Sat, 1400-1800 Sun.
Min Mail Order UK: Nmc
Min Mail Order EU: Nmc
Cat. Cost: Sae
Credit Cards: Visa, Access
Specialities: Unusual plants for the mild coastal climate of Ireland. Conservatory plants. Sole Irish agents for Chase Organic Seeds.
Notes: No mail order outside Ireland & UK. Euro accepted.
Map Ref: I, D1

IDic **DICKSON NURSERIES**
Milecross Road, Newtownards, Co. Down, N. Ireland BT23 4SS
Ⓣ 028 9181 2206
Ⓔ mail@dickson-roses.co.uk
Ⓦ www.dickson-roses.co.uk
Contact: Colin Dickson
Opening Times: 0800-1230 & 1300-1515 Mon-Thu. 0800-1230 Fri.
Min Mail Order UK: Nmc
Min Mail Order EU: £25.00 + p&p
Cat. Cost: Free
Credit Cards: None
Specialities: Roses esp. modern Dickson varieties. Limited selection, check website. Most varieties available in small quantities only.
Notes: Also sells wholesale. Only glasshouses accessible for wheelchairs.
Map Ref: I, B3

IFoB **FIELD OF BLOOMS** ♿
Ballymackey, Lisnamoe, Nenagh, Co. Tipperary, Rep. of Ireland
Ⓣ +353 67 29974
Ⓜ +353 8764 06044
Ⓔ guy2002@eircom.net
Ⓦ www.fieldofblooms.ie
Contact: Guy de Schrijver
Opening Times: Strictly by appt.
Min Mail Order UK: Nmc
Min Mail Order EU: Nmc
Cat. Cost: Online only.
Credit Cards: None
Specialities: Hellebores, herbaceous, hardy perennials, ornamental grasses, woodland plants & some alpines.
Notes: Euro accepted. Wheelchair accessible.
Map Ref: I, C2

IFro **FROGSWELL NURSERY**
Clooncolan, Straide, Foxford, Co. Mayo, Rep. of Ireland
Ⓜ +353 8621 06166
Ⓔ frogswell@gmail.com
Ⓦ www.frogswellhardyplants.com
Contact: Celia Graebner
Opening Times: Feb-Oct by appt. Please phone first. Also charity Open Days & occasional on-site workshops; see website or contact nursery for details.

Credit Cards: None
Specialities: A small garden-based nursery specialising in shade & spring woodland plants incl. hybrid hellebores & hardy geraniums, plus unusual perennial bee & wild pollinator plants for the Irish climate, all raised on site & without chemical inputs. Some in very limited quantities.
Notes: Group visits & on- and off-site talks by arrangement. See website for location map. Euro accepted.
Map Ref: I, B1 **OS Grid Ref:** M2497

I

ILea **Leamore Nursery**
Cronroe, Ashford, Co. Wicklow A67 Y681, Rep of Ireland
Ⓣ +353 87 227 8850
Ⓕ +353 404 70126
Ⓔ info@leamorenursery.com
Ⓦ www.leamorenursery.com
Contact: Phil Havercroft
Opening Times: Not open to the public.
Min Mail Order UK: €25
Min Mail Order EU: €25
Cat. Cost: Online only.
Credit Cards: All major credit/debit cards
Specialities: *Paeonia* & other perennials. Most items in large quantities. Itoh peonies & some more unusual items only available in small quantities.
Notes: Bare-root peonies supplied in autumn, available to order from July (on website). Founding members of the Irish Specialist Nursery Association (ISNA). Also sells wholesale. Delivers to shows. Sterling & Euro accepted.
Map Ref: I, C3 **OS Grid Ref:** SG235520

IMou **Mount Venus Nursery** ♿
The Walled Garden, Mutton Lane, Dublin 16, Rep. of Ireland
Ⓣ +353 1 493 3813
Ⓜ +353 08632 18789
Ⓔ mountvenusnursery@gmail.com
Ⓦ www.mountvenusnursery.com
Contact: Oliver & Liat Schurmann
Opening Times: 1000-1800 Mon-Sat, Feb-Nov. 1300-1700 Sun, Apr-Oct.
Min Mail Order UK: €20
Min Mail Order EU: €35
Credit Cards: All major credit/debit cards
Specialities: Specialist perennials. Grasses & bamboos. Unusual woodland plants.
Notes: Also sells wholesale. Delivers to shows. Euro accepted. Wheelchair accessible.
Map Ref: I, C3

IPot **The Potting Shed** ♿
Bolinaspick, Camolin, Enniscorthy, Co. Wexford Y21 TD93 Rep. of Ireland
Ⓣ +353 5393 83629
Ⓔ susan@camolinpottingshed.com
Ⓦ www.camolinpottingshed.com
Contact: Susan Carrick
Opening Times: 1100-1700, Wed-Sat (incl.), Mar-Sep 2016. Other times by appt.
Min Mail Order UK: Nmc
Min Mail Order EU: Nmc
Cat. Cost: 3 × 1st class.
Credit Cards: MasterCard, Visa
Specialities: We grow a wide range of unusual, hard to find and new introductions of herbaceous perennials, ornamental grasses and *Clematis*, many of which can be seen growing to their full potential in our many display beds.
Notes: Member of the Irish Specialist Nursery Assoc. (ISNA). Orders outside Ireland can only be delivered by courier, charges at cost. Delivers to shows. Euro accepted. Wheelchair accessible.
Map Ref: I, C3

IRhd **Ringhaddy Daffodils**
Ringhaddy Road, Killinchy, Co. Down, N. Ireland BT23 6TU
Ⓣ 028 9754 1007
Ⓜ 07762 337534
Ⓔ info@ringhaddy-daffodils.com
Ⓦ www.ringhaddy-daffodils.com
Contact: Nial Watson
Opening Times: Mail order only. Not open.
Min Mail Order UK: £20.00 + p&p
Min Mail Order EU: £50.00 + p&p
Cat. Cost: £3.00
Credit Cards: Paypal
Specialities: Daffodil bulbs, some varieties only available in small numbers.
Notes: Exports beyond EU. Euro accepted.

IRob **Ballyrobert Cottage** ♿
154 Ballyrobert Road, Nr Templepatrick & Ballyclare, Co. Antrim, N. Ireland BT39 9RT
Ⓣ 028 9332 2952
Ⓜ 07463 793160
Ⓔ information@ballyrobertgardens.com
Ⓦ www.ballyrobertgardens.com
Contact: Paul Parkinson
Opening Times: 1000-1700 Mon-Sat, 1st Mar-1st Nov. Closed Sun.
Min Mail Order UK: £4.99
Min Mail Order EU: £4.99
Credit Cards: All major credit/debit cards
Specialities: Family-run garden & nursery in business over 25 years, selling hardy perennials that have performed successfully in own garden.
Notes: RHSI Partner Garden containing around 5000 cvs, open to the public. Euro accepted. Wheelchair accessible.
Map Ref: I, B3 **OS Grid Ref:** NW418462

IRos **Ros Ban Wildlife Garden** ♿
Common, Raphoe, Co. Donegal,
Rep. of Ireland
Ⓣ +353 74 91 45336
Ⓜ +353 8608 05214
Ⓔ Rosbangarden@gmail.com
Contact: Ann Kavanagh
Opening Times: Garden open, morning to evening, Easter to Sep.
Credit Cards: None
Notes: Plants available in season from the garden. Please check plant availability with nursery before travelling. Euro accepted. Wheelchair accessible.
Map Ref: I, A2 **OS Grid Ref:** F93HH0X

ITim **Timpany Nurseries & Gardens** ♿
77 Magheratimpany Road,
Ballynahinch, Co. Down, N. Ireland
BT24 8PA
Ⓣ 028 9756 2812
Ⓜ 07711 428477
Ⓔ s.tindall@btconnect.com
Ⓦ www.timpanynurseries.com
Contact: Susan Tindall
Opening Times: 1000-1730 Tue-Sat, Sun by appt.
Min Mail Order UK: £40.00 + p&p
Min Mail Order EU: £40.00 + p&p
Cat. Cost: £2.00
Credit Cards: All major debit/credit cards except American Express
Specialities: *Androsace*, *Campanula*, *Cassiope*, *Celmisia*, *Cyclamen*, *Dianthus*, *Galanthus*, *Meconopsis*, *Primula*, *Primula auricula*, *Rhodohypoxis* & *Saxifraga*.
Notes: Delivers to shows. Wheelchair accessible.
Map Ref: I, B3

London Area

LAma **Jacques Amand International Ltd** ♿
The Nurseries, 145 Clamp Hill, Stanmore, Middlesex HA7 3JS
Ⓣ 020 8420 7110
Ⓕ 020 8954 6784
Ⓔ bulbs@jacquesamand.co.uk
Ⓦ www.jacquesamandintl.com
Contact: Stuart Chapman
Opening Times: 0900-1700 Mon-Fri, 1000-1600 Sat.
Min Mail Order UK: Nmc
Min Mail Order EU: Nmc
Cat. Cost: 1 × 1st class.
Credit Cards: All major credit/debit cards
Specialities: Rare and unusual species bulbs esp. *Arisaema*, *Trillium*, *Fritillaria*, tulips.
Notes: Also sells wholesale. Exports beyond EU. Delivers to shows. Euro accepted. Wheelchair accessible.
Map Ref: L, B3 **OS Grid Ref:** TQ154919

LAyl **Aylett Nurseries Ltd** ♿
North Orbital Road, St Albans, Hertfordshire AL2 1DH
Ⓣ (01727) 822255
Ⓕ (01727) 823024
Ⓔ info@aylettnurseries.co.uk
Ⓦ www.aylettnurseries.co.uk
Contact: Julie Aylett
Opening Times: 0830-1730 Mon-Fri, 0830-1700 Sat, 1030-1630 Sun.
Cat. Cost: Free.
Credit Cards: All major credit/debit cards
Specialities: *Dahlia*. 2-acre trial ground adjacent to garden centre.
Notes: Wheelchair accessible.
Map Ref: L, B3 **OS Grid Ref:** TL169049

LBee **Beechcroft Nursery** ♿
127 Reigate Road, Ewell, Surrey KT17 3DE
Ⓣ 020 8393 4265
Ⓕ 020 8393 4265
Ⓔ enquiries@beechcroft-nursery.co.uk
Ⓦ www.beechcroft-nursery.co.uk
Contact: C Kimber
Opening Times: 1000-1600 Mon-Sat, 1000-1400 Sun and B/hols. Closed Xmas-New Year week.
Cat. Cost: None issued.
Credit Cards: All major credit/debit cards
Specialities: Conifers.
Notes: Wheelchair accessible.
Map Ref: L, C3

LBuc **Buckingham Nurseries** ♿ ◆
14 Tingewick Road, Buckingham MK18 4AE
Ⓣ (01280) 822133
Ⓕ (01280) 815491
Ⓔ enquiries@buckingham-nurseries.co.uk
Ⓦ www.buckingham-nurseries.co.uk
Contact: R J & P L Brown
Opening Times: 0830-1730 (1800 in summer) Mon-Sat, 1000-1600 Sun.
Min Mail Order UK: Nmc
Min Mail Order EU: Nmc
Cat. Cost: Free.
Credit Cards: Visa, MasterCard, Maestro
Specialities: Bare-rooted and container grown hedging. Fruit trees, soft fruit, trees, shrubs, herbaceous perennials, alpines, grasses & ferns.
Notes: Garden centre with restaurant. Wheelchair accessible.
Map Ref: L, A2 **OS Grid Ref:** SP675333

LCla **Clay Lane Nursery**
3 Clay Lane, South Nutfield, Nr Redhill, Surrey RH1 4EG

Ⓣ (01737) 823307
Ⓔ claylane.nursery@btinternet.com
Ⓦ www.claylane-fuchsias.co.uk
Contact: K W Belton
Opening Times: Not open to general visitors. Pre-ordered plants can be collected by arrangement.
Min Mail Order UK: £11.00
Cat. Cost: 3 × 2nd class.
Credit Cards: None
Specialities: *Fuchsia*. Many varieties in small quantities only.
Notes: Mail order by telephone pre-arangement. Pre-arranged collections from the nursery.
Map Ref: L, C4

L

LCro **Crocus.co.uk**
Nursery Court, London Road, Windlesham, Surrey GU20 6LQ
Ⓣ (01344) 578000
Ⓕ (01344) 629600
Ⓔ customerservices@crocus.co.uk
Ⓦ www.crocus.co.uk
Contact: Customer Care Team
Opening Times: Mail order only. Order lines open 24hrs, 7 days. Nursery has four Open Days a year; see website or phone for details.
Min Mail Order UK: Nmc + delivery charges.
Cat. Cost: Free.
Credit Cards: All major debit/credit cards except American Express
Specialities: Large general nursery.
Notes: Also sells wholesale.
Map Ref: L, C3

LEdu **Edulis** ♿
(Office) 1 Flowers Piece, Ashampstead, Reading, Berkshire RG8 8SG
Ⓣ (01635) 578113
Ⓜ 07802 812781
Ⓔ edulisnursery@gmail.com
Ⓦ www.edulis.co.uk
Contact: Paul Barney
Opening Times: 1000-1600 Tues & Wed, & by appt. Apr-Oct. Nov-Mar by appt. only. See website or contact nursery for additional Open Days.
Min Mail Order UK: £20.00 + p&p
Min Mail Order EU: £30.00 + p&p
Cat. Cost: Online only.
Credit Cards: All major debit/credit cards except American Express
Specialities: Unusual edibles, architectural plants, permaculture plants & many of our own collections.
Notes: Nursery is at The Walled Garden, Tidmarsh Lane, Pangbourne, RG8 8HT. Also sells wholesale. Euro accepted. Delivers to shows. Wheelchair accessible.
Map Ref: L, B2 **OS Grid Ref:** SU615747

LHom **Home Farm Plants**
Home Farm, Shantock Lane, Bovingdon, Hertfordshire HP3 0NG
Ⓜ 07773 798068
Ⓔ enquiries@homefarmplants.com
Ⓦ www.homefarmplants.co.uk
Contact: Graham Austin
Opening Times: 0900-1730 Fri & Sat, 1000-1600 Sun, viewing by appointment only Mon-Thu, 1st Apr-end Oct (subject to weather conditions).
Cat. Cost: 1st class sae for list.
Credit Cards: None
Specialities: *Delphinium elatum* (over 60 varieties). Also hardy perennials & seasonal cut flowers. Show area of 200+ delphiniums (contact nursery for flowering times). Some varieties only available in small quantities.
Notes: If travelling, please contact nursery to confirm plant availability. Limited wheelchair access. Delivers to shows.

LLHF **Little Heath Farm (UK)** ♿
Little Heath Lane, Potten End, Berkhamsted, Hertfordshire HP4 2RY
Ⓣ (01442) 864951
Ⓜ 07835 200789
Ⓔ lhfnursery@gmail.com
Ⓦ www.littleheathfarmnursery.co.uk
Contact: John Spokes
Opening Times: 1000-1700 or dusk if earlier, 7 days.
Cat. Cost: Online only.
Credit Cards: Visa, MasterCard
Specialities: Large range of alpines, herbaceous, shrubs, many available in small quantities only.
Notes: Delivers to shows. Wheelchair accessible.
Map Ref: L, B3 **OS Grid Ref:** TL019085

LLWG **Lilies Water Gardens** ♿
Broad Lane, Newdigate, Surrey RH5 5AT
Ⓣ (01306) 631064
Ⓜ 07801 166244
Ⓔ mail@lilieswatergardens.co.uk
Ⓦ www.lilieswatergardens.co.uk
Contact: Simon Harman
Opening Times: 0900-1700 Wed-Sat, Mar-Aug. By appt. only Sep-Feb.
Min Mail Order UK: Nmc but flat rate £6.50 delivery charge.
Min Mail Order EU: Nmc
Cat. Cost: Online only.
Credit Cards: All major credit/debit cards
Specialities: Waterlilies, moist perennials, bog-garden plants, primulas, marginal plants, ferns, oxygenating plants. Pond plants, incl. submerged & free-floating, aquatic, water iris, water-garden, floating, stream & deep-water

plants. Alpine, rock & creeping plants. Rushes & grasses.
Notes: Wheelchair accessible.

LMaj **Majestic Trees**
Chequers Meadow, Chequers Hill, Flamstead, St Albans, Hertfordshire AL3 8ET
Ⓣ (01582) 843881
Ⓕ (01582) 843882
Ⓔ info@majestictrees.co.uk
Ⓦ www.majestictrees.co.uk
Contact: Andy Miles
Opening Times: 0830-1700 Mon-Fri. 1000-1600 Sat, Nov-Feb, 1000-1700 Sat, Mar-Oct. Closed Sun, B/hols, Xmas/New Year.
Credit Cards: MasterCard, Visa, Switch, Maestro
Specialities: Semi-mature & mature containerised trees grown in airpots from 50ltr to 5000 ltr.
Notes: Also sells wholesale. Disabled access by golf buggy can be arranged by appt. Euro accepted. Delivers to shows.

LMea **Meadowview Nursery**
8 Bourne Way, Addlestone, Surrey KT15 2BT
Ⓣ (01932) 988631
Ⓜ 07989 474767
Ⓕ (01932) 843475
Ⓔ chris@mvnltd.co.uk
Ⓦ www.meadowviewnursery.co.uk
Contact: Chris Glazier
Opening Times: Not open. Mail order only. Online orders taken 0800-1700 Mon-Fri.
Min Mail Order UK: Nmc
Min Mail Order EU: Nmc
Cat. Cost: Online only
Credit Cards: None
Specialities: *Paeonia*: herbaceous, tree, Itoh. *Iris germanica, Hemerocallis* & *Helleborus*.
Notes: Euro accepted. Also sells wholesale.

LMil **Millais Nurseries** ♿
Crosswater Farm, Crosswater Lane, Churt, Farnham, Surrey GU10 2JN
Ⓣ (01252) 792698
Ⓔ sales@rhododendrons.co.uk
Ⓦ www.rhododendrons.co.uk
Contact: David Millais
Opening Times: 1000-1700 Mon-Fri all year. Daily in spring. Please phone or see website for weekend opening in spring.
Min Mail Order UK: Nmc
Min Mail Order EU: Nmc
Cat. Cost: Free list on request. Full catalogue Online.
Credit Cards: All major credit/debit cards
Specialities: Rhododendrons, azaleas, magnolias, camellias & acers. Garden open in spring.
Notes: Mail order all year. Also sells wholesale.

Wheelchair accessible.
Map Ref: L, C3 **OS Grid Ref:** SU856397

LOPS **RHS Plant Shop: RHSplants.co.uk** ◆
Nursery Court, London Road, Windlesham, Surrey GU20 6LQ
Ⓣ (01344) 578822
Ⓕ (01344) 629600
Ⓔ customerservices@rhsplants.co.uk
Ⓦ www.rhsplants.co.uk
Contact: Customer Care Team
Opening Times: Not open. Online mail order only.
Min Mail Order UK: Nmc
Credit Cards: All major debit/credit cards except American Express

LPai **Painshill Park Trust** ♿
Portsmouth Road, Cobham, Surrey KT11 1JE
Ⓣ 01932 868113
Ⓔ AndyMills@painshill.co.uk
Ⓦ www.painshill.co.uk
Contact: Andy Mills
Opening Times: 7 days, 1030-1800 Mar to Oct, 1030-1600 Nov to Feb. Closed Xmas Day & Boxing Day.
Specialities: Small selection of surplus stock of annuals and perennials grown on site, available in very small quantities only. All funds raised contribute to the continuing restoration & conservation of Charles Hamilton's landscape garden at Painshill.
Notes: Wheelchair accessible.

LPla **The Plant Specialist**
7 Whitefield Lane, Great Missenden, Buckinghamshire HP16 0BH
Ⓣ (01494) 866650
Ⓕ (01494) 866650
Ⓔ enquire@theplantspecialist.co.uk
Ⓦ www.theplantspecialist.co.uk
Contact: Sean Walter
Opening Times: 1000-1700 Wed-Sat, 1000-1600 Sun, Apr-Oct. 1000-1600 B/hol Mons.
Cat. Cost: None issued.
Credit Cards: All major credit/debit cards
Specialities: Herbaceous perennials, grasses, half-hardy perennials, bulbs.
Notes: Limited wheelchair access. Delivers to shows.

LPmr **Primrose Hall Nursery**
Dingley Dell Nursery, Toddington Road, Westoning, Bedfordshire MK45 5AH
Ⓣ (01525) 878924
Ⓕ (01525) 878924
Ⓔ enquiries@primrosehall.co.uk
Ⓦ www.primrosehall.co.uk
Contact: Alec White

Opening Times: 0900-1600 Mon-Sat. Closed Wed & Sun.
Min Mail Order UK: Nmc
Min Mail Order EU: £50.00
Credit Cards: All major debit/credit cards except American Express
Specialities: *Paeonia* & *Alstroemeria*.
Notes: Also sells wholesale. Delivers to shows. Euro accepted.

L

LPra **Practicality Brown Ltd**
Swan Road, Iver, Buckinghamshire SL0 9LA
Ⓣ (01753) 652022
Ⓕ (01753) 653007
Ⓔ hedge@pracbrown.co.uk
Ⓦ www.pracbrown.co.uk
Contact: Ginny Lemarie
Opening Times: 0800-1700 Mon-Fri.
Credit Cards: All major credit/debit cards
Specialities: Established over 30 years. Large shrubs, topiary and semi-mature trees incl. yew, holly, box, beech & hornbeam. Everything to create a mature garden finish.
Notes: Also sells wholesale.

LRHS **Wisley Plant Centre (RHS)** ♿ ◆
RHS Garden, Wisley, Woking, Surrey GU23 6QB
Ⓣ (01483) 211113
Ⓕ (01483) 212372
Ⓔ wisleyplantcentre@rhs.org.uk
Ⓦ www.rhs.org.uk/wisleyplantcentre
Contact: Any member of staff
Opening Times: 0900-1700 Mon-Sat, Oct-Feb. 0900-1800 Mon-Sat, Mar-Sep. 1100-1700 Sun all year, browsing from 1030.
Credit Cards: All major credit/debit cards
Specialities: Over 12,000 plants, many rare or unusual, reflecting the range of the RHS flagship garden at Wisley. Also houseplants, bedding plants, bulbs & seed potatoes, plus a range of garden sundries.
Notes: Plants subject to seasonal availability. For plants not in stock, a reservation service is operated. All plants must be collected from Wisley as no mail order service. Wheelchair accessible.
Map Ref: L, C3

LSds **Seeds of Italy** ♿
Unit D2, Phoenix Industrial Estate, Rosslyn Crescent, Harrow, Middlesex HA1 2SP
Ⓣ 0208 427 5020
Ⓕ 0208 427 5051
Ⓔ grow@italianingredients.com
Ⓦ www.seedsofitaly.com
Contact: Paolo Arrigo
Opening Times: 0930-1730, Mon-Fri.
Min Mail Order UK: Nmc
Cat. Cost: Free.
Credit Cards: All major credit/debit cards
Specialities: Franchi Italian vegetable seeds.
Notes: Also sells wholesale. Wheelchair accessible.
Map Ref: L, B3

LSou **Southon Plants** ♿
Mutton Hill, Dormansland, Lingfield, Surrey RH7 6NP
Ⓣ (01342) 870150
Ⓔ lyn@southon-plants.co.uk
Ⓦ www.southon-plants.co.uk
Contact: Mr Southon
Opening Times: 0900-1700, 1000-1700 w/ends, Mar-Oct. Closed Mon (apart from Easter-end Jun). For Nov, Dec, Jan & Feb times, please phone first or see website for up-to-date opening hours.
Cat. Cost: Online only.
Credit Cards: All major credit/debit cards
Specialities: New & unusual hardy & tender perennials, specialising in *Agapanthus* (over 30 varieties), & *Heuchera* (over 30 varieties). Many new varieties for tender perennials/patio plants.
Notes: Wheelchair accessible.
Map Ref: L, C4

LSRN **Spring Reach Nursery** ♿
Long Reach, Ockham, Guildford, Surrey GU23 6PG
Ⓣ (01483) 284769
Ⓜ 07884 432666
Ⓕ (01483) 284769
Ⓔ info@springreachnursery.co.uk
Ⓦ www.springreachnursery.co.uk
Contact: Nick & Lissa Hourhan
Opening Times: 7 days. 1000-1700 Mon-Sat, 1030-1630 Sun. Open B/hols. Closed 23rd Dec-2nd Jan.
Min Mail Order UK: Nmc
Min Mail Order EU: Nmc
Credit Cards: All major credit/debit cards
Specialities: Shrubs, evergreen climbers, *Clematis*, perennials, roses, grasses, ferns, bamboos, trees, hedging, soft fruit & top fruit. Plants for chalk & clay. Deer & rabbit proof plants. Specimen & acid-loving plants.
Notes: Please ring for mail order details. Also sells wholesale. Delivers to shows. Wheelchair accessible.

LSun **Sunnyside Nursery**
Upper Allotments, New Road, Northchurch, Hertfordshire HP4 1NJ
Ⓜ 07743 552154
Ⓔ philsmith2004@yahoo.co.uk
Contact: Philip Smith
Opening Times: 0900-1700 Mon-Fri. Closed Mon, Sat, Sun & B/hols. Some w/end shows, please phone for details.

Cat. Cost: Availability list on request.
Credit Cards: All major credit/debit cards
Specialities: Hardy perennials, alpines & ornamental grasses. Some plants available in small quantities only.
Notes: Please phone for stock availability & updates. Trade discounts available with orders of £100+.

LSvl **Savill Gardens** ♿
Windsor Great Park, Windsor, Berkshire SL4 2HT
Ⓣ (01784) 435544
Ⓦ www.windsorgreatpark.co.uk
Contact: Veronique Serre
Opening Times: 0930-1800 (summer), 0930-1630 (winter).
Credit Cards: All major debit/credit cards except American Express
Specialities: Woody plants, incl. Windsor magnolias, herbaceous, *Ligularia* & *Mahonia*. Available in small numbers only.
Notes: Wheelchair accessible.
Map Ref: L, B3

LToo **Toobees Exotics**
20 Inglewood, St Johns, Woking, Surrey GU21 3HX
Ⓣ (01483) 722600
Ⓜ 07836 334011
Ⓕ (01483) 751995
Ⓔ bbpotter@woking.plus.com
Ⓦ www.toobees-exotics.com
Contact: Bob Potter
Opening Times: Not open. Mail order & online shop only. Visits by appt. only.
Min Mail Order UK: Nmc
Min Mail Order EU: Nmc
Cat. Cost: Sae
Specialities: South African & Madagascan succulents, many rare & unusual species, *Euphorbia* & *Pachypodium*. Stock constantly changes.
Notes: Credit cards accepted online only. Exports beyond EU. Euro accepted.

LTop **Topiary Arts**
(Office) 224 Hospital Bridge Road, Whitton, Twickenham, Middlesex TW2 6LF
Ⓣ 020 8894 2816
Ⓜ 07775 602704
Ⓔ jcb@topiaryarts.com
Ⓦ www.topiaryarts.com
Contact: James Crebbin-Bailey
Opening Times: By appt. only.
Min Mail Order UK: £30
Cat. Cost: Online only.
Credit Cards: None
Specialities: Topiary. Small quantities of *Buxus, Philyrea, Taxus* & *Ligustrum*.
Notes: Nursery is at Copped Hall Walled Garden, Upshire, Epping, Essex CM16 5HS. Also sells wholesale. Delivers to shows.

LYaf **Yaffles** ♿
Harvest Hill, Bourne End, Buckinghamshire SL8 5JJ
Ⓣ (01628) 525455
Contact: I Butterfield
Opening Times: 0900-1300 & 1400-1700. Please phone beforehand in case we are attending shows.
Min Mail Order UK: Nmc
Min Mail Order EU: £30.00 + p&p
Cat. Cost: 2 × 2nd class.
Credit Cards: None
Specialities: *Pleione*.
Notes: Only *Pleione* by mail order. Delivers to shows. Wheelchair accessible.

Midlands

MArl **Arley Hall Nursery** ♿
Northwich, Cheshire CW9 6NA
Ⓣ (01565) 777479
Ⓔ arleyhallplantnursery@gmail.com
Ⓦ www.arleyhallandgardens.com
Contact: Rob Groom
Opening Times: 0930-1730 Mon-Fri, 1100-17.30 Sat & Sun, 1st Mar-29th Sep.
Cat. Cost: 4 × 1st class.
Credit Cards: All major credit/debit cards
Specialities: Wide range of herbaceous incl. many unusual varieties, some in small quantities. Wide range of unusual pelargoniums.
Notes: Nursery is beside car park at Arley Hall Gardens. Wheelchair accessible.
Map Ref: M, A1 **OS Grid Ref:** SJ673808

MAsh **Ashwood Nurseries Ltd** ♿
Ashwood Lower Lane, Ashwood, Kingswinford, West Midlands DY6 0AE
Ⓣ (01384) 401996
Ⓕ (01384) 401108
Ⓔ mailorder@ashwoodnurseries.com
Ⓦ www.ashwoodnurseries.com
Contact: Karrina Gilbert & Steve Lampitt
Opening Times: 0900-1700 Mon-Sat & 0930-1700 Sun, excl. Xmas & Boxing Day.
Min Mail Order UK: Nmc
Min Mail Order EU: Nmc
Cat. Cost: 4 × 1st class.
Credit Cards: All major credit/debit cards
Specialities: Large range of hardy plants, shrubs & dwarf conifers. Roses, alpines & herbaceous plants. Also specialises in *Auricula, Cyclamen, Galanthus*, hellebores, *Hepatica, Hydrangea* & *Salvia*. Nat. Collection of *Lewisia*.

M

Notes: Tea room overlooking display garden. Ample parking. Regular events. Groups by appt. to visit private garden. Wheelchair accessible.
Map Ref: M, C2 **OS Grid Ref:** SO865879

MAus **DAVID AUSTIN ROSES LTD** ♿ ◆
Bowling Green Lane, Albrighton, Wolverhampton, West Midlands WV7 3HB
Ⓣ (01902) 376300
Ⓕ (01902) 375177
Ⓔ retail@davidaustinroses.co.uk
Ⓦ www.davidaustinroses.com
Contact: Customer Services Dept
Opening Times: 0830-1800 Mon-Fri, 0830-1630 Sat, 1000-1400 Sun.
Min Mail Order UK: Nmc
Min Mail Order EU: Nmc
Cat. Cost: Free.
Credit Cards: All major credit/debit cards
Specialities: Roses. Nat. Collection of English Roses.
Notes: Also sells wholesale. Exports beyond EU. Euro accepted. Wheelchair accessible.

M

MAvo **AVONDALE NURSERY** ♿
(Office) 3 Avondale Road, Earlsdon, Coventry, Warwickshire CV5 6DZ
Ⓣ (024) 766 73662
Ⓜ 07979 093096
Ⓔ enquiries@avondalenursery.co.uk
Ⓦ www.avondalenursery.co.uk
Contact: Brian Ellis
Opening Times: 1000-1230, 1400-1700 Mon-Sat, 1030-1630 Sun, Mar-Sep. Other times by appt.
Cat. Cost: 4 × 1st class.
Credit Cards: All major credit/debit cards
Specialities: Rare & unusual perennials esp. asters, *Eryngium*, *Leucanthemum*, *Geum*, *Crocosmia*, *Sanguisorba* & grasses. Nat. Collections of *Symphyotrichum novae-angliae*, *Anemone nemorosa* & *Sanguisorba*. Display garden open. Groups welcome.
Notes: Nursery is at Russell's Nursery, Mill Hill, Baginton, Nr Coventry, CV8 3AG. Delivers to shows. Wheelchair accessible.
Map Ref: M, C2 **OS Grid Ref:** SP339751

MBel **BLUEBELL COTTAGE NURSERY** ♿
Lodge Lane, Dutton, Cheshire WA4 4HP
Ⓣ (01928) 713718
Ⓔ info@bluebellcottage.co.uk
Ⓦ www.bluebellcottage.co.uk
Contact: Sue Beesley
Opening Times: 1000-1700 Wed-Sun & B/hols, 1st Apr-end Sep. By appt. only outside these dates.
Min Mail Order UK: £6.50
Cat. Cost: Online only.
Credit Cards: All major credit/debit cards
Specialities: *Achillea*, *Anthemis*, *Brunnera*, *Centaurea*, *Echinacea*, *Geranium*, *Geum*, *Lychnis*, *Persicaria*, *Potentilla*, *Sanguisorba*, *Thalictrum* & ornamental grasses. Some items stocked in small quantities. Mail order plants are fully established, ready to plant out.
Notes: Mail order available all year round. RHS Partner Garden open Apr-Sep. Refreshments available. Delivers to shows. Wheelchair accessible.
Map Ref: M, A1 **OS Grid Ref:** SJ586779

MBlu **BLUEBELL ARBORETUM & NURSERY** ♿
Annwell Lane, Smisby, Nr Ashby de la Zouch, Derbyshire LE65 2TA
Ⓣ (01530) 413700
Ⓕ (01530) 417600
Ⓔ sales@bluebellnursery.com
Ⓦ www.bluebellnursery.com
Contact: Robert & Suzette Vernon
Opening Times: 0900-1700 Mon-Sat & 1030-1630 Sun Mar-Oct, 0900-1600 Mon-Sat (not Sun) Nov-Feb. Closed 24th Dec-1st Jan incl. & Easter Sun.
Min Mail Order UK: £8.95
Min Mail Order EU: Nmc
Cat. Cost: £1.50 + 3 × 1st class.
Credit Cards: Visa, Access, Switch, MasterCard
Specialities: Specialists in rare & unusual plants. Uncommon trees & shrubs. Rare *Acer*, *Betula*, *Cornus*, *Fagus*, *Magnolia*, *Liquidambar*, *Quercus* & *Tilia*. Woody climbers.
Notes: 9-acre woodland garden & arboretum surrounds nursery. RHS partner garden. Guide dogs only. Working nursery, so wear appropriate clothing & sturdy footwear when visiting. Delivers to shows. Wheelchair accessible but please call to check after wet weather.
Map Ref: M, B2 **OS Grid Ref:** SK344187

MBNS **BARNSDALE GARDENS** ♿
Exton Avenue, Exton, Oakham, Rutland LE15 8AH
Ⓣ (01572) 813200
Ⓔ mailorder@barnsdalegardens.co.uk
Ⓦ www.barnsdalegardens.co.uk
Contact: Nick Hamilton
Opening Times: 0900-1700 Mar-May & Sep-Oct, 0900-1900 Jun-Aug, 1000-1600 Nov-Feb, 7 days. Closed 24th & 25th Dec.
Min Mail Order UK: Nmc
Min Mail Order EU: Nmc
Cat. Cost: Online only.
Credit Cards: All major credit/debit cards
Specialities: Wide range of choice & unusual garden plants but specialising in perennials.

Notes: Mail order from website or by telephone ordering only. Delivers to shows. Wheelchair accessible.
Map Ref: M, B3 **OS Grid Ref:** SK912108

MBrN **Bridge Nursery** ♿
Tomlow Road, Napton-on-the-Hill, Nr Rugby, Warwickshire CV47 8HX
Ⓣ (01926) 812737
Ⓔ philipemartino@gmail.com
Ⓦ www.Bridge-Nursery.co.uk
Contact: Christine Dakin & Philip Martino
Opening Times: 1000-1600 Thu-Sun mid Feb-mid Nov, plus B/hol Mons. Other times by appt.
Min Mail Order UK: £10.00
Cat. Cost: Online only.
Credit Cards: All major credit/debit cards
Specialities: Ornamental grasses, sedges & bamboos. Also range of shrubs & perennials. Display garden.
Notes: Limited range available by mail order, please check with nursery. Also sells wholesale. Euro accepted. Wheelchair accessible.
Map Ref: M, C2 **OS Grid Ref:** SP463625

MCms **Chrysanthemums Direct**
Holmes Chapel Road, Over Peover, Knutsford, Cheshire WA16 9RA
Ⓣ 0800 046 7443
Ⓜ 07977 312 593
Ⓔ sales@chrysanthemumsdirect.co.uk
Ⓦ www.chrysanthemumsdirect.co.uk
Contact: Martyn Flint
Opening Times: Not open. Mail order only.
Min Mail Order UK: Nmc
Min Mail Order EU: Nmc
Cat. Cost: 4 × 1st class.
Credit Cards: All major credit/debit cards
Specialities: Chrysanthemums. Young plants grown to order. Delivery within 14 days. Winner Protected Ornamental Grower of the Year at the UK Grower Awards 2015.
Notes: Delivers to shows.

MCoo **Cool Temperate**
(Office) 45 Stamford Street, Awsworth, Nottinghamshire NG16 2QL
Ⓣ (0115) 916 2673
Ⓜ 07952 019376
Ⓕ (0115) 916 2673
Ⓔ phil.corbett@cooltemperate.co.uk
Ⓦ www.cooltemperate.co.uk
Contact: Phil Corbett
Opening Times: 0900-1700, 7 days. Please ring/write first.
Min Mail Order UK: £30.00
Min Mail Order EU: £50.00
Cat. Cost: Online or via email.
Credit Cards: None
Specialities: Tree fruit, soft fruit, nitrogen-fixers, hedging, own-root fruit trees. Many species available in small quantities only.
Notes: Nursery at Newton's Lane, Cossall, Notts. Also sells wholesale. Exports beyond EU.
Map Ref: M, B2 **OS Grid Ref:** SK475433

MCot **Coton Manor Garden**
Guilsborough, Northampton, Northamptonshire NN6 8RQ
Ⓣ (01604) 740219
Ⓔ nursery@cotonmanor.co.uk
Ⓦ www.cotonmanor.co.uk
Contact: Caroline Tait
Opening Times: 1200-1730 Tue-Sat, 1st Apr-27th Sep. Also Sun Apr, May & B/hol w/ends. Other times in working hours by appt.
Cat. Cost: Online only.
Credit Cards: All major credit/debit cards
Specialities: Wide-range of herbaceous perennials (1200+ varieties), some available in small quantities only. Also many tender perennials & selected shrubs.
Notes: Garden open. Tea rooms. Garden school. Partial wheelchair access.
Map Ref: M, C3 **OS Grid Ref:** SP675715

MCri **Crin Gardens**
79 Partons Road, Kings Heath, Birmingham B14 6TD
Ⓜ 07805 591475
Ⓔ cringardens@tiscali.co.uk
Ⓦ www.cringardens.co.uk
Contact: M Milinkovic
Opening Times: Not open. Mail order only.
Min Mail Order UK: Nmc
Min Mail Order EU: Nmc
Cat. Cost: 2 × 1st class + 1 × 2nd.
Credit Cards: None
Specialities: Lilies. Limited stock available on first come, first served basis.
Notes: Euro accepted.

MCtn **Chiltern Seeds Ltd**
Crowmarsh Battle Barns, 114 Preston Crowmarsh, Wallingford, Oxfordshire OX10 6SL
Ⓣ (01491) 824675
Ⓔ info@chilternseeds.co.uk
Ⓦ www.chilternseeds.co.uk
Contact: Any member of staff
Opening Times: Mail order only. Normal office hours, Mon-Fri.
Min Mail Order UK: Nmc
Min Mail Order EU: Nmc
Cat. Cost: Free.
Credit Cards: All major debit/credit cards except American Express
Specialities: Around 3,500 items of all kinds:

M

wild flowers, trees, shrubs, cacti, annuals, houseplants, vegetables & herbs.
Notes: Exports beyond EU. Customer's responsibility to ensure no restrictions & special import requirements apply.

MDon **Donington Nurseries Ltd** ♿
Kings Mills, Park Lane, Castle Donington, Derbyshire DE74 2RS
Ⓣ (01332) 853004
Ⓕ (01332) 853793
Ⓔ sales@doningtonnurseries.co.uk
Ⓦ www.doningtonnurseries.co.uk
Contact: Rebecca Faulkner
Opening Times: Open daily (hours vary depending on season).
Cat. Cost: None.
Credit Cards: All major credit/debit cards
Specialities: Family-owned nursery stocking wide range of trees, shrubs, perennials & alpines. 50% of stock grown on nursery set within 4-acre former walled garden of Donington Hall. Home grown *Prunus laurocerasus* (laurel) & *Thuja* hedging available in large quantities.
Notes: Wheelchair accessible.

MEch **Echium World**
Edwinstowe House, High Street, Edwinstowe, Nottinghamshire NG21 9PR
Ⓜ 07957 602073
Ⓔ echiumworld@gmail.com
Ⓦ www.echiumworld.co.uk
Contact: Linda Heywood
Opening Times: Plants sales at Echium Garden Open Days: Sun 15th, 22nd, 29th May & 5th Jun 2016. Other times by arrangement only.
Min Mail Order UK: £6.95
Credit Cards: Paypal
Specialities: Nat. Collection of *Echium* species & cvs from the Macaronesian Islands. Specialist growers & suppliers of *Echium* varieties incl. rare & threatened species & cvs from other countries. Exhibits at the Echium Garden, Nottinghamshire & at garden shows around the UK.

MFie **Field House Nursery** ♿
Leake Road, Gotham, Nottinghamshire NG11 0JN
Ⓣ (01159) 830278
Ⓜ 07504 125209
Ⓔ val.woolley@btinternet.com
Contact: Valerie A Woolley & Bob Taylor
Opening Times: By appt. only.
Cat. Cost: 4 × 1st class (auriculas/primulas). 2 × 1st class (astrantias).
Credit Cards: Visa, MasterCard, Electron, Maestro, Solo
Specialities: *Primula auricula* & seed, *Astrantia*. Nat. Collections of *Primula auricula* (show & alpine) & *Astrantia*.
Notes: Mail order for *Astrantia*, *Primula* & auricula seeds. Delivers to shows. Wheelchair accessible.

MGil **John Gillies** ♿
at Russell's Garden Centre, Mill Hill, Baginton, Warwickshire CV8 3AG
Ⓜ 07546 064961
Ⓔ enquiries@gilliesrareplants.com
Ⓦ www.gilliesrareplants.com
Contact: John Gillies
Opening Times: 1000-1700 Mon, Wed & Sat, 1030-1630 Sun, Mar-Sep. Closed Easter Sun. 1000-1600 Wed-Sat, Oct-Nov. Other times by appt.
Cat. Cost: Online only.
Credit Cards: All major credit/debit cards
Specialities: A range of choice & rare plants incl., but not limited to, *Azara*, *Clethra*, *Daphne*, *Diostea*, *Embothrium*, *Ercilla*, *Iochroma*, *Lomatia* & *Rhapiolepis*. Most available in small quantities only. Contact nursery if plant not on plant list.
Notes: Nursery situated beside Avondale Nursery. Please contact before visiting to ensure plant is currently in stock. Wheelchair accessible.
Map Ref: M, C2 **OS Grid Ref:** SP337750

MGos **Goscote Nurseries Ltd** ♿
Syston Road, Cossington, Leicestershire LE7 4UZ
Ⓣ (01509) 812121
Ⓔ enquiries@goscote.co.uk
Ⓦ www.goscote.co.uk
Contact: James Toone
Opening Times: 7 days, year round, apart from between Xmas & New Year.
Cat. Cost: Online only.
Credit Cards: Visa, Access, MasterCard, Delta, Switch
Specialities: Japanese maples, rhododendrons & azaleas, *Magnolia*, *Camellia*, *Pieris* & other *Ericaceae*. Ornamental trees & shrubs, conifers, fruit, heathers, alpines, roses, *Clematis* & unusual climbers.
Notes: Design & landscaping service available. Café & show garden. Also sells wholesale. Wheelchair accessible.
Map Ref: M, B3 **OS Grid Ref:** SK602130

MHCG **Hill Close Gardens** ♿
Bread and Meat Close, Warwick, Warwickshire CV34 6HF
Ⓣ (01926) 493339
Ⓜ 07533 401934
Ⓔ headgardener@hcgt.org.uk

Ⓦ www.hillclosegardens.com
Contact: Gary Leaver
Opening Times: 1100-1700, 7 days, Apr-Oct. 1100-1600 Mon-Fri only, Nov-Mar.
Cat. Cost: 2 × 1st class or online.
Credit Cards: All major credit/debit cards
Specialities: Small retail nursery attached to heritage garden which is open to the public. Hold dispersed National Collection of hardy *Chrysanthemum*. Also specialise in *Symphyotrichum* (asters) & *Galanthus*.
Notes: Wheelchair accessible.
Map Ref: M, C2 **OS Grid Ref:** SP277647

MHed HEDGEXPRESS
Buckland Road, Bampton, Oxfordshire OX18 2AA
Ⓣ (01993) 850979
Ⓔ info@hedgexpress.co.uk
Ⓦ www.hedgexpress.co.uk
Contact: Gavin Stevens
Opening Times: 0900-1600, Mon-Fri.
Min Mail Order UK: £100 + VAT
Cat. Cost: Online only.
Credit Cards: All major credit/debit cards, Paypal
Specialities: Hedging & lavenders.
Notes: Also sells wholesale.
Map Ref: M, D2 **OS Grid Ref:** SP322024

MHer THE HERB NURSERY ♿
Thistleton, Oakham, Rutland LE15 7RE
Ⓣ (01572) 767658
Ⓔ herbnursery@southwitham.net
Ⓦ www.herbnursery.co.uk
Contact: Peter Bench
Opening Times: 0900-1700 Mon-Sat, 1000-1600 Sun. Closed 2 weeks after Xmas.
Cat. Cost: Free with A5 sae.
Credit Cards: All major credit/debit cards
Specialities: Herbs, wild flowers, cottage garden plants, scented-leaf pelargoniums. *Thymus, Mentha, Lavandula*.
Notes: Wheelchair accessible.
Map Ref: M, B3

MHol HOLLIES FARM PLANT CENTRE
Uppertown, Bonsall, Nr Matlock, Derbyshire DE4 2AW
Ⓣ (01629) 822734
Ⓔ rbrt.wells@gmail.com
Ⓦ www.holliesfarmplantcentre.co.uk
Contact: Robert or Linda Wells
Opening Times: 0900-1700 every day except Wed.
Credit Cards: None
Specialities: Range of rare & unusual herbaceous perennials.
Notes: Garden designers welcome.

MHom HOMESTEAD PLANTS
The Homestead, Normanton, Bottesford, Nottingham NG13 0EP
Ⓣ (01949) 842745
Ⓦ www.homesteadplants.com
Contact: Mrs S Palmer
Opening Times: By appt.
Min Mail Order UK: Nmc
Cat. Cost: 2 × 2nd class.
Credit Cards: None
Specialities: Unusual hardy & half-hardy perennials, esp. *Argyranthemum, Galanthus* & heliotrope. Most available only in small quantities. Nat. Collection of *Heliotropium* cultivars.
Notes: Mail order not offered year round. Please check with nursery for details.
Map Ref: M, B3 **OS Grid Ref:** SK812407

MJac JACKSON'S NURSERIES
Clifton Campville, Nr Tamworth, Staffordshire B79 0AP
Ⓣ (01827) 373307
Contact: N Jackson
Opening Times: 0900-1800 Mon & Wed-Sat, 1000-1700 Sun.
Cat. Cost: 2 × 1st class.
Credit Cards: None
Specialities: *Fuchsia*.
Notes: Also sells wholesale.

MJak JACKSON'S NURSERIES ♿
Thorney Edge Road, Bagnall, Stoke-on-Trent, Staffordshire ST9 9LE
Ⓣ (01782) 502741
Ⓕ (01782) 504932
Ⓔ sales@jacksonsnurseries.co.uk
Ⓦ www.jacksonsnurseries.co.uk
Contact: Shaun Goldstraw
Opening Times: 0800-1700 7 days, Mar-Oct. 0800-1630, Nov-Feb.
Min Mail Order UK: Nmc.
Credit Cards: MasterCard, Visa
Specialities: Good general range.
Notes: Family-run nursery, established for over 50 years, a short distance from the Peak District. Tea room. Also sells wholesale. Wheelchair accessible.
Map Ref: M, B2 **OS Grid Ref:** SJ934504

MLea LEA RHODODENDRON GARDENS LTD ♿
Lea, Matlock, Derbyshire DE4 5GH
Ⓣ (01629) 534380/534260
Ⓕ (01629) 534260
Ⓔ lea.gardens@hotmail.co.uk
Ⓦ www.leagarden.co.uk
Contact: Peter Tye
Opening Times: 1000-1730 7 days 20 Mar-30 Jun. Out of season by appt.

M

Min Mail Order UK: £15.00 + p&p
Min Mail Order EU: £15.00 + p&p
Cat. Cost: 30p + sae.
Credit Cards: All major credit/debit cards
Specialities: Rhododendrons & azaleas.
Notes: Exports beyond EU. Wheelchair accessible.
Map Ref: M, B2 **OS Grid Ref:** SK324571

MLod **LODGE FARM PLANTS & WILDFLOWERS** ♿
Case Lane, Fiveways, Hatton, Warwickshire
CV35 7JD
Ⓣ (01926) 484649
Ⓜ 07977 631368
Ⓔ lodgefarmplants@btinternet.com
Ⓦ www.lodgefarm-plants.com
Contact: Janet Cook & Nick Cook
Opening Times: Open 7 days all year, except Xmas Day & Boxing Day.
Min Mail Order UK: Nmc
Cat. Cost: Availability list online.
Credit Cards: All major credit/debit cards
Specialities: All forms of fruit trees: bush; espalier; fan; stepovers; cordons. Soft fruit. Native trees & hedging. Ornamental trees.
Notes: Courier service to all UK. Offers online & phone sales as well as at nursery. Also sells wholesale. Euro accepted. Wheelchair accessible.
Map Ref: M, C2 **OS Grid Ref:** SP223700

M

MMoz **MOZART HOUSE NURSERY GARDEN**
84 Central Avenue, Wigston, Leicestershire
LE18 2AA
Ⓣ (0116) 288 9548
Contact: Des Martin
Opening Times: Please phone for appt.
Cat. Cost: None issued.
Credit Cards: None
Specialities: A collection of bamboos, ornamental grasses, rushes & sedges, ferns, shade & woodland plants growing in a third acre display garden. Many specialities available in small quantities only.
Notes: Talks given to gardening clubs and societies using live plant material. Delivers to shows.
Map Ref: M, B3

MMrt **MORTON NURSERIES LTD** ♿
Morton, Retford, Nottinghamshire
DN22 8HE
Ⓣ (01777) 702530
Ⓜ 07940 434398
Ⓔ enquiries@morton-nurseries.com
Ⓦ www.morton-nurseries.co.uk
Contact: Gill McMaster
Opening Times: 1000-1600 Mon-Fri, 1400-1700 Sat & Sun.
Min Mail Order UK: £5.00 + p&p
Cat. Cost: None issued.
Credit Cards: All major credit/debit cards
Specialities: Shrubs & perennials.
Notes: Delivers to shows. Wheelchair accessible.
Map Ref: M, A3

MMuc **MUCKLESTONE NURSERIES** ♿
Rock Lane, Mucklestone,
Nr Market Drayton, Shropshire
TF9 4FA
Ⓣ (01630) 674284
Ⓜ 07714 241668
Ⓔ info@botanyplants.co.uk
Ⓦ www.botanyplants.co.uk
Contact: William & Louise Friend
Opening Times: 0930-1700 (or dusk) Wed-Sat. Closed Sat in winter. Mon/Tue phone for assistance. Closed Sun. If travelling far, please phone/email first.
Min Mail Order UK: Nmc
Cat. Cost: Online.
Credit Cards: All major credit/debit cards
Specialities: Trees, shrubs, grasses, bamboos, rhododendrons, ferns & perennials for acid & damp soils of the north & west UK. Our nursery in Kent grows complementary range for dry, chalk & coast. Extensive grounds where plants can be seen growing. Small numbers only of each variety available.
Notes: Any plants on website or listed under nursery code SEND (in Kent) can be collected to order or sent/delivered. Evening garden tours & talks for garden groups in Staffs, Salop or Cheshire by appt., see website or phone for full list & details. Wheelchair accessible.
Map Ref: M, B1 **OS Grid Ref:** SJ728373

MNHC **THE NATIONAL HERB CENTRE** ♿
Banbury Road, Warmington, Nr Banbury,
Oxfordshire OX17 1DF
Ⓣ (01295) 690999
Ⓕ (01295) 690034
Ⓔ info@herbcentre.co.uk
Ⓦ www.herbcentre.co.uk
Contact: Plant Centre Staff
Opening Times: 0900-1730 Mon-Sat, 1030-1700 Sun.
Min Mail Order UK: Nmc but carriage charge of £10.00 for orders valued up to £50, more for larger orders.
Credit Cards: All major credit/debit cards
Specialities: Herbs, culinary & medicinal. Extensive selection of rosemary, thyme & lavender in particular.
Notes: Next day delivery UK mainland only, signature required. Wheelchair accessible.
Map Ref: M, C2 **OS Grid Ref:** SP413471

MNrw **Norwell Nurseries** ♿
Woodhouse Road, Norwell, Newark, Nottinghamshire NG23 6JX
Ⓣ (01636) 636337
Ⓔ wardha@aol.com
Ⓦ www.norwellnurseries.co.uk
Contact: Dr Andrew Ward
Opening Times: 1000-1700 Mon, Wed-Fri & Sun (Wed-Mon May & Jun). By appt. Aug & 20th Oct-1st Mar.
Min Mail Order UK: £20.00 + p&p
Min Mail Order EU: £40.00
Cat. Cost: 3 × 1st class or online.
Credit Cards: None
Specialities: A large collection of over 2500 unusual & choice herbaceous perennials esp., hardy geraniums, *Geum*, pond & bog plants, cottage garden plants, *Hemerocallis*, grasses, *Trillium* & woodland plants. Over 2500 different species & cvs grown. Nat. Collection of Hardy Chrysanthemums.
Notes: One acre garden & tea room. Talks given. Also sells wholesale. Delivers to shows. Wheelchair accessible.
Map Ref: M, B3 **OS Grid Ref:** SK767616

MOld **Old Hall Nursery** ♿
Winkhill, Leek, Staffordshire ST13 7PN
Ⓣ (01538) 308257
Ⓜ 07866 175881
Ⓔ oldhallnursery@hotmail.co.uk
Ⓦ www.oldhallnursery.com
Contact: Sandra Henshall
Opening Times: 1000-1600, Tue-Sat.
Cat. Cost: Not available.
Credit Cards: None
Specialities: Large selection of herbaceous, herbs & alpines. Also shrubs, climbers & fruit trees. All hardy.
Notes: Wheelchair accessible.
Map Ref: M, B2 **OS Grid Ref:** SK051521

MPhe **Phedar Nursery**
42 Bunkers Hill, Romiley, Stockport, Cheshire SK6 3DS
Ⓣ (0161) 430 3772
Ⓔ mclewin@phedar.com
Ⓦ www.phedar.com
Contact: Will McLewin
Opening Times: Frequent but irregular. Please phone to arrange appt.
Min Mail Order UK: Nmc
Min Mail Order EU: Nmc
Cat. Cost: Online or write for printed version.
Credit Cards: None
Specialities: *Helleborus*, *Paeonia*. Limited stock of some rare items.
Notes: Exports beyond EU subject to destination & on an ad hoc basis only. Please contact nursery for details. Also sells wholesale. Euro accepted.
Map Ref: M, A2 **OS Grid Ref:** SJ936897

MPie **Piecemeal Plants** ♿
Whatton House Gardens, Nr Kegworth, Loughborough, Leicestershire LE12 5BG
Ⓣ (01509) 672056
Ⓜ 07950 757444
Ⓔ nursery@piecemealplants.co.uk
Ⓦ www.piecemealplants.co.uk
Contact: Mary Thomas
Opening Times: 1300-1600 (1700 in summer) early Apr-mid Sep, Thu, Fri & some Sun. For up to date details please ring or see website. Also open by arrangement throughout the year.
Cat. Cost: Online only.
Credit Cards: None
Specialities: Wide range of interesting herbaceous perennials & bulbs, many unusual. Some half-hardy or tender. Majority in small quantities.
Notes: Nursery located at entrance to Whatton Gardens, off A6 between Kegworth & Hathern. Car parking in front of Whatton House at top of drive. Delivers to shows. Wheelchair accessible.
Map Ref: M, B3 **OS Grid Ref:** SK494242

MPkF **Packhorse Farm Nursery** ♿
Sandyford House, Lant Lane, Tansley, Matlock, Derbyshire DE4 5FW
Ⓣ (01629) 57206
Ⓜ 07974 095752
Ⓕ (01629) 57206
Contact: Hilton W Haynes
Opening Times: 1000-1700 Tues & Wed, 1st Mar-31st Oct. Any other time by appt. only.
Cat. Cost: 2 × 1st class for plant list.
Credit Cards: None
Specialities: *Acer*, rare stock is limited in supply. Other more unusual hardy shrubs, trees & conifers.
Notes: Delivers to shows. Wheelchair accessible.
Map Ref: M, B2 **OS Grid Ref:** SK322617

MPnt **Plantagogo.com**
Jubilee Cottage Nursery, Snape Lane, Englesea Brook, Crewe, Cheshire CW2 5QN
Ⓣ (01270) 820335
Ⓜ 07713 518271
Ⓔ info@plantagogo.com
Ⓦ www.plantagogo.com
Contact: Vicky & Richard Fox
Opening Times: Visitors are welcome by appt. only. Also Open Days (no appointment required): 1000-1600 8th, 9th & 10th Apr; 4th & 5th Jun; 30th Sep, 1st & 2nd Oct 2016.

Min Mail Order UK: £9.95 single payment.
Min Mail Order EU: Price on application or see website.
Cat. Cost: 4 × 1st class.
Credit Cards: All major credit/debit cards
Specialities: *Heuchera, Heucherella, Tiarella,* also large selection of perennials. Nat. Collections of *Heuchera, Heucherella* & *Tiarella.* Plants listed in the *RHS Plant Finder* are available in good quantities. Others, not listed here, are available from our collections on request.
Notes: Also sells wholesale. Delivers to shows. Limited wheelchair access.
Map Ref: M, B1 **OS Grid Ref:** SJ750516

M

MRai **Rainsbrook Nursery**
6 Barby Lane, Rugby, Warwickshire CV22 5QJ
Ⓣ (01788) 842906
Ⓔ sales@gb-online.co.uk
Ⓦ www.gb-online.co.uk
Contact: Graeme Bale
Opening Times: Not open. Mail order only.
Min Mail Order UK: Nmc
Min Mail Order EU: Nmc
Cat. Cost: Online only.
Credit Cards: Paypal, All major debit/credit cards except American Express
Specialities: *Malus, Prunus, Ficus, Vitis, Mespilus, Pyrus, Diospyros, Cydonia, Juglans, Corylus, Carya* & *Castenea.*
Notes: Plant passported grower and seller of unusual fruit and nut trees, rootstock and scions via mail order. Also sells wholesale. Exports beyond EU. Euro accepted.

MRav **Ravensthorpe Nursery** ♿
6 East Haddon Road, Ravensthorpe, Northamptonshire NN6 8ES
Ⓣ (01604) 770548
Ⓕ (01604) 770548
Ⓔ ravensthorpenursery@hotmail.com
Contact: Jean & Richard Wiseman
Opening Times: 1000-1800 (or dusk if earlier) Tue-Sat. B/hol Mons in May.
Min Mail Order UK: Nmc
Cat. Cost: None issued.
Credit Cards: Visa, MasterCard, Delta
Specialities: Huge range of perennials, shrubs & trees with numerous unusual varieties, many of which can be seen growing in the display garden.
Notes: Search & delivery service for large orders, winter months only. Wheelchair accessible.
Map Ref: M, C3 **OS Grid Ref:** SP665699

MSCN **Stonyford Cottage Nursery** ♿
Stonyford Lane, Cuddington, Northwich, Cheshire CW8 2TF
Ⓣ (01606) 888970/888128 (answerphone)
Ⓜ 07714 205177
Ⓔ stonyfordcottage@yahoo.co.uk
Ⓦ www.stonyfordcottagenursery.co.uk
Contact: Andrew Overland
Opening Times: 1000-1700 Tue-Sun & B/hol Mons 1st Feb-31st Oct.
Min Mail Order UK: Nmc
Min Mail Order EU: Nmc
Cat. Cost: None.
Credit Cards: All major credit/debit cards
Specialities: Wide range of herbaceous perennials, *Iris,* hardy *Geranium,* moisture-loving & bog plants. *Sempervivum, Paeonia,* candelabra *Primula.*
Notes: Also sells wholesale. Wheelchair accessible.
Map Ref: M, A1 **OS Grid Ref:** SJ580710

MShS **Shelley Seeds**
5 Speedwell Close, Huntingdon, Chester, Cheshire CH3 6DX
Ⓣ (01244) 317165
Ⓜ 07710 545118
Ⓔ shelleyseeds@chester137.fsnet.co.uk
Contact: James Shelley
Opening Times: Not open. Mail order only.
Min Mail Order UK: £1.75
Min Mail Order EU: £4.50
Notes: Also sells wholesale.

MSKA **Sweet Knowle Aquatics** ♿
Wimpstone-Ilmington Road, Stratford-upon-Avon, Warwickshire CV37 8NR
Ⓣ (01789) 450036
Ⓕ (01789) 450036
Ⓔ sweetknowleaquatics@hotmail.com
Ⓦ www.sweetknowleaquatics.co.uk
Contact: Zoe Harding
Opening Times: 0930-1700 Sun-Fri, closed Sat. Open B/hols.
Min Mail Order UK: Nmc
Min Mail Order EU: Nmc
Cat. Cost: By email only.
Credit Cards: All major credit/debit cards
Specialities: Aquatics. Hardy & tropical water lilies, marginals & oxygenators. 2-acre display garden open to the public (no charge).
Notes: Wheelchair accessible.
Map Ref: M, C2 **OS Grid Ref:** SP207480

MSmi **John Smith & Son** ♿
Fuchsia Centre, Thornton Nurseries, Thornton, Leicestershire LE67 1AN
Ⓣ (01530) 230331
Ⓕ (01530) 230331
Ⓔ sales@fuchsiaplants.co.uk
Ⓦ www.fuchsiaplants.co.uk
Contact: David Smith
Opening Times: 0800-1730 Mon-Fri, 1000-

1600 Sat & Sun all year round.
Min Mail Order UK: Nmc
Cat. Cost: Online only.
Credit Cards: None
Specialities: Hardy, half-hardy & large American fuchsias.
Notes: Also sells wholesale. Wheelchair accessible.
Map Ref: M, B3

MSpe **SPECIALPERENNIALS.COM**
Yew Tree House, Hall Lane, Hankelow, Crewe, Cheshire CW3 0JB
Ⓣ (01270) 811443
Ⓜ 07716 990695
Ⓔ plants@specialperennials.com
Ⓦ www.specialperennials.com
Contact: Janet & Martin Blow
Opening Times: Mail order only. Not open except for collection of orders by appt. only.
Min Mail Order UK: £25.00
Cat. Cost: Online or A5 sae for descriptive catalogue.
Credit Cards: Paypal
Specialities: Herbaceous perennials. *Geum*, border *Phlox*, *Hemerocallis*, *Monada* & *Persicaria*. Nat. Collections of *Helenium* cvs & *Centaurea*. All plants available in small quantities only.
Notes: All plants grown in garden nursery, most in small quantities & some sell out quickly. Orders can be delivered to Plant Hunters' Fairs. See website or phone for details.

MSwo **SWALLOWS NURSERY** ♿
Mixbury, Brackley, Northamptonshire NN13 5RR
Ⓣ (01280) 847721
Ⓔ enq@swallowsnursery.co.uk
Ⓦ www.swallowsnursery.co.uk
Contact: Chris Swallow
Opening Times: 0900-1300 & 1400-1700 (earlier in winter) Mon-Fri, 0900-1300 Sat.
Min Mail Order UK: £19.50
Cat. Cost: 3 × 1st class (plus phone number).
Credit Cards: All major credit/debit cards
Specialities: Growing a wide range, particularly shrubs, climbers, trees & roses.
Notes: Trees not for mail order unless part of larger order. Nursery transport used where possible, esp. for trees. Also sells wholesale. Wheelchair accessible.
Map Ref: M, C3 **OS Grid Ref:** SP607336

MTin **THE TINY PLANT COMPANY**
25 Owley Wood Road, Weaverham, Cheshire CW8 3LF
Ⓣ (01606) 851146
Ⓔ thetinyplantco@hotmail.com
Ⓦ www.tinyplantcompany.co.uk
Contact: Matt Wood
Opening Times: Not open. Mail order only.
Min Mail Order UK: Nmc
Cat. Cost: Online only.
Credit Cards: All major credit/debit cards
Specialities: Newly-opened small nursery. All plants available in very small quantities only.
Notes: Delivers to shows.

MTis **TISSINGTON NURSERY** ♿
The Old Kitchen Gardens, Tissington, Ashbourne, Derbyshire DE6 1RA
Ⓣ (01335) 390650
Ⓜ 07929 720284
Ⓔ info@tissington-nursery.co.uk
Ⓦ www.tissington-nursery.co.uk
Contact: Mairi Longdon
Opening Times: 1100-1700 daily, end Mar-end Sep.
Min Mail Order UK: Nmc
Cat. Cost: 4 × 1st class or online.
Credit Cards: All major credit/debit cards
Specialities: Choice & unusual perennials esp. *Achillea*, *Aster*, *Dianthus*, *Geranium*, *Geum*, *Helenium*, *Helianthus*, *Nepeta*, *Phlox*, *Salvia*, *Sanguisorba* & *Sedum*.
Notes: Delivers to shows. Wheelchair accessible.
Map Ref: M, B2 **OS Grid Ref:** SK176521

MWat **WATERPERRY GARDENS LTD** ♿
Waterperry, Nr Wheatley, Oxfordshire OX33 1JZ
Ⓣ (01844) 339226/254
Ⓜ 07864 678864
Ⓕ (01844) 339883
Ⓔ rjacobs@waterperrygardens.co.uk
Ⓦ www.waterperrygardens.co.uk
Contact: Mr R Jacobs
Opening Times: 1000-1730 summer. 1000-1700 winter.
Min Mail Order UK: £30.00
Cat. Cost: Online only.
Credit Cards: All major credit/debit cards
Specialities: General, large range of herbaceous esp. Asters, also Nat. Collection of *Saxifraga* (subsect. *Kabschia* & *Engleria*).
Notes: Also sells wholesale. Wheelchair accessible.
Map Ref: M, D3 **OS Grid Ref:** SP630064

MWht **WHITELEA NURSERY** ♿
Whitelea Lane, Tansley, Matlock, Derbyshire DE4 5FL
Ⓣ (01629) 55010
Ⓔ sales@uk-bamboos.co.uk
Ⓦ www.uk-bamboos.co.uk
Contact: David Wilson
Opening Times: By appt.

Min Mail Order UK: Nmc
Cat. Cost: Online only. Price list available 2 × 1st class.
Credit Cards: None
Specialities: Bamboos. Substantial quantities of 45 cvs & species of bamboo, remainder stocked in small numbers only. Limited stocks of grasses, trees & shrubs.
Notes: Mail order limited by carrier restrictions, please contact nursery or see website for details. Also sells wholesale. Wheelchair accessible.
Map Ref: M, B2 **OS Grid Ref:** SK325603

MWts **WATERSIDE NURSERY**
Sharnford, Leicestershire
Ⓣ (01455) 273730
Ⓜ 07931 557082
Ⓔ info@watersidenursery.co.uk
Ⓦ www.watersidenursery.co.uk
Contact: Linda Smith
Opening Times: Mail order only.
Min Mail Order UK: Nmc
Cat. Cost: Online only.
Credit Cards: All major credit/debit cards
Specialities: Aquatics, marginal pond plants, miniature waterlilies, waterlilies, submerged oxygenating plants, bog garden plants & moisture-loving plants.

N

NORTHERN

NBid **BIDE-A-WEE COTTAGE GARDENS** ♿
Stanton, Netherwitton, Morpeth, Northumberland NE65 8PR
Ⓣ (01670) 772238
Ⓜ 07976 559416
Ⓕ (01670) 772238
Ⓔ info@bideawee.co.uk
Ⓦ www.bideawee.co.uk
Contact: Mark Robson
Opening Times: 1330-1700 Sat & Wed, 16th Apr-31st Aug 2016. Group visits at other times, except Sun.
Min Mail Order UK: £28.00
Cat. Cost: Online only.
Credit Cards: All major credit/debit cards
Specialities: Unusual herbaceous perennials, *Agapanthus*, *Primula*, ferns, grasses. Nat. Collection of *Centaurea*.
Notes: Wheelchair accessible.
Map Ref: N, B2 **OS Grid Ref:** NZ132900

NBre **BREEZY KNEES NURSERIES** ♿
Common Lane, Warthill, York YO19 5XS
Ⓣ (01904) 488800
Ⓦ www.breezyknees.co.uk
Contact: Any member of staff
Opening Times: 1000-1700 7 days (open 1100 Sun), 1st Apr-30th Sep.
Credit Cards: All major credit/debit cards
Specialities: Very wide range of perennials. All can be viewed in 15-acre gardens (open 1st May-30th Sep).
Notes: Wheelchair accessible.
Map Ref: N, C3 **OS Grid Ref:** SE675565

NBro **BROWNTHWAITE HARDY PLANTS** ♿
Fell Yeat, Casterton, Kirkby Lonsdale, Lancashire LA6 2JW
Ⓣ (01524) 271340 (after 1800 hours).
Ⓦ www.hardyplantsofcumbria.co.uk
Contact: Chris Benson
Opening Times: 1000-1700, 1st Apr-20th Sep.
Min Mail Order UK: Nmc
Cat. Cost: 5 × 1st class for *Hydrangea* list. 2 × 1st for fern list.
Credit Cards: None
Specialities: Herbaceous perennials incl. *Geranium*, *Hosta*, *Primula*, hardy ferns, *Hydrangea paniculata* & *H. serrata* varieties.
Notes: Follow brown signs from A65 between Kirkby Lonsdale & Cowan Bridge. Mail order for *Hydrangea* & ferns. Delivers to shows. Wheelchair accessible.
Map Ref: N, C1 **OS Grid Ref:** SD632794

NCft **CRAFTY PLANTS**
(Office) 21 Wood Green Drive, Radcliffe, Lancashire
M26 1BF
Ⓣ 0161 820 8606
Ⓔ sales@craftyplants.co.uk
Ⓦ www.craftyplants.co.uk
Contact: Graham Sigsworth
Opening Times: Mail order only. Not open except for nursery Open Days (see website or phone for details).
Min Mail Order UK: Nmc
Min Mail Order EU: Nmc
Cat. Cost: Online only.
Credit Cards: All major debit/credit cards except American Express
Specialities: *Tillandsia*.
Notes: Also sells wholesale. Euro accepted. Nursery at Eezitill, Startley Nook, Preston PR4 4XW. No wheelchair access.

NChi **CHIPCHASE CASTLE NURSERY** ♿
Chipchase Castle, Wark, Hexham, Northumberland NE48 3NT
Ⓣ (01434) 230083
Ⓜ 07575 714002
Ⓔ chipchaseplants@aim.com
Ⓦ www.chipchaseplants.com
Contact: Mark Cummings
Opening Times: 1000-1700 Wed-Sun & B/hol Mons, 2nd Apr (or Easter if earlier)-end Sep.

Min Mail Order UK: Nmc
Min Mail Order EU: Nmc
Cat. Cost: A5 sae for list
Credit Cards: All major credit/debit cards
Specialities: Rare & unusual herbaceous esp. *Eryngium*, *Geum* & *Geranium* and some herbs. Some plants only available in small quantities.
Notes: Delivers to shows. Suitable for accompanied wheelchair users.
Map Ref: N, B2 **OS Grid Ref:** NY880758

NCou COURTYARD PLANTERS ♿
9 Westgate, Otley, West Yorkshire LS21 3AT
Ⓣ (01943) 462390
Ⓔ katie@courtyardplanters.co.uk
Ⓦ www.courtyardplanters.co.uk
Contact: Katie Burnett
Opening Times: 0930-1700 Tue-Sat. Closed all Jan.
Min Mail Order UK: Nmc
Cat. Cost: Online only.
Credit Cards: All major debit/credit cards except American Express
Specialities: Perennials. Plants for heavy clay soils. Peat free.
Notes: Gardening classes & workshops. Also sells wholesale. Wheelchair accessible.
Map Ref: N, C2 **OS Grid Ref:** SE201455

NDal DALESIDE NURSERIES LTD ♿
Ripon Road, Killinghall, Harrogate, North Yorkshire HG3 2AY
Ⓣ (01423) 506450
Ⓕ (01423) 527872
Ⓔ contact@dalesidenurseries.co.uk
Ⓦ www.dalesidenurseries.co.uk
Contact: Any Member of Staff
Opening Times: 0830-1700 Mon-Sat, 1030-1630 Sun. (Closed Sun in Jan).
Cat. Cost: Online only.
Credit Cards: All major debit/credit cards except American Express
Specialities: Many plants & trees not generally available. Container-grown fruit trees: apples, pears & soft fruit. Container-grown trees. Conifers, *Clematis*, & hardy perennials.
Notes: Wheelchair accessible.
Map Ref: N, C2 **OS Grid Ref:** SE287590

NDav DAVE PARKINSON PLANTS
4 West Bank, Carlton, Goole, East Yorkshire DN14 9PZ
Ⓣ (01405) 860693
Ⓜ 07773 564945
Ⓦ www.daveparkinsonplants.co.uk
Contact: Mary Parkinson
Opening Times: Not open. Mail order only. Sells at RHS & Orchid Shows.
Min Mail Order UK: £12 + p&p
Min Mail Order EU: Nmc
Cat. Cost: 1st class stamp.
Credit Cards: None
Specialities: Hardy orchids. Terrestrial South African *Disa* orchids, species & hybrids.
Notes: Delivers to shows.

NDov DOVE COTTAGE NURSERY & GARDEN ♿
Shibden Hall Road, Halifax, West Yorkshire HX3 9XA
Ⓣ (01422) 203553
Ⓔ info@dovecottagenursery.co.uk
Ⓦ www.dovecottagenursery.co.uk
Contact: Stephen & Kim Rogers
Opening Times: 1000-1700 Wed-Sun, 2nd Mar-30th Sep & B/hols Mons. Other times by appt.
Cat. Cost: £2.00.
Credit Cards: All major credit/debit cards
Specialities: Herbaceous perennials & selected grasses, many displayed in adjoining naturalistic garden.
Notes: Wheelchair accessible.
Map Ref: N, D2 **OS Grid Ref:** SE115256

NDro DROINTON NURSERIES ♿
Plaster Pitts, Norton Conyers, Ripon, North Yorkshire HG4 5EF
Ⓣ (01765) 641849
Ⓜ 07909 971529
Ⓔ info@auricula-plants.co.uk
Ⓦ www.auricula-plants.co.uk
Contact: Robin & Annabel Graham
Opening Times: Open days in spring, otherwise by appt. only.
Min Mail Order UK: Nmc
Min Mail Order EU: Nmc
Cat. Cost: 4 × 1st class.
Credit Cards: All major credit/debit cards
Specialities: *Primula auricula*. More than 1000 cvs of show, alpine, double & border auriculas. Limited stock of any one cultivar. Nat. Collection of *Primula auricula* (Borders).
Notes: Also sells wholesale. Exports beyond EU. Delivers to shows. Wheelchair accessible.
Map Ref: N, C2 **OS Grid Ref:** SE315753

NEgg EGGLESTON HALL GARDENS ♿
Eggleston, Barnard Castle, Co. Durham DL12 0AG
Ⓣ (01833) 650230
Ⓜ 07747 620908
Ⓔ lahock@btinternet.com
Ⓦ www.egglestonhallgardens.co.uk.
Contact: Lisa Hockham
Opening Times: 1000-1700 7 days. Closed 24th Dec to 6th Jan each year.

Cat. Cost: Online only.
Credit Cards: All major credit/debit cards
Notes: Collection from nursery only. Euro accepted. Wheelchair accessible.
Map Ref: N, C2 **OS Grid Ref:** NY997233

NEoE **East of Eden Nursery** ♿
Ainstable, Carlisle, Cumbria CA4 9QN
Ⓣ (01768) 896604
Ⓜ 07788 142969
Ⓔ roger@east-of-eden-nursery.co.uk
Ⓦ www.east-of-eden-nursery.co.uk
Contact: Roger Proud
Opening Times: Mar-Oct. Days & times variable, so please phone or email before calling.
Min Mail Order UK: £10.00
Cat. Cost: None issued
Credit Cards: All major credit/debit cards
Specialities: Interesting & unusual shrubs, perennials & alpines, esp. astilbes and geums with over 60 new *Geum* cvs, bred & raised on nursery.
Notes: Mail order available for geums & astilbes only. Also sells wholesale (geums only). Delivers to shows. Wheelchair accessible.
Map Ref: N, B1 **OS Grid Ref:** NY467504

NEqu **Equatorial Plant Co.**
The Dovecote, Newgate, Barnard Castle, Co. Durham DL12 8NW
Ⓣ (01833) 908127
Ⓕ (01833) 908127
Ⓔ Equatorial9@gmail.com
Ⓦ www.equatorialplants.com
Contact: Dr Richard Warren
Opening Times: Mail order only. Open by appt. only.
Min Mail Order UK: Nmc
Min Mail Order EU: Nmc
Cat. Cost: Free.
Credit Cards: Visa, Access, Paypal
Specialities: Laboratory-raised orchids only.
Notes: Also sells wholesale. Exports beyond EU. Delivers to shows. Euro accepted.

NGBl **Garden Blooms**
Fieldgate, Mill Field Road, Fishlake, Doncaster, Yorkshire DN7 5GH
Ⓣ (01302) 288145
Ⓔ info@gardenblooms.co.uk
Ⓦ www.gardenblooms.co.uk
Contact: Liz Webster
Opening Times: Open by appt. or on Open Days only. Contact nursery for details. **Min Mail Order UK:** Nmc
Cat. Cost: Online only.
Credit Cards: MasterCard, Visa
Specialities: Hardy & tender perennials & small range of conservatory/house plants. Some plants available in small quantities only.
Notes: Delivers to shows.
Map Ref: N, D3 **OS Grid Ref:** SE659148

NGdn **Garden House Nursery** ♿
The Square, Dalston, Carlisle, Cumbria CA5 7LL
Ⓣ (01228) 710297
Ⓜ 07595 219082
Ⓔ stephickso@hotmail.co.uk
Ⓦ www.gardenhousenursery.co.uk
Contact: Stephen Hickson
Opening Times: 0900-1700 7 days Mar-Oct.
Cat. Cost: Plant list online only.
Credit Cards: None
Specialities: *Geranium*, *Hosta*, *Hemerocallis*, *Iris*, grasses, *Brunnera*, *Pulmonaria* & *Aconitum*.
Notes: Also sells wholesale. Wheelchair accessible.
Map Ref: N, B1 **OS Grid Ref:** NY369503

NHal **Halls of Heddon**
West Heddon Nurseries, Heddon-on-the-Wall, Northumberland NE15 0JS
Ⓣ (01661) 852445
Ⓕ (01661) 852398
Ⓔ enquiry@hallsofheddon.co.uk
Ⓦ www.hallsofheddon.co.uk
Contact: David Hall
Opening Times: 0900-1700 Mon-Sat 1000-1700 Sun.
Min Mail Order UK: £10.00
Min Mail Order EU: £35.00
Cat. Cost: 3 × 2nd class
Credit Cards: MasterCard, Visa, Switch, Delta
Specialities: *Chrysanthemum* & *Dahlia*.
Notes: Also sells wholesale.
Map Ref: N, B2 **OS Grid Ref:** NZ122679

NHaw **The Hawthornes Nursery** ♿
Marsh Road, Hesketh Bank, Nr Preston, Lancashire PR4 6XT
Ⓣ (01772) 812379
Ⓔ richardhaw@talktalk.net
Ⓦ www.hawthornes-nursery.co.uk
Contact: Irene & Richard Hodson
Opening Times: 0900-1800 7 days, Mar-Jun & Thu-Sun, July-Oct. Gardens open for NGS. Check with nursery for National Collection Open Day 2016.
Min Mail Order UK: £10.00
Min Mail Order EU: Nmc
Cat. Cost: None issued.
Credit Cards: None
Specialities: *Clematis*. Nat. Collection of *Clematis viticella*.
Notes: Euro accepted. Wheelchair accessible.

NHim **HIMALAYAN GARDENS**
The Hutts, Hutts Lane, Grewelthorpe, Ripon, North Yorkshire
HG4 3DA
Ⓣ (01765) 658009
Ⓕ (01765) 658912
Ⓔ info@himalayangarden.com
Ⓦ www.himalayangarden.com
Contact: Peter Roberts
Opening Times: 1000-1600, Tues-Sun & B/hol Mon, mid Apr-mid Jun. During the rest of the year by appt. only.
Min Mail Order UK: £10.00 to £15.00
Cat. Cost: Online only.
Credit Cards: All major credit/debit cards
Specialities: Rare and unusual species & hybrid rhododendrons, azaleas, magnolias & *Cornus*, as well as other Himalayan plants.
Notes: Also sells wholesale. Euro accepted. Delivers to shows. Very limited wheelchair access.

NHip **HIPPOPOTTERING NURSERY**
Orchard House, East Lound, Nr Doncaster, South Yorkshire DN9 2LR
Ⓜ 07979 764677
Ⓔ hippomaples@hotmail.co.uk
Ⓦ www.hippopottering.com
Contact: Pat Gibbons
Opening Times: By appt. only & Open Days.
Min Mail Order UK: £15.00 + p&p
Cat. Cost: Online only.
Credit Cards: Visa, MasterCard
Specialities: Japanese maples. Many available only from us.
Notes: Mail order to UK throughout year; to EU during winter. Delivers to shows. Wheelchair accessible in dry weather only.

NHpl **HARPERLEY HALL FARM NURSERIES** ♿
Harperley, Stanley, Co. Durham DH9 9UB
Ⓣ (01207) 233318
Ⓜ 07944 644126
Ⓔ enquiries@harperleyhallfarmnurseries.co.uk
Ⓦ www.harperleyhallfarmnurseries.co.uk
Contact: Gary McDermott
Opening Times: Nursery is only open on set days. See website or phone for details.
Min Mail Order UK: Nmc
Min Mail Order EU: Nmc
Cat. Cost: None issued.
Credit Cards: All major credit/debit cards
Specialities: Growers of a wide range of alpine & woodland plants, including *Meconopsis* & *Primula*, many of which are rare or unusual. Also growers of a wide range of autumn-flowering gentians.
Notes: Euro accepted. Also sells wholesale. Wheelchair access. Delivers to shows.
Map Ref: N, B2

NHsp **HARE SPRING COTTAGE PLANTS**
Hare Spring Cottage, Finkle Street Lane, Wortley, Sheffield, Yorkshire
S35 7DH
Ⓜ 07792 376805
Ⓔ harespringcottageplants@hotmail.co.uk
Ⓦ www.harespringcottageplants.co.uk
Contact: Stella Exley
Opening Times: Not open. Sells online & at plant fairs.
Min Mail Order UK: Nmc
Specialities: Hardy, mainly herbaceous perennials, especially *Camassia*, *Uvularia* & *Sidalcea*. National Collection of *Camassia* applied for. Some specialist plants available in small quantities only.
Notes: Sells at & delivers to specialist plant fairs. Talks to specialist groups & societies by arrangement.

NJRG **JRG DAHLIAS**
22 Summerville Road, Milnthorpe, Cumbria
LA7 7DF
Ⓣ (01539) 562691
Ⓔ jack@jrg-dahlias.co.uk
Ⓦ www.jrg-dahlias.co.uk
Contact: Jack Gott
Opening Times: By appt. only.
Min Mail Order UK: £10.00 + p&p
Min Mail Order EU: Price with order.
Cat. Cost: Sae: 110mm × 220mm, 2nd class.
Credit Cards: None
Specialities: *Dahlia*. Some available in small quantities only.
Notes: Delivers to shows.
Map Ref: N, C1

NLar **LARCH COTTAGE NURSERIES** ♿ ◆
Melkinthorpe, Penrith, Cumbria
CA10 2DR
Ⓣ (01931) 712404
Ⓕ (01931) 712727
Ⓔ plants@larchcottage.co.uk
Ⓦ www.larchcottage.co.uk
Contact: Peter & Joanne Stott
Opening Times: Daily from 1000-1730 (or dusk in winter), all year round.
Min Mail Order UK: £20.00
Min Mail Order EU: Nmc
Cat. Cost: £7.00
Credit Cards: All major credit/debit cards
Specialities: Comprehensive plant collection in unique garden setting. Rare & unusual plants, particularly shrubs, trees, perennials, dwarf conifers & Japanese maples. *Acer*, *Hamamelis*, *Magnolia* & *Cornus kousa* cvs. Old-fashioned roses, bamboo & alpines.
Notes: Terraced restaurant & art gallery. Wheelchair accessible.
Map Ref: N, C1 **OS Grid Ref:** NY315602

NLos **The Lost World Nursery** ♿
The Hawthorns, Hesketh Bank,
Nr Preston, Lancashire
PR4 6XT
Ⓜ 07810 547629
Ⓔ plants@thelostworldnursery.com
Ⓦ www.thelostworldnursery.com
Contact: Phil Ball
Opening Times: Please check website or contact nursery for opening times.
Min Mail Order UK: Nmc
Min Mail Order EU: Nmc
Cat. Cost: Online.
Credit Cards: All major credit/debit cards
Specialities: Carnivorous plants: *Sarracenia, Nepenthes*. Also ferns, bromeliads, bananas, palms, grasses, gingers, bamboo. Plants for exotic effect.
Notes: Plants may be pre-ordered for collection either at the nursery or at shows or plant fairs. Delivers to shows. Euro accepted. Wheelchair access in dry weather.
Map Ref: N, D1 **OS Grid Ref:** SD447239

NMen **Mendle Nursery** ♿
Holme, Scunthorpe, North Lincolnshire
DN16 3RF
Ⓣ (01724) 850864
Ⓔ annearnshaw@lineone.net
Ⓦ www.mendlenursery.co.uk
Contact: Mrs A Earnshaw
Opening Times: 1000-1600 Tue-Sun.
Min Mail Order UK: Nmc
Min Mail Order EU: Nmc
Credit Cards: Paypal
Specialities: *Jovibarba, Saxifraga* & *Sempervivum.*
Notes: Wheelchair accessible.

NMir **Mires Beck Nursery** ♿
Low Mill Lane, North Cave, Brough,
East Riding, Yorkshire HU15 2NR
Ⓣ (01430) 421543
Ⓕ (01430) 421543
Ⓔ admin@miresbeck.co.uk
Ⓦ www.miresbeck.co.uk
Contact: Martin Rowland
Opening Times: 1000-1600 7 days, 1st Mar-30th Sep. 1000-1600 Mon-Fri 1st Oct-30th Apr..
Min Mail Order UK: Nmc
Cat. Cost: 3 × 1st class.
Credit Cards: All major debit/credit cards except American Express
Specialities: Wildflower plants of Yorkshire provenance.
Notes: Mail order for wildflower plants & plugs only. Also sells wholesale. Wheelchair accessible.
Map Ref: N, D3 **OS Grid Ref:** SE889316

NNor **Norcroft Nurseries** ♿
Roadends, Intack, Southwaite, Carlisle,
Cumbria CA4 0LH
Ⓣ (01697) 473933
Ⓔ info@norcroftnurseries.co.uk
Ⓦ www.norcroftnurseries.co.uk
Contact: Keith Bell
Opening Times: Every afternoon excl. Mon (open B/hol), Apr-Jul, or ring for appt.
Min Mail Order UK: Nmc
Cat. Cost: 2 × 2nd class
Credit Cards: None
Specialities: Hardy herbaceous, *Dianthus, Aquilegia, Hosta, Papaver.*
Notes: Also sells wholesale. Wheelchair accessible.
Map Ref: N, B1 **OS Grid Ref:** NY474433

NOra **Orange Pippin Ltd**
(Office) 33 Algarth Rise, Pocklington,
York, Yorkshire
YO42 2HX
Ⓣ (01759) 392007
Ⓔ trees@orangepippin.com
Ⓦ www.orangepippintrees.co.uk
Contact: Maureen Borrie
Opening Times: Not open. Mail order online only.
Min Mail Order UK: Nmc
Min Mail Order EU: Nmc
Cat. Cost: Online only.
Credit Cards: MasterCard, Visa
Specialities: Wide range of fruit trees & ornamentals, incl. traditional & modern varieties. Wide choice of rootstocks & tree forms. Fruit tree expert available most days. Website incl. extensive tasting notes & variety comparisons.
Notes: Website for ornamental trees: www.pippintrees.co.uk. Order online all year round, deliveries from Aug-Apr. Exports beyond EU (to USA).

NPer **Perry's Plants** ♿
The River Garden, Sleights, Whitby,
North Yorkshire YO21 1RR
Ⓜ 07879 498623
Ⓔ richardperry008@hotmail.co.uk
Ⓦ www.perrysplants.co.uk
Contact: Sharon & Richard Perry
Opening Times: 1000-1700 mid-March to Oct.
Cat. Cost: None published.
Credit Cards: None
Specialities: *Lavatera, Malva, Erysimum, Euphorbia, Anthemis, Osteospermum* & *Hebe.* Uncommon hardy & container plants & aquatic plants.
Notes: Euro accepted. Wheelchair accessible.
Map Ref: N, C3 **OS Grid Ref:** NZ869082

NPla **The Plant Directory**
Scawsby Hall Nurseries, Barnsley Road, Scawsby, Doncaster, South Yorkshire DN5 7UB
Ⓣ (01302) 783434
Ⓔ mail@the-plant-directory.co.uk
Ⓦ www.the-plant-directory.co.uk
Contact: David Lawson
Opening Times: Not open. Mail order only.
Min Mail Order UK: Nmc
Cat. Cost: None issued
Credit Cards: Visa, American Express, MasterCard, Paypal
Specialities: A wide range of herbaceous perennials, hardy trees, shrubs & indoor plants. Some indoor & aquatic plants in small quantities only.

NPnk **Primrose Bank** ♿
Redroofs, Dauby Lane, Kexby, York, Yorkshire YO41 5LH
Ⓣ (01759) 380220
Ⓜ 07774 944447
Ⓔ suegoodwill@yahoo.co.uk
Ⓦ www.primrosebank.co.uk
Contact: Sue Goodwill
Opening Times: 1000-1700, Thu-Sun, 12th Mar-26th Jun. By appt. only Jul-Sep. Please ring for weekly opening times Jul-Sep. Please ring before travelling, as occasionally closed during shows.
Min Mail Order UK: Nmc
Cat. Cost: None issued.
Credit Cards: All major credit/debit cards
Specialities: Hardy perennials.
Notes: Delivers to shows. Wheelchair accessible.
Map Ref: N, C3 **OS Grid Ref:** SE695508

NPoe **Poets Cottage Shrub Nursery** ♿
Lealholm, Whitby, North Yorkshire YO21 2AQ
Ⓣ (01947) 897424
Ⓜ 07813 252303
Ⓔ enquiries@poetscottage.co.uk
Ⓦ www.poetscottage.co.uk
Contact: Ilona J McGivern
Opening Times: 1300-1530 Feb, 0900-1700 Mar-Christmas, 7 days. Closed Jan.
Cat. Cost: None issued.
Credit Cards: All major credit/debit cards
Specialities: Dwarf conifers, *Acer* & herbaceous shrubs.
Notes: Wheelchair accessible.
Map Ref: N, C3

NPol **Polemonium Plantery**
28 Sunnyside, Trimdon Grange, Co. Durham TS29 6HF
Ⓣ (01429) 881529
Ⓔ dandd@polemonium.co.uk
Ⓦ www.polemonium.co.uk
Contact: David or Dianne Nichol-Brown
Opening Times: By appt. only.
Min Mail Order UK: £10.00
Cat. Cost: 3 × 1st class
Credit Cards: None
Specialities: Nat. Collections of *Polemonium*, *Collomia*, *Gilia*, *Leptodactylon* (*Polemoniaceae*) & *Hakonechloa*.
Notes: Also sells wholesale. Delivers to shows.
Map Ref: N, B2 **OS Grid Ref:** NZ369353

NPri **Primrose Cottage Nursery** ♿
Ringway Road, Moss Nook, Wythenshawe, Manchester M22 5WF
Ⓣ (0161) 437 1557
Ⓜ 07798 754457
Ⓔ info@primrosecottagenursery.co.uk
Ⓦ www.primrosecottagenursery.co.uk
Contact: Caroline Dumville
Opening Times: 0900-1730 Mon-Sat, 0930-1730 Sun (summer). 0900-1700 Mon-Sat, 0930-1700 Sun (winter).
Credit Cards: All major credit/debit cards
Specialities: Perennials, herbs, roses, patio & hanging basket plants. Shrubs, houseplants, ornamental trees, fruit trees, soft fruit bushes & vegetable plants. New & unusual varieties.
Notes: Refreshments area open daily. Wheelchair accessible.
Map Ref: N, D2

NQui **Quiet Corner Plants**
(Office) 20 Grove Road, Brandon, Co. Durham DH7 8AW
Ⓜ 079321 59204
Ⓔ hal@uwclub.net
Ⓦ www.quietcornerplants.co.uk
Contact: Howard Leslie
Opening Times: 1100-1700 (or sunset in winter), Sat only.
Min Mail Order UK: Nmc
Cat. Cost: Online only.
Credit Cards: All major credit/debit cards
Specialities: Hardy herbaceous & shrubby perennials, incl. small quantities of lesser known and harder to find plants.
Notes: Nursery is at Misty Blue Farm, Rock Road, Kirk Merrington, Co. Durham DL16 7HJ. Also sells wholesale. Delivers to shows.
Map Ref: N, B2

NRHS **Harlow Carr Plant Centre (RHS)** ◆
RHS Garden Harlow Carr, Crag Lane, Harlow Carr, Harrogate, North Yorkshire HG3 1QB
Ⓣ (01423) 724666
Ⓕ (01423) 569521

Ⓔ nigeleaton@rhs.org.uk
Ⓦ www.rhs.org.uk
Contact: Any member of staff
Specialities: Wide general range, particularly alpines.
Notes: Programme of free plant events throughout the year. Please ring or check website for details. Customer ordering system for plants which need to be collected from the plant centre (no mail order).

NRib **Ribblesdale Nurseries** ♿
Newsham Hall Lane, Woodplumpton, Preston, Lancashire PR4 0AS
Ⓣ (01772) 863081
Ⓔ philsd@btinternet.com
Ⓦ www.ribblesdalenurseries.co.uk
Contact: Mr & Mrs Dunnett
Opening Times: 0900-1800 Mon-Sat Apr-Sep, 0900-1700 Mon-Sat Oct-Mar. 1030-1630 Sun.
Credit Cards: All major credit/debit cards
Specialities: Trees, shrubs & perennials. Conifers, hedging, alpines, fruit, climbers, herbs, aquatics, ferns & wildflowers. Own grown plants in peat-free compost.
Notes: Wheelchair accessible.

NRob **W Robinson & Son (Seeds & Plants) Ltd** ♿
Sunny Bank, Forton, Nr Preston, Lancashire PR3 0BN
Ⓣ (01524) 791210
Ⓕ (01524) 791933
Ⓔ info@mammothonion.co.uk
Ⓦ www.mammothonion.co.uk
Contact: Miss Robinson
Opening Times: 1000-1600 7 days Mar-Jun, 0800-1700 Mon-Fri Jul-Feb.
Min Mail Order UK: Nmc
Min Mail Order EU: Nmc
Cat. Cost: Free.
Credit Cards: All major credit/debit cards
Specialities: Mammoth vegetable seed. Onions, leeks, tomatoes & beans. Range of vegetable plants in the spring.
Notes: Also sells wholesale. Euro accepted. Exports beyond EU. Delivers to shows. Wheelchair accessible.

NRog **R V Roger Ltd** ♿
The Nurseries, Pickering, North Yorkshire YO18 7JW
Ⓣ (01751) 472226
Ⓕ (01751) 476749
Ⓔ sales@rvroger.co.uk
Ⓦ www.rvroger.co.uk
Contact: Ian Roger
Opening Times: 0900-1700 Mon-Sat, 1000-1600 Sun.
Min Mail Order UK: Nmc
Min Mail Order EU: Nmc
Cat. Cost: £1.00
Credit Cards: All major credit/debit cards
Specialities: Holders of National Collection of *Erythronium*.
Notes: Also sells wholesale. Wheelchair accessible. Exports beyond EU.
Map Ref: N, C3 **OS Grid Ref:** SE801827

NRya **Ryal Nursery** ♿
East Farm Cottage, Ryal, Northumberland NE20 0SA
Ⓣ (01661) 886562
Ⓔ alpines@ryal.freeserve.co.uk
Contact: R F Hadden
Opening Times: Mar-Jul by appt., please phone in advance.
Cat. Cost: Sae.
Credit Cards: None
Specialities: Alpine & woodland plants, mainly available in small quantities only. Nat. Collection of *Primula marginata*.
Notes: Also sells wholesale. Delivers to shows. Wheelchair accessible.
Map Ref: N, B2 **OS Grid Ref:** NZ015744

NSla **Slack Top Nurseries**
Alpine House, 22A Slack Top, Hebden Bridge, West Yorkshire HX7 7HA
Ⓣ (01422) 845348
Ⓜ 07508 953804
Ⓔ enquiries@slacktopnurseries.co.uk
Ⓦ www.slacktopnurseries.co.uk
Contact: Michael & Allison Mitchell
Opening Times: 1000-1700 Fri-Sun, Mar-Aug & B/hols. Other times by appt.
Min Mail Order UK: £20.00
Min Mail Order EU: £50.00
Cat. Cost: 2 × 1st class A5 sae or online.
Credit Cards: None
Specialities: Alpine, rockery & woodland plants.
Notes: Talks given to gardening clubs & other groups by appt. Delivers to shows. Euro accepted. Some areas of garden inaccessible for wheelchairs.
Map Ref: N, D2 **OS Grid Ref:** SD977286

NSti **Stillingfleet Lodge Nurseries** ♿
Stewart Lane, Stillingfleet, York, YO19 6HP
Ⓣ (01904) 728506
Ⓔ info@stillingfleetlodgenurseries.co.uk
Ⓦ www.stillingfleetlodgenurseries.co.uk
Contact: Vanessa Cook
Opening Times: 1300-1700 Wed & Fri, 1st Apr-30th Sep. 1300-1700, 1st & 3rd Sat & Sun in each month.

Cat. Cost: Online only.
Credit Cards: All major credit/debit cards
Specialities: Foliage & unusual perennials. Hardy geraniums, *Pulmonaria*, variegated plants & grasses.
Notes: Wheelchair accessible.
Map Ref: N, D2

NSue **Sue Proctor Plants**
69 Ings Mill Avenue, Clayton West, Huddersfield, West Yorkshire HD8 9QG
Ⓣ (01484) 866189
Ⓜ 07917 006636
Ⓔ hostas@sueproctorplants.co.uk
Ⓦ www.sueproctorplants.co.uk
Contact: Richard Proctor
Opening Times: By appt. only. Please phone first.
Min Mail Order UK: £3.50
Cat. Cost: Large 1st sae.
Credit Cards: All major credit/debit cards
Specialities: *Hosta*, especially miniature hostas.
Notes: Delivers to shows.
Map Ref: N, D2

NSum **Summerdale Garden Nursery**
Summerdale House, Cow Brow, Lupton, Carnforth, Lancashire LA6 1PE
Ⓣ (01539) 567210
Ⓔ sheals@btinternet.com
Ⓦ www.summerdalegardenplants.co.uk
Contact: Gail Sheals
Opening Times: 1000-1630 Thu, Fri & Sat, 1st Apr-31st Aug. Other times by appt. only.
Min Mail Order UK: Nmc
Cat. Cost: Online only.
Credit Cards: None
Specialities: Wide variety of perennials, large collection of *Primula*. Many moist and shade-loving plants incl. *Meconopsis* & hellebores.
Notes: Mail order for primulas only.
Map Ref: N, C1 **OS Grid Ref:** SD545819

NTPC **Tree Peony Company**
Willow Cottage, Rillington, Malton, North Yorkshire YO17 8JU
Ⓣ (01944) 758280
Ⓔ info@treepeony.co.uk
Ⓦ www.treepeony.co.uk
Contact: Thelma Scruton, Roger Scruton
Min Mail Order UK: £12.00
Min Mail Order EU: Nmc
Cat. Cost: None.
Credit Cards: None
Specialities: Tree peonies. *Paeonia suffruticosa*. *P.* Gansu Group. *P. rockii*.
Notes: Also sells wholesale. Euro accepted. Delivers to shows.

NTre **Treetyme**
Prospect Hill House, Kirkoswald, Penrith, Cumbria CA10 1ER
Ⓣ (01768) 800238
Ⓕ (01768) 897138
Ⓔ sales@treetyme.co.uk
Ⓦ www.treetyme.co.uk
Contact: Hugh Povey
Opening Times: Not open. Mail order via website only. Visits by appt. only.
Min Mail Order UK: Nmc
Min Mail Order EU: Nmc
Cat. Cost: Online only.
Credit Cards: All major credit/debit cards
Specialities: *Cercis*. Stock available in small quantities only. National Collection of *Cercis*.
Notes: Also sells wholesale.

NWad **Waddow Lodge Garden** ♿
Clitheroe Road, Waddington, Clitheroe, Lancashire BB7 3HQ
Ⓣ (01200) 429145
Ⓔ peterfoleyhcn@hotmail.co.uk
Ⓦ www.gardentalks.co.uk
Contact: Peter Foley
Opening Times: By appt. only all year. Also open under NGS 1300-1700 29th May & 31st Jul 2016 with plant sales for Plant Heritage NW Group.
Min Mail Order UK: Nmc
Min Mail Order EU: Nmc
Cat. Cost: Online only.
Credit Cards: None
Specialities: A developing plantsman's garden with an ever-changing & interesting plant collection. Some plants may only be available in small numbers.
Notes: Open for group visits by appt., incl. evenings. Wheelchair accessible.
Map Ref: N, C1 **OS Grid Ref:** SD732434

NWms **Woodmoss Fuchsias** ♿
Woodmoss Lane Nursery, Woodmoss Lane, Scarisbrick, Ormskirk, Lancashire L40 9RJ
Ⓣ (01253) 980667
Ⓜ 07849 080248
Ⓔ woodmossfuchsia@yahoo.co.uk
Contact: Brian Houghton & Keith Middleton
Opening Times: 0900-1600 Mon-Fri, 0900-1230 Sat, Jan-end Jun. B/hols & w/ends by appt.
Min Mail Order UK: £13.50 for 6 plants.
Cat. Cost: Free, or by email.
Credit Cards: None
Specialities: *Fuchsia*. New varieties may be available in small quantities only.
Notes: Wheelchair accessible.

NWsh **Westshores Nurseries**
82 West Street, Winterton, Scunthorpe, Lincolnshire DN15 9QF

Ⓣ (01724) 733940
Ⓜ 07875 732535
Ⓔ westshnur@aol.com
Ⓦ www.westshores.co.uk
Contact: Gail & John Summerfield
Opening Times: 1st Mar-31st Oct. Please check before visiting.
Min Mail Order UK: £15.00
Cat. Cost: Online only.
Credit Cards: All major credit/debit cards
Specialities: Ornamental grasses, autumn flowering perennials & scented pelargoniums.
Notes: Wide selection of talks (21) for gardening clubs and Hardy Plant Society groups.
Map Ref: N, D3 **OS Grid Ref:** SE927187

SOUTHERN

S

SAdn **ASHDOWN FOREST GARDEN CENTRE & NURSERY** ♿
Duddleswell, Ashdown Forest, East Sussex
TN22 3JP
Ⓣ (01825) 712300
Ⓔ victoria@ashdownforestgardencentre.co.uk
Ⓦ www.ashdownforestgardencentre.co.uk
Contact: Victoria Falletti
Opening Times: 0900-1700 winter, 0900-1700 summer.
Min Mail Order UK: Nmc
Cat. Cost: Online only.
Credit Cards: All major credit/debit cards
Specialities: Ornamental grasses, *Lapageria*, *Fuchsia*, conservatory climbers, unusual shrubs. Available in small quantities only.
Notes: Wheelchair accessible.
Map Ref: S, C4 **OS Grid Ref:** TQ468283

SAdu **ADUR VALLEY GROWERS**
(Office) 4 Newland Road, Upper Beeding, Steyning, West Sussex
BN44 3JJ
Ⓣ (01903) 813780
Ⓔ clivethecannaman@gmail.com
Ⓦ www.adurvalleygrowers.co.uk
Contact: Clive Parker
Opening Times: Not open. Mail order only.
Min Mail Order UK: Nmc
Min Mail Order EU: Nmc
Cat. Cost: Online only.
Credit Cards: Paypal
Specialities: A wide range of disease-free *Canna*, many only available in very small numbers. All plants grown in own peat-free compost without the use of chemical pesticides. Will propagate to order. *Iris reticulata* & *I. histrioides* hybrids also available in season.
Notes: Plants only available from May-Oct. Euro accepted.

SAko **AKORN AND OAKE**
18 Twyford Avenue, Southampton, Hampshire
SO15 5NP
Ⓣ (023) 8034 4040
Ⓜ 07973 149404
Ⓔ stefan.rau@hotmail.co.uk
Contact: Stefan Rau
Opening Times: Open by appt. only.
Specialities: *Saxifraga*.
Notes: Delivers to shows.

SAll **ALLWOODS** ♿
London Road, Hassocks, West Sussex
BN6 9NA
Ⓣ (01273) 844229
Ⓔ info@allwoods.net
Ⓦ www.allwoods.net
Contact: David & Emma James
Opening Times: Office 0900-1630 Mon-Fri. Answer machine all other times. Garden nursery open to visitors all year round, check website or contact nursery for detailed opening times.
Min Mail Order UK: Nmc
Min Mail Order EU: Nmc
Cat. Cost: 2 × 1st class.
Credit Cards: Access, Visa, MasterCard, Switch, Maestro
Specialities: Large collection of *Dianthus*, incl. hardy border carnations, pinks, perpetual flowering & spray carnations, Malmaisons & *D. allwoodii*. Unusual & collectors' geraniums & pelargoniums. *Fuchsia*, Penstemons & other garden plants. Succulents.
Notes: All listed varieties available as plugs but choice varies depending on time of year. Please phone before travelling to avoid disappointment and/or to ensure order is ready for collection. Also sells wholesale. Wheelchair accessible.
Map Ref: S, D4

SArc **ARCHITECTURAL PLANTS LTD** ♿
Stane Street, North Heath, Pulborough, West Sussex RH20 1DJ
Ⓣ (01798) 879213
Ⓔ enquiries@architecturalplants.com
Ⓦ www.architecturalplants.com
Contact: Cindy Hines
Opening Times: 0900-1700 Mon-Sat & B/hols. Closed Sun. Café open 1030-1600 Thu-Sat & B/hols.
Cat. Cost: Free
Credit Cards: All major debit/credit cards except American Express
Specialities: Architectural plants & hardy exotics esp. rare evergreen broadleaved trees & seaside exotics, spiky plants, yuccas/agaves, climbers, topiary & bamboos.
Notes: Also sells wholesale. Delivers to shows.

Wheelchair accessible (& available on site).
Map Ref: S, C3 **OS Grid Ref:** TQ192262

SBch **Birchwood Plants**
(Office) 10 Westering, Romsey, Hampshire SO51 7LY
Ⓣ (01794) 502192
Ⓜ 07874 678175
Ⓔ info@birchwoodplants.co.uk
Ⓦ www.birchwoodplants.co.uk
Contact: Lesley Baker
Opening Times: Not open to the public. Plants can be collected by arrangement from nursery or from sales & shows, see website or phone for details.
Min Mail Order UK: £15 + p&p
Min Mail Order EU: £15+ p&p
Cat. Cost: Online only.
Credit Cards: Paypal
Specialities: Alpines & drought-tolerant plants. Plants to attract bees & butterflies. Unusual plants. Predominantly growing peat-free. National Collection of *Geranium nodosum*. Most stock only available in very small quantities unless ordered well in advance.
Notes: Nursery at Silverwood House, Gardener's Lane, Nr Romsey, SO51 6AD. Mail order mostly for small plants. No mail order sent Dec-Jan. Delivers to shows.
Map Ref: S, D2 **OS Grid Ref:** SU333190

SBee **Beechbridge Plants**
Goudhurst Road, Marden, Tonbridge, Kent TN12 9NN
Ⓣ (01622) 832237
Ⓜ 07914 019943
Ⓔ info@beechbridgeplants.co.uk
Ⓦ www.beechbridgeplants.co.uk
Contact: Victoria Mummery
Opening Times: Open by appt. only.
Min Mail Order UK: Nmc
Cat. Cost: Online only.
Credit Cards: None
Specialities: A small family-run nursery specialising in herbaceous perennials and grasses, many of which are unusual or hard to find. Virtually all plants are grown on the nursery. Stock only available in small quantities.
Notes: Please contact nursery before travelling a long distance to check current availability & make an appt.
Map Ref: S, C5 **OS Grid Ref:** TQ738436

SBig **Big Plant Nursery** ♿ ◆
Hole Street, Ashington, West Sussex RH20 3DE
Ⓣ (01903) 891466
Ⓕ (01903) 892829
Ⓔ info@bigplantnursery.co.uk
Ⓦ www.bigplantnursery.co.uk
Contact: Bruce Jordan
Opening Times: 0900-1700 Mon-Sat, 1000-1600 Sun & B/hols.
Min Mail Order UK: Please phone for further info.
Cat. Cost: Online only.
Credit Cards: All major credit/debit cards
Specialities: Bamboos, hardy exotics & palms, *Ginkgo*, *Betula*. Architectural plants, evergreens.
Notes: Programme of events & propagation tuition, see website or phone for details. Also sells wholesale. Wheelchair accessible.
Map Ref: S, D3 **OS Grid Ref:** TQ132153

SBir **Birchfleet Nurseries** ♿ ◆
Greenfields Close, Nyewood, Petersfield, Hampshire GU31 5JQ
Ⓣ (01730) 821636
Ⓕ (01730) 821636
Ⓔ gammoak@aol.com
Ⓦ www.birchfleetnurseries.co.uk
Contact: John & Daphne Gammon
Opening Times: By appt. only. Please phone. Open Days 15th & 16th Oct 2016.
Cat. Cost: 2 × 1st class.
Credit Cards: None
Specialities: Oaks. Beech. *Nyssa*. Nat. Collection of *Liquidambar*.
Notes: Also sells wholesale. Nursery accessible for wheelchairs in dry weather.
Map Ref: S, C3

SBod **Bodiam Nursery**
Bodiam, Robertsbridge, East Sussex TN32 5RA
Ⓣ (01580) 830811
Ⓜ 07971 419302
Ⓔ enquiries@bodiamnursery.co.uk
Ⓦ www.bodiamnursery.co.uk
Contact: Jill Kaye
Opening Times: 1000-1700 Tue-Sun, 1st Mar-31st Oct. Closed Nov-Feb.
Cat. Cost: None issued.
Credit Cards: All major credit/debit cards
Specialities: Wide range of *Acer palmatum*, available in small numbers of each variety. Coastal & Mediterranean plants. Many other compact & slow-growing shrubs, conifers & perennials suitable for small gardens & containers.
Notes: Between Great Dixter & Merriments Gardens, opposite Bodiam Castle, next to the level crossing for the steam railway. Delivers to shows.

SBri **Brickwall Cottage Nursery**
1 Brickwall Cottages, Frittenden, Cranbrook, Kent TN17 2DH
Ⓣ (01580) 852425

Ⓜ 07714 529946
Ⓔ suemartin41@icloud.com
Ⓦ www.geumcollection.co.uk
Contact: Sue Martin
Opening Times: By appt. only.
Min Mail Order UK: Nmc
Min Mail Order EU: Nmc
Credit Cards: None
Specialities: Hardy perennials. Stock available in small quantities only. Nat. Collection of *Geum*.
Notes: Limited wheelchair access.
Map Ref: S, C5 **OS Grid Ref:** TQ815410

SBrt **BRIGHTON PLANTS** ♿
New Hall Lane, Small Dole, Sussex BN5 9YJ
Ⓜ 07955 744802
Ⓔ brighton.plants@gmail.com
Ⓦ www.brightonplants.blogspot.com
Contact: Steve Law
Opening Times: 1000-1700 w/ends, May-Oct & B/hols. Please email/phone first.
Min Mail Order UK: Nmc
Min Mail Order EU: Nmc
Cat. Cost: 4 × 1st class.
Credit Cards: All major credit/debit cards
Specialities: Hardy herbaceous and woody plants. Drought-tolerant plants.
Notes: Exports beyond EU. Delivers to shows. Euro accepted. Wheelchair accessible.
Map Ref: S, D3 **OS Grid Ref:** TQ208132

S

SCac **CACTI & SUCCULENTS**
Hammerfield, Crockham Hill, Edenbridge, Kent TN8 6RR
Ⓣ (01732) 866295
Contact: Geoff Southon
Opening Times: Flexible. Please phone first.
Min Mail Order UK: Nmc
Cat. Cost: None issued.
Credit Cards: None
Specialities: *Echeveria* & related genera & hybrids. A large range of *Aeonium*, both species & hybrids, possibly the largest collection in the country. Many available in small quantities only.

SCam **CAMELLIA GROVE NURSERY** ♿
Market Garden, Lower Beeding, West Sussex RH13 6PP
Ⓣ (01403) 891412
Ⓔ lp@hortic.com
Ⓦ www.camellia-grove.com
Contact: Chris Loder
Opening Times: 1000-1600 Mon-Sat, please phone first so we can give you our undivided attention.
Min Mail Order UK: Nmc
Min Mail Order EU: Nmc
Cat. Cost: 2 × 1st class.
Credit Cards: All major debit/credit cards except American Express
Specialities: *Camellia japonica*, *C. williamsii*, *C. sasanqua* & *C. reticulata*, from the purest white to richest red flowers.
Notes: Also sells wholesale. Exports beyond EU. Delivers to shows. Euro accepted. Wheelchair accessible.
Map Ref: S, C3 **OS Grid Ref:** TQ221255

SChF **CHARLESHURST FARM NURSERY**
Loxwood Road, Plaistow, Billingshurst, West Sussex RH14 0NY
Ⓣ (01403) 752273
Ⓜ 07736 522788
Ⓔ Charleshurstfarm@aol.com
Ⓦ www.charleshurstplants.co.uk
Contact: Clive Mellor
Opening Times: Normally 0900-1730 Fri, Sat, Sun, Feb-Oct, but please ring before travelling.
Min Mail Order UK: Nmc
Min Mail Order EU: Nmc
Cat. Cost: 2 × 1st class.
Credit Cards: All major credit/debit cards
Specialities: Shrubs including some more unusual species. Good range of daphnes & Japanese maples.
Notes: Delivers to shows. Euro accepted.
Map Ref: S, C3 **OS Grid Ref:** TQ015308

SChr **JOHN CHURCHER**
47 Grove Avenue, Portchester, Fareham, Hampshire PO16 9EZ
Ⓣ (023) 9232 6740
Ⓜ 07717 495861
Ⓔ johnchurcher47@btinternet.com
Contact: John Churcher
Opening Times: By appt. only. Please phone or email.
Min Mail Order UK: Nmc
Min Mail Order EU: Nmc
Cat. Cost: None issued.
Credit Cards: None
Specialities: Hardy exotics for the Mediterranean-style garden, incl. palms, tree ferns, *Musa*, hedychiums, cycads, *Agave*, *Aloe*, *Opuntia* & echiums. Stock available in small quantities only.
Map Ref: S, D2 **OS Grid Ref:** SU614047

SCit **THE CITRUS CENTRE** ♿
West Mare Lane, Marehill, Pulborough, West Sussex RH20 2EA
Ⓣ (01798) 872786
Ⓔ enquiries@citruscentre.co.uk
Ⓦ www.citruscentre.co.uk
Contact: Amanda & Chris Dennis
Opening Times: 0930-1600 Tue-Sat. Phone for Xmas & B/hol opening times.
Min Mail Order UK: Nmc

Min Mail Order EU: Nmc
Cat. Cost: Online.
Credit Cards: Visa, MasterCard
Specialities: *Citrus* & *Citrus* relatives.
Notes: Wheelchair accessible.
Map Ref: S, D3

SCmr **CROMAR NURSERY** ♿
39 Livesey Street, North Pole, Wateringbury, Maidstone, Kent ME18 5BQ
Ⓣ (01622) 812380
Ⓔ CromarNursery@aol.com
Ⓦ www.cromarnursery.co.uk
Contact: Debra & Martin Cronk
Opening Times: 0930-1630 Thu, Fri, Sat, Sun. Please check website or phone if travelling far.
Min Mail Order UK: Nmc
Min Mail Order EU: Nmc
Cat. Cost: 2 × 1st class.
Credit Cards: All major credit/debit cards
Specialities: Ornamental & fruit trees.
Notes: Wheelchair accessible.
Map Ref: S, C4 **OS Grid Ref:** TQ697547

SCob **COBLANDS NURSERIES**
Trench Road, Tonbridge, Kent TN11 9NG
Ⓣ (01732) 770999
Ⓔ info@coblands.co.uk
Ⓦ www.coblands.co.uk
Contact: Stephen Derbyshire
Opening Times: 0900-1630 Mon-Sat, all year. Closed for Xmas/New Year.
Min Mail Order UK: Nmc
Min Mail Order EU: Nmc
Cat. Cost: Online & seasonal postings to existing customers.
Credit Cards: All major credit/debit cards
Specialities: Wide range of plants esp. herbaceous perennials of garden-worthiness incl. many new varieties, *Hebe*, *Hydrangea*, *Phormium*, *Brunnera*, *Echinacea*, *Epimedium*, *Heuchera*, *Hosta*, *Rudbeckia* & ferns. Wide range of established specimen plants. New introductions may be in limited supply.
Notes: Direct online ordering service. Ornamental trees & hedging available seasonally. Also sells wholesale.
Map Ref: S, C4 **OS Grid Ref:** TQ586487

SCoo **COOLING'S NURSERIES LTD** ♿
Rushmore Hill, Knockholt, Sevenoaks, Kent TN14 7NN
Ⓣ (01959) 532269
Ⓕ (01959) 534092
Ⓔ Plantfinder@coolings.co.uk
Ⓦ www.coolings.co.uk
Contact: Mark Reeve or Garry Norris
Opening Times: 0900-1700 Mon-Sat & 0900-1630 Sun.
Min Mail Order UK: Nmc
Cat. Cost: None issued
Credit Cards: All major debit/credit cards except American Express
Specialities: Large range of perennials, conifers & bedding plants. Many unusual shrubs & trees. Third generation family business.
Notes: Display garden. Coffee shop. Wheelchair accessible.
Map Ref: S, C4 **OS Grid Ref:** TK477610

SDay **A LA CARTE DAYLILIES**
Little Hermitage, St Catherine's Down, Ventnor, Isle of Wight PO38 2PD
Ⓣ (01983) 730512
Ⓔ andy@alacartedaylilies.co.uk
Ⓦ www.alacartedaylilies.co.uk
Contact: Jan & Andy Wyers
Opening Times: Mail order only. Open by appt. only. Difficult to find on an unmade private road, phone/email for directions.
Min Mail Order UK: Nmc
Min Mail Order EU: Nmc
Cat. Cost: 3 × 1st class.
Credit Cards: None
Specialities: *Hemerocallis*. Nat. Collections of Miniature & Small Flowered *Hemerocallis* & Large Flowered *Hemerocallis* (post-1960 award-winning cultivars).
Notes: Euro accepted.
Map Ref: S, D2 **OS Grid Ref:** SZ499787

SDea **DEACON'S NURSERY** ◆
Moor View, Godshill, Isle of Wight PO38 3HW
Ⓣ (01983) 840750 (24 hrs) or (01983) 522243
Ⓕ (01983) 523575
Ⓔ info@deaconsnurseryfruits.co.uk
Ⓦ www.deaconsnurseryfruits.co.uk
Contact: G D & B H W Deacon
Opening Times: 0800-1600 Mon-Fri May-Sep, 0800-1700 Mon-Fri 0800-1200 Sat Oct-Apr.
Min Mail Order UK: Nmc
Min Mail Order EU: Nmc
Cat. Cost: Free.
Credit Cards: All major credit/debit cards
Specialities: Over 300 varieties of apple, old & new, apricots, cherries, damsons, gages, nectarines, peaches, pears, plums. Modern soft fruit, grapes, hops, nuts & family trees.
Notes: Also sells wholesale. Exports beyond EU. Euro accepted.
Map Ref: S, D2

SDeJ **P. DE JAGER & SONS LTD** ♿ ◆
Church Farm, Ulcombe, Maidstone, Kent ME17 1DN
Ⓣ (01622) 840229

Ⓕ (01622) 844073
Ⓔ flowerbulbs@dejager.co.uk
Ⓦ www.dejager.co.uk
Contact: George Clowes
Opening Times: Mail order only. Orders taken from 0900-1700 Mon-Fri
Min Mail Order UK: Nmc
Min Mail Order EU: Nmc
Cat. Cost: Free.
Credit Cards: All major credit/debit cards
Specialities: Wide range of all flower bulbs.
Notes: Also sells wholesale. Exports beyond EU. Euro accepted. Wheelchair accessible.

SDir **Direct Bulbs**
Mault Ley, Hillside Close, Winchester, Hampshire SO22 5LW
Ⓣ (01962) 840038
Ⓔ jo@directbulbs.com
Ⓦ www.directbulbs.co.uk
Contact: Jo Woodland
Opening Times: 0900-1700 Mon-Fri.
Min Mail Order UK: £5.95
Min Mail Order EU: £20.00
Credit Cards: All major credit/debit cards
Specialities: Bulbs.

S

SDow **Downderry Nursery** ♿
Pillar Box Lane, Hadlow, Nr Tonbridge, Kent TN11 9SW
Ⓣ (01732) 810081
Ⓔ info@downderry-nursery.co.uk
Ⓦ www.downderry-nursery.co.uk
Contact: Dr Simon Charlesworth
Opening Times: 1000-1700 Thu-Sun 1st May-30th Sep & B/hols. Other times by appt.
Min Mail Order UK: Nmc
Min Mail Order EU: Nmc
Cat. Cost: None issued.
Credit Cards: Delta, MasterCard, Maestro, Visa
Specialities: Nat. Collections of *Lavandula* and *Rosmarinus*.
Notes: Exports beyond EU. Euro accepted. Wheelchair accessible.
Map Ref: S, C4 **OS Grid Ref:** TQ625521

SDys **Dysons Nurseries** ♿
Great Comp Garden, Platt, Sevenoaks, Kent TN15 8QS
Ⓣ (01732) 885094
Ⓜ 07887 997663
Ⓔ dysonsorders@greatcompgarden.co.uk
Ⓦ www.dysonsalvias.com
Contact: William T Dyson
Opening Times: 1100-1700 7 days 1st Apr-31st Oct. Other times by appt.
Cat. Cost: Online only.
Credit Cards: All major credit/debit cards
Specialities: Salvias & an eclectic range of choice and uncommon plants.
Notes: Delivers to shows. Wheelchair accessible.
Map Ref: S, C4

SEle **Eleplants Nursery**
32 Framfield Road, Uckfield, East Sussex TN22 5AH
Ⓣ (01825) 760356
Ⓜ 07810 660109
Ⓔ eleplantsnursery@talk21.com
Ⓦ www.eleplantsnursery.co.uk
Contact: Martin Batchelor
Opening Times: Not open but can be visited by prior appt. only.
Min Mail Order UK: Nmc
Min Mail Order EU: Nmc
Credit Cards: All major credit/debit cards, Paypal
Specialities: Shrubs.
Notes: Exports beyond EU. Delivers to shows.
Map Ref: S, C4

SEND **East Northdown Farm & Gardens** ♿
George Hill Road (B2052), Margate, Kent CT9 3TS
Ⓣ (01843) 862060
Ⓜ 07714 241668 or 241667
Ⓔ info@botanyplants.co.uk
Ⓦ www.botanyplants.co.uk
Contact: Louise & William Friend
Opening Times: 0900-1700 7 days, all year except Sun in winter. Closed Xmas week.
Min Mail Order UK: Nmc
Cat. Cost: Online only.
Credit Cards: All major credit/debit cards
Specialities: Chalk & coast-loving plants. Specimen shrubs & bamboos available. Complimentary range of plants for damp/acid conditions available to order from our Mucklestone Nursery (MMuc). Collection of rare Mediterranean plants.
Notes: Free consultation/advice. Plant selection service. Tea room & gardens. Close to Botany Bay. Lectures given to gardening groups in Kent. Garden tours by appt. See website or contact nursery for full list & details. Wheelchair accessible.
Map Ref: S, B6 **OS Grid Ref:** TR383702

SEWo **English Woodlands** ♿
Burrow Nursery, Herrings Lane, Cross-in-Hand, Heathfield, East Sussex TN21 0UG
Ⓣ (01435) 862992
Ⓕ (01435) 867742
Ⓔ sales@englishwoodlands.com
Ⓦ www.englishwoodlands.com
Contact: Joanne Carter
Opening Times: 0800-1700 Mon-Fri. 0800-

1630 Sat. Closed Sun & B/hols.
Min Mail Order UK: £25.00
Cat. Cost: Free.
Credit Cards: All major debit/credit cards except American Express
Specialities: Trees, shrubs, hedging. Phone to check plant availability before visiting.
Notes: Also sells wholesale. Wheelchair accessible.
Map Ref: S, C4 **OS Grid Ref:** TQ567222

SFai **Fairweather's Garden Centre** ♿
High Street, Beaulieu, Hampshire SO42 7YB
Ⓣ (01590) 612307
Ⓕ (01590) 612519
Ⓔ info@fairweathers.co.uk
Ⓦ www.fairweathers.co.uk
Contact: Sue Greaves
Opening Times: 0900-1700 7 days.
Min Mail Order UK: Nmc
Cat. Cost: None issued.
Credit Cards: Visa, MasterCard
Specialities: *Agapanthus* & *Lavandula*.
Notes: Wheelchair accessible.
Map Ref: S, D2

SGbt **Gilbert's Nursery** ♿
Dandy's Ford Lane, Sherfield English, Romsey, Hampshire SO51 6DT
Ⓣ (01794) 322566
Ⓔ gilbertsnursery@aol.com
Ⓦ www.gilbertsnursery.co.uk
Contact: Nick Gilbert
Opening Times: 0900-1700 Tue-Sat, 10.00-16.30 Sun, all year round. *Dahlia* field open from 2nd week Aug to 2nd week Oct.
Min Mail Order UK: Nmc
Min Mail Order EU: Nmc
Cat. Cost: 2 × 1st class
Credit Cards: All major debit/credit cards except American Express
Specialities: *Dahlia*. Proper plant nursery with many unusual plants & staff happy to share their knowledge & help with plant selection.
Notes: *Dahlia* field with over 400 cvs on view (grass pathways). See above for opening times or go to www.gilbertsdahlias.co.uk. Tea room. Delivers to shows. Wheelchair accessible.
Map Ref: S, C2

SGol **Golden Hill Nurseries** ♿
Lordsfield, Goudhurst Road, Marden, Kent TN12 9LT
Ⓣ (01622) 833218
Ⓜ 07826 523655
Ⓕ (01622) 832528
Ⓔ enquiries@goldenhillplants.com
Ⓦ www.goldenhillplants.com
Contact: Roger Butler
Opening Times: 0900-1700 Mon-Sat, 1st Mar-31st Oct. 0900-1600 Mon-Sat, 1st Nov-28th Feb. 1100-1600 Sun from 3rd Sun in Feb until Xmas.
Min Mail Order UK: Nmc
Cat. Cost: Online only.
Credit Cards: All major credit/debit cards
Specialities: Specimen plants, shrubs, grasses, bamboos, Japanese maples, conifers & trees.
Notes: Also sells wholesale. Euro accepted. Wheelchair accessible.

SHaC **Hart Canna** ♿
27 Guildford Road West, Farnborough, Hampshire GU14 6PS
Ⓣ (01252) 514421
Ⓜ 07762 950000
Ⓔ sales@hartcanna.com
Ⓦ www.hartcanna.co.uk
Contact: Keith Hayward
Opening Times: By arrangement.
Min Mail Order UK: Nmc
Min Mail Order EU: Nmc
Cat. Cost: Online only.
Credit Cards: All major credit/debit cards
Specialities: *Canna*. Nat. Collection of *Canna*.
Notes: Also sells wholesale. Euro accepted. Delivers to shows. Wheelchair accessible.
Map Ref: S, C3

SHal **Hall's Court Nursery** ♿
Pluckley Road, Bethersden, Ashford, Kent TN26 3ET
Ⓣ (01233) 820828
Ⓜ 07729 418275
Ⓔ info@hallscourt.co.uk
Ⓦ www.hallscourt.co.uk
Contact: Jeanette Jahnz
Opening Times: 0900-1700 every w/end, end Mar-beginning Oct. Weekdays by arrangement.
Cat. Cost: Online only.
Credit Cards: Visa, MasterCard, Maestro
Specialities: At least 90 varieties of hardy geraniums. Over 20 varieties of scented leaf pelargoniums, plus some species, zonal & ivy leaf. Perennials, grasses, hardy fuchsias, alpines, herbs & some succulents. Some plants available in small quantities only.
Notes: Small nursery, situated midway between Ashford and Tenterden in rural Kent. Euro accepted. Wheelchair accessible.
Map Ref: S, C5 **OS Grid Ref:** TQ919414

SHar **Hardy's Cottage Garden Plants** ♿
Priory Lane Nursery, Freefolk Priors, Whitchurch, Hampshire RG28 7FA
Ⓣ (01256) 896533
Ⓔ info@hardys-plants.co.uk

Ⓦ www.hardys-plants.co.uk
Contact: Rosemary Hardy
Opening Times: 1000-1700 7 days, 1st Mar-30th Sep. 1000-1600 Mon-Fri, Oct, 1000-1500 Mon-Fri, 1st Nov-28th Feb. Closed 23rd Dec-4th Jan.
Min Mail Order UK: Nmc
Cat. Cost: Online only.
Credit Cards: Visa, Access, Electron, Switch, Solo
Specialities: Wide range of herbaceous perennials incl. *Achillea, Gaura, Geum, Geranium, Hemerocallis, Heuchera, Lathryus vernus, Paeonia, Penstemon* & *Salvia.*
Notes: Accepts HTA Gift Tokens. Offers trade discount. Euro accepted. Delivers to shows. Wheelchair accessible.
Map Ref: S, C2

S

SHeu **HEUCHERAHOLICS** ♿
Boldre Nurseries, Southampton Road, Lymington, Hampshire SO41 8ND
Ⓣ (01590) 670581
Ⓜ 07973 291062
Ⓔ jooles.heucheraholics@gmail.com
Ⓦ www.heucheraholics.co.uk
Contact: Julie Burton/Sean Atkinson
Opening Times: Visits to nursery by appt. only. Please phone first. No need to make an appt. for Open Days, see website or contact nursery for details.
Min Mail Order UK: Nmc
Cat. Cost: No charge.
Credit Cards: All major credit/debit cards
Specialities: *Heuchera, Heucherella, Pulmonaria* & *Tiarella.* Other foliage plants. *Hellebore.*
Notes: Toilet facilities. Well-behaved dogs can bring their owners. Also sells wholesale. Delivers to shows. Wheelchair accessible.
Map Ref: S, D2 **OS Grid Ref:** SZ310934

SHmp **HAMPSHIRE CARNIVOROUS PLANTS**
Stroudwood Nursery, Stroudwood Lane, Lower Upham, Southampton, Hampshire SO32 1HG
Ⓣ (023) 8047 3314
Ⓜ 07703 258296
Ⓕ (023) 8047 3314
Ⓔ sales@hantsflytrap.com
Ⓦ www.hantsflytrap.com
Contact: Matthew Soper
Opening Times: Mail order only. Open by appt. only.
Min Mail Order UK: Nmc
Min Mail Order EU: £50.00 + p&p
Credit Cards: All major credit/debit cards
Specialities: Carnivorous plants esp. *Cephalotus, Darlingtonia, Dionaea, Drosera, Heliamphora, Nepenthes, Pinguicula, Sarracenia* & *Utricularia.*
Notes: Also sells wholesale. Exports beyond the EU. Euro accepted.

SHyH **HYDRANGEA HAVEN** ♿
Market Garden, Lower Beeding, West Sussex RH13 6PP
Ⓣ (01403) 891412
Ⓔ lp@hortic.com
Ⓦ www.hydrangea-haven.com
Contact: Chris Loder
Opening Times: 1000-1600 Mon-Sat, please phone first, so we can give you our undivided attention.
Min Mail Order UK: Nmc
Min Mail Order EU: Nmc
Cat. Cost: 2 × 1st class.
Credit Cards: All major debit/credit cards except American Express
Specialities: *Hydrangea*: mophead, lacecap & panicle. *Agapanthus.*
Notes: Also sells wholesale. Exports beyond EU. Delivers to shows. Euro accepted. Wheelchair accessible.
Map Ref: S, C3 **OS Grid Ref:** TQ221255

SIri **IRIS OF SISSINGHURST**
Roughlands Farm, Goudhurst Road, Marden, Kent TN12 9NH
Ⓣ (01622) 831511
Ⓔ orders@irisofsissinghurst.com
Ⓦ www.irisofsissinghurst.com
Contact: Sue Marshall
Opening Times: Contact nursery or see website for opening times.
Min Mail Order UK: Nmc
Min Mail Order EU: Nmc
Cat. Cost: Online only.
Credit Cards: None
Specialities: *Iris*, short, intermediate & tall bearded, *ensata, sibirica* & many species.
Notes: Euro accepted.

SKee **KEEPERS NURSERY**
Gallants Court, Gallants Lane, East Farleigh, Maidstone, Kent ME15 0LE
Ⓣ (01622) 326465
Ⓔ sales@keepers-nursery.co.uk
Ⓦ www.keepers-nursery.co.uk
Contact: Hamid Habibi
Opening Times: Only on a limited number of Open Days & for collection of order by arrangement.
Min Mail Order UK: Nmc
Cat. Cost: Online only.
Credit Cards: Visa, MasterCard, Switch, Maestro
Specialities: A very large range of old & rare as well as modern fruit trees varieties. Soft fruit plants & nut trees.

SKin **KINGS BARN TREES**
Kings Barn Farm, Kent Street,
Cowfold, West Sussex
RH13 8BB
Ⓣ (01403) 865405
Ⓜ 07908 708915
Ⓔ sales@kingsbarntrees.co.uk
Ⓦ www.kingsbarntrees.co.uk
Contact: Adrian Rumble
Opening Times: Not open. Mail order via website only.
Min Mail Order UK: £9.95
Min Mail Order EU: £9.95
Cat. Cost: Not available.
Credit Cards: All major credit/debit cards
Specialities: Mainly grow containerised trees, specialising in *Eucalyptus*. Also grow willow for sale as whips & setts during the winter/early spring. *Eucalyptus* available in small quantities only.

SLau **THE LAURELS NURSERY**
Benenden, Cranbrook, Kent
TN17 4JU
Ⓣ (01580) 240463
Ⓦ www.thelaurelsnursery.co.uk
Contact: Peter or Sylvia Kellett
Opening Times: 0800-1600 Wed-Fri, 0900-1200 Sat, Sun by appt. only.
Min Mail Order UK: £30
Cat. Cost: Free.
Credit Cards: All major credit/debit cards
Specialities: Open ground & container ornamental trees, shrubs & climbers especially birch, beech & *Wisteria*.
Notes: Mail order of small *Wisteria* only. Also sells wholesale. Euro accepted.
Map Ref: S, C5 **OS Grid Ref:** TQ815313

SLay **LAYHAM GARDEN CENTRE & NURSERY** ♿
Lower Road, Staple, Nr Canterbury, Kent
CT3 1LH
Ⓣ (01304) 813267
Ⓕ (01304) 814007
Ⓔ info@layhamgardencentre.co.uk
Ⓦ www.layhamgardencentre.co.uk
Contact: Ellen Wessel
Opening Times: 0900-1700 Mon-Sat, 1000-1630 Sun.
Min Mail Order UK: Nmc
Min Mail Order EU: £25.00 + p&p
Cat. Cost: Free.
Credit Cards: Visa, MasterCard
Specialities: Roses, herbaceous, shrubs, trees & hedging plants.
Notes: Mail order roses only. Also sells wholesale. Euro accepted. Wheelchair accessible.
Map Ref: S, C6 **OS Grid Ref:** TR276567

SLBF **LITTLE BROOK FUCHSIAS** ♿
Ash Green Lane West, Ash Green,
Nr Aldershot, Hampshire GU12 6HL
Ⓣ (01252) 329731
Ⓔ carol.gubler@ntlbusiness.com
Ⓦ www.littlebrookfuchsias.co.uk
Contact: Carol Gubler
Opening Times: 1000-1700 Wed-Sun 1st Jan-26th Jun.
Cat. Cost: 70p + sae.
Credit Cards: All major credit/debit cards
Specialities: Fuchsias, old & new.
Notes: Nursery located off White Lane in Ash Green. Wheelchair accessible.
Map Ref: S, C3 **OS Grid Ref:** SU901496

SLdr **LODER PLANTS** ♿
Market Garden, Lower Beeding, West Sussex
RH13 6PP
Ⓣ (01403) 891412
Ⓔ sales@rhododendrons.com
Ⓦ www.rhododendrons.com
Contact: Chris Loder
Opening Times: 1000-1600 Mon-Sat, please ring first so we can give you our undivided attention.
Min Mail Order UK: Nmc
Min Mail Order EU: Nmc
Cat. Cost: 2 × 1st class.
Credit Cards: All major debit/credit cards except American Express
Specialities: Rhododendrons & azaleas in all sizes. Some in very limited quantities only. *Agapanthus*.
Notes: Also sells wholesale. Exports beyond EU. Delivers to shows. Euro accepted. Wheelchair accessible.
Map Ref: S, C3 **OS Grid Ref:** TQ221255

SLim **LIME CROSS NURSERY** ♿
Herstmonceux, Hailsham, East Sussex
BN27 4RS
Ⓣ (01323) 833229
Ⓔ info@limecross.co.uk
Ⓦ www.limecross.co.uk
Contact: Vicky Tate, Anita Green
Opening Times: 0830-1700 Mon-Sat & 1000-1700 Sun.
Min Mail Order UK: Nmc
Min Mail Order EU: £50.00
Cat. Cost: Online only.
Credit Cards: All major credit/debit cards
Specialities: Conifers, trees & shrubs, climbers.
Notes: Wheelchair accessible.
Map Ref: S, D4 **OS Grid Ref:** TQ642125

SLon **LONGSTOCK PARK NURSERY** ♿
Longstock, Stockbridge, Hampshire
SO20 6EH
Ⓣ (01264) 810894

Ⓕ (01264) 810924
Ⓔ longstock.park.nursery@waitrose.co.uk
Ⓦ www.longstocknursery.co.uk
Contact: Mark Pitman
Opening Times: 0900-1730 Mon-Sat, 1000-1600 Sun. Closed 25th-27th Dec & 1st Jan.
Min Mail Order UK: £15.00
Credit Cards: All major credit/debit cards
Specialities: A wide range, over 2000 varieties, of trees, shrubs, perennials, climbers, aquatics & ferns. Extensive collection of *Penstemon*. Nat. Collections of *Buddleja* & *Clematis viticella*.
Notes: Wheelchair accessible.
Map Ref: S, C2 **OS Grid Ref:** SU365389

SMad **Madrona Nursery** ♿
Pluckley Road, Bethersden, Kent TN26 3DD
Ⓣ (01233) 820100
Ⓕ (01233) 820091
Ⓔ madrona@hotmail.co.uk
Ⓦ www.madrona.co.uk
Contact: Liam Mackenzie
Opening Times: 1000-1700 Sat-Tue 15th Mar-28th Oct. Other times by appt.
Cat. Cost: Free
Credit Cards: All major credit/debit cards
Specialities: Unusual shrubs, conifers & perennials. *Eryngium*, *Colletia*.
Notes: Delivers to shows. Euro accepted. Wheelchair accessible.
Map Ref: S, C5 **OS Grid Ref:** TQ918419

SMor **Morehavens**
Stocks Lane, Meonstoke, Hampshire SO32 3NQ
Ⓣ (01489) 878501
Ⓔ morehavens@camomilelawns.co.uk
Ⓦ www.camomilelawns.co.uk
Contact: E. Clements
Opening Times: Mail order only. Open for collection only.
Min Mail Order UK: £18.00
Min Mail Order EU: £18.00 + p&p
Cat. Cost: Free.
Credit Cards: Paypal
Specialities: *Camomile nobile* 'Treneague' and *C. nobile* dwarf.
Notes: Also sells wholesale.

SMHy **Marchants Hardy Plants** ♿
2 Marchants Cottages, Mill Lane, Laughton, East Sussex BN8 6AJ
Ⓣ (01323) 811737
Ⓔ graham@marchantsplants.plus.com
Ⓦ www.marchantshardyplants.co.uk
Contact: Graham Gough
Opening Times: 0930-1730 Wed-Sat, 16th Mar-22nd Oct 2016.
Cat. Cost: 3 × 2nd class
Credit Cards: Visa, MasterCard
Specialities: Uncommon herbaceous perennials. *Agapanthus*, *Erodium*, choice grasses, *Galanthus*, *Miscanthus*, *Molinia*.
Notes: Euro accepted. Wheelchair accessible.
Map Ref: S, D4 **OS Grid Ref:** TQ506119

SNig **Nightingale Nursery** ♿
Gardeners Lane, East Wellow, Romsey, Hampshire SO51 6AD
Ⓣ (023) 8081 4350
Ⓔ gfnightingale4@gmail.com
Ⓦ www.nightingalenursery.co.uk
Contact: Graham Farmiloe
Opening Times: 0800-1700 Mon-Fri & open 7 days from mid-Mar to mid-Jun.
Cat. Cost: Free.
Credit Cards: All major debit/credit cards except American Express
Specialities: *Clematis*. Also climbers & wall shrubs; herbaceous; seasonal bedding; hanging baskets.
Notes: Also sells wholesale. Wheelchair accessible.
Map Ref: S, D2

SPad **Paddock Plants**
The Paddock, Upper Toothill Road, Rownhams, Southampton, Hampshire SO16 8AL
Ⓣ (023) 8073 9912
Ⓜ 07763 386717
Ⓔ rob@paddockplants.co.uk
Ⓦ www.paddockplants.co.uk
Contact: Rob & Joanna Courtney
Opening Times: By appt. only. Please telephone in advance.
Min Mail Order UK: £10.00
Cat. Cost: Online only.
Credit Cards: All major credit/debit cards
Specialities: A family-run nursery offering an interesting range of perennials, grasses, ferns & shrubs, incl. some more unusual varieties or plants new to the UK market. All plants are grown in a peat-free medium. Some varieties grown in small quantities.
Notes: Local delivery by our own transport. Courier delivery throughout UK. Delivers to shows.
Map Ref: S, D2 **OS Grid Ref:** SU383177

SPav **Pavilion Plants**
18 Pavilion Road, Worthing, West Sussex BN14 7EF
Ⓣ (01903) 821338
Ⓜ 07776 409498
Ⓔ pavilionplants.worthing@yahoo.co.uk
Contact: Andrew Muggeridge
Opening Times: Please phone for details.
Min Mail Order UK: Nmc

Cat. Cost: 4 × 1st class.
Credit Cards: None
Specialities: Perennials and bulbs. *Digitalis*.
Notes: Also sells wholesale. Delivers to shows.
Map Ref: S, D3

SPer **PERRYHILL NURSERIES LTD** ♿
Edenbridge Road, Hartfield, East Sussex
TN7 4JP
Ⓣ (01892) 770377
Ⓕ (01892) 770929
Ⓔ sales@perryhillnurseries.co.uk
Ⓦ www.perryhillnurseries.co.uk
Contact: P J Chapman
Opening Times: 0900-1700 7 days 1st Mar-31st Oct. 0900-1630 1st Nov-28th Feb.
Min Mail Order UK: Nmc
Cat. Cost: Online only.
Credit Cards: Maestro, Visa, Access, MasterCard
Specialities: Wide range of trees, shrubs, perennials, roses, fruit trees, soft fruit. Unusual & rare plants may be available in small quantities.
Notes: Mail order despatch depends on size & weight of plants. Wheelchair accessible.
Map Ref: S, C4 **OS Grid Ref:** TQ480375

SPet **PETTET'S NURSERY** ♿
Drainless Road, Eastry, Sandwich, Kent
CT13 0EA
Ⓣ (01304) 613869
Ⓜ 07940 337520
Ⓕ (01304) 613869
Ⓔ pettets.nursery@btconnect.com
Ⓦ www.pettetsnursery.co.uk
Contact: Terry Pettet
Opening Times: 1000-1600 Tue-Sun, Mar-Oct. Closed Mon (except B/hol). Closed Nov-Feb.
Min Mail Order UK: £10.00
Cat. Cost: Online only.
Credit Cards: None
Specialities: *Pelargonium*: scented-leaf, decorative regal, unique, angel. *Fuchsia*.
Notes: Delivers to shows. Wheelchair accessible.
Map Ref: S, C6

SPhm **PARHAM HOUSE & GARDENS** ♿
Storrington, Nr Pulborough, West Sussex
RH20 4HS
Ⓣ (01903) 742021
Ⓔ gardens@parhaminsussex.co.uk
Ⓦ www.Parhaminsussex.co.uk
Contact: Tom Brown
Opening Times: 1030-1700 Wed, Thur, Fri, Sun & Bank Hols. 5th Apr-27th Oct.
Cat. Cost: None issued
Credit Cards: All major debit/credit cards except American Express
Specialities: Hardy perennials.
Notes: House open 1400-1700 on same days/dates as gardens. Wheelchair accessible.
Map Ref: S, D3

SPhx **PHOENIX PERENNIAL PLANTS**
Paice Lane, Medstead, Alton, Hampshire
GU34 5PR
Ⓣ (01420) 560695
Ⓜ 07909 528191
Ⓕ (01420) 563640
Ⓔ marina@phoenixperennialplants.co.uk
Contact: Marina Christopher
Opening Times: Open by appt. only.
Credit Cards: All major credit/debit cards
Specialities: Perennials, many uncommon & hardy, selected for beneficial insects particularly pollinators. *Agastache*, *Centaurea*, *Monarda*, *Sanguisorba*, *Sedum*, *Thalictrum*, *Verbascum*, bulbs, prairie plants, umbellifers & late-flowering perennials.
Notes: Also sells wholesale. Delivers to shows.
Map Ref: S, C2 **OS Grid Ref:** SU657362

SPin **JOHN AND LYNSEY'S PLANTS** ♿
2 Hillside Cottages, Trampers Lane, North Boarhunt, Fareham, Hampshire PO17 6DA
Ⓣ (01329) 832786
Ⓔ landjpink@tiscali.co.uk
Contact: Mrs Lynsey Pink
Opening Times: By appt. only.
Cat. Cost: None issued.
Credit Cards: None
Specialities: Mainly *Salvia* with a wide range of other unusual perennials. Stock is only available in small quantities but we are happy to try & propagate anything that we have. Nat. Collection of species *Salvia*.
Notes: Wheelchair accessible.
Map Ref: S, D2 **OS Grid Ref:** SU603109

SPlb **PLANTBASE** ♿
Sleepers Stile Road, Cousley Wood, Wadhurst, East Sussex TN5 6QX
Ⓣ (01892) 785599
Ⓜ 07967 601064
Ⓔ graham@plantbase.freeserve.co.uk
Ⓦ www.plantbase.co.uk
Contact: Graham Blunt
Opening Times: 1000-1700, 7 days all year (appt. advisable).
Min Mail Order UK: Nmc
Min Mail Order EU: Nmc
Cat. Cost: Online only.
Credit Cards: All major credit/debit cards
Specialities: Wide range of alpines, perennials, shrubs, climbers, waterside plants, herbs, Australasian, South African & South American plants in particular. Some available in small

quantities only.
Notes: Delivers to shows. Euro accepted. Wheelchair accessible.
Map Ref: S, C5

SPoG **The Potted Garden Nursery** ♿
Ashford Road, Bearsted, Maidstone, Kent ME14 4NH
Ⓣ (01622) 737801
Ⓦ www.thepottedgarden.co.uk
Contact: Any staff member
Opening Times: 0900-1730 (dusk in winter), 7 days. Xmas/New Year period opening times on website or answerphone.
Credit Cards: All major credit/debit cards
Notes: Mail order not available. Wheelchair accessible.
Map Ref: S, C5 **OS Grid Ref:** TQ810550

S

SPol **Pollie's Perennials and Daylily Nursery** ♿
Lodore, Mount Pleasant Lane, Sway, Lymington, Hampshire SO41 8LS
Ⓣ (01590) 682577
Ⓜ 07712 713765
Ⓕ (01590) 682577
Ⓔ terry.maasz@btinternet.com
Ⓦ www.polliesdaylilies.co.uk
Contact: Pollie Maasz
Opening Times: 1000-1730 w/ends & 1400-1730 Mon-Fri during the daylily season, late-May to mid-Aug. Other times by appt. only.
Min Mail Order UK: Nmc
Min Mail Order EU: £20.00
Cat. Cost: 2 × 1st class.
Credit Cards: Paypal
Specialities: *Hemerocallis*. Stock available in small quantities only. Nat. Collection of Spider & Unusual Form *Hemerocallis*. 1700+ different cvs can be viewed, mid Jun-mid Sep.
Notes: Mail order, daylilies only. Euro accepted. Wheelchair accessible.
Map Ref: S, D2

SPop **Pops Plants**
Pops Cottage, Barford Lane, Downton, Salisbury, Wiltshire SP5 3PZ
Ⓣ (01725) 511421
Ⓔ pops08@btinternet.com
Ⓦ www.popsplants.com
Contact: Lesley Roberts
Opening Times: By appt. only, please.
Min Mail Order UK: 5 plants.
Min Mail Order EU: 5 plants.
Cat. Cost: £2.50
Credit Cards: Paypal
Specialities: *Primula auricula*. Some varieties in limited numbers. Nat. Collection of Show, Alpine, Double & Striped Auriculas.
Notes: Credit cards accepted online only. Exports beyond EU: min. mail order outside EU 10 plants. Euro accepted.

SPre **Plants4Presents** ◆
The Glasshouses, Fletching Common, Newick, Lewes, East Sussex BN8 4JJ
Ⓣ (01825) 721162
Ⓔ plants@4presents.co.uk
Ⓦ www.plants4presents.co.uk
Contact: Emily Rae
Opening Times: Not open. Mail order only.
Min Mail Order UK: Nmc
Cat. Cost: Online only.
Credit Cards: All major credit/debit cards
Specialities: Well-established nursery offering a range of unusual flowering and fruiting plants, incl. citrus trees.
Notes: Delivers to shows.

SPtp **Plantstoplant**
Fromefield Nurseries Ltd, Church Lane, Awbridge, Romsey, Hampshire SO51 0HN
Ⓣ (01794) 341123
Ⓕ (01794) 341351
Ⓔ info@plantstoplant.com
Ⓦ www.plantstoplant.com
Contact: David West
Opening Times: Not open. Mail order only.
Min Mail Order UK: £12.00
Cat. Cost: Online only.
Credit Cards: All major credit/debit cards, Paypal
Specialities: Unusual plants.
Notes: Also sells wholesale.

SReu **G Reuthe Ltd**
Crown Point Nursery, Sevenoaks Road, Ightham, Nr Sevenoaks, Kent TN15 0HB
Ⓣ (01732) 865614
Ⓔ reuthe@hotmail.co.uk
Contact: Sales
Opening Times: 0900-1600 Thu-Sat. Closed Jan, Feb, Jul & Aug. Please phone before visiting as we are sometimes closed due to circumstances beyond our control. Please ask for details of special spring openings.
Credit Cards: Visa, Access
Specialities: Rhododendrons & azaleas, trees, shrubs & climbers. Some plants only available in larger sizes. Large specimen plants available in pots & open ground.
Notes: Deliveries can be arranged at cost. Landscaping & planting service.
Map Ref: S, C4

SRGP **Rosie's Garden Plants**
Fieldview Cottage, Pratling Street, Aylesford, Kent ME20 7DG
Ⓣ (01622) 715777
Ⓜ 07740 696277

Ⓕ (01622) 715777
Ⓔ jcaviolet@aol.com
Ⓦ www.rosiesgardenplants.biz
Contact: J C Aviolet
Opening Times: Not open. Mail order only.
Min Mail Order UK: Nmc
Min Mail Order EU: Nmc
Cat. Cost: Online only.
Specialities: Hardy *Geranium*, *Buddleja* & *Aster*. Herbaceous & shrubs. Roses. Grows & sells asters, hardy geraniums, roses, plants & shrubs with people's names.
Notes: Exports beyond EU. Delivers to shows. Check web for dates of shows, talks & Farmers' Markets.

SRiv **River Garden Nurseries**
Troutbeck, Otford, Sevenoaks, Kent TN14 5PH
Ⓣ (01959) 525588
Ⓔ box@river-garden.co.uk
Ⓦ www.river-garden.co.uk
Contact: Jenny Alban Davies
Opening Times: By appt. only.
Min Mail Order UK: £10.00 + p&p
Min Mail Order EU: £50.00 + p&p
Cat. Cost: 2 × 1st class.
Credit Cards: None
Specialities: *Buxus* species & cultivars. *Buxus* topiary.
Notes: Also sells wholesale. Euro accepted. Delivers to shows.
Map Ref: S, C4 **OS Grid Ref:** TQ523593

SRkn **Rapkyns Nursery** ♿
Street End Lane, Broad Oak, Heathfield, East Sussex TN21 8UB
Ⓣ (01825) 830065
Ⓜ 07771 916933
Ⓔ rapkynsnursery@hotmail.com
Ⓦ www.rapkynsnursery.co.uk
Contact: Steven Moore
Opening Times: 1000-1700 Tue, Thu & Fri, Mar-Oct incl. or by appt.
Min Mail Order UK: Nmc
Min Mail Order EU: Nmc
Cat. Cost: 2 × 1st class or online.
Credit Cards: None
Specialities: Unusual shrubs, perennials & climbers. Asters, campanulas, *Ceanothus*, geraniums, lavenders, *Clematis*, penstemons & grasses. New collections of *Crocosmia*, *Anemone*, *Heuchera*, *Heucherella*, *Phlox*, *Coreopsis* & *Helleborus*. Extensive range of salvias.
Notes: Nursery next door to Scotsford Farm, TN21 8UB. Mail order Sep-Apr incl. Also sells wholesale. Delivers to shows. Wheelchair accessible.
Map Ref: S, C4 **OS Grid Ref:** TQ604248

SRms **Rumsey Gardens** ♿
117 Drift Road, Clanfield, Waterlooville, Hampshire PO8 0PD
Ⓣ (023) 9259 3367
Ⓔ info@rumsey-gardens.co.uk
Ⓦ www.rumsey-gardens.co.uk
Contact: Mrs M A Giles
Opening Times: 0900-1700 Mon-Sat & 1000-1600 Sun & B/hols. Closed Sun Nov-Feb.
Min Mail Order UK: £15.00
Cat. Cost: Online only.
Credit Cards: American Express, Visa, MasterCard
Specialities: Wide general range. Herbaceous, alpines, heathers & ferns. Nat. & International Collection of *Cotoneaster*.
Notes: Wheelchair accessible.
Map Ref: S, D2

SRot **Rotherview Nursery** ♿
Ivy House Lane, Three Oaks, Hastings, East Sussex TN35 4NP
Ⓣ (01424) 756228
Ⓔ rotherview@btinternet.com
Ⓦ www.rotherview.com
Contact: Ray & Wendy Bates
Opening Times: 1000-1700 Mar-Oct, 1000-1530 Nov-Feb, Tue to Sun.
Min Mail Order UK: Nmc
Min Mail Order EU: Nmc
Cat. Cost: 6 × 1st class.
Credit Cards: All major credit/debit cards
Specialities: Alpines. Ferns. *Camellia*.
Notes: Nursery is on same site as Coghurst Camellias. Also sells wholesale. Delivers to shows. Euro accepted. Wheelchair accessible.
Map Ref: S, D5

SSea **Seale Rose Garden**
Seale Nurseries, Seale Lane, Seale, Farnham, Surrey GU10 1LD
Ⓣ (01252) 782410
Ⓔ catherine@sealenurseries.demon.co.uk
Ⓦ www.sealenurseries.co.uk
Contact: David & Catherine May
Opening Times: 1000-1600 Tue-Sat. Other times by appt.
Cat. Cost: None issued.
Credit Cards: Visa, Access, Delta, MasterCard
Specialities: Roses & *Pelargonium*. Some varieties in short supply, please phone first.
Map Ref: S, C3 **OS Grid Ref:** SU887477

SSFT **Sussex Fruit Trees**
Hook Farm, Nettlesworth Lane, Heathfield, East Sussex TN21 9EN
Ⓜ 07745 379526
Ⓔ mark@sussexfruittrees.co.uk
Ⓦ www.sussexfruittrees.co.uk

Contact: Mark Piper
Opening Times: 0800-1700, 7 days.
Specialities: Grows & sells a wide range of fruit trees on various rootstocks. Some Sussex apple tree cultivars.
Notes: Also provides delivery, planting, pruning, grafting, orchard maintenance & tree sundries.
Map Ref: S, D4

SSta **Starborough Nursery** ♿
Starborough Road, Marsh Green, Edenbridge, Kent
TN8 5RB
Ⓣ (01732) 865614
Ⓔ starborough@hotmail.co.uk
Contact: Sales
Opening Times: 0900-1600 Thu, Fri & Sat. Closed Jan, Jul & Aug.
Credit Cards: Visa, Access
Specialities: Rare & unusual shrubs esp. *Daphne*, *Acer*, rhododendrons & azaleas, *Magnolia* & *Nyssa*. Some plants only available in larger sizes.
Notes: Mail order only between Oct & Apr. Deliveries can be made at cost. Planting & landscaping services available. Wheelchair accessible.
Map Ref: S, C4

S

SSut **Dan Sutton** ◆
(Office) 142 Hawks Road, Hailsham, East Sussex BN27 1NA
Ⓣ (01323) 845270
Ⓜ 07772 869645
Ⓔ suttonnursery@gmail.com
Ⓦ www.suttonnursery.co.uk
Contact: Dan Sutton
Opening Times: By appt. only.
Min Mail Order UK: £5.80.
Cat. Cost: Online only.
Credit Cards: Paypal
Specialities: Herbaceous perennials, bulbs/corms, incl. *Crocosima*, grasses, specimen bamboos, *Fargesia robusta*, *F. scabrida* & *Borinda boliana*.
Notes: Also offers landscape design. Nursery at Park Wood Farmhouse, Upper Dicker, Hailsham, BN27 3QL. Also sells wholesale.

STPC **The Plant Company** ♿
Coolham Road, West Chiltington, Pulborough, West Sussex RH20 2LH
Ⓣ (01403) 740100
Ⓔ sales@theplantco.co.uk
Ⓦ www.theplantco.co.uk
Contact: Tim Ricketts
Opening Times: 0900-1730 Mon-Sat.
Min Mail Order UK: £8.95
Min Mail Order EU: Nmc
Cat. Cost: Online only.
Credit Cards: Visa, MasterCard
Specialities: A range of herbaceous, shrubs and grasses.
Notes: Also sells wholesale. Delivers to shows. Wheelchair accessible.
Map Ref: S, C3 **OS Grid Ref:** TQ111196

STrG **Terrace Gardener**
(Office) Thickets, Copthall Road, Ightham, Kent TN15 9DU
Ⓣ (01732) 883776
Ⓔ info@terracegardener.com
Ⓦ www.terracegardener.co.uk
Contact: Mike McGonigle
Opening Times: Not open. Mail order only, incl. online & telephone orders.
Min Mail Order UK: Nmc
Cat. Cost: Online only
Credit Cards: All major debit/credit cards except American Express
Specialities: Patio plants & topiary trees. Container gardening. Architectural & hardy exotics. Containers & pots.

SVen **Ventnor Botanic Garden** ♿
Undercliff Drive, Ventnor, Isle of Wight
PO38 1UL
Ⓣ (01983) 855397
Ⓔ sales@botanic.co.uk
Ⓦ www.botanic.co.uk
Contact: Chris Kidd
Opening Times: 1000-1700 7 days, all year.
Min Mail Order UK: Nmc
Min Mail Order EU: Nmc
Cat. Cost: None issued
Credit Cards: All major debit/credit cards except American Express
Specialities: Coastal, drought-tolerant, Mediterranean & southern hemisphere plants. Rare & esoteric half-hardy trees, shrubs & perennials. Nat. Collection of Hardy & Half-hardy *Puya*.
Notes: Wheelchair accessible.
Map Ref: S, D2 **OS Grid Ref:** SZ548768

SVic **Victoriana Nursery Gardens** ♿
Challock, Ashford, Kent TN25 4DG
Ⓣ (01233) 740529
Ⓔ help@victoriananursery.co.uk
Ⓦ www.victoriananursery.co.uk
Contact: Serena Shirley
Opening Times: 0930-1630 (or dusk if sooner) Mon-Fri, 1030-1500 (or dusk if sooner) Sat.
Min Mail Order UK: Nmc
Cat. Cost: Free by post or online.
Credit Cards: All major credit/debit cards
Specialities: Heritage & unusual vegetable plants, seeds, fruit trees & bushes. Specialist

grower of chillies & tomatoes, with annual tasting days. Also 600+ varieties of *Fuchsia*.
Notes: Also sells wholesale. Wheelchair accessible.
Map Ref: S, C5 **OS Grid Ref:** TR018501

SWCr **Wych Cross Nurseries** ♿
Wych Cross, Forest Row, East Sussex
RH18 5JW
Ⓣ (01342) 822705
Ⓕ (01342) 828246
Ⓔ jp@wychcross.co.uk
Ⓦ www.wychcross.co.uk
Contact: Stan Wyatt
Opening Times: 0900-1730 Mon-Sat.
Min Mail Order UK: Nmc
Cat. Cost: Free
Credit Cards: All major credit/debit cards
Specialities: Roses.
Notes: Wheelchair accessible.
Map Ref: S, C3 **OS Grid Ref:** TQ420320

SWeb **Web Garden Centre**
Meadow Farm, Sway Road, Tiptoe,
Nr Lymington, Hampshire SO41 6FR
Ⓣ (01590) 683487
Ⓜ 07786 064018
Ⓔ info@webgardencentre.com
Ⓦ www.webgardencentre.com
Contact: Stanley Jackson
Opening Times: By appt. only. Phone to arrange.
Min Mail Order UK: Nmc
Min Mail Order EU: Nmc
Cat. Cost: Online only.
Credit Cards: All major credit/debit cards
Specialities: Bespoke & traditional topiary, specimen ornamental plants, evergreen hedging (up to 6 metres tall) and 'window blockers'. Also a wide range of shrubs as well as citrus, olive, bay, *Buxus* & *Taxus*, as well as perennials, herbs & alpines.
Notes: Orders taken online. Euro accepted. Also sells wholesale.

SWhi **John Hall Plants Ltd** ♿
Whitehall Nursery, Red Lane (Off Churt Road), Headley Down, Hampshire GU35 8SR
Ⓣ (01428) 715505
Ⓜ 07714 344327
Ⓔ info@johnhallplants.com
Ⓦ www.johnhallplants.com
Contact: John Hall
Opening Times: 0900-1630 Mon-Fri, 0900-1300 Sat, by appt. only.
Min Mail Order UK: Nmc
Min Mail Order EU: Nmc
Cat. Cost: By email only.
Credit Cards: None
Specialities: *Erica*, *Calluna* & *Daboecia*.
Notes: Planting plans supplied. Also sells wholesale. Exports beyond EU. Euro accepted. Wheelchair accessible.
Map Ref: S, C3 **OS Grid Ref:** SU837371

SWvt **Wolverton Plants Ltd** ♿ ◆
Wolverton Common, Tadley, Hampshire
RG26 5RU
Ⓣ (01635) 298453
Ⓕ (01635) 299075
Ⓔ Julian@wolvertonplants.co.uk
Ⓦ www.wolvertonplants.co.uk
Contact: Julian Jones
Opening Times: 0900-1700 (or dusk Nov-Feb), 7 days. Closed Xmas/New Year.
Credit Cards: All major credit/debit cards
Specialities: Wide range of herbaceous perennials & shrubs grown on a commercial scale for the public.
Notes: Horticultural club visits welcome by prior arrangement. Also sells wholesale. Euro accepted. Wheelchair accessible.
Map Ref: S, C2 **OS Grid Ref:** SU555589

W

Wales and the West

WAbe **Aberconwy Nursery**
Graig, Glan Conwy, Conwy LL28 5TL
Ⓣ (01492) 580875
Contact: Keith & Tim Lever
Opening Times: 1000-1600 Tue-Sun Mar-Sep incl.
Cat. Cost: 2 × 2nd class.
Credit Cards: Visa, MasterCard
Specialities: Alpines, including specialist varieties, esp. gentians, dionysias, dwarf *Dianthus*, *Primula*, *Saxifraga* & dwarf ericaceous plants. Some choice shrubs & woodland plants incl. smaller ferns.
Notes: Delivers to shows.
Map Ref: W, A3 **OS Grid Ref:** SH799744

WAln **L. A. Allen**
Windy Ridge, Llandrindod Wells, Powys
LD1 5NY
Ⓔ leslie.allen@mypostoffice.co.uk
Contact: Les Allen
Opening Times: Mail order only. Open by prior appt.
Min Mail Order UK: Nmc
Min Mail Order EU: Nmc
Cat. Cost: 6 × 1st class.
Credit Cards: None
Specialities: All sections of *Primula auricula*: alpine auricula, show-edged, show-self, doubles, show-stripe. Surplus plants from private collection so available in small quantities. Occasionally only 1 or 2 available of some cvs.
Notes: Also sells wholesale.

WArt **Artisan Plant Nurseries** ♿
CLM Keder Greenhouses, Newtown, Evesham, Worcestershire
WR11 8RZ
Ⓜ 07460 661165
Ⓔ helen@artisanplantnurseries.com
Ⓦ www.artisanplantnurseries.com
Contact: Andi Strachan, Helen Lockwood
Opening Times: Open by appt. only.
Min Mail Order UK: Nmc
Min Mail Order EU: Nmc
Cat. Cost: Online only.
Credit Cards: Paypal, All major credit/debit cards
Specialities: Wide range of rare & unusual hardy perennials, especially many species plants that are beneficial to wildlife. Building collections of *Primula*, *Digitalis*, *Verbascum*, *Salvia* & *Iris*.
Notes: Group visits welcome. Talks available Jul-Mar. Plant displays for special events. Also sells wholesale. Wheelchair accessible. Delivers to shows.
Map Ref: W, C5 **OS Grid Ref:** SP066462

W

WAul **Aulden Farm**
Aulden, Leominster, Herefordshire
HR6 0JT
Ⓣ (01568) 720129
Ⓔ pf@auldenfarm.co.uk
Ⓦ www.auldenfarm.co.uk
Contact: Alun Whitehead
Opening Times: Flexible. Individuals & groups welcome. Please contact nursery. Also open for NGS.
Min Mail Order UK: £25.00
Cat. Cost: Online only.
Credit Cards: Paypal
Specialities: Nat. Collection of Siberian *Iris*.
Notes: Informal three acre country garden. Talks given.
Map Ref: W, C4 **OS Grid Ref:** SO462548

WAvo **Pershore College** ♿
Avonbank, Pershore, Worcestershire
WR10 3JP
Ⓣ (01386) 551177
Ⓔ avonbanknurseries@warwickshire.ac.uk
Ⓦ www.warwickshire.ac.uk/plantcentre
Contact: Josh Egan-Wyer
Opening Times: 0900-1700 Mon-Sat, 1000-1630 Sun (1600 in winter).
Cat. Cost: £3.50 incl. p&p
Credit Cards: All major credit/debit cards
Specialities: Extensive range of specialist plants incl. Nat. Collections of *Penstemon* (pre-1995 cvs) & *Philadelphus* cvs.
Notes: Also sells wholesale. Wheelchair accessible.
Map Ref: W, C5 **OS Grid Ref:** SO957447

WBor **Bordervale Plants** ♿
Nantyderi, Sandy Lane, Ystradowen, Cowbridge, Vale of Glamorgan CF71 7SX
Ⓣ (01446) 774036
Ⓔ bordervaleplants@gmail.com
Ⓦ www.bordervale.co.uk
Contact: Claire E Jenkins
Opening Times: 1000-1700 Fri-Sun & B/hols Mar-Sep. Very often open Mon-Thu but please make an appt. on these days if travelling some distance.
Min Mail Order UK: £20.00 + p&p
Cat. Cost: 3 × 1st class.
Specialities: Unusual herbaceous perennials, trees, shrubs & roses, as well as cottage garden plants, many displayed in the 2-acre garden.
Notes: Mail order available for smaller items, subject to season. Garden open mid-May to Sep when nursery open. Also open for NGS. See website or contact nursery for details. Delivers to shows. Nursery wheelchair accessible.
Map Ref: W, D3 **OS Grid Ref:** ST022776

WBrk **Brockamin Plants** ♿
Brockamin, Old Hills, Callow End, Worcestershire WR2 4TQ
Ⓣ (01905) 830370
Ⓔ stone.brockamin@btinternet.com
Contact: Margaret Stone
Opening Times: By appt. only.
Cat. Cost: Free.
Credit Cards: None
Specialities: Nat. Collections of *Symphyotrichum novae-angliae*, *Geranium sanguineum*, *G. macrorrhizum* & *G.* × *cantabrigiense*. Plants available in small quantities only.
Notes: Wheelchair accessible.
Map Ref: W, C5 **OS Grid Ref:** SO830488

WBuc **Bucknell Nurseries** ♿
Bucknell, Shropshire SY7 0EL
Ⓣ (01547) 530606
Ⓕ (01547) 530699
Ⓔ nickcoull@yahoo.co.uk
Contact: A N Coull
Opening Times: 0800-1700 Mon-Fri & 1000-1300 Sat.
Min Mail Order UK: Nmc
Cat. Cost: Free
Credit Cards: All major credit/debit cards
Specialities: Bare-rooted hedging conifers & forest trees.
Notes: Also sells wholesale. Euro accepted. Wheelchair accessible.
Map Ref: W, C4 **OS Grid Ref:** SO356736

WCAu **Claire Austin Hardy Plants**
White Hopton Farm, Wern Lane, Sarn, Newtown, Powys SY16 4EN

Ⓣ (01686) 670342
Ⓔ enquiries@claireaustin-hardyplants.co.uk
Ⓦ www.claireaustin-hardyplants.co.uk
Contact: Claire Austin
Opening Times: Mail order only. Open Day towards start of Jun. See website for details.
Min Mail Order UK: Nmc
Min Mail Order EU: Nmc
Cat. Cost: Free, UK only.
Credit Cards: MasterCard, Visa, Switch
Specialities: *Paeonia*, *Iris*, *Hemerocallis* & hardy plants. Nat. Collections of Bearded *Iris*.

WCFE **CHARLES F ELLIS**
Oak Piece Nurseries, Stanway Road, Stanton, Nr Broadway, Worcestershire WR12 7NQ
Ⓣ (01386) 584077
Ⓔ ellisplants@cooptel.net
Ⓦ www.ellisplants.co.uk
Contact: Charles Ellis
Opening Times: 1000-1600 Wed-Sun, 1st Apr-30th Sep incl.
Min Mail Order UK: £10.00
Cat. Cost: None issued.
Credit Cards: All major debit/credit cards except American Express
Specialities: Wide range of shrubs, conifers, climbers & perennials, some unusual. Some available in small quantities only.
Notes: Euro accepted.
Map Ref: W, C5

WChG **CHENNELS GATE GARDENS & NURSERY** ♿
Eardisley, Herefordshire HR3 6LT
Ⓣ (01544) 327288
Ⓔ mark.richard.dawson60@gmail.com
Contact: Mark Dawson
Opening Times: 1000-1700 7 days Mar-Oct.
Cat. Cost: None issued.
Credit Cards: None
Specialities: Interesting & unusual cottage garden plants, grasses & shrubs.
Notes: Wheelchair accessible.
Map Ref: W, C4

WCot **COTSWOLD GARDEN FLOWERS**
Sands Lane, Badsey, Evesham, Worcestershire WR11 7EZ
Ⓣ nursery: (01386) 833849 or mail order: (01386) 422829
Ⓜ 07812 833849
Ⓕ nursery: (01386) 49844
Ⓔ info@cgf.net
Ⓦ www.cgf.net
Contact: Mandie Potter, Bob Brown
Opening Times: 0900-1730 Mon-Fri &1000-1730 Sat & Sun, Mar-Sep. 0900-1630 Mon-Fri only, Oct-Feb. Closed from Xmas Eve for 10 days.
Min Mail Order UK: Nmc
Min Mail Order EU: Nmc
Cat. Cost: Free.
Credit Cards: All major debit/credit cards except American Express
Specialities: A very wide range of easy & unusual perennials.
Notes: Delivers to shows. Euro accepted. Limited wheelchair access.
Map Ref: W, C5 **OS Grid Ref:** SP077426

WCru **CRÛG FARM PLANTS** ♿
Caernarfon, Gwynedd LL55 1TU
Ⓣ (01248) 670232
Ⓜ 07774 980842
Ⓔ mailorder@crug-farm.co.uk
Ⓦ www.mailorder.crug-farm.co.uk
Contact: B and S Wynn-Jones
Opening Times: 0930-1630 Thu-Sat, 1st Sat in Apr to 2nd Sat in Sep. Or Mon-Fri by appt. all year.
Min Mail Order UK: Nmc
Min Mail Order EU: Nmc
Cat. Cost: Online only.
Credit Cards: All major credit/debit cards
Specialities: Unusual & rare inc. trees, shrubs, herbaceous & bulbous, mostly self-collected new introductions from the Far East & the Americas. Rare woody & climbers esp. *Acer*, *Araliaceae*, *Carpinus*, *Hydrangeaceae* & *Magnolia* with many other extraordinary introductions. Shade plants esp. *Asparagaceae*, *Convallariaceae*, *Liliaceae*, *Ranunculaceae* & *Saxifragaceae*. Many supplied bare-rooted. Nat. Collections of *Coriaria*, *Paris* & *Polygonatum*.
Notes: Delivery by overnight carrier for UK & Ireland. Courier for rest of EU. Delivers to shows. Wheelchair accessible.
Map Ref: W, A2 **OS Grid Ref:** SH509652

WDib **DIBLEYS NURSERIES** ♿ ◆
Llanelidan, Ruthin, Denbighshire LL15 2LG
Ⓣ (01978) 790677
Ⓕ (01978) 790668
Ⓔ sales@dibleys.com
Ⓦ www.dibleys.com
Contact: R Dibley
Opening Times: 1000-1700 7 days, Apr-Aug. 1000-1700 Mon-Fri, Mar, Sep & Oct.
Min Mail Order UK: Nmc
Min Mail Order EU: Nmc
Cat. Cost: Free
Credit Cards: Visa, Access, Switch, Electron, Solo
Specialities: *Streptocarpus*, *Columnea*, *Solenostemon*, *Saintpaulia* & other gesneriads & *Begonia*. Nat. Collections of *Streptocarpus*, *Saintpaulia* & *Petrocosmea*.
Notes: Also sells wholesale. Euro accepted.

Delivers to shows. Wheelchair accessible.
Map Ref: W, A3

WFar **FARMYARD NURSERIES** ♿
Dol Llan Road, Llandysul, Carmarthenshire SA44 4RL
Ⓣ (01559) 363389
Ⓜ 01267 220259
Ⓕ (01559) 362200
Ⓔ sales@farmyardnurseries.co.uk
Ⓦ www.farmyardnurseries.co.uk
Contact: Richard Bramley
Opening Times: 0900-1700 7 days, excl. Xmas Day, Boxing Day & New Year's Day.
Min Mail Order UK: Nmc
Min Mail Order EU: Nmc
Cat. Cost: None issued.
Credit Cards: Visa, Switch, MasterCard
Specialities: Large range of home grown shrubs & herbaceous perennials, incl. *Geranium*, *Helleborus* & *Primula*. Trees, shrubs, climbers, alpines, conifers & bedding plants.
Notes: Additionally sells from shop/yard in Carmarthen. Also sells wholesale. Euro accepted. Wheelchair accessible.
Map Ref: W, C2 **OS Grid Ref:** SN421406

WFib **FIBREX NURSERIES LTD** ♿
Honeybourne Road, Pebworth, Stratford-on-Avon, Warwickshire CV37 8XP
Ⓣ (01789) 720788
Ⓔ sales@fibrex.co.uk
Ⓦ www.fibrex.co.uk
Contact: U Key-Davis & R L Godard-Key
Opening Times: 0900-1700 Mon-Fri, 1st Mar-31st Aug. 0900-1600 Mon-Fri, 1st Sep-28th Feb. 1030-1600 Sat & Sun, 2nd Apr-26th Jun. Closed last 2 weeks Dec & 1st week Jan. Closed Easter Sun & Aug B/hol Mon.
Min Mail Order UK: £10.00 + p&p
Min Mail Order EU: £20.00 + p&p
Cat. Cost: 3 × 1st class.
Credit Cards: MasterCard, Visa, Maestro
Specialities: *Hedera*, ferns, *Pelargonium*, named tuberous begonias, *Hibiscus rosa-sinensis* cvs, hardy geraniums. Nat. Collections of *Pelargonium* & *Hedera*. Plant collections subject to time of year, please check by phone.
Notes: Also sells wholesale. Delivers to shows. Wheelchair accessible.
Map Ref: W, C5 **OS Grid Ref:** SP133458

WGob **THE GOBBETT NURSERY**
Farlow, Kidderminster, Worcestershire DY14 8TD
Ⓣ (01746) 718647
Ⓔ chrislink59@gmail.com
Ⓦ www.thegobbettnursery.co.uk
Contact: C H Link
Opening Times: By appt. only.
Min Mail Order UK: £10.00
Min Mail Order EU: £50.00
Cat. Cost: None issued.
Credit Cards: None
Specialities: *Syringa*, & *Cornus*. Some varieties available in small quantities only.
Notes: Delivers to shows.

WGoo **WILDEGOOSE NURSERY HOME OF BOUTS VIOLAS**
The Walled Garden, Lower Millichope, Munslow, Craven Arms, Shropshire SY7 9HE
Ⓣ (01584) 841890
Ⓜ 07798 628762
Ⓔ flowers@boutsviolas.co.uk
Ⓦ www.boutsviolas.co.uk
Contact: Laura Willgoss
Opening Times: Mail order only. Open strictly by appt. only.
Min Mail Order UK: Nmc
Min Mail Order EU: Nmc
Cat. Cost: 1st class sae.
Credit Cards: All major credit/debit cards
Specialities: *Viola*, incl. *Viola* stock from Bouts Cottage Nursery.
Notes: Delivers to shows. Euro accepted.

WGrn **GREEN'S LEAVES** ♿
36 Ford House Road, Newent, Gloucestershire GL18 1LQ
Ⓣ (01531) 820154
Ⓜ 07890 413036
Ⓔ r.paul.green@hotmail.co.uk
Ⓦ www.greensleavesnursery.co.uk
Contact: Paul Green
Opening Times: By appt. only. Please phone to arrange collection of orders from house (nursery site not open).
Min Mail Order UK: £10.00 + p&p
Cat. Cost: 4 × 2nd class.
Credit Cards: None
Specialities: Range of rare & choice shrubs, also some perennials. Ornamental grasses & sedges. Coloured foliage plants.
Notes: Also sells wholesale. Delivers to shows. Wheelchair accessible.
Map Ref: W, C4 **OS Grid Ref:** SO732273

WGSt **ROSS GARDEN STORE** ♿
The Engine Shed, Station Approach, Ashburton, Ross-on-Wye, Herefordshire HR9 7BW
Ⓣ (01989) 568999
Ⓕ (01989) 568157
Ⓔ sales@rossgardenstore.co.uk
Ⓦ www.rossgardenstore.com
Contact: Glyn Price
Opening Times: 0900-1700, Mon-Sat, incl. B/hols. 1000-1630 Sun.
Credit Cards: All major credit/debit cards

Specialities: Good general range, incl. specimen Italian stock.
Notes: Café. Garden design service. Also sells wholesale. Wheelchair accessible.

WGwG **Gwynfor Growers**
Gwynfor, Pontgarreg, Llangrannog, Llandysul, Ceredigion SA44 6AU
Ⓣ (01239) 654151
Ⓔ info@gwynfor.co.uk
Ⓦ www.gwynfor.co.uk
Contact: Steve & Angie Hipkin
Opening Times: Usually 1000-1800 or sunset if earlier, Wed, Thu & Sun, all year round.
Min Mail Order UK: Nmc
Cat. Cost: Online only.
Credit Cards: Paypal
Specialities: National Collection of *Rosmarinus* cvs. Specialist supplier of Welsh fruit trees. Classic & contemporary plants grown organically & peat-free. Some plants available in small quantities only. Rarities propagated to order.
Notes: Plants also available at local farmers' markets, plant fairs & some NGS Open Gardens. Delivers to shows.
Map Ref: W, C2 **OS Grid Ref:** SN331536

WHal **Hall Farm Nursery**
Vicarage Lane, Kinnerley, Nr Oswestry, Shropshire SY10 8DH
Ⓣ (01691) 682135
Ⓔ info@hallfarmnursery.co.uk
Ⓦ www.hallfarmnursery.co.uk
Contact: Christine & Nick Ffoulkes-Jones
Opening Times: 1000-1700, Tues-Sat, 1st Mar-1st Oct 2016.
Min Mail Order UK: £30.00 +p&p
Cat. Cost: Online only.
Credit Cards: Visa, MasterCard, Electron, Maestro
Specialities: Wide range of herbaceous perennials, woodland plants, alpine & scree plants.
Notes: Partially accessible for wheelchairs.
Map Ref: W, B4 **OS Grid Ref:** SJ333209

WHar **Harley Nursery** ♿
Harley, Shrewsbury, Shropshire SY5 6LN
Ⓣ (01952) 510241
Ⓔ plants@harleynursery.co.uk
Ⓦ www.harleynursery.co.uk
Contact: Nick Murphy & Debbie Plant
Opening Times: 0900-1730 Mon-Sat, 1000-1600 Sun & B/hols. Winter hours 0830-1630 Mon-Sat, 1000-1600 Sun & B/hols.
Cat. Cost: Online only.
Credit Cards: All major credit/debit cards
Specialities: Wide range of trees & shrubs. Large selection of fruit trees & bushes, many old & unusual varieties. Seasonal selection of conifers, climbing & herbaceous plants. Wide range of hedging & forestry plants, many available bare-root.
Notes: Wheelchair accessible.
Map Ref: W, B4 **OS Grid Ref:** SJ598020

WHCr **Hergest Croft Gardens**
Kington, Herefordshire HR5 3EG
Ⓣ (01544) 230160
Ⓜ 07968 435627
Ⓕ (01544) 232031
Ⓔ gardens@hergest.co.uk
Ⓦ www.hergest.co.uk
Contact: Stephen Lloyd
Opening Times: 1200-1730, 7 days, Apr-Oct.
Cat. Cost: None issued
Credit Cards: All major credit/debit cards
Specialities: *Acer*, *Betula* & unusual woody plants.
Notes: Limited wheelchair access.

WHer **The Herb Garden & Historical Plant Nursery**
Frondeg, Gilfachreda, New Quay, Ceredigion SA45 9SP
Ⓣ (01545) 580893
Ⓔ corinnetremaine@gmail.com
Ⓦ www.HistoricalPlants.co.uk
Contact: Corinne Tremaine
Opening Times: By appt. only.
Min Mail Order UK: Nmc
Min Mail Order EU: £50.00 + p&p sterling only.
Cat. Cost: Online only.
Credit Cards: None
Specialities: Rarer herbs, rare natives & wild flowers; rare & unusual & historical perennials, old roses, heritage pinks & Parma violets.

WHil **Hillview Hardy Plants** ♿
(off B4176), Worfield, Nr Bridgnorth, Shropshire WV15 5NT
Ⓣ (01746) 716454
Ⓜ 07974 391608
Ⓕ (01746) 716454
Ⓔ hillview@onetel.net
Ⓦ www.hillviewhardyplants.com
Contact: Ingrid, John & Sarah Millington
Opening Times: 0930-1700 Mon-Sat, Mar-mid Oct. At other times, please phone first.
Min Mail Order UK: £10.00 + p&p
Min Mail Order EU: £10.00 + p&p
Cat. Cost: Online only.
Credit Cards: All major credit/debit cards
Specialities: Choice herbaceous perennials incl. *Acanthus*, *Albuca*, *Aquilegia*, *Primula auricula*, *Eucomis*, *Ixia*, South African bulbs. Nat. Collections of *Acanthus* & *Albuca*.

Notes: Also sells wholesale. Exports beyond EU. Delivers to shows. Euro accepted. Wheelchair accessible.
Map Ref: W, B4 **OS Grid Ref:** SO772969

WHlf **HAYLOFT PLANTS**
Manor Farm, Pensham, Pershore, Worcestershire WR10 3HB
Ⓣ (01386) 554440 or (01386) 562999
Ⓕ (01386) 553833
Ⓔ info@hayloftplants.co.uk
Ⓦ www.hayloftplants.co.uk
Contact: Yvonne Walker
Opening Times: Not open. Mail order only.
Min Mail Order UK: Nmc
Min Mail Order EU: Nmc
Cat. Cost: Free.
Credit Cards: All major debit/credit cards except American Express

WHoo **HOO HOUSE NURSERY** ◆
Hoo House, Gloucester Road, Tewkesbury, Gloucestershire GL20 7DA
Ⓣ (01684) 293389
Ⓕ (01684) 293389
Ⓔ nursery@hoohouse.co.uk
Ⓦ www.hoohouse.co.uk
Contact: Julie & Robin Ritchie
Opening Times: 1000-1700 Mon-Sat, 1100-1700 Sun. Please ring to check Nov-Jan.
Cat. Cost: 3 × 1st class.
Credit Cards: All major credit/debit cards
Specialities: Wide range of herbaceous & alpines grown peat-free. *Aster*, *Cyclamen*, *Geranium*, *Penstemon*, *Saxifraga* & many later-flowering varieties.
Notes: Also sells wholesale. Euro accepted. Partially wheelchair accessible.
Map Ref: W, C5 **OS Grid Ref:** SO893293

WHor **HORTICULTURAL SALES**
Upper Brockington, Berrington Street, Bodenham, Herefordshire HR1 3HT
Ⓣ (01568) 797747
Ⓜ 07966 635005
Ⓔ pdavies@hortsales.fsnet.co.uk
Ⓦ www.hortplants.co.uk
Contact: Peter Davies
Opening Times: By appt. only.
Min Mail Order UK: Nmc
Min Mail Order EU: Nmc
Cat. Cost: Free but available by email only.
Credit Cards: Paypal
Specialities: Wide selection of less commonly grown shrubs, available in small quantities only.
Notes: Plant finding service. 39 years experience in trade. Also sells wholesale. Euro accepted.
Map Ref: W, C4

WHrl **HARRELLS HARDY PLANTS**
(Office) 15 Coxlea Close, Evesham, Worcestershire WR11 4JS
Ⓣ (01386) 443077
Ⓜ 07799 577120 or 07733 446606
Ⓔ mail@harrellshardyplants.co.uk
Ⓦ www.harrellshardyplants.co.uk
Contact: Liz Nicklin & Kate Phillips
Opening Times: By appt. only. Please telephone.
Min Mail Order UK: Nmc
Min Mail Order EU: Nmc
Cat. Cost: Online plant list.
Credit Cards: None
Specialities: Display gardens showcase wide range of hardy perennials, esp. *Hemerocallis* & grasses.
Notes: Nursery located off Rudge Rd, Evesham. Please phone for directions or see website. Partial wheelchair access.
Map Ref: W, C5 **OS Grid Ref:** SP033443

WJas **PAUL JASPER TREES**
(Office) The Lighthouse, Bridge Street, Leominster, Herefordshire HR6 8DX
Ⓔ jaspertreescouk@aol.com
Ⓦ www.jaspertrees.co.uk
Contact: Paul Jasper
Opening Times: Not open. Mail order only.
Min Mail Order UK: £20.00 + p&p
Cat. Cost: Online only.
Credit Cards: All major credit/debit cards
Specialities: Full range of fruit & ornamental trees. Over 100 modern and traditional fruit tree varieties plus 100 ornamental tree varieties, all direct from the grower. Many unusual varieties of *Malus domestica* & *Prunus*.
Notes: Regular updates & notes on website. Also sells wholesale. Delivers to shows.
Map Ref: W, C4 **OS Grid Ref:** SO495595

WJPR **JPR ENVIRONMENTAL**
The Malt House, Standish, Stonehouse, Gloucestershire GL10 3DL
Ⓣ (01453) 811537
Ⓔ enquiries@jprenvironmental.co.uk
Ⓦ www.jprwillow.co.uk
Contact: John Robinthwaite
Opening Times: Not open. Mail order only. 0900-1700, Mon-Fri.
Min Mail Order UK: £6.00
Credit Cards: All major debit/credit cards except American Express
Specialities: *Salix*.
Notes: Also sells wholesale.

WKif **KIFTSGATE COURT GARDENS** ♿
Kiftsgate Court, Chipping Camden, Gloucestershire GL55 6LN
Ⓣ (01386) 438777

Ⓕ (01386) 438777
Ⓔ anne@kiftsgate.co.uk
Ⓦ www.kiftsgate.co.uk
Contact: Mrs J Chambers
Opening Times: 1200-1800 Sat-Wed, May, Jun & Jul. 1400-1800 Sat-Wed, Aug. 1400-1800 Sun, Mon & Wed, Apr & Sep.
Cat. Cost: None issued
Credit Cards: All major debit/credit cards except American Express
Specialities: Small range of unusual plants.
Notes: Wheelchair accessible.
Map Ref: W, C5 **OS Grid Ref:** SP170430

WMAq MEREBROOK WATER PLANTS
Kingfisher Barn, Merebrook Farm, Hanley Swan, Worcestershire WR8 0DX
Ⓣ (01684) 310950
Ⓜ 07876 777066
Ⓔ enquiries@pondplants.co.uk
Ⓦ www.pondplants.co.uk
Contact: Roger Kings & Biddi Kings
Opening Times: Not open. Mail order only.
Min Mail Order UK: Nmc
Min Mail Order EU: £25.00
Cat. Cost: Online only.
Credit Cards: All major credit/debit cards
Specialities: *Nymphaea*, Louisiana irises & other aquatic plants. International Waterlily & Water Gardening Soc. accredited collection.

WMil ANNE MILNER
Meadow House, Baunton, Cirencester, Gloucestershire GL7 7BB
Ⓣ (01285) 643731
Ⓔ anne.milner@btinternet.com
Ⓦ www.blissiris.co.uk
Contact: Anne Milner
Opening Times: By appt. only.
Min Mail Order UK: Nmc
Min Mail Order EU: Nmc
Cat. Cost: 50p (UK) £1.00 (EU) to cover postage.
Credit Cards: None
Specialities: Nat. Collection of *Iris* (A.J. Bliss introductions). Available in small quantities only.
Notes: Euro accepted. Delivers to some shows, check with nursery.

WMon NATIONAL COLLECTION OF MONARDA
Glyn Bach, Pont Hywel, Efailwen, Pembrokeshire SA66 7JP
Ⓣ (01994) 419104
Ⓜ 07828 199303
Ⓔ carole.whittaker7@btinternet.com
Ⓦ www.glynbachgardens.co.uk
Contact: Carole Whittaker
Opening Times: Open by appt. & May-Oct for collection of orders only.
Min Mail Order UK: Nmc
Min Mail Order EU: Nmc
Cat. Cost: Online only.
Credit Cards: None
Specialities: National Collection of *Monarda*. Limited stock available.
Notes: Gardens open under NGS and by appt. Talks given. If travelling some distance please contact nursery to check plant availability.
Map Ref: W, C2 **OS Grid Ref:** SN132275

WMoo MOORLAND COTTAGE PLANTS
Rhyd-y-Groes, Brynberian, Crymych, Pembrokeshire SA41 3TT
Ⓣ (01239) 891363
Ⓦ www.moorlandcottageplants.co.uk
Contact: Jennifer Matthews
Opening Times: 1030-1700 daily excl. Wed 1st Mar-30th Sep.
Min Mail Order UK: £40.00 + carriage
Cat. Cost: 4 × 1st class.
Credit Cards: All major credit/debit cards
Specialities: Traditional & unusual hardy perennials raised outside. Many garden-worthy rarities. Cottage garden plants incl. many *Astilbe*, *Crocosmia*, *Geum*, *Geranium*, *Monarda*, *Potentilla*, *Persicaria* & *Veronicastrum*. Plants for shade incl. ferns, moisture lovers & ornamental grasses. Colourful ground cover.
Notes: Display garden with mountain & moorland views open for NGS from mid-May to end Sep. Partial wheelchair access.
Map Ref: W, C2 **OS Grid Ref:** SN091343

WMou MOUNT PLEASANT TREES LTD ♿
Rockhampton, Berkeley, Gloucestershire GL13 9DU
Ⓣ (01454) 260348
Ⓔ info@mountpleasanttrees.com
Ⓦ www.mountpleasanttrees.com
Contact: Tom Locke & Elizabeth Murphy
Opening Times: 0830-1630 Mon-Fri, 0830-1230 Sat, Oct-Apr.
Min Mail Order UK: Nmc but p&p quoted on individual basis.
Cat. Cost: Free.
Credit Cards: All major credit/debit cards
Specialities: Wide range of trees for forestry, hedging, woodlands & gardens esp. *Populus*, *Salix*, *Tilia* & *Quercus*.
Notes: Mail order available for plants under 1m in height, quotes on request. Also sells wholesale. Wheelchair accessible.
Map Ref: W, D4 **OS Grid Ref:** ST654929

WNHG NEW HOPE GARDENS ♿
(Office) The Old Chapel, Cefn Einion, Nr Bishops Castle, Shropshire SY9 5LF
Ⓣ Office: (01588) 630750

Ⓔ newhopegardensmz@aol.com
Ⓦ www.newhopegardens.com
Contact: Mark Zenick
Opening Times: Open w/ends: 1000-1700 Sat & Sun, 25th/26th Jun; 2nd/3rd, 9th/10th, 16th/17th, 23rd/24th, 30th/31st Jul. Or by appt.
Min Mail Order UK: Nmc
Min Mail Order EU: Nmc
Cat. Cost: Online only. Plant list on request.
Credit Cards: All major credit/debit cards
Specialities: American bred, British grown, *Hemerocallis*. Ships bare-rooted plants. Daylily plants are growing and for sale at New Hope Gardens, Colebatch Farm, Shropshire on open w/ends.
Notes: Wheelchair accessible.
Map Ref: W, B4 **OS Grid Ref:** SO872317

WNPC NEWENT PLANT CENTRE ♿
Little Verzons Farm, Hereford Road, Ledbury, Herefordshire
HR8 2PZ
Ⓣ (01531) 670121
Ⓔ markmoir999@btinternet.com
Ⓦ www.newentplantcentre.co.uk
Contact: Mark Moir
Opening Times: 0900-1700 Mon-Sat, 1000-1600 Sun.
Credit Cards: All major credit/debit cards
Specialities: Extensive range of *Heuchera* & *Euphorbia*. Herbaceous perennials, climbers, shrubs, trees, alpines, herbs, roses & fruit.
Notes: Delivers to shows. Wheelchair accessible.
Map Ref: W, C4 **OS Grid Ref:** SO665395

WOld OLD COURT NURSERIES
Colwall, Nr Malvern, Worcestershire
WR13 6QE
Ⓣ (01684) 540416
Ⓜ 07971 522891
Ⓔ oldcourtnurseries@btinternet.com
Ⓦ www.autumnasters.co.uk
Contact: Paul, Meriel or Helen Picton
Opening Times: 1400-1700 Wed-Sat, May-Aug. 1100-1700 Wed-Sun, Aug. 1100-1700 7days, 1st week Sep-2nd week Oct. Also by appt. May to Oct.
Min Mail Order UK: Nmc
Min Mail Order EU: Nmc
Cat. Cost: Free.
Credit Cards: All major debit/credit cards except American Express
Specialities: Nat. Collection of Michaelmas Daisies. Herbaceous perennials.
Notes: Mail order sent in spring only. Display garden open Aug-Oct.
Map Ref: W, C4 **OS Grid Ref:** SO759430

WOth OTHER FELLOW FUCHSIAS
25 Spring Meadow Road, Lydney, Gloucestershire GL15 5LF
Ⓣ (01594) 844452
Ⓜ 07564 357637
Ⓔ info@otherfellow.co.uk
Ⓦ otherfellow.co.uk
Contact: Nick Egginton
Opening Times: Not open. Mail order only. No public access. Phones open 0830-1730 Mon-Fri, 0900-1300 Sat.
Min Mail Order UK: Nmc
Min Mail Order EU: £10.50 + p&p
Cat. Cost: Online or printed list only free. Full colour catalogue £2.25.
Credit Cards: All major credit/debit cards
Specialities: Large collection of *Fuchsia*, esp. unusual, single & exhibition varieties. Small selection of *Salvia* & *Brugmansia*. Some stock available in small quantities only. Can propagate to order.
Notes: Exports beyond EU. Euro accepted.

WOut OUT OF THE COMMON WAY
(Office) Penhyddgan, Boduan, Pwllheli, Gwynedd LL53 8YH
Ⓣ office: (01758) 721577 or nursery: (01407) 720431
Ⓔ ziggymen22@hotmail.co.uk
Contact: Joanna Davidson (nursery) Margaret Mason (office & mail order)
Opening Times: By arrangement.
Min Mail Order UK: Nmc
Min Mail Order EU: Nmc
Cat. Cost: A5 sae large letter rate postage.
Credit Cards: None
Specialities: *Labiates*, esp. *Nepeta* & *Salvia*. *Symphyotrichum*, *Geranium* & *Crocosmia*. Native plants. Some plants propagated in small quantities only. Will propagate salvias to order.
Notes: Nursery is at Pandy Treban, Bryngwran, Anglesey. Delivers to shows. Euro accepted. Partially accessible for wheelchairs.
Map Ref: W, A2 **OS Grid Ref:** SH370778

WPGP PAN-GLOBAL PLANTS ♿
The Walled Garden, Frampton Court, Frampton-on-Severn, Gloucestershire
GL2 7EX
Ⓣ (01452) 741641
Ⓜ 07801 275138
Ⓔ info@panglobalplants.com
Ⓦ www.panglobalplants.com
Contact: Nick Macer
Opening Times: 1100-1700 Wed-Sun 1st Feb-31st Oct. Also B/hols. Closed 2nd Sun in Sep. Winter months by appt., please phone first.
Min Mail Order UK: £22.00

Min Mail Order EU: £25.00
Cat. Cost: 6 × 1st class.
Credit Cards: Maestro, MasterCard, Visa, Solo, Delta
Specialities: A serious plantsman's nursery offering a very wide selection of correctly named, rare & desirable trees, shrubs, herbaceous, bamboos, exotics, climbers, ferns etc. Specialities incl. *Magnolia*, *Hydrangea*, *Tilia*, *Betula*, *Sorbus*, *Bamboo* & *Agavaceae*.
Notes: Wheelchair accessible.
Map Ref: W, D5 **OS Grid Ref:** SO750080

WPnP **Penlan Perennials** ♿
Wern Rhos, Newchapel, Boncath, Pembrokeshire SA37 0EN
Ⓣ (01239) 842260
Ⓜ 07857 675312
Ⓔ info@penlanperennials.co.uk
Ⓦ www.penlanperennials.co.uk
Contact: Richard Cain
Opening Times: Open for collection of orders & by appt..
Min Mail Order UK: Nmc
Min Mail Order EU: Nmc
Cat. Cost: Online PDF, or sae for CD-ROM.
Credit Cards: All major credit/debit cards
Specialities: Aquatic, marginal & bog plants. Shade-loving & woodland perennials, ferns & hardy geraniums, all grown organically in peat-free compost.
Notes: Mail order all year, next day delivery. Secure online web ordering. Also sells wholesale. Euro accepted. Delivers to shows. Wheelchair accessible.
Map Ref: W, C2 **OS Grid Ref:** SN217392

WPtf **Pantyfod Garden & Nursery**
Llandewi Brefi, Tregaron, Ceredigion SY25 6PE
Ⓣ (01570) 400564 (answering service)
Ⓜ 74739 22858
Ⓔ suepantyfod@gmail.com
Ⓦ www.pantyfodgarden.co.uk
Contact: Susan Rowe
Opening Times: 1200-1800 Sat only, mid Apr-mid Sep, nursery & garden. Other times by arrangement. Garden open under the NGS with plants for sale. Please check with NGS for Open Days.
Min Mail Order UK: Nmc
Min Mail Order EU: Nmc
Cat. Cost: Online only.
Credit Cards: Paypal
Specialities: Hardy geraniums, unusual hardy perennials, grasses, plants for moist soil, black plants, woodland plants. All plants grown largely peat-free. Many plants available in small quantities only.
Notes: Stock changes throughout the year as new varieties are added. Not all plants available for mail order. Mail order plants may be sent bare-rooted when dormant. Some listed plants ready later in the year. See website for regular updates or phone/email.
Map Ref: W, C3 **OS Grid Ref:** SN654540

WRHF **Red House Farm** ♿
Flying Horse Lane, Bradley Green, Nr Redditch, Worcestershire B96 6QT
Ⓣ (01527) 821269
Ⓔ redhousenursery@googlemail.com
Ⓦ www.redhousefarmgardenandnursery.co.uk
Contact: Mrs Maureen Weaver
Opening Times: 1000-1700 Mon-Sat all year. 1000-1700 Sun & B/hols.
Cat. Cost: 2 × 1st class.
Credit Cards: None
Specialities: Cottage garden perennials.
Notes: Wheelchair accessible.
Map Ref: W, C5 **OS Grid Ref:** SO986623

WSFF **Saith Ffynnon Wildlife Plants** ♿
Whitford, Holywell, Flintshire CH8 9EQ
Ⓣ (01352) 711198
Ⓕ (01352) 716777
Ⓔ jan@7wells.org
Ⓦ www.7wells.co.uk
Contact: Jan Miller
Opening Times: By appt. only.
Min Mail Order UK: Nmc
Min Mail Order EU: Nmc
Cat. Cost: 2 × 1st class (list only) or full catalogue online.
Credit Cards: All major credit/debit cards
Specialities: Plants and seeds to attract bees, butterflies & other wildlife. Natural dye plants. Nat. Collection of *Eupatorium*. Stock available in small quantities unless ordered well in advance.
Notes: Percentage of profits go to conservation. Credit cards accepted via website only. Also sells wholesale. Euro accepted. Wheelchair accessible.

WSHC **Stone House Cottage Nurseries** ♿
Church Lane, Stone, Nr Kidderminster, Worcestershire DY10 4BG
Ⓜ 07817 921146
Ⓔ louisa@shcn.co.uk
Ⓦ www.shcn.co.uk
Contact: L N Arbuthnott
Opening Times: 1000-1700 Wed-Sat, late Mar-early Sep only.
Cat. Cost: Sae
Credit Cards: None
Specialities: Small general range esp. wall shrubs, climbers & unusual plants.
Notes: Wheelchair accessible.
Map Ref: W, C5 **OS Grid Ref:** SO863750

WShi **SHIPTON BULBS**
Y Felin, Henllan Amgoed, Whitland, Carmarthenshire SA34 0SL
Ⓣ (01994) 240637
Ⓕ (01994) 240637
Ⓔ admin@shiptonbulbs.co.uk
Ⓦ www.shiptonbulbs.co.uk
Contact: John Shipton & Astra Shipton
Opening Times: By appt. only.
Min Mail Order UK: Nmc
Min Mail Order EU: Nmc
Cat. Cost: Sae.
Credit Cards: All major credit/debit cards
Specialities: Native British bulbs. Bulbs & plants for naturalising.
Notes: Also sells wholesale. Euro accepted.
Map Ref: W, D2 **OS Grid Ref:** SN188207

WSpi **SPINNEYWELL NURSERY**
Spinneywell Farm, Waterlane, Oakridge, Stroud, Gloucestershire GL6 7PH
Ⓣ (01452) 770092
Ⓜ 07986 887158
Ⓕ (01452) 770151
Ⓔ spinneywellsales@btconnect.com
Ⓦ www.plantproviders.co.uk
Contact: Wendy Asher
Opening Times: 0900-1700 Sat only, otherwise by prior appt. only. Also advertised Open Days. Check website or contact nursery for details.
Min Mail Order UK: £10.00 + p&p
Min Mail Order EU: £30.00 + p&p
Cat. Cost: Online only.
Credit Cards: All major credit/debit cards
Specialities: *Buxus*, *Taxus* & unusual herbaceous & shrubs. Hellebores, euphorbias, *Ceanothus*, hardy geraniums.
Notes: Plant sourcing service available. Mail order only. Also sells wholesale. Delivers to shows.

WSSs **SHROPSHIRE SARRACENIAS** ♿
5 Field Close, Malinslee, Telford, Shropshire TF4 2EH
Ⓣ (01952) 501598
Ⓔ mike@carnivorousplants.uk.com
Ⓦ www.carnivorousplants.uk.com
Contact: Mike King
Opening Times: By appt. only.
Min Mail Order UK: Nmc
Min Mail Order EU: Nmc
Cat. Cost: 2 × 1st class.
Credit Cards: Paypal
Specialities: *Sarracenia*. *Dionaea muscipula* & forms. Some stock available in small quantities only. Nat. Collections of *Sarracenia* & *Dionaea*.
Notes: Exports beyond EU. Delivers to shows. Euro accepted. Wheelchair accessible.
Map Ref: W, B4 **OS Grid Ref:** SJ689085

WTan **TAN-Y-LLYN NURSERIES**
Meifod, Powys SY22 6YB
Ⓣ (01938) 500370
Ⓔ info@tanyllyn-nursery.co.uk
Ⓦ www.tanyllyn-nursery.co.uk
Contact: Callum Johnston
Opening Times: By appt. only. Please phone.
Cat. Cost: None issued
Specialities: Herbs, alpines, perennials.
Map Ref: W, B3 **OS Grid Ref:** SJ167125

WThu **THUYA ALPINE NURSERY**
Glebelands, Hartpury, Gloucestershire GL19 3BW
Ⓣ (01452) 700548 (ring between 1900-2100 hours)
Contact: S W Bond
Opening Times: 1000-dusk Sat & B/hols. 1100-dusk Sun, Weekdays appt. advised.
Min Mail Order UK: £6.00 + p&p
Min Mail Order EU: £12.00 + p&p
Cat. Cost: 4 × 2nd class.
Credit Cards: None
Specialities: Wide and changing range including rarities, available in smallish numbers.
Notes: Will deliver plants to AGS shows only. Partially accessible for wheelchair users.
Map Ref: W, C5

WTor **TORTWORTH PLANTS LTD**
Old Lodge Farm, Tortworth, Wotton-under-Edge, Gloucestershire GL12 8HF
Ⓣ (01454) 260020
Ⓕ (01454) 260020
Ⓔ info@tortworthplants.co.uk
Ⓦ www.tortworthplants.co.uk
Contact: Rebecca Flint or Tim Hancock
Opening Times: By appt. only.
Min Mail Order UK: Nmc
Cat. Cost: Online or 2 × 1st for plant list.
Credit Cards: All major credit/debit cards
Specialities: Herbaceous perennials & alpines, incl. rare & unusual.
Notes: Also sells wholesale. Partial wheelchair access. Delivers to shows.
Map Ref: W, D4

WTre **WALLED GARDEN TREBERFYDD**
Llangasty, Brecon, Powys LD3 7PX
Ⓣ (01874) 730169
Ⓜ 07711 222700
Ⓔ alison@walledgardentreberfydd.com
Ⓦ www.walledgardentreberfydd.com
Contact: Alison Sparshatt
Opening Times: 1000-1700 daily, Apr-Oct. 1000-1600 daily, Nov-Mar.
Credit Cards: All major debit/credit cards except American Express

Specialities: Old-fashioned plant nursery in a 2-acre walled garden. Hardy plants grown in Wales which are structural, unusual, herbal or fragrant. Special emphasis on herbs & wild flowers. Display beds for all plants on sale. All plants grown peat-free.
Notes: Tea & cake available.
Map Ref: W, C4 **OS Grid Ref:** SO128255

WTSh **Tree Shop Ltd**
Unit 16, Harts Barn, Monmouth Road, Longhope, Gloucestershire
GL17 0QD
Ⓣ (01452) 832100
Ⓕ (01452) 831273
Ⓔ office@tree-shop.co.uk
Ⓦ www.tree-shop.co.uk
Contact: Helen Conneely & Lorraine Organ
Opening Times: By appt. only 0830-1600 Mon-Fri. Please phone first.
Min Mail Order UK: Nmc
Cat. Cost: Free.
Credit Cards: All major debit/credit cards except American Express
Specialities: Trees, hedging, shrubs.

WViv **Viv Marsh Postal Plants** ♿
Hunkington Nurseries, Walford Heath, Shrewsbury, Shropshire SY4 2HT
Ⓣ (01939) 291475
Ⓔ mail@postalplants.co.uk
Ⓦ www.postalplants.co.uk
Contact: Mr Viv Marsh
Opening Times: Open 2 w/ends a year. Please phone or see website for details.
Min Mail Order UK: 3 *Alstroemeria* or 4 *Iris.*
Min Mail Order EU: 3 *Alstroemeria* or 4 *Iris.*
Cat. Cost: Free.
Credit Cards: All major credit/debit cards
Specialities: Specialists in *Alstroemeria*. Nat. Collection of *Alstroemeria*, viewing by appt.
Notes: Wheelchair access to tunnels but no disabled toilet.
Map Ref: W, B4 **OS Grid Ref:** SJ445197

WWct **Walcot Organic Nursery**
Lower Walcot Farm, Walcot Lane, Drakes Broughton, Pershore, Worcestershire
WR10 2AL
Ⓣ (01905) 841587
Ⓜ 07780 547983
Ⓔ enquiries@walcotnursery.co.uk
Ⓦ www.walcotnursery.co.uk
Contact: Kevin O'Neill
Opening Times: 0800-1700 Mon-Fri. 1000-1300 Sat. Nov-Mar only.
Min Mail Order UK: £12.50
Cat. Cost: Free.
Credit Cards: All major credit/debit cards
Specialities: Organic fruit trees. Apples, plums, pears, cherries, quinces etc on different rootstocks.
Notes: Also sells wholesale.
Map Ref: W, C5 **OS Grid Ref:** SO944461

WWFP **Whitehall Farmhouse Plants**
Sevenhampton, Cheltenham, Gloucestershire
GL54 5TL
Ⓣ (01242) 820772
Ⓜ 07711 021034
Ⓔ info@wfplants.co.uk
Ⓦ www.wfplants.co.uk
Contact: Victoria Logue
Opening Times: By appt. only.
Min Mail Order UK: Nmc
Credit Cards: None
Specialities: A small nursery producing a range of interesting & easy hardy perennials for the garden. Some plants held in small quantities only.
Notes: Delivers to shows.
Map Ref: W, C5 **OS Grid Ref:** SP018229

WWtn **Westonbury Mill Water Garden** ♿
Pembridge, Herefordshire HR6 9HZ
Ⓣ (01544) 388650
Ⓕ (01544) 388650
Ⓔ westonburymillnursery@gmail.com
Ⓦ www.westonburymillwatergardens.com
Contact: Richard Pim
Opening Times: 1100-1700 daily, 1st Apr-30th Sep. By appt. only at other times & to arrange collection. Please contact nursery for orders outside open season.
Specialities: Range of herbaceous plants suitable for a wide range of growing conditions, with special emphasis on plants for the water garden & bog areas. Plants available in small quantities & seasonally. Contact nursery to confirm availability before travelling.
Notes: Café. Wheelchair accessible.
Map Ref: W, C4

Abroad

XAbr **Abriherbs**
La Gigude, Soulatge 11330, France
Ⓣ +33 685 651155
Ⓕ +33 685 651155
Ⓔ abriherbs@gmail.com
Contact: Jocasta Lyman-Dixon
Opening Times: By appt. only.
Min Mail Order UK: Nmc
Min Mail Order EU: Nmc
Cat. Cost: Sae for free plant list.
Specialities: Natural medicinal and rare plants.
Notes: Exports beyond EU. Euro accepted.

XBar **Barnhaven Primroses**
Keranguiner, Plestin-les-grèves 22310, France
Ⓣ +33 2 9635 6841
Ⓜ +33 6 6124 7739
Ⓕ +33 2 9635 6841
Ⓔ info@barnhaven.com
Ⓦ www.barnhaven.com
Contact: Lynne Lawson & Rob Mitchell
Opening Times: 1400-1700 Feb-Apr. For visits outside this period, please phone first.
Min Mail Order UK: Nmc
Min Mail Order EU: Nmc
Credit Cards: Visa, MasterCard, Paypal
Specialities: *Primula*. French Nat. Collection of Barnhaven *Primula* hybrids. Certified collection of *Primula auricula* cvs. Old-fashioned and double primroses. Large collection of Asiatic and Alpine *Primula*. Seeds & plants available worldwide.
Notes: Exports beyond EU. Euro & sterling accepted. Delivers to shows.

XBlo **Table Bay View Nursery**
PO Box 12123, Mill Street, Cape Town 8010, South Africa
Ⓣ +27 21 683 5108
Ⓕ +27 21 683 5108
Ⓔ info@tablebayviewnursery.co.za
Contact: Terence Bloch
Opening Times: Mail order only. No personal callers.
Min Mail Order UK: £15.00 + p&p
Min Mail Order EU: £15.00
Cat. Cost: £3.40 (postal order)
Credit Cards: None
Specialities: Tropical & sub-tropical ornamental & fruiting plants. Self-harvested seed, predominently from our own inventory of mother stock plants.
Notes: Due to high local bank charges, cannot accept foreign bank cheques, only undated postal orders. To comply with UK import regulations, prospective buyers must register with DEFRA before placing an order. Exports beyond EU. Euro accepted.

XEll **Ellebore**
La Chamotière, 61360 Saint-Jouin-de-Blavou, France
Ⓣ +33 2 3383 3772
Ⓜ +33 6802 28674
Ⓕ +33 2 3383 3773
Ⓔ pepiniere.ellebore@orange.fr
Ⓦ www.pepiniere-ellebore.fr
Contact: Nadine Albouy & Christian Geoffroy
Opening Times: 1000-1800 Wed-Sat, mid-Feb to late Jun & Sep-Dec. 1500-1800 Thu, Fri & Sat, Jul, Aug & Jan to mid-Feb.
Min Mail Order UK: Nmc
Min Mail Order EU: Nmc
Cat. Cost: Free.
Credit Cards: All major credit/debit cards
Specialities: *Helleborus*. Bulbs. *Clematis*.
Notes: Also sells wholesale. Euro accepted. Delivers to shows. Exports beyond EU.

XFro **Frosch Exclusive Perennials**
Ziegelstadelweg 5, D-83623 Dietramszell-Lochen, Germany
Ⓣ +49 172 842 2050
Ⓕ +49 8027 904 9975
Ⓔ info@cypripedium.de
Ⓦ www.cypripedium.de
Contact: Michael Weinert
Opening Times: Not open. Mail order only. Orders taken between 0700-2200 hours.
Min Mail Order UK: £350.00 + p&p
Min Mail Order EU: £350.00 + p&p
Cat. Cost: Online only.
Credit Cards: None
Specialities: *Cypripedium* hybrids. Hardy orchids.
Notes: Also sells wholesale. Exports beyond EU. Euro accepted.

XGra **Graefswinning**
Diestersteenweg 222, 3850 Nieuwerkerken, Belgium
Ⓣ +32 1188 3611
Ⓔ info@graefswinning.be
Ⓦ www.graefswinning.be
Contact: Jeaninne Lemmens
Opening Times: Open Apr-Jun to view flower fields. Check website for further information.
Min Mail Order UK: Nmc
Min Mail Order EU: Nmc
Cat. Cost: Online only.
Credit Cards: MasterCard, Visa, Paypal
Specialities: Herbaceous, tree & Itoh peonies. Several acres of peonies in the field. Containerised peonies in sturdy 7L pots as well as bare-root plants. Landscape & cut-flower varieties.
Notes: Bare-root peonies are shipped in autumn to countries within the EU. Container plants available at nursery & garden shows. Exports beyond EU. Euro accepted.

XHod **SCEA Hodnik**
1 Place du 19 Mars 1962, 45700 St Maurice sur Fessard, France
Ⓣ (33) 02 3897 8459
Ⓕ (33) 02 3897 8939
Ⓔ contact@hodnik.com
Ⓦ www.hodnik.com
Contact: André Hodnik
Opening Times: Not open except by appt. Mail order only.
Min Mail Order UK: Nmc

Min Mail Order EU: Nmc
Cat. Cost: Online only.
Credit Cards: All major credit/debit cards
Specialities: A large number of tropical & Mediterreanean plants which can be grown in a conservatory. French National Collection nationale of *Bougainvillea* & *Brugmansia*.
Notes: Weekly shipments to the UK. Euro accepted.

XLum **Lumen Plantes Vivaces**
Les Coutets, 24100 Creysse-Bergerac, Occitania, France
Ⓣ +33 5 5357 6215
Ⓔ ets.lumen@gmail.com
Ⓦ www.lumen.fr
Contact: Jordi & Amélie Tura
Opening Times: 0800-1730 Mon-Sat. Closed Sun.
Min Mail Order UK: Nmc
Min Mail Order EU: Nmc
Cat. Cost: Online only.
Credit Cards: Visa, MasterCard, Paypal
Specialities: Hardy perennials. French Nat. Collection of *Miscanthus*.
Notes: Also sells wholesale. Exports beyond EU. Delivers to shows. Euro accepted.
OS Grid Ref: N44 51.789 E0 32.0518

XPou **Koen Van Poucke** ♿
Heistraat 106, Sint-Niklaas, Oost-Vlaanderen 9100, Belgium
Ⓣ +32 0377 77642
Ⓕ +32 0376 61698
Ⓔ kvanpoucke@skynet.be
Ⓦ www.koenvanpoucke.be
Contact: Koen Van Poucke
Opening Times: 0900-1230 & 1300-1800, Tue-Sat. Closed Sun & Mon. Closed Jul. Check website or contact nursery before travelling a long distance.
Min Mail Order UK: €100
Min Mail Order EU: €100
Credit Cards: None
Specialities: *Epimedium*. Also rare Asian shade plants. *Dahlia*.
Notes: Mail order Sep-Apr. Collector's garden open to the public. Delivers to shows. Euro accepted. Wheelchair accessible.

XSen **GAEC Senteurs Du Quercy** ♿
Mas de Fraysse, Escamps, Lot 46230, France
Ⓣ +33 5 652 10167
Ⓔ contact@senteursduquercy.com
Ⓦ www.senteursduquercy.com
Contact: Frédéric Prévot
Opening Times: 1400-1800 spring & summer (excl. Aug). Other times, incl. Aug by appt.
Min Mail Order UK: Nmc
Min Mail Order EU: Nmc
Cat. Cost: €5.00
Specialities: *Salvia*, *Iris*, *Phlomis*, *Teucrium*, *Lavandula* and drought tolerant plants. French Nat. Coll. of *Salvia* species.
Notes: Euro accepted. Delivers to shows. Wheelchair accessible.

XTur **Etablissements Pierre Turc** ♿ ◆
63 Route de Seiches, 49630 Mazé, France
Ⓣ +33 02 4180 6408
Ⓜ +33 06 4756 3327
Ⓕ +33 02 4180 2696
Ⓔ export@turcieflor.com
Ⓦ www.turcieflor.com
Contact: Mark Hodson
Opening Times: 0800-1200 & 1330-1630 Mon-Fri.
Min Mail Order UK: Nmc + p&p
Min Mail Order EU: Nmc + p&p
Cat. Cost: Online only.
Specialities: *Alstroemeria*, *Agapanthus* & *Canna*. Also *Arum*, *Begonia*, *Dahlia*, *Fuchsia* & *Hippeastrum*. French National Collection of *Alstroemeria* cvs.
Notes: Accepts payment by electronic transfer or cheques. Also sells wholesale. Exports beyond EU. Delivers to shows. Euro accepted. Wheelchair accessible.

Nursery Index by Name

Nurseries that are included in the *RHS Plant Finder* for the first time this year (or have been reintroduced after a significant absence) are marked in **bold type**.

Full details of the nurseries will be found in **Nursery Details by Code** on page 840. For a key to the geographical codes, see the start of **Nurseries**.

Old Hall Nursery	MOld
Old Hall Plants	EOHP
Orange Pippin Ltd	NOra
Other Fellow Fuchsias	WOth
Out of the Common Way	WOut
Packhorse Farm Nursery	MPkF
Paddock Plants	SPad
Painshill Park Trust	**LPai**
Palm House, The	CPHo
Pan-Global Plants	WPGP
Pantyfod Garden & Nursery	WPtf
Parham House & Gardens	**SPhm**
Parham Bungalow Plants	CPBP
Dave Parkinson Plants	NDav
Parks Perennials	CPar
Paugers Plants Ltd	EPau
Pavilion Plants	SPav
Penberth Plants (formerly Trewidden Nursery)	CPbh
Penlan Perennials	WPnP
Pernewood Plants	EPed
Perrie Hale Nursery	CPer
Perry's Plants	NPer
Perryhill Nurseries Ltd	SPer
Pershore College	WAvo
Pettet's Nursery	SPet
Phedar Nursery	MPhe
Alan Phipps Cacti	CPhi
Phoenix Perennial Plants	SPhx
Piecemeal Plants	MPie
Pine Cottage Plants	CPne
Place for Plants, The	EPfP
Plant Company, The	STPC
Plant Directory, The	NPla
Plant Specialist, The	LPla
Plant World Botanic Gardens	CPla
Plantagogo.com	MPnt
Plantbase	SPlb
Plants4Presents	SPre
Plants for Small Gardens	CSma
Plants, Shoots and Leaves	GPSL
Plantsman's Preference, The	EPPr
Plantstoplant	SPtp
Poets Cottage Shrub Nursery	NPoe
Polemonium Plantery	NPol
Pollie's Perennials and Daylily Nursery	SPol
Pomona Fruits Ltd	EPom
Pops Plants	SPop
Potash Nursery	EPts
Potted Garden Nursery, The	SPoG
Pottertons Nursery	EPot
Potting Shed, The	IPot
Koen Van Poucke	**XPou**
Pounsley Plants	CPou
Poyntzfield Herb Nursery	GPoy
Practicality Brown Ltd	**LPra**
Primrose Bank	NPnk
Primrose Cottage Nursery	NPri
Primrose Hall Nursery	**LPmr**
Priory Plants	EPri
Sue Proctor Plants	NSue
ProperPlants.com	CPrp
Quality Daffodils	CQua
Quercus Garden Plants Ltd	GQue
Quiet Corner Plants	NQui
Rainsbrook Nursery	MRai
Rapkyns Nursery	SRkn
Sarah Raven	**CRav**
Ravensthorpe Nursery	MRav
Reads Nursery	ERea
Really Wild Flowers	CRea
Red House Farm	WRHF
G Reuthe Ltd	SReu
RHS Plant Shop: RHSplants.co.uk	LOPS
Ribblesdale Nurseries	NRib
Ringhaddy Daffodils	IRhd
River Garden Nurseries	SRiv
Roadford Water Gardens	CRoa
W Robinson & Son (Seeds & Plants) Ltd	NRob
Rodings Plantery, The	ERod
R V Roger Ltd	NRog
Ros Ban Wildlife Garden	IRos
Rose Cottage Plants	ERCP
Roseland House Nursery	CRHN
Rosemoor Plant Centre (RHS)	CRos
Rosie's Garden Plants	SRGP
Ross Garden Store	**WGSt**
Rotherview Nursery	SRot
Rumsey Gardens	SRms
Ryal Nursery	NRya
St Bridget Nurseries Ltd	CSBt
Saith Ffynnon Wildlife Plants	WSFF
Sampford Shrubs	CSam
Savill Gardens	**LSvl**
SCEA Hodnik	XHod
Seagate Irises	ESgI
Seale Rose Garden	SSea
Seeds of Italy	**LSds**
Shelley Seeds	**MShS**
Shipton Bulbs	WShi
Shropshire Sarracenias	WSSs
Shrubland Park Nurseries	EShb
Simpson's Nurseries Ltd	ESps
Slack Top Nurseries	NSla
John Smith & Son	MSmi
Snape Cottage	CSna
Southon Plants	LSou
Special Plants	CSpe
SpecialPerennials.com	MSpe
Spinneywell Nursery	**WSpi**
Spring Reach Nursery	LSRN
Staddon Farm Nurseries	CSta
Starborough Nursery	SSta
Stillingfleet Lodge Nurseries	NSti
Stone House Cottage Nurseries	WSHC

INDEX MAP

The maps on the following pages show the approximate location of the nurseries whose details are listed in this directory.

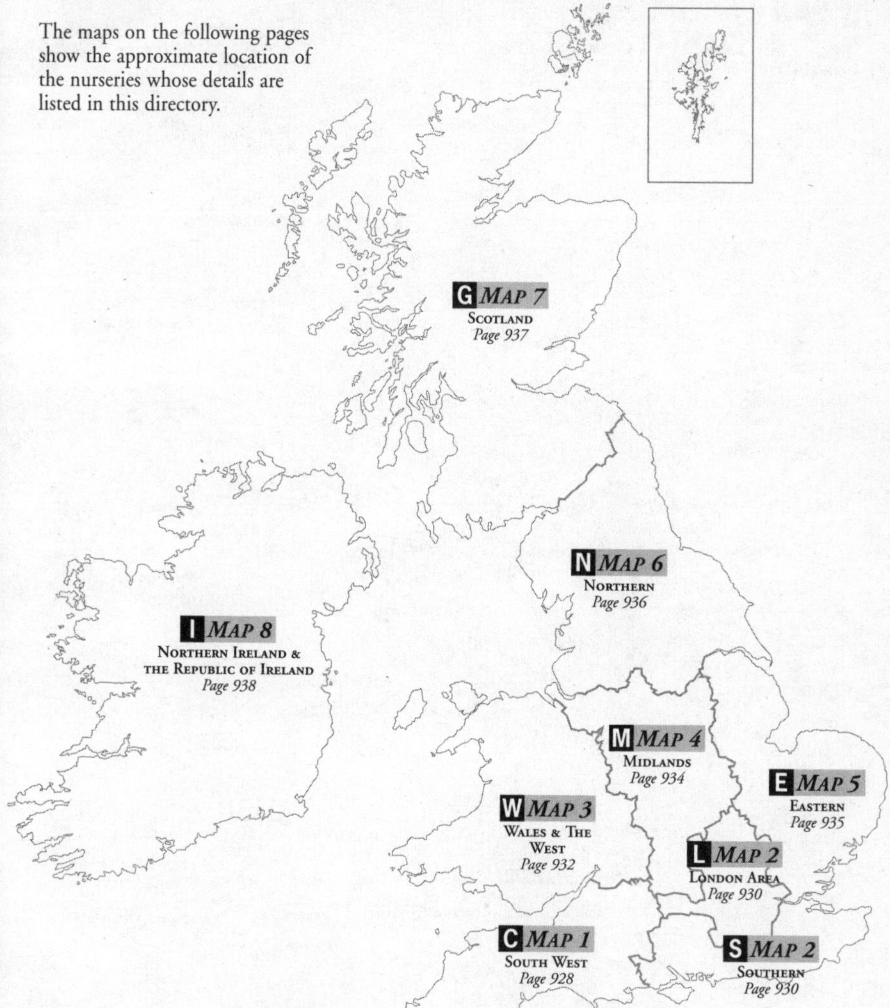

KEY

WCru Details of nurseries with letter codes in boxes are given in the Nursery Details by Code Index starting on page 840.

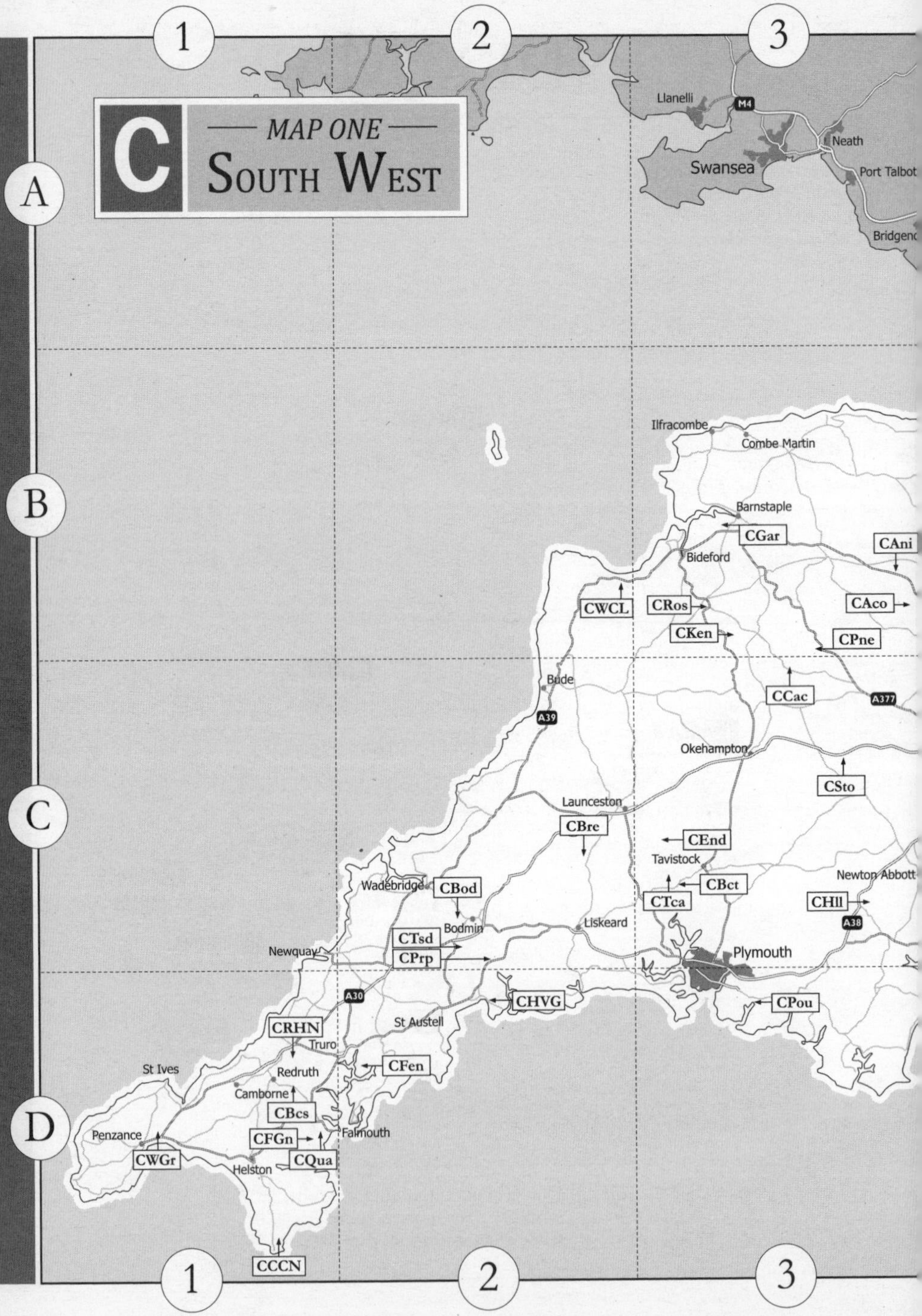

C
MAP ONE
SOUTH WEST
1
2
3
A
B
C
D
Llanelli
M4
Swansea
Neath
Port Talbot
Bridgend
Ilfracombe
Combe Martin
Barnstaple
CGar
CAni
Bideford
CWCL
CRos
CAco
CKen
CPne
Bude
CCac
A39
A377
Okehampton
CSto
Launceston
CBre
CEnd
Tavistock
Newton Abbott
Wadebridge
CBod
CBct
CTca
CHll
Bodmin
Liskeard
A38
CTsd
Newquay
CPrp
Plymouth
A30
CHVG
CPou
CRHN
St Austell
Truro
CFen
St Ives
Redruth
Camborne
CBcs
Penzance
CFGn
Falmouth
CWGr
Helston
CQua
CCCN

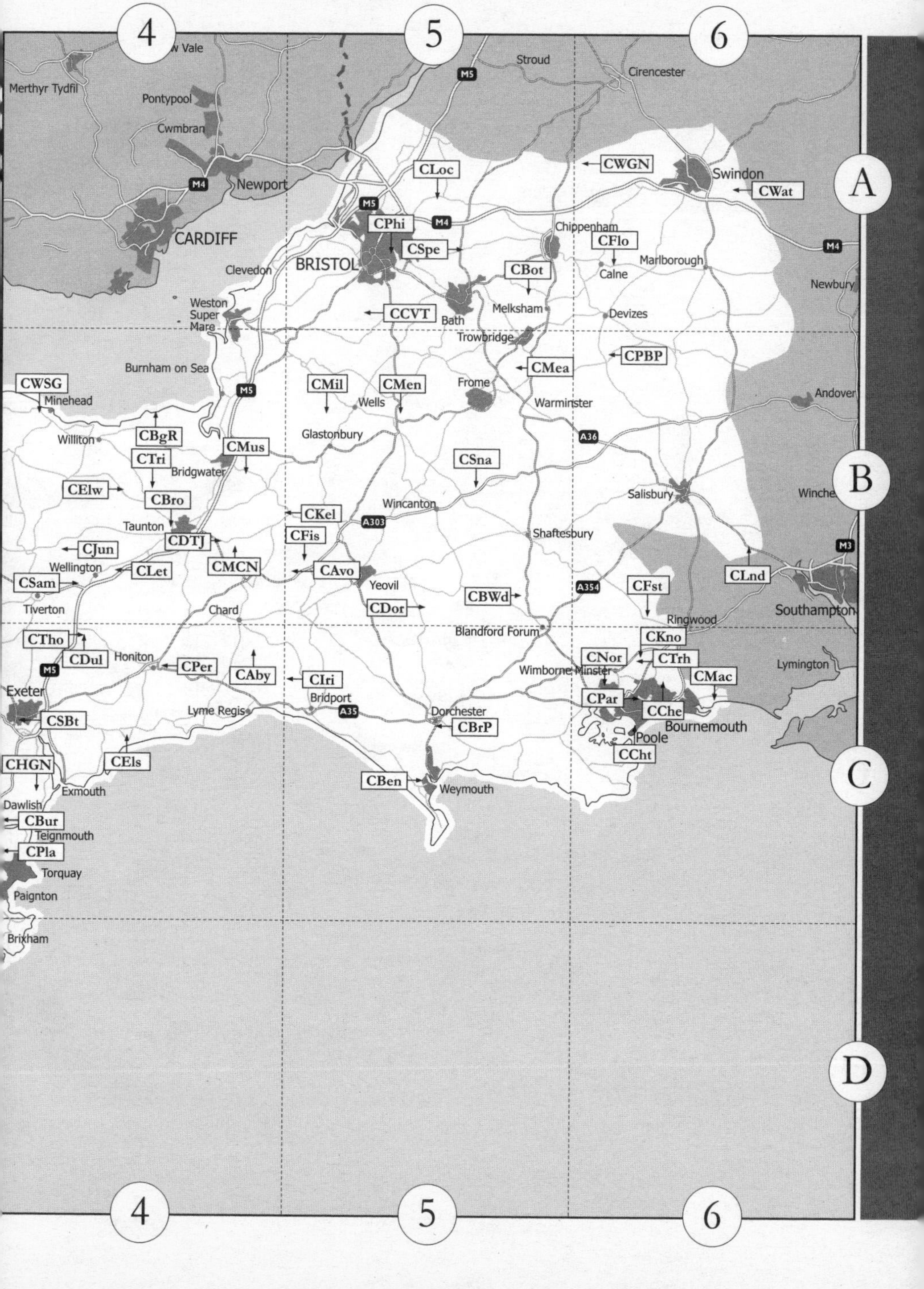
4
5
6
A
B
C
D
Merthyr Tydfil
Pontypool
Cwmbran
Newport
CARDIFF
Stroud
Cirencester
Swindon
CWGN
CWat
CLoc
CPhi
CSpe
BRISTOL
Clevedon
Weston Super Mare
Chippenham
CFlo
Calne
Marlborough
CBot
Melksham
Bath
CCVT
Devizes
Newbury
Trowbridge
CPBP
CMea
Burnham on Sea
CWSG
Minehead
CMil
CMen
Frome
Wells
Warminster
Andover
Williton
CBgR
Glastonbury
CMus
CTri
Bridgwater
CSna
CElw
CBro
Salisbury
Taunton
CKel
Wincanton
CDTJ
CFis
Shaftesbury
CJun
Wellington
CLet
CMCN
CAvo
Yeovil
CLnd
CSam
Tiverton
CBWd
CFst
Southampton
Chard
CDor
Ringwood
Blandford Forum
CKno
CTho
CDul
Honiton
CNor
CTrh
Lymington
CPer
CAby
CIri
Wimborne Minster
CMac
Exeter
Bridport
CPar
CChe
CSBt
Lyme Regis
Dorchester
CBrP
Bournemouth
Poole
CCht
CHGN
CEls
Exmouth
CBen
Weymouth
Dawlish
CBur
Teignmouth
CPla
Torquay
Paignton
Brixham
M4
M5
M3
A36
A303
A354
A35

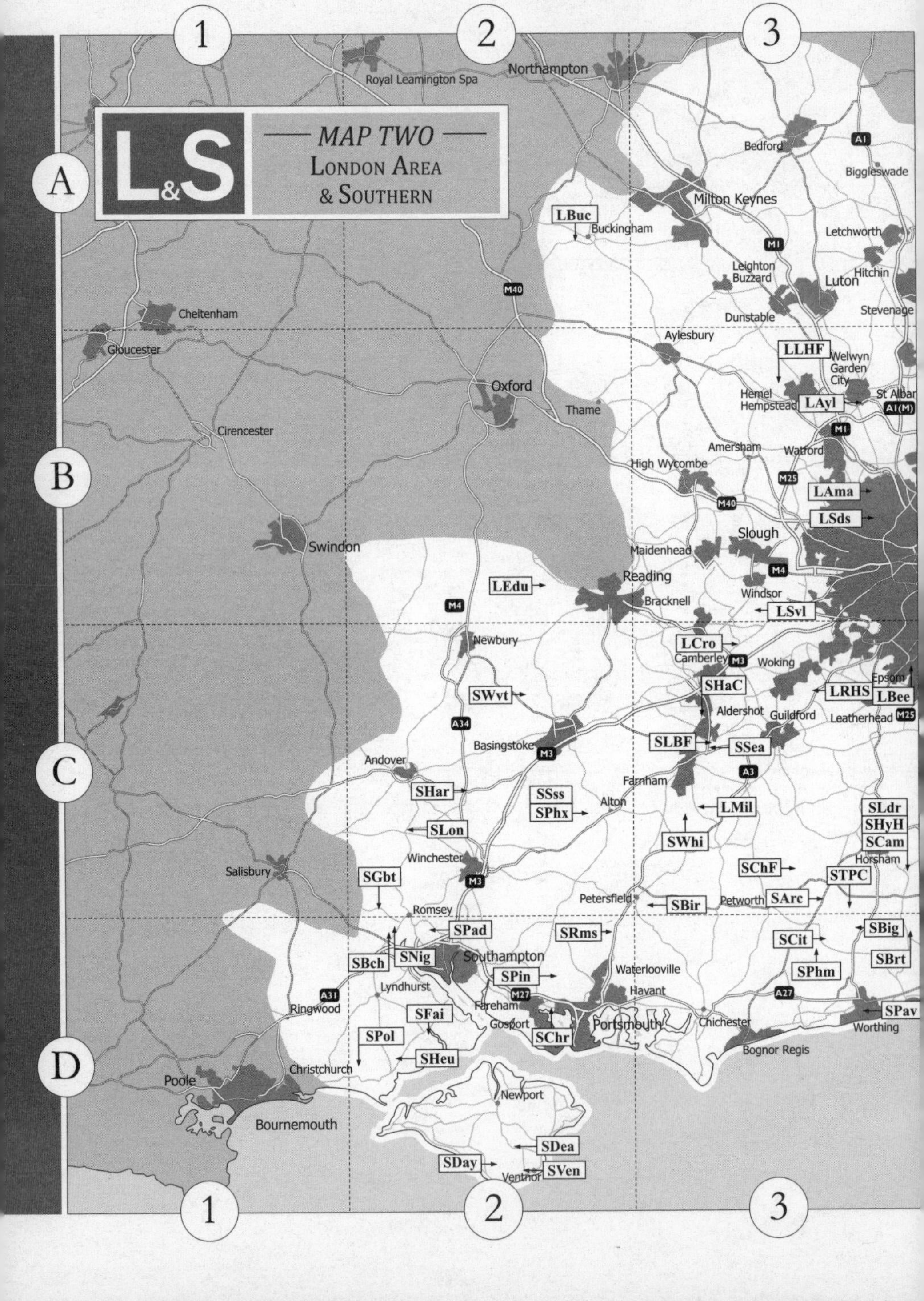
L&S
MAP TWO
LONDON AREA
& SOUTHERN
1
2
3
A
B
C
D
Royal Leamington Spa
Northampton
Bedford
Biggleswade
Milton Keynes
LBuc
Buckingham
Letchworth
Leighton Buzzard
Hitchin
Luton
Stevenage
Dunstable
Cheltenham
Gloucester
Aylesbury
LLHF
Welwyn Garden City
Oxford
Hemel Hempstead
LAyl
St Alban
Thame
Cirencester
Amersham
Watford
High Wycombe
LAma
LSds
Slough
Swindon
Maidenhead
Reading
LEdu
Bracknell
Windsor
LSvl
Newbury
LCro
Camberley
Woking
SHaC
Epsom
SWvt
LRHS
LBee
Aldershot
Guildford
Leatherhead
Basingstoke
SLBF
SSea
Andover
Farnham
SHar
SSss
SPhx
Alton
LMil
SLdr
SHyH
SCam
SLon
SWhi
Horsham
Winchester
SChF
STPC
Salisbury
SGbt
Petersfield
SBir
Petworth
SArc
Romsey
SPad
SRms
SBig
SCit
SBch
SNig
Southampton
SBrt
SPin
Waterlooville
SPhm
Lyndhurst
Havant
Ringwood
Fareham
SFai
Chichester
SPav
Gosport
Portsmouth
Worthing
SPol
SChr
Bognor Regis
SHeu
Christchurch
Poole
Newport
Bournemouth
SDea
SDay
Ventnor
SVen
M1
M40
M25
M4
M3
M27
A1
A1(M)
A34
A3
A31
A27

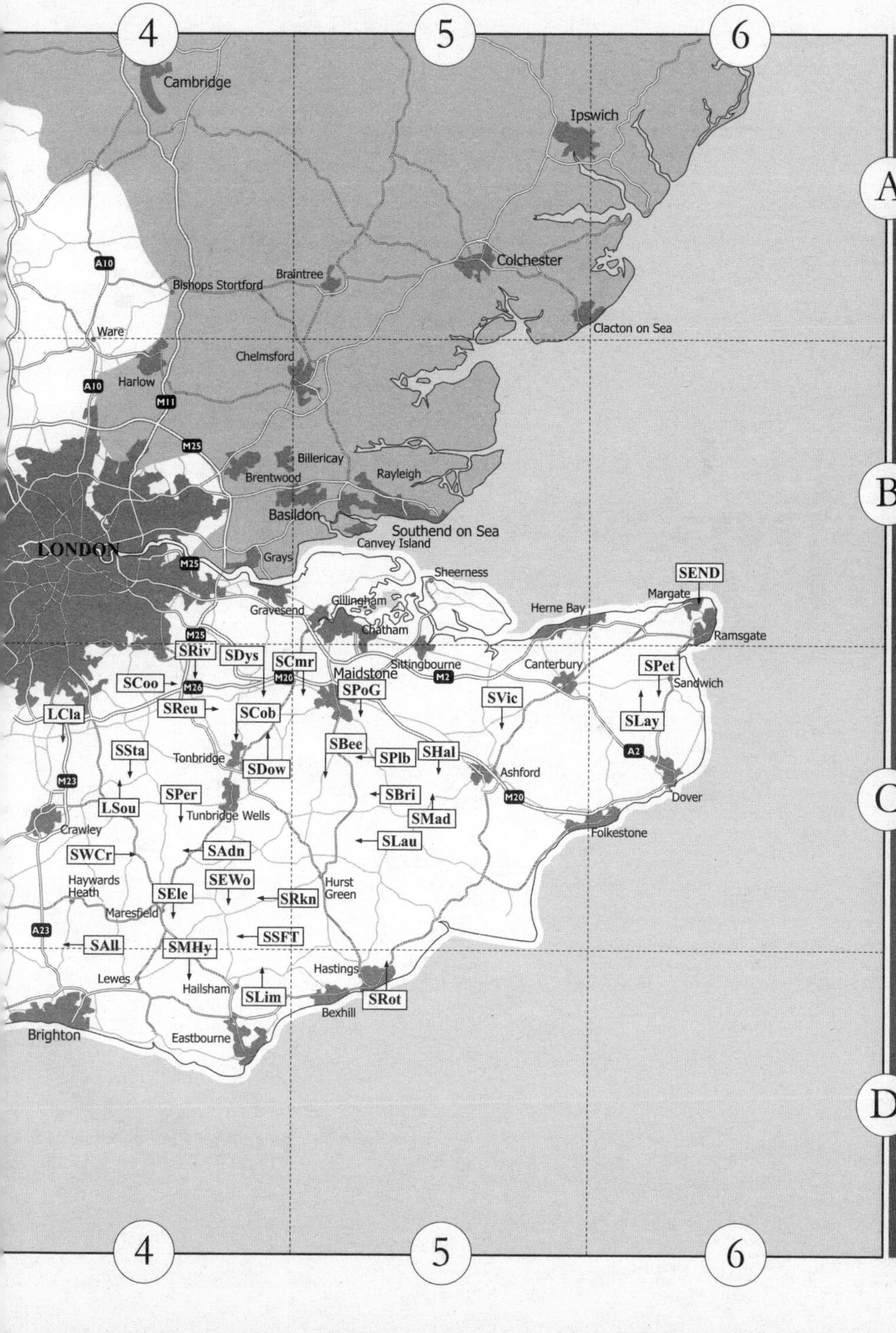
4
5
6
A
B
C
D
Cambridge
Ipswich
A10
Bishops Stortford
Braintree
Colchester
Ware
Clacton on Sea
Chelmsford
Harlow
M11
M25
Billericay
Brentwood
Rayleigh
Basildon
Southend on Sea
Canvey Island
LONDON
Grays
Sheerness
SEND
Margate
Gillingham
Gravesend
Herne Bay
Chatham
Ramsgate
M25
SRiv
SDys
SCmr
Sittingbourne
Canterbury
SPet
SCoo
M26
M20
Maidstone
M2
Sandwich
SPoG
SVic
SReu
SCob
LCla
SLay
SSta
SBee
SPlb
SHal
A2
Tonbridge
SDow
Ashford
M23
SBri
SPer
M20
LSou
SMad
Dover
Tunbridge Wells
Crawley
SLau
Folkestone
SWCr
SAdn
SEWo
Haywards Heath
SEle
SRkn
Hurst Green
Maresfield
A23
SSFT
SAll
SMHy
Hastings
Lewes
Hailsham
SLim
SRot
Bexhill
Brighton
Eastbourne
4
5
6

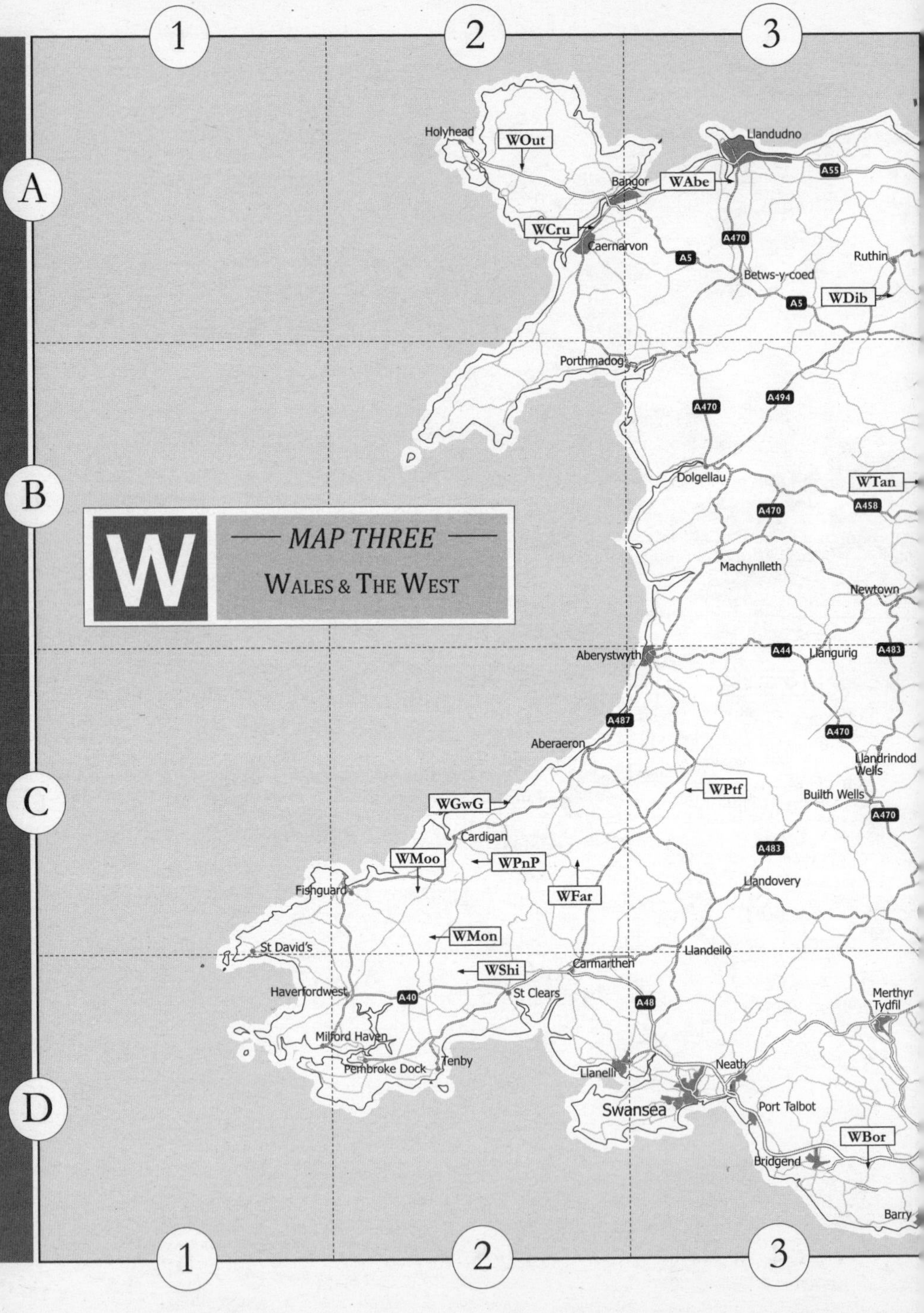
1
2
3
A
B
C
D
W
MAP THREE
WALES & THE WEST
Holyhead
WOut
Llandudno
A55
Bangor
WAbe
WCru
Caernarvon
A470
A5
Ruthin
Betws-y-coed
A5
WDib
Porthmadog
A470
A494
Dolgellau
WTan
A470
A458
Machynlleth
Newtown
Aberystwyth
A44
Llangurig
A483
A487
A470
Aberaeron
Llandrindod Wells
WPtf
Builth Wells
WGwG
A470
Cardigan
WMoo
WPnP
A483
Fishguard
WFar
Llandovery
WMon
St David's
Llandeilo
WShi
Carmarthen
Haverfordwest
A40
St Clears
A48
Merthyr Tydfil
Milford Haven
Pembroke Dock
Tenby
Llanelli
Neath
Swansea
Port Talbot
WBor
Bridgend
Barry
1
2
3

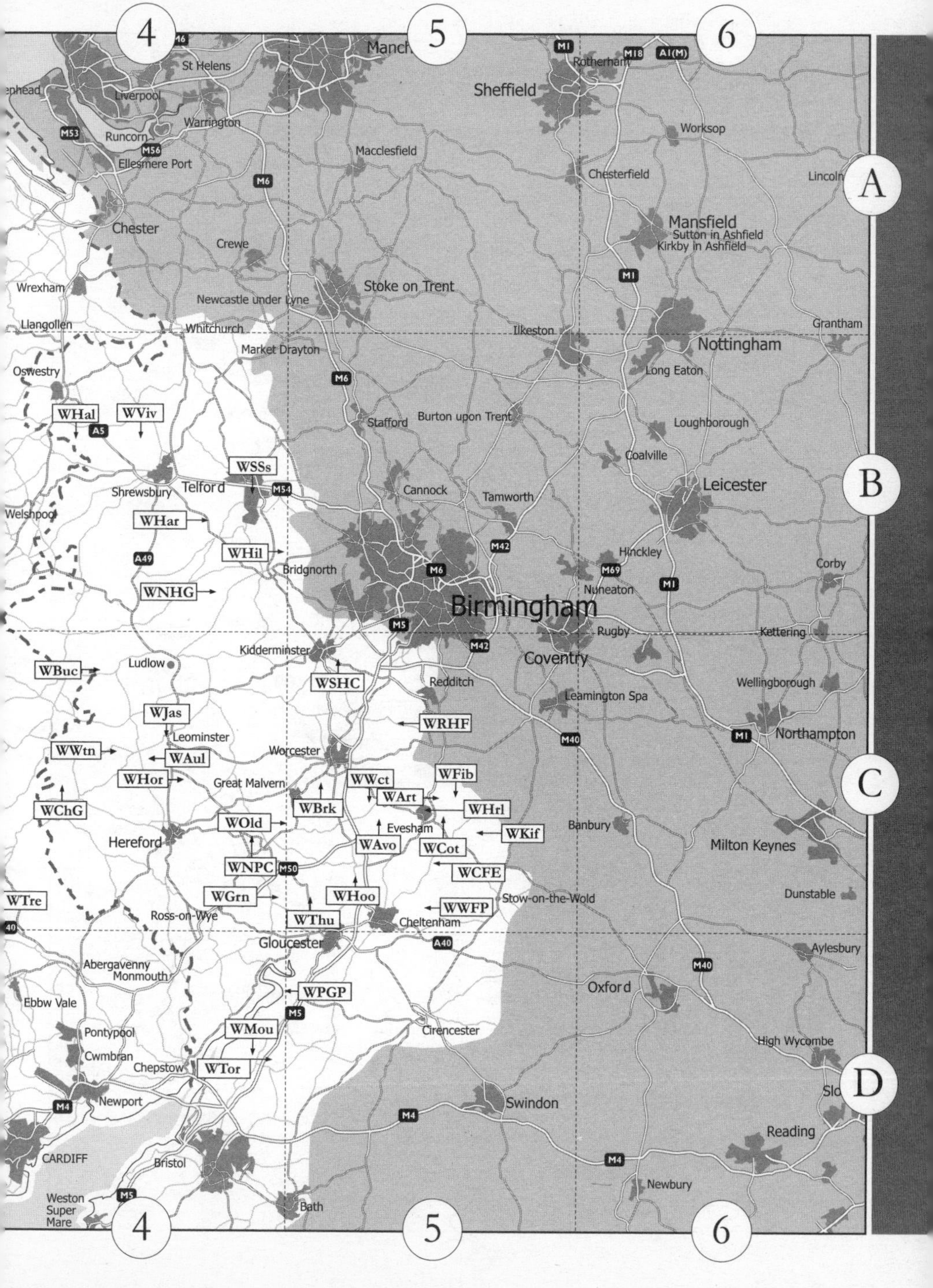

4
5
6
A
B
C
D
St Helens
Liverpool
Runcorn
Warrington
Ellesmere Port
Chester
Crewe
Wrexham
Llangollen
Whitchurch
Oswestry
Shrewsbury
Telford
Welshpool
Bridgnorth
Ludlow
Leominster
Kidderminster
Worcester
Great Malvern
Hereford
Ross-on-Wye
Gloucester
Cheltenham
Evesham
Redditch
Stow-on-the-Wold
Abergavenny
Monmouth
Ebbw Vale
Pontypool
Cwmbran
Chepstow
Newport
CARDIFF
Bristol
Weston
Super
Mare
Bath
Cirencester
Swindon
Oxford
Newbury
Reading
High Wycombe
Aylesbury
Dunstable
Milton Keynes
Northampton
Wellingborough
Kettering
Corby
Banbury
Leamington Spa
Coventry
Rugby
Birmingham
Nuneaton
Hinckley
Leicester
Coalville
Loughborough
Long Eaton
Nottingham
Ilkeston
Grantham
Tamworth
Cannock
Stafford
Burton upon Trent
Market Drayton
Newcastle under Lyne
Stoke on Trent
Macclesfield
Sheffield
Rotherham
Worksop
Chesterfield
Lincoln
Mansfield
Sutton in Ashfield
Kirkby in Ashfield
M6
M53
M56
M1
M18
A1(M)
A5
M54
A49
M42
M69
M5
M40
M50
A40
M4
WHal
WViv
WSSs
WHar
WHil
WNHG
WBuc
WSHC
WJas
WRHF
WWtn
WAul
WHor
WChG
WOld
WBrk
WWct
WArt
WFib
WHrl
WKif
WAvo
WCot
WCFE
WNPC
WGrn
WHoo
WWFP
WThu
WTre
WPGP
WMou
WTor

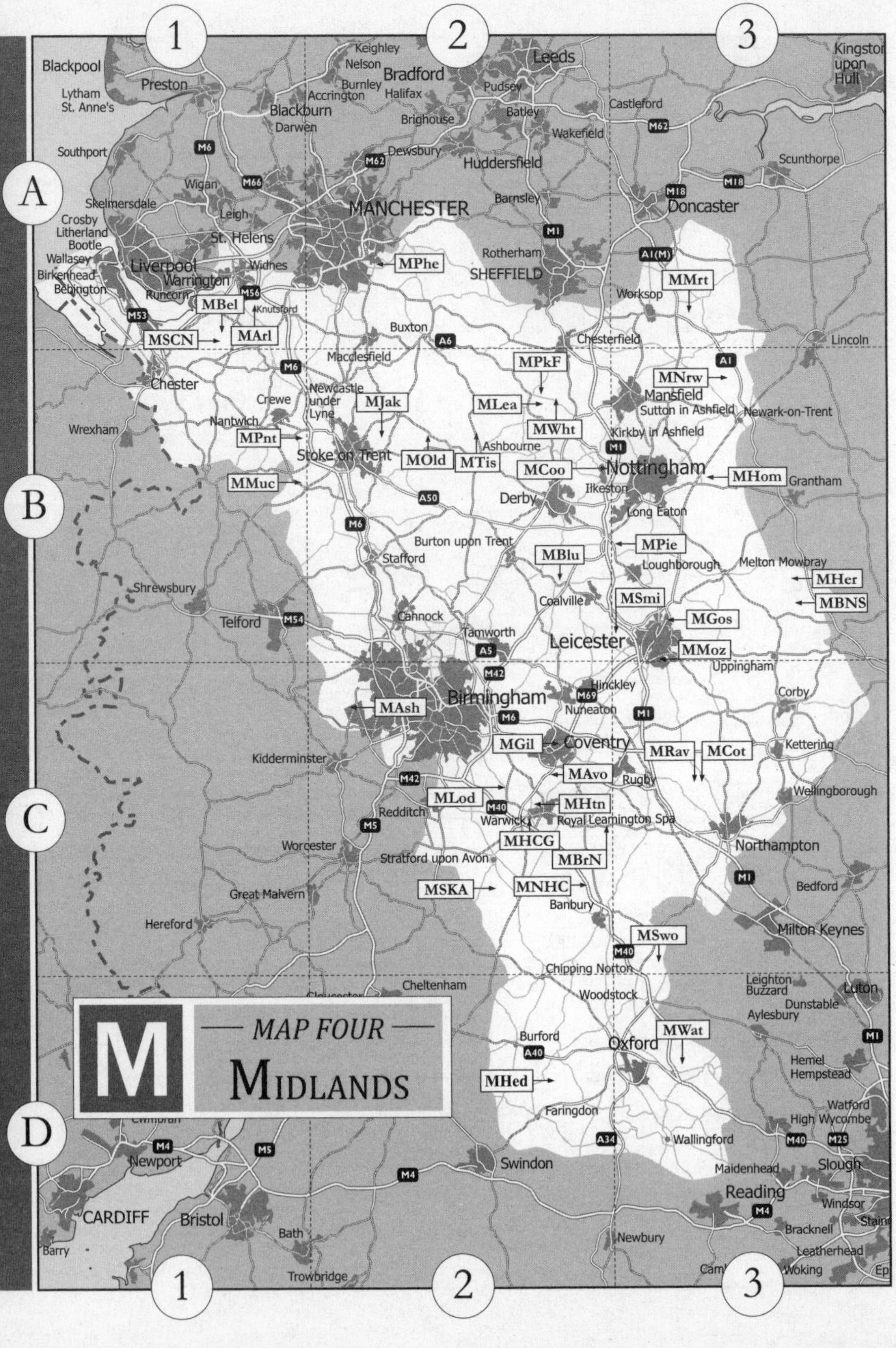
M
MAP FOUR
MIDLANDS
1
2
3
A
B
C
D
1
2
3
Blackpool
Preston
Lytham St. Anne's
Keighley
Nelson
Burnley
Bradford
Accrington
Halifax
Blackburn
Darwen
Leeds
Pudsey
Batley
Castleford
Kingston upon Hull
Brighouse
Wakefield
Southport
Dewsbury
Huddersfield
Scunthorpe
Wigan
Skelmersdale
Leigh
MANCHESTER
Barnsley
Doncaster
Crosby
Litherland
Bootle
Wallasey
St. Helens
Liverpool
Birkenhead
Bebington
Widnes
Warrington
Runcorn
Knutsford
Rotherham
SHEFFIELD
Worksop
Buxton
Chesterfield
Lincoln
Macclesfield
Chester
Crewe
Newcastle under Lyne
Nantwich
Wrexham
Mansfield
Sutton in Ashfield
Newark-on-Trent
Kirkby in Ashfield
Ashbourne
Stoke on Trent
Nottingham
Grantham
Ilkeston
Derby
Long Eaton
Burton upon Trent
Stafford
Loughborough
Melton Mowbray
Shrewsbury
Coalville
Telford
Cannock
Tamworth
Leicester
Uppingham
Hinckley
Birmingham
Nuneaton
Corby
Coventry
Kettering
Kidderminster
Rugby
Wellingborough
Redditch
Warwick
Royal Leamington Spa
Worcester
Northampton
Stratford upon Avon
Great Malvern
Banbury
Bedford
Hereford
Milton Keynes
Chipping Norton
Cheltenham
Woodstock
Leighton Buzzard
Luton
Dunstable
Aylesbury
Burford
Oxford
Hemel Hempstead
Faringdon
Watford
High Wycombe
Wallingford
Newport
Swindon
Maidenhead
Slough
Reading
Windsor
CARDIFF
Bristol
Bath
Bracknell
Barry
Newbury
Leatherhead
Woking
Trowbridge
M6
M66
M62
M18
M1
A1(M)
M56
M53
A6
A1
M6
A50
M6
M54
A5
M42
M69
M6
M1
M42
M40
M5
M1
M40
A40
M1
A34
M40
M25
M4
M5
M4
M4
MPhe
MMrt
MBel
MSCN
MArl
MPkF
MNrw
MJak
MLea
MWht
MPnt
MOld
MTis
MCoo
MHom
MMuc
MBlu
MPie
MHer
MSmi
MBNS
MGos
MMoz
MAsh
MGil
MRav
MCot
MAvo
MLod
MHtn
MHCG
MBrN
MSKA
MNHC
MSwo
MWat
MHed

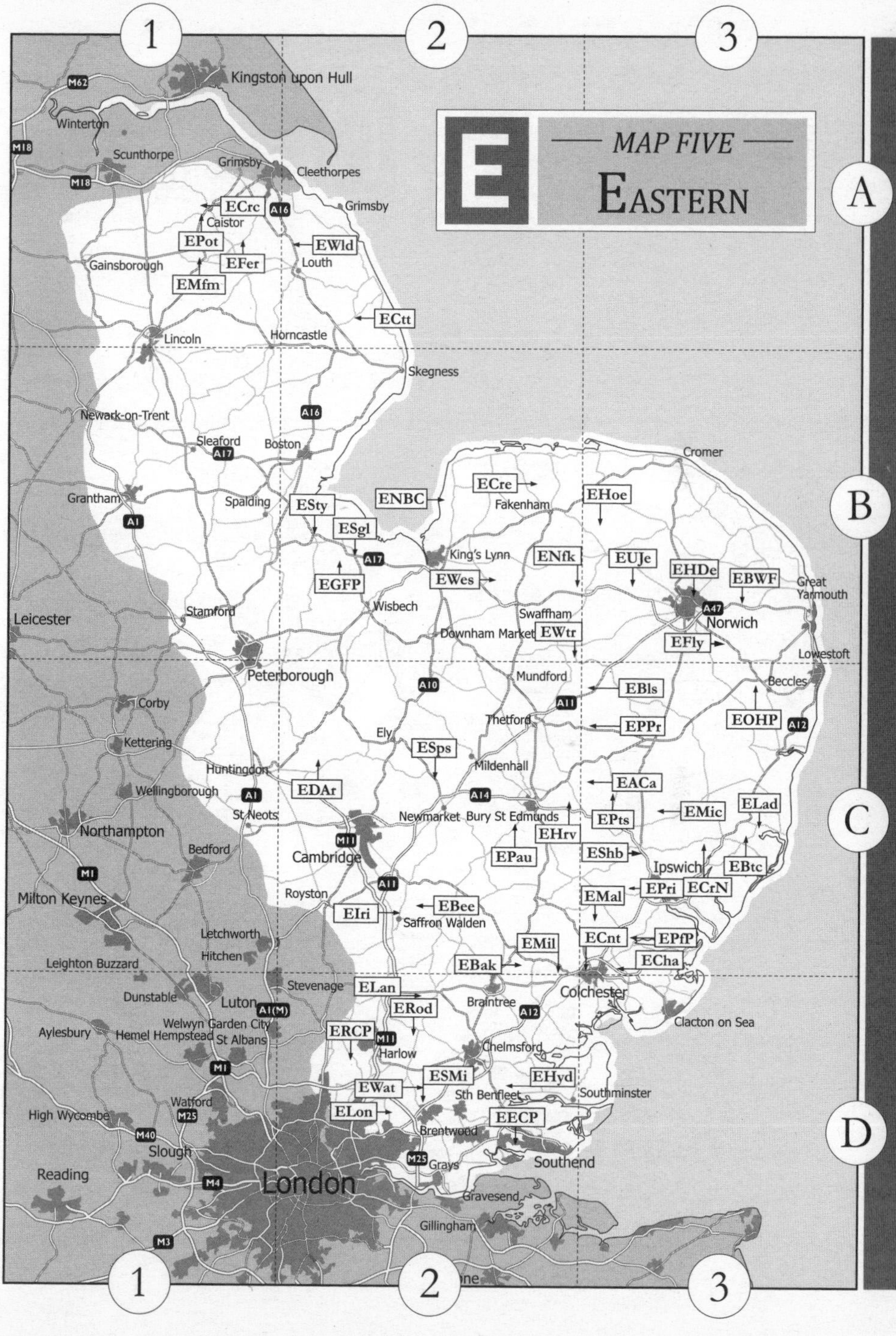
E
MAP FIVE
EASTERN
1
2
3
A
B
C
D
Kingston upon Hull
M62
Winterton
M18
Scunthorpe
Grimsby
Cleethorpes
Grimsby
A16
ECrc
Caistor
EPot
EFer
EWld
Louth
Gainsborough
EMfm
ECtt
Lincoln
Horncastle
Skegness
A16
Newark-on-Trent
Sleaford
A17
Boston
Cromer
ECre
Grantham
Spalding
ESty
ENBC
Fakenham
EHoe
A1
ESgl
A17
King's Lynn
ENfk
EUJe
EHDe
EBWF
Great Yarmouth
EGFP
EWes
Wisbech
Swaffham
A47
Norwich
Leicester
Stamford
Downham Market
EWtr
EFly
Lowestoft
Peterborough
Mundford
EBls
Beccles
Corby
A10
A11
Thetford
EPPr
EOHP
A12
Kettering
Ely
ESps
Mildenhall
Huntingdon
EDAr
EACa
Wellingborough
A1
A14
ELad
St Neots
Newmarket
Bury St Edmunds
EPts
EMic
Northampton
EHrv
Bedford
M11
EPau
EShb
Cambridge
Ipswich
EBtc
M1
A11
EPri
ECrN
Milton Keynes
Royston
EMal
EBee
EIri
Saffron Walden
Letchworth
EMil
ECnt
EPfP
Hitchen
EBak
ECha
Leighton Buzzard
Stevenage
ELan
Colchester
Dunstable
Luton
A1(M)
ERod
Braintree
A12
Clacton on Sea
Aylesbury
Welwyn Garden City
Hemel Hempstead
St Albans
ERCP
M11
Harlow
Chelmsford
M1
ESMi
EHyd
EWat
Southminster
Sth Benfleet
Watford
High Wycombe
M25
ELon
EECP
M40
Brentwood
Slough
M25
Grays
Southend
Reading
M4
London
Gravesend
Gillingham
M3

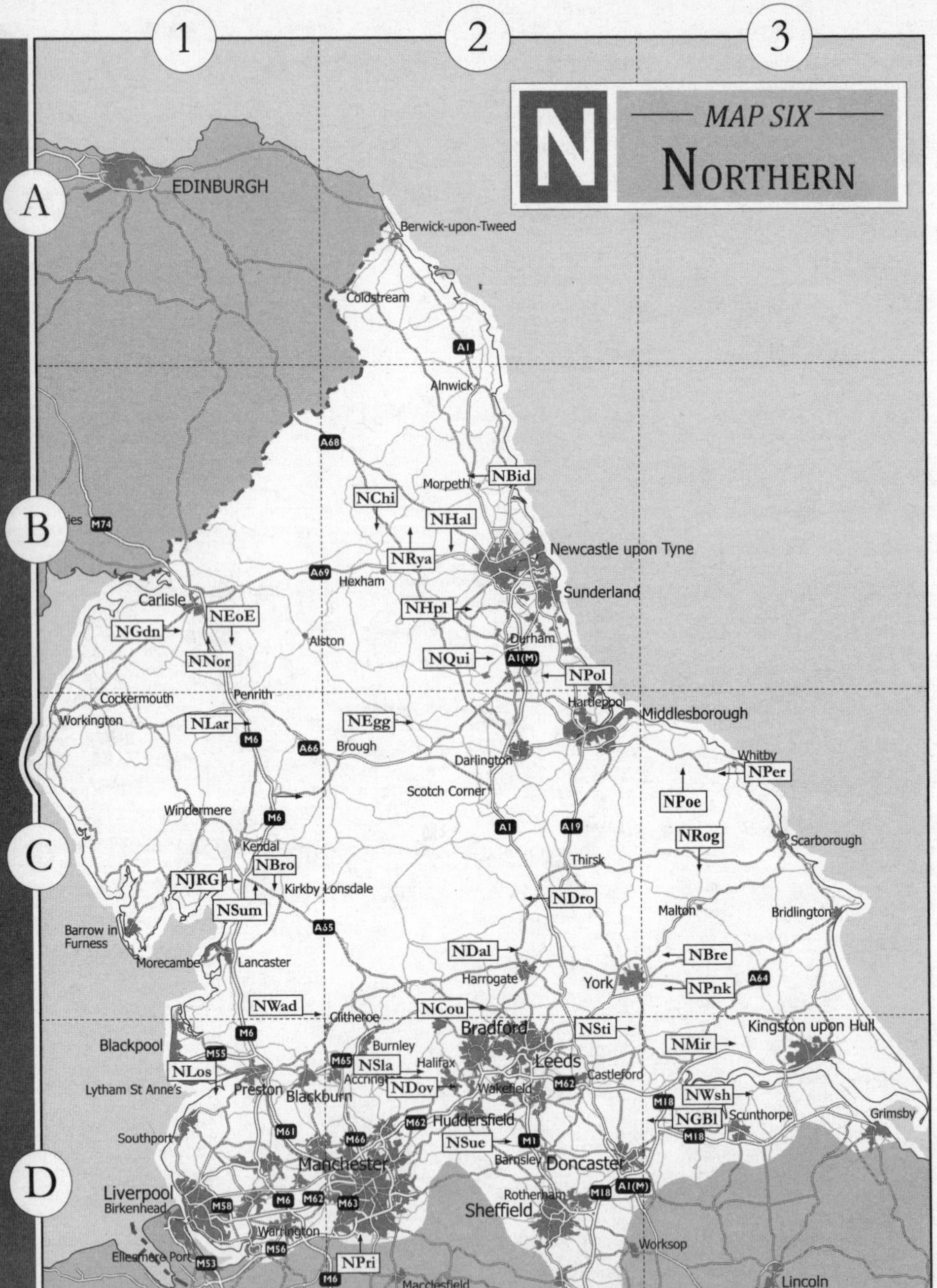

1
2
3
A
B
C
D
N
MAP SIX
NORTHERN
EDINBURGH
Berwick-upon-Tweed
Coldstream
A1
Alnwick
A68
Morpeth
NBid
NChi
NHal
NRya
Newcastle upon Tyne
M74
A69
Hexham
Sunderland
Carlisle
NEoE
NGdn
NHpl
Alston
Durham
NQui
A1(M)
NNor
NPol
Cockermouth
Penrith
Hartlepool
Middlesborough
Workington
NLar
M6
NEgg
A66
Brough
Darlington
Whitby
NPer
Scotch Corner
NPoe
Windermere
A1
A19
NRog
Kendal
Scarborough
NBro
Thirsk
NJRG
Kirkby Lonsdale
NDro
NSum
Malton
Bridlington
Barrow in Furness
A65
NDal
NBre
Morecambe
Lancaster
Harrogate
York
A64
NPnk
NWad
Clitheroe
NCou
Bradford
NSti
Kingston upon Hull
Blackpool
Burnley
NMir
M55
M65
NSla
Halifax
Leeds
NLos
Accrington
Castleford
Lytham St Anne's
Preston
Blackburn
NDov
Wakefield
M62
NWsh
M18
NGBl
Scunthorpe
Grimsby
M61
M66
Huddersfield
Southport
NSue
M1
Manchester
Barnsley
Doncaster
Liverpool
Birkenhead
M58
M63
Rotherham
Sheffield
Warrington
M56
Worksop
Ellesmere Port
M53
NPri
Macclesfield
Lincoln
Chesterfield
Chester
Mansfield

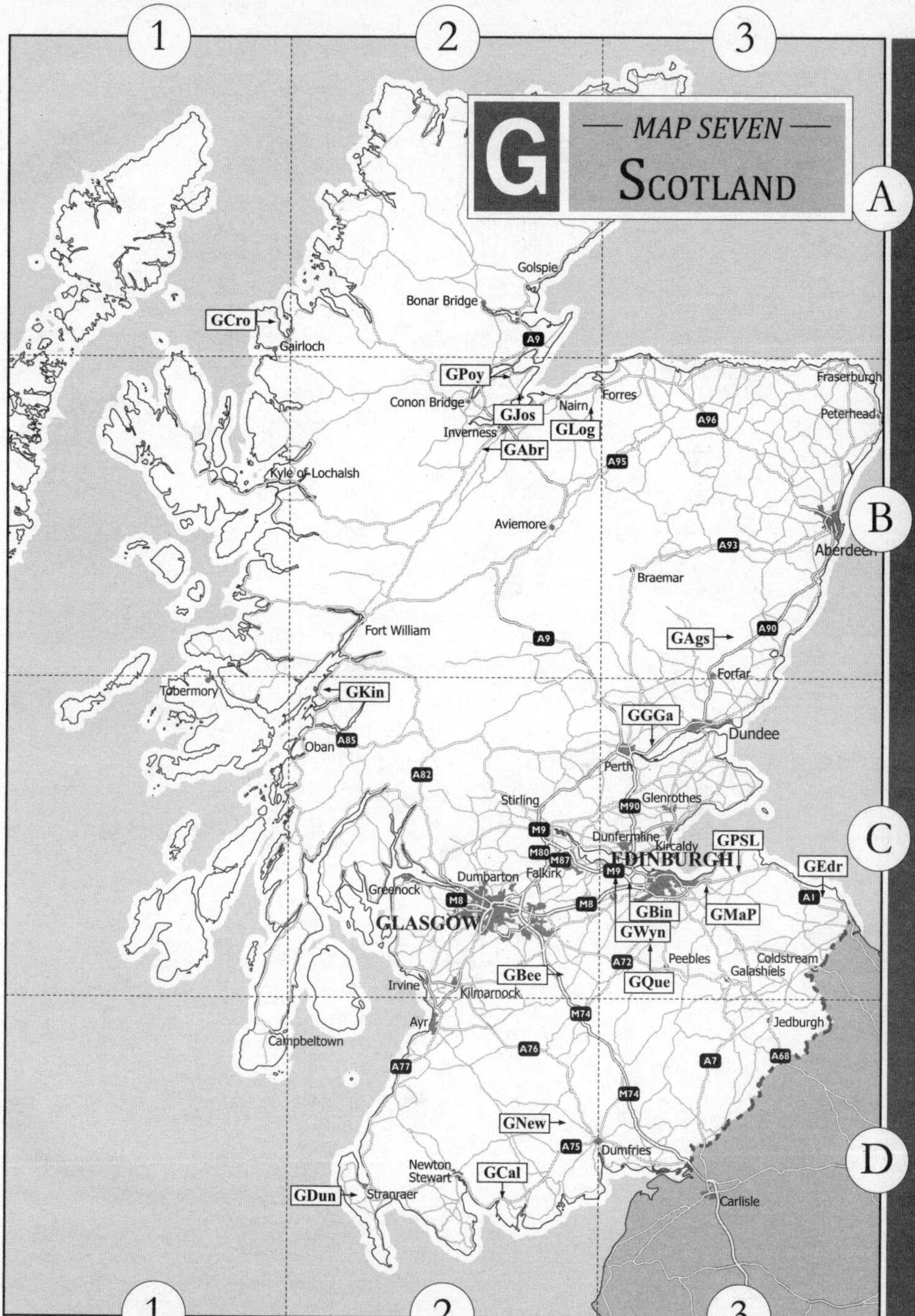

G
— MAP SEVEN —
SCOTLAND
1
2
3
A
B
C
D
Golspie
Bonar Bridge
GCro
Gairloch
A9
GPoy
Conon Bridge
GJos
Nairn
Forres
GLog
Inverness
GAbr
Kyle of Lochalsh
Fraserburgh
Peterhead
A96
A95
Aviemore
A93
Aberdeen
Braemar
Fort William
A9
GAgs
A90
Forfar
Tobermory
GKin
GGGa
Dundee
Oban
A85
Perth
A82
Stirling
Glenrothes
M90
M9
Dunfermline
Kircaldy
GPSL
EDINBURGH
GEdr
M80
M87
Falkirk
M9
Dumbarton
Greenock
M8
M8
A1
GBin
GMaP
GLASGOW
GWyn
A72
Peebles
Coldstream
Galashiels
GBee
GQue
Irvine
Kilmarnock
M74
Ayr
Jedburgh
Campbeltown
A76
A7
A68
A77
M74
GNew
A75
Dumfries
Newton Stewart
GCal
GDun
Stranraer
Carlisle

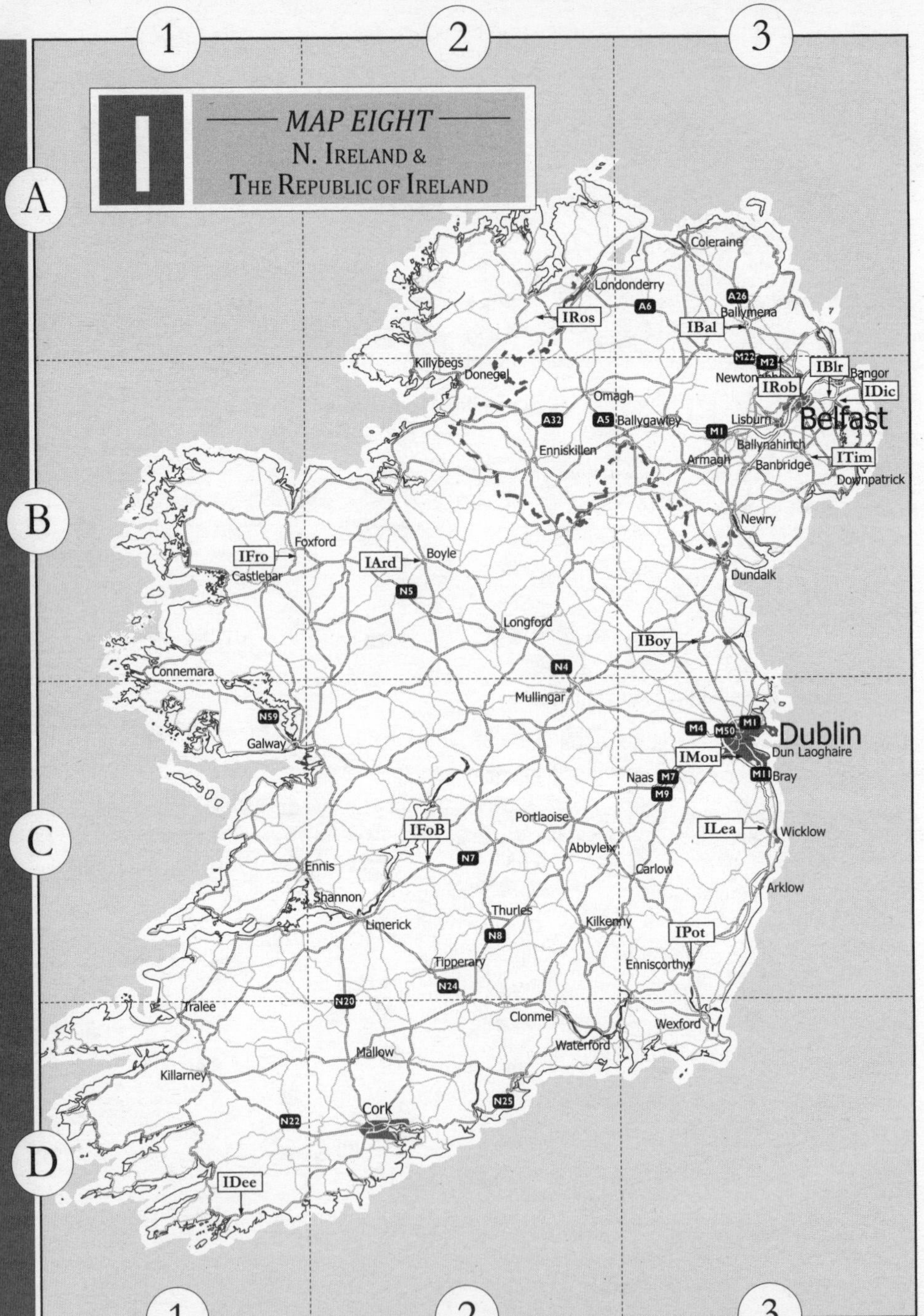
1
2
3
A
B
C
D
I
MAP EIGHT
N. Ireland &
The Republic of Ireland
Coleraine
Londonderry
A26
A6
Ballymena
IRos
IBal
Killybegs
Donegal
M22
M2
Newtownabbey
IBlr
Bangor
IRob
IDic
Omagh
Belfast
A32
A5
Ballygawley
M1
Lisburn
Enniskillen
Ballynahinch
Armagh
Banbridge
ITim
Downpatrick
Newry
IFro
Foxford
IArd
Boyle
Castlebar
Dundalk
N5
Longford
IBoy
N4
Connemara
Mullingar
N59
M4
M50
M1
Dublin
Galway
IMou
Dun Laoghaire
Naas
M7
M11
Bray
M9
Portlaoise
IFoB
ILea
Wicklow
N7
Abbyleix
Ennis
Carlow
Shannon
Arklow
Thurles
Limerick
Kilkenny
N8
IPot
Tipperary
Enniscorthy
N24
N20
Tralee
Clonmel
Wexford
Waterford
Mallow
Killarney
N25
Cork
N22
IDee
1
2
3

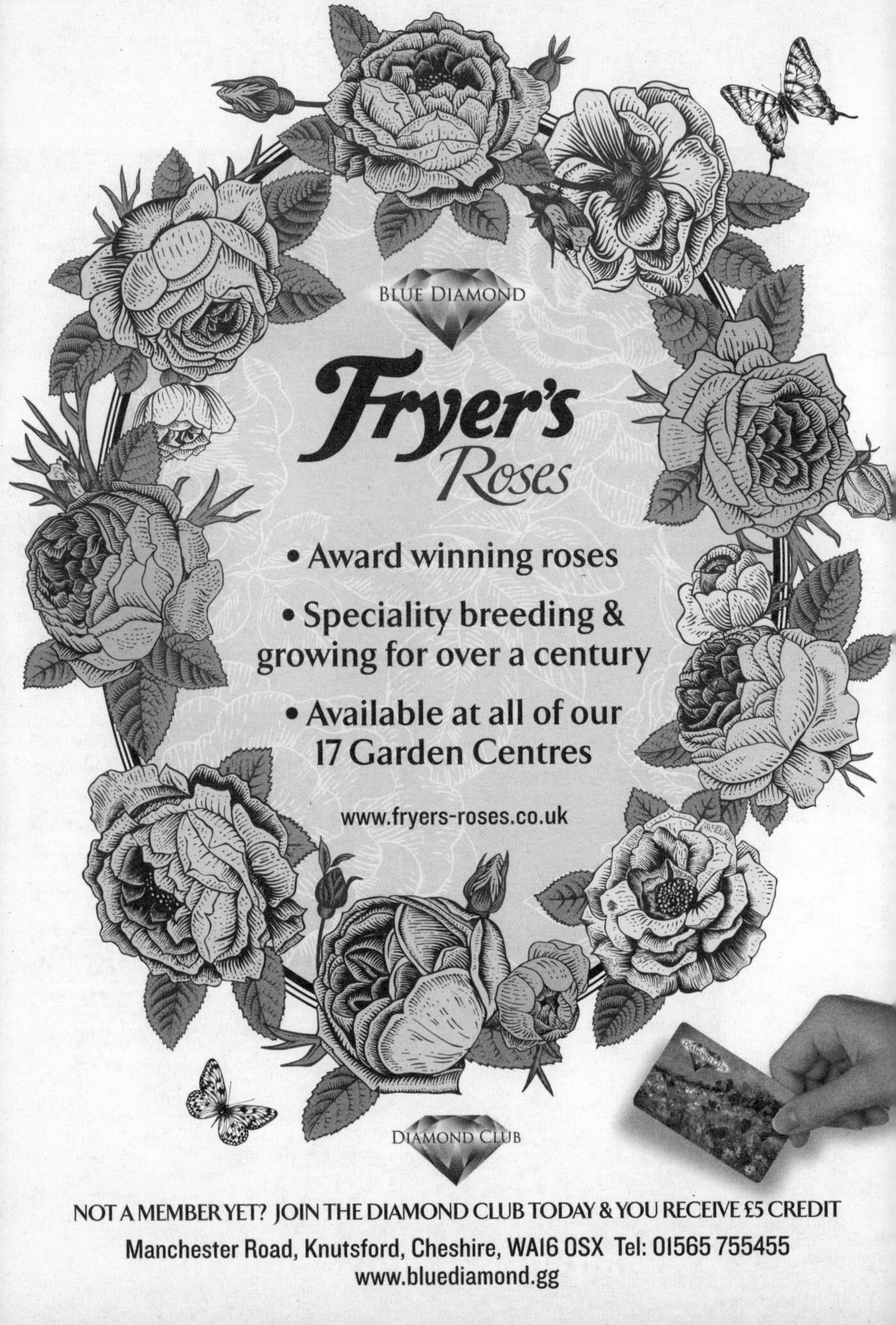
BLUE DIAMOND
Fryer's
Roses
• Award winning roses
• Speciality breeding & growing for over a century
• Available at all of our 17 Garden Centres
www.fryers-roses.co.uk
DIAMOND CLUB
NOT A MEMBER YET? JOIN THE DIAMOND CLUB TODAY & YOU RECEIVE £5 CREDIT
Manchester Road, Knutsford, Cheshire, WA16 0SX Tel: 01565 755455
www.bluediamond.gg

deJager
Top Quality, Top Size Bulbs
Flower Bulb Specialists Since 1868
Order direct online at
www.dejager.co.uk
Retail and
Wholesale
Tel: 01622 840229
FOR A FREE CATALOGUE

Plants4Presents specialise
in Delivering Plants as Gifts
Choose from a huge range of
citrus trees, flowering plants,
herbs and exotics delivered
gift wrapped for birthdays,
anniversarys and events
throughout the year.
Plants4Presents
01825 721162
www.plants4presents.co.uk

BREEDER & GROWER
Alstroemerias, Agapanthus, cannas
Turcieflor
Ets PIERRE TURC
young plants / pot plants
Tel : 0033 (0) 241 80 64 08
Mob : 0033 (0) 647 56 33 27
Email : export@turcieflor.com
www.turcieflor.com

Est. over 60 years
HEDGING, TREES,
SHRUBS, CONIFERS
ORNAMENTAL & FRUIT TREES
Over 200 different varieties of hedging
plants and young trees to choose from plus
fruit trees, soft fruit, ground cover plants etc.
Telephone or
write for your
FREE
COLOUR
BROCHURE
Buckingham Nurseries
14 Tingewick Rd, Buckingham MK18 4AE
Tel: (01280) 822133 Fax: (01280) 815491
www.hedging.co.uk

Swinesmeadow
Farm Nursery
Exotic and Rare Plants
Hosting HPS Plant Fairs on
17th April and 3rd July 2016
Opening hours: Mon-Sat 9-5, Sun 10-4
Close at 4pm in winter months
47 Towngate East, Market Deeping, Peterborough, PE6 8LQ
Tel: 01778 343340 Email: ceveandsons@btconnect.com
www.swinesmeadowfarmnursery.co.uk

Hoo House
Nursery
Gloucester Road, Tewkesbury,
Gloucestershire, GL20 7DA.
Tel/Fax 01684 293389
www.hoohouse.co.uk
Open 10-5pm Mon-Sat, 11-5pm Sun
Perennials & Alpines grown peat-free

Open
7 days
9am-5pm
Winter
9am - Dusk
Wolverton Plants
We
Accept
all Major
Credit Cards
Wolverton Common,
Nr. Tadley, Hampshire. RG26 5RU
Growers of a wide range: Hardy Perennials, Shrubs, Conifers, Climbing
Plants, Grasses, Hedging, Basket, Bedding and much more at realistic
prices. We also offer Plant Find Service to our Customers.
Tel:
01635
298453
We sell and redeem
National Garden Vouchers
Fax:
01635
299075
HTA
HTA
www.wolvertonplants.co.uk

INDEX OF ADVERTISERS